DESIGN OF WELDED STRUCTURES

BY

Omer W. Blodgett

Published as a Service to Education

by

THE JAMES F. LINCOLN ARC WELDING FOUNDATION

First Printing 5,000 June 1966
Second Printing 10,000 November 1966
Third Printing 15,000 August 1967
Fourth Printing 15,000 July 1968
Fifth Printing 10,000 May 1972
Sixth Printing 10,000 February 1974
Seventh Printing 10,000 October 1975
Eighth Printing 10,000 July 1976

Special acknowledgment is herewith made to

Watson N. Nordquist

who has contributed much to the editing
and organization of the material from
which this manual has been prepared

Price:

$7.00 in U.S.A. (Postage Included)

Overseas and Quantity Prices Upon Request

FB–37

Library of Congress Catalog Card Number: 66–23123

Printed in U.S.A.

PREFACE

WELDED STRUCTURAL CONNECTIONS have long been used in the construction of buildings, bridges, and other structures. The first welded buildings were erected in the '20s—the greatest application being in low-level buildings of many types. The American Welding Society first published specifications for welded bridges in 1936. But early progress came slowly.

During that year, 1936, The James F. Lincoln Arc Welding Foundation was created by The Lincoln Electric Company to help advance the progress in welded design and construction. Through its award programs and educational activities, the Foundation provided an exchange of experience and gave impetus to the growing application of welding.

Thus, within the last decade and particularly the past few years, unitized welded design has become widely accepted for high-rise buildings and bridges of nobler proportions in addition to the broad base of more modest structures.

Now, the Foundation publishes this manual for further guidance and challenge to architects, structural engineers, fabricators and contractors who will build the structures of tomorrow . . . and to the educators who will prepare young people for these professions. This material represents an interpretation of the best in accumulated experience of all who have participated in prior Foundation activities. The author has coordinated this with a continuing study of current welding research conducted both in the United States and Europe, and against a background of participation on various code-writing committees. Much of the direct instructional information that resulted has been pretested in over 70 structural seminars attended by over 4000 engineers.

The production of this manual has spanned several years during which constant effort was made to eliminate errors. The author will appreciate having called to his attention any errors that have escaped his attention and invites correspondence on subjects about which the reader may have questions. Neither the author nor the publisher, however, can assume responsibility for the results of designers using values and formulas contained in the manual since so many variables affect every design.

Charles Herbruck, Secretary

The James F. Lincoln Arc Welding Foundation

June 1966

CREDITS

The author and the publisher gratefully acknowledge the organizations and individuals who have contributed photographs or other illustrative material:

Allied Steel Corporation
Allison Steel Mfg. Co.
Allison Structural Steel Co.
American Bridge Division,
U.S. Steel Corporation
American Institute of Steel Construction
American Iron & Steel Institute
American Welding Society
Barber-Magee & Hoffman
John F. Beasley Construction Co.
Bethlehem Fabricating Co.
Bethlehem Steel Corporation
J. G. Bouwkamp
Burkhardt Steel Company
The California Co.
California State Division of Highways
Canadian Welding Magazine
J. A. Cappuccilli, Architect
Column Research Council
Connecticut State Highway Dept.
Dinwiddie Construction Company
Dominion Bridge Company, Ltd.
Dominion Structural Steel Co., Ltd.
B. M. Dornblatt & Associates, Inc.
Dreier Structural Steel Co.
Edmundson, Kochendoerfer & Kennedy
Engineering News-Record
Englert Engineering Company
Flint Steel Corporation
Frankel Steel Company
General Electric Company,
Industrial Heating Dept.
David R. Graham & Associates
Granco Steel Products Co.
Harley, Ellington, Cowin & Stirton, Inc.
Haven-Busch Co.
Herzberg & Associates
Hewitt-Robins, Inc.
Nathan N. Hoffman
Hoyle, Doran & Berry
Inland Steel Company
Jackson & Moreland Division,
United Engineers and Constructors, Inc.
Kaiser Steel Corp.
Kansas City Structural Steel Co.
Felix M. Kraus, Consulting Engineer
Lehigh Construction Company
Lehigh University, Fritz Engineering Laboratory
Robert Charles Lesser, Architect
R. C. Mahon Company
P. H. Mallog Co.
McGraw-Hill Book Co.
Midwest Steel & Iron Works
Nelson Stud Welding Division,
Gregory Industries, Inc.
New England Construction Magazine
Pacific Car & Foundry Co.
Pacific Iron and Steel Corporation
Phillips-Carter-Osborn, Inc.
Pittsburgh-Des Moines Steel Co.
H. Platt Company
Port of New York Authority
Product Engineering Magazine
Republic Steel Corporation
Joseph T. Ryerson & Sons, Inc.
Van Rensselaer P. Saxe, Engineer
Schact Steel Construction, Inc.
Steel Joist Institute
Tennessee Gas Pipeline Co.
United States Steel Corporation
Vermont Structural Steel Co.
Paul Weidlinger, Consulting Engineers
Welding Engineer Magazine
Welding Research Council
West Coast Steel Works
Minoru Yamasaki-Smith, Hinchman & Grylls

In certain subject areas, the author has made adaptations of work done by earlier investigators, to wit:

Friedrich Bleich
"Buckling Strength of Metal Structures"
McGraw-Hill Book Co., New York, N. Y.

Raymond Roark
"Formulas for Stress and Strain"
McGraw-Hill Book Co., New York, N. Y.

F. R. Shanley
"Strength of Materials"
McGraw-Hill Book Co., New York, N. Y.

S. Timoshenko
"Theory of Elasticity"
McGraw-Hill Book Co., New York, N. Y.

S. Timoshenko and S. Woinowsky Krieger
"Theory of Plates and Shells"
McGraw-Hill Book Co., New York, N. Y.

S. Timoshenko and James Gere
"Theory of Elastic Stability"
McGraw-Hill Book Co., New York, N. Y.

The publisher regrets any omissions from this list, and would appreciate being advised about them so that the records can be corrected.

Other Books Published by

THE JAMES F. LINCOLN ARC WELDING FOUNDATION

Metals and How to Weld Them. This dual purpose textbook and reference manual clearly describes the internal structure of metals and its relation to mechanical and physical properties and weldability. The book thoroughly discusses the metallurgical aspects of welding various metals used in Industry, describing welding processes and procedures that are applicable in each case. 400 pages, 195 illustrations. $2.00 U.S.A., postpaid.

Modern Welded Structures, Vol. I. A behind-the-scenes look at how 83 noted architects, engineers and designers chose welded design to economically improve the function and aesthetic appeal of varied structures. Adapted from outstanding papers submitted in the 1962 Awards Program for Progress in the Design of Arc Welded Structures sponsored by The James F. Lincoln Arc Welding Foundation. Each study relates the design problem, then tells and explains the solution found with arc-welded steel. 150 pages, 333 illustrations. $2.00 U.S.A., postpaid.

Modern Welded Structures, Vol. II. Welded design aspects of 64 exciting projects developed by some of the country's leading architects and engineers are described in this book. These men tell you in their own words how they approached the design problem and solved it; how they applied the latest concepts and techniques in arc-welded design and construction to improve function, add beauty, lower costs. Studies are adapted from the best entries in The James F. Lincoln Arc Welding Foundation's 1964 Awards Program for Progress in the Design of Arc Welded Structures. 280 pages, 335 illustrations. $2.50 U.S.A., postpaid.

Design of Weldments. Authoritative combined textbook and reference manual describes in detail many design techniques for creating machinery designs in arc-welded steel. Much of this material not available elsewhere. Theoretical analysis and problem-solution examples explain how to design machinery components for manufacturing economies and improvement of product performance. 464 pages, 923 illustrations, nomographs and charts. $5.00 U.S.A., postpaid.

Overseas and Quantity Prices Available Upon Request

The James F. Lincoln Arc Welding Foundation
P. O. Box 3035, Cleveland, Ohio, 44117

TABLE OF

Part One

INTRODUCTION

Part Two

LOAD & STRESS ANALYSIS

Part Three

COLUMN-RELATED DESIGN

Part Four

GIRDER-RELATED DESIGN

CONTENTS

Part Five
WELDED-CONNECTION DESIGN

Part Six
MISCELLANEOUS STRUCTURE DESIGN

Part Seven
JOINT DESIGN AND PRODUCTION

Part Eight
REFERENCE DESIGN FORMULAS

LIST OF SYMBOLS AND DEFINITIONS

α = angular acceleration (radians/sec/sec); included angle of beam curvature (degrees); form factor

Δ = perpendicular deflection (in.), bending (Δ_b) or shear (Δ_s)

ϵ = unit strain, elongation or contraction (in./in.)

ϵ_s = unit shear strain (in./in.)

ν = Poisson's ratio (steel = 0.3 usually); unit shear force

ω = leg size of fillet weld (in.); rate of angular motion about an axis (radians/sec)

ϕ = unit angular twist (radians/linear inch); included angle; angle of rotation

Σ = sum

σ = normal stress, tensile or compressive (psi); strength (psi)

σ_b = bending stress (psi)

σ_y = yield strength (psi)

τ = shear stress (psi); shear strength (psi)

θ = angle of twist (radians; 1 radian = 57.3 degrees); angle of rotation (radians); slope of tapered girder; any specified angle

a = area of section beyond plane where stress is desired or applied (in.^{2}); length of plate (in.); acceleration or deceleration (ft/min, ft/sec); clear distance between transverse stiffeners of girder (in.)

b = width of section (in.); distance of area's center of gravity to reference axis (in.)

c = distance from neutral axis to extreme fiber (in.); distance of elastic center from reference axis

d = depth of section (in.); moment arm of force (in.); distance (in.); distance between centers of gravity of girder flanges (in.)

d_w = clear distance between girder flanges (in.)

e = eccentricity of applied load (in.); total axial strain (in.); moment arm of force (in.); effective width (in.); length of Tee section in open-web girder (in.)

f = force per linear inch of weld (lbs/in.); horizontal shear force (lbs/in.); (vectorial) resultant force (lbs/in.); allowable strength of weld (lbs/in.)

f_c' = compressive strength of concrete (psi)

g = acceleration of gravity (386.4"/sec^2)

h = height; height of fall; distance of expansion on open-web girder (in.)

k = any specified constant or amplification factor

m = mass; statical moment of transformed concrete (composite construction)

n = distance of section's neutral axis from reference axis (in.); number of units in series

p = internal pressure (psi)

q = allowable force on shear connector

r = radius (in.); radius of gyration

s = length of curved beam segment (in.); clear distance between ends of increments of weld (in.)

t = thickness of section (in.); time (min.); time interval (sec)

u = material's tensile modulus of resilience (in.-lb/in.^{3})

u_u = material's ultimate energy resistance (in.-lb/in.^{3})

w = uniformly distributed load (lbs/linear inch)

x = length of moment arm (curved beam)

y = distance of area's center of gravity to neutral axis of entire section (in.)

A = area (in.^{2}); total area of cross-section

C = stiffness factor used in moment distribution; any specified constant

E = modulus of elasticity, tension (psi); arc voltage (volts)

E_s = modulus of elasticity in shear (psi)

E_t = tangential modulus of elasticity (psi)

E_k = kinetic energy

E_p = potential energy

F = total force (lbs); radial force (lbs)

I = moment of inertia (in.^{4}); welding current (amps)

J = polar moment of inertia (in.^{4}); heat input (joules/in. or watt-sec/in.)

K = ratio of minimum to maximum load (fatigue); ratio of web depth to web thickness; distance from outer face of beam flange to web toe of fillet (in.); thermal conductivity; any specified constant

L = length of member (in. or ft.); span between supports (in.)

L_e = effective length of column

M = bending moment (in.-lbs)

M_o = applied bending moment (in.-lbs)

M_p = plastic moment at connection (in.-lbs)

N = number of service cycles; minimum bearing length of beam on seat (in.)

P = concentrated load (lbs)

Q = shear center; statical moment of cover plate area about neutral axis of cover-plated beam section

R = reaction (lbs); torsional resistance of member (in.^{4}); weld cooling rate (°F/sec)

S = section modulus (in.^{3}) = I/c

T = torque or twisting moment (in.-lbs); temperature (°F)

U = stored energy

V = vertical shear load (lbs); shear reaction; velocity; volume; arc speed (in./min)

W = total load (lbs); weight (lbs); total width (in.)

Y = effective bearing length on base plate (in.)

Z = plastic section modulus (in.^{3})

C.G. = center of gravity

HP = horsepower

N.A. = neutral axis

RPM = revolutions per minute

Introduction to Welded Construction

1. WELDING'S IMPORTANCE TO STRUCTURAL FIELD

Welding has been an important factor in our economy. The progress made in welding equipment and electrodes, the advancing art and science of designing for welding, and the growth in trust and acceptance of welding have combined to make welding a powerful implement for an expanding construction industry.

More and more buildings and bridges are being built according to the precepts of good welded design. The economies inherent in welding are helping to offset evolutionary increases in the prices of materials and cost of labor. In addition, the shortened production cycles, made possible by welding, have helped effect a quickening in the pace of new construction.

Welded construction has paid off handsomely for many architects, structural engineers, contractors, and their client-customers. It will become increasingly important as more people acquire a greater depth of knowledge and experience with it.

2. RECOGNITION OF WELDING

The widespread recognition of welding as a safe means of making structural connections has come about only after years of diligent effort, pioneering action by the more progressive engineers and builders, and heavy documentation of research findings and successes attained.

Today, there just aren't many men in industry who speak disparagingly of welding. Most regulatory agencies of local and federal government now accept welded joints which meet the requirements imposed by codewriting bodies such as the American Institute of Steel Construction and the American Welding Society.

With this acceptance, there remains however a considerable task of education and simple dissemination of information to achieve maximum efficiency in the application of welded design. And, there is even a continuing need for more thorough understanding of welding by codewriting bodies who fail to use the full strength of welded joints.

3. WHY WELDED CONSTRUCTION?

There are many reasons for using welded design and construction, but probably the two basic ones are 1) welded design offers the opportunity to achieve more efficient use of materials, and 2) the speed of fabrication and erection can help compress production schedules, enabling the entire industry to be more sensitive and react faster to rapidly shifting market needs.

Freedom of Design

Welding permits the architect and structural engineer complete freedom of design—freedom to develop and use modern economical design principles, freedom to

FIG. 1 Indicative of the design freedom offered by unitized welding design, the Yale Rare Book Library's four outside walls are each a 5-story high Vierendeel truss. Each is a network of Greek-type crosses. The structure is all welded—shop and field.

employ the most elementary or most daring concepts of form, proportion and balance to satisfy the need for greater aesthetic value. Just about anything the designer may envision can now be given reality . . . because of welding.

Welded construction imposes no restrictions on the thinking of the designer. Already, this has resulted in wide usage of such outstanding design advancements as open-web expanded beams and girders, tapered beams and girders, Vierendeel trusses, cellular floor construction, orthotropic bridge decks, composite floor construction, and tubular columns and trusses.

Weld Metal Superior to Base Metal

A welded joint basically is one-piece construction. All of the other methods of connecting members are mechanical lap joints. A properly welded joint is stronger than the material joined. The fused joints create a rigid structure in contrast to the nonrigid structure made with mechanical joints. The compactness and calculable degree of greater rigidity permits design assumptions to be realized more accurately. Welded joints are better for fatigue loads, impact loads, and severe vibration.

Welding Saves Weight, Cuts Costs

Connecting steel plates are reduced or eliminated since they often are not required. Welded connections save steel because no deductions need be made for holes in the plate: the gross section is effective in carrying loads. They offer the best method of making rigid connections, resulting in reduced beam depth and weight.

This reduced beam depth can noticeably lower the overall height of a building. The weight of the structure and therefore static loading is greatly reduced. This saves column steel, walls and partitions, facia, and reduced foundation requirements.

Welded connections are well suited to the new field of plastic design, resulting in further appreciable weight savings over conventional rigid frame design.

Savings in transportation, handling time, and erection are proportional to the weight savings.

Available Standards

Arc welding, either in the shop or in the field, has been used long enough to have been proved thoroughly dependable. The AWS and AISC have set up dependable standards for all phases of structural activity. These standards are backed up by years of research and actual testing. They simplify the design of welded connections and facilitate acceptance by purchasers and inspectors.

Other Advantages

Less time is required on detailing, layout and fabrication since fewer pieces are used. Punching or drilling, and reaming or countersinking are eliminated—a substantial saving on large projects.

The typical welded joint produces a smooth, uncluttered connection that can be left exposed, without detracting from the appearance of the structure. Welded

FIG. 2 The athletic unit of Ladue Jr. High School (Missouri) features an all-welded steel lamella roof frame spanning 252′, expressing the strength of one-piece welded construction.

joints exhibit less corrosion and require little or no maintenance. The smooth welded joints also make it easier to install masonry, facia and other close fitting members, often reducing the thickness of walls or floors in buildings.

Structures can be erected in relative silence, a definite asset in building in downtown areas, near office buildings or hospitals.

4. HOW GOOD IS A WELD?

Many engineers are unaware of the great reserve of strength that welds have, and in many cases this is not recognized by code bodies.

Notice in Table 1 that the minimum yield strengths of the ordinary E60xx electrodes are about 50% higher than the corresponding values of the A7, A373 and A36 structural steels with which they would be used.

TABLE 1—Comparison of Typical Weld Metals and Steels

Material		Minimum Yield Strength	Minimum Tensile Strength
AWS A5.1 &	E6010	50,000 psi	62,000 psi
ASTM A233	E6012	55,000	67,000
Weld	E6024	50,000	62,000
Metal	E6027	50,000	62,000
(as welded)	E70xx	60,000	72,000
	A7	33,000	60,000 to 75,000
ASTM	A373	32,000	58,000 to 75,000
Steels	A36	36,000	58,000 to 80,000
	A441	42,000	63,000
		46,000	67,000
		50,000	70,000

Many of the commercial E60xx electrodes also meet E70xx specifications. Used on the same A7, A373 and A36 steels, they have about 75% higher yield strength than the steel.

There are numerous reasons why weld metal has higher strength than the corresponding plate. The two most important are:

1. The core wire used in the electrode is of premium steel, held to closer specifications than the plate.

2. There is complete shielding of the molten metal during welding. This, plus the scavenging and deoxidizing agents and other ingredients in the electrode coating, produces a uniformity of crystal structure and physical properties on a par with electric furnace steel.

Because of these, properly deposited welds have a tremendous reserve of strength or factor of safety, far beyond what industry specifications usually recognize. But even without a reduced safety factor, there is a considerable cost advantage.

Inspection and Quality

Much money is spent annually by industry and government in obtaining and inspecting for a specified weld quality. Usually the weld quality specified is obtained, but too often the quality specified has little or no relation to service requirements.

Welds that meet the actual service requirements, at the least possible cost, are the result of—

1) proper design of connections and joints,
2) good welding procedure,
3) good weldor technique and workmanship, and
4) intelligent, responsible inspection.

In the following examples (Figures 3, 4, 5 and 6) test specimens exhibit undercut, undersize, lack of fusion, and porosity. In spite of these adverse conditions,

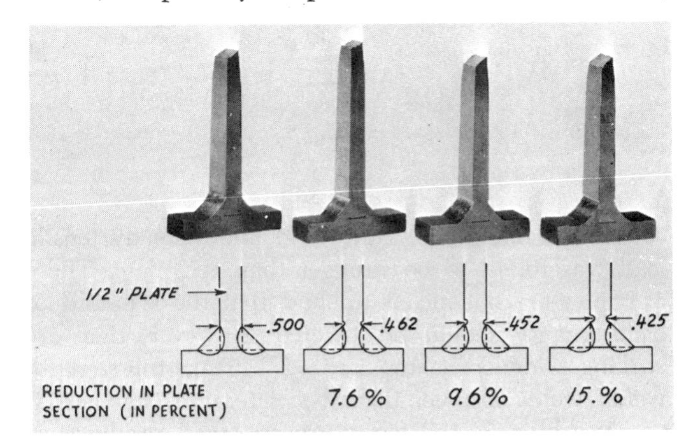

FIG. 3 Test samples prepared to show effect of undercut. Samples were pulled in tension under a static load; in all cases failure occurred in the plate and not in the weld.

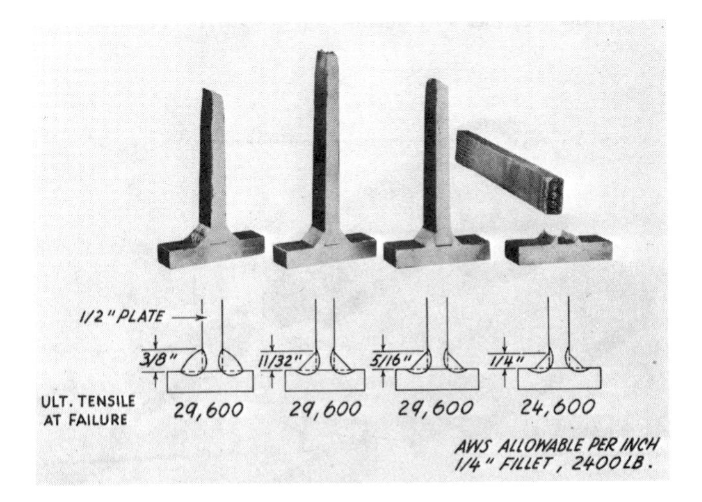

FIG. 4 One rule of thumb says fillet size should equal 3/4 plate thickness to develop full plate strength. Using this method, a 3/8" fillet weld on 1/2" plate should "beat the plate". But so did 11/32" and 5/16" fillets. Not until fillet size was reduced to 1/4" did weld failure occur . . . at a stress of 12,300 lbs/linear in., more than 5 times the AWS allowable.

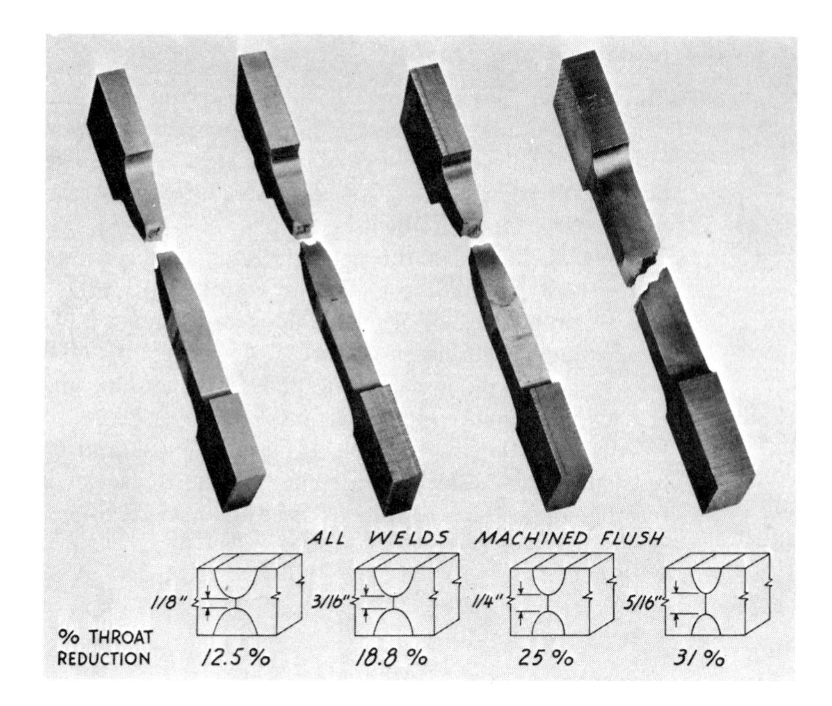

FIG. 5 Weld samples were made, with varying degrees of lack of fusion, as reduced-section tensile specimens. Welds were machined flush before testing, and weld failure did not occur until the unpenetrated throat dimension had reached 31% of the total joint throat.

considered individually, the weld under steady tensile load was found to be stronger than the plate. These examples are not meant to show that the standard of weld quality should be lowered. However, they are striking evidence of how easy it is to make full-strength welds, welds stronger than the plate.

Welding is the only process that produces a unitized, or one-piece, construction. The welded plate is so sound, strong, and ductile as to permit some testing procedures that frequently are impossible or impractical to perform with other connection methods.

The weld is so ductile that it can be readily bent around a small radius, Figure 7. Apparently because it is possible to do so, bend tests are often required. Unfortunately, U-bend test results do not correlate well with actual service performance.

Because it is possible to examine a welded joint by radiographic inspection, some engineers feel this must be done.

Most radiographic inspection is based on responsible standards. These specifications assure the quality required, yet are realistic. Frequently, however, local decisions are made to require more perfect radiographic soundness than the specifications demand.

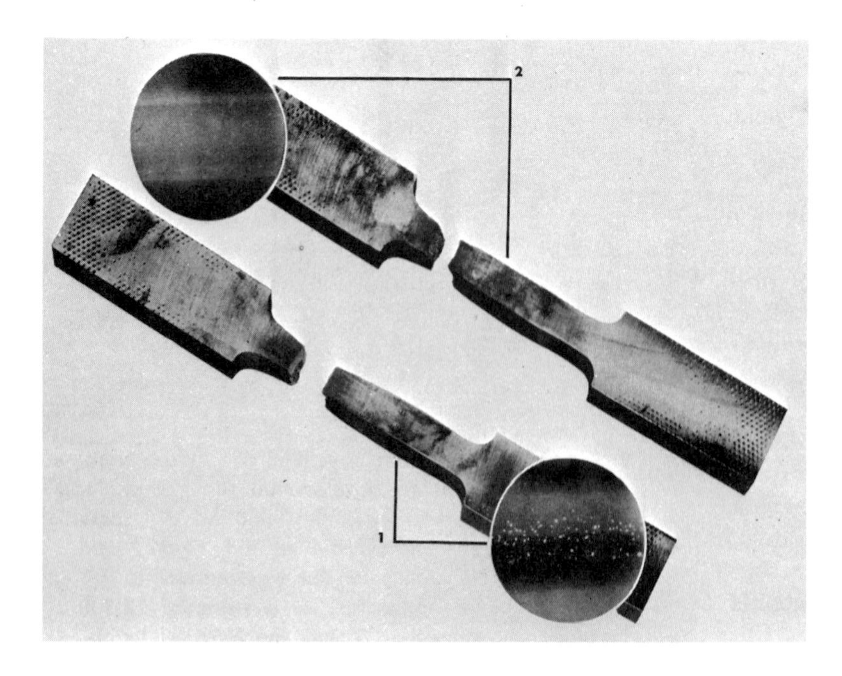

FIG. 6 Excessive porosity (weld 1) as shown by radiograph did not weaken the joint. Weld 2 shows perfect. In both cases the weld was stronger than the plate. Specimens broke in the plate at approximately 60,100 psi.

How Important Is Porosity?

Normally, porosity if it should exist is not a problem, because each void is spherical. It does not represent a notch. Even with a slight loss in section because of the void, its spherical shape allows a smooth flow of stress around the void without any measurable loss in strength.

Tests have shown that a weld can contain a large amount of porosity without materially changing the tensile or impact strength and ductility of the weld. This porosity could amount in total volume to a void equal to 7% of the weld's cross-section without impairing the joint's performance.

The ASME Boiler and Pressure Vessel Code, Section VIII and X, will allow porosity in a weld to the extent shown on charts incorporated into the Code. These charts consider size, distribution, and alignment of voids, versus plate thickness.

The AWS Building Code will allow a slight porosity if well dispersed in the weld. This is defined as "gas pockets and any similar generally globular type voids."

The AWS Bridge Specification allows some porosity. For porosity above $1/16''$ in void size, a table shows minimum clearance between voids and maximum size of void for any given plate thickness.

5. DESIGN FOR WELDING

A designer must know the fundamental differences between welding and other assembly methods if he is to detail economical welded members. If a welded girder,

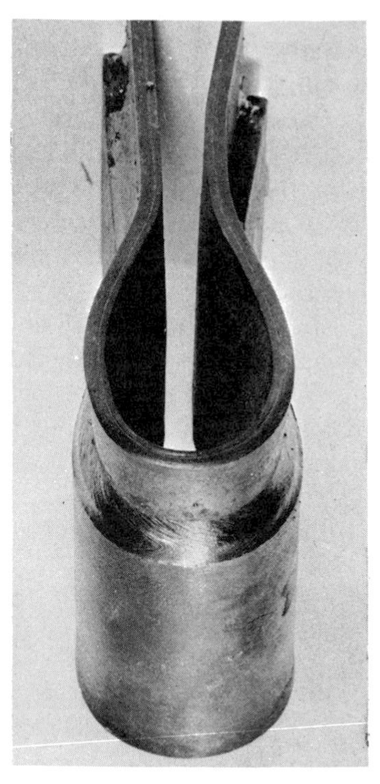

FIG. 7 Weld metal in well-designed joints demonstrate much greater ductility than would be required in any type of structures.

for example, were constructed with multiple cover plates, the cost would be excessive. The use of only one flange plate with a reasonable number of butt welded splices, at points where the plate thickness can be reduced, is usually adequate and also gives improved fatigue resistance.

The selection of a connecting system should be made at the design level; for some types of structures, may even influence the architectural concept itself.

FIG. 8 Many contemporary structures are using exposed steel framing as part of the artistic scheme. Welding provides the unencumbered simplicity of form essential to the modern look in architecture, typified in this showcase building.

The most efficient use of steel is achieved with welded design, the advantages of which grow with the size of the structure. In fact, the full advantages of using steel in competition with other materials will only be realized when the structure is erected as a welded design, and when fabricators and erectors use modern techniques of welding, production scheduling, and materials handling.

A welded office building in Dallas, Texas, is an example of the economies possible in structural welding. The building is 413 feet high, has 34 floors, and contains 600,000 square feet of usable floor space. The savings are impressive. The contractor states that by designing for welding he saved 650 tons of steel. Comparison estimates show an additional saving of approximately $16.00 per ton in fabrication and erection. Futhermore, approximately six months in construction time will be saved as a result of using a welded steel frame.

FIG. 9 Welded connections contributed to safer and more economical erection of the stately 33-story Hartford Building in San Francisco, California's tallest skyscraper. Semi-automatic welding, using self-shielding cored electrode, speeded completion of 80 beam-to-column connections per floor.

Comparative experience has proved that had this type structure involved welded connections that were simply converted from another type of connection, there still would have been savings but substantially less than when designing specifically for welding.

6. WELDED DESIGN OF BUILDINGS

The taller that buildings grow, the greater the role of welding. This applies to the shop fabrication of columns and other structurals, and also to the field welding associated with erection.

A majority of the more recently built skyscrapers are of welded design. These are found in all sections of the country, including earthquake-prone San Francisco.

Expanded open-web beams and girders—fabricated from standard rolled beams—are providing great savings in both bridge and building design. An open-web girder designed to have the required moment of inertia will result in a weight saving as high as 50%. In multi-story buildings, where utility supply lines can be run through these beams and girders rather than suspended below, the overall building height is substantially shortened. This results in significant savings in material costs—for columns, facia, stairs, etc.

The ease with which tapered beams and girders can be fabricated from standard rolled beams permits an endless variety of savings in building design. Tapered spandrel beams are often made deep enough at the column end to reduce the bending force and eliminate need for column stiffeners. The spandrel beam is shop welded to the column for lowest cost and shipped to the site.

Special built-up columns can be used to obtain open, column-free interiors, to mount facia economically, to provide the steel-and-glass look which dominates today's downtown and industrial park architecture.

The new look in building design—especially research centers, office buildings, libraries and museums —calls for a heavy use of exposed steels, including the corrosion-resistant steels such as ASTM A242. The clean trim lines which are demanded with this use of exposed steel can be achieved only by welding.

Light, airy roof supporting space frames—three-dimensional truss systems—are being shop-fabricated in sections, final assembled on the ground at the site and lifted into place. Welding facilitates the use of such designs, since there is a lack of extraneous material in the multiplicity of connections as would be the case with any other means of assembly.

Plastic design does not use the conventional allowable stresses, but rather the calculated ultimate load-carrying capacity of the structure. In the case of rigid framing, plastic design requires less engineering time than does conventional elastic design and, in most cases, results in significant savings in steel over the use of elastic design. Welding is the most practical method of making connections for plastic design. This is because the connection must allow the members to reach their full plastic moments with sufficient strength, adequate rotational ability, and proper stiffness.

7. WELDED CONSTRUCTION OF BRIDGES

Today bridges of every type—suspension, arch, truss, plate and box girder, etc.—are constructed of steel because of strength, dependability, and permanence. Because there are no limitations placed on welding, the bridge engineer is not limited or restricted in his thinking. Due to this new freedom of design effected by welding, some rather unusual and unique bridges have appeared in recent years.

The State of Connecticut has favored welding design for its highway bridges for over 20 years. The Turnpike has 28 all-welded bridges, the largest of which is the 24-span, 2661-foot Mianus River Bridge at Greenwich. The experience of the States of Connecticut, New York, Texas, California and Kansas has clearly shown that substantial savings are possible in properly designed welded bridges.

Bridge girders of variable depth enhance the appearance of the structure, while placing the metal where needed and taking it away where shallower section depth is permissible—thereby saving tons of steel.

A 900′ long welded bridge spanning the tracks of the Erie Railroad on the New York Thruway had to be shaped to meet site requirements. The Thruway at this point is on both a vertical grade and a horizontal curve, requiring superelevation. It is estimated that more-flexible welded design also developed a 50% savings in the weight of steel.

In both building and bridge construction, the development of welded shear connectors and specialized welding equipment for attaching such connectors has accelerated the use of composite floor construction —where the concrete and steel act together with a strength greater than either component, resulting in large savings.

Orthotropic bridge design, long accepted in Europe, is coming into prominence in America as a major approach to reduction of bridge costs. This concept calls for the complete deck to act as a unit. Orthotropic design could not be executed without welding.

FIG. 10 Large bridge sections are shop-fabricated, shipped to the site, and lifted into position. This lowers erection costs and compresses the project timetable.

8. WELDED CONSTRUCTION OF OTHER STRUCTURES

Welding has facilitated the design and construction of a great variety of structures with the contemporary look. Even water towers have taken on a beauty that complements adjacent architecture.

Stadiums for big-league sports clubs and for big-name colleges are leaning heavily on welding. Among these are Shea Stadium, Anaheim's new home for the Angels, and others. A very unique feature of the modern stadium resulting from welded steel design is the cantilevered roof which removes columns as obstructions to spectator vision and pleasure.

Towers, space needles, huge radio telescopes, radar antennas, off-shore drilling rigs, ore unloaders, and many other structures are being designed for welded construction.

9. REVOLUTION IN SHOP FABRICATION & ERECTION

Today's structure goes up quickly due to welding. The trend is to build the structure on a sub-assembly basis, doing as much work as possible under ideal shop conditions where mass-production techniques can be fully employed.

The progress made in recent years in automatic and semi-automatic welding equipment and in positioners and manipulators has made shop fabrication of special girders, knees, and built-up columns extremely attractive. In many cases, the ingenious designer can make tremendous savings through the design of special structural members. This includes members having complex cross-sectional configuration and hybrid members that are a mix of steels having different analyses.

Modern structural fabricating shops have fixtures for assembling plates into columns and girders, manipulators for welding automatically, and positioners for supporting members so that attaching plates may be welded in the flat position.

Welding developments in the past few years have greatly increased welding speeds, while assuring high quality welds. In submerged-arc welding the use of multiple arcs, with two and three welding heads has tremendously increased welding speeds. Continuous wire processes for semi-mechanized welding for both shop and field applications have substantially increased productivity.

Much progress has been made in automatic manipulators, enabling the welding head to be put into proper alignment with the joint of the member in a matter of seconds. This alignment is automatically maintained along the length of the joint during welding. These manipulators represent a major cost reduction possibility. As the size of the structure increases, the total arc time on a welded job becomes a decreasingly smaller percentage of the total fabricating time. Thus savings in handling time and increasing manufacturing cycle efficiency are the major potentials for cost reduction.

Semi-automatic field welding is speeding up erection and lowering costs. Submerged-arc has long been used in the field for flat welding. Recently the use of self-shielding cored electrode wire, automatically fed, has greatly extended the speed and uniform quality inherent with semi-automatic welding. This process is rapidly winning general acceptance. It is not affected by rather severe wind and other adverse climatic conditions. Both submerged-arc and certain cored electrode processes are considered low hydrogen.

1/2" FILLETS ON BEAMS AND COLUMNS

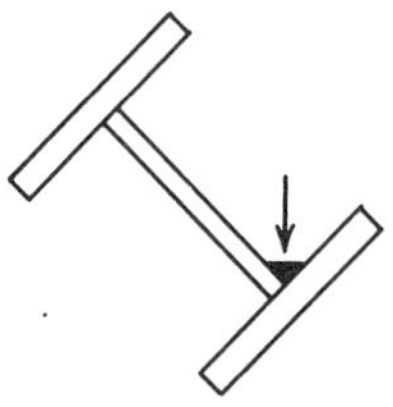

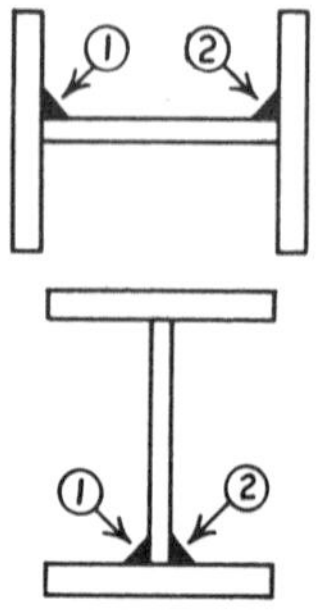

WELDING METHOD	ARC SPEED IN./MIN.
STICK ELECTRODE (E7028)	5 1/2
SINGLE ARC SEMI-AUTOMATIC (SUB-ARC)	12
SINGLE ARC SEMI-AUTOMATIC (INNERSHIELD)	12
SINGLE ARC AUTOMATIC (SUB-ARC)	15
TWIN ARC AUTOMATIC (SUB-ARC)	25
TANDEM ARC AUTOMATIC (SUB-ARC)	30
TANDEM AUTOMATICS (SUB-ARC) ① (BOTH WELDS ① AND ② SIMULTANEOUSLY = 36 IN. 1/2 FILLET/MIN.)	18 (2=36)
TRIPLE TANDEM AUTOMATICS (SUB-ARC) ① (BOTH WELDS ① AND ② SIMULTANEOUSLY = 50 IN. 1/2 FILLET/MIN)	25 (2=50)

FIG. 11 Many fabricating shops have realized substantial savings through step up in selection of welding process and equipment. This chart shows numerous ways to make the 1/2" fillet weld, which is common to many large structural members.

Properties of Materials

1. IMPORTANCE OF PROPERTIES

All materials have certain properties which must be known in order to promote their proper use. These properties are essential to selection of the best material for a given member.*

In the design of structural members, the properties of materials which are of primary concern are those that indicate material behavior under certain types of load. Some property of material is called for in each of the basic design formulas.

Properties commonly found in engineering handbooks and suppliers catalogs are these:

1. ultimate tensile strength
2. yield strength in tension
3. elongation
4. modulus of elasticity
5. compressive strength
6. shear strength
7. fatigue strength

Other properties such as modulus of resilience and ultimate energy resistance, may also be given.

Tables 1 and 2 present physical properties and chemical composition of various steels. These are proprietary steels that are not provided for by the ASTM specifications for basic steels used in the structural field. The specification steels are covered in Section 7.1 on the Selection of Structural Steel.

* Also see "Metals and How to Weld Them" by T. B. Jefferson and G. Woods; James F. Lincoln Arc Welding Foundation.

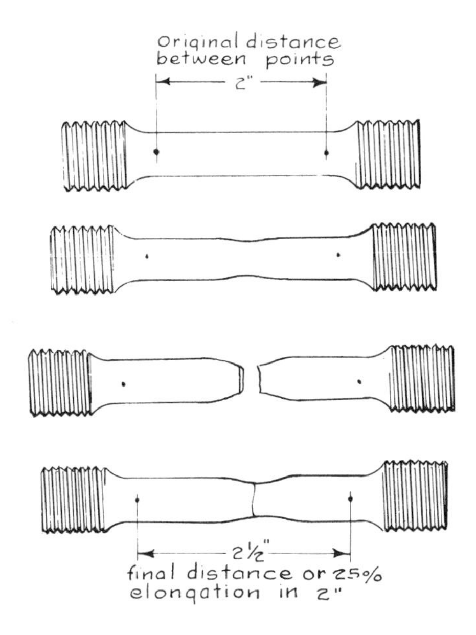

FIG. 1 Tensile test specimen before and after testing to failure, showing maximum elongation.

TABLE 1—Properties and Composition of Constructional Alloy Steels

Producer	Alloy	Yield Point, psi	Ult. Strength, psi	Elong., %	C	Mn	Si	Cu	Mo	Cr	Ni	Other
					Nominal Composition, %							
Great Lakes Steel	N-A-Xtra 80	80,000	95,000	18	0.15	0.80	0.70		0.20	0.65		0.09 Zr
	90	90,000	105,000	18	0.15	0.80	0.70		0.20	0.65		0.09 Zr
	100	100,000	115,000	18	0.15	0.80	0.70		0.20	0.65		0.09 Zr
	110	110,000	125,000	18	0.15	0.80	0.70		0.20	0.65		0.09 Zr
Jones & Laughlin	Jalloy-S-90	90,000	105,000	18	0.15	1.25	0.25		0.25			
	Jalloy-S-100	100,000	115,000	18	0.15	1.25	0.25		0.25			Cb
	Jalloy-S-110	110,000	125,000	18	0.15	1.25	0.25		0.25			Cb
Lukens Steel	T-1	100,000	115,000	18	0.15	0.80	0.25	0.35	0.55	0.60	0.85	V, B
Republic Steel	Republic 65	65,000	85,000	20	0.15	1.00	0.15	1.15	0.25		1.25	
	70	70,000	90,000	18	0.20	1.00	0.15	1.25	0.25		1.50	
US Steel	T-1	100,000	115,000	18	0.15	0.80	0.25	0.35	0.55	0.60	0.85	V, B
Youngstown Sheet & Tube	Yoloy S	65,000	95,000	20	0.12	0.60	0.30	1.00			1.80	

— Table courtesy PRODUCT ENGINEERING Magazine

TABLE 2—Properties and Composition of High-Strength Low Alloy Steels

Producer	Alloy	Yield Point, psi	Ult. Strength, psi	Elong., %	Nominal Composition, % C	Mn	Si	Cu	Mo	Cr	Ni	Other
Alan Wood Steel	Dynalloy I	50,000	70,000	22	0.15	0.80	0.30	0.45	0.10		0.55	
	Dynalloy II	45,000	62,000	25	0.15	0.80	0.30	0.45	0.10		0.55	
Armco Steel	High Strength No. 1	50,000	70,000	22	0.15	0.70	0.15	0.60			0.75	
	2	45,000	64,000		0.15	0.70	0.15	0.60			0.75	
	3	40,000	60,000	35	0.10	0.60	0.10	0.20				0.02 V
	4	50,000	70,000	22	0.25	1.35	0.25	0.20				
	5	45,000	60,000	25	0.22	1.25	0.30	0.20				0.02 V
Bethlehem Steel	Mayari R	50,000	70,000	22	0.12	0.75	0.55	0.50		0.70	1.0	0.10 Zr
	Medium Manganese	50,000	75,000	20	0.25	1.35	0.30	0.30				
	Manganese Vanadium	50,000	70,000	22	0.22	1.25	0.30	0.20				0.02 V
Crucible Steel of America	Maxeloy	50,000	70,000	22	0.15	1.20	0.50	0.20			0.50	
Colorado Fuel & Iron	Clay-Loy	50,000	70,000		0.22	1.25	0.35	0.50				0.2 V
Inland Steel	Hi-Steel	50,000	70,000	22	0.12	0.75	0.15	0.95	0.18		0.55	
	Hi-Man	50,000	75,000	20	0.25	1.35	0.30	0.20				
	Hi-Man 440 (A440)	50,000	70,000		0.28	1.35	0.30	0.20				
	Tri-Steel	50,000	70,000	22	0.22	1.25	0.30	0.20				0.02 V
Jones & Laughlin	Jalten No. 1	50,000	70,000	22	0.15	1.30	0.10	0.30				0.05 V
	2	50,000	70,000	22	0.15	1.40	0.10	0.30				
	3	50,000	70,000	22	0.25	1.50	0.25	0.20				
	JLX-45-W	45,000	65,000	22	0.15	0.75	0.10					0.03 Cb
	-50-W	50,000	70,000	22	0.15	0.75	0.10					0.03 Cb
	-55-W	55,000	75,000	22	0.15	0.75	0.10					0.03 Cb
	-60-W	60,000	80,000	22	0.15	0.75	0.10					0.03 Cb
Kaiser Steel	Kaisaloy No. 1	50,000	70,000	23	0.20	1.25	0.60	0.35	0.15	0.25	0.60	V, Ti
	2	45,000	60,000	25	0.12	0.60	0.50	0.30	0.10	0.25	0.60	V, Ti
	3	58,000	83,000	15	0.30	1.50	0.35	0.35	0.10	0.25	0.40	V, Ti
	Structural High Strength	50,000	75,000	18	0.27	1.60	0.30	0.20				
Lukens Steel	Cor-Ten	50,000	70,000	22	0.12	0.35	0.50	0.40		0.80	0.65	
National Steel (Great Lakes Steel and Weirton Steel)	GLX-45-W	45,000	65,000	22	0.15	0.75	0.10					0.03 Cb
	GLX-50-W	50,000	70,000	22	0.15	0.75	0.10					0.03 Cb
	GLX-55-W	55,000	75,000	22	0.15	0.75	0.10					0.03 Cb
	GLX-60-W	60,000	80,000	22	0.15	0.75	0.10					0.03 Cb
	N-A-X High Tensile	50,000	70,000	22	0.15	0.75	0.75	0.25	0.20	0.55		0.10 Zr
	N-A-X High Manganese	50,000	70,000	22	0.25	1.35	0.30	0.20				
Pittsburgh Steel	Pitt-Ten No. 1	50,000	70,000	22	0.12	0.75	0.20	0.85			0.70	
Republic Steel	Republic 50	50,000	70,000	22	0.15	0.75		0.65	0.10	0.30	0.75	
	Republic M	50,000	75,000	20	0.25	1.35	0.30	0.20				
US Steel	Cor-Ten	50,000	70,000	22	0.12	0.35	0.50	0.40		0.80	0.65	
	Ex-Ten-45	45,000			0.20	0.75	0.10					0.01 Cb
	Ex-Ten-50	50,000			0.25	0.75	0.10					0.01 Cb
	Man-Ten	50,000	75,000	20	0.25	1.35	0.30	0.20				
	Man-Ten (A440)	50,000	70,000		0.28	1.35	0.30	0.20				
	Par-Ten	45,000	62,000	28	0.12	0.75	0.10					0.04 V
	Tri-Ten	50,000	70,000	22	0.22	1.25	0.30	0.20				0.02 V
Youngstown Sheet & Tube	Yoloy	50,000	70,000	22	0.15	0.75	0.30	1.00			1.70	
	Yoloy A242	50,000	70,000	22	0.22	1.25	0.30	0.20				0.02 V
	Yoloy E HSX	45,000	80,000	25	0.18	1.00	0.30	0.35		0.40	0.70	
	Yoloy EHS	50,000	70,000	22	0.18	1.00	0.30	0.35	0.40	0 40	0.70	
	Yoloy M-A	50,000	70,000	20	0.25	1.60	0.30	0.35				
	Yoloy M-B	45,000	70,000	22	0.23	1.40	0.25	0.20				
	Yoloy 45W	45,000	65,000	30	0.15	0.65						Cb
	Yoloy 50W	50,000	70,000	28	0.15	0.65						Cb

- Table courtesy PRODUCT ENGINEERING Magazine

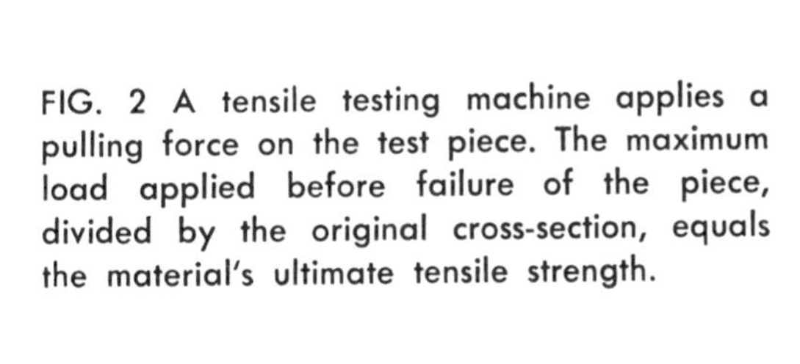

FIG. 2 A tensile testing machine applies a pulling force on the test piece. The maximum load applied before failure of the piece, divided by the original cross-section, equals the material's ultimate tensile strength.

The various properties are best defined by a description of what happens when a specimen of the material is subjected to load during laboratory tests.

2. TENSILE PROPERTIES

In a tensile test, the machined and ground specimen of the material is marked with a centerpunch at two points 2″ apart, as shown in Figure 1. The specimen is placed in a tensile testing machine, and an axial load is applied to it by pulling the jaws holding the ends of the specimen in opposing directions at a slow and constant rate of speed, Figure 2.

As the pulling progresses, the specimen elongates at a uniform rate which is proportionate to the rate at which the load or pulling force increases. The load divided by the cross-sectional area of the specimen within the gage marks represents the unit stress or resistance of the material to the pulling or tensile force. This *stress* (σ) is expressed in pounds per square inch, psi. The elongation of the specimen represents the *strain* (ϵ) induced in the material and is expressed in inches per inch of length, in./in. Stress and strain are plotted in a diagram, shown in simplified form in Figure 3.

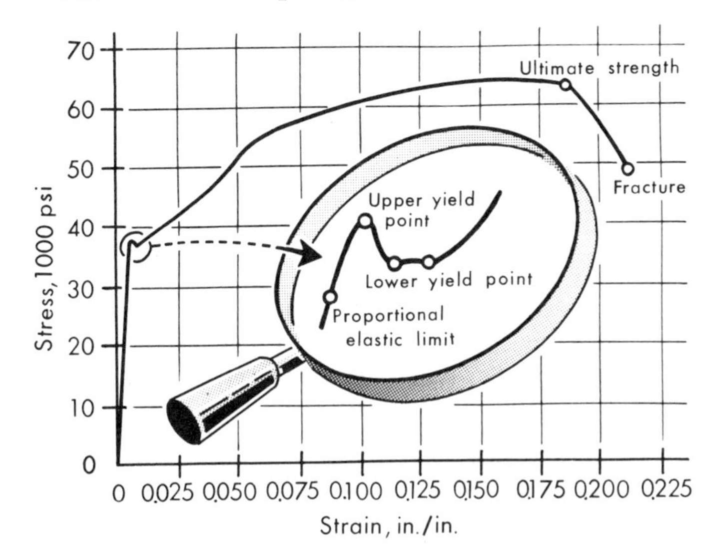

FIG. 3 A stress-strain diagram for mild steel, showing ultimate tensile strength and other properties. Here, the most critical portion of the curve is magnified.

The proportional relationship of load to elongation, or of stress to strain, continues until a point is reached where the elongation begins to increase at a faster rate. This point, beyond which the elongation of the specimen no longer is proportional to the loading, is the *proportional elastic limit* of the material. When the load is removed, the specimen returns to its original dimensions.

Beyond the elastic limit, further movement of the test machine jaws in opposing directions causes a permanent elongation or deformation of the specimen material. In the case of a low- or medium-carbon steel, a point is reached beyond which the metal stretches briefly without an increase in load. This is the yield point.

For low- and medium-carbon steels, the unit stress at the yield point is considered to be the material's *tensile yield strength* (σ_y).* For other metals, the yield strength is the stress required to strain the specimen by a specified small amount beyond the elastic limit. For ordinary commercial purposes, the elastic limit is assumed to coincide with the yield strength.

Beyond the material's elastic limit, continued pulling causes the specimen to neck down across its diameter or width. This action is accompanied by a

* The symbols commonly used for yield strength, ultimate strength, and axial strain do not indicate the type of load.

further acceleration of the axial elongation, which is now largely confined within the relatively short necked-down section.

The pulling force eventually reaches a maximum value and then falls off rapidly, with little additional elongation of the specimen before failure occurs. In failing, the specimen breaks in two within the necked-down portion. The maximum pulling load, expressed as a stress in psi of the original cross-sectional area of the specimen, is the material's ultimate tensile strength (σ_u).

Ductility and Elasticity

The two halves of the specimen are then put together, and the distance between the two punch marks is measured (Fig. 1). The increase in length gives the *elongation* of the specimen in 2″, and is usually expressed as a percentage. The cross-section at point of failure is also measured to give the *reduction in area,* which is usually expressed as a percentage. Both elongation percentage and reduction of area percentage indicate the material's *ductility.*

In the design of most members, it is essential to keep the stresses resulting from loading within the elastic range. If the elastic limit (very close to the material's yield strength) is exceeded, permanent deformation takes place due to plastic flow or slippage along molecular slip planes. When this happens, the material is strain-hardened and thereafter has a higher effective elastic limit and higher yield strength.

Under the same amount of stress, some materials stretch less than others. The *modulus of elasticity* (E) of a material simplifies the comparison of its stiffness

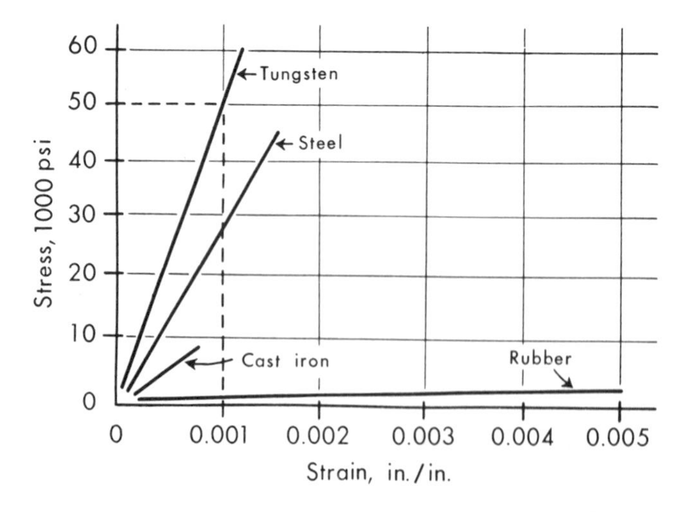

FIG. 4 Stress-strain curves for several materials show their relative elasticity. Only that portion of curve displaying a proportional relationship between stress and strain is diagrammed.

with that of another material. This property is the ratio of the stress to the strain within the elastic range:

$$\frac{\text{Stress } \sigma}{\text{Strain } \epsilon} = \text{Modulus of elasticity E}$$

On a stress-strain diagram, the modulus of elasticity is represented visually by the straight portion of the curve where the stress is directly proportional to the strain. The steeper the curve, the higher the modulus of elasticity and the stiffer the material (Fig. 4).

Any steel has a modulus of elasticity in tension of approximately 30,000,000 psi. AISC in their specifications still use a more conservative value of 29,000,000 psi for the modulus of elasticity of steel. The modulus of elasticity will vary for other metals. Steel, however, has the highest value of any commercially available metal used in the structural field.

3. COMPRESSIVE STRENGTH

The general design practice is to assume that the compressive strength of a steel is equal to its tensile strength. This practice is also adhered to in some rigidity design calculations, where the modulus of elasticity of the material in tension is used even though the loading is compressive.

The actual *ultimate compressive strength* of steels may be somewhat greater than the ultimate tensile strength. The variation in compressive values is at least partially dependent on the condition of the steel: the compressive strength of an annealed steel is closer to its tensile strength than would be the case with a cold-worked steel. (There is less of a relationship between the compressive strength and the tensile strength of cast iron and non-ferrous metals.)

A compressive test is conducted similar to that for tensile properties, but a short specimen is subjected to a compressive load. That is, force is applied on the specimen from two directions in axial opposition. The ultimate compressive strength is reached when the specimen fails by crushing.

A stress-strain diagram is developed during the test, and values are obtained for *compressive yield strength* and other properties. However, instead of the Young's modulus of elasticity conventionally used, the *tangential modulus of elasticity* (E_t) is usually obtained. This will be discussed in Section 3.1 on Compression.

Compression of long columns is more complex, since failure develops under the influence of a bending moment that increases as the deflection increases. Geometry of the member has much to do with its capacity to withstand compressive loads, and this will

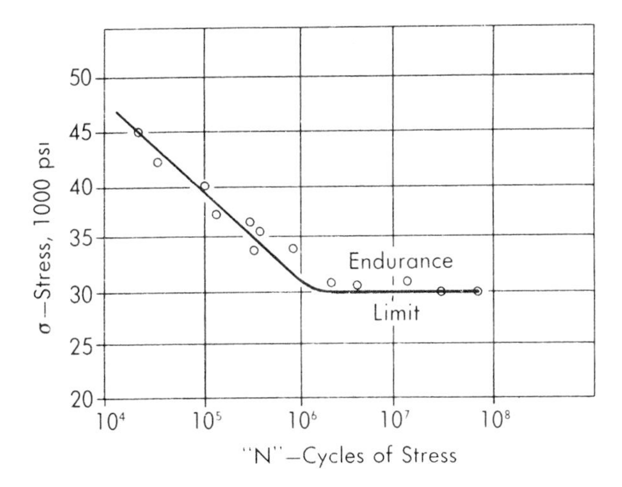

FIG. 5 Fatigue test results are plotted on σ–N diagram; stress vs. number of cycles before failure.

be discussed more completely under Section 3.1.

With long columns, the effect of eccentric loading is more severe in the case of compression than tension.

4. SHEAR STRENGTH

There is no recognized standard method of testing for shear strength of a material. Fortunately, pure shear loads are seldom encountered in structural members but shear stresses frequently develop as a by-product of principal stresses or the application of transverse forces.

The ultimate shear strength is often obtained from an actual shearing of the metal, usually in a punch-and-die setup using a ram moving slowly at a constant rate of speed. The maximum load required to punch through the metal is observed, and ultimate shear strength is calculated from this.

Where it is not practical to physically determine it, the *ultimate shear strength* (τ) is generally assumed to be ¾ the material's ultimate tensile strength for most structural steels.

5. FATIGUE STRENGTH

When the load on a member is constantly varying in value, is repeated at relatively high frequency, or constitutes a complete reversal of stresses with each operating cycle, the material's fatigue strength must be substituted for the ultimate strength where called for by the design formulas.

Under high load values, the variable or fatigue mode of loading reduces the material's effective ultimate strength as the number of cycles increases. At a given high stress value, the material has a definite service life, expressed as "N" cycles of operation.

A series of identical specimens are tested, each under a specific load value expressible as a unit stress. The unit stress is plotted for each specimen against the number of cycles before failure. The result is a σ–N diagram (Fig. 5).

The *endurance limit* (usually σ_r) is the maximum stress to which the material can be subjected for an indefinite service life. Although the standards vary for various types of members and different industries, it is a common practice to accept the assumption that carrying a certain load for several million cycles of stress reversals indicates that load can be carried for an indefinite time.

Theoretically the load on the test specimens should be of the same nature as the load on the proposed member, i.e. tensile, torsional, etc. (Fig. 6).

Since the geometry of the member, the presence of local areas of high stress concentration, and the condition of the material have considerable influence on the real fatigue strength, prototypes of the member or its section would give the most reliable information as test specimens. This is not always practical however. Lacking any test data or handbook values on endurance limit, see Section 2.9 on Fatigue.

6. IMPACT PROPERTIES

Impact strength is the ability of a metal to absorb the energy of a load rapidly delivered onto the member. A metal may have good tensile strength and good ductility under static loading, and yet break if subjected to a high-velocity blow.

The two most important properties that indicate the material's resistance to impact loading are obtained from the stress-strain diagram (Fig. 7). The first of these is the *modulus of resilience* (u) which is a measure of how well the material absorbs energy providing it is not stressed above the elastic limit or yield

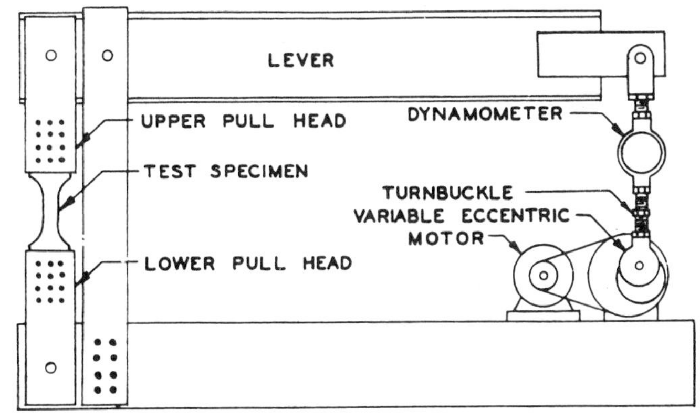

FIG. 6 Typical setup for fatigue testing under pulsating axial stresses.

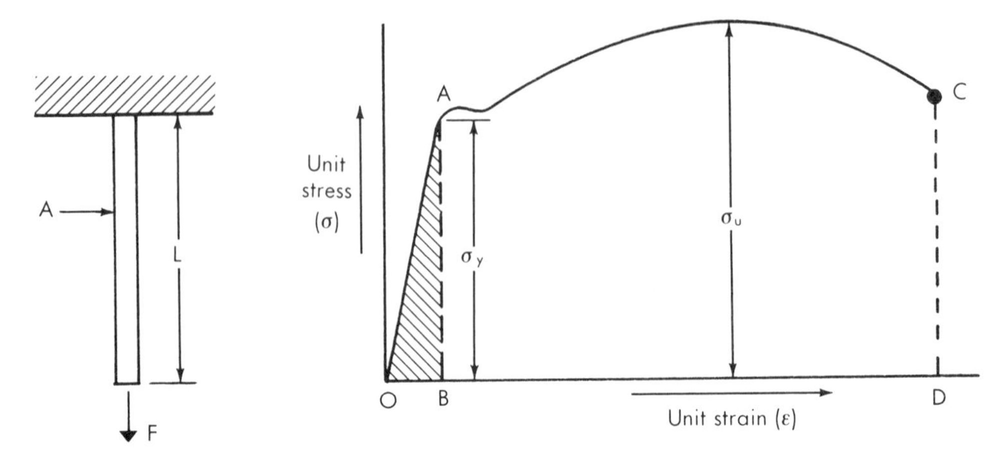

FIG. 7 In the stress-strain diagram for impact, the elongation at moment of ultimate stress is a factor in determining the toughness of the material in terms of ultimate energy resistance.

point. It indicates the material's resistance to deformation from impact loading. (See Section 2.8 on Impact.)

The modulus of resilience (u) is the triangular area OAB under the stress-strain curve having its apex at the elastic limit. For practicality let the yield strength (σ_y) be the altitude of the right triangle and the resultant strain (ϵ_y) be the base. Thus,

$$u = \frac{\sigma^2}{2\,E}$$

where E = modulus of elasticity.

Since the absorption of energy is actually a volumetric property, the u in psi = u in in.-lbs/cu. in.

When impact loading exceeds the elastic limit (or yield strength) of the material, it calls for toughness in the material rather than resilience. Toughness, the ability of the metal to resist fracture under impact loading, is indicated by its *ultimate energy resistance* (u_u). This is a measure of how well the material absorbs energy without fracture.

The ultimate energy resistance (u_u) is the total area OACD under the stress-strain curve. For practicality the following formula can be used:

$$u_u = \frac{\sigma_y + \sigma_u}{2}\,\epsilon_u$$

where:

σ_y = material's shear strength
σ_u = material's ultimate strength
ϵ_u = strain of the material at point of ultimate stress

Since the absorption of energy is actually a volumetric property, the u_u in psi = u_u in in.-lbs/cu. in.

Tests developed for determining the impact strength of materials are often misleading in their results. Nearly all testing is done with notched specimens, in which case it is more accurately the testing for notch toughness.

The two standard tests are the Izod and Charpy. The two types of specimens used in these tests and the method of applying the load are shown in Figure 8. Both tests can be made in a universal impact testing machine. The minimum amount of energy in a falling pendulum required to fracture the specimen is considered to be a measure of the material's impact strength. In actuality, test conditions are seldom duplicated in the working member and application of these test data is unrealistic.

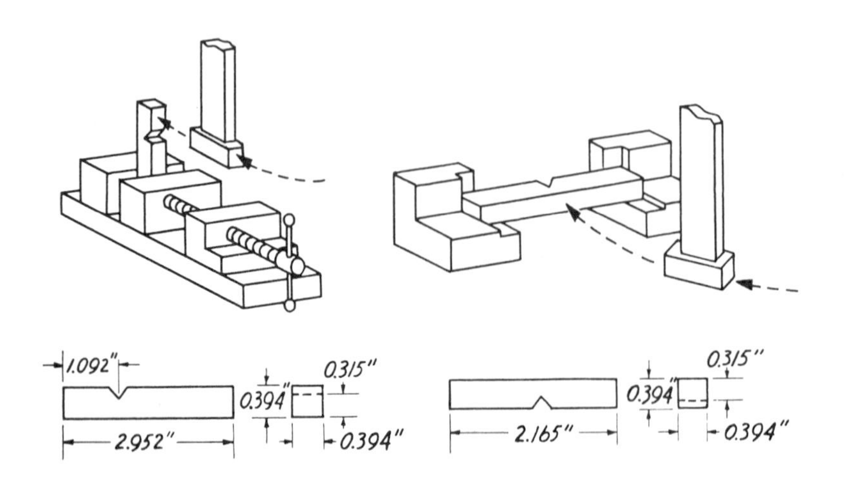

FIG. 8 Typical Izod (left) and Charpy (right) impact test specimens, methods of holding and of applying the test load. The V-notch specimens shown have an included angle of 45° and a bottom radius of 0.010" in the notch.

Properties of Sections

1. IMPORTANCE OF SECTION PROPERTY

The basic formulas used in the design of structural members include as one factor the critical property of the material and as another factor the corresponding critical property of the member's cross-section. The property of the section dictates how efficiently the property of the material will be utilized.

The property of section having the greatest importance is the section's area (A). However, most design problems are not so simple that the area is used directly. Instead there is usually a bending aspect to the problem and, therefore, the rigidity factor normally is the section's moment of inertia (I) and the simple strength factor is the section modulus (S).

Another property of section that is of major importance is the section's torsional resistance (R), a modified value for standard sections.

2. AREA OF THE SECTION (A)

The *area* (A) of the member's cross-section is used directly in computations for simple tension, compression, and shear. Area (A) is expressed in square inches.

If the section is not uniform throughout the length of the member, it is necessary to determine the section in which the greatest unit stresses will be incurred.

3. MOMENT OF INERTIA (I)

Whereas a *moment* is the tendency toward rotation about an axis, the *moment of inertia* of the cross-section of a structural member is a measure of the resistance to rotation offered by the section's geometry and size. Thus, the moment of inertia is a useful property in solving design problems where a bending moment is involved.

The moment of inertia is needed in solving any rigidity problem in which the member is a beam or long column. It is a measure of the stiffness of a beam. Moment of inertia is also required for figuring the value of the polar moment of inertia (J), unless a formula is available for finding torsional resistance (R).

The moment of inertia (I) is used in finding the section modulus (S) and thus has a role in solving simple strength designs as well as rigidity designs. The moment of inertia of a section is expressed in inches raised to the fourth power ($in.^4$).

Finding the Neutral Axis

In working with the section's moment of inertia, the *neutral axis* (N.A.) of the section must be located. In a member subject to a bending load for example, the neutral axis extends through the length of the member parallel to the member's structural axis and perpendicular to the line of applied force. The neutral axis represents zero strain and therefore zero stress. Fibers between the neutral axis and the surface to the inside of the arc caused by deflection under load, are under compression. Fibers between the neutral axis and the surface to the outside of the arc caused by deflection under load, are under tension.

For practical purposes this neutral axis is assumed to have a fixed relationship (n) to some reference axis, usually along the top or bottom of the section. In Figure 1, the reference axis is taken through the base line of the section. The total section is next broken into rectangular elements. The moment (M) of each element about the section's reference axis, is determined:

M = area of element multiplied by the distance (y) of element's center of gravity from reference axis of section

The moments of the various elements are then all added together. This summation of moments is next divided by the total area (A) of the section. This gives the distance (n) of the neutral axis from the reference axis, which in this case is the base line or extreme fiber.

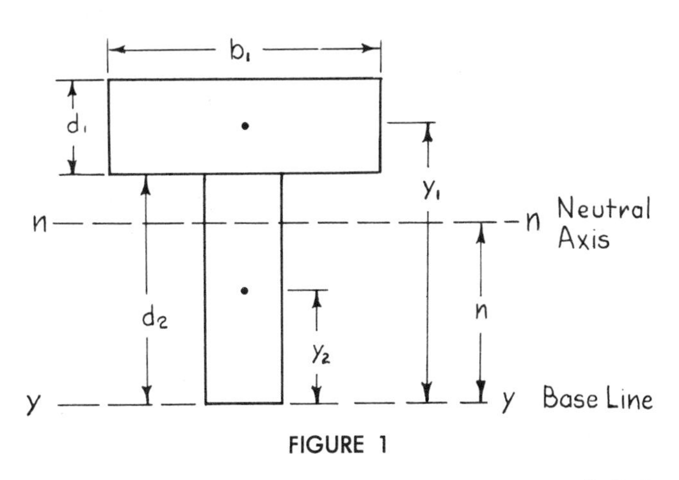

FIGURE 1

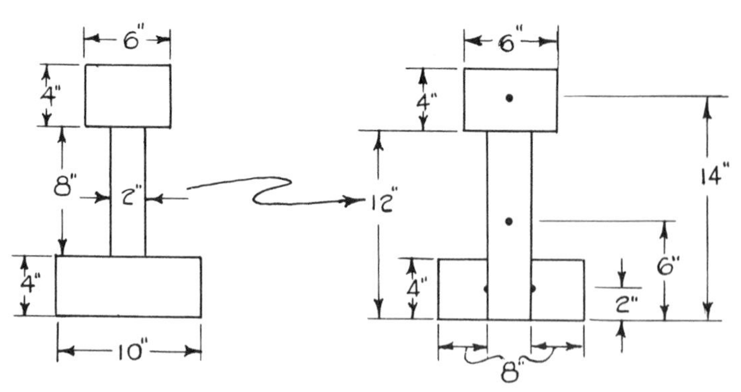

FIGURE 2

Problem 1

The neutral axis of the compound section shown in Figure 2 is located in the following manner:

$$n = \frac{\Sigma M}{\Sigma A} \text{ or } \frac{\text{sum of all moments}}{\text{total area}} \quad \ldots\ldots\ldots\ldots (1)$$

$$= \frac{(4 \cdot 6 \cdot 14) + (2 \cdot 12 \cdot 6) + (4 \cdot 8 \cdot 2)}{(4 \cdot 6) \quad + \quad (2 \cdot 12) \quad + \quad (4 \cdot 8)}$$

$$= \frac{336 + 44 + 64}{24 + 24 + 32} = \frac{544}{80}$$

$$= 6.8''$$

Thus, the neutral axis is located 6.8″ above the reference axis or base line and is parallel to it.

Finding the Moment of Inertia

There are various methods to select from to get the value of moment of inertia (I). Four good methods are presented here.

Moment of Inertia for Typical Sections (First Method)

The first method for finding the moment of inertia is to use the simplified formulas given for typical sections. These are shown in Table 1. This method for finding I is the most appropriate for simple sections that cannot be broken down into smaller elements. In using these formulas, be sure to take the moment of inertia about the correct line. Notice that the moment of inertia for a rectangle about its neutral axis is —

$$I_n = \frac{bd^3}{12} \quad \ldots\ldots\ldots\ldots (2)$$

but the moment of inertia for a rectangle about its base line is —

$$I_b = \frac{bd^3}{3} \quad \ldots\ldots\ldots\ldots (3)$$

where b = width of rectangle, and
d = depth of rectangle

Moment of Inertia by Elements (Second Method)

In the second method, the whole section is broken into rectangular elements. The neutral axis of the whole section is first found. Each element has a moment of inertia about its own centroid or center of gravity (C.G.) equal to that obtained by the formula shown for rectangular sections. (See Table 1.)

In addition, there is a much greater moment of inertia for each element because of the distance of its center of gravity to the neutral axis of the whole section. This moment of inertia is equal to the area of the element multiplied by the distance of its C.G. to the neutral axis squared.

Thus, the moment of inertia of the entire section about its neutral axis equals the summation of the two moments of inertia of the individual elements.

Problem 2

Having already located the neutral axis of the section in Figure 2, the resulting moment of inertia of the section (detailed further in Fig. 3) about its neutral axis is found as follows:

$$I_n = \frac{6 \cdot 4^3}{12} + (6 \cdot 4 \cdot 7.2^2) + \frac{2 \cdot 8^3}{12} +$$

$$(2 \cdot 8 \cdot 1.2^2) + \frac{10 \cdot 4^3}{12} + (10 \cdot 4 \cdot 4.8^2)$$

$$= 32 + 1244 + 85.3 + 23 + 53.3 + 921.6$$

$$= \underline{2359 \text{ in.}^4}$$

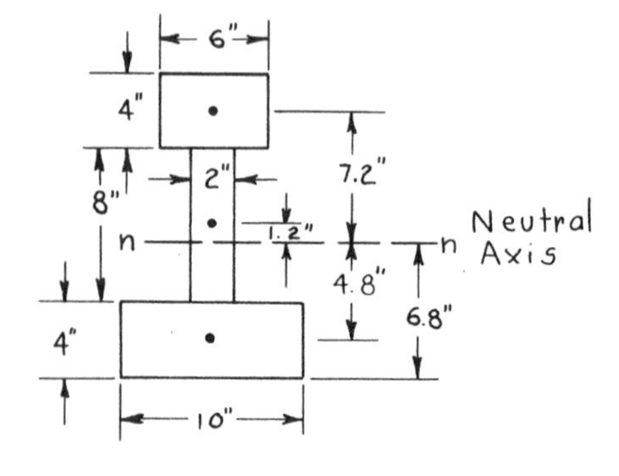

FIGURE 3

Moment of Inertia by Adding Areas (Third Method)

With the third method it is possible to figure moment of inertia of built-up sections without first directly making a calculation for the neutral axis.

This method is recommended for use with built-up girders and columns because the designer can stop briefly as a plate is added to quickly find the new moment of inertia. If this value is not high enough, he simply continues to add more plate and again checks this value without losing any of his previous calculations. Likewise if the value is too high, the designer may deduct some of the plates and again check his result. This is done in the same manner as one using an adding machine, whereby you can stop at any time during adding and take a sub-total, and then proceed along without disrupting the previous figures.

Using the parallel axis theorem for shifting the axis for a moment of inertia, the moment of inertia of the whole section about the reference line y-y is —

$$\boxed{I_y = I_n + A\,n^2} \quad \ldots\ldots\ldots\ldots\ldots\ldots\ldots (4)$$

or

$$\boxed{I_n = I_y - A\,n^2} \quad \ldots\ldots\ldots\ldots\ldots\ldots\ldots (5)$$

$$\text{Since } n = \frac{\text{total moments about base}}{\text{total area}} = \frac{M}{A}$$

$$\text{and of course } n^2 = \frac{M^2}{A^2}$$

Substituting this back into equation (5):

$$I_n = I_y - \frac{A\,M^2}{A^2}$$

Note: neutral axis (n) has dropped out

Thus:

$$\boxed{I_n = I_y - \frac{M^2}{A}} \quad \ldots\ldots\ldots\ldots\ldots\ldots\ldots (6)$$

where:

I_n = moment of inertia of whole section about its neutral axis, n-n

I_y = sum of the moments of inertia of all elements about a common reference axis, y-y

M = sum of the moments of all elements about the same reference axis, y-y

A = total area, or sum of the areas of all elements of section

Although I_y for any individual element is equal to its area (A) multiplied by the distance squared from its center of gravity to the reference axis (y^2), each element has in addition a moment of inertia (I_g) about its own center of gravity. This must be added in if it is large enough, although in most cases it may be neglected:

$$\boxed{I_n = I_y + I_g - \frac{M^2}{A}} \quad \ldots\ldots\ldots\ldots\ldots\ldots (7)$$

The best way to illustrate this method is to work a problem.

TABLE 1—Properties of Standard Sections

	Moment of Inertia I	Section Modulus S	Radius of Gyration r
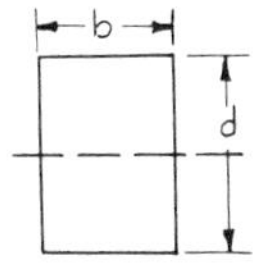	$\frac{bd^3}{12}$	$\frac{bd^2}{6}$	$\frac{d}{\sqrt{12}}$
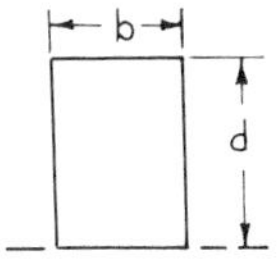	$\frac{bd^3}{3}$	$\frac{bd^2}{3}$	$\frac{d}{\sqrt{3}}$
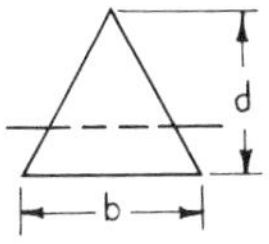	$\frac{bd^3}{36}$	$\frac{bd^2}{24}$	$\frac{d}{\sqrt{18}}$
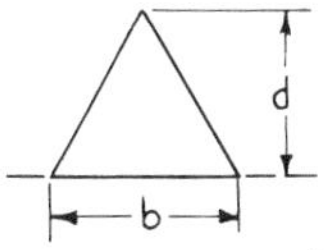	$\frac{bd^3}{12}$	$\frac{bd^2}{12}$	$\frac{d}{\sqrt{6}}$
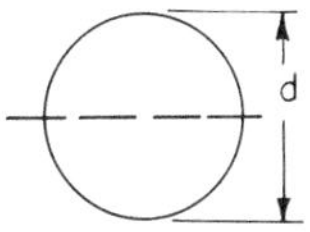	$\frac{\pi d^4}{64}$	$\frac{\pi d^3}{32}$	$\frac{d}{4}$
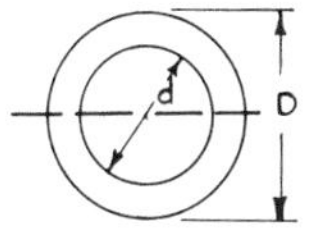	$\frac{\pi}{64}(D^4-d^4)$	$\frac{\pi}{32}\frac{(D^4-d^4)}{D}$	$\frac{\sqrt{D^2+d^2}}{4}$
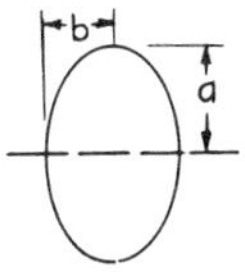	$\frac{\pi a^3 b}{4}$	$\frac{\pi a^2 b}{4}$	$\frac{a}{2}$
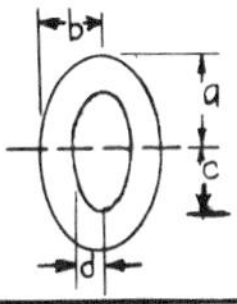	$\frac{\pi}{4}\left(a^3b-c^3d\right)$	$\frac{\pi(a^3b-c^3d)}{4a}$	$\frac{1}{a}\sqrt{\frac{a^3b-c^3d}{ab-cd}}$

Problem 3

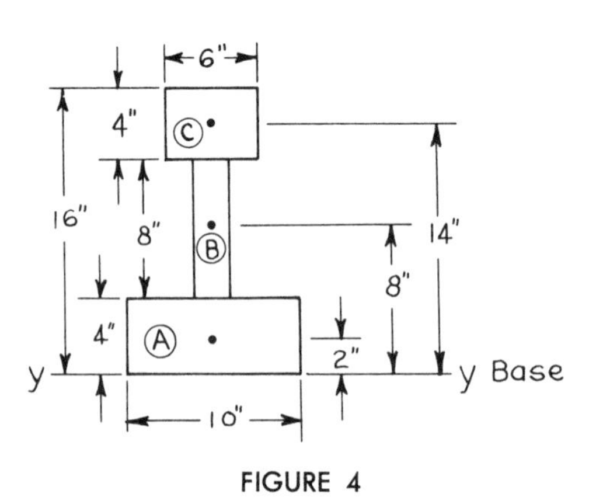

FIGURE 4

The base of this section will be used as a reference axis, y-y. Every time a plate is added, its dimensions are put down in table form, along with its distance (y) from the reference axis. No other information is needed. It is suggested that the plate section size be listed as width times depth ($b \times d$); that is, its width first and depth last.

Plate	Size	Distance y	$A = b \cdot d$ in.^{2}	$M = A \cdot y$ in.^{3}	$I_y = Ay^2 = My$ in.^{4}	$I_g = \frac{bd^3}{12}$ in.^{4}
(A)	10″x4″	2″				
(B)	2″x8″	8″				
(C)	6″x4″	14″				
	Total					

The above table has been filled out with all of the given information from the plates. The rest of the computations are very quickly done on slide rule or calculator and placed into the table. Notice how easy and fast each plate is taken care of.

Starting with plate A, 10″ is multiplied by 4″ to give an area of 40 sq. in. This value is entered into the table under A. Without resetting the slide rule, this figure for A is multiplied by (distance y) 2″ to give 80 inches cubed. This value for the element's moment is placed under M in the table. Without resetting the slide rule, this figure for M is multiplied by (distance y) 2″ again to give 160 inches to the fourth power. This value for the element's moment of inertia about the common reference axis y-y is recorded under (I_y) in the table.

If the moment of inertia (I_g) of the plate about its own center of gravity appears to be significant, this value is figured by multiplying the width of the plate by the cube of its depth and dividing by 12. This value for I_g is then placed in the extreme right-hand column, to be later added in with the sum of I_y. Thus,

$$I_g = \frac{bd^3}{12}$$

$$= \frac{10 \cdot 4^3}{12}$$

$$= 53.3 \text{ in.}^4$$

Usually the value of I_g is small enough that it need not be considered. In our example, this value of 53.3 could be considered, although it will not make much difference in the final value. The greater the depth of any element relative to the maximum width of the section, the more the likelihood of its I_g value being significant.

The table will now be filled out for plates B and C as well:

Plate	Size	Distance y	$A = b \cdot d$ in.^{2}	$M = A \cdot y$ in.^{3}	$I_y = Ay^2 = My$ in.^{4}	$I_g = \frac{bd^3}{12}$ in.^{4}
(A)	10″x4″	2″	40.0	80.0	160.0	53.3
(B)	2″x8″	8″	16.0	128.0	1024.0	85.3
(C)	6″x4″	14″	24.0	336.0	4704.0	32.0
	Total		80.0	544.0	5888.0	170.6
					6058	

$$I_n = I_y + I_g - \frac{M^2}{A}$$

$$= 5888 + 170.6 - \frac{(544)^2}{80} = 6059 - 3700$$

$$= 2359 \text{ in.}^4$$

$$\text{and } n = \frac{M}{A} = \frac{544}{80}$$

$$= 6.8'' \text{ (up from bottom)}$$

A recommended method of treating M^2/A on the slide rule, is to divide M by A on the rule. Here we have 544 divided by 80 which gives us 6.8. This happens to be the distance of the neutral axis from the base reference line. Then without resetting the slide rule, multiply this by 544 again by just sliding the indicator of the rule down to 544 and read the answer as 3700. It is often necessary to know the neutral axis, and it can be found without extra work.

Problem 4

To show a further advantage of this system, assume that this resulting moment of inertia (2359 in.^{4}) is not large enough and the section must be made larger. Increasing the plate size at the top from 6″ × 4″ to 8″ × 4″ is the same as adding a 2″ × 4″ area to the already existing section. See Figure 5. The previous column totals are carried forward, and properties of only the added area need to be entered. I_n is then solved, using the corrected totals.

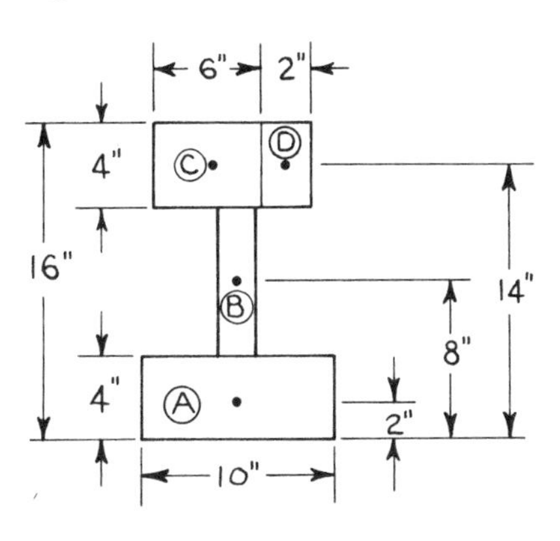

FIGURE 5

Plate	Size	Distance y	$A = b \cdot d$ in.²	$M = A \cdot y$ in.³	$I_y = Ay^2 = My$ in.⁴	$I_g = \frac{bd^3}{12}$ in.⁴
Previous Section		———	80.0	544.0	5888.0	170.6
New D	2″x4″	14″	8.0	112.0	1568.0	10.6
	Total		88.0	656.0	7456.0	181.2
					7637	

$$I_n = I_y + I_g - \frac{M^2}{A}$$

$$= 7637 - \frac{(656)^2}{88}$$

$$= 2747 \text{ in.}^4$$

$$\text{and } n = \frac{M}{A} = \frac{656}{88}$$

$$= 7.45'' \text{ (up from bottom)}$$

Moment of Inertia of Rolled Sections (Fourth Method)

The fourth method is the use of steel tables found in the A.I.S.C. handbook and other steel handbooks. These values are for any steel section which is rolled, and should be used whenever standard steel sections are used.

Positioning the Reference Axis

The designer should give some thought to positioning the reference axis (y-y) of a built-up section where it will simplify his computations.

The closer the reference axis (y-y) is to the final neutral axis (N.A.), the smaller will be the values of (I_y and I_g) and M^2/A. Hence, the more accurate these values will be if a slide rule is used.

If the reference axis (y-y) is positioned to lie through the center of gravity (C.G.) of one of the elements (the web, for example), this eliminates any subsequent work on this particular element since $y = 0$ for this element.

If the reference axis (y-y) is positioned along the base of the whole section, the distance of the neutral axis ($n = M/A$) from the reference axis (y-y) then automatically becomes the distance (c_b) from the neutral axis to the outer fiber at the bottom.

The following problem illustrates these points.

Problem 5

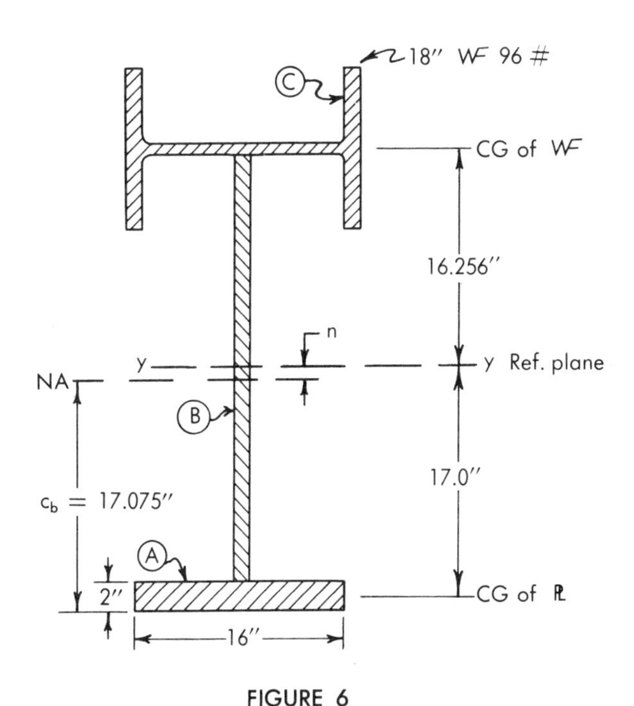

FIGURE 6

It is very easy to incorporate a rolled section into a built-up member, for example this proposed column to resist wind moments. See Figure 6. Find the moment of inertia of the whole section about its neutral axis (I_n) and then find its section modulus (S).

Choosing reference axis (y-y) through the center of gravity (C.G.) of the web plate (B) makes $y = 0$, and thus eliminates some work for (B).

Properties of the standard 18″ WF 96# section are given by the steel handbook as —

$A = 28.22 \text{ in.}^2 \quad I_y = 206.8 \text{ in.}^4 \quad t_w = .512''$

The handbook value of $I_y = 206.8$ in.^{4} can be inserted directly into the following table, for the I_g of this WF section C .

By adding areas and their properties:

	Size	y	A	M	I_y	I_g
A	16″ x 2″	−17.0″	32.00	−544.00	+9248.0	+10.7
B	1″ x 32″	0	32.00	0	0	+2730.7
A	18 WF 96#	+16.256″	28.22	+458.74	+7456.62	+206.8
		Total	92.22	− 85.26	+19,652.8	

moment of inertia about neutral axis

$$I_n = I_y + I_g - \frac{M^2}{A}$$

$$= (19{,}652.8) - \frac{(-85.26)^2}{(92.22)}$$

$$= 19{,}574 \text{ in.}^4$$

distance of neutral axis from reference axis

$$n = \frac{M}{A}$$

$$= \frac{(-85.26)}{(92.22)}$$

$$= -.925'' \text{ from axis y-y}$$

distance from N.A. to outer fiber

$$c_b = 18.00 - .925$$

$$= 17.075''$$

section modulus (see Topic 4 which follows)

$$S = \frac{I_n}{c_b}$$

$$= \frac{(19{,}574 \text{ in.}^4)}{(17.075'')}$$

$$= 1146 \text{ in.}^3$$

4. SECTION MODULUS (S)

The *section modulus* (S) is found by dividing the moment of inertia (I) by the distance (c) from the neutral axis to the outermost fiber of the section:

$$S = \frac{I}{c} \quad \text{.......... (8)}$$

Since this distance (c) can be measured in two directions, there are actually two values for this property, although only the smaller value is usually available in tables of rolled sections because it results in the greater stress. If the section is symmetrical, these two values are equal. Section modulus is a measurement of the strength of the beam in bending. In an unsymmetrical section, the outer face having the greater value of (c) will have the lower value of section modulus (S) and of course the greater stress. Since it has the greater stress, this is the value needed.

With some typical sections it is not necessary to solve first for moment of inertia (I). The section modulus can be computed directly from the simplified formulas of Table 1.

In many cases, however, the moment of inertia (I) must be found before solving for section modulus (S). Any of the previously described methods may be applicable for determining the moment of inertia.

Problem 6

Using a welded "T" section as a problem in finding the section modulus, its neutral axis is first located, Figure 7.

Using the standard formula (#1) for determining the distance (n) of the neutral axis from any reference axis, in this case the top horizontal face of the flange:

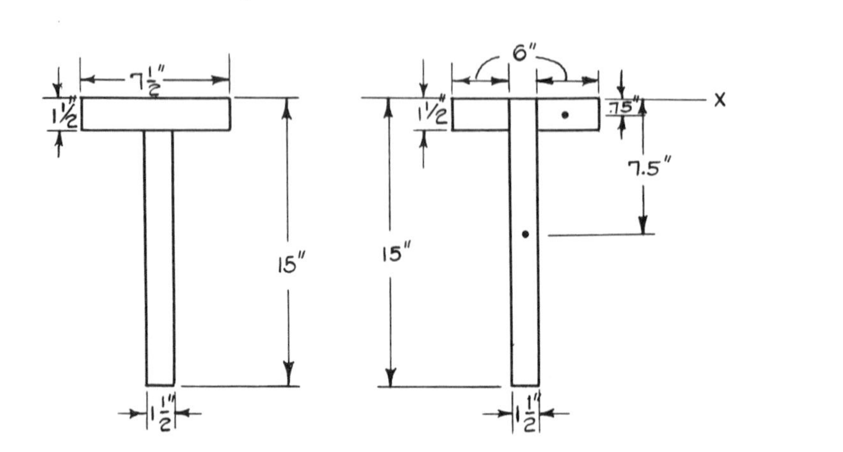

FIGURE 7

$$n = \frac{M}{A} = \frac{\text{Sum of moments}}{\text{Total area of section}}$$

$$= \frac{(6 \cdot 1.5 \cdot 0.75) + (15 \cdot 1.5 \cdot 7.5)}{(6 \cdot 1.5) \quad + \quad (15 \cdot 1.5)}$$

$$= \frac{6.75 + 168.75}{9.0 + 22.5}$$

$$= 5.56''$$

Next, the section's moment of inertia is determined, using the elements method (Figure 8):

$$I_n = \frac{6 \cdot 1.5^3}{12} + (6 \cdot 1.5 \cdot 4.81^2) + \frac{1.5 \cdot 15^3}{12} +$$

$$(1.5 \cdot 15 \cdot 1.94^2)$$

$$= 1.69 + 208.22 + 421.87 + 84.68$$

$$= 716.5 \text{ in.}^4$$

This value is slightly higher than the required $I = 700$ in.^{4} because depth of section was made $d = 15''$ instead of $14.9''$.

Finally, the section modulus (S) is determined:

$$S = \frac{I}{c} = \frac{716.5}{9.44}$$

$$= 75.8 \text{ in.}^3$$

5. RADIUS OF GYRATION (r)

The *radius of gyration* (r) is the distance from the neutral axis of a section to an imaginary point at which the whole area of the section could be concentrated and still have the same moment of inertia. This property is used primarily in solving column problems. It is found by taking the square root of the moment of inertia divided by the area of the section and is expressed in inches.

$$r = \sqrt{\frac{I}{A}} \qquad \text{.............................(9)}$$

6. POLAR MOMENT OF INERTIA (J)

The *polar moment of inertia* (J) equals the sum of any two moments of inertia about axes at right angles to each other. The polar moment of inertia is taken about an axis which is perpendicular to the plane of the other two axes.

$$J = I_x + I_y \qquad \text{........................(10)}$$

Polar moment of inertia is used in determining the polar section modulus (J/c) which is a measure

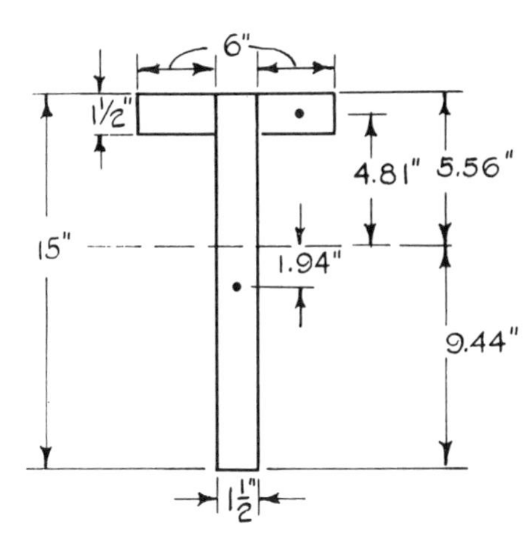

FIGURE 8

of strength under torsional loading of round solid bars and closed tubular shafts.

7. TORSIONAL RESISTANCE (R)

Torsional resistance (R) has largely replaced the less accurate polar moment of inertia in standard design formula for angular twist of open sections. It should be employed where formulas have been developed for the type of section. These are given in the later Section 2.10 on Torsion.

8. PROPERTIES OF THIN SECTIONS

Because of welding, increasingly greater use is being found for structural shapes having thin cross-sections. Thin sections may be custom roll-formed, rolled by small specialty steel producers, brake-formed, or fabricated by welding. Properties of these sections are needed by the designer, but they are not ordinarily listed among the standard rolled sections of a steel handbook. Properties of thin sections customarily are found by the standard formulas for sections.

With a thin section, the inside dimension is almost as large as the outside dimension; and, in most cases, the property of the section varies as the cubes of these two dimensions. This means dealing with the difference between two very large numbers. In order to get any accuracy, it would be necessary to calculate this out by longhand or by using logarithms rather than use the usual slide rule.

To simplify the problem, the section may be "treated as a line", having no thickness. The property of the "line", is then multiplied by the thickness of the section to give the approximate value of the section property within a very narrow tolerance. Table 2 gives simplified formulas for nine properties of six different cross-sections. In this table: d = mean depth, b = mean width of the section, and t = thickness.

TABLE 2—Properties of Thin Sections
Where thickness (t) is small, b = mean width, and d = mean depth of section

Section						
I_x	$\frac{t\,d^3\,(4\,b+d)}{12\,(b+d)}$	$\frac{t\,d^2}{12}\,(6\,b+d)$	$\frac{t\,d^2}{6}\,(3\,b+d)$	$\frac{t\,d^3\,(2\,b+d)}{3\,(b+2\,d)}$	$\frac{t\,d^3\,(4\,b+d)}{12\,(b+d)}$	$t\,\pi\,r^3$
S_x	$\frac{t\,d^2\,(4\,b+d)}{6\,(2\,b+d)}$ bottom $\frac{t\,d}{6}\,(4\,b+d)$ top *	$\frac{t\,d}{6}\,(6\,b+d)$ *	$\frac{t\,d}{3}\,(3\,b+d)$ *	$\frac{t\,d}{3}\,(2\,b+d)$ top $\frac{t\,d^2\,(2\,b+d)}{3\,(b+d)}$ bottom *	$\frac{t\,d}{6}\,(4\,b+d)$ top $\frac{t\,d^2\,(4\,b+d)}{6\,(2\,b+d)}$ bottom *	$t\,\pi\,r^2$
I_y	$\frac{t\,b^3}{12}$	$\frac{t\,b^3}{6}$	$\frac{t\,b^2}{6}\,(b+3\,d)$	$\frac{t\,b^2}{12}\,(b+6\,d)$	$\frac{t\,b^3\,(b+4\,d)}{12\,(b+d)}$	———
S_y	$\frac{t\,b^2}{6}$	$\frac{t\,b^2}{3}$	$\frac{t\,b}{3}\,(b+3\,d)$ *	$\frac{t\,b}{6}\,(b+6\,d)$ *	$\frac{t\,b^2\,(b+4\,d)}{6\,(b+2\,d)}$ right side $\frac{t\,b}{6}\,(b+4\,d)$ left side *	———
I_{xy}	0	0	0	0	$\frac{t\,b^2\,d^2}{4\,(b+d)}$	0
R	$\frac{t^3}{3}\,(b+d)$	$\frac{t^3}{3}\,(2\,b+d)$	$\frac{2\,t\,b^2\,d^2}{b+d}$	$\frac{t^3}{3}\,(b+2\,d)$	$\frac{t^3}{3}\,(b+d)$	$2t\,\pi\,r^3$
r_x max. or min.	$\sqrt{\frac{\frac{d^3\,(4\,b+d)}{12}}{b+d}}$	$\sqrt{\frac{d^2\,(6\,b+d)}{12\,(2\,b+d)}}$	$\sqrt{\frac{d^2\,(3\,b+d)}{12\,(b+d)}}$	$\frac{\sqrt{\frac{d^3}{3}\,(2\,b+d)}}{(b+2\,d)}$		0.7071 r
NA	$\frac{d^2}{2\,(b+d)}$ down from top			$\frac{d^2}{b+2\,d}$ down from top	$\frac{d^2}{2\,(b+d)}$ down from top $\frac{b^2}{2\,(b+d)}$	———
r_y min. or max.	$\sqrt{\frac{b^3}{12\,(b+d)}}$	$\sqrt{\frac{b^3}{6\,(2\,b+d)}}$	$\sqrt{\frac{b^2\,(b+3\,d)}{12\,(b+d)}}$	$\sqrt{\frac{b^2\,(b+d)}{12\,(b+2\,d)}}$		———

(* = add t/2 to c for S)

The error in calculating the moment of inertia by this Line Method versus the conventional formula is represented by the curve in Figure 9, using a square tubular section as an example. As indicated, the error increases with the ratio of section thickness (t) to depth (d).

An excellent example of the savings in design time offered by use of the Line Method exists as (column) Problem 4 in Section 3.1.

Table 3 gives the most important properties of additional thin sections of irregular but common configurations.

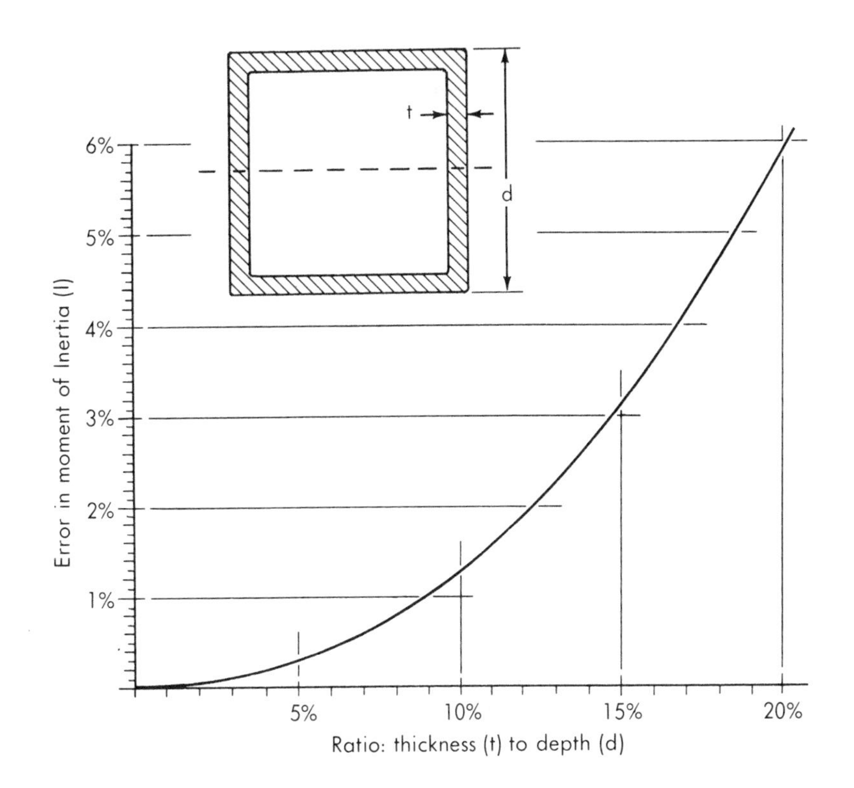

FIG. 9 Possible error in using Line Method is minimal with low ratio of section thickness to depth.

For additional formulas and reference tables, see "Light Gage Cold-Formed Steel Design Manual" 1962, American Iron & Steel Institute.

9. SHEAR AXIS AND SHEAR CENTER

Since the bending moment decreases as the distance of the load from the support increases, bending force f_1 is slightly less than force f_2, and this difference $(f_2 - f_1)$ is transferred inward toward the web by the longitudinal shear force (f_s). See Figure 10.

$$f_s = f_s' + \frac{P\,a\,y}{I_x} \quad \text{.....................(11)}$$

This force also has an equal component in the transverse direction. A transverse force applied to a beam sets up transverse (and horizontal) shear forces within the section. See Figure 11.

In the case of a symmetrical section, A, a force (P) applied in line with the principal axis (y-y) does not result in any twisting action on the member. This

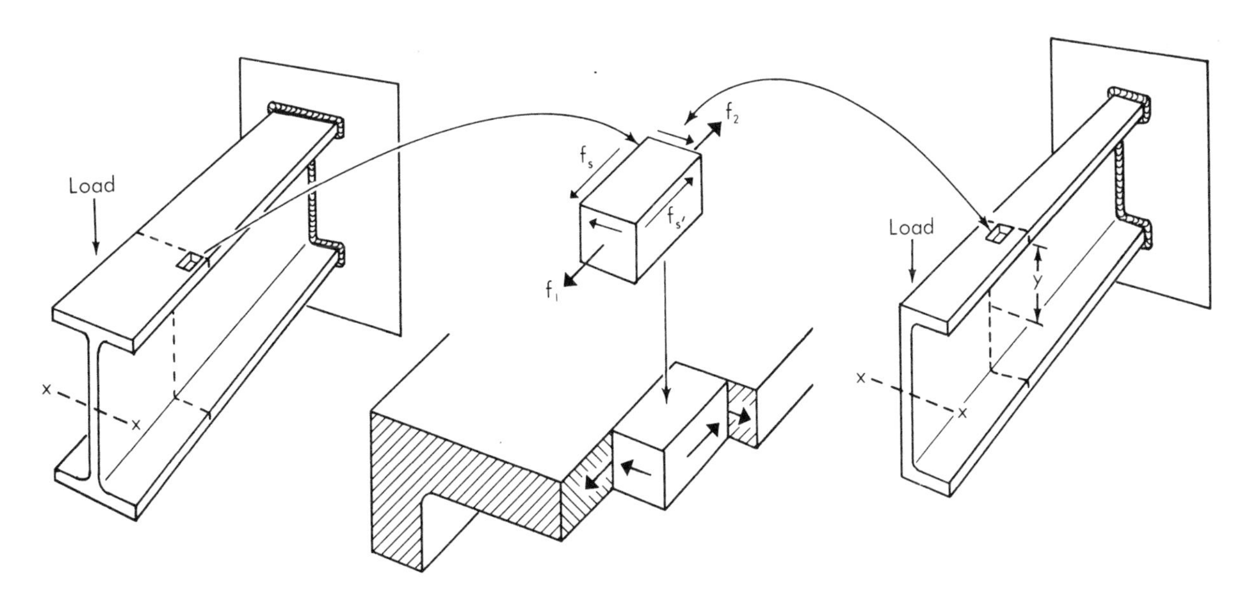

FIGURE 10

TABLE 3—Properties of Typical Irregular Thin Sections

Where thickness (t) is small, b = mean width, and d = mean depth of section

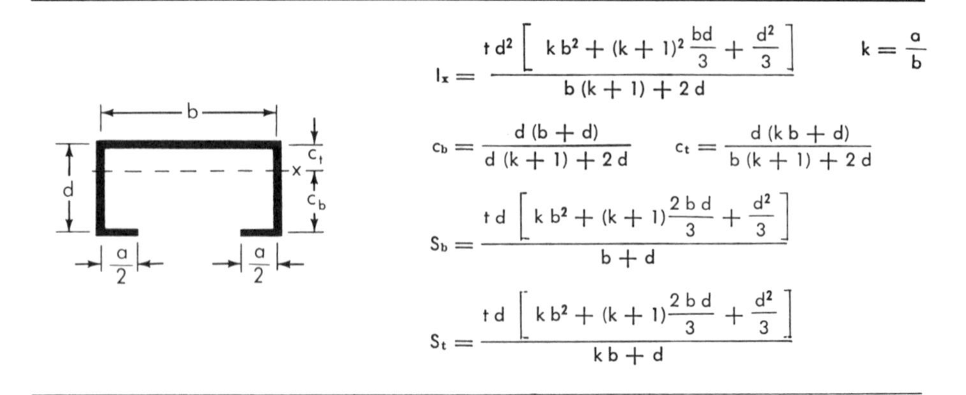

$$I_x = \frac{t\,d^2\left[k\,b^2 + (k+1)^2\frac{bd}{3} + \frac{d^2}{3}\right]}{b\,(k+1) + 2\,d} \qquad k = \frac{a}{b}$$

$$c_b = \frac{d\,(b+d)}{d\,(k+1) + 2\,d} \qquad c_t = \frac{d\,(k\,b+d)}{b\,(k+1) + 2\,d}$$

$$S_b = \frac{t\,d\left[k\,b^2 + (k+1)\frac{2\,b\,d}{3} + \frac{d^2}{3}\right]}{b+d}$$

$$S_t = \frac{t\,d\left[k\,b^2 + (k+1)\frac{2\,b\,d}{3} + \frac{d^2}{3}\right]}{k\,b+d}$$

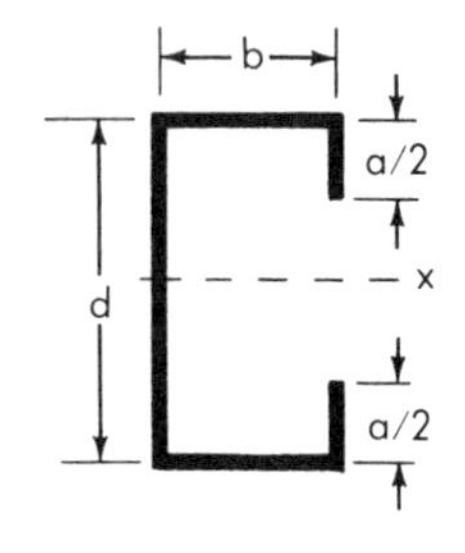

$$I_x = \frac{t\,d^3}{12}(k^3 - 3\,k^2 + 3\,k + 1) + \frac{t\,b\,d^2}{2}$$

$$k = \frac{a}{d}$$

$$S_x = \frac{t\,d^2}{6}(k^3 - 3\,k^2 + 3\,k + 1) + t\,b\,d$$

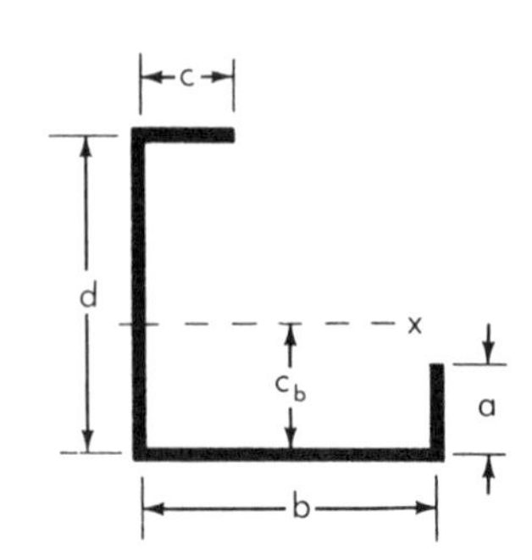

$$c_b = \frac{a^2 + 2\,c\,d + d^2}{2\,(a+b+c+d)}$$

$$I_x = \frac{t\,(a^3 + 3\,c\,d^2 + d^3)}{3} - \frac{t\,(a^2 + 2\,c\,d + d^2)^2}{4\,(a+b+c+d)}$$

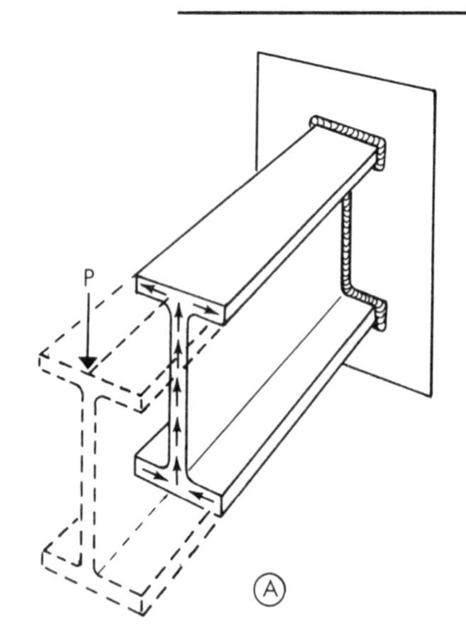

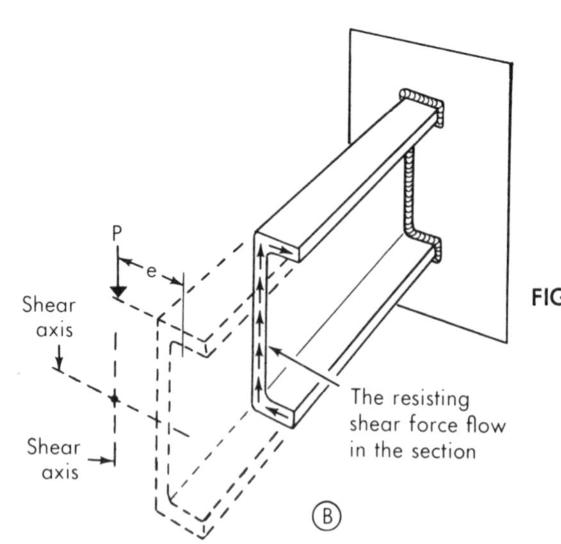

FIGURE 11

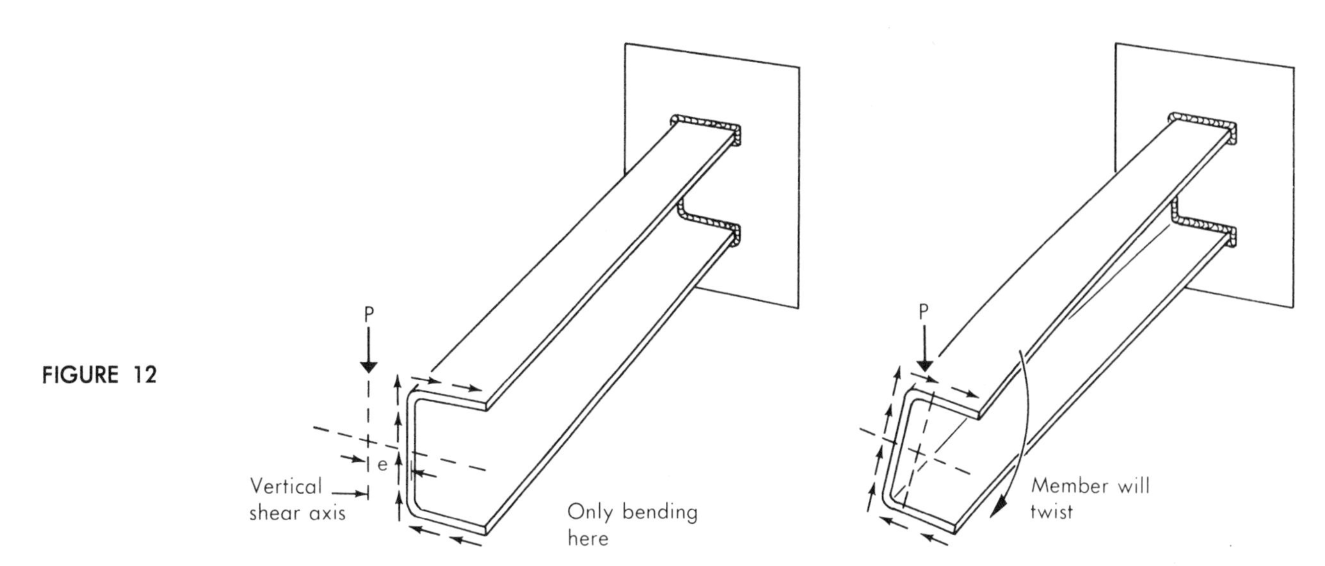

FIGURE 12

is because the torsional moment of the internal transverse shear forces (⟶) is equal to zero.

On the other hand, in the case of an unsymmetrical section, B, the internal transverse shear forces (⟶) form a twisting moment. Therefore, the force (P) must be applied eccentrically at a proper distance (e) along the shear axis, so that it forms an external torsional moment which is equal and opposite to the internal torsional moment of the transverse shear forces. If this precaution is not taken, there will be a twisting action applied to the member which will twist under load, in addition to bending. See Figure 12.

Any axis of symmetry will also be a shear axis.

There will be two shear axes and their intersection forms the shear center (Q).

A force, if applied at the shear center, may be at any angle in the plane of the cross-section and there will be no twisting moment on the member, just transverse shear and bending.

As stated previously, unless forces which are applied transverse to a member also pass through the shear axis, the member will be subjected to a twisting moment as well as bending. As a result, this beam should be considered as follows:

1. The applied force P should be resolved into a force P′ of the same value passing through the shear center (Q) and parallel to the original applied force P. P′ is then resolved into the two components at right angles to each other and parallel to the principal axes of the section.

2. A twisting moment (T) is produced by the applied force (P) about the shear center (Q).

The stress from the twisting moment (T) is computed separately and then superimposed upon the stresses of the two rectangular components of force P′.

This means that the shear center must be located. Any axis of symmetry will be one of the shear axes.

For open sections lying on one common neutral axis (y-y), the location of the other shear axis is —

$$e = \frac{\Sigma\, I_x\, X}{\Sigma\, I_x}$$

Notice the similarity between this and the following:

$$d = \frac{\Sigma\, M}{\Sigma\, A} = \frac{\Sigma\, A\, d}{\Sigma\, A}$$

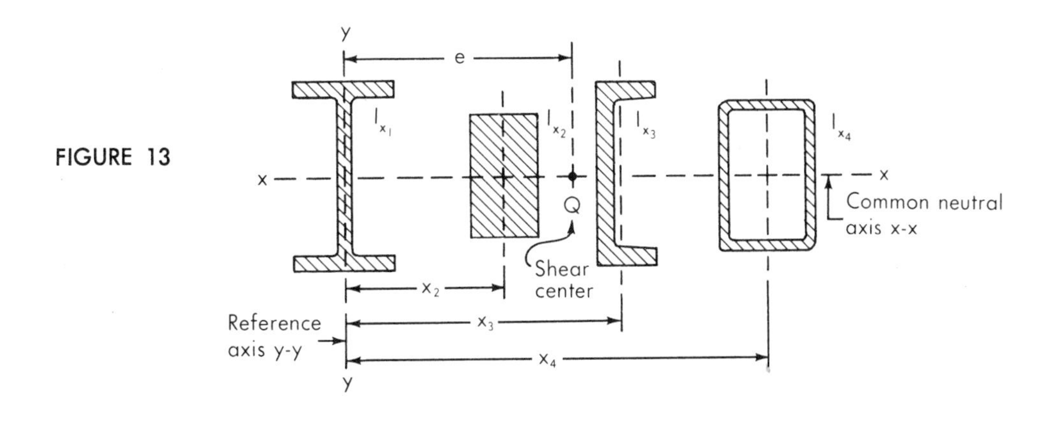

FIGURE 13

which is used to find the neutral axis of a built-up section.

Just as the areas of individual parts are used to find the neutral axis, now the moments of inertia of individual areas are used to find the shear axis of a composite section, Figure 13. The procedure is the same; select a reference axis (y-y), determine I_x for each member section (about its own neutral axis x-x) and the distance X this member section lies from the reference axis (y-y). The resultant (e) from the formula will then be the distance from the chosen reference axis (y-y) to the parallel shear axis of the built-up section.

Here:

$$e = \frac{I_{x1} X_1 + I_{x2} X_2 + I_{x3} X_3 + I_{x4} X_4}{I_{x1} + I_{x2} + I_{x3} + I_{x4}}$$

or:

$$\boxed{e = \frac{\Sigma I_x X}{\Sigma I_x}} \quad \text{.........................(12)}$$

Locating Other Shear Centers

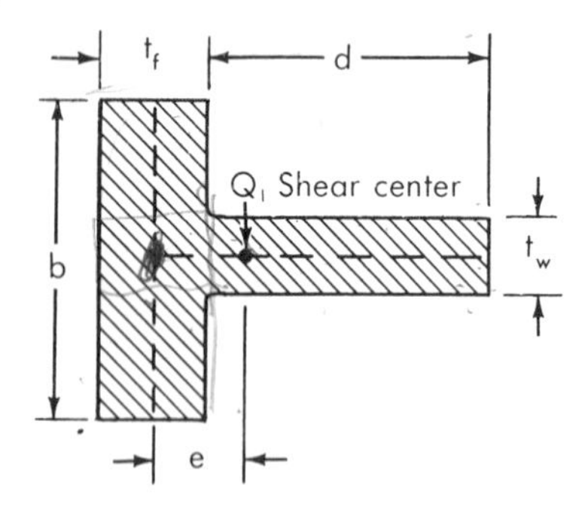

FIGURE 14

Here:

$$e = \frac{\Sigma I_x X}{\Sigma I_x} = \frac{\frac{t_f b^3}{12} \times 0 + \frac{d t_w^3}{12} \times \frac{t_f + d)}{2}}{I_x}$$

$$= \frac{d t_w^3 (t_f + d)}{24 I_x}$$

Normally Q might be assumed to be at the intersection of the centerlines of the web and the flange.

The James F. Lincoln Arc Welding Foundation also publishes collections of award-winning papers describing the best and most unique bridges, buildings and other structures in which modern arc welding is used effectively.

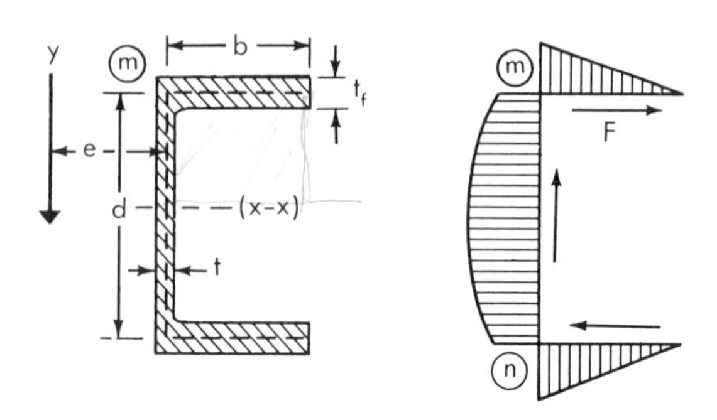

FIGURE 15

Here, at point M:

$$f_s = \frac{V a y}{I_x} = \frac{V (b t_f)(d/2)}{I_x}$$

$$F = ½ f_s b = \frac{V b^2 d t_f}{4 I_x}$$

$$\Sigma M_n = 0 = + F d - V e = 0$$

$$e = \frac{F d}{V} = \frac{V b^2 d^2 t_f}{V 4 I_x}$$

$$= \frac{b^2 d^2 t_f}{4 I_x}$$

or, since areas have a common (x-x) neutral axis:

$$e = \frac{\Sigma I_x X}{\Sigma I_x} = \frac{\frac{t d^3}{12} \times 0 + 2 \times (b t_f)(d/2)^2 \frac{b}{2}}{I_x}$$

$$= \frac{b^2 d^2 t_f}{4 I_x}$$

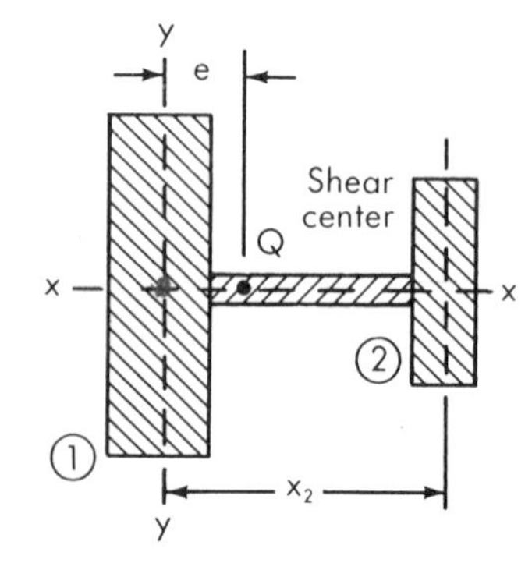

FIGURE 16

Here:

$$e = \frac{\Sigma I_x X}{\Sigma I_x} = \frac{I_{x1} 0 + I_{x2} X_2}{I_{x1} + I_{x2}}$$

$$= \frac{X_2 I_{x2}}{I_x}$$

Figure 17 suggests an approach to locating shear axes of some other typical sections.

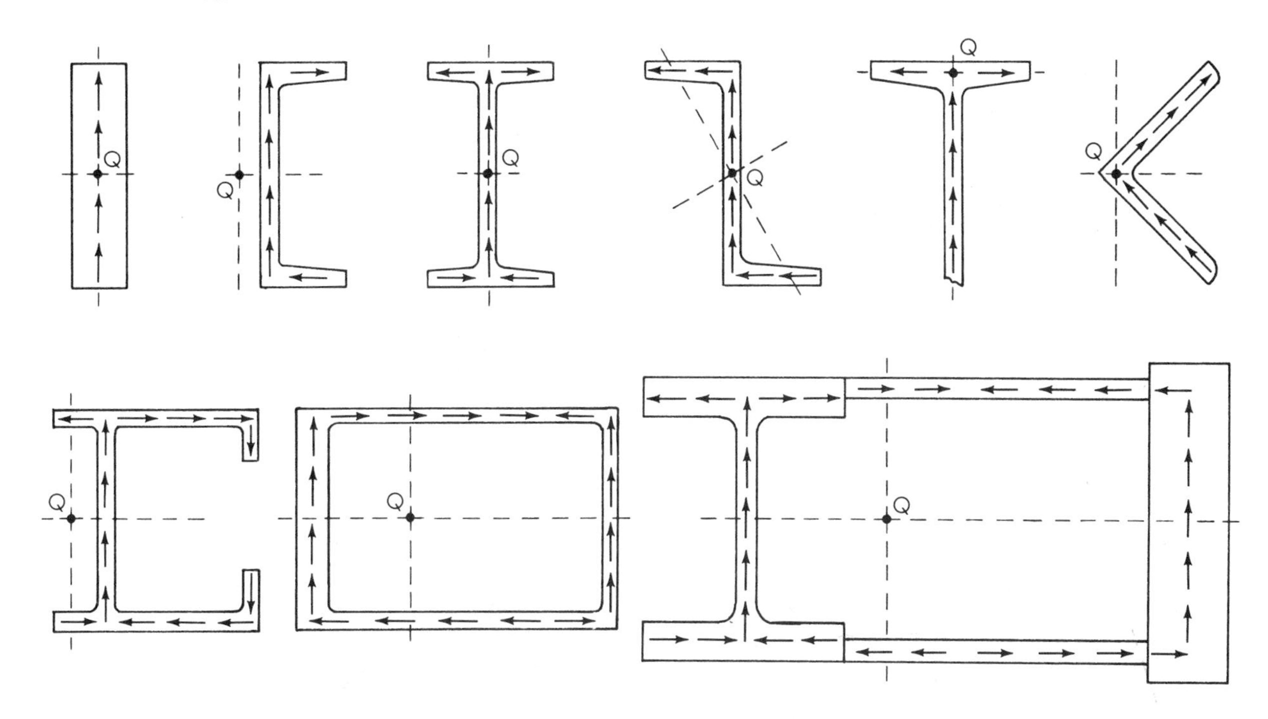

FIGURE 17

Structural steel for Gateway Towers, 26-story Pittsburgh apartment building was erected in tiers of three floors each by two derricks. Shop and field welding combined to facilitate erection; nearly 15 tons of electrode were used.

Eighty-foot hollow steel masts and suspension cables help support the continuous roof framing system of the 404′ x 1200′ Tulsa Exposition Center. Welds holding brackets (arrow) to which cables are anchored are designed to withstand the high tensile forces involved in such a structure.

Built-Up Tension Members

1. TENSILE STRESS

The simplest type of loading on a member is tension. A tensile load applied (axially) in line with the center of gravity of the section will result in tensile stresses distributed uniformly across the plane of the cross-section lying at right angles to the line of loading. The formula for the stress is —

$$\boxed{\sigma_t = \frac{P}{A}} \quad \ldots\ldots\ldots\ldots\ldots\ldots\ldots\ldots (1)$$

where:

P = the tensile force applied to the member

A = area of cross-section at right angles to line of force

σ_t = unit tensile stress

A tensile load that is not applied in line with the center of gravity of the section, but with some eccentricity, will introduce some bending stresses. These must be combined with the original tensile stresses.

2. TENSILE STRAIN

The unit elongation or strain of the member under tension is found by the following relationship:

$$\boxed{\epsilon = \frac{\sigma_t}{E}} \quad \ldots\ldots\ldots\ldots\ldots\ldots\ldots\ldots (2)$$

where:

ϵ = unit elongation (tensile strain)

σ_t = unit tensile stress

E = modulus of elasticity (tension)

The total elongation or displacement is equal to this unit strain (ϵ) multiplied by the length (L) of the member.

$$\text{Elongation} = \epsilon \cdot L$$

Problem 1

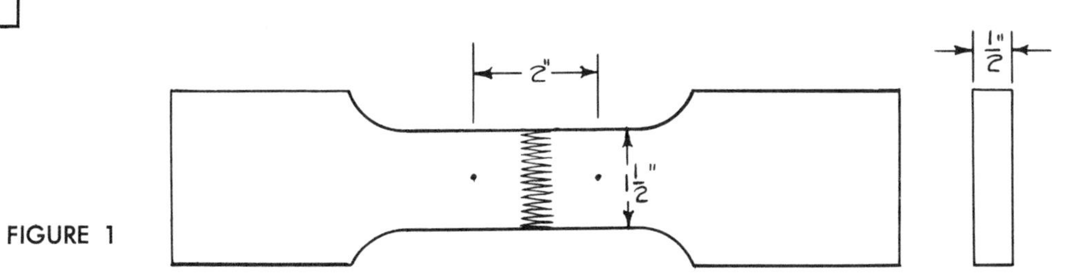

FIGURE 1

A welded tensile coupon (test specimen) measures ½" x 1½" at the reduced section, and has two punch marks 2" apart with which to later measure elongation. Just after the test is started, a load of 10,000 lbs is reached.

Find (1) the unit tensile stress on the reduced section, and (2) the total elongation as measured within the two marks.

(1) $$\sigma_t = \frac{P}{A} = \frac{10{,}000}{\frac{1}{2} \cdot 1\frac{1}{2}}$$

$$= 13{,}333 \text{ psi}$$

(2) $$\epsilon = \frac{\sigma_t}{E} = \frac{13{,}330}{30{,}000{,}000}$$

$$= 0.000444 \text{ in./in.}$$

and elon. $= \epsilon \cdot L = 0.000444 \cdot 2''$

$= 0.00089''$ in $2''$

In any calculation for strain or elongation it is understood that the stresses are held below the yield point. Beyond the yield point, the relationship of stress to strain is no longer proportional and the formula does not apply.

3. WELDING OF BUILT-UP TENSION MEMBERS

AISC Section 1.18.3 has established the requirements illustrated in Figure 2.

Plate to a rolled shape, or 2 plates in contact with each other

t

s ≦ 24t ≦ 12″

P

t = thickness of thinner element

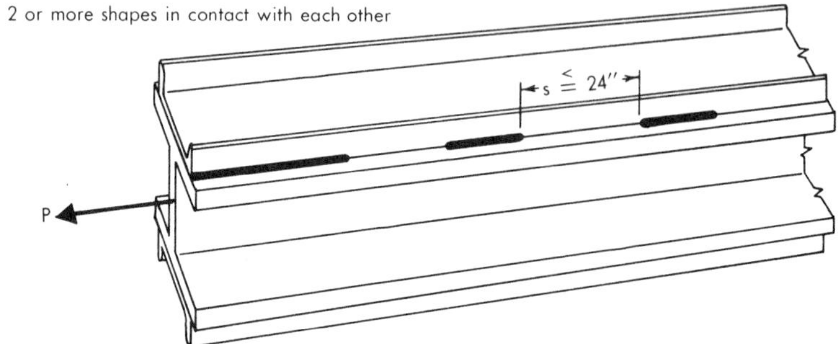

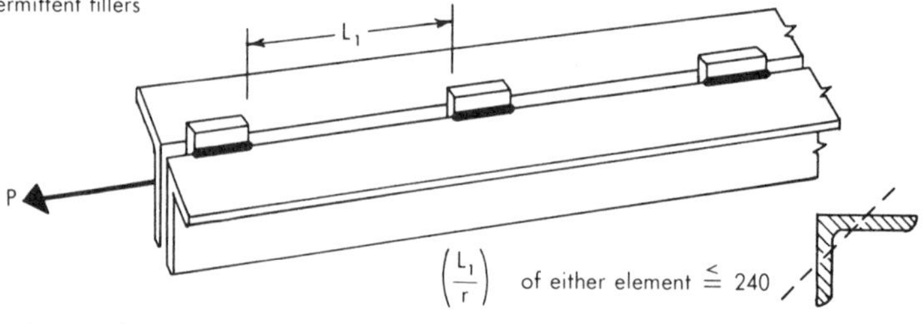

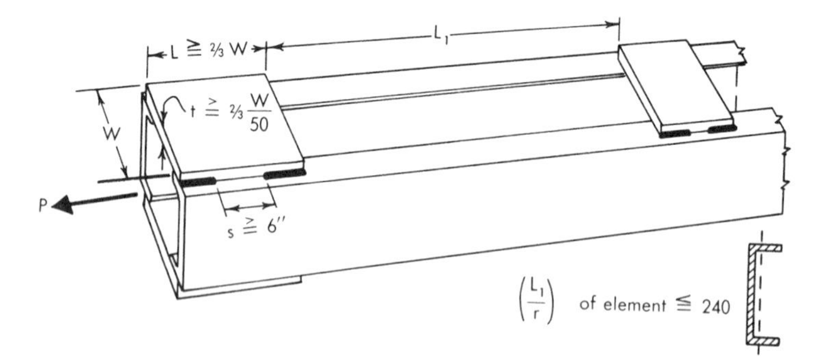

FIGURE 2—Welding of Built-Up Tension Members

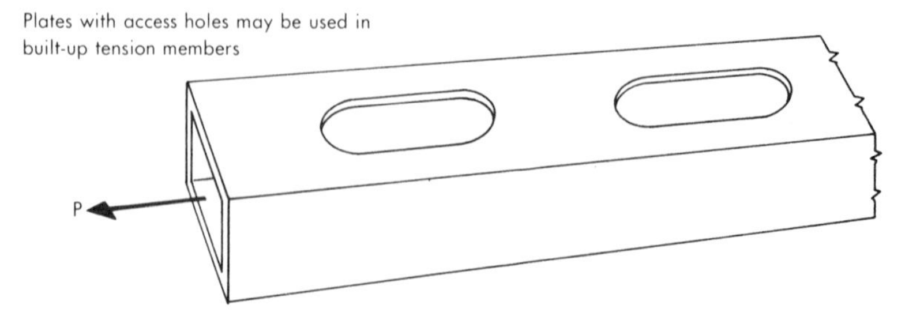

Plates with access holes may be used in built-up tension members
P

Analysis of Bending

1. BENDING STRESS

Any force applied transversely to the structural axis of a partially supported member sets up bending moments (M) along the length of the member. These in turn stress the cross-sections in bending.

As shown in Figure 1, the bending stresses are zero at the neutral axis, and are assumed to increase linearly to a maximum at the outer fiber of the section. The fibers stressed in tension elongate; the fibers stressed in compression contract. This causes each section so stressed to rotate. The cumulative effect of this movement is an over-all deflection (or bending) of the member.

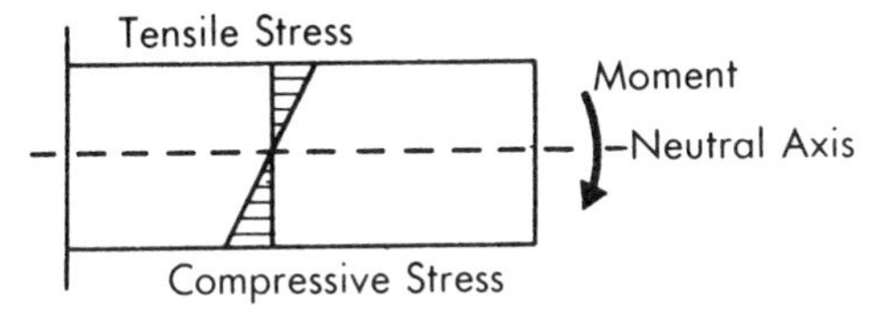

FIGURE 1

The cantilever beam shown in Figure 1 is in tension along the top and in compression along the bottom. In contrast, the relationship of the applied force and the points of support on the member shown in Figure 2 is such that the curve of deflection is inverted, and the member is in tension along the bottom and in compression along the top.

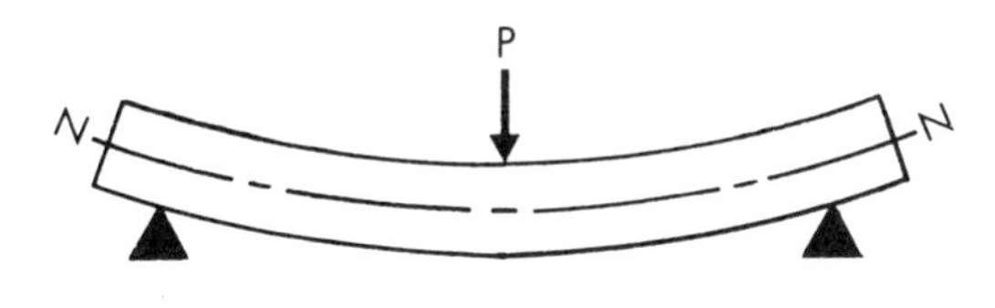

FIGURE 2

Within the elastic range (i.e. below the proportional elastic limit or the yield point), the bending stress (σ_b) at any point in the cross-section of a beam is —

$$\boxed{\sigma_b = \frac{M\,c}{I}} \quad \ldots\ldots(1)$$

where:

M = bending moment at the section in question, in.-lbs

I = moment of inertia of the section, in.⁴

c = distance from neutral axis to the point at which stress is desired, in.

σ_b = bending stress, may be tension or compression, psi

TABLE 1—Beam Diagrams

Type of Beam	Maximum moment	Maximum deflection	Maximum shear
P	$M = PL$ Fixed end	$\Delta = \frac{PL^3}{3EI}$ Free end	$V = P$
P	$M = \frac{PL}{4}$ center	$\Delta = \frac{PL^3}{48EI}$ center	$V = \frac{P}{2}$
P	$M = \frac{3PL}{16}$ Fixed end	$\Delta = \frac{PL^3}{48EI\sqrt{5}}$	$V = \frac{11}{16}P$
P, Guided Free	$M = \frac{PL}{2}$ both ends	$\Delta = \frac{PL^3}{12EI}$ guided end	$V = P$
P	$M = \frac{PL}{8}$ center & ends	$\Delta = \frac{PL^3}{192EI}$ center	$V = \frac{P}{2}$
P	$M = \frac{PL}{2}$ Fixed end	$\Delta = \frac{PL^3}{8EI}$ Free end	$V = P$
P	$M = \frac{PL}{8}$ center	$\Delta = \frac{5PL^3}{384EI}$ center	$V = \frac{P}{2}$
P	$M = \frac{PL}{8}$ Fixed end	$\Delta = \frac{PL^3}{185EI}$	$V = \frac{5}{8}P$
P, Guided Free	$M = \frac{PL}{3}$ Fixed end	$\Delta = \frac{PL^3}{24EI}$ guided end	$V = P$
P	$M = \frac{PL}{12}$ both ends	$\Delta = \frac{PL^3}{384EI}$ center	$V = \frac{P}{2}$
e, P, L, P, e, L	$M = Pe$ whole beam	$\Delta = \frac{PeL^2}{2EI}$ right angles to force	$V = O$

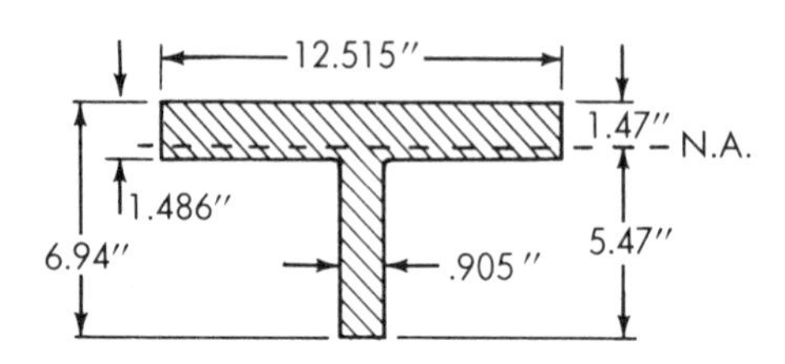

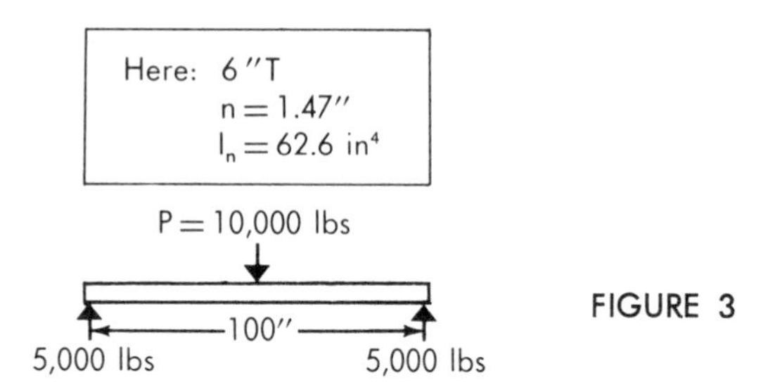

FIGURE 3

The bending moment (M) may be determined from standard beam diagrams. Table 1 lists several of these, along with the formulas for bending moment, shear, and deflection. A more complete presentation is included in the Reference Section on Beam Diagrams.

Normally there is no interest in knowing what the bending stresses are somewhere inside a beam. Usually the bending stress at the outer fiber is needed because it is of maximum value. In an unsymmetrical section, the distance *c* must be taken in the correct direction across that portion of the section which is in tension or that portion which is in compression, as desired. Ordinarily only the maximum stress is needed and this is the stress at the outer fiber under tension, which rests at the greater distance *c* from the neutral axis.

Problem 1

A standard rolled "T" section (ST–6″ wide flange, 80.5 lbs) is used as a beam, 100″ long, supported on each end and bearing a concentrated load of 10,000 lbs at the middle. Find the maximum tensile and maximum compressive bending stresses.

Figure 3 shows the cross-section of this beam, together with its load diagram.

Referring to Table 1, the formula for the bending moment of this type of beam is found to be—

$$M = \frac{PL}{4} \text{ and therefore}$$

$$= \frac{(10{,}000)(100)}{4}$$

$$= 250{,}000 \text{ in.-lbs}$$

Since the bottom portion of the beam is stressed in tension, substituting appropriate known values into the formula:

$$\sigma_t = \frac{M\ c}{I}$$

$$= \frac{(250{,}000)(5.47)}{(6.26)}$$

$$= \underline{21{,}845 \text{ psi}} \text{ (tension)}$$

The top portion of the beam being in compression,

$$\sigma_c = \frac{M\ c}{I}$$

$$= \frac{(250{,}000)(1.47)}{62.6}$$

$$= \underline{5{,}870 \text{ psi}} \text{ (compression)}$$

Problem 2

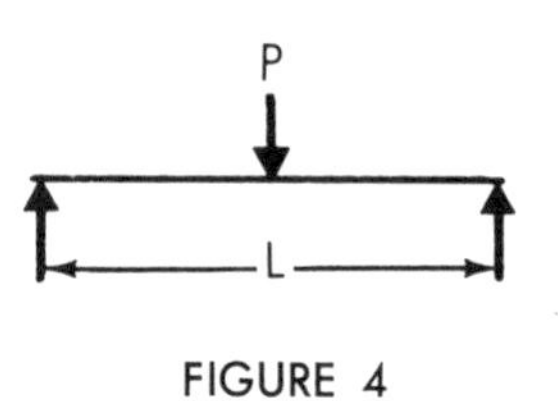

FIGURE 4

Find the maximum deflection of the previous beam under the same loading. From the beam diagrams, Table 1, the appropriate formula is found to be—

$$\Delta_{max} = \frac{P\ L^3}{48\ E\ I} \text{ and therefore}$$

$$= \frac{(10{,}000)(100)^3}{48(30 \times 10^6)(62.6)}$$

$$= \underline{.111''}$$

2. HORIZONTAL SHEAR STRESS

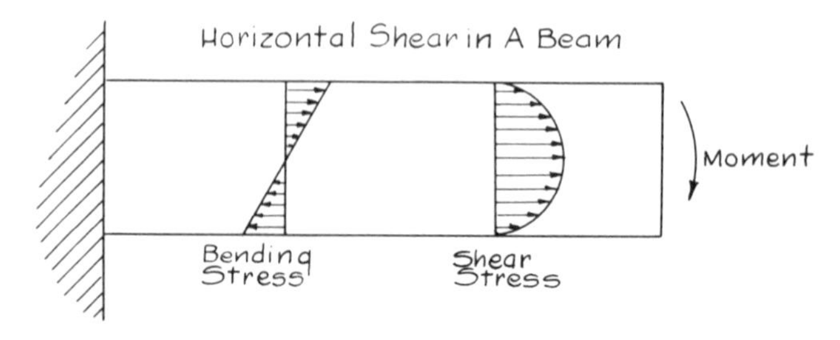

FIGURE 5

In addition to pure bending stresses, horizontal shear stress is often present in beams, Figure 5. It depends on vertical shear and only occurs if the bending moment varies along the beam. (Any beam, or portion of the beam's length, that has uniform bending moment has no vertical shear and therefore no horizontal shear).

Unlike bending stress, the horizontal shear stress is zero at the outer fibers of the beam and is maximum at the neutral axis of the beam. It tends to cause one part of the beam to slide past the other.

The horizontal shear stress at any point in the cross-section of a beam, Figure 6, is —

$$\tau = \frac{V\,a\,y}{I\,t} \qquad (2)$$

where:

V = external vertical shear on beam, lbs

I = moment of inertia of whole section, in.^{4}

t = thickness of section at plane where stress is desired, in.

a = area of section beyond plane where stress is desired, in.^{2}

y = distance of center of gravity of area to neutral axis of entire section, in.

Problem 3

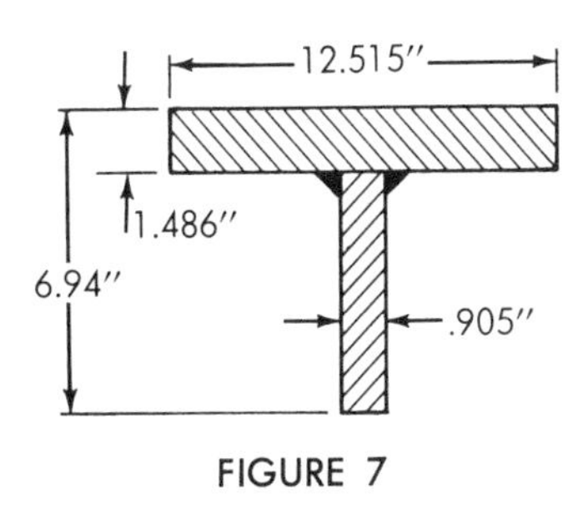

FIGURE 7

Assume that the "T" beam in our previous example (Problem 1) is fabricated by welding. Under the same load conditions,

(a) Find the horizontal shear stress in the plane where the web joins the flange.

(b) Then find the size of continuous fillet welds on both sides, joining the web to the flange.

From the beam diagrams, Table 1, the appropriate formula for vertical shear (V) is found to be —

$$V = \frac{P}{2} \text{ and thus}$$

$$= \frac{10{,}000}{2}$$

$$= 5{,}000 \text{ lbs}$$

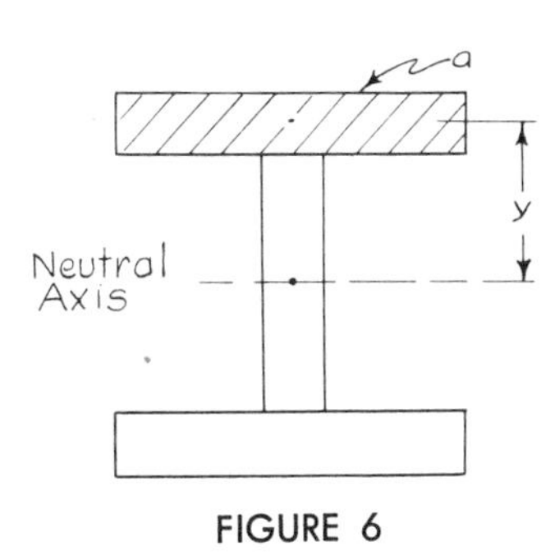

FIGURE 6

The following values also are known or determined to be —

I = 62.6 in.^{4}

$a = 1.486 \times 12.515 = 18.6$ in.^{2}

y = 0.727″

t = 0.905″

(a) Substituting the above values into the formula, the horizontal shear stress (τ) is found:

$$\tau = \frac{V\,a\,y}{I\,t}$$

$$= \frac{(5000)(18.6)(0.727)}{(62.6)(0.905)}$$

$$= \underline{1196 \text{ psi}}$$

(b) Since the shear force is borne entirely by the web of the "T", the horizontal shear force (f) depends on the thickness of the web in the plane of interest:

$$f = \tau\, t \text{ and thus}$$

$$= 1196 \times 0.905$$

$$= 1080 \text{ lbs/in.}$$

There are two fillet welds, one on each side of the "T" joining the flange to the web. Each will have to support half of the shear force or 540 lbs/in. and its leg size would be:

$$\omega = \frac{540}{9600}$$

$$= .056''$$

This would be an extremely small continuous fillet weld. Based upon the AWS, the minimum size fillet weld for the thicker 1.47″ plate would be 5/16″.

If manual intermittent fillet welds are to be used, the percentage of the length of the joint to be welded would be:

FIGURE 8—Required Section Modulus of Beam Under Bending Load
(Strength Nomograph)

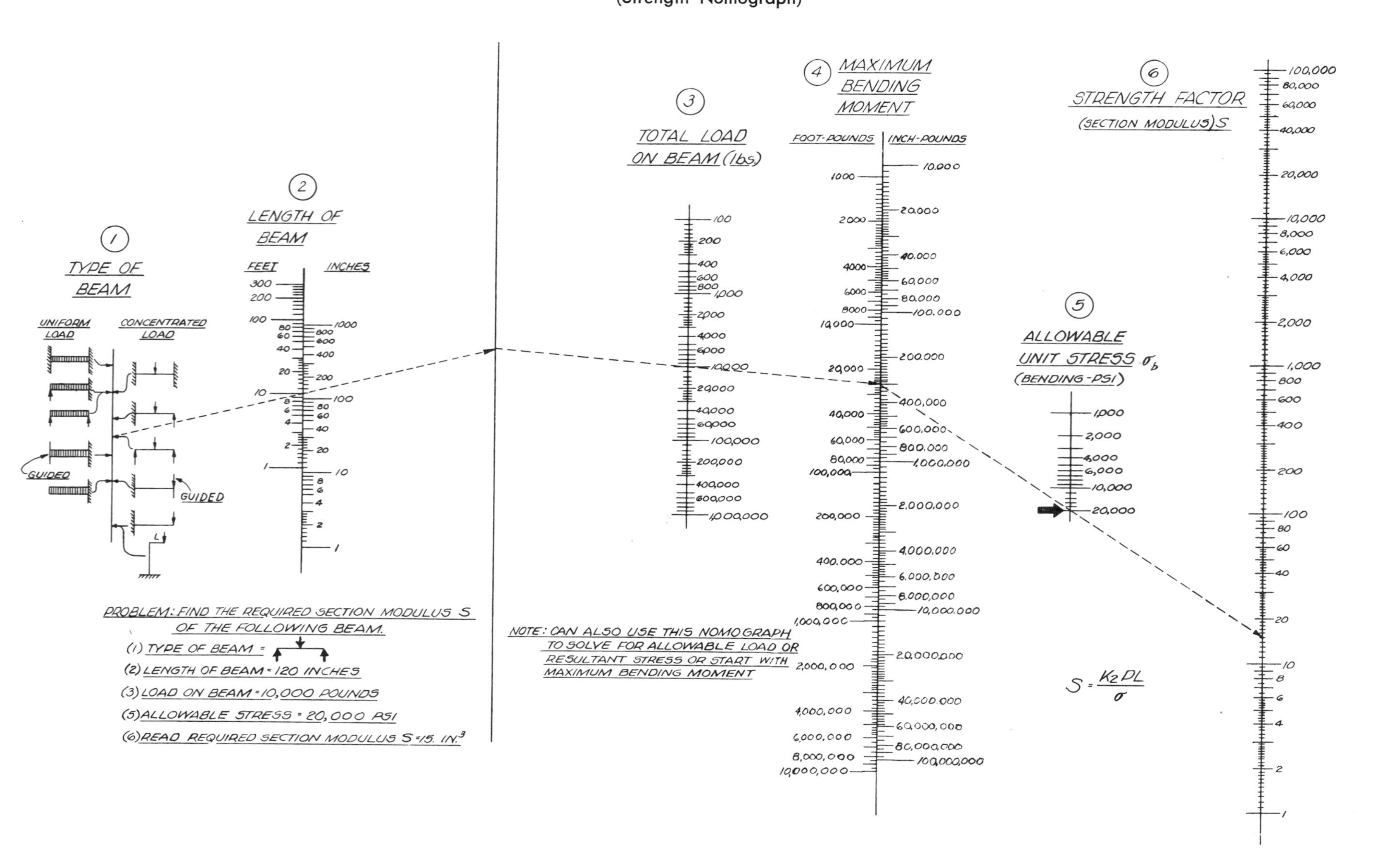

$$\% = \frac{\text{calculated leg size of continuous fillet weld}}{\text{actual leg size of intermittent fillet weld used}} \times 100$$

$$= \frac{.056}{5/16} = 18\%$$

A 5/16 ◣ 3–12 fillet weld would satisfy this requirement because it results in 25% of the length of the joint being welded.

3. QUICK METHOD FOR FINDING REQUIRED SECTION MODULUS (STRENGTH) OR MOMENT OF INERTIA (STIFFNESS)

To aid in designing members for bending loads, the following two nomographs have been constructed. The first nomograph determines the required strength of a straight beam. The second nomograph determines the required stiffness of the beam.

In both nomographs several types of beams are included for concentrated loads as well as uniform loads. The length of the beam is shown both in inches and in feet, the load in pounds. In the first nomograph (Fig. 8) an allowable bending stress (σ_b) is shown and the strength property of the beam is read as section modulus (S). In the second nomograph (Fig. 9) an allowable unit deflection (Δ/L) is shown. This is the resulting deflection of the beam divided by the length of the beam. The stiffness property of the beam is read as moment of inertia (I).

By using these nomographs the designer can quickly find the required section modulus (strength) or moment of inertia (stiffness) of the beam. He can then refer to a steel handbook to choose a steel section that will meet these requirements.

If he wishes to fabricate the section from welded steel, he may use any of the methods for building up a steel section having the required values of section modulus or moment of inertia discussed in Properties of Sections.

More than a carload of welding electrode was employed in the fabrication of this huge bucket-wheel iron ore reclaiming machine at the Eagle Mountain Mine. Steel pipe was used extensively in the 170′ long all-welded truss, of triangular cross-section, that is the main load-carrying member.

FIGURE 9—Required Moment of Inertia of Beam Under Bending Load
(Stiffness Nomograph)

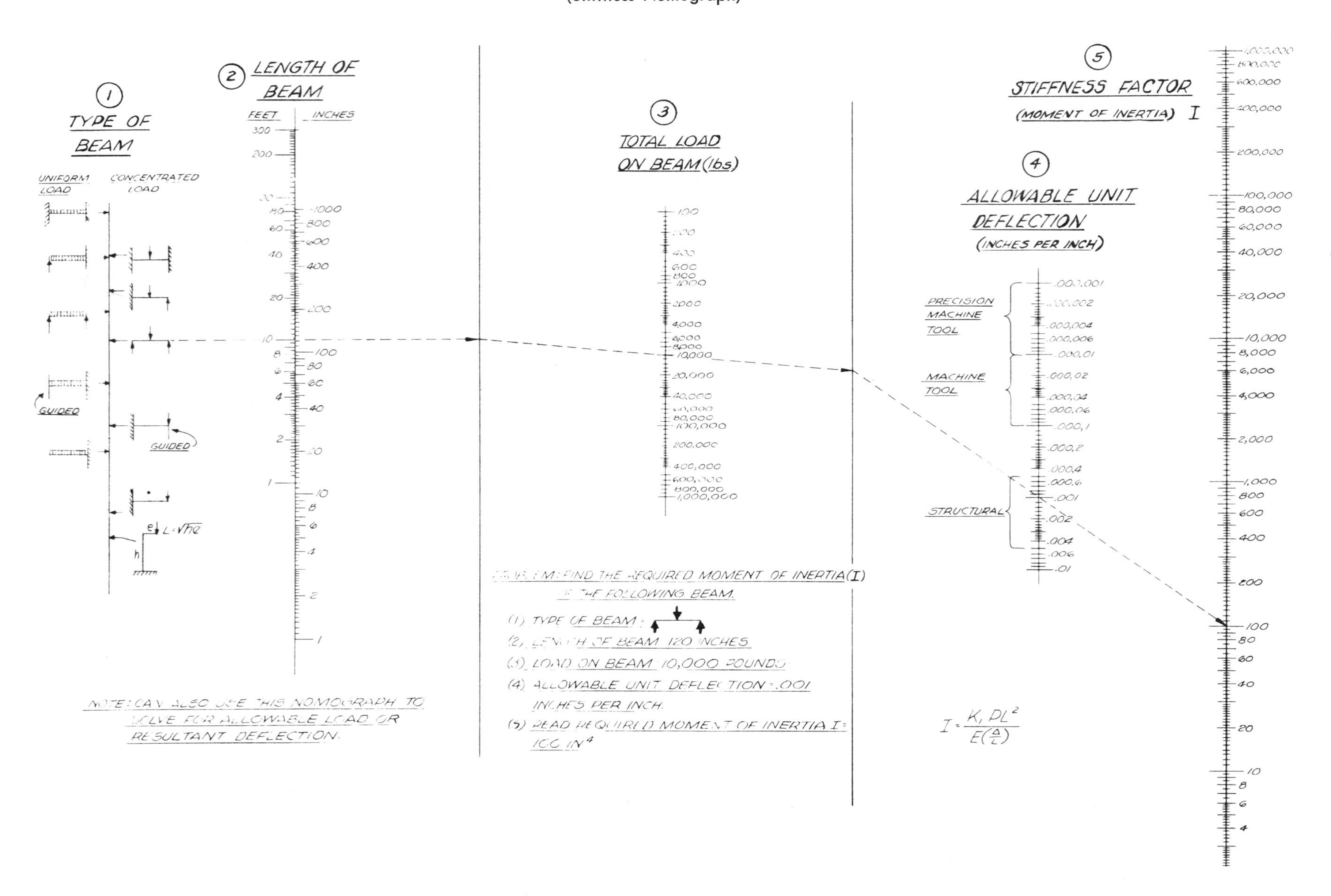

Deflection by Bending

1. RIGIDITY DESIGN

Under a transverse bending load, the normally straight neutral axis of a beam becomes a curved line. The deflection of interest is the linear displacement of some point on the neutral axis along a path parallel to the line of applied force. Usually it is the maximum deflection that is of value on our computations, although occasionally the deflection at a specific point is needed.

Rigidity design formulas for use when bending loads are experienced, are based on the maximum deflection being—

$$\boxed{\Delta_{max} = k \frac{P L^3}{E I}} \quad \text{.........................(1)}$$

Two of the components in this formula have been discussed previously in detail. The critical property of the material is its modulus of elasticity (E). In the case of all steels, this has the very high value of 30,000,000 psi. The related property of the section is its moment of inertia (I), which is dependent on dimensions of the beam cross-section.

If the values for E and I are held constant, and the load (P) is a specified value, the length of the beam span (L) is one variable which will influence the deflection. The constant (k) is a function of the type of loading and also the manner in which the load is supported, and thus is subject to the designer's will. In practice "I" also is subject to the designer's will.

The several components of the basic formula are best handled by constructing a bending moment diagram from the actual beam, and then applying the appropriate standard simplified beam formula. These formulas are available in the Reference Section on Beam Diagrams included at the end of this book.

There are several methods for finding the deflection of a beam. Four of these will be shown:

1. Successive integration method
2. Virtual work method
3. Area moment method
4. Conjugate beam method

2. FUNDAMENTALS OF BEAM DEFLECTION

A transverse load placed on a beam causes bending moments along the length of the beam. These bending moments set up bending stresses (σ) across all sections of the beam. See Figure 1a, where at any given section:

$$\sigma_x = \frac{M_x \, c}{I_x}$$

It is usually assumed that the bending stress (σ) is zero at the neutral axis and then increases linearly to a maximum at the outer fibers. One surface is under compression, while the other surface is under tension. Within the elastic limit, assuming a straight-line relationship between stress and strain, the distribution of bending stress can be converted over into a distribution of strain. Correspondingly, there would be no strain (ϵ) along the neutral axis and the strain would increase linearly to a maximum at the outer fiber. See Figure 1b where at any given section:

$$\epsilon_x = \frac{\sigma_x}{E} = \frac{M_x \, c}{E \, I_x}$$

Considering a segment of the beam having only a

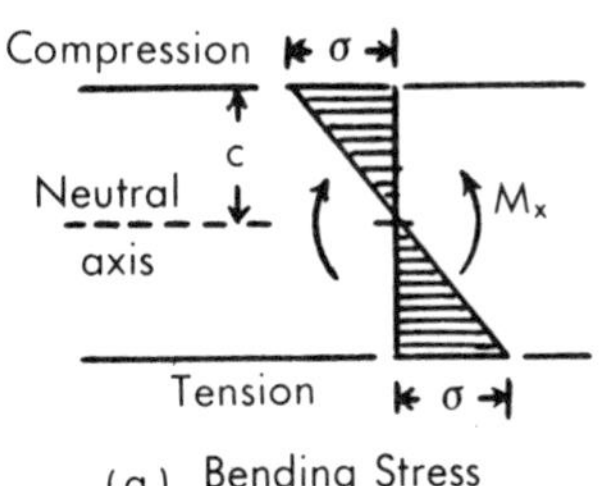

(a) Bending Stress

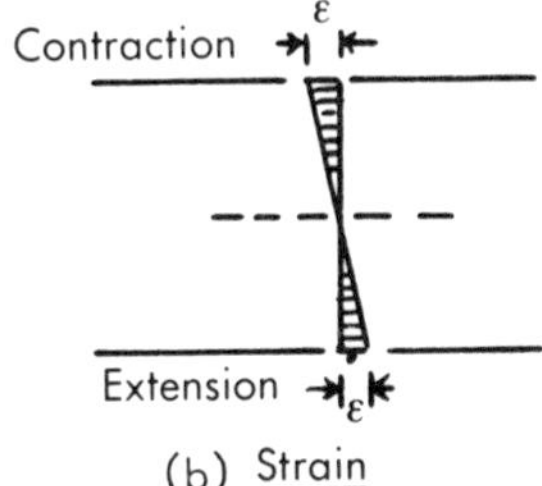

(b) Strain

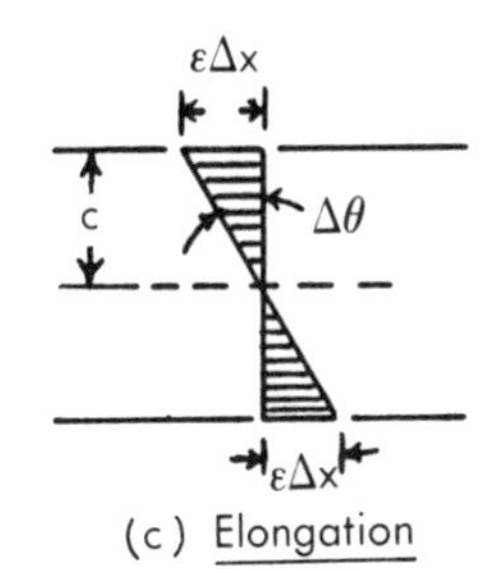

(c) Elongation

FIGURE 1

very small increment in length (Δx), Figure 1c, the elongation within this small increment would be $\epsilon\,(\Delta x)$. Also, here it can be seen that the small angular rotation ($\Delta\theta$) would be the elongation at the outer fiber divided by the distance (c) to the outer fiber from the neutral axis.

This can be expressed as —

$$\epsilon(\Delta x) = c\,(\Delta\theta)$$

$$\therefore \Delta\theta = \frac{\epsilon\,(\Delta x)}{c} = \frac{M\,c\,(\Delta x)}{E\,I\,c}$$

or:

$$(\theta\Delta)_x = \frac{M_x\,(\Delta x)}{E\,I_x}$$

In other words, the infinitesimal angle change in any section of the beam is equal to the area under the moment diagram ($M_x\,\Delta x$) divided by the ($E\,I_x$) of the section.

The angular rotation relative to stress and strain is further illustrated by Figure 2.

Figure 2a represents a straight beam under zero bending moment. Here any two given sections (a and b) would parallel each other and, in a stress-free condition, would then have a radius of curvature (R_x) equal to infinity (∞). These two sections (a and b) can be set close together to define the segment of very small increment in length (Δx).

At Figure 2b, the beam is subjected to a bending moment and this small segment (Δx) will compress on one side and will elongate on the other side where the outer fiber is in tension. This can be related to a small angular movement within this increment. It can be seen that sections *a* and *b* are no longer parallel but would converge at some point (0) in space, forming a radius of curvature (R_x).

In the sketch to the right of Figure 2b, dotted lines (a and b) represent the initial incremental segment (Δx) with zero moment, while the solid lines reflect the effect of applied load: $\Delta x\,(1 - \epsilon)$ at the surface under compression.

The total angular change (θ) between any two points (a and b) of the beam equals the sum of the incremental changes, or:

$$\theta = \int_{x=a}^{x=b} (\Delta\theta)_x = \int_{x=a}^{x=b} \frac{M_x\,(\Delta x)}{E\,I_x} \qquad \text{.............(2)}$$

It is also observed from Figure 2b that —

$$(\Delta\theta)_x = \frac{\Delta x}{R_x} = \frac{M_x\,(\Delta x)}{E\,I_x}$$

and since —

$$(\Delta\theta)_x = \frac{M_x\,(\Delta x)}{E\,I_x}$$

the reciprocal of the radius of curvature (1/R) at any given point (x) of the beam is —

$$\boxed{\frac{1}{R_x} = \frac{M_x}{E\,I_x}} \qquad \text{..............................(3)}$$

The next logical step would seem to be application of the Successive Integration Method to determine the beam deflection.

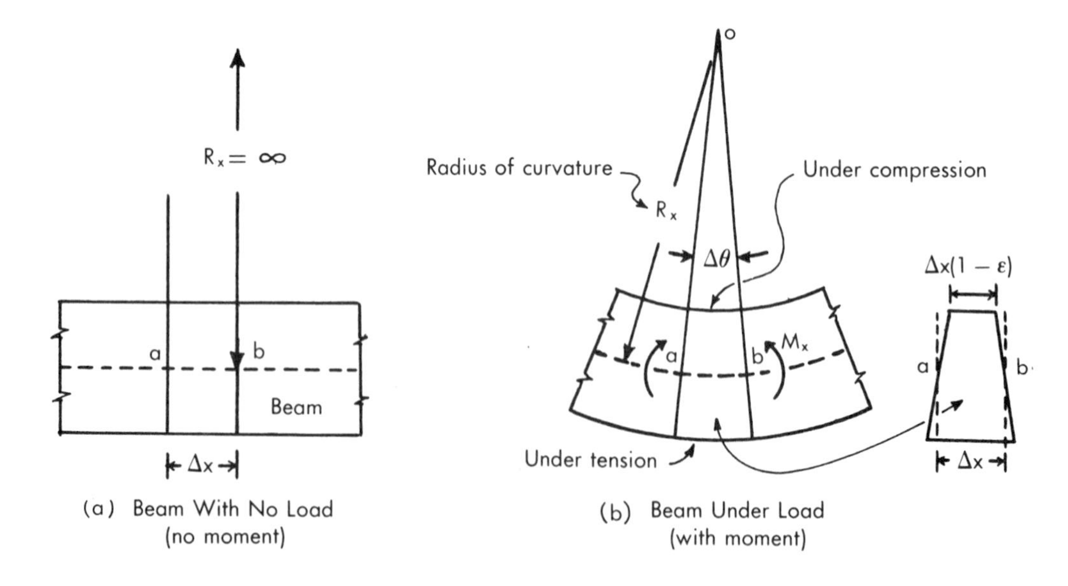

(a) Beam With No Load (no moment)

(b) Beam Under Load (with moment)

FIGURE 2

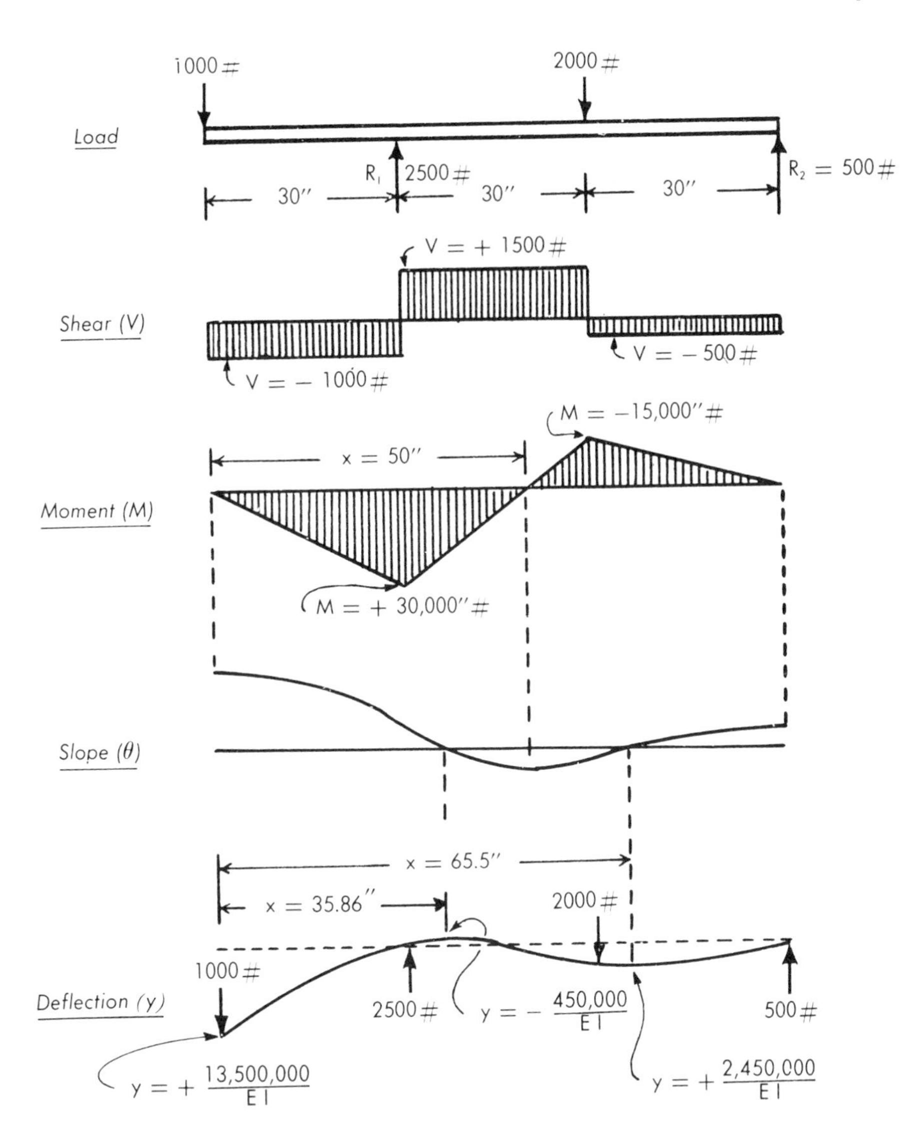

FIGURE 3

3. SUCCESSIVE INTEGRATION METHOD

For any given beam with any given load, if the load (w_x) at any point (x) can be expressed mathematically as a function of (x) and if such load condition is known for the entire beam, then:

load

$$\boxed{w_x = f_1(x)} \qquad (4)$$

and by successive integrations —

shear

$$\boxed{V_x = \int_{x_1}^{x_2} w_x\,(dx)} \qquad (5)$$

moment

$$\boxed{M_x = \int_{x_1}^{x_2} V_x\,(dx)} \qquad (6)$$

slope

$$\boxed{\theta_x = \int_{x_1}^{x_2} \frac{M_x\,(dx)}{E\,I_x}} \qquad (7)$$

deflection

$$\boxed{y_x = \int_{x_1}^{x_2} \frac{\theta_x(dx)}{E\,I_x} = \iint_{x_1}^{x_2} \frac{M_x\,(dx)}{E\,I_x}} \qquad (8)$$

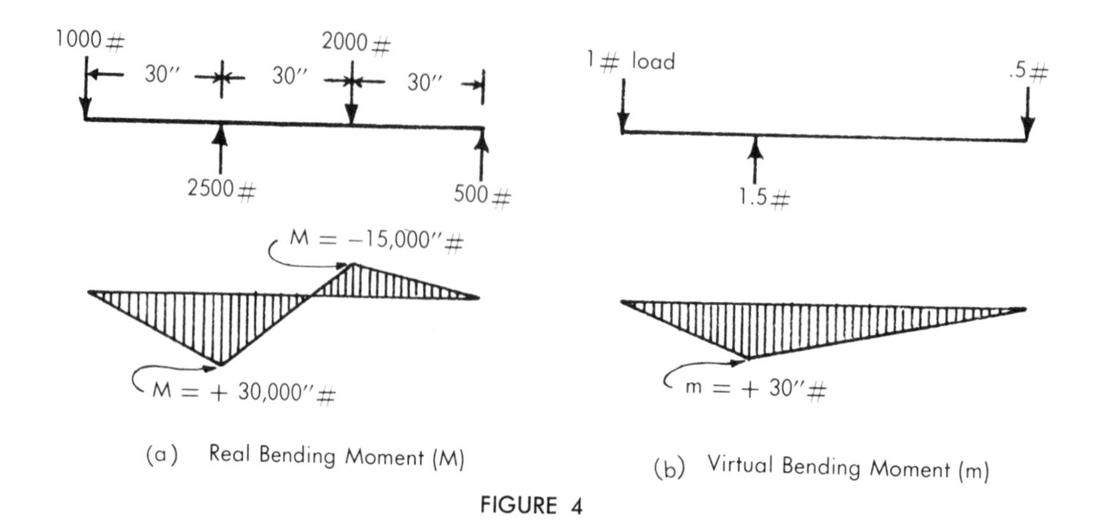

FIGURE 4

Unfortunately, it is usually difficult to get a mathematical expression for the load in terms of x for the entire length of the beam for any but the simplest of beam loadings. The method is cumbersome, especially if various loads are applied, if there are various types of support, or if there are various changes in section.

For every integration, there is a constant of integration (C) which must be solved. This is done by setting up known conditions of the beam; for example, the deflection of a beam over a support is zero, the slope of a beam at a fixed end is zero, etc.

This method means several equations must be used and integrated within certain limits of x, with considerable time expended and with the possibility of compounded error.

If possible, integrate graphically rather than mathematically, this process takes on greater importance. Most of the methods in actual use for computing deflection are based on a graphical solution of the problem.

Problem 1

The example in Figure 3 will be worked through in several ways. In this case, the problem was previously worked out by longhand so it is known exactly what it looks like. Then several methods will be used in finding the deflection (y or Δ) under the conditions illustrated, to show that in each case the answer comes out the same:

$$y = \frac{13{,}500{,}000}{E\ I} \text{ inches}$$

4. VIRTUAL WORK METHOD

This is used frequently for finding the deflection of a point on a beam in any direction, caused by the beam load. A virtual load of one pound (or one kip) is placed on the beam at the point where the amount of deflection is desired and in the same direction.

Virtual bending moments (m) caused by the 1-lb load are determined along the entire length of the beam. The internal energy of the beam after deflecting is determined by integration. This is then set equal to the external energy of the 1-lb virtual load moving a distance (y) equal to the deflection.

$$1\# \cdot y = \int \frac{M_x\ m_x\ dx}{E\ I_x} \quad \text{.....................(9)}$$

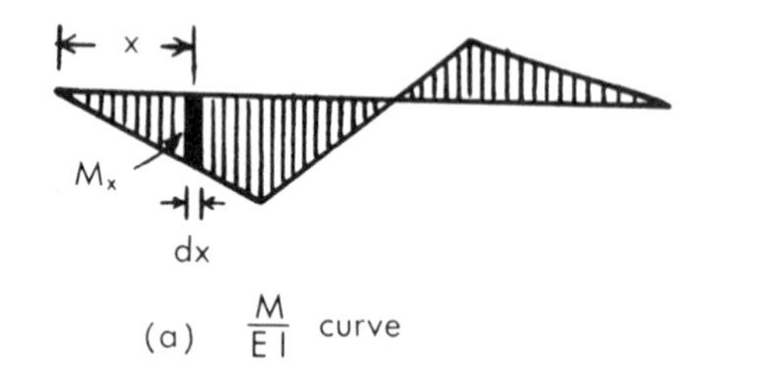

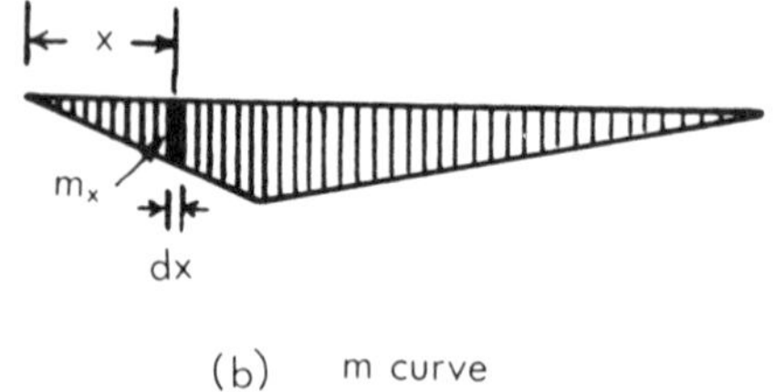

FIGURE 5

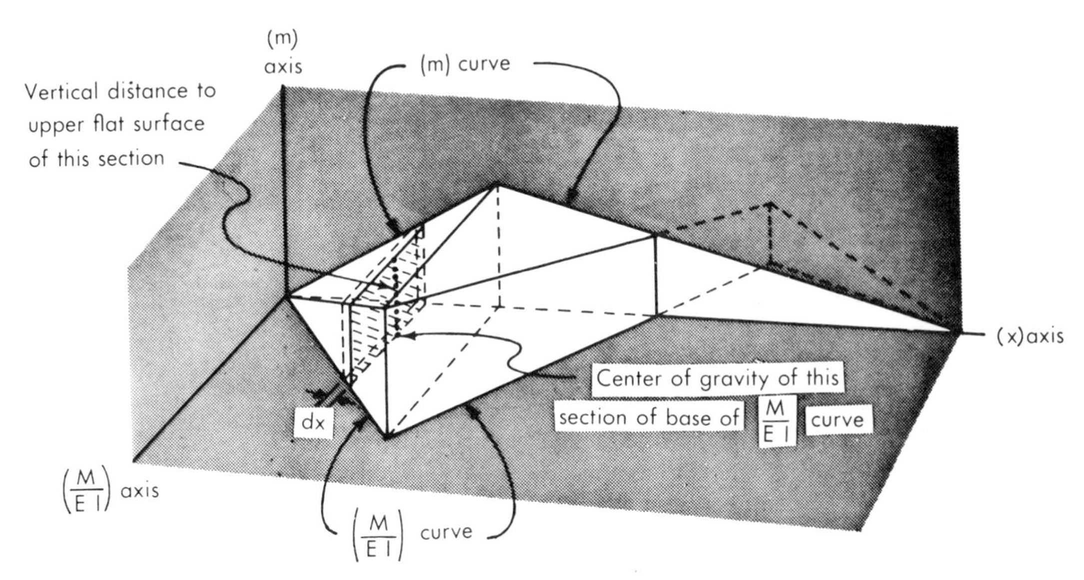

FIGURE 6

where:

m = virtual bending moment at any point caused by the 1-lb load

M = real bending moment at the same point

I = moment of inertia at this same point

dx = length of small increment of the beam

E = modulus of elasticity in tension of the material

This equation can be worked out by calculus; however, its real value is that it lends itself to a graphical approach.

The first step is to apply all of the forces (Problem 1, Fig. 3) to the member, Figure 4a, and to compute the bending diagram—the real bending moment (M) on the beam. The next step is to remove the real load and replace it with a 1-lb load at the point where the deflection is desired and also in the same direction, Figure 4b. The bending moment of this particular load is then computed; this is known as the virtual bending moment (m).

The real moment diagram can be broken down into standard geometric areas; for example, triangles and rectangles for concentrated loads, and parabolas for uniformly distributed loads. The virtual moment diagram by the very nature of the single 1-lb concentrated force is always triangular in shape.

This means that the integration of these moment diagrams to obtain the internal energy may be replaced by working directly with these areas, since their properties are known. This will greatly simplify the work.

Figure 5 separates the two moment diagrams that must be combined in the basic equation #9.

It is seen from the equation that $M_x\ m_x\ dx$ is a segment of a volume.

In the triaxial representation, Figure 6, diagrams for both the real moment (M) divided by EI and the virtual moment (m) have a common base line (the x axis). The M/EI curve for the real bending moment lies flat in the horizontal plane. The m curve for the virtual bending moment is shown in the vertical plane established by the m axis and the x axis. The solid thus defined is a series of smaller volumes with simple geometric faces.

The volume of any element of this solid equals the area of the element's base surface multiplied by the vertical distance from the center of gravity of the base surface to the upper flat surface. This vertical distance is shown by a dotted line.

Thus, in Figure 7, with the M/EI and m diagrams lined up one above the other, it is necessary to know

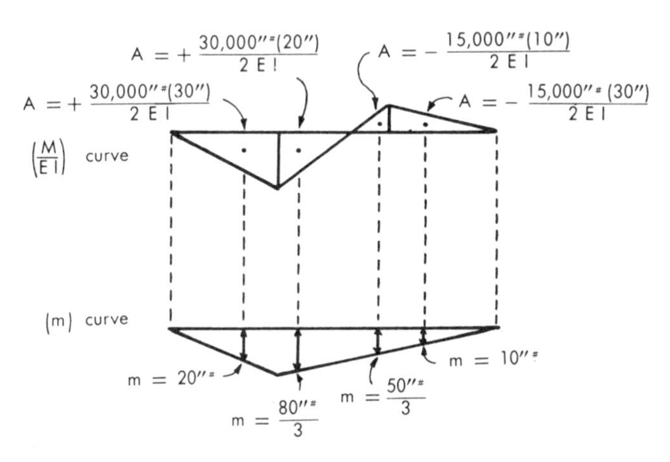

FIGURE 7

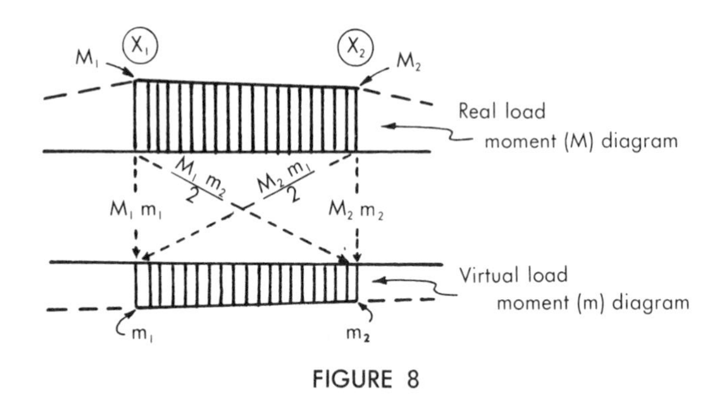

FIGURE 8

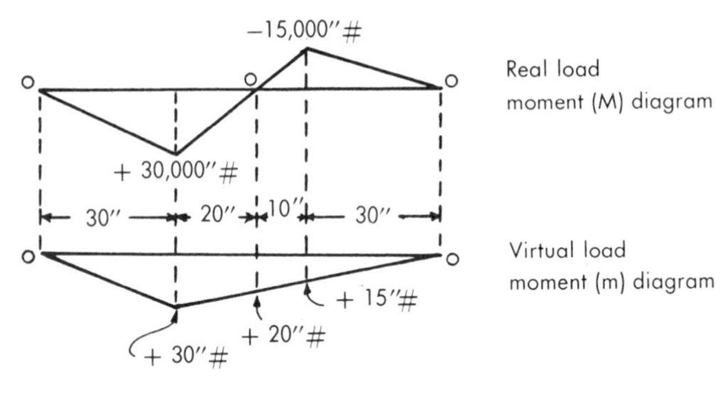

FIGURE 9

only the height of the virtual moment diagram at the same distance (x) as on the real moment diagram. The M/EI diagram is then divided into simple geometric shapes (in this case, right triangles), and the area of each is found and multiplied by the height of the m diagram along a line through the particular M/EI area's center of gravity.

From this the volume is obtained:

$$\text{Volume} = \frac{(30{,}000)(30)(20)}{2\,E\,I} + \frac{(30{,}000)(20)}{2\,E\,I}\left(\frac{80}{3}\right) - \frac{(15{,}000)(10)}{2\,E\,I}\left(\frac{50}{3}\right) - \frac{(15{,}000)(30)(10)}{2\,E\,I}$$

$$= + \frac{13{,}500{,}000}{E\,I}$$

and since:

$$\text{Volume} = 1'' \cdot y$$

the deflection in inches is—

$$y = \frac{13{,}500{,}000}{E\,I}$$

The value of I can now be inserted in this to give the deflection (y) in inches. However, if the beam has a variable section, several values of I would have to be inserted earlier in the computation—for the section taken through the center of gravity of each geometrical area of the M/EI diagram.

To simplify this further, a method of cross-multiplying has been found to give the same results. The general approach is illustrated by Figure 8, where some segment of the real moment (M) diagram between points x_1 and x_2 is at the top and a corresponding segment of the virtual moment (m) diagram is below.

The required volume can be found directly by multiplying M_1 by m_1 and M_2 by m_2 and then by cross-multiplying M_1 by m_2 and M_2 by m_1 using only ½ of the products of cross-multiplication. This is more fully related to the basic integration equation by the following:

$$\int_{x=1}^{x=2} \frac{M\,m\,dx}{E\,I} = \frac{L}{3\,E\,I}\left(M_1m_1 + M_2m_2 + \frac{M_1m_2}{2} + \frac{M_2m_1}{2}\right)$$

where L = the distance between points x_1 and x_2.

Figure 9 shows application of this method to the original Problem 1.

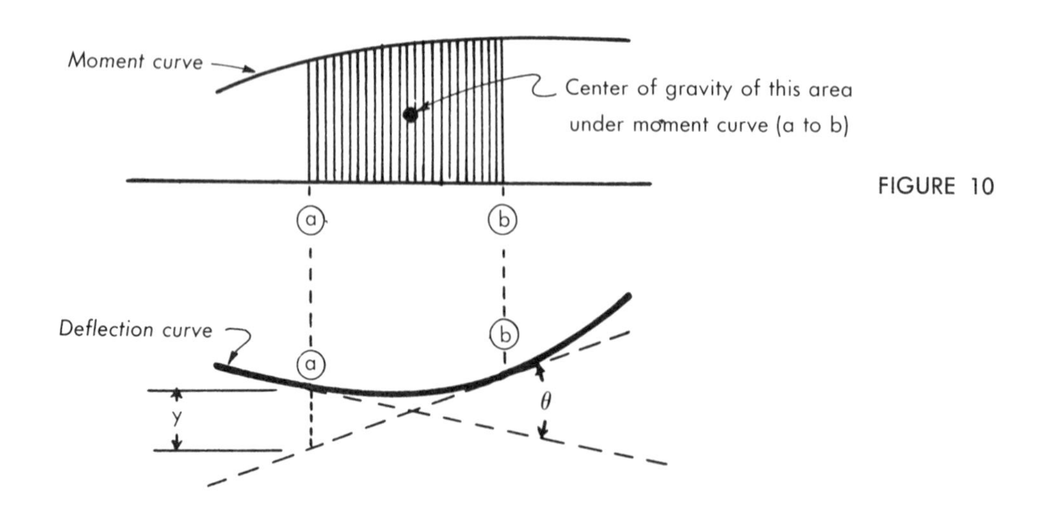

FIGURE 10

From Figure 9:

$$y = \left(\frac{30}{3}\right)\left(\frac{30 \times 30{,}000}{E\,I}\right) + \left(\frac{20}{3}\right)\left(\frac{30 \times 30{,}000}{E\,I}\right) + \left(\frac{20}{3}\right)$$
$$\left(\frac{20 \times 30{,}000}{2\,E\,I}\right) - \left(\frac{10}{3}\right)\left(\frac{15 \times 15{,}000}{E\,I}\right) - \left(\frac{10}{3}\right)$$
$$\left(\frac{20 \times 15{,}000}{2\,E\,I}\right) - \left(\frac{30}{3}\right)\left(\frac{15 \times 15{,}000}{E\,I}\right)$$
$$= \frac{13{,}500{,}000}{E\,I}$$

5. AREA MOMENT METHOD

This a very useful tool for engineers and is illustrated in Figure 10 by a general moment diagram and the corresponding deflection curve. Here points *a* and *b* represent any two points defining a simple geometric area of an actual moment diagram.

The two fundamental rules for use of this method are:

> The change in slope (radians) between two points (a and b) of a loaded beam equals the area under the moment curve, divided by E I, between these two points (a and b).

> The distance of point *a* of the beam to the tangent at point *b* of the beam equals the moment of the area under the moment diagram taken about point *a*, divided by E I.

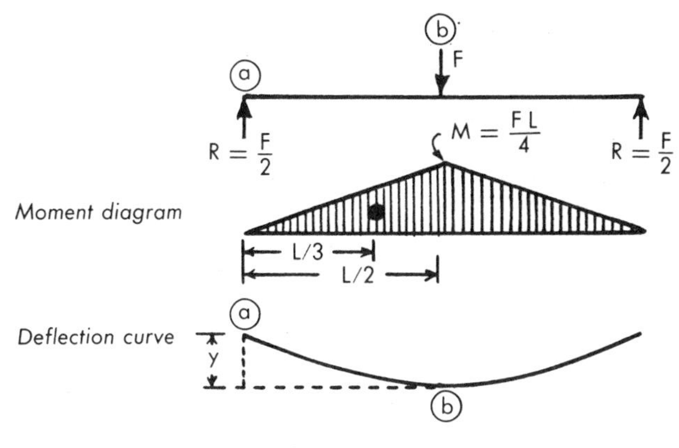

FIGURE 11

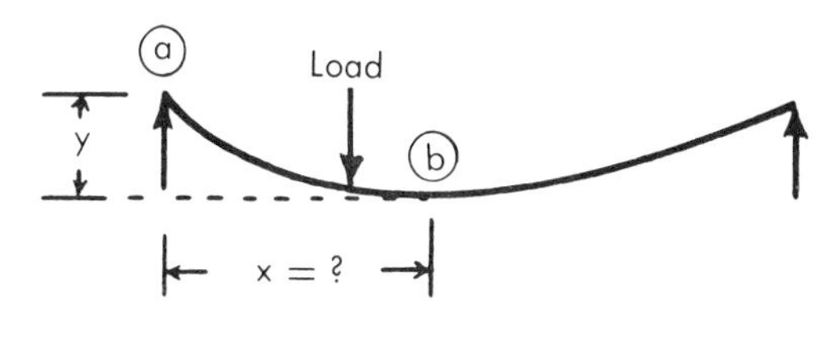

FIGURE 12

For symmetrically loaded, simply supported beams this is a convenient method with which to find the maximum deflection of the beam, because in this case the slope of the beam is zero at the mid-span (b) and the distance from *a* to the tangent at *b* equals the maximum deflection we are seeking. See Figure 11.

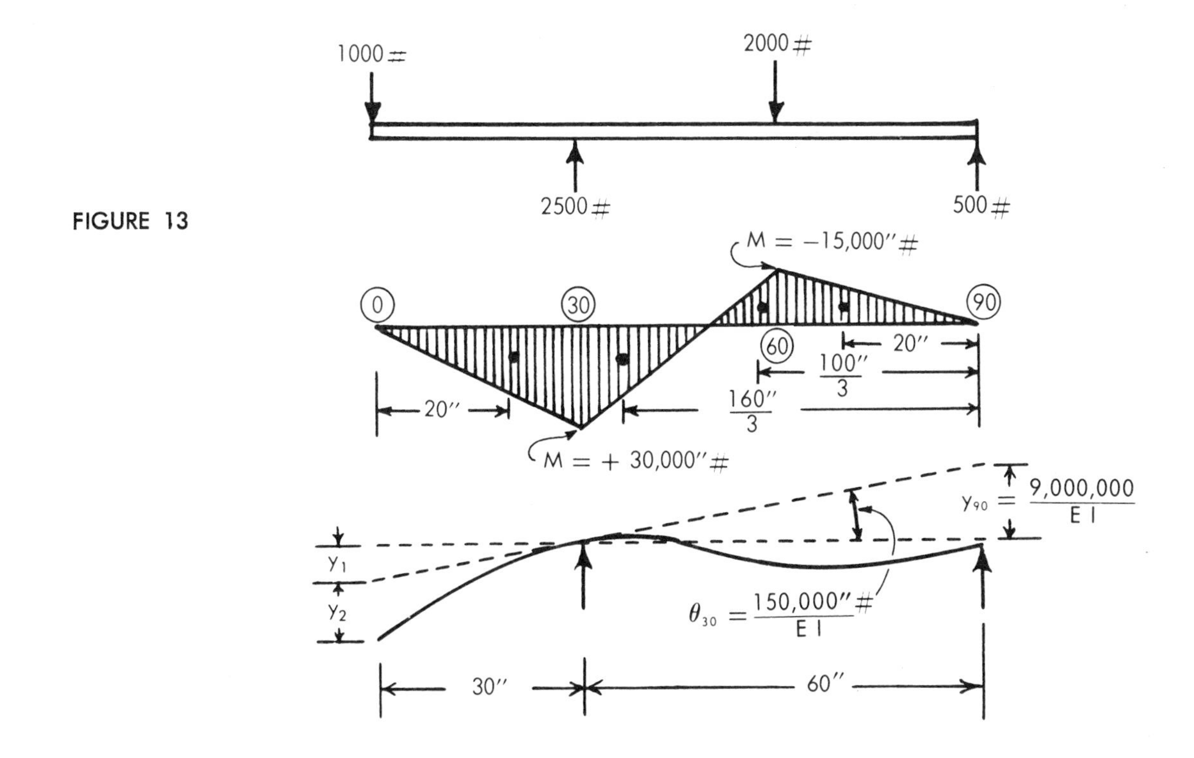

FIGURE 13

From Figure 11:

$$y = \frac{1}{2}\left(\frac{M}{E\ I}\right)\left(\frac{L}{2}\right)\left(\frac{2}{3} \times \frac{L}{2}\right) = \frac{1}{2}\left(\frac{F\ L}{4\ E\ I}\right)\left(\frac{L}{2}\right)\left(\frac{L}{3}\right)$$

$$= \frac{F\ L^3}{48\ E\ I}$$

However, for an unsymmetrically loaded beam, the point of the beam having zero slope, or maximum deflection, is unknown (Fig. 12). There are ways of getting around this.

The conditions of Problem 1 are here illustrated by Figure 13. The moments of the area under the moment curve (from point zero to point 30) is taken about point zero to give the vertical distance between point zero and the tangent to the deflection curve at point 30. This becames y_2. This is not the actual deflection, because the slope of the deflection curve at point 30 is not level. This slope is yet to be found.

First find the vertical distance between point 90 and the tangent to the deflection curve at point 30. To find this distance (y_{90}), take the moments, about point 90, of the area of the moment diagram from point 30 to point 90.

$$y_{90} = \frac{(30{,}000)(20)}{2\,E\,I}\left(\frac{160}{3}\right) - \frac{(15{,}000)(10)}{2\,E\,I}\left(\frac{100}{3}\right) - \frac{(15{,}000)(30)(20)}{2\,E\,I}$$

$$= \frac{9{,}000{,}000}{E\ I}$$

TABLE 1—Comparative Conditions of Real and Conjugate Beams

Real Beam	Conjugate Beam
1. Simple supported ends a) zero deflection b) maximum slopes	1. Simply supported ends because — a) zero moment b) maximum shear
2. Fixed ends a) zero deflection b) zero slope	2. Free ends because — a) zero moment b) zero shear hence no support
3. Free ends a) a maximum deflection b) a maximum slope	3. Fixed ends because — a) a maximum moment b) a maximum shear hence a support
4. Interior supports of a continuous beam a) no deflection b) gradual change in slope	4. A hinge without support a) no moment b) gradual change in shear hence no support
5. Point of maximum deflection	5. Located at point of zero shear because this is a point of maximum moment
6. Either statically determinate or statically indeterminate	6. Always statically determinate

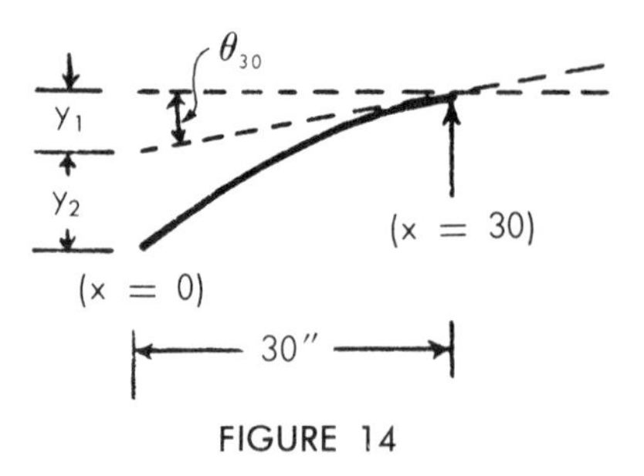

FIGURE 14

The angle of this tangent line to the horizon (θ_{30}) is then found by dividing this vertical distance (y_{90}) by the horizontal distance between point 30 and point 90.

$$\theta_{30} = \frac{y_{90}}{60''} = \frac{9{,}000{,}000}{60\ E\ I} = \frac{150{,}000}{E\ I}$$

This angle (θ_{30}) is the same to the left of point 30, Figure 14, and defines the vertical deflection (y_1) at point zero. This angle then, multiplied by the horizontal distance from point zero to point 30, gives the vertical displacement (y_1).

$$y_1 = \theta_{30}\ 30 = \frac{150{,}000}{E\ I}\ 30 = \frac{4{,}500{,}000}{E\ I}$$

Adding this to the initial displacement—

$$y_2 = \frac{(30{,}000)(30)(20)}{2\ E\ I} = \frac{9{,}000{,}000}{E\ I}$$

gives the total deflection at point zero of—

$$y = \frac{13{,}500{,}000}{E\ I}$$

6. CONJUGATE BEAM METHOD

In using this method, the bending moment diagram of the real beam is constructed. A substitutional beam or conjugate beam is then set up; the load on this is the moment of the real beam divided by the E I of the real beam; in other words it is loaded with the M/EI of the real beam.

Five conditions must be met:

1. The length of the conjugate beam equals the length of the real beam.

TABLE 2—Typical Real Beams and Corresponding Conjugate Beams

Real Beam	Conjugate Beam
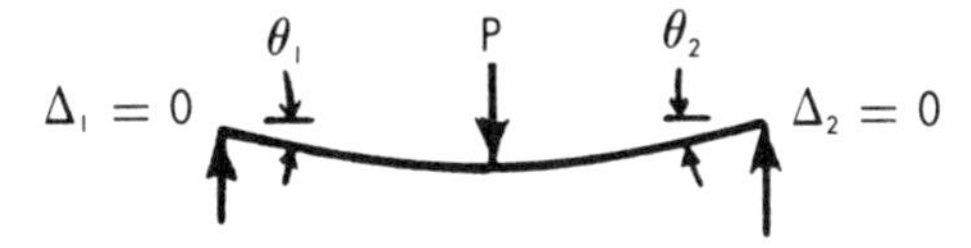 θ_1 P θ_2 $\Delta_1 = 0$ $\Delta_2 = 0$	 $M_1 = 0$ $M_2 = 0$ $R_1 = \theta_1$ $R_2 = \theta_2$
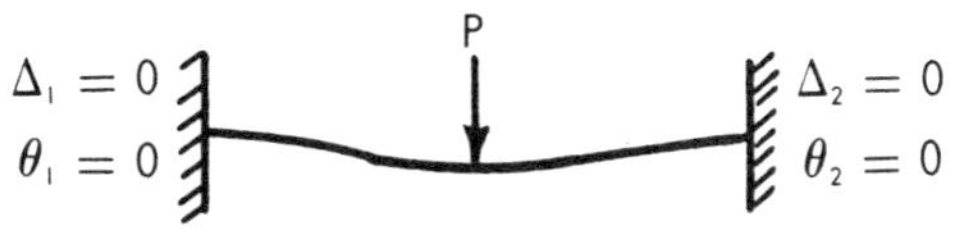 P $\Delta_1 = 0$ $\Delta_2 = 0$ $\theta_1 = 0$ $\theta_2 = 0$	 $M_1 = 0$ $M_2 = 0$ $R_1 = 0$ $R_2 = 0$ No supports
 P $\Delta_2 = 0$ Δ_1 $\theta_2 = 0$ θ_1	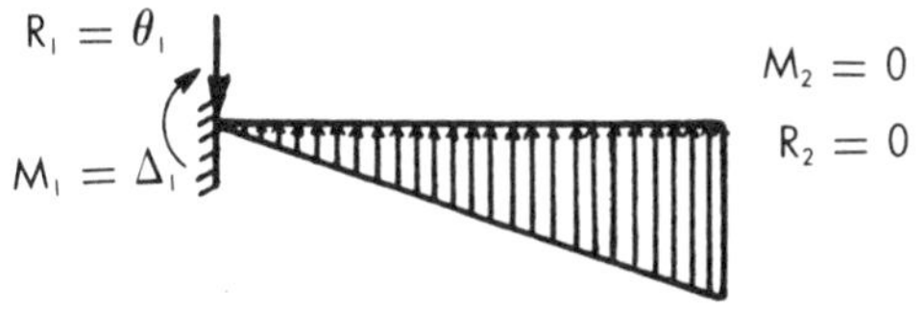 $R_1 = \theta_1$ $M_2 = 0$ $M_1 = \Delta_1$ $R_2 = 0$
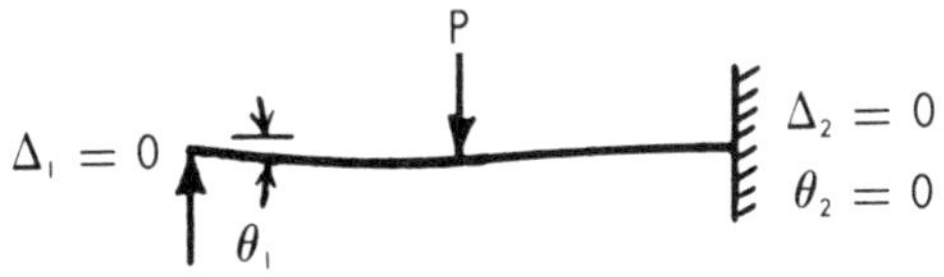 P $\Delta_1 = 0$ $\Delta_2 = 0$ θ_1 $\theta_2 = 0$	 $M_1 = 0$ $M_2 = 0$ $R_1 = \theta_1$ $R_2 = 0$
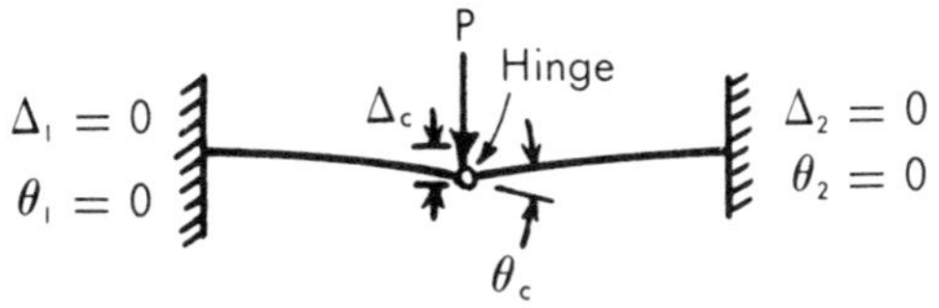 P Hinge $\Delta_1 = 0$ Δ_c $\Delta_2 = 0$ $\theta_1 = 0$ $\theta_2 = 0$ θ_c	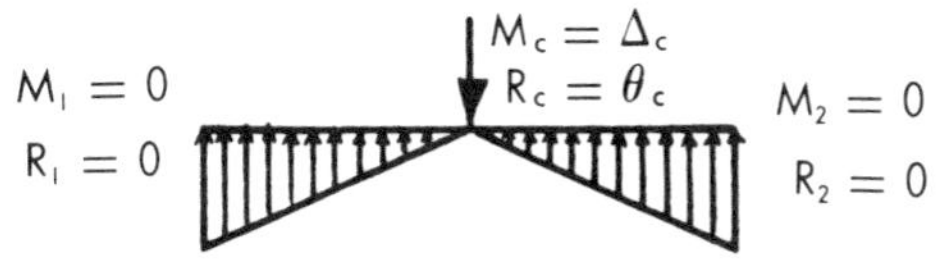 $M_c = \Delta_c$ $R_c = \theta_c$ $M_1 = 0$ $M_2 = 0$ $R_1 = 0$ $R_2 = 0$
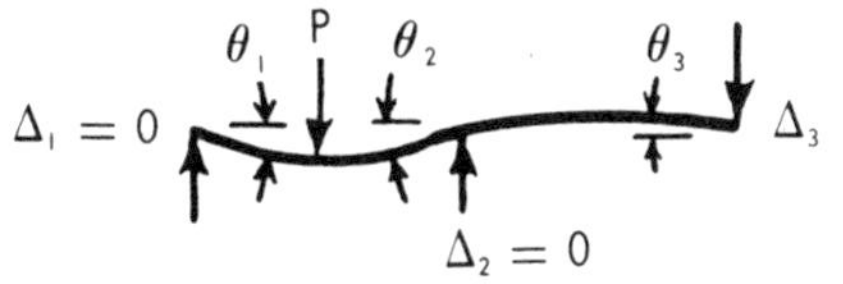 θ_1 P θ_2 θ_3 $\Delta_1 = 0$ Δ_3 $\Delta_2 = 0$	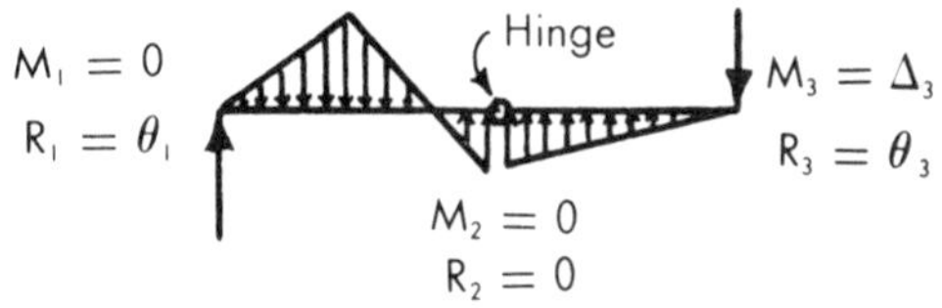 Hinge $M_1 = 0$ $M_3 = \Delta_3$ $R_1 = \theta_1$ $R_3 = \theta_3$ $M_2 = 0$ $R_2 = 0$

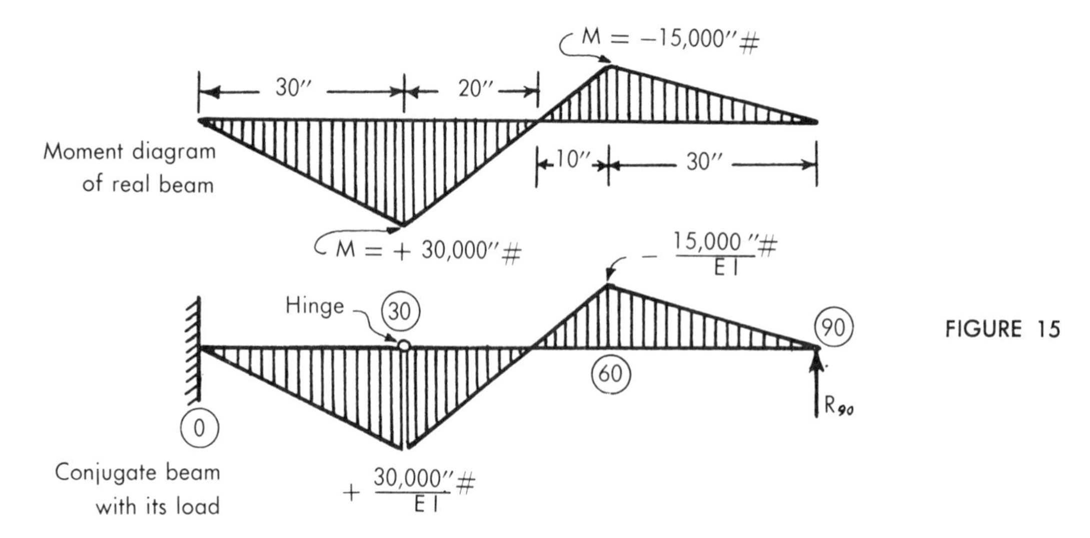

FIGURE 15

2. There are two equations of equilibrium—
   - The sum of forces acting in any one direction on the conjugate beam equals zero.
   - The sum of moments about any point of the conjugate beam equals zero.

3. The load at any point of the conjugate beam equals the moment of the real beam divided by the E I of the real beam at the same point. The real beam could have variable I.

4. The vertical shear at any point of the conjugate beam equals the slope of the real beam at the same point.

5. The bending moment at any point of the conjugate beam equals the deflection of the real beam at the same point.

The conjugate beam must be so supported that conditions 4 and 5 are satisfied. The above statements of condition may be reversed.

By knowing some of the conditions of the real beam, it will be possible to reason the nature of the support of the conjugate beam. The comparative statements of Table 1 will help in setting up the conjugate beam.

Some examples of real beams and their corresponding conjugate beams are presented in Table 2.

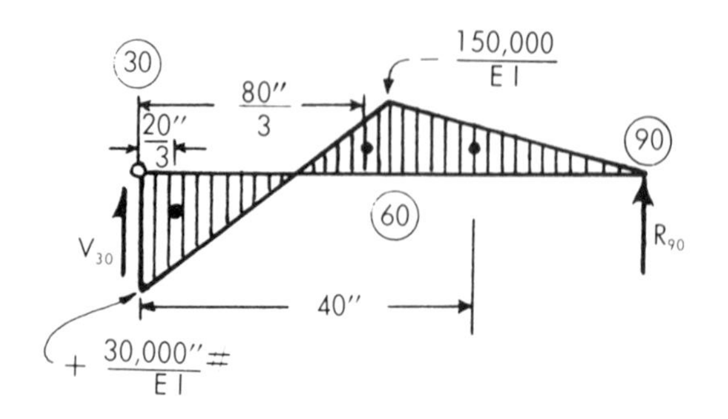

FIGURE 16

Notice that the support of the conjugate beam can be very unlike the support of the real beam.

The last example in Table 2 is similar to the Problem 1 beam to which several methods of solving deflection have already been applied. Here the conjugate beam is hinged at the point of second support of the real beam, and without this hinge the Conjugate Beam Method would not be workable.

The same Problem 1 is illustrated in Figure 15, where the real beam moment is first diagrammed. This is then divided by E I of the real beam for the load on the conjugate beam shown next.

To find the right hand reaction (R_{90}) take moments, about point 30, on the conjugate beam between points 30 and 90. See Figure 16.

Since:

$$\Sigma M_{30} = 0$$

$$\frac{1}{2}\left(\frac{+\ 300{,}000}{E\ I}\right)(20)\left(\frac{20}{3}\right) + \frac{1}{2}\left(\frac{-\ 15{,}000}{E\ I}\right)(10)\left(\frac{80}{3}\right) + \frac{1}{2}\left(\frac{-\ 15{,}000}{E\ I}\right)(30)(40) - R_{90}(60) = 0$$

$$\therefore R_{90} = -\ \frac{150{,}000\ \text{in.}^2\text{-lbs}}{E\ I}$$

This negative sign means the reaction is directed opposite to our original assumption; hence it is directed downward.

Since the sum of vertical forces equals zero, V_{30} may be found:

$$\underbrace{-\ V_{30}}_{\text{assume upward}} + \frac{1}{2}\left(\frac{+\ 30{,}000}{E\ I}\right)(20) + \frac{1}{2}\left(\frac{-\ 15{,}000}{E\ I}\right)(40) + \overbrace{\frac{150{,}000}{E\ I}}^{\text{downward } R_{90}} = 0$$

$$\therefore V_{30} = + \frac{150{,}000 \text{ in.}^2\text{-lbs}}{E\ I}$$

This positive sign means original assumption was correct and shear is directed upward.

The left hand moment (M_0) of the conjugate beam may be found by taking moments of the isolated element, between points zero and 30. See Figure 17.

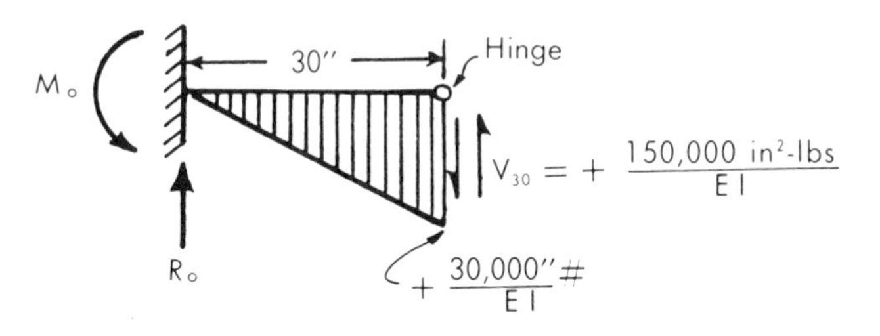

FIGURE 17

directed downward
V_{30}

$$M_o = \frac{1}{2}\left(\frac{+\ 30{,}000}{E\ I}\right)(30)(20) + \left(\frac{150{,}000}{E\ I}\right)(30)$$

$$= + \frac{13{,}500{,}000 \text{ in.}^3\text{-lbs}}{E\ I}$$

The deflection of the real beam at point zero (y_o or Δ_{max}) equals the moment of the conjugate beam at this point (M_o); hence:

$$y_o = \frac{13{,}500{,}000}{E\ I} \text{ inches}$$

This would be the solution of this problem; however, to get the deflection at other points it would be necessary to continue this work and find the moment of the conjugate beam throughout its length.

The maximum deflection of the real beam on the right side occurs at the same point as zero shear of the conjugate beam. By observation this would occur somewhere between points 60 and 90, and the distance

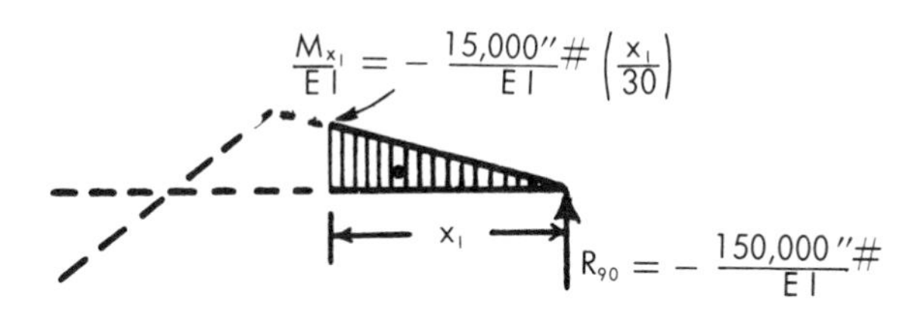

FIGURE 18

of this point of maximum deflection from point 90 is set as x_1. See Figure 18.

Since:

$$\Sigma\ V = 0$$

$$\frac{1}{2}\left(\frac{-\ 15{,}000}{E\ I}\right)\left(\frac{x_1}{30}\right) x_1 + \frac{150{,}000}{E\ I} = 0$$

$$250\ x_1^2 = 150{,}000$$

$$x_1^2 = 600$$

and:

$$x_1 = 24.5''$$

The moment of the conjugate beam at this point is —

$$M_x = \frac{1}{2}\left(\frac{-\ 15{,}000}{E\ I}\right)\left(\frac{x_1}{30}\right) x_1 \left(\frac{x_1}{3}\right) + \frac{150{,}000}{E\ I}\ x_1$$

$$= \frac{2{,}450{,}000}{E\ I}$$

and therefore the maximum deflection (y_{max} or Δ_{max}) of the real beam, Figure 19 —

$$y_{max} = \frac{2{,}450{,}000 \text{ in.}^3\text{-lbs}}{E\ I} \text{ inches}$$

7. DEFLECTION OF BEAM WITH VARIABLE SECTION

The area moment method may be used very nicely to find the deflection of beams in which no portion of the beam has a constant moment of inertia.

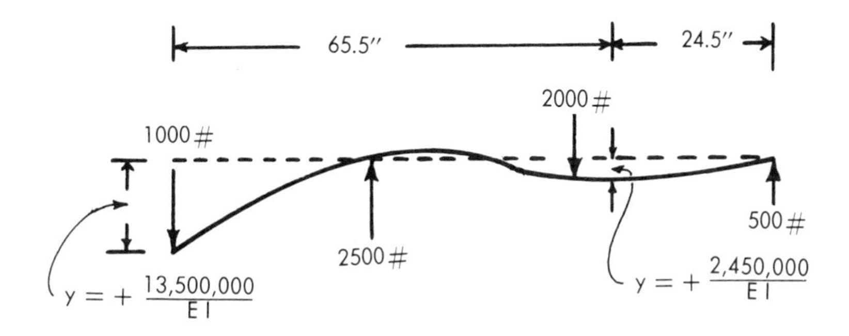

FIGURE 19

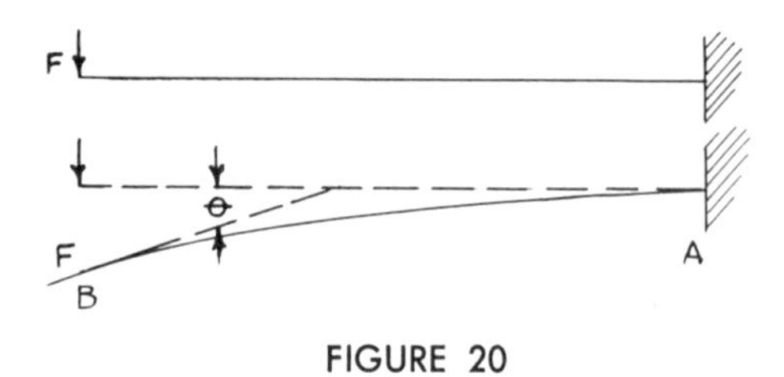

FIGURE 20

The angle between the tangents at A and B = θ = the area of the moment diagram between A and B, divided by EI.

Subdividing this beam into 10 or more segments of equal length (s):

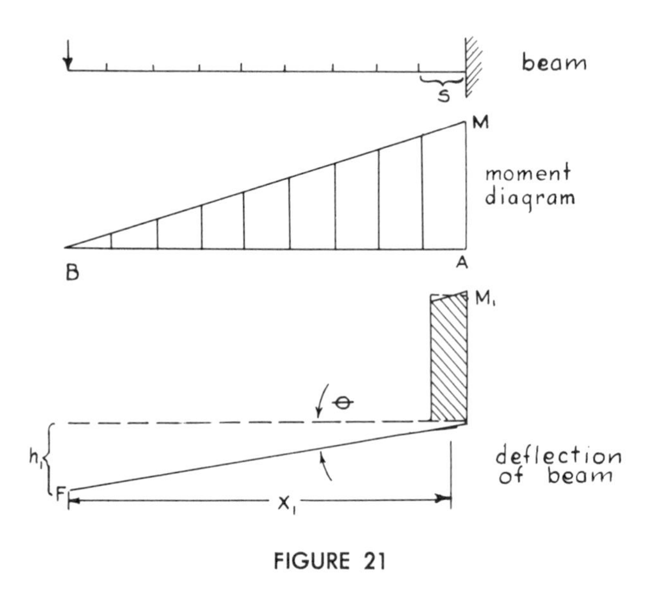

FIGURE 21

Each segment of bending moment causes the beam in this segment to bend or rotate. The angle of bend θ = area of moment diagram of this segment divided by EI, or —

$$\theta_n = \frac{M_n\ s}{E\ I_n} \qquad (10)$$

The resultant vertical momement (h_n) of the load, at the left end of the beam, is —

$$h_n = \theta_n\ X_n = \frac{M_n\ s\ X_n}{E\ I_n} \qquad (11)$$

Each segment of the beam bends under its individual bending moment and its angle change causes the end of the beam to deflect. See Figure 22.

The total deflection at the end of the beam equals the sum of the deflections at the end of the beam caused by the angle change of each segment of the beam. See Figure 23.

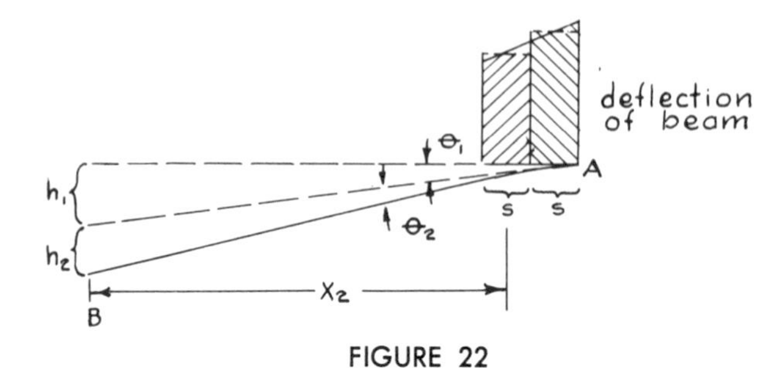

FIGURE 22

Restating the preceding, the vertical deflection of B is —

$$\Delta = \Sigma \frac{M_n\ X_n\ s}{E\ I_n} \qquad (12)$$

or:

$$\Delta = \frac{s}{E} \Sigma \frac{M_n\ X_n}{I_n} \qquad (13)$$

Note: $\dfrac{M_n\ X_n}{I_n}$ is found for each segment. These values are added together, and this sum is multiplied by s/E to give the total deflection.

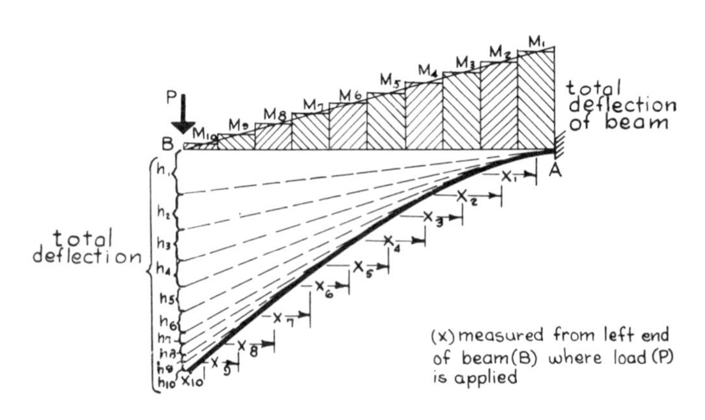

FIGURE 23

Problem 2

The following tapered beam is 30′ long. It has 1″ × 10″ flange plates and a ½″ thick web. It is 11″ deep at the ends and 33″ deep at centerline. It supports two 50-kip loads at the ⅓ points. Find the maximum deflection of the beam. See Figure 24.

Divide the length of the beam into 12 equal segments. The greater the number of segments or divisions, the more accurate will be the answer. Normally 10 divisions would give a fairly accurate result (Fig. 25).

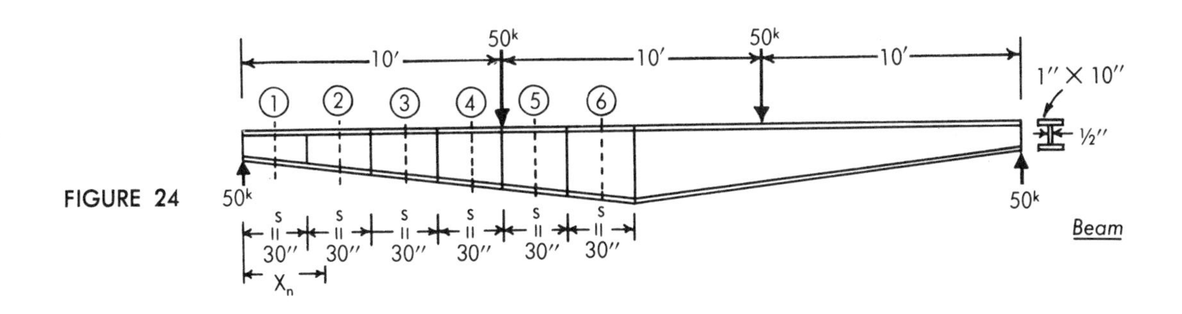

FIGURE 24

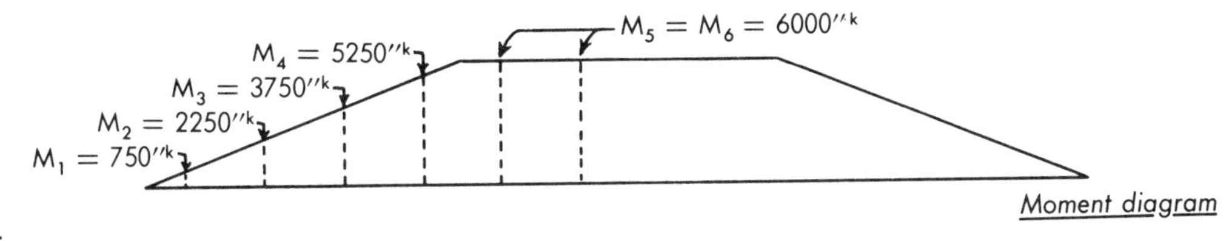

FIGURE 25

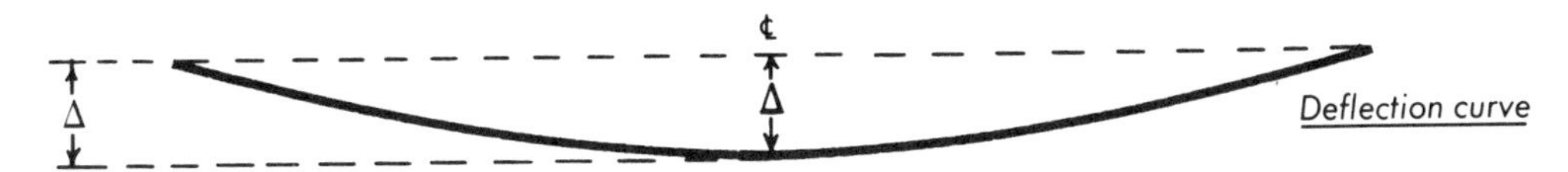

Here: $s = 30''$

and $\Delta_{total} = \dfrac{s}{E} \Sigma \dfrac{M_n X_n}{I_n}$

The moment of inertia of each segment (I_n) is taken at the sectional centroid of the segment.

The formula components M_n, X_n, and I_n are easier to handle in table form:

Seg-ment	Depth of Web	I_n	X_n	Moment (M_n), in.-lbs	$\dfrac{M_n X_n}{I_n}$ psi
1	10″	646.67	15″	$50^k \times 15''$ = 750,000	17,400
2	14″	1239.33	45″	$50^k \times 45''$ = 2,250,000	81,700
3	18″	2048.00	75″	$50^k \times 75''$ = 3,750,000	137,320
4	22″	3088.67	105″	$50^k \times 105''$ = 5,250,000	178,480
5	26″	4377.33	135″	$50^k \times 135'' - 50^k \times 15''$ = 6,000,000	185,040
6	30″	5930.33	165″	$50^k \times 165'' - 50^k \times 45''$ = 6,000,000	166,940
				Total ➠	766,880

Total vertical deflection —

$$\Delta_{total} = \frac{s}{E} \Sigma \frac{M_n X_n}{I_n}$$

$$= \frac{(30'')(766{,}880 \text{ psi})}{(30{,}000{,}000 \text{ psi})}$$

$$= \underline{.77''}$$

8. DESIGNING FOR MULTIPLE LOADS

Normally, the calculation of the maximum deflection of members subjected to bending loads is very complex. The point of maximum deflection must first be found; then, from this, the maximum deflection is found. Unless there are no more than two loads of equal value and equal distance from the ends of the beam (Fig. 26), existing beam tables in handbooks do not cover this problem.

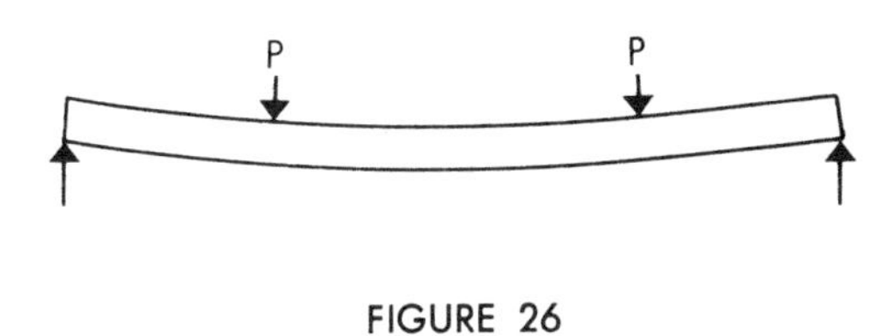

FIGURE 26

For example, most beams have more than two loads (Fig. 27). The maximum deflection usually does not occur at the middle or centerline of the beam (Fig. 28). Two things can be done to simplify this problem.

First, consider only the deflection at the middle or centerline of the member, rather than the maximum deflection at some point which is difficult to determine. This is justified, since the deflection at midpoint or centerline is almost as great as the maximum deflection,

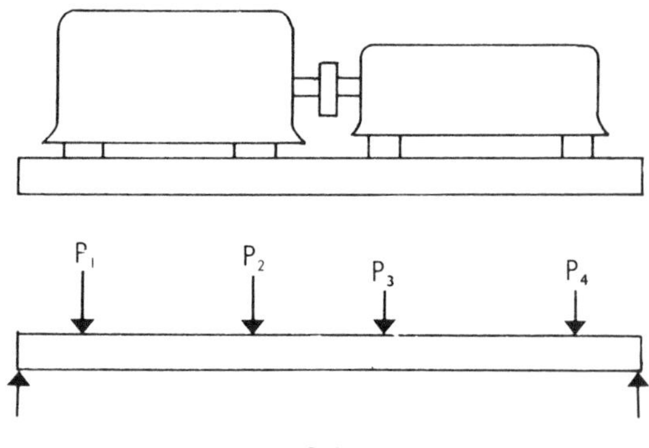

FIGURE 27

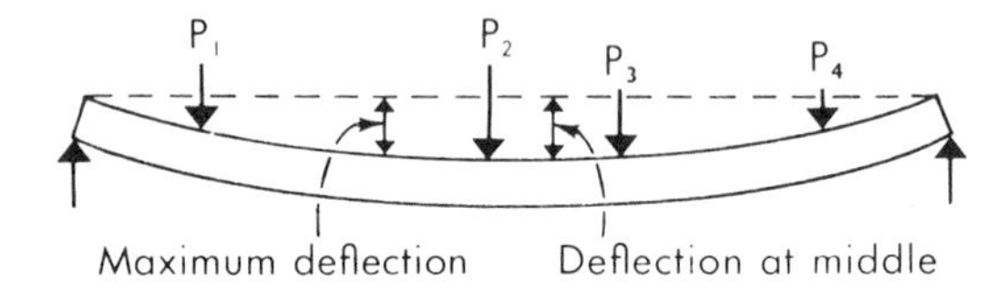

FIGURE 28

the greatest deviation coming within 1 or 2% of this value. For example, a simply supported beam with a single concentrated load at the one-quarter point has a deflection at centerline = 98.5% of the maximum deflection.

Secondly, a simple method of adding the required moments of inertia required for each individual load can be used.

For a given size member, Figure 29, it is found that each load, taken one at a time, will cause a certain amount of deflection at the middle or centerline. The total deflection at the centerline will equal the sum of these individual deflections caused by each load.

This principle of adding deflections may be used in a reverse manner to find the required section of the member (I), Figure 30. For a given allowable deflection (Δ) at the centerline, each individual load, taken one at a time, will require the member to have a certain section (I_1, I_2, etc.).

The moment of inertia (I) of the beam section required to support all of the vertical loads within this allowable vertical deflection (Δ) will equal the sum of the individual moments of inertia (I_n) required for the several loads.

Any torque or couple applied horizontal to the beam will cause it to deflect vertically. This can be handled in the same manner. The required moment of inertia of the member (I_n) for each torque acting separately is found and added into the total requirement for the property of the section (I).

The following two formulas may be used to find the individual properties of the section (I_n):

for each force

$$I_n = \frac{P_n \, L^2}{48 \, E\left(\frac{\Delta}{L}\right)}(3 \, K_n - 4 \, K_n^3) \quad \ldots\ldots\ldots(14)$$

for each couple

$$I_n = \frac{C_n \, L}{16 \, E\left(\frac{\Delta}{L}\right)}(4 \, K_n^2 - 1) \quad \ldots\ldots\ldots\ldots(15)$$

where:

$$K_n = \frac{a_n}{L}$$

The two formulas have been simplified into the formulas given below in which the expression K_n now produces a constant (A or B) which is found in Table 3.

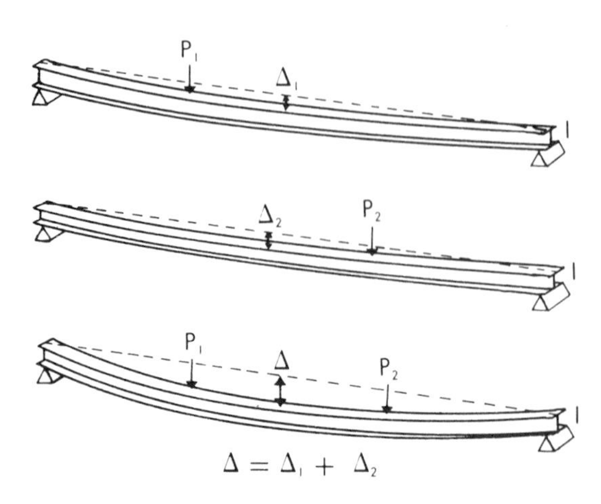

FIGURE 29

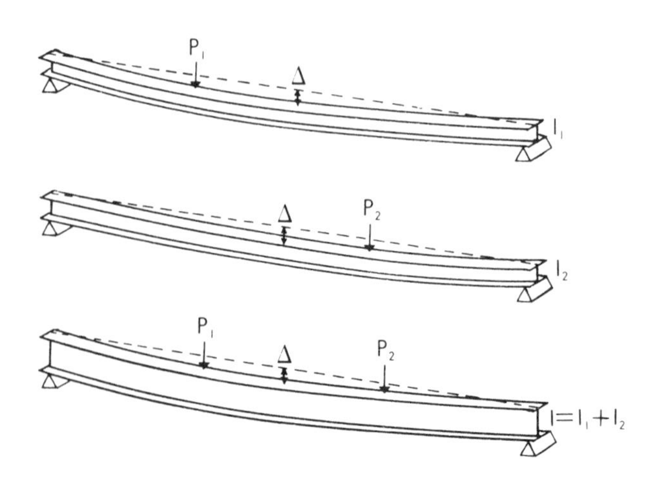

FIGURE 30

FIGURE 31—Required Moment of Inertia to Resist Bending

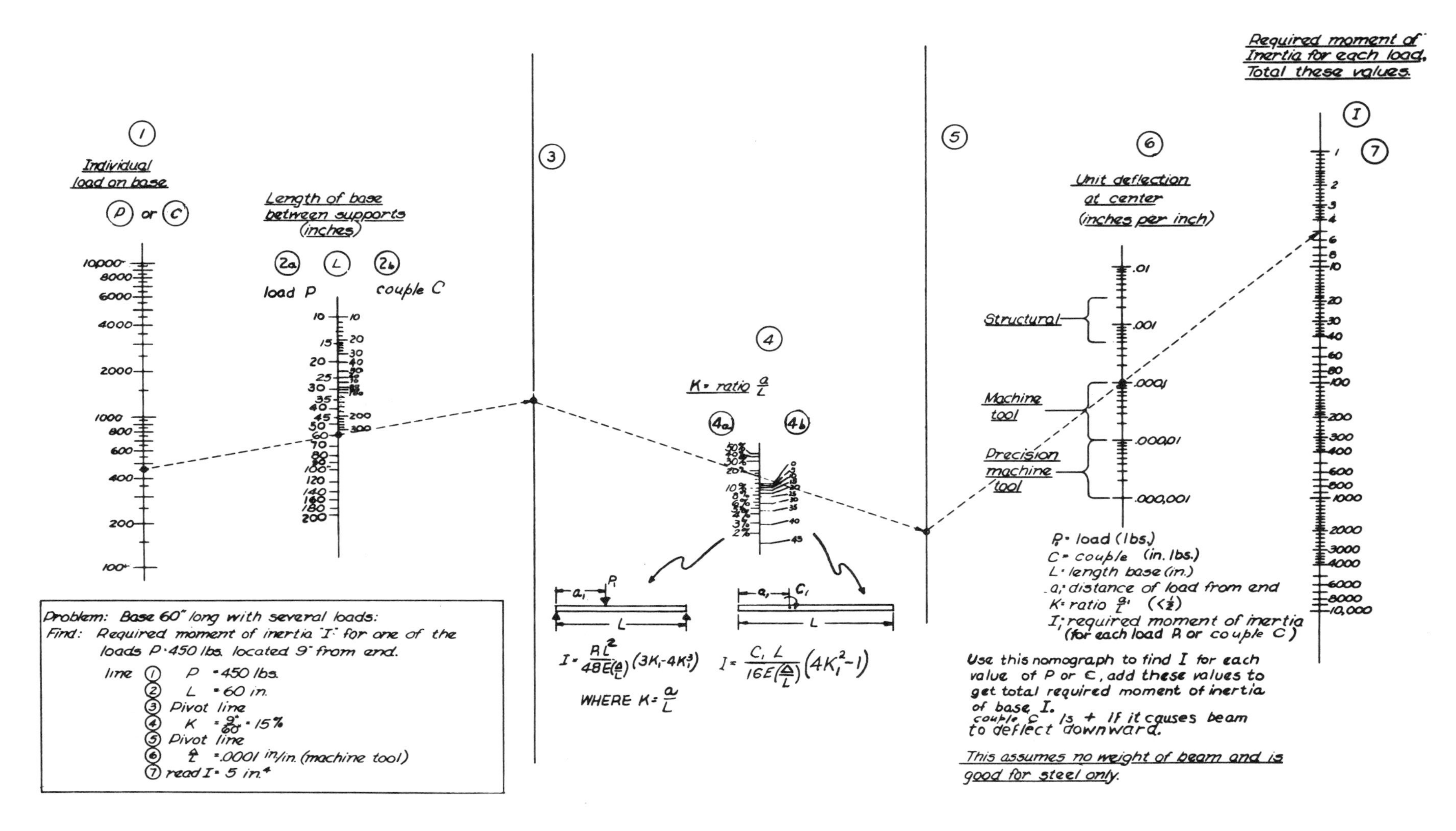

TABLE 3—Values of Constants (A and B) for Simplified Formulas (16 and 17)

K	A	B	K	A	B	K	A	B
0	0	2.083×10^{-9}	.17	3.045×10^{-10}	1.842×10^{-9}	.34	5.002×10^{-10}	1.120×10^{-9}
.01	$.2083 \times 10^{-10}$	2.083	.18	3.588	1.813	.35	6.101	1.063
.02	.4166	2.080	.19	3.768	1.783	.36	6.204	1.003
.03	.6243	2.076	.20	3.944	1.750	.37	6.301	.9425
.04	.8312	2.070	.21	4.118	1.715	.38	6.392	.8900
.05	1.038	2.063	.22	4.268	1.680	.39	6.477	.8158
.06	1.244	2.053	.23	4.453	1.642	.40	6.556	.7500
.07	1.449	2.043	.24	4.616	1.603	.41	6.627	.6825
.08	1.653	2.030	.25	4.774	1.563	.42	6.692	.6133
.09	1.855	2.016	.26	4.928	1.520	.43	6.750	.5425
.10	2.056	2.000	.27	5.079	1.476	.44	6.801	.4700
.11	2.355	1.983	.28	5.224	1.430	.45	6.844	.3958
.12	2.452	1.963	.29	5.364	1.381	.46	6.880	.3221
.13	2.647	1.942	.30	5.500	1.333	.47	6.898	.2425
.14	2.847	1.920	.31	5.631	1.282	.48	6.928	.1633
.15	3.031	1.896	.32	5.756	1.209	.49	6.940	.0825
.16	3.219	1.870	.33	5.876	1.176	.50	7.000	0

for each force

$$I_n = \frac{P_n L^2 A_n}{\left(\frac{\Delta}{L}\right)} \qquad \text{(16)}$$

for each couple

$$I_n = \frac{C_n L B_n}{\left(\frac{\Delta}{L}\right)} \qquad \text{(17)}$$

The value of K_n is equal to the ratio a_n/L, where a_n is the distance from the point at which the specific force or couple is applied to the nearest point of support. L is the span or length of beam between supports. From the value of K for any given load (P), the substitute constant A or B is obtained from Table 3.

When a force is applied to the member, use the constant A and substitute into the first formula. When a couple is applied to the member, use the constant B and substitute into the second formula.

A shorter method would be to make use of the nomograph in Figure 31.

9. INFLUENCE LINE FOR REACTIONS

Maxwell's Theorem of Reciprocal Deflections may be used to find the reactions of a continuous beam or frame, and is especially adaptable to model analysis.

Consider the continuous beam represented by the diagram at Figure 32a. The problem here is to find the reactions of the supports for various positions of the load (P_x).

According to Maxwell's theorem, the deflection at point 1 (Δ_b) due to the load (P_b) at point x, Figure 32b, equals the deflection at point x (Δ_c) due to the same amount of load (P_c) applied to point 1, Figure 32c. There is a similar relationship between an applied load or moment and the resulting rotation of a real beam.

Figures 32b and 32c constitute a simple reversal

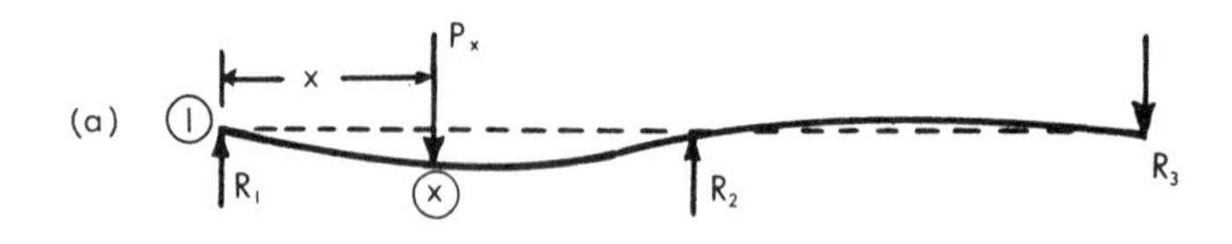

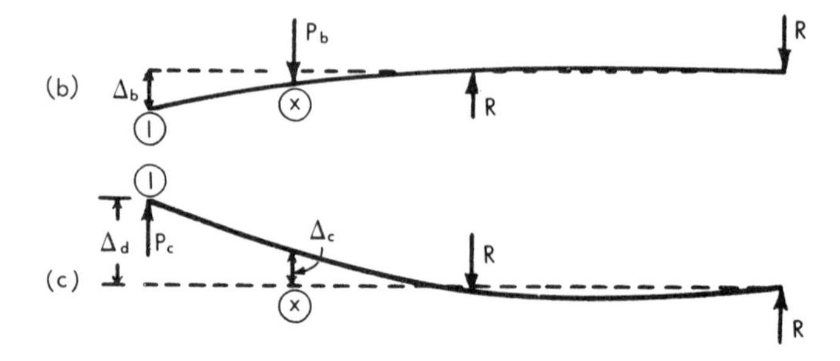

FIGURE 32

of points at which the pressure is applied. This concept supplies a very useful tool for finding influence lines for reactions, deflections, moments, or shear. In this case, the interest is in reactions.

To find the value of the reaction (R_1) at the left-hand support in Figure 32a, the support is removed; this causes the left end to deflect (Δ_b), as at Figure 32b. In order to restore the left end to its initial position, an upward reaction (P_c) must be applied, as in Figure 32c.

In extending Maxwell's theorem of reciprocal deflections to Figure 32b and Figure 32c, it is noticed:

$$\text{if } P_b = P_c \qquad \text{then } \Delta_b = \Delta_c$$

However, in order to return the beam to the initial condition of Figure 32a, Δ_d must be reduced until it equals Δ_b. To do this the upward reaction (P_c) must be reduced by the factor: Δ_b/Δ_d. And since $\Delta_b = \Delta_c$, this reduction factor becomes Δ_c/Δ_d.

$\therefore R_1 = P_b \dfrac{\Delta_c}{\Delta_d}$ or, using Figure 32a —

$$\boxed{R_1 = P_x \frac{\Delta_c}{\Delta_d}} \qquad (18)$$

This means that if the model beam (as in Fig. 32c) is displaced in the same direction and at the same point as the reaction in question, the resulting deflection curve becomes the plot of the reaction as the load is moved across the length of the beam.

This is called an "influence curve". Considering the conditions of the real beam represented by Figure 32a, the reaction (R_1) at point 1 due to a load (P_x) at point x will be proportional to the ratio of the two ordinates at points x and 1 of the deflection curve.

In other words:

$$\boxed{R_1 = P_x \frac{\Delta_x}{\Delta_1}} \qquad (19)$$

For continuous beams of constant cross-section, a wire model may be set up on a drawing board, with the wire beam supported by thumb tacks spaced so as to represent the supports on the real beam. See Figure 33. A load diagram of the real beam is shown at the bottom. Notice that the thumb tacks used for supports of the wire must be located vertically so as to function in the opposite direction to reactions on the real beam.

The point of the model beam at the reaction in question (R_1) is raised upward some convenient distance, for example ½" or 1", and the deflection curve of the wire beam is traced in pencil. This is shown immediately below the model.

The final value for the reaction (R_1) is equal to

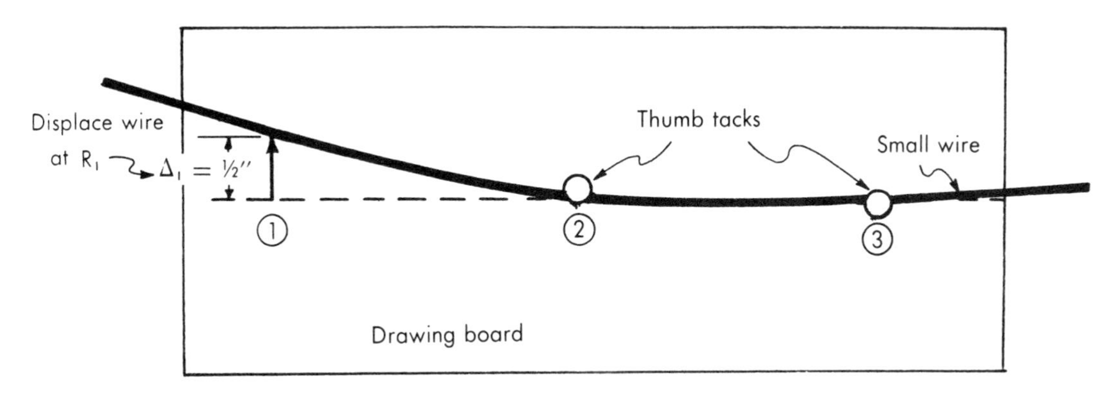

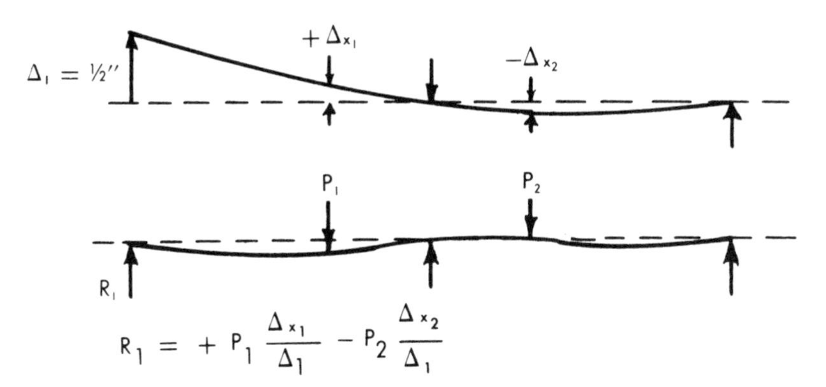

$$R_1 = +P_1 \frac{\Delta_{x1}}{\Delta_1} - P_2 \frac{\Delta_{x2}}{\Delta_1}$$

FIGURE 33

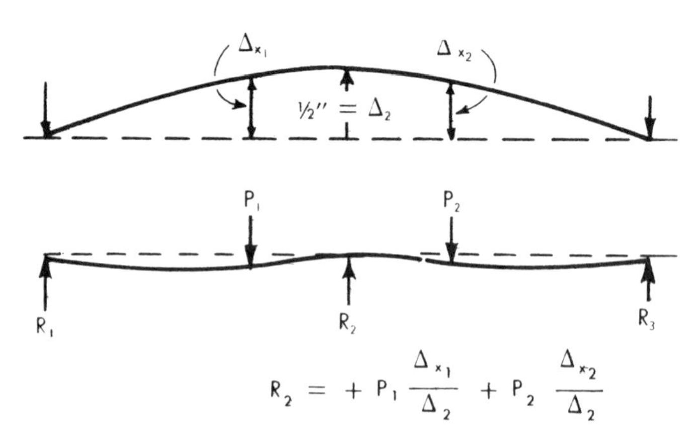

$$R_2 = +P_1\frac{\Delta_{x1}}{\Delta_2} + P_2\frac{\Delta_{x2}}{\Delta_2}$$

FIGURE 34

the sum of the actual applied forces multiplied by the ratio of their ordinates of this curve to the original displacement at R_1.

The influence curve for the central reaction (R_2) may also be found in the same manner. See Figure 34.

Deflection curve of the wire model is shown first and then the load diagram of the real beam.

Problem 3

A continuous beam has 5 concentrated loads and 4 supports. The problem is to find the reactions at the supports.

The reactions are found by comparing the ordinates of the deflection curve of a wire representing the beam. See Figure 35, where the critical dimensions appear on the (upper) load diagram.

For the ends, reactions R_1 and R_4, displace the end of the wire a given amount as shown. The portion of each applied load (P) to be transferred to the reaction R_1 is proportional to the ordinate of the deflection curve under the load (P) and the given displacement at R_1.

For the interior reactions R_2 and R_3, displace the wire a given amount at R_2. From the ordinates of this

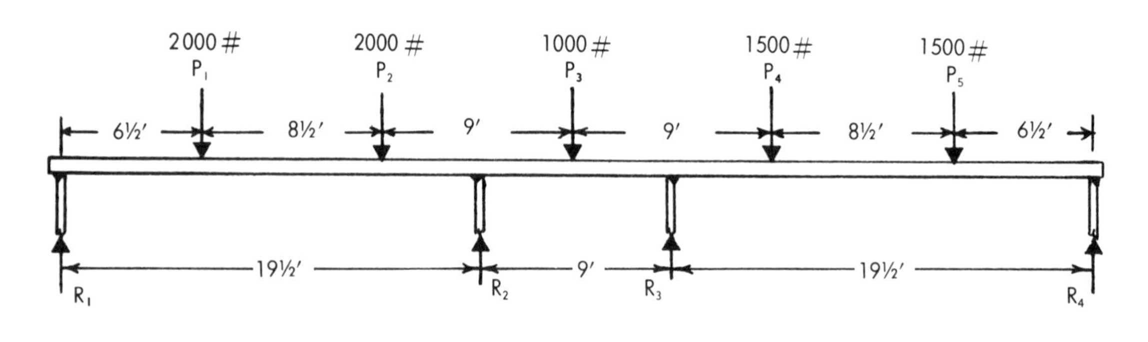

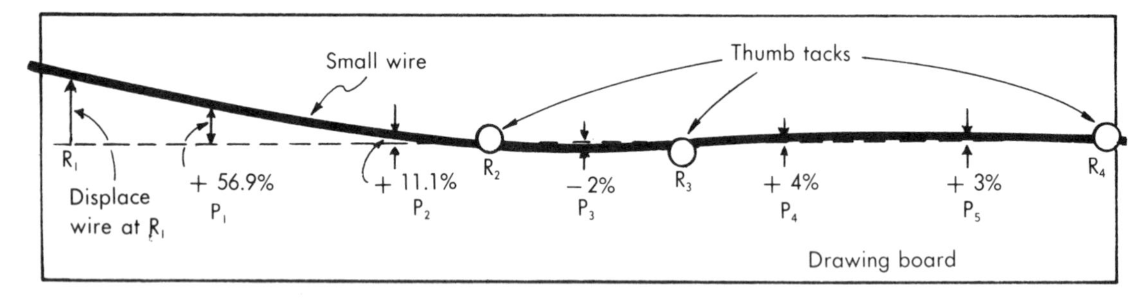

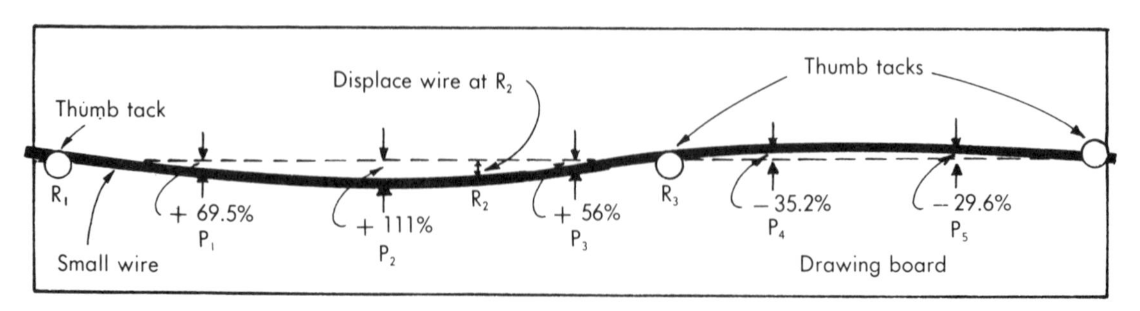

FIGURE 35

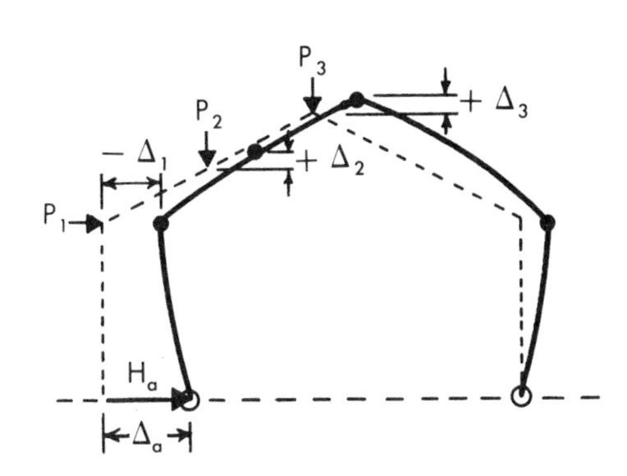

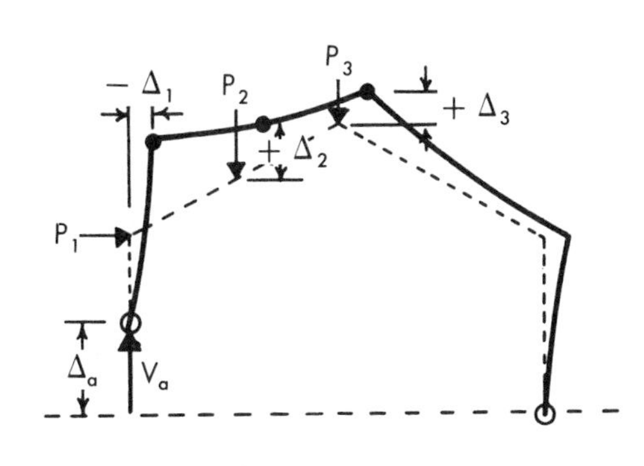

FIGURE 36

deflected wire, determine the ratios of each applied load (P) for the reaction at R_2.

The computation of forces for the reactions R_1 and R_4 is as follows:

$$R_1 = +\ .569\ P_1 + .111\ P_2 - .02\ P_3 + .04\ P_4 + .03\ P_5$$

$$= .569(2000\#) + .111(2000\#) - .02(1000\#) + .04(1500\#) + .03(1500\#)$$

$$= +\ 1445 \text{ lbs}$$

$$R_2 = +\ .695\ P_1 + 1.11\ P_2 + .56\ P_3 - .352\ P_4 - .296\ P_5$$

$$= .695(2000\#) + 1.11(2000\#) + .56(1000\#) - .352(1500\#) - .296(1500\#)$$

$$= +\ 3198 \text{ lbs}$$

Reactions R_3 and R_4 can be found in like manner.

Application to Frames

This same method may be extended to the analysis of frames. If the frame has a constant moment of inertia, a stiff wire may be bent into the shape of the frame. If the frame has a variable moment of inertia, the model may be made of a sheet of plastic or cardboard proportioned to the actual moments of inertia.

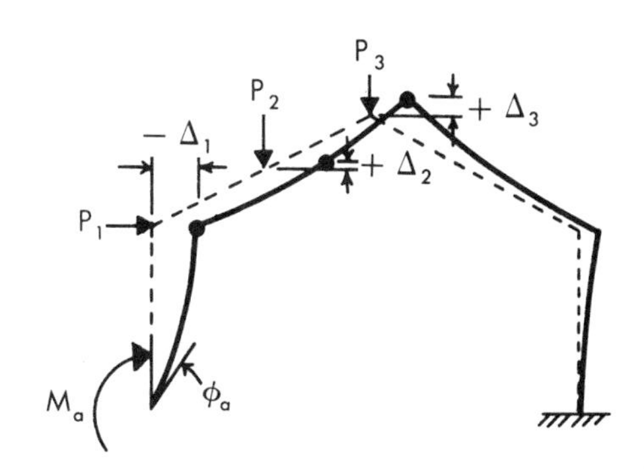

FIGURE 37

Reactions, either horizontal (H) or vertical (V) at the supports, may be found by displacing the frame at the support a given amount in the direction of the desired reaction. See Figure 36. The outline of the displaced model frame is traced in pencil, and this becomes the curve showing the influence of any load (at any point) upon this reaction.

The displacement of each point of the model frame (Δ) where a load is applied is measured in the same direction as the application of the load, and the resulting reaction may be computed from the following:

horizontal reaction

$$H_a = P_1\left(\frac{-\ \Delta_1}{\Delta_a}\right) + P_a\left(\frac{+\ \Delta_2}{\Delta_2}\right) + P_3\left(\frac{+\ \Delta_3}{\Delta_a}\right)$$

vertical reaction

$$V_a = P_1\left(\frac{-\ \Delta_1}{\Delta_a}\right) + P_2\left(\frac{+\ \Delta_2}{\Delta_a}\right) + P_3\left(\frac{+\ \Delta_3}{\Delta_a}\right)$$

Moments at the ends of the frame (or at any point in the frame) may be found by rotating the point in question a given angle (ϕ_a) and again drawing the resulting displaced model frame. See Figure 37.

The displacement of each point of the model frame (Δ) where a load is applied is measured in the same direction as the application of the load, and the resulting moment may be computed from the following:

moment at left-hand support

$$M_a = \frac{P_1\ (-\ \Delta_1) + P_2\ (+\ \Delta_2) + P_3\ (+\ \Delta_3)}{\phi_a}$$

It is necessary to displace the model a considerable distance in order that some accuracy may be obtained in the readings. Therefore, some error may be introduced because the final shape of the frame may alter the real load conditions. This error can be reduced greatly by measuring the displacements between one

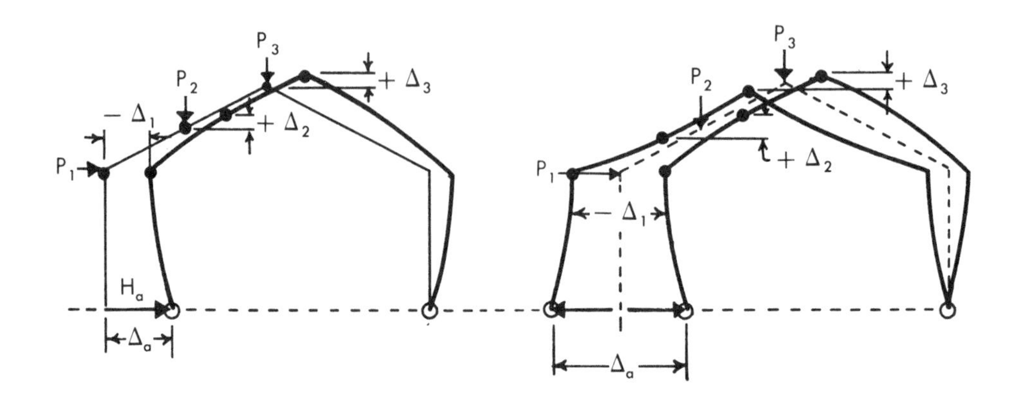

(a) Measuring displacement of model frame from initial condition to displaced condition

(b) Measuring displacement of model frame from one displaced condition to an equal and opposite displaced condition

FIGURE 38

condition and the opposite condition. See Figure 38.

This method of equal to opposite displacement may also be applied to moments in which the frame is rotated an equal amount in both directions, and measurements taken from one extreme to the other.

10. INFLUENCE LINE FOR DEFLECTION

In like manner, the use of a wire model based on Maxwell's Theorem of Reciprocal Deflection is useful in finding the deflections of a beam under various loads or under a moving load.

If a 1-lb load is placed at a particular point on a beam, the resulting deflection curve becomes the plot of the deflection (Δ) at this point as the 1-lb load is moved across the length of the beam. This is called the influence line for deflection at this particular point.

TABLE 4—Incremental Deflections of Real Beam

Point	Load (Lbs)	Ordinate x 10^{-3}	Deflection At Free End (In.)
0	100	0	0
3′	150	— .60	— .030
8′	300	—1.06	— .318
15′	400	—1.60	— .640
21′	750	—1.56	—1.170
23′	750	—1.36	—1.020
28′	375	— .70	— .262
33′	150	+ .70	+ .105
37′	325	+2.00	+ .650
40′	100	+3.25	+ .325
Total	3300 lbs		—2.360″

Problem 4

To determine the deflection of the overhung portion of this trailer, Figure 39, under the various loads. Assume a cross-section moment of inertia (I) of 2 × 11.82 in.[4]

Using the standard beam formula for this type of beam, the deflection of the free (right) end is determined for a 1-lb load placed at that point:

$$\Delta_{end} = \frac{P\ a^2}{3\ E\ I}(L + a)$$

$$= \frac{1\#\ (120)^2}{3(30 \times 10^6)(2 \times 11.82)}(360 - 120)$$

$$= 3.25 \times 10^{-3} \text{ inches}$$

A wire model of this beam is held at the two supports (trailer hitch and the wheel assembly) with thumb tacks on a drawing board. The outer end is displaced an amount equal to 3.25 on a suitable scale. The deflection curve is traced in pencil from this displaced wire beam. The ordinates of this resulting deflection curve become the actual deflections at the free end as the 1-lb load is moved across the length of the beam.

Multiplying each of the loads on the real beam by the ordinate at that point gives the deflection at the free end caused by each load on the real beam. See Table 4. Summing these incremental deflections gives the total deflection:

$$\Delta = \underline{2.36'' \text{ upward}}$$

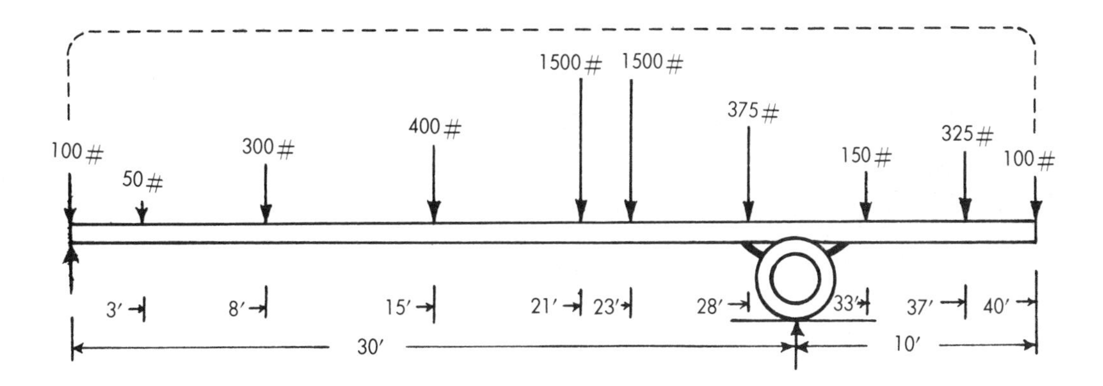

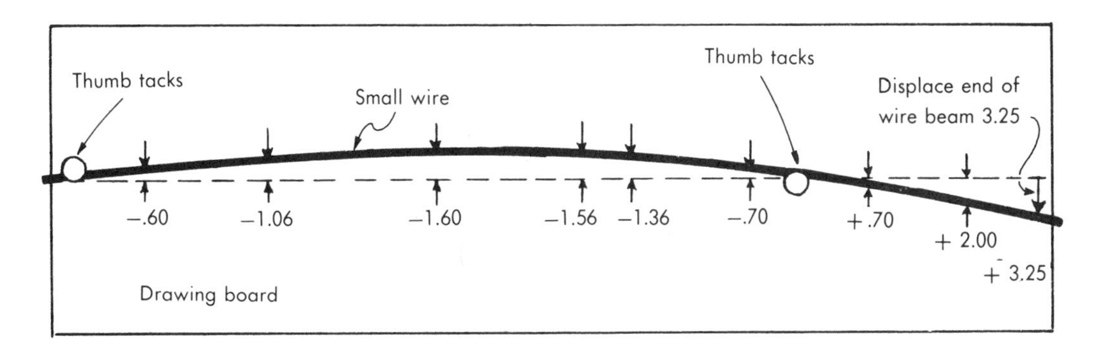

FIGURE 39

Erection of the 32-story Commerce Towers in Kansas City, Missouri was speeded with the aid of modern semi-automatic arc welding. Field use of self-shielding cored electrode quadrupled the rate of weld metal deposition. The weldor shown here is making a field splice of two sections of the heavy building column.

Complex antenna systems needed in age of space communications are sensitive to bending deflections caused by high wind loads. Good engineering, including the specification of high strength steels and rigid welded connections, is essential to the satisfactory performance of such structures. In the parabolic antenna dish shown, 6400 sq ft of expanded metal mesh are welded to a space frame of tubular welded trusses.

Shear Deflection in Beams

1. NATURE OF SHEAR DEFLECTION

Shear stresses in a beam section cause a displacement or sliding action on a plane normal to the axis of the beam, as shown in the right hand view of Figure 1. This is unlike the deflection resulting from bending in a beam, which is shown in the left hand view of Figure 1.

Normally deflection due to shear in the usual beam is ignored because it represents a very small percentage of the entire deflection. Figure 2 shows that the deflection due to shear increases linearly as the length of the beam increases, whereas the deflection

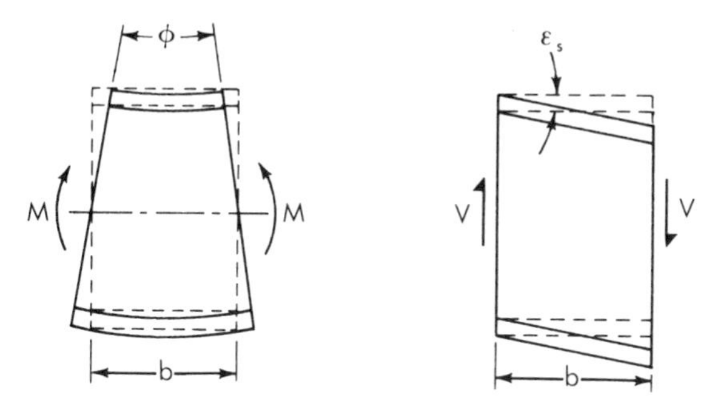

FIG. 1 Deflection in beam caused by bending moment, left, and by shear, right.

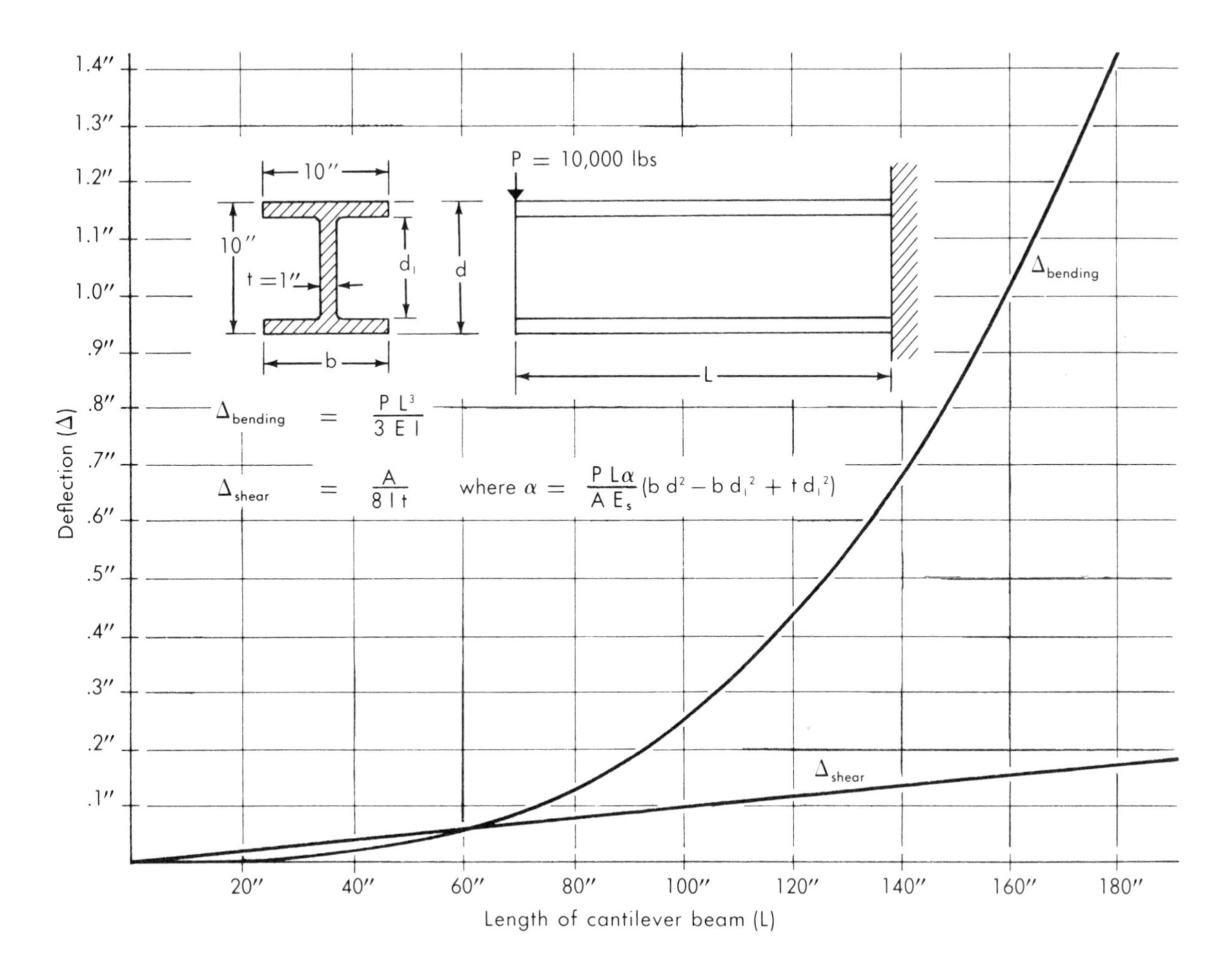

FIG. 2 Deflection caused by shear increases linearly as length of beam, but that caused by bending increases as the third power of beam length.

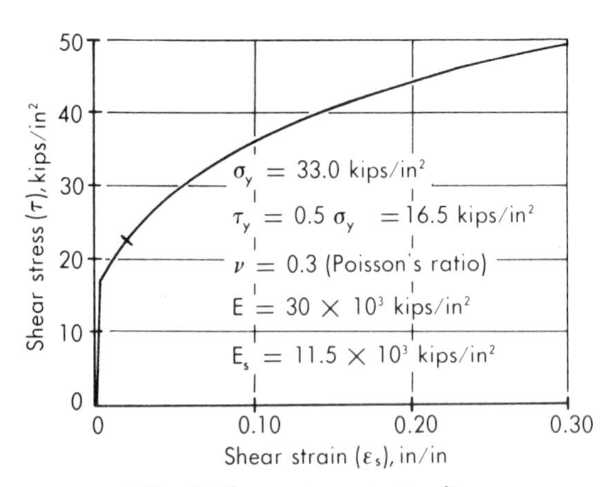

FIG. 3 Shear stress-strain diagram.

due to bending increases very rapidly as a third power of the length of the beam. For this reason the deflection due to shear is not an important factor except for extremely short spans where deflection due to bending drops off to a very small value.

The deflection due to shear is dependent entirely on the shear distribution across the cross-section of the member and also the value of the shear stress (τ). Figure 3 shows the shear stress-strain diagram which is similar to the usual stress-strain diagram, although the shear yield strength is much lower than the tensile yield strength of the same material. After the shear yield strength is reached, the shear strain (ϵ_s) increases rapidly and the shear strength increases because of strain hardening.

2. DETERMINING SHEAR DEFLECTION

The theory of deflection caused by shear stress is rather simple. However, the actual determination of the shear stresses and their distribution across the beam section (which two factors cause the deflection) is more difficult. In all cases, some kind of a form factor (α) must be determined, and this is simply a matter of expressing the distribution of shear stress throughout the web of the section. Since there is practically no shear stress in the flange area, this particular area has negligible effect on the deflection due to shear (Δ_s).

The following formulas are valid for several types of beams and loading:

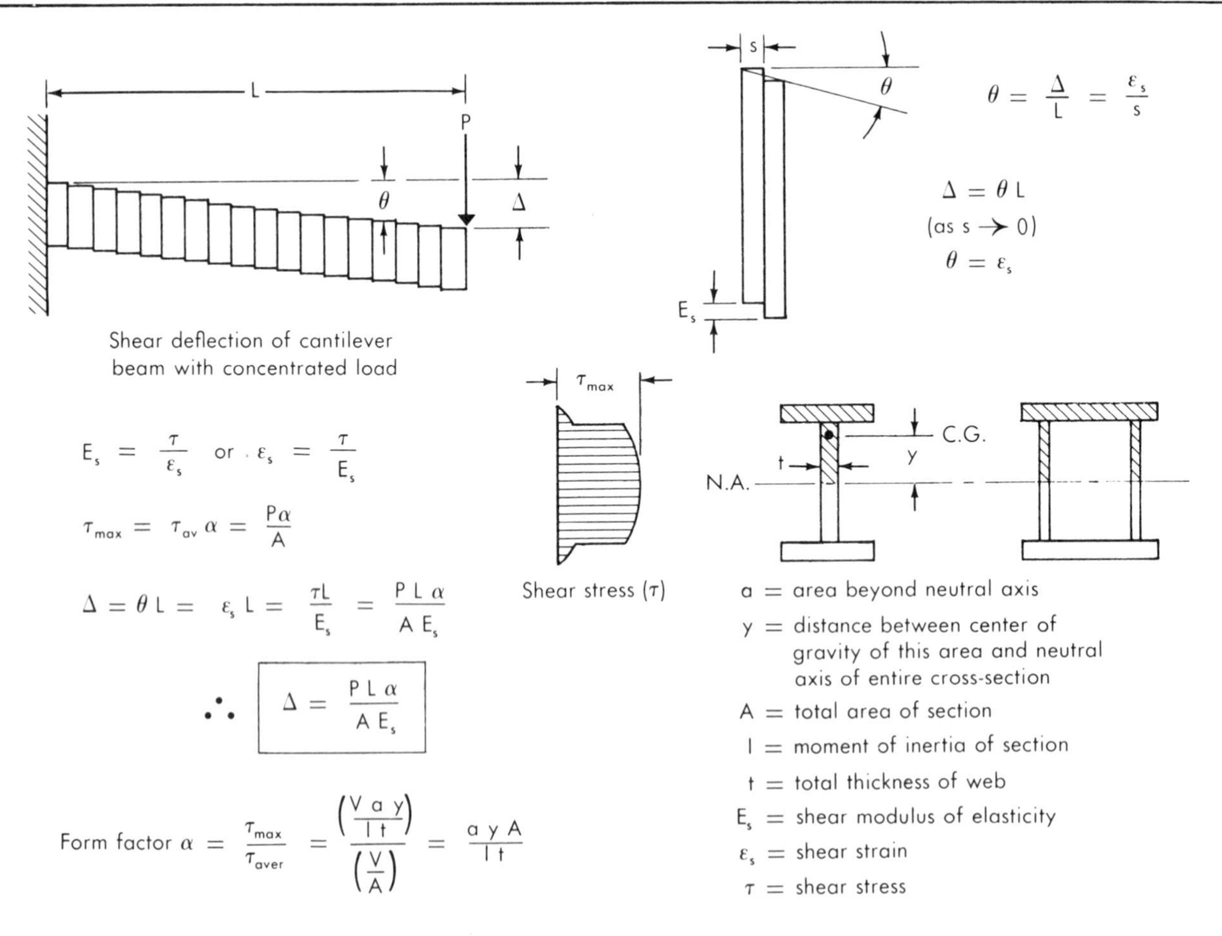

FIG. 4 Form factor for shear deflection in built-up beams.

simply supported beam; uniform load (w)

$$\Delta_s = \frac{w\,L^2\,\alpha}{8\,A\,E_s} \quad \cdots\cdots (1)$$

simply supported beam; concentrated load (P)

$$\Delta_s = \frac{P\,L\,\alpha}{4\,A\,E_s} \quad \cdots\cdots (2)$$

cantilever beam; uniform load (w)

$$\Delta_s = \frac{w\,L^2\,\alpha}{2\,A\,E_s} \quad \cdots\cdots (3)$$

cantilever beam; concentrated load (P)

$$\Delta_s = \frac{P\,L\,\alpha}{A\,E_s} \quad \cdots\cdots (4)$$

where:

P = total load, lbs

A = area of entire section

E_s = modulus of elasticity in shear (steel = 12,000,000 psi)

w = distributed load, lbs/linear in.

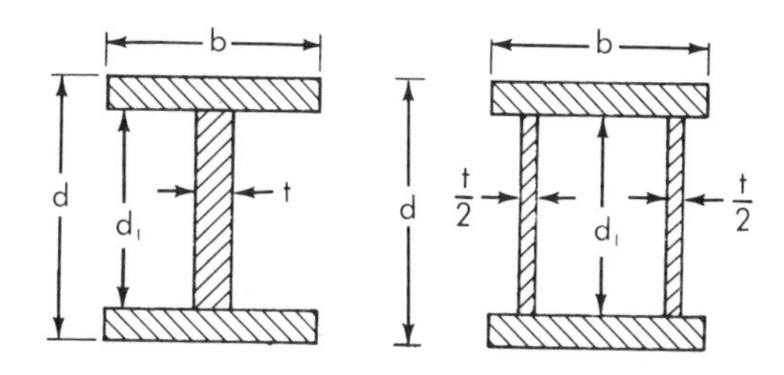

FIG. 5 Beam sections for which Eq. 5 applies.

The slope of the deflection curve (θ) is equal at each cross-section to the shearing strain (ϵ_s) at the centroid of this cross-section. α is a factor with which the average shearing stress (τ_{av}) must be multiplied in order to obtain the shearing stress (τ_{max}) at the centroid of the cross-sections.

On this basis, the form factor (α) for an I beam or box beam would be:

$$\alpha = \frac{A}{8\,I\,t}(b\,d^2 - b\,d_1^2 + t\,d_1^2) \quad \cdots\cdots (5)$$

where Figure 5 applies. Don't compute area (A) in this formula because it will cancel out when used in the formulas for shear deflection.

Welding was used extensively in the fabrication and erection of this steel-framed, 8-story, balconized apartment building which features cantilevered cross beams in the upper stories. The building was designed basically as a rigid structure with main beams designed plastically and light X-braces used to accommodate wind moments. The welded steel design cost 16¢/sq ft less than a reinforced concrete building would have.

Both shop and field welding were used extensively in building the Anaheim Stadium, home of the Los Angeles Baseball club—the Angels. The steelwork was designed as an earthquake-resistant frame, with high moment carrying capacity in both directions. Having very good torsional resistance in addition to bending strength in both directions, the tapered box section frames can be located more widely (45′ centers along straight sides) and eliminate the need for conventional cross-bracing between bents.

Deflection of Curved Beams

1. AREA MOMENT METHOD FOR CURVED CANTILEVER BEAM

In Sect. 2.5, Figures 20 to 23, the area moment method was used to find the deflection of a straight cantilever beam of variable section. This same method may be extended to a curved cantilever beam of variable section.

As before, the beam is divided into 10 segments of equal length (s) and the moment of inertia (I_n) is determined for each segment. See Figure 1.

The moment applied to any segment of the beam is equal to the applied force (P) multiplied by the distance (X_n) to the segment, measured from and at right angles to the line passing through and in the same direction as the load (P).

This moment (M_n) applied to the segment causes it to rotate (θ_n), and—

$$\theta_n = \frac{M_n}{E\ I_n} \quad \text{.......... (1)}$$

The resulting deflection (Δ_n) at the point of the beam where the deflection is to be determined is equal to the angle of rotation of this segment(θ_n) multiplied by the distance (Y_n) to the segment, measured from and at right angles to the line passing through and in the same direction as the desired deflection(Δ).

$$\Delta_n = \frac{M_n\ Y_n\ s}{E\ I_n} = \frac{P\ X_n\ Y_n\ s}{E\ I_n} \quad \text{.......... (2)}$$

The distances (X_n and Y_n) and the moment of inertia (I_n) are determined for each of the 10 segments and placed in table form. In most cases, the deflection to be determined is in line with the applied force so that these two distances are equal and the formula becomes—

$$\Delta_n = \frac{P\ X_n^2\ s}{E\ I_n} \quad \text{.......... (3)}$$

The values of X_n^2/I_n are found and totaled. From this the total deflection (Δ) is found:

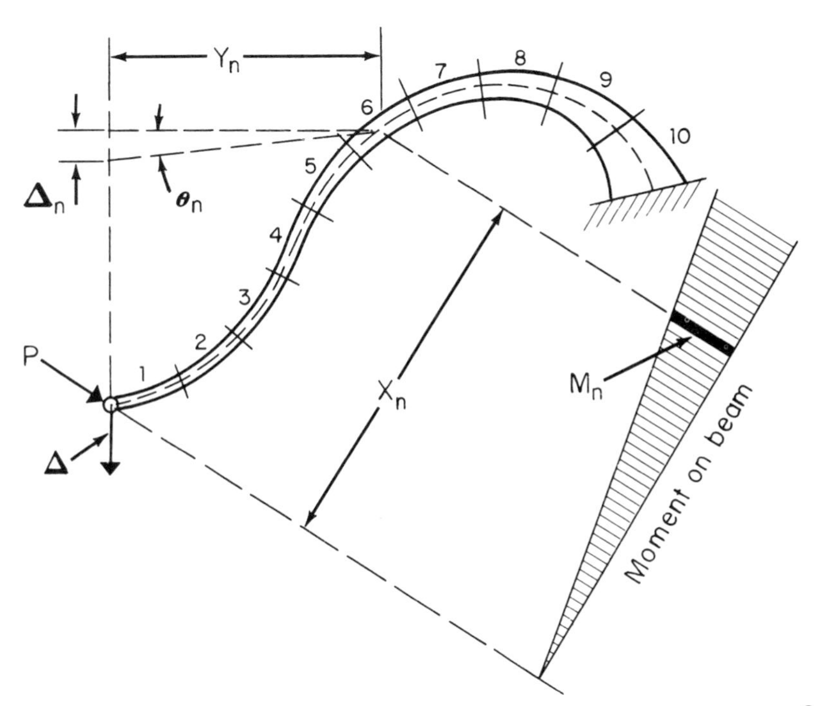

FIG. 1 To find deflection of curved cantilever beam of variable section, first divide it into segments of equal length.

$$\Delta = \frac{P\,s}{E}\sum\frac{X_n^2}{I_n} \quad \text{.......................(4)}$$

A symmetrical beam forming a single continuous arc, for example, is comparable to two equal cantilever beams connected end to end. Thus, the prediction of deflection in a curved beam can be approached in a manner similar to finding the deflection in a straight cantilever beam.

Problem 1

The total vertical deflection (Δ) is needed on a curved beam that will carry a maximum load (P) of 100,000 lbs. See Figure 2. Given the segment length (s) = 10″ and the various values of X_n and I_n, complete the computation.

Segment	X_n	I_n	$\frac{X_n^2}{I_n}$
1	5″	119 in.⁴	.21
2	15	216	1.04
3	23	358	1.48
4	29	550	1.53
5	32	800	1.28
6	32	800	1.28
7	29	550	1.53
8	23	358	1.48
9	15	216	1.04
10	5	119	.21
			$\sum\frac{X_n^2}{I_n} = 11.08$

$$\Delta = \frac{P\,s}{E}\sum\frac{X_n^2}{I_n}$$

$$= \frac{100{,}000 \times 10}{30{,}000{,}000}\,11.08$$

$$= 0.369''$$

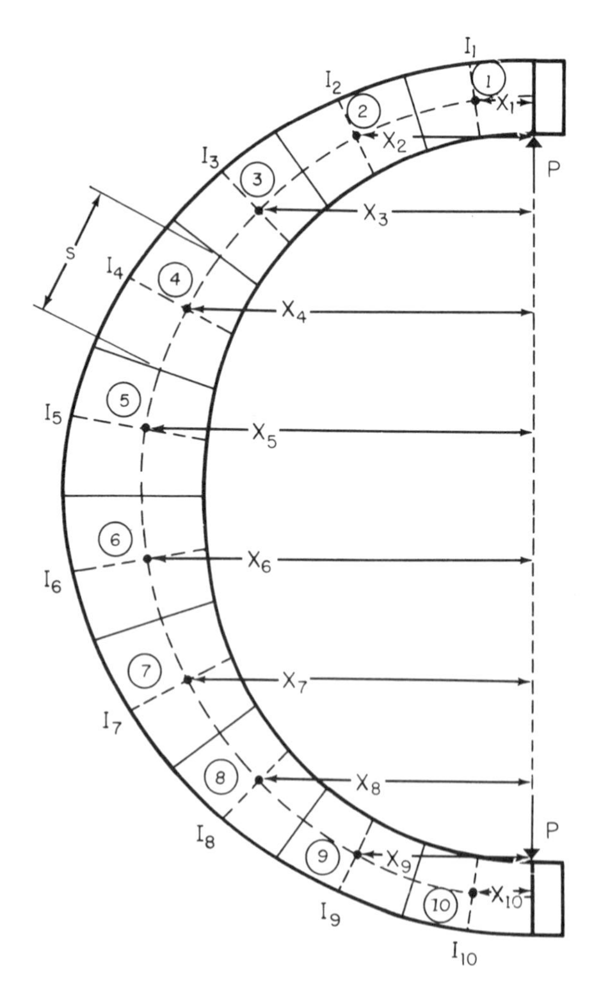

Deflection of Curved Beams

Solving for deflection

by using formula $\Delta = \frac{Ps}{E}\sum\frac{X_n^2}{I_n}$

first calculate value of X_n^2/I_n

by using stiffness nomograph

graphically find value of PX_n^2/EI_n

for use in formula $\Delta = s\sum\frac{PX_n^2}{EI}$

Segment	X_n	I_n	
1			
2			
3			
4			
5			
6			
7			
8			
9			
10			
		$\Sigma =$	

FIG. 2 For deflection of simple curved beam, use Eq. 4 or nomograph, Fig. 3.

FIGURE 3—Deflection of Curved Beam (Stiffness Nomograph)

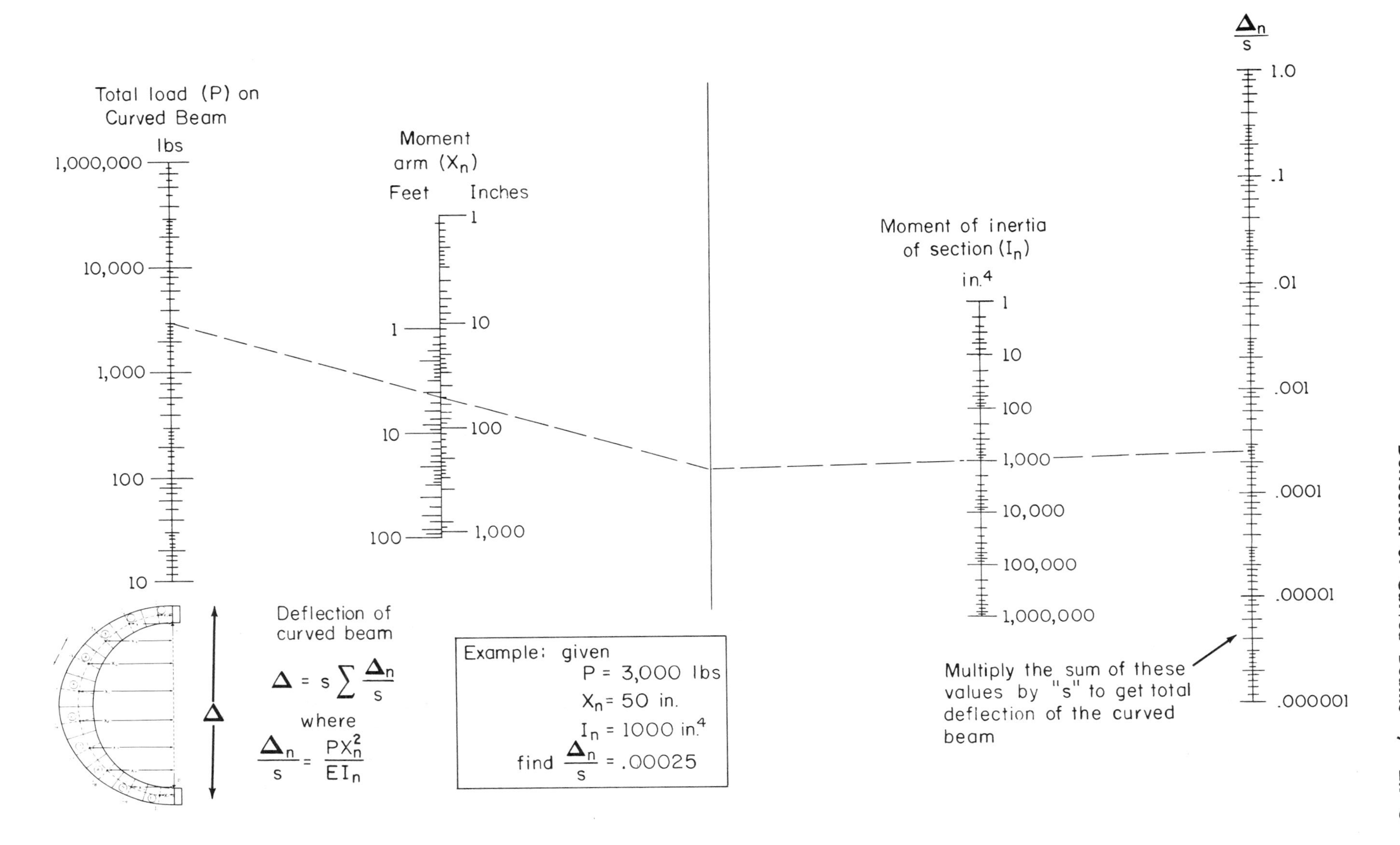

2. SIMPLIFICATION USING NOMOGRAPH

By using the stiffness nomograph, Figure 3, the computation can be considerably shortened with no significant loss of accuracy. The nomograph is based on the modified formula:

$$\Delta = s \sum \frac{P\ X_n^{\,2}}{E\ I_n} \qquad (5)$$

Readings are obtained from the nomograph for $PX_n^{\,2}/EI_n$ for each segment and entered in the last column of the table. These are then added and their sum multiplied by s to give the total vertical deflection.

Problem 2

Use the same beam example as in Problem 1, the same values for P, s, X_n and I_n, and the same form of table. Complete the computation.

Segment	X_n	I_n	$\frac{P\ X_n^{\,2}}{E\ I_n}$
1	5	119	.0006
2	15	216	.0036
3	23	358	.0048
4	29	550	.0050
5	32	800	.0043
6	32	800	.0043
7	29	550	.0050
8	23	358	.0048
9	15	216	.0036
10	5	119	.0006
			$\sum \frac{P\ X_n^{\,2}}{E\ I_n} = .0366$

$$\Delta = s \sum \frac{P\ X_n^{\,2}}{E\ I_n}$$

$$= 10 \times .0366$$

$$= 0.366''$$

Engineers of the Whiskey Creek Bridge in No. California specified that the 300′ welded steel girders across each span utilize three types of steel in order to meet stress requirements economically while maintaining uniform web depth and thickness and uniform flange section. High strength quenched and tempered steel was prescribed for points of high bending moment, A-373 where moments were low, and A-242 elsewhere.

Designing for Impact Loads

1. NATURE OF IMPACT LOADING

Impact loading results not only from actual impact (or blow) of a moving body against the member, but by any sudden application of the load (Fig. 1). It may occur in any of the following methods:

1. *A direct impact,* usually by another member or an external body moving with considerable velocity, for example:
   (a) A pile driver hammer striking the top of a pile.
   (b) The die striking the workpiece in a drop forge press or punch press.
   (c) A large rock dropped from a height onto a truck.
2. *A sudden application of force,* without a blow being involved.
   (a) The sudden creation of a force on a member as during the explosive stroke in an engine, the ignition or misfire of a missile motor when mounted on a test stand.
   (b) The sudden moving of a force onto a member, as when a heavy loaded train or truck moves rapidly over a bridge deck, or a heavy rock rolls from the bucket of a shovel onto a truck without any appreciable drop in height.
3. *The inertia of the member* resisting high acceleration or deceleration.
   (a) Rapidly reciprocating levers.
   (b) A machine subject to earthquake shocks or explosives in warfare.
   (c) The braking of a heavy trailer.

2. APPROACH TO DESIGN PROBLEM

In many cases it is difficult to evaluate impact forces quantitatively. The analysis is generally more qualitative and requires recognition of all of the factors involved and their inter-relationship.

The designer can follow one of two methods:

1. Estimate the maximum force exerted on the resisting member by applying an impact factor. Consider this force to be a static load and use in standard design formulas.

2. Estimate the energy to be absorbed by the resisting member, and design it as an energy-absorbing member.

The properties of the material and the dimensions of the resisting member that give it maximum resistance to an energy load, are quite different from those that give the member maximum resistance to a static load.

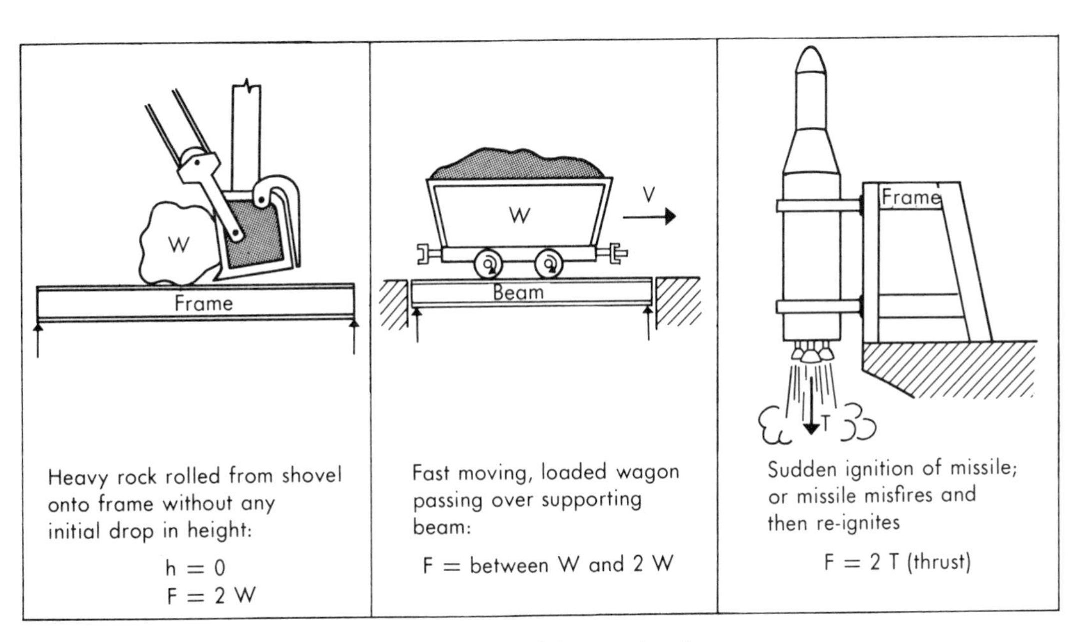

FIG. 1 Types of impact loading.

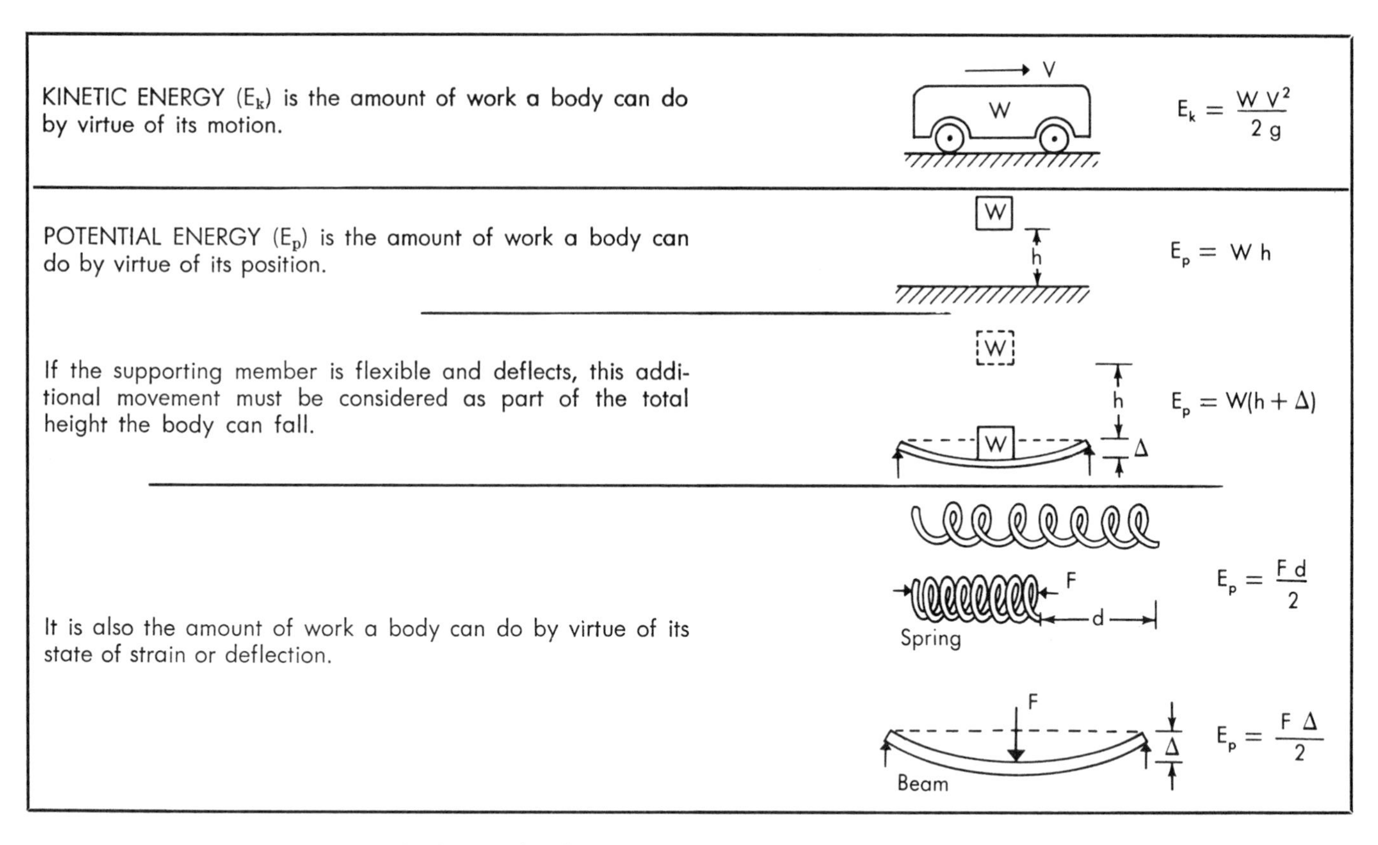

KINETIC ENERGY (E_k) is the amount of work a body can do by virtue of its motion.
V
W
$E_k = \frac{W V^2}{2 g}$
POTENTIAL ENERGY (E_p) is the amount of work a body can do by virtue of its position.
W
h
$E_p = W h$
If the supporting member is flexible and deflects, this additional movement must be considered as part of the total height the body can fall.
W
h
Δ
$E_p = W(h + \Delta)$
It is also the amount of work a body can do by virtue of its state of strain or deflection.
F
d
Spring
$E_p = \frac{F d}{2}$
F
Δ
Beam
$E_p = \frac{F \Delta}{2}$

FIG. 2 Formulas for kinetic energy and potential energy.

3. INERTIA FORCES

Inertia is the property of a member which causes it to remain at rest or in uniform motion unless acted on by some external force. Inertia force is the resisting force which must be overcome in order to cause the member to accelerate or decelerate, equal but opposite to—

$$F = \frac{W_m}{g} a$$

where:

W_m = weight of member, lbs

a = acceleration or deceleration of member, in./sec² or ft/sec²

g = acceleration of gravity (386.4 in./sec² or 32.2 ft/sec²

4. IMPACT FORCES

A moving body striking a member produces a force on the member due to its deceleration to a lower velocity or perhaps to zero velocity:

$$F = \frac{W_b a}{g}$$

where:

W_b = weight of body, lbs

a = deceleration of body, in./sec² or ft/sec²

g = acceleration of gravity (386.4 in./sec² or 32.2 ft/sec²)

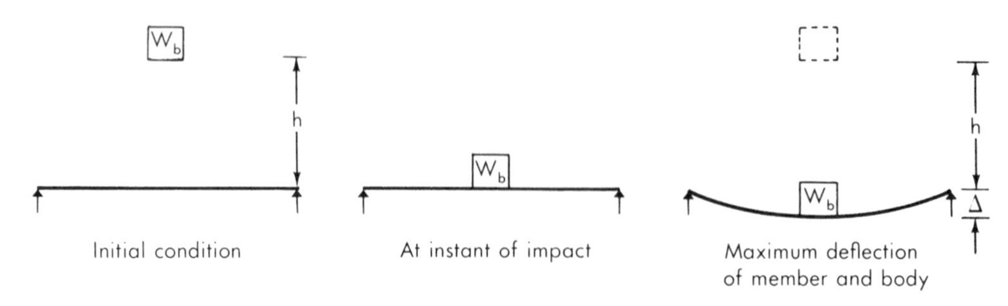

FIG. 3 Effect of member's inertia.

Fortunately the member will deflect slightly and allow a certain time for the moving body (W_b) to come to rest, thereby reducing this impact force (F).

Since the time interval is usually unknown, the above formula cannot be used directly to find the force (F). However, it is usually possible to solve for this force by finding the amount of kinetic energy (E_k) or potential energy (E_p) that must be absorbed by the member (Fig. 2).

This applied energy (E_k) or (E_p) may then be set equal to the energy (U) absorbed by the member within a given stress (σ), see Table 2.

5. POTENTIAL ENERGY OF FALLING BODY ON MEMBER

(See Figure 3)

Potential energy of falling body (W_b):

$$E_p = W_b (h + \Delta)$$

Potential energy received by deflected member:

$$E_p = \frac{F \Delta}{2}$$

Then:

$$W_b h + W_b \Delta = \frac{F \Delta}{2}$$

but $K = \frac{F}{\Delta}$ being the spring constant of the beam

$$W_b h + W_b \frac{F}{K} = \frac{F^2}{2K}$$

and $F^2 - 2 W_b F - 2 K W_b h = 0$

or

$$\boxed{F = W_b + \sqrt{W_b^2 + 2 K W_b h}}$$

or since $V = \sqrt{2 g h}$

$$\boxed{F = W_b + \sqrt{W_b^2 + \frac{K W_b V^2}{g}}}$$

If the body (W_b) is suddenly applied to the member without any appreciable drop in height (h = 0), the maximum force due to impact is twice that of the applied load (W_b):

$$F = 2 W_b$$

Thus, it is common practice to apply an impact factor to a load and design as though it were a steady load. As the weight of the supporting member (W_m) increases, this impact factor of (2) becomes less.

In a similar manner, it is possible to express the resultant impact deflection in terms of steady load deflection.

$$\boxed{\Delta = \Delta_{st} + \sqrt{\Delta_{st}^2 + 2 h \Delta_{st}}}$$

or

$$\boxed{\Delta = \Delta_{st} + \sqrt{\Delta_{st}^2 + \frac{\Delta_{st} V^2}{g}}}$$

Again, if h = 0, then $\Delta = 2 \Delta_{st}$

TABLE 1—Basic Laws Used in Analysis of Impact

	Linear	Angular
Mass	(1) $M = \frac{W}{g}$	(10) $I = \frac{W}{g} r^2$ r = radius of gyration
Force	(2) F	(11) T = F d d = perpendicular distance from center of rotation to line of force
Velocity	(3) $V = \frac{d}{t}$	(12) $\omega = \frac{\theta}{t} = 2\pi RPM = \frac{V}{r}$ r = radius of point for which ω is to be found
Acceleration	(4) $a = \frac{V - V_o}{t}$	(13) $a = \frac{\omega - \omega_o}{t}$
Force of Impact	(5) $F = \frac{W}{g} a$	(14) $T = I a$
Impulse	(6) F t	(15) T t
Momentum	(7) $\frac{W}{g} V$	(16) $I \omega$
Kinetic Energy	(8) $\frac{W}{2 g} V^2$	(17) $\frac{I \omega^2}{2}$
Work	(9) F d	(18) $T \theta$

6. EFFECT OF MEMBER'S INERTIA

If the weight (W_m) of the supporting member is relatively high, some of the applied energy will be absorbed because of the inertia of the member to movement. A good example is the effect of the mass of

TABLE 2—Impact Formulas for Common Member-Load Conditions

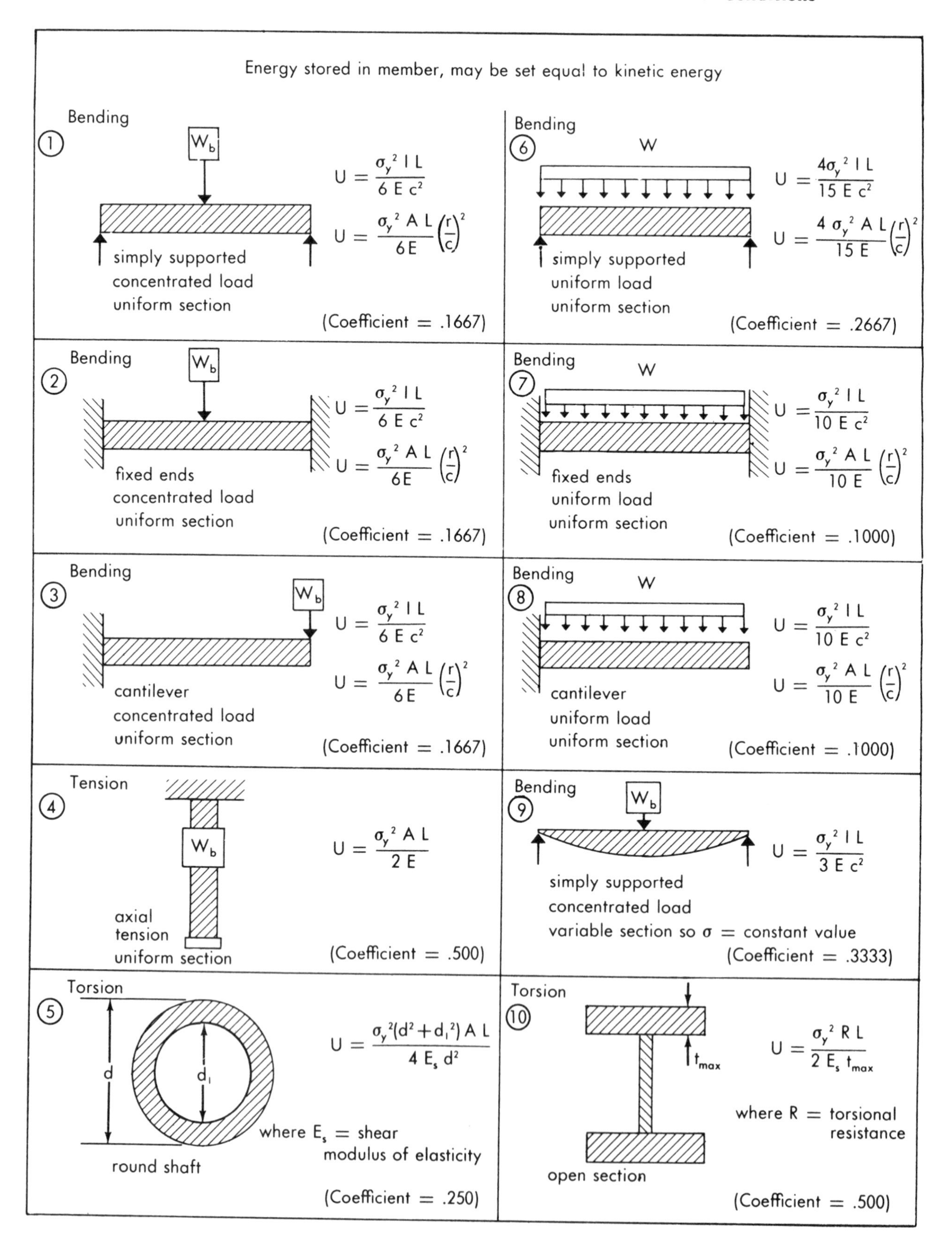

a concrete bridge deck in reducing the impact forces transferred into the member supporting it.

If the applied energy is expressed in terms of the velocity of the body (V), the reduced velocity (V_e) at instant of impact is—

$$V_e = V\left(\frac{W_b}{W_b + W_e}\right) = \left(\frac{V}{1+\frac{W_e}{W_b}}\right)$$

where:

W_b = weight of the body

W_e = equivalent weight of the member

If the member were compact and concentrated at a point, the entire weight of the member would be effective in reducing the velocity of the body. However, the supporting member is spread out in the form of a beam or frame and therefore only a portion of its weight is effective in moving along with the body and slowing it down. Timoshenko shows the portion of the weight of the member to be used is:

- Simply supported beam with concentrated load at midpoint

$$W_e = .486\ W_m$$

- Cantilever beam with concentrated load at end

$$W_e = .236\ W_m$$

The reduced kinetic energy (E_k) applied to the member causing stress and deflection would be

$$E_k = \frac{(W_b + W_e)\ V_e^2}{2\ g} = \frac{W_b\ V^2}{2\ g}\left(\frac{1}{1 + \frac{W_e}{W_b}}\right)$$

If the applied energy is expressed in terms of the height of fall of the body (h), the reduced velocity (V_e) may be expressed in terms of a reduced effective height (h_e):

$$h_e = \frac{V_e^2}{2\ g}$$

This represents the effective height the body would have to fall in order to have the reduced velocity (V_e) at the instant of impact with the member.

7. ENERGY-ABSORBING CAPACITY OF MEMBER

The allowable energy load, or load that can be absorbed elastically (without plastic deformation) by the member in bending, is basically—

$$\boxed{U = k\ \frac{\sigma_y^2\ I\ L}{E\ c^2}} \qquad \text{(1)}$$

where (k) is a constant for a specific type of beam with a specific type of loading. Table 2 shows the application of this formula to various member and load conditions, with numerical values substituted for the (k) factor.

Observation shows that the critical property of the section is $\frac{I}{c^2}$, while that of the material is $\frac{\sigma_y^2}{2\ E}$.

8. IMPACT PROPERTIES OF MATERIAL

The two most important properties of a material that indicate its ability to absorb energy are obtained from the stress-strain diagram (Fig. 4).

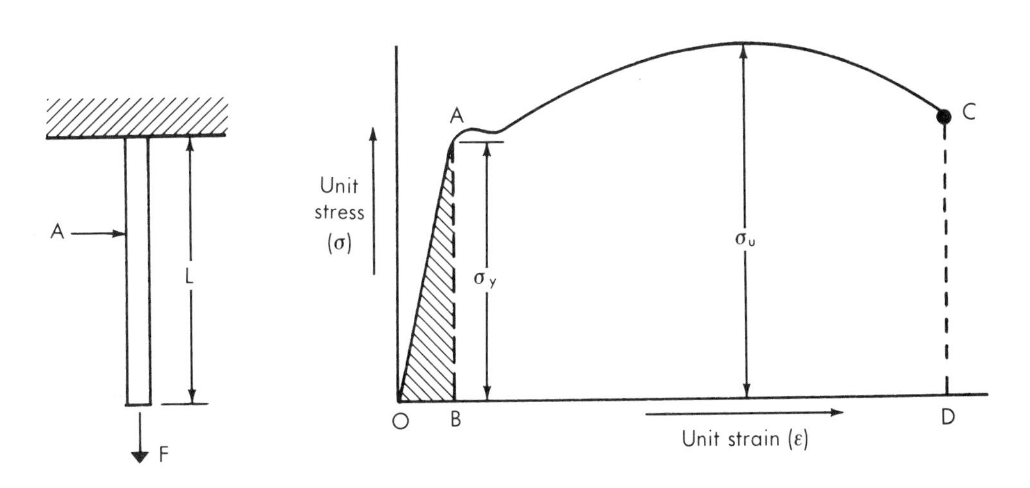

FIG. 4 Stress-strain diagram: basis for material's impact properties.

The *modulus of resilience* (u) of a material is its capacity to absorb energy within its elastic range, i.e. without permanent deformation. This is represented on the tensile stress-strain diagram by the area under the curve defined by the triangle O A B, having its apex A at the elastic limit.

$$u = \frac{\sigma_y^2}{2\ E} \qquad (2)$$

Since the absorption of energy is actually a volumetric property, the u in (in.-lbs/in.^{3}) = u in psi.

When impact loading exceeds the elastic limit (or yield strength) of the material, it calls for toughness in the material rather than resilience.

The *ultimate energy resistance* (u_u) of a material indicates its toughness or ability to resist fracture under impact loading. This is a measure of how well the material absorbs energy without fracture. A material's ultimate energy resistance is represented on the stress-strain diagram by the total area OACD under the curve. Here point A is at the material's yield strength (σ_y) and point C at its ultimate strength (σ_u). For ductile steel, the ultimate energy resistance is approximately—

$$u_u = A_{OACD} = \frac{\sigma_y + \sigma_u}{2}\ \epsilon_u \qquad (3)$$

where:

ϵ_u = ultimate unit elongation, in./in.

Since the absorption of energy is actually a volumetric property, u_u in (in.-lbs/in.^{3}) = u_u in psi.

Impact properties of common design materials are charted in Table 3.

9. IMPACT PROPERTIES OF SECTION

The section property which is needed to withstand impact loads or to absorb energy in bending is I/c^2.

This is very important because as moment of inertia (I) increases with deeper sections, the distance from the neutral axis to the outer fiber (c) increases *as its square*. So, increasing only the depth of a section will increase the section's moment of inertia but with little or no increase in impact property.

For example, suppose there is a choice between these two beams:

Section Property	Beam A 12" WF 65# Beam	Beam B 24" WF 76# Beam
I	533.4 in.^{4}	2096.4 in.^{4}
c	6.06 in.	11.96 in.
Steady load strength $S = \frac{I}{c}$	$\frac{533.4}{6.06} = 88.2$ in.^{3}	$\frac{2096.4}{11.96} = 175$ in.^{3}
Impact load strength $\frac{I}{c^2}$	$\frac{533.4}{(6.06)^2} = 14.5$ in.^{2}	$\frac{2096.4}{(11.96)^2} = 14.6$ in.^{2}

The new beam (B) with twice the depth, has about 4 times the bending stiffness (I), and 2 times the steady load strength (I/c), but for all practical purposes there is no increase in the impact load strength (I/c^2). In this example, there would be no advantage in changing from (A) to (B) for impact.

10. IMPROVING ENERGY ABSORPTION CAPACITY

The basic rule in designing members for maximum energy absorption is to have the maximum volume of the member subjected to the maximum allowable stress. If possible, this maximum stress should be uniform on every cubic inch of the member.

1. For any given cross-section, have the maximum amount of the area stressed to the maximum allowable. In the case of beams, place the greatest area of the section in the higher stressed portion at the outer fibers.

2. Choose sections so the member will be stressed to the maximum allowable stress along the entire length of the member.

For a member subjected to impact in axial tension, specifying a constant cross-section from end to end will uniformly stress the entire cross-section to the maximum value along the full length.

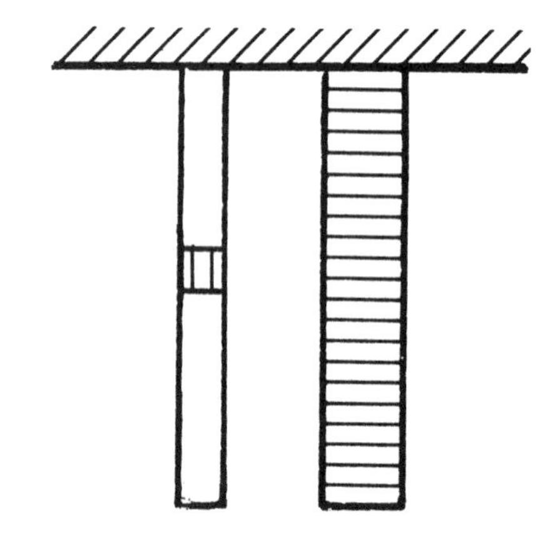

TABLE 3—Impact Properties of Common Design Materials

Material	σ_y Tensile Proportional limit lbs/in.^{2}	σ_u Tensile Ultimate Strength lbs/in.^{2}	E Tensile Modulus of Elasticity lbs/in.^{2}	ϵ_u Ultimate Unit Elongation in./in.	u Tensile Modulus of Resilience in.-lbs/in.^{3}	u_u Toughness - Ultimate Energy Resistance in.-lbs/in.^{3}
Mild Steel	35,000	60,000	30×10^6	0.35	20.4	16,600
Low Alloy (under ¾")	50,000	70,000	30×10^6	.18	41.6	
(¾ to 1½")	46,000	67,000	30×10^6	.19	35.2	
(over 1½ to 4")	42,000	63,000	30×10^6	.19	29.4	
Medium carbon steel	45,000	85,000	30×10^6	0.25	33.7	16,300
High carbon steel	75,000	120,000	30×10^6	0.08	94.0	5,100
T-1 Steel	100,000	115,000 to 135,000	30×10^6	0.18	200.0*	about 19,400
Alloy Steel	200,000	230,000	30×10^6	0.12	667.0	22,000
Gray Cast Iron	6,000	20,000	15×10^6	0.05	1.2	70
Malleable Cast Iron	20,000	50,000	23×10^6	0.10	17.4	3,800

* Based on integrator-measured area under stress-strain curve.

A beam can be designed for constant bending stress along its entire length, by making it of variable depth. Although the cross-section at any point is not uniformly stressed to the maximum value, the outer fiber is stressed to the maximum value for the entire length of the member.

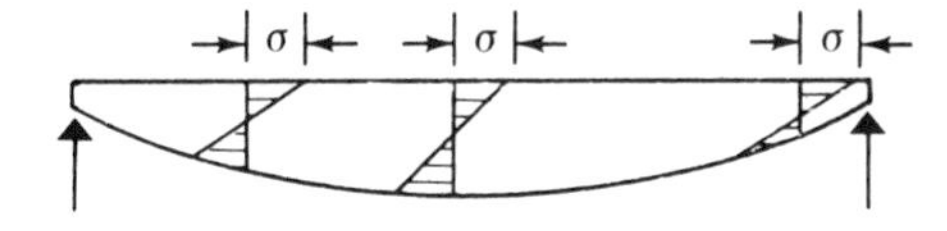

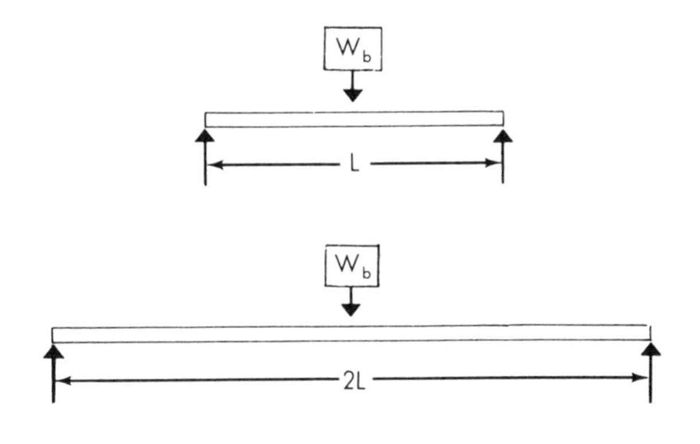

FIGURE 5

In Table 3 the member in tension (No. 4) has three times the energy-absorption capacity of the simple beam with a concentrated load (No. 1). This is because the tensile member (No. 4) has its entire cross-section uniformly stressed to maximum for its full length. In contrast, the maximum bending stress in beam No. 1 is at the outer fibers only; and this bending stress decreases away from the central portion of the beam, being zero at the two ends.

Notice that decreasing the depth of the beam at its supports, so the maximum bending stress is uniform along the entire length of the beam, doubles the energy-absorbing capacity of the beam. See (1) and (9).

For a steady load, doubling the length of a beam will double the resulting bending stress. However, for an impact load, doubling the length of the beam will reduce the resulting impact stress to 70.7% of the original.

Two identical rectangular beams can theoretically absorb the same amount of energy and are just as strong under impact loading. The section property which determines this is I/c^2, and this is constant for a given rectangular area regardless of its position.

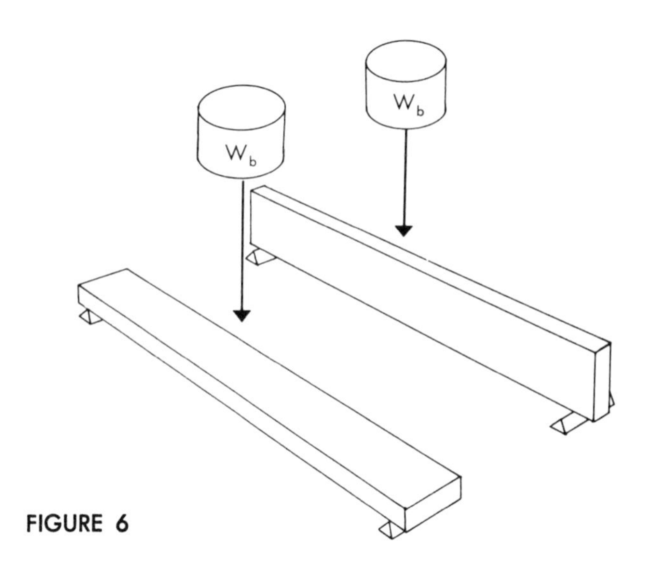

FIGURE 6

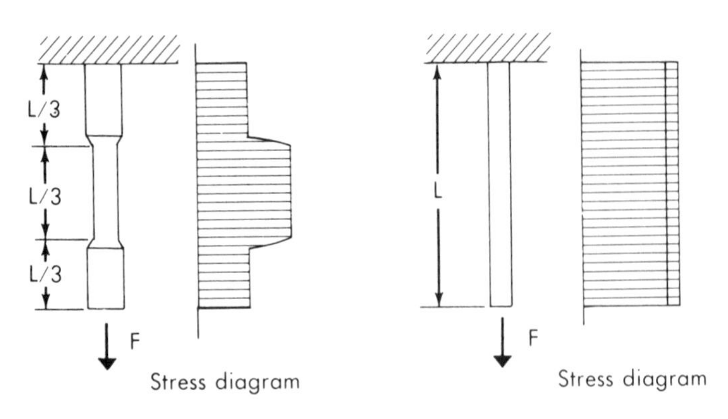

FIGURE 7

The two tensile bars shown in Figure 5 have equal strength under steady loads; yet, the bar on the right, having uniform cross-section, is able to absorb much more energy and can withstand a greater impact load.

Summary

1. The property of the section which will reduce the impact stress in tension is increased volume (AL).

2. The property of the section which will reduce the impact stress in a simple beam is:

$$\text{increased} \sqrt{\frac{I\ L}{c^2}} \text{ or } = \frac{r}{c}\sqrt{A\ L}$$

3. In a simple beam, a decrease in length (L) will decrease the static stress, but will increase the stress due to impact.

4. In a simple tensile bar of a given uniform cross-section, increasing the length (l) will not alter the static stress yet it will decrease the stress due to impact.

11. NOTCH EFFECT ON ENERGY ABSORBING CAPACITY

In Figure 8, diagrams e and f represent the energy absorbed along the length of a member. The total energy absorbed corresponds to the area under this diagram.

Assume the notch produces a stress concentration of twice the average stress (d). Then for the same maximum stress, the average stress will be reduced to ½ and the energy absorbed (f) will be ¼ of the energy absorbed if no notch were present (e). For a stress concentration of three times the average stress, the energy absorbed will be 1/9, etc.

Notched bar impact test results are of limited value to the design engineer, and can be misleading:

(a) The test is highly artificial in respect to severe notch condition and manner of load condition.

(b) The results can be altered over a wide range by changing size, shape of notch, striking velocity, and temperature.

(c) The test does not simulate a load condition likely to be found in service.

(d) The test does not give quantitative values of the resistance of the material to energy loads.

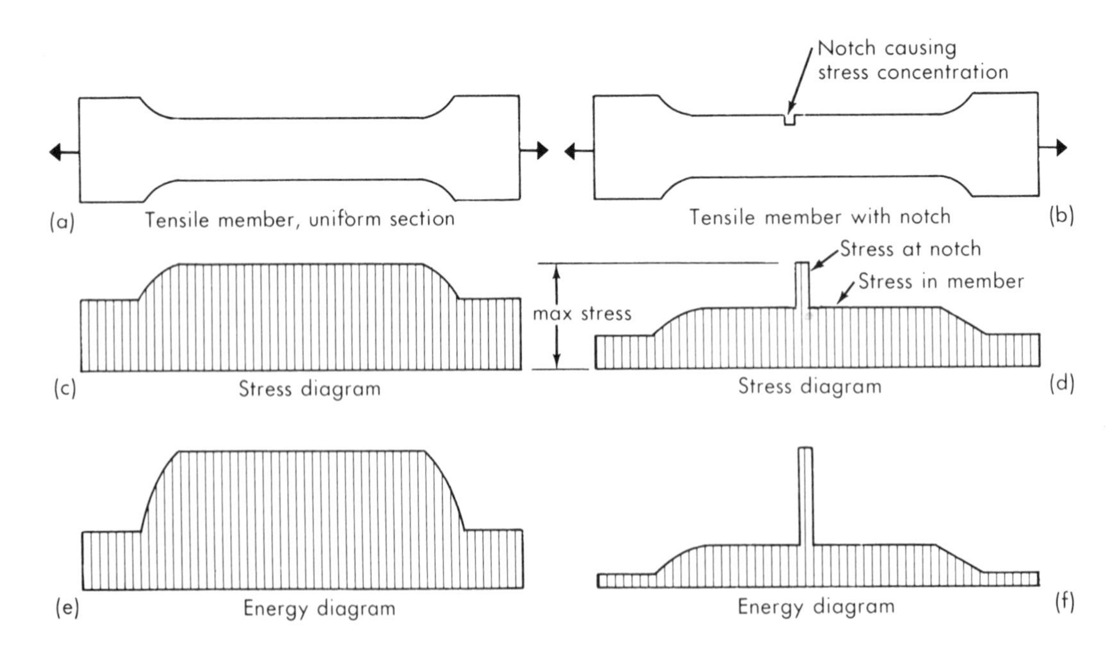

FIGURE 8

12. GUIDES TO DESIGNING FOR IMPACT LOADS

1. Design the member as an energy-absorbing system, that is have the maximum volume of material stressed to the highest working stress; this increases the energy absorbed.
2. For any given cross-section of the member, have the maximum area subjected to the maximum allowable stress; also stress the entire length to this value.
3. The property of the section which will reduce the impact stress in tension is increased volume (A L).
4. The property of the section which will reduce the impact stress in bending is increased I/c^2.
5. Increasing the length (L) of a beam will increase the static stress, but will decrease stress due to impact.
6. Increasing the length (L) of a tensile member of uniform cross-section will not change the static stress, but will decrease stress due to impact.
7. Use the basic formula, or those shown in Table 3, as a guide to select the required property of section and property of material.
8. Select material that has a high modulus of resilience $u = \frac{\sigma_y^2}{2\,E}$. Materials having lower modulus of elasticity (E) generally have lower values of yield strength (σ_y), and this latter value is more important because it is squared. Therefore steels with higher yield strengths have higher values of modulus of resilience and are better for impact loads.
9. The material should be ductile enough to plastically relieve the stress in any area of high stress concentration; and have good notch toughness.
10. The material should have high fatigue strength if the impact load is repeatedly applied.
11. The material should have good notch toughness, and for low temperature service, a low transition temperature.
12. Reduce stress concentrations to a minimum and avoid abrupt changes in section.
13. If possible, place material so that the direction of hot rolling (of plate or bar in steel mill) is in line with impact force.
14. For inertia forces, decrease the weight of the member, while maintaining proper rigidity of the member for its particular use. This means lightweight, well-stiffened members having sufficient moment of inertia (I) should be used.
15. One aid against possible inertia forces caused by the rapid movement of the member due to explosive energy, earthquakes, etc., is the use of flexible supports, to decrease the acceleration and/or deceleration of the member.

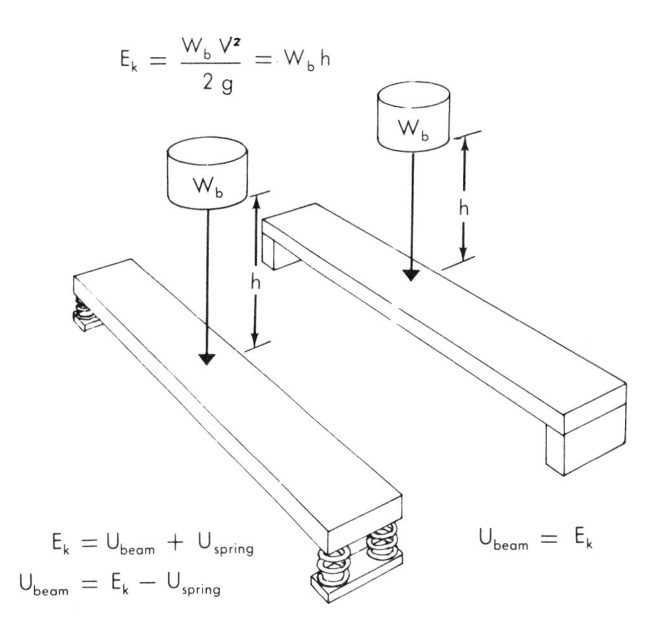

FIGURE 9

Problem 1	*Accelerating a Load*

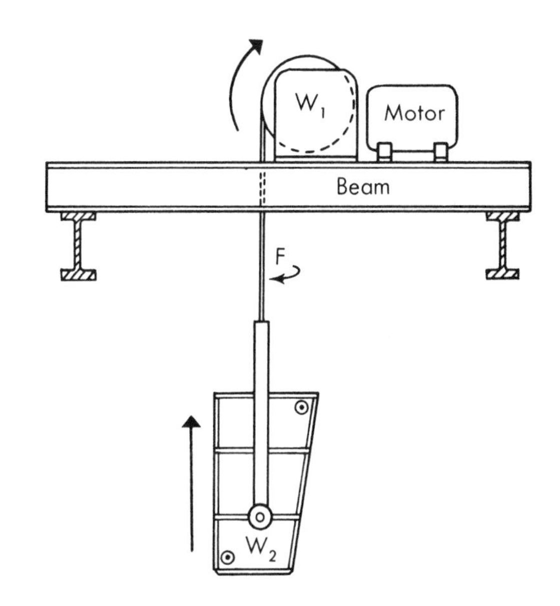

FIGURE 10

Find the load placed on the supporting beam for a hoisting unit in the shaft of a mine if the 5000-lb load (W_2) is accelerated upward to a velocity (V) of 1800 feet per minute in 5 seconds (t). The dead weight of the hoisting unit is 1000 lbs (W_1).

acceleration

$$a = \frac{V_2 - V_1}{t}$$

$$= \frac{\left(\frac{1800}{60}\right) - 0}{(5)}$$

$$= 6 \text{ ft/sec}^2$$

force of acceleration

$$F_a = \frac{W_2}{g} a$$

$$= \frac{(5000)}{(32.2)} (6)$$

$$= 931 \text{ lbs}$$

total load on beam

$$W_1 + W_2 + F_a = (1000) + (5000) + (931)$$

$$= 6931 \text{ lbs}$$

Problem 2 ***Decelerating a Load***

Assume the truck brakes the trailer, because brakes on trailer have failed, and stops from a speed of 60 miles per hour within 15 seconds.

$$V_1 = 60 \text{ MPH} = \frac{(5280)\ (60)}{(3600)}$$

$$= 88 \text{ ft/sec}$$

deceleration

$$a = \frac{V_2 - V_1}{t}$$

$$= \frac{0 - (88)}{(15)}$$

$$= -5.86 \text{ ft/sec}^2$$

force of deceleration

$$F = \frac{W}{g} a$$

$$= \frac{(40{,}000)}{(32.2)} (5.86)$$

$$= 7275 \text{ lbs}$$

The king pin on the fifth wheel, connecting the trailer to the tractor must be designed to transfer this force.

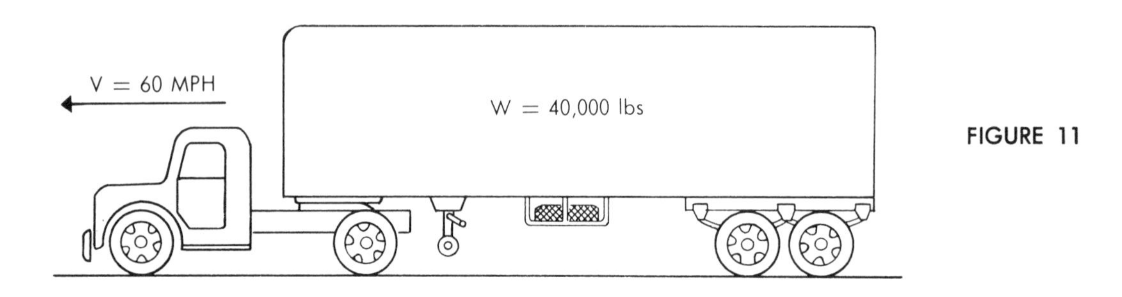

FIGURE 11

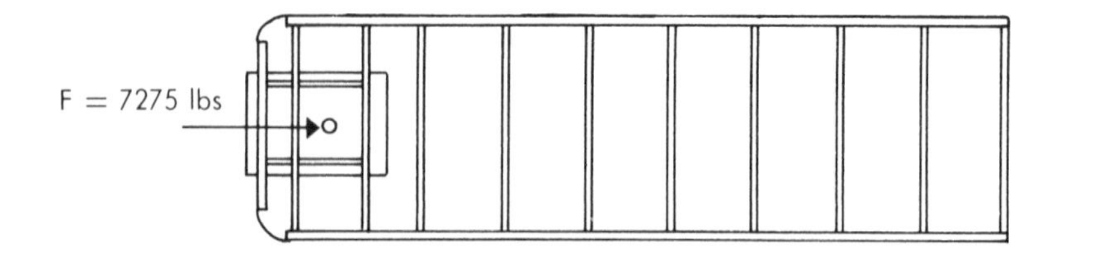

FIGURE 12

Designing for Fatigue Loads

1. ENDURANCE LIMIT

When the load on a member is constantly varying in value, or is repeated at relatively high frequency, or constitutes a complete reversal of stresses with each operating cycle, the material's endurance limit must be substituted for the ultimate strength where called for by design formulas.

Under high load values, the variable or fatigue mode of loading reduces the material's effective ultimate strength as the number of cycles increases. At a given high stress value, the material has a definite service or fatigue life, expressed as N cycles of operations. Conversely, at a given number of service cycles the material has a definite allowable fatigue strength.

The endurance limit is the maximum stress to which the material can be subjected for a given service life.

2. NATURE OF FATIGUE LOADING

Fatigue failure is a progressive failure over a period of time which is started by a plastic movement within a localized region. Although the average unit stresses across the entire cross-section may be below the yield point, a non-uniform distribution of these stresses may cause them to exceed the yield point within a small area and cause plastic movement. This eventually produces a minute crack. The localized plastic movement further aggravates the non-uniform stress ditribution, and further plastic movement causes the crack to progress. The stress is important only in that it causes the plastic movement.

Any fatigue test usually shows considerable scatter in the results obtained. This results from the wide range of time required before the initial crack develops in the specimen. Once this has occurred, the subsequent time to ultimate failure is fairly well confined and proceeds in a rather uniform manner.

The designer when first encountering a fatigue loading problem will often use the material's endurance limit or fatigue strength value given in his engineering handbook, without fully considering what this value represents and how it was obtained. This procedure could lead to serious trouble.

There are many types of fatigue tests, types of loading, and types of specimens. Theoretically the fatigue value used by the designer should be determined in a test that exactly duplicates the actual service conditions. The sample used should preferably be identical to the member, the testing machine should reproduce the actual service load, and the fatigue cycle and frequency should be the same as would be encountered in actual service. For example, if thc problem is a butt weld in tension, the allowable fatigue strength used in the design must come from data obtained from loading a butt weld in axial tension on a pulsating type of fatigue testing machine, with the same range of stress.

3. ANALYZING THE FATIGUE LOAD

Figure 1 illustrates a typical fatigue load pattern, the curve representing the applied stress at any given moment of time.

There are two ways to represent this fatigue load:

1. As a mean or average stress (σ_m) with a superimposed variable stress (σ_v).

2. As a stress varying from maximum value (σ_{max}) to a minimum (σ_{min}). Here, the cycle can be represented by the ratio—

$$K = \frac{\sigma_{min}}{\sigma_{max}}$$

FIGURE 1

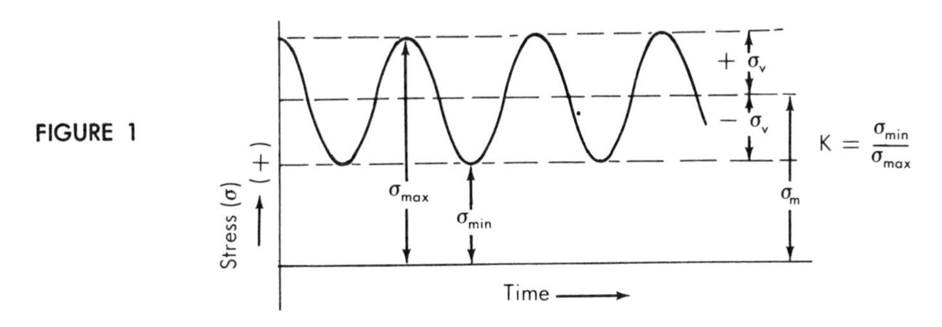

One approach to this problem is to let the variable stress (σ_v) be the ordinate and the steady or mean stress (σ_m) be the abscissa. When the mean stress (σ_m) is zero, see Figure 2, the varible stress (σ_v) becomes the value for a complete reversal of stress (σ_r). This value would have to be determined by experimental testing, and becomes point *b* in the diagram. When there is no variation in stress, i.e. a steady application of stress, σ_v becomes zero, and the maximum resulting mean stress (σ_m) is equal to the ultimate stress for a steady load (σ_u); this becomes point *a*.

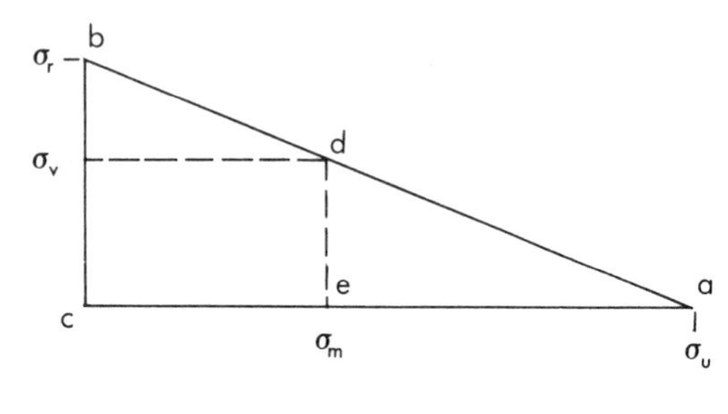

FIGURE 2

where:

σ_r = fatigue strength for a complete reversal of stress

σ_v = variable stress which is superimposed upon steady stress

σ_u = ultimate strength under steady load (Some set σ_u equal to the yield strength, σ_y)

σ_m = mean stress (average stress)

A line connecting points *b* and *a* will indicate the relationship between the variable stress (σ_v) and the mean stress (σ_m) for any type of fatigue cycle, for a given fatigue life (N). This straight line will yield conservative values; almost all of the test data will lie just outside of this line.

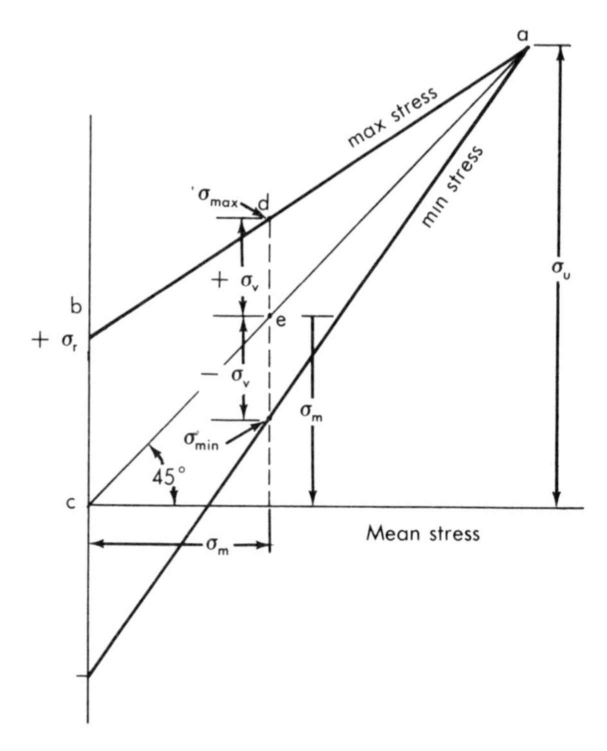

FIGURE 3

From similar triangles it is found that—

$$\frac{\sigma_v}{\sigma_r} + \frac{\sigma_m}{\sigma_u} = 1$$

A Goodman diagram, Figure 3, is constructed from Figure 2 by moving point *a* vertically to a height equal to σ_u; in other words, line a-c now lies at a 45° angle.

It can be shown by similar triangles that the same relationship holds:

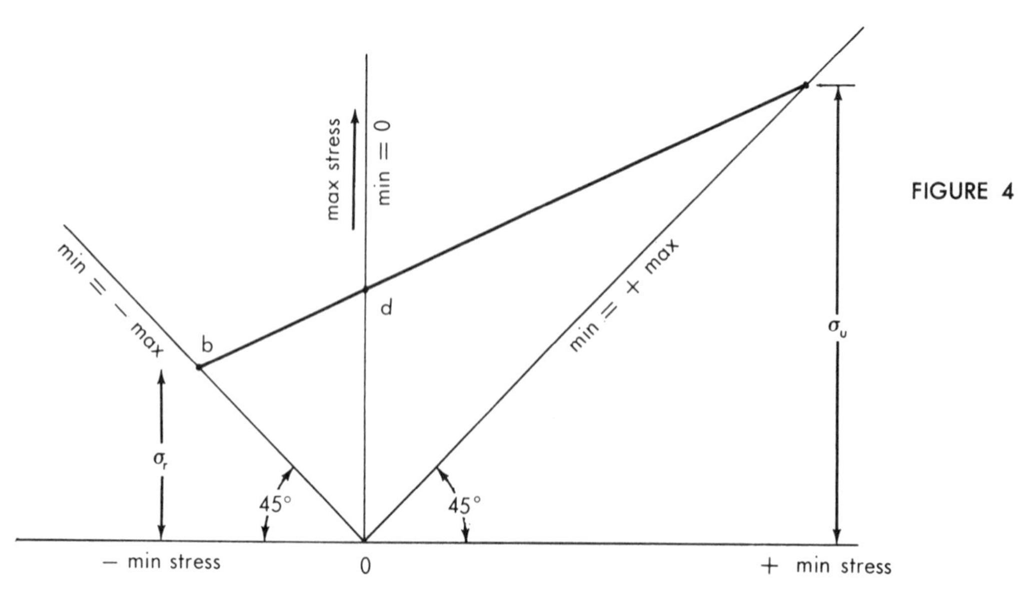

FIGURE 4

$$\frac{\sigma_v}{\sigma_r} + \frac{\sigma_m}{\sigma_u} = 1$$

The Goodman diagram of Figure 3 may be modified so that the ordinate becomes the maximum stress (σ_{max}) and the abscissa becomes the minimum stress (σ_{min}); see Figure 4. It can be proved that all three diagrams yield the same results. The American Welding Society (Bridge Specification) uses this last type of diagram to illustrate their fatigue data test results.

If the maximum stress (σ_{max}) lies on line a-b, this value is found to be—

$$\sigma_{max} = \frac{2\ \sigma_r\ \sigma_u}{\sigma_u + \sigma_r - K(\sigma_u - \sigma_r)}$$

where $K = \dfrac{\sigma_{min}}{\sigma_{max}}$

The next diagram, Figure 5, is constructed with the values for complete reversal (σ_r) and the ultimate strength (σ_u) for butt welds in tension. The fatigue data from test results are also plotted. Notice the values lie on or slightly above these straight lines for service life (N) of 100,000 cycles and that of 2 million cycles.

These "dependable values" have been reduced to some extent below the minimum values obtained in the test. A factor of safety is applied to obtain allowable values; these are shown by dotted lines. This is expressed as a formula along with a value which should not be exceeded. In this case, the maximum allowable is 18,000 psi. This formula represents the slanting line, but a maximum value must be indicated so that it is not carried too far.

Figure 6 illustrates several types of fatigue cycles, with corresponding K values to be used in the fatigue strength formulas.

4. ALLOWABLE MAXIMUM STRESS

Fatigue strength formulas, for determining the allowable maximum stress for a given service life of N cycles, are presented in Table 1 for A7 mild steel, A373 and A36 steels, in Table 2 for A441 steel, and in Table 3 for T-1, quenched and tempered high yield strength steel.

Required fatigue life or number of cycles will vary but usually starts at several hundred thousand cycles. It is assumed that by the time the value of several million cycles is reached, the fatigue strength has

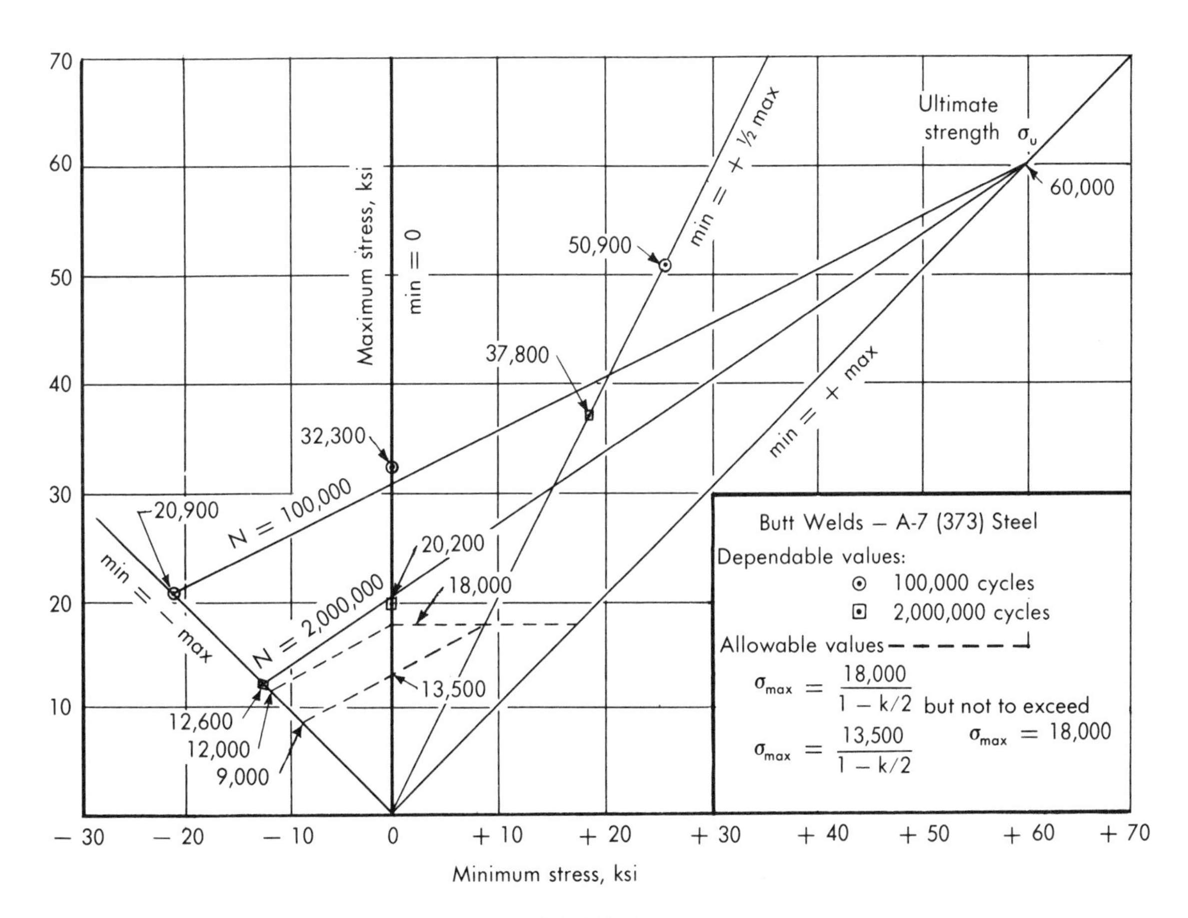

FIGURE 5

leveled off and further stress cycles would not produce failure. For any particular specimen and stress cycle there is a relationship between the fatigue strength (σ) and fatigue life (N) in number of cycles before failure. The following empirical formula may be used to convert fatigue strengths from one fatigue life to another:

$$\sigma_a = \sigma_b \left(\frac{N_b}{N_a}\right)^k$$

where:

σ_a = fatigue strength for fatigue life N_a
σ_b = fatigue strength for fatigue life N_b
N_a = fatigue life for fatigue strength σ_a
N_b = fatigue life for fatigue strength σ_b

The constant (k) will vary slightly with the specimen; however, 0.13 has been widely used for butt welds and 0.18 for plate in axial loading (tension and/or compression).

The curve in Figure 7 illustrates the general increase in fatigue life when the applied fatigue stress is reduced. As an example, in this case, reducing the fatigue stress to 75% of its normal value will in general increase the fatigue life about nine times.

Problem 1

Test data indicates a fatigue life of N_a = 1,550,000 cycles when the member is stressed to σ_a = 30,000 psi. What would be the fatigue strength at a life of 2,000,000 cycles?

TABLE 1—Allowable Fatigue Stress
For A7, A373 and A36 Steels and Their Welds

	2,000,000 cycles	600,000 cycles	100,000 cycles	But Not to Exceed
Base Metal In Tension Connected By Fillet Welds	(1) $\sigma = \frac{7500}{1 - 2/3\,K}$ psi	(3) $\sigma = \frac{10{,}500}{1 - 2/3\,K}$ psi	(5) $\sigma = \frac{15{,}000}{1 - 2/3\,K}$ psi	$\frac{2\,P_c}{3\,K}$ psi
But not to exceed →	P_t	P_t	P_t	
Base Metal Compression Connected By Fillet Welds	(2) $\sigma = \frac{7500}{1 - 2/3\,K}$ psi	(4) $\sigma = \frac{10{,}500}{1 - 2/3\,K}$ psi	(6) $\sigma = \frac{15{,}000}{1 - 2/3\,K}$ psi	P_c psi $\frac{P_c}{1 - \frac{K}{2}}$ psi
Butt Weld In Tension	(7) $\sigma = \frac{16{,}000}{1 - \frac{8}{10}K}$ psi	(11) $\sigma = \frac{17{,}000}{1 - \frac{7}{10}K}$ psi	(15) $\sigma = \frac{18{,}000}{1 - \frac{K}{2}}$ psi	P_t psi
Butt Weld Compression	(8) $\sigma = \frac{18{,}000}{1 - K}$ psi	(12) $\sigma = \frac{18{,}000}{1 - .8K}$ psi	(16) $\sigma = \frac{18{,}000}{1 - \frac{K}{2}}$ psi	P_c psi
Butt Weld In Shear	(9) $\tau = \frac{9{,}000}{1 - \frac{K}{2}}$ psi	(13) $\tau = \frac{10{,}000}{1 - \frac{K}{2}}$ psi	(17) $\tau = \frac{13{,}000}{1 - \frac{K}{2}}$ psi	13,000 psi
Fillet Welds ω = Leg Size	(10) $f = \frac{5100\,\omega}{1 - \frac{K}{2}}$ lb/in.	(14) $f = \frac{7100\,\omega}{1 - \frac{K}{2}}$ lb/in.	(18) $f = \frac{8800\,\omega}{1 - \frac{K}{2}}$ lb/in.	8800 ω lb/in.

Adapted from AWS Bridge Specifications. K = min/max
P_c = Allowable unit compressive stress for member.
P_t = Allowable unit tensile stress for member.

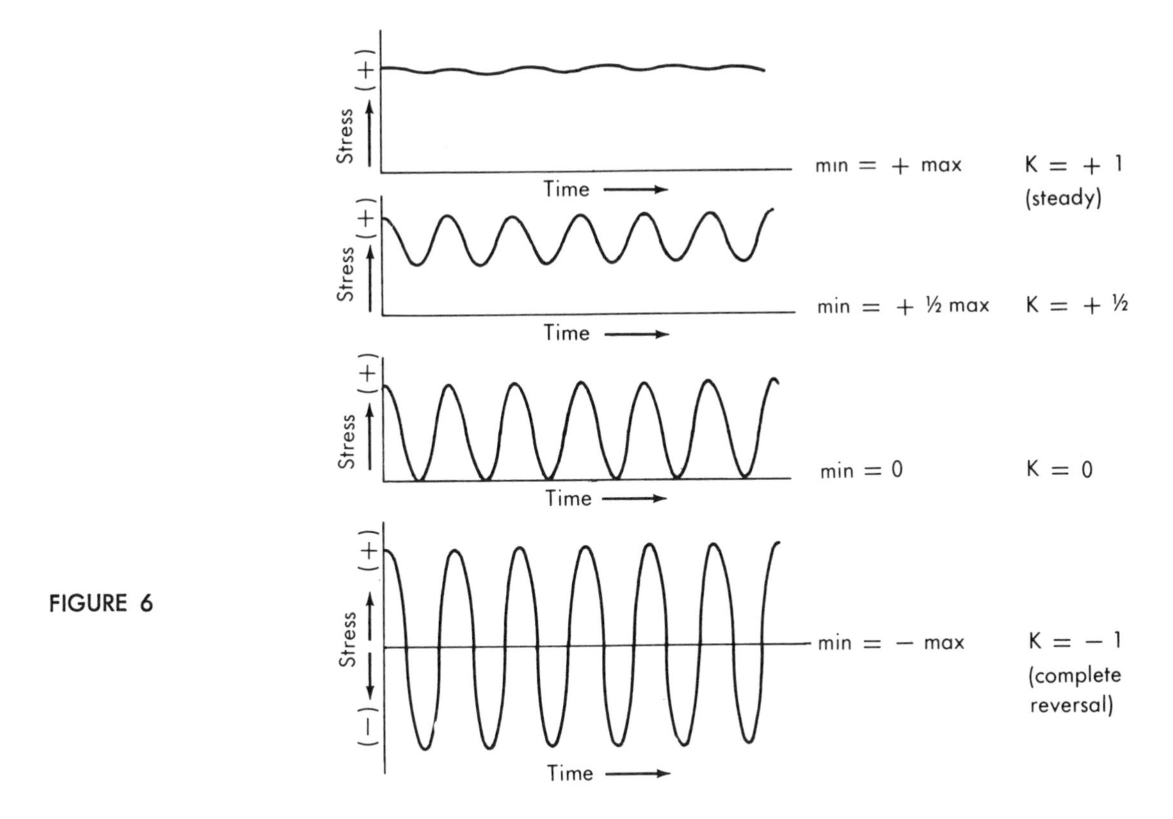

FIGURE 6

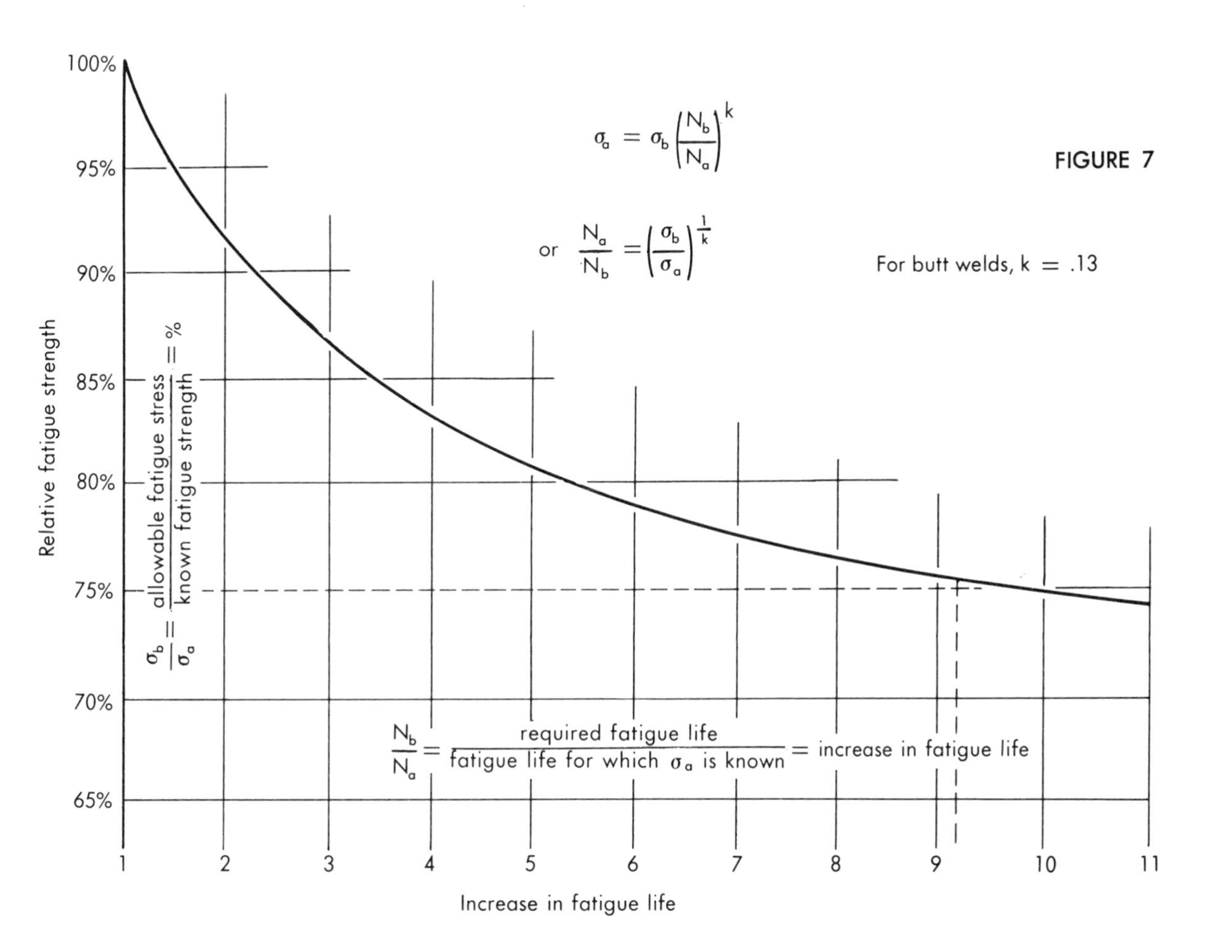

FIGURE 7

TABLE 2—Allowable Fatigue Stress
For A441 Steel and Its Welds

	2,000,000 cycles	600,000 cycles	100,000 cycles	But Not to Exceed
Base Metal In Tension Connected By Fillet Welds	(1) $\sigma = \dfrac{7500}{1 - 2/3\,R}$ psi	(3) $\sigma = \dfrac{10{,}500}{1 - 2/3\,R}$ psi	(5) $\sigma = \dfrac{15{,}000}{1 - 2/3\,R}$ psi	$\dfrac{2\,P_c}{3\,R}$ psi P_t psi
Base Metal Compression Connected By Fillet Welds	(2) $\sigma = \dfrac{7500}{1 - 2/3\,R}$ psi	(4) $\sigma = \dfrac{10{,}500}{1 - 2/3\,R}$ psi	(6) $\sigma = \dfrac{15{,}000}{1 - 2/3\,R}$ psi	$\dfrac{P_c}{1 - \frac{1}{2}\,R}$ psi P_c psi
Butt Weld In Tension	(7) $\sigma = \dfrac{16{,}000}{1 - .8\,R}$ psi	(11) $\sigma = \dfrac{19{,}000}{1 - .7\,R}$ psi	(15) $\sigma = \dfrac{24{,}000}{1 - \frac{1}{2}\,R}$ psi	P_t psi
Butt Weld Compression	(8) $\sigma = \dfrac{24{,}000}{1 - 1.7\,R}$ psi	(12) $\sigma = \dfrac{24{,}000}{1 - R}$ psi	(16) $\sigma = \dfrac{24{,}000}{1 - \frac{1}{2}\,R}$ psi	P_c psi
Butt Weld In Shear	(9) $\sigma = \dfrac{9000}{1 - \frac{1}{2}\,R}$ psi	(13) $\sigma = \dfrac{10{,}000}{1 - \frac{1}{2}\,R}$ psi	(17) $\sigma = \dfrac{13{,}000}{1 - \frac{1}{2}\,R}$ psi	13,000 psi
Fillet Welds ω = leg size	(10) $f = \dfrac{5100\,\omega}{1 - \frac{1}{2}\,R}$ lb/in.	(14) $f = \dfrac{7100\,\omega}{1 - \frac{1}{2}\,R}$ lb/in.	(18) $f = \dfrac{8800\,\omega}{1 - \frac{1}{2}\,R}$ lb/in.	* $f = 10{,}400\,\omega$ lb/in.

Adapted from AWS Bridge Specifications.
* if SAW-1, use 8800
R = min/max load
P_t = Allowable unit tensile stress for member.
P_c = Allowable unit compressive stress for member.

TABLE 3—Allowable Fatigue Stress
For Quenched and Tempered Steels of High Yield Strength and Their Welds

	2,000,000 cycles	600,000 cycles	100,000 cycles	But Not to Exceed
Base Metal In Tension—Not Adjacent to Welds	(1) $\sigma = \dfrac{29{,}000}{1 - .65\,K}$ psi	(2) $\sigma = \dfrac{33{,}000}{1 - .60\,K}$ psi	(3) $\sigma = \dfrac{39{,}500}{1 - .50\,K}$ psi	$\sigma = 54{,}000$ psi
Butt Weld In Tension	(4) $\sigma = \dfrac{16{,}500}{1 - .80\,K}$ psi	(5) $\sigma = \dfrac{21{,}000}{1 - .75\,K}$ psi	(6) $\sigma = \dfrac{31{,}000}{1 - .60\,K}$ psi	$\sigma = 54{,}000$ psi
Fillet Weld ω = leg size	(7) $f = \dfrac{6{,}360\,\omega}{1 - .80\,K}$ lbs/in.	(8) $f = \dfrac{9{,}900\,\omega}{1 - .75\,K}$ lbs/in.	(9) $f = \dfrac{14{,}500\,\omega}{1 - .60\,K}$ lbs/in.	$f = 26{,}160\,\omega$ lbs/in.

Above values adapted from "The Fabrication and Design of Structures of T-1 Steel" by Gilligan and England, United States Steel Corporation.

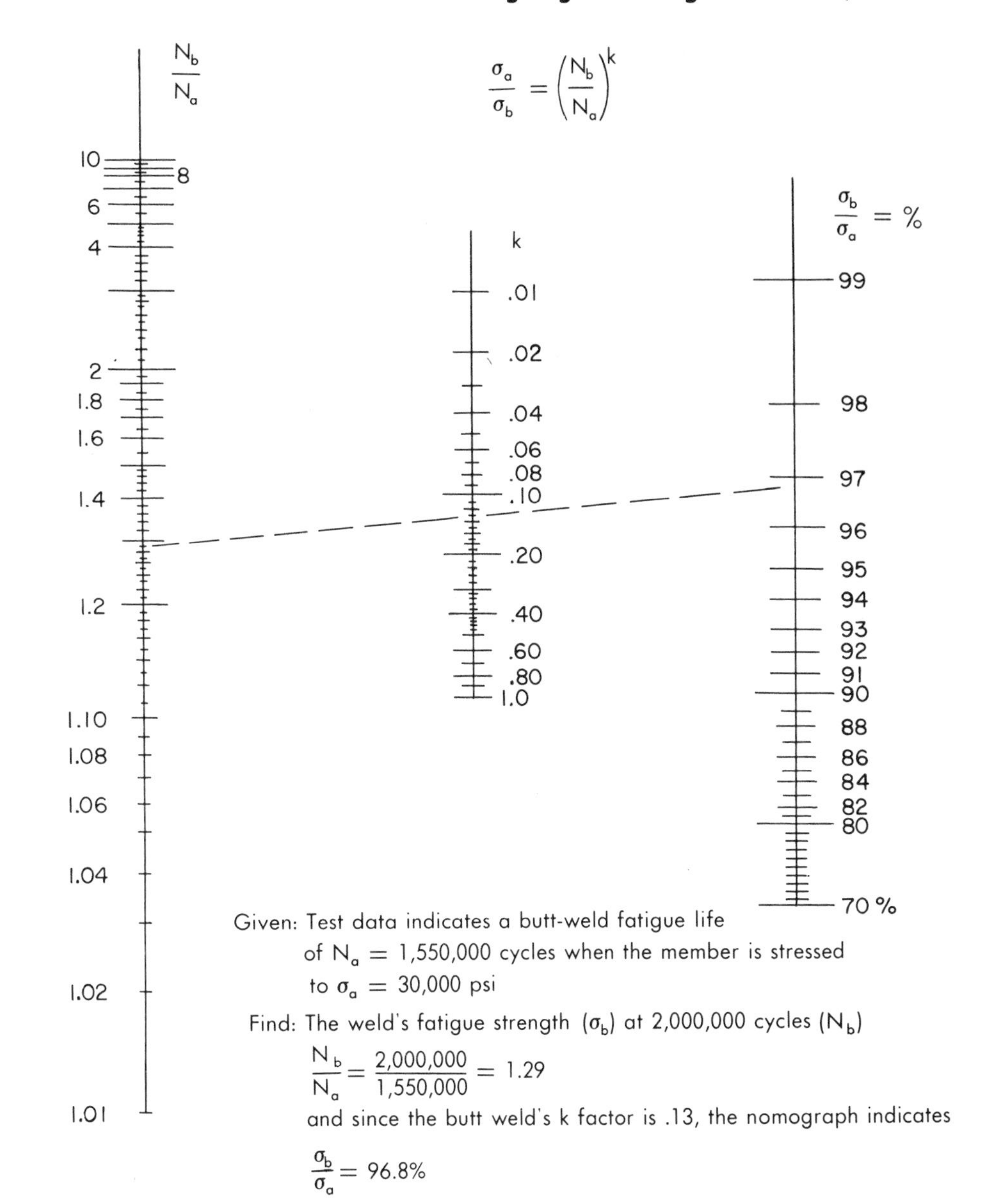

$\frac{N_b}{N_a}$
$\frac{\sigma_a}{\sigma_b} = \left(\frac{N_b}{N_a}\right)^k$
k
$\frac{\sigma_b}{\sigma_a} = \%$
10 8 6 4 2 1.8 1.6 1.4 1.2 1.10 1.08 1.06 1.04 1.02 1.01
.01 .02 .04 .06 .08 .10 .20 .40 .60 .80 1.0
99 98 97 96 95 94 93 92 91 90 88 86 84 82 80 70 %
Given: Test data indicates a butt-weld fatigue life of N_a = 1,550,000 cycles when the member is stressed to σ_a = 30,000 psi
Find: The weld's fatigue strength (σ_b) at 2,000,000 cycles (N_b)
$\frac{N_b}{N_a} = \frac{2,000,000}{1,550,000} = 1.29$
and since the butt weld's k factor is .13, the nomograph indicates
$\frac{\sigma_b}{\sigma_a} = 96.8\%$
or σ_b = 30,000 × 96.8% = 29,000 psi

FIGURE 8
FATIGUE NOMOGRAPH

Since:

$$\frac{\sigma_a}{\sigma_b} = \left(\frac{N_b}{N_a}\right)^k \quad \text{(For butt welds, k = 0.13) or:}$$

$$\frac{\sigma_b}{\sigma_a} = \left(\frac{N_a}{N_b}\right)^k \quad \text{and:}$$

$$\frac{\sigma_b}{30{,}000} = \left(\frac{1{,}550{,}000}{2{,}000{,}000}\right)^{.13} = (0.775)^{.13}$$

Using logarithms* for the right hand side:

$$= 0.13(\log 0.775) = 0.13(9.88930 - 10)$$

$$\begin{array}{llr} = 1.285609 & - 1.3 & \text{(add 8.7 to left side and} \\ + 8.7 & - 8.7 & \text{subtract 8.7 from right} \\ \hline 9.985609 & -10.0 & \text{side)} \end{array}$$

The anti-log of this is 0.96740; hence:

$$\frac{\sigma_b}{30{,}000} = 0.96740$$

$$\sigma_b = 30{,}000 \times 0.96740$$

$$= \underline{29{,}020} \text{ psi at } N_b = 2{,}000{,}000 \text{ cycles)}$$

The nomograph, Figure 8, further facilitates such conversion and permits quickly finding the relative allowable stress for any required fatigue life provided the fatigue strength at some one fatigue life is known and that the constant k value has been established. Conversely, the relative fatigue life can be readily found for any given stress and any constant (k).

* A log-log slide rule could be used to find the value of 0.775 raised to the 0.13 power.

5. RELATIVE SEVERITY OF FATIGUE PROBLEM

In Figure 9, the allowable fatigue stress is the vertical axis (ordinate) and the type of fatigue stress cycle (K = min/max) is the horizontal axis (abscissa).

The extreme right-hand vertical line (K = + 1) represents a steady stress. As we proceed to the left, the severity of the fatigue cycle increases; finally at the extreme left-hand axis (K = − 1) there is a complete reversal of stress. This is just one method of illustrating fatigue stress conditions. The important thing to be noticed here is that actual fatigue strength or allowable fatigue values are not reduced below the steady stress condition until the type of cycle (K = min/max) has progressed well into the fatigue type of loading.

In the case of 2 million cycles, the minimum stress must drop down to ½ of the maximum stress before there is any reduction of allowable strength. In the case of 100,000 cycles, the minimum stress can drop to zero before any reduction of allowable strength takes place. Even at these levels, the member and welds would be designed as though they were subjected to a steady load. The stress cycle must extend into a wider range of fluctuation before it becomes necessary to use lower fatigue allowables.

In other words, a fatigue problem occurs only if—

1. Stress is very high,
2. Anticipated service extends for a great number of cycles,
3. Stress fluctuates over a wide range.

And it generally requires all three of these situations occurring simultaneously to produce a critical fatigue condition worthy of consideration.

The allowable fatigue strength values obtained from the formulas in Table 1 take all three of these into consideration, and it is believed they will result in a conservative design.

6. COMBINED FATIGUE STRESSES

Several formulas are available for this consideration but very little actual testing has been done on this. In many cases there is not very good agreement between the actual test and the formulas.

1. Principal-stress theory—

$$\sigma_e = \frac{\sigma_x + \sigma_y}{2} + \tfrac{1}{2}\sqrt{(\sigma_x - \sigma_y)^2 + 4\,\tau_{xy}{}^2}$$

2. Maximum shear-stress theory—

$$\sigma_e = \sqrt{(\sigma_x - \sigma_y)^2 + 4\,\tau_{xy}{}^2}$$

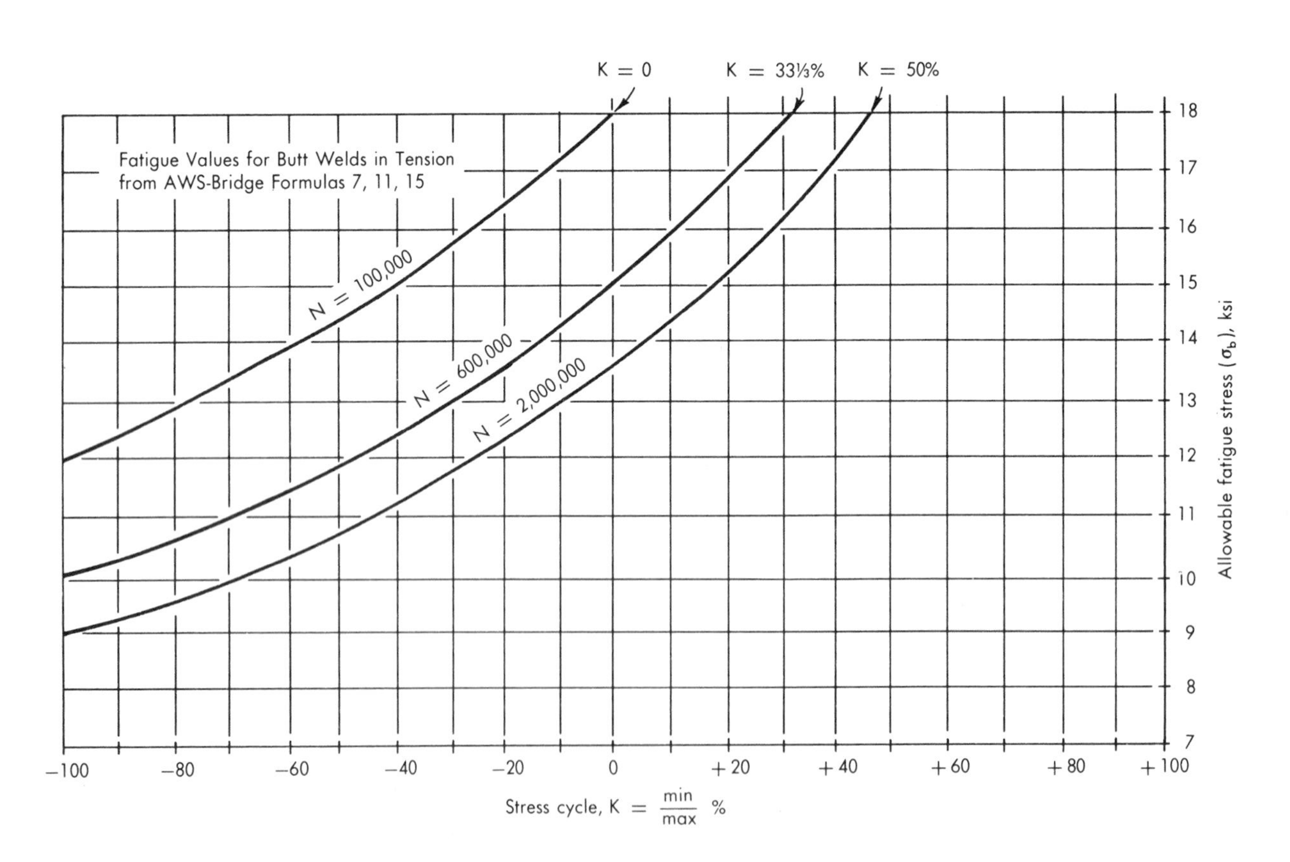

FIG. 9 Severity of fatigue depends on stress value and range of fluctuation, as well as service life.

TABLE 4—Fatigue Strength of Butt Welds
Summary of Results, Using 7/8-In. Carbon-Steel Plates

Description of Specimen	FATIGUE STRENGTH IN 1000's OF PSI					
	TENSION TO AN EQUAL COMPRESSION		0 TO TENSION		TENSION TO TENSION 1/2 AS GREAT	
	N = 100,000	N = 2,000,000	N = 100,000	N = 2,000,000	N = 100,000	N = 2,000,000
As Welded	22.3	14.4	33.1	22.5	53.3	36.9
Reinforcement On Stress Relieved	21.3	15.1	31.9	23.7		37.6
Reinforcement Machined Off Not Stress Relieved	28.9		48.8	28.4		43.7
Reinforcement Machined Off Stress Relieved	24.5	16.6	49.4	27.8		42.6
Reinforcement Ground Off Not Stress Relieved	26.8		44.5	26.3		
Plain Plate Mill Scale On	27.7	17.1	49.8	31.6		50.0
Plain Plate Mill Scale Machined Off and Surface Poished			59.6			
Butt Weld. Reinforcement and Mill Scale Machined Off and Surface Polished			53.9			

3. Shear-stress-invariant theory—

$$\sigma_e = \sqrt{\sigma_x^2 - \sigma_x\sigma_y + \sigma_y^2 + 3\,\tau_{xy}^2}$$

4. Combined bending and torsion. Findley corrected shear-stress theory for anistropy—

$$\sigma_e = \sqrt{\sigma_x^2 + \left(\frac{\sigma_b}{\tau}\right)^2 \tau_{xy}^2}$$

where σ_b/τ is the ratio of fatigue strength in pure bending to that in pure tension.

5. Combined tensile stresses. Gough suggests—

$$\frac{\sigma_x^2}{\sigma_{ox}^2} + \frac{\sigma_y^2}{\sigma_{oy}^2} = 1$$

where:

σ_{ox} = fatigure strength in (x) direction

σ_{oy} = fatigue strength in (y) direction

σ_x and σ_y = applied stresses

7. INFLUENCE OF JOINT DESIGN

Any abrupt change of section along the path of stress flow will reduce the fatigue strength. It is not welding that effects a reducing of the fatigue strength but the resultant shape or geometry of the section. It is for this reason that fillet welds have lower fatigue strength. simply because they are used in lap joints and all lap joints including riveted joints have lower fatigue strength.

TABLE 5—Effect of Transverse Attachments On Fatigue Strength

$K = \frac{min}{max.} = -1$	5/8"	5/16"	5/16", 5/16"
100,000 cycles	25,800 psi	25,400 psi	22,900 psi
2,000,000 cycles	22,800 psi	18,900 psi	13,100 psi

By means of Table 4, we can see that removing the reinforcement of a butt weld increases its fatigue strength to that of unwelded plate, also that stress relieving the weld has no appreciable effect on its fatigue strength.

Table 5 illustrates the effect of transverse fillet welds upon the fatigue strength of plate; this is ⅝″ plate.

The attachment causes an abrupt change in section, and this reduces the fatigue strength of the plate. It is believed these results could be duplicated by machining these joints out of solid plate, without any welding.

8. GUIDES TO DESIGNING FOR FATIGUE LOADING

I. Usually a member is stressed to the full maximum value for only a portion of its fatigue life or cycles. For most of its fatigue life, the member is stressed to a much lower value, and not to its full rated capacity; hence, most fatigue loading is not as severe as it may first appear.

Consider actual stress rather than average stress.

Reduce if possible the range of stress without increasing the maximum or average stress.

2. Fatigue loading requires careful fabrication, smooth transition of sections.

Avoid attachments and openings at locations of high stress.

Avoid sharp corners.

Use simple butt weld instead of lap or T fillet weld.

Grinding the reinforcement off of butt welds will increase the fatigue strength. This weld will have about the same fatigue strength as unwelded plate. Grinding, however, should not be specified unless essential, since it does add to the final unit cost.

Avoid excessive reinforcement, undercut, overlap, lack of penetration, roughness of weld.

Avoid placing weld in an area which flexes.

Stress relieving the weld has no appreciable effect upon fatigue strength.

Difficulties are sometimes caused by the welds being too small, or the members too thin.

3. Under critical loading, place material so that the direction of rolling (of plate in steel mill) is in line with force, because the fatigue strength may be higher in this direction than if placed at right angles with the direction of rolling. See Figure 10.

4. Where possible, form member into shape that it tends to assume under load, and hence prevent the resulting flexial movement.

5. Avoid operating in the critical or resonant frequency of individual member or whole structure to avoid excessive amplitude.

6. Perhaps consider prestressing a beam in axial compression. This will reduce the tensile bending stress and lessen chance for fatigue failure even though the compressive bending stress is increased to some extent.

7. Avoid eccentric application of loads which may cause additional flexing with each application of load.

8. Stiffeners decrease flexibility of panel and result in better fatigue strength, unless they cause a more abrupt change of section.

9. A rigid frame type of structure or statically indeterminate type of structure may be better than a simple structure since the load is shared by other members; hence, the structure is less likely to collapse immediately if a fatigue failure starts in one member.

10. Avoid biaxial and triaxial stresses, avoid restrained internal sections.

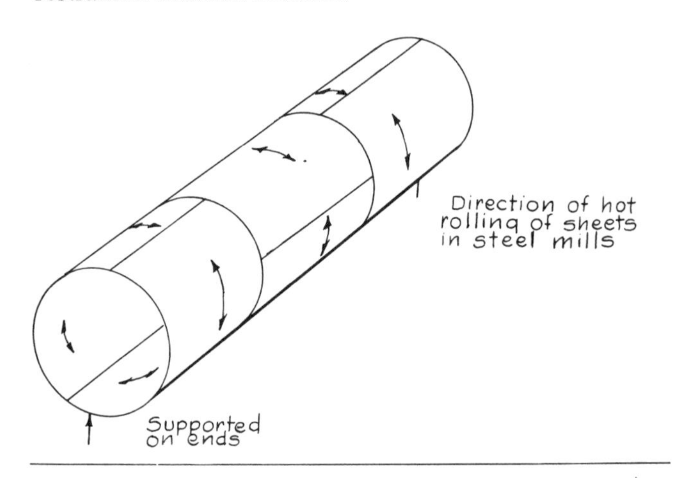

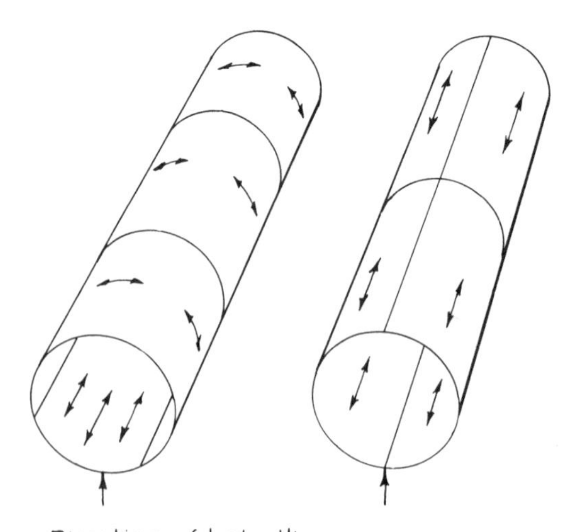

FIG. 10 Grain direction of sheet or plate should be in line with force, for greater fatigue strength.

Designing for Torsional Loading

1. NATURE OF TORSIONAL LOADING

Torsional loading is the application of a force that tends to cause the member to twist about its structural axis.

Torsion is usually referred to in terms of torsional moment or torque (T), which is basically the product of the externally applied force and the moment arm or force arm. The moment arm is the distance of the centerline of rotation from the line of force and perpendicular to it. This distance often equals the distance from the member's center of gravity to its outer fiber (radius of a round shaft, for example), but not always.

The principal deflection caused by torsion is measured by the angle of twist, or by the vertical movement of one corner of the frame.

Steel, in rolled structural shapes or built-up sections, is very efficient in resisting torsion. With steel, torsionally rigid sections are easily developed by the use of stiffeners.

Here are the three basic rules for designing structural members to make the best use of steel where torsional loads are a problem:

1. Use closed sections where possible.
2. Use diagonal bracing.
3. Make rigid end connections.

2. POLAR MOMENT OF INERTIA

When a round shaft is subjected to a twisting or torsional moment (torque), the resulting shear stress in the shaft is—

$$\boxed{\tau = \frac{T\,c}{J}} \quad \cdots\cdots (1)$$

where:

τ = shear stress, psi

c = distance from center of section to outer fiber

T = torque, in.-lbs.

J = polar moment of inertia of section, $in.^4$
$= I_x + I_y = 2I$

The angular twist of a round shaft is—

$$\boxed{\theta = \frac{T\,L}{E_s\,J}} \quad \cdots\cdots (2)$$

where:

θ = over-all angular twist of shaft, in radians (1 radian = 57.3° approx.)

L = length of shaft, in inches

E_s = modulus of elasticity in shear (steel E_s = 12,000,000 psi)

In most cases, the designer is interested in holding the torsional moment within the material's elastic limit. Where the torsional strength of a round shaft *is* required (i.e. the stress it can take without failure), the polar section modulus is J/c, and the allowable torque is thus—

$$T = \tau_u \frac{J}{c}$$

where, lacking test data, the ultimate shear strength of steel (τ_u) is assumed to be in the order of 75% of the material's ultimate tensile strength.

The above three formulas are true for solid round or tubular round shafts. For non-circular sections the shear stresses are not uniform, and therefore the standard torsional formulas no longer hold.

3. TORSIONAL RESISTANCE

Values of torsional resistance (R)—stiffness factor—have been established for various standard sections and provide more reliable solutions to torsional rigidity problems. Values of R are expressed in inches to the fourth power.

Table 1 shows the formulas for shear stress and torsional resistance of various sections. The formulas for solid rectangular sections call for values, of α and β, which are derived from the ratio of section width (b) to depth (d), as shown in the table.

Actual tests show that the torsional resistance (R) of an open section made up of rectangular areas, nearly equals the sum of the torsional resistances of all the individual rectangular areas. For example, the torsional resistance of an I beam is approximately

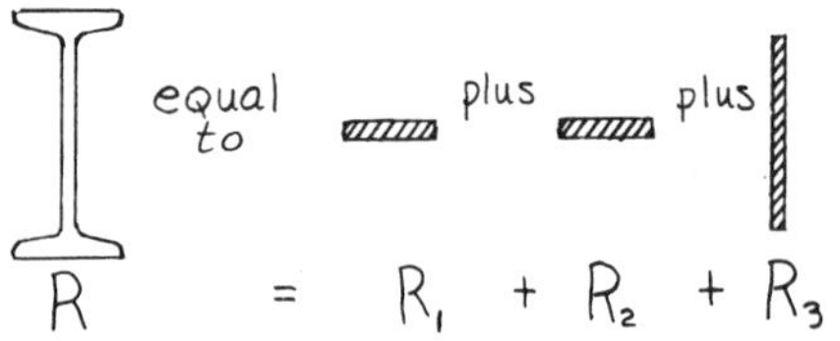

equal to plus plus

$$R = R_1 + R_2 + R_3$$

FIGURE 1

equal to the sum of the torsional resistances of the two flanges and web (Fig. 1).

Figure 2 shows the results of twisting an I beam made of three equal plates. Calculated values of twist by using the conventional polar moment of inertia (J) and the torsional resistance (R) are compared with the actual results. This shows greater accuracy by using torsional resistance (R).

This means that the torsional resistance of a flat

Angle of twist		
all loadings identical	t = .055,  2	t = .055, 2, 2 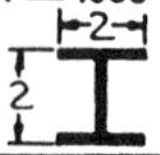
Conventional method J polar moment of inertia	.065°	.007°
Method using R Torsional Resistance	21.8°	7.3°
Actual Twist	22°	9.5°

FIGURE 2

TABLE 1—Torsional Properties of Various Sections

Section	Shear Stress	(for steel) R-torsional Resistance
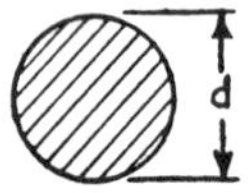 Solid circle, diameter d	$\tau = \frac{16\,T}{\pi\,d^3}$	$R = .0982\,d^4$
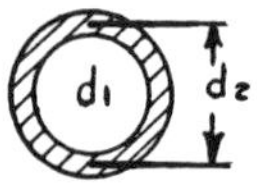 Hollow circle, inner diameter d_1, outer diameter d_2	$\tau = \frac{16\,T\,d_2}{\pi\,(d_2^4 - d_1^4)}$	$R = .0982\,(d_2^4 - d_1^4)$
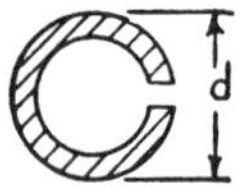 Split tube, diameter d	$\tau = \frac{3\,T}{\pi\,d\,t^2}$	$R = 1.0472\,t^3 d$
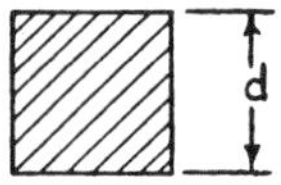 Square, side d	$\tau = \frac{4.8\,T}{d^3}$	$R = .1406\,d^4$
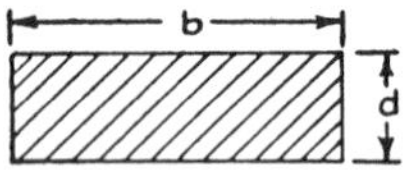 Rectangle, width b, depth d	$\tau = \frac{T}{\alpha\,b\,d^2}$	$R = \beta\,b\,d^3$

for solid rectangular sections	1.00	1.50	1.75	2.00	2.50	3.00	4.00	6	8	10	∞
$\frac{b}{d}$ =	1.00	1.50	1.75	2.00	2.50	3.00	4.00	6	8	10	∞
α	.208	2.31	.239	.246	.258	.267	.282	.299	.307	.313	.333
β	.141	.196	.214	.229	.249	.263	.281	.299	.307	.313	.333

Use this for diagonal bracing		R (I of diagonal brace)
	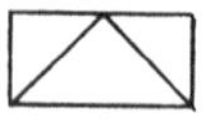 single brace	$R = 3.54\,I$
	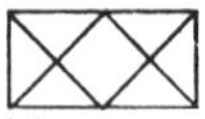 double brace	$R = 10.6\,I$

	Angle of twist				
	a	b	c	d	e
all loadings identical	t = .060	t = .060	t = .060	t = .060	t = .060
Conventional method J polar moment of inertia	.01°	.006°	.04°	.04°	.045°
Method using R Torsional Resistance	9.5°	9.7°	10°	.04°	.06°
Actual Twist	9°	9.5°	11°	too small to measure	too small to measure

FIGURE 3

plate is approximately the same whether it is used as such or is formed into an angle, channel, open tube section, etc. This is illustrated in Figure 3. Samples of different sections made of 16-gage steel are subjected to torsion. The flat section twists 9°. The same piece of steel formed into a channel (b) twists 9½°. When rolled into a tube with an open beam (c), it twists 11°.

When the same section is made into a closed section (d) by placing a single tack weld in the middle of the open seam, the torsional resistance increases several hundred times. When the tube becomes a closed section, the torsional stresses are distributed more evenly over the total area, thus permitting a greater load.

Notice the error in using polar moment of inertia (J) for the angle of twist of open sections, and the good agreement by using torsional resistance (R).

> Design Rule No. 1: USE CLOSED SECTIONS WHERE POSSIBLE

The solid or tubular round closed section is best for torsional loading since the shear stresses are uniform around the circumference of the member.

Next to a tubular section, the best section for resisting torsion is a closed square or rectangular tubular section.

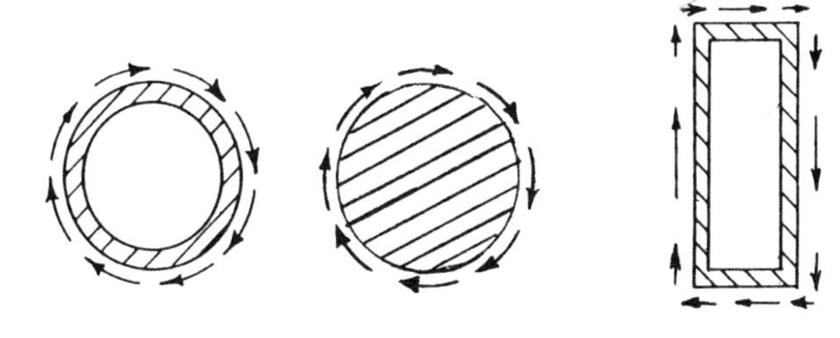

FIGURE 4

Table 2 provides formulas for determining the torsional resistance (R) of various closed tubular sections. It also provides the basic formulas for determining the shear stress (τ) at any given point along the sidewall of any closed section regardless of configuration or variation of thickness, and for determining the section's torsional resistance (R).

The poorest sections for torsional loading are open sections, flat plates, angle sections, channel sections, Z-bar sections, T-bar sections, I-beam sections, and tubular sections which have a slot.

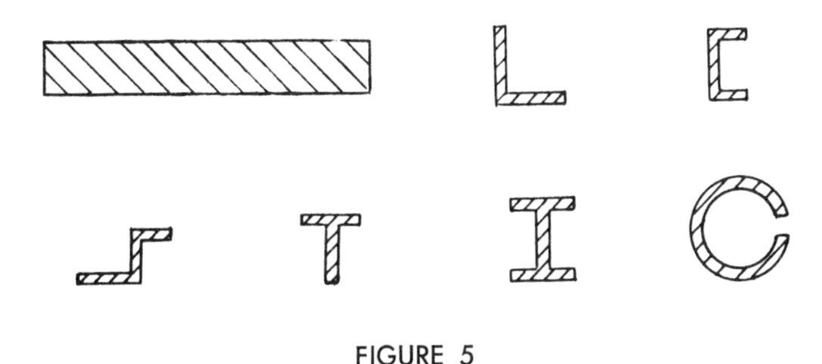

FIGURE 5

After the R values of all areas in a built-up section have been added together, their sum is inserted into the following formula or a modification of it:

$$\theta = \frac{T\,L}{E_s\,R} \quad \text{.......} (3)$$

Torque (T) in in.-lbs may be obtained from one of the formulas in Table 3, such as—

$$T = \frac{63{,}000 \times HP}{RPM}$$

$$\text{or } T = P\,e$$

where:

HP = horsepower

RPM = speed of revolution

P = applied force, lbs

e = moment arm of force (the perpendicular distance from the center of rotation to the line of force)

Problem 1

As an example, consider the torsional resistance of a closed round tube and one that is slotted. The tube has an O.D. of 4″, and I.D. of 3″, a length of 100″, and is subjected to a torque of 1000 in.-lbs.

Case 1

From Table 1, the torsional resistance of the closed round tube is found to be—

$$R = 0.0982\ (d_2^4 - d_1^4)$$
$$= 0.0982\ (4^4 - 3^4)$$
$$= \underline{17.19\ \text{in.}^4}$$

and the angular twist is—

$$\theta = \frac{T\ L}{E_s\ R} = \frac{(1000)(100)}{(12 \times 10^6)17.19}$$
$$= 0.000485 \text{ radians, or } \underline{0.0278°}$$

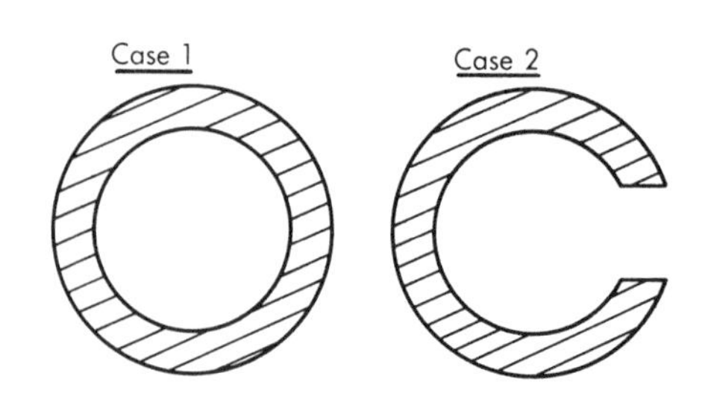

FIGURE 6

Case 2

From Table 1, the torsional resistance of the slotted round tube is found to be—

TABLE 2—Torsional Resistance (R) of Closed Tubular Sections

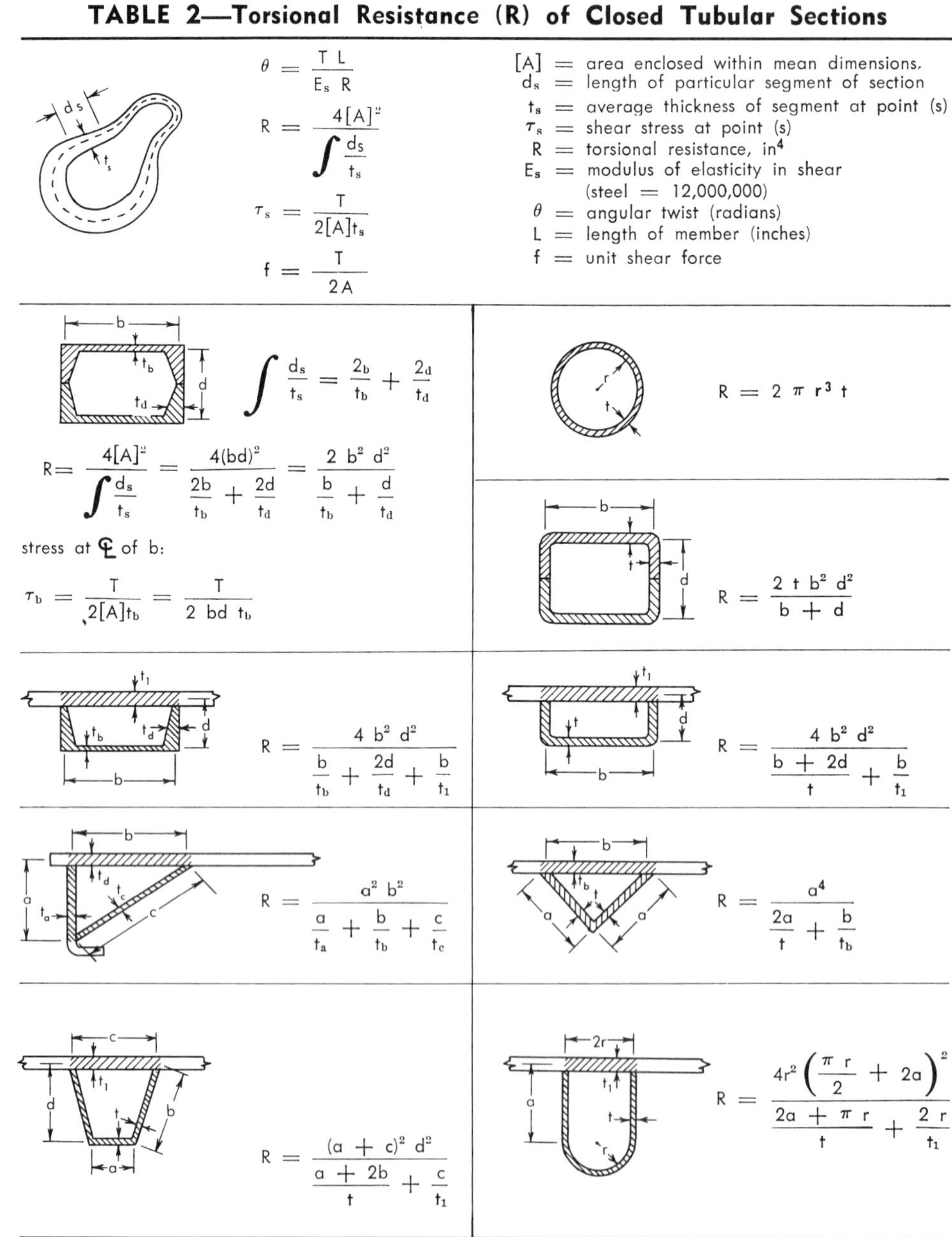

$\theta = \frac{T\ L}{E_s\ R}$
$R = \frac{4[A]^2}{\int \frac{d_s}{t_s}}$
$\tau_s = \frac{T}{2[A]t_s}$
$f = \frac{T}{2A}$
[A] = area enclosed within mean dimensions.
d_s = length of particular segment of section
t_s = average thickness of segment at point (s)
τ_s = shear stress at point (s)
R = torsional resistance, in⁴
E_s = modulus of elasticity in shear (steel = 12,000,000)
θ = angular twist (radians)
L = length of member (inches)
f = unit shear force
$\int \frac{d_s}{t_s} = \frac{2b}{t_b} + \frac{2d}{t_d}$
$R = \frac{4[A]^2}{\int \frac{d_s}{t_s}} = \frac{4(bd)^2}{\frac{2b}{t_b} + \frac{2d}{t_d}} = \frac{2\ b^2\ d^2}{\frac{b}{t_b} + \frac{d}{t_d}}$
stress at ℄ of b:
$\tau_b = \frac{T}{2[A]t_b} = \frac{T}{2\ bd\ t_b}$
$R = 2\ \pi\ r^3\ t$
$R = \frac{2\ t\ b^2\ d^2}{b + d}$
$R = \frac{4\ b^2\ d^2}{\frac{b}{t_b} + \frac{2d}{t_d} + \frac{b}{t_1}}$
$R = \frac{4\ b^2\ d^2}{\frac{b + 2d}{t} + \frac{b}{t_1}}$
$R = \frac{a^2\ b^2}{\frac{a}{t_a} + \frac{b}{t_b} + \frac{c}{t_c}}$
$R = \frac{a^4}{\frac{2a}{t} + \frac{b}{t_b}}$
$R = \frac{(a + c)^2\ d^2}{\frac{a + 2b}{t} + \frac{c}{t_1}}$
$R = \frac{4r^2\left(\frac{\pi\ r}{2} + 2a\right)^2}{\frac{2a + \pi\ r}{t} + \frac{2\ r}{t_1}}$

$$R = 1.0472\ t^3\ d$$
$$= 1.0472\ (\tfrac{1}{2})^3\ 3\tfrac{1}{2}$$
$$= \underline{0.459\ \text{in.}^4}$$

and the angular twist is—

$$\theta = \frac{T\ L}{E_s\ R}$$
$$= \frac{(1000)(100)}{(12 \times 10^6).459}$$
$$= 0.018 \text{ radians, or } \underline{1.04°}$$

Thus, the tube without the slot is many times more rigid than the slotted tube.

Problem 2

Two 6″ × 2″ × 10½-lb channels are to be used in making a 100″-long frame, which will be subjected to a torque of 1000 in.-lbs. In what relationship to each other will these channels offer the greatest resistance to twist?

Case 1

These two channels when separated but fastened together by end plates do not have much torsional resistance.

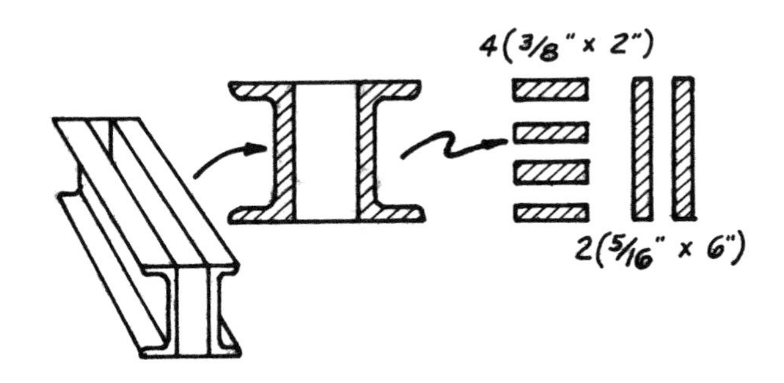

FIGURE 7

From Table 1, the value of R for each of the flanges is found to be—

$$R_1 = 0.0306\ \text{in.}^4$$

and that of each web is—

$$R_2 = 0.0586\ \text{in.}^4$$

and thus the total angular twist is—

$$\theta = \frac{1000 \times 100}{(12 \times 10^6)\ (4 \times .0306 + 2 \times .0586)}$$
$$= 0.0348 \text{ radians, or } \underline{2.0°}$$

TABLE 3—Formulas for Determining Safe Torque Under Various Conditions

Based on tangential load:

$$T = P\ e$$

Based on horsepower transmitted:

$$T = \frac{63{,}030 \times HP}{RPM}$$

Based on strength of shaft:

$$T = \frac{.19635\ S_s\ (d_2^4 - d_1^4)}{d_2}$$

where $S_s = 15{,}000$

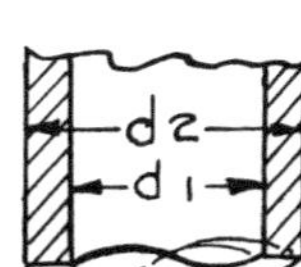

$$T = \frac{2945\ d_2^4 - d_1^4}{d_2}$$

Based on safe twist of shaft (.08°/ft):

$$T = 137\ (d_2^4 - d_1^4)$$

Based on fillet weld leg size around shaft or hub:

$$T = \frac{3781}{d + \omega}\left[(d + \omega)^4 - d^4\right]$$

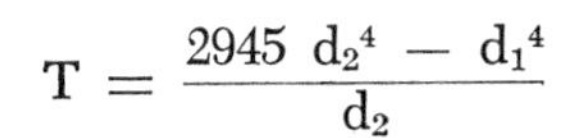

Based on butt weld size around hub:

$$T = 20{,}420\ d^2\ t$$

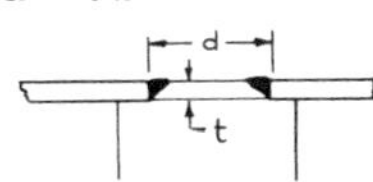

Case 2

When these two channels are securely fastened back to back, there is suitable resistance to any slip or movement due to horizontal shear. Here the two webs are considered as one solid web, and the top and bottom flanges are considered solid.

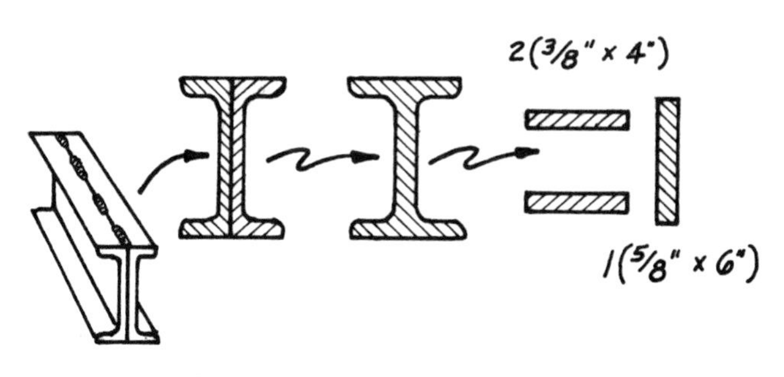

FIGURE 8

From Table 1, the value of R for each of the two composite flanges is found to be—

$$R_1 = 0.066 \text{ in.}^4$$

and that of the composite web is—

$$R_2 = 0.459 \text{ in.}^4$$

and thus the total angular twist is—

$$\theta = \frac{1000 \times 100}{(12 \times 10^6)\ (2 \times .066 + .459)}$$

$$= 0.0141 \text{ radians, or } \underline{0.81°}$$

which is much less than in Case 1.

Case 3

If these two channels were welded toe to toe to form a box section, the torsional resistance would be greatly increased.

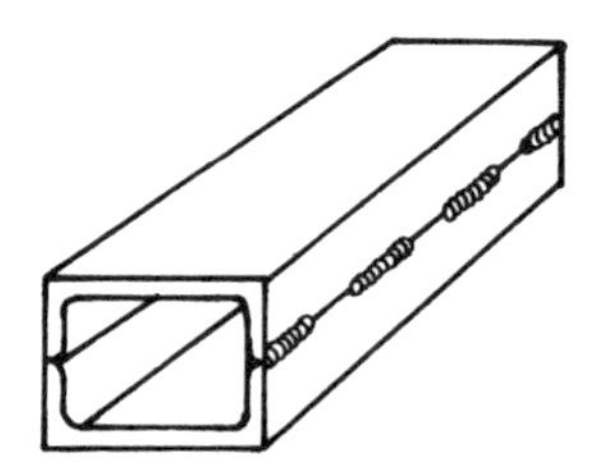

FIGURE 9

From Table 2, the value of R for a box section is found to be—

$$R = \frac{2b^2\ d^2}{\frac{b}{t_b} + \frac{d}{t_d}}$$

where:

$$b = 6 - \tfrac{3}{8} = 5.625''$$

$$d = 4 - \tfrac{5}{16} = 3.6875''$$

$$= \frac{2(5.625)^2(3.6875)^2}{\frac{5.625}{5/16} + \frac{3.6875}{3/8}}$$

$$= 30.91 \text{ in.}^4$$

and the angular twist is—

$$\theta = \frac{1000 \times 100}{(12 \times 10^6)\ 30.91}$$

$$= 0.00027 \text{ radians, or } \underline{0.015°}$$

which is far less than in Case 2, which in turn was much better than Case 1.

Torsional Resistance Nomograph

A panel or other member may be sufficiently resistant to deflection by bending, and yet have very low torsional resistance.

The nomograph, Figure 10, permits the designer to quickly find the torsional resistance of a proposed design. The total torsional resistance of a built-up design equals the sum of the resistances offered separately by the members.

On this nomograph:

Line 1 = Type of section, or element of a built-up section. Observe caution as to meaning of letter symbols. For a solid rectangular section use the ratio of width (a) divided by thickness (b); for a hollow rectangular section use width (b) divided by depth (c).
Line 2 = Dimension (a), in.
Line 3 = Pivot line
Line 4 = Dimension (b), in.
Line 5 = Torsional resistance of the section (R), in.^{4} These values for each element are added together to give the total torsional resistance of the section, and the resistances of the sections are added to give the total torsional resistance of the frame or base. This is used in the design formula for angular twist, or in the next nomograph, Figure 14.

In the case of a member having a built-up cross-section, such as a T or I beam, read the Figure 10 nomograph for the R value of each element or area making up the section. Start at vertical Line 1 in the nomograph, using the scale to the right of it that expresses the rectangular element's a/b ratio. In the case of solid squares or rounds, and closed or open round tubes, go directly to the point on the scale indicated by the visual representation of the cross-section.

Notice that the meaning of *a* and *b* varies. In the case of a rectangular element, *a* is the longer dimension; but in the case of a hollow rectangle, *a* is the wall or plate thickness. The value of *a* or *b* on Lines 1, 2 and 4 must correspond, according to the type of section or element for which torsional resistance (R) is sought.

For hollow rectangular sections (of uniform wall or plate thickness), use the scale along the left of vertical Line 1 that expresses the ratio b/c. Here b = the section's width and c = its depth.

4. MAXIMUM SHEAR STRESS IN BUILT-UP SECTIONS

The maximum shear stress of a rectangular section in torsion lies on the surface at the center of the long side.

For the maximum shear stress on a narrow rectangular section or section element—

FIGURE 10—TORSIONAL RESISTANCE OF MEMBER

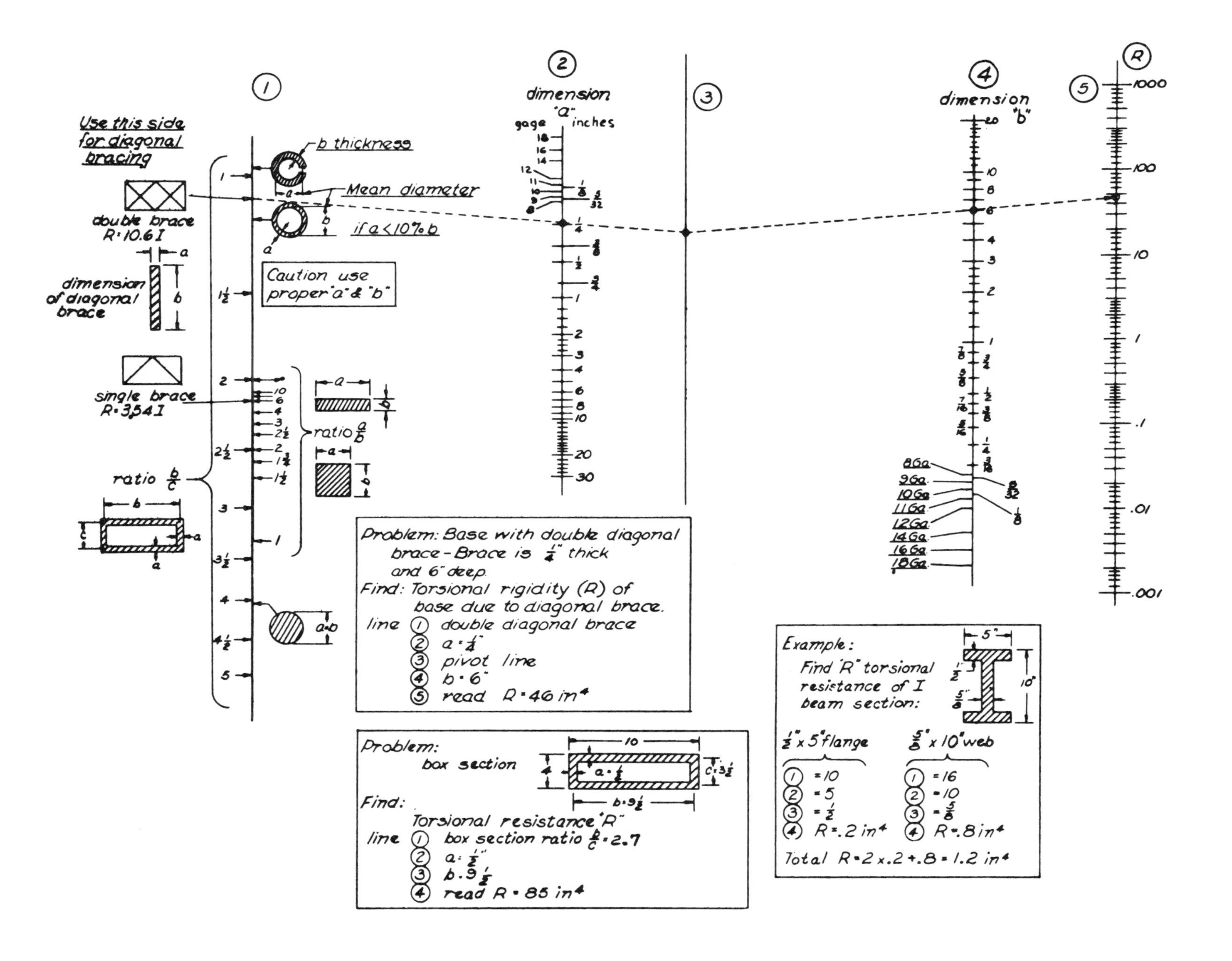

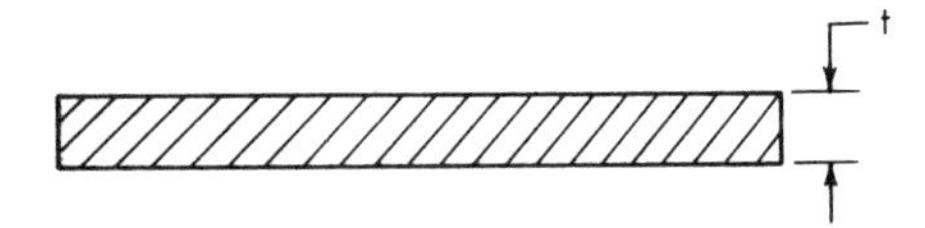

FIGURE 11

$$\tau = \phi \ t \ E_s = \frac{T \ t}{R}$$

where:

ϕ = unit angular twist of whole section (each element twists this amount), in radians/linear inch of member

t = thickness of rectangular section

R = torsional resistance of entire member, not necessarily just this one flat element

This formula can be used for a flat plate, or the flat plate of a built-up section not forming a closed section (i.e. channel, angle, T- or I-beam section).

In such a built-up open section, the unit angular twist (ϕ) of the whole member is first found:

$$\phi = \frac{\theta}{L}$$

and then the maximum shear stress in the specific rectangular element.

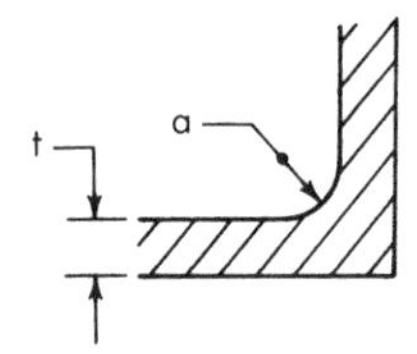

FIGURE 12

Shear stresses tend to concentrate at re-entrant corners. In this case, the maximum stress value should be used and is—

$$\tau_{max} = \tau\left(1 + \frac{t}{4a}\right)$$

where a = inside corner radius.

Problem 3

A 6″ × 2″ × 10½-lb channel is subjected to a torque of T = 1000 in.-lbs. Find the shear stress along the web. See Figure 13.

Applying the formula for rectangular sections from Table 1, find the torsional resistance of each of the two identical 2″ × ⅜″ flanges (R_1) and of the 6″ × 5/16″ web (R_2):

$$R_1 = .0306 \text{ in.}^4$$

$$R_2 = .0586 \text{ in.}^4$$

$$\therefore \ R = 2R_1 + R_2$$

$$= 2\ (.0306) + .0586$$

$$= .1208 \text{ in.}^4$$

Then:

$$\tau = \frac{t \ T}{R}$$

$$= \frac{5/16 \times 1000}{.1208}$$

$$= \underline{2{,}580 \text{ psi}}$$

Problem 4

Two 6″ × 2″ × 10½-lb channels are welded toe to toe, to form a short box section. This is subjected to a torque of T = 100,000 in.-lbs. Find the horizontal shear stress at the toes and the amount of groove welding required to hold these channels together for this torsional load. See Figure 14.

From Table 2, the shear stress at mid-length of the short side is found to be—

$$\tau = \frac{T}{2\ [A]\ t}$$

where:

$$b = 6 - \tfrac{3}{8} = 5.625''$$

$$d = 4 - \tfrac{5}{16} = 3.6875''$$

$$[A] = bd$$

$$= \frac{100{,}000}{2(5.625 \times 3.687)\tfrac{3}{8}}$$

$$= 6420 \text{ psi}$$

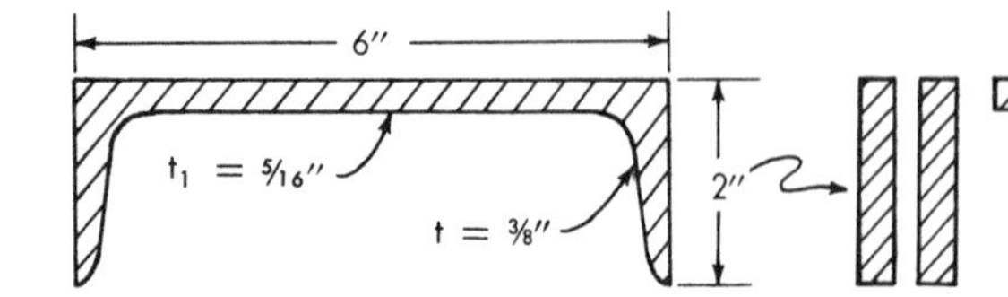

FIGURE 13

FIGURE 14

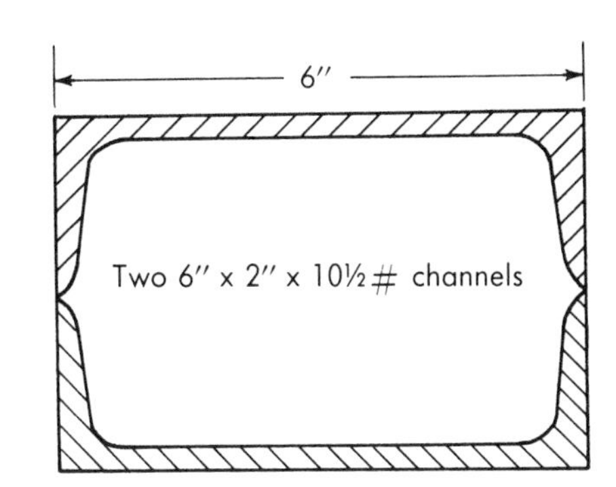

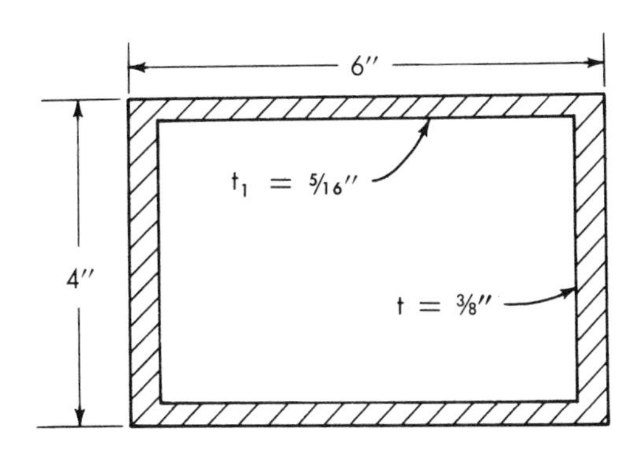

The horizontal shear force is then—

$$f = \tau\, t$$
$$= 6420 \times .375$$
$$= 2410 \text{ lbs/linear inch}$$

Since weld metal is good for 13,000 psi in shear, the throat or depth of the continuous butt weld must be—

$$f = \tau_{weld}\, t$$
$$2410 = 13{,}000\, t$$
$$\text{or } t = \frac{2410}{13{,}000}$$
$$= .185'' \text{ or } \underline{3/16''}$$

The groove weld connecting the channels must have a throat depth of at least 3/16″. Of course, if the torsional load is applied suddenly as an impact load, it would be good practice to add a safety factor to the computed load. This would then necessitate a deeper throat for the butt weld.

Problem 5

Check the following built-up spandrel beam supporting a wall 12′ high, made of 4″ of limestone and 9″ of brick. The beam's span is 20′, and the dead load of the wall is applied 6″ off the beam's centerline.

FIGURE 15

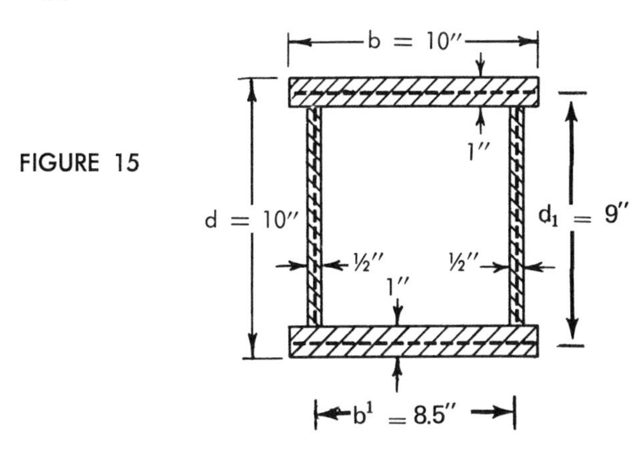

4″ limestone + 9″ brick = 140 lbs/sq ft

Since the wall is 12′ high, this is a load of 1680 lbs/linear ft or 140 lbs/linear in. Or, use w = 150 lbs/lin in. to include beam weight.

bending resistance (moment of inertia)

$$I_x = \frac{(10)(10)^3}{12} - \frac{(9)(8)^3}{12}$$
$$= 449.3 \text{ in.}^4$$

torsional resistance

$$R = \frac{2\, b_1{}^2\, d_1{}^2}{\dfrac{b_1}{t_b} + \dfrac{d_1}{t_d}}$$
$$= \frac{2\ (8.5)^2(9)^2}{\dfrac{(8.5)}{(1)} + \dfrac{(9)}{(\frac{1}{2})}}$$
$$= 442 \text{ in.}^4$$

The eccentricity of the dead load applies torque to the beam. From torsional member diagrams in Reference Section 8.2:

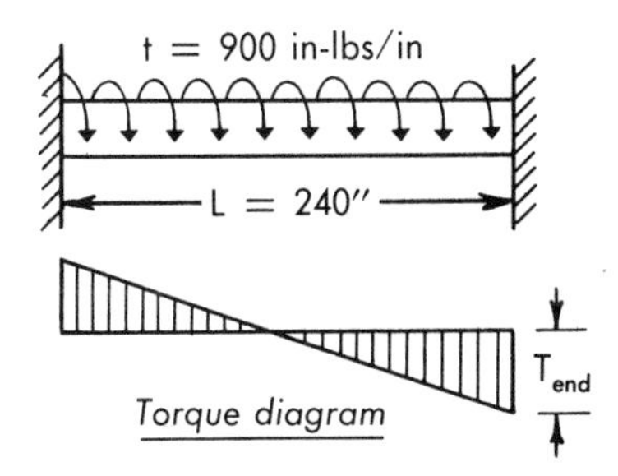

uniform torque

$$t = 150 \text{ lbs/in.} \times 6''$$
$$= 900 \text{ in.-lbs/in.}$$

angular twist at center of beam

$$\theta_{\text{℄}} = \frac{t\ L^2}{8\ E_s\ R} = \frac{(900)(240)^2}{8(12 \times 10^6)(442)}$$
$$= .00122 \text{ radians (or .07°)}$$

torque at end

$$T = \frac{t\ L}{2}$$

$$= \frac{(900)(240)}{2}$$

$$= 108{,}000 \text{ in.-lbs}$$

torsional shear stress

$$\tau = \frac{T}{2\ [A]\ t_s}$$

where:

t_s = thickness of single web

$$= \frac{(108{,}000)}{2(8.5 \times 9)\frac{1}{2}}$$

$$= 1410 \text{ psi}$$

unit shear force from torque

$$f_t = \tau\ t$$

$$= (1410)(\tfrac{1}{2})$$

$$= 700 \text{ lbs/in.}$$

unit shear force along N.A. from bending

$$V = w\ L/2$$

$$= (150)(120)$$

$$= 18{,}000 \text{ lbs}$$

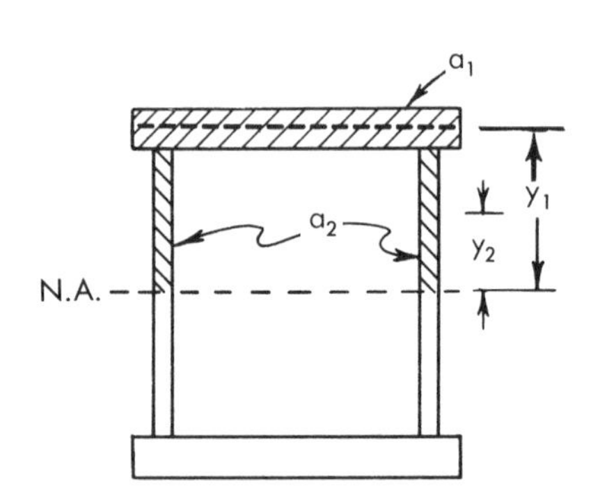

FIGURE 16

$$f_b = \frac{V\ (a_1\ y_1 + a_2\ y_2)}{I\ n}$$

$$= \frac{(18{,}000)(10 \times 4.5 + 1 \times 2.0)}{(449.3)(2 \text{ webs})}$$

$$= 860 \text{ lbs/in.}$$

total unit shear force on beam web (each)

$$f_s = f_t + f_b$$

$$= (700) + (860)$$

$$= 1560 \text{ lbs/in.}$$

total shear stress

$$\tau = \frac{f_s}{t_s}$$

$$= \frac{(2050)}{(\frac{1}{2})}$$

$$= 4100 \text{ psi} \quad \underline{\text{OK}}$$

Then to determine the required size of fillet weld between flange and web:

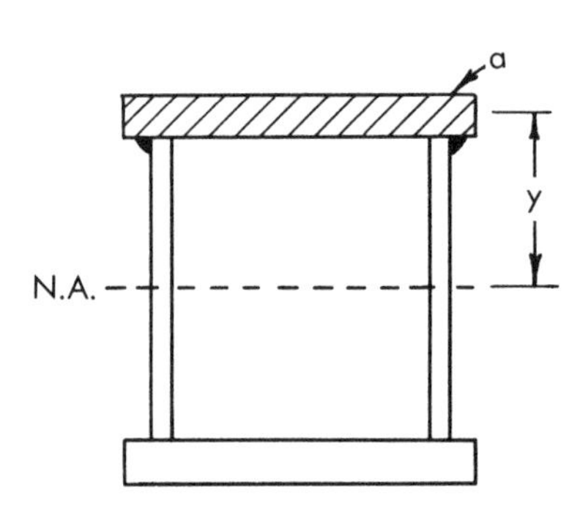

FIGURE 17

unit shear force at weld from bending

$$f_b = \frac{V\ a\ y}{I\ n}$$

$$= \frac{(18{,}000)(10)(4\frac{1}{2})}{(449.3)(2)}$$

$$= 900 \text{ lbs/in.}$$

unit shear force at weld from torque

$$f_t = 700 \text{ lbs/in.}$$

total unit shear force at weld

$$f_s = f_t + f_b$$

$$= (700) + (900)$$

$$= 1600 \text{ lbs/in.}$$

required leg size of fillet weld (E70)

$$\omega = \frac{\text{actual force}}{\text{allowable force}}$$

$$= \frac{(1600)}{(11{,}200)}$$

$$= .143'' \text{ or } \tfrac{3}{16}''\ \triangle$$

However, because of the 1" flange, AWS Bldg. 212, AWS Bridge 217 and AISC 1.17.4 would require a $\underline{\tfrac{5}{16}''\ \triangle}$.

5. BUILT-UP FRAMES

The principles of torsion which determine the best sections for resisting twist apply to built-up frames. Just as the torsional resistance of the section is equal to the total of the resistances of its individual areas, so is the torsional resistance of a frame approximately equal to the total resistance of its individual parts.

The torsional resistance of the frame whose longitudinal members are two channels would be approximately equal to twice the torsional resistance of each channel section, Figure 18. The distance between these members for purpose of this example is considered to have no effect. Since the closed section is best for resisting twist, the torsional resistance of this frame could be greatly increased by making the channels into rectangular box sections through the addition of plate.

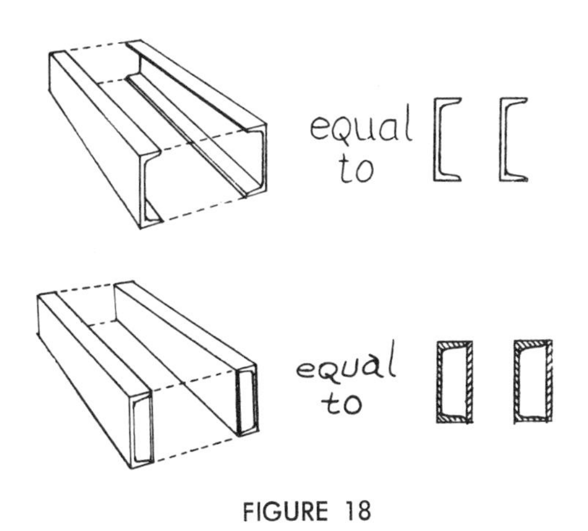

FIGURE 18

Problem 6

A frame is made of two 6″ standard pipes, spaced 24″ between centers, and having a length of 60″. This frame supports a 10-hp motor running at 1800 rpm and driving a pump. Find the approximate twist of the frame under the load.

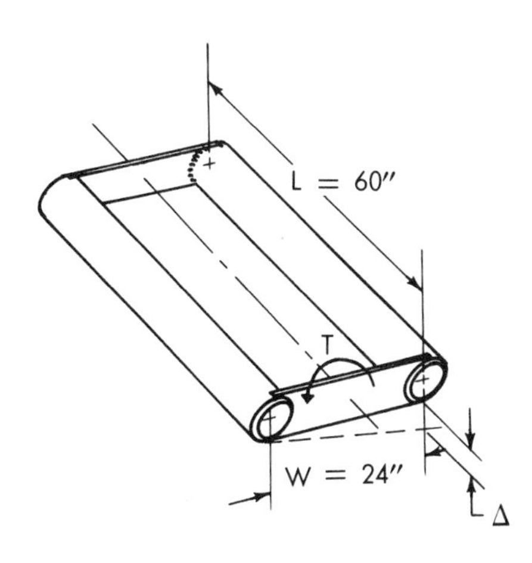

FIGURE 19

The 6″ standard pipe has O.D. = 6.625″ and I.D. = 6.065″. In finding the torsional resistance of each tube:

$$R = .0982\ (d_2^4 - d_1^4)$$
$$= .0982\ (6.625^4 - 6.065^4)$$
$$= 56.30 \text{ in.}^4$$

The torque is easily found:

$$T = \frac{63{,}030 \times HP}{RPM}$$
$$= \frac{63{,}030 \times 10}{1800}$$
$$= 350 \text{ in.-lbs}$$

Then, adding together the R of each tube, the angular twist is:

$$\theta = \frac{T\ L}{E_s\ R}$$
$$= \frac{350 \times 60}{(12 \times 10^6)\ (2 \times 56.30)}$$
$$= 0.0000156 \text{ radians, or } 0.00089°$$

Maximum deflection in the frame is the vertical displacement (Δ), which is the product of angular twist (θ) and frame width (W) between centers:

$$\Delta = \theta\ W$$
$$= 0.0000156 \times 24''$$
$$= 0.00037''$$

6. DEFLECTION OF BUILT-UP FRAMES

In analyzing the resistance and strength of a built-up frame against twisting, consider the torque applied as two forces in the form of a couple at each end of the frame. In this manner, it is seen that these same forces apply a torque transverse to the frame as well as longitudinal to it.

This helps to show that the over-all resistance against twisting is the sum of the resistances of all the members, longitudinal as well as transverse. It is usually more convenient to express the resulting angular twist in terms of vertical deflection of the frame corner which receives the vertical load.

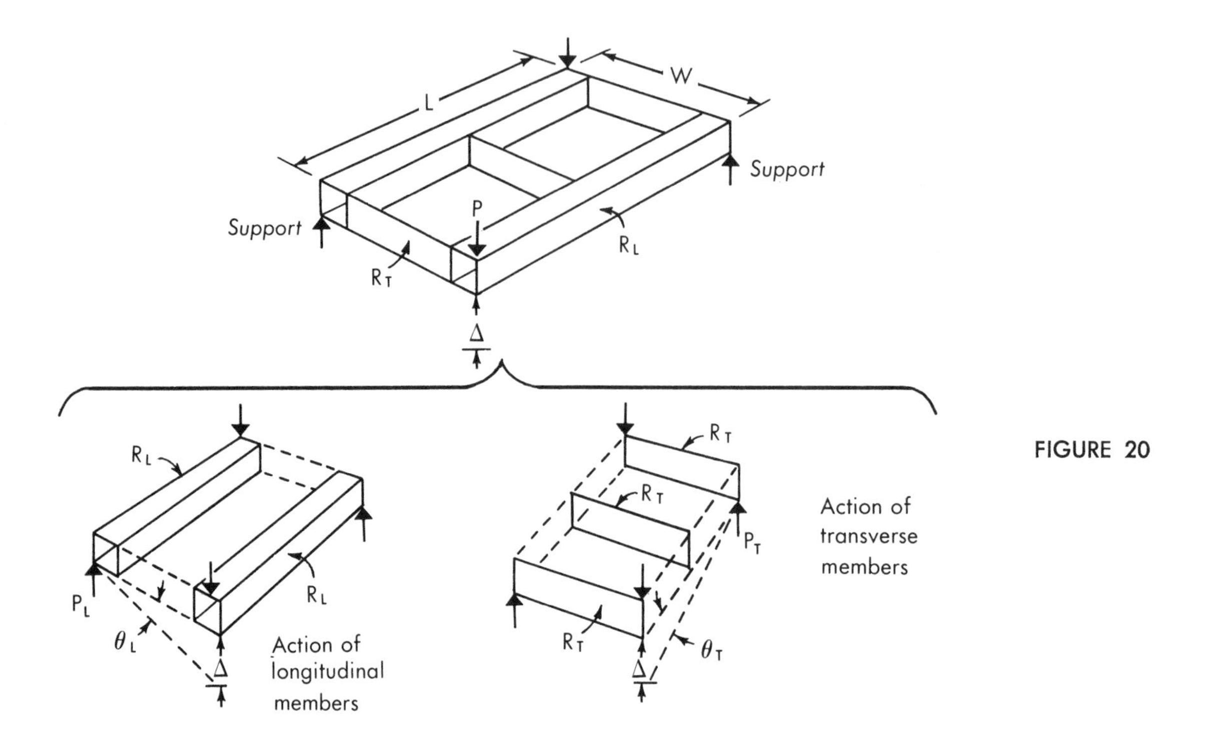

FIGURE 20

The longitudinal members are now considered to make up a frame of their own. When the vertical force (P_L) applied at the corner reaches the proper value, the frame will deflect vertically the given distance (Δ) and each longitudinal member will twist (θ_L). The same separate analysis is also made of the transverse members.

By observation we find—

$$\Delta = \theta_L \, W = \theta_T \, L$$

Then:

$$\theta_L = \frac{\Delta}{W} \text{ and } \theta_T = \frac{\Delta}{L}$$

Using the common formula for angular twist—

$$\theta_L = \frac{T_L \, L}{E_s \, n_L \, R_L} \text{ and } \theta_T = \frac{T_T \, W}{E_s \, n_T \, R_T}$$

and substituting for θ_L and θ_T —

$$\frac{\Delta}{W} = \frac{T_L \, L}{E_s \, n_L \, R_L} \text{ and } \frac{\Delta}{L} = \frac{T_T \, W}{E_s \, n_T \, R_T}$$

Then:

$$T_L = \frac{\Delta \, E_s \, n_L \, R_L}{W \, L} \text{ and } T_T = \frac{\Delta \, E_s \, n_T \, R_T}{W \, L}$$

Since the applied torque is—

$$T_L = P_L \, W \text{ and } T_T = P_T \, L$$

$$\therefore P_L = \frac{T_L}{W} \text{ and } P_T = \frac{T_T}{L}$$

and substituting for P_L and P_T —

$$P_L = \frac{\Delta \, E_s \, n_L \, R_L}{W^2 \, L} \text{ and } P_T = \frac{\Delta \, E_s \, n_T \, R_T}{W \, L^2}$$

Since the external force (P) applied at the corner is the sum of these two forces:

$$P = P_L + P_T = \frac{\Delta \, E_s \, n_L \, R_L}{W^2 \, L} + \frac{\Delta \, E_s \, n_T \, R_T}{W \, L^2}$$

$$= \frac{\Delta \, E_s}{W \, L} \left(\frac{n_L \, R_L}{W} + \frac{n_T \, R_T}{L} \right)$$

$$\therefore \boxed{\Delta = \frac{P \, L \, W}{E_s} \left[\frac{1}{\dfrac{n_L \, R_L}{W} + \dfrac{n_T \, R_T}{L}} \right]} \quad \cdots\cdots\cdots (4)$$

where:

L = length of whole frame, in.

W = width of whole frame, in.

R_L = torsional resistance of longitudinal member, $in.^4$

R_T = torsional resistance of transverse member, $in.^4$

n_L = number of longitudinal members

n_T = number of transverse members

P = load applied at corner, lbs

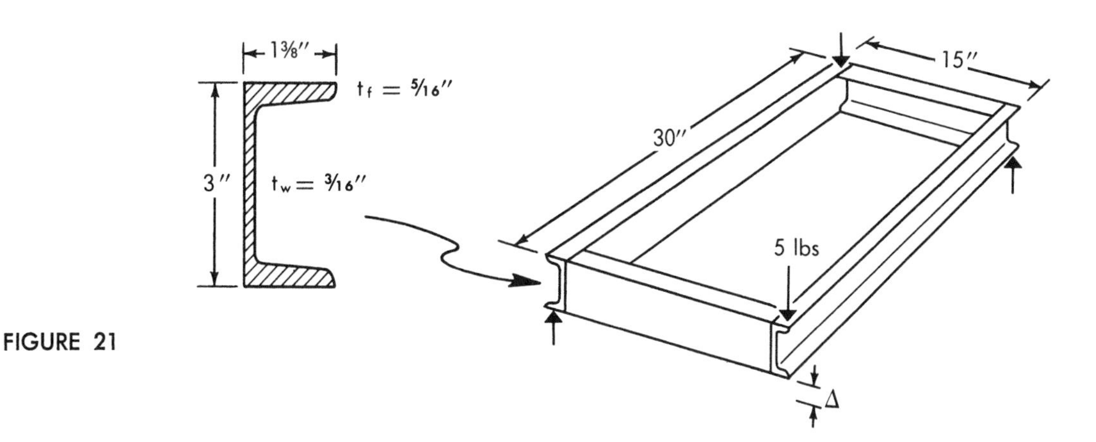

FIGURE 21

E_s = modulus of elasticity in shear (steel: 12×10^6), psi

Δ = vertical deflection, in.

It can be seen that the torque on a given member is actually produced by the transverse forces supplied by the cross members attached to them. These same forces subject the cross members to bending. In other words, the torque applied to a member equals the end moment of the cross member attached to it. There is some deflection due to bending of all the members, and this would slightly increase the over-all deflection of the frame. For simplicity this has been neglected in this analysis.

Problem 7

To illustrate the use of the preceding deflection formula, consider a small elevator frame 15″ wide and 30″ long, made of standard 3″ channel, Figure 21. Find the

TABLE 4—Torsional Resistance of Frame and Various Sections

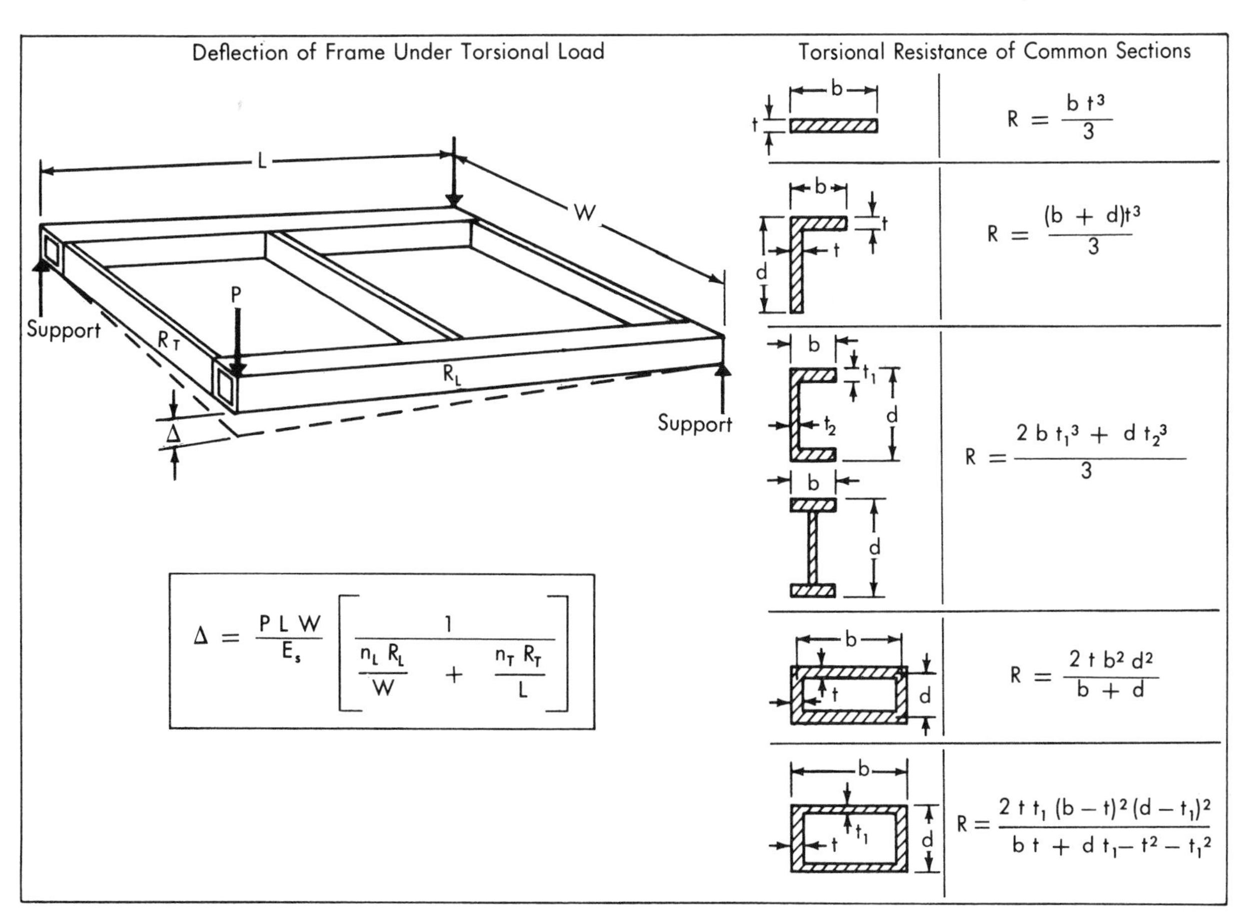

Deflection of Frame Under Torsional Load
L
W
P
Support
R_T
R_L
Support
Δ
$$\Delta = \frac{P\,L\,W}{E_s}\left[\frac{1}{\frac{n_L R_L}{W} + \frac{n_T R_T}{L}}\right]$$
Torsional Resistance of Common Sections
$$R = \frac{b\,t^3}{3}$$
$$R = \frac{(b + d)t^3}{3}$$
$$R = \frac{2\,b\,t_1^3 + d\,t_2^3}{3}$$
$$R = \frac{2\,t\,b^2\,d^2}{b + d}$$
$$R = \frac{2\,t\,t_1\,(b - t)^2\,(d - t_1)^2}{b\,t + d\,t_1 - t^2 - t_1^2}$$

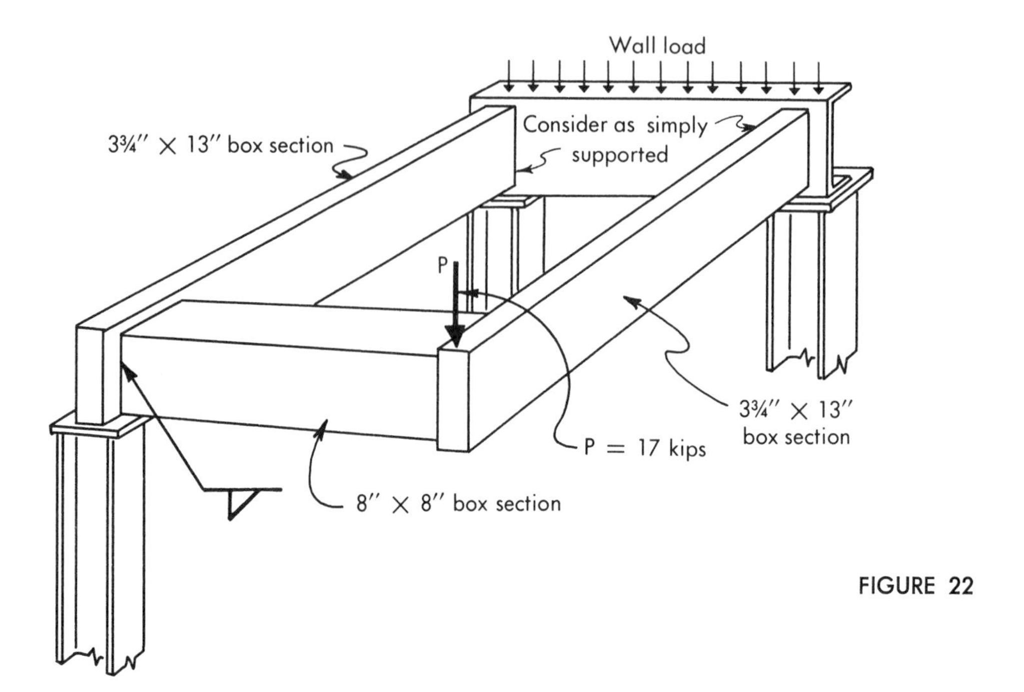

FIGURE 22

vertical deflection of the unsupported corner when under a load of 5 lbs.

Using the appropriate formula from Table 4, torsional resistance of the U channel cross-section is —

$$R = \frac{2\ bt_1^3 + dt_2^3}{3} = \frac{2\ bt_f^3 + dt_w^3}{3}$$

$$= \frac{2\ (1.375)(.3125)^3}{3} + \frac{3(\ 1875)^3}{3}$$

$$= .0346 \text{ in.}^4$$

Substituting actual values into formula #4:

$$\Delta = \frac{P\ L\ W}{E_s}\left[\frac{1}{\dfrac{n_L\ R_L}{W} + \dfrac{n_T\ R_T}{L}}\right]$$

$$= \frac{(5)(30)(15)}{(12 \times 10^6)}\left[\frac{1}{\dfrac{2(.0346)}{15} + \dfrac{2(.0346)}{30}}\right]$$

$$= \underline{.027''}$$

The actual deflection when tested was —

$$\Delta = .030''$$

Problem 8

The structural frame of Figure 22, simply supported at three corners, is designed to support a 17-kip load at its unsupported corner. Here the width between centerlines of the longitudinal members is 34.75″, and the latter are 82″ long. Determine:

a) The approximate vertical deflection of the unsupported corner,

b) the shear stress in longitudinal and transverse members, and

c) the size of the connecting weld between the longitudinal and transverse members.

torsional resistance of longitudinal members

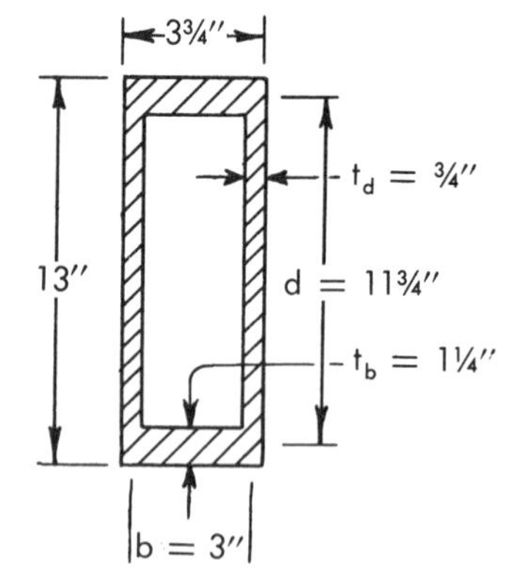

FIGURE 23

$$R_L = \frac{2\ b^2\ d^2}{\dfrac{b}{t_b} + \dfrac{d}{t_d}}$$

$$= \frac{2(3)^2\ (11\tfrac{3}{4})^2}{\dfrac{(3)}{(1\tfrac{1}{4})} + \dfrac{(11\tfrac{3}{4})}{(\tfrac{3}{4})}}$$

$$= 137.5 \text{ in.}^4$$

torsional resistance of transverse member
(only one in this example)

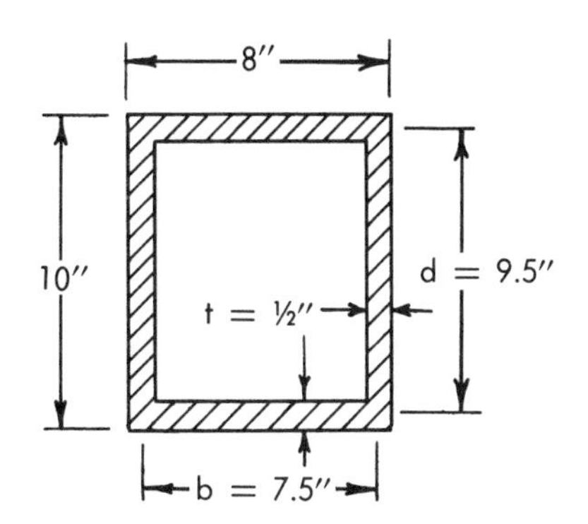

FIGURE 24

$$R_T = \frac{2\ b^2\ d^2}{\frac{b}{t_b} + \frac{d}{t_d}}$$

$$= \frac{2(7.5)^2(9.5)^2}{\frac{(7.5)}{(½)} + \frac{(9.5)}{(½)}}$$

$$= 298.3 \text{ in.}^4$$

vertical deflection of frame

$$\Delta = \frac{P\ W\ L}{E_s}\left[\frac{1}{\frac{n_L\ R_L}{W} + \frac{n_T\ R_T}{L}}\right]$$

$$= \frac{(17{,}000)(34¾)(82)}{(12 \times 10^6)}\left[\frac{1}{\frac{(2)(137.5)}{(34¾)} + \frac{(1)(298.3)}{(82)}}\right]$$

$$= .35''$$

shear stress in longitudinal member

The applied torque on only one longitudinal member is —

$$T_L = \frac{\Delta\ E_s\ n_L\ R_L}{W\ L}$$ See formula development, p. 2.10-12

$$= \frac{(35)(12 \times 10^6)(1)(137.5)}{(34¾)(82)}$$

$$= 202{,}500 \text{ in.-lbs, each member}$$

The shear stress at midpoint of the longitudinal member, on the short side of its cross-section is —

$$\tau_b = \frac{T_L}{2\ [A]\ t_b}$$

$$= \frac{(202{,}500)}{2(3 \times 11¾)(1¼)}$$

$$= 2300 \text{ psi}$$

and the shear stress at midpoint of the member, on the long side of its cross-section is —

$$\tau_d = \frac{T_T}{2\ [A]\ t_d}$$

$$= \frac{(202{,}500)}{2(3 \times 11¾)(¾)}$$

$$= 3820 \text{ psi}$$

shear stress in transverse member

In a similar manner it is found that the applied torque on the transverse member is —

$$T_T = \frac{\Delta\ E_s\ n_t\ R_t}{W\ L}$$

See formula development, p. 2.10-12

$$= \frac{(.35)(12 \times 10^6)(1)(298.3)}{(34¾)(82)}$$

$$= 438{,}500 \text{ in.-lbs}$$

Since the cross-section of the transverse member is a hollow rectangle of uniform thickness, the shear stress at mid-length along either side of the section is —

$$\tau = \frac{T_L}{2\ [A]\ t}$$

$$= \frac{(438{,}500)}{2(7.5 \times 9.5)(½)}$$

$$= 6160 \text{ psi}$$

size of connecting fillet weld

Treating the weld as a line —

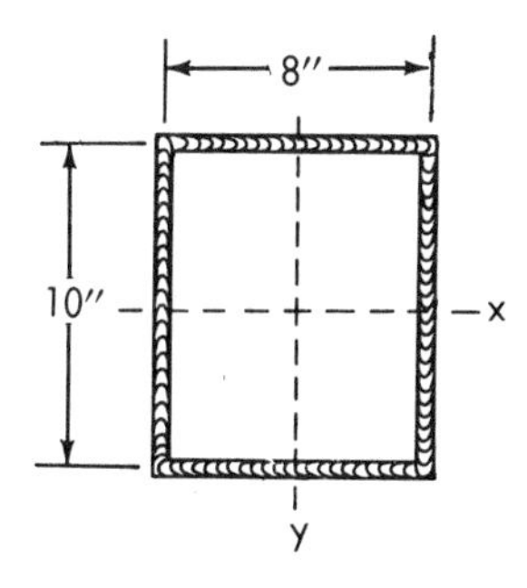

FIGURE 25

$$I_x = \frac{b\ d^2}{2} + \frac{d^3}{6}$$

$$= \frac{(8)(10)^2}{2} + \frac{(10)^3}{6}$$

$$= 566.7 \text{ in.}^3$$

$$I_y = \frac{b^2\,d}{2} + \frac{b^3}{6}$$

$$= \frac{(8)^2(10)}{2} + \frac{(8)^3}{6}$$

$$= 405.3 \text{ in.}^3$$

and the polar moment of inertia is —

$$J_w = I_x + I_y$$

$$= (566.7) + (405.3)$$

$$= 972 \text{ in.}^3$$

Assuming just two vertical welds transfer vertical shear (V), the length of the weld is —

$$L_w = 2 \times 10 = 20''$$

torque on weld

From the standard design formula for torsion —

$$\tau = \frac{T\,c}{J} \text{ lbs/in.}^2 \text{(stress)}$$

the corresponding formula for total weld force is obtained —

$$f_t = \frac{T\,c}{J} \text{ lbs/in. (force per linear inch of weld)}$$

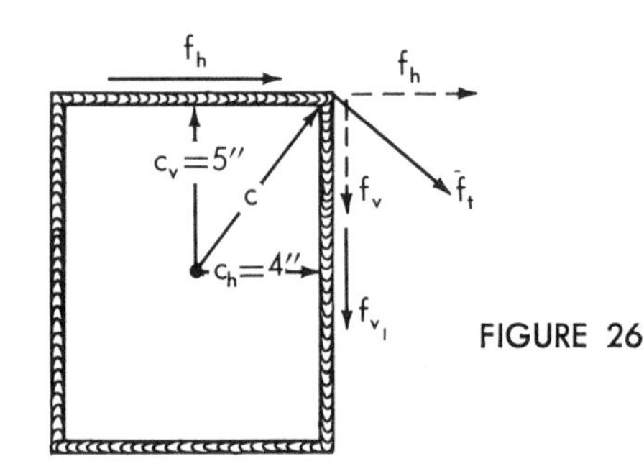

FIGURE 26

The horizontal component of this torque is —

$$f_h = \frac{T\,c_v}{J_w}$$

$$= \frac{(438{,}500)(5)}{(972)}$$

$$= 2250 \text{ lbs/in.}$$

and the vertical component of this torque is —

$$f_v = \frac{T\,c_h}{J_w}$$

$$= \frac{(438{,}500)(4)}{972}$$

$$= 1805 \text{ lbs/in.}$$

vertical shear on weld

Since the vertical shear on the joint is —

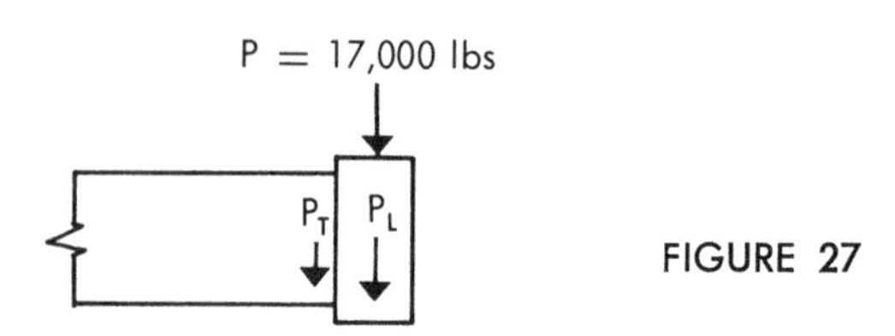

FIGURE 27

$$V = P_T = \frac{T_L}{W}$$

$$= \frac{(202{,}500)}{(34\tfrac{3}{4})}$$

$$= 5825 \text{ lbs}$$

the resultant force on the vertical welds is —

$$f_{v1} = \frac{V}{A_w} \qquad \boxed{A_w = L_w}$$

$$A_w = L_w$$

$$= \frac{(5825)}{(20'')}$$

$$= 290 \text{ lbs/in.}$$

Notice that, if the load (P) is applied to the end of the transverse member instead of the longitudinal member, the portion going back into the longitudinal member (P_L = 17,000 − 5825 = 11,175 lbs) must be transferred through the connecting weld and the resulting unit force from vertical shear is:

$$f_{v1} = \frac{V}{A_w}$$

$$= \frac{(11{,}175)}{(20)}$$

$$= 560 \text{ lbs/in. instead of 290 lbs/in.}$$

moment on weld

Since the bending moment on the joint is—

$$M = T_L$$

$$= 202{,}500 \text{ in.-lbs}$$

the resultant force on the weld is —

$$f_m = \frac{M\,c}{I_x}$$

$$= \frac{(202{,}500)(5)}{(566.7)}$$

$$= 1785 \text{ lbs/in.}$$

Resolving combined forces on weld at point of greatest effect—

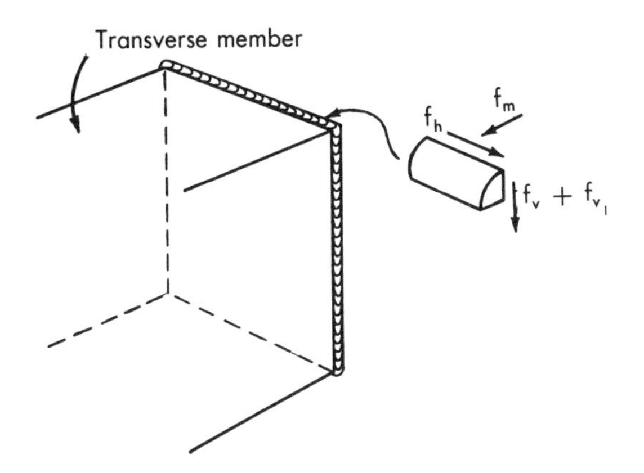
Transverse member
f_h
f_m
$f_v + f_{v_1}$

FIGURE 28

$$f_r = \sqrt{f_h^2 + f_m^2 + (f_v + f_{v1})^2}$$
$$= \sqrt{(2250)^2 + (1785)^2 + (1805 + 290)^2}$$
$$= 3560 \text{ lbs/in.}$$

Since 11,200 lbs is the accepted allowable load per linear inch of fillet weld having a 1″ leg size, the minimum leg size for this application is—

$$\omega = \frac{3560}{11{,}200} \leftarrow \text{(E70-weld allowable)}$$

$$= .318''$$

or use 5/16″ fillet weld.

7. BRACING OF FRAMES

The two main stresses on a member under torsional loading are (1) transverse shear stresses and (2) longitudinal shear stresses.

These two stresses combine to produce diagonal tensile and compressive stresses which are maximum at 45°. At 45°, the transverse and longitudinal shear stresses cancel each other. Therefore, there is no twisting stress or action on a diagonal member placed at 45° to the frame.

In a frame made up of flat members, the transverse shear stresses cause the longitudinal members to twist. The longitudinal shear stresses cause the cross braces and end members to twist.

On a diagonal member at 45° to axis of twist, the transverse and longitudinal shear stress components are opposite in direction to each other and cancel out, but in line with this member they combine to produce diagonal tensile and compressive stresses which tend

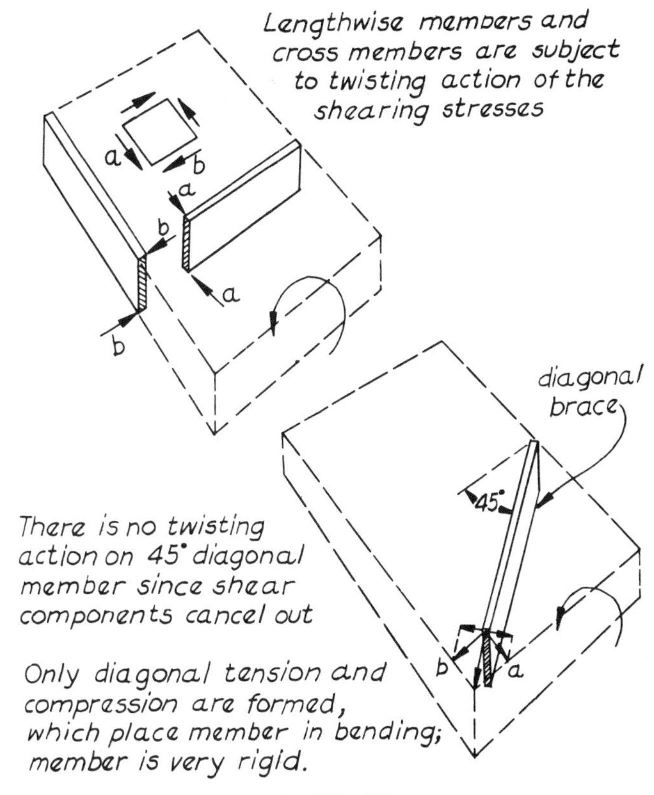
Lengthwise members and cross members are subject to twisting action of the shearing stresses
a
b
a
b
a
b
diagonal brace
45°
There is no twisting action on 45° diagonal member since shear components cancel out
Only diagonal tension and compression are formed, which place member in bending; member is very rigid.
b
a

FIGURE 29

to cause bending rather than twisting. See Figure 29.

Since these two shear stresses cancel out, there is no tendency for a diagonal member placed in this direction to twist.

The diagonal tensile and compressive stresses try to cause this diagonal member to bend; but being very resistant to bending, the diagonal member greatly stiffens the entire frame against twisting.

Design Rule No. 2: USE DIAGONAL BRACING

Stiffening the Braces

Previous experience in designing longitudinal side members for bending is now used to design these diagonal members.

It is important that the diagonal members have a high moment of inertia to provide sufficient stiffness so there will be no failure from local buckling, under severe torsional loads.

Since the diagonal brace is not subjected to any twisting action, it is not necessary to use a closed box section.

For short diagonal braces, use a simple flat bar. The top and/or bottom panel of the frame will stiffen this to some extent (Fig. 30). As the unsupported length of the diagonal brace becomes longer, it may become necessary to add a flange (Fig. 31). This is

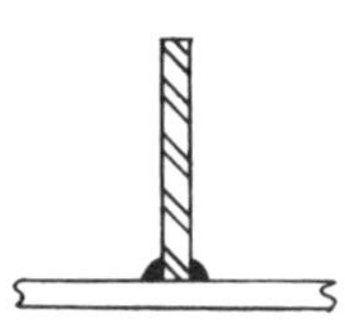

FIGURE 30

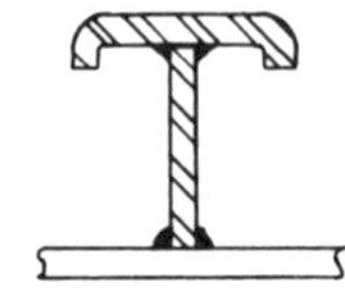

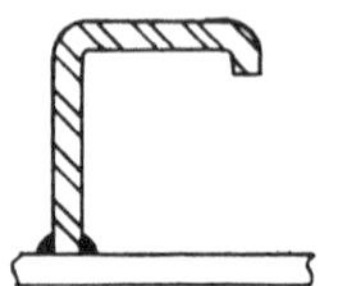

FIGURE 31

done by flanging one edge of the brace or using an angle bar or T section. The flange of the brace may also be stiffened to keep it from buckling.

For open frames with no flat panel, it is better to use a channel or I beam section having two flanges (Fig. 32).

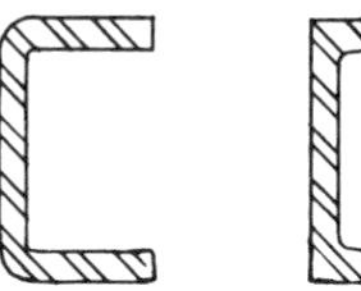

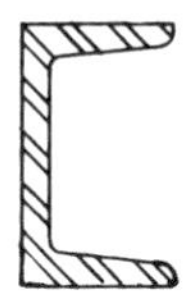

FIGURE 32

Relative Effectiveness of Bracing

Tests were made on scale models of typical machine frames to illustrate increase in resistance to twist as a result of the diagonal bracing.

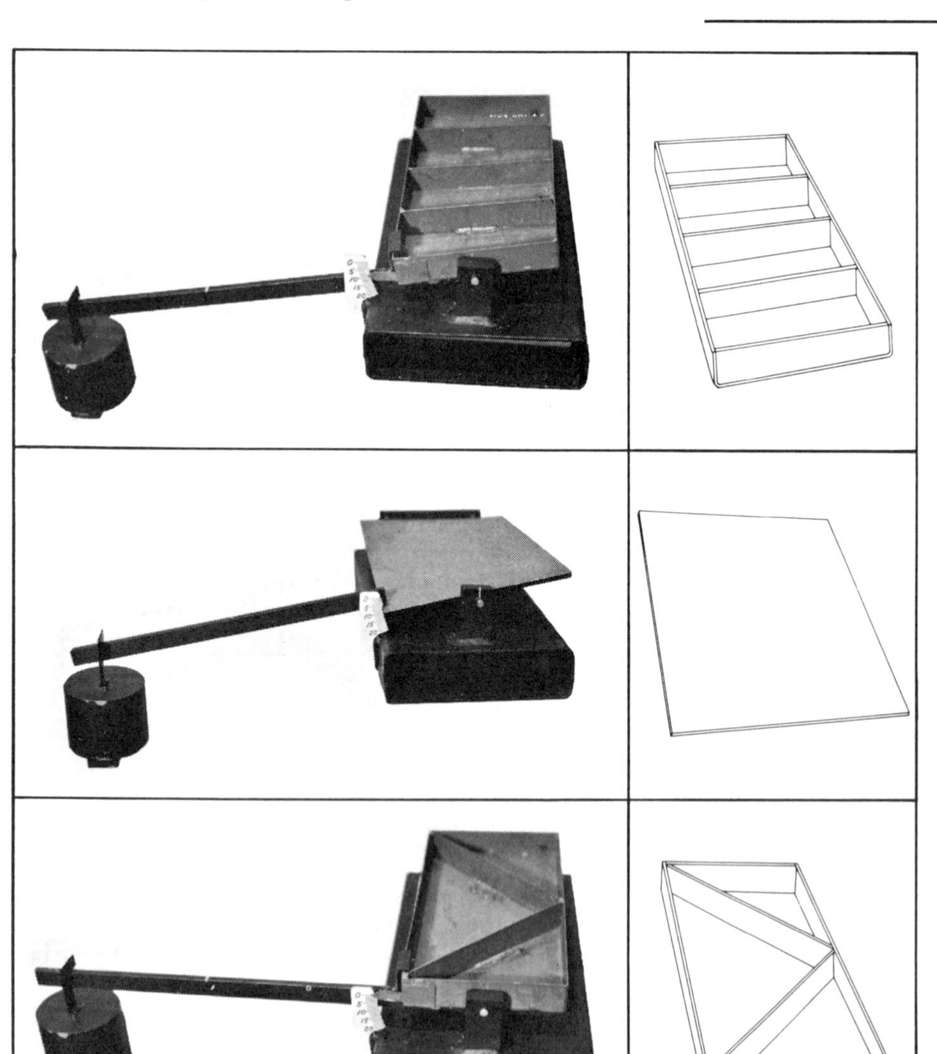

FIGURE 33

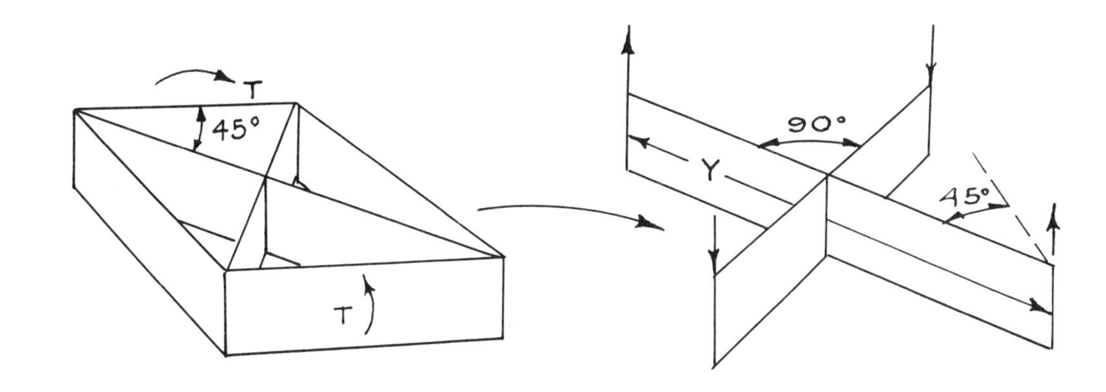

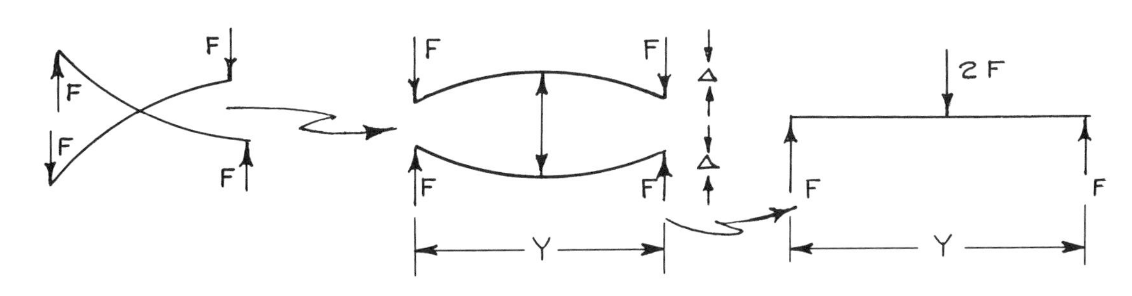

FIGURE 34

The top frame in Figure 33 has conventional cross bracing at 90° to side members. It twisted 9°.

The above frame is little better in resistance to twist than a flat sheet of the same thickness, as shown in the middle. The plain sheet twisted 10°.

The bottom frame has diagonal braces at 45° with side members. It twisted only ¼°. It is 36 times as resistant to twisting as the first frame, yet uses 6% less bracing material.

8. DIAGONAL BRACING (Double)

(See Figure 34)

An approximate indication of the angular twist of a frame using double diagonal bracing (in the form of an X) may be made by the following procedure. Here each brace is treated as a beam.

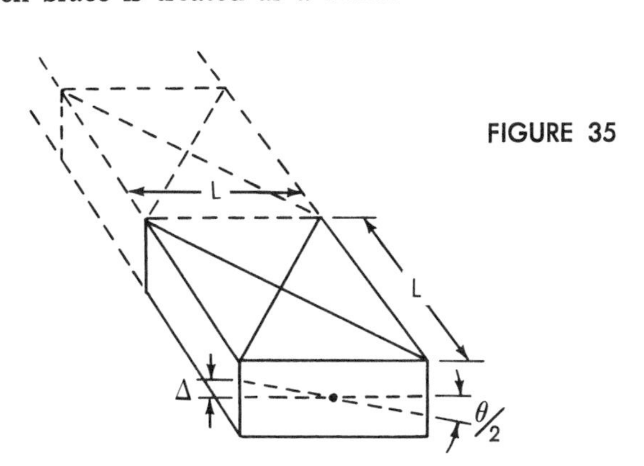

FIGURE 35

$$\Delta = \frac{(2\ F)\ Y^3}{48\ E\ I} \qquad \text{(simply supported)}$$

$$\theta/2 = \frac{\Delta}{\frac{1}{2}\ L} = \frac{2\ \Delta}{L} = \frac{F\ Y^3}{12\ E\ I\ L}$$

Since $T = F\ L$, then $F = \frac{T}{L}$

$$\therefore\ \theta = \frac{T\ Y^3}{6\ E\ I\ L^2}$$

Since $Y = \sqrt{2}\ L$

$$\theta = \frac{T\ (\sqrt{2})^3\ L^3}{6\ E\ I\ L^2} = \frac{\sqrt{2}\ T\ L}{3\ E\ I}$$

also $\theta = \frac{T\ L}{E_s\ R}$ Hence $\frac{\sqrt{2}\ T\ L}{3\ E\ I} = \frac{T\ L}{E_s\ R}$

and $R = \frac{3\ E\ I}{\sqrt{2}\ E_s} = 5.3\ I$

$E = 30 \times 10^6$
$E_s = 12 \times 10^6$

For fixed ends, $R = 21.2\ I$

For the usual frame, the following is suggested:

$$R = 10.6\ I$$

which appeared in Table 1.

Therefore: For a double diagonal brace use $R = 10.6\ I$ and substitute this value into the standard formula: $\theta = \frac{T\ L}{E_s\ R}$

to get the frame's angular twist (radians).

Problem 9

Two ¼″ × 10″ plates, 40″ long, spaced 20″ apart to make a frame 40″ long, are subjected to a torque of T = 1000 in.-lbs. Find the relative angular twist on the frame, when using conventional and diagonal bracing.

Case 1 (Conventional bracing)

Here the torsional resistance of the plate section is known, from Table 4, to be—

$$R = \frac{b\ t^3}{3}$$

$$\therefore R = 2\ \frac{(10)(.25)^3}{3}$$

$$= .104 \text{ in.}^4 \text{ (both sides)}$$

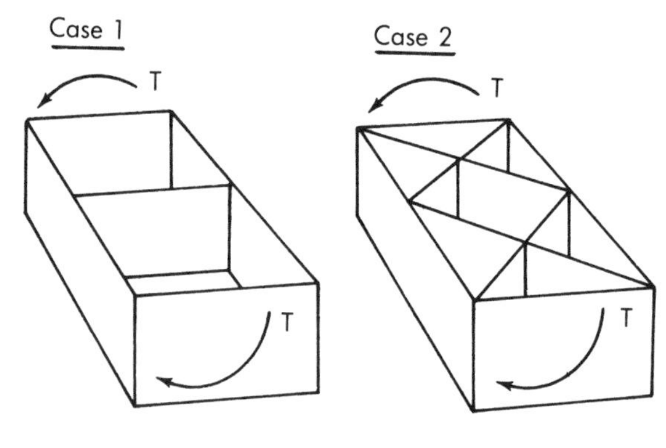

FIGURE 36

The total angular twist is then—

$$\theta = \frac{T\ L}{E_s\ R}$$

$$= \frac{(1000)(40)}{(12 \times 10^6)(.104)}$$

$$= .0321 \text{ radians or } \underline{1.84°}$$

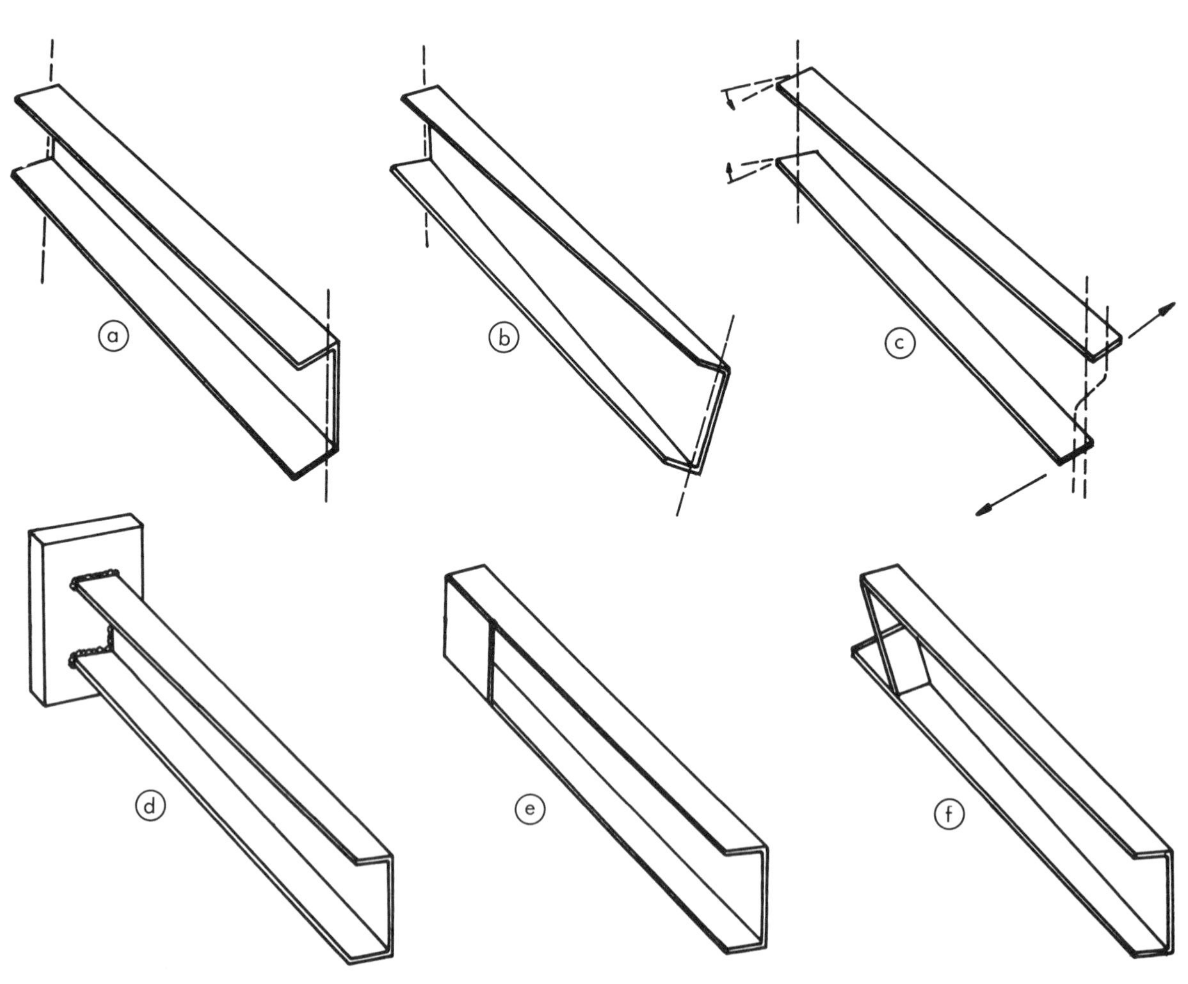

FIGURE 37

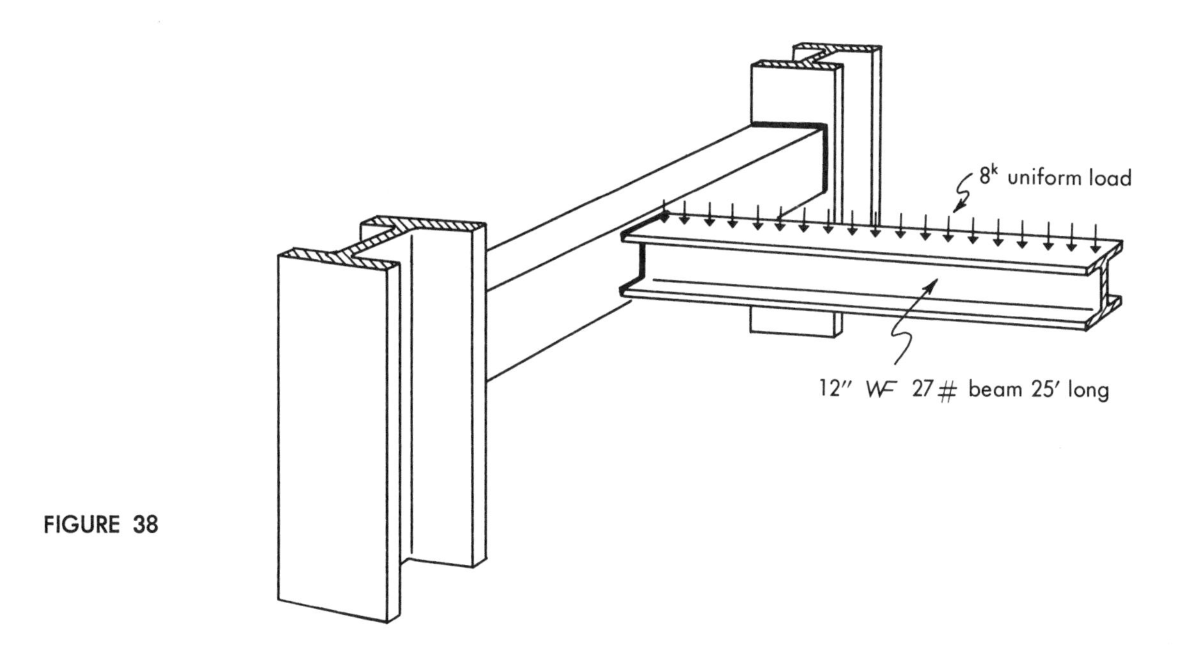

FIGURE 38

Case 2 (Diagonal bracing)

Since this is "double" bracing, the Table 1 formula for this type of frame is used—

$$R = 10.6\ I$$

First find the moment of inertia for the cross-section of a brace, which is a simple rectangle, assuming the brace also is ¼″ × 10″:

$$I = \frac{b\ d^3}{12}$$

where b = the section width (plate thickness), and d = the section depth

$$I = \frac{.25(10)^3}{12}$$

$$= 20.83 \text{ in.}^4$$

then substituting into the formula for R—

$$R = 10.6\ (20.83)$$

$$= 221 \text{ in.}^4$$

The angular twist on the frame is then—

$$\theta = \frac{T\ L}{E_s\ R}$$

$$= \frac{(1000)(40)}{(12 \times 10^6)(221)}$$

$$= .0000152 \text{ radians or } \underline{.00087°}$$

9. END CONNECTIONS OF TORSION MEMBERS

When a member having an open section is twisted, the cross-section warps (see b, in Fig. 37) if ends of the member are free. The flanges of these members not only twist, but they also swing outward (see c), allowing the member to twist more. If the ends of the flanges can be locked in place in relation to each other, this swinging will be prevented.

Design Rule No. 3: MAKE RIGID END CONNECTIONS

There are several methods of locking the flanges together. The simplest is to weld the end of the member to the supporting member as in (d). If the supporting member is then neither thick enough nor rigid enough, a thin, square plate may be welded to the two flanges at the end of the member (e). Another method is to use diagonal braces between the two flanges at the two ends of the member (f).

Either of these methods reduces the angular twist by about ½.

Members having a box section, when butt welded directly to a primary member, have the fully rigid end connections required for high torsional resistance.

Problem 10

A 12″ WF 27-lb beam, 25′ long, with a uniformly distributed load of 8 kips, is supported at each end by a box girder. See Figure 38. If the beam is continuously welded to these girders, estimate a) the resulting end

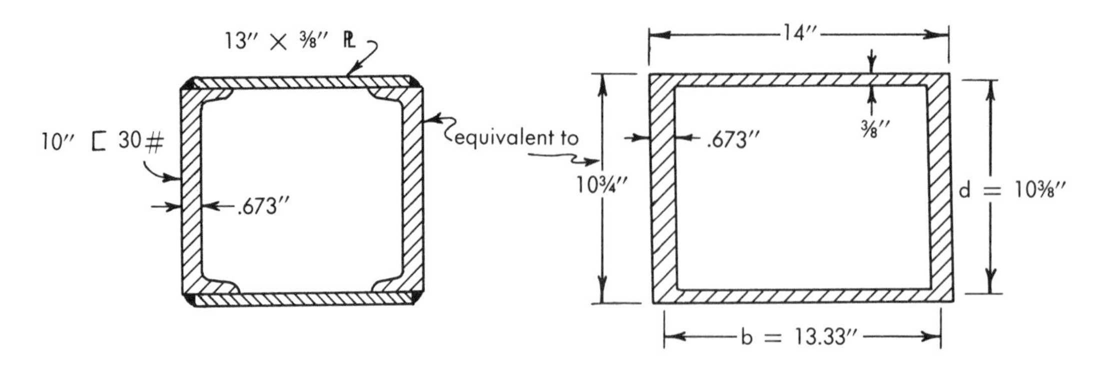

FIGURE 39

moments in the beam, b) the torsional stresses in the girder, and c) the weld size required to hold the box girder together.

torsional resistance of box girder

$$R = \frac{2\, b^2\, d^2}{\frac{b}{t_b} + \frac{d}{t_d}} \qquad \text{(See Figure 39)}$$

$$= \frac{2(13.33)^2(10\tfrac{3}{8})^2}{\frac{(13.33)}{(\tfrac{1}{2})} + \frac{(10\tfrac{3}{8})}{(.673)}}$$

$$= 910 \text{ in.}^4$$

Torque in the central section of the box girder support is equal to the end moment of the supporting beam.

end moment of beam

See Sect. 8.1 Beam Formulas.

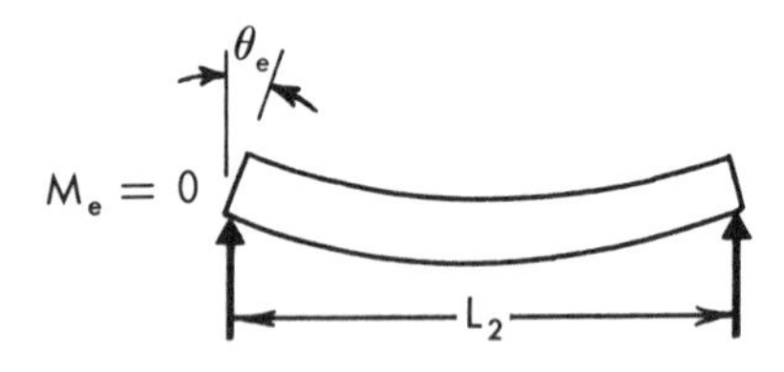

If the beam is simply supported without any end restraint, the end moment (M_e) is zero, and the slope of the beam at the end is—

$$\theta_e = \frac{W\, L_2^{\,2}}{24\, E\, I_2}$$

$$= \frac{(8^k)(25' \times 12'')^2}{24(30 \times 10^6)(204.1)}$$

$$= .0049 \text{ radians}$$

Now, if the ends of the beam are so restrained that it cannot rotate, the end moment becomes—

$$M_e = \frac{W\, L_2}{12}$$

$$= \frac{(8^k)(25' \times 12'')^2}{12}$$

$$= 200 \text{ in.-kips}$$

torque on box girder

See Sect. 8.2 Torsional Member Formulas.

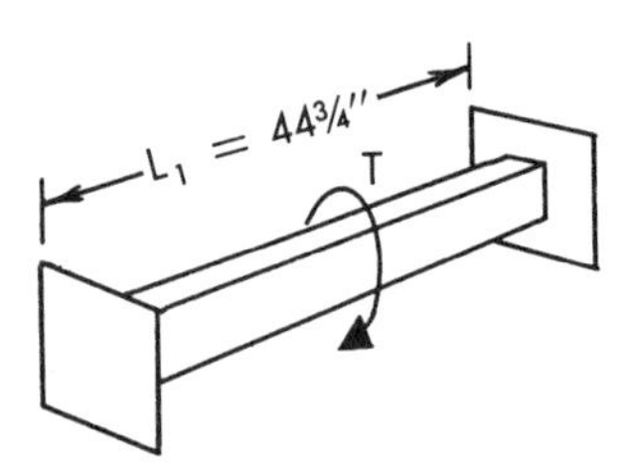

Determine what torque must be applied to the central section of the supporting box girder to cause it to rotate the same amount as the end rotation of the supported beam, if simply supported (θ_e = .0049 radians):

$$\theta_{℄} = \frac{T\, L_1}{4\, E_s\, R}$$

$$\text{or } T = \frac{4\, E_s\, R\, \theta_{℄}}{L_1}$$

$$= \frac{4(12 \times 10^6)(910)(.0049)}{(44\tfrac{3}{4}'')}$$

$$= 4780 \text{ in.-kips}$$

A moment-rotation chart shows the relationship; see Figure 40. A straight line represents the end moment (M_e) and end rotation (θ_e) of the supported beam

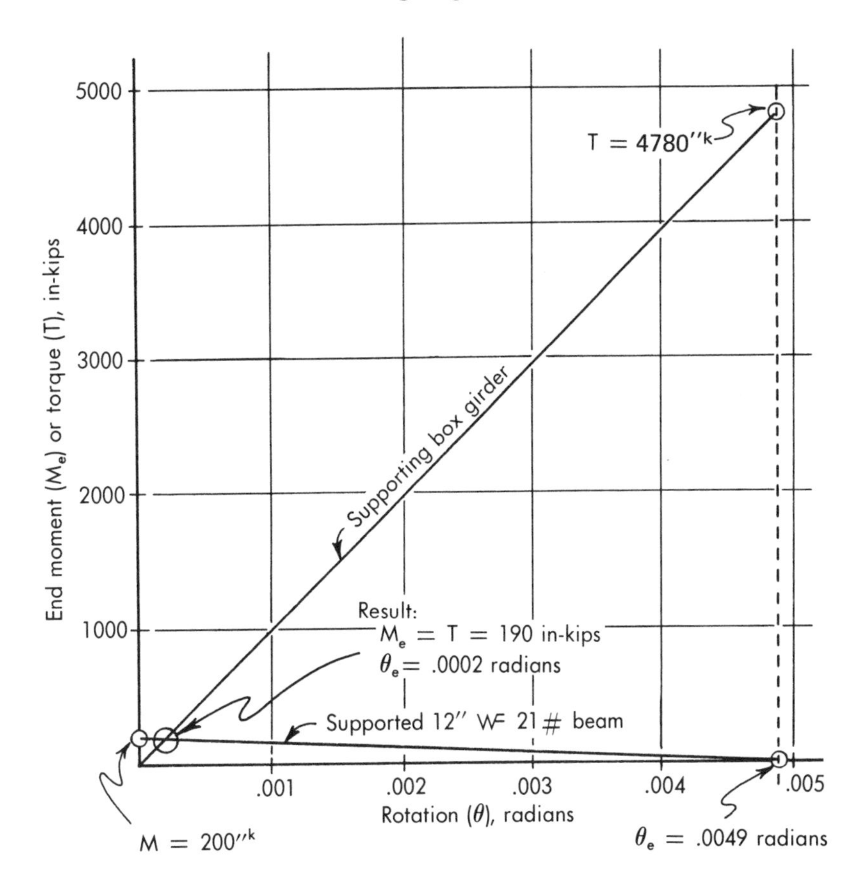

FIGURE 40

under all conditions of end restraint. A similar straight line, but in the opposite direction, represents the applied torque (T) and angular rotation (θ) at the central section of the supporting box girder.

These two lines are plotted, and where they intersect is the resulting end moment (M_e) or torque (T) and the angular rotation (θ):

$$M_e = T = 190 \text{ in.-kips}$$

$$\theta_e = .0002 \text{ radians}$$

torsional shear stresses in box girder

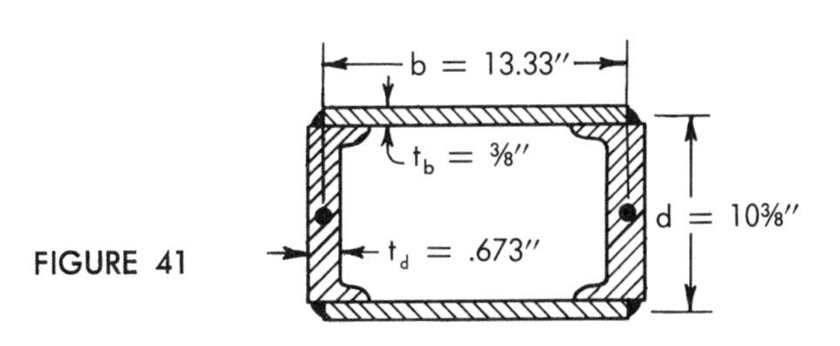

FIGURE 41

$$\tau_b = \frac{T}{2\,[A]\,t_b}$$

$$= \frac{(190''^{k})}{2(13.33 \times 10\tfrac{3}{8})(\tfrac{3}{8})}$$

$$= 1830 \text{ psi}$$

torsional shear force on fillet weld

$$f_1 = \tau_b\, t_b$$

$$= (1830)(\tfrac{3}{8})$$

$$= 690 \text{ lbs/lin in.}$$

which must be transferred by the fillet weld joining the top and bottom plates to the side channels, to make up the box girder.

horizontal shear force on fillet weld due to bending

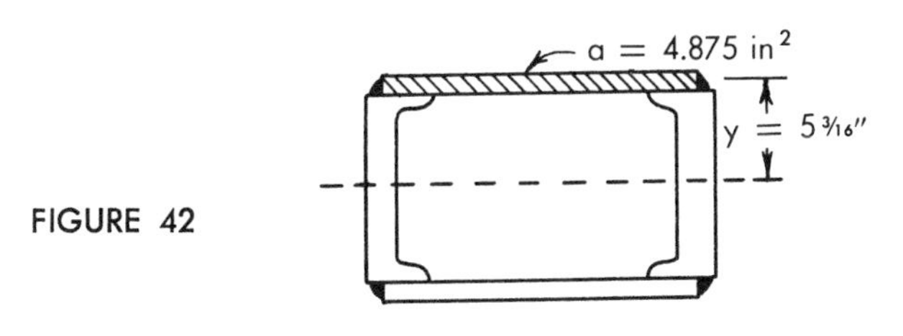

FIGURE 42

$$I = 2(103.0) + 2(4.875)(5\tfrac{3}{16})^2$$

$$= 468 \text{ in.}^4$$

Half of the 8-kip load goes to each end of the beam, or a 4-kip load is applied to the central section of each box girder. And V = 2 kips.

$$\therefore f_2 = \frac{V\ a\ y}{I\ n}$$

$$= \frac{(2^k)(4.875)(5\tfrac{5}{16})}{(468)(2\ \text{welds})}$$

$$= 54 \text{ lbs/lin in.}$$

total shear force on weld

$$f = f_1 + f_2$$

$$= (690) + (54)$$

$$= 744 \text{ lbs/lin in.}$$

required leg size of fillet weld (E70 welds)

$$\omega = \frac{\text{actual force}}{\text{allowable force}}$$

$$= \frac{744}{11{,}200}$$

$$= .066'' \text{ (continuous)}$$

However, AWS and AISC would require a minimum fillet weld leg size of $\tfrac{3}{16}''$ (See Section 7.4).

If intermittent fillet welds are to be used, the length and spacing of the welds would be—

$$\% = \frac{\text{calculated leg size of continuous weld}}{\text{actual leg size of intermittent weld used}}$$

$$= \frac{(.066)}{(\tfrac{3}{16})}$$

$$= 35\%$$

or use $\tfrac{3}{16}''$ ⊿ 3″ — 8″

Alternate Design

As a matter of interest, consider the support to be provided by a 10″ WF 39-lb beam.

(See Figure 43)

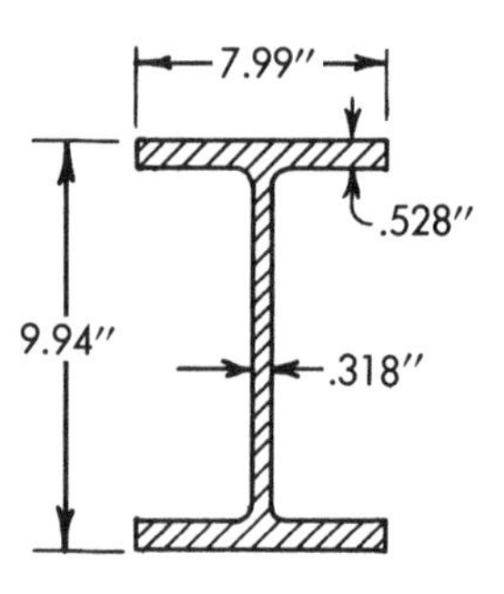

FIGURE 43

torsional resistance of supporting beam

$$R = \frac{2\ b\ t_f^3}{3} + \frac{d\ t_w^3}{3}$$

$$= \frac{2(7.99)(.528)^3}{3} + \frac{(9.94)(.318)^3}{3}$$

$$= 0.89 \text{ in.}^4$$

torque on supporting beam

Determine what torque must be applied to the central section of this supporting beam for it to rotate the same amount as the end rotation of the supported beam, if simply supported (θ_e = .0049 radians):

$$\theta = \frac{T\ L_1}{4\ E_s\ R}$$

$$\text{or } T = \frac{4\ E_s\ R\ \theta}{L_1}$$

$$= \frac{4(12 \times 10^6)(0.89)(.0049)}{(44\ \tfrac{3}{4})}$$

$$= 4.67 \text{ in.-kips}$$

The moment-rotation diagram, Figure 44, shows the resulting end moment on the supported beam to be 4.67 in.-kips. Thus, this beam could be connected as a

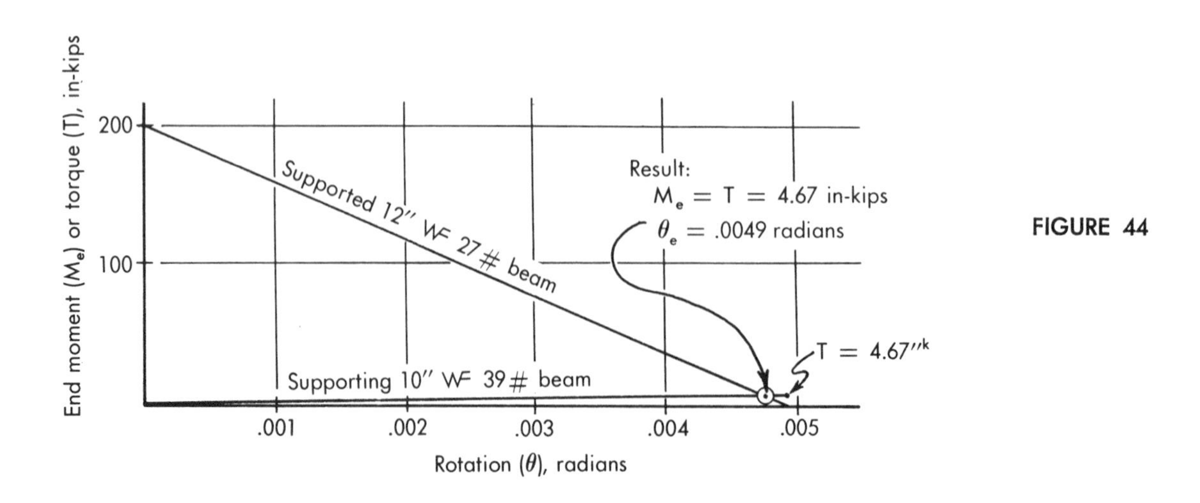

FIGURE 44

simply supported beam with just vertical welds on the web sufficient to carry the 4-kip shear reaction. The end restraint is about 2.3%.

10. MEMBRANE ANALOGY

Membrane analogy is a very useful method to understand the behavior of open sections when subjected to torsion. To make use of this method, holes are cut into a thin plate making the outline of various shaped sections. A membrane material such as soap film is spread over the open surface and air pressure is applied to the film. The mathematical expressions for the slope and volume of this membrane or film covering the openings representing different cross-sections are the same as the expressions for the shear stresses and torsional resistance of the actual member being studied. It is from this type of analysis that formulas for various types of open sections subjected to torsion have been developed and confirmed.

If several outlines are cut into the thin plate and the same pressure applied to each membrane, the following will be true:

1. The volumes under the membranes will be proportional to the torsional resistances of the corresponding sections.
2. The slope of the membrane's surface at any point is proportional to the shear stress of the section at this point.
3. A narrow section (thin plate) has practically the same torsional resistance regardless of the shape of the section it is formed into. Notice a, b, and c in Figure 45. For a given area of section, the volume under the membrane remains the same regardless of the shape of the section.

It is possible to determine the torsional resistance of these open sections by comparing them with a standard circle on this same test plate whose torsional resistance can readily be calculated.

By comparing the membrane of the slotted open tube, (c) in Figure 45, to that of the membrane of the closed tube (e), it is readily seen why the closed tube is several hundred times more resistant to twist, when it is remembered that the volume under the membrane is proportional to the torsional resistance.

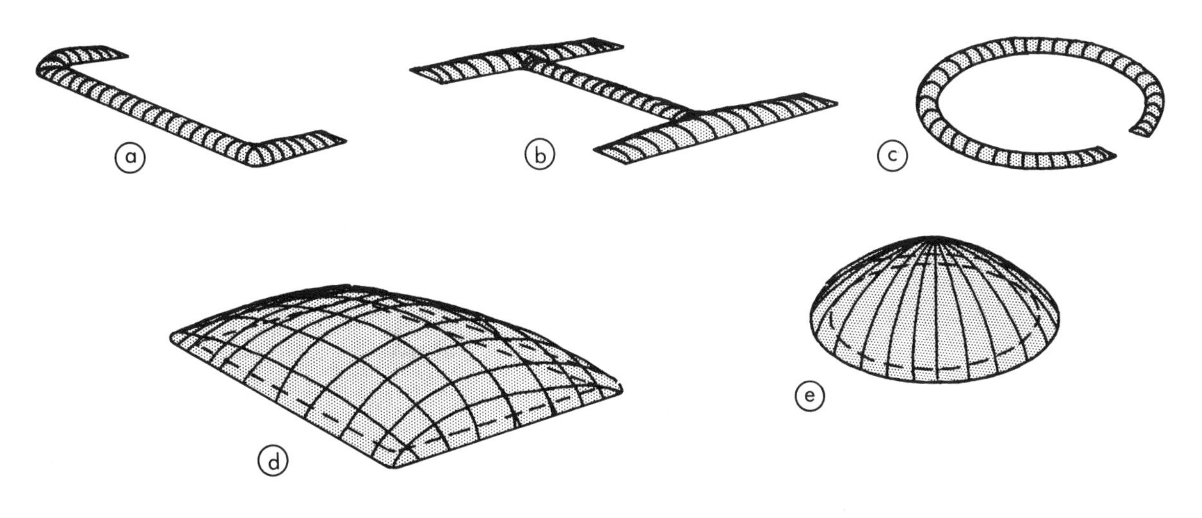

FIGURE 45

Modern structural steel shops are equipped with highly efficient equipment for the welding of fabricated plate girders. Here an automatic submerged-arc welder runs a transverse splice in 7/8″ web plate to full width, with the aid of a small runout tab previously tacked in place.

This automatic submerged-arc welder mounted on a track-mounted, gantry type manipulator runs a web-to-flange fillet weld the full 84′ girder length. Welding generators travel with the manipulator.

Analysis of Combined Stresses

1. CONCEPT OF CUBICAL UNIT

Structural members are often subject to combined loading, such as axial tension and transverse bending. These external forces induce internal stresses as forces of resistance. Even without combined loading, there may be combined stress at points within the member.

The analysis of combined stresses is based on the concept of a cubic unit taken at any point of intersection of three planes perpendicular to each other. The total forces in play against these planes result in proportionate forces of the same nature acting against faces of the cube, tending to hold it in equilibrium. Since any member is made up of a multitude of such cubes, the analysis of stresses at a critical point is the key to analysis of the member's resistance to combined external forces.

2. COMBINING STRESSES

Biaxial and triaxial stresses are tensile and compressive stresses combined together.

Combined stresses are tensile and compressive stresses combined together.

Principal planes are planes of no shear stress.

Principal stresses are normal stresses (tensile or compressive) acting on these principal planes. These are the greatest and smallest of all the normal stresses in the element.

Normal stresses, either tensile or compressive, act normal or at right angles to their reference planes. Shear stresses act parallel to their reference planes.

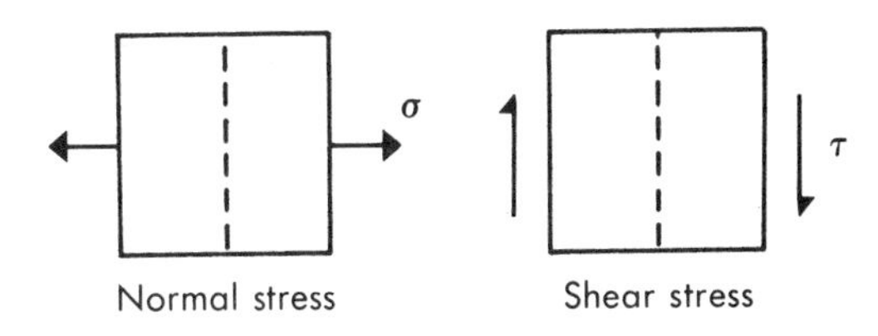

FIGURE 1

These stresses may be represented graphically on Mohr's circle of stress. By locating the points (σ_3, τ_1) and (σ_2, τ_1) on a graph, Figure 2, and drawing a circle through these two points, the other stresses at various planes may be determined.

By observation of Mohr's circle of stress, it is found that—

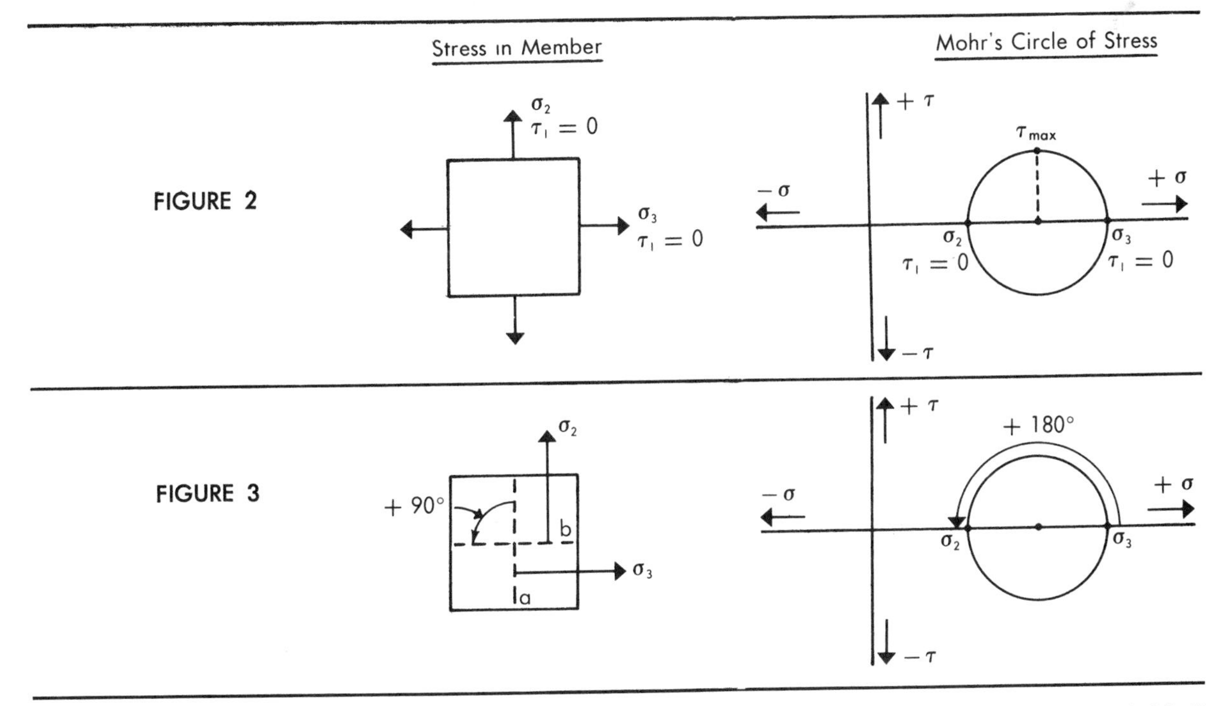

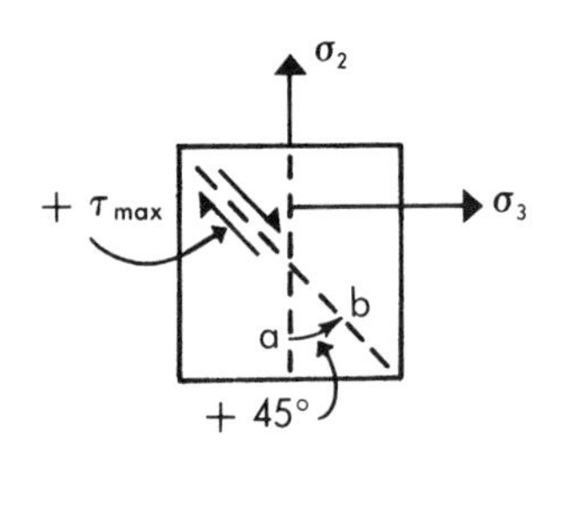

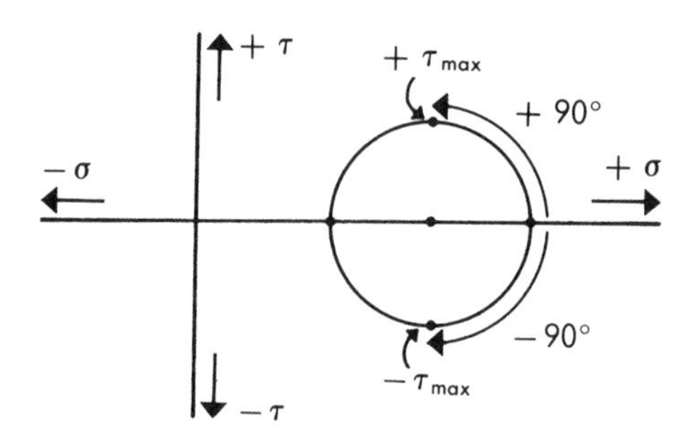

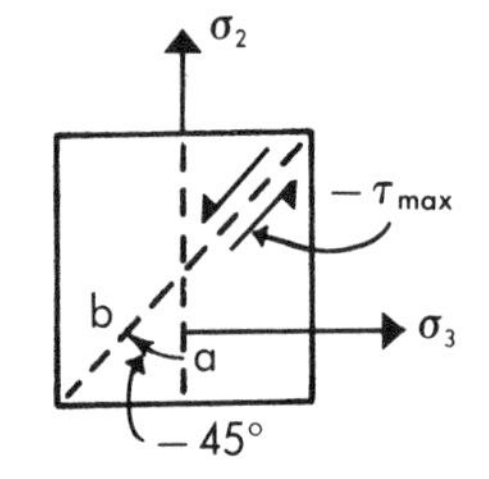

FIGURE 4

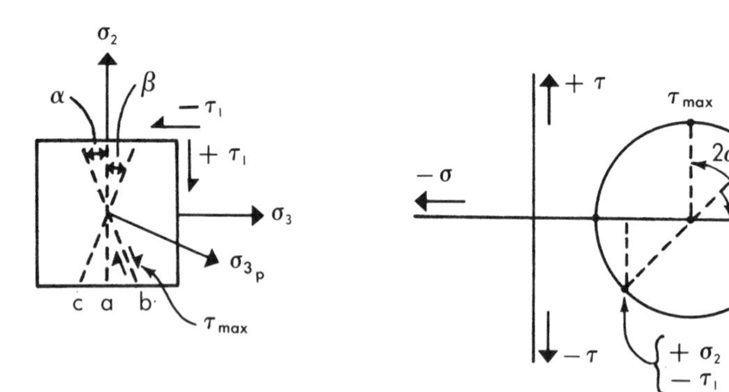

FIGURE 5

$$\tau_{max} = \frac{\sigma_3 - \sigma_2}{2} \qquad (1)$$

In this case, σ_3 and σ_2 are principal stresses σ_{3p} and σ_{2p} since they act on planes of zero shear stress.

For any angle of rotation on Mohr's circle of stress, the corresponding planes on which these stresses act in the member rotate through just half this angle and in the same direction.

Notice in Figure 3, σ_2 lies at $+ 180°$ from σ_3 in Mohr's circle of stress, and the plane (b) on which σ_2 acts in the member lies at $+ 90°$ from the plane (a) on which σ_3 acts.

Notice in Figure 4, τ_{max} lies at $+ 90°$ from σ_3 and the plane (b) on which τ_{max} acts in the member lies at $+ 45°$ from the plane (a) on which σ_3 acts. In this case σ_2 and σ_3 are principal stresses because there is no applied shear on these planes.

This is a simple method to graphically show how stresses within a member combine; see Figure 5. On the graph, right, locate the two stress points $(+ \sigma_3, + \tau_1)$ and $(+ \sigma_2, - \tau_1)$ and draw a circle through these points. Now determine maximum normal and shear stresses.

By observation of Mohr's circle of stress, it is found that—

$$\sigma_{3p}\ (\text{max}) = \frac{\sigma_3 + \sigma_2}{2} + \sqrt{\left(\frac{\sigma_3 - \sigma_2}{2}\right)^2 + \tau_1^2} \qquad (2)$$

$$\tau_{max} = \sqrt{\left(\frac{\sigma_3 - \sigma_2}{2}\right)^2 + \tau_1^2} \qquad (3)$$

The above formula for the maximum shear stress (τ_{max}) is true for the flat plane considered; however, there are really two other planes not yet considered and their maximum shear stress could possibly be greater than this value.

This is a very common mistake among engineers. To be absolutely sure, when dealing with biaxial

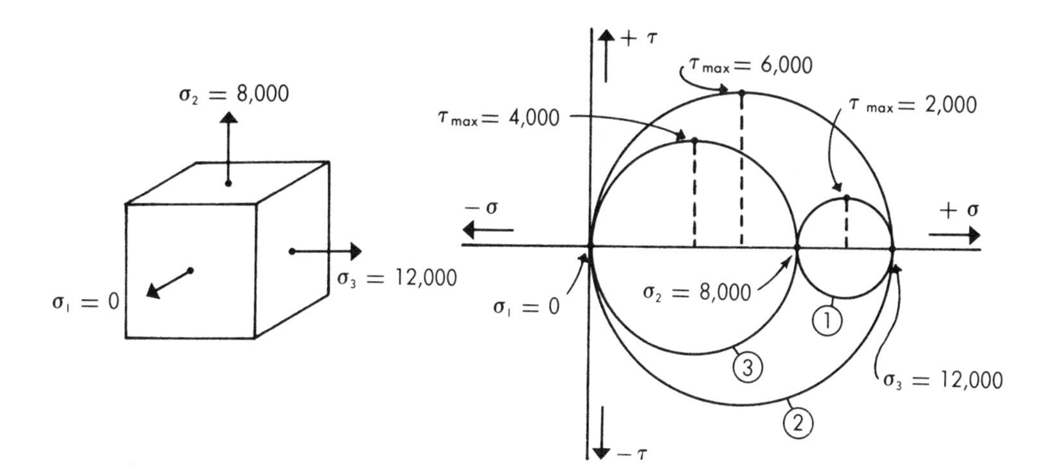

FIGURE 6

stresses, always let the third normal stress be zero instead of ignoring it, and treat the problem as a triaxial stress problem.

The example in Figure 2 will now be reworked, Figure 6, and the third normal stress (σ_1) will be set equal to zero.

Here,

$\sigma_3 = +\ 12,000$ psi $\qquad \tau_3 = 0$

$\sigma_2 = +\ 8,000$ psi $\qquad \tau_2 = 0$

$\sigma_1 = 0 \qquad \tau_1 = 0$

On graph, right: Locate stress points (σ_1) (σ_2), (σ_3) and draw three circles through these points. Now determine the three maximum shear stresses.

There are three values for the maximum shear stress, each equal to half of the difference between two principal (normal) stresses. The plane of maximum shear stress (shaded in the following sketches) is always at 45° to the planes of principal stress.

Circle 1

$$\tau_{max} = \frac{\sigma_3 - \sigma_2}{2} = \frac{12,000\text{-}8,000}{2} = 2,000 \text{ psi}$$

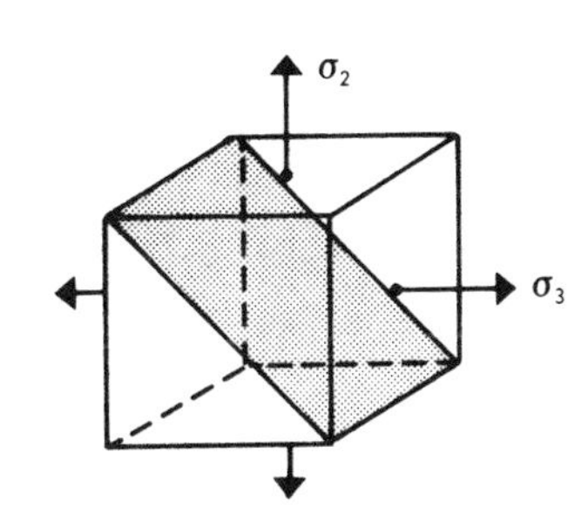

Circle 2

$$\tau_{max} = \frac{\sigma_3 - \sigma_1}{2} = \frac{12,000\text{–}0}{2} = 6,000 \text{ psi}$$

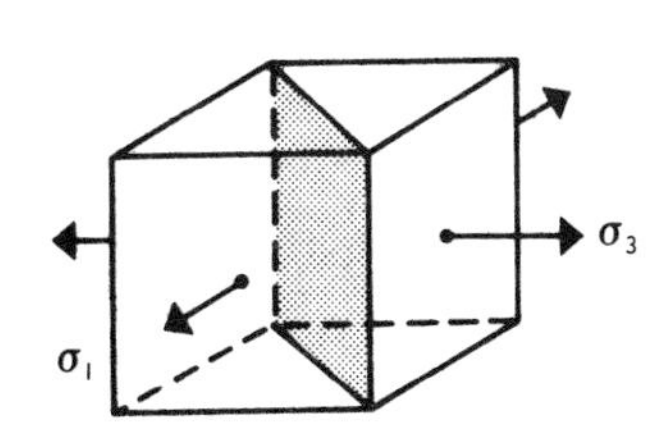

Circle 3

$$\tau_{max} = \frac{\sigma_2 - \sigma_1}{2} = \frac{8,000\text{–}0}{2} = 4,000 \text{ psi}$$

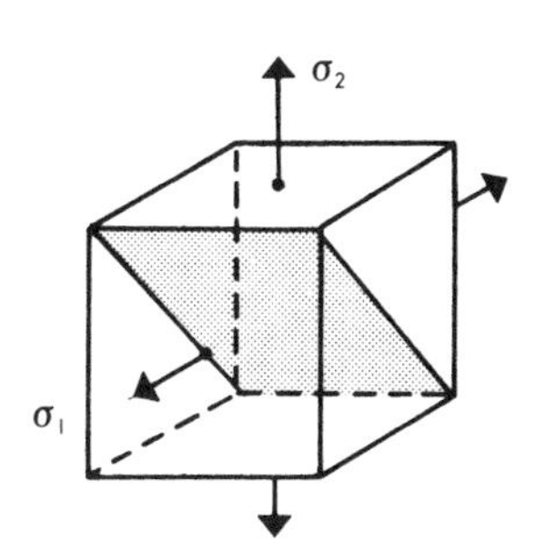

It is seen that, in this example, the maximum shear stress is 6,000 psi, and not the 2,000 psi value that would usually be found from the conventional formulas for biaxial stress.

3. TRIAXIAL STRESS COMBINED WITH SHEAR STRESS (See Figure 7)

The three principal stresses (σ_{1p}, σ_{2p}, σ_{3p}) are given by the three roots (σ_p) of this cubic equation:

$$\begin{aligned}\sigma_{p3} &- (\sigma_1 + \sigma_2 + \sigma_3)\sigma_p^2 \\ &+ (\sigma_1\sigma_2 + \sigma_2\sigma_3 + \sigma_1\sigma_3 - \tau_1^2 - \tau_2^2 - \tau_3^2)\sigma_p \\ &- (\sigma_1\sigma_2\sigma_3 + 2\,\tau_1\tau_2\tau_3 - \sigma_1\tau_1^2 - \sigma_2\tau_2^2 - \sigma_3\tau_3^2) = 0\end{aligned} \quad (4)$$

For maximum shear stress, use the two principal stresses (σ_p) whose algebraic difference is the greatest. The maximum shear stress (τ_{max}) is equal to half of this difference.

*Since a, b, and c are coefficients of this equation:

$$a = -(\sigma_1 + \sigma_2 + \sigma_3)$$

$$b = \sigma_1\sigma_2 + \sigma_2\sigma_3 + \sigma_1\sigma_3 - \tau_1^2 - \tau_2^2 - \tau_3^2$$

$$c = \sigma_1\tau_1^2 + \sigma_2\tau_2^2 + \sigma_3\tau_3^2 - \sigma_1\sigma_2\sigma_3 - 2\,\tau_1\tau_2\tau_3$$

*Solution of Cubic Equation from "Practical Solution of Cubic Equations", G. L. Sullivan, MACHINE DESIGN, Feb. 21, 1957.

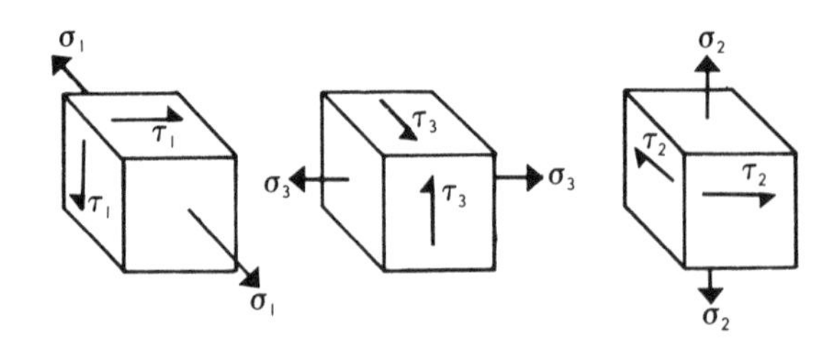

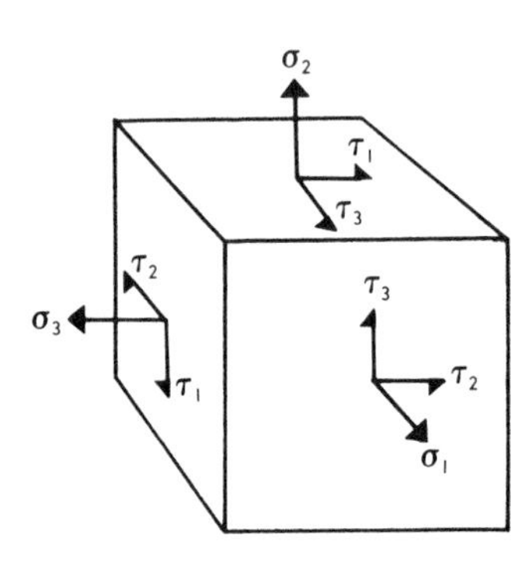

FIGURE 7

Let $N = \frac{b}{3} - \left(\frac{a}{3}\right)^2$

and $Q = \frac{c}{2} - \frac{a\ b}{6} + \left(\frac{a}{3}\right)^3$

Then calculate—

$K = \frac{N^3}{Q^2}$ as a test ratio.

Case 1

When $(1 + K)$ is positive (one real root) or when $(1 + K)$ is zero (three real roots, two of which are equal)
calculate—

$$S = \sqrt[3]{Q\left[1 + \sqrt{1 + K}\right]}$$

and compute the root—

$$\sigma_{1p} = \frac{N}{S} - S - \frac{a}{3}$$

Case 2

When $(1 + K)$ is negative (three real and unequal roots)
calculate—

$$T = \sqrt{-K}$$

and compute the root—

$$\sigma_{1p} = \mp\sqrt{-3N\left(\frac{T + 0.386}{T + 0.2}\right)} - \frac{a}{3}$$

The ambiguous sign is opposite to the sign of Q (approximate, but very accurate).

For either Case 1 or Case 2

The additional two roots (σ_{2p}, σ_{3p}) of the general cubic equation are calculated by solving for σ_p using the exact quadratic:

$$\sigma_p^2 + (a + \sigma_{1p})\sigma_p - \frac{c}{\sigma_{1p}} = 0$$

$$\text{or } \sigma_p = \frac{-(a + \sigma_{1p}) \pm \sqrt{(a + \sigma_{1p})^2 + \frac{4c}{\sigma_{1p}}}}{2}$$

Problem 1

Determine the maximum normal and shear stress in this web section, Figure 8:

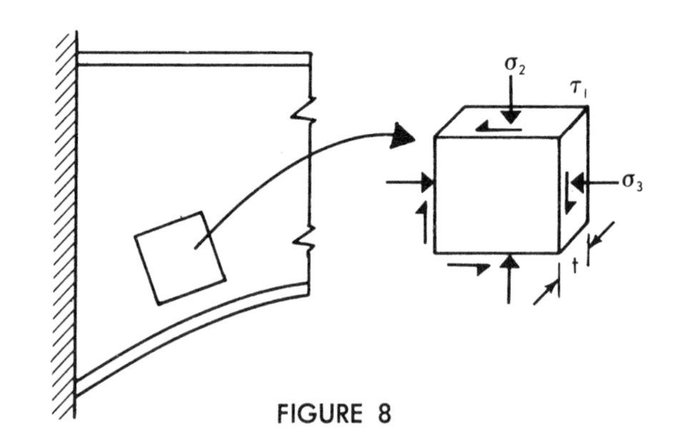

FIGURE 8

where:

$\sigma_1 = 0$ $\tau_1 = 11{,}000$ psi
$\sigma_2 = -13{,}650$ psi $\tau_2 = 0$
$\sigma_3 = -14{,}500$ psi $\tau_3 = 0$

Substituting these values into the general cubic equation:

$$\sigma_p^3 - (-13{,}650 - 14{,}500)\sigma_p^2 + [(-13{,}650)(-14{,}500) - (11{,}000)^2]\,\sigma_p = 0$$

$$\sigma_p^2 + 28{,}150\,\sigma_p + 76{,}925{,}000 = 0$$

the three principal normal stresses are—

$\sigma_{1p} = 0$
$\sigma_{2p} = -25{,}075$ psi $\sigma_{3p} = -3{,}075$ psi

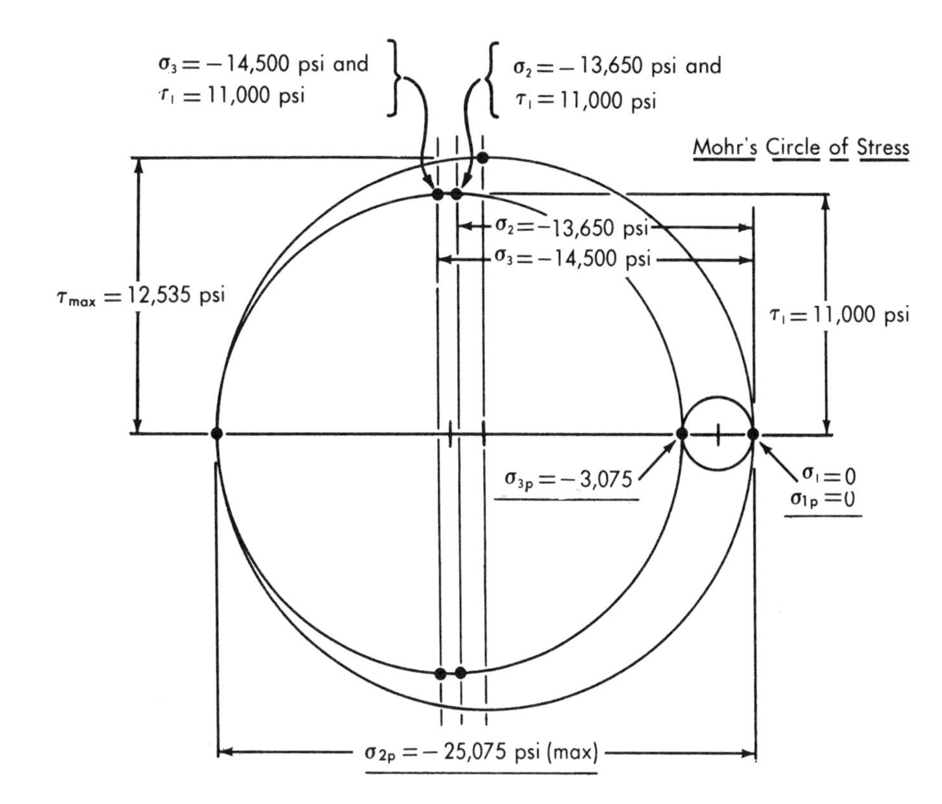

FIGURE 9

and taking one-half of the greatest difference of two principal stresses:

$$\tau_{max} = \frac{25{,}075 - 0}{2} = \underline{12{,}535 \text{ psi}}$$

These various values are shown diagramed on Mohr's Circle of Stress, Figure 9.

Checking Effect of Applied Stresses

The Huber-Mises formula is convenient for checking the effect of applied stresses on the yielding of the plate. If a certain combination of normal stresses (σ_x and σ_y) and shear stress (τ_{xy}) results in a critical stress (σ_{cr}) equal to the yield strength (σ_y) of the steel when tested in uniaxial tension, this combination of stresses is assumed to just produce yielding in the steel.

$$\sigma_{cr} = \sqrt{\sigma_x^2 - \sigma_x \, \sigma_y + \sigma_y^2 + 3 \, \tau_{xy}}$$

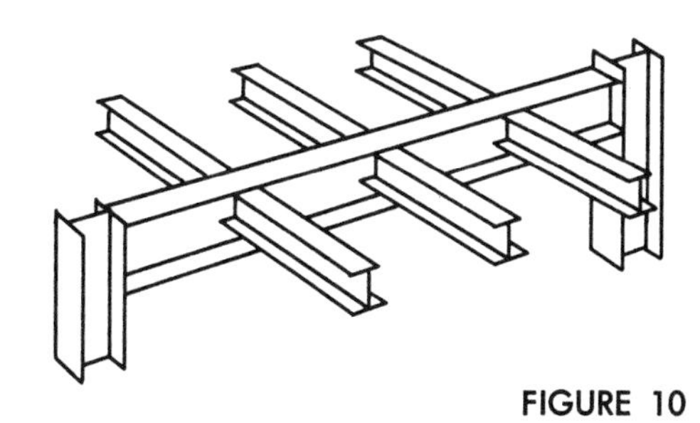

FIGURE 10

Problem 2

For the beam-to-girder network represented by Figure 10, assume the combination of stresses represented by Figure 11.

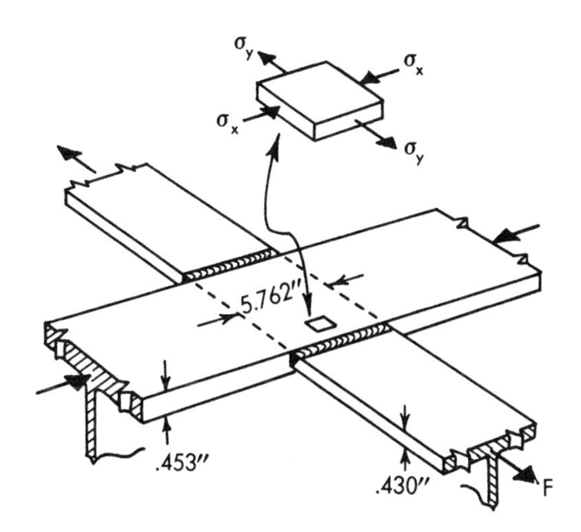

FIGURE 11

Here:

$$\sigma_{cr} = \sqrt{\sigma_x^2 - \sigma_x \, \sigma_y + \sigma_y^2 + 3 \, \tau_{xy}}$$

$$= \sqrt{(-14{,}350)^2 - (-14{,}350(15{,}900) + (15{,}900)^2 + 0}$$

$$= 21{,}600 \text{ psi}$$

The apparent factor of yielding is

$$k = \frac{\sigma_y}{\sigma_{cr}}$$

$$= \frac{(36{,}000)}{(21{,}600)}$$

$$= 1.67$$

This seems reasonable and under these conditions, the beam flange could be groove welded directly to the edge of the girder flange without trying to isolate the two intersecting flanges.

4. STRENGTH UNDER COMBINED LOADING

A very convenient method of treating combined loadings is the interaction method. Here each type of load is expressed as a ratio of the actual load (P,M,T) to the ultimate load (P_u,M_u,T_u) which would cause failure if acting alone.

axial load	*bending load*	*torsional load*
$R_a = \frac{P}{P_u}$	$R_b = \frac{M}{M_u}$	$R_t = \frac{T}{T_u}$

In the general example shown in Figure 12, the effect of two types of loads (x) and (y) upon each other is illustrated.

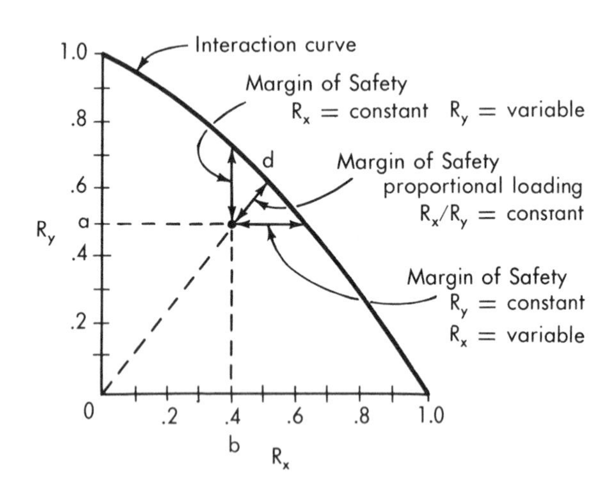

FIGURE 12

The value of $R_y = 1$ at the upper end of the vertical axis is the ultimate value for this type of load on the member. The value $R_x = 1$ at the extreme right end of the horizontal axis is the ultimate value for this type of load on the member. These values are determined by experiment; or when this data is not available, suitable calculations may be made to estimate them.

The interaction curve is usually determined by actual testing of members under various combined-load conditions, and from this a simple formula is derived to express this relationship.

If points *a* and *b* are the ratios produced by the actual loads, point *c* represents the combination of these conditions, and the margin of safety is indicated by how close point *c* lies to the interaction curve. A suitable factor of safety is then applied to these values.

Combined Bending and Torsion

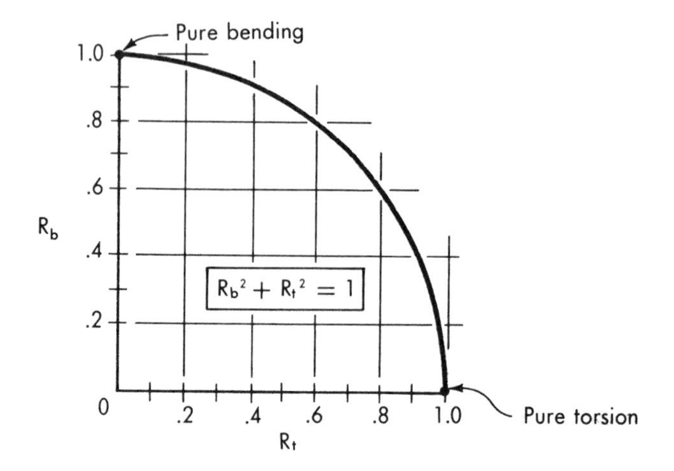

FIGURE 13

Combined Axial Loading and Torsion

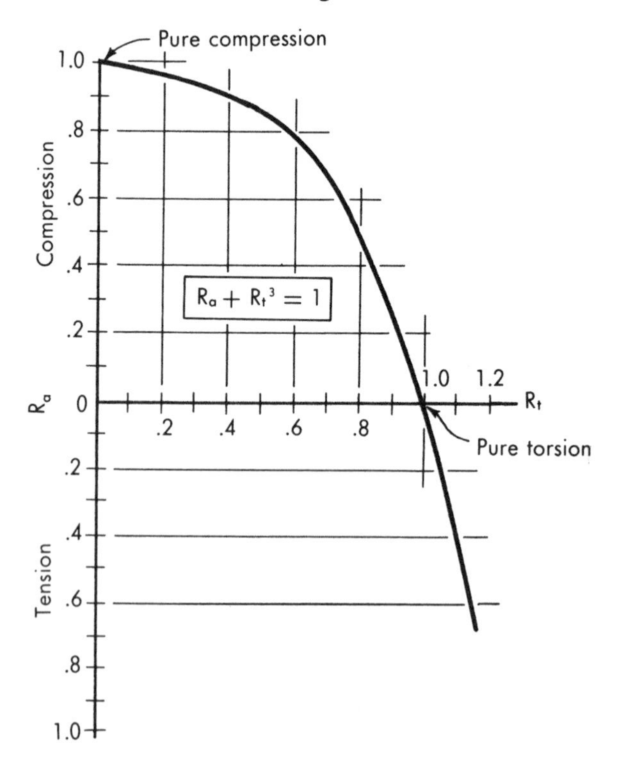

FIGURE 14

Combined Axial Compression and Bending

In this case, the axial compression will cause additional deflection, which in turn increases the moment of the bending load. This increase can easily be taken care of by an amplification factor (k). See Figures 15 and 16.

For sinusoidal initial bending moment curve

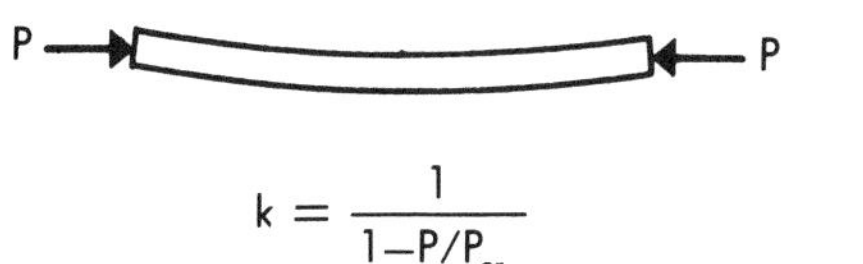

$$k = \frac{1}{1 - P/P_{cr}}$$

FIGURE 15

For constant bending moment

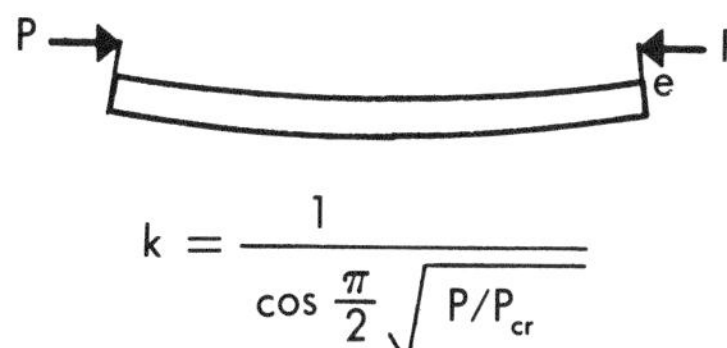

$$k = \frac{1}{\cos \frac{\pi}{2} \sqrt{P/P_{cr}}}$$

FIGURE 16

Here:

$$P_{cr} = \frac{\pi^2 \, E \, I}{L^2}$$

The bending moment applied to the member (chosen at the cross-section where it is maximum) is then multiplied by this amplification factor (k), and this value is then used as the applied moment (M) in the ratio:

$$R_b = \frac{M}{M_u}$$

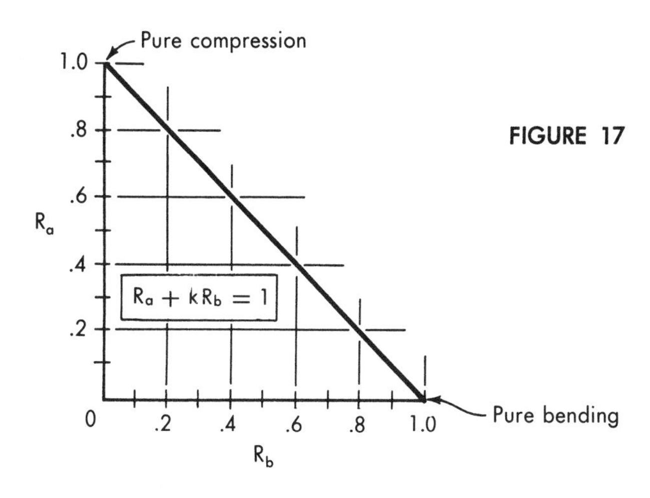

FIGURE 17

The chart in Figure 18 is used to determine the amplification factor (k) for the bending moment

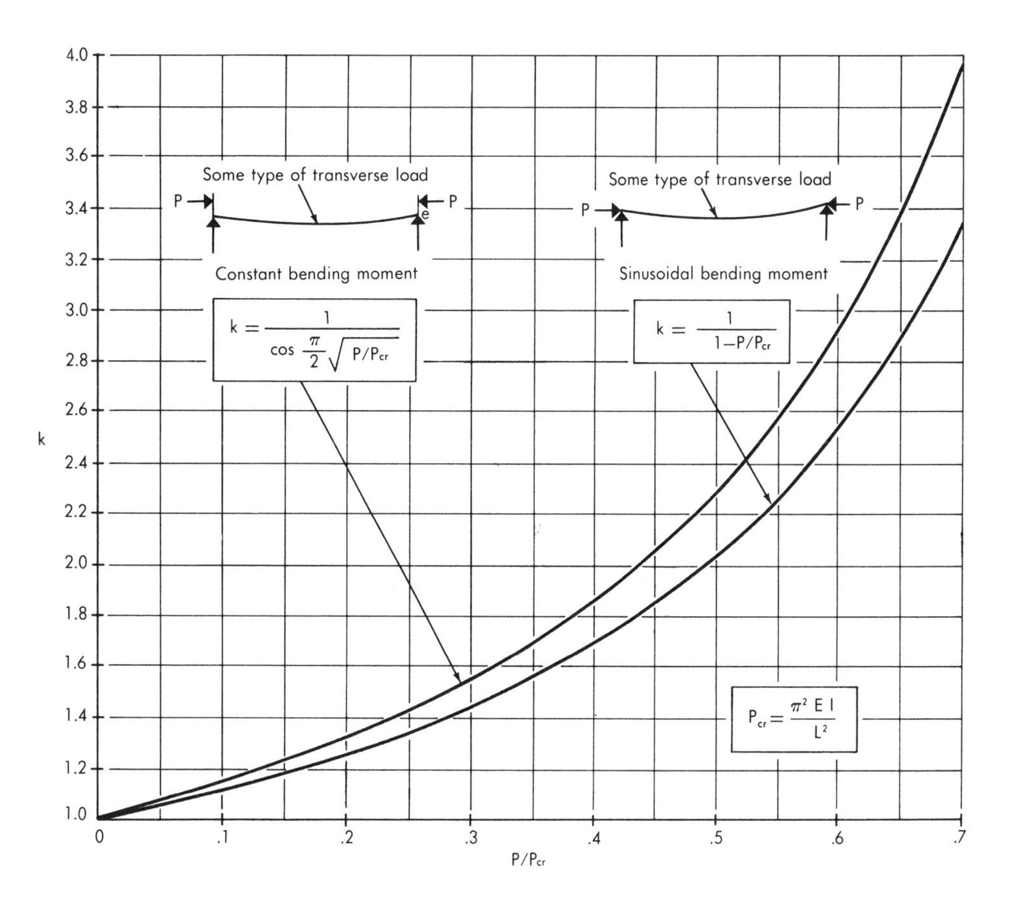

FIG. 18 Amplification factor (k) for bending moment on beam also subject to axial compression.

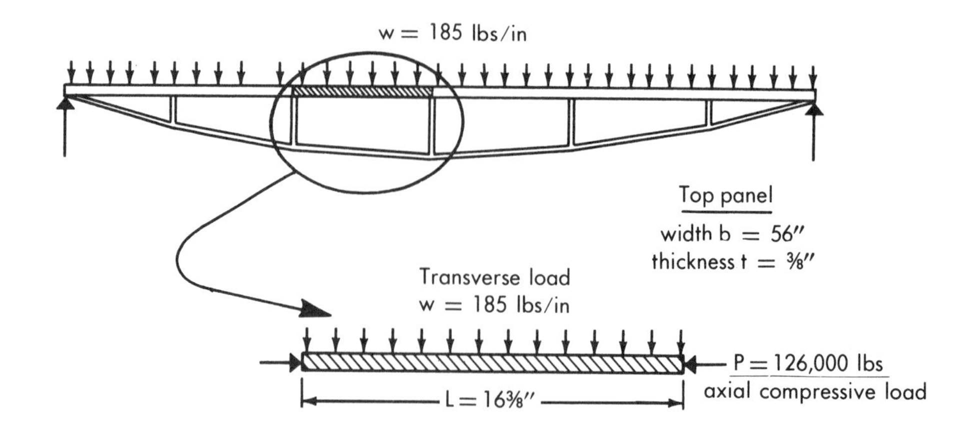

FIGURE 19

applied to a beam when it is also subject to axial compression.

The resulting combined stress is found from the following formula:

$$\sigma = \frac{P}{A} \pm \frac{k\ M\ c}{I}$$

Problem 3

A loading platform is made of a ⅜″ top plate and a 10-gage bottom sheet. The whole structure is in the form of a truss, Figure 19.

Determination of combined stress (axial compression and bending) in top compression panel:

With $L = 16⅜''$

$A = 21 \text{ in.}^2$

$I = .247 \text{ in.}^4$

First the critical load—

$$P_{cr} = \frac{\pi^2\ E\ I}{L^2}$$

$$= \frac{\pi^2\ (30 \times 10^6)\ (.247)}{(16⅜)^2}$$

$$= 272{,}000 \text{ lbs}$$

Then the ratio—

$$P/P_{cr} = \frac{126{,}000}{272{,}000}$$

$$= .464$$

The bending moment—

$$M = \frac{w\ L^2}{8}$$

$$= \frac{(185)\ (16⅜)^2}{8}$$

$$= 6200 \text{ in.-lbs}$$

Obtaining the amplification factor (k) for the sinusoidal bending moment from the curve, Figure 18—

$$k = 1.87$$

The actual applied moment due to extra deflection is found to be—

$$k\ M = (1.87)(6200)$$

$$= 11{,}600 \text{ in.-lbs.}$$

The resulting combined stress formula being—

$$\sigma = \frac{P}{A} \pm \frac{k\ M\ c}{I}$$

of which there are two components:

(a) the compressive stress above the neutral axis of the top panel being—

$$\sigma_c = \frac{126{,}000}{21} + \frac{11{,}600(3/16)}{.247}$$

$$= \underline{14{,}800 \text{ psi}}$$

(b) and the tensile stress below the neutral axis of the top panel being—

$$\sigma_t = \frac{126{,}000}{21} - \frac{11{,}600(3/16)}{.247}$$

$$= 2{,}800 \text{ psi}$$

Determination of Factor of Safety

The ultimate load values for this member in compression alone and in bending alone are unknown, so the following are used.

For *compression* alone —

*Since $\frac{L}{r} = 150$ (where r = radius of gyration)

assume $P_u = P_{cr} = 272{,}000$ lbs

For *bending* alone—

The plastic or ultimate bending moment is—

$$M_u = \left(b\ \sigma_y\ \frac{t}{2}\right)\frac{t}{2} = \frac{b\ t^2\ \sigma_y}{4}$$

$$= \frac{(56)\ (3/8)^2\ (33{,}000)}{4}$$

$$= 64{,}900 \text{ in.-lbs}$$

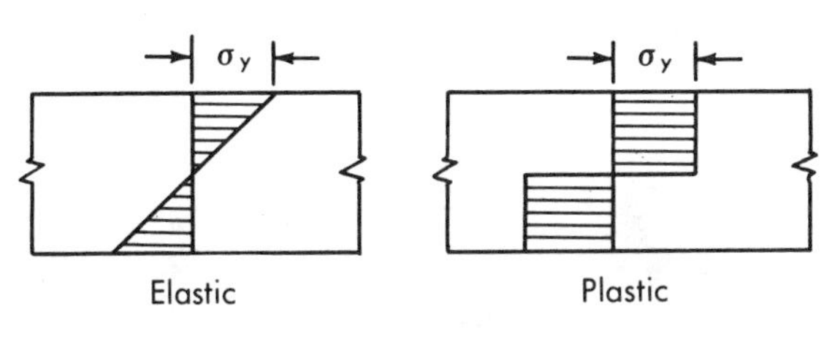

FIGURE 20

These ultimate values are represented on the following interaction curve, Figure 21. Plotting the present load values at *a* against the curve, indicates there is about a *2:1 factor of safety* before the top compression panel will buckle.

*This L/r ratio of 150 is high enough so we can assume the ultimate load carrying capacity of the column (P_u) is about equal to the critical value (P_{cr}). If this had been an extremely short column (very low L/r ratio), the critical value (P_{cr}) could be quite a bit higher than the actual ultimate value (P_u).

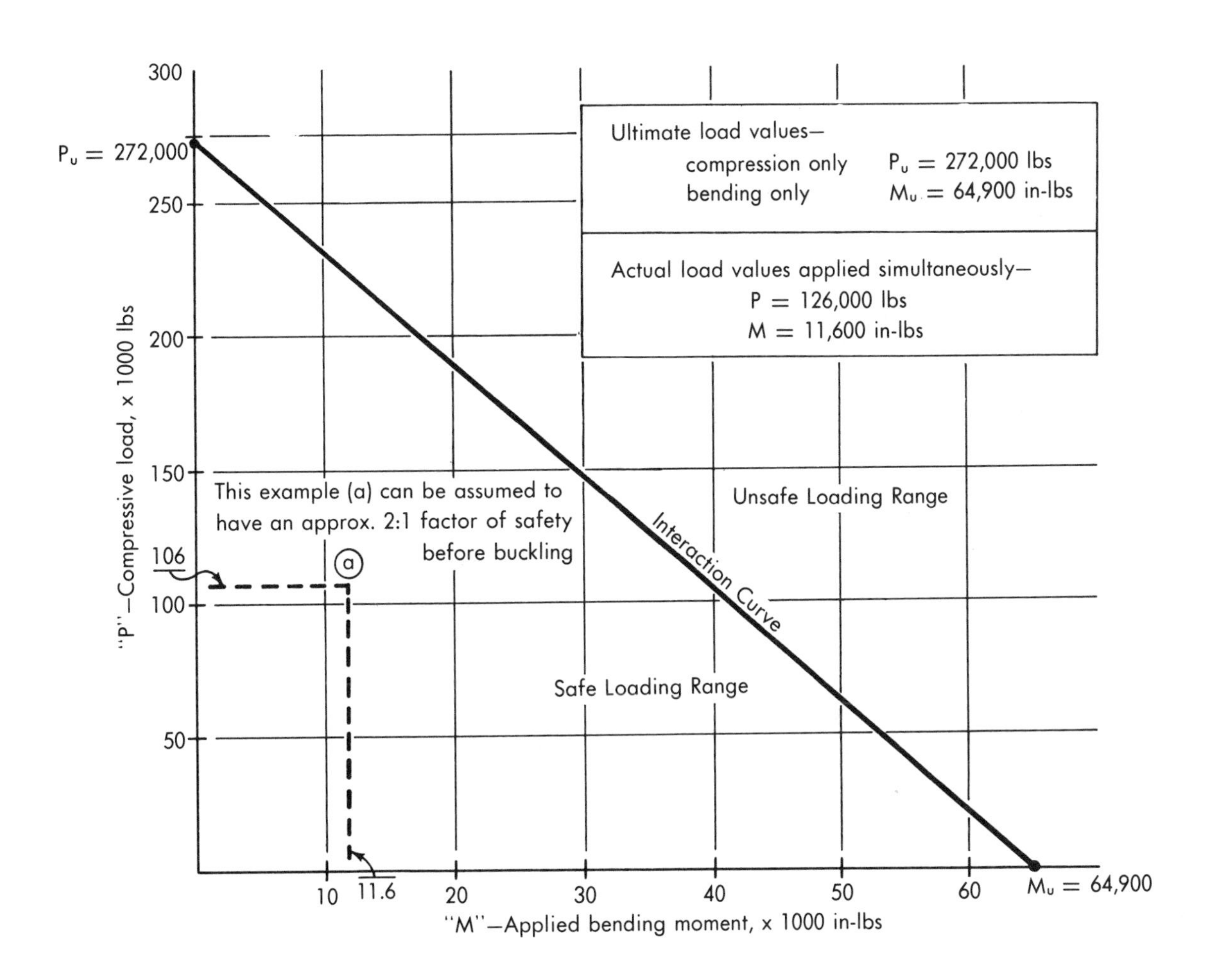

FIG. 21 Interaction Curve for Problem 3

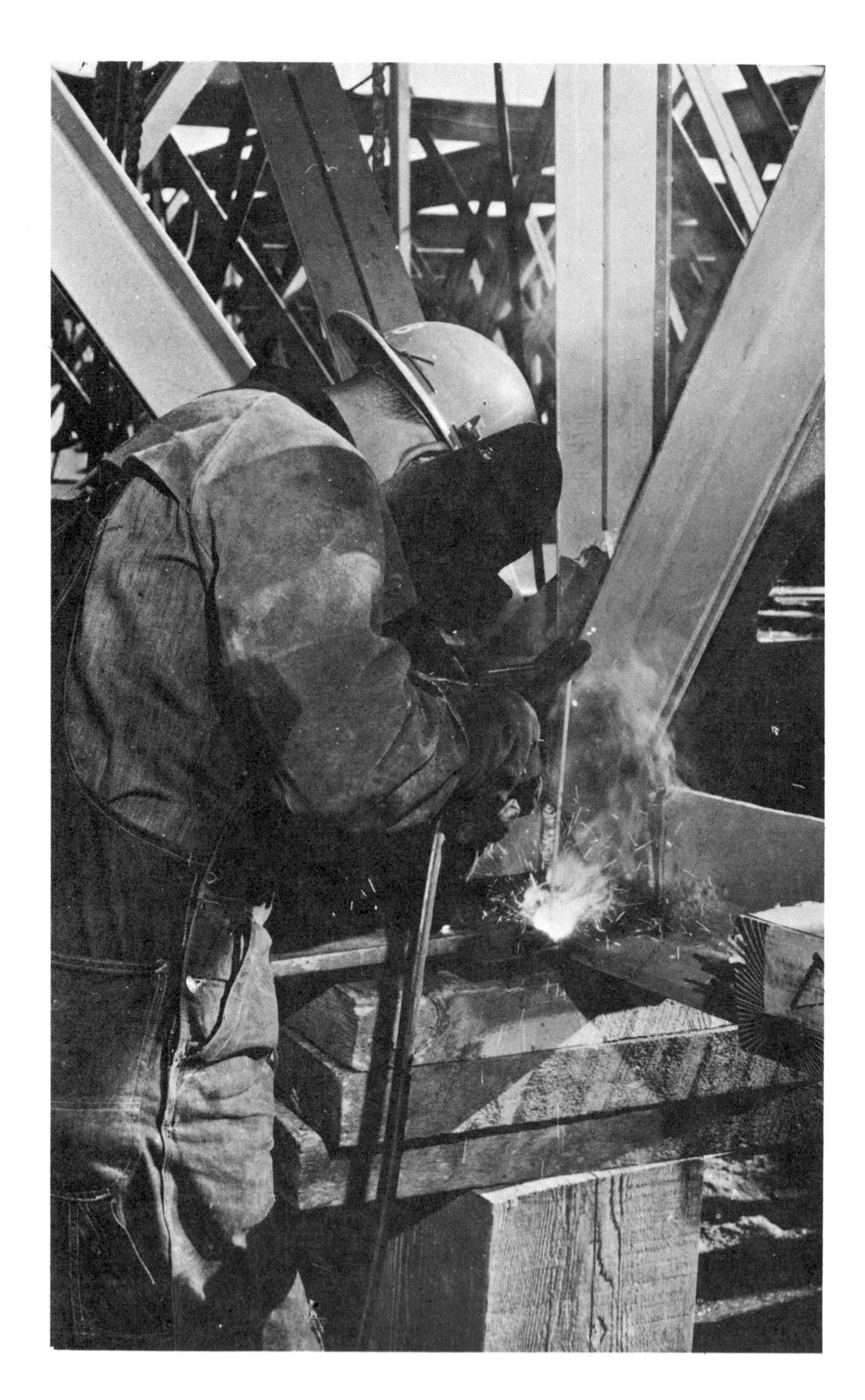

The Air Force Academy Dining Hall (seating the entire student body) at Colorado Springs was built on the ground and jacked into position atop columns. The complexity of joints, the heavy cantilevered construction and large lateral forces offered unique problems in combined stresses. Welding was the only practical approach to the complex connections required to join members of this three-dimensional truss system.

Buckling of Plates

1. CAUSES OF BUCKLING

Buckling of flat plates may be experienced when the plate is excessively stressed in compression along opposite edges, or in shear uniformly distributed around all edges of the plate, or a combination of both. This necessitates establishment of values for the critical buckling stress in compression (σ_{cr}) and in shear (τ_{cr}).

2. BUCKLING OF PLATES IN EDGE COMPRESSION

The critical compressive stress of a plate when subject to compression (σ_{cr}) can be found from the following:

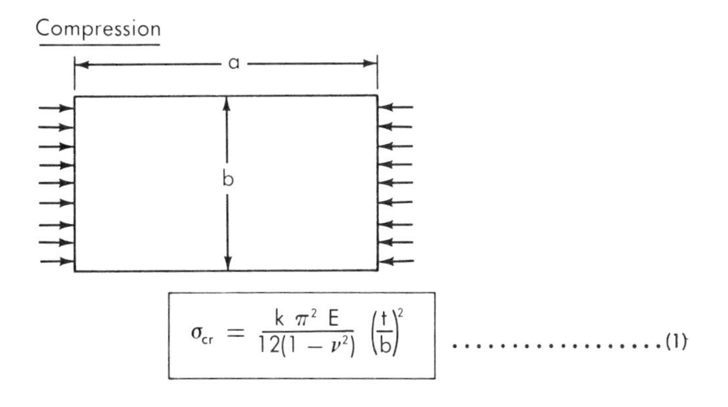

$$\sigma_{cr} = \frac{k \pi^2 E}{12(1-\nu^2)} \left(\frac{t}{b}\right)^2 \qquad (1)$$

FIGURE 1

where:

E = modulus of elasticity in compression (Steel = 30,000,000 psi)

t = thickness of plate, inches

b = width of plate, inches

a = length of plate, inches

ν = Poisson's ratio (for steel, usually = 0.3)

k = constant; depends upon plate shape b/a and support of sides. See Tables 1 and 3.

If the resulting critical stress (σ_{cr}) from this formula is below the proportional limit (σ_p), buckling is said to be elastic and is confined to a portion of the plate away from the supported side; this does not mean complete collapse of the plate at this stress. This is represented by the portion of the curve C to D in Figure 2. If the resulting value (σ_{cr}) is above the proportional limit (σ_p), indicated by the portion of the curve A to C, buckling is said to be inelastic. Here, the tangent modulus (E_t) must be used in some form to replace Young's or secant modulus (E) in the formula for determining σ_{cr}.

This problem can be simplified by limiting the maximum value of the critical buckling stress (σ_{cr}) to the yield strength (σ_y). However, the value of the critical buckling stress (σ_{cr}) may be calculated if required.

Above the proportional limit (σ_p), the ratio $E = \sigma/\epsilon$ is no longer constant, but varies, depending upon

TABLE 1—Compression Load on Plate

Support (long plates)	Values for Plate Factor (k) to be Used in Formula	Critical Stress on Plate to Cause Buckling (σ'_{cr})
supported / free (σ)	$k = 0.425$	$\sigma'_{cr} = \sigma_{cr}$
fixed / free (σ)	$k = 1.277$	$\sigma'_{cr} = \sigma_{cr}$
supported / supported (σ)	$k = 4.00$	$\sigma'_{cr} = \sigma_{cr}$
supported / fixed (σ)	$k = 5.42$	$\sigma'_{cr} = \sigma_{cr}$
fixed / fixed (σ)	$k = 6.97$	$\sigma'_{cr} = \sigma_{cr}$

—Bleich, "Buckling Strength of Metal Structures," p. 330

the type of steel (represented by its stress-strain diagram) and the actual stress under consideration (position on the stress-strain diagram). See Figure 3.

Above the proportional limit (σ_p), the modulus of elasticity (E) must be multiplied by a factor (λ) to give the tangent modulus (E_t). The tangent modulus (E_t) is still the slope of the stress-strain diagram and $E_t = \sigma/\epsilon$, but it varies.

If it is assumed that the plate is "isotropic" (i.e., having the same properties in both directions x and y), the critical buckling formula becomes—

where:

$$\lambda = \frac{E_t}{E}$$

$$\sigma_{cr} = \frac{\pi^2 \, E \, \lambda}{12(1 - \nu^2)} \left(\frac{t}{b}\right)^2 k \qquad \ldots\ldots\ldots\ldots(2)$$

If it is assumed that the plate has "anisotropic" behavior (i.e. *not* having the same properties in both directions x and y), the tangent modulus (E_t) would be used for stresses in the x direction when the critical stress (σ_{cr}) is above the proportional limit (σ_p). However, the modulus of elasticity (E) would be used in the y direction because any stress in this direction would be below the proportional limit (σ_p). In this case, the above formula #2 would be conservative and the following would give better results:

$$\sigma_{cr} = \frac{\pi^2 \, E \, \sqrt{\lambda}}{12(1 - \nu^2)} \left(\frac{t}{b}\right)^2 k \qquad \ldots\ldots\ldots\ldots(3)$$

For steel, this becomes—

$$\sigma_{cr} = 2.710 \times 10^7 \sqrt{\lambda} \left(\frac{t}{b}\right)^2 k \qquad \ldots\ldots\ldots(4)$$

If the critical buckling stress (σ_{cr}) is *less* than the proportional limit (σ_p) then $\lambda = E_t/E = 1$ and formula #4 could be used directly in solving for critical stress (σ_{cr}).

However, if the critical buckling stress (σ_{cr}) is *greater* than the proportional limit (σ_p), then $\lambda < 1$ and formula #4 cannot be used directly. It would be better to divide through by $\sqrt{\lambda}$ and express the formula as—

$$\frac{\sigma_{cr}}{\sqrt{\lambda}} = 2.710 \times 10^7 \left(\frac{t}{b}\right)^2 k \qquad \ldots\ldots\ldots\ldots(5)$$

From the value of $\sigma_{cr}/\sqrt{\lambda}$, formula #6 will give the value of σ_{cr}. Obtain proper value for the plate factor (k) from Table 1 or 3.

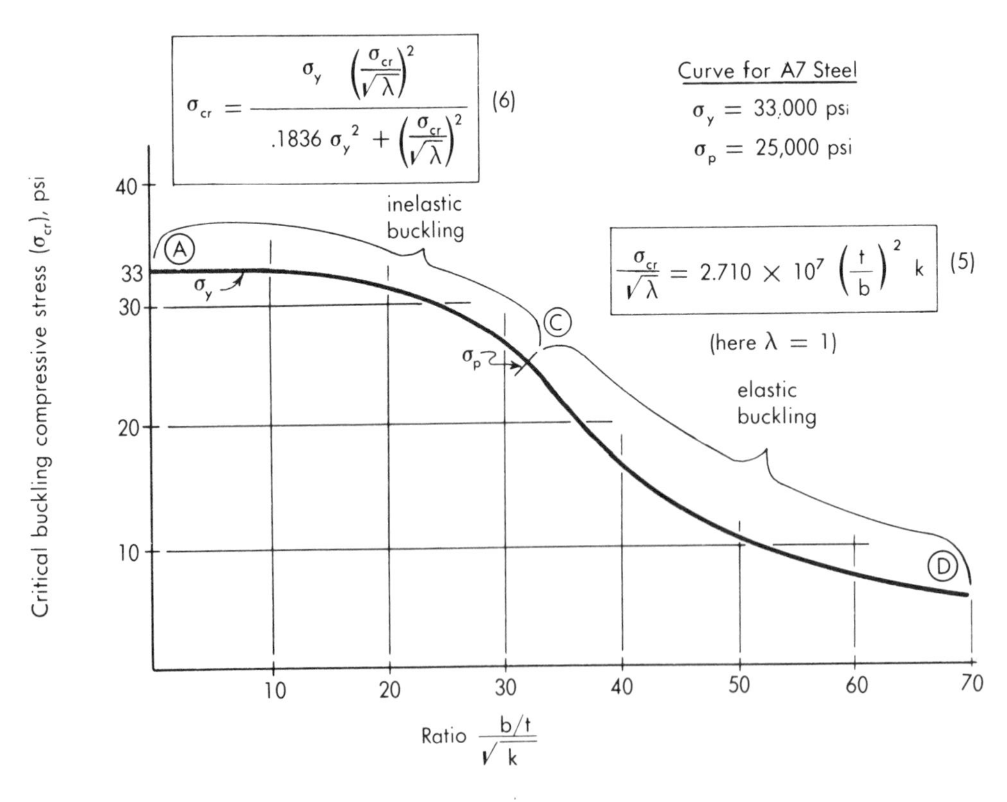

FIG. 2 Buckling stress curve for plates in compression.

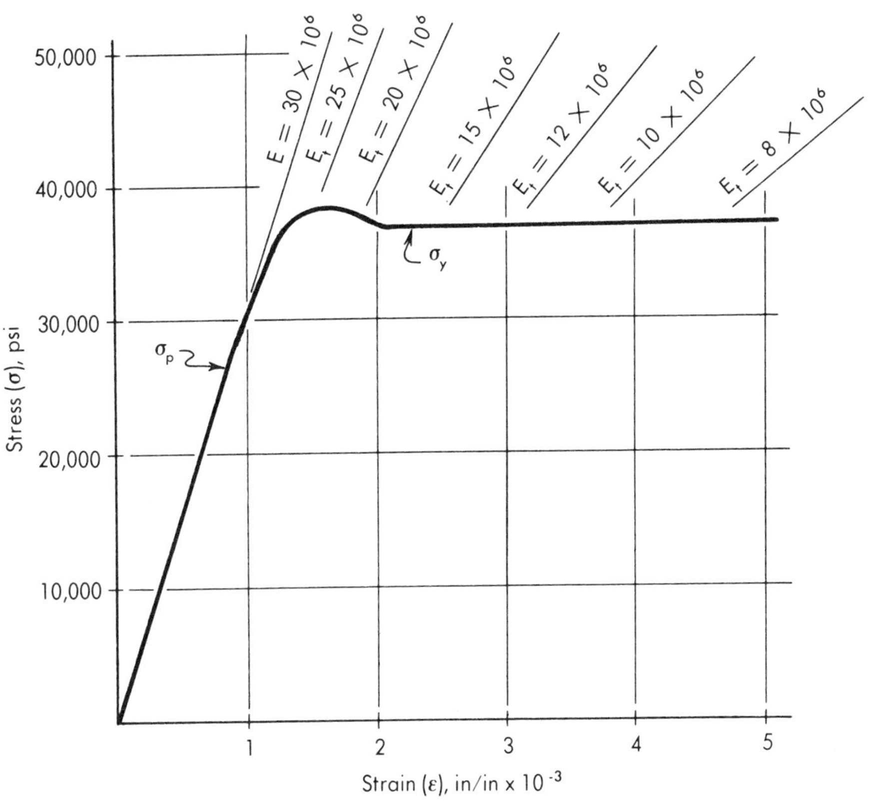

FIG. 3 Stress-strain diagram showing where tangent modulus need be applied to determine critical stress.

Determining Tangent Modulus Factor (λ)

Bleich in "Buckling Strength of Metal Structures", p. 54, gives the following expression for this factor ($\lambda = E_t/E$):

$$\lambda = \frac{(\sigma_y - \sigma_{cr})\ \sigma_{cr}}{(\sigma_y - \sigma_p)\ \sigma_p}$$

where:

σ_y = yield point

σ_p = proportional limit

σ_{cr} = critical buckling stress

If we use a ratio of—

$$\frac{\sigma_y}{\sigma_p} = 1.32 \quad \text{or} \quad \sigma_p = \frac{\sigma_y}{1.32}$$

the expression becomes—

$$\lambda = \frac{(\sigma_y - \sigma_{cr})\ \sigma_{cr}}{\left(\sigma_y - \dfrac{\sigma}{1.32}\right)\dfrac{\sigma}{1.32}}$$

$$= \frac{\sigma_y\ \sigma_{cr} - \sigma_{cr}^2}{.1836\ \sigma_y^2}$$

$$\therefore\ .1836\ \sigma_y^2\ \lambda = \sigma_y\ \sigma_{cr} - \sigma_{cr}^2$$

$$\text{or } .1836\ \sigma_y^2\ \lambda + \sigma_{cr}^2 = \sigma_y\ \sigma_{cr}$$

Then, multiply through by $\dfrac{\sigma_{cr}}{\lambda}$

$$.1836\ \sigma_y^2\ \sigma_{cr} + \frac{\sigma_{cr}^3}{\lambda} = \frac{\sigma_y\ \sigma_{cr}^2}{\lambda}$$

$$\sigma_{cr}\left(.1836\ \sigma_y^2 + \frac{\sigma_{cr}^2}{\lambda}\right) = \frac{\sigma_y\ \sigma_{cr}^2}{\lambda}$$

or

$$\boxed{\sigma_{cr} = \frac{\sigma_y \left(\dfrac{\sigma_{cr}}{\sqrt{\lambda}}\right)^2}{.1836\ \sigma_y^2 + \left(\dfrac{\sigma_{cr}}{\sqrt{\lambda}}\right)^2}} \quad \text{..............(6)}$$

TABLE 2—Shear Load on Plate

Support	Values for Plate Factor (k) to be Used in Formula	Critical Stress on Plate to Cause Buckling (τ'_{cr})
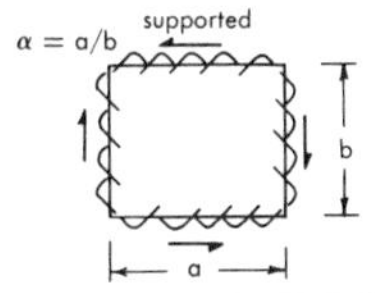	$k = 5.34 + \dfrac{4}{\alpha^2}$	$\tau'_{cr} = \dfrac{\sigma_{cr}}{\sqrt{3}}$
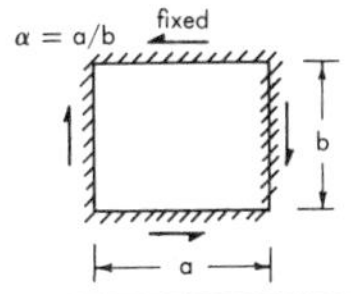	$k = 8.98 + \dfrac{5.6}{\alpha^2}$	$\tau'_{cr} = \dfrac{\sigma_{cr}}{\sqrt{3}}$

—Bleich, "Buckling Strength of Metal Structures," p. 395

See Figure 2 for curves representing these formulas applied to the critical buckling compressive stress of plates of A7 steel (σ_y = 33,000 psi).

3. BUCKLING OF PLATES UNDER SHEAR

The critical buckling shearing stress (τ_{cr}) of a plate when subject to shear forces (τ t) may be expressed by the formula in Figure 4 (similar to that used for the critical buckling stress for plates in edge compression).

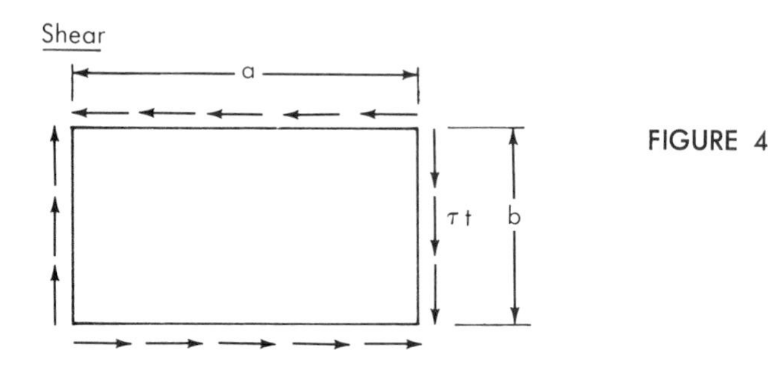

FIGURE 4

$$\tau_{cr} = \frac{k \pi^2 E}{12(1 - \nu^2)} \left(\frac{t}{b}\right)^2 \qquad \text{......(7)}$$

where:

E = modulus of elasticity in compression (Steel = 30,000,000 psi)

t = thickness of plate, inches

b = width of plate, inches

a = length of plate, inches (*a* is always the larger of the plate's dimensions)

ν = Poisson's ratio (for steel, usually = 0.3)

k = constant; depends upon plate shape b/a and edge restraint, and also accounts for the modulus of elasticity in shear (E_s). See Tables 2 and 3.

It is usual practice to assume the edges simply supported.

Shear yield strength of steel (τ) is usually considered as $\frac{1}{\sqrt{3}}$ of the tensile yield strength (σ_y), or .58 σ_y.

Since

$$\tau_{cr} = \frac{\sigma_{cr}}{\sqrt{3}}$$

$$\sigma_{cr} = \frac{\sqrt{3}\, k\, \pi^2 E}{12(1 - \nu^2)} \left(\frac{t}{b}\right)^2$$

TABLE 3—Critical Stress for Rectangular Plates Supported On 4 Sides
(Applies to Web of Girders Between Stiffeners and to Web of Frame Knee Between Stiffeners)

Load	Values for Plate Factor (k) to be Used in Formulas 3, 4, 5, and 6		Critical Stress τ'_{cr} and σ'_{cr}
Compression, $\sigma_1 = \sigma_2$, $\alpha = a/b$	when $\alpha \geqq 1$	$k = 4$	$\sigma'_{cr} = \sigma_{cr}$
	when $\alpha \leqq 1$	$k = \left(\alpha + \frac{1}{\alpha}\right)^2$	
Compression, $\sigma_2 = 0$, $\alpha = a/b$	when $\alpha \geqq 1$	$k = 7.7$	$\sigma'_{cr} = \sigma_{cr}$
	when $\alpha \leqq 1$	$k = 7.7 + 33\,(1 - \alpha)^3$	
Compression, $\sigma_1 = -\sigma_2$, $\alpha = a/b$	when $\alpha \geqq 2/3$	$k = 24$	$\sigma'_{cr} = \sigma_{cr}$
	when $\alpha \leqq 2/3$	$k = 24 + 73\,(2/3 - \alpha)^2$	
Shear, $\alpha = a/b$	when $\alpha \geqq 1$	$k = \sqrt{3}\left(5.34 + \frac{4}{\alpha^2}\right)$	$\tau'_{cr} = \frac{\sigma_{cr}}{\sqrt{3}}$
	when $\alpha \leqq 1$	$k = \sqrt{3}\left(4 + \frac{5.34}{\alpha^2}\right)$	

Since the plate constant (k) can be adjusted to contain the $\sqrt{3}$ factor, this becomes—

$$\sigma_{cr} = \frac{k\,\pi^2\,E}{12(1-\upsilon^2)}\left(\frac{t}{b}\right)^2$$

As before in the buckling of plates by compression, in the inelastic range the critical stress (σ_{cr}) exceeds the proportional limit (σ_p), and the tangent modulus (E_t) is introduced by the factor ($\lambda = E_t/E$). Therefore, formulas #5 and #6 would be used also in the buckling of plates by shear.

Proper values for the plate factor (k) are obtained from Table 2, for pure shear load, and Table 3, for shear load combined with compression.

TABLE 3—Critical Stress for Rectangular Plates Supported On 4 Sides — Continued —

(Applies to Web of Girder Between Stiffeners and to Web of Frame Knee Between Stiffeners)

Load	Values for Plate Factor (k) to be Used in Formulas 3, 4, 5, and 6	Critical Stress τ'_{cr} and σ'_{cr}
Compression and shear, $\sigma_1 = \sigma_2$; $\alpha = a/b$ $\beta = \sigma_1/\tau$	when $\sigma \geqq 1$: $k = 2\,\eta^2\beta\sqrt{\beta^2+3}\left[-1+\sqrt{1+\frac{4}{\beta^2\eta^2}}\right]$ where $\eta = \frac{4}{3} + \frac{1}{\alpha^2}$	$\tau'_{cr} = \frac{\sigma_{cr}}{\sqrt{\beta^2+3}}$
	when $\frac{1}{2} \leqq \alpha \leqq 1$: $k = \frac{\eta^2}{2}\left(\alpha + \frac{1}{\alpha^2}\right)^2\beta\sqrt{\beta^2+3}\left[-1+\sqrt{1+\frac{4}{\beta^2\eta^2}}\right]$ where $\eta = \frac{4\,\alpha^2 + 5.34}{(\alpha^2+1)^2}$	$\sigma'_{cr} = \frac{\beta\,\sigma_{cr}}{\sqrt{\beta^2+3}}$
Compression and shear, $\sigma_2 = 0$; $\alpha = a/b$ $\beta = \sigma_1/\tau$	when $\alpha \geqq 1$: $k = 3.85\,\eta^2\beta\sqrt{\beta^2+3}\left[-1+\sqrt{1+\frac{4}{\beta^2\eta^2}}\right]$ where $\eta = \frac{5.34 + 4/\alpha^2}{7.7}$	$\tau'_{cr} = \frac{\sigma_{cr}}{\sqrt{\beta^2+3}}$
	when $\frac{1}{2} \leqq \alpha \leqq 1$: $k = 3.85\,\eta^2\beta\sqrt{\beta^2+3}\left[-1+\sqrt{1+\frac{4}{\beta^2\eta^2}}\right]$ where $\eta = \frac{4 + 5.34/\alpha^2}{7.7 + 33\,(1-\alpha)^3}$	$\sigma'_{cr} = \frac{\beta\,\sigma_{cr}}{\sqrt{\beta^2+3}}$
Compression and shear, $\sigma_1 = -\sigma_2$; $\alpha = a/b$ $\beta = \sigma_1/\tau$	when $\alpha \geqq 1$: $k = 24\,\eta\sqrt{\beta^2+3}\sqrt{\frac{1}{1+\beta^2\eta^2}}$ where $\eta = \frac{2}{9} + \frac{1}{6\,\alpha^2}$	$\tau'_{cr} = \frac{\sigma_{cr}}{\sqrt{\beta^2+3}}$
	when $\frac{1}{2} \leqq \alpha \leqq 1$: $k = 24\,\eta\sqrt{\beta^2+3}\sqrt{\frac{1}{1+\beta^2\eta^2}}$ where $\eta = \frac{1}{6} + \frac{2}{9\,\alpha^2}$	$\sigma'_{cr} = \frac{\beta\,\sigma_{cr}}{\sqrt{\beta^2+3}}$

4. SUMMARY FOR DETERMINING CRITICAL BUCKLING STRESS OF PLATE

1. The value of the plate factor (k) to be used in formula #5 comes from Tables 1, 2 or 3, adapted from "Buckling Strength of Metal Structures", Bleich, pp 330, 395, 410.

2. Solve for $\sigma_{cr}/\sqrt{\lambda}$ from formula #5.

a. If $\sigma_{cr}/\sqrt{\lambda} \leqq \sigma_p$, this is the value of σ_{cr}, so go to step 4.

b. If $\sigma_{cr}/\sqrt{\lambda} > \sigma_p$, go to step 3.

3. Insert this value $(\sigma_{cr}/\sqrt{\lambda})$ into formula #6, and solve for the critical buckling stress (σ_{cr}).

4. After the critical stress (σ_{cr}) has been determined, the critical buckling stress of the given plate $(\sigma'_{rc}$ or $\tau'_{cr})$ is determined from the relationship shown in the right-hand column of Tables 1, 2, or 3.

5. BUCKLING STRESS CURVES (Compression)

In regard to plates subjected only to compression or only to shear, H. M. Priest and J. Gilligan in their "Design Manual for High Strength Steels" show the curve patterns, Figure 5 (compression) and Figure 10 (shear). They have divided the buckling curve into three distinct portions (A-B, B-C, and C-D), and have lowered the critical stress values in the elastic buckling region by 25% to more nearly conform to actual test results.

Values indicated on this typical curve are for ASTM A-7 (mild) steel, having a yield strength of 33,000 psi.

The buckling curve (dashed line) of Figure 2 has been superimposed on the Priest-Gilligan curve for comparison.

TABLE 4—Buckling Stress Formulas (Compression)

Portion of Curve	Factor $\frac{b/t}{\sqrt{k}}$	Critical Buckling Compressive Stress (σ_{cr}) Determined by
A to B	0 to $\frac{3820}{\sqrt{\sigma_y}}$	$\sigma_{cr} = \sigma_y$
B to C	$\frac{3820}{\sqrt{\sigma_y}}$ to $\frac{5720}{\sqrt{\sigma_y}}$	$\sigma_{cr} = 1.8\,\sigma_y - n\,\frac{b/t}{\sqrt{k}}$ where: $n = \frac{\sqrt{\sigma_y^3}}{4770}$
C to D	$\frac{5720}{\sqrt{\sigma_y}}$ and over	$\sigma_{cr} = \left[\frac{4434}{\left(\frac{b/t}{\sqrt{k}}\right)}\right]^2$

The horizontal line (A to B) is the limit of the yield strength (σ_y). Here σ_{cr} is assumed equal to σ_y.

The curve from B to C is expressed by—

$$\sigma_{cr} = 1.8\,\sigma_y - n\,\frac{(b/t)}{\sqrt{k}}$$

where:

$$n = \frac{\sqrt{\sigma_y^3}}{4770}$$

The curve from C to D is 75% of the critical buckling stress formula, Figure 1, or:

$$\sigma_{cr} = .75\,\frac{k\,\pi^2\,E}{12\,(1-\nu^2)}\left(\frac{t}{b}\right)^2$$

$$= \left[\frac{4434}{\frac{b/t}{\sqrt{k}}}\right]^2$$

All of this is expressed in terms of the factor

$\frac{b/t}{\sqrt{k}}$ See Table 4.

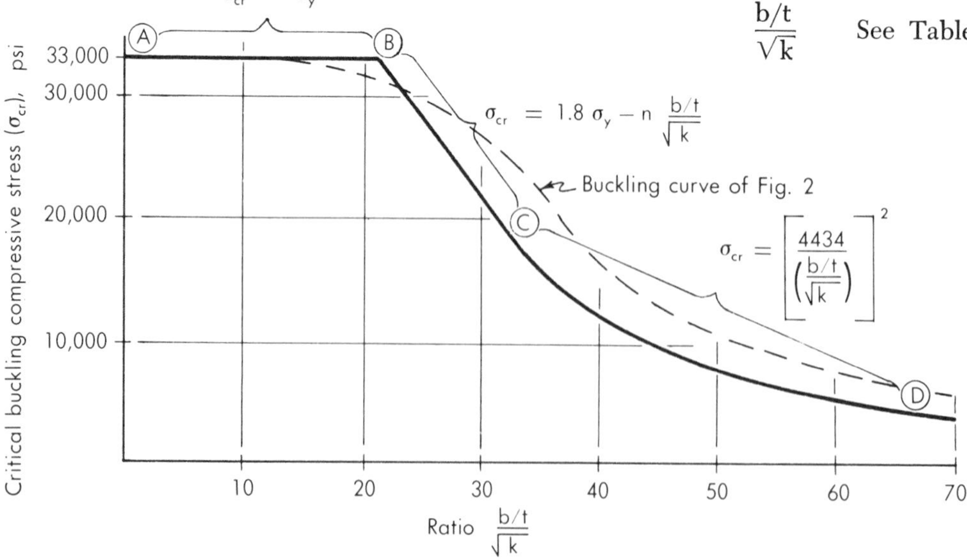

FIG. 5 Buckling stress curves for plates in edge compression.

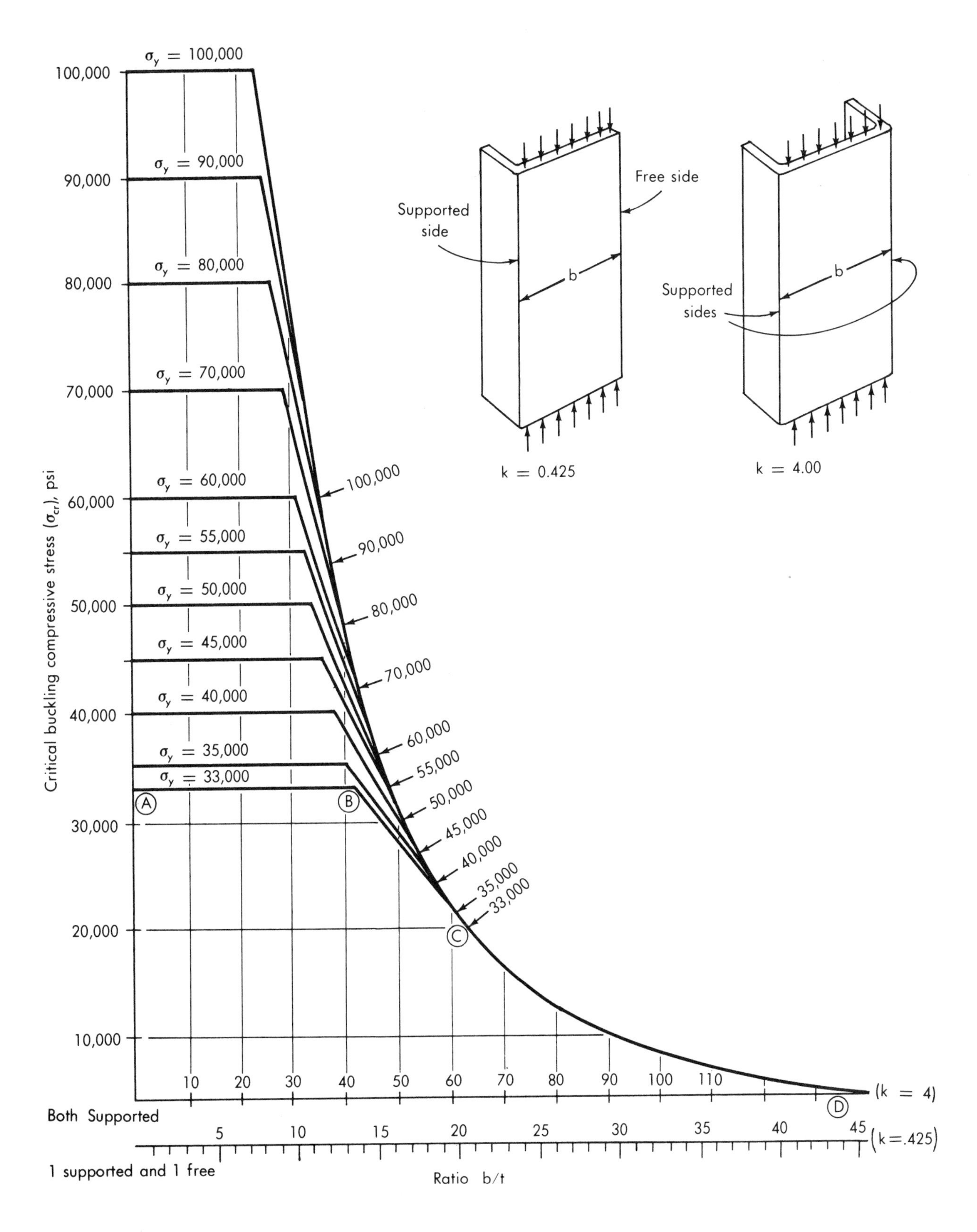

FIG. 6 Buckling stress curves (plates in edge compression) for various steels.

TABLE 5—Factors for Buckling Formulas

Yield Strength of Steel σ_y psi	$\left(\frac{b/t}{\sqrt{k}}\right)$ for Point B $= \frac{3820}{\sqrt{\sigma_y}}$	$\left(\frac{b/t}{\sqrt{k}}\right)$ for Point C $= \frac{5720}{\sqrt{\sigma_y}}$	$n = \frac{\sqrt{\sigma_y^3}}{4770}$
33,000	21.0	31.5	1260
35,000	20.4	30.6	1370
40,000	19.1	28.6	1680
45,000	18.0	27.0	2000
50,000	17.1	25.6	2340
55,000	16.3	24.4	2700
60,000	15.6	23.4	3080
70,000	14.4	21.6	3470
80,000	13.5	20.2	4740
90,000	12.7	19.1	5660
100,000	12.1	18.1	6630

TABLE 6—Limiting Values of b/t *(Code)*

Side Conditions	Yield Strength σ_y psi	AISC	AASHO	AREA
One simply supported; the other free	33,000	13 & 16	12	12
	50,000	11 & 13	—	—
Both simply supported	33,000	44	40	40
	50,000	36	34	32

AISC—American Institute of Steel Construction
AASHO—American Association of State Highway Officials
AREA—Amercan Railway Engineers Association

Factors needed for the formulas of curves in Figure 5, for steels of various yield strengths, are given in Table 5.

Figure 6 is just an enlargement of Figure 5, with additional steels having yield strengths from 33,000 psi to 100,000 psi.

For any given ratio of plate width to thickness (b/t), the critical buckling stress (σ_{cr}) can be read directly from the curves of this figure.

6. FACTOR OF SAFETY

A suitable factor of safety must be used with these values of b/t since they represent ultimate stress values for buckling.

Some structural specifications limit the ratio b/t to a maximum value (point B) at which the critical buckling stress (σ_{cr}) is equal to the yield strength (σ_y). By so doing, it is not necessary to calculate the buckling stress. These limiting values of b/t, as specified by several codes, are given in Table 6.

In general practice, somewhat more liberal values of b/t are recognized. Table 7, extended to higher yield strengths, lists these limiting values of b/t.

7. EFFECTIVE WIDTH OF PLATES IN COMPRESSION

The 20″ × ¼″ plate shown in Figure 7, simply supported along both sides, is subjected to a compressive load.

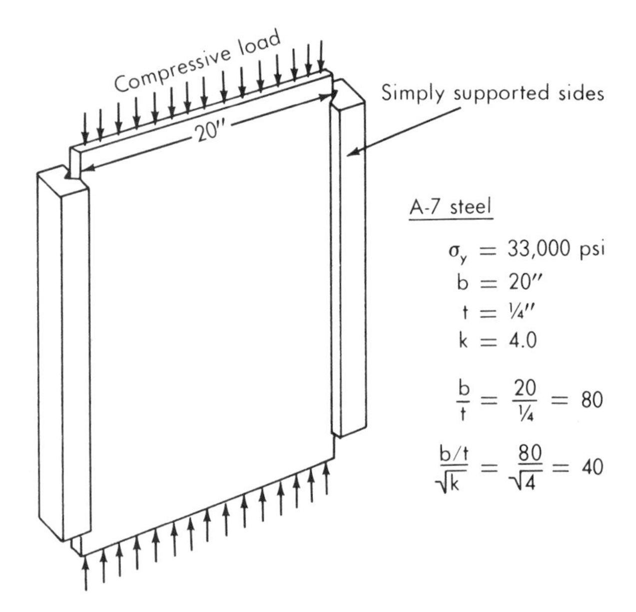

FIGURE 7

Under these conditions, the critical buckling compressive stress (σ_{cr}) as found from the curve (σ_y = 33,000 psi) in Figure 6 is—

$$\sigma_{cr} = 12{,}280 \text{ psi}$$

TABLE 7—Usual Limiting Values of b/t

Yield Strength σ_y psi	One Edge Simply Supported; the Other Edge Free	Both Edges Simply Supported
33,000	13.7	42.0
35,000	13.3	40.8
40,000	12.5	38.2
45,000	11.7	36.0
50,000	11.1	34.2
55,000	10.6	32.6
60,000	10.1	31.2
70,000	9.4	28.8
80,000	8.8	27.0
90,000	8.3	25.4
100,000	7.9	24.2

This value may also be found from the formulas in Table 4.

Since the ratio $\frac{b/t}{\sqrt{k}}$ is 40.0 and thus exceeds the value of 31.5 for point C, the following formula must be used—

$$\sigma_{cr} = \left[\frac{4434}{\frac{b/t}{\sqrt{k}}}\right]^2 = \left[\frac{4434}{40}\right]^2$$

$$= 12{,}280 \text{ psi}$$

At this stress, the middle portion of the plate would be expected to buckle, Figure 8. The compressive load at this stage of loading would be—

$$P = A\,\sigma = (20'' \times 1/4'')\ 12{,}280$$

$$= 61{,}400 \text{ lbs}$$

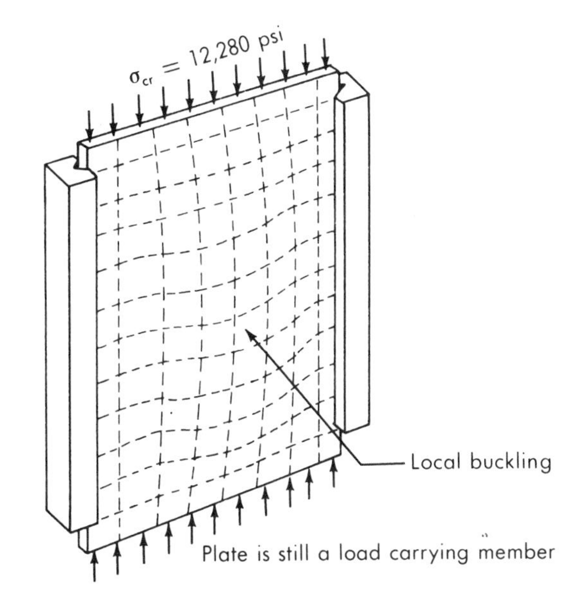

FIGURE 8

The over-all plate should not collapse since the portion of the plate along the supported sides could still be loaded up to the yield point (σ_y) before ultimate collapse.

This portion of the plate, called the "effective width" can be determined by finding the ratio b/t when (σ_{cr}) is set equal to yield strength (σ_y) or point B.

From Figure 6 we find—

$$\frac{b}{t} = 42.0$$

or from Table 4 we find—

$$\frac{b/t}{\sqrt{k}} = 21.0$$

Since k = 4.0 (both sides simply supported), the ratio—

$$\frac{b}{t} = 21.0\sqrt{k}$$

$$= 42.0$$

Since the plate thickness t = 1/4" width, b = 42.0 t or b = 10.5".

This is the effective width of the plate which may be stressed to the yield point (σ_y) before ultimate collapse of the entire plate.

The total compressive load at this state of loading would be as shown in Figure 9.

The total compressive load here would be—

$$P = A_1\,\sigma_1 + A_2\,\sigma_2$$

$$= (10\tfrac{1}{2} \times \tfrac{1}{4})(33{,}000) + (9\tfrac{1}{2} \times \tfrac{1}{4})(12{,}280)$$

$$= \underline{115{,}800 \text{ lbs}}$$

Another method makes no allowance for the central buckled portion as a load carrying member, it being assumed that the load is carried only by the supported portion of the plate. Hence the total compressive load would be—

$$P = A_1\,\sigma_1$$

$$= (10\tfrac{1}{2} \times \tfrac{1}{4})(33{,}000)$$

$$= \underline{86{,}600 \text{ lbs}}$$

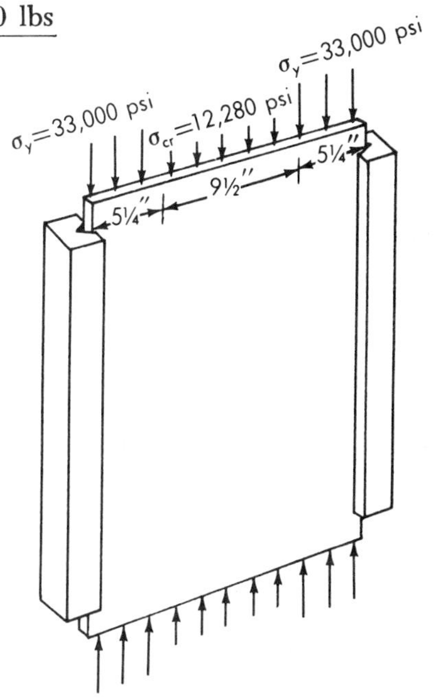

FIGURE 9

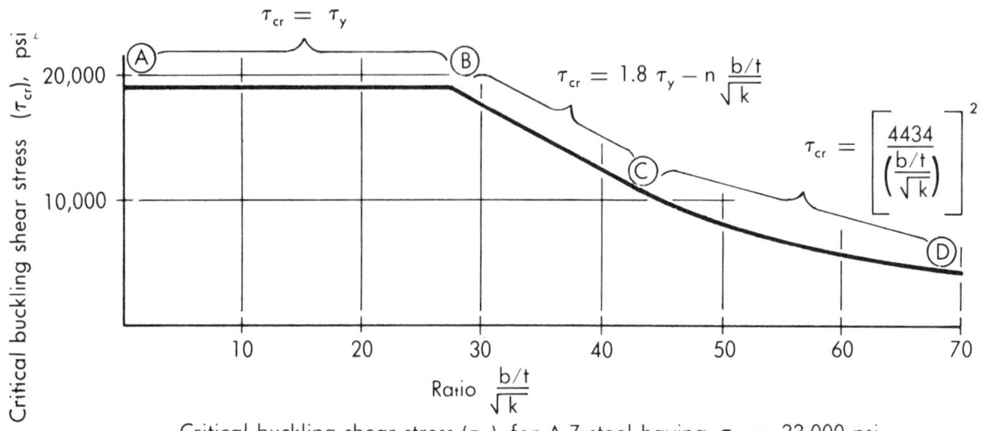

FIG. 10 Buckling stress curves for flate plates in shear.

8. BUCKLING STRESS CURVES (Shear)

The Priest & Gilligan curve, corresponding to Figure 5, when applied to the buckling of plates in shear is shown in Figure 10.

The curve is expressed in terms of $\left(\frac{b/t}{\sqrt{k}}\right)$. See Table 8. Comparison of Figure 10 and Table 8 with Figure 5 and Table 4 reveals the parallelism of critical buckling stress for compression (σ_{cr}) and for shear (τ_{cr}).

Figure 11 is just an enlargement of Figure 10, with additional steels having yield strengths from 33,000 psi to 100,000 psi. Factors needed for the formulas of curves in Figure 11 are given in Table 9.

For any value of $\left(\frac{b/a}{\sqrt{k}}\right)$ the critical buckling shear stress (τ_{cr}) can be read directly from the curves of this figure.

A suitable factor of safety must be used with these values since they represent ultimate stress values for buckling.

By holding the ratio of $\left(\frac{b/a}{\sqrt{k}}\right)$ to the value at point B, $\tau_{cr} = \tau_y$ and it will not be necessary to compute the critical shear stress (τ_{cr}). Assuming the edges are simply supported, the value of $k = 5.34 + 4(b/a)^2$ Then using just the three values of b/a as 1 (a square panel), ½ (the length twice the width of panel) and zero (or infinite length), the required b/t value is obtained from Table 10 for steels of various yield strengths. The plate thickness is then adjusted as necessary to meet the requirement.

Notice in Figure 10 and Table 8 that the critical buckling stress in shear is given directly as (τ_{cr}). In Tables 2 and 3 it is given first as (σ_{cr}) and then changed to (τ_{cr}).

TABLE 8—Buckling Stress Formulas *(Shear)*

Portion of Curve	Factor $\frac{b/t}{\sqrt{k}}$	Critical Buckling Shear Stress (τ_{cr}) Determined by
A to B	0 to $\frac{3820}{\sqrt{\tau_y}}$	$\tau_{cr} = \tau_y$
B to C	$\frac{3820}{\sqrt{\tau_y}}$ to $\frac{5720}{\sqrt{\tau_y}}$	$\tau_{cr} = 1.8\ \tau_y - n \frac{b/t}{\sqrt{k}}$ where: $n = \frac{\sqrt{\tau_y^3}}{4770}$
C to D	$\frac{5720}{\sqrt{\tau_y}}$ and over	$\tau_{cr} = \left[\frac{4434}{\frac{b/t}{\sqrt{k}}}\right]^2$

TABLE 9—Factors for Buckling Formulas *(Shear)*

Yield Strength of Steel σ_y psi	Corresponding Shearing Yield Strength $\tau_y = .58\ \sigma_y$ psi	$\frac{b/t}{\sqrt{k}}$ for point B $= \frac{3820}{\sqrt{\tau_y}}$	$\frac{b/t}{\sqrt{k}}$ for point C $= \frac{5720}{\sqrt{\tau_y}}$	$n = \frac{^2\sqrt{\tau_y^3}}{4770}$
33,000	19,100	27.6	41.4	550
35,000	20,300	27.6	40.2	610
40,000	23,200	25.1	37.6	740
45,000	26,100	23.6	35.4	880
50,000	29,000	22.4	33.6	1030
55,000	31,900	21.4	32.1	1200
60,000	34,800	20.5	30.7	1360
70,000	40,600	19.0	28.4	1680
80,000	46,400	17.7	26.6	2100
90,000	52,200	16.7	25.1	2500
100,000	58,000	15.9	23.8	2920

TABLE 10—Maximum Values of b/t To Avoid Formulas

Maximum Values of b/t to Hold τ_{cr} to τ_y (Panels with simply supported edges)			
Tensile Yield Strength σ_y psi	b/a = 1 (square panel)	b/a = ½ (panel with length twice the width)	b/a = 0 (panel with infinite length)
33,000	84.5	69.6	63.9
35,000	82.0	67.6	62.0
40,000	76.7	63.2	58.0
45,000	72.3	59.6	54.7
50,000	68.6	56.5	51.9
55,000	65.4	53.9	49.5
60,000	62.6	51.6	47.4
70,000	58.0	47.8	43.9
80,000	54.2	44.7	41.0
90,000	51.1	42.1	38.7
100,000	48.5	40.0	36.7

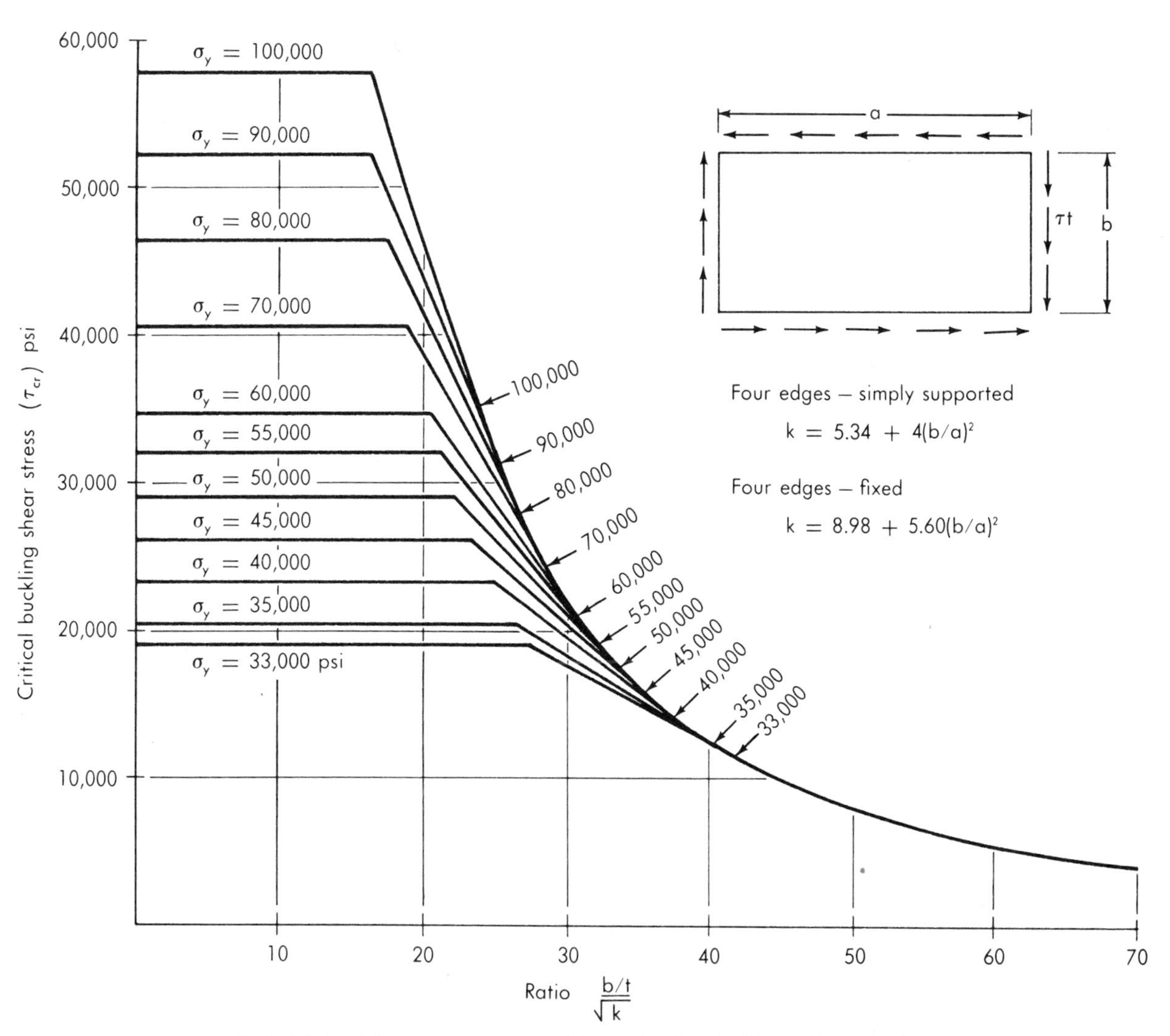

FIG. 11 Buckling stress curves (plates in shear) for various steels.

United Airlines hangar at San Francisco features double-cantilevered roof over areas into which large jet aircraft are wheeled, nosing up to the 3-story inner "core" for servicing. Center girder section half (at left) is completely shop welded. Large plate girders like this one are stiffened to prevent web buckling due to edge compression. Cantilevered welded plate girders weigh 125 tons.

Analysis of Compression

1. COMPRESSIVE STRESS

Compressive loading of a member when applied (axially) concentric with the center of gravity of the member's cross-section, results in compressive stresses distributed uniformly across the section. This compressive unit stress is —

$$\sigma_c = \frac{P}{A} \qquad (1)$$

A *short* column (slenderness ratio L/r equal to about unity or less) that is overloaded in compression may fail by crushing. From a design standpoint, short compression members present little problem. It is important to hold the compressive unit stress within the material's compressive strength.

For steel, the yield and ultimate strengths are considered to be the same in compression as in tension.

Any holes or openings in the section in the path of force translation will weaken the member, unless such openings are completely filled by another member that will carry its share of the load.

Excessive compression of *long* columns may cause failure by buckling. As compressive loading of a long column is increased, it eventually causes some eccentricity. This in turn sets up a bending moment, causing the column to deflect or buckle slightly. This deflection increases the eccentricity and thus the bending moment. This may progress to where the bending moment is increasing at a rate greater than the increase in load, and the column soon fails by buckling.

2. SLENDERNESS RATIO

As the member becomes longer or more slender, there is more of a tendency for ultimate failure to be caused by buckling. The most common way to indicate this tendency is the slenderness ratio which is equal to —

$$\frac{L}{r}$$

where L = unsupported length of member

r = the least radius of gyration of the section

and—

$$r = \sqrt{\frac{I}{A}} \qquad (2)$$

If the member is made longer, using the same cross-section and the same compressive load, the resulting compressive stress will remain the same, although the tendency for buckling will increase. The slenderness ratio increases as the radius of gyration of the section is reduced or as the length of the member is increased. The allowable compressive load which may be applied to the member decreases as the slenderness ratio increases.

The various column formulas (Tables 3 and 4) give the allowable average compressive stress ($\underline{\sigma}$) for the column. They do not give the actual unit stress developed in the column by the load. The unit stress resulting from these formulas may be multiplied by the cross-sectional area of the column to give the allowable load which may be supported.

3. RADIUS OF GYRATION

The radius of gyration (r) is the distance from the neutral axis of a section to an imaginary point at which the whole area of the section could be concentrated and still have the same amount of inertia. It is found by the expression: $r = \sqrt{I/A}$.

In the design of unsymmetrical sections to be used as columns, the least radius of gyration (r_{min}) of the section must be known in order to make use of the slenderness ratio (L/r) in the column formulas.

If the section in question is not a standard rolled section the properties of which are listed in steel handbooks, it will be necessary to compute this least radius of gyration. Since the least radius of gyration is —

$$r_{min} = \sqrt{\frac{I_{min}}{A}} \qquad (3)$$

the minimum moment of inertia of the section must be determined.

Minimum Moment of Inertia

The maximum moment of inertia (I_{max}) and the minimum moment of inertia (I_{min}) of a cross-section are

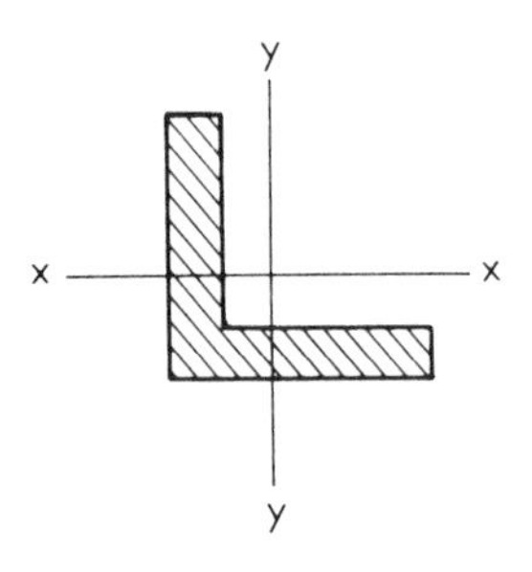

FIGURE 1

found on principal axes, 90° to each other.

$$I_{\substack{max \\ min}} = \frac{I_x + I_y}{2} \pm \sqrt{\left(\frac{I_x - I_y}{2}\right)^2 + I_{xy}^2} \quad \ldots .(4)$$

Knowing I_x, I_y, and I_{xy} it will be possible to find I_{min}.

Problem I

Locate the (neutral) x-x and y-y axes of the offset T section shown in Figure 2:

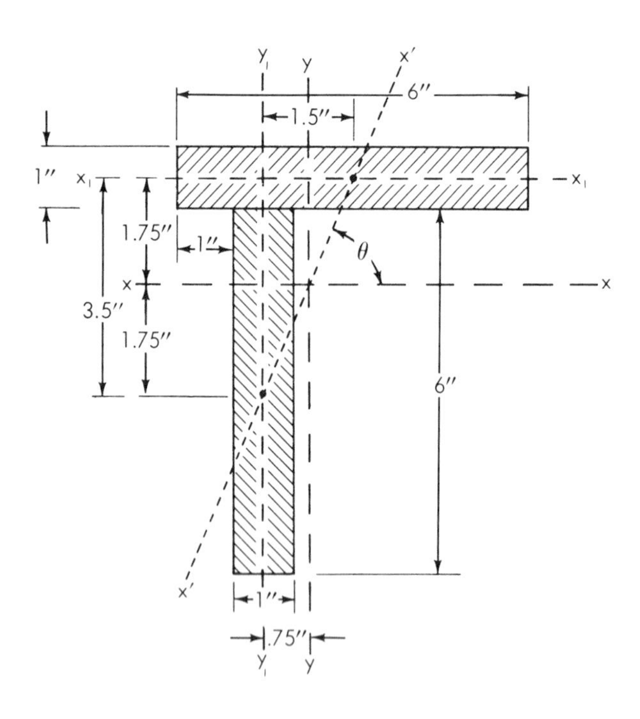

FIGURE 2

to locate neutral axis x-x:

	A	d	M
6" × 1"	6.0	0	0
1" × 6"	6.0	− 3.5	− 21.0
Total ⟶	12.0		− 21.0

where d = distance from center of gravity of element area to parallel axis (here: x_1-x_1)

and, applying formula #1 from Section 2.3, the distance of neutral axis x-x from its parallel axis x_1-x_1 is —

$$NA_{x\text{-}x} = \frac{\Sigma M}{\Sigma A} = \frac{-21.0}{12.0} = -1.75''$$

to locate neutral axis y-y:

	A	d	M
1" × 6"	6.0	+ 1.5	+ 9.0
6" × 1"	6.0	0	0
Total ⟶	12.0		+ 9.0

$$NA_{y\text{-}y} = \frac{\Sigma M}{\Sigma A} = \frac{+9.0}{12.0} = +.75''$$

product of inertia

It will be necessary to find the product of inertia (I_{xy}) of the section. This is the area (A) times the product of distances d_x and d_y as shown in Figure 3.

(See Figure 3 on facing page).

In finding the moment of inertia of an area about a given axis (I_x or I_y), it is not necessary to consider the signs of d_x or d_y. However, in finding the product of inertia, it is necessary to know the signs of d_x and d_y because the product of these two could be either positive or negative and this will determine the sign of the resulting product of inertia. The total product of inertia of the whole section, which is the sum of the values of the individual areas, will depend upon these signs. Areas in diagonally opposite quadrants will have products of inertia having the same sign.

The product of inertia of an individual rectangular area, the sides of which are parallel to the x-x and y-y axes of the entire larger section is —

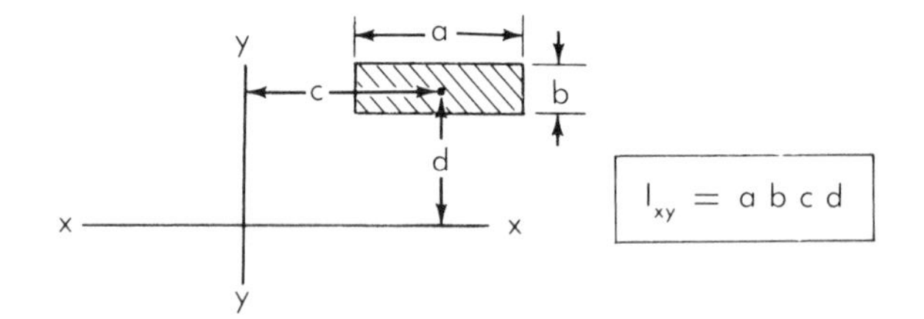

FIGURE 4

where:

a and b = dimensions of rectangle (= A)

d and c = distance of area's center of gravity to the x-x and y-y axes (= d_x and d_y)

The product of inertia of a T or angle section is — (See Figure 5).

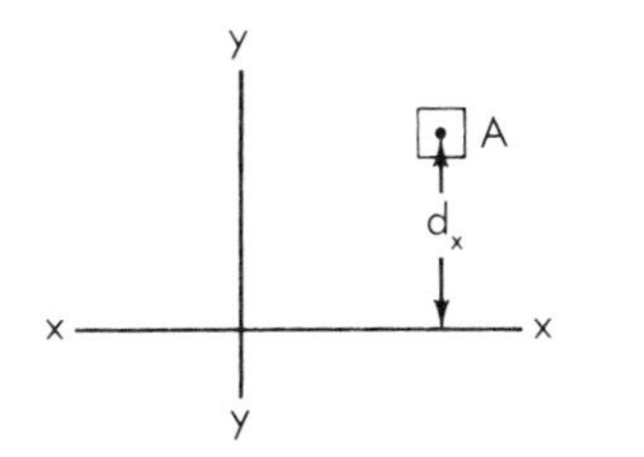

$I_x = A\,d_x^2$
Moment of inertia about x-x axis

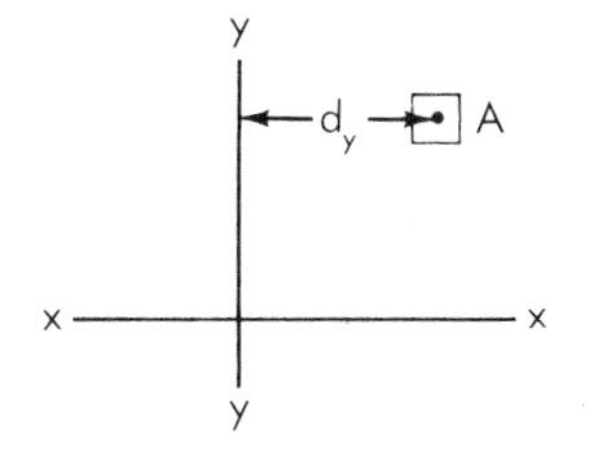

$I_y = A\,d_y^2$
Moment of inertia about y-y axis

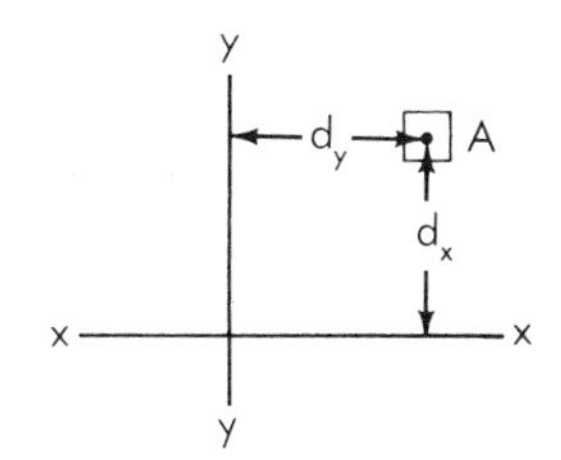

$I_{xy} = A\,d_x\,d_y$
Product of inertia about x-x and y-y axes

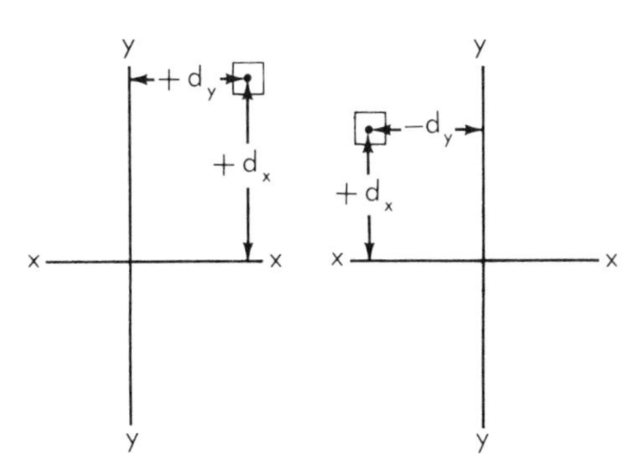

1st Quadrant
$I_{xy} = +A\,d_x\,d_y$

2nd Quadrant
$I_{xy} = -A\,d_x\,d_y$

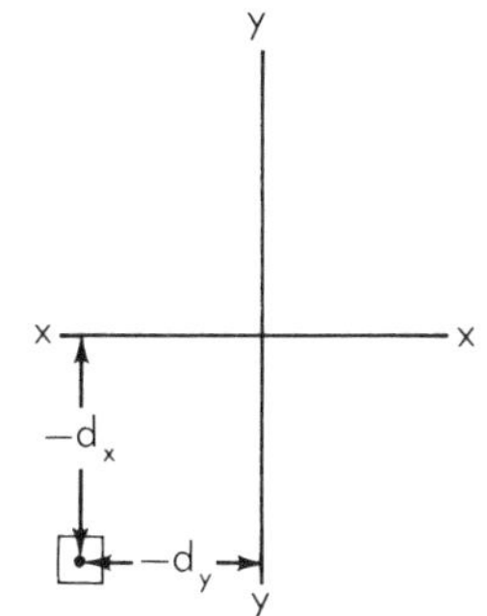

3rd Quadrant
$I_{xy} = +A\,d_x\,d_y$

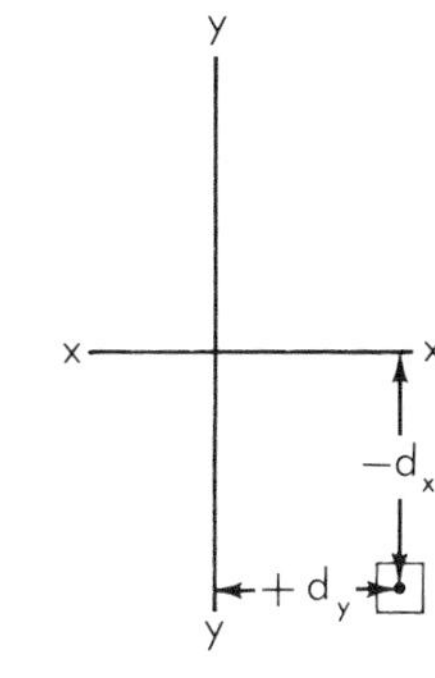

4th Quadrant
$I_{xy} = -A\,d_x\,d_y$

FIGURE 3

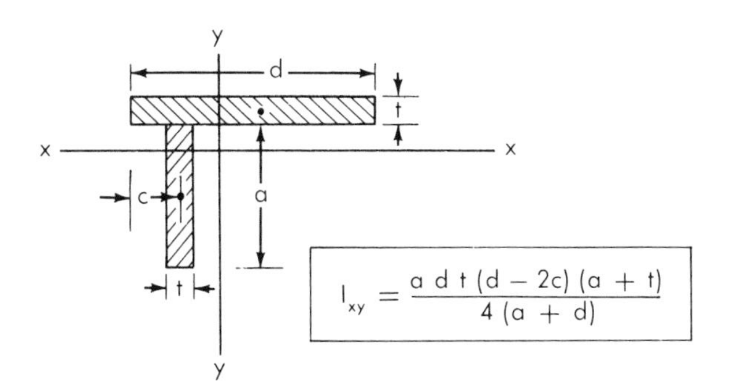

FIGURE 5

Here, determine sign by inspection.

Problem 2

Determine the product of inertia of this offset T section about the x-x and y-y axes:

$$
\begin{aligned}
I_{xy} &= \Sigma A\,(d_x)(d_y) \\
&= 2.5\,(+1)(+.555) + 2\,(-1.25)(-.695) \\
&= +1.388 + 1.737 \\
&= \underline{+3.125 \text{ in.}^4}
\end{aligned}
$$

Now use formula given previously for product of inertia of such a section:

$$
\begin{aligned}
I_{xy} &= \frac{a\,d\,t\,(d - 2c)(a + t)}{4\,(a + d)} \\
&= \frac{(4)(5)(\tfrac{1}{2})(5 - 2.5)(4 + \tfrac{1}{2})}{4\,(4 + 5)} \\
&= \underline{+3.125 \text{ in.}^4}
\end{aligned}
$$

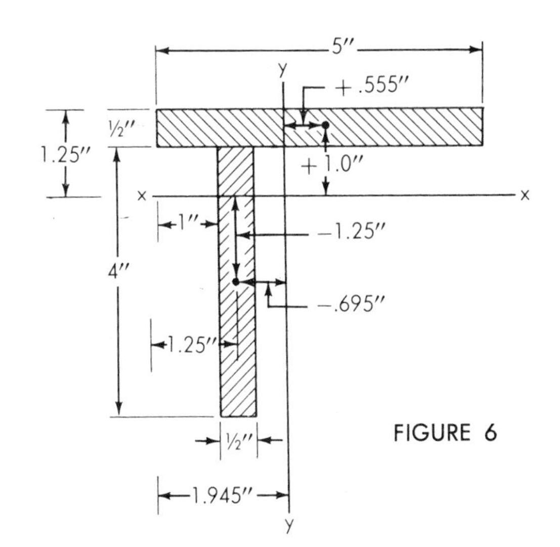

FIGURE 6

Problem 3

Determine the minimum radius of gyration of the offset T section shown previously (Fig. 2) and repeated here:

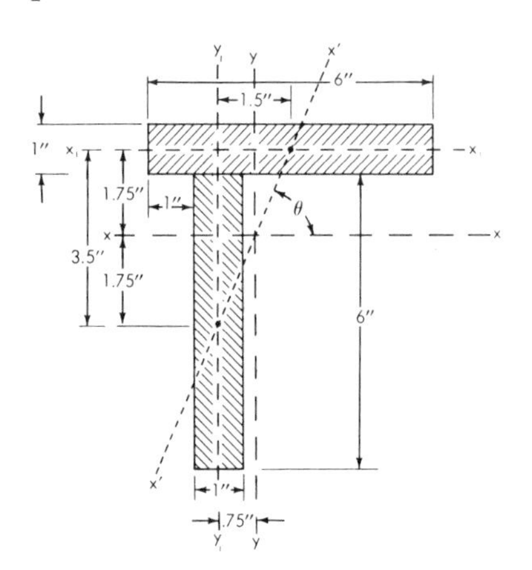

FIGURE 7

moment of inertia about axis x-x

	A	d	M	I	I_g
6″ × 1″	6.0	0	0	0	.50
1″ × 6″	6.0	− 3.5	− 21.0	+ 73.5	18.00
Total ⟶	12.0		− 21.0	+ 92.00	

$$NA_{x\text{-}x} = \frac{\Sigma M}{\Sigma A} = \frac{-21.0}{12.0} = -1.75'' \text{ and}$$

$$I_x = I - \frac{M^2}{A} = 92.00 - 36.75 = 55.25 \text{ in.}^4$$

moment of inertia about axis y-y

	A	d	M	I	I_g
1″ × 6″	6.0	+ 1.5	+ 9.0	13.5	18.00
6″ × 1″	6.0	0	0	0	.50
Total ⟶	12.0		+ 9.0	+ 32.00	

$$NA_{y\text{-}y} = \frac{\Sigma M}{\Sigma A} = \frac{+9.0}{12.0} = +.75'' \text{ and}$$

$$I_y = I - \frac{M^2}{A} = 32.00 - 6.75 = 25.25 \text{ in.}^4$$

product of inertia

$$I_{xy} = \Sigma A\,(d_x)(d_y)$$
$$= (1 \times 6)(+1.75)(+.75) + (1 \times 6)(-1.75)(-.75)$$
$$= +15.75 \text{ in.}^4$$

minimum moment of inertia

$$I_{min} = \frac{I_x + I_y}{2} - \sqrt{\left(\frac{I_x + I_y}{2}\right)^2 + I_{xy}^2}$$

$$= \frac{55.25 + 25.25}{2} - \sqrt{\left(\frac{55.25 - 25.25}{2}\right)^2 + (15.75)^2}$$

$$= 40.25 - 21.75$$
$$= 18.50 \text{ in.}^4$$

minimum radius of gyration

$$r_{min} = \sqrt{\frac{I_{min}}{A}}$$
$$= \sqrt{\frac{18.50}{12.0}} = \sqrt{1.542}$$
$$= \underline{1.24''}$$

As a matter of interest, this r_{min} is about axis x′-x′, the angle (θ) of which is—

$$\tan 2\theta = -\frac{2\,I_{xy}}{I_x - I_y} \quad \text{(See sketch below).}$$

$$= -\frac{2\,(15.75)}{55.25 - 25.25} = -1.05$$

$$2\theta = -46.4° \text{ or } +133.6°$$
$$\text{and } \theta = +66.8°$$

Any ultimate buckling could be expected to occur about this axis (x′-x′).

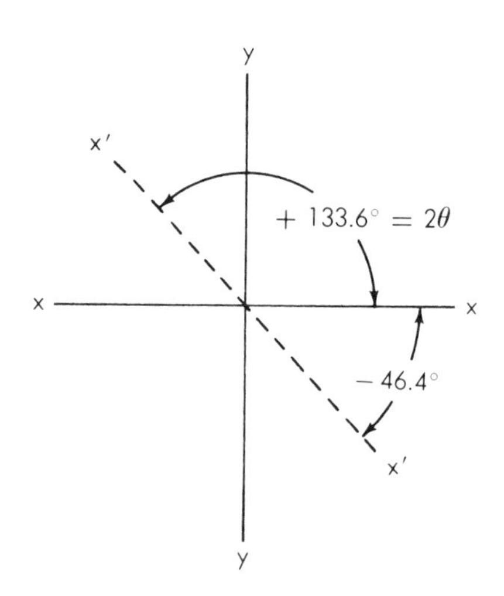

Problem 4

The channel section, Figure 8, is to be used as a column. Determine its radius of gyration about its x-x axis.

Using the conventional formulas for the properties of the section—

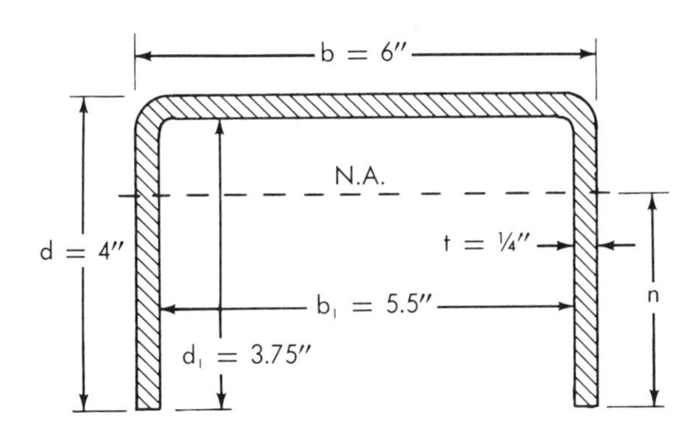

FIGURE 8

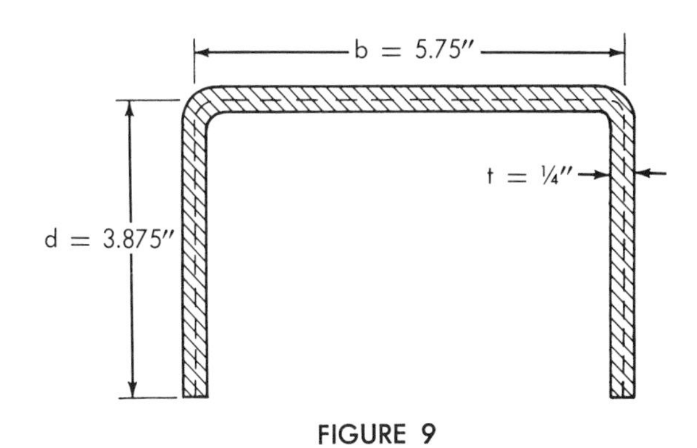

FIGURE 9

area of the section

$$A = bd - b_1d_1 = (6)(4) - (5.5)(3.75)$$
$$= 3.375 \text{ in.}^2$$

distance of neutral axis

$$n = d - \frac{2\ d^2t + b_1t^2}{2\ db - 2\ b_1d_1}$$
$$= 4 - \frac{2(4)^2(.25) + (5.5)(.25)^2}{2(4)(6) - 2(5.5)(3.75)}$$
$$= 2.764''$$

moment of inertia

$$I = \frac{2\ d^3t + b_1t^3}{3} - A(d - n)^2$$
$$= \frac{2(4)^3(.25) + (5.5)(.25)^3}{3} - 3.375\ (4 - 2.764)^2$$
$$= 5.539''$$

radius of gyration

$$r = \sqrt{\frac{I}{A}}$$
$$= \sqrt{\frac{5.539}{3.375}}$$
$$= \underline{1.281''}$$

If a slide rule had been used, assuming a possible error of ± one part in 1000 for every operation, this answer could be as high as 1.336″ and as low as 1.197″. This represents an error of + 4.3% and − 6.6%. For this reason it is necessary, when using these conventional formulas, to make use of logarithms or else do the work longhand. To do this requires about 30 minutes.

The radius of gyration will now be found directly, using the properties of thin sections, treating them as a line. See Table 2. Section 2.2.

Mean dimensions b and d are used, Figure 9.

$$r_x = \frac{\sqrt{d^3/3(2b + d)}}{b + 2d}$$
$$= \frac{\sqrt{3.875^3/3(2 \times 5.75 + 3.875)}}{5.75 + 2(3.875)}$$
$$= \underline{1.279''}$$

The exact value obtained from this formula for r is 1.279″. The value obtained by using the conventional formula is 1.281″.

Assuming a possible error of ± one part in 1000 for every operation of the slide rule, it would be possible to get an answer as high as 1.283″ and as low as 1.275″. This represents an error of about ¼ of the error using the conventional formulas with slide rule. The time for this last calculation was 2 minutes.

Moment of Inertia About Any Axis

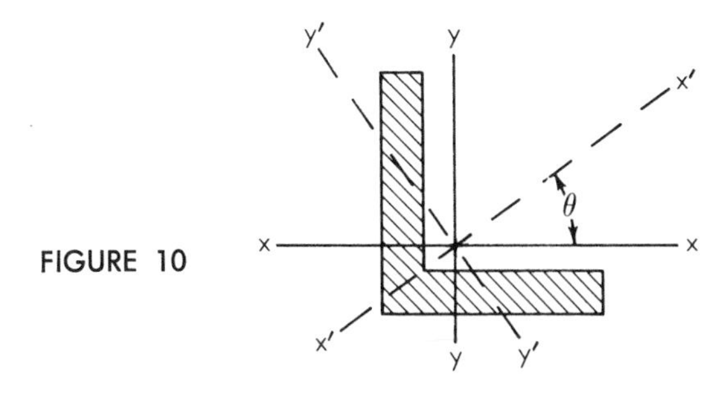

FIGURE 10

Sometimes (as in Problem 3) the moment of inertia of a section is needed about an axis lying at an angle (θ) with the conventional x-x axis. This may be found by using the product of inertia (I_{xy}) of the section about the conventional axes (x-x and y-y) with the moments of inertia (I_x) and (I_y) about these same axes in the following formula:

$$\boxed{I_x' = I_x\cos^2\theta + I_y\sin^2\theta - I_{xy}\sin^2\theta} \quad \ldots\ldots\ldots (7)$$

$$\boxed{I_y' = I_x\sin^2\theta + I_y\cos^2\theta - I_{xy}\sin^2\theta} \quad \ldots\ldots\ldots (8)$$

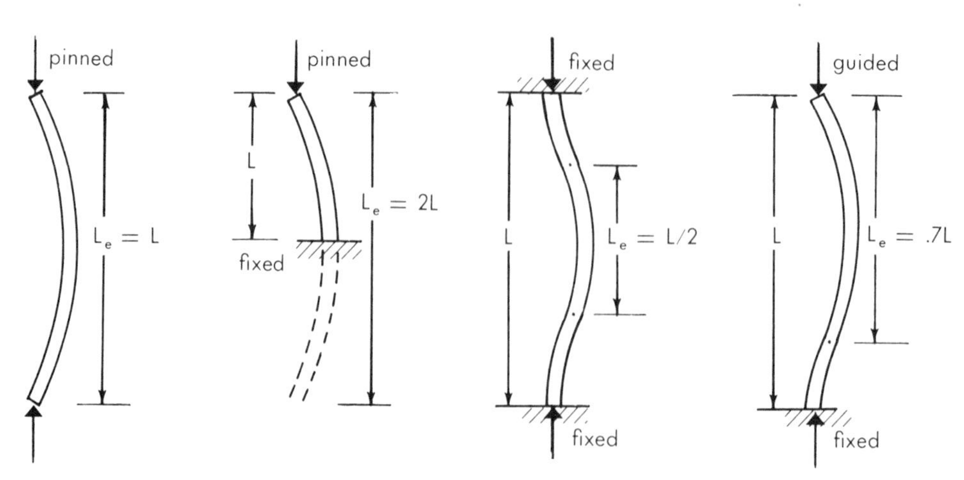

FIGURE 11

4. CRITICAL COMPRESSIVE STRESS

The critical load on a column as given by the Euler-formula is —

$$P_{cr} = \frac{\pi^2 E I}{L_e^2} \quad \text{.........................(9)}$$

where L_e = effective length of column.

This can be changed into terms of average critical stress by dividing by the cross-sectional area of the column. Since $A = I/r^2$, this becomes —

$$\sigma_{cr} = \frac{\pi^2 E}{(L_e/r)^2} \quad \text{.........................(10)}$$

Because this formula gives excessively high values for short columns, Engesser modified it by substituting the tangent modulus (E_t) in place of the usual Young's modulus of elasticity (E).

The modified formula then becomes —

$$\sigma_{cr} = \frac{\pi^2 E_t}{(L_e/r)^2} \quad \text{.........................(11)}$$

where:

E_t = tangent modulus of elasticity, corresponding to the modulus of elasticity when stressed to σ_{cr}.

r = least radius of gyration of the cross-section

L_e = effective length of the column, corresponding to the length of a pinned column that would have the same critical load. See Figure 11.

The Engesser formula is also called the Tangent Modulus formula and checks well with experimental values.

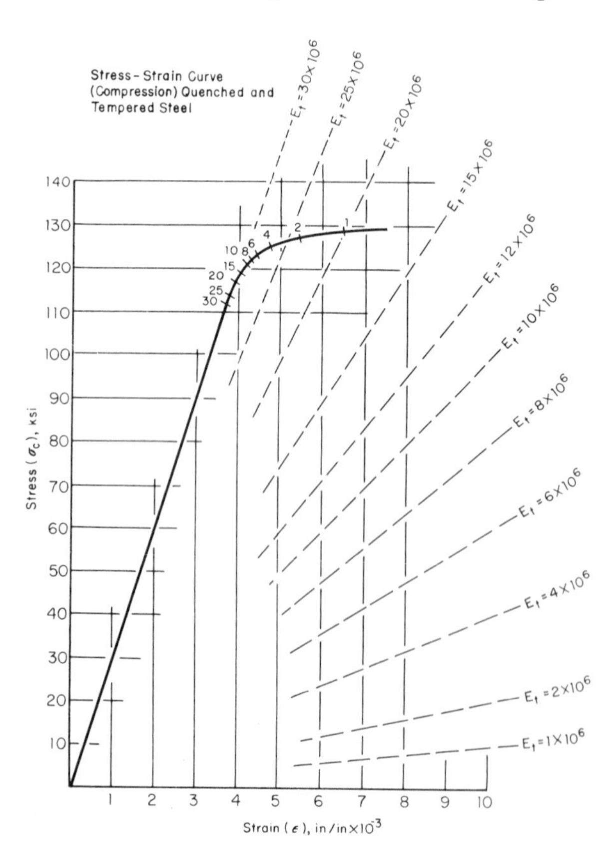

FIGURE 12

5. TANGENT MODULUS

Use of the Tangent Modulus formula necessitates a stress-strain curve (preferably in compression) of the material. See Figure 12, stress-strain curve for a quenched and tempered steel in compression. Whereas the usual Young's modulus of elasticity represents a fixed value for steel (30×10^6) according to the ratio

Slenderness Ratios: Quenched & Tempered Steel

TABLE 1

σ_c	E_t	L_e/r
110,000	30.2×10^6	52.1
112,000	30.0	51.4
114,000	26.5	47.9
116,000	22.0	43.4
118,000	17.5	38.3
120,000	13.0	32.7
122,000	9.0	27.0
124,000	5.5	20.9
126,000	3.3	16.1
128,000	1.5	10.8

Engesser portion of curve
(inelastic bending)

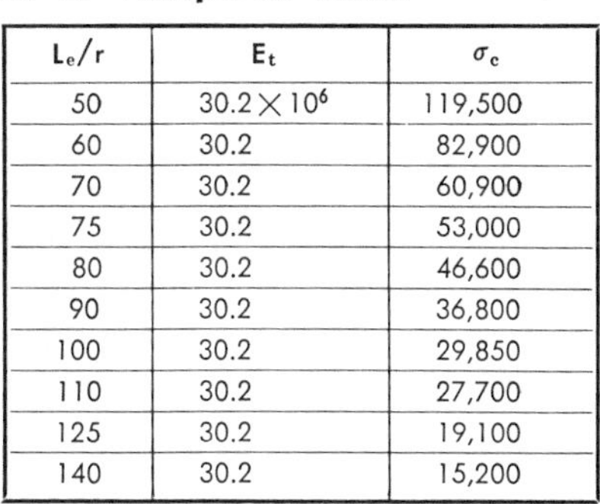

L_e/r	E_t	σ_c
50	30.2×10^6	119,500
60	30.2	82,900
70	30.2	60,900
75	30.2	53,000
80	30.2	46,600
90	30.2	36,800
100	30.2	29,850
110	30.2	27,700
125	30.2	19,100
140	30.2	15,200

TABLE 2

Euler portion of curve
(elastic bending)

of stress to strain below the proportional limit, the tangent modulus of elasticity takes into consideration the changing effect of plastic strain beyond this point corresponding to the actual stress involved.

Notice, in Figure 12, the broken lines representing the slope for various values of tangent modulus of elasticity (E_t), in this case from 1×10^6 psi up to 30×10^6. The compressive stress level (σ_c) at which a given E_t value applies is determined by moving out parallel from that reference modulus line (dotted), by means of parallel rule or other suitable device, until the stress-strain curve is intersected at one point only. The line is tangent at this point.

The compressive stress-strain curve for any material can be superimposed on this graph and the values of E_t at a given stress level (σ_c) read by the same technique.

The values of tangent modulus (E_t) for quenched and tempered steel, as read from Figure 12, are now plotted against the corresponding compressive stress (σ_c). This is shown in Figure 13.

The Engesser or tangent modulus formula for critical stress (σ_{cr}) is then put into the following form —

$$\frac{L_e}{r} = \pi \sqrt{\frac{E_t}{\sigma_{cr}}} \qquad (12)$$

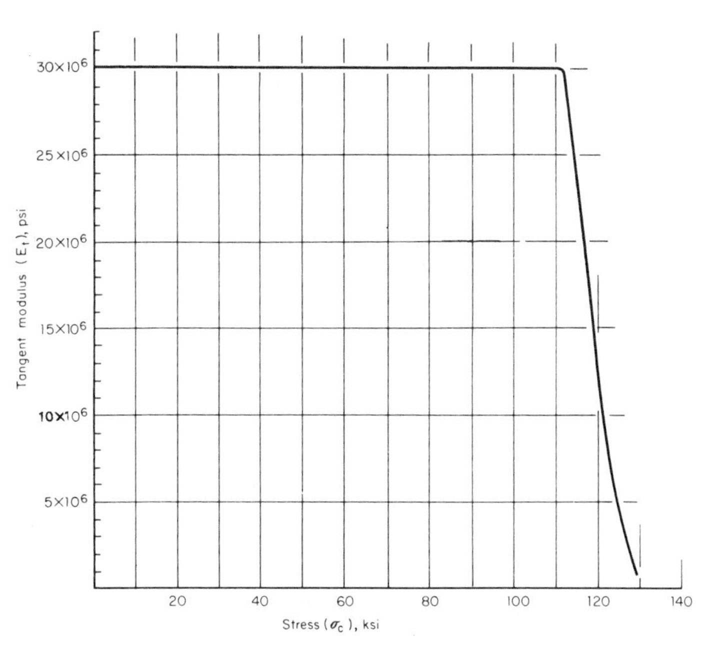

FIGURE 13

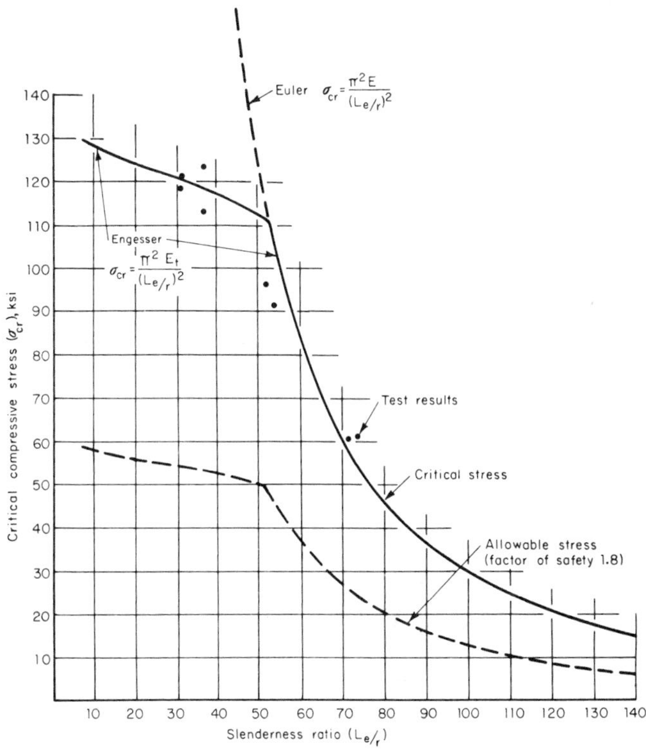

FIGURE 14

and the critical slenderness ratio (L_e/r) is determined for various values of stress (σ_c), resulting in Tables 1 and 2 for quenched and tempered steel only.

Table 1 gives corresponding values of slenderness ratio (L_e/r) for given values of stress (σ_c) above the proportional limit of a quenched and tempered steel.

Below the material's proportional limit, the use of Young's modulus (E) or tangent modulus (E_t) provide the same value. Table 2 for quenched and tempered steel gives the slenderness ratio (L_e/r) for stress levels (σ_c) within the proportional portion of the stress-strain curve. Since the original Euler formula for σ_{cr} applies here, this portion of the curve is often called the Euler curve.

6. PLOTTING ALLOWABLE STRESS CURVE

These values from Tables 1 and 2 are now plotted to form the curve in Figure 14. The Euler portion of the curve is extended upward by a broken line to indicate the variance that would be obtained by continuing to use the Euler formula beyond the proportional limit. This must be kept in mind in designing compression members having a low slenderness ratio (L/r).

A few test results are also shown to indicate the close relationship between the Tangent Modulus formula and actual values.

Note that a corresponding curve has been plotted below the main curve, representing the allowable stress ($\underline{\sigma}$) after applying a factor of safety of 1.8.

TABLE 3—Allowable Compressive Stress (AISC)

Range of $\frac{L_e}{r}$ Values	Average Allowable Compressive Unit Stress ($\underline{\sigma}$)
0 to C_c	$\underline{\sigma} = \left[1 - \dfrac{\left(\frac{KL}{r}\right)^2}{2C_c^2}\right]\dfrac{\sigma_y}{F.S.}$
C_c to 200	$\underline{\sigma} = \dfrac{149{,}000{,}000}{\left(\frac{KL}{r}\right)^2} = \left(\dfrac{12{,}210}{\frac{KL}{r}}\right)^2$

where:

$$C_c = \sqrt{\frac{2\,\pi^2\,E}{\sigma_r}}$$

$$F.S. = \frac{5}{3} + \frac{3}{8}\left(\frac{\frac{KL}{r}}{C_c}\right) - \frac{1}{8}\left(\frac{\frac{KL}{r}}{C_c}\right)^3$$

For very short columns, this factor of safety (F.S.) is equal to that of members in tension (F.S. = 1.67). For longer columns, the safety of factor increases gradually to a maximum of F.S. = 1.92.

K = effective length factor

7. BASIC FORMULAS FOR COMPRESSION MEMBERS

In "Buckling Strength of Metal Structures," page 53, Bleich introduces a parabolic formula to express this tangent modulus curve for compression. By applying a factor of safety (F.S.), this becomes the allowable compressive stress. The basic parabolic formula thus modified is—

$$\underline{\sigma} = \frac{\sigma_y}{F.S.} - \frac{\sigma_p(\sigma_y - \sigma_p)}{\pi^2\,E\,F.S.}\left(\frac{L_e}{r}\right)^2 \quad \ldots\ldots(13)$$

E = modulus of elasticity

σ_p = proportional limit

σ_y = yield point

F.S. = factor of safety

Any residual compressive stress (σ_{rc}) in the member tends to lower the proportional limit (σ_p), or straight-line portion of the stress-strain curve in compression, without affecting the yield point. For the purpose of the above formula, it is assumed that

$$\sigma_p = \sigma_y - \sigma_{rc}$$

Also assuming this value of residual compressive stress is about half of the yield point, or $\sigma_{rc} = \frac{1}{2}\,\sigma_y$, Formula #13 becomes:

$$\underline{\sigma} = \frac{\sigma_y}{F.S.} - \frac{\sigma_y^2}{4\,\pi^2\,E\,F.S.}\left(\frac{L_e}{r}\right)^2 \quad \ldots\ldots(14)$$

This formula provides a parabolic curve, starting at a slenderness ratio of ($L_e/r = 0$) with values at yield stress (σ_y), and extending down to one-half of this stress where it becomes tangent with the Euler curve at the upper limit of elastic bending.

The slenderness ratio at this point is:

$$\frac{L_e}{r} = \sqrt{\frac{2\,\pi^2\,E}{\sigma_y}} = \frac{23{,}925}{\sqrt{\sigma_y}} \text{ for steel} \quad \ldots(15)$$

Above this slenderness ratio, the Euler formula is used:

$$\underline{\sigma} = \frac{\pi^2\,E}{F.S.\left(\frac{L_e}{r}\right)^2} = \frac{1}{F.S.}\left[\frac{16{,}918}{\frac{L_e}{r}}\right]^2 \text{ for steel} \quad (16)$$

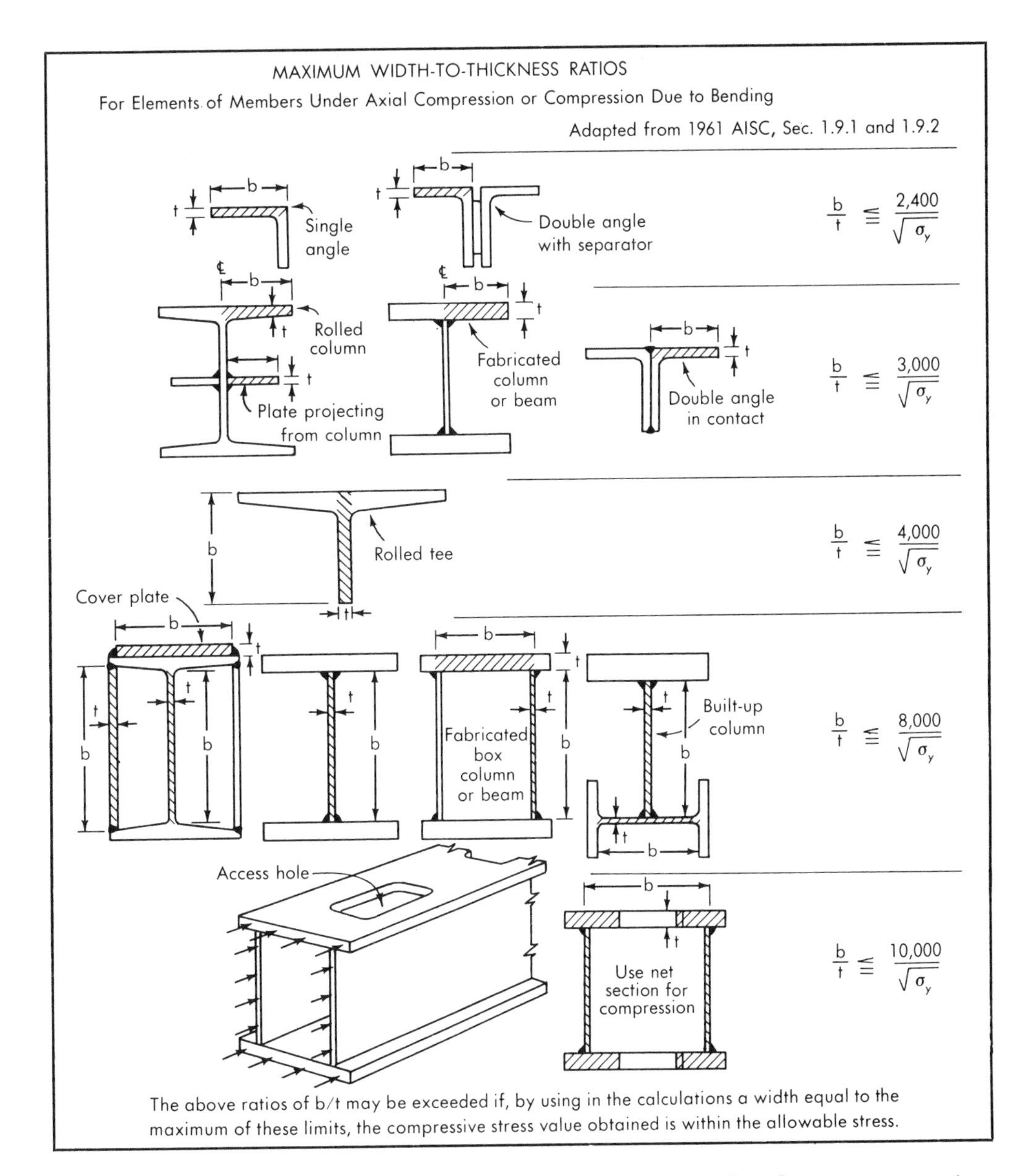

FIGURE 15

8. AISC FORMULAS FOR COMPRESSION MEMBERS

The AISC has incorporated (1963) these basic column formulas endorsed by the Column Research Council Report in its specifications for structural buildings.

The slenderness ratio where the Euler and parabolic portions of the curve intersect, Formula 15, has been designated in the AISC Specification as (C_c). This is also incorporated into Formula 13.

AISC uses a value of E = 29,000,000 psi (instead of the usual 30,000,000 psi) for the modulus of elasticity of steel. For the Euler portion of the curve, Formula 16, AISC uses a factor of safety of 1.92.

The resulting new AISC column formulas are shown in Table 3.

Tables 6 through 14 give the AISC compression allowables for several strengths of structural steel.

For various conditions of column cross-section, Figure 15, there is a limiting ratio of element width to thickness (b/t). This ratio is expressed as being equal to or less than ($\leq$) a certain value divided by the square root of the material's yield strength. The related Table 4 permits direct reading of a compression element's b/t ratio for various yield strengths of steel.

At times it may be desirable to exceed the limiting b/t ratio of an element. This can be done if, in the calculations, substituting the shorter maximum width allowed (by the Fig. 15 limits) would give a compressive unit stress value within the allowable stress.

To help in visualizing relative savings in metal by the use of higher-strength steels, Figure 16 indicates the allowable compressive strength (σ) obtained from the Table 3 formulas for 8 different yield strengths. Notice that the advantage of the higher strengths drops off as the column becomes more slender.

TABLE 4—Limiting b/t Ratios of Section Elements Under Compression

Limits of Ratio of Width to Thickness of Compression Elements for Different Yield Strengths of Steel

Fig. 15 Ratio \ σ_y	33,000	36,000	42,000	45,000	46,000	50,000	55,000	60,000	65,000	* 90,000	* 95,000	* 100,000
$\frac{2{,}400}{\sqrt{\sigma_y}}$	13.2	12.6	11.7	11.3	11.2	10.7	10.2	9.8	9.4	8.0	7.8	7.6
$\frac{3{,}000}{\sqrt{\sigma_y}}$	16.5	15.8	14.6	14.1	14.0	13.4	12.8	12.2	11.8	10.0	9.7	9.5
$\frac{4{,}000}{\sqrt{\sigma_y}}$	22.0	21.0	19.5	18.9	18.7	17.9	17.1	16.3	15.7	13.3	13.0	12.6
$\frac{8{,}000}{\sqrt{\sigma_y}}$	44.0	42.1	39.0	37.7	37.3	35.8	34.1	32.6	31.4	26.6	25.9	25.3
$\frac{10{,}000}{\sqrt{\sigma_y}}$	55.0	52.6	48.7	47.1	46.6	44.7	42.6	40.8	39.2	33.4	32.4	31.6

Round off to the nearest whole number.
* Quenched and tempered steels: yield strength at 0.2% offset.

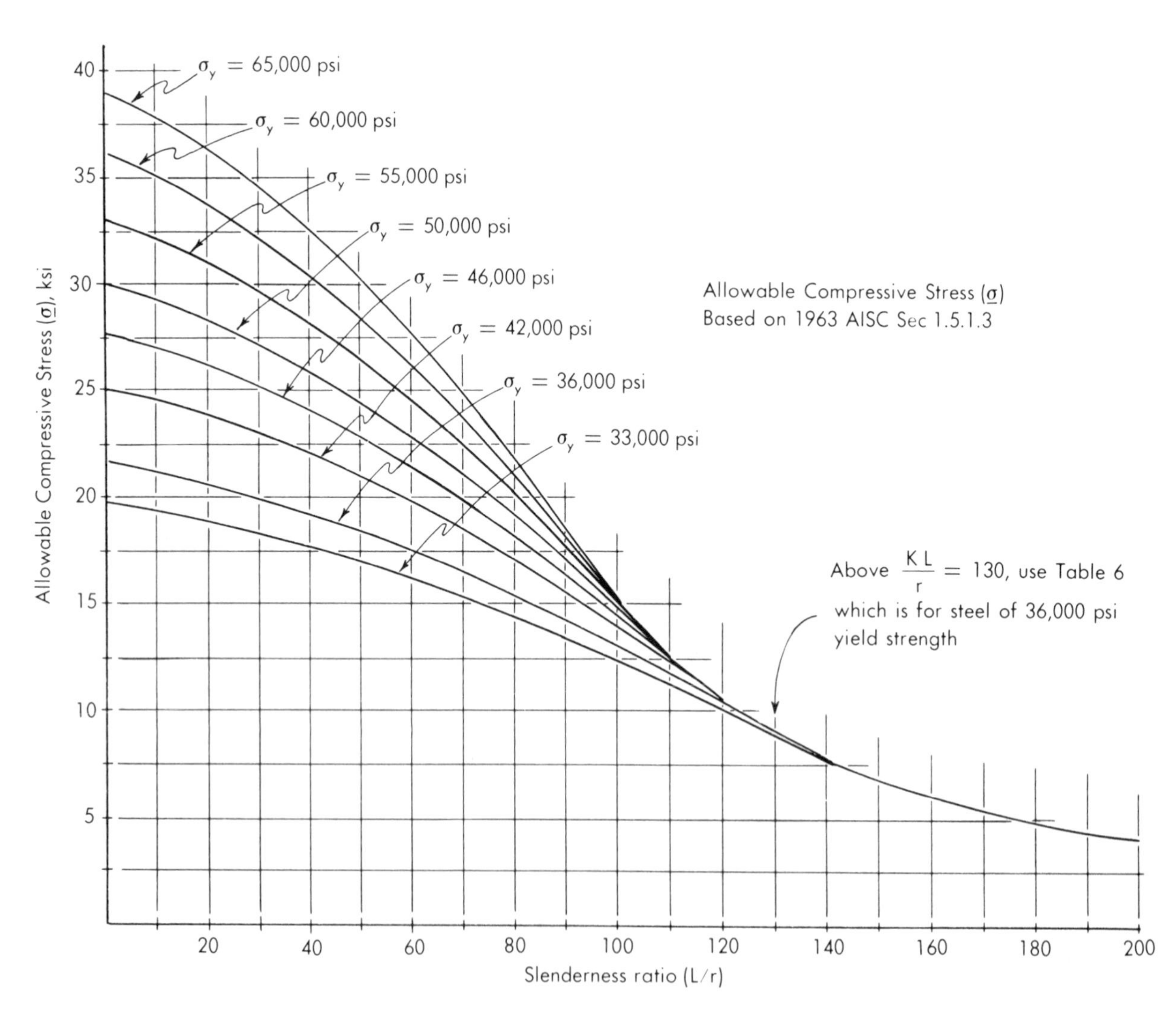

FIGURE 16

If the allowable stress curve of quenched and tempered steel (Fig. 14) were now superimposed on this graph, the even greater, strength advantage of quenched and tempered steel at lower slenderness ratios would be readily apparent.

The allowable compressive unit stress ($\underline{\sigma}$) for a given slenderness ratio ($\overline{KL/r}$), from unity through 200, is quickly read from Tables 6 through 14 for steels of various yield strengths.

Above KL/r of 130, the higher-strength steels offer no advantage as to allowable compressive stress ($\underline{\sigma}$). Above this point, use Table 7 for the more economical steel of 36,000 psi yield strength.

9. OTHER FORMULAS FOR COMPRESSION MEMBERS

Table 5 gives the AASHO formulas, which are applicable to bridge design.

As a matter of general interest, the column formula established for use of quenched and tempered steel on the Carquinez Strait Bridge (California) is—

$$\sigma = 36{,}000 - 1.75 \left(\frac{L}{r}\right)^2$$

TABLE 5—AASHO Allowable Stress for Compression Members *Having Rigid Ends and Concentric Loads*

	A-441 (or A-242)		
A-7 and A-373	3/4" and under $\sigma_y = 50{,}000$ psi	over 3/4" to 1 1/2" $\sigma_y = 46{,}000$ psi	over 1 1/2" to 4" $\sigma_y = 42{,}000$ psi
$\sigma = 15{,}000 - \frac{1}{4}\left(\frac{L}{r}\right)^2$	$\sigma = 22{,}000 - .56\left(\frac{L}{r}\right)^2$	$\sigma = 20{,}000 - .46\left(\frac{L}{r}\right)^2$	$\sigma = 18{,}000 - .39\left(\frac{L}{r}\right)^2$
$\frac{L}{r}$ to 140	$\frac{L}{r}$ to 125	$\frac{L}{r}$ to 125	$\frac{L}{r}$ to 125

Steel skeleton for 10-story Buffalo, New York apartment building features unique shop-welded construction. Principal erection element is a "bent" consisting of a 50' floor girder or "needle beam" threaded through the web of column section near each end and welded. Girder is supported mainly by an angle bracket or "saddle" previously welded to the column web. Girders cantilever out as much as 13' from column.

TABLES 6 through 14—Allowable Compressive ($\underline{\sigma}$) Values (1963 AISC), Main Members

TABLE 6—33,000 psi yield steel

$\frac{KL}{r}$ ratio		1	2	3	4	5	6	7	8	9
		19,770	19,730	19,690	19,660	19,620	19,580	19,540	19,500	19,460
10	19,410	19,370	19,320	19,280	19,230	19,180	19,130	19,080	19,030	18,980
20	18,930	18,880	18,820	18,770	18,710	18,660	18,600	18,540	18,840	18,420
30	18,360	18,300	18,240	18,180	18,110	18,050	17,980	17,920	17,850	17,780
40	17,710	17,640	17,570	17,500	17,430	17,360	17,290	17,220	17,140	17,070
50	16,990	16,920	16,840	16,760	16,680	16,600	16,520	16,440	16,360	16,280
60	16,200	16,120	16,030	15,950	15,860	15,780	15,690	15,610	15,520	15,430
70	15,340	15,250	15,160	15,070	14,980	14,890	14,800	14,700	14,610	14,510
80	14,420	14,320	14,230	14,130	14,030	13,930	13,840	13,740	13,640	13,530
90	13,430	13,330	13,230	13,130	13,020	12,920	12,810	12,710	12,600	12,490
100	12,380	12,280	12,170	12,060	11,950	11,830	11,720	11,610	11,900	11,380
110	11,270	11,150	11,040	10,920	10,800	10,690	10,570	10,450	10,330	10,210
120	10,090	9,996	9,840	9,720	9,590	9,470	9,340	9,220	9,090	8,960
130	8,830	8,700	8,570	8,440	8,320	8,190	8,070	7,960	7,840	7,730
140	7,620	7,510	7,410	7,300	7,200	7,100	7,010	6,910	6,820	6,730
150	6,640	6,550	6,460	6,380	6,300	6,220	6,140	6,060	5,980	5,910
160	5,830	5,760	5,690	5,620	5,550	5,490	5,420	5,350	5,290	5,230
170	5,170	5,110	5,050	4,990	4,930	4,880	4,820	4,770	4,710	4,660
180	4,610	4,560	4,510	4,460	4,410	4,360	4,320	4,270	4,230	4,180
190	4,140	4,090	4,050	4,010	3,970	3,930	3,890	3,850	3,810	3,770
200	3,730									

TABLE 7—36,000 psi yield steel

$\frac{KL}{r}$ ratio		1	2	3	4	5	6	7	8	9
		21,560	21,520	21,480	21,440	21,390	21,350	21,300	21,250	21,210
10	21,160	21,100	21,050	21,000	20,950	20,890	20,830	20,780	20,720	20,660
20	20,600	20,540	20,480	20,410	20,350	20,280	20,220	20,150	20,080	20,010
30	19,940	19,870	19,800	19,730	19,650	19,580	19,500	19,420	19,350	19,270
40	19,190	19,110	19,030	18,950	18,860	18,780	18,700	18,610	18,530	18,440
50	18,350	18,260	18,170	18,080	17,990	17,900	17,810	17,710	17,620	17,530
60	17,430	17,330	17,240	17,140	17,040	16,940	16,840	16,740	16,640	16,530
70	16,430	16,330	16,220	16,120	16,010	15,900	15,790	15,690	15,580	15,470
80	15,360	15,240	15,130	15,020	14,900	14,790	14,670	14,560	14,440	14,320
90	14,200	14,090	13,970	13,840	13,720	13,600	13,480	13,350	13,230	13,100
100	12,980	12,850	12,720	12,590	12,470	12,330	12,200	12,070	11,940	11,810
110	11,670	11,540	11,400	11,260	11,130	10,990	10,850	10,710	10,570	10,430
120	10,280	10,140	9,990	9,850	9,700	9,550	9,410	9,260	9,110	8,970
130	8,840	8,700	8,570	8,440	8,320	8,190	8,070	7,960	7,840	7,730
140	7,620	7,510	7,410	7,300	7,200	7,100	7,010	6,910	6,820	6,730
150	6,640	6,550	6,460	6,380	6,300	6,220	6,140	6,060	5,980	5,910
160	5,830	5,760	5,690	5,620	5,550	5,490	5,420	5,350	5,290	5,230
170	5,170	5,110	5,050	4,990	4,930	4,880	4,820	4,770	4,710	4,660
180	4,610	4,560	4,510	4,460	4,410	4,360	4,320	4,270	4,230	4,180
190	4,140	4,090	4,050	4,010	3,970	3,930	3,890	3,850	3,810	3,770
200	3,730									

TABLE 8—42,000 psi yield steel

$\frac{KL}{r}$ ratio		1	2	3	4	5	6	7	8	9
		25,150	25,100	25,050	24,990	24,940	24,880	24,820	24,760	24,700
10	24,630	24,570	24,500	24,430	24,360	24,290	24,220	24,150	24,070	24,000
20	23,920	23,840	23,760	23,680	23,590	23,510	23,420	23,330	23,240	23,150
30	23,060	22,970	22,880	22,780	22,690	22,590	22,490	22,390	22,290	22,190
40	22,080	21,980	21,870	21,770	21,660	21,550	21,440	21,330	21,220	21,100
50	20,990	20,870	20,760	20,640	20,520	20,400	20,280	20,160	20,030	19,910
60	19,790	19,660	19,530	19,400	19,270	19,140	19,010	18,880	18,750	18,610
70	18,480	18,340	18,200	18,060	17,920	17,780	17,640	17,500	17,350	17,210
80	17,060	16,920	16,770	16,620	16,470	16,320	16,170	16,010	15,860	15,710
90	15,550	15,390	15,230	15,070	14,910	14,750	14,590	14,430	14,260	14,090
100	13,930	13,760	13,590	13,420	13,250	13,080	12,900	12,730	12,550	12,370
110	12,190	12,010	11,830	11,650	11,470	11,280	11,100	10,910	10,720	10,550
120	10,370	10,200	10,030	9,870	9,710	9,560	9,410	9,260	9,110	8,970

*

TABLE 9—45,000 psi yield steel

$\frac{KL}{r}$ ratio		1	2	3	4	5	6	7	8	9
		26,950	26,890	26,830	26,770	26,710	26,640	26,580	26,510	26,440
10	26,370	26,300	26,220	26,150	26,070	25,990	25,910	25,820	25,740	25,650
20	25,570	25,480	25,390	25,290	25,200	25,110	25,010	24,910	24,810	24,710
30	24,610	24,500	24,400	24,290	24,180	24,070	23,960	23,850	23,740	23,620
40	23,510	23,390	23,270	23,150	23,030	22,900	22,780	22,660	22,530	22,400
50	22,270	22,140	22,010	21,880	21,740	21,610	21,470	21,330	21,190	21,050
60	20,910	20,770	20,630	20,480	20,340	20,190	20,040	19,890	19,740	19,590
70	19,440	19,280	19,130	18,970	18,810	18,650	18,490	18,330	18,170	18,000
80	17,840	17,670	17,510	17,340	17,170	17,000	16,830	16,650	16,480	16,300
90	16,130	15,950	15,770	15,590	15,410	15,220	15,040	14,850	14,660	14,480
100	14,290	14,100	13,900	13,710	13,510	13,320	13,120	12,920	12,720	12,520
110	12,320	12,110	11,910	11,670	11,470	11,270	11,070	10,880	10,700	10,520
120	10,350	10,180	10,010	9,850	9,690	9,540	9,390	9,240	9,090	8,950

*

TABLE 10—46,000 psi yield steel

$\frac{KL}{r}$ ratio		1	2	3	4	5	6	7	8	9
		27,540	27,480	27,420	27,360	27,300	27,230	27,160	27,090	27,020
10	26,950	26,870	26,790	26,720	26,630	26,550	26,470	26,380	26,290	26,210
20	26,110	26,020	25,930	25,830	25,730	25,640	25,540	25,430	25,330	25,230
30	25,120	25,010	24,900	24,790	24,680	24,560	24,450	24,330	24,210	24,100
40	23,970	23,850	23,730	23,600	23,480	23,350	23,220	23,090	22,960	22,830
50	22,690	22,560	22,420	22,280	22,140	22,000	21,860	21,720	21,570	21,430
60	21,280	21,130	20,980	20,830	20,680	20,530	20,370	20,220	20,060	19,900
70	19,740	19,580	19,420	19,260	19,100	18,930	18,760	18,600	18,430	18,260
80	18,080	17,910	17,740	17,560	17,390	17,210	17,030	16,850	16,670	16,480
90	16,300	16,120	15,930	15,740	15,550	15,360	15,170	14,970	14,780	14,580
100	14,390	14,190	13,990	13,790	13,580	13,380	13,170	12,960	12,750	12,540
110	12,330	12,120	11,900	11,690	11,490	11,290	11,100	10,910	10,720	10,550
120	10,370	10,200	10,030	9,870	9,710	9,560	9,410	9,260	9,110	8,970

*

* Above $\frac{KL}{r}$ of 130, the higher-strength steels offer no advantage as to allowable compressive stress ($\underline{\sigma}$). Above this point, use Table 7 for the more economical steel of 36,000 psi yield strength.
K multiplied by actual length (L) = effective length.
Table values computed by Research Dept., Bethlehem Steel Co.

TABLE 11—50,000 psi yield steel

$\frac{KL}{r}$ ratio		1	2	3	4	5	6	7	8	9
		29,940	29,870	29,800	29,730	29,660	29,580	29,500	29,420	29,340
10	29,260	29,170	29,080	28,990	28,900	28,800	28,710	28,610	28,510	28,400
20	28,300	28,190	28,080	27,970	27,860	27,750	27,630	27,520	27,400	27,280
30	27,150	27,030	26,900	26,770	26,640	26,510	26,380	26,250	26,110	25,970
40	25,830	25,690	25,550	25,400	25,260	25,110	24,960	24,810	24,660	24,510
50	24,350	24,190	24,040	23,880	23,720	23,550	23,390	23,220	23,060	22,890
60	22,720	22,550	22,370	22,200	22,020	21,850	21,670	21,490	21,310	21,120
70	20,940	20,750	20,560	20,380	20,190	19,990	19,800	19,610	19,410	19,210
80	19,010	18,810	18,610	18,410	18,200	17,990	17,790	17,580	17,370	17,150
90	16,940	16,720	16,500	16,290	16,060	15,840	15,620	15,390	15,170	14,940
100	14,710	14,470	14,240	14,000	13,770	13,530	13,290	13,040	12,800	12,570
110	12,340	12,120	11,900	11,690	11,490	11,290	11,100	10,910	10,720	10,550
120	10,370	10,200	10,030	9,870	9,710	9,560	9,410	9,260	9,110	8,970

*

TABLE 12—55,000 psi yield steel

$\frac{KL}{r}$ ratio		1	2	3	4	5	6	7	8	9
		32,930	32,850	32,770	32,690	32,600	32,510	32,420	32,330	32,230
10	32,130	32,030	31,930	31,820	31,720	31,600	31,490	31,380	31,260	31,140
20	31,010	30,890	30,760	30,630	30,500	30,370	30,230	30,090	29,950	29,810
30	29,670	29,520	29,370	29,220	29,070	28,910	28,760	28,600	28,440	28,270
40	28,110	27,940	27,770	27,600	27,430	27,260	27,080	26,900	26,730	26,540
50	26,360	26,180	25,990	25,800	25,610	25,420	25,220	25,030	24,830	24,630
60	24,430	24,230	24,020	23,820	23,610	23,400	23,190	22,970	22,760	22,540
70	22,320	22,100	21,880	21,660	21,430	21,200	20,970	20,740	20,510	20,280
80	20,040	19,800	19,560	19,320	19,070	18,830	18,580	18,330	18,080	17,830
90	17,570	17,310	17,050	16,790	16,530	16,260	16,000	15,730	15,460	15,180
100	14,910	14,630	14,350	14,040	13,780	13,510	13,260	13,010	12,770	12,540
110	12,310	12,090	11,880	11,670	11,470	11,270	11,070	10,880	10,700	10,520
120	10,350	10,180	10,010	9,850	9,690	9,540	9,390	9,240	9,090	8,950

*

TABLE 13—60,000 psi yield steel

$\frac{KL}{r}$ ratio		1	2	3	4	5	6	7	8	9
		35,920	35,830	35,740	35,640	35,540	35,440	35,340	35,230	35,120
10	35,010	34,890	34,770	34,650	34,520	34,400	34,270	34,130	34,000	33,860
20	33,710	33,570	33,420	33,270	33,120	32,960	32,810	32,650	32,480	32,320
30	32,150	31,980	31,810	31,630	31,460	31,280	31,090	30,910	30,720	30,530
40	30,340	30,150	29,950	29,760	29,560	29,350	29,150	28,940	28,730	28,520
50	28,310	28,100	27,880	27,660	27,440	27,210	26,990	26,760	26,530	26,300
60	26,060	25,830	25,590	25,350	25,110	24,860	24,610	24,360	24,110	23,860
70	23,610	23,350	23,090	22,830	22,560	22,300	22,030	21,760	21,490	21,210
80	20,940	20,660	20,380	20,090	19,810	19,520	19,230	18,940	18,640	18,340
90	18,040	17,740	17,440	17,130	16,820	16,510	16,190	15,880	15,510	15,200
100	14,900	14,610	14,320	14,040	13,780	13,510	13,260	13,010	12,770	12,540
110	12,310	12,090	11,880	11,670	11,470	11,270	11,070	10,880	10,700	10,520
120	10,350	10,180	10,010	9,850	9,690	9,540	9,390	9,240	9,090	8,950

*

TABLE 14—65,000 psi yield steel

$\frac{KL}{r}$ ratio		1	2	3	4	5	6	7	8	9
		38,900	38,810	38,700	38,590	38,480	38,370	38,250	38,130	38,000
10	37,870	37,740	37,600	37,460	37,320	37,180	37,030	36,870	36,720	36,560
20	36,390	36,230	36,060	35,890	35,710	35,530	35,350	35,170	34,980	34,790
30	34,600	34,400	34,210	34,010	33,800	33,600	33,390	33,170	32,960	32,740
40	32,520	32,300	32,070	31,850	31,620	31,380	31,150	30,910	30,670	30,430
50	30,180	29,930	29,680	29,430	29,180	28,920	28,660	28,390	28,130	27,860
60	27,590	27,320	27,040	26,770	26,490	26,200	25,920	25,630	25,340	25,050
70	24,760	24,460	24,160	23,860	23,550	23,240	22,930	22,620	22,300	21,990
80	21,670	21,340	21,020	20,690	20,360	20,020	19,690	19,350	19,000	18,660
90	18,310	17,960	17,600	17,240	16,860	16,510	16,170	15,840	15,510	15,200
100	14,900	14,610	14,320	14,040	13,780	13,510	13,260	13,010	12,770	12,540
110	12,310	12,090	11,880	11,670	11,470	11,270	11,070	10,880	10,700	10,520
120	10,350	10,180	10,010	9,850	9,690	9,540	9,390	9,240	9,090	8,950

*

* See note on previous page

Design of Compression Members

1. INTRODUCTION

The preceding Section 3.1 covers the general Analysis of Compression, along with an evaluation of the methods for determining stress allowables.

This present section deals more specifically with the actual design of columns and other compression members. For purposes of illustration, the term "column" is used quite liberally. This is due partly to much of the material having been originally developed expressly for columns. However, the information is generally applicable to all compression members.

2. RESTRAINT AND EFFECTIVE LENGTH OF MEMBER

Section 3.1 explained how a compression member's slenderness ratio (L/r) relates to its buckling strength. The degree of end restraint on a member results in its having an effective length which may vary considerably from its actual unbraced length. This ratio (K) of effective length to actual unbraced length is used as a multiplier in determining the effective length (L_e) of a compression member.

$$L_e = K\,L \qquad (1)$$

where:

L = actual length of the column

L_e = effective length of the column to be used in column formulas

K = effective length factor

Table 1 lists theoretical values of K and the Column Research Council's corresponding recommended values of K for the effective length (L_e) of columns under ideal conditions.

Where End Conditions Can't Be Classified

In actual practice it will be more difficult to classify the end conditions. If classification is doubtful, the Column Research Council recommends the following method based on the relative stiffness of connecting beams and columns.

The stiffness factor of any member is given as I/L, its moment of inertia divided by its length.

These values are determined for the column or columns in question (I_c/L_c), as well as for any beam or other restraining member lying in the plane in which buckling of the column is being considered (I_g/L_g).

The moments of inertia (I_c and I_g) are taken about an axis perpendicular to the plane of buckling being considered.

The values of G for each end (A and B) of the column are determined:

$$G = \frac{\sum \frac{I_c}{L_c}}{\sum \frac{I_g}{L_g}} \qquad (2)$$

TABLE 1—Effective Length (L_e) of Compression Members

Buckled shape of member is shown by dashed line	(a)	(b)	(c)	(d)	(e)	(f)
Theoretical K value	0.5	0.7	1.0	1.0	2.0	2.0*
Recommended design value when ideal conditions are approximated	0.65	0.80	1.2	1.0	2.10**	2.0

End condition		
(fixed symbol)	rotation fixed	translation fixed
(pinned symbol)	rotation free	translation fixed
(hatched box symbol)	rotation fixed	translation free
(free symbol)	rotation free	translation free

*K may be greater than 2.0
**Top end assumed truly rotation free

From "Guide to Design Criteria for Metal Compression Members" 1960, p. 28, Column Research Council

FIGURE 1—Effective Length Factor In Column Design

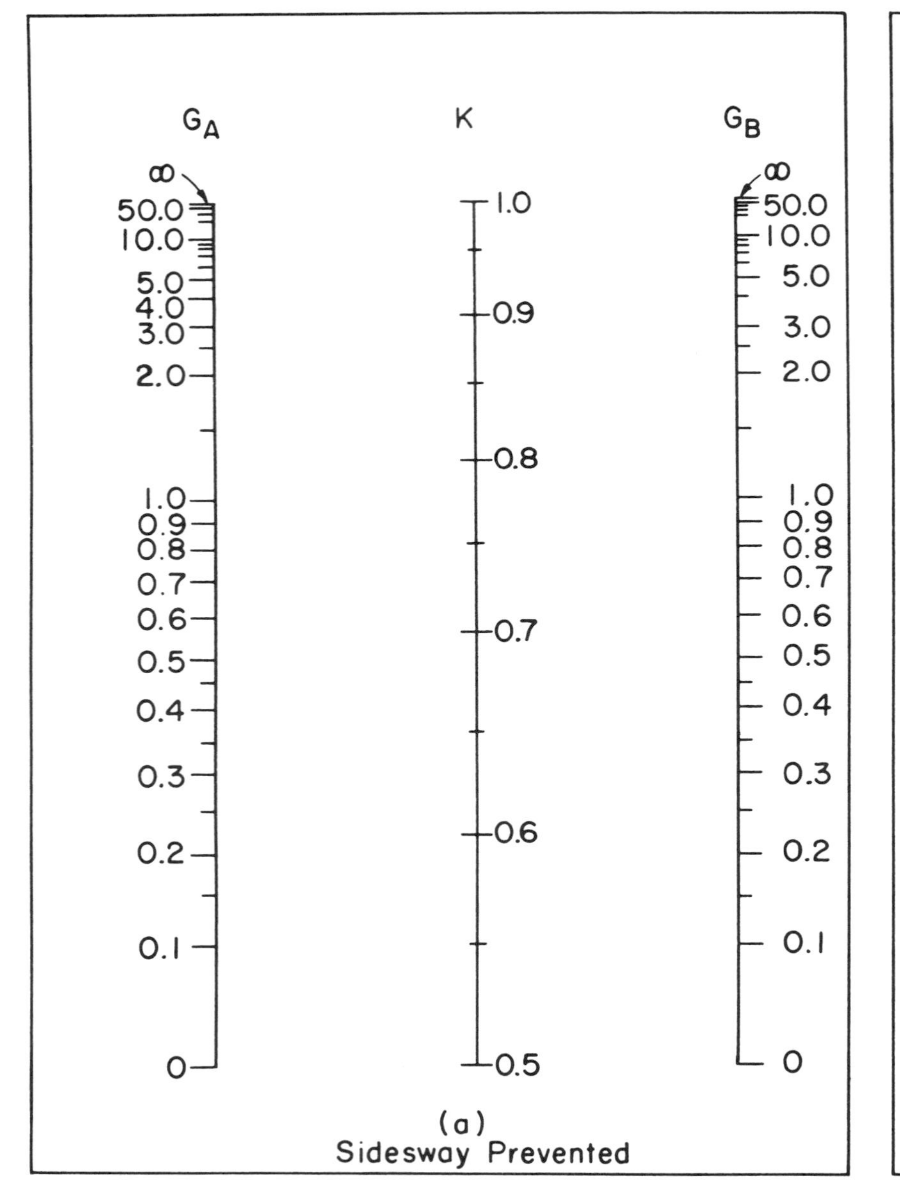

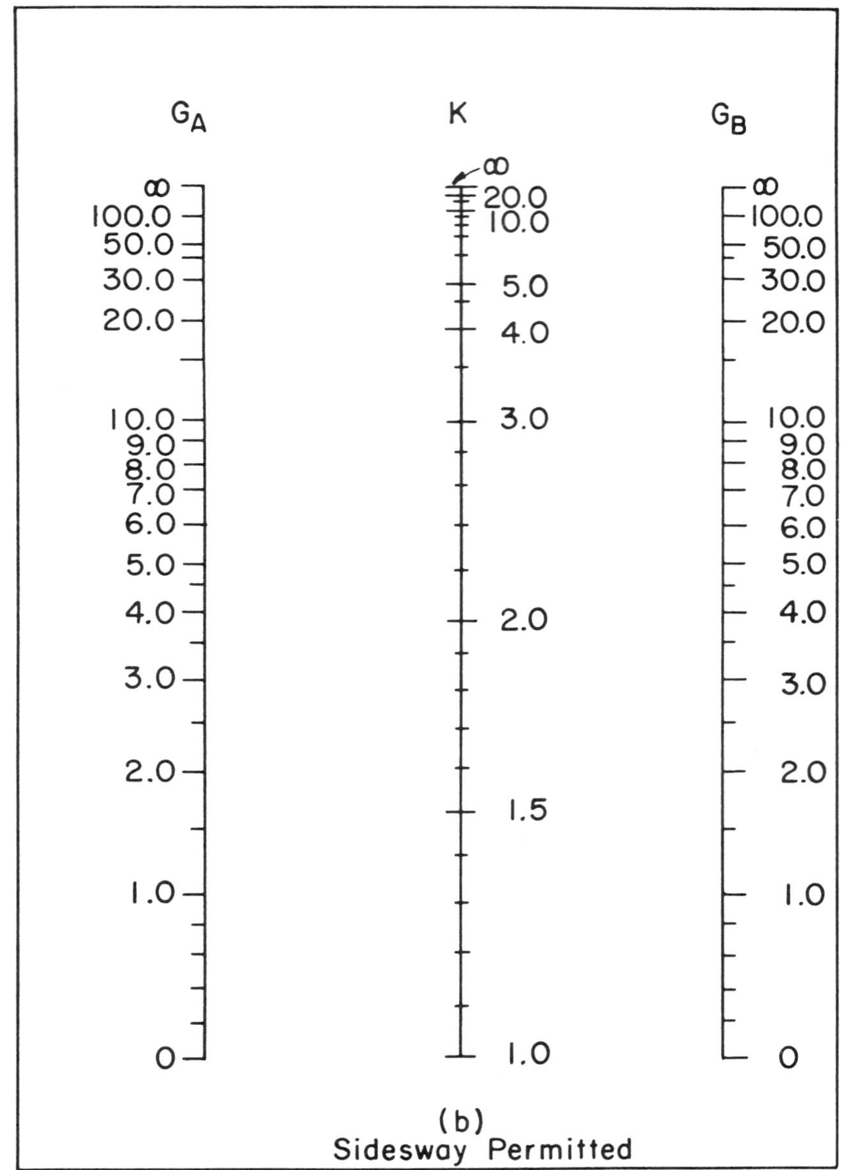

where:

$\sum \frac{I_c}{L_c}$ = the total for the columns meeting at the joint considered.

$\sum \frac{I_g}{L_g}$ = the total for the beams or restraining members meeting at the joint considered.

For a column end that is supported, but not fixed, the moment of inertia of the support is zero, and the resulting value of G for this end of the column would be ∞. However in practice, unless the footing were designed as a frictionless pin, this value of G would be taken as 10.

If the column end is fixed, the moment of inertia of the support is ∞, and the resulting value of G for this end of the column would be zero. However in practice, there is some movement and G may be taken as 1.0.

If the beam or restraining member is either pinned ($G = \infty$) or fixed against rotation ($G = 0$) at its far end, further refinements may be made by multiplying the stiffness (I/L) of the beam by the following factors:

sidesway prevented

far end of beam pinned = 1.5
far end of beam fixed = 2.0

sidesway permitted

far end of beam pinned = 0.5

For any given column, knowing the values (G_A and G_B) for each end, the nomograph, Figure 1, may be used to determine the value of K so that the effective length (L_e) of the column may be found:

$$L_e = K\ L$$

This nomograph is taken from the Column Research Council's "Guide to Design Criteria for Metal Compression Members", 1960, p. 31. The nomograph was developed by Jackson & Moreland Division of United Engineers and Constructors, Inc.

3. STRENGTH OF COMPRESSION MEMBERS UNDER COMBINED LOADING

A very convenient method of treating combined loadings is the interaction method. (Also see Sect. 2.11, Analysis of Combined Stresses.) Here each type of

Problem 1

Find the effective length factor (K) for column A-B under the following conditions:

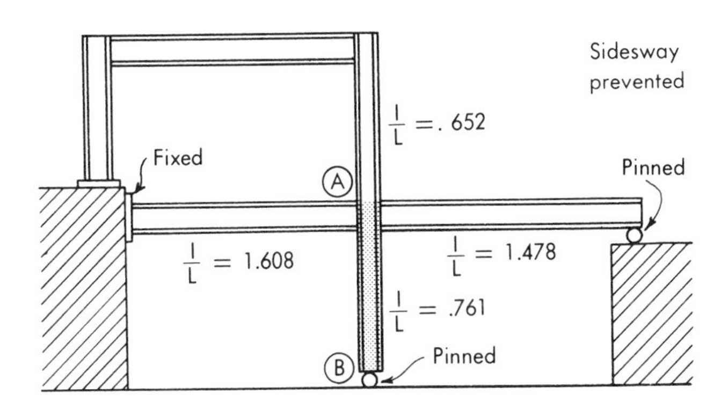

FIGURE 2

Here:

$$G_A = \frac{.652 + .761}{2(1.608) + 1.5(1.478)}$$

$$= .260$$

$$G_B = \infty;\ \text{use } 10.$$

From the nomograph, read K = .76

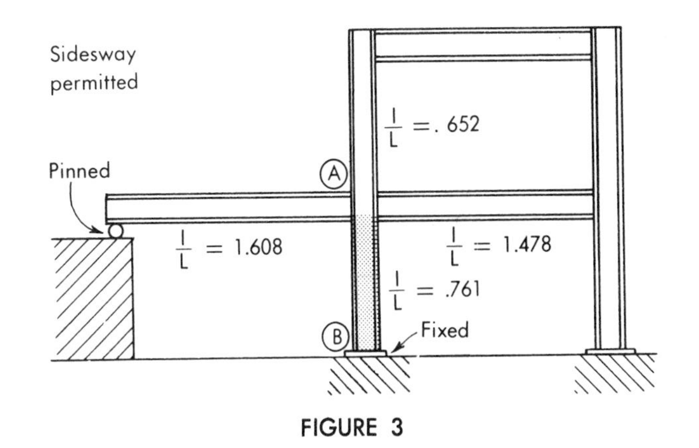

FIGURE 3

Here:

$$G_A = \frac{.652 + .761}{.5(1.608) + 1.478}$$

$$= .620$$

$$G_B = \text{zero; use } 1.0$$

From the nomograph, read K = 1.26

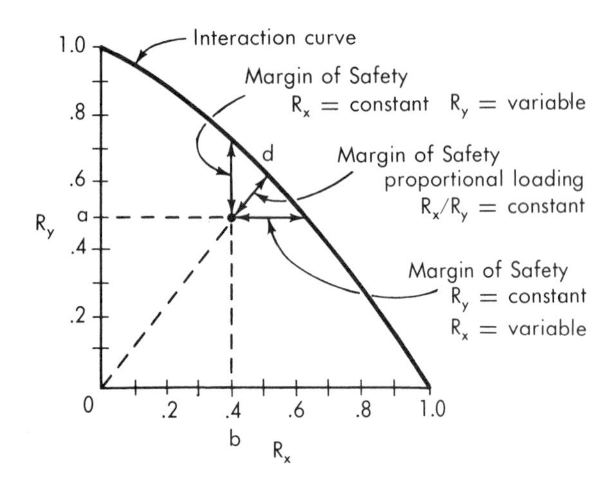

FIGURE 4

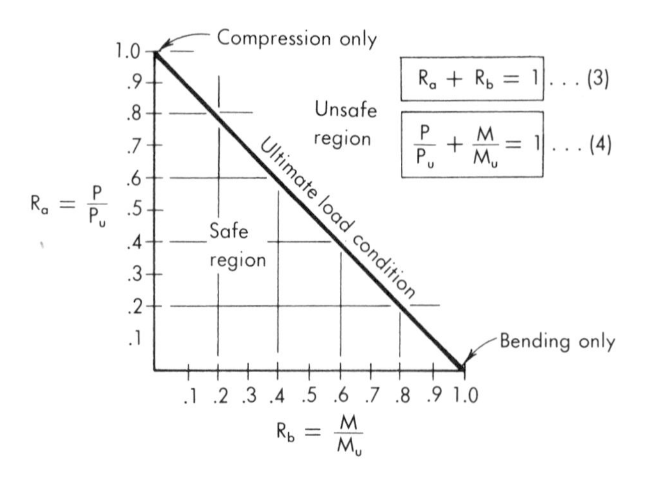

FIGURE 5

load is expressed as a ratio of the actual load to the ultimate load which would cause failure if acting alone.

axial load

$$R_a = \frac{P}{P_u}$$

bending load

$$R_b = \frac{M}{M_u}$$

torsional load

$$R_t = \frac{T}{T_u}$$

In the general example shown in Figure 4, the effect of two types of loads (X and Y) upon each other is illustrated.

The value of $R_y = 1$ at the upper end of the vertical axis is the ultimate value for this type of load on the member when acting alone. The value of $R_x = 1$ at the extreme right end of the horizontal axis is the ultimate value for this type of load on the member when acting alone. These ultimate values are determined by experiment; or when this data is not available, suitable calculations may be made to estimate these values.

The interaction curve is usually determined by actual testing of members under various combined-load conditions. From this, a simple formula is derived to fit the curve and express this relationship.

If points a and b are the ratios produced by the actual loads, point c represents the combination of these conditions. The margin of safety is indicated by how close point c lies to the interaction curve. A suitable factor of safety is then applied to these values.

Figure 5 illustrates this for axial compression and bending.

However, the applied bending moment (M_1) causes the column to bend, and the resulting displacement or eccentricity induces a secondary moment from the applied axial force. See Figure 6.

Assume that the moment (M_1) applied to the column is sinusoidal in nature; Figure 7.

A sinusoidal moment applied to a pinned end member results in a sinusoidal deflection curve, whose maximum deflection is equal to—

$$\Delta_1 = \frac{M_1 \, L_b^2}{\pi^2 \, E \, I}$$

Since the critical Euler load is—

$$\boxed{P_e = \frac{\pi^2 \, E \, I}{L_b^2}} \quad \text{.......................(5)}$$

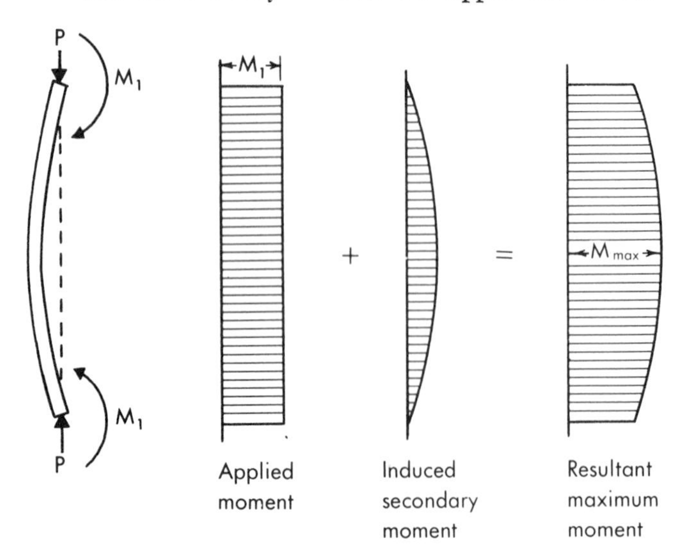

FIGURE 6

this becomes

$$\Delta_1 = \frac{M_1}{P_e}$$

When the axial load (P) is also applied to this deflected column, a secondary moment is induced and this is also sinusoidal in nature, its maximum value being—

$$M_2 = P\ \Delta_1$$

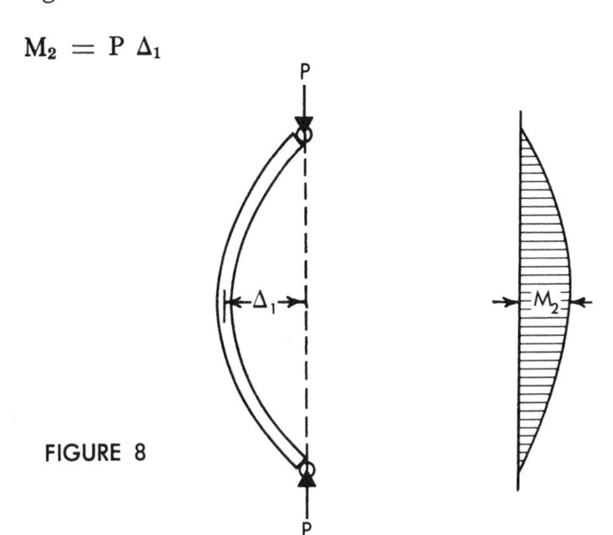

FIGURE 8

This slightly higher moment ($M_2 + M_1$) will in the same manner produce a slightly greater deflection ($\Delta_2 + \Delta_1$), etc. Each successive increment in deflection becomes smaller and smaller.

The final values would be—

$$\Delta_{max} = \frac{M_{max}}{P_e}$$

since

$$M_{max} = M_1 + P\ \Delta_{max} \quad \text{then}$$

$$M_{max} = M_1 + P\left(\frac{M_{max}}{P_e}\right) \quad \text{or}$$

$$M_{max} = \frac{M_1}{1 - \frac{P}{P_e}}$$

Accommodating Increased Moment Due to Deflection

This increase in the moment of the bending load caused by deflection is easily taken care of in the basic interaction formula by an amplification factor (k):

$$k = \frac{M_{max}}{M_1}$$

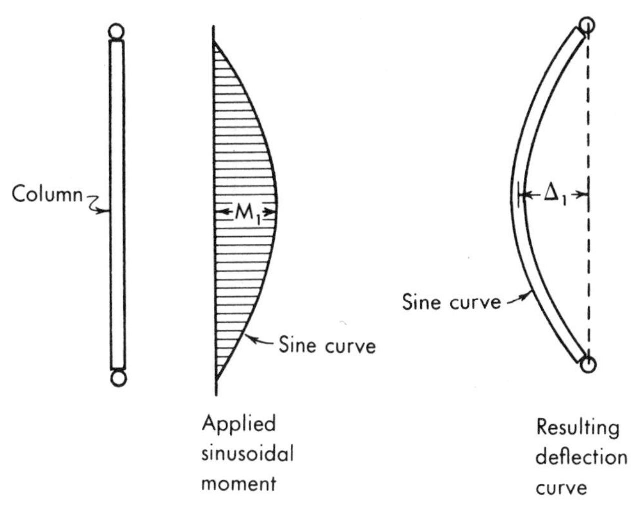

FIGURE 7

$$\therefore \boxed{k = \frac{1}{1 - \frac{P}{P_e}}} \qquad \text{(6)}$$

The interaction Formula #4 then becomes—

$$\boxed{\frac{P}{P_u} + \frac{M_1}{M_u}\left(\frac{1}{1 - \frac{P}{P_e}}\right) = 1} \qquad \text{(7)}$$

(ultimate load condition)

Each ultimate load condition factor in the above formula is equal to the corresponding factor for working conditions multiplied by the factor of safety (n); or

$$\frac{n\ P_w}{n\ P_A} + \frac{n\ M_w}{n\ M_A}\left(\frac{1}{1 - \frac{n\ P_w}{P_e}}\right) \leqq 1 \quad \text{and}$$

$$\frac{P_w}{P_A} + \frac{M_w}{M_A}\left(\frac{1}{1 - \frac{n\ P_w}{P_e}}\right) \leqq 1$$

where: subscript $_w$ is for working loads
subscript $_A$ is for allowable loads

Notice:

$$P_e = \frac{\pi^2\ E\ I}{L_b{}^2} = \frac{\pi^2\ E\ A}{\left(\frac{L_b}{r_b}\right)^2}$$

so: $$\sigma_e = \frac{\pi^2\ E}{\left(\frac{L_b}{r_b}\right)^2}$$

Or, on a stress basis —

$$\frac{\sigma_a}{\underline{\sigma_a}} + \frac{\sigma_b}{\underline{\sigma_b}}\left(\frac{1}{1 - \frac{n\,\sigma_a}{\sigma_e}}\right) \leq 1 \qquad (8)$$

(allowable load condition)

where:

σ_a = computed axial stress

σ_b = computed compressive bending stress at point considered

$\underline{\sigma_a}$ = allowable axial stress permitted if there is no bending moment; use largest (L/r) ratio, regardless of plane of bending

$\underline{\sigma_b}$ = allowable compressive bending stress permitted if there is no axial force. (AISC Sec. 1.5.1.4)

The AISC Specification Sec. 1.6.1 uses the same amplification factor. They use the term (F'_e) which is the Euler stress (σ_e) divided by the factor of safety (n). The term (σ'_e) is used here in place of AISC's (F'_e).

$$\sigma'_e = \frac{\sigma}{n} = \frac{\pi^2 E}{\left(\frac{L_b}{r_b}\right)^2 n}$$

$$= \frac{149{,}000{,}000}{\left(\frac{L_b}{r_b}\right)^2} = \left(\frac{12{,}210}{\frac{L_b}{r_b}}\right)^2$$

AISC uses E = 29,000,000 psi and n = 1.92 in the above.

Here:

r_b = radius of gyration about an axis normal to the plane of bending

L_b = actual unbraced length of column in the plane of bending

TABLE 2—Euler Stress Divided By Factor of Safety

Values of $\sigma'_e = \dfrac{149{,}000{,}000}{\left(\frac{KL_b}{r_b}\right)^2} = \left(\dfrac{12{,}210}{\frac{KL_b}{r_b}}\right)^2$

For All Grades of Steel ***AISC 1963***

$\frac{KL_b}{r_b}$		1	2	3	4	5	6	7	8	9
20		338,130	308,090	281,880	258,890	238,590	220,580	204,550	190,200	177,310
30	165,680	155,170	145,620	136,930	128,990	121,730	115,060	108,930	103,270	98,040
40	93,200	88,710	84,530	80,650	77,020	73,640	70,470	67,510	64,730	62,110
50	59,650	57,330	55,150	53,090	51,140	49,300	47,560	45,900	44,440	42,840
60	41,430	40,070	38,790	37,570	36,410	35,290	34,240	33,220	32,250	31,320
70	30,440	29,580	28,770	27,990	27,240	26,510	25,820	25,150	24,510	23,890
80	23,300	22,730	22,180	21,650	21,130	20,640	20,160	19,700	19,260	18,830
90	18,410	18,010	17,620	17,240	16,880	16,530	16,180	15,850	15,530	15,210
100	14,910	14,620	14,340	14,060	13,730	13,530	13,280	13,020	12,800	12,570
110	12,340	12,120	11,900	11,690	11,490	11,290	11,100	10,910	10,730	10,550
120	10,370	10,200	10,030	9,870	9,710	9,560	9,410	9,260	9,110	8,970
130	8,840	8,700	8,570	8,440	8,320	8,190	8,070	7,960	7,840	7,730
140	7,620	7,510	7,410	7,300	7,200	7,100	7,010	6,910	6,820	6,730
150	6,640	6,550	6,460	6,380	6,300	6,220	6,140	6,060	5,980	5,910
160	5,830	5,760	5,690	5.620	5,550	5,490	5,420	5,360	5,290	5,230
170	5,170	5,110	5,050	4,990	4,930	4,880	4,820	4,770	4,710	4,660
180	4,610	4,560	4,510	4,460	4,410	4,360	4,320	4,270	4,230	4,180
190	4,140	4,090	4,050	4,010	3,970	3,930	3,890	3,850	3,810	3,770
200	3,730									

L_b = actual unbraced length of column in the plane of bending
r_b = radius of gyration about the axis of bending

According to AISC Sec. 1.5.6, this value (σ'_e) may be increased ⅓ for wind loads.

Table 2 lists the values of σ'_e (Euler stress divided by factor of safety) for $\frac{KL_b}{r_b}$ ratios from 20 to 200. These values apply for all grades of steel, but are based on the conservative factor of safety = 1.92.

The derivation of the amplification factor has been based on a member with pinned ends and a sinusoidal moment applied to it. In actual practice these conditions will vary; however this factor will be reasonably good for most conditions. AISC Sec. 1.6.1 applies a second factor (C_m) to adjust for more favorable conditions of applied end moments or transverse loads.

applied end moments

$$C_m = 0.6 + 0.4 \frac{M_1}{M_2} \geqq 0.4 \qquad \text{.............. (9)}$$

applied transverse loads

$$C_m = 1 + \psi \frac{\sigma_a}{\sigma'_e} \qquad \text{..................... (10)}$$

where:

M_1 and M_2 are end moments applied to the column.

$M_1 \leqq M_2$, and the ratio (M_1/M_2) is positive when the column is bent in a single curve and negative when bent in reverse curve.

$$\psi = \frac{\pi^2 \, \Delta \, E \, I}{M \, L^2} - 1$$

(see Table 3 for values ψ and C_m for several load conditions)

Here:

Δ = maximum deflection due to transverse load

L = actual length of member also used in deflection (Δ) calculation

M = maximum moment between supports due to transverse load

AISC Formulas For Checking

When

$$\frac{\sigma_a}{\underline{\sigma}_a} \leqq .15$$

the influence of the amplification factor is generally small and may be neglected. Hence the following formula will control:

TABLE 3—Value of ψ for Several Load Conditions

Case	ψ	C_m
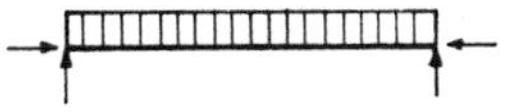	0	1.0
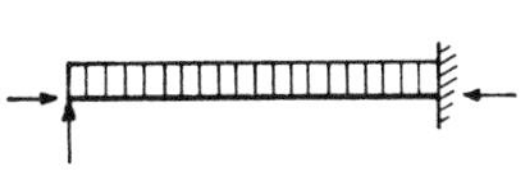	—0.3	$1 - .3\frac{\sigma_a}{\sigma'_e}$
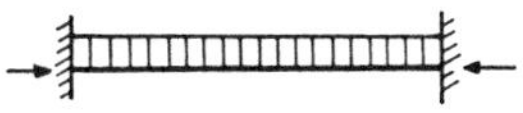	—0.4	$1 - .4\frac{\sigma_a}{\sigma'_e}$
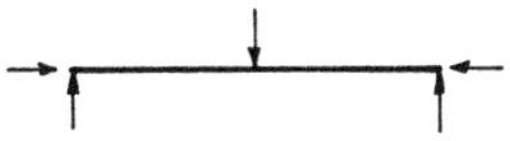	—0.2	$1 - .2\frac{\sigma_a}{\sigma'_e}$
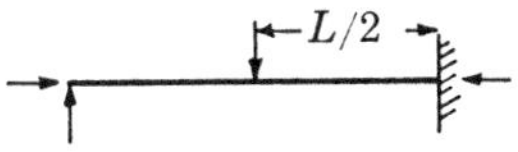	—0.4	$1 - .4\frac{\sigma_a}{\sigma'_e}$
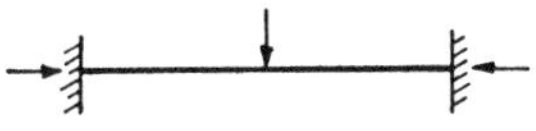	—0.6	$1 - .6\frac{\sigma_a}{\sigma'_e}$

AISC 1963 Commentary

$$\frac{\sigma_a}{\underline{\sigma}_a} + \frac{\sigma_b}{\underline{\sigma}_b} \leqq 1.0$$

(AISC Formula 6)

When

$$\frac{\sigma_a}{\underline{\sigma}_a} > .15$$

the amplification factor must be used.

Formula #8 now becomes—

$$\frac{\sigma_a}{\underline{\sigma}_a} + \frac{C_m \; \sigma_b}{\left(1 - \frac{\sigma_a}{\sigma'_e}\right) \underline{\sigma}_b} \leqq 1.0 \qquad \text{........... (11)}$$

(AISC Formula 7a)

This formula provides a check for column stability.

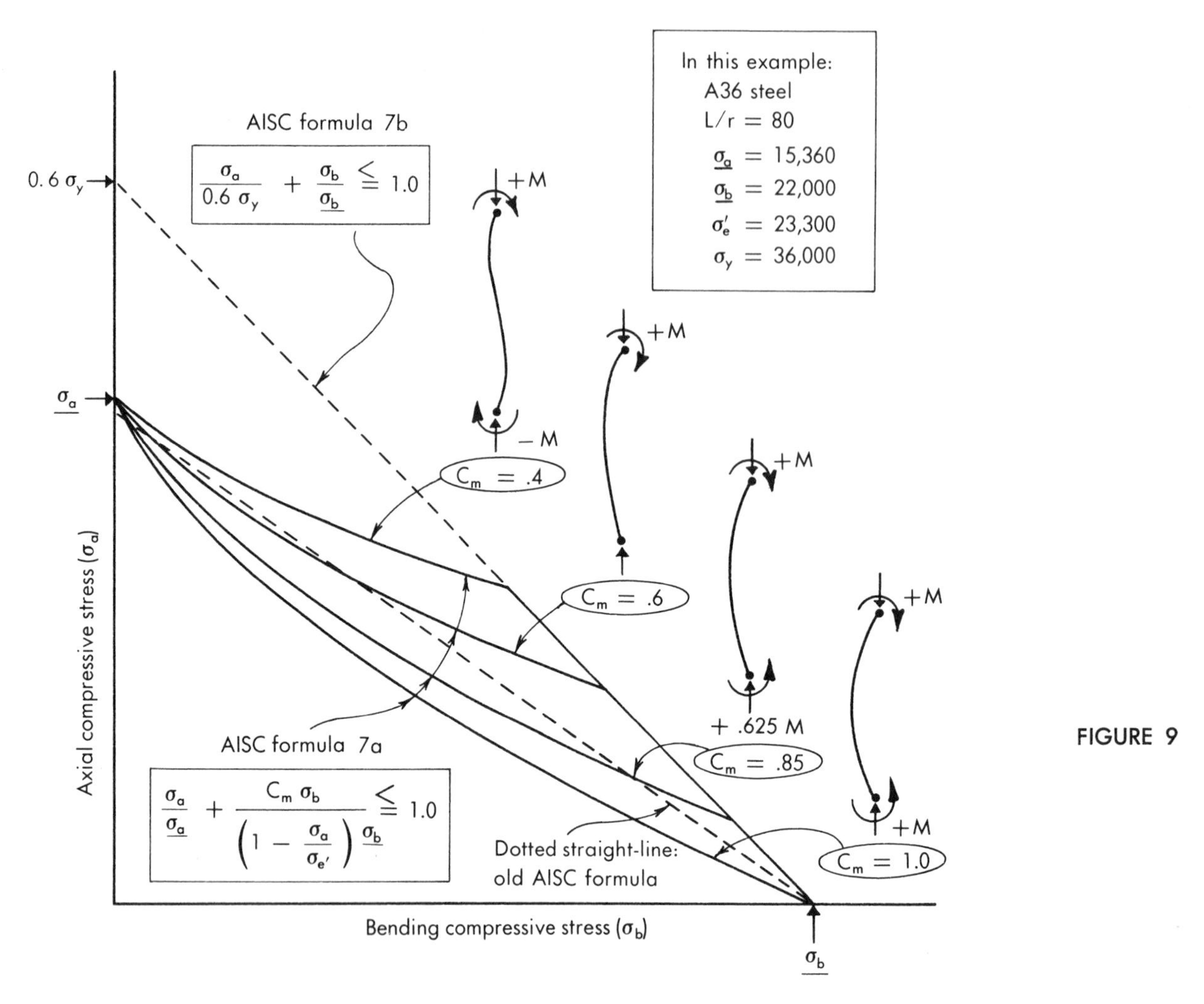

FIGURE 9

It is an attempt to estimate the total bending stress in the central portion of the column and to hold the axial compressive stress down to a safe level.

As L/r increases, this formula will reduce the axial load carrying capacity of the column. This is because the Euler stress (σ_e) decreases as L/r increases.

As C_m increases, caused by a less favorable condition of applied end moments or transverse forces, Formula #11 will reduce the axial load carrying capacity of the column.

The end of the member also must satisfy the straight-line interaction formula:

$$\frac{\sigma_a}{0.6\,\sigma_y} + \frac{\sigma_b}{\underline{\sigma}_b} \leq 1.0 \quad \text{(AISC Formula 7b)} \qquad \cdots\cdots(12)$$

In this formula, the allowable for compression ($\underline{\sigma}_a$) is for a column having a slenderness ratio of L/r = 0, hence $\underline{\sigma}_a = .60\,\sigma_y$.

This formula provides a check for the limiting stress at the ends of the column, and as such applies only at braced points.

Figure 9 is an example of the relationship of AISC Formulas 7a and 7b in the design of a specific member, under various loading conditions.

For bending moments applied about both axes of the column, these formulas become:

$$\frac{\sigma_a}{\underline{\sigma}_a} + \frac{\sigma_{bx}}{\underline{\sigma}_{bx}} + \frac{\sigma_{by}}{\underline{\sigma}_{by}} \leq 1.0 \quad \text{(AISC Formula 6)} \qquad \cdots\cdots(13)$$

$$\frac{\sigma_a}{\underline{\sigma}_a} + \frac{C_{mx}\,\sigma_{bx}}{\left(1 - \frac{\sigma_a}{\sigma'_{ex}}\right)\underline{\sigma}_{bx}} + \frac{C_{my}\,\sigma_{by}}{\left(1 - \frac{\sigma_a}{\sigma'_{ey}}\right)\underline{\sigma}_{by}} \leq 1.0 \quad \text{(AISC Formula 7a)} \qquad \cdots\cdots(14)$$

$$\frac{\sigma_a}{.60\,\sigma_y} + \frac{\sigma_{bx}}{\underline{\sigma}_{bx}} + \frac{\sigma_{by}}{\underline{\sigma}_{by}} \leq 1.0 \quad \text{(AISC Formula 7b)} \qquad \cdots\cdots(15)$$

4. DESIGN OUTLINES

The design procedure is simplified by following the appropriate outline in Tables 4, 5, or 6. Table 4 applies to compression members under combined loading (interaction problems). Table 5 applies to open-sectioned members under compression in bending. Table 6 applies to box members under compression in bending.

Each of these tables categorize the member-load conditions which must be satisfied, and then presents the required formulas with which to determine the allowable compressive stress.

TABLE 4—Design Outline for Compression Members Under Combined Loading *(Interaction Problems)*

If $\dfrac{\sigma_a}{\underline{\sigma}_a} \leqq .15$ check $\dfrac{\sigma_a}{\underline{\sigma}_a} + \dfrac{\sigma_b}{\underline{\sigma}_b} \leqq 1$ (AISC Formula 6) using $\sigma_b = \dfrac{M}{S}$

If $\dfrac{\sigma_a}{\underline{\sigma}_a} > .15$

Category (A)	Category (B)	Category (C)
Columns in frames with computed moments maximum at the ends with no transverse loading, and sidesway is permitted. Here the lateral stability of the frame depends upon the bending stiffness of its members.	Columns with computed moments maximum at the ends with no transverse loading, and sidesway is prevented	Compression members with additional transverse loads; for example a compressive chord of a truss with transverse loading between supports (panel points).
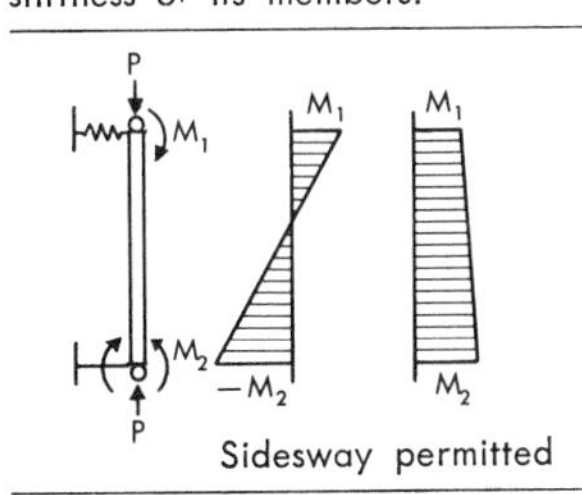 Sidesway permitted	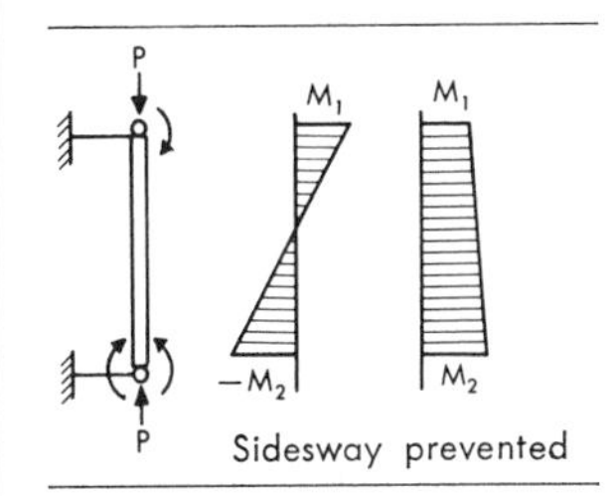 Sidesway prevented	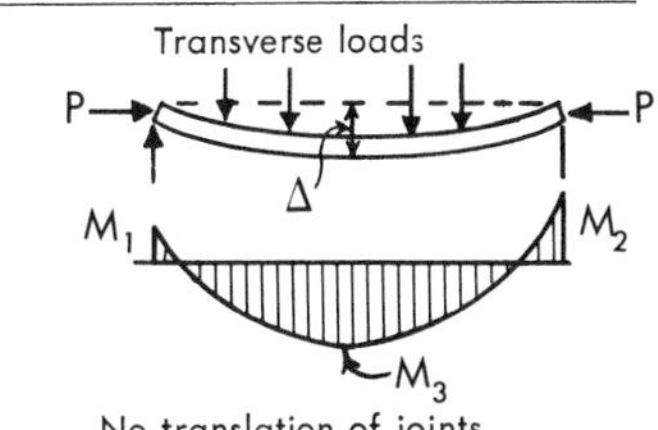 No translation of joints
$C_m = 0.85$	$C_m = 0.6 + 0.4 \dfrac{M_1}{M_2} \geqq 0.4$	$C_m = 1 + \psi \dfrac{\sigma_a}{\sigma'_e}$ $\psi = \dfrac{\pi^2 \Delta E I}{M_3 L^2} - 1$ Δ = max deflection due to transverse loading M_3 = max moment between supports due to trans. loading Use KL in computing $\underline{\sigma}_a$ Use L_b in computing moments (M)
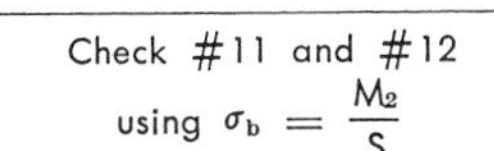 Check #11 and #12 using $\sigma_b = \dfrac{M_2}{S}$	Check #11 and #12 using $\sigma_b = \dfrac{M_2}{S}$	Check #11 using $\sigma_b = \dfrac{M_3}{S}$ Check #12 using $\sigma_b = \dfrac{M_2}{S}$

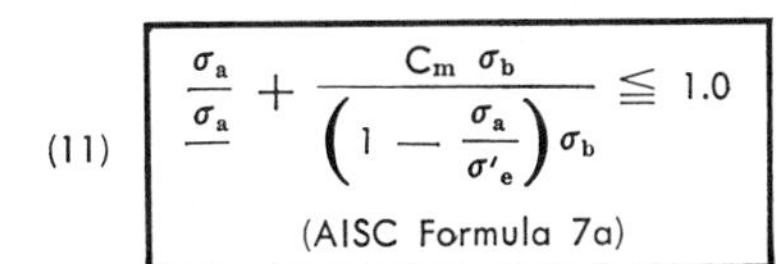

$$\frac{\sigma_a}{\underline{\sigma}_a} + \frac{C_m \sigma_b}{\left(1 - \dfrac{\sigma_a}{\sigma'_e}\right) \underline{\sigma}_b} \leqq 1.0 \quad (11)$$

(AISC Formula 7a)

$$\frac{\sigma_a}{.6\, \sigma_y} + \frac{\sigma_b}{\underline{\sigma}_b} \leqq 1.0 \quad (12)$$

(AISC Formula 7b)

$\underline{\sigma}_a$, $\underline{\sigma}_b$ and .60 σ_y may be increased ⅓ for wind (AISC Sec 1.5.6)

TABLE 5—Design Outline for Compression Members Under Compression In Bending

Members Which Are Symmetrical About An Axis In Plane of Bending And Having Some Lateral Support of Compression Flange

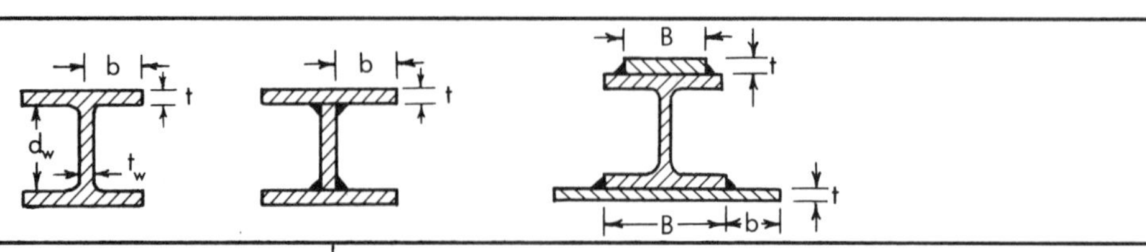

<table>
<tr>
<td>

Compression elements which are not "compact" but meet the following AISC Sec 1.9 requirements

$b/t \leqq \dfrac{3000}{\sqrt{\sigma_y}}$ *

$B/t \leqq \dfrac{8000}{\sqrt{\sigma_y}}$ *

</td>
<td>

If in addition, lateral support of compression flange does not exceed:

A7, A373, A36 steels
$13\ b_f$

Other stronger steels

$\dfrac{2300\ b_f}{\sqrt{\sigma_y}}$ or $\dfrac{20{,}000{,}000\ A_f}{d\ \sigma_y}$ (in.)

</td>
</tr>
<tr>
<td>

Having an axis of symmetry in the plane of its web:
AISC 1.5.1.4.5

(4)

$$\underline{\sigma_b} = \left[1.0 - \frac{\left(\frac{L}{r}\right)^2}{2C_c^2\ C_b}\right] .6\ \sigma_y$$

when $\dfrac{L}{r} \leqq 40$ don't need AISC Formula 4

(5)

$$\underline{\sigma_b} = \frac{12{,}000{,}000}{\dfrac{L\ d}{A_f}}$$

Use the larger value of (4) or (5) but $\leqq .60\ \sigma_y$

</td>
<td>

and compression elements meet the following AISC Sec 1.5.1.4.1 "compact section" requirements:

$b/t \leqq \dfrac{1600}{\sqrt{\sigma_y}}$ ‡

$B/t \leqq \dfrac{6000}{\sqrt{\sigma_y}}$

$\dfrac{d_w}{t_w} \leqq \dfrac{13{,}300}{\sqrt{\sigma_y}}\left(1 - 1.43\ \dfrac{\sigma_a}{\underline{\sigma_a}}\right)$

but need not be less than $\dfrac{8000}{\sqrt{\sigma_y}}$

$\underline{\sigma_b} = .66\ \sigma_y$ † (1.5.1.4.1)

</td>
</tr>
</table>

* This ratio may be exceeded if the bending stress, using a width not exceeding this limit, is within the allowable stress.
† For "compact" columns (AISC Sec. 1.5.1.4.1) which are symmetrical about an axis in the plane of bending, with the above lateral support of its compression flange and $\sigma_a = .15\ \sigma_a$ use 90% of the moments applied to the ends of the column if caused by the gravity loads of the connecting beams.
‡ For rolled sections, an upward variation of 3% may be tolerated.

In Tables 5 and 6:

L = unbraced length of the compression flange

b_f = width of compression flange

d = depth of member treated as a beam

r = radius of gyration of a Tee section comprising the compression flange plus 1/6 of the web area; about an axis in the plane of the web. For shapes symmetrical about their x axis of bending, substitution of r_y of the entire section is conservative

A_f = area of the compression flange

M_1 is the smaller and M_2 the larger bending moment at the ends of the unbraced length, taken about the strong axis of the member, and where M_1/M_2 is the ratio of end moments. This ratio is positive when M_1 and M_2 have the same sign, and negative when they have different signs. When the bending moment within an unbraced length is larger than that at both ends of this length, the ratio shall be taken as unity.

$$C_b = 1.75 - 1.05\left(\frac{M_1}{M_2}\right) + .3\left(\frac{M_1}{M_2}\right)^2$$

$$C_c = \sqrt{\frac{2\ \pi^2\ E}{\sigma_y}}$$

(but not more than 2.3 can conservatively be taken as 1.0)

TABLE 6—Design Outline for Box Members Under Compression In Bending
Members Which Are Symmetrical About An Axis In Plane of Bending

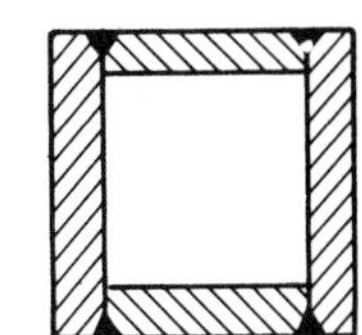

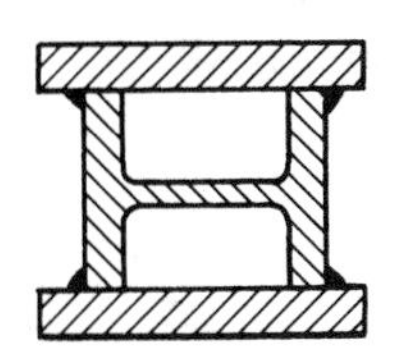

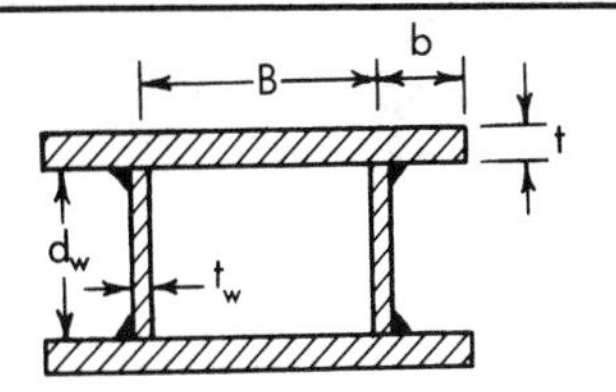

No AISC limit on lateral support of compression flange because box section is torsionally rigid	And if lateral support does not exceed: A7, A373, A36 steels $13\ b_f$ Other stronger steels $\frac{2400\ b_f}{\sqrt{\sigma_y}}$ or $\frac{20{,}000{,}000\ A_f}{d\ \sigma_y}$ (in.)
Compression elements which are not "compact" but meet the following AISC Sec 1.9 requirements (1.5.1.4.3) $b/t = \frac{3000}{\sqrt{\sigma_y}}$ * $B/t = \frac{8000}{\sqrt{\sigma_y}}$ *	And comparison elements meet the following AISC Sec 1.5.1.4.1 "compact section" requirements: $b/t \leqq \frac{1600}{\sqrt{\sigma_y}}$ ‡ $B/t \leqq \frac{6000}{\sqrt{\sigma_y}}$ $\frac{d_w}{t_w} \leqq \frac{13{,}300}{\sqrt{\sigma_y}}\left(1 - 1.43\frac{\sigma_a}{\sigma_a}\right)$ but need not be less than $\frac{8000}{\sqrt{\sigma_y}}$
$\sigma_b = .60\ \sigma_y$	$\sigma_b = .66\ \sigma_y$ †

Note: All notes from Table 5 apply equally to this Table 6.

TABLE 6A

		33,000	36,000	42,000	45,000	46,000	50,000	55,000	60,000	65,000	90,000*	95,000*	100,000*
		yield strength of steel											
Allowable bending stress	$\sigma = .60\ \sigma_y$	20,000	22,000	25,000	27,000	27,500	30,000	33,000	36,000	39,000	54,000	57,000	60,000
	$\sigma = .66\ \sigma_y$	22,000	24,000	28,000	29,500	30,500	33,000	36,500	39,500	43,000	59,400	62,700	66,000
Width-to-thickness ratio not to exceed:	$\frac{1600}{\sqrt{\sigma_y}}$	8.8	8.4	7.8	7.5	7.5	7.2	6.8	6.5	6.3	5.3	5.2	5.1
	$\frac{3000}{\sqrt{\sigma_y}}$	16.5	15.8	14.6	14.1	14.0	13.4	12.8	12.2	11.8	10.0	9.7	9.5
	$\frac{6000}{\sqrt{\sigma_y}}$	33.0	31.6	29.2	28.3	28.0	26.8	25.6	24.5	23.5	20.0	19.5	19.0
	$\frac{8000}{\sqrt{\sigma_y}}$	44.0	42.1	39.0	37.7	37.3	35.8	34.1	32.6	31.4	26.6	25.9	25.3
	$\frac{13{,}300}{\sqrt{\sigma_y}}$	73.2	70.0	64.8	62.6	62.0	59.5	56.7	54.3	52.2	44.4	43.1	42.1
Lateral support of compression flange of "compact" sections not to exceed:	$\frac{2400}{\sqrt{\sigma_y}}$	$13.2 b_f$	$12.6 b_f$	$11.7 b_f$	$11.3 b_f$	$11.2 b_f$	$10.7 b_f$	$10.2 b_f$	$9.8 b_f$	$9.4 b_f$	$8.0 b_f$	$7.8 b_f$	$7.6 b_f$
	$\frac{20{,}000{,}000\ A_f}{\sigma_y\ d}$	$606\frac{A_f}{d}$	$555\frac{A_f}{d}$	$476\frac{A_f}{d}$	$444\frac{A_f}{d}$	$435\frac{A_f}{d}$	$400\frac{A_f}{d}$	$364\frac{A_f}{d}$	$333\frac{A_f}{d}$	$308\frac{A_f}{d}$	$222\frac{A_f}{d}$	$210\frac{A_f}{d}$	$200\frac{A_f}{d}$
	$C_c = \sqrt{\frac{2\pi^2 E}{\sigma_y}}$	131.7	126.1	116.7	112.8	111.6	107.0	102.0	97.7	93.8	79.8	77.6	75.7
1.18.2.3: max. longitudinal spacing between intermittent fillet welds attaching compression flange to girders	$S \leqq \frac{4000}{\sqrt{\sigma_y}}\ t \leqq 12''$	22.0t	21.0t	19.5t	18.9t	18.7t	17.9t	17.1t	16.3t	15.7t	13.3t	13.0t	12.6t

*Quenched & Tempered Steels: yield strength at 0.2% offset
Round off to nearest whole number

5. BUILT-UP COMPRESSION MEMBERS

The basic requirements of welds on built-up compression members, as specified by AISC, are summarized by Figures 10, 11, 12, and 13.

Welding at the ends of built-up compression members bearing on base plates or milled surfaces (AISC 1.18.2.2):

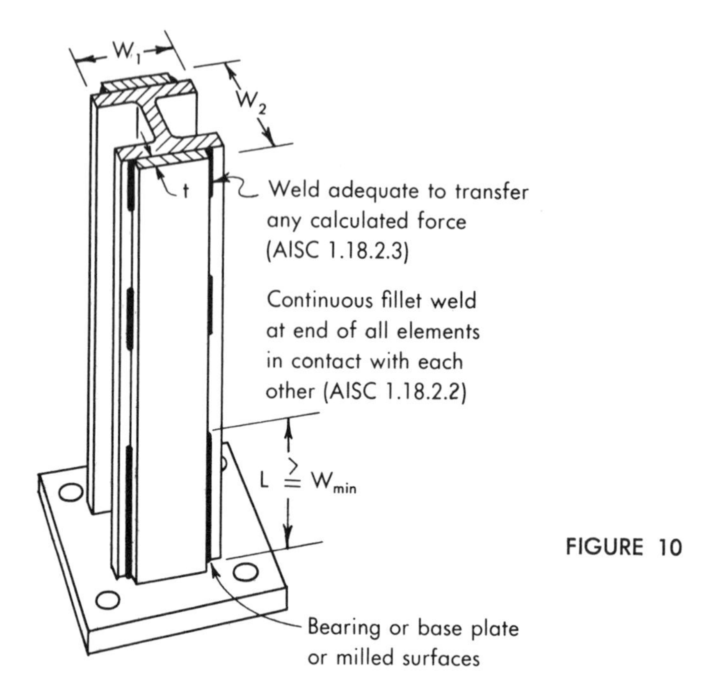

FIGURE 10

Plate in contact with a shape (AISC 1.18.2.3):

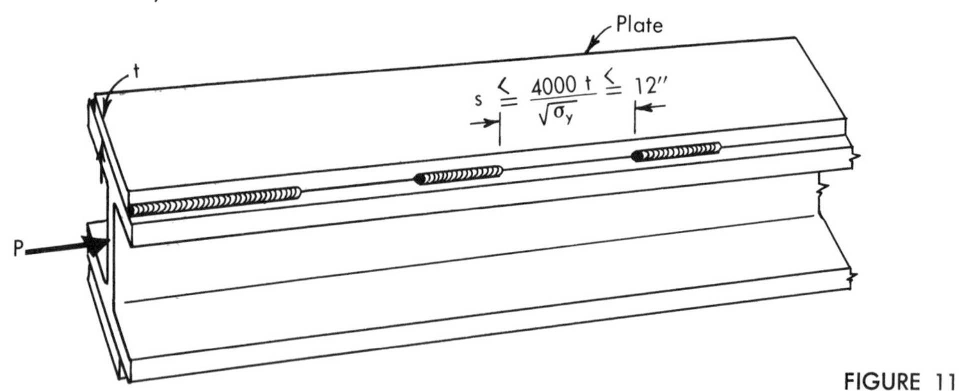

FIGURE 11

Two rolled shapes in contact with each other (AISC 1.18.2.3):

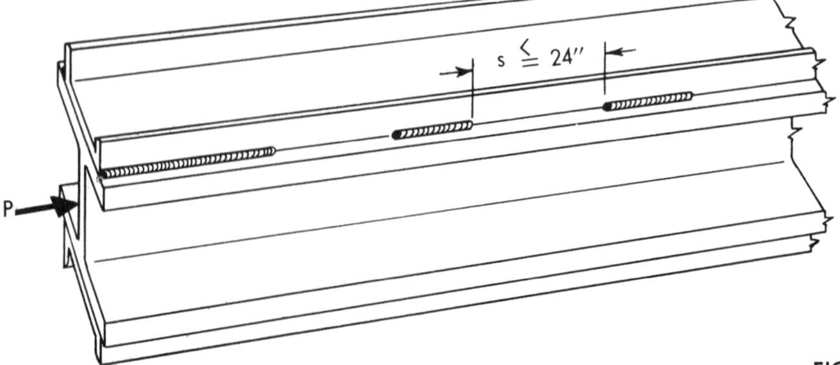

FIGURE 12

Two or more rolled shapes separated by intermittent fillers (AISC 1.18.2.4):

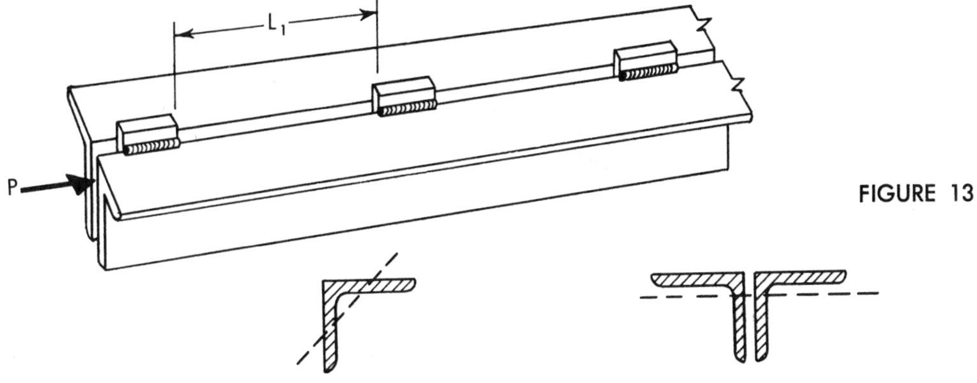

FIGURE 13

$$\left(\frac{L_1}{r}\right) \text{ of either member } \leqq \left(\frac{L}{r}\right) \text{ of whole member}$$

Tie Plates and Lacing

Main compression member built-up from plates or shapes and carrying a calculated force:

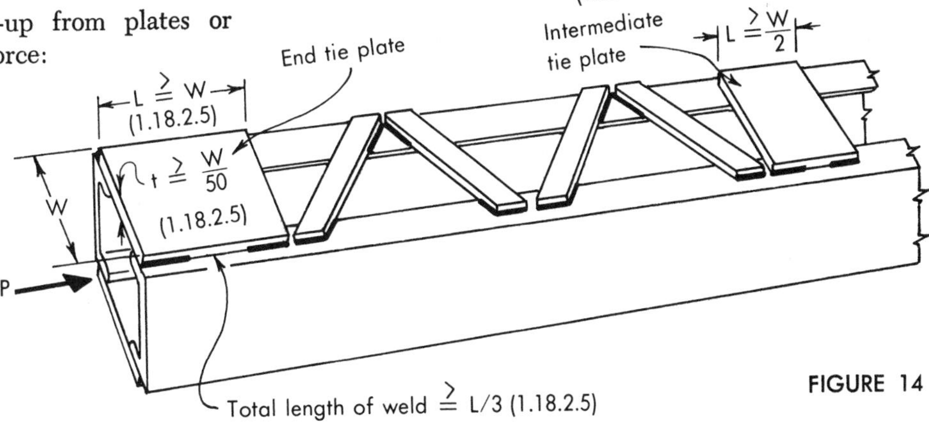

FIGURE 14

The spacing of lacing must be such (AISC 1.18.2.6) that—

$$\left(\frac{S}{r_1}\right) \text{ of element } \leqq \left(\frac{L}{r}\right) \text{ of whole member}$$

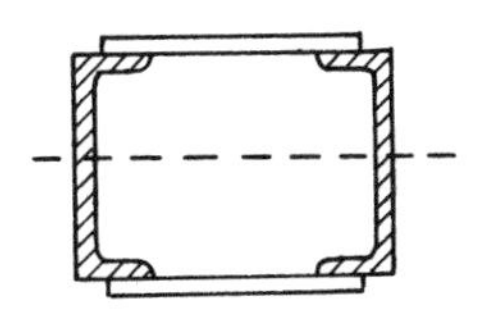

FIGURE 15

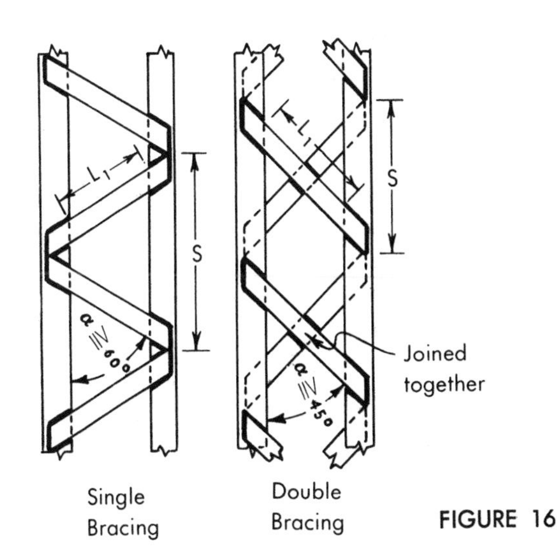

FIGURE 16

For single bracing:

$$\left(\frac{L_1}{r_1}\right) \leqq 140$$

For double bracing:

$$\left(\frac{L_1}{r_1}\right) \leqq 200$$

When the spacing between intermittent welds S > 15″, preferably use double bracing or braces made from angles (AISC 1.18.2.6).

Design lacing bar for axial compressive force (F):

$$F = \frac{V}{n \sin \alpha}$$

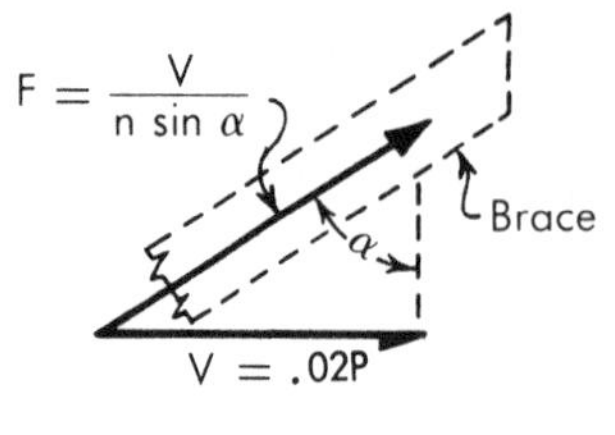

(AISC 1.18.2.6)

where:

n = number of bars carrying shear (V)

Determine allowable compressive stress ($\underline{\sigma_a}$) from one of the following two formulas:

If $\left(\frac{L_1}{r}\right) \leqq 120$*

$$\underline{\sigma_a} = \frac{\left[1 - \frac{\left(\frac{KL_1}{r}\right)^2}{2\ C_c^2}\right]}{F.S.}\ \sigma_y \qquad \text{(16)}$$ *

(AISC Formula 1)

(Use Tables 6 through 14, Section 3.1)

If $\left(\frac{L_1}{r}\right) > 120$*

$$\underline{\sigma_a} = \frac{\underline{\sigma_a} \text{ from Form. \#15}}{1.6 - \frac{1}{200}\left(\frac{L_1}{r}\right)} \qquad \text{(17)}$$ *

(AISC Formula 3)

here K = 1

On continuous cover plates with access holes (AISC 1.18.2.7):

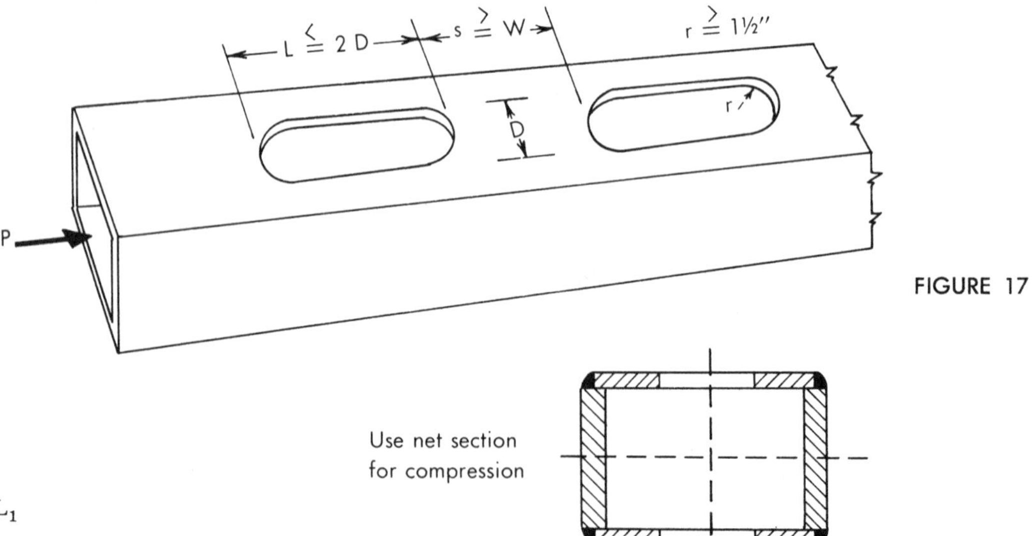

FIGURE 17

*For double brace, use .70 L_1

Typical Built-Up Compression Members

Figure 18 shows a number of examples of compression members built up from common shapes by means of welded construction. As indicated in lower views, perforated plates are often substituted for lacing bars for aesthetic effect.

Problem 2

To check the design of the following built-up section for the hoist of a boom. The 15′ column is fabricated from A36 steel by welding four 4″ x 3½″ x ½″ angles together with lacing bars.

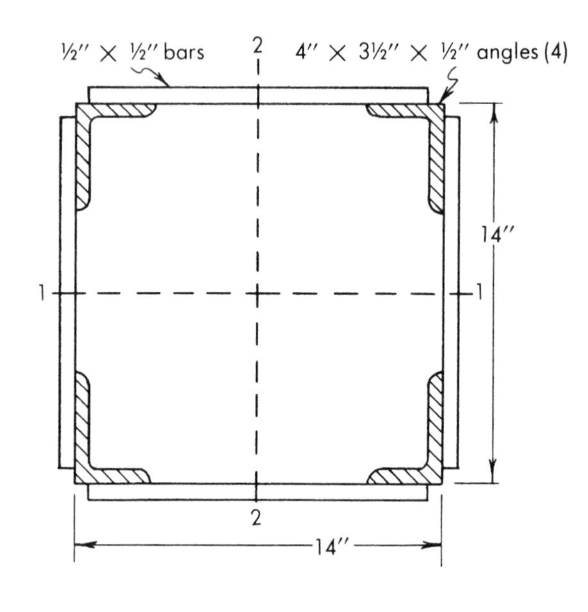

FIGURE 19

FIGURE 18—Typical Built-Up Compression Members

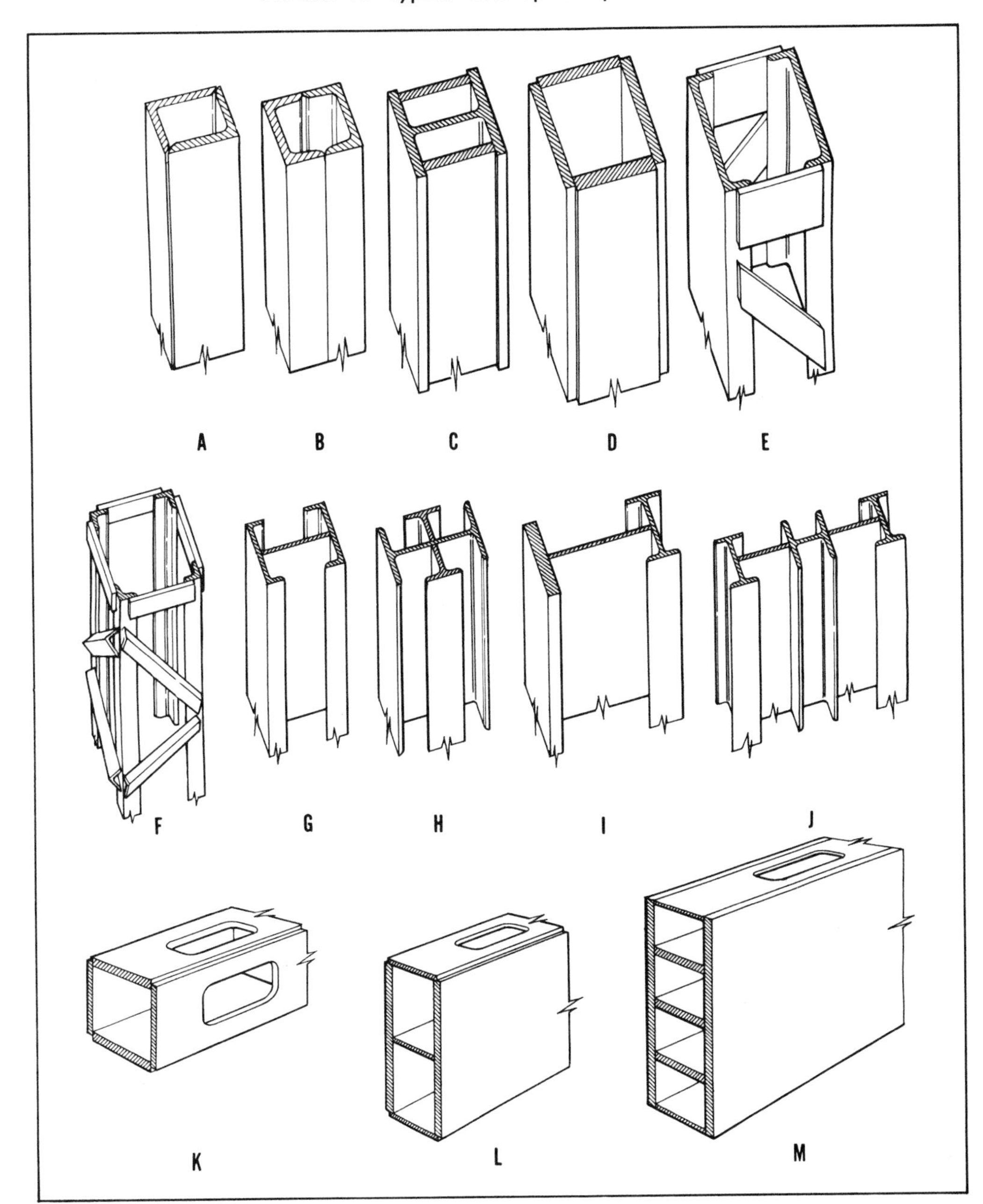

properties of each corner angle

$A = 3.5$ in.^{2}

$r_z = .72''$

$I_x = 5.3$ in.^{4}

$I_y = 3.8$ in.^{4}

$x = 1.0''$

$y = 1.25''$

moment of inertia of built-up section about axis 1-1

$$I_1 = 4(3.5)(5.75)^2 + 4(5.3) = 484 \text{ in.}^4$$

moment of inertia of built-up section about axis 2-2

$$I_2 = 4(3.5)(6)^2 + 4(3.8) = 519 \text{ in.}^4$$

least radius of gyration

$$r_1 = \sqrt{\frac{I_1}{A}}$$

$$= \sqrt{\frac{(484)}{4(3.5)}}$$

$$= 5.89''$$

slenderness ratio

$$\frac{L}{r} = \frac{(15')(12)}{(5.89)}$$

$$= 30.6$$

Then from Table 7 in Sect. 3.1, the allowable compressive stress is $\underline{\sigma_c} = 19{,}900$ psi and the allowable compressive load is —

$$P = \underline{\sigma_c}\, A$$

$$= (19{,}900)(14)$$

$$= 278.6 \text{ kips}$$

Check slenderness ratio of single 4″ x 3½″ x ½″ angle between bracing:

$$\frac{L}{r_z} = \frac{(16.2)}{(.72)}$$

$$= 22.4 < 30.6 \quad \underline{\text{OK}}$$

(AISC Sec. 1.18.2.6)

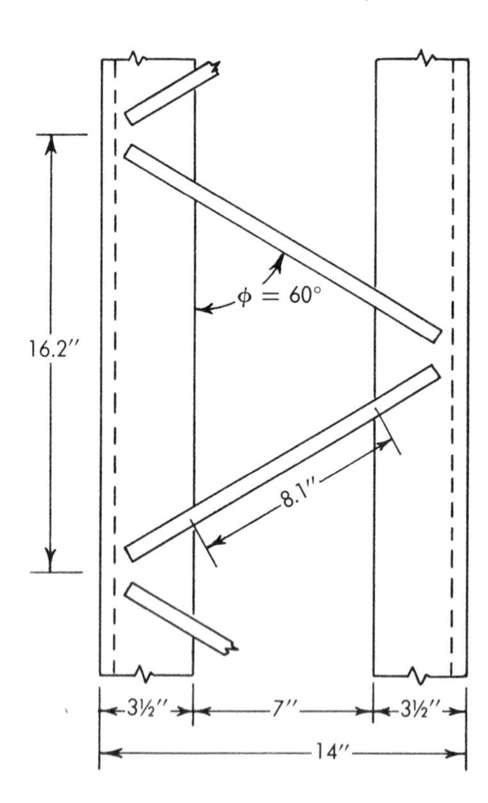

FIGURE 20

Design of Lacing Bars

AISC specifies that lacing bars be proportioned to resist a shearing force normal to the axis of the member and equal to 2% of the total compressive force on the member (Sec. 1.18.2.6):

$$V = 2\%\ P$$

$$= (.02)(278.6^k)$$

$$= 5.57^k \quad (2 \text{ bars})$$

The axial force on each bar is—

$$F = \frac{1}{2}\left(\frac{5.57}{.866}\right)$$

$$= 3.22^k$$

The unsupported length of the lacing bar between connecting welds is —

$$L = \frac{14'' - (2 \times 3\tfrac{1}{2}'')}{.866}$$

$$= 8.1''$$

The least radius of gyration of the ½″ x ½″ bar is obtained thusly —

$$A = \tfrac{1}{4} \text{ in.}^2$$

$$I = \frac{(\frac{1}{2})(\frac{1}{2})^3}{12}$$

$$= \frac{1}{192}$$

$$r = \sqrt{\frac{I}{A}}$$

$$= \sqrt{\left(\frac{1}{192}\right)\left(\frac{4}{1}\right)}$$

$$= .144$$

And the slenderness ratio of the lacing bars is —

$$\frac{L}{r} = \frac{(8.1)}{(.144)}$$

$$= 56.3 < 140 \quad \underline{\text{OK}} \text{ single lacing}$$

(AISC Sec. 1.18.2.6)

From Table 7 in Sect. 3.1, the allowable compressive stress on the bas is —

$$\underline{\sigma_c} = 17{,}780 \text{ psi}$$

The allowable compressive force on the bar is —

$$F = \sigma_c\, A$$

$$= (17{,}780)(.25)$$

$$= 4.45^k > 3.22^k \quad \underline{\text{OK}}$$

If each end of each bar is connected to the angles by two 1½″ long $^3\!/_{16}$″ (E70) fillet welds, this will provide an allowable force of —

$$F = 2 \times 1\tfrac{1}{2} \times 2100 \text{ lbs/in} = 6.3^k > 4.45^k \quad \underline{\text{OK}}$$

Problem 3

A multi-story building, having no interior columns, has a typical welded built-up column with the section shown in Figure 21.

A36 steel and E70 welds are employed.

The following three load conditions are recognized:

Case A	Case B	Case C
dead and live loads no wind P = 2500 kips M_x = 250 ft-kips M_y = 0	dead and live loads with wind in y-y direction P = 2700 kips M_x = 2200 ft-kips M_y = 0	dead and live loads with wind in x-x direction P = 2800 kips M_x = 250 ft-kips M_y = 1200 ft-kips

properties of the 14″ WF 426# section

$$A = 125.25 \text{ in.}^2$$

$$I_x = 6610.3 \text{ in.}^4$$

$$I_y = 2359.5 \text{ in.}^4$$

moment of inertia about x-x

Let reference axis be a-a here

Parts	d	A	M	I_a	I_g
20 x 4	— 19.0	80.0	— 1520.0	+ 28,880	107
1½ x 34	0	51.0	0	0	4913
14 WF 426#	+ 17.94	125.25	+ 2247.0	+ 40,310	2360
Total		256.25	+ 727	+ 76,570	

$$I_x = 76{,}570 - \frac{+727^2}{256.25}$$

$$= 74{,}507 \text{ in.}^4$$

$$NA = \frac{+727}{256.25}$$

$$= +2.84'' \quad \text{(from a-a)}$$

$$r_x = \sqrt{\frac{I_x}{A}}$$

$$= \sqrt{\frac{(74{,}507)}{(256)}}$$

$$= 17.05''$$

moment of inertia about y-y

$$I_y = \frac{4 \times 20^3}{12} + \frac{34\ (1\tfrac{1}{2})^3}{12} + 6610$$

$$= 9287 \text{ in.}^4$$

$$r_y = \sqrt{\frac{I_y}{A}} = \sqrt{\frac{(9287)}{(256)}}$$

$$= 6.03''$$

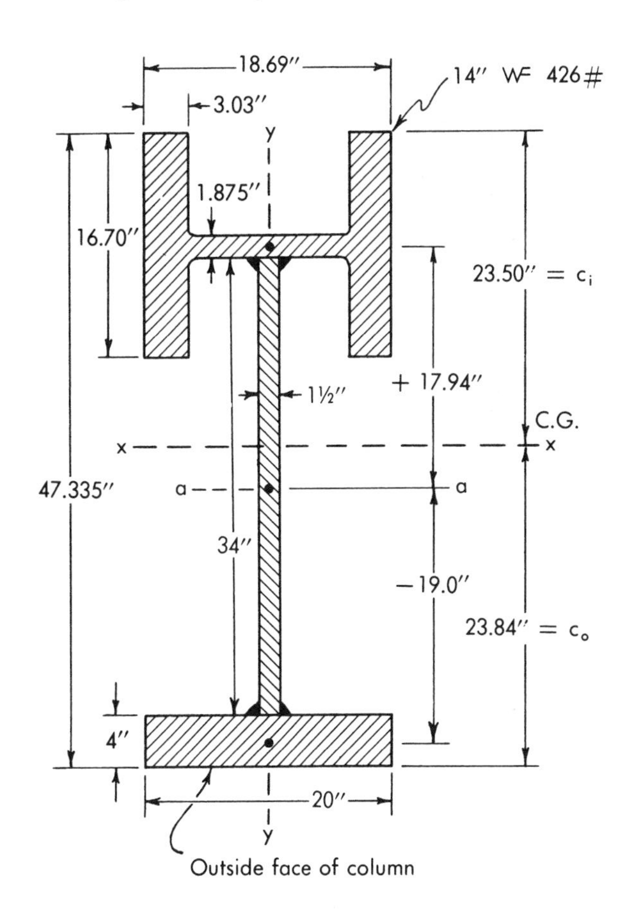

FIGURE 21

Allowable Stresses

The various axial compressive stresses and bending stresses on the built-up column are checked according to Formulas #11 and 12 (AISC Sec. 1.6.1, Formulas 6, 7a, and 7b).

When wind loads are included, the basic allowable stresses are increased by ⅓, provided the resulting section is not less than that required for dead load, live loads, and any impact (AISC Sec. 1.5.6).

Compression members are considered "compact" when symmetrical about an axis in the plane of bending, with lateral support of the column's compression flange not exceeding a distance equal to 13 times its width (A36 steel) (AISC Sec. 1.5.1.4.1). For "compact" columns, the engineer can use just 90% of moments applied to ends of the column if caused by gravity loads on connecting beams (no wind loads) and $\sigma_a \leqq .15\ \underline{\sigma_a}$ (AISC Sec 1.5.1.4.1).

If the section is not "compact", AISC Formulas 4 and 5 must be used to determine the allowable compressive bending stress ($\underline{\sigma_{bx}}$ and $\underline{\sigma_{by}}$).

check for lateral support

L_c = maximum unbraced length of compression flange for "compact" section

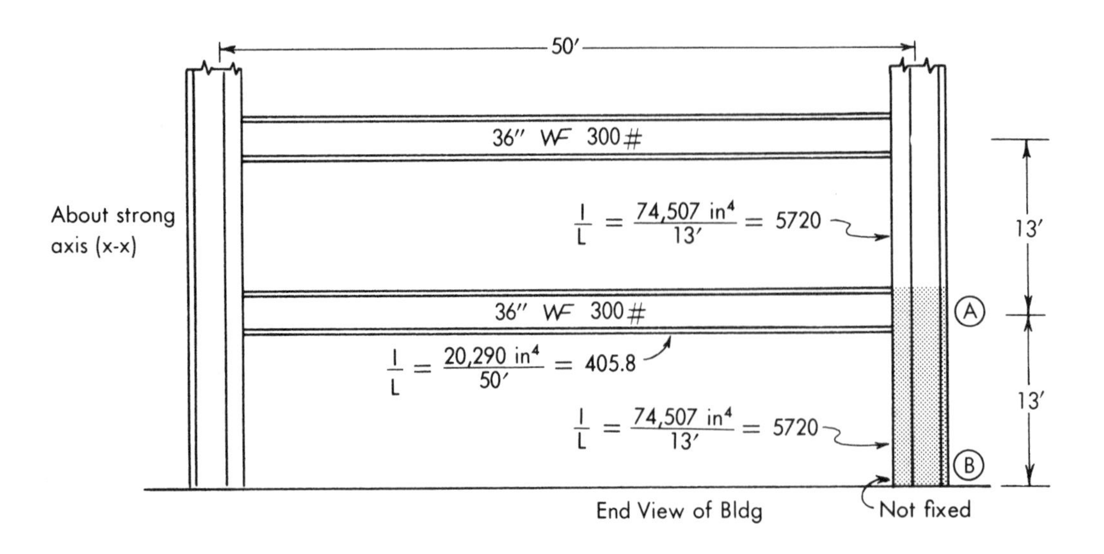

FIGURE 22 (a)

$L_{cx} = 13\ b_{fx}$

$= 13(18\tfrac{3}{4}'')$

$= 244''$ or $20.3' > 13'$ OK

$L_{cy} = 13\ b_{fy}$

$= 13(16\tfrac{3}{4}'')$

$= 218''$ or $18.2' > 13'$ OK

check for "compact" section
flange half, width to thickness

(a) outer flange plate

$$\frac{b_f}{t_f} = \frac{10''}{4''}$$

$$= 2.5 < \frac{1600}{\sqrt{\sigma_y}} \quad \text{or } 8.4 \quad \text{OK}$$

(b) inner WF section

$$\frac{b_f}{t_f} = \frac{8.35''}{3.03''}$$

$$= 2.75 < \frac{1600}{\sqrt{\sigma_y}} \quad \text{or } 8.4 \quad \text{OK}$$

check web depth to web thickness

$$\text{Actual } \frac{d_w}{t_w} = \frac{34''}{1\tfrac{1}{2}} = 22.6$$

$$\text{Allowable } \frac{d_w}{t_w} \leq \frac{13{,}300}{\sqrt{\sigma_y}}\left(1 - 1.43\ \frac{\sigma_a}{\underline{\sigma_a}}\right)$$

but need not be less than $\dfrac{8000}{\sqrt{\sigma_y}}$

$$\frac{d_w}{t_w} \leq 70\left(1 - 1.43 \times \frac{9{,}760}{17{,}970}\right) \leq 17.3$$

but need not be less than 42.1

$42.1 > 22.6$ OK

Therefore it is a "compact" section and following can be used:

$$\underline{\sigma_{bx}} = \underline{\sigma_{by}} = .66\ \sigma_y \text{ or } 24{,}000 \text{ psi}$$

Euler stress (σ'_{ex}) *and* (σ'_{ey})

About strong axis (x-x):

$$\frac{K_x L_x}{r_x} = \frac{569''}{17.05''} = 33.4$$

From Table 2, read $\sigma'_{ex} = 133{,}750$ psi.

About weak axis (y-y):

$$\frac{K_y L_y}{r_y} = \frac{328''}{6.03''} = 54.4$$

From Table 2, read $\sigma'_{ey} = 50{,}400$ psi.

allowable axial compressive stress

$$G_A = \frac{\sum \frac{I_c}{L_c}}{\sum \frac{I_g}{L_g}}$$

$$= \frac{2(5720)}{1(\ 406)}$$

$$= 28.2$$

$G_B = \infty$ or 10

Sidesway being permitted, from the nomograph (Fig. 1):

$K = 3.65$ and

$L_e = K\ L$

$= (3.65)(13' \text{ x } 12'')$

$= 569''$

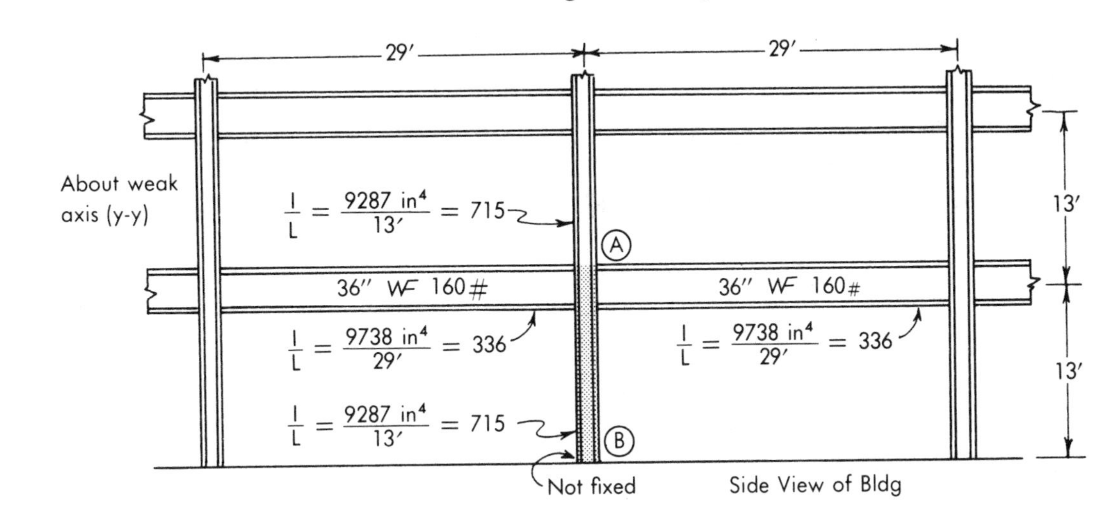

FIGURE 22 (b)

$$\frac{L_e}{r_x} = \frac{(569'')}{(17.05'')}$$

$$= 33.4$$

$$G_A = \frac{\sum \frac{I_c}{L_c}}{\sum \frac{I_g}{L_g}}$$

$$= \frac{2(715)}{2(336)}$$

$$= 2.13$$

$$G_B = \infty \text{ or } 10$$

Sidesway being permitted, from the nomograph (Fig. 1):

$$K = 2.1 \text{ and}$$

$$L_e = K\ L$$

$$= 2.1\ (13' \times 12'')$$

$$= 328''$$

$$\frac{L_e}{r_y} = \frac{(328'')}{(6.03'')}$$

$$= 54.4$$

This value of $r_y = 54.4$ governs, and from Table 7 in Sect. 3.1 (A36 steel)

$$\sigma_a = 17{,}970 \text{ psi}$$

Column Analysis

The following three analyses of the column (Cases A, B, and C) are for columns with computed moments maximum at the ends with no transverse loading and with sidesway being permitted.

This would be category A on Table 4. In this case ($C_m = .85$) for both axes (x-x) and (y-y).

CASE A Dead and Live Loads; No Wind

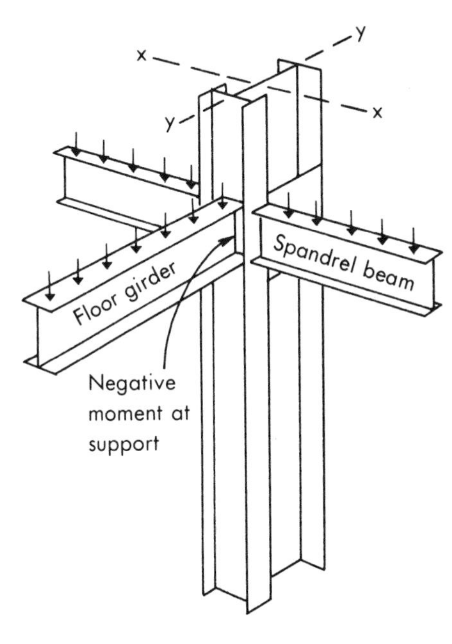

FIGURE 23

applied loads

$$P = 2500 \text{ kips}$$

$$M_x = 250 \text{ ft-kips}$$

$$M_y = 0$$

applied stresses

$$\sigma_a = \frac{P}{A}$$

$$= \frac{(2500 \times 1000)}{(256.25)}$$

$$= 9760 \text{ psi}$$

$$\sigma_{bx} = \frac{M_x \, c}{I_x}$$

$$= \frac{(250 \times 1000 \times 12)(23.50)}{(74{,}507)}$$

$= 947$ psi (max at 4″ x 20″ flange ℄)

$\sigma_{by} = 0$

> If $\frac{\sigma_a}{\underline{\sigma_a}} = .15$, $.9M_x$ can be used (Sec 1.5.1.4.1); but in this case, $\frac{\sigma_a}{\underline{\sigma_a}} = \frac{9760}{17{,}970} = .54$
> $= .54 > .15$ so full value of M_x must be used.

allowable stresses

$\underline{\sigma_a} = 17{,}970$ psi

Since it is a "compact" section laterally supported within 13 times its compression flange width (Sec 1.5.1.4.1):

$\underline{\sigma_{bx}} = \underline{\sigma_{by}} = .66\ \sigma_y \quad = 24{,}000$ psi

$\sigma'_{ex} = 133{,}750$ psi

$0.60\ \sigma_y = 22{,}000$ psi

checking against Formula #14 (AISC 7a)

$$\frac{\sigma_a}{\underline{\sigma_a}} + \frac{C_{mx}\ \sigma_{bx}}{\left(1 - \frac{\sigma_a}{\sigma'_{ex}}\right)\underline{\sigma_{bx}}} + \frac{C_{my}\ \sigma_{by}}{\left(1 - \frac{\sigma_a}{\sigma'_{ey}}\right)\underline{\sigma_{by}}} \leqq 1$$

> Here $C_m = .85$ because sidesway is permitted

$$\frac{(9760)}{(17{,}970)} + \frac{(.85)(947)}{\left(1 - \frac{9760}{133{,}750}\right)(24{,}000)}$$

$= .579 < 1.0$ OK

checking against Formula #15 (AISC 7b)

$$\frac{\sigma_a}{0.6\ \sigma_y} + \frac{\sigma_{bx}}{\underline{\sigma_{bx}}} + \frac{\sigma_{by}}{\underline{\sigma_{by}}} \leqq 1$$

$$\frac{(9760)}{(22{,}000)} + \frac{(947)}{(24{,}000)} = .482 < 1.0 \text{ OK}$$

CASE B Dead and Live Loads; Wind in Y Direction

applied loads

$P = 2700$ kips $\quad M_x = 2200$ ft-kips $\quad M_y = 0$

applied stresses

$$\sigma_a = \frac{P}{A} = \frac{2700 \times 1000}{256.25} = 10{,}520 \text{ psi}$$

$$\sigma_{bx} = \frac{M_x \, c}{I_x}$$

$$= \frac{(2200 \times 1000 \times 12)(23.50)}{74{,}507}$$

$= 8330$ psi (max at 4″ × 20″ flange ℄)

We cannot use .9 M_x, because wind loading is involved; hence full value of M_x must be used.

$\sigma_{by} = 0$

allowable stresses

$\underline{\sigma_a} = 17{,}970 \times 1.33$ Wind in addition (Sec 1.5.6)

$\underline{\sigma_{bx}} = 24{,}000 \times 1.33$ Wind in this direction (Sec 1.5.6)

$\underline{\sigma_{ex}} = 133{,}750 \times 1.33$ Wind in this direction (Sec 1.6.1 and 1.5.6)

checking against Formula #14 (AISC 7a)

$$\frac{\sigma_a}{\underline{\sigma_a}} + \frac{C_{mx}\ \sigma_{bx}}{\left(1 - \frac{\sigma_a}{\sigma'_{ex}}\right)\underline{\sigma_{bx}}} + \frac{C_{my}\ \sigma_{by}}{\left(1 - \frac{\sigma_a}{\sigma'_{ex}}\right)\underline{\sigma_{by}}} \leqq 1.0$$

$$\frac{(10{,}520)}{(17{,}970 \times 1.33)}$$

$$+ \frac{(.85)(8330)}{\left(1 - \frac{10{,}520}{133{,}750 \times 1.33}\right)(24{,}000 \times 1.33)}$$

$= .676 < 1.0$ OK

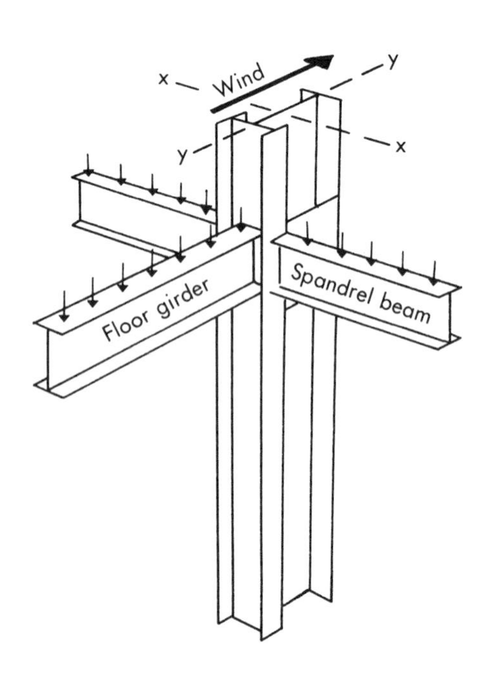

FIGURE 24

checking against Formula #15 (AISC 7b)

$$\frac{\sigma_a}{0.6\ \sigma_y} + \frac{\sigma_{bx}}{\underline{\sigma_{bx}}} + \frac{\sigma_{by}}{\underline{\sigma_{by}}} \leqq 1.0$$

$$\frac{(10{,}520)}{(22{,}000 \times 1.33)} + \frac{(8330)}{(24{,}000 \times 1.33)}$$

$$= .621 < 1.0 \quad \underline{\text{OK}}$$

CASE C Dead and Live Loads; Wind in X Direction

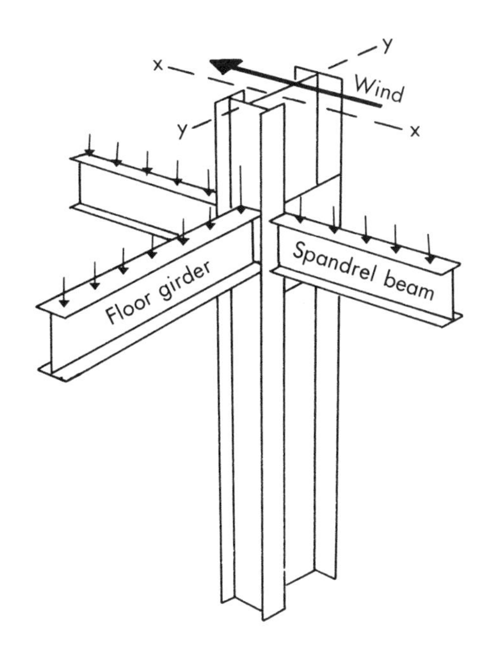

FIGURE 25

applied loads

$P = 2800$ kips

$M_x = 250$ ft-kips

$M_y = 1200$ ft-kips

applied stresses

$$\sigma_a = \frac{P}{A}$$

$$= \frac{(2800 \times 1000)}{(256.25)}$$

$$= 10{,}920 \text{ psi}$$

$$\sigma_{bx} = \frac{M_x\ c}{I_x}$$

$$= \frac{(250 \times 1000 \times 12)(23.50)}{(74{,}507)}$$

$= 947$ psi (max at 4″ × 20″ flange ⅊)

$$\sigma_{by} = \frac{M_y\ c}{I_y}$$

$$= \frac{(1200 \times 1000 \times 12)(9.35)}{(9286)}$$

$= 14{,}500$ psi (max at flange of WF section)

$$\text{or } = \frac{(1200 \times 1000 \times 12)(10.0)}{(9286)}$$

$= 15{,}500$ psi (max at outer edge of 4″ × 20″ ⅊)

We cannot use .9 M, because wind loading is involved; hence full value of (M_x) and (M_y) must be used.

allowable stresses

$\sigma_a = 17{,}970 \times 1.33$	Wind in addition (Sec 1.5.6)
$\sigma_{bx} = 24{,}000$	No wind in this direction
$\sigma_{by} = 24{,}000 \times 1.33$	Wind in this direction (Sec 1.5.6)
$\sigma'_{ex} = 133{,}750$	No wind in this direction
$\sigma'_{ey} = 50{,}400 \times 1.33$	Wind in this direction

checking against Formula #11 (AISC 7a)

$$\frac{\sigma_a}{\underline{\sigma_a}} + \frac{C_m\ \sigma_{bx}}{\left(1 - \frac{\sigma_a}{\sigma'_{ex}}\right)\underline{\sigma_{bx}}} + \frac{C_m\ \sigma_{by}}{\left(1 - \frac{\sigma_a}{\sigma'_{ey}}\right)\underline{\sigma_{by}}} \leqq 1.0$$

$$\frac{(10{,}920)}{(17{,}970 \times 1.33)} + \frac{(.85)(947)}{\left(1 - \frac{10{,}920}{133{,}750}\right)(24{,}000)}$$

$$+ \frac{(.85)(15{,}500)}{\left(1 - \frac{10{,}920}{50{,}400 \times 1.33}\right)(24{,}000 \times 1.33)}$$

$$= .986 < 1.0 \text{ OK}$$

If there is any question about this built-up column section being a "compact" section about the y-y axis, we must use $\underline{\sigma_{by}} = 22{,}000$. This would result in $1.03 > 1.0$. However, this could be overcome by re-adjusting the 4″ × 20″ flange plate down to a distance within the depth of the WF (18.69″). Then $\sigma_{by} = 14{,}500$ and this would result in $.996 < 1.0$ OK.

checking against Formula #11 (AISC 7b)

$$\frac{\sigma_a}{0.6\ \sigma_y} + \frac{\sigma_{bx}}{\underline{\sigma_{bx}}} + \frac{\sigma_{by}}{\underline{\sigma_{by}}} = 1.0$$

$$\frac{(10{,}920)}{(22{,}000 \times 1.33)} + \frac{(947)}{(24{,}000)} + \frac{(15{,}500)}{(24{,}000 \times 1.33)}$$

$$= .898 < 1.0 \quad \underline{\text{OK}}$$

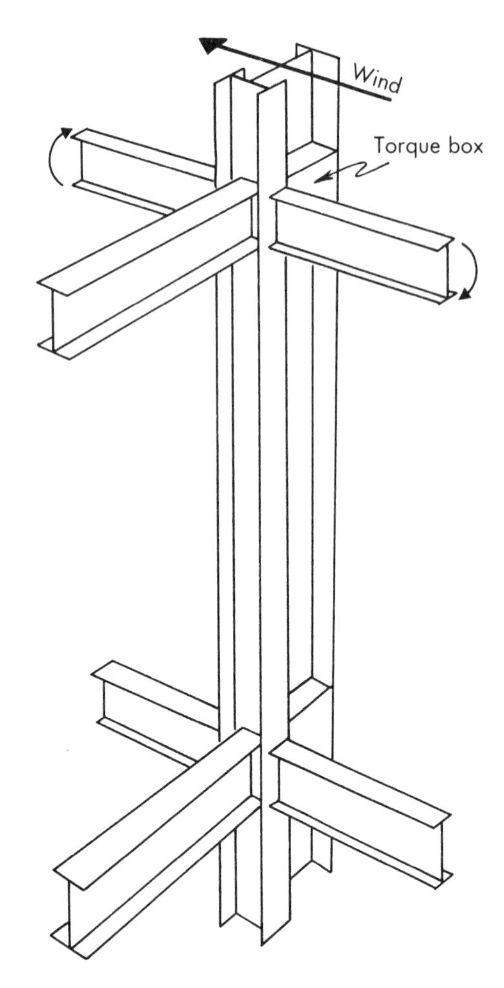

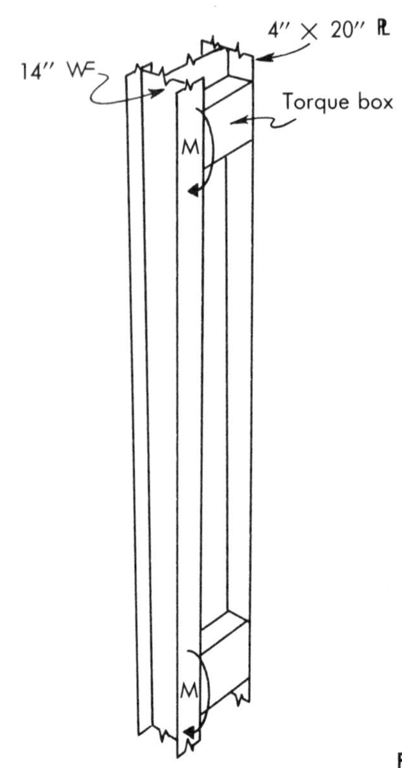

FIGURE 26

Torsion on Built-Up Column

One item left to investigate in the built-up column is the twisting action applied to it. In Case C, the wind in the x-x direction causes a moment of $M_y = 1200$ ft-kips because of the restraint of the spandrel beams.

(1) One way to analyze this problem is to assume that this moment (M_y) is resisted by the elements (the 14″ WF section and the 4″ × 20″ flange plate) of the built-up column in proportion to their moments of inertia about axis y-y. See Figure 26.

Since:

$$I_{WF} = 6610 \text{ in.}^4$$

$$I_{℄} = 2667 \text{ in.}^4$$

The moment resisted by the 4″ × 20″ flange plate is—

$$M_{℄} = \frac{(1200 \text{ ft-kip})(2667)}{(6610 + 2667)}$$

$$= 346 \text{ ft-kips} = 4{,}152{,}000 \text{ in.-lbs}$$

This moment is to be transferred as torque from the 14″ WF section to the 4″ × 20″ plate through a torque box, made by adding ½″-thick plates to the built-up column in line with the beam connections.

This torque box is checked for shear stress; Figure 27.

$$\tau = \frac{T}{2\ t\ b\ d}$$

$$= \frac{(4{,}152{,}000)}{2(\tfrac{1}{2})(18.2)(34.5)}$$

$$= 6600 \text{ psi } \underline{\text{OK}}$$

(2) Another method of checking this twisting action is to consider the moment (M_y) as applying torque to the built-up column. See Figure 28.

This applied moment may be considered as two flange forces: in this case, 411 kips in the upper and the lower flanges of the spandrel beam, but in opposite directions. Since these forces are not applied at the "shear center" of the column, a twisting action will be applied to the column about its longitudinal axis within the region of the beam connection where these forces are applied; there is no twisting action along the length of the column in between these regions.

Since an "open" section such as this built-up

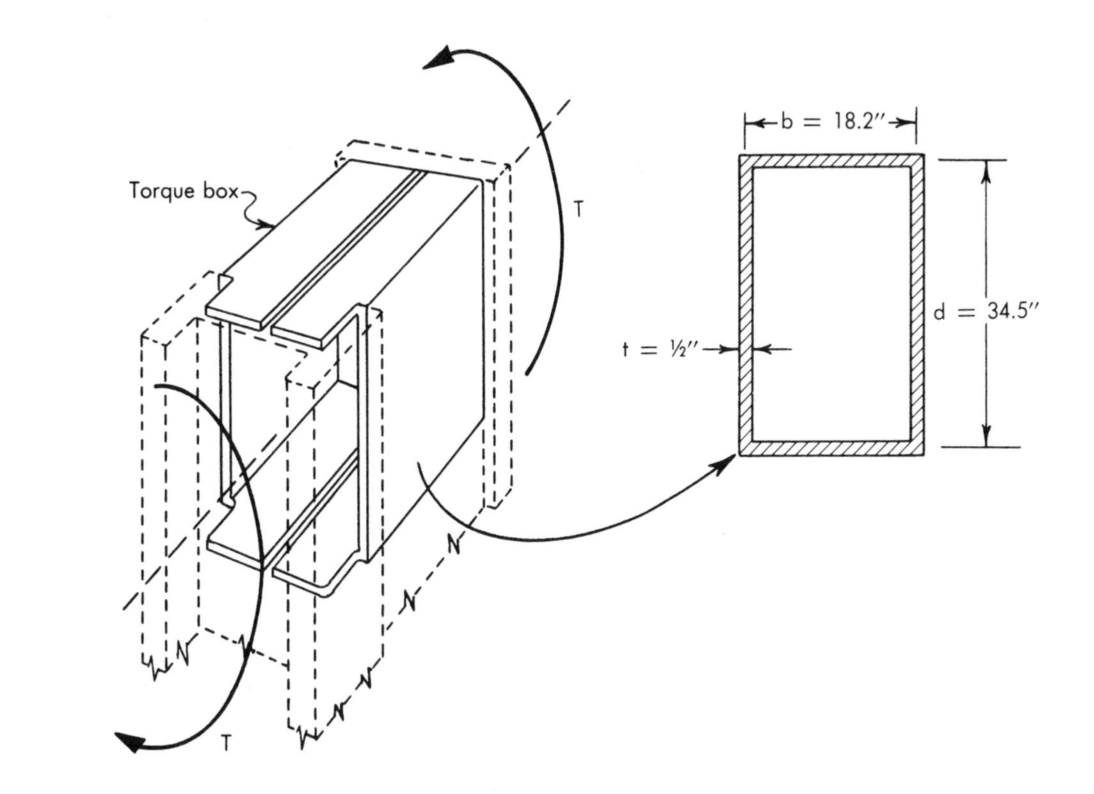

FIGURE 27

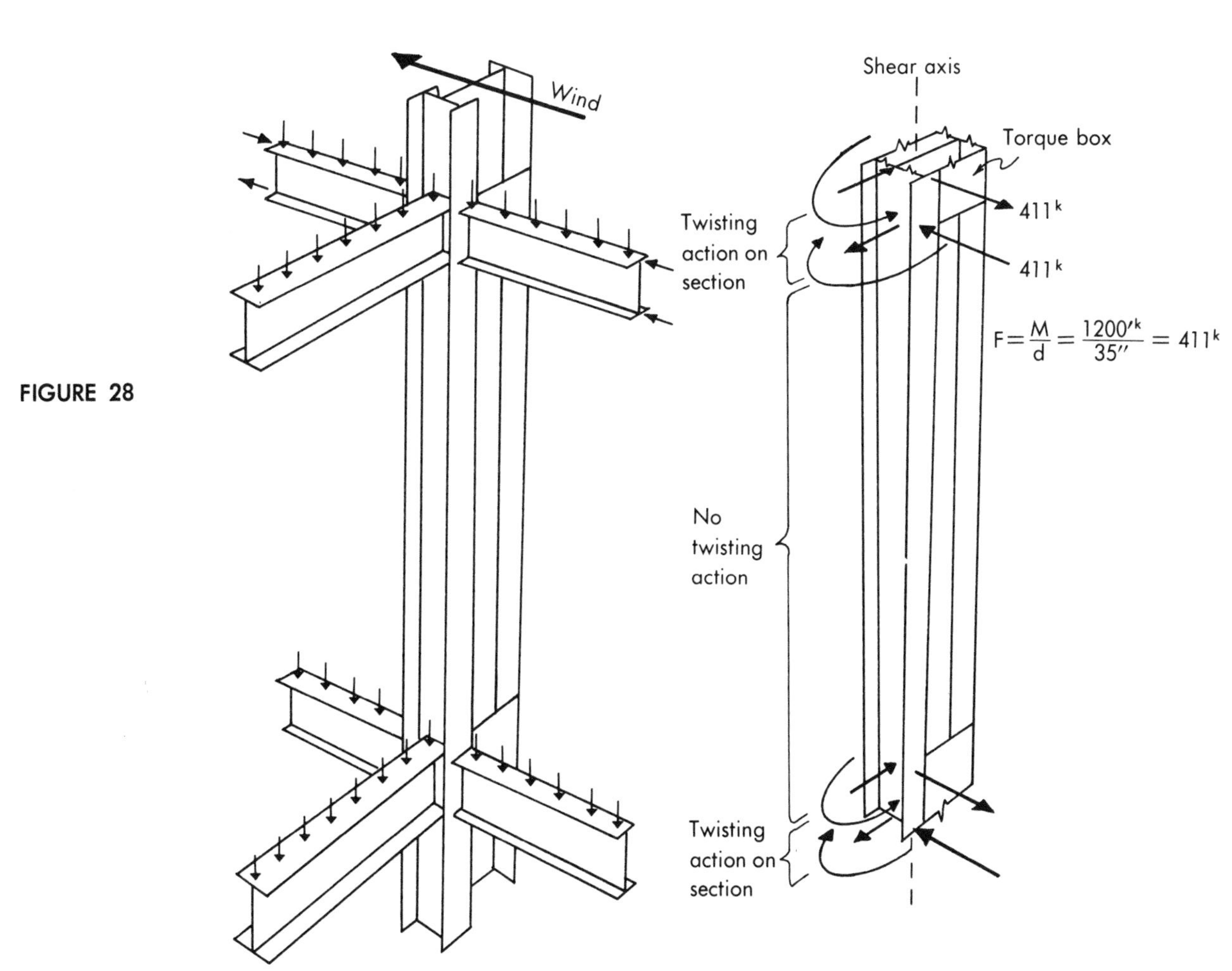

FIGURE 28

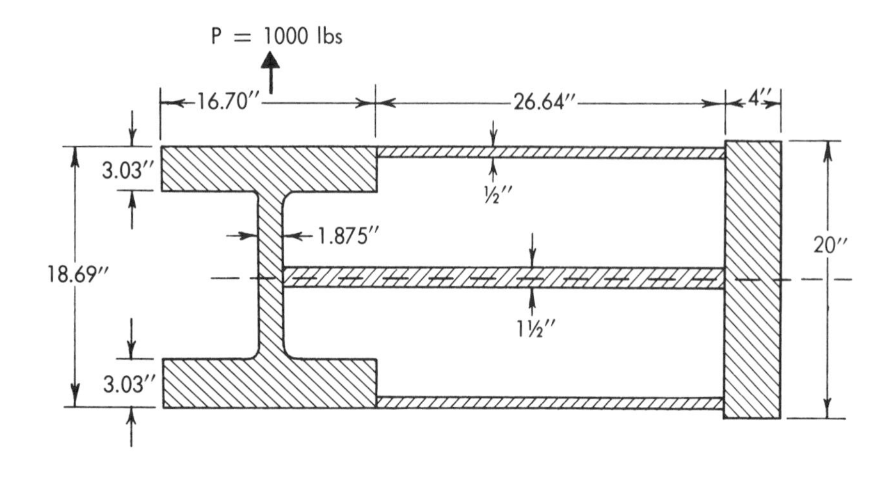

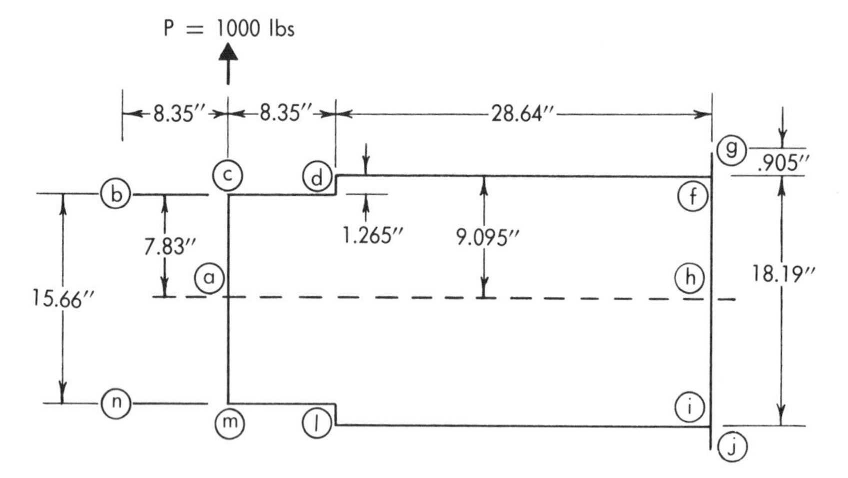

FIGURE 29

column offers very little torsional resistance, two plates will be added within this region to form a closed section about the shear axis to transfer this torque. See Figure 29.

If this torque had to be transferred from one floor to the next, these plates would have to be added the full length of the column. However, this torque is only within the region of the connecting beams which apply these forces, hence plates are only added within this short distance.

$$I_y = 6610.3 + 2(26.64 \times \tfrac{1}{2})(9.095)^2 + \frac{4 \times 20^3}{12}$$

$$+ 2\,\frac{26.64(\tfrac{1}{2})^2}{12} + \frac{34(1\tfrac{1}{2})^3}{12}$$

$$= 11{,}491 \text{ in.}^4$$

In our analysis of the column under Case C loading conditions, a transverse force of 1 kip was assumed to be applied in line with the web of the WF section of the built-up column (this is the position of the spandrel beams). This cross-section is in the plane of the top flange of the spandrel beam. Just below this, in the plane of the lower flange of the spandrel beam, this 1-kip force will be applied in the opposite direction.

Treating this short section of the built-up column as a beam, the shear forces due to this 1-kip force will be analyzed on the basis of shear flow. In an open section it is not difficult to do this because there is always one or more starting points, the unit shear force at the outer edges always being zero. But in a closed section such as this, it is necessary to assume a certain value (usually zero) at some convenient point, in this case at the midpoint of the web of the WF section. The unit shear forces are then found, starting from this point and working all the way around the section using the general formula—

$$q_2 = q_1 + \frac{V\,a\,y}{I}$$

where:

V = transverse force applied to section (lbs)

I = moment of inertia of built-up section about the axis normal to the applied force (in.^{4})

a = area of portion of section considered (in.^{2})

y = distance between center of gravity of this

area and the neutral axis of the built-up section (in.)

q_1 = unit shear force at the start of this area (lbs/in.)

q_2 = unit shear force at the end of this area (lbs/in.)

This work is shown as Computation A. Below, in Figure 30, the total shear force (Q) in the various areas of this section are found; these are indicated by arrows. This work is shown as Computation B. By Computation C, these shear forces are seen to produce an unbalanced moment of 70.519 in-lbs, which if unresisted will cause this section of the column to twist.

In order to counterbalance this moment, a negative moment of the same value is set up by a constant shear force flow of—

$$q = -54.1 \text{ lbs per linear inch}$$

When this is superimposed upon the original shear flow, Figure 30, we obtain the final flow shown in Figure 31. The resulting shear stress (τ) is obtained by dividing the unit shear force (q) by the thickness of the section. Also the values must be increased because the actual force is 411 kips instead of 1 kip, the work and resulting shear stresses are shown as Computation D. See Figure 32 also. These shear stresses seem reasonable.

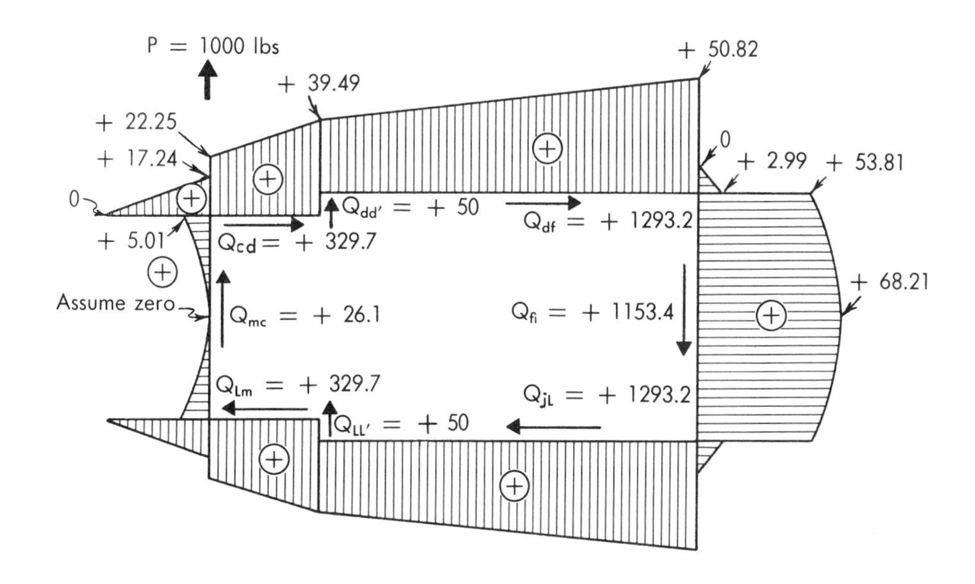

FIGURE 30

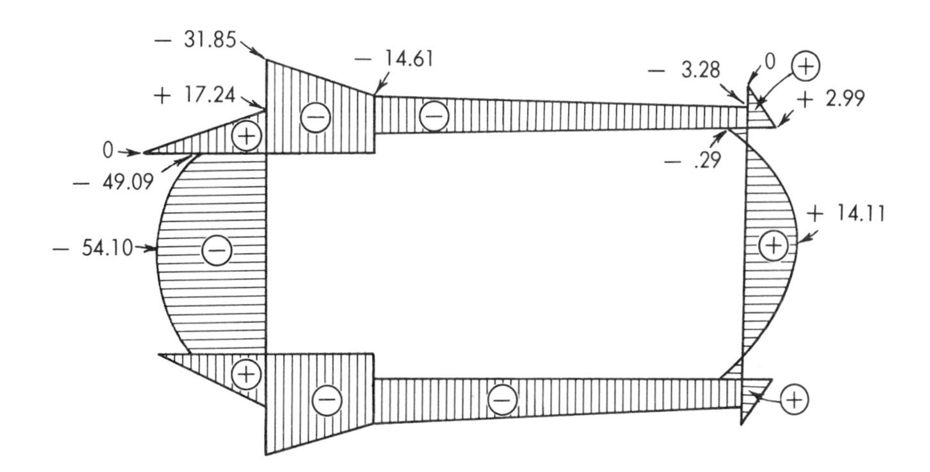

FIGURE 31

Computation A

1. $q_a = 0$ — **0**

2. $q_c = 0 + \frac{V\,a\,y}{I} = 0 + \frac{(1000)(7.83 \times 1.875)(3.92)}{11{,}491.} = 0 + 5.01 =$ — **5.01**

3. $q_b = 0$ — **0**

4. $q_c' = q_b + \frac{V\,a\,y}{I} = 0 + \frac{(1000)(8.35 \times 3.03)(7.83)}{11{,}491.} = 0 + 17.24 =$ — **17.24**

5. $q_c'' = q_c + q_c' = 5.01 + 17.24 =$ — **22.25**

6. $q_d = q_c'' + \frac{V\,a\,y}{I} = 22.25 + \frac{(1000)(8.35 \times 3.03)(7.83)}{11{,}491.} = 22.25 + 17.24 =$ — **39.49**

7. $q_f = q_d + \frac{V\,a\,y}{I} = 39.49 + \frac{(1000)(28.64 \times 1/2)(9.095)}{11{,}491.} = 39.49 + 11.33 =$ — **50.82**

8. $q_g = 0$ — **0**

9. $q_f' = q_g + \frac{V\,a\,y}{I} = 0 + \frac{(1000)(.905 \times 4)(9.548)}{11{,}491.} = 0 + 2.99 =$ — **2.99**

10. $q_f'' = q_f' + q_f = 2.99 + 50.82 =$ — **53.81**

11. $q_h = q_f'' + \frac{V\,a\,y}{I} = 53.81 + \frac{(1000)(9.095 \times 4)(4.548)}{11{,}491.} = 53.81 + 14.40 =$ — **68.21**

Computation B

12. $Q_{mc} = (2/3 \times 0 + 1/3 \times 5.01)\ 15.66 = 26.1\ \#$

13. $Q_{bd} = (1/2 \times 17.24 \times 8.35) + \frac{22.25 + 39.49}{2} \times 8.35) = 329.7\ \#$

14. $Q_{dd'} = 39.49 \times 1.265 = 50.0\ \#$

15. $Q_{df} = \frac{39.49 + 50.82}{2} \times 28.64 = 1293.2\ \#$

16. $Q_{fi} = (2/8 \times 68.21 + 1/3 \times 53.81)\ 18.19 = 1153.4\ \#$

Check $\Sigma V = 0$

$+ 1000 + 26.1 + 50.0 - 1153.4 + 50.0 = 1126.1 - 1153.4 = -27.3$ OK (Close)

Computation C

Now, take moments about (m)

$M_m = (+329.7)(15.66) - (100)(8.35) + (1293.2)(18.19) + (1153.4)(36.99) = 70{,}519$

The unbalanced moment is 70,519 in-lbs

Make $\Sigma M_m = 0$ a constant shear force flow, which must be added to form a negative moment of — 70,519.

The resulting shear force is —

$$q = \frac{-M}{2[A]} = \frac{-70{,}519}{2(651.7)} = -54.1 \text{ lbs/in.}$$

Where [A] = area enclosed by centerline of web, flanges, and plates
[A] = (15.66)(8.35) + (18.19)(28.64) = 651.7 in²

This gives the true shear flow (Fig. 31).

Computation D

If this force is P = 441,000 lbs, the shear stresses in the section are —

(a) $\tau_a = \frac{q}{t} = \frac{411 \times 54.10}{1.875} = 11{,}850$ psi

(c'') $\tau_c'' = \frac{q}{t} = \frac{411 \times 31.85}{3.03} = 4320$ psi

(d) $\tau_d = \frac{q}{t} = \frac{411 \times 14.61}{1/2} = 12{,}000$ psi

(f) $\tau_f = \frac{q}{t} = \frac{411 \times 3.28}{1/2} = 2690$ psi

(h) $\tau_h = \frac{q}{t} = \frac{411 \times 14.11}{4} = 1450$ psi

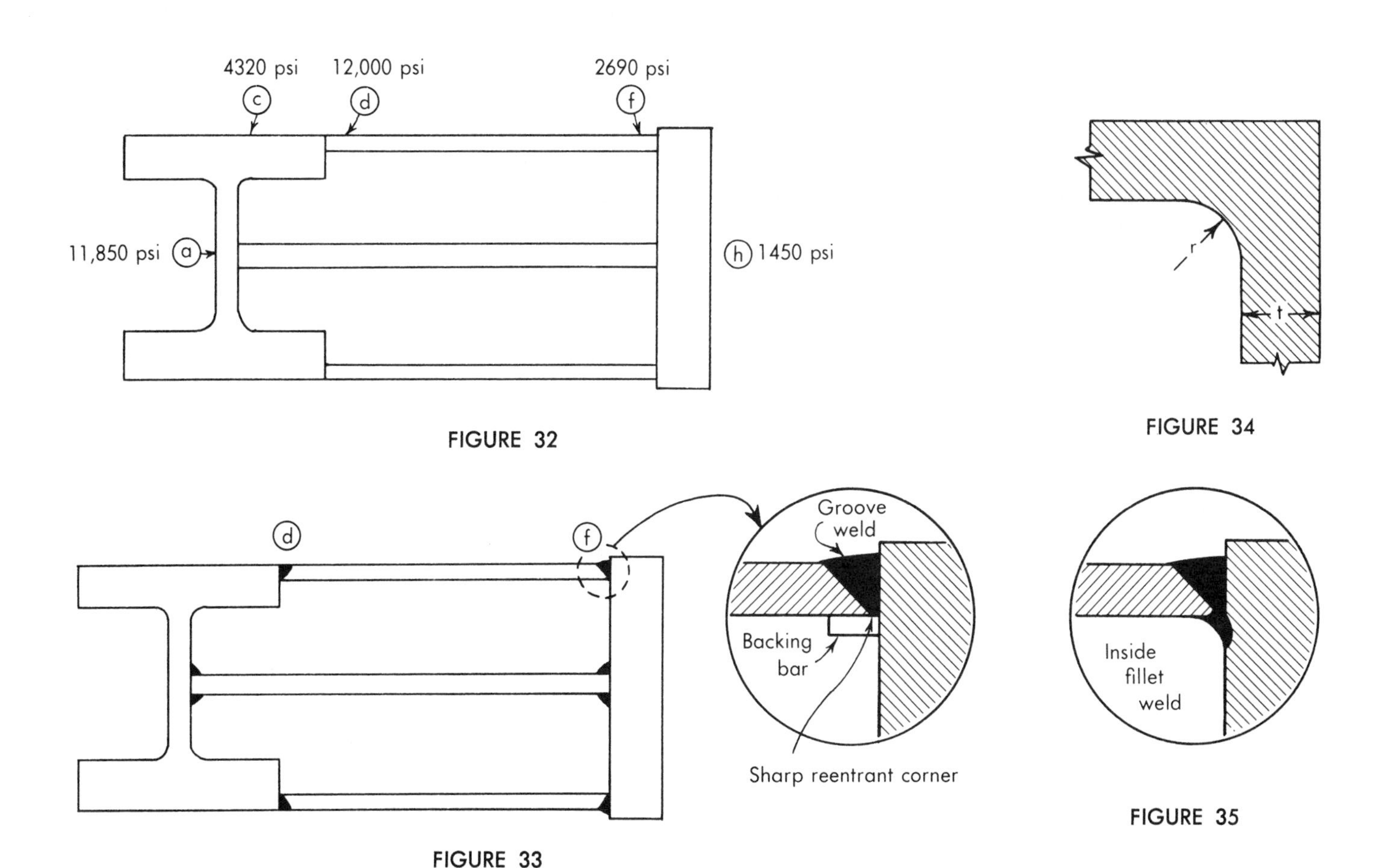

FIGURE 32

FIGURE 33

FIGURE 34

FIGURE 35

Reentrant Corners (Figures 33 and 34)

The only other concern on this built-up construction is the sharp reentrant corner at points (d) and (f).

Timoshenko in "Theory of Elasticity", p. 259, indicates the following shear stress increase for a reentrant corner:

$$\tau_{max} = \tau\left(1 + \frac{t}{4r}\right)$$

In structural steel, any stress concentration in this area probably would be relieved through plastic flow and could be neglected unless fatigue loading were a factor or there were some amount of triaxial stress along with impact loading.

Of course if a fillet weld could be made on this inside corner, it would eliminate this problem. See Figure 35. This is possible in this case, because these plates for the torque box are not very long and the welding operator could reach in from each end to make this weld.

6. SIZE OF WELDS FOR FABRICATED COLUMN

The welds that join the web of a built-up column to its inside WF section and its outside flange plate, are subject to longitudinal shear forces resulting from the changing moment along the length of the column.

As an example, continue with the conditions stated for the preceding Problem 3.

The bending force in the flanges of the girder applied to the column is found by dividing this moment (M_x) by the depth of the girder:

$$F = \frac{M_x}{d}$$

$$= \frac{2200 \text{ ft-kip} \times 12''}{35''}$$

$$= 754 \text{ kips}$$

The point of contraflexure, or zero moment, is assumed at about midheight of the column. The horizontal force at this point, or transverse shear in the column, may be found by dividing half of the moment applied to the column at the connection by about one-half of the column height. This assumes half of applied moment enters upper column and half enters lower column.

$$F_h = \frac{M}{\frac{1}{2}\,h}$$

$$= \frac{1100 \text{ ft-kip}}{6.5'}$$

$$= 170 \text{ kips}$$

The moment and shear diagrams for the column when loaded with dead and live loads and wind in the y-y direction (Case B) are given in Figure 36.

This shear diagram indicates the transverse shear within the region of the beam connection is $V_2 = 584$ kips, and that in the remaining length of the column is $V_1 = 170$ kips.

The size of the connecting weld shall be determined for the larger shear within the region of the beam connection, and for the lower shear value for the remaining length of the column. The minimum fillet weld size is also dependent on the maximum thickness of plate joined (AWS Building Article 212 a 1, and AISC Sec. 1.17.4).

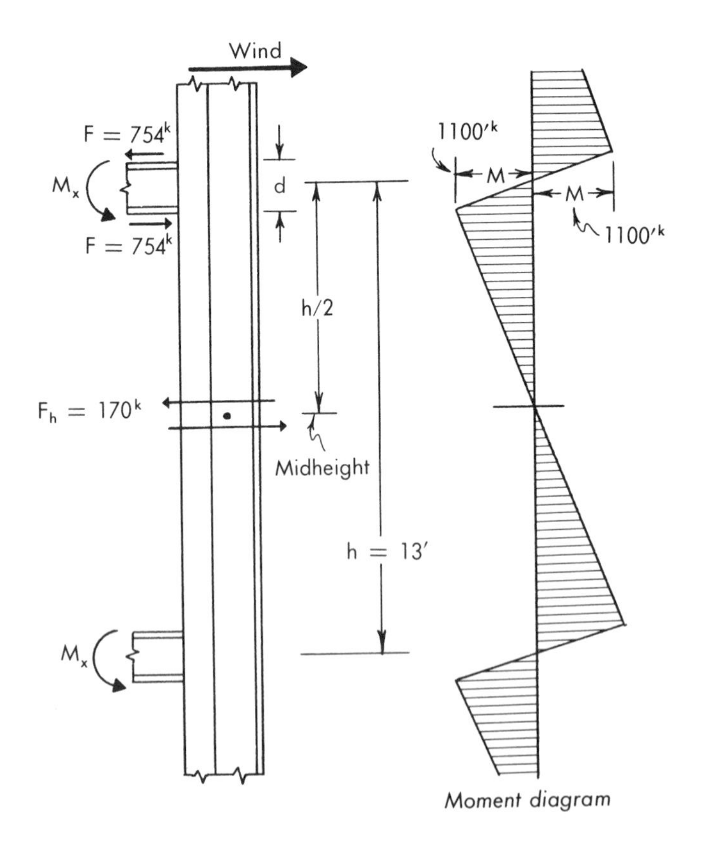

Moment diagram

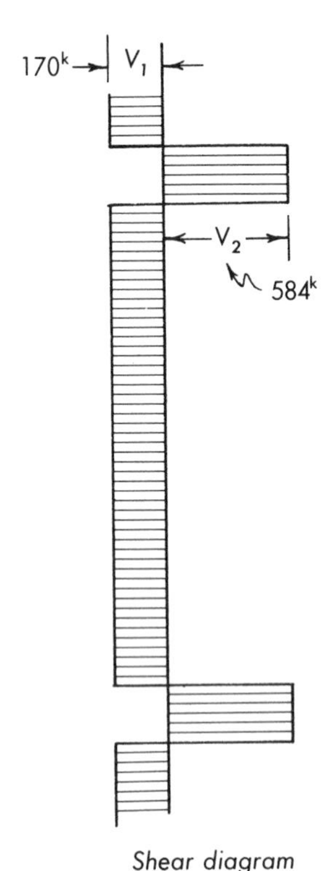

Shear diagram
This is also a picture of the amount and location of the connecting welds to hold column together

FIGURE 36

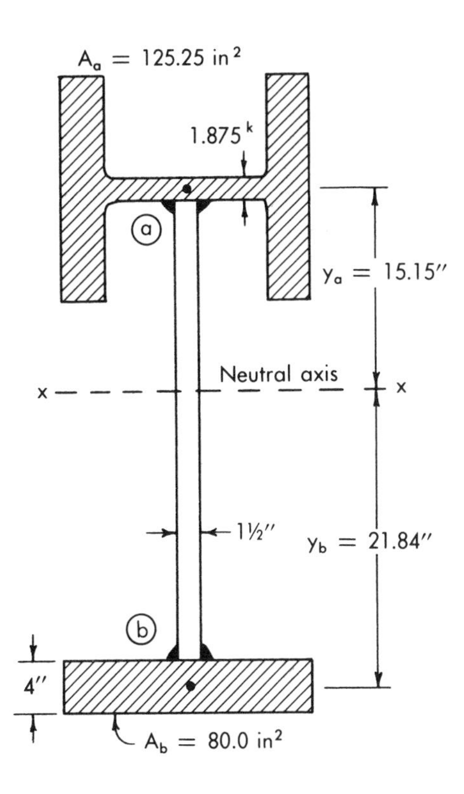

FIGURE 37

where:

$A = 256.25$ in.²

$I_x = 74{,}507$ in.⁴

The following allowable shear force for the fillet weld will be used:

$f = 11{,}200\omega$ (A36 steel and E70 weld metal)

We will not reduce the shear carrying capacity of the fillet weld due to the axial compressive stress on it.

weld (a) in the way of the beam connection

$$f_a = \frac{V_2\ a_a\ y_a}{I\ n}$$

$$= \frac{(584^k)(125.25)(1515)}{(74{,}507)(2 \text{ welds})}$$

$$= 7450 \text{ lbs/in}$$

$$\text{leg size } \omega = \frac{7450}{11{,}200}$$

$$= .665'' \text{ or use } 3/4''$$

weld (a) for the remaining length of the column

$V_1 = 170^k$ or 29% of V_2

hence use 29% of the leg size or .192″. However, the maximum thickness of plate here is 1⅞″, and the minimum size of fillet weld for this thickness is ⅜″ (AWS Bldg Art 212 and AISC Sec. 1.17.4). Hence use $\omega = 3/8''$.

Weld (b) in line with the beam connection

$$f_b = \frac{V_2\ a_b\ y_b}{I\ n}$$

$$= \frac{(584^k)(80)(21.84)}{(74{,}507)(2 \text{ welds})}$$

$$= 6860 \text{ lbs/in.}$$

$$\text{leg size } \omega = \frac{6860}{11{,}200}$$

$$= .612'' \text{ or use } 5/8''$$

weld (b) for the remaining length of the column

$V_1 = 170^k$ or 29% of V_2

hence use 29% of the above leg size, or leg size ω = .178″ or 3/16″; however, the maximum thickness of plate here is 4″ and the minimum size of fillet weld for this thickness is ½″ (AWS Bldg Art 212 and AISC Sec. 1.17.4). Hence use ½″.

When the column is subjected to the dead and live loads and wind in the x-x direction, bending is about the y-y axis. Here the inside and outside portions of the column are continuous throughout the cross-section of the column, and the connecting welds do not transfer any force; hence, the weld size as determined above for Case B would control.

Perhaps weld (a) should be further increased within the region of the beam connection, to transfer the horizontal forces of the beam end moment back into the column web. The horizontal stiffeners in the column at this point, however, would undoubtedly take care of this.

7. SQUARE AND RECTANGULAR HOT-ROLLED SECTIONS FOR COLUMNS

Square and rectangular tubular shapes are now being hot rolled from A7 (33,000 psi yield) and A36 (36,000 psi yield) steel at about the same price as other hot-rolled sections.

These sections have exceptionally good compressive and torsional resistance. See Tables 7 and 8 for dimensions and properties of stock sizes.

Many engineers feel that the round tubular section is the best for a column since it has a rather high radius of gyration in all directions. This is much better than the standard WF or I sections, which have a much lower radius of gyration about the weaker y-y axis.

Unfortunately the usually higher cost of round tubular sections prohibits their universal use for columns.

However, a square tube is slightly better than the round section; for the same outside dimensions and cross-sectional area the square tube has a larger radius of gyration. This of course would allow higher compressive stresses. Consider the following two sections, 12′ long, made of A36 steel:

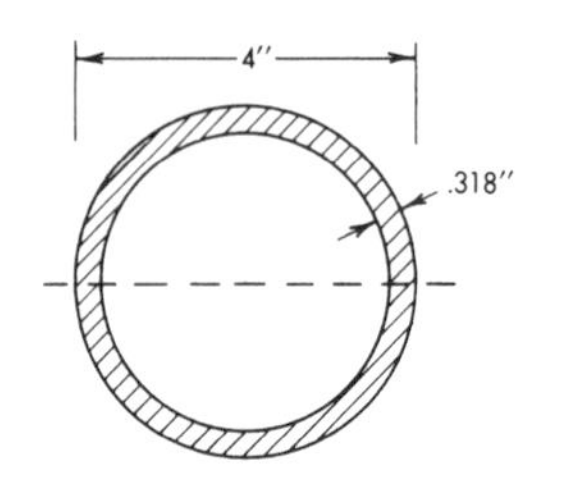

FIGURE 38

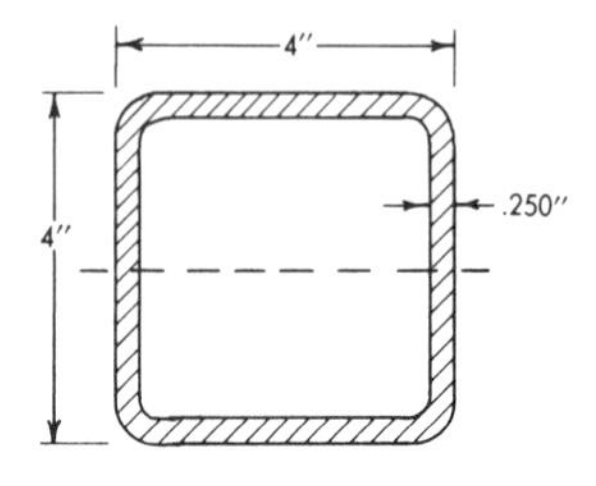

FIGURE 39

3½″ extra-heavy pipe

$A = 3.678 \text{ in.}^2$

$W_t = 12.51 \text{ lbs/ft}$

$r_{min} = 1.31''$

$$\frac{L}{r} = \frac{(144'')}{(1.31'')} = 110.0$$

$\underline{\sigma_c} = 11{,}670 \text{ psi}$

$P = (11{,}670)(3.678) = 42.9^k$

4″ × 4″ square tubing

$A = 3.535 \text{ in.}^2$

$W_t = 12.02 \text{ lbs/ft}$

$r_{min} = 1.503''$

$$\frac{L}{r} = \frac{(144'')}{(1.503'')} = 95.8$$

$\underline{\sigma_c} = 13{,}500 \text{ psi}$

$P = (13{,}500)(3.535) = 47.6^k$

In this example, the square tube has 3.9% less weight and yet has an allowable load 11% greater. Its radius of gyration is 14.7% greater.

For another example, consider the following A36 section:

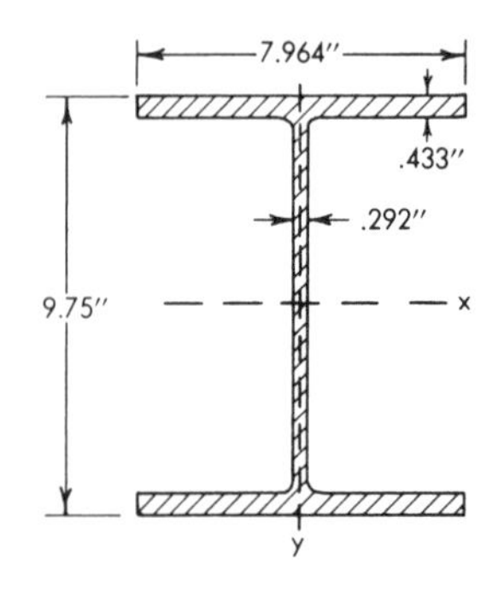

FIGURE 40

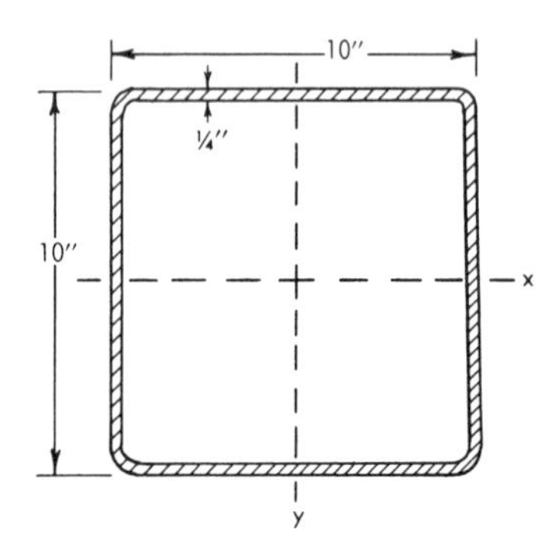

FIGURE 41

10″ WF 33#

$A = 9.71 \text{ in.}^2$

$r_x = 4.20''$

$r_y = 1.94''$

$$\frac{L}{r} = \frac{(144'')}{(1.94'')} = 74.2$$

$\underline{\sigma_c} = 15{,}990 \text{ psi}$

$P = (15{,}990)(9.71) = 155.0^k$

10″ □ 32#

$A = 9.48 \text{ in.}^2$

$r_{min} = 3.949''$

$$\frac{L}{r} = \frac{(144'')}{(3.95'')} = 36.5$$

$\underline{\sigma_c} = 19{,}460 \text{ psi}$

$P = (19{,}460)(9.48) = 184.3^k$

The 32-lb/ft 10″ square tubular section has a radius of gyration which is more than twice that about the weak y-y axis of the 33-lb/ft 10″ WF section. This results in an allowable compressive load 19% greater.

The second advantage to the square and rectangular sections is the flat surface they offer for connections. This results in the simplest and most direct type of joint with minimum preparation and welding. Also by closing the ends, there would be no maintenance problem. It is common practice in many tubular structures not to paint the inside.

TABLE 7
Square Hollow Structural Tubing*

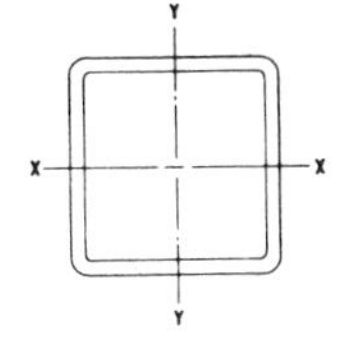

Size, Inches	Wall, Inches	Weight per foot, pounds	Area of metal, sq. inches	Moment of inertia	Section modulus	Radius of gyration
2x2	.1875	4.31	1.2688	.6667	.6667	.7249
	.250	5.40	1.5890	.7612	.7612	.6921
2½x2½	.1875	5.59	1.6438	1.4211	1.1369	.9298
	.250	7.10	2.0890	1.6849	1.3479	.8981
	.3125	8.44	2.4829	1.8585	1.4868	.8652
3x3	.1875	6.86	2.0188	2.5977	1.7318	1.1344
	.250	8.80	2.5890	3.1509	2.1006	1.1032
	.3125	10.57	3.1079	3.5664	2.3776	1.0712
3½x3½	.1875	8.14	2.3938	4.2904	2.4517	1.3388
	.250	10.50	3.0890	5.2844	3.0196	1.3079
	.3125	12.69	3.7329	6.0826	3.4758	1.2765
4x4	.1875	9.31	2.7383	6.4677	3.2338	1.5369
	.250	12.02	3.5354	7.9880	3.9940	1.5031
	.3125	14.52	4.2720	9.2031	4.6016	1.4677
	.375	16.84	4.9543	10.152	5.0760	1.4315
	.500	20.88	6.1416	11.234	5.6169	1.3524
5x5	.1875	11.86	3.4883	13.208	5.2831	1.9458
	.250	15.42	4.5354	16.595	6.6380	1.9128
	.3125	18.77	5.5220	19.489	7.7955	1.8786
5x5	.375	21.94	6.4543	21.946	8.7784	1.8440
	.500	27.68	8.1416	25.521	10.208	1.7705
6x6	.1875	14.41	4.2383	23.496	7.8322	2.3545
	.250	18.82	5.5354	29.845	9.9482	2.3220
	.3125	23.02	6.7720	35.465	11.822	2.2884
	.375	27.04	7.9543	40.436	13.479	2.2547
	.500	34.48	10.142	48.379	16.126	2.1841
7x7	.1875	16.85	4.9577	37.698	10.771	2.7575
	.250	22.04	6.4817	48.052	13.729	2.7228
	.3125	26.99	7.9389	57.306	16.373	2.6867
	.375	31.73	9.3339	65.544	18.727	2.6499
	.500	40.55	11.927	78.913	22.547	2.5722
8x8	.250	25.44	7.4817	73.382	18.346	3.1318
	.3125	31.24	9.1889	88.095	22.024	3.0963
	.375	36.83	10.834	101.46	25.366	3.0603
	.500	47.35	13.927	124.08	31.021	2.9849
	.625	56.98	16.761	141.41	35.353	2.9046
10x10	.250	32.23	9.4817	147.89	29.578	3.9494
	.3125	39.74	11.689	179.12	35.824	3.9146
	.375	47.03	13.834	208.21	41.642	3.8795
	.500	60.95	17.927	259.81	51.962	3.8069
	.625	73.98	21.761	302.94	60.587	3.7311

TABLE 8
Rectangular Hollow Structural Tubing*

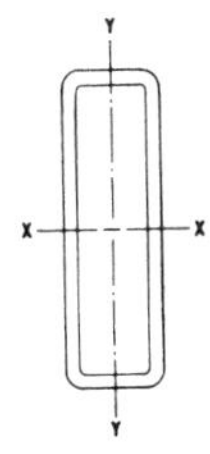

Size, inches Axis Y-Y	Size, inches Axis X-X	Wall, inches	Weight per foot, pounds	Area of metal, square inches	Axis X-X Moment of inertia	Axis X-X Section modulus	Axis X-X Radius of gyration	Axis Y-Y Moment of inertia	Axis Y-Y Section modulus	Axis Y-Y Radius of gyration
3	2	.1875	5.59	1.6438	1.8551	1.2367	1.0623	.9758	.9758	.7704
		.250	7.10	2.0890	2.2030	1.4687	1.0269	1.1466	1.1466	.7409
		.3125	8.44	2.4829	2.4327	1.6218	.9898	1.2528	1.2528	.7103
4	2	.1875	6.86	2.0188	3.8654	1.9327	1.3837	1.2849	1.2849	.7978
		.250	8.80	2.5890	4.6893	2.3447	1.3458	1.5321	1.5321	.7692
		.3125	10.57	3.1079	5.3041	2.6520	1.3064	1.7029	1.7029	.7402
4	3	.1875	8.14	2.3938	5.2291	2.6146	1.4780	3.3404	2.2269	1.1813
		.250	10.50	3.0890	6.4498	3.2249	1.4450	4.0988	2.7326	1.1519
		.3125	12.69	3.7329	7.4338	3.7169	1.4112	4.7000	3.1333	1.1221
5	3	.1875	9.31	2.7383	8.8629	3.5452	1.7991	4.0118	2.6746	1.2104
		.250	12.02	3.5354	10.949	4.3797	1.7598	4.9195	3.2797	1.1796
		.3125	14.52	4.2720	12.612	5.0448	1.7182	5.6255	3.7504	1.1475
		.375	16.84	4.9543	13.907	5.5628	1.6754	6.1552	4.1034	1.1146
		.500	20.88	6.1416	15.355	6.1418	1.5812	6.6839	4.4559	1.0432
6	3	.1875	10.58	3.1133	13.991	4.6637	2.1199	4.7545	3.1697	1.2358
		.250	13.72	4.0354	17.438	5.8128	2.0788	5.8675	3.9116	1.2058
		.3125	16.65	4.8970	20.287	6.7622	2.0353	6.7592	4.5061	1.1748
		.375	19.39	5.7043	22.612	7.5373	1.9910	7.4560	4.9706	1.1433
		.500	24.28	7.1416	25.629	8.5431	1.8944	8.2672	5.5115	1.0759
6	4	.1875	11.86	3.4883	17.160	5.7198	2.2179	9.1952	4.5976	1.6236
		.250	15.42	4.5354	21.574	7.1913	2.1810	11.509	5.7544	1.5930
		.3125	18.77	5.5220	25.346	8.4487	2.1424	13.463	6.7313	1.5614
		.375	21.94	6.4543	28.553	9.5178	2.1033	15.097	7.5486	1.5294
		.500	27.68	8.1416	33.213	11.071	2.0198	17.400	8.7002	1.4619
7	5	.1875	14.41	4.2383	29.380	8.3943	2.6329	17.552	7.0210	2.0350
		.250	18.82	5.5354	37.341	10.669	2.5973	22.241	8.8963	2.0045
		.3125	23.02	6.7720	44.396	12.685	2.5604	26.365	10.546	1.9731
		.375	27.04	7.9543	50.646	14.470	2.5233	29.985	11.994	1.9416
		.500	34.48	10.142	50.642	17.326	2.4453	35.688	14.275	1.8759
8	4	.1875	14.41	4.2383	34.828	8.7070	2.8666	11.923	5.9614	1.6772
		.250	18.82	5.5354	44.230	11.058	2.8267	15.030	7.5148	1.6478
		.3125	23.02	6.7720	52.533	13.133	2.7852	17.722	8.8160	1.6177
		.375	27.04	7.9543	59.864	15.966	2.7433	20.042	10.021	1.5874
		.500	34.48	10.142	71.475	17.869	2.6548	23.567	11.784	1.5244
8	6	.1875	16.85	4.9577	45.772	11.443	3.0385	29.548	9.8493	2.4413
		.250	22.04	6.4817	58.362	14.590	3.0007	37.608	12.536	2.4088
		.3125	26.99	7.9389	69.617	17.404	2.9613	44.784	14.928	2.3751
		.375	31.73	9.3339	79.643	19.911	2.9211	51.143	17.048	2.3408
		.500	40.55	11.927	95.916	23.979	2.8358	61.374	20.458	2.2684
10	6	.250	25.44	7.4817	100.35	20.070	3.6623	45.879	15.293	2.4763
		.3125	31.24	9.1889	120.45	24.089	3.6205	54.903	18.301	2.4444
		.375	36.83	10.834	138.69	27.739	3.5780	63.026	21.009	2.4119
		.500	47.35	13.927	169.48	33.896	3.4884	76.541	25.514	2.3443
10	8	.250	28.83	8.4818	124.12	24.824	3.8254	88.403	22.101	3.2284
		.3125	35.49	10.439	149.78	29.957	3.7880	106.57	26.643	3.1916
		.375	41.93	12.334	173.45	34.690	3.7501	123.28	30.821	3.1616
		.500	54.15	15.927	214.64	42.929	3.6711	152.25	38.062	3.0918
12	6	.250	28.83	8.4818	157.30	26.217	4.3065	54.150	18.050	2.5267
		.3125	35.49	10.439	189.65	31.609	4.2624	65.022	21.674	2.4958
		.375	41.93	12.334	219.41	36.589	4.2178	74.909	24.969	2.4644
		.500	54.15	15.927	270.89	45.149	4.1241	91.708	30.569	2.3996

*(1) Tables 7 and 8 are used here by permission of United States Steel Corporation.

(2) Standard sizes listed represent outside dimensions.

(3) These sizes of tubing are normally in stock and available for immediate delivery; other sizes will be stocked or rolled as required.

(4) The weight, area, and other properties given were calculated on the basis of a section with rounded corners and consequently show the actual section properties rather than the idealized version considering the corners as square.

Four all-welded multilayer Vierendeel trusses make up the exposed frame of the beautiful Rare Book Library of Yale University. Weld-fabricated tapered box sections are used in the trusses. Good planning held field welding to a minimum, the trusses being shop built in sections. Here, a cruciform vertical member of the grilled truss is field spliced.

Column Bases

1. BASIC REQUIREMENTS

Base plates are required on the ends of columns to distribute the concentrated compressive load (P) of the column over a much larger area of the material which supports the column.

The base plate is dimensioned on the assumption that the overhanging portion of the base plate acts as a cantilever beam with its fixed end just inside of the column edges. The upward bending load on this cantilever beam is considered to be uniform and equal to the bearing pressure of the supporting material.

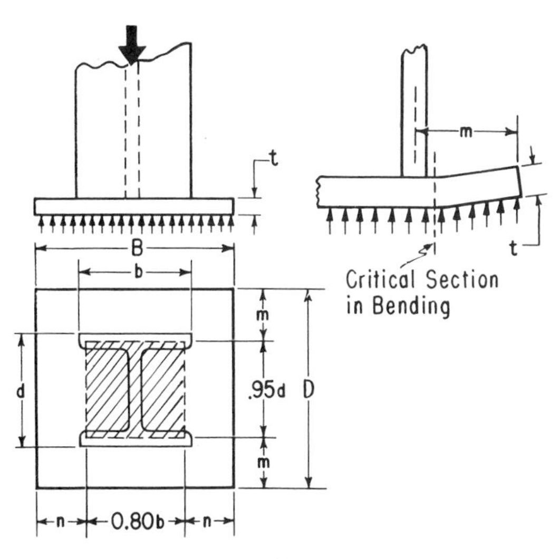

FIGURE 1

AISC suggests the following method to determine the required thickness of bearing plate, using a maximum bending stress of .75 σ_y psi (AISC Sec 1.5.1.4.8):

1. Determine the required minimum base plate area, $A = P/p$. The column load (P) is applied uniformly to the base plate within a rectangular area (shaded). The dimensions of this area relative to the column section's dimensions are .95 d and .80 b.

The masonry foundation is assumed to have a uniform bearing pressure (p) against the full area ($A = B \times D$) of the base plate. See Table 1 for allowable values of p.

2. Determine plate dimensions B and D so that dimensions m and n are approximately equal. As a guide, start with the square root of required plate area (A). Table 2 lists standard sizes of rolled plate used for bearing plates.

3. Determine overhanging dimensions m and n, the projection of the plate beyond the assumed (shaded) rectangle against which the load (P) is applied.

$$m = \tfrac{1}{2}\,(D - .95\ d)$$

$$n = \tfrac{1}{2}\,(B - .80\ b)$$

4. Use the larger value of m or n to solve for required plate thickness (t) by one of the following formulas:

$$t = m\sqrt{\frac{3p}{\sigma}} \qquad t = n\sqrt{\frac{3p}{\sigma}} \qquad \cdots\cdots\cdots(1)$$

Derivation of Formula #1

The primary function of the plate thickness is to provide sufficient resistance to the bending moment (M) on the overhang of the plate just beyond the rectangular area contacted by the column. Treating this over-

TABLE 1—Masonry Bearing Allowables

(AISC Sec 1.5.5)

On sandstone and limestone	p = 400 psi
On brick in cement mortar	p = 250 psi
On full area of concrete support	p = 0.25 f'_c
On ⅓ area of concrete support	p = 0.375 f'_c

where f'_c is the specified compression strength of the concrete at 28 days (In this text, σ'_c is used as equivalent to AISC's f'_c.)

TABLE 2—Standard Sizes of Rolled Plate For Bearing Plates

14 × 1¼	28 × 3	44 × 6	60 × 7	72 × 9½
14 × 1½	28 × 3½	48 × 5½	60 × 7½	72 × 10
16 × 1½	32 × 3½	48 × 6	60 × 8	78 × 9
16 × 2	32 × 4	48 × 6½	66 × 7½	78 × 10
20 × 2	36 × 4	52 × 6	66 × 8	84 × 9½
20 × 2½	36 × 4½	52 × 6½	66 × 8½	84 × 10
20 × 3	40 × 4½	52 × 7	66 × 9	
24 × 2	40 × 5	56 × 6½	72 × 8	
24 × 2½	44 × 5	56 × 7	72 × 8½	
24 × 3	44 × 5½	56 × 8	72 × 9	

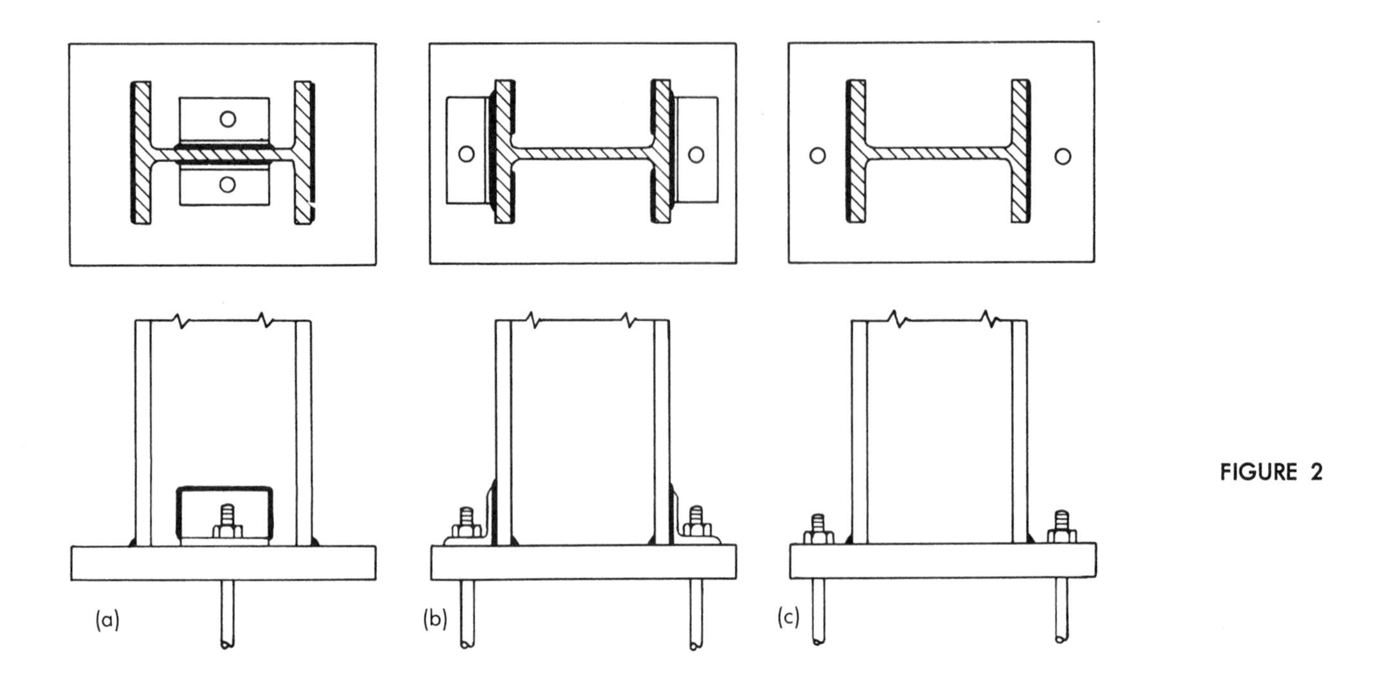

FIGURE 2

hang (m or n) as a cantilever beam with M being maximum at the fixed or column end:

bending moment

$$M = \frac{p\ m^2}{2} \text{ parallel to the column's x-x axis and}$$

$$M = \frac{p\ n^2}{2} \text{ parallel to the column's y-y axis}$$

bending stress in plate

$$\sigma = \frac{M}{S}$$

where, assuming a 1″ strip:

$$S = \frac{(1'')\ t^2}{6}$$

$$\therefore\ t^2 = 6\ S$$

and by substitution:

$$t^2 = 6\ \frac{M}{\sigma}$$

$$= \frac{6\ p\ m^2}{2\ \sigma} = \frac{3\ p\ m^2}{\sigma} \text{ and}$$

$$t = m\sqrt{\frac{3\ p}{\sigma}} \text{ or Formula \#1.}$$

(similarly for dimension n)

Finishing of Bearing Surfaces

AISC Sec 1.21.3 prescribes that column base plates be finished as follows:

"1. Rolled steel bearing plates, 2″ or less in thickness, may be used without planing, provided a satisfactory contact bearing is obtained; rolled steel bearing plates over 2″ but not over 4″ in thickness may be straightened by pressing; or, if presses are not available, by planing for all bearing surfaces (except as noted under requirement 3) to obtain a satisfactory contact bearing; rolled steel bearing plates over 4″ in thickness shall be planed for all bearing surfaces (except as noted under requirement 3).

"2. Column bases other than rolled steel bearing plates shall be planed for all bearing surfaces (except as noted under requirement 3).

"3. The bottom surfaces of bearing plates and column bases which are grouted to insure full bearing contact on foundations need not be planed."

The above requirements assume that the thinner base plates are sufficiently smooth and flat as rolled, to provide full contact with milled or planed ends of column bases. Thicker plates (exceeding 2″) are likely to be slightly bowed or cambered and thus need to be straightened and/or made smooth and flat.

2. STANDARD DETAILING PRACTICE

Figure 2 shows typical column bases. Note the simplicity of these designs for arc-welded fabrication.

Designs *a* and *b* are intended for where column and base plate are erected separately. The angles are shop welded to the column, and the column field welded to the base plate after erection. Design *c* is a standard of fabrication for light columns. Here the base plate is first punched for anchor bolts, then shop welded to the column.

If the end of the column is milled, there must be just sufficient welding to the base plate to hold all parts securely in place (AISC Sec 1:15.8). If the end of the column is not milled, the connecting weld must be large enough to carry the compressive load.

Welding Practices

In most cases, during fabrication, the columns are placed horizontally on a rack or table with their ends overhanging. The base plate is tack welded in place (Fig. 3), using a square to insure proper alignment, and is then finish welded.

As much as possible of the welding is done in the downhand position because of the increased welding speed through higher welding currents and larger electrodes. After completing the downhand welding, along the outside of the top flange, the column is rolled over and the downhand welding is applied to the other flange.

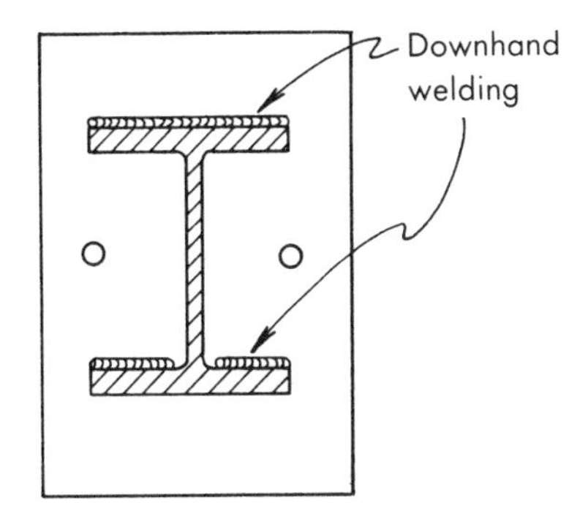

FIGURE 4

It is possible to weld the base plate to the column without turning. See Figure 4. With the web in the vertical position and the flanges in the horizontal position, the top flange is welded on the outside and the lower flange is welded on the inside. This will provide sufficient welding at the flanges without further positioning of the column.

FIGURE 3

3. ANCHOR ATTACHMENTS TO COLUMN BASES

Anchor bolt details can be separated into two general classes.

First, those in which the attachments serve only for erection purposes and carry no important stresses in the finished structure. These include all columns that have no uplift. The design of these columns is governed by direct gravity loads and slenderness ratios set up by specifications for a given column formula.

Here the columns can be shop welded directly to the base plate, unless the detail is too cumbersome for shipment. The anchor bolts preset in the masonry are made to engage the base plate only. See Figure 5a. Large base plates are usually set and levelled separately before beginning column erection. In this case clip angles may be shop welded to the column web or flanges, and in field erection the anchor bolts engage both base plate and clip angle. See Figure 5b.

Secondly, those in which the attachments are designed to resist a direct tension or bending moment, or some combination in which the stability of the

FIGURE 5

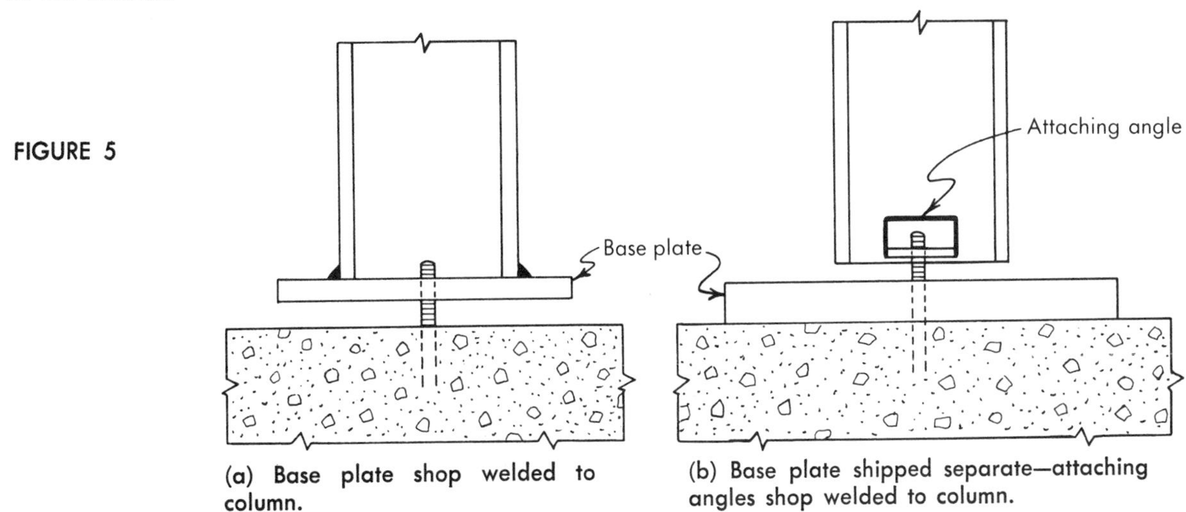

(a) Base plate shop welded to column.

(b) Base plate shipped separate—attaching angles shop welded to column.

finished structure is dependent on the anchor attachments. These include all columns having direct loads combined with bending stresses, caused by the eccentric applications of gravity loads or horizontal forces; for example, wind, cable reactions, sway or temperature, etc. These are found in everyday practice in such structures as mill buildings, hangers, rigid frames, portals and towers, crane columns, etc.

In large structures that extend several hundred feet between expansion joints in each direction, the columns at ends and corners of the structure may be plumb only at normal temperature. As temperatures rise and fall, milled-end bearing conditions at edges or corners of the column base may prove very unsatisfactory, even though shop work were perfect. Such columns should have anchor bolt details designed to hold the column firmly fixed, in square contact with the base plate.

The combined effects of the direct load and overturning moments (due to wind, crane runway, etc.) can always be considered by properly applying the direct load at a given eccentricity, even though the bending stresses sometimes occur in two directions simultaneously. Design of the anchor bolts resolves itself into a problem of bending and direct stress.

4. HOLD-DOWN ANGLES

If there is any appreciable uplift on the column, angles may be welded to the base of the column and anchored by means of hold-down bolts. Under load, the angle is subject to a bending action, and its thickness may be determined from this bending moment.

Treating the cross-section of the angle as a frame, the problem is to know the end conditions.

Some engineers treat the horizontal leg as a cantilever beam, fixed at one end by the clamping action of the hold-down bolts. See Figure 6. This is not quite a true picture because there is some restraint offered by the other leg of the angle.

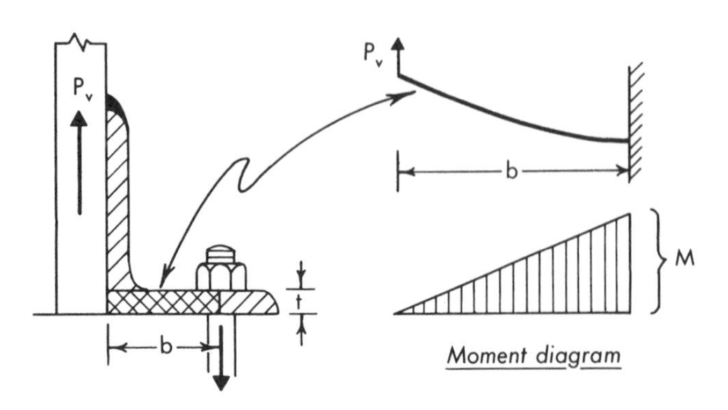

FIGURE 6

$$\boxed{M = P_v\, b} \qquad \text{(2)}$$

Other engineers have assumed the horizontal leg of the angle acts as a beam with both ends fixed. In this case the resulting moment at either end of the portion being considered, the heel of the angle or the end at the bolt, is only half that indicated by the previous approach. See Figure 7.

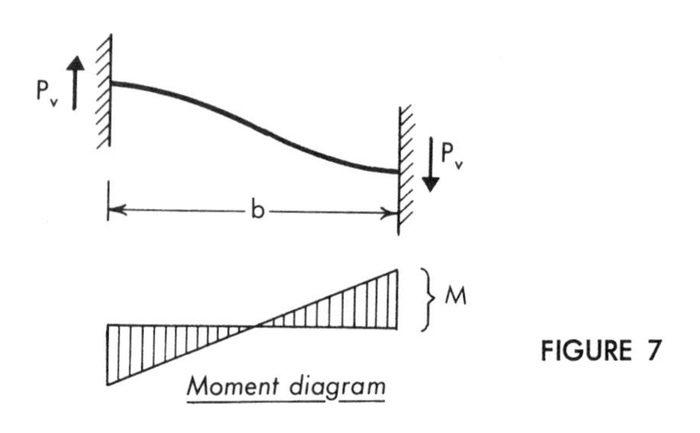

FIGURE 7

$$\boxed{M = \frac{P_v\, b}{2}} \qquad \text{(3)}$$

However, it might be argued that the vertical leg is not completely fixed and that this will increase the moment in the horizontal leg near the bolt. The following analysis, made on this basis, is probably more nearly correct. See Figure 8.

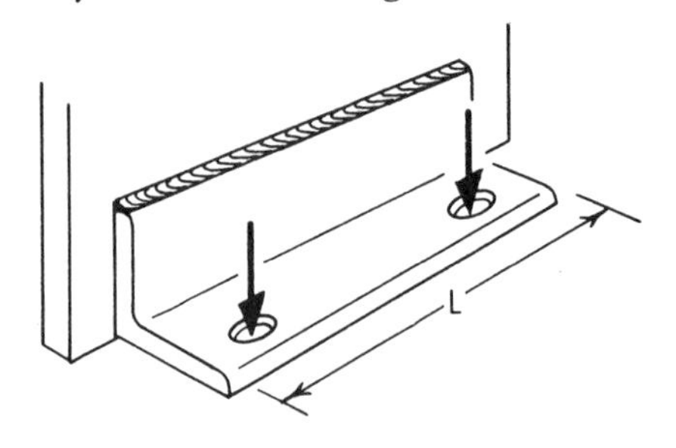

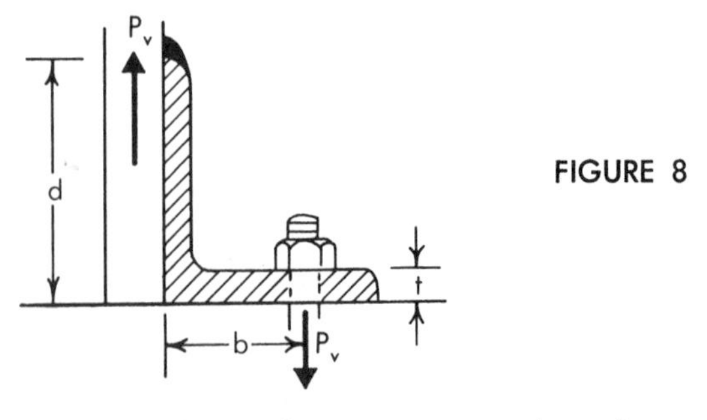

FIGURE 8

1. Considering first just one angle and temporarily ignoring the effect of the other, the upper end of the vertical leg if not restrained would tend to move in horizontally (Δ_h) when an uplift force (P_v) is applied to the column.

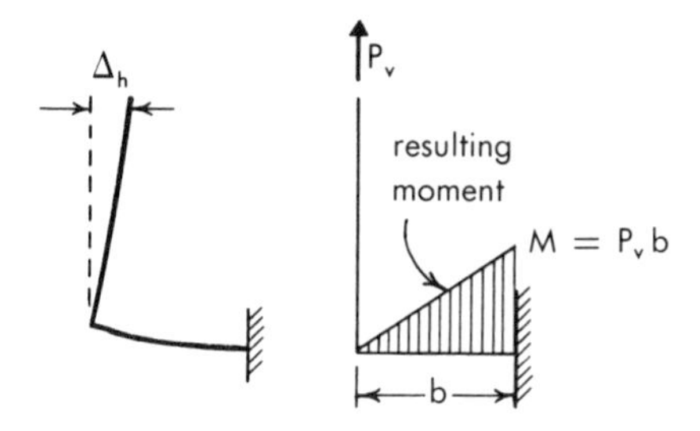

The resulting moment is

$M = P_v\ b$ and

$$\Delta_{hv} = \frac{\text{area of moment diagram}}{E\ I} \times \text{moment arm}$$

$$= \frac{\tfrac{1}{2}\ (P_v\ b)(b)(d)}{E\ I}$$

$$= \frac{P_v\ b^2\ d}{2\ E\ I}$$

2. Since the opposite angle does provide restraint, a horizontal force (P_h) is applied to pull the vertical leg back to its support position. The resulting moment is

$M = P_h\ d$ and

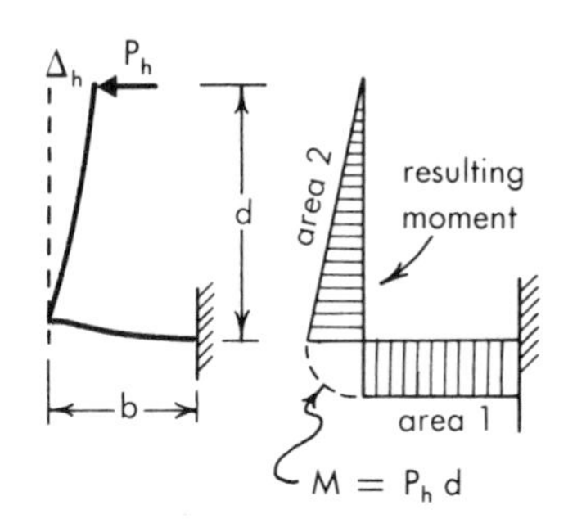

$$\Delta_{hh} = \frac{\text{area 1} \times \text{moment arm 1}}{E\ I} + \frac{\text{area 2} \times \text{moment arm 2}}{E\ I}$$

$$= \frac{(P_h\ d)b\ d}{E\ I} + \frac{\tfrac{1}{2}(P_h\ d)(d)\tfrac{2}{3}\ d}{E\ I}$$

$$= \frac{P_h\ d}{3\ E\ I}(3b + d)$$

Since the horizontal movement is the same in each direction:

$$\Delta_{hh} = \Delta_{hv}$$

$$\therefore \frac{Ph_h\ d}{3\ E\ I}\ (3b + d) = \frac{P_v\ b^2\ d}{2\ E\ I} \quad \text{or}$$

$$P_h = \frac{3\ P_v\ b^2}{2\ d(3b + d)}$$

3. Combining the initial moment resulting from the uplift force (1) and the secondary moment resulting from the restraint offered by the opposite angle (2):

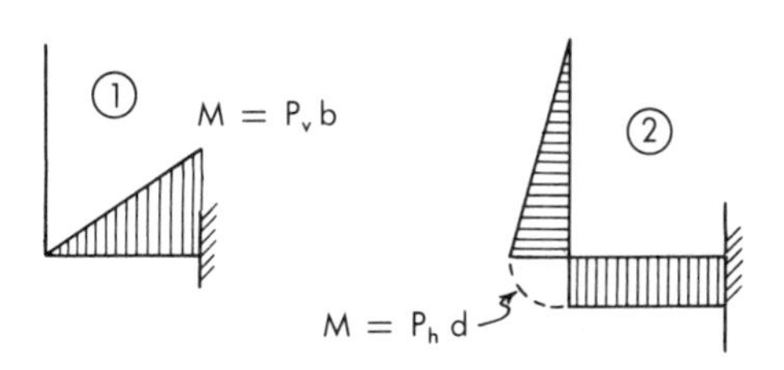

gives—

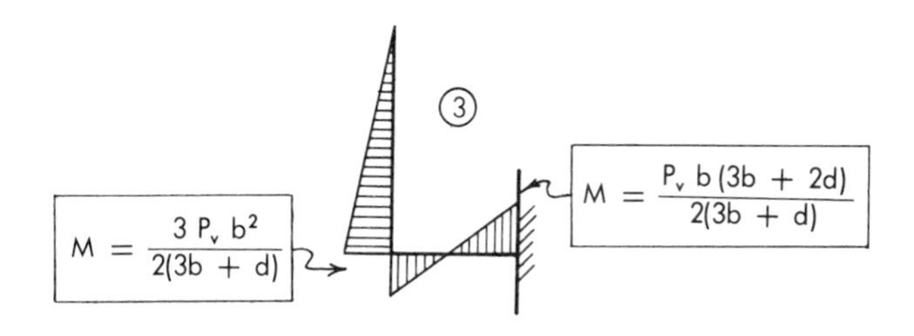

Substituting into the previous equations:

$$\boxed{M = \frac{3\ P_v\ b^2}{2(3b + d)}} \quad \ldots\ldots\ldots\ldots\ldots\ldots\ldots (4)$$

at the heel of the angle, and

$$\boxed{M = \frac{P_v\ b\ (3b + 2d)}{2(3b + d)}} \quad \ldots\ldots\ldots\ldots\ldots (5)$$

which is the critical moment and is located at the hold-down bolts.

Required Thickness of Angle

The leg of the angle has a section modulus of—

$$S = \frac{L\ t^2}{6}$$

or required thickness of

$$t = \sqrt{\frac{6\ S}{L}}$$

where: $S = \dfrac{M}{\sigma}$

or, see Figure 9, where the vertical leg of the angle is welded its full length to the column providing a fixed-end condition (Case A); here formula #3 applies—

$$\boxed{t = \sqrt{\frac{3\ P_v\ b}{L\ \sigma}} \quad \text{Case (A)}} \quad \ldots\ldots\ldots\ldots (6)$$

or where, the vertical leg of the angle is welded only

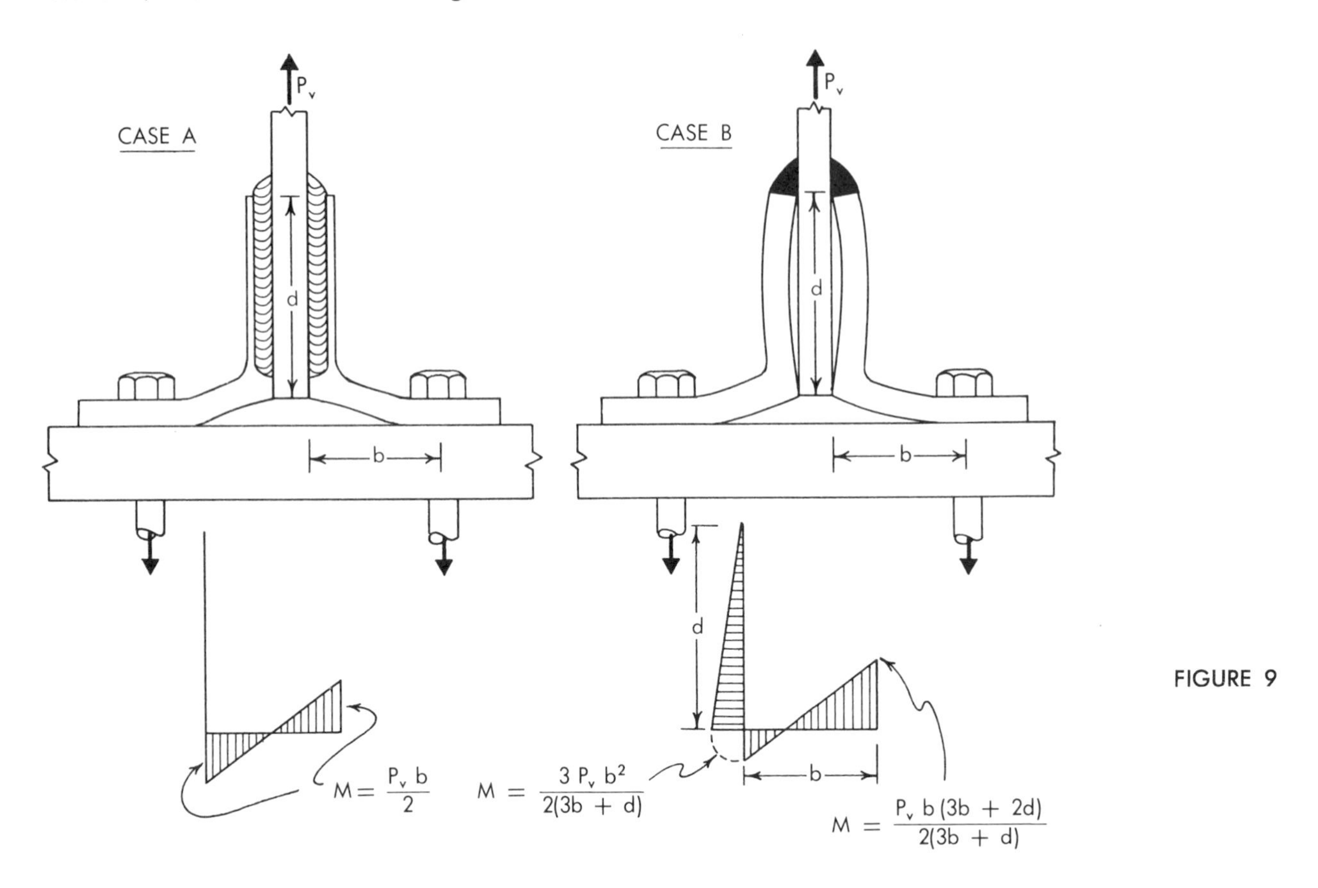

FIGURE 9

at its toe to the column (Case B); here formula #5 applies—

$$t = \sqrt{\frac{3 P_v b (3b + 2d)}{L (3b + d) \sigma}} \quad \text{Case (B)} \qquad \ldots(7)$$

Allowable Stresses

Table 3 presents the allowable stresses for holddown bolts used in building (AISC) and in bridge (AASHO) construction. Also included are dimensions of standard bols. (Table 3A).

TABLE 3—Allowable Stresses for Hold-Down Bolts

Allowable unit tension and shear stresses on bolts and threaded parts (psi of unthreaded body area):

AISC 1.5.2.1 (Building)	Tension psi	Shear psi
A307 bolts and threaded parts of A7 and A373 steel	14,000	10,000
A325 bolts when threading is <u>not</u> excluded from shear planes	40,000	15,000
A325 bolts when threading <u>is</u> excluded from shear planes	40,000	22,000
A354, Grade BC, bolts when threading is <u>not</u> excluded from shear planes	50,000	20,000
A354, Grade BC, when threading <u>is</u> excluded from shear planes	50,000	24,000

AASHO 1.4.2 (Bridge)	psi
tension — bolts at root of thread	13,500
shear — turned bolts	11,000
bearing — turned bolts	20,000

Effective bearing area of a pin or bolt shall be its diameter multiplied by the thickness of the metal on which it bears.

5. BASE PLATE FOR COLUMN LOADED WITH MOMENT

When a moment (M) is applied to a column already subjected to an axial compressive force (P_c), it is more convenient to express this combined load as the same axial force (P_c) applied at some eccentricity (e) from the neutral axis of the column.

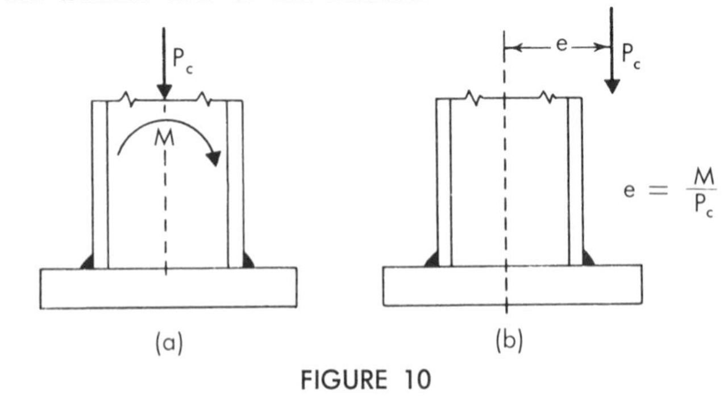

FIGURE 10

In either representation, there is a combination of axial compressive stress and bending stress acting on a cross-section of the column. See Figure 11.

Multiplying this stress by the width of the flange (or the thickness of the web) over which the stresses are applied, gives the following force distribution

TABLE 3A—Standard Bolt Dimensions

Bolt Diameter	No. of threads per inch	Area of bolt	Net area at root of thread	Bolt Diameter	No. of threads per inch	Area of bolt	Net area at root of thread
¼″	20	.049	.026	2″	4½	3.142	2.302
5⁄16″	18	.076	.045	2¼″	4½	3.976	3.023
⅜″	16	.110	.068	2½″	4	4.909	3.719
7⁄16″	14	.150	.093	2¾″	4	5.940	4.620
½″	13	.196	.126				
9⁄16″	12	.248	.162	3″	3½	7.069	5.428
⅝″	11	.307	.202	3¼″	3½	8.296	6.510
¾″	10	.442	.302	3½″	3¼	9.621	7.548
⅞″	9	.601	.419	3¾″	3	11.045	8.641
1″	8	.785	.551	4″	3	12.566	9.963
1⅛″	7	.994	.694	4¼″	2⅞	14.186	11.340
1¼″	7	1.227	.893	4½″	2¾	15.904	12.750
1⅜″	6	1.485	1.057	4¾″	2⅝	17.721	14.215
1½″	6	1.767	1.295				
1⅝″	5½	2.074	1.515	5″	2½	19.635	15.760
1¾″	5	2.405	1.746	5¼″	2½	21.648	17.570
1⅞″	5	2.761	2.051	5½″	2⅜	23.758	19.260
				5¾″	2⅜	25.967	21.250
				6″	2¼	28.274	23.090

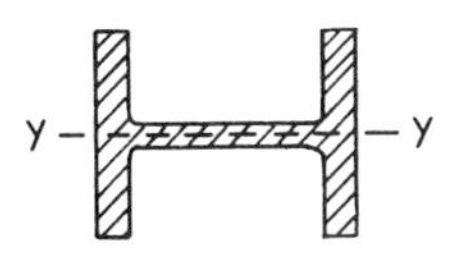

Compressive stress

$$\sigma = \frac{P_c}{A}$$

Bending stress

$$\sigma = \frac{P_c e}{S}$$

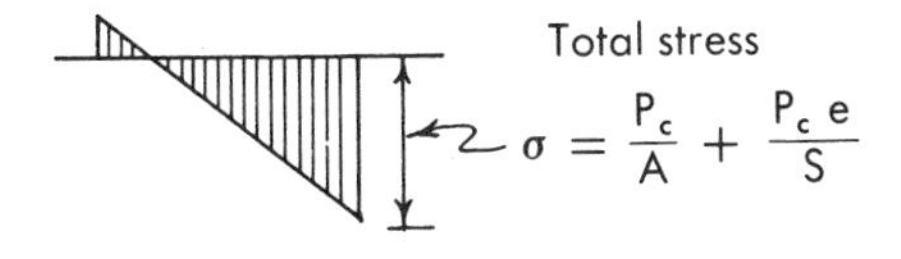

FIGURE 11

across the depth of the column. This force is transferred to the base plate. See Figure 12. This assumes that the column flanges are welded directly to the base plate.

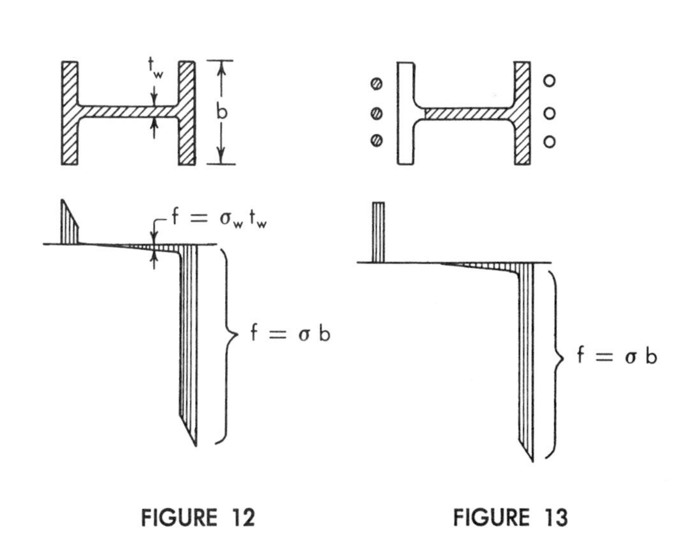

FIGURE 12

FIGURE 13

If anchor hold-down bolts transfer the tensile forces, then—

The column is usually set with the eccentricity (e) lying within the plane of the column web (axis y-y), as in Figure 11. Thus the column flanges will carry most of the resulting forces because of their having relatively greater cross-sectional area, and being located in areas of higher stress. See Figure 14.

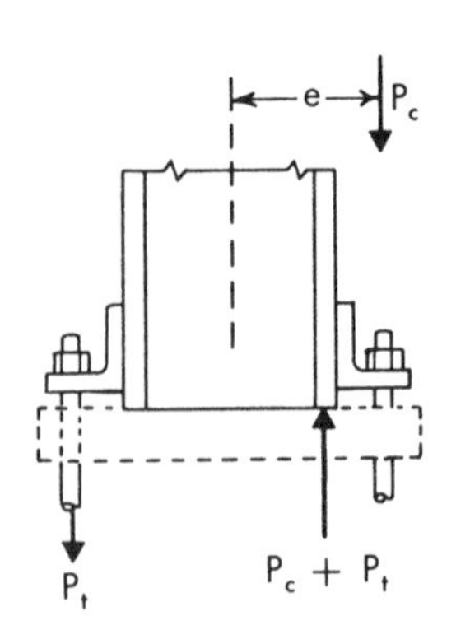

FIGURE 14

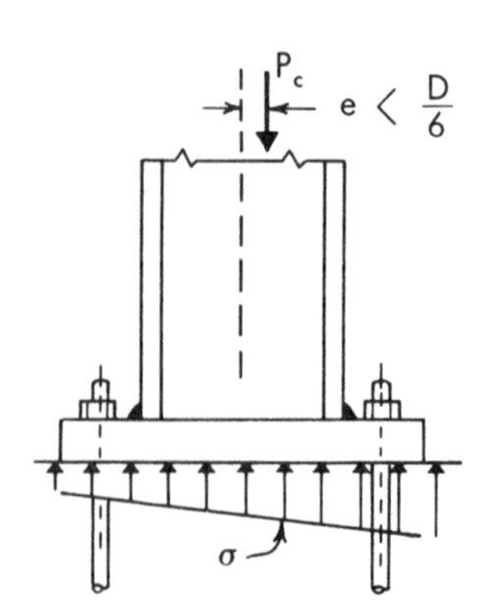

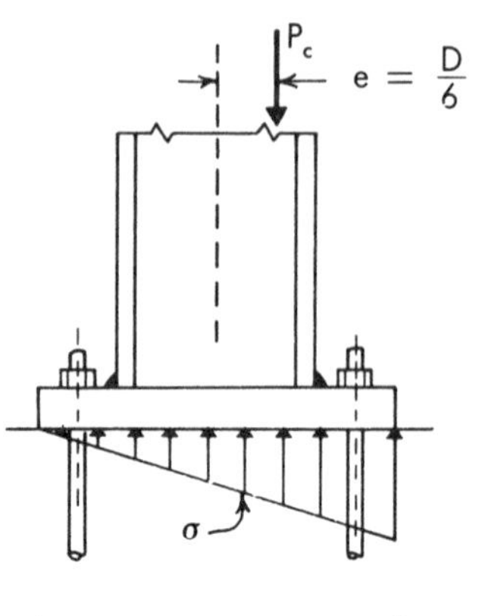

FIGURE 15

If the eccentricity (e) *is less than* 1/6 D, there is no uplift of the base plate at the surface of the masonry support (Figure 15):

section modulus of base plate

$$S = \frac{B\ D^2}{6} \qquad A = B \times D$$

stress in base plate

$$\sigma_T = \sigma_1 \text{ compression} \pm \sigma_2 \text{ bending}$$

$$= \frac{P_c}{A} \pm \frac{P_c\ e}{S}$$

When the eccentricity (e) *exceeds* 1/6 D, there is uplift on the base plate which is resisted by the anchor hold-down bolts. The bearing stress on the masonry support is maximum at the extreme edge of the bearing plate. It is assumed this stress decreases linearly back along the plate for a distance (Y); however, there is some question as to how far this extends. One problem analysis approach treats this section as a reinforced concrete beam.

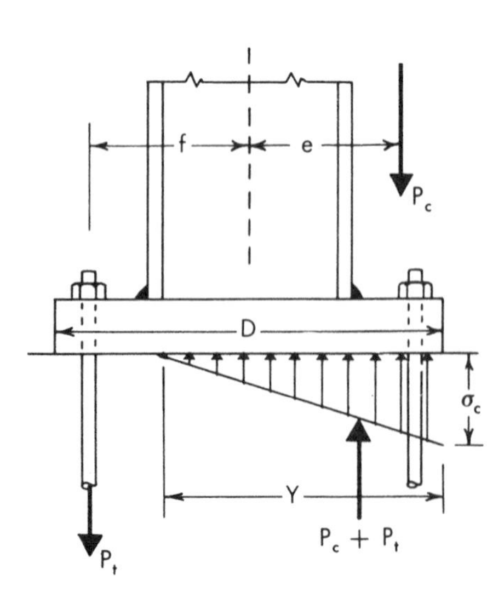

FIGURE 16

Basic Method (If Uplift)

There are three equations, and three unknowns (P_t), (Y), and (σ_c):

1. $\Sigma\ V = 0$

$$\tfrac{1}{2}\ Y\ \sigma_c\ B - P_t - P_c = 0$$

or

$$P_c + P_t = \frac{\sigma_c\ Y\ B}{2} \qquad \text{(8a)}$$

and

$$\sigma_c = \frac{2(P_c + P_t)}{Y\ B} \qquad \text{(8b)}$$

where: σ_c = pressure supplied by masonry supporting material

2. $\Sigma\ M = 0$ (About N.A. of column)

$$P_t\ f + (P_c + P_t)\left(\frac{D}{2} - \frac{Y}{3}\right) - P_c\ e = 0$$

or

$$P_c = -P_t \left[\frac{\frac{D}{2} - \frac{Y}{3} + f}{\frac{D}{2} - \frac{Y}{3} - e}\right] \qquad \text{(9a)}$$

and

$$P_t = -P_c \left[\frac{\frac{D}{2} - \frac{Y}{3} - e}{\frac{D}{2} - \frac{Y}{3} + f}\right] \qquad \text{(9b)}$$

3. Representing the elastic behavior of the concrete support and the steel hold-down bolt (see Figure 17):

$$\frac{a}{b} = \frac{\epsilon_s}{\epsilon_c} = \frac{\frac{\sigma_s}{E_s}}{\frac{\sigma_c}{E_c}} = \frac{\sigma_s\, E_c}{\sigma_c\, E_s}$$

since: $E_s = \dfrac{\sigma_s}{\epsilon_s}$, $E_c = \dfrac{\sigma_c}{\epsilon_c}$

Also

$$\sigma_s = \frac{P_t}{A_s}$$

and letting

$$n = \frac{E_s}{E_c}$$

then

$$\frac{a}{b} = \frac{\frac{P_t}{A_s}}{\sigma_c\, n} = \frac{P_t}{A_s\, \sigma_c\, n}$$

and from similar triangles

$$\frac{a}{b} = \frac{\frac{D}{2} - Y + f}{Y}$$

where:

A_s = total area of steel hold-down bolts under tension

σ_s = stress in steel bolt

ϵ_s = strain in steel bolt

E_s = modulus of elasticity of steel bolt

and:

σ_c = stress in concrete support

ϵ_c = strain in concrete support

E_c = modulus of elasticity of concrete support

n = modular ratio of elasticity, steel to concrete

so

$$\frac{P_t}{A_s\, \sigma_c\, n} = \frac{\frac{D}{2} - Y + f}{Y}$$

or

$$\boxed{\sigma_c = \frac{P_t\, Y}{A_s\, n\left(\frac{D}{2} - Y + f\right)}} \qquad \ldots\ldots\ldots\ldots(10)$$

* * *

Substituting formula #10 into formula #8a:

$$P_c + P_t = \frac{P_t\, Y}{A_s\, n\left(\frac{D}{2} - Y + f\right)}\left(\frac{Y\, B}{2}\right)$$

or

$$\boxed{P_c + P_t = \frac{P_t\, Y^2\, B}{2\, A_s\, n\left(\frac{D}{2} - Y + f\right)}} \qquad \ldots.(11)$$

Substituting formula #9a into formula #11:

$$-P_t\left[\frac{\frac{D}{2} - \frac{Y}{3} + f}{\frac{D}{2} - \frac{Y}{3} - e}\right] + P_t = \frac{P_t\, Y^2\, B}{2\, A_s\, n\left(\frac{D}{2} - Y + f\right)}$$

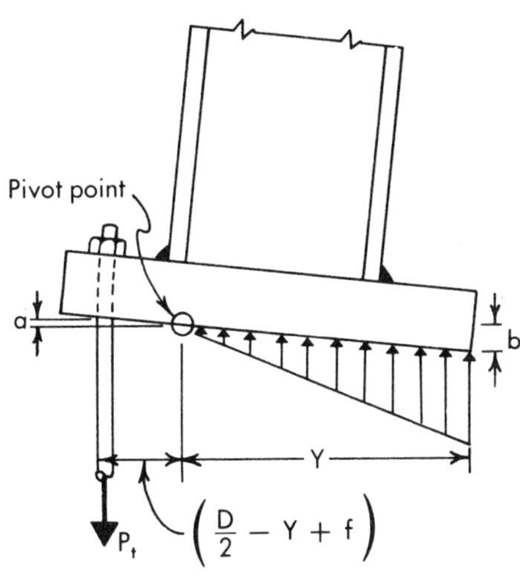

FIGURE 17

Solve for Y:

$$-2\, n\, A_s\left(\frac{D}{2} - Y + f\right)\left(\frac{D}{2} - \frac{Y}{3} + f\right) + \left(\frac{D}{2} - \frac{Y}{3} - e\right)\left(2\, n\, A_s\right)\left(\frac{D}{2} - Y + f\right) = Y^2\, B\left(\frac{D}{2} - \frac{Y}{3} - e\right)$$

or

$$-\frac{n\, A_s\, D^2}{2} + \frac{4\, n\, A_s\, D\, Y}{3} - 2\, n\, A_s\, D\, f - \frac{2\, n\, A_s\, Y^2}{3} + \frac{8\, n\, A_s\, f\, Y}{3} - 2\, n\, A_s\, f^2 + \frac{n\, A_s\, D^2}{2} - \frac{4\, n\, A_s\, D\, Y}{3} - n\, A_s\, D\, e + \frac{2\, n\, A_s\, Y^2}{3} + 2\, n\, A_s\, e\, Y + n\, A_s\, D\, f - \frac{2\, n\, A_s\, f\, Y}{3} - 2\, n\, A_s\, e\, f = \frac{B\, D}{2}\, Y^2 - \frac{B\, Y^3}{3} - B\, e\, Y^2$$

This reduces to—

$$\boxed{Y^3 + 3\left(e - \frac{D}{2}\right)Y^2 + \frac{6\, n\, A_s}{B}\left(f + e\right)Y - \frac{6\, n\, A_s}{B}\left(\frac{D}{2} + f\right)(f + e) = 0} \qquad ..(12)$$

or to express it in a manner to facilitate repetitive use, let—

$$K_1 = 3\left(e - \frac{D}{2}\right)$$

$$K_2 = \frac{6\, n\, A_s}{B}\left(f + e\right)$$

$$K_3 = -\, K_2\left(\frac{D}{2} + f\right)$$

then—

$$Y^3 + K_1 Y^2 + K_2 Y + K_3 = 0 \quad \text{.......(13)}$$

There are several ways to solve this cubic equation. Perhaps the easiest is to plot a few points, letting Y = simple whole numbers, for example, 9, 10, etc., and reading the value of Y on the graph where the curve crosses zero.

Having found the effective bearing length (Y) in this manner, formula #9b can be used to solve for the tensile force (P_t) in the hold-down bolts. Formula #10 then gives the amount of bearing stress in the masonry support.

Alternative Shorter Method

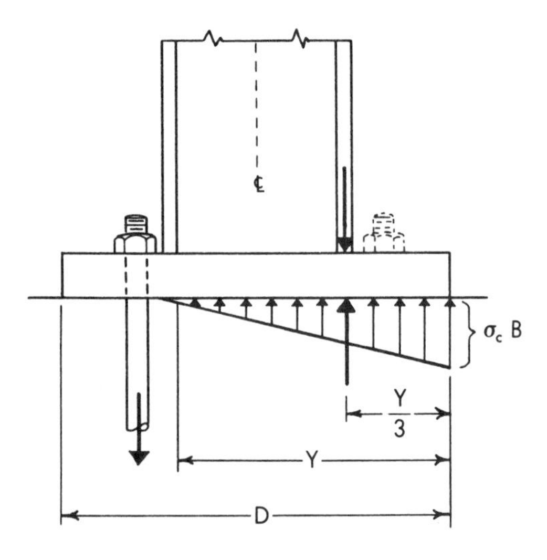

FIGURE 18

Another approach to determining the effective bearing length, involving less work, assumes the same triangular distribution of bearing forces from the supporting masonry against the bearing plate. However, the center of gravity of the triangle, or the concentrated force representing this triangle, is assumed to be fixed at a point coinciding with the concentrated compressive force of the column flange. See Figure 18.

From this assumption, the overhang of the bearing plate, i.e. the distance from the column flange to the plate's outer edge, is seen to equal ⅓ the effective bearing length.

Problem 1

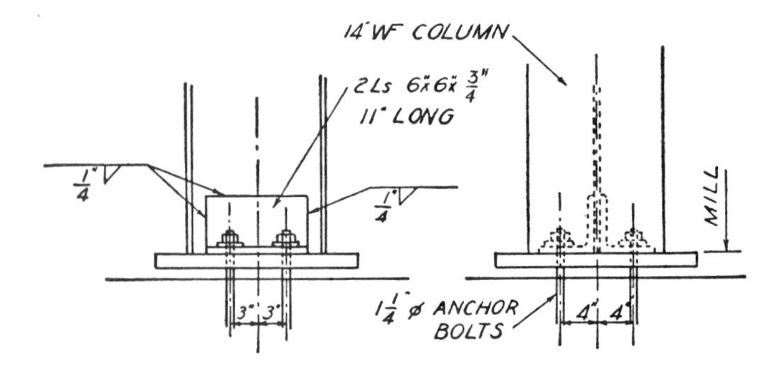

FIGURE 19

Figure 19 shows a column base detail. The columns have a maximum load of 186 kips, and receive no uplift under normal wind. See Figure 19. Under heavier wind load and in combination with temperature, they may receive up to 20 kips direct uplift. See Figure 20. Four bolts are provided, attached by means of 6″ × 6″ × ¾″ clip angles, 11″ long on a 4″ gauge.

To be effective, the angles must carry this load on the anchor bolts into the column web. This causes a bending moment on the outstanding legs of the angles. Analysis follows that for formula #3. The bolt tension fixes the toe of the angle against the base plate and causes an inflection point between the bolts and the vertical leg of the angle, so that the bolt load is cantilevered only about halfway.

$$M_{max} = \frac{P\ b}{2}$$

To compute the bending stress in the angles:

$$\sigma_b = \frac{M\ c}{I}$$

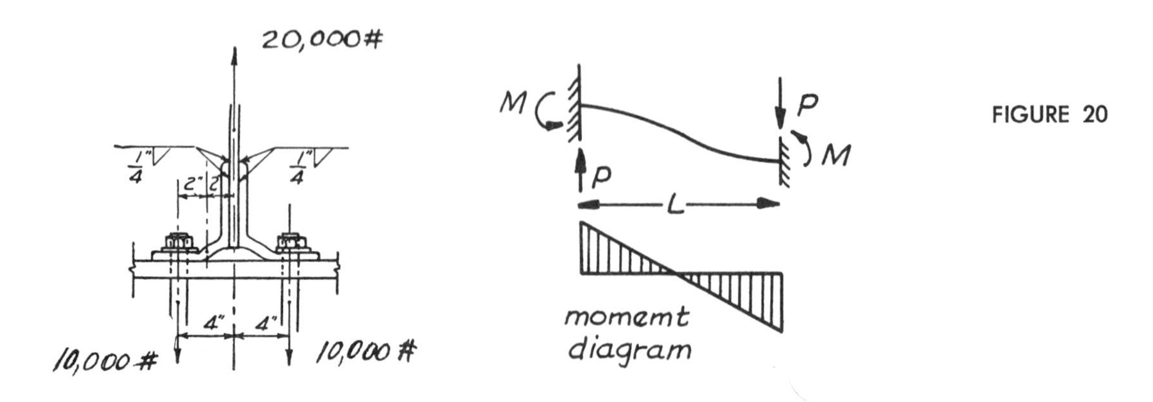

FIGURE 20

where:

σ_b = stress in outer fibers

M = bending moment

c = distance to neutral axis

I = moment of inertia

Since:

$$I = \frac{(11'')(3/4'')^3}{12}$$

$$= .386 \text{ in.}^4$$

$$\therefore \sigma_b = \frac{M\ c}{I}$$

$$= \frac{(10{,}000\ \# \times 2'')(3/8'')}{(.386)}$$

$$= 19{,}400 \text{ psi}$$

Hence, the detail with 3/4" angles is <u>OK</u> for this load.

Check Welds to Column Web

The angles are welded to the column web with 1/4" fillet welds; this will now be checked.

The heel of the angle is in compression against the web of the column and is equivalent to an additional weld across the bottom for resisting moment. On this basis, the section modulus of the weld is calculated. For simplicity, the weld is treated as a line without any cross-sectional area. From Table 5, Sect. 7.4, the section modulus of a rectangular connection is:

$$S_w = b\ d + \frac{d^2}{3}$$

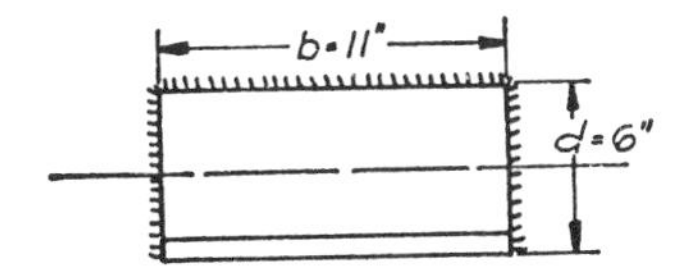

and here:

$$S_w = (11)(6) + \frac{(6)^2}{3}$$

$$= 78 \text{ in.}^2$$

Normally, section modulus is expressed as inches to the third power; however, here where the weld has no area, the resulting section modulus is expressed as inches squared.

When a standard bending formula is used, the answer (σ) is stress in lbs/in.^{2}; however, when this new section modulus is used in the bending formula, the answer (f) is force on the weld in lbs/linear in.

bending

$$f_b = \frac{M}{S_w}$$

$$= \frac{(10{,}000\# \times 4'')}{(78 \text{ in.}^2)}$$

$$= 513 \text{ lbs/in.}$$

shear

$$f_s = \frac{P}{L_w}$$

$$= \frac{(10{,}000\#)}{(23'')}$$

$$= 435 \text{ lbs/in.}$$

resultant force on weld

$$f_r = \sqrt{f_b^2 + f_s^2}$$

$$= \sqrt{(513)^2 + (435)^2}$$

$$= 673 \text{ lbs/in.}$$

leg size of (E70) fillet weld

$$\omega = \frac{\text{actual force}}{\text{allowable force}}$$

$$= \frac{(673)}{(11{,}200)}$$

$$= .06''$$

but 3/4"-thick angle requires a minimum of <u>1/4" ◺</u> (Table 3, Section 7.4).

If it is desired to increase the anchor bolt capacity of the clip angle detail, thicker angles should be used with large plate washers on top of the angle. The attachments should be made to the column flanges, since the welds are more accessible there and the bolts have better leverage.

Problem 2

To illustrate how the column flange can be checked to determine whether or not it is too thin, consider a clip angle anchored with two 1¼" bolts centered 2½" out from the face of the column flange; see Figure 21. The angle is attached to the column flange by fillet welds across the top and down each side.

The capacity of the two bolts at 14,000 psi allowable stress on unthreaded area (AISC Sec 1.5.2) is—

$$2\ (1.227)(14{,}000) = 34{,}400 \text{ lbs} > 28{,}500 \text{ lbs} \quad \underline{\text{OK}}$$

The bending moment on the weld is—

$$(28{,}500 \text{ lbs})(2\tfrac{1}{2}'') = 71{,}250 \text{ in.-lbs}$$

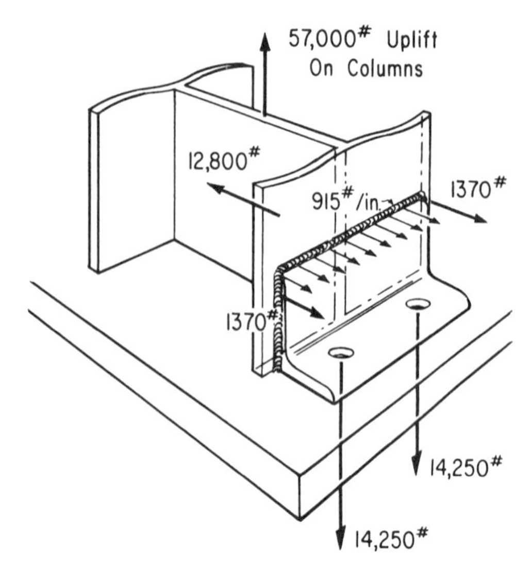

FIGURE 21

As in the previous example, the heel of the angle is in compression against the web of the column and is replaced with an equivalent weld. The welds are treated as a line, and the section modulus of the welded connection is found to be—

$$S_w = b\ d + \frac{d^2}{3}$$

$$= (11)\ 6) + \frac{(6)^2}{3}$$

$$= 78 \text{ in.}^2 \quad \text{(See Problem 1)}$$

The bending force is—

$$f_b = \frac{M}{S_w}$$

$$= \frac{71{,}250 \text{ in.-lbs}}{78 \text{ in.}^2}$$

$$= 915 \text{ lbs/in.}$$

all along the top edge of the angle, pulling outward on the column flange. This is the force on the horizontal top weld. At the ends of the angle, the force couple is $\frac{(915)(3)}{2} = 1370$ lbs centered 1″ below the top toe of the angle. See Figure 22.

This is the force on each of the vertical welds at ends of the angle. Since these forces are not resisted by anything but the flange, they have to be carried transversely by bending stresses in the flange until they reach the resistance in the column web.

The bending moment in the column flange is computed as follows:

$$\text{Force along top of angle} = 915 \times 5.5 = 5040 \text{ lbs}$$

$$M_h = 5040 \times 2.75 = 13{,}860 \text{ in.-lbs}$$

$$M_v = 1370 \times 5.5 = 7{,}535 \text{ in.-lbs}$$

$$\text{Total M} = 21{,}395 \text{ in.-lbs}$$

If we assume a 6″ wide strip of the column flange to resist this load, this moment will cause a bending stress of 45,300 psi in the 14″ WF 87-lb column with a flange 11/16″ thick.

This is calculated as follows:

$$I = \frac{(6'')(11/16'')^3}{12}$$

$$= .1625 \text{ in.}^4$$

$$\sigma_b = \frac{M\ c}{I}$$

$$= \frac{(21{,}395)(11/32)}{(.1625)}$$

$$= 45{,}300 \text{ psi}$$

Obviously, since this stress distribution along the welds is capable of bending the column flange beyond the yield point, the column flange will deflect outward sufficiently to relieve these stresses and cause a redistribution. The resultant stresses in the weld metal on the toe of the clip angle will be concentrated opposite the column web.

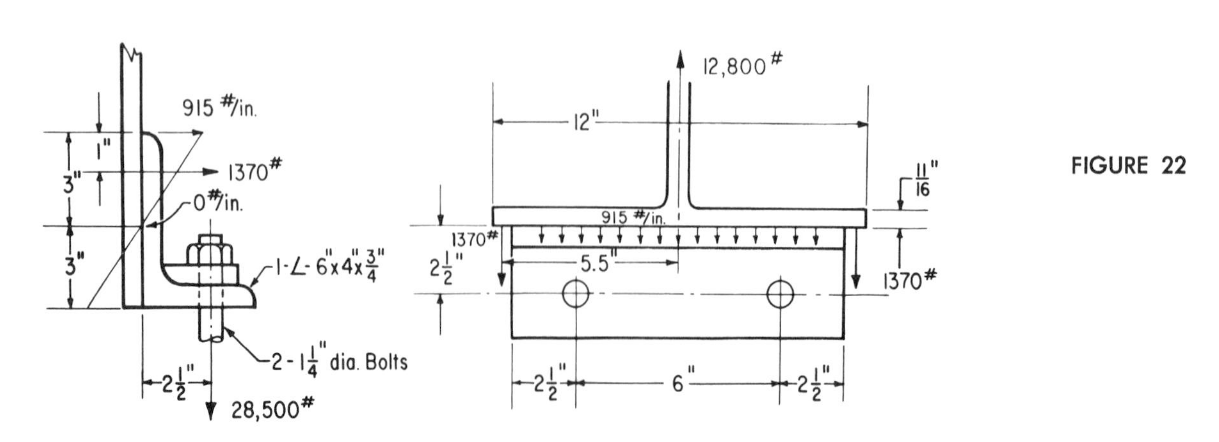

FIGURE 22

Thus, the capacity of this anchor bolt detail is limited by the bending strength of the column flange even after the clip angle has been satisfactorily stiffened.

The force back through the column web is:

$$F = (915 \text{ lbs/in.})\ (11'') + 2\ (1370 \text{ lbs})$$
$$= 12{,}800 \text{ lbs}$$

A ½″ fillet weld 3 inches long on the top of the angle opposite the column web will satisfactorily resist the force couple:

$$F = (3'')\ (5600 \text{ lbs/in.}) \qquad \text{E70 welds}$$
$$= 16{,}800 \text{ lbs.} \qquad \underline{\text{OK}}$$

For greater anchor bolt capacities than shown in Figure 22, either horizontal stiffeners or diaphragms should be provided to prevent bending of the column flanges.

Problem 3

A rather simple detail, whereby a wide-flanged channel serves as a stiffener, is shown in Figure 23.

This detail was used with three 1⅝″-dia anchor bolts on a 14″ × 87-lb mill building column designed to resist a wind bending moment of 175,000 ft-lbs combined with a direct load downward of 130,000 lbs.

The tension on the bolts is determined by taking moments about the right-hand compression flange of the column after first determining the eccentricity at which the direct load will cause a moment of 175,000 ft-lbs about the centerline of the column. The eccentricity is—

$$e = \frac{(175{,}000)(12)}{(130{,}000)}$$
$$= 16.15''$$

The load on the bolts is—

$$F = \frac{(130{,}000)(9.49)}{(15.66)}$$
$$= 78{,}800 \text{ lbs}$$

The area of the three 1⅝″ dia. bolts in the unthreaded body area is—

$$A = (3)(2.074)$$
$$= 6.22 \text{ in.}^2$$

The tensile stress in the bolts is:

$$\sigma = \frac{(78{,}800)}{(6.22)}$$
$$= 12{,}700 \text{ psi} < 14{,}000 \text{ psi} \qquad \underline{\text{OK}}$$

(AISC Sec 1.5.2)

The compression flange reaction (R) is the sum of the 130,000-lb column load plus the 78,800-lb pull of the anchor bolts, or 208,800 lbs. The 13″ ship channels are set up just clear of the bearing on the base plate so that the end of the column will take the compressive load of 208,800 lbs without overloading channels.

Bearing stress on masonry

The bearing stress on the masonry support is maximum at the extreme edge of the bearing plate, and is assumed to decrease linearly back along the plate. This bearing stress would resemble a triangle in which

FIGURE 23

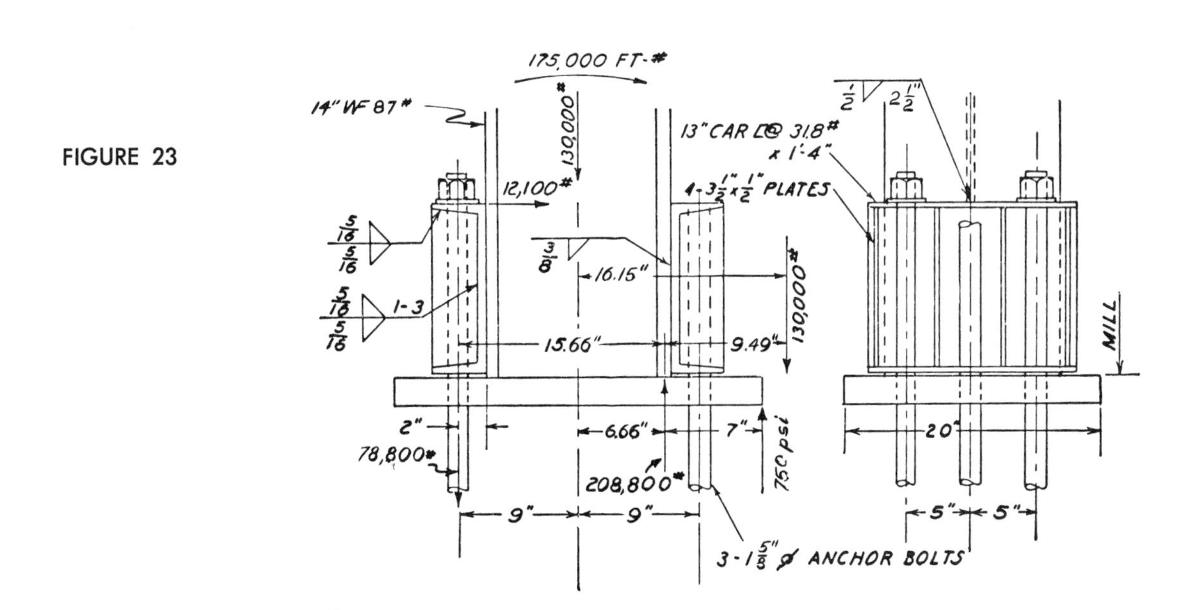

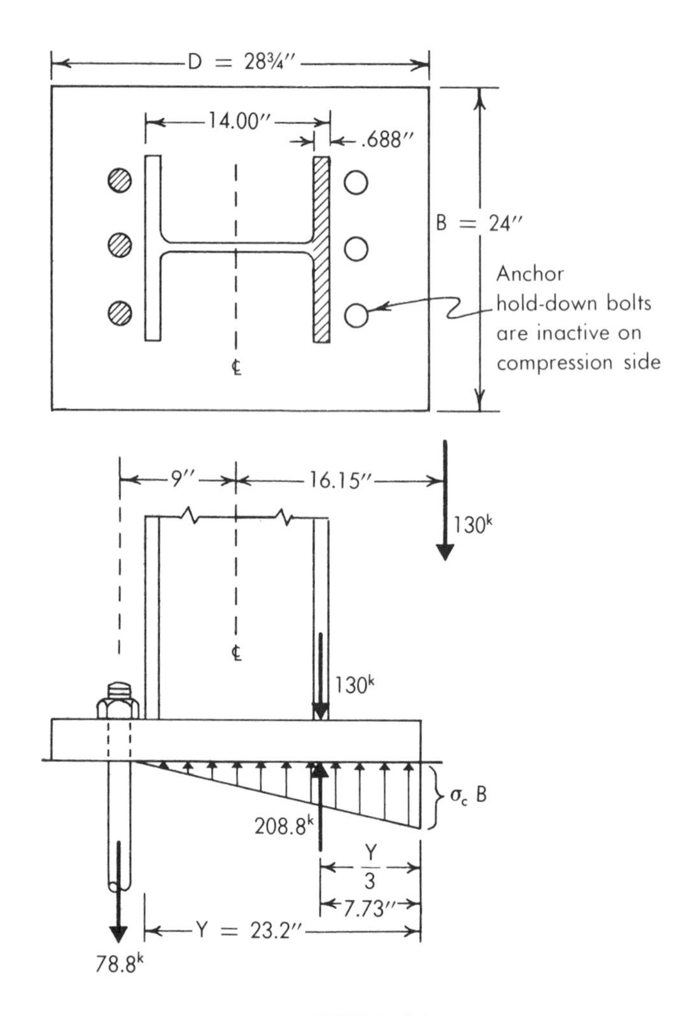

FIGURE 24

the altitude is the maximum bearing stress at the edge of the plate, and the base of the triangle is the effective bearing length (Y) against the plate. (See short method described on page 10.) Since the area of this triangle has a center of gravity ⅓ Y back from the altitude, the bearing pressure may be resolved into a concentrated force at this point. This point will be assumed to lie where the column flange's concentrated compressive load of 208,800 lbs is applied.

Hence, the distance from the compressive force of the flange out to the edge of the bearing plate (in other words, the overhang of the bearing plate) equals ⅓ the effective distance of the bearing support. See Figure 24.

area of triangle

$$A = \tfrac{1}{2}\,\sigma_c\,Y$$

$$= P_c + P_t$$

effective bearing length of base plate (from formula #8)

$$Y = \frac{2(P_c + P_t)}{\sigma_c\,B}$$

$$= \frac{2(130^k + 78.8^k)}{(750)(24)}$$

$$= 23.2''$$

$$\text{and } \frac{Y}{3} = 7.73'' \text{ overhang}$$

Let:

$$B = 24''$$

$$\sigma_c = .25\,\sigma'_c$$

$$= .25\ (3000 \text{ psi})$$

$$= 750 \text{ psi}$$

$$\therefore D = 7.73'' + 13.31'' + 7.73''$$

$$= 28.77'' \text{ or use } 28\tfrac{3}{4}''$$

Bolt load

The load on the bolts is supported by the top flange of the 13″ channel, reinforced by four 3⅝″ × ½″ stiffener plates welded between the channel flanges. See Figure 23.

The two interior plates each support a full bolt load of ⅓ (78,800 lbs) or 26,300 lbs. These stiffeners are attached to the channel web with four 1″ × 5⁄16″ intermittent fillet welds on each side of the plate, and to both flanges by continuous 5⁄16″ fillet welds on each side of the plate. See Figure 25. The welds at the channel flanges transmit the moment to the channel flanges, and the welds at the channel web support most of the shearing load.

The 2″ eccentricity of the bolt load to column flange is transposed to a force couple acting on the channel flanges. This couple is obtained by dividing

FIGURE 25

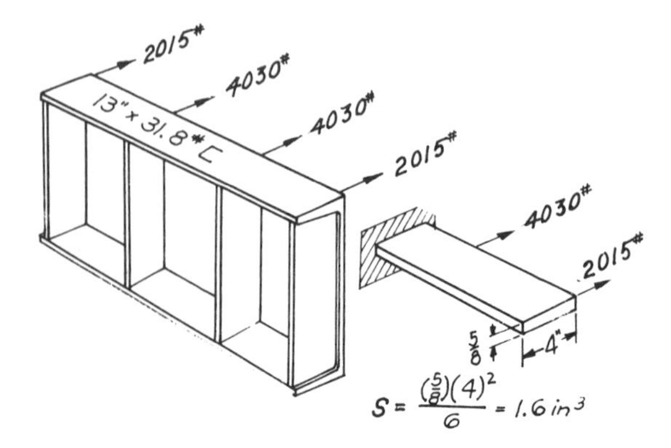

the moment by the depth of the stiffeners:

$$C = \frac{(78{,}800)(2)}{(13)}$$
$$= 12{,}100 \text{ lbs}$$

This is a horizontal load acting at right angles to the column flange. It is delivered as four concentrated loads at the tops of stiffeners and then carried horizontally by the channel flange to a point opposite the column web where it is attached to the column with a 2½" × ½" fillet weld.

2½" × 5600 lbs/in. = 14,000 lbs.

The concentrated load values are 2015 lbs at each end stiffener for one-half a bolt load, and 4030 lbs at each interior stiffener.

The total moment on the flanges is:

$$(2{,}015)(7.5) = 15{,}200 \text{ in.-lbs}$$
$$(4{,}030)(2.5) = 10{,}100 \text{ in.-lbs}$$
$$M = 25{,}300 \text{ in.-lbs}$$

It causes a bending stress in the channels 4" × ⅝" top flange section of approximately—

$$\sigma_b = \frac{M}{S}$$
$$= \frac{(25{,}300)}{(1.6)}$$
$$= 15{,}800 \text{ psi}$$

To keep the channel section from sliding parallel to the column flange, the direct vertical pull of the bolts is supported by two 13" × 5⁄16" continuous fillet welds between the edge of the column flanges and the web of the 13" channel section. The shear on these welds is—

$$f_s = \frac{(78{,}800)}{(2)(13)}$$
$$= 3030 \text{ lbs/in.}$$

$$\omega = \frac{(3030)}{(11{,}200)} \qquad \text{E70-weld allowable}$$
$$= .276'' \text{ or } \underline{\text{use } 5/16'' \text{ fillet}}$$

The problem in Figure 23 has been analyzed on the basis of simple levers with the compression load concentrated on the column flange. It ignores the compression area under the web of the column and illustrates the problem where the channel flange of the anchor bolt attachment does not bear against the base plate.

For simplicity, this analysis has assumed that the effective bearing length (Y) was such that the center of gravity of the triangular bearing stress distribution, C.G. at ⅓ Y, lies along the centerline of the column flange where the compressive force of the column is applied.

Problem 4

With the same column base detail as in Problem 3, we will now use the original derivation for this effective bearing length (Y), treating the analysis as a reinforced concrete beam and solving the resulting cubic equation. The work may take longer, but results are more accurate. See Figure 26, temporarily ignoring the anchor-bolt channel attachments.

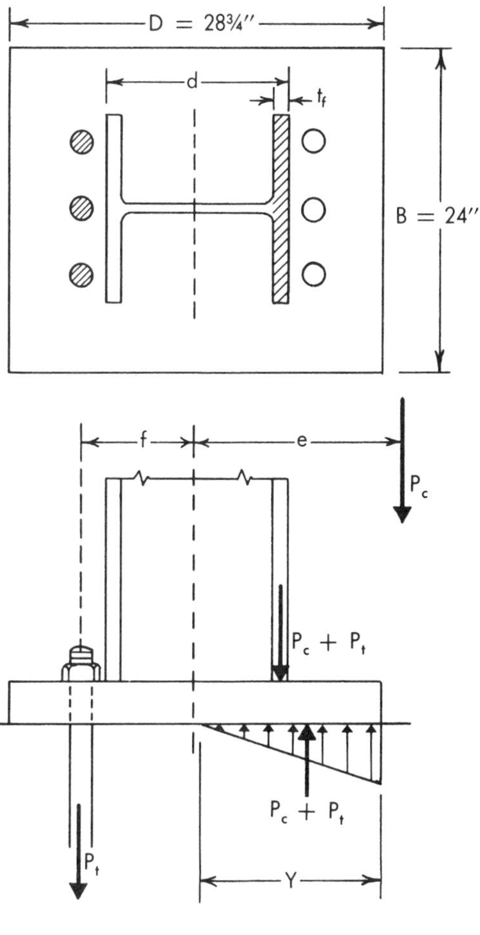

FIGURE 26

Here:

$$e = 16.15''$$
$$f = 9''$$
$$D = 28\tfrac{3}{4}''$$
$$B = 24''$$

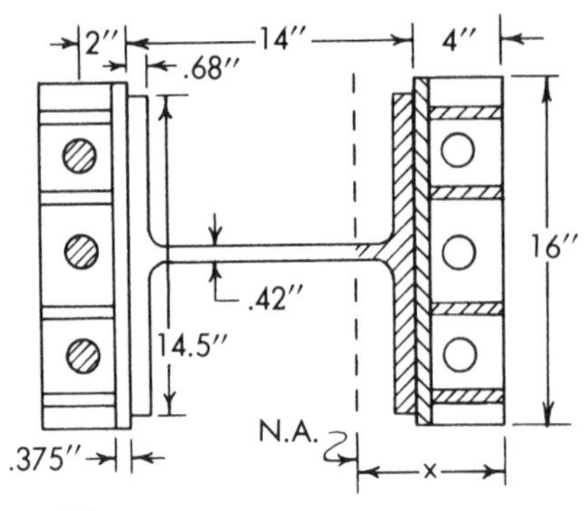

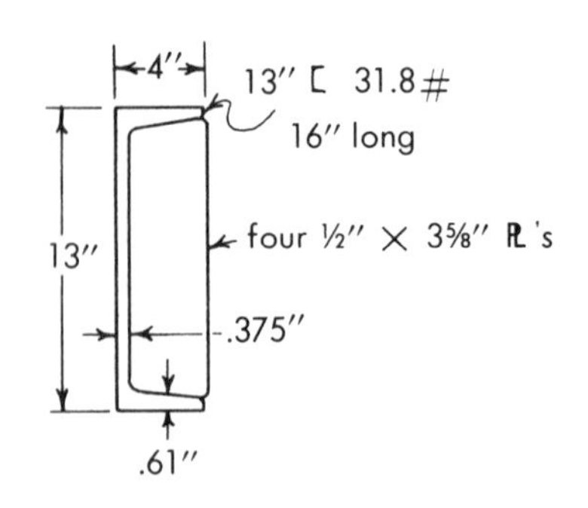

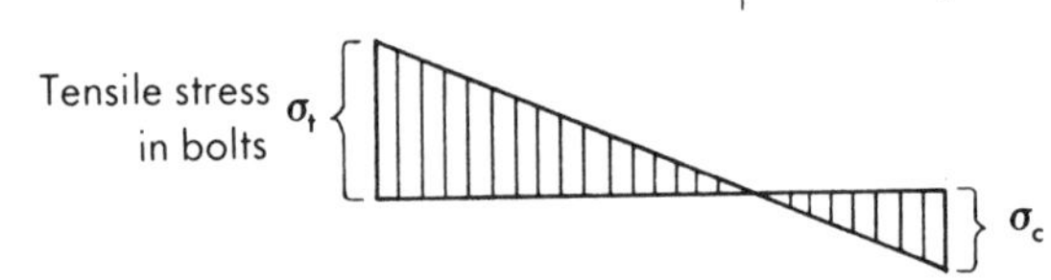

FIGURE 27

$$n = \frac{E_s}{E_c} = 10 \quad (E_c = 3000 \text{ psi})$$

1⅝″ bolts

$$A_s = 3\ (2.074)$$

$$= 6.22 \text{ in.}^2 \text{ (bolts under tension)}$$

$$P_c = 130 \text{ kips}$$

from formula #13 (cubic equation)

$$Y^3 + K_1\, Y^2 + K_2\, Y + K_3 = 0$$

where:

$$K_1 = 3\left(e - \frac{D}{2}\right)$$

$$= 3\left(16.15 - \frac{28\tfrac{3}{4}}{2}\right)$$

$$= 5.33$$

$$K_2 = \frac{6\ n\ A_s}{B}(f + e)$$

$$= \frac{6\ (10)(6.22)}{24}(9 + 16.15)$$

$$= 392$$

$$K_3 = -\,K_2\left(\frac{D}{2} + f\right)$$

$$= -\,392\left(\frac{28\tfrac{3}{4}}{2} + 9\right)$$

$$= -\,9160$$

Therefore, substituting into formula #13:

$$Y^3 + 5.33\ Y^2 + 392\ Y - 9160 = 0$$

Letting Y = +10, +12, and +15 provides the following solutions to the cubic equation as the function of Y:

$$Y = +10 \longrightarrow -3707$$

$$Y = +12 \longrightarrow -1960$$

$$Y = +15 \longrightarrow +1294$$

Plotting these three points, the curve is observed to pass through zero at—

$$Y = \underline{13.9''}$$

which is the effective bearing length.

from formula #9b

$$P_t = -\,P_c\left[\frac{\frac{D}{2} - \frac{Y}{3} - e}{\frac{D}{2} - \frac{Y}{3} + f}\right]$$

$$= -\,130^k\left[\frac{\frac{28\tfrac{3}{4}}{2} - \frac{13.9}{3} - 16.15}{\frac{28\tfrac{3}{4}}{2} - \frac{13.9}{3} + 9}\right]$$

$$= +\,44.5^k$$

which is the tensile load on the hold-down bolts.

from formula #8b

$$\sigma_c = \frac{2(P_c + P_t)}{Y\ B}$$

$$= \frac{2(130^k + 44.5^k)}{(13.9)(24)}$$

$$= 1050 \text{ psi}$$

which is the bearing pressure of the masonry support against the bearing plate.

If the anchor hold-down bolt detail is milled with the column base so that it bears against the base plate, it must be made strong enough to support the portion of the reaction load ($P_c + P_t$) which tends to bear upward against the portions of the bolt detail outside the column flange. This upward reaction on the compression side ($P_c + P_t$) is much larger than the downward load of the bolts on the tension side (P_t).

The area of section effective in resisting this reaction includes all the area of the compression material—column flange, portion of column web, the channel web, and stiffeners—plus the area of the anchor bolts on the tension side. See shaded area in Figure 27.

The anchor bolts on the compression side do not act because they have no way of transmitting a compressive load to the rest of the column. In like manner, the column flange and web on the tension side do not act because they have no way of transmitting a tensile stress across the milled joint to the base plate. The tension flange simply tends to lift off the base plate and no stress is transmitted in the tensile area except by the hold-down bolts attached to the column.

Determining moment of inertia

To determine the moment of inertia of this effective area of section, the area's neutral axis must be located. Properties of the elements making up this effective area are entered in the table shown here. Moments are taken about a reference axis (y-y) at the outermost edge of the channel stiffeners on the compression side (Fig. 27). See Section 2.2 for method.

Having obtained the 1st totals of area (A) and moment (M), solve for the location (n) of the neutral axis relative to the reference axis:

$$n = \frac{\Sigma M}{\Sigma A}$$

$$= \frac{(199.98 + .21\ n^2)}{(27.36 + .42\ n)}$$

$$199.98 + .21\ n^2 = 27.36 + .42\ n^2$$

$$n^2 + 130.28\ n - 952.47 = 0$$

$$n = \frac{-130.28 \pm \sqrt{130.28^2 + 4(952.47)}}{2}$$

$$= 6.93'' \text{ distance of N.A. to ref. axis y-y}$$

$$\therefore c = 6.93'' \text{ distance of N.A. to outer fiber}$$

Now, having the value of n, properties of the effective portion of the column web can be fixed and the table completed. With the 2nd totals of area (A), moment (B), and also moments of inertia ($I_y + I_g$), solve for the moment of inertia about the neutral axis (I_n):

$$I_n = I_y + I_g - \frac{M^2}{A}$$

$$= (2789.93) - \frac{(210.07)^2}{(30.27)}$$

$$= 1326 \text{ in.}^4$$

Since the concentrated compressive load (P_c) is applied at an eccentricity (e) of 16.15″ to provide for the wind moment of 175,000 kips, the moment arm of the 130-kip load is—

9.15″ from face of column flange

5.15″ from outer edge of channel stiffeners

12.08″ from neutral axis of effective area

compressive stress at outer edge of channel stiffeners

$$\sigma_c = \frac{M\,c}{I} + \frac{P_c}{A}$$

$$= \frac{(130^k \times 12.08)(6.93)}{(1326)} + \frac{130^k}{30.27}$$

$$= 8220 + 4300 = 12,150 \text{ psi}$$

	Distance: C.G. to ref. axis y-y (y)	Area (A)	Moment (M)	Moment of inertia (I_y)	(I_g)
3 bolts	20.0	6.22	124.40	2448.0	
Portion of web	$\frac{4.688 + n}{2} = 2.344 + .5n$	$(n - 4.688)(.42) = .42n - 1.969$	$(2.344 + .5n)(.42n - 1.969) = .21n^2 - 4.615$		
	= 5.809	= .94	= + 5.47	31.77	
Column flange	4.344	9.86	42.83	186.05	
Channel web	3.812	6.00	22.87	87.19	
Channel stiffeners	2.00	7.25	14.50	29.00	7.92
	First Total →	27.36 + .42 n	199.98 + .21 n²		
By substituting value of n = 6.93″:	Second Total →	30.27	210.07	2789.93	

tensile stress in hold-down bolts

$$\sigma_t = \frac{M\ c}{I} - \frac{P_c}{A}$$

where c is distance of N.A. from extreme fiber of tensile area

$$= \frac{(130^k \times 12.08)(13.07)}{(1326)} - \frac{130^k}{30.27}$$

$$= 15{,}500 \text{ psi} - 4{,}300 = 11{,}200 \text{ psi}$$

total force in hold-down bolts

$$P_t = A_s\ \sigma_t$$

$$= (6.22)(11{,}200)$$

$$= 69.6 \text{ kips}$$

Size of Welds Attaching Stiffeners to Channel Web

Compressive force is carried by each of the four channel stiffeners. The average compressive stress on these stiffeners is—

$$\sigma_c = \frac{5.15''}{6.93''}(8220 \text{ psi}) + 4300 \text{ psi}$$

$$= 6110 \text{ psi} + 4300 \text{ psi} = 10{,}410 \text{ psi}$$

$$\therefore\ F = \sigma_c\ A$$

$$= (10{,}410)(\tfrac{1}{2} \times 3\tfrac{5}{8}'')$$

$$= 18{,}850 \text{ lbs}$$

This compressive force on each channel stiffener is transferred to the channel web by two vertical fillet welds, each 11″ long. The force on each weld is thus—

$$f = \frac{F}{2\ L}$$

$$= \frac{(18{,}850 \text{ lbs})}{2(11'')}$$

$$= 856 \text{ lbs/linear inch}$$

and the required fillet weld leg size is—

$$\omega = \frac{856}{11{,}200} \leftarrow \text{for E70 welds (Table 5, Sect. 7.4)}$$

$$= .076'' \text{ or use } \tfrac{3}{16}'' \qquad \text{(Table 2, Sect. 7.4)}$$

With this leg size, intermittent welds can be used instead of continuous welding—

TABLE 4—Four Methods of Welding Channel Assembly to Column Flange

(a)	(b)	(c)	(d)
b = 14½″, d = 13″; bottom	b = 14½″, d = 13″	b = 14½″, d = 13″	b = 14½″, d = 13″
$S_w = \frac{d^2(2b+d)}{3(b+d)}$	$S_w = bd + \frac{d^2}{3}$	$S_w = \frac{d^2}{3}$	$S_w = bd$
$= \frac{(13)^2(2 \times 14.5 + 13)}{3(14.5+13)}$	$= (14.5)(13) + \frac{(13)^2}{3}$	$= \frac{(13)^2}{3}$	$= (14.5)(13)$
$= 86.1 \text{ in.}^2$	$= 242.2 \text{ in.}^2$	$= 56.3 \text{ in.}^2$	$= 185.9 \text{ in.}^2$
$f_b = \frac{M}{S_w}$	$f_b = \frac{M}{S_w}$	$f_b = \frac{M}{S_w}$	$f_b = \frac{M}{S_w}$
$= \frac{(174{,}200)}{(86.1)}$	$= \frac{(174{,}200)}{(242.2)}$	$= \frac{(174{,}200)}{(56.3)}$	$= \frac{(174{,}200)}{(185.9)}$
= 2020 lbs/in.	= 720 lbs/in.	= 3100 lbs/in.	= 935 lbs/in.
$f_s = \frac{V}{L}$	$f_s = \frac{V}{L}$	$f_s = \frac{V}{L}$	$f_s = \frac{V}{L}$
$= \frac{(123{,}400)}{2(13)+(14.5)}$	$= \frac{(123{,}400)}{2(13+14.5)}$	$= \frac{(123{,}400)}{2\ (13)}$	$= \frac{(123{,}400)}{2\ (14.5)}$
= 3050 lbs/in.	= 2240 lbs/in.	= 4750 lbs/in.	= 4260 lbs/in.
$f_r = \sqrt{f_b^2 + f_s^2}$	$f_r = \sqrt{f_b^2 + f_s^2}$	$f_r = \sqrt{f_b^2 + f_s^2}$	$f_r = \sqrt{f_b^2 + f_s^2}$
$= \sqrt{(2020)^2 + (3050)^2}$	$= \sqrt{(720)^2 + (2240)^2}$	$= \sqrt{(3100)^2 + (4750)^2}$	$= \sqrt{(935)^2 + (4260)^2}$
= 3670 lbs/in.	= 2350 lbs/in.	= 5680 lbs/in.	= 4360 lbs/in.
$\omega = \frac{\text{actual force}}{\text{allowable force}}$	$\omega = \frac{\text{actual force}}{\text{allowable force}}$	$\omega = \frac{\text{actual force}}{\text{allowable force}}$	$\omega = \frac{\text{actual force}}{\text{allowable force}}$
$= \frac{(3670)}{(11{,}200)} \leftarrow$ E70	$= \frac{(2350)}{(11{,}200)}$	$= \frac{(5680)}{(11{,}200)}$	$= \frac{(4360)}{(11{,}200)}$
= .328″ or 5/16″ Δ	= .210″ or ¼″ Δ	= .506″ or ½″ Δ	= .389″ or 7/16″ Δ

$$L = \frac{\frac{1}{2}\,(18{,}850\text{ lbs})}{2100}$$

$$= 4.49''$$

or a total length of 4½″ of 3/16″ fillet welds on each side of each stiffener.

Size of Weld Connecting Channel Assembly to Column Flange

The average compressive stress on the channel web is—

$$\sigma_c = \frac{3.12''}{6.93''} \quad 8220 + 4300$$

$$= 3700 + 4300 = 8000 \text{ psi}$$

$$\therefore \quad F = \sigma A$$

$$= 8000$$

$$= 48{,}000 \text{ lbs}$$

total compressive force on channel assembly

$$F = 48{,}000 + 4(18{,}850)$$

$$= 123{,}400 \text{ lbs}$$

The fillet welds connecting the assembly to the column flange must transfer this total compressive force into the column flange. There are four ways to weld this, as shown in Table 4. Assume the welds carry all of the compressive force, and ignore any bearing of the channel against the column flange.

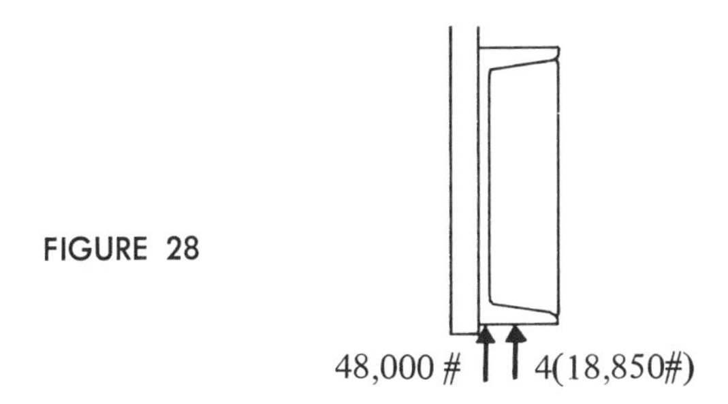

FIGURE 28

First find the moment applied to the weld, Figure 28, which applies in each case of Table 4:

$$M = 4(18{,}850\text{ lbs})\ (2.187'') + (48{,}000\text{ lbs})\,(3/16'')$$

$$= 174{,}200 \text{ in.-lbs}$$

Then, making each weld pattern in turn, treat the weld as a line to find its section modulus (S_w), the maximum bending force on the weld (f_b), the vertical shear on the weld (f_s), the resultant force on the weld (f_r), and the required weld leg size (ω).

Perhaps the most efficient way to weld this is method (d) in which two transverse ¼″ fillet welds are placed across the column flange and channel flange, with no longitudinal welding along the channel web.

5. USE OF WING PLATES

When large wing plates are used to increase the leverage of an anchor bolt, the detail should always be checked for weakness in bearing against the side of the column flange.

Problem 5

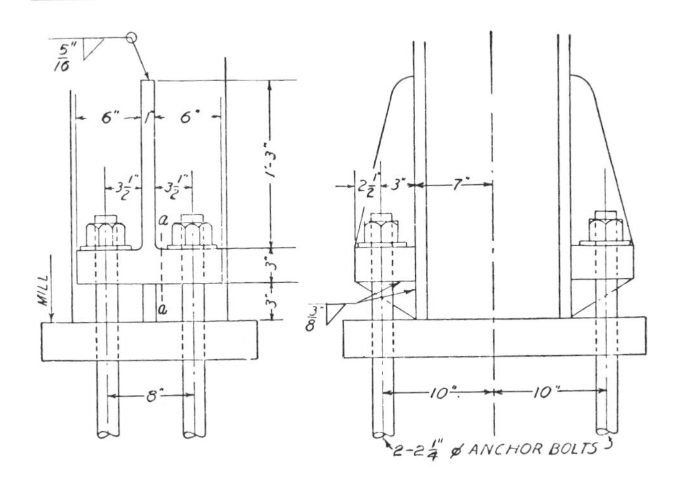

FIGURE 29

Figure 29 illustrates a wing-plate type of column base detail that is not limited with respect to size of bolts or strength of column flange. A similar detail, with bolts as large as 4½″ diameter, has been used on a large terminal project.

The detail shown is good for four 2¼″-dia. anchor bolts. Two of these bolts have a gross area of 6.046 in.² and are good for 84,600 lbs tension at a stress of 14,000 psi.

In this detail, the bolt load is first carried laterally to a point opposite the column web by the horizontal bar which is 5½″ wide by 3″ thick.

section modulus of section a-a

$$S = \frac{5\frac{1}{2}''\ (3'')^2}{6}$$

$$= 8.25 \text{ in.}^3$$

bending moment on bar

$$M = 42{,}300\# \times 3\tfrac{1}{2}''$$

$$= 148{,}000 \text{ in.-lbs.}$$

resulting bending stress

$$\sigma = \frac{M}{S}$$

$$= \frac{(148{,}000)}{(8.25)}$$

$$= 18{,}000 \text{ psi}$$

At the center of the 3″ bar, the bolt loads are supported by tension and compression forces in the 1″ thick web plates above and below the bar. The web plates are attached to the column flange, opposite the column web, by welds that carry this moment and shear into the column.

The shear and moment caused by the anchor bolt forces, which are not in the plane of the weld, determine the size of the vertical welds. The welds extend 15″ above and 3″ below the 3″ transverse bar.

The properties and stresses on the vertical welds are figured on the basis of treating the welds as a line, having no width. See Figure 30.

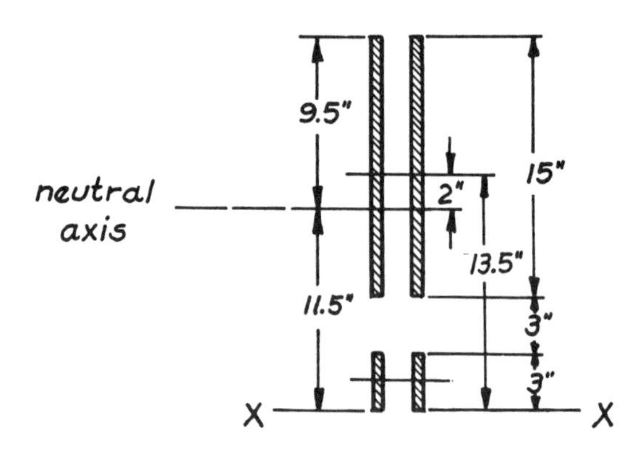

FIGURE 30

Take area moments about the base line (y-y):

	A	y	M	I_y	I_g
2 welds × 3″	6	1.5	9.0	13.5	4.5
2 welds × 15″	30	15.3	405.0	5467.5	562.5
Total	36		414.0	6048	

moment of inertia about N.A.

$$I_n = I_y + I_g - \frac{M^2}{A}$$

$$= (6048) - \frac{(414)^2}{(36)}$$

$$= 1288 \text{ in.}^3$$

$$n = \frac{M}{A}$$

$$= \frac{(414)}{(36)}$$

$$= 11.5'' \text{ (up from base line y-y)}$$

distance of N.A. from outer fiber

$$c_{bottom} = 11.5''$$

$$c_{top} = 9.5''$$

section modulus of weld

$$S_{bottom} = \frac{(1288)}{(11.5)}$$

$$= 112 \text{ in.}^2$$

$$S_{top} = \frac{(1288)}{(9.5)}$$

$$= 135.5 \text{ in.}^2$$

maximum bending force on weld

$$\text{(top) } f_b = \frac{M}{S_w}$$

$$= \frac{(84{,}600)(3)}{(135.5)}$$

$$= 1870 \text{ lbs/in.}$$

shear force on weld

$$f_s = \frac{V}{L_w}$$

$$= \frac{(84{,}600)}{(36)}$$

$$= 2340 \text{ lbs/in.}$$

resultant force on weld

$$f_r = \sqrt{f_b^2 + f_s^2}$$

$$= \sqrt{(1870)^2 + (2340)^2}$$

$$= 3000 \text{ lbs/in.}$$

required fillet weld size

$$\omega = \frac{3000}{11{,}200} \leftarrow \text{E70 allowable}$$

$$= .268'' \text{ or use } 5/16''$$

This requires continuous 5/16″ fillet welds on both sides for the full length of the 1″ vertical web plate. If greater weld strength had been required, the 1″ web plate could be made thicker or taller.

For bolts of ordinary size, the upper portion of the plates for this detail can be cut in one piece from column sections of 14″ flanges. This insures full continuity of the web-to-flange in tension for carrying the bolt loads. By welding across the top and bottom edges of the horizontal plate to the column flange, the required thickness of flange plate in bending is reduced by having support in two directions.

6. TYPICAL COLUMN BASES

In (a) of Figure 31, small brackets are groove butt

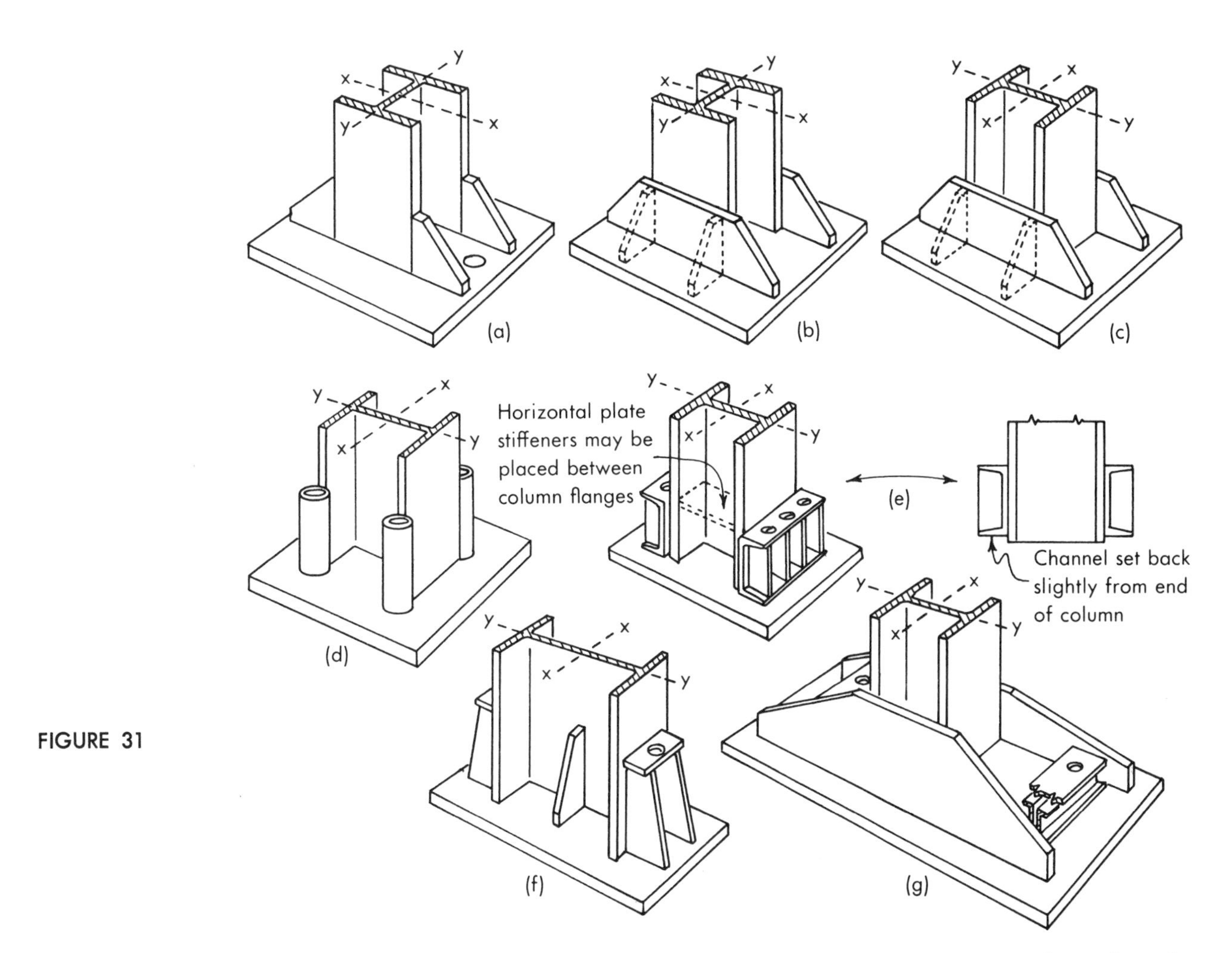

FIGURE 31

welded to the outer edges of the column flanges to develop greater moment resistance for the attachment to the base plate. This will help for moments about either the x-x or the y-y axis. A single bevel or single V joint is prepared by beveling just the edge of the brackets; no beveling is done on the column flanges.

For column flanges of nominal thickness, it might be easier to simply add two brackets, fillet welded to the base of the column; see (b) and (c). No beveling is required, and handling and assembling time is reduced because only two additional pieces are required.

In (b) the bracket plates are attached to the face of the column flange; in (c) the plates are attached to the outer edge of the column flange. In any rolled section used as a column, greater bending strength and stiffness is obtained about the x-x axis. If the moment is about the x-x axis, it would be better to attach the additional plates to the face of the column as in (b). This will provide a good transverse fillet across the column flange and two longitudinal fillet welds along the outer edge of the column flange with good accessibility for welding. The attaching plates and the welds connecting them to the base plate are in the most effective position and location to transfer this moment. The only slight drawback is that the attaching plates will not stiffen the overhung portion of the base plate for the bending due to tension in the hold-down bolts, or due to the upward bearing pressure of the masonry support. However if this is a problem, small brackets shown in dotted lines may be easily added.

The plates can be fillet welded to the outer edges of the column flange as in (c), although there is not good accessibility for the welds on the inside. Some of these inside fillet welds can be made before the unit is assembled to the base plate.

For thick flanges, detail (a) might represent the least amount of welding and additional plate material.

Short lengths of pipe have been welded to the outer edge of the column flange to develop the necessary moment for the hold-down bolts; see (d). The length and leg size of the attaching fillet welds are sufficient for the moment.

In (e) two channels with additional stiffeners are welded to the column flanges for the required moment from the hold-down bolts. By setting this channel assembly back slightly from the milled end of the column, it does not have to be designed for any bear-

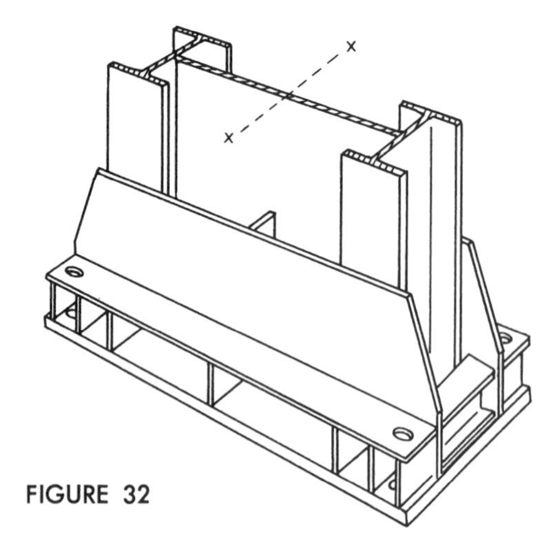
FIGURE 32

ing, but just the tension from the hold-down bolts. If this assembly is set flush with the end of the column and milled to bear, then this additional bearing load must be considered in its design. Any vertical tensile load on the assembly from the holddown bolts, or vertical bearing load from the base plate (if in contact), will produce a horizontal force at the top which will be applied transverse to the column flange. If the column flange is too thin, then horizontal plate stiffeners must be added between the column flanges to effectively transfer this force. These stiffeners are shown in (e) by dotted lines.

In (f) built-up, hold-down bolt supports are welded to the column flanges. These may be designed to any size for any value of moment.

In (g), the attaching plates have been extended out farther for very high moments. This particular detail uses a pair of channels with a top plate for the hold-down bolts to transfer this tensile force back to the main attaching plates, and in turn back to the column.

One of the many possible details for the base of a built-up crane runway girder column in a steel mill is shown in Figure 32. Two large attaching plates are fillet welded to the flanges of the rolled sections of the column. This is welded to a thick base plate. Two long narrow plates are next welded into the assembly, with spacers or small diaphragms separating them from the base plate. This provides additional strength and stiffness of the base plate through beam action for the forces from the hold-down bolts. Short sections of I beam can also be welded across the ends between the attaching plates.

7. HIGH-RISE REQUIREMENTS

Columns for high-rise buildings may use brackets on their base plates to help distribute the column load out over the larger area of the base plate to the masonry support.

Problem 6

A 14″ WF 426# column of A36 steel is to carry a compressive load of 2,000 kips. Using a bearing load of 750 psi, this would require a 50″ × 60″ base plate. Use E70 welds.

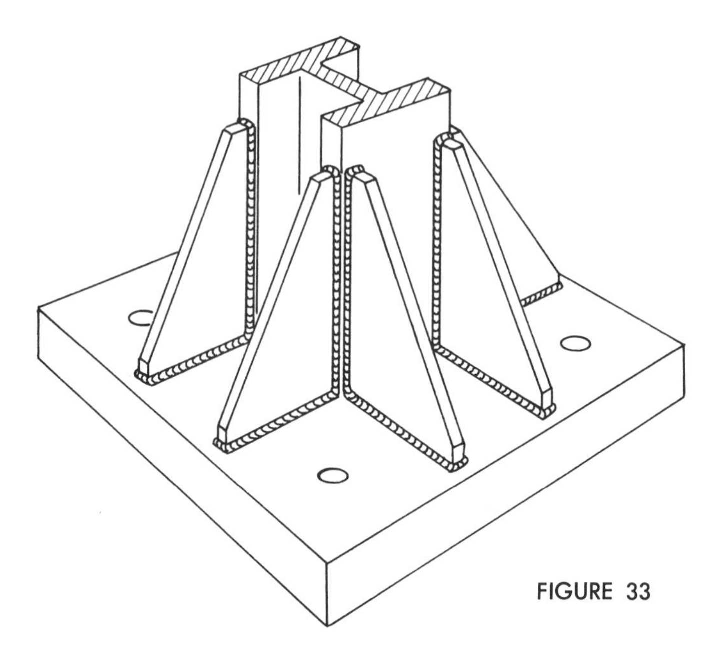
FIGURE 33

For simplicity, each set of brackets together with a portion of the base plate formed by a diagonal line from the outer corner of the plate back to the column flange, will be assumed to resist the bearing pressure of the masonry support; see Figure 34. This is a conservative analysis because the base plate is not cut along these lines and these portions do not act independently of each other.

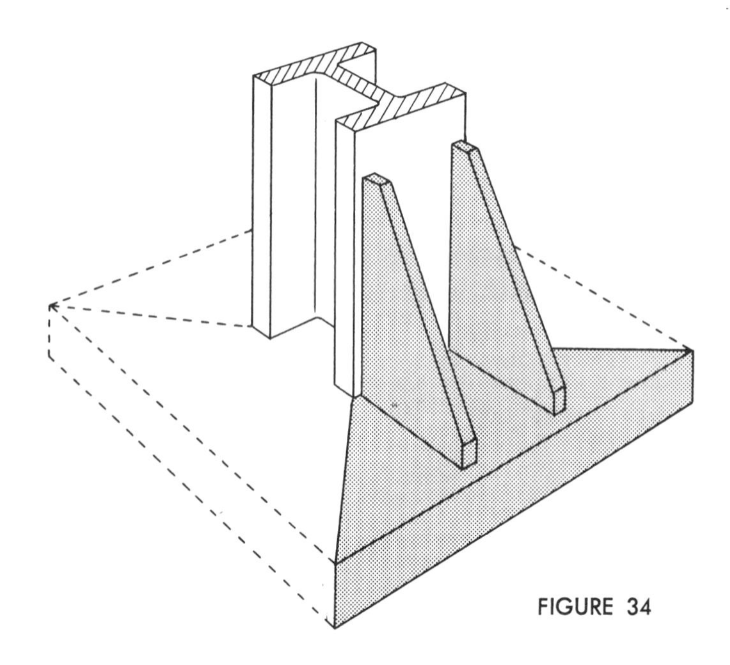
FIGURE 34

This portion of the assembly occupies a trapezoidal area; Figure 35.

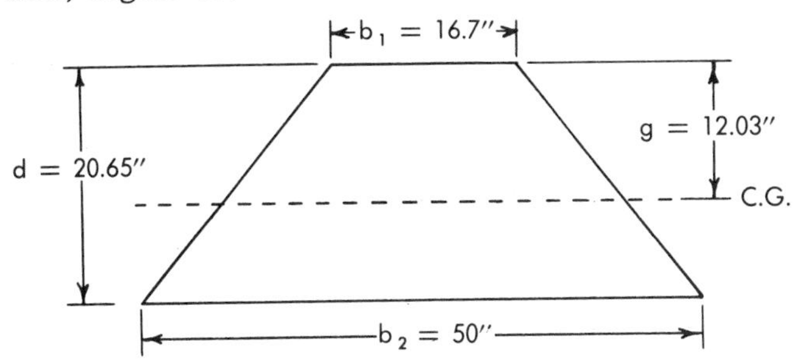

FIGURE 35

$$g = \frac{d(b_1 + 2\ b_2)}{3(b_1 + b_2)}$$

$$= \frac{20.65\ (16.7 + 2 \times 50)}{3\ (16.7 + 50)}$$

$$= 12.03''$$

$$A = (b_1 + b_2)\frac{d}{2}$$

$$= (16.7 + 50)\ \frac{20.65}{2}$$

$$= 690\ \text{in.}^2$$

$$P = A\ \sigma$$

$$= (690\ \text{in.}^2)(750\ \text{psi})$$

$$= 516\ \text{kips}$$

$$M = P\ g$$

$$= (516^k)(12.03'')$$

$$= 6.225\ \text{in.-kips}$$

Determining thickness of base plate

To get an idea of the thickness of the base plate (t), consider a 1" wide strip as a uniformly loaded, continuous beam supported at two points (the brackets) and overhanging at each end. See Figure 36.

From beam formula #6Bb in Section 8.1:

$$M_{max}\ (\text{at support}) = \frac{-w\ a^2}{2}$$

$$= \frac{-(750)(18.4)^2}{2}$$

$$= -126{,}500\ \text{in.-lbs}$$

Since:

$$M = \sigma\ S$$

$$S = \frac{M}{\sigma} \qquad = \frac{1''\ t^2}{6}$$

or:

$$t = \sqrt{\frac{6\ M}{\sigma}}$$

where: $\sigma = .75\ \sigma_y$ (AISC 1.5.1.4.8)

$$= \sqrt{\frac{6(126{,}500)}{(25{,}000)}}$$

$$= \sqrt{30.4}$$

$$= 5.51''\ \text{or use 6''-thick plate}$$

Check bending stresses & shear stresses in base plate bracket section

Start with 1½"-thick brackets (2 × 1½" = 3" flange thickness) at right angles to face of column flange. Find moment of inertia of the vertical section through brackets and base plate, Figure 37, using the method of adding areas:

	A	y	M	I_y	I_g
16.7" × 6"	100.2	+ 3	300.6	902	301
3" × 24"	72.0	+ 18	1296.0	23,328	3456
Total	172.2		1596.6	27,990	

moment of inertia about N.A.

$$I_n = I_y + I_g - \frac{M^2}{A}$$

$$= (27{,}990) - \frac{(1596.6)^2}{(172.2)}$$

$$= 13{,}190\ \text{in.}^4$$

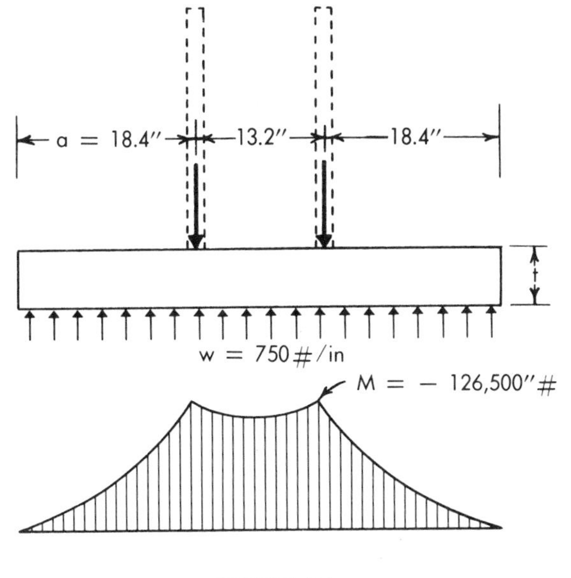

FIGURE 36

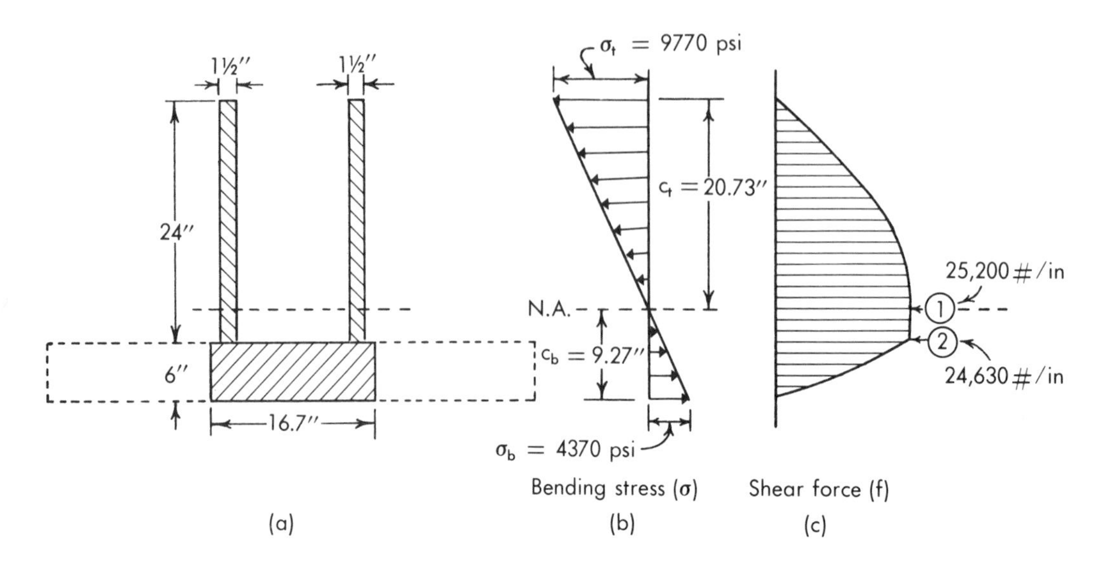

FIGURE 37

$$n = \frac{M}{A}$$

$$= \frac{(1596.6)}{(172.2)}$$

$$= 9.27''$$

distance of N.A. to outer fiber

$$c_b = 9.27''$$

$$c_t = 30'' - 9.27''$$

$$= 20.73''$$

bending stresses

$$\sigma_b = \frac{M\ c_b}{I}$$

$$= \frac{(6225)(9.27)}{(13{,}190)}$$

$$= 4370 \text{ psi}$$

$$\sigma_t = \frac{M\ c_t}{I}$$

$$= \frac{(6225)(20.73)}{(13{,}190)}$$

$$= 9770 \text{ psi} \quad \underline{\text{OK}}$$

maximum shear force at neutral axis

$$f_1 = \frac{V\ a\ y}{I}$$

$$= \frac{(516.5^k)(3'' \times 20.73'')(10.37'')}{(13{,}190)}$$

$$= 25{,}200 \text{ lbs/in.}$$

corresponding shear stress in brackets

$$\tau = \frac{f}{t}$$

$$= \frac{(25{,}200 \text{ lbs/in.})}{(3'')}$$

$$= 8400 \text{ psi} \quad \underline{\text{OK}}$$

shear force at face of 6″ base plate
(to be transferred through fillet welds)

$$f_2 = \frac{V\ a\ y}{I}$$

$$= \frac{(516.5^k)(6'' \times 16.7'')(6.27'')}{(13{,}190)}$$

$$= 24{,}630 \text{ lbs/in.}$$ (to be carried by four fillet welds at 1½″ thick brackets)

leg size of each fillet weld joining base plate to brackets

$$\omega = \frac{\frac{1}{4}\ (24{,}630)}{(11{,}200)}$$ ← E70 allowable

$$= .545'' \text{ or use } \tfrac{9}{16}''$$ ◺

(The minimum fillet weld leg size for 6″ plate is ½″ ◺ .)

Determining vertical weld requirements

In determining fillet weld sizes on the usual beam seat bracket, it is often assumed that the shear reaction is uniformly distributed along the vertical length of the bracket. The two unit forces resulting from shear and bending are then resolved together (vectorially added), and the resultant force is then divided by the allowable force for the fillet weld to give the weld size. This is of course conservative, because the maximum unit bending force does not occur on the fillet weld at the same region as does the maximum unit shear force. However the analysis does not take long:

bending force on weld

$$f_b = \sigma\ t$$
$$= (9770\ psi)(1½'')$$
$$= 14{,}660\ lbs/in.\ \text{(one bracket and two fillet welds)}$$

or

$$= 7330\ lbs/in.\ \text{(one fillet weld)}$$

vertical shear force on weld
(assuming uniform distribution)

$$f_s = \frac{516.5^k}{4 \times 30''}$$
$$= 4310\ lbs/in.$$

resultant force on weld

$$f_r = \sqrt{f_b^2 + f_s^2}$$
$$= \sqrt{(7330)^2 + (4310)^2}$$
$$= 8500\ lbs/in.$$

required leg size of vertical fillet weld

$$\omega = \frac{\text{actual force}}{\text{allowable force}}$$
$$= \frac{(8500)}{(11{,}200)}$$
$$= .758''\ \text{or}\ \underline{\text{use}\ ¾''}$$

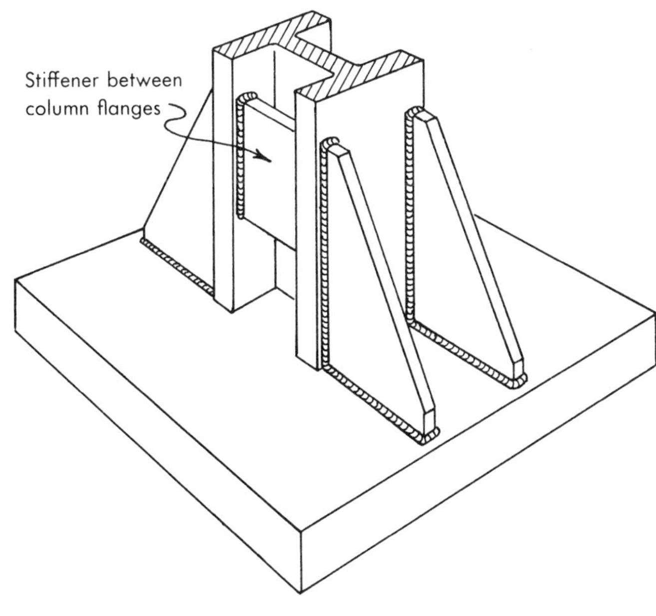

FIGURE 38

Alternate method. In cases where the forces are high, and the requirement for welding is greater, it would be well to look further into the analysis in order to reduce the amount of welding.

In Figure 37, it is seen that the maximum unit force on the vertical weld due to bending moment occurs at the top of the bracket connection (b) in a region of very low shear transfer. Likewise the maximum unit shear force occurs in a region of low bending moment (c). In the following analysis, the weld size is determined both for bending and for shear, and the larger of these two values are used:

vertical shear requirement
(maximum condition at N.A.)

$$f_1 = 25{,}200\ lbs/in.$$

to be carried by four fillet welds.

$$\omega = \frac{\text{actual force}}{\text{allowable force}}$$
$$= \frac{¼\ (25{,}200)}{(11{,}200)}$$
$$= .562''\ \text{or}\ 9/16''$$

bending requirement
(maximum condition at top of bracket)

$$f_b = 7330\ lbs/in.$$

$$\omega = \frac{\text{actual force}}{\text{allowable force}}$$
$$= \frac{(7330)}{(11{,}200)}$$
$$= .654''\ \text{or}\ ¾''$$

Hence use the larger of the two, or ¾" fillet welds. Although this alternate method required a slightly smaller fillet weld (.654") as against (.758"), they both ended up at ¾" when they were rounded off. So, in this particular example, there was no saving in using this method.

Column stiffeners

A rather high compressive force in the top portion of these brackets is applied horizontally to the column flange. It would be well to add stiffeners between the column flanges to transfer this force from one bracket through the column to the opposite column flange; Figure 38.

It might be argued that, if the brackets are milled to bear against the column flanges, the bearing area may then be considered to carry the compressive horizontal force between the bracket and the column flange. Also, the connecting welds may then be considered to

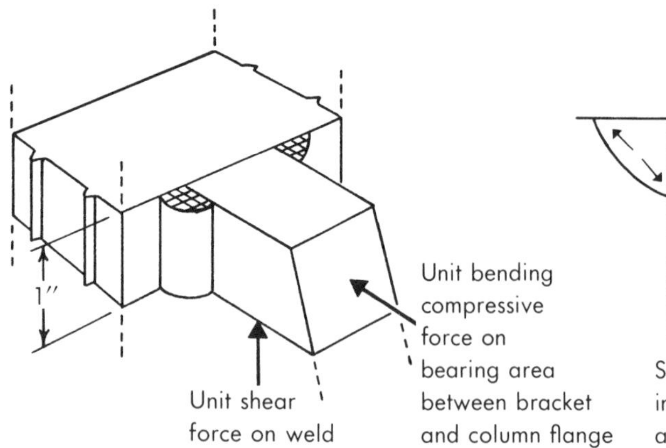

FIGURE 39

carry only the vertical shear forces. See Figure 39, left.

If the designer questions whether the weld would load up in compression along with the bearing area of the bracket, it should be remembered that weld shrinkage will slightly prestress the weld in tension and the end of the bracket within the weld region in compression. See Figure 39, right. As the horizontal compression is applied, the weld must first unload in tension before it would be loaded in compression. In the meantime, the bracket bearing area continues to load up in compression.

This is very similar to standard practice in welded plate girder design. Even though the web is not milled along its edge, it is fitted tight to the flange and simple fillet welds join the two. In almost all cases, these welds are designed just for the shear transfer (parallel to the weld) between the web and the flange; any distributed floor load is assumed to transfer down through the flange (transverse to the weld) into the edge of the web which is in contact with the flange. Designers believe that even if this transverse force is transferred through the weld, it does not lower the capacity of the fillet weld to transfer the shear forces.

Refer to Figure 37(b) and notice that the bending action provides a horizontal compressive force on the vertical connecting welds along almost their entire length. Only a very small length of the welds near the base plate is subjected to horizontal tension, and these forces are very small. The maximum tensile forces occur within the base plate, which has no connecting welds.

shear force on vertical weld
(assuming uniform distribution)

$$f_s = \frac{516.5^k}{4 \times 30''}$$

$$= 4310 \text{ lbs/in. (one weld)}$$

vertical weld size
(assuming it to transfer shear force only)

$$\omega = \frac{\text{actual force}}{\text{allowable force}}$$

$$= \frac{(4310)}{(11{,}200)}$$

$$= .385''$$

but 3″ thick column flange would require a minimum ½″ ◺ (Table 2, Sect. 7.4).

If partial-penetration groove welds are used (assuming a tight fit) the following applies:

allowables (E70 welds)

compression: same as plate

shear: $\tau = 15{,}800$ psi

shear force on one weld

$$f_s = 4310 \text{ lbs/in.}$$

required effective throat

$$t_e = \frac{f_s}{\tau}$$

$$= \frac{(4310)}{(15{,}800)}$$

$$= .273''$$

if using bevel joint

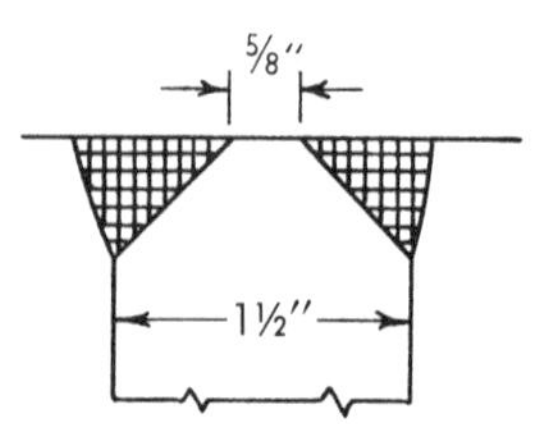

$$t = t_e + \tfrac{1}{8}''$$

$$= .273'' + \tfrac{1}{8}''$$

$$= .398''$$

$$\text{root face (land)} = 1\tfrac{1}{2}'' - 2(.398'')$$

$$= .704'' \text{ or } \underline{\text{use } \tfrac{5}{8}''}$$

if using J joint

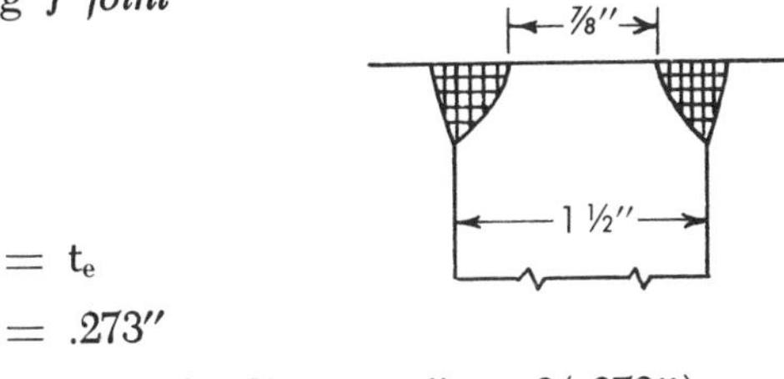

$t = t_e$

$= .273''$

root face (land) $= 1\frac{1}{2}'' - 2(.273'')$

$= .954''$ or use $\frac{7}{8}''$

A portion of the shear transfer represented by the shear force distribution in Figure 37 (c) lies below a line through the top surface of the base plate. It might be reasoned that this portion would be carried by the base plate and not the vertical connecting welds between the bracket and the column flange. If so, this triangular area would approximately represent a shear force of

$\frac{1}{2}$ (24,630#/in.) 6" $= 73.9^k$

to be deducted:

$516.5^k - 73.9^k = 442.6^k$

$$f = \frac{442.6^k}{4 \times 30''} = 3690 \text{ lbs/in.}$$

$$\omega = \frac{3690}{11{,}200} = .33'' \text{ or } \frac{3}{8}''$$

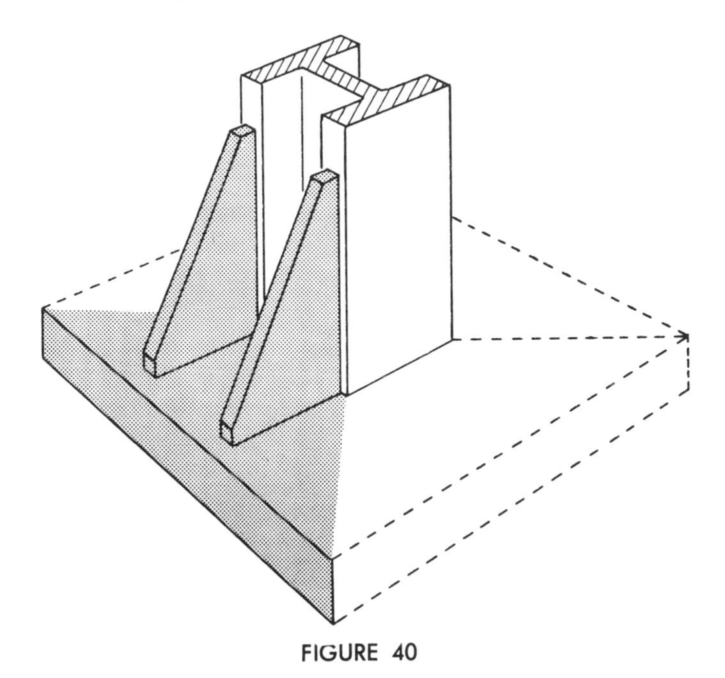

FIGURE 40

However, in this example, the column flange thickness of 3" would require a ½" fillet weld to be used.

Brackets to column flange edges

The base section consisting of the brackets attached to the edge of the column flanges, Figure 40, is now considered in a similar manner. From this similar analysis, the brackets will be made of 1¼"-thick plate.

Figure 41 shows the resulting column base detail.

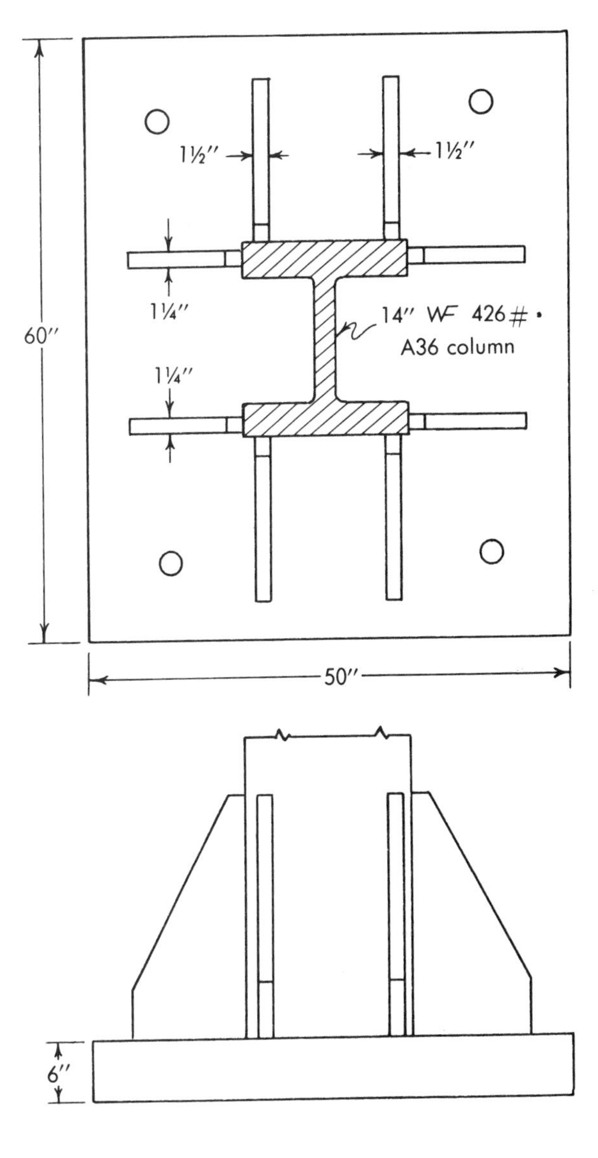

FIGURE 41

COLUMN BASE PLATE DIMENSIONS (AISC, 1963)

COLUMN BASE PLATES

Dimensions for maximum column loads

For A36 Columns

Base plates, ASTM A36, F_b = 27 ksi
Concrete, f'_c = 3000 psi

Column			Unit Pressure on Support $F_p = 0.25 f'_c$ = 750 psi						Unit Pressure on Support $F_p = 0.375 f'_c$ = 1125 psi					
Nom. Size & Designation	Wt. per Ft.	Max. Load	Dimensions		Thickness of Plate			Gross Wt.	Dimensions		Thickness of Plate			Gross Wt.
			B	C	Calc.	Fin.	Rolled		B	C	Calc.	Fin.	Rolled	
In.	Lb.	Kips	In.	In.	In.	In.	In.	Lb.	In.	In.	In.	In.	In.	Lb.
14 × 16 WF	426	2605	57	61	6.30	6¼	6¾	6649	46	51	5.84	5⅞	6¼	4154
	398	2433	55	59	6.02	6	6½	5976	45	49	5.56	5⅝	6	3748
	370	2261	53	57	5.76	5¾	6¼	5349	43	47	5.28	5¼	5⅝	3221
	342	2090	51	55	5.51	5½	5⅞	4669	41	46	5.14	5⅛	5½	2939
	320	1954	50	53	5.30	5¼	5⅝	4223	40	44	4.92	5	5⅜	2680
	314	1917	49	53	5.25	5¼	5⅝	4138	40	43	4.75	4¾	5⅛	2497
	287	1752	47	50	4.91	5	5⅜	3578	38	41	4.44	4½	4⅞	2152
	264	1611	45	48	4.65	4⅝	5	3060	36	40	4.29	4¼	4⅝	1887
	246	1501	44	46	4.48	4½	4⅞	2795	36	38	4.06	4⅛	4½	1744
	237	1446	43	45	4.36	4⅜	4¾	2604	35	37	3.92	4	4	1467
	228	1391	42	45	4.26	4¼	4⅝	2476	34	37	3.82	3⅞	3⅞	1381
	219	1335	41	44	4.15	4⅛	4½	2300	33	36	3.70	3¾	3¾	1262
	211	1287	40	43	4.04	4	4	1949	33	35	3.58	3⅝	3⅝	1186
	202	1231	40	42	3.91	4	4	1904	32	35	3.52	3½	3½	1111
	193	1176	39	41	3.78	3¾	3¾	1699	31	34	3.39	3⅜	3⅜	1008
	184	1121	38	40	3.65	3⅝	3⅝	1561	31	33	3.22	3¼	3¼	942
	176	1072	37	39	3.52	3½	3½	1431	30	32	3.08	3⅛	3⅛	850
	167	1017	36	38	3.40	3⅜	3⅜	1308	29	32	3.08	3⅛	3⅛	822
	158	963	35	37	3.27	3¼	3¼	1192	28	31	2.94	3	3	738
	150	913	34	36	3.15	3⅛	3⅛	1084	28	29	2.76	2¾	2¾	633
	142	867	33	36	3.13	3⅛	3⅛	1052	27	29	2.63	2⅝	2⅝	582
14 × 14½ WF	136	826	32	35	3.00	3	3	952	26	29	2.61	2⅝	2⅝	561
	127	771	31	34	2.87	2⅞	2⅞	858	25	28	2.47	2½	2½	496
	119	722	30	33	2.74	2¾	2¾	771	24	27	2.33	2⅜	2⅜	436
	111	674	29	31	2.50	2½	2½	637	24	25	2.17	2¼	2¼	382
	103	625	28	30	2.37	2⅜	2⅜	565	23	25	1.99	2	2	326
	95	577	27	29	2.23	2¼	2¼	499	22	24	1.84	1⅞	1⅞	280
	87	527	26	28	2.09	2⅛	2⅛	438	21	23	1.69	1¾	1¾	239
14 × 12 WF	84	503	24	28	2.10	2⅛	2⅛	405	20	23	1.81	1⅞	1⅞	244
	78	467	24	26	2.08	2⅛	2⅛	376	19	22	1.66	1¾	1¾	207
14 × 10 WF	74	435	22	27	1.99	2	2	337	17	23	1.67	1¾	1¾	194
	68	400	21	26	1.85	1⅞	1⅞	290	17	21	1.58	1⅝	1⅝	164
	61	359	20	24	1.73	1¾	1¾	238	16	20	1.41	1½	1½	136
14 × 8 WF	53	302	17	24	1.54	1⅝	1⅝	188	13	21	1.36	1⅜	1⅜	106
	48	273	16	23	1.42	1½	1½	156	13	19	1.15	1¼	1¼	87
	43	245	15	22	1.29	1⅜	1⅜	129	12	19	1.04	1⅛	1⅛	73

Note: Rolled plate thicknesses above 4 inches are based on finished thickness plus suggested allowances for finishing one side, and may be modified to suit fabricating plant practice. When it is required to finish both surfaces of base plates, additional allowance must be made.

American Institute of Steel Construction

—This and following tables presented here by courtesy of American Institute of Steel Construction.

For A36 Columns

COLUMN BASE PLATES

Dimensions for maximum column loads

Base plates, ASTM A36, F_b = 27 ksi
Concrete, f'_c = 3000 psi

Column			Unit Pressure on Support $F_p = 0.25 f'_c$ = 750 psi						Unit Pressure on Support $F_p = 0.375 f'_c$ = 1125 psi					
Nom. Size & Designation	Wt. per Ft.	Max. Load	Dimensions		Thickness of Plate			Gross Wt.	Dimensions		Thickness of Plate			Gross Wt.
			B	C	Calc.	Fin.	Rolled		B	C	Calc.	Fin.	Rolled	
In.	Lb.	Kips	In.	In.	In.	In.	In.	Lb.	In.	In.	In.	In.	In.	Lb.
12 × 12 WF	190	1143	38	41	3.97	4	4	1766	30	34	3.59	3⅝	3⅝	1048
	161	969	34	38	3.58	3⅝	3⅝	1327	28	31	3.17	3¼	3¼	799
	133	799	31	35	3.19	3¼	3¼	999	25	29	2.85	2⅞	2⅞	591
	120	721	30	33	2.92	3	3	841	24	27	2.56	2⅝	2⅝	482
	106	636	28	31	2.68	2¾	2¾	676	23	25	2.32	2⅜	2⅜	387
	99	593	27	30	2.55	2⅝	2⅝	602	22	24	2.16	2¼	2¼	337
	92	552	26	29	2.43	2½	2½	534	21	24	2.10	2⅛	2⅛	303
	85	509	25	28	2.29	2⅜	2⅜	471	20	23	1.95	2	2	261
	79	473	24	27	2.17	2¼	2¼	413	20	22	1.79	1⅞	1⅞	234
	72	431	23	25	1.93	2	2	326	19	21	1.62	1⅝	1⅝	184
	65	389	22	24	1.79	1⅞	1⅞	280	18	20	1.47	1½	1½	153
12 × 10 WF	58	342	19	24	1.79	1⅞	1⅞	242	16	19	1.41	1½	1½	129
	53	312	19	22	1.58	1⅝	1⅝	192	15	19	1.32	1⅜	1⅜	111
12 × 8 WF	50	286	17	23	1.63	1⅝	1⅝	180	13	20	1.47	1½	1½	110
	45	257	16	22	1.50	1½	1½	150	13	18	1.15	1¼	1¼	83
	40	229	15	21	1.37	1⅜	1⅜	123	12	17	1.00	1	1	58
10 × 10 WF	112	663	28	32	3.04	3	3	762	23	26	2.67	2¾	2¾	466
	100	593	27	30	2.77	2¾	2¾	631	22	24	2.42	2½	2½	374
	89	527	26	28	2.52	2½	2½	516	21	23	2.23	2¼	2¼	308
	77	456	24	26	2.27	2¼	2¼	398	19	22	2.07	2⅛	2⅛	252
	72	426	23	25	2.16	2¼	2¼	367	19	20	1.92	2	2	215
	66	390	22	24	2.03	2	2	299	18	20	1.76	1¾	1¾	178
	60	355	21	23	1.90	2	2	274	17	19	1.62	1⅝	1⅝	149
	54	319	20	22	1.76	1¾	1¾	218	16	18	1.47	1½	1½	122
	49	289	19	21	1.63	1⅝	1⅝	184	15	18	1.47	1½	1½	115
10 × 8 WF	45	258	17	21	1.61	1⅝	1⅝	164	13	18	1.47	1½	1½	99
	39	224	16	19	1.38	1⅜	1⅜	118	13	16	1.14	1¼	1¼	74
	33	189	14	18	1.26	1¼	1¼	89	12	14	1.00	1	1	48
8 × 8 WF	67	387	22	24	2.21	2¼	2¼	337	18	20	1.98	2	2	204
	58	335	21	22	2.05	2⅛	2⅛	278	17	18	1.82	1⅞	1⅞	163
	48	277	18	21	1.84	1⅞	1⅞	201	15	17	1.55	1⅝	1⅝	117
	40	230	17	19	1.57	1⅝	1⅝	149	13	16	1.43	1½	1½	88
	35	201	15	18	1.48	1½	1½	115	12	15	1.28	1⅜	1⅜	70
	31	178	14	17	1.36	1⅜	1⅜	93	12	14	1.10	1⅛	1⅛	54
8 × 6½ WF	28	155	13	16	1.20	1¼	1¼	74	10	14	1.11	1⅛	1⅛	45
	24	133	12	15	1.07	1⅛	1⅛	57	10	12	.84	⅞	⅞	30
8 × 5¼ WF	20	102	10	14	.89	1	1	40	8	12	.73	¾	¾	20
	17	86	9	13	.77	⅞	⅞	29	7	11	.60	⅝	⅝	14

American Institute of Steel Construction

COLUMN BASE PLATE DIMENSIONS (AISC, 1963)

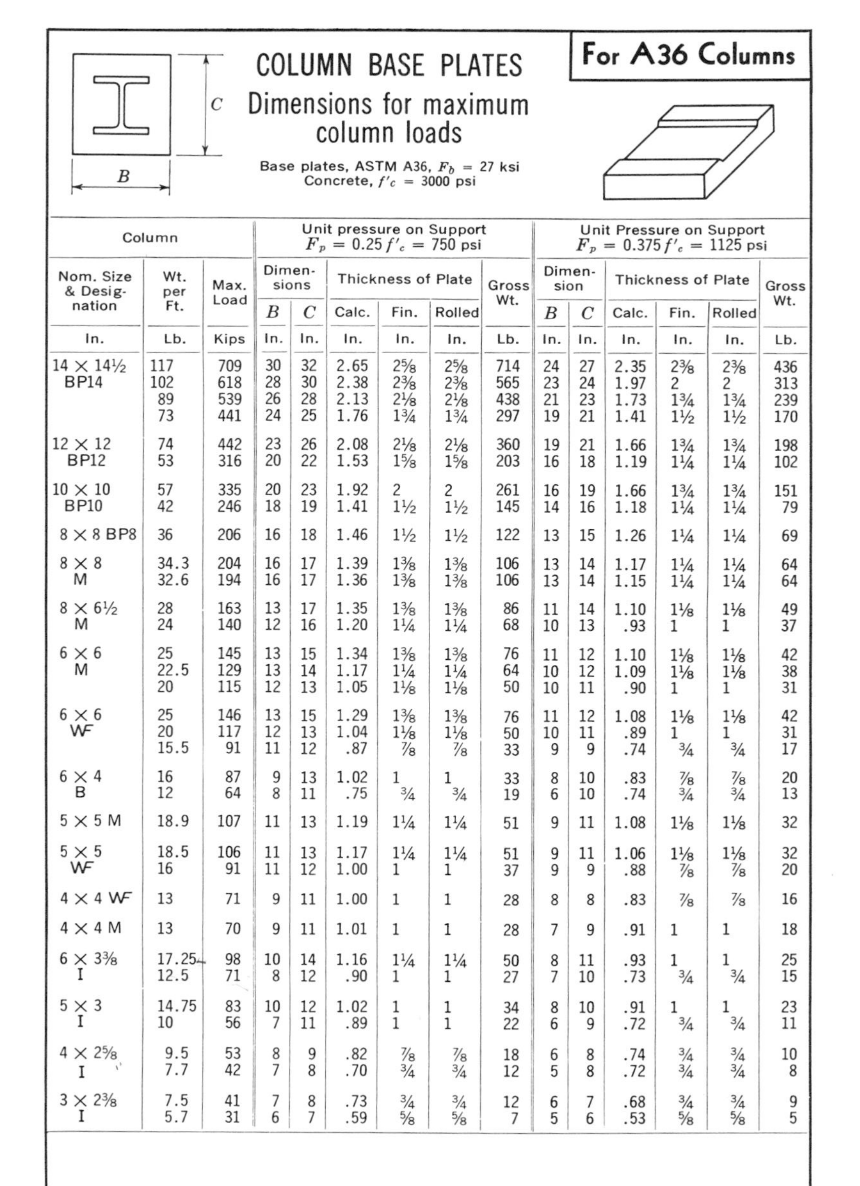

COLUMN BASE PLATES

Dimensions for maximum column loads

For A36 Columns

Base plates, ASTM A36, $F_b = 27$ ksi
Concrete, $f'_c = 3000$ psi

Column			Unit pressure on Support $F_p = 0.25 f'_c = 750$ psi						Unit Pressure on Support $F_p = 0.375 f'_c = 1125$ psi					
Nom. Size & Designation	Wt. per Ft.	Max. Load	Dimensions		Thickness of Plate			Gross Wt.	Dimension		Thickness of Plate			Gross Wt.
			B	C	Calc.	Fin.	Rolled		B	C	Calc.	Fin.	Rolled	
In.	Lb.	Kips	In.	In.	In.	In.	In.	Lb.	In.	In.	In.	In.	In.	Lb.
14 × 14½ BP14	117	709	30	32	2.65	2⅝	2⅝	714	24	27	2.35	2⅜	2⅜	436
	102	618	28	30	2.38	2⅜	2⅜	565	23	24	1.97	2	2	313
	89	539	26	28	2.13	2⅛	2⅛	438	21	23	1.73	1¾	1¾	239
	73	441	24	25	1.76	1¾	1¾	297	19	21	1.41	1½	1½	170
12 × 12 BP12	74	442	23	26	2.08	2⅛	2⅛	360	19	21	1.66	1¾	1¾	198
	53	316	20	22	1.53	1⅝	1⅝	203	16	18	1.19	1¼	1¼	102
10 × 10 BP10	57	335	20	23	1.92	2	2	261	16	19	1.66	1¾	1¾	151
	42	246	18	19	1.41	1½	1½	145	14	16	1.18	1¼	1¼	79
8 × 8 BP8	36	206	16	18	1.46	1½	1½	122	13	15	1.26	1¼	1¼	69
8 × 8 M	34.3	204	16	17	1.39	1⅜	1⅜	106	13	14	1.17	1¼	1¼	64
	32.6	194	16	17	1.36	1⅜	1⅜	106	13	14	1.15	1¼	1¼	64
8 × 6½ M	28	163	13	17	1.35	1⅜	1⅜	86	11	14	1.10	1⅛	1⅛	49
	24	140	12	16	1.20	1¼	1¼	68	10	13	.93	1	1	37
6 × 6 M	25	145	13	15	1.34	1⅜	1⅜	76	11	12	1.10	1⅛	1⅛	42
	22.5	129	13	14	1.17	1¼	1¼	64	10	12	1.09	1⅛	1⅛	38
	20	115	12	13	1.05	1⅛	1⅛	50	10	11	.90	1	1	31
6 × 6 WF	25	146	13	15	1.29	1⅜	1⅜	76	11	12	1.08	1⅛	1⅛	42
	20	117	12	13	1.04	1⅛	1⅛	50	10	11	.89	1	1	31
	15.5	91	11	12	.87	⅞	⅞	33	9	9	.74	¾	¾	17
6 × 4 B	16	87	9	13	1.02	1	1	33	8	10	.83	⅞	⅞	20
	12	64	8	11	.75	¾	¾	19	6	10	.74	¾	¾	13
5 × 5 M	18.9	107	11	13	1.19	1¼	1¼	51	9	11	1.08	1⅛	1⅛	32
5 × 5 WF	18.5	106	11	13	1.17	1¼	1¼	51	9	11	1.06	1⅛	1⅛	32
	16	91	11	12	1.00	1	1	37	9	9	.88	⅞	⅞	20
4 × 4 WF	13	71	9	11	1.00	1	1	28	8	8	.83	⅞	⅞	16
4 × 4 M	13	70	9	11	1.01	1	1	28	7	9	.91	1	1	18
6 × 3⅜ I	17.25	98	10	14	1.16	1¼	1¼	50	8	11	.93	1	1	25
	12.5	71	8	12	.90	1	1	27	7	10	.73	¾	¾	15
5 × 3 I	14.75	83	10	12	1.02	1	1	34	8	10	.91	1	1	23
	10	56	7	11	.89	1	1	22	6	9	.72	¾	¾	11
4 × 2⅝ I	9.5	53	8	9	.82	⅞	⅞	18	6	8	.74	¾	¾	10
	7.7	42	7	8	.70	¾	¾	12	5	8	.72	¾	¾	8
3 × 2⅜ I	7.5	41	7	8	.73	¾	¾	12	6	7	.68	¾	¾	9
	5.7	31	6	7	.59	⅝	⅝	7	5	6	.53	⅝	⅝	5

COLUMN BASE PLATES

Dimensions for maximum column loads

For A242-A440-A441 Columns

Base plates, ASTM A36, $F_b = 27$ ksi
Concrete, $f'_c = 3000$ psi

Column			Unit Pressure on Support $F_p = 0.25 f'_c = 750$ psi						Unit Pressure on Support $F_p = 0.375 f'_c = 1125$ psi					
Nom. Size & Designation	Wt. per Ft.	Max. Load	Dimensions		Thickness of Plate			Gross Wt.	Dimensions		Thickness of Plate			Gross Wt.
			B	C	Calc.	Fin.	Rolled		B	C	Calc.	Fin.	Rolled	
In.	Lb.	Kips	In.	In.	In.	In.	In.	Lb.	In.	In.	In.	In.	In.	Lb.
14 × 16 WF	426	3028	61	67	7.07	7	7½	8684	49	55	6.58	6⅝	7	5344
	398	2827	59	64	6.72	6¾	7¼	7756	48	53	6.26	6¼	6¾	4865
	370	2628	57	62	6.46	6½	7	7008	46	51	5.99	6	6½	4320
	342	2429	55	59	6.10	6⅛	6½	5976	45	48	5.64	5⅝	6	3672
	320	2271	54	57	5.87	5⅞	6¼	5450	43	47	5.48	5½	5⅞	3364
	314	2228	53	57	5.82	5⅞	6¼	5349	43	47	5.37	5⅜	5¾	3292
	287	2036	51	54	5.46	5½	5⅞	4584	41	45	5.08	5⅛	5½	2875
	264	1872	48	52	5.24	5¼	5⅝	3978	39	43	4.81	4⅞	5¼	2494
	246	1744	47	50	4.96	5	5⅜	3578	38	41	4.51	4½	4⅞	2152
	237	1680	46	49	4.85	4⅞	5¼	3352	38	40	4.43	4½	4⅞	2099
	228	1616	45	48	4.73	4¾	5⅛	3136	37	39	4.29	4¼	4⅝	1891
	219	1551	44	47	4.61	4⅝	5	2929	36	39	4.19	4¼	4⅝	1840
	211	1634	46	48	4.78	4¾	5⅛	3206	37	40	4.39	4⅜	4¾	1992
	202	1563	45	47	4.64	4⅝	5	2996	36	39	4.25	4¼	4⅝	1840
	193	1493	44	46	4.50	4½	4⅞	2795	35	38	4.11	4⅛	4½	1696
	184	1423	43	45	4.36	4⅜	4¾	2604	35	37	3.93	4	4	1467
	176	1361	42	44	4.22	4¼	4⅝	2421	34	36	3.78	3¾	3¾	1300
	167	1291	41	42	4.12	4⅛	4½	2195	33	35	3.64	3⅝	3⅝	1186
	158	1222	39	42	4.00	4	4	1856	32	34	3.49	3½	3½	1079
	150	1159	38	41	3.86	3⅞	3⅞	1710	31	34	3.47	3½	3½	1045
	142	1100	37	40	3.73	3¾	3¾	1572	30	33	3.34	3⅜	3⅜	947
14 × 14½ WF	136	1135	38	40	3.77	3¾	3¾	1615	31	33	3.37	3⅜	3⅜	978
	127	1060	37	39	3.61	3⅝	3⅝	1482	30	32	3.20	3¼	3¼	884
	119	993	35	38	3.49	3½	3½	1319	29	31	3.03	3	3	764
	111	926	34	37	3.34	3⅜	3⅜	1203	28	30	2.86	2⅞	2⅞	684
	103	858	33	35	3.08	3⅛	3⅛	1023	27	29	2.70	2¾	2¾	610
	95	792	32	33	2.94	3	3	897	26	28	2.54	2⅝	2⅝	541
	87	725	31	32	2.76	2¾	2¾	773	25	26	2.36	2⅜	2⅜	437
14 × 12 WF	84	689	29	32	2.78	2¾	2¾	723	23	27	2.38	2⅜	2⅜	418
	78	639	28	31	2.63	2⅝	2⅝	645	22	26	2.23	2¼	2¼	365
14 × 10 WF	74	593	26	31	2.57	2⅝	2⅝	599	21	26	2.25	2¼	2¼	348
	68	545	25	30	2.41	2½	2½	531	20	25	2.08	2⅛	2⅛	301
	61	488	23	29	2.25	2¼	2¼	425	19	23	1.94	2	2	248
14 × 8 WF	53	408	20	28	2.10	2⅛	2⅛	337	16	23	1.71	1¾	1¾	182
	48	369	19	26	1.86	1⅞	1⅞	262	15	22	1.57	1⅝	1⅝	152
	43	330	18	25	1.71	1¾	1¾	223	14	21	1.41	1½	1½	125

Note: Rolled plate thicknesses above 4 inches are based on finished thickness plus suggested allowances for finishing one side, and may be modified to suit fabricating plant practice. When it is required to finish both surfaces of base plates, additional allowance must be made.

COLUMN BASE PLATE DIMENSIONS (AISC, 1963)

For A242-A440-A441 Columns

COLUMN BASE PLATES
Dimensions for maximum column loads

Base plates, ASTM A36, $F_b = 27$ ksi
Concrete, $f'_c = 3000$ psi

Column			Unit Pressure on Support $F_p = 0.25 f'_c = 750$ psi						Unit Pressure on Support $F_p = 0.375 f'_c = 1125$ psi					
Nom. size & Desig-nation	Wt. per ft.	Max. Load	Dimen-sions		Thickness of Plate			Gross Wt.	Dimen-sions		Thickness of Plate			Gross Wt.
			B	C	Calc.	Fin.	Rolled		B	C	Calc.	Fin.	Rolled	
In.	Lb.	Kips	In.	In.	In.	In.	In.	Lb.	In.	In.	In.	In.	In.	Lb.
12 × 12 WF	190	1448	42	46	4.67	4¾	5⅛	2805	34	38	4.29	4¼	4⅝	1693
	161	1226	39	42	4.18	4¼	4⅝	2146	32	35	3.83	3⅞	3⅞	1230
	133	1011	35	39	3.77	3¾	3¾	1450	29	31	3.38	3⅜	3⅜	860
	120	912	34	36	3.47	3½	3½	1214	28	29	3.21	3¼	3¼	748
	106	872	33	36	3.39	3⅜	3⅜	1136	27	29	3.03	3	3	665
	99	813	32	34	3.21	3¼	3¼	1002	26	28	2.86	2⅞	2⅞	593
	92	756	31	33	3.05	3⅛	3⅛	906	25	27	2.69	2¾	2¾	526
	85	698	30	32	2.89	2⅞	2⅞	782	24	26	2.52	2½	2½	442
	79	648	28	31	2.77	2¾	2¾	676	23	26	2.47	2½	2½	424
	72	590	27	30	2.61	2⅝	2⅝	602	22	24	2.18	2¼	2¼	337
	65	533	26	28	2.35	2⅜	2⅜	490	21	23	2.01	2	2	274
12 × 10 WF	58	466	23	28	2.33	2⅜	2⅜	433	19	22	1.93	2	2	237
	53	425	22	26	2.09	2⅛	2⅛	344	18	21	1.77	1¾	1¾	188
12 × 8 WF	50	387	20	26	2.07	2⅛	2⅛	313	16	22	1.82	1⅞	1⅞	187
	45	347	19	25	1.93	2	2	269	15	21	1.67	1¾	1¾	156
	40	309	18	23	1.68	1¾	1¾	205	14	20	1.52	1½	1½	119
10 × 10 WF	112	906	33	37	3.76	3¾	3¾	1297	27	30	3.38	3⅜	3⅜	774
	100	809	31	35	3.52	3½	3½	1076	25	29	3.25	3¼	3¼	668
	89	719	30	32	3.14	3⅛	3⅛	850	24	27	2.93	3	3	551
	77	622	28	30	2.86	2⅞	2⅞	684	23	25	2.59	2⅝	2⅝	428
	72	581	27	29	2.73	2¾	2¾	610	22	24	2.45	2½	2½	374
	66	532	26	28	2.58	2⅝	2⅝	541	21	23	2.30	2⅜	2⅜	325
	60	484	24	27	2.49	2½	2½	459	20	22	2.14	2⅛	2⅛	265
	54	435	23	26	2.33	2⅜	2⅜	402	19	21	1.98	2	2	226
	49	394	22	24	2.09	2⅛	2⅛	318	18	20	1.83	1⅞	1⅞	191
10 × 8 WF	45	349	20	24	2.04	2⅛	2⅛	289	16	20	1.81	1⅞	1⅞	170
	39	302	19	22	1.79	1⅞	1⅞	222	15	18	1.52	1½	1½	115
	33	255	17	20	1.55	1⅝	1⅝	157	14	17	1.34	1⅜	1⅜	93
8 × 8 WF	67	525	25	28	2.81	2⅞	2⅞	570	21	23	2.51	2½	2½	342
	58	454	24	26	2.51	2½	2½	442	20	21	2.33	2⅜	2⅜	283
	48	375	21	24	2.29	2⅜	2⅜	339	17	20	2.09	2⅛	2⅛	205
	40	311	19	22	2.04	2⅛	2⅛	252	16	18	1.76	1¾	1¾	143
	35	272	18	21	1.88	1⅞	1⅞	201	15	17	1.60	1⅝	1⅝	117
	31	241	17	19	1.64	1⅝	1⅝	149	14	16	1.45	1½	1½	95
8 × 6½ WF	28	207	15	19	1.61	1⅝	1⅝	131	12	16	1.44	1½	1½	82
	24	178	14	17	1.36	1⅜	1⅜	93	11	15	1.29	1⅜	1⅜	64
8 × 5¼ WF	20	134	12	15	1.12	1⅛	1⅛	57	9	14	1.08	1⅛	1⅛	40
	17	112	10	15	1.07	1⅛	1⅛	48	8	13	.93	1	1	29

Note: Rolled plate thicknesses above 4 inches are based on finished thickness plus suggested allowances for finishing one side, and may be modified to suit fabricating plant practice. When it is required to finish both surfaces of base plates, additional allowance must be made.

COLUMN BASE PLATES
Dimensions for maximum column loads

For A242-A440-A441 Columns

Base plates, ASTM A36, $F_b = 27$ ksi
Concrete, $f'_c = 3000$ psi

Column			Unit Pressure on Support $F_p = 0.25 f'_c = 750$ psi						Unit Pressure on Support $F_p = 0.375 f'_c = 1125$ psi					
Nom. Size & Desig-nation	Wt. per Ft.	Max. Load	Dimen-sions		Thickness of Plate			Gross Wt.	Dimen-sions		Thickness of Plate			Gross Wt.
			B	C	Calc.	Fin.	Rolled		B	C	Calc.	Fin.	Rolled	
In.	Lb.	Kips	In.	In.	In.	In.	In.	Lb.	In.	In.	In.	In.	In.	Lb.
14 × 14½ BP14	117	974	35	38	3.49	3½	3½	1319	28	31	3.09	3⅛	3⅛	768
	102	849	33	35	3.10	3⅛	3⅛	1023	27	28	2.68	2¾	2¾	589
	89	740	31	32	2.77	2¾	2¾	773	25	27	2.41	2½	2½	478
	73	573	27	29	2.29	2⅜	2⅜	527	22	24	1.92	2	2	299
12 × 12 BP12	74	604	27	30	2.66	2¾	2¾	631	22	25	2.36	2⅜	2⅜	370
	53	422	23	25	1.97	2	2	326	19	20	1.65	1¾	1¾	188
10 × 10 BP10	57	456	24	26	2.35	2⅜	2⅜	420	19	22	2.17	2¼	2¼	266
	42	335	21	22	1.84	1⅞	1⅞	245	17	18	1.56	1⅝	1⅝	141
8 × 8 BP8	36	278	19	20	1.78	1⅞	1⅞	202	15	17	1.63	1⅝	1⅝	117
8 × 8 M	34.3	279	18	21	1.92	2	2	214	15	17	1.64	1⅝	1⅝	117
	32.6	266	18	20	1.78	1⅞	1⅞	191	15	16	1.52	1½	1½	102
8 × 6½ M	28	221	16	19	1.62	1⅝	1⅝	140	13	16	1.44	1½	1½	88
	24	190	15	17	1.41	1½	1½	108	12	15	1.27	1⅜	1⅜	70
6 × 6 M	25	196	16	17	1.60	1⅝	1⅝	125	13	14	1.44	1½	1½	77
	22.5	175	15	16	1.47	1½	1½	102	12	13	1.29	1⅜	1⅜	61
	20	156	14	15	1.34	1⅜	1⅜	82	11	13	1.27	1⅜	1⅜	56
6 × 6 WF	25	199	16	17	1.59	1⅝	1⅝	125	13	14	1.42	1½	1½	77
	20	159	14	16	1.42	1½	1½	95	11	13	1.25	1¼	1¼	51
	15.5	124	12	14	1.19	1¼	1¼	59	10	12	1.07	1⅛	1⅛	38
6 × 4 B	16	115	11	14	1.16	1¼	1¼	55	9	12	1.04	1⅛	1⅛	34
	12	84	9	13	1.03	1⅛	1⅛	37	7	11	.92	1	1	22
5 × 5 M	18.9	144	13	15	1.47	1½	1½	83	11	12	1.26	1¼	1¼	47
5 × 5 WF	18.5	143	13	15	1.45	1½	1½	83	11	12	1.24	1¼	1¼	47
	16	123	12	14	1.32	1⅜	1⅜	65	10	11	1.10	1⅛	1⅛	35
4 × 4 WF	13	94	11	12	1.13	1⅛	1⅛	42	9	10	1.03	1⅛	1⅛	29
4 × 4 M	13	92	11	12	1.14	1¼	1¼	47	9	10	1.05	1⅛	1⅛	29
6 × 3⅜ I	17.25	133	12	15	1.33	1⅜	1⅜	70	10	12	1.25	1¼	1¼	42
	12.5	97	10	13	1.06	1⅛	1⅛	41	8	11	.93	1	1	25
5 × 3 I	14.75	112	11	14	1.32	1⅜	1⅜	60	9	12	1.23	1¼	1¼	38
	10	75	9	12	1.01	1	1	31	7	10	.91	1	1	20
4 × 2⅝ I	9.5	71	9	11	1.02	1	1	28	7	10	1.04	1⅛	1⅛	22
	7.7	57	8	10	.87	⅞	⅞	20	6	9	.89	1	1	15
3 × 2⅜ I	7.5	54	8	9	.89	1	1	20	6	8	.91	1	1	14
	5.7	41	7	8	.73	¾	¾	12	6	7	.68	¾	¾	9

Column base plates for the 32-story Commerce Towers, Kansas City, Mo., were shop-fabricated and shipped separately. At the site they were positioned and bolted to the concrete. The heavy columns were then erected and field welded to base plates. This was facilitated by use of semi-automatic arc welding with self-shielding cored electrode wire. Process quadrupled the speed of manual welding and produced sounder welds.

Ten-ton weldments were required for tower bases on lift bridges along the St. Lawrence Seaway. Edges of attaching members were double-beveled to permit full penetration. Iron powder electrodes were specified for higher welding speeds and lower costs. Because of high restraint, LH-70 (low hydrogen) E7018 electrodes were used on root passes to avoid cracking, while E6027 was used on subsequent passes to fill the joint.

In designing a scenic highway bridge with 700′ arch span, near Santa Barbara, Cal., engineers called for tower columns to be anchored to the concrete skew-backs by means of $1\frac{3}{8}$″ prestressing rods. The bottom of the column is slotted to accommodate the base, an "eggbox" grill made up of vertical plates welded together and to the box column. The towers support heavy vertical girder loads but also safely transmit horizontal wind and seismic loads from the deck system to the foundation.

Column Splices

1. INTRODUCTION

AISC specifies that, where full-milled tier-building columns are spliced, there shall be sufficient welding to hold them securely in place. These connections shall be proportioned to resist any horizontal shear forces, and any tension that would be developed by specified wind forces acting in conjunction with 75% of the calculated dead load stress and no live load, if this condition will produce more tension than full dead load and live load applied. (AISC Sec 1.15.8).

Figures 1 and 2 show various designs of column splices which eliminate punching of the columns. Note that these details require only handling and punching of small pieces of angles or plates which are easily carried to, and welded to, the columns in the shop. The details provide for temporary bolted connections in the field prior to making the permanent welded connections.

Sometimes the column connections are placed about midway in height, in order to get the connection away from the region of heavy bending moment caused by windloads, etc. The result is a connection sufficient to hold the columns in place and designed for horizontal shear and axial compression only.

2. TYPES OF SPLICES

In Figure 1(a), a plate and two angles are punched or, if necessary, drilled. The plate is shop welded to the top of the lower column. The two angles are shop welded to the web at the lower end of the upper column. The upper column is erected on top of the lower column and erection bolts are inserted. The upper column is then field welded to the connecting plate. Where additional clearance is needed for erection of beams framing into the web of the lower column, it might be necessary to shop weld the plate to the upper column and then field weld in the overhead position to the lower column.

If the upper and lower columns differ in size, the connecting plate is designed as a member in bending due to misalignment of the flanges, and its thickness is determined from this; Figure 1(b). If the lower column's section is much deeper than the upper column, stiffeners can be welded directly below the flanges of the upper column. These stiffeners will reduce the required thickness of the connecting plate; Figure 1(c).

A splice for heavy columns is shown in Figure 1(d). Two small plates are punched with holes aligned as indicated. They are then carried to the column sec-

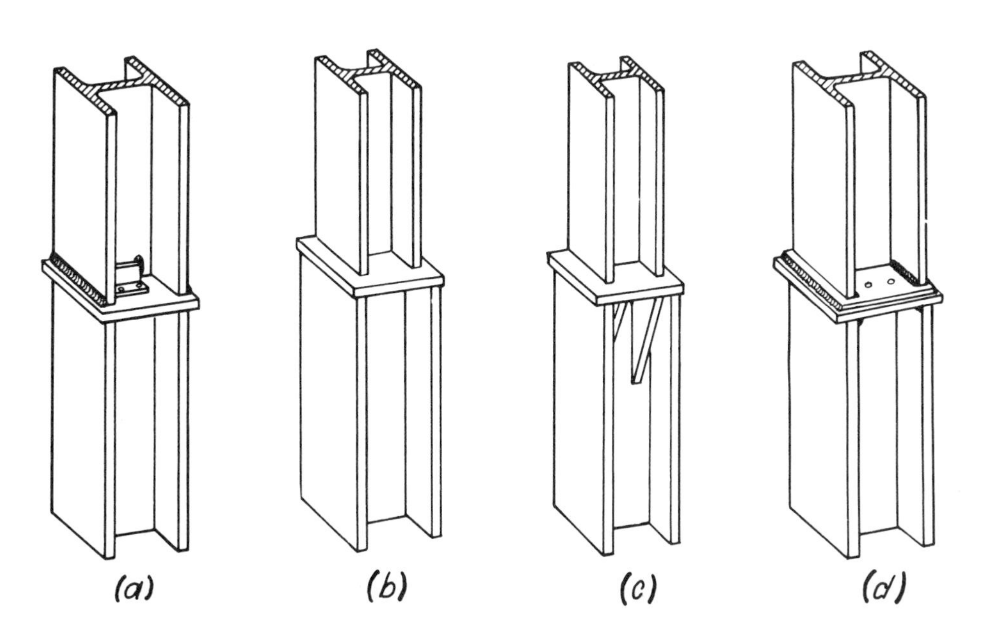

FIG. 1—Typical Column Splices

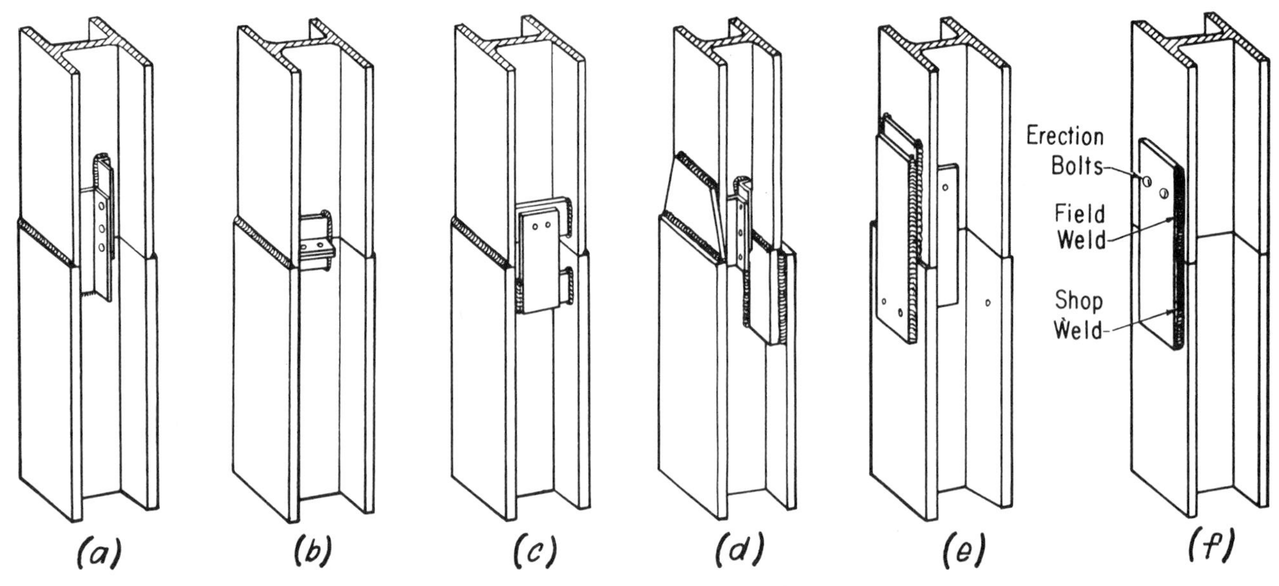

FIG. 2 — Typical Column Splices

tions and welded thereto. In the field the column sections are bolted temporarily prior to welding, as indicated at (d).

In Figure 2(a) the ends of both column sections are first milled for a square bearing surface. Then the two lower erection splice angles are shop welded on opposite sides of the web of the heavier column section, so as to project past the end of the column. The outstanding legs of these angles are provided with holes for erection bolts to engage the outstanding legs of the other two angles that are shop welded to the upper column section. In this type of detail where lighter connecting material projects from heavy main sections, care should be taken in handling to prevent damage to the lighter material.

The flanges on the lower end of the upper column section are partially beveled or "J" grooved, and this partial penetration groove joint is then welded in the field.

The purpose of the angles is to splice and hold the two adjacent columns together temporarily while they are being field welded.

These erecting angles may be placed horizontally

TABLE 1—Allowables for Weld Metal in Partial-Penetration Groove Welds *For Field Splices of Columns*

	E60 Welds SAW-1	E70 Welds SAW-2
compression	same as plate	same as plate
tension transverse to cross-section of throat area	13,600 psi	15,800 psi
shear	13,600 psi	15,800 psi

AWS Building Par 205(a) and AISC Sec. 1.5.3

on the web of the columns, Figure 2(b). The advantage of this position is that they do not extend beyond the ends of the column for possible damage during transit or erection.

Four plates are punched, then shop welded between the flanges of the two column sections as shown in Figure 2(c), leaving enough space between the back of the plates and the column web to insert a wrench. Two splice plates are also punched and shop welded to the lower column section before shipping to the erection site. After bolting in the field as indicated, the permanent connection is made by welding.

The splice in Figure 2(d) is similar to that at (a) but is for connecting two columns of different sizes. The flanges of the upper column lie inside of the flanges of the lower column. Before shop welding the erecting angles, splice plates are first shop fillet welded to the inside face of the flange of the lower column. They are milled with the lower column section. As an alternate to this, splice plates with their lower edges prepared for welding are shop fillet welded to the outside face of the flanges on the upper column.

In case only one side of the column is accessible, for example when new steel is erected adjacent to an old structure, a combination of this procedure may be used. Place the lower splice plates on the inside face of the lower column and the upper splice plate on the outside face of the upper column; See Figure 2(d). In this manner all field welds on both column flanges can be made from the one side.

Where splice plates are used and filler plates are needed because of the difference in sizes of the upper and lower columns, these plates are welded to the upper column. See Figure 2(e). This allows the greater amount of welding to be done in the shop where larger electrodes and higher welding currents used in

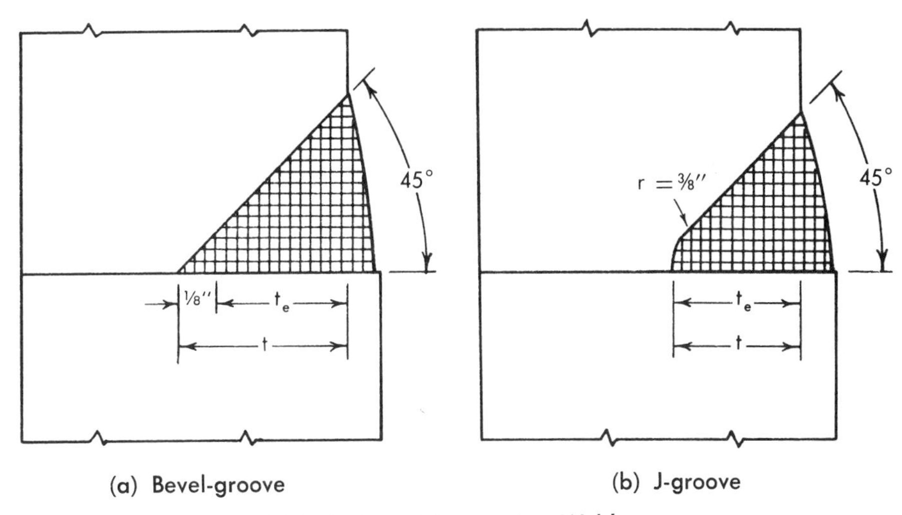

(a) Bevel-groove (b) J-groove

FIG. 3—Partial-Penetration Welds

the flat position result in higher welding speeds and lower cost. After erection the splice plate is field welded to the lower column.

Two attaching plates are shop welded to the upper end of the lower column. The column may be hoisted by attaching the cable to the erection holes of these plates. After erecting the upper columns, these plates are field welded to the upper column.

3. WELD ALLOWABLES

Both the AWS Building Code and the AISC Specifications allow partial-penetration groove welds, either a bevel or a J preparation, to be used on column field splices.

For a J joint, the effective throat (t_e) is equal to the actual throat (t).

For a beveled joint, the effective throat (t_e) equals the actual throat (t) less ⅛″. This reduction in throat is made because the weld may not extend all the way down into the very root of the joint. The ⅛″ reduction is very conservative. No reduction is made in the throat of the J preparation because there is no problem in reaching the root of the joint.

A beveled joint is usually flame cut along the end of the column flange. A J groove must be machined or else gouged out by the air carbon-arc process. Although it may seem that the beveled groove might require more weld metal because it must be ⅛″ deeper than required, the J groove on the other hand must start with a ⅜″ radius and an included angle of 45°. There may be no reduction in the amount of weld metal by using the J groove; see Figure 3. A decision on joint design should be made only after all factors are carefully evaluated.

Since it is impossible to properly read radiographs of this partial penetration groove joint, because of the unwelded portion, these field splices should never be subject to radiographic inspection.

4. EXAMPLES

Figure 4 illustrates a typical field splice used on columns of the Detroit Bank & Trust Building in Detroit, Michigan. These fabricated columns were spliced by partial-penetration bevel joints in the column

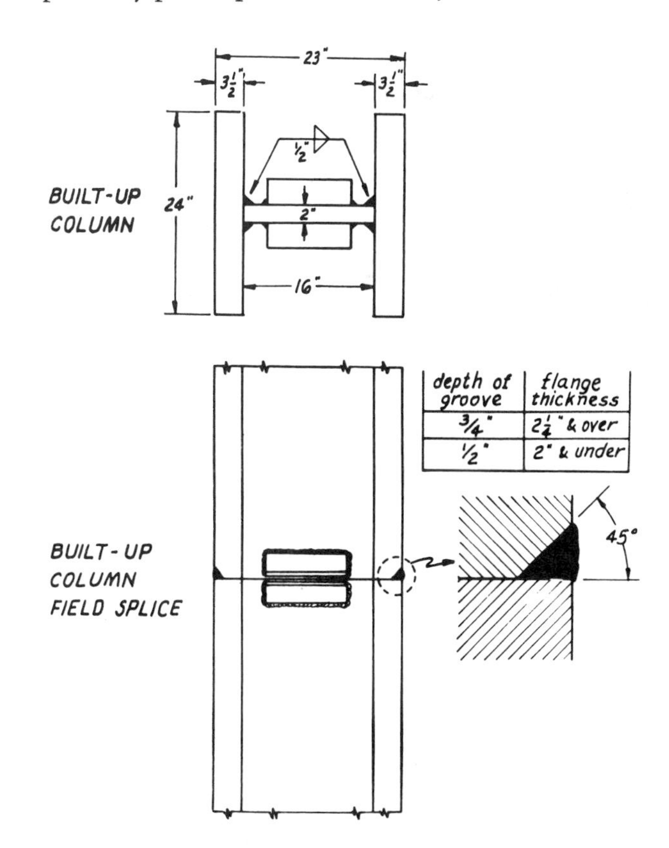

FIG. 4—Typical column splice on Detroit Bank & Trust Building.

flanges. These A36 steel columns were welded with E70 low-hydrogen electrodes. Notice the schedule of weld sizes. The angles were shop welded to column ends and field bolted during erection, using high-tensile bolts. These bolts were left in place and carried any horizontal shear in the direction of the column web, hence no field welding was required on the web of the columns.

Figure 5 illustrates the field splice of columns in the Michigan Consolidated Gas Co. Building in Detroit, Michigan. These fabricated A36 steel box-shaped columns were field welded with E70 low-hydrogen electrodes. Partial-penetration J-groove welds were used on all four flanges around the periphery of the column. Notice the schedule of weld sizes.

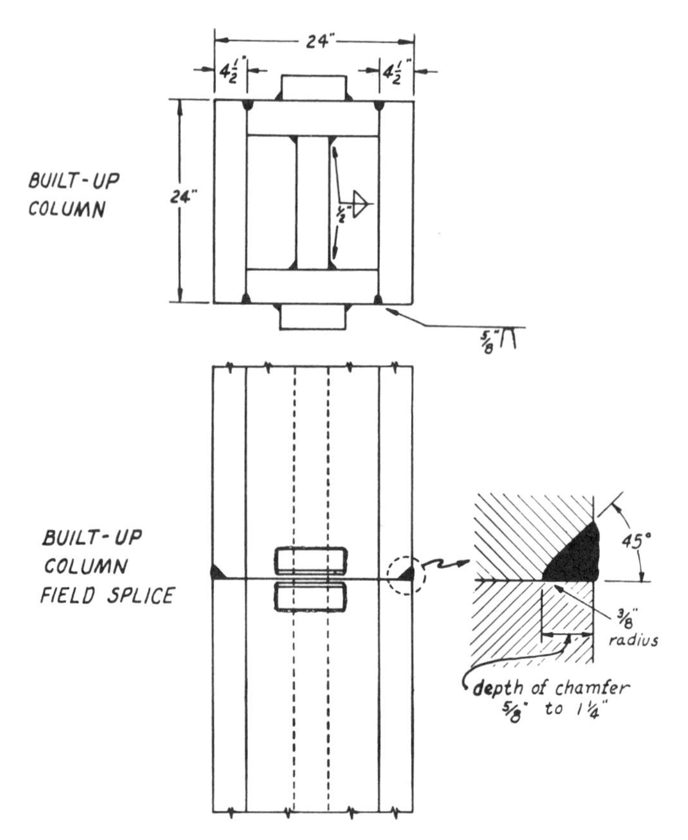

FIG. 5—Typical column splice on Michigan Consolidated Gas Co. Building.

FIG. 6—Typical column splice in sections of same depth. Plate on the web is for bolting to facilitate erection.

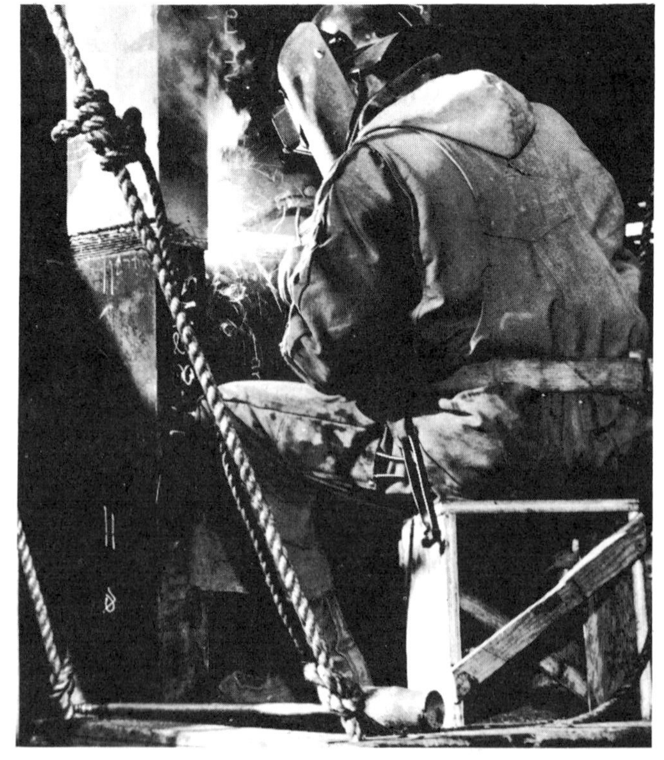

FIG. 7—Field splicing of column flanges, using vapor-shielded arc welding process.

Bearing-Pin Connections

1. TYPICAL CONNECTION

Figure 1 illustrates a suggested detail for a pin connection at the end of a built-up compression member of an arch bridge, subject to a reaction of 90 kips.

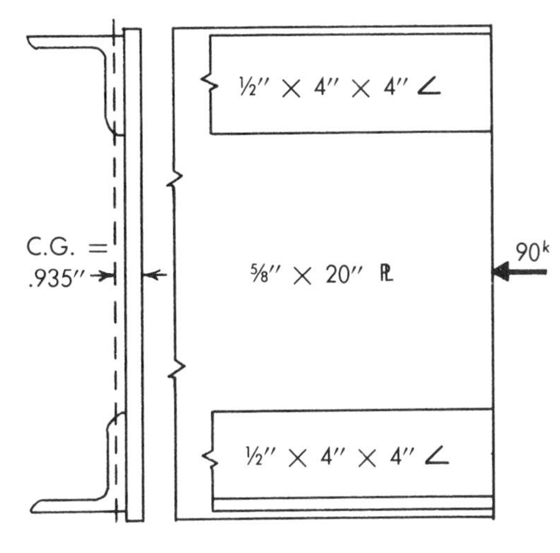

FIGURE 1

There are many approaches to this type of problem and, of course, many solutions. This is simply one analysis and one solution. One of the design requirements in this particular example is to have a smooth-appearing surface on the outside or facia side of the arch compression member.

Notice in the sketch of the cross-section of the built-up compression member, Figure 1, that the center of gravity is .935″ in from the outer face.

By selecting an attaching plate of sufficient thickness for its center of gravity to line up with the compression member's center of gravity, the compression load will be transferred in a direct line without any eccentricity.

The bearing pin is subjected to a double-shear load: 90,000 lbs on two areas, or 45,000 lbs each. See Figure 2. According to AASHO (Sec 3.4.2), the allowable stress on this pin is 13,500 psi.

$$\therefore A = \frac{45{,}000}{13{,}500}$$

$$= 3.33 \text{ in.}^2 \text{ required pin area}$$

or use a 2¼″-dia pin having A = 3.98 in.²

FIGURE 2

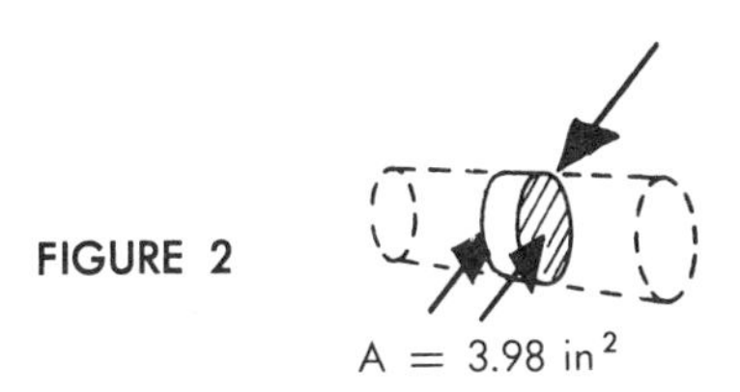

The next step is to compute the thickness of the connecting plate. This is based on the minimum required bearing area of the plate because of the pin reaction against the plate, Figure 3. The 90,000-lb load is divided by the allowable bearing pressure, which in this case is 24,000 psi assuming no rotation, (AASHO 3.4.2) and the minimum bearing area comes out to be 3.75 in.²

$$A = \frac{90{,}000}{24{,}000}$$

$$= 3.75 \text{ in.}^2$$

2¼″ dia

2″

FIGURE 3

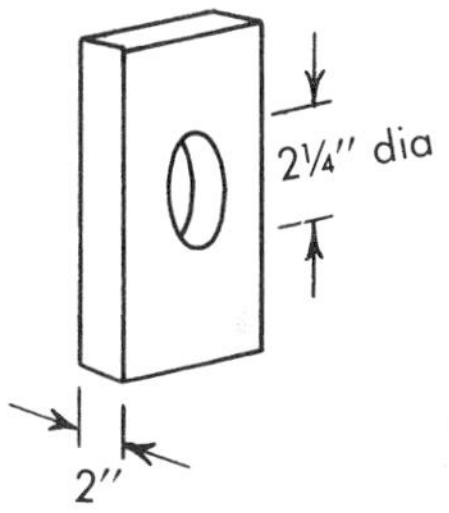

Since the pin's diameter has been computed to be 2¼″, the required plate thickness to make up this bearing area would be—

$$t = \frac{3.75}{2.25}$$

$$= 1.67''$$

but use 2″-thick plate

since this will also line up with the center of gravity of the compression member (CG = .935″).

The next step is a simple determination of the required depth (d) of this connecting plate. See Figure 4. In this analysis, some structural designers consider this connecting plate as a beam supported at the center, or pin, and withstanding the compression loads transmitted from the compression member.

In most cases, the compression load (here 90 kips) is assumed to be equally distributed throughout the various parts of the compression member by the ratio of the individual areas to the total area. Accordingly, the compression load carried by each angle would be—

$$P_{\angle} = (90^k)\,\frac{3.75}{20}$$

$$= 16.9 \text{ kips}$$

and the compression load carried by the ⅝″ × 20″ web plate would be—

$$P_{PL} = (90^k)\,\frac{12.5}{20}$$

$$= 56 \text{ kips}$$

throughout its entire width. Dividing this load by 20″ results in a uniform load of—

$$f = \frac{56^k}{20''}$$

$$= 2.8 \text{ kips/linear in.}$$

Treat this connecting plate as a cantilever beam from the centerline with these two loads:

(1) the concentrated load of 16.9 kips at 8.75″ from center, and

(2) the uniform load of 2.8 kips/in. for a distance of 10″.

The resulting bending moment is then computed:

$$M = M_a + M_b$$

$$= (16.9^k)(8.75'') + \frac{(2.8 \text{ k/in.})(10'')^2}{2}$$

$$= 288 \text{ in.-kips}$$

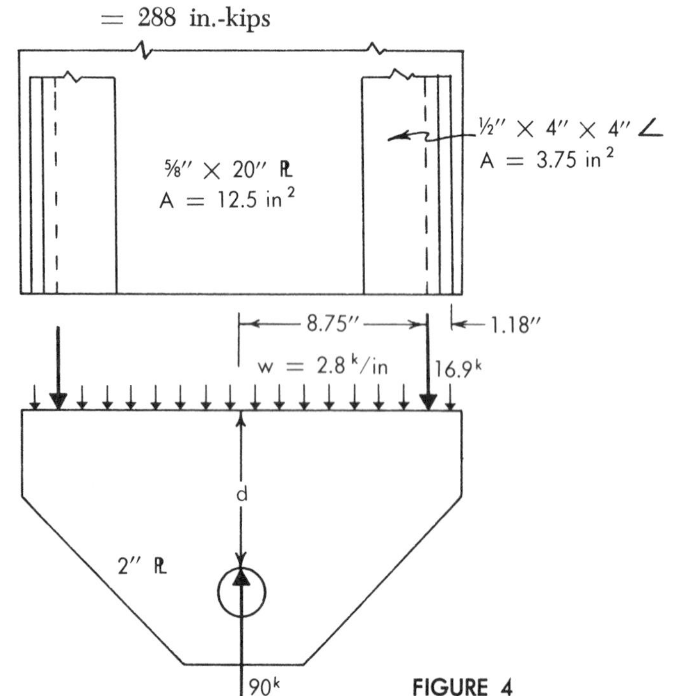

FIGURE 4

Since the required section modulus is in terms of (d):

$$M = \sigma\, S$$

$$\text{and } S = \frac{M}{\sigma}$$

$$= \frac{(288{,}000 \text{ in.-lbs})}{(20{,}000 \text{ psi})}$$

$$= 14.4$$

Since

$$S = \frac{t\, d^2}{6}$$

$$d^2 = \frac{6\, S}{2}$$

$$= 3 \times 14.4$$

$$= 43.2''$$

and the minimum depth of upper plate is found to be—

$$d = 6.58''$$

or 7″ deep beyond the pinhole would be sufficient.

2. FINALIZING THE DETAIL

The final detail has been sketched in Figure 5. The outer leg of each angle might be trimmed back slightly so as to fit to the 2″ connecting plate. Whether this is cut back or not, there will be a loss of 2⅝″ of the angle leg. This area (A = 2 × ½″ × 2.625″ = 2.625 in.²) is made up by additional attaching stiffening plates. These have been chosen to be two ¾″ × 3″ plates (A = 4.5 in.²) and two ½″ × 1⅜″ bars (A = 1.375 in.²). The total added area is thus 5.875 square inches. The entire built-up compression member has an area of 20 square inches. These additional attaching plates simply mean that the cross-sectional area in contact with the 2″ connecting plate is in excess of the required 20 square inches.

After the compression member has been welded, its end might be milled to provide a flat, smooth surface for bearing against the 2″ plate. If this is done, the entire section would not have to be welded 100% all the way through. Under these conditions, it is suggested that a bevel be made part way through these plates of the compression member and that a groove weld be made on the outside. Reinforcing fillet welds should then be made on the inner side of this compression member where it connects with the 2″ plate.

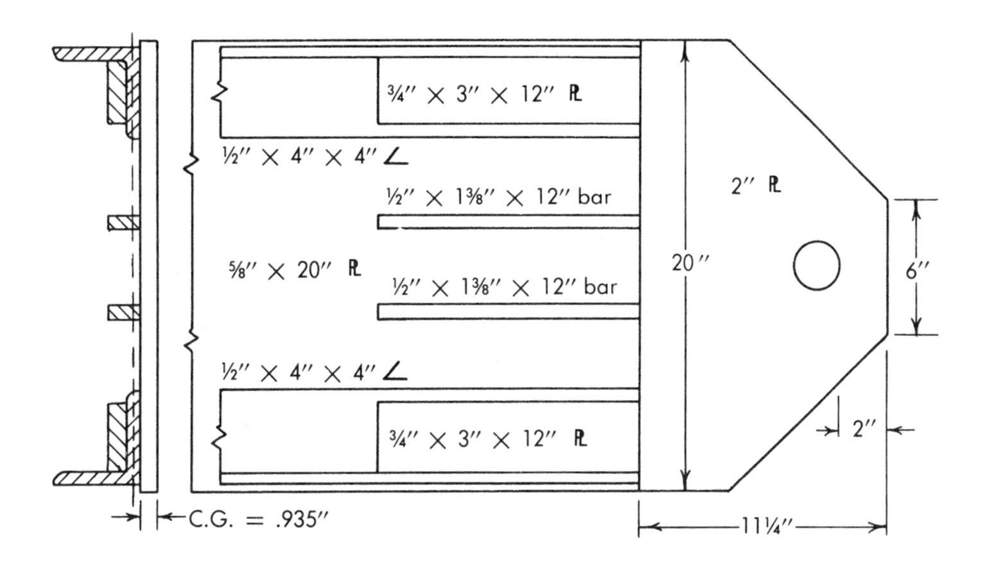
¾″ × 3″ × 12″ ℞
½″ × 4″ × 4″ ∠
½″ × 1⅜″ × 12″ bar
⅝″ × 20″ ℞
½″ × 1⅜″ × 12″ bar
½″ × 4″ × 4″ ∠
¾″ × 3″ × 12″ ℞
2″ ℞
20″
6″
2″
C.G. = .935″
11¼″

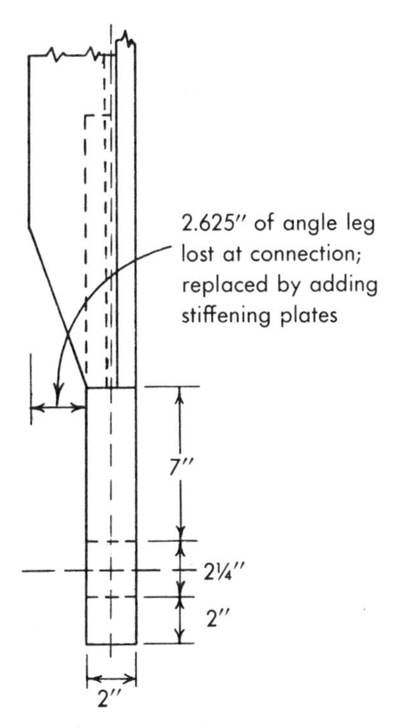
2.625″ of angle leg
lost at connection;
replaced by adding
stiffening plates
7″
2¼″
2″
2″

FIGURE 5

Bearing-pin connections like those shown on this bridge over Michigan's John C. Lodge Expressway must be designed to transfer the compression load without eccentricity. Note simplicity and beauty of the welded rigid frame employed in this bridge design.

Designing Built-Up Columns

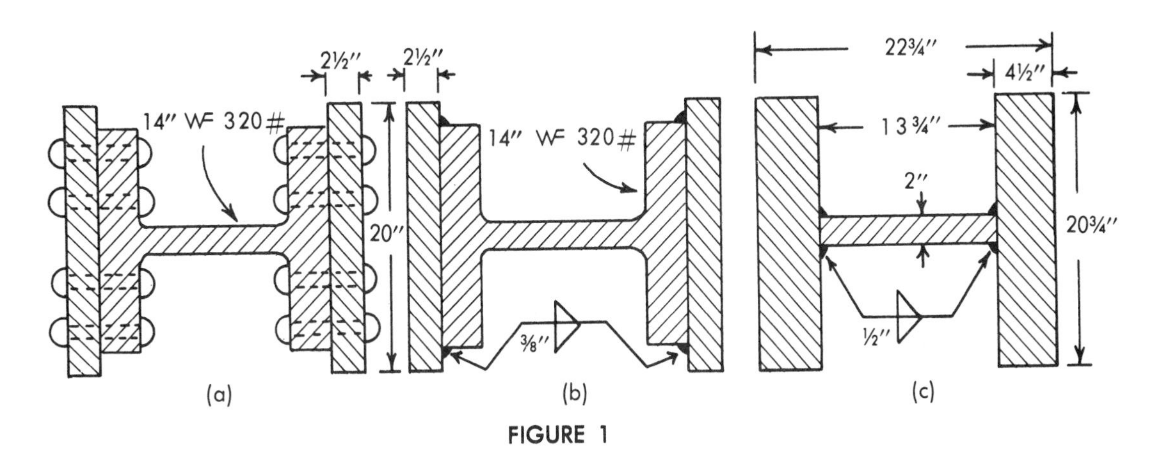

FIGURE 1

1. ADVANTAGES OF WELDED BUILT-UP COLUMNS

In the past, when engineers required steel columns of heavier section than those commercially available, they designed the columns to be made by riveting cover plates to the flanges of 14″ WF rolled sections. See Figure 1(a). The cover plates were sized to produce the required additional section area.

In recent years, fabricating shops have simply substituted fillet welds for rivets and produced the same column section; Figure 1(b). This practice has presented a design problem in getting an efficient transfer of tensile force from the beam flange through the cover plate into the column without pulling the cover plate away from the column flange. The cover plate, being attached only along its two outer edges, tends to bow outward; Figure 2. This results in uneven distribution of forces on the beam-to-column weld.

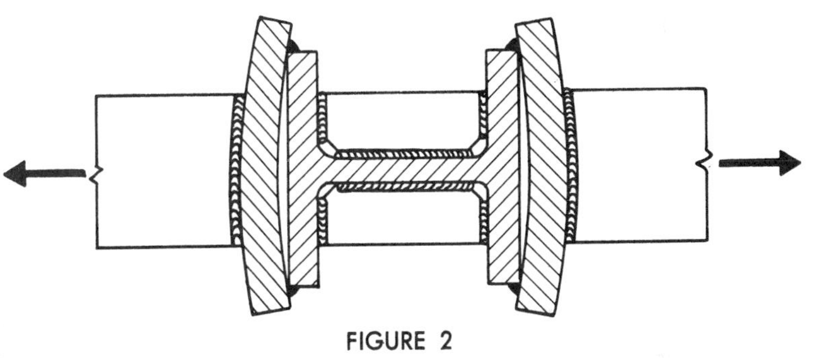

FIGURE 2

The best design is a completely welded built-up column; Figure 1(c). This gives the exact section required without any increase in welding, and there is no problem in transferring tensile forces from the beam flange through the column.

FIGURE 3

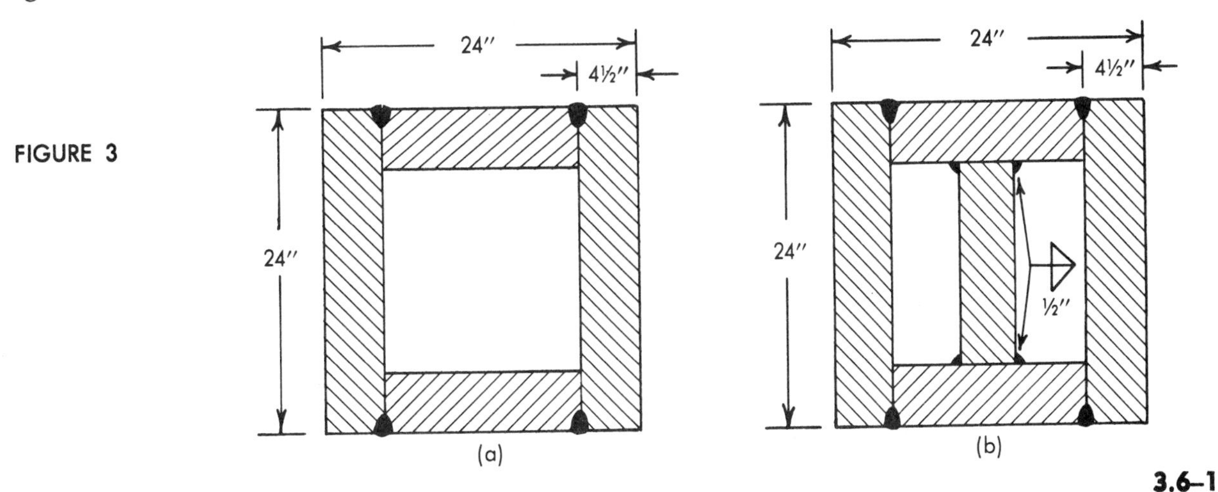

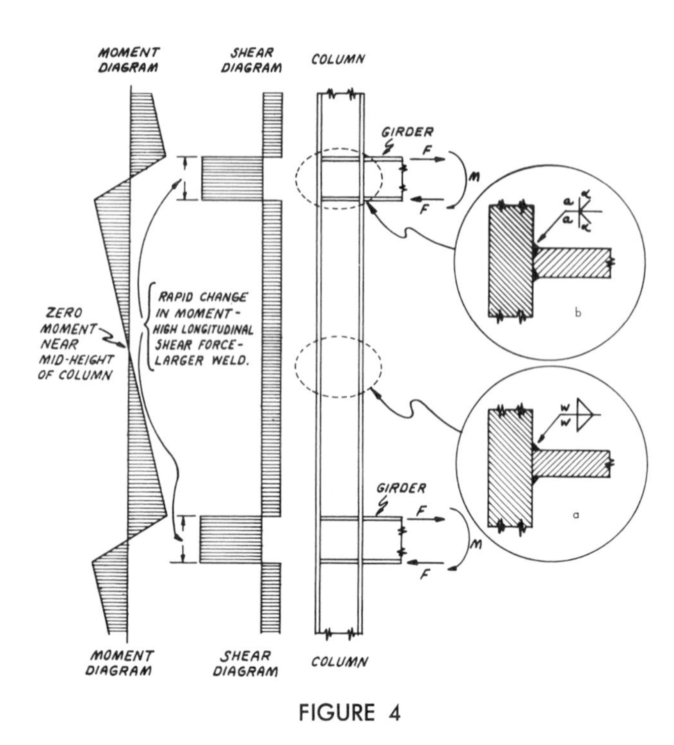

FIGURE 4

For very large column sections, 4 plates can be welded together to form a box section; Figure 3(a). Sometimes a web plate is added to this box for additional area in the lower part of a building; Figure 3(b). Moving up the building, the point is reached where this web plate can be omitted without changing the outer section dimensions.

2. WELD REQUIREMENTS

There are two general requirements for the welds holding the plates of the columns together; Figure 4.

a. The entire length of the column must have sufficient welds to withstand any longitudinal shear resulting from moments applied to the column from wind or beam loads; Figure 4(a). Notice at the left the rather low change in moment along most of the column length.

b. Within the region where the beams connect to the column, this longitudinal shear is much higher because of the abrupt change in moment within this region; Figure 4(b). Also the tensile force from the beam flange will be transferred through a portion of this weld. These two conditions require heavier welds in the connection region.

Various types of welds are employed in fabricating:

a. *Fillet welds* (Fig. 5) require no plate preparation. They can be made to any size simply by making more passes. However, since the amount of weld metal varies as the square of the leg size, these welds can require a large amount of weld metal for the larger sizes. For nominal size welds (approx. ½″ to ¾″), fillet welds are usually used. When their size becomes too large, they are replaced with some type of groove weld because less weld metal is required.

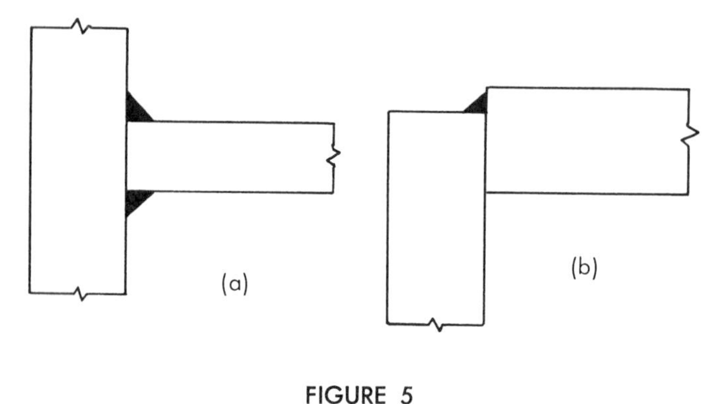

FIGURE 5

b. *Bevel and Vee groove welds* (Fig. 6) require joint edges of the plate to be beveled, usually by the oxygen cutting process. On larger size welds, this additional preparation cost is offset by the reduction in weld metal required. AWS and AISC deduct the first ⅛″ of weld to compensate for any slight lack of penetration into the very bottom of the bevel joint, if welded manually.

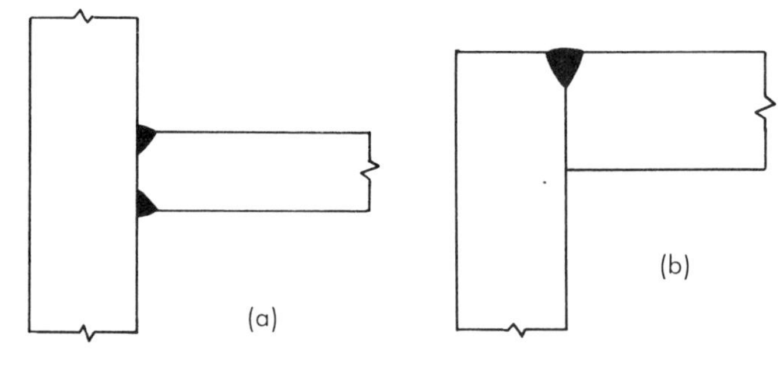

FIGURE 6

c. *J and U groove welds* (Fig. 7) require the plates to be gouged or machined. Machining is seldom used in the structural field, although air carbon-arc gouging is becoming more popular. The J and U welds may not require as much weld metal as the bevel or Vee weld. AWS and AISC allow the full throat or depth of groove to be used.

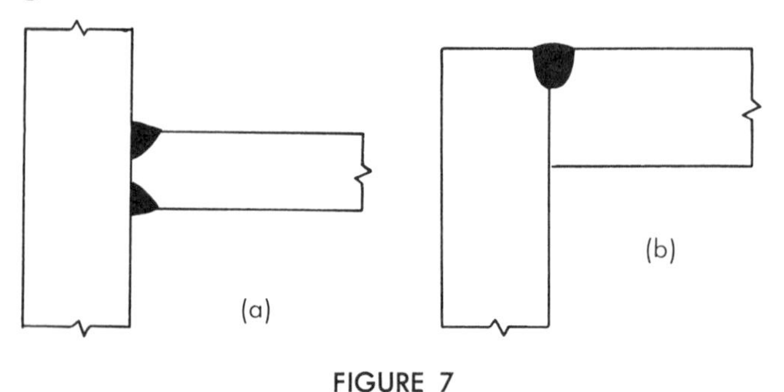

FIGURE 7

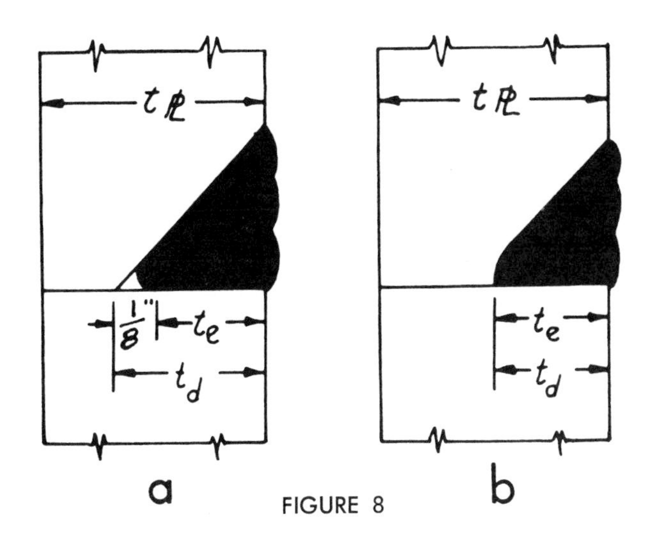

FIGURE 8

3. PARTIAL-PENETRATION GROOVE WELDS

Partial-penetration groove welds are allowed in the Building field. They have many applications; for example, field splices of columns, built up columns, built-up box sections for truss chords, etc.

If a vee J or U groove is used, it is assumed the welder can easily reach the bottom of the joint. Thus, the effective throat of the weld (t_e) is equal to the actual throat of the prepared groove (t), see Fig. 8(b).

If a bevel groove is used, it is assumed that the weldor may not quite reach the bottom of the groove, therefore AWS and AISC deduct ⅛" from the prepared groove. Here the effective throat (t_e) will equal the throat of the groove (t) minus ⅛", see Fig. 8(a).

TABLE 1—AISC Allowables for Weld Metal

1.5.3.1 1.5.3.2 1.17.2	A36 **E60 & SAW-1** A7, A373 steel E60 & SAW-1 E70 & SAW-2	A36, A242*, A441* steel E70 & SAW-2
FILLET WELDS		
for any direction of force	τ = 13,600 psi f = 9600 ω	τ = 15,800 psi f = 11,300 ω
PARTIAL PENETRATION GROOVE WELDS		
shear	τ = 13,600 psi	τ = 15,800 psi
# tension transverse to axis of weld	σ = 13,600	σ = 15,800 psi
tension parallel to axis of weld	same as plate	same as plate
compression bearing	same as plate	same as plate
COMPLETE PENETRATION GROOVE WELDS		
tension compression bending shear bearing	same as plate	same as plate

* low hydrogen E60 & SAW-1 may be used for fillet welds & partial penetration groove welds on A242 or A441 steel. (at the lower allowable τ = 13,600 psi)

\# only for splices or connections of columns or other members subject primarily to axial compression stress

TABLE 2—Partial-Penetration Groove Welds and Fillet Welds

depth of groove or leg size of fillet weld	WEIGHT	FORCE	WEIGHT	FORCE	WEIGHT	FORCE	WEIGHT
½"	.482	4,800 5,600	.850	6,800 7,900	.536	5,100 5,925	.425
⅝"	.754	6,000 7,000	1.12	8,500 9,875	.837	6,800 7,900	.664
¾"	1.085	7,200 8,400	1.40	10,200 11,850	1.21	8,500 9,875	.956
⅞"	1.427	8,400 9,800	1.71	11,900 13,825	1.64	10,200 11,850	1.30
1"	1.93	9,600 11,200	2.03	13,600 15,800	2.15	11,900 13,825	1.70
1⅛"	2.44	10,800 12,600	2.37	15,300 17,775	2.72	13,600 15,800	2.15
1¼"	3.02	12,000 14,000	2.74	17,000 19,750	3.35	15,300 17,775	2.66
1⅜"	3.65	13,200 15,400	3.12	18,700 21,725	4.06	17,000 19,750	3.21
1½"	4.34	14,400 16,800	3.52	20,400 23,700	4.83	18,700 21,725	3.82
1⅝"	5.09	15,600 18,200	3.94	22,100 25,675	5.66	20,400 23,700	4.49
1¾"	5.91	16,800 19,600	4.38	23,800 27,650	6.57	22,100 25,675	5.21
1⅞"	6.79	18,000 21,000	4.84	25,500 29,625	7.55	23,800 27,650	5.98
2"	7.72	19,200 22,400	5.32	27,200 31,600	8.58	25,550 29,625	6.80
2⅛"	8.71	20,400 23,800	5.82	28,900 33,575	9.69	27,200 31,600	7.68
2¼"	9.76	21,600 25,200	6.33	30,600 35,550	10.88	28,900 33,575	8.61
2⅜"	10.88	22,800 26,600	6.87	32,300 37,525	12.10	30,600 35,550	9.59
2½"	12.06	24,000 28,000	7.42	34,000 39,500	13.30	32,300 37,525	10.62
2⅝"	13.32	25,200 29,400	8.00	35,700 41,475	14.80	34,000 39,500	11.72
2¾"	14.60	26,400 30,800	8.72	37,400 43,450	16.23	35,700 41,475	12.87
2⅞"	15.96	27,600 32,200	9.21	39,100 45,425	17.75	37,400 43,450	14.07
3"	17.37	28,800 33,600	9.84	40,800 47,400	19.300	39,100 45,425	15.30

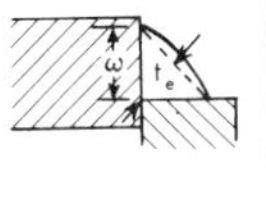

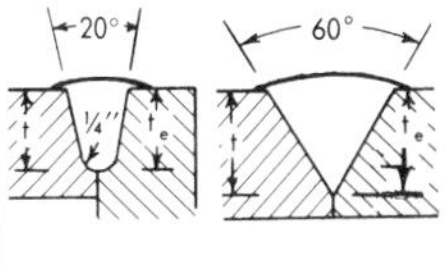

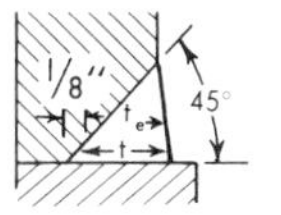

force — lbs per linear inch — upper value A7, A373 steel & E60 welds
lower value A36, A441 steel & E70 welds
weight of weld metal — lbs per foot.

Tension applied parallel to the weld's axis, or compression in any direction, has the same allowable stress as the plate.

Tension applied transverse to the weld's axis, or shear in any direction, has reduced allowable stress, equal to that for the throat of a correspanding fillet weld.

Just as fillet welds have a minimum size for thick plates because of fast cooling and greater restraint, so partial-penetration groove welds have a minimum effective throat (t_e) of—

$$t_e \geqq \sqrt{\frac{t_p}{6}}$$

where:

t_p = thickness of thinner plate

TABLE 3—Partial-Penetration Groove Weld *Reinforced by a Fillet Weld*

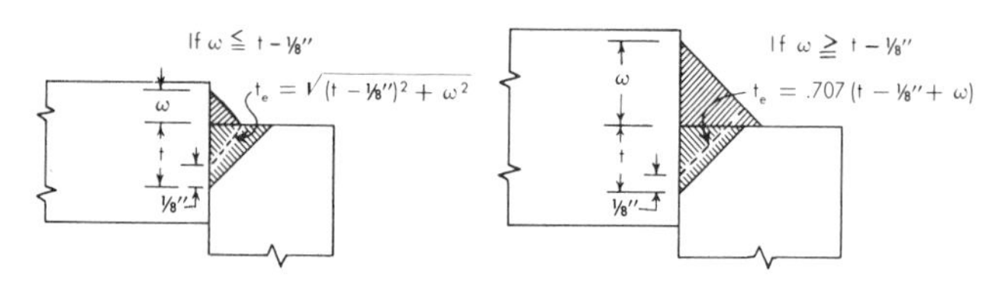

depth of groove	leg size of fillet weld 1/2"	5/8"	3/4"	7/8"	1"	1 1/8"	1 1/4"
1/2"	8,400 9,770 .970	9,610 11,160 1.18	10,810 12,540 1.51	12,010 13,930 1.85	13,010 15,320 2.36	14,410 16,720 2.87	15,620 18,130 3.44
5/8"	9,610 11,160 1.15	10,810 12,540 1.42	12,010 13,930 1.75	13,210 15,320 2.09	14,410 16,720 2.59	15,620 18,130 3.10	16,820 19,530 3.68
3/4"	10,870 12,620 1.44	12,010 13,930 1.71	13,200 15,320 2.04	14,410 16,720 2.38	15,620 18,130 2.89	16,820 19,530 3.40	18,020 20,930 3.97
7/8"	12,250 14,220 1.78	13,270 15,410 2.05	14,410 16,720 2.39	15,620 18,130 2.73	16,820 19,530 3.23	18,020 20,930 3.74	19,220 22,310 4.32
1"	14,000 16,270 2.18	14,620 16,980 2.45	15,660 18,170 2.79	16,820 19,530 3.13	18,020 20,930 3.63	19,220 22,310 4.14	20,420 23,700 4.72
1 1/8"	15,200 17,650 2.63	16,030 18,620 2.90	17,000 19,740 3.24	18,080 21,000 3.58	19,220 22,310 4.08	20,420 23,700 4.59	21,610 25,100 5.17
1 1/4"	16,710 19,400 3.14	17,480 20,320 3.41	18,350 21,300 3.75	19,380 22,530 4.09	20,520 23,800 4.59	21,610 25,100 5.10	22,820 26,470 5.68
1 3/8"	18,300 21,240 3.69	19,000 22,060 3.96	19,700 22,860 4.30	20,730 24,040 4.64	21,750 25,250 5.14	22,830 26,550 5.65	24,000 27,850 6.23
1 1/2"	19,900 23,120 4.30	20,510 23,810 4.57	21,260 24,680 4.91	22,180 25,780 5.25	23,100 26,830 5.75	24,160 28,060 6.26	25,240 29,350 6.84
1 5/8"	21,460 24,930 4.97	22,100 25,670 5.24	22,800 26,460 5.58	23,600 27,400 5.92	24,510 28,450 6.42	25,470 29,600 6.93	26,550 30,830 7.51
1 3/4"	23,100 26,830 5.63	23,650 27,500 5.96	24,350 28,300 6.30	25,100 29,200 6.64	25,950 30,170 7.14	26,850 31,220 7.65	27,900 32,400 8.23

1st value force lbs per linear inch A7, A373 steel & E60 welds
2nd value force lbs per linear inch A36, A441 steel & E70 welds
3rd value weight of weld metal lbs per foot

4. ALLOWABLES AND WELD METAL REQUIREMENTS

Table 1 lists the AWS and AISC allowable stresses in welds used on Buildings. Values for both partial-penetration and full-penetration groove welds and for fillet welds are included.

Table 2 translates the Table 1 values into allowable forces (lbs/linear in.) and required weld metal (lbs/ft) for fillet welds and several types of partial-penetration groove welds. These values cover weld sizes from ½" to 3".

Table 3 provides allowable forces for partial-penetration groove welds reinforced by a fillet weld.

Table 4 directly compares a number of joints to carry a given force, illustrating their relative requirements in weight of weld metal.

TABLE 4—Joints to Carry Force of 20,000 lbs./lin inch
A36 Steel E70 Welds

		ALLOWABLE FORCE	WEIGHT OF WELD METAL
ω = 1⅞"; 1⅞"	ω = 1 7/8"	21,000#/in	6.79#/ft
t = 1⅜"	t = 1 3/8"	21,725#/in	3.12#/ft
t = 1⅜"; t_e = 1⅜"	t = 1 3/8"	21,725#/in	4.06#/ft
⅛"; t_e = 1⅜"; t = 1½"	t = 1 1/2"	21,725#/in	3.82#/ft
ω = 1¼"; t = ¾"; ⅛"	ω = 1 1/4" t = 3/4"	20,930#/in	3.97#/ft
ω = ½"; t = 1⅜"; ⅛"	ω = 1/2" t = 1 3/8"	21,240#/in	3.69#/ft

5. COMBINING WELD TYPES

There are several ways in which different types of welds can be combined in economically fabricating built-up columns to meet the two basic requirements: a) welds from end-to-end of column to withstand longitudinal shear resulting from (wind and beam load) applied moments, and b) heavier welds in connection regions to withstand higher longitudinal shear due to abrupt change in moment, and to carry tensile force from the beam flange. The following cases illustrate combinations that permit optimum use of automatic welding:

Case 1

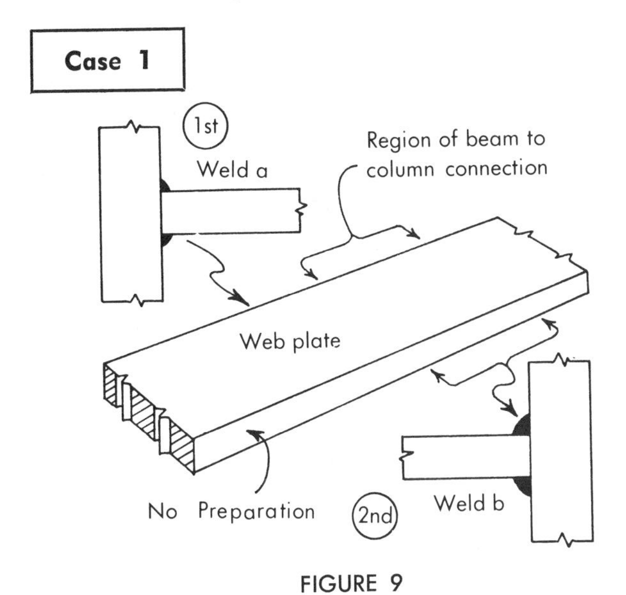

FIGURE 9

If the weld sizes are not too large, the column may be first fillet welded with weld (a) along its entire length. Second, additional passes are made in the connection region to bring the fillet weld up to the proper size for weld (b).

Case 2

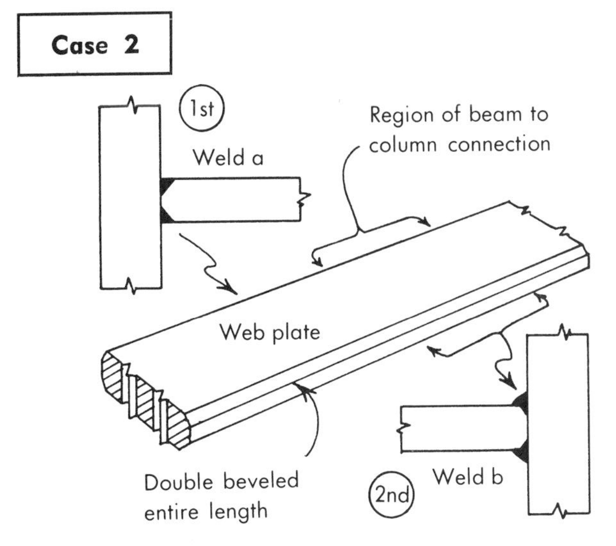

FIGURE 10

The web plate is beveled to the proper depth on all 4 edges along the entire length. Groove weld (a) is first made along the entire length. Second, fillet weld (b) is made over the groove weld within the connection region to bring it up to the proper size.

Case 3

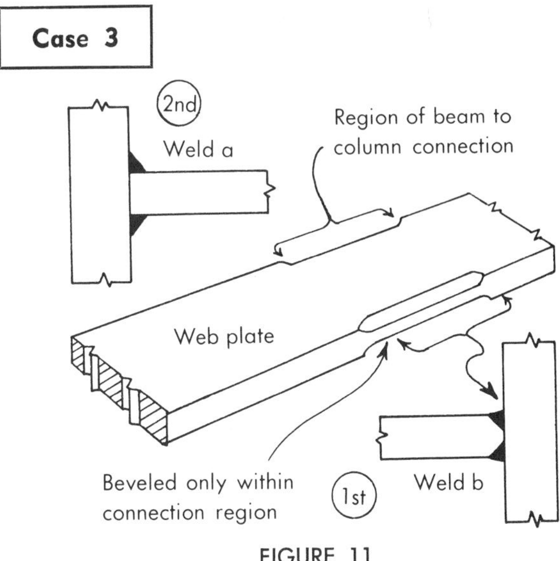

FIGURE 11

The web plate is beveled to the proper depth along short lengths within the connection region. First, groove weld (b) is made flush with the surface within the connection region. Second, fillet weld (a) is made along the entire length of the column.

Case 4

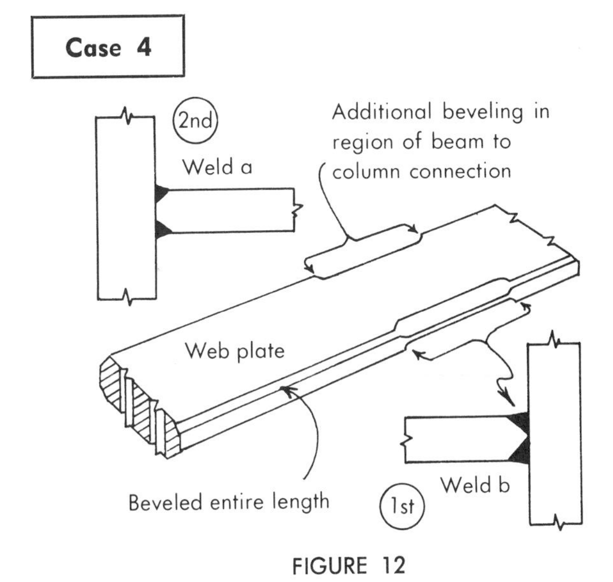

FIGURE 12

The web plate is beveled to the proper depth on all 4 edges along the entire length. Within the connection region, the web is further beveled to a deeper depth. First, groove weld (b) is made within the connection region until the plate edge is built up to the height of the first bevel. Second, groove weld (a) is made along the entire length.

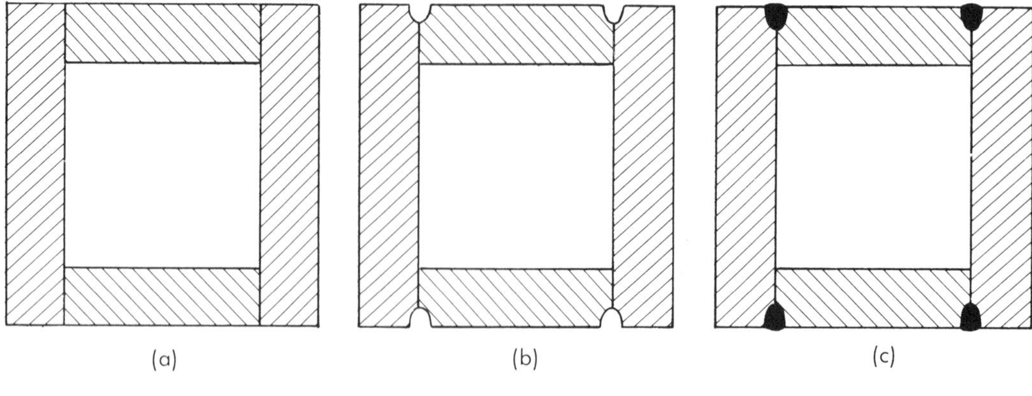

FIGURE 13

6. BOX SECTIONS

In column box sections, J and U groove welds may be substituted for bevel and Vee groove welds if the fabricator is equipped to gouge and prefers to do so rather than bevel. Since beveling is a cutting method, the plates must be beveled before assembling them together. Gouging, however, may be done either before or after assembling. Further, heavy J or U groove welds normally require less weld metal than the bevel or Vee groove welds.

Some fabricators, in making built-up box sections, have assembled and lightly tack welded the plates together without any preparation; Figure 13(a). The joints are next air carbon-arc gouged to the desired depth for very short distances and further tack welded; Figure 13(b). Next, the longer distances in between tack welds are air carbon-arc gouged. When this is completed, the entire length is automatically submerged-arc welded together; Figure 13(c).

7. BEAMS FRAMING INTO BUILT-UP BOX COLUMNS

At first glance it might be thought that the requirements for a beam flange welded to the flange of a built-up box column, Figure 14(a), would be similar to the beam flange welded to the flange of an I shaped column, Figure 14(b). This is because the box column flange is treated as a beam simply supported at its two outer edges, Figure 14(c); it has the same maximum bending moment as the WF column flange treated as a beam supported at its center, Figure 14(d).

The following analysis of a beam flange welded to

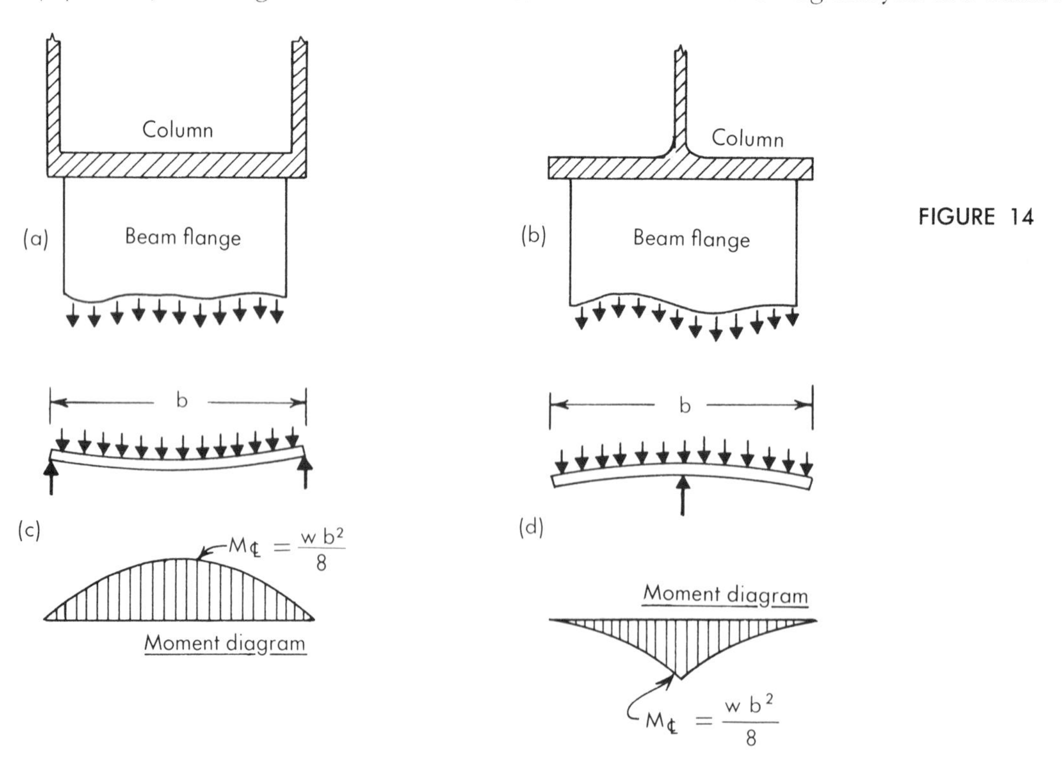

FIGURE 14

a box column, Figure 15(a), is based upon a similar analysis of a line force applied to a cover-plated WF column, Figure 15(b). The latter analysis was made by Dr. T. R. Higgins, Director of Engineering and Research of the AISC.

The following assumptions are made:

1. The length of the box column flange resisting this line force is limited to a distance equal to 6 times its thickness above and below the application of the line force. See Figure 16.

2. The edge welds offer no restraining action to this flange plate. In other words, these two edges are just supported. The upper and lower boundary of this portion of the column flange are fixed.

3. The tensile line force applied to this flange area is uniformly distributed.

At ultimate load (P_u), it is assumed that this rectangular plate has failed as a mechanism with plastic hinges forming along the dotted lines.

The internal work done by the resisting plate equals the summation of the plastic moments (M_p)

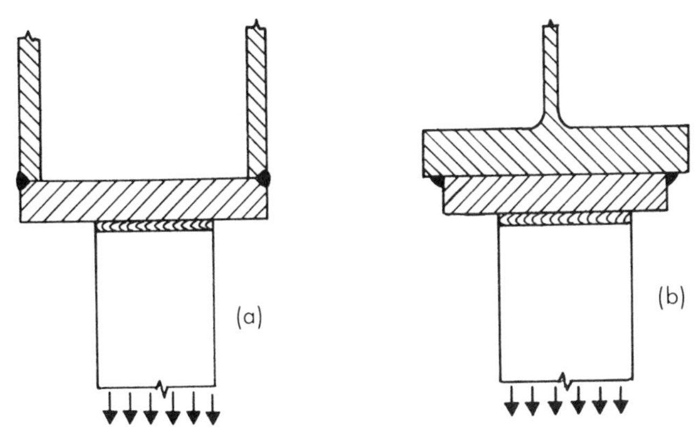

FIGURE 15

multiplied by the angle change (ϕ) along these edges.

The external work done equals the ultimate load (P_u) multiplied by the virtual displacement (Δ).

By setting these two expressions equal to each other, it is possible to solve for the ultimate load (P_u) which may be applied to this portion of the flange plate.

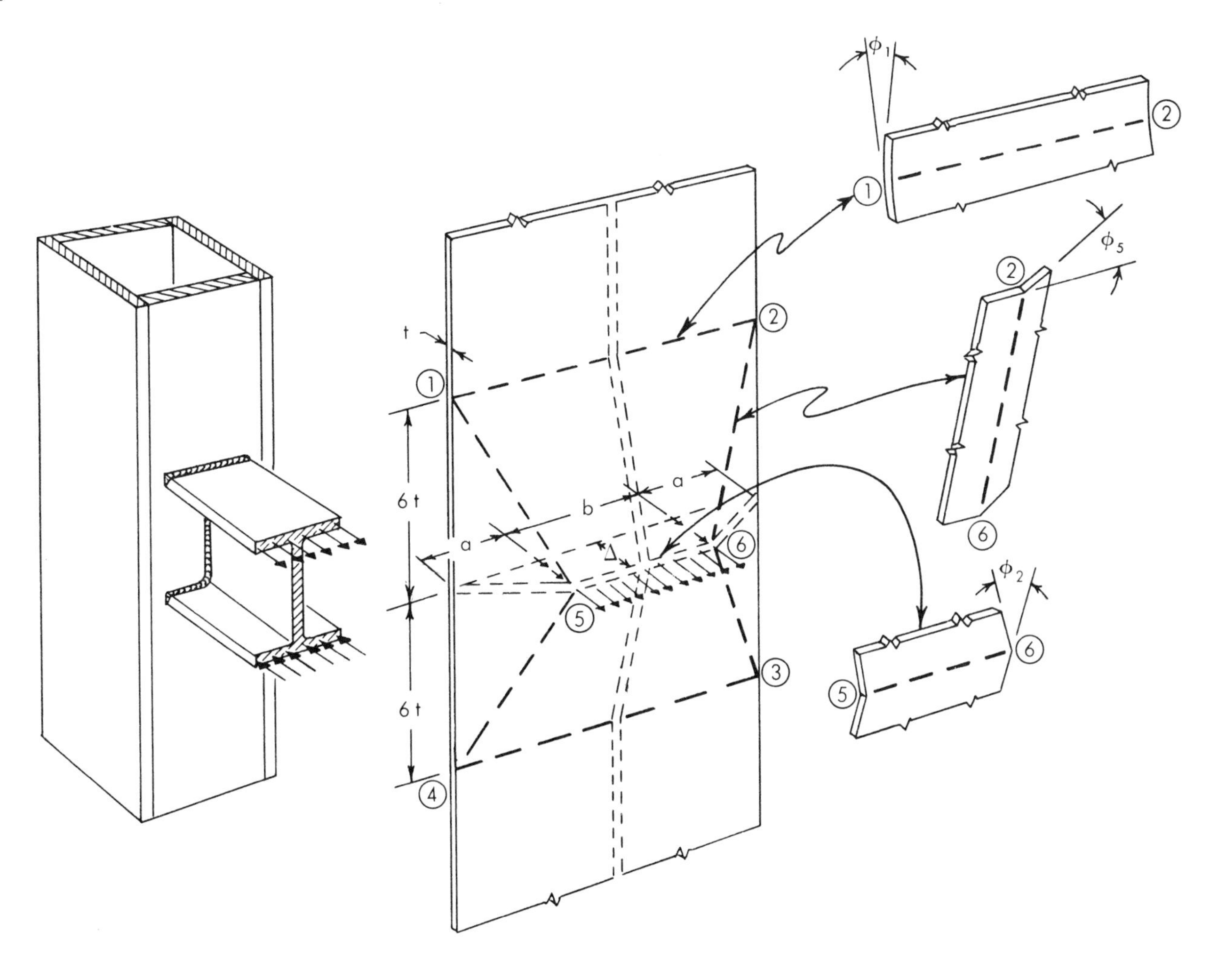

FIGURE 16

At ultimate loading (P_u), plastic moments (M_p) will build up along the dashed lines (Fig. 16) to form plastic hinges. The internal work done, when this plate is pulled out, will be the plastic moment (M_p) multiplied by the corresponding angle changes (ϕ) along these lengths:

angle ϕ_1 along ①—② & ③—④

angle ϕ_2 along ⑤—⑥

angle ϕ_5 along ①—⑤, ②—⑥, ③—⑥ & ④—⑤

With reference to Figure 17:

Distance ②—⑥ $= \sqrt{a^2 + 36\,t^2}$

$$\frac{⑥—Ⓨ}{\sqrt{a^2 + 36\,t^2}} = \frac{6\,t}{a}$$

or distance ⑥—Ⓨ $= \dfrac{a}{6\,t}\sqrt{a^2 + 36\,t^2}$

$$\tan\phi_6 = \frac{\sqrt{a^2 + 36\,t^2}}{Ⓨ—Ⓨ} \text{ also } = \frac{a}{6\,t}$$

or distance Ⓨ—Ⓨ $= \dfrac{6\,t}{a}\sqrt{a^2 + 36\,t^2}$

Now find the angle changes (ϕ) along the hinges at ultimate load:

$$\phi_1 = \frac{\Delta}{6\,t}$$

$$\phi_2 = 2\,\phi_1 = \frac{\Delta}{3\,t}$$

and since

$$\phi_3 = \frac{\Delta\,a}{6\,t\sqrt{a^2 + 36\,t^2}}$$

and

$$\phi_4 = \frac{6\,\Delta\,t}{a\sqrt{a^2 + 36\,t^2}}$$

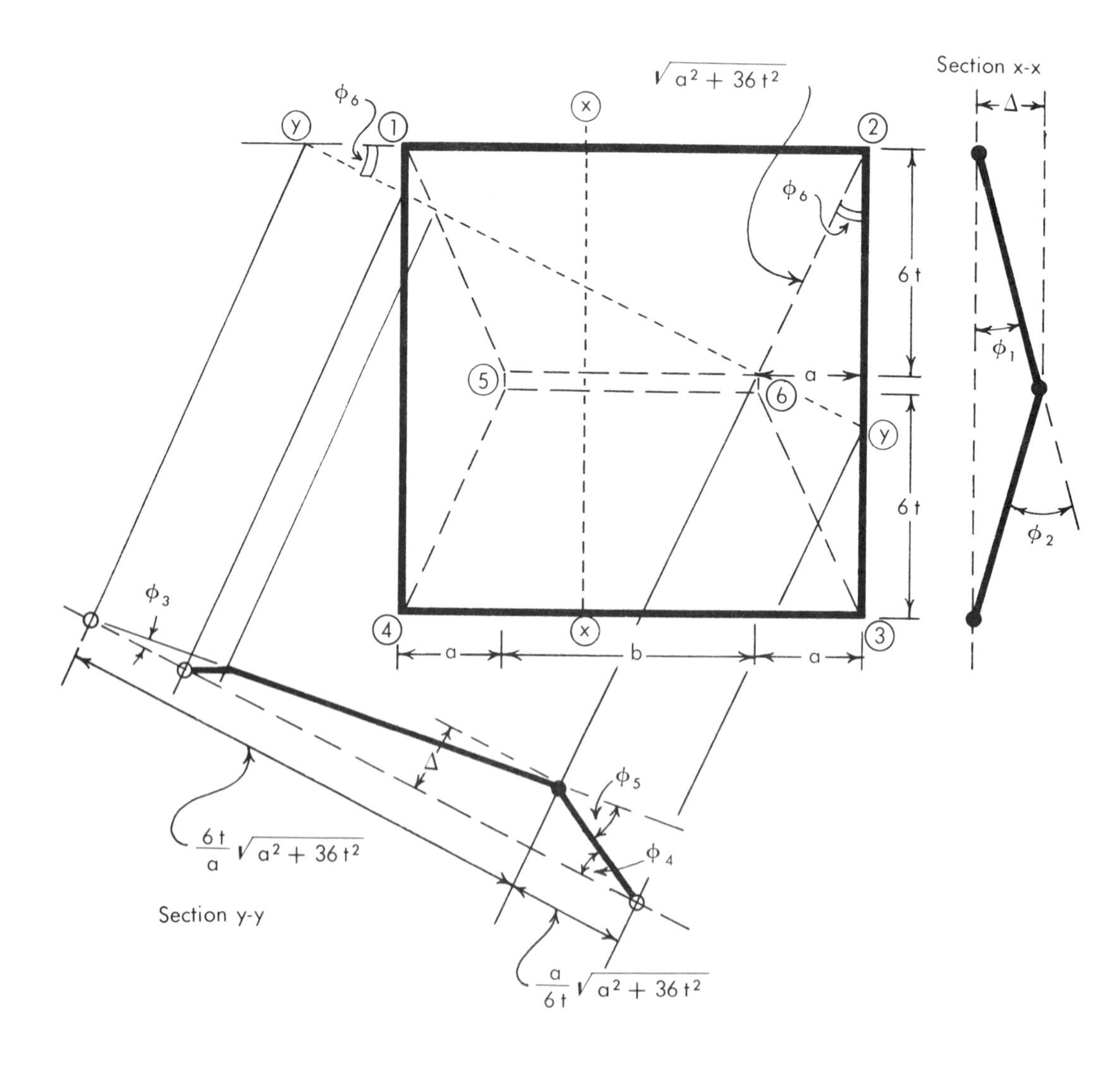

FIGURE 17

$$\therefore\ \phi_5 = \phi_3 + \phi_4 = \frac{\Delta}{6\ at}\ \sqrt{a^2 + 36\ t^2}$$

internal work

$$= M_p \left[\phi_1\, 2(2\,a + b) + \phi_2\, b + \phi_5\, 4\sqrt{a^2 + 36\,t^2} \right]$$

$$= M_p \left[\frac{\Delta}{6\,t}\, 2(2\,a + b) + \frac{\Delta\, b}{3\,t} + \frac{\Delta}{6\ a\ t} \left(\sqrt{a^2 + 36\,t^2}\right)\left(4\sqrt{a^2 + 36\,t^2}\right) \right]$$

$$= M_p\ \Delta \left[\frac{2(a + b)}{3\ t} + 4\left(\frac{a^2 + 36\ t^2}{6\ a\ t}\right) \right]$$

$$= \frac{2\ M_p\ \Delta}{3\ t}\left(2\ a + b + 36\frac{t^2}{a}\right)$$

where the plastic moment (M_p), in in.-lbs/linear inch is—

$$M_p = 2\left(\sigma_y \times \frac{t}{2} \times 1'' \times \frac{t}{4}\right) = \frac{\sigma_y\ t^2}{4}$$

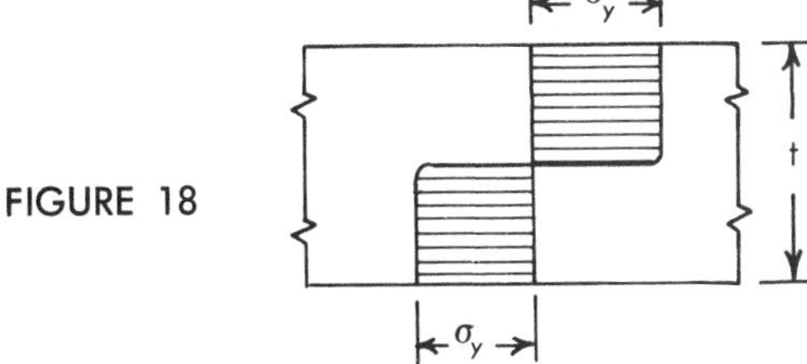

FIGURE 18

external work

$$= P_u\ \Delta$$

allowable force

external work = internal work

$$P_u\ \Delta = \left(\frac{2\ \Delta}{3\ t}\right)\left(\frac{\sigma_y\ t^2}{4}\right)\left(2\ a + b + 36\ \frac{t^2}{a}\right)$$

$$= \frac{\Delta\ \sigma_y\ t}{6}\left(2\ a + b + 36\frac{t^2}{a}\right)$$

Applying a load factor of 2, and using the yield strength (σ_y), the allowable force (P) which may be applied to the plate would be—

$$\boxed{P = \frac{t\ \sigma_y}{12}\left(2\ a + b + 36\frac{t^2}{a}\right)}$$

Example

Here:

t = 3½″

a = 5″

b = 14″

σ = 22,000 psi

calculated tensile force on beam flange = 386 kips

The allowable force:

$$P = \frac{t\ \sigma_y}{12}\left(2\ a + b + 36\ \frac{t^2}{a}\right)$$

$$= \frac{(3\tfrac{1}{2})(36\ \text{kips/sq in.})}{12}\left(2 \times 5'' + 14'' + 36\,\frac{(3\tfrac{1}{2})^2}{5}\right)$$

$$= 1178\ \text{kips} > 386\ \text{kips} \quad \underline{\text{OK}}$$

FIGURE 19

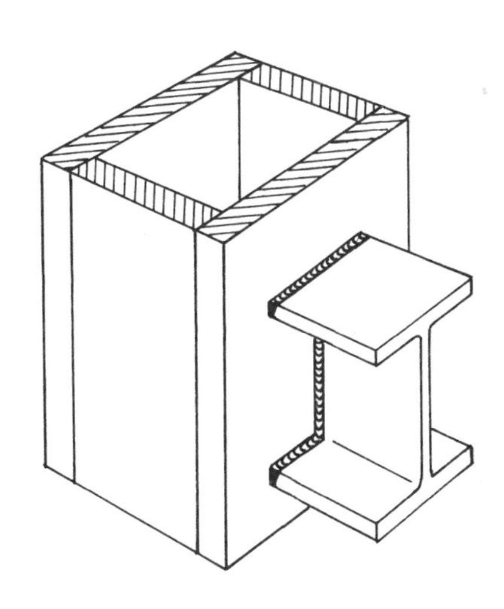

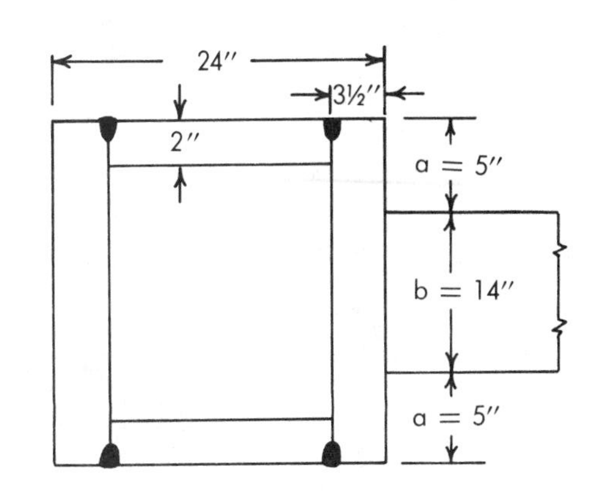

8. TYPICAL APPLICATIONS

Equitable Life Assurance Building

Columns for the Equitable Life Assurance building in San Francisco, an earthquake area, were built and erected in 3-story lengths. The columns were uniformly tapered $\frac{3}{32}$ in./ft from the base to the 14th story.

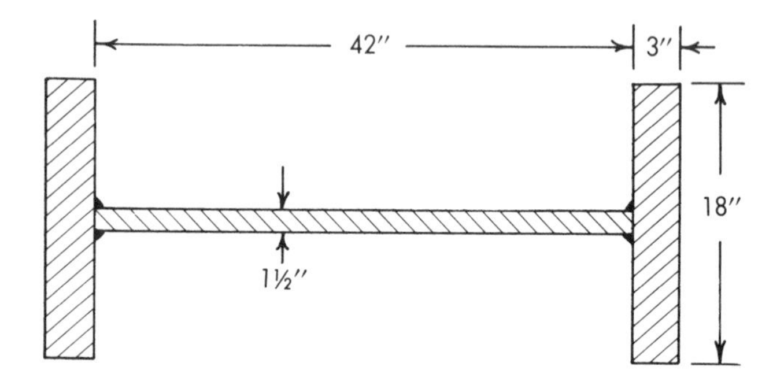

FIGURE 20

FIGURE 22

Exterior columns started with a 42″ web at the bottom, tapering to a 12″ web at the 14th story level; Figure 20. Flanges were 18″ × 3″ at the base. The tapered columns were fabricated by welding two flange plates and a web together. L-shaped columns were used at the corners of the building.

C.IL. House

The 32-story C.I.L. House in Montreal, Canada has the heaviest "H" section columns ever constructed. The fabricated columns weigh as much as 2,000 lbs/ft. A typical column, Figure 21, consists of two 7⅛″ × 28″ flange plates welded to a 5″ × 16½″ web plate.

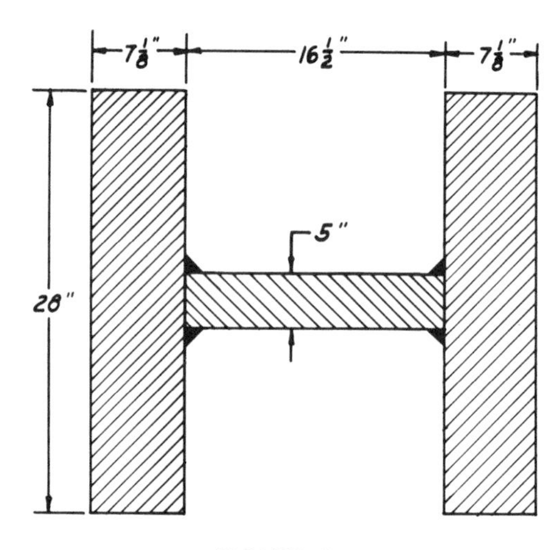

FIGURE 21

Automatic submerged-arc welding was used in fabricating these columns; Figure 22. Simple continuous fillet welds of about ¾″ leg size join the column flanges to the web. Because of the greater forces within the beam-to-column connection region, these welds were increased in size by beveling the web.

The depth of the bevel for this double beveled T-joint varied with the forces to be transferred, but ranged from a minimum of ½″ on each side of the web up to 100%. Less than 10% of these groove welds required 100% beveling. The grooved joints extended in length slightly above and below the depth of the connecting beam and ranged in length from 2′ to 5′.

Joint preparation involved beveling with oxygen cutting equipment at a 22° to 30° angle to the correct depth. After tacking the flange to the web, the weldor lightly air carbon-arc gouged the bottom of the joint prior to welding to open it up for the root pass; the result was a modified J-groove.

The columns, 2 stories high, range from 22′ to 34′ in length. Flange and web plates were clamped in heavy fixtures to maintain proper alignment during welding; Figure 22. After tack welding, trunnions were

FIGURE 23

attached to the column ends so that all welds could be deposited in the flat position. The columns with trunnions attached were then transferred to the automatic welding unit. After preheating to the correct temperature, using natural gas torches, the shorter-length groove welds were made first. The remaining length of unwelded column was then fillet welded.

After welding, trunnions were removed and the column ends machine faced to proper length. Connection plates were attached after machining, with most welds positioned downhand to achieve maximum welding speed. Preheating preceded the manual welding of these plates in position, using low-hydrogen electrodes; Figure 23.

Inland Steel Building
& North Carolina National Bank Building

Elimination of interior columns in a building designed for welded construction is not unique, but usually requires the design and fabrication of special columns; Figure 24.

The column design on the right was used in the Inland Steel Building in Chicago. The inner portion of the built-up column is a standard WF section; the outer portion is a flat plate from 1″ to 3″ thick. A web plate, from ⅝″ to 1½″ thick, joins these two segments. Notice that a section of the main girder was shop welded to the fabricated column. Dotted lines show the spandrel beams and remainder of the girder that were field welded to produce a rigid connection. The main girders span 60′.

On the left is a typical column from the North Carolina National Bank Building in Charlotte. A specially rolled WF section is the main segment of this column. Wing plates have been added to one flange and a cover plate to the other to develop the needed column properties. The main girders and spandrels (dotted sections) were later attached by field welding.

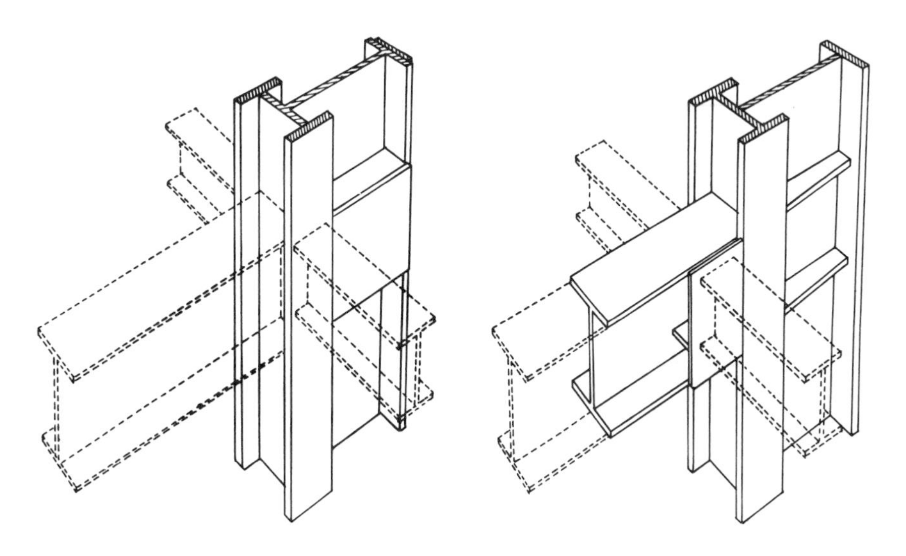

FIGURE 24

FIGURE 25

Fabrication of special column sections demand low cost, high production assembly and welding techniques. Submerged-arc automatic welding is used extensively in fabricating these columns. The welding head, Figure 25, is mounted on a universal, track traveling type welding manipulator. The manipulator, flux recovery unit, and welding generators are mounted on a self-propelled carriage having a 65 ft track travel distance. Two identical welding fixtures are positioned parallel to and on either side of the carriage track. This has reduced handling time for setup and repositioning of the columns.

FIGURE 26

During fabrication of columns for the North Carolina National Bank Building, they were placed in a specially designed trunnion fixture; Figure 26. This stood the columns on end. Shop welding of connection details could then be performed in the flat and horizontal position. This facilitated use of semi-automatic, submerged-arc welding and minimized weld costs.

Commerce Towers Building

Columns of similar section configuration were used in the 32-floor Commerce Towers Building in Kansas City. Here, heavy floor loading due to the modern electronic business machines to be installed necessitated very heavy sections.

Column sections were built up by first welding plates into an I section and a T section, and then joining the end of the T section web to the middle of the I section web. The typical column length is 34′ and the lower columns use 5″ flange plates and 5″ web plates.

Tandem-arc automatic submerged-arc welding was used in joining the flange plates to web; Figure 27. The basic weld was a ½″ fillet deposited at 32-36 ipm. Preheat torches ran ahead of the arc.

In joining together the I and T sections, they are assembled in an air-clamping fixture and tack welded; Figure 28. Automatic submerged-arc welding is then used, with the fixture on a rail-mounted carriage.

FIGURE 27

FIGURE 28

FIGURE 29

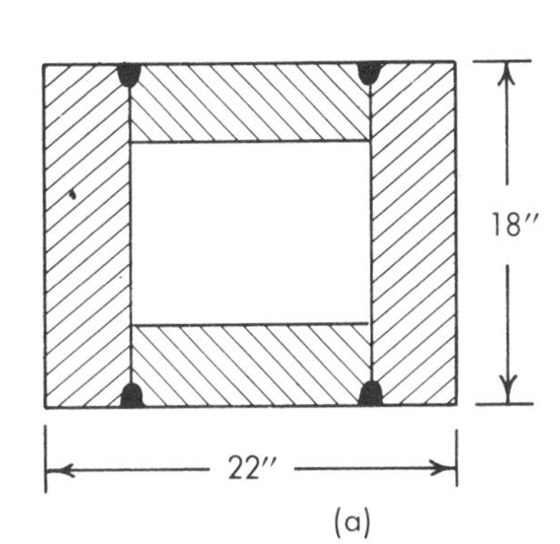

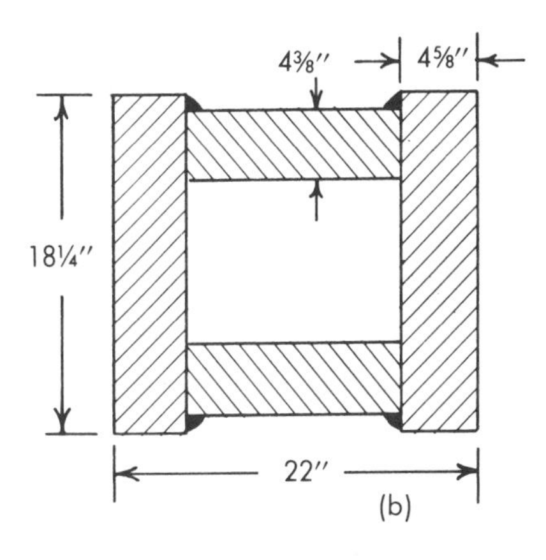

First Federal Savings & Loan Co. Building

On this project in Detroit, Michigan, the engineer originally detailed the fabricated columns to the 17th floor as built-up box sections, flush around the outside periphery. U-groove welds were to be used; Figure 29(a). This would have meant grooving the plates for the entire length of the column.

The fabricator, chose to set one set of plates slightly in or out; Figure 29(b). This would allow use of continuous fillet welds for the basic welding. The fabricator obtained permission to exceed the original outside column dimension in one direction by ¼″. Any further adjustment was precluded because of the already detailed curtain walls, etc.

The original outside dimensions of the columns were 18″ × 22″ to the 5th floor, 18″ × 20″ to the 11th floor, 18″ × 19″ to the 13th floor, and 18″ × 18″ to the 17th floor. Above the 17th floor, WF sections were used. The modified box section on the lower floors were then built up from two 18¼″ × 4⅝″ flange plates, with two 12¾″ × 4⅜″ web plates recessed slightly to permit the fillet welding. Above the 5th floor, the smaller plates were set out slightly.

In general, these full-length welds were ½″ fillets; with ⅜″ fillets for plates 2¼″ or less in thickness. This eliminated plate preparation except for short distances in the region of the beam-to-column connections. Here the plates were previously beveled, to the required depth, varying from ⅜″ to ⁵⁄₁₆″ depending upon load requirements. The typical joint consisting of the beveled groove weld topped by the continuous fillet weld extended 9″ above and below the beam-to-column connection.

9. FIELD SPLICES

Partial-penetration groove welds; either single bevel or single J, may be used for the field splicing of columns. The information presented previously under "Partial-Penetration Groove Welds" will apply here.

Attaching angles shop-welded to the columns serve to temporarily hold the column sections in alignment. For the H column in Figure 30, using high tensile bolts, this connection was considered sufficient to transfer any horizontal shear force across the

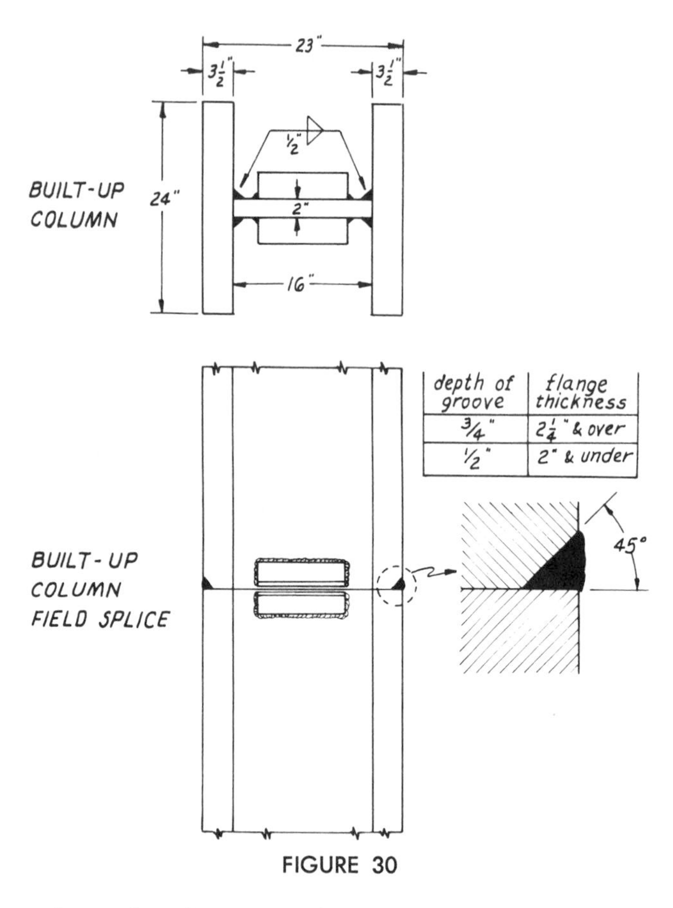

depth of groove	flange thickness
¾"	$2\frac{1}{4}$" & over
½"	2" & under

FIGURE 30

24"
$4\frac{1}{2}$"
$4\frac{1}{2}$"
BUILT-UP COLUMN
24"
½"
⅝"
BUILT-UP COLUMN FIELD SPLICE
45°
⅜" radius
depth of chamfer ⅝" to 1¼"

FIGURE 31

web in this direction. The column field splice, consisting of two single bevel, partial-penetration groove welds, would transfer any horizontal shear in the other direction.

FIGURE 32

For the box column in Figure 31, the column field splice consisted of a partial-penetration J groove weld on all four sides of the column. These four welds would transfer any horizontal shear in the column splice. The attaching angles here were used simply to facilitate erection.

Partial-penetration welds on column splices permit fast semi-automatic welding techniques to be used in the field. In the Commerce Towers project, semi-automatic arc welding with self-shielding, cored electrode permitted deposition of 100 lbs/man/8-hour day; Figure 32.

10. CONCLUSION

The full economic impact of welded steel built-up columns in construction of tall multi-story buildings, can be realized by carefully considering the major cost factors. These are column design, placement of welds, joint design, weld size, and procedure. The dominating objective is the fullest use of automatic arc welding methods in the shop, with an extension of these benefits into the field by use of semi-automatic arc welding for beam-to-column connections and for field splices.

Built-up columns are a key design feature of the 28-story Michigan Consolidated Gas Co. Building in Detroit. Welding was considered to be the only practical method for fabricating these columns which carry a maximum load of approximately 6800 kips. Photo shows a field splice of the column, revealing the shop beveling that facilitated welding. Clip angles shown are for temporary use during erection.

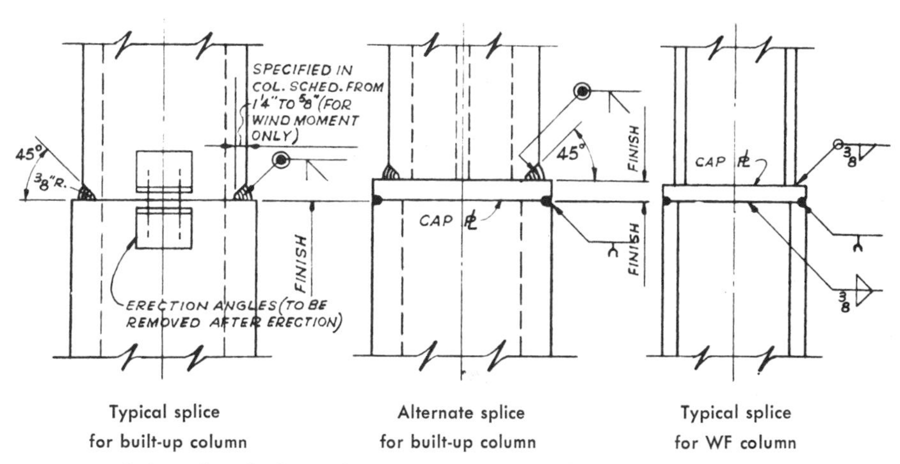

Typical splice for built-up column

Alternate splice for built-up column

Typical splice for WF column

Splice details from the Michigan Consolidated project show how maximum use was made of material at minimum weight.

Automatic submerged-arc welding was used extensively in shop fabricating the unique and complex built-up columns for the 500′ space tower which overlooked the Seattle World's Fair. Approximately 50% of all shop welding was with the submerged-arc process; 25% with self-shielding cored wire, semi-automatically; and the remainder manual stick electrode. At the top of the tower is a five-story observatory and restaurant. The structure required 3400 tons of structural steel.

Welded Plate Girders for Buildings

1. DIMENSIONING THE GIRDER

Plate girders are fabricated for requirements which exceed those of a rolled beam, or a rolled beam with added cover plate. The usual welded plate girder is made of two flange plates fillet welded to a single web plate. Where needed, web stiffeners are attached to one or both sides of the web. Box girders are made of two flange plates fillet welded to two web plates. Internal stiffening of these is accomplished with diaphragm plates.

The flange-area method is used to get an approximate dimension of the girder. This assumes that the flanges will carry all the bending moment and the web will carry all the shear forces.

The required web area is—

$$\boxed{A_w = \frac{V}{\tau}} \quad \cdots\cdots (1)$$

where:

V = vertical shear applied to cross-section to be considered

τ = allowable shear stress on web section

The formula for required flange area is derived from properties of the girder:

$$I = 2\,A_f\,\frac{d^2}{2} + \frac{t_w\,d^3}{12} \quad \text{or}$$

$$= \frac{A_f\,d^2}{2} + \frac{A_w\,d^2}{12} \qquad \text{since } A_w = t_w\,d$$

For simplicity, this assumes web depth is equal to (d), the distance between the centers of gravity of the two flange plates.

$$S = \frac{I}{d/2} \quad \text{or}$$

$$= A_f\,d + \frac{A_w\,d}{6}$$

Also,

$$S = \frac{M}{\sigma}$$

Therefore, the required flange area is—

$$\boxed{A_f = \frac{M}{\sigma\,d} - \frac{A_w}{6}} \quad \cdots\cdots (2)$$

where:

M = bending moment applied to section

σ = allowable bending stress

d = distance between centers of gravity of flange plates

This method will require some approximate knowledge of what the girder depth should be and some adjustment of the resulting figures before the design is finalized.

Guides to Girder Depth

The previous AISC specification held the depth of girders to a minimum value of 1/24 of the span. The Commentary on the new AISC specifications suggests, as a guide, that the girder depth should not exceed the following:

Floors: σ_y / 800,000 times the span
Roof purlins: σ_y / 1,000,000 times the span

This translates into the Table 1 limiting values of depth-to-length for girders used in floors. These values are for general guidance only.

TABLE 1—Suggested Girder Depth Limits (AISC)

AISC Steels			Others	
	σ_y	d/L	σ	d/L
A7, A373	33,000	1/24.2	45,000	1/17.8
A36	36,000	1/22.2	50,000	1/16.0
A441	42,000	1/19.0	55,000	1/14.6
	46,000	1/17.4	60,000	1/13.3
	50,000	1/16.0	65,000	1/12.3
			90,000*	1/8.8
			95,000*	1/8.4
			100,000*	1/8.0

* Quenched & tempered steels: Yield strength at 0.2% offset.

TABLE 2—Allowable Bending Stresses For Plate and Box Girders

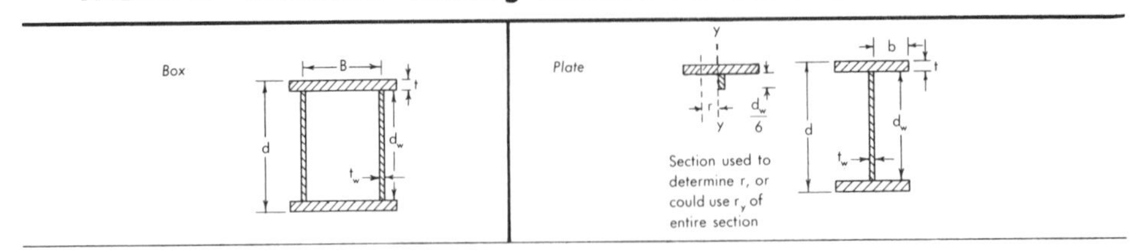

Compression elements which are not "compact" but meet the following AISC Sec 1.9 requirements—

$$* \quad \frac{b}{t} \leqq \frac{3{,}000}{\sqrt{\sigma_y}} \qquad (1.9.1)$$

$$* \quad \frac{B}{t} \leqq \frac{8{,}000}{\sqrt{\sigma_y}} \qquad (1.9.2)$$

$$\frac{d_w}{t_w} \leqq \frac{14{,}000{,}000}{\sqrt{\sigma_y(\sigma_y + 16{,}500)}} \qquad (1.10.2)$$

box girder		plate girder	
tension $\sigma = .60\ \sigma_y$	(1.5.1.4.3)	**tension** $\sigma = .60\ \sigma_y$	(1.5.1.4.4.)
compression $\sigma = .60\ \sigma_y$	(1.5.1.4.3)	**compression** $\sigma = \left[1.0 - \dfrac{\left(\frac{L}{r}\right)^2}{2\ C_c^2\ C_b}\right] .60\ \sigma_y$ (AISC Formula 4) $\quad \sigma = \dfrac{12{,}000{,}000}{\frac{Ld}{A_f}}$ (AISC Formula 5) Use the larger of (4) or (5) but not to exceed .60 σ_y If $\frac{L}{r} < 40$, don't need to use (4)	(1.5.1.4.5)

reduction in allowable compressive bending stress due to possible lateral displacement of web. (1.10.6)

when $\dfrac{d_w}{t_w} < \dfrac{24{,}000}{\sqrt{\sigma_b}}$ $\qquad \sigma_b$ = allowable compression stress from above

$$\text{use } \sigma = \sigma_b \left[1.0 - .0005\ \frac{A_w}{A_c}\left(\frac{d_w}{t_w} - \frac{24{,}000}{\sqrt{\sigma_b}}\right)\right]$$

(AISC Formula 11)

* This ratio may be exceeded if the compressive bending stress, using a width not exceeding this limit, is within the allowable stress. The above toble does not include the higher bending stress ($\sigma = .66\ \sigma_y$) for "compact" sections because most fabricated plate and box girders will exceed the width-thickness ratio of "compact" sections.

Allowable Bending Stresses

Table 2 summarizes the AISC allowable bending stresses for plate and box girders.

In Table 2:

L = span or unbraced length of compression flange

r = radius of gyration of a Tee section comprising the compression flange plus 1/6 of the web area, about the y-y axis (in the plane of the web). For girders symmetrical about their x-x axis of bending, substitution of r_y of the entire section is conservative

A_f = area of the compression flange

$$C_b = 1.75 - 1.05\ \frac{M_1}{M_2} + .3\left(\frac{M_1}{M_2}\right)^2$$

(but not more than 2.3; can conservatively be taken as 1.0)

$$C_c = \sqrt{\frac{2\ \pi^2\ E}{\sigma_y}}$$

σ_b = allowable compressive bending stress from above

M_1 is the smaller, and M_2 is the larger bending moment at the ends of the unbraced length (L), taken about the strong axis of the member. M_1/M_2 is the ratio of these end moments. When M_1 and M_2 have

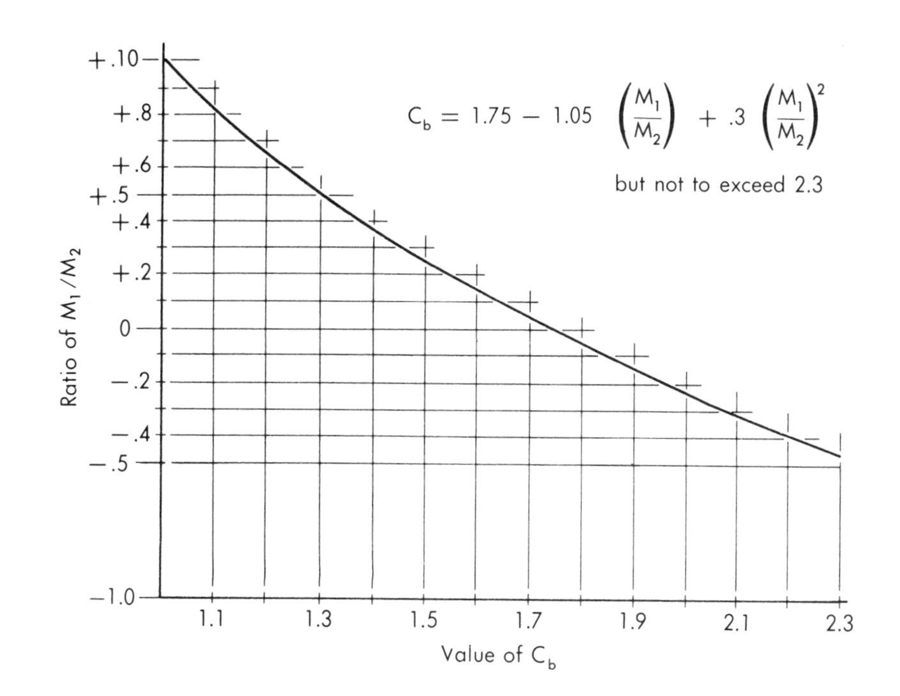

FIGURE 1

the same signs, this ratio is positive; when they have different signs, it is negative. When the bending moment within an unbraced length is larger than that at both ends of this length, the ratio is taken as unity.

Figure 1 is a graph showing the value of C_b for any given ratio of M_1/M_2.

When the bending moment within an unbraced length is larger than that at both ends of this length, the ratio shall be taken as unity, and C_b becomes 1.0.

2. TRANSVERSE INTERMEDIATE STIFFENERS

Loads applied to beams and girders cause bending moments along the length of the member. When these moments are non-uniform along the length of the member, both horizontal and vertical shear stresses are set up because shear is equal to the rate of change of moment.

The horizontal shear forces would cause the flange of a plate girder to slide past the web if it were not for the fillet welds joining them.

These horizontal and vertical shear stresses combine and produce both diagonal tension and compression, each at 45° to the shear stresses. In steel structures, tension is not the problem; however, the diagonal compression could be high enough to cause the web to buckle. Stiffeners are used to prevent the web from buckling in regions of high shear stress.

The ratio of web thickness to clear depth of web in the older specifications was based on predications of the plate buckling theory: the web being subjected to shear throughout its depth, and to compressive bending stresses over a portion of its depth. See Figure 2.

The plate buckling theory assumes the portion of the web between stiffeners to be an isolated plate; however, in the plate girder, the web is part of a built-up member. When the critical buckling stress in the web is reached, the girder does not collapse. This is because the flanges carry all of the bending moment,

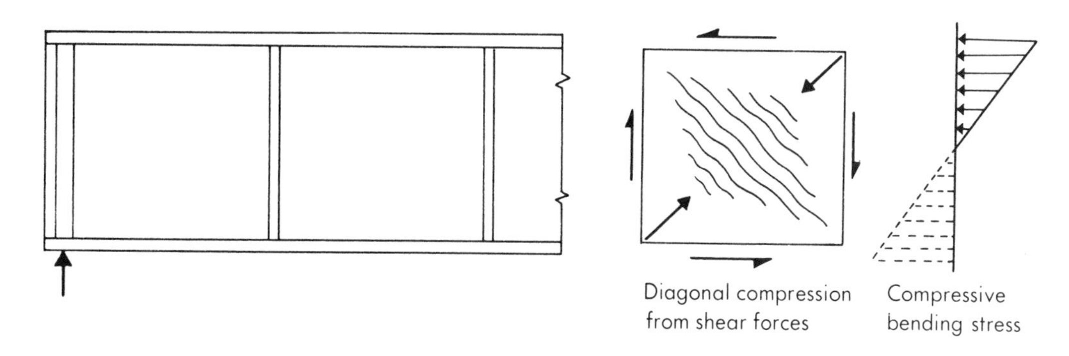

FIGURE 2

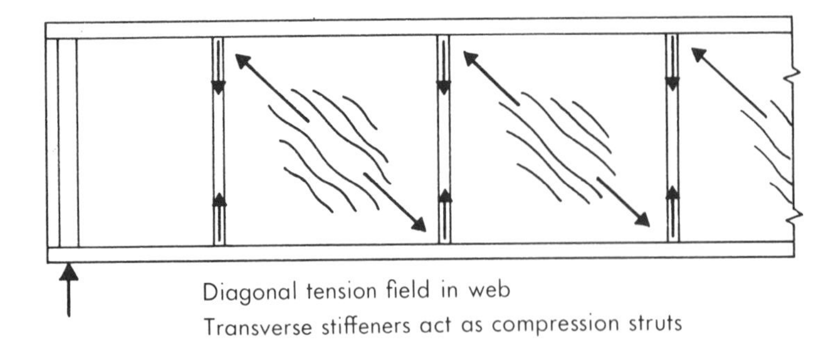

Diagonal tension field in web
Transverse stiffeners act as compression struts

FIGURE 3

the buckled web then serves as a tension diagonal, and the transverse stiffeners become the vertical compression struts. This in effect makes the plate girder act as a truss. See Figure 3.

The carrying capacity of the plate girder is greater under this analysis, being equal to that supported by the beam action shear (Fig. 2) and that supported by the diagonal tension field in the web (Fig. 3). AISC Formulas 8 and 9 will meet this requirement. These formulas appear further along on this page.

AISC Specifications

Intermediate stiffeners are not required when the ratio (d_w/t_w) is less than 260 and the maximum web shear stress is less than that permitted by AISC Formula 9 (AISC 1.10.5.3).

Figure 4 partially summarizes the AISC specifications for intermediate stiffeners.

These requirements apply:

1. If single stiffeners are used, they must be welded to compression flange (AISC 1.10.5.4).

2. Intermediate stiffeners may be cut short of tension flange for a distance less than 4 t_w when not needed for bearing (AISC 1.10.5.4).

3. For intermittent fillet welds, clear spacing (s) between lengths of weld must $\leqq$ 16 t_w and $\leqq$ 10″ (AISC 1.10.5.4).

4. Welds joining stiffeners to web must be sufficient to transfer a total unit shear force of—

$$f_s = d_w \sqrt{\left(\frac{\sigma_y}{3400}\right)^3} \qquad \text{(AISC 1.10.5.4)}$$

This shear force to be transferred may be reduced in same proportion that the largest computed shear stress (τ) in the adjacent panel is less than that allowed by AISC Formula 8 (AISC 1.10.5.4).

5. If lateral bracing is attached to stiffener, welds connecting stiffener to compression flange must be sufficient to transfer a horizontal force (F) = 1% of flange force (AISC 1.10.5.4).

When intermediate stiffeners are required, their maximum spacing (a) depends on three items: a/d_w, d_w/t_w, and shear stress (τ).

The largest average web shear stress ($\tau_{av} = V/A_w$) in any panel between transverse intermediate stiffeners shall not exceed the following (AISC 1.10.5.2):

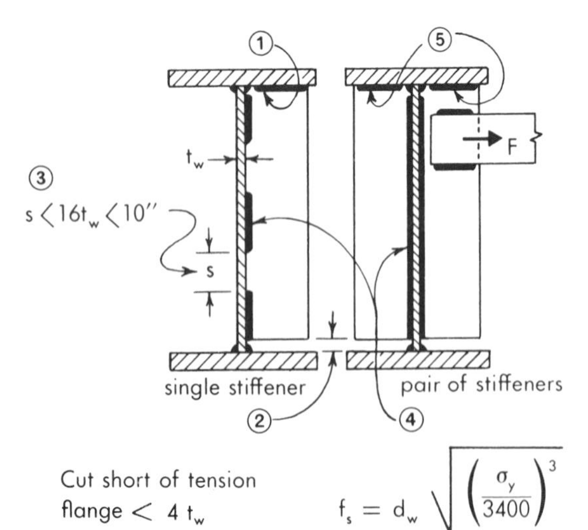

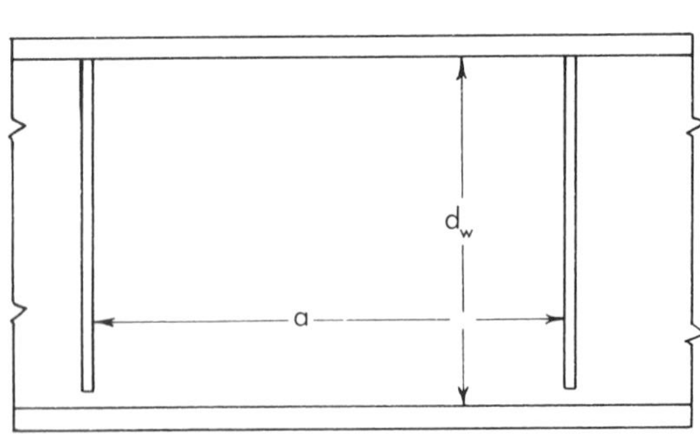

FIGURE 4

when $C_v < 1.0$

$$\tau \leq \frac{\sigma_y}{2.89}\left[C_v + \frac{1 - C_v}{1.15\sqrt{1 + \left(\frac{a}{d_w}\right)^2}}\right] \quad \text{(AISC Formula 8)} \qquad \text{..(3a)}$$

This provides an allowable shear stress (τ) up to about .35 σ_y and takes advantage of tension field action.

when $C_v > 1.0$ or when no stiffeners are used

$$\tau \leq \frac{\sigma_y\, C_v}{2.89} < .40\, \sigma_y \quad \text{(AISC Formula 9)} \qquad \text{................(3b)}$$

This provides an allowable shear stress (τ) within the range of .347 σ_y to .40 σ_y and does not take advantage of tension field action.

where:

a = clear distance between transverse stiffeners, in.

d_w = clear distance between flanges, in.

t_w = thickness of web, in.

σ_y = yield strength of girder steel, psi

when $C_v < .8$

$$C_v = \frac{45{,}000{,}000\ k}{\sigma_y\ (d_w/t_w)^2}$$

when $C_v > .8$

$$C_v = \frac{6{,}000}{(d_w/t_w)}\sqrt{\frac{k}{\sigma_y}}$$

when $a/d_w < 1.0$

$$k = 4.00 + \frac{5.34}{(a/d_w)^2}$$

when $a/d_w > 1.0$

$$k = 5.34 + \frac{4.00}{(a/d_w)^2}$$

Above, the one C_v formula picks up exactly where the other leaves off. The value of C_v may be read directly from the nomograph, Figure 5, without separately computing the value of k.

Both ASIC Formulas 8 and 9 contain a basic factor $\left(\frac{\sigma_y\, C_v}{2.89}\right)$ which you will notice is the same as $\left(\frac{.60\, \sigma_y\, C_v}{\sqrt{3}}\right)$ or (.347 σ_y C_v). The expression (.60 σ_y) is recognized as the basic allowable tensile stress and $\left(\frac{\sigma_y}{\sqrt{3}}\right)$ as (τ_y).

For greater depth to thickness of web (d_w/t_w) and greater stiffener spacing (a/d_w), the values of (C_v) will become lower. This will result in lower values for the allowable shear stress in the web. For these conditions, AISC Formula 8 has an additional factor which takes advantage of the increased carrying capacity provided by the diagonal tension field and results in a higher shear allowable. When $C_v = 1$, this factor becomes zero and AISC Formula 8 becomes Formula 9.

The ratio a/d_w shall not exceed (AISC 1.10.5.3):

$$a/d_w \leq \frac{260}{d_w/t_w} \qquad \text{..........................(4)}$$

nor

$$a/d_w \leq 3.0 \qquad \text{..........................(5)}$$

These arbitrary values provide a girder which will facilitate handling during fabrication and erection.

When a/d_w exceeds 3.0, its value is taken as infinity. Then AISC Formula 8 reduces to AISC Formula 9 and $k = 5.34$ (AISC 1.10.5.2).

This work can be greatly simplified by using the appropriate AISC Table 3 for the specific yield point of steel. See AISC's "Specification for the Design, Fabrication and Erection of Structural Steel for Buildings" and Bethlehem Steel Corp's *Steel Design File* on "V Steels—Recommended Allowable Stresses for Building Design."

In end panels and panels containing large holes, the smaller dimension (a or d_w) shall not exceed (AISC 1.10.5.3)—

$$a \text{ or } d_w \leq \frac{11{,}000\ t_w}{\sqrt{\tau}} \qquad \text{....................(6)}$$

where τ is the computed average shear stress in the web:

$$\tau = \frac{V}{A_w}$$

It is necessary that the stiffeners have sufficient cross-sectional area for them to act as compressive struts to resist the vertical component of the tension field in the web.

This cross-sectional area, in square inches, of intermediate stiffeners when spaced in accordance with

FIG. 5 Value of C_v to Determine Allowable Web Shear Stress (1.10.5.2)

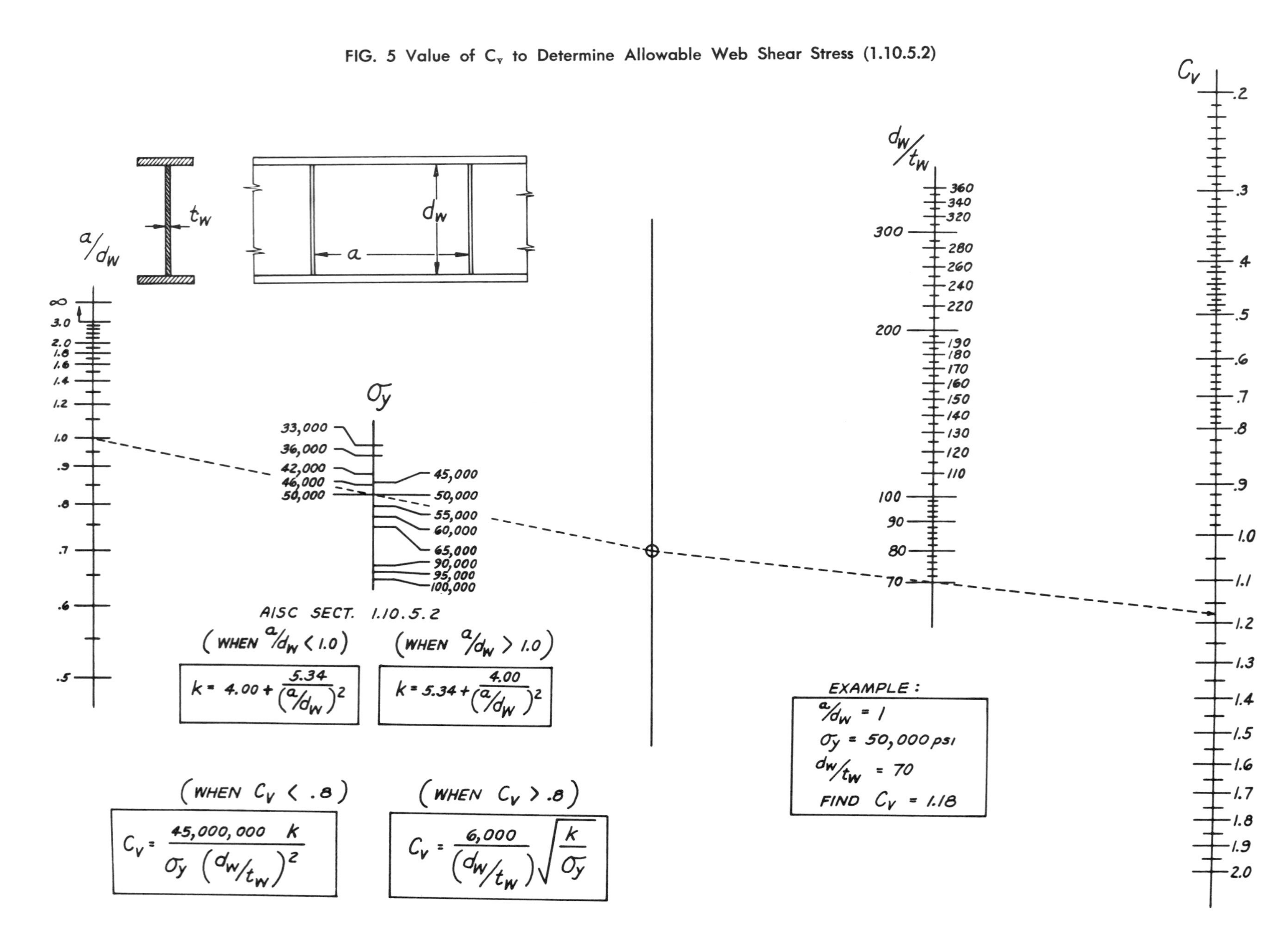

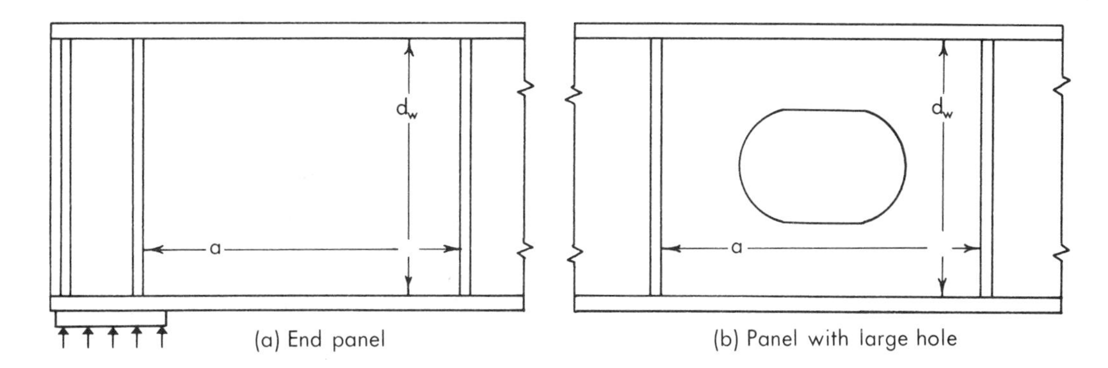

(a) End panel

(b) Panel with large hole

FIGURE 6

AISC Formula 8 (total area when in pairs) must not be less than (AISC 1.10.5.4)—

$$A_s \geqq \frac{1 - C_v}{2}\left[\frac{a}{d_w} - \frac{(a/d_w)^2}{\sqrt{1 + (a/d_w)^2}}\right] Y\, D\, d_w\, t \qquad (7)$$

(AISC Formula 10)

(See the appropriate AISC Table 3)

where:

$$Y = \frac{\text{yield point of web steel}}{\text{yield point of stiffener steel}}$$

D = 1.0 for a pair of stiffeners
1.8 for a single angle stiffener
2.4 for a single plate stiffener

When the greatest shear stress (τ) in a panel is less than that permitted by AISC Formula 8, this area (A_s) requirement may be reduced in like proportion (AISC 1.10.5.4).

The moment of inertia of a pair of stiffeners or a single stiffener, with reference to an axis in the plane of the web, shall not be less than (AISC 1.10.5.4)—

$$I_s \geqq \left(\frac{d_w}{50}\right)^4 \qquad \text{(8)}$$

See Tables 3, 4, and 5.

Plate girder webs, subjected to a combination of bending tensile stress and shear stress shall be checked according to the following interaction formula:

$$\underline{\sigma_b} \leqq \left(0.825 - 0.375 \frac{\tau}{\underline{\tau}}\right) \sigma_y \text{ or } .60\, \sigma_y \qquad \text{(9)}$$

(AISC Formula 12)

where:

τ = computed average web shear stress $= \dfrac{V}{A_w}$

$\underline{\tau}$ = allowable web shear stress from AISC Formulas 8 or 9

$\underline{\sigma_b}$ = allowable bending tensile stress

It can be shown that this formula will result in—

a) full bending tensile stress allowable, if the concurrent shear stress is not greater than 60% of the full allowable value, or

b) full shear stress allowable, if the concurrent bending tensile stress is not greater than 75% of the full allowable value.

See Table 6B for abbreviated Formula 12 to use for a specific yield strength of steel.

3. BEARING STIFFENERS

Concentrated loads cause high compressive stress at the web toe of the fillet along a distance of N + K for end reactions, and N + 2K for interior loads.

If there are no bearing stiffeners, this compressive stress shall not exceed (AISC 1.10.10.1)—

for end reactions

$$\sigma = \frac{R}{t_w(N + K)} \leqq .75\, \sigma_y \qquad \text{(10a)}$$

(AISC Formula 14)

for interior loads

$$\sigma = \frac{R}{t_w(N + 2K)} \leqq .75\, \sigma_y \qquad \text{(10b)}$$

(AISC Formula 13)

Also, the sum of the compressive stresses from concentrated and distributed loads on the compression edge of the web plate not supported directly by bearing stiffeners shall not exceed (AISC 1.10.10.2)—

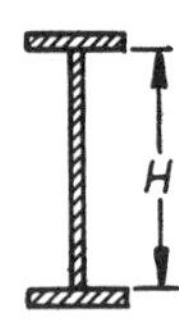

TABLE 3—Minimum Moment of Inertia of Intermediate Stiffener

For a Given Web Depth (d_w)

$$I_s \geqq \left(\frac{d_w}{50}\right)^4$$

d_w	I_s	d_w	I_s	d_w	I_s	d_w	I_s	d_w	I_s
10	.00160	45	.656	80	6.56	115	28.0	150	81.0
11	.00234	46	.717	81	6.89	116	29.0	151	83.2
12	.00332	47	.781	82	7.24	117	30.0	152	85.3
13	.00457	48	.849	83	7.60	118	31.0	153	87.7
14	.00615	49	.924	84	7.96	119	32.0	154	90.0
15	.00810	50	1.00	85	8.36	120	33.1	155	92.3
16	.0105	51	1.08	86	8.76	121	34.3	156	94.7
17	.0134	52	1.17	87	9.17	122	35.4	157	97.2
18	.0168	53	1.26	88	9.60	123	36.6	158	99.7
19	.0208	54	1.36	89	10.0	124	37.8	159	102.0
20	.0256	55	1.46	90	10.5	125	39.1	160	104.5
21	.0311	56	1.57	91	11.0	126	40.3	161	107.3
22	.0375	57	1.69	92	11.5	127	41.6	162	110.0
23	.0448	58	1.81	93	12.0	128	42.9	163	112.7
24	.0531	59	1.94	94	12.5	129	44.3	164	115.7
25	.0625	60	2.07	95	13.0	130	45.7	165	118.3
26	.0731	61	2.22	96	13.6	131	47.1	166	121.5
27	.0850	62	2.37	97	14.2	132	48.6	167	124.3
28	.0984	63	2.52	98	14.8	133	50.1	168	127.5
29	.113	64	2.68	99	15.4	134	51.6	169	130.2
30	.130	65	2.86	100	16.0	135	53.2	170	133.5
31	.148	66	3.04	101	16.7	136	54.8	171	136.5
32	.168	67	3.22	102	17.3	137	56.3	172	140.0
33	.190	68	3.42	103	18.0	138	58.1	173	143.3
34	.214	69	3.63	104	18.7	139	59.8	174	146.4
35	.240	70	3.84	105	19.4	140	61.5	175	150.0
36	.269	71	4.06	106	20.2	141	63.2	176	153.0
37	.300	72	4.30	107	21.0	142	65.1	177	156.7
38	.334	73	4.54	108	21.8	143	66.8	178	160.0
39	.370	74	4.80	109	22.6	144	68.7	179	164.0
40	.410	75	5.06	110	23.4	145	70.8	180	168.0
41	.451	76	5.34	111	24.3	146	72.7		
42	.499	77	5.62	112	25.2	147	74.7		
43	.547	78	5.82	113	26.1	148	76.7		
44	.600	79	6.23	114	27.0	149	78.8		

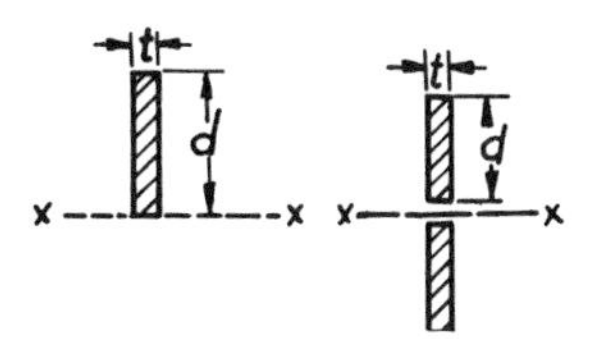

TABLE 4—Moment of Inertia of Single Flat Bar Stiffener

Double These Values for Stiffeners on Both Sides of Girder Web

$$I_s = \frac{t\,d^3}{3}$$

Thickness of bar (t)

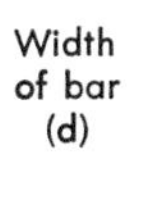

Width of bar (d)	1/4"	5/16"	3/8"	7/16"	1/2"	5/8"	3/4"	7/8"	1"
2"	.66	.82	.99	1.16	1.32	1.65	1.98	2.31	2.66
2 1/2"	1.46	1.83	2.19	2.56	2.93	3.66	4.39	5.21	5.85
3"	2.25	2.81	3.37	3.94	4.49	5.62	6.75	7.87	8.99
3 1/2"	3.55	4.44	5.32	6.21	7.10	8.88	10.6	12.4	14.2
4"	5.33	6.66	8.00	9.32	10.7	13.3	16.0	18.6	21.2
4 1/2"	7.59	9.49	11.4	13.3	15.2	19.0	22.8	26.6	30.4
5"	10.4	13.0	15.6	18.2	20.9	26.1	31.3	36.5	41.7
5 1/2"		17.3	20.8	24.2	27.7	34.7	41.6	48.5	55.5
6"		22.5	27.0	31.5	36.0	44.9	54.0	63.0	72.0
6 1/2"			34.3	40.0	45.7	57.1	68.5	80.0	91.4
7"			46.9	50.0	57.2	71.4	85.7	100.	114.
7 1/2"			52.8	61.6	70.4	88.0	105.	123.	141.
8"				74.8	85.5	107.	128.	150.	171.
8 1/2"				89.6	102.	128.	154.	179.	204.
9"				106.	121.	152.	182.	212.	243.
9 1/2"					142.	178.	214.	250.	285.
10"					166.	208.	249.	291.	333.

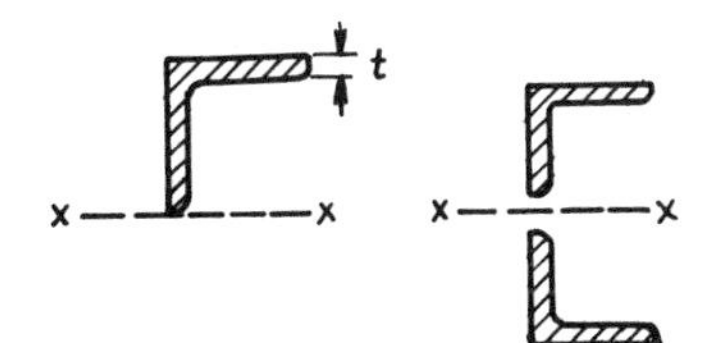

TABLE 5—Moment of Inertia of Single Angle Stiffener

Double These Values for Stiffeners on Both Sides of Girder Web

Thickness of angle stiffener(t)

Angle size	1"	7/8"	3/4"	5/8"	9/16"	1/2"	7/16"	3/8"	5/16"	1/4"
8" × 8"	564.5	506.4	444.0	379.3	354.1	310.2				
6" × 6"	224.0	201.9	178.5	153.8	140.4	127.2	113.0	98.3	79.9	
5" × 5"		111.7	99.8	86.2		71.8	63.8	55.8	47.3	
4" × 4"			48.2	42.1		35.4	31.7	27.8	23.6	19.4
3 1/2" × 3 1/2"						23.0	20.7	18.3	15.7	12.8
3" × 3'						14.0	12.6	11.2	9.6	7.9
2 1/2" × 2 1/2"						7.6		6.2	5.4	4.5
2" × 2"								3.0	2.6	2.2

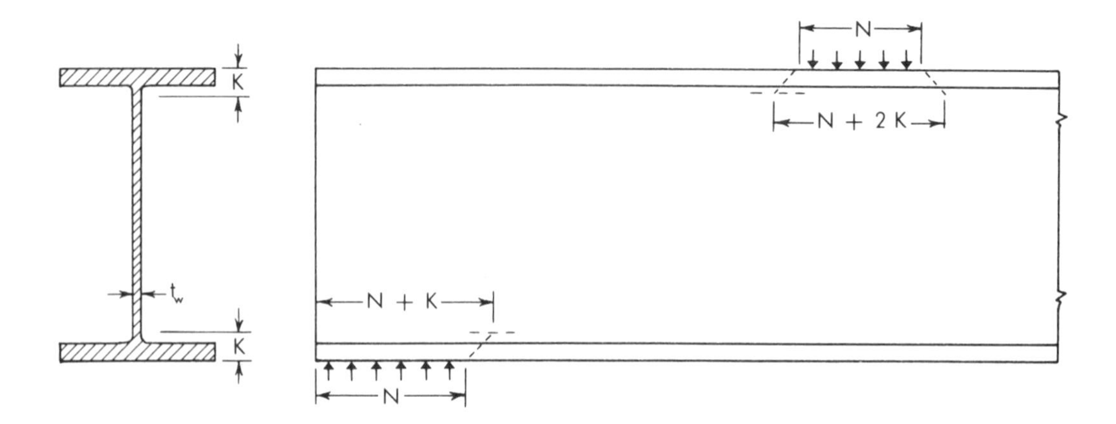

FIGURE 7

if flange restrained against rotation

$$\sigma \leqq \left[5.5 + \frac{4}{(a/d_w)^2} \right] \frac{10{,}000{,}000}{(d_w/t_w)^2} \quad \text{(AISC Formula 15)} \qquad \ldots\ldots(11a)$$

if flange not restrained against rotation

$$\sigma \leqq \left[2 + \frac{4}{(a/d_w)^2} \right] \frac{10{,}000{,}000}{(d_w/t_w)^2} \quad \text{(AISC Formula 16)} \qquad \ldots\ldots(11b)$$

Concentrated loads and loads distributed over a partial length of panel shall be divided by either the product of the web thickness and the girder depth or the length of panel in which the load is placed, whichever is the smaller panel dimension. Any other distributed loading, in lbs/linear in. of length, shall be divided by the web thickness.

If the above stress limits are exceeded, bearing stiffeners shall be placed in pairs at unframed ends and at points of concentrated loads, Figure 8.

Bearing stiffeners with the above sections of web are designed as columns (AISC 1.10.5.1).

These requirements apply:

1. Bearing stiffeners shall extend almost to edge of flange (AISC 1.10.5.1).

2. Bearing stiffeners shall have close bearing against flange or flanges to which load is applied (AISC 1.10.5.1).

3. Clear spacing of intermittent fillet welds $< 16\, t_w < 10''$ (AISC 1.10.5.4.).

4. Deduct leg of fillet weld or corner snipe for width of stiffener (b_s) effective in bearing at 90% σ_y (AISC 1.5.1.5.1). If parts have different yield strengths, use the lower value.

5. The limiting ratio of stiffener width to thickness shall be—

$$\frac{b_s}{t_s} \leqq \frac{3000}{\sqrt{\sigma_y}} \quad \text{(AISC 1.9.1)}$$

6. Use $L_e \geqq \frac{3}{4}\, d_w$ for slenderness ratio (L_e/r) of column section to determine allowable compressive stress (AISC 1.10.5.1); r is figured about an axis in the plane of the web.

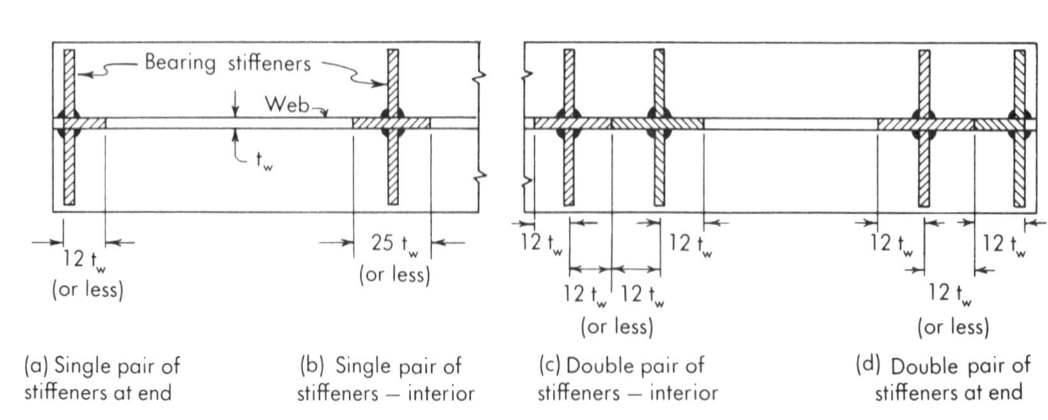

FIGURE 8

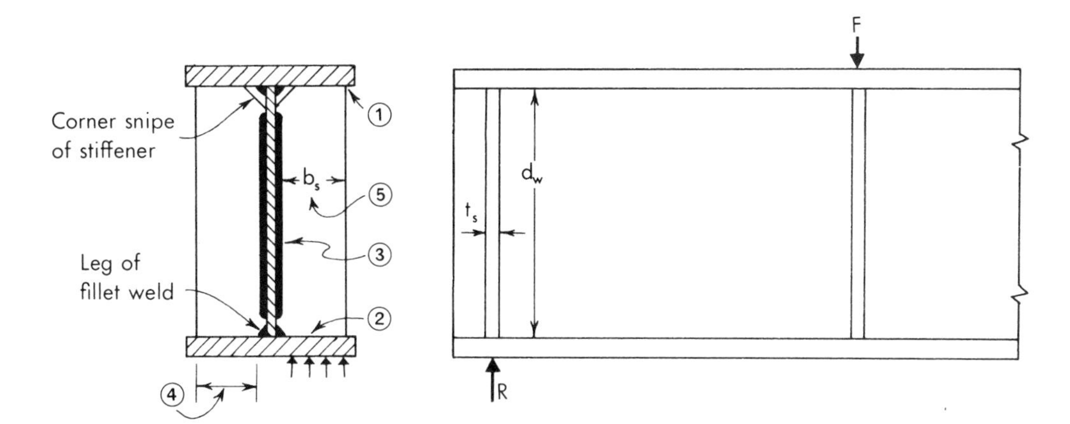

FIGURE 9

4. LONGITUDINAL FILLET WELDS

If intermittent fillet welds are used in plate or box girders, their longitudinal clear spacing shall not exceed—

tension flange (AISC 1.18.3.1)

$$s \leq 24 \times \text{thickness of thinner plate} \leq 12'' \qquad (12)$$

compression flange (AISC 1.18.2.3)

$$s \leq \frac{4000\ t_w}{\sqrt{\sigma_y}} \leq 12'' \qquad (13)$$

The longitudinal shear force on fillet weld between flange and web is—

$$f = \frac{V\ a\ y}{I\ n} \text{ lbs/linear in.}$$

where:

V = external shear on section

a = area of flange held by welds

y = distance between center of gravity of flange area held by welds, and neutral axis of entire section

I = moment of inertia of entire section

n = number of fillet welds holding flange area, usually 2 welds

5. SUMMARY OF SPECIFICATIONS

Table 6 summarizes the principal AISC specifications in easy to use form, permitting direct readout of the limiting value for the specific yield strength steel being used.

Problem 1

Design a welded plate girder to support a 120-kip uniformly distributed load, and a 125-kip concentrated load at midspan; Figure 11. Girder is to be simply supported, have a span of 50′, and have sufficient lateral support for its compressive flange. Use A36 steel and E70 or SA-2 weld metal.

FIGURE 10

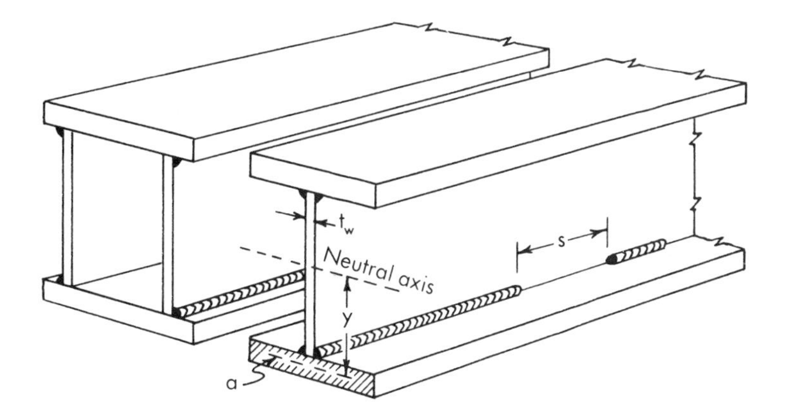

TABLE 6A—Summary of AISC Allowables and Limiting Ratios (Expanded to Include Some Proprietary Steels)

σ_y	33,000	36,000	42,000	45,000	46,000	50,000	55,000	60,000	65,000	90.000*	95,000*	100,000*
Max depth to span of girder (suggested) $\frac{d}{L} \geqq \frac{800,000}{\sigma_y}$ (AISC Commentary, p. 26)	1/24.2	1/22.2	1/19.0	1/17.8	1/17.4	1/16.0	1/14.6	1/13.3	1/12.2	1/8.8	1/8.4	1/8.0
Max width to thickness ratio of compression element $\frac{3,000}{\sqrt{\sigma_y}}$ (1.9.1)	16.5	15.8	14.6	14.1	14.0	13.4	12.8	12.2	11.8	10.0	9.7	9.5
Max width to thickness ratio of compression element $\frac{8,000}{\sqrt{\sigma_y}}$ (1.9.2)	44.0	42.1	39.0	37.7	37.3	35.8	34.1	32.6	31.4	26.6	25.9	25.3
Max width to thickness ratio of web $\frac{d_w}{t_w} \leqq \frac{14,000,000}{\sqrt{\sigma_y (\sigma_y + 16,500)}}$ (1.10.2) Up to this limit the web is capable of providing vertical support for the compression flange	345	320	282	266	260	243	223	207	192	143	136	130
Bending stress allowable (tensile) $\sigma \leqq .60\ \sigma_y$ (1.5.1.4.4) (1.5.1.4.3)	20,000	22,000	25,000	27,000	27,500	30,000	33,000	36,000	39,000	54,000	57.000	60,000
Max width to thickness ratio of web for no reduction in allowable compressive bending stress due to possible lateral displacement of web (1.10.6) $\frac{d_w}{t_w} \leqq \frac{24,000}{\sqrt{\sigma_b}}$ (if $\sigma_b = .60\ \sigma_y$)	171	163	151	146	145	139	132	127	122	103.2	100.6	98.0
$C_c = \sqrt{\frac{2\pi^2 E}{\sigma_y}}$ (1.5.1.3)	131.7	126.1	116.7	112.8	111.6	107.0	102.0	97.7	93.8	79.8	77.6	75.7
Shear force on fillet welds between stiffener and web (1.10.5.4) $f_s = d_w \sqrt{\left(\frac{\sigma_y}{3400}\right)^3}$	30 d_w	35 d_w	43 d_w	48 d_w	50 d_w	56 d_w	65 d_w	74 d_w	84 d_w	136 d_w	153 d_w	159.5 d_w
Web crippling allowable $\sigma \leqq .75\ \sigma_y$ for use in formulas (13) & (14) (1.10.10)	25,000	27,000	31,500	34,000	34,500	37,500	41,500	45,000	48,500	67,500	71,250	75,000
Max longitudinal spacing between intermittent fillet welds attaching compression flange to girder $s \leqq \frac{4,000}{\sqrt{\sigma_y}} t \leqq 12'$ (1.18.2.3)	22.0 t	21.0 t	19.5 t	18.9 t	18.7 t	17.9 t	17.1 t	16.3 t	15.7 t	13.3 t	13.0 t	12.6 t

* Quenched & tempered steels: yield strength at 0.2% offset.

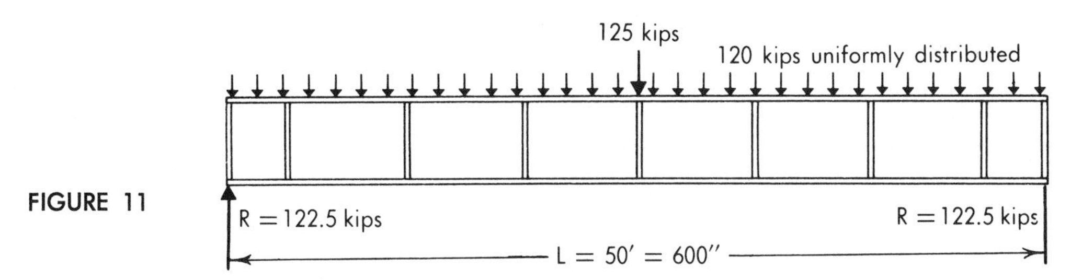

FIGURE 11

bending moment

for the uniform load,

$$M_{\mathfrak{E}} = \frac{W\ L}{8} = \frac{(120)(600)}{8} = 9{,}000 \text{ in.-kips}$$

for the concentrated load,

$$M_{\mathfrak{E}} = \frac{F\ L}{4} = \frac{(125)(600)}{4} = 18{,}750 \text{ in.-kips}$$

$$\text{Total } M_{\mathfrak{E}} = 27{,}750 \text{ in.-kips}$$

shear

$$V = 122.5 \text{ kips}$$

Design Procedure

1. Design the girder web for the shear requirements, assuming it held to a depth of 66″.

$$A_w = \frac{V}{\tau_{av}} = t_w\ d_w$$

TABLE 6B—AISC Allowable Bending Strengths
(Expanded to Include Some Important Proprietary Steels)

σ_y	AISC Formula 4 (1.5.1.4.5)	AISC Formula 12 (1.10.7)
33,000	$\sigma_b = 20{,}000 - \frac{.576}{C_b}\left(\frac{L}{r}\right)^2$	$\sigma_b = 27{,}000 - 12{,}500 \frac{\tau}{\tau_a} \leq 20.000$
36,000	$\sigma_b = 22{,}000 - \frac{.692}{C_b}\left(\frac{L}{r}\right)^2$	$\sigma_b = 29{,}500 - 13{,}500 \frac{\tau}{\tau_a} \leq 22{,}000$
42,000	$\sigma_b = 25{,}000 - \frac{.925}{C_b}\left(\frac{L}{r}\right)^2$	$\sigma_b = 34{,}500 - 15{,}500 \frac{\tau}{\tau_a} \leq 25{,}000$
45,000	$\sigma_b = 27{,}000 - \frac{1.06}{C_b}\left(\frac{L}{r}\right)^2$	$\sigma_b = 37{,}000 - 17{,}000 \frac{\tau}{\tau_a} \leq 27{,}000$
46,000	$\sigma_b = 27{,}500 - \frac{1.110}{C_b}\left(\frac{L}{r}\right)^2$	$\sigma_b = 38{,}000 - 17{,}000 \frac{\tau}{\tau_a} \leq 27{,}500$
50,000	$\sigma_b = 30{,}000 - \frac{1.310}{C_b}\left(\frac{L}{r}\right)^2$	$\sigma_b = 41{,}000 - 18{,}500 \frac{\tau}{\tau_a} \leq 30{,}000$
55,000	$\sigma_b = 33{,}000 - \frac{1.59}{C_b}\left(\frac{L}{r}\right)^2$	$\sigma_b = 45{,}500 - 20{,}500 \frac{\tau}{\tau_a} \leq 33{,}000$
60,000	$\sigma_b = 36{,}000 - \frac{1.89}{C_b}\left(\frac{L}{r}\right)^2$	$\sigma_b = 49{,}500 - 22{,}500 \frac{\tau}{\tau_a} \leq 36{,}000$
65,000	$\sigma_b = 39{,}000 - \frac{2.22}{C_b}\left(\frac{L}{r}\right)^2$	$\sigma_b = 53{,}500 - 24{,}500 \frac{\tau}{\tau_a} \leq 39{,}000$
90,000*	$\sigma_b = 54{,}000 - \frac{4.24}{C_b}\left(\frac{L}{r}\right)^2$	$\sigma_b = 74{,}250 - 33{,}750 \frac{\tau}{\tau_a} \leq 54{,}000$
95,000*	$\sigma_b = 57{,}000 - \frac{4.73}{C_b}\left(\frac{L}{r}\right)^2$	$\sigma_b = 78{,}375 - 35{,}625 \frac{\tau}{\tau_a} \leq 57{,}000$
100,000*	$\sigma_b = 60{,}000 - \frac{5.23}{C_b}\left(\frac{L}{r}\right)^2$	$\sigma_b = 82{,}500 - 37{,}500 \frac{\tau}{\tau_a} \leq 60{,}000$
* Quenched & tempered steels: yield strength at 0.2% offset.		τ = average shear stress in web $= \frac{V}{A_w}$ τ_a = allowable shear stress in web from formulas (8) or (9) or table 3

Consider the following average shear stress (τ_{av}) and maximum panel length (a) for various web thicknesses (t_w):

t_w	$\tau_{av} = \frac{\text{Actual } V}{A_w}$ (max)	Actual d_w/t_w	$a/d_w = \left(\frac{260}{d_w/t_w}\right)^2$ (max)
¼″	7430 psi	264	.97
5/16″	5950	211	1.52
⅜″	4950	176	2.18

Although the ¼″ thick web would result in a reasonable shear stress of 7430 psi, the greatest stiffener spacing (a) allowed would be 97% of the web depth (d_w); this would require more intermediate stiffeners. It would be more practical, in this example, to increase the web thickness to 5/16″, thus allowing a greater distance between stiffeners.

$$A_w = (66)(5/16) = 20.6 \text{ in.}^2$$

$$I_w = \frac{(5/16)(66)^3}{12} = 7487 \text{ in.}^4$$

$$d_w/t_w = 211$$

2. Design the flange to make up the remainder of the moment requirements. Assume a bending stress of about $\sigma = 21{,}000$ psi.

section modulus required of girder

$$S = \frac{M}{\sigma} = \frac{(27{,}750 \text{ in.-kips})}{(21{,}000 \text{ psi})} = 1320 \text{ in.}^3$$

distance from neutral axis of girder to outer fiber assuming a flange thickness of about 1″

$$c = \tfrac{1}{2}\, d_w + t_f = (33'') + (1'') = 34''$$

total moment of inertia required of girder

$$I_t = S\, c = (1320)(34) = 44{,}880 \text{ in.}^4$$

remaining moment of inertia required of flanges

$$I_f = I_t - I_w = (44{,}880) - (7487) = 37{,}393 \text{ in.}^4$$

and since

$$I_f = 2\, A_f\, c_f^2$$

here:

$$c_f = 33'' + \tfrac{1}{2}'' = 33.5''$$

area of flange required

$$A_f = \frac{I_f}{2\, c_f^2} = \frac{(37{,}393)}{2(33.5)^2} = 16.67 \text{ in.}^2$$

or *use two 17″ × 1″ flange plates.*

final properties of girder

$$I = 2\,(17 \text{ in.}^2)(33.5'')^2 + \frac{(5/16'')(66'')^3}{12} = 46{,}766 \text{ in.}^4 > 44{,}880 \text{ in.}^4 \quad \underline{OK}$$

$$S = \frac{I}{c} = \frac{(46{,}766 \text{ in.}^4)}{(34'')} = 1375 \text{ in.}^3 > 1320 \text{ in.}^3 \quad \underline{OK}$$

actual bending stress in girder

$$\sigma = \frac{M}{S} = \frac{(27{,}750 \text{ in.-kips})}{(1375 \text{ in.}^3)} = 20{,}200 \text{ psi}$$

reduced allowable compressive bending stress in flange due to possible lateral displacement of the web in the compression region (AISC 1.10.6)

$$\sigma_b \leqq \sigma_b \left[1.0 - .005 \frac{A_w}{d_f}\left(\frac{d_w}{t_w} - \frac{24{,}000}{\sqrt{\sigma_b}}\right)\right]$$

$$= (22{,}000)\left[1.0 - .0005 \frac{(20.6)}{(17)}(211 - 162)\right]$$

$$= 21{,}347 \text{ psi} > 20{,}200 \text{ psi actual} \quad \underline{OK}$$

where:

σ_b = allowable bending stress
= .60 σ_y
= 22,000 psi

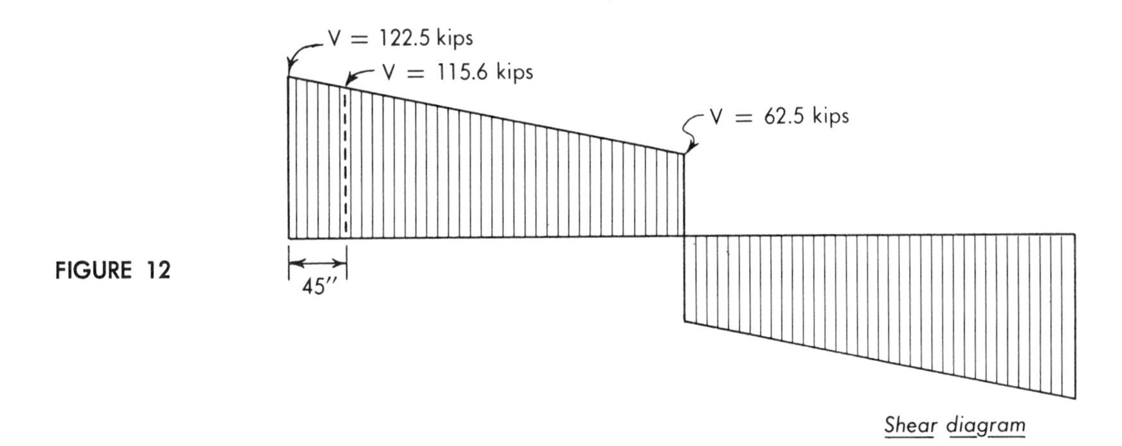

FIGURE 12

3. Design the transverse intermediate stiffeners. Figure 12 is a shear diagram of the girder.

end panel distance between intermediate stiffeners (AISC 1.10.5.3)

$$a \leqq \frac{11{,}000\ t_w}{\sqrt{\tau}}$$

$$\leqq \frac{11{,}000\ (5/16)}{\sqrt{5950}}$$

$$\leqq 45.6'' \text{ or use } 45''$$

maximum shear just inside of this stiffener

$$V = (122.5 \text{ kips} - 62.5 \text{ kips})\left(\frac{255''}{300''}\right) + 62.5 \text{ kips}$$

$$= 155.6 \text{ kips}$$

maximum spacing between remaining intermediate stiffeners (AISC 1.10.5.3)

$$a/d_w \leqq 3.0 \text{ or}$$

$$\leqq \left(\frac{260}{d_w/t_w}\right)^2$$

$$\leqq \left(\frac{260}{211}\right)^2$$

$$\leqq 1.52$$

$$\text{or}\quad a \leqq 1.52\ d_w$$

$$\leqq 1.52\ (66'')$$

$$\leqq 100''$$

required number of panels

$$600'' - 2(45'') = 510''$$

$$\frac{510''}{100''} = 5.1$$

so use 6 panels of a = 85″ each.

check the allowable shear stress in the web and determine required area of stiffener

Since the girder web's ratio is—

$$d_w/t_w = 211$$

and the ratio of panel width to web thickness is—

$$a/d_w = \frac{85''}{66''} = 1.29$$

the maximum allowable shear stress (τ) to be carried by the girder, web and the total area of stiffener (A_s) to resist this shear are found from Table 3-36 in the following manner:

	$a/d_w = 1.2$	$a/d_w = 1.3$	$a/d_w = 1.4$
$d_w/t_w = 200$	8.4 10.4		7.8 10.0
$d_w/t_w = 210$		$\tau = 8000$ psi $A_s = 10.5\%\ A_w$	
$d_w/t_w = 220$	8.2 11.0		7.5 10.6

Within the above limited area of the larger AISC table, the values in the four corner cells are read directly from the AISC table. Then the required values obtained by interpolation are filled into the center cell. Within each cell, the upper value is the allowable shear stress (τ) and the lower value is the required area of stiffener (A_s).

Thus, for our problem:

$$\tau = 8.0 \text{ kips or } 8000 \text{ psi} > 5950 \text{ psi} \quad OK$$

$$A_s = 10.5\%\ A_w$$

$$= 10.5\%\ (20.6) \qquad = 2.16 \text{ in.}^2$$

width of stiffener (if using $t_s = 3/8''$)

$$b_s = \frac{A_w}{2\ t_s}$$

$$= \frac{(2.16)}{2(3/8)}$$

$$= 2.88'' \text{ or } use\ 3\tfrac{1}{2}''$$

Since: $A_w = 2 b_s\ t_s$

also check AISC Sec 1.9.1:

$$\frac{b_s}{t_s} = \frac{3\frac{1}{2}}{\frac{3}{8}}$$

$$= 9.3 \leqq \frac{3000}{\sqrt{\sigma_y}} \text{ or } 16 \quad \underline{OK}$$

required moment of inertia

$$I_s = \left(\frac{d_w}{50}\right)^4$$

$$= \left(\frac{66}{50}\right)^4$$

$$= 3.04 \text{ in.}^4$$

actual moment of inertia

$$I_s = \frac{(2 \times 3\frac{1}{2}'' + \frac{5}{16}'')^3 \; \frac{3}{8}''}{12}$$

$$= 12.2 \text{ in.}^4 > 3.04 \text{ in.}^4 \quad \underline{OK}$$

4. Determine the size of fillet weld joining intermediate stiffeners to the girder web.

unit shear force per linear inch of stiffener

$$f_s = d_w \sqrt{\left(\frac{\sigma_y}{3400}\right)^3}$$

$$= (66) \sqrt{\left(\frac{36{,}000}{3400}\right)^3}$$

$$= 2280 \text{ lbs/in.}$$

or $f_s = 1140$ lbs/in. for a single fillet weld (one on each side).

leg size of fillet weld

$$\omega = \frac{1140}{11{,}200}$$

$= .102''$ or use $\frac{3}{16}''$ continuous fillet

or, for a $\frac{3}{16}''$ intermittent fillet weld

$$\% = \frac{.102''}{\frac{3}{16}''}$$

$= 58.6\%$ or use $\frac{3}{16}''$ 3-5 or $\frac{3}{16}''$ 3-5

or, for a $\frac{1}{4}''$ intermittent fillet weld

$$\% = \frac{.102''}{\frac{1}{4}''}$$

$= 44\%$ or use $\frac{1}{4}''$ 3-7 or $\frac{1}{4}''$ 3-7

5. Check the combined bending tensile stress and shear stress in the girder web according to

$$\sigma_b \leqq \left(0.825 - 0.375 \frac{\tau}{\underline{\tau}}\right) \sigma_y \text{ or } .60 \; \sigma_y$$

(AISC Formula 12)

wherever the calculated shear stress exceeds 60% of that allowed according to AISC Formulas 8 and 9.

The allowable shear stress was found to be $\underline{\tau} = 8000$ psi and 60% of this would be 4800 psi.

This would correspond to a shear force of

$$V = \underline{\tau} \, A_w$$

$$= (4800 \text{ psi})(\tfrac{5}{16} \times 66)$$

$$= 99.0 \text{ kips}$$

and would occur at $x = 125''$.

The bending moment at this point is—

$$M = 122.5^k \, (125'') - \left(\frac{120^k}{600''}\right) \frac{(125'')^2}{2}$$

$$= 13{,}750 \text{ in.-kips}$$

and the bending stress is—

$$\sigma_b = \frac{M}{S}$$

$$= \frac{13{,}750 \text{ in.-kips}}{1375 \text{ in.}^3}$$

$$= 10{,}000 \text{ psi}$$

It is only when the shear stress exceeds 60% of the allowable that the allowable bending stress must be reduced according to AISC Formula 12.

Since the calculated bending stress at this point ($x = 125''$) is only 10,000 psi or 45% of the allowable, and it rapidly decreases as we approach the ends, there will be no problem of the combined bending tensile stress and shear stress exceeding the allowable values of AISC Formula 12.

6. Determine the size of fillet weld joining flanges to the girder web, Figure 13.

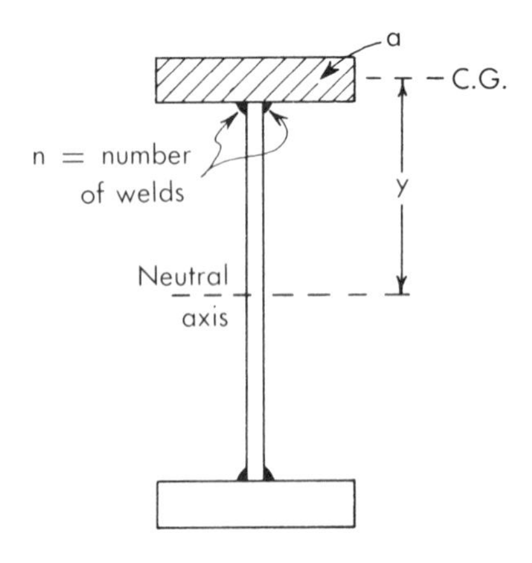

FIGURE 13

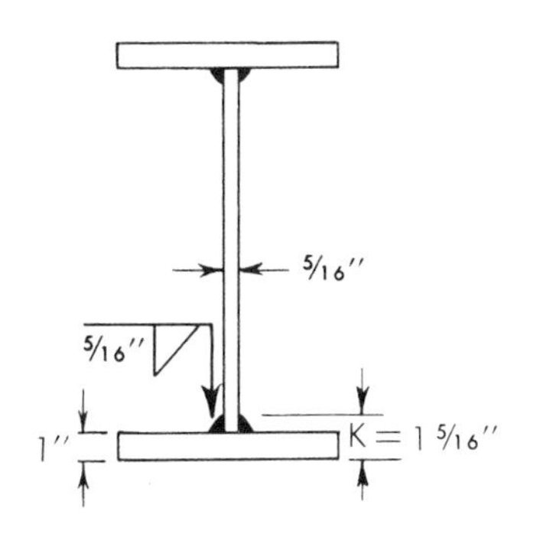

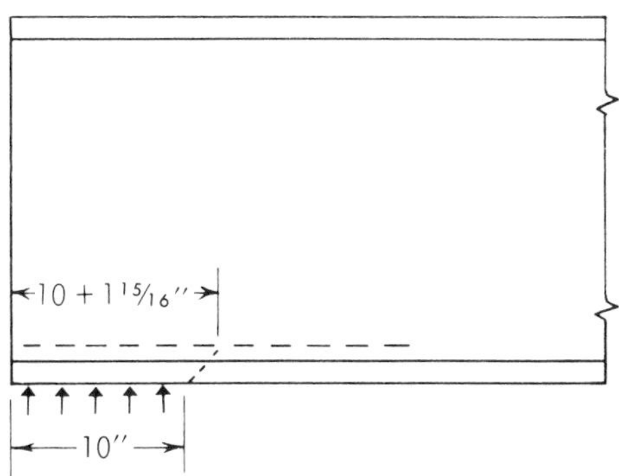

FIGURE 14

force on weld

$$f = \frac{V\ a\ y}{I\ n}$$

$$= \frac{(122.5 \text{ kips})(17 \text{ in.}^2)(33.5'')}{(46{,}776 \text{ in.}^4)(2 \text{ welds})}$$

$$= 746 \text{ lbs/in.}$$

leg size of fillet weld

$$\omega = \frac{746}{11{,}200}$$

$$= .066''$$

but because of 1″ thick flange plates, use $\frac{5}{16}''$ ◺

Bearing Stiffeners

6. Check to see if bearing stiffeners are needed at the girder ends (AISC 1.10.10.1); Figure 14.

compressive stress at web toe of girder fillet

$$\sigma = \frac{R}{t_w(N + K)}$$

$$= \frac{(122.5 \text{ kips})}{\frac{5}{16}(10'' + 1\frac{5}{16}'')}$$

$$= 34{,}700 \text{ psi} > 27{,}000 \text{ psi, or } .75\ \sigma_y$$

This stress is too high; bearing stiffeners are needed. Try a single pair and treat the stiffeners along with a portion of the web as a column. Assume an acceptable compressive stress of about 20,000 psi.

7. Determine size of bearing stiffeners.

sectional area required to carry this stress

$$A = \frac{R}{\sigma}$$

$$= \frac{(122.5 \text{ kips})}{(20{,}000 \text{ psi})}$$

$$= 6.1 \text{ in.}^2$$

portion of web acting with stiffeners to form column

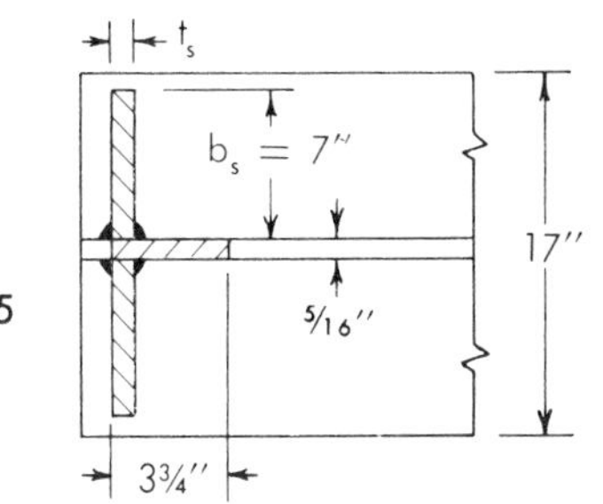

FIGURE 15

$$= 12\ t_w$$

$$= 12\ (\tfrac{5}{16}'')$$

$$= 3\tfrac{3}{4}''$$

area of this web portion

$$= (3\tfrac{3}{4}'')(\tfrac{5}{16}'')$$

$$= 1.17 \text{ in.}^2$$

required area of bearing stiffeners

$$6.10 - 1.17 = 4.93 \text{ in.}^2$$

If stiffeners extend almost the full width of the flange, a width of 7″ will be needed on each side.

$$A_s = 2\ (7'')\ t_s$$

$$= 4.93 \text{ in.}^2$$

$$\therefore t_s = \frac{4.93}{2(7'')}$$

$$= .352 \text{ or } \textit{use } \tfrac{3}{8}'' \textit{ thickness}$$

8. Check stiffener profile for resistance to compression (AISC 1.9.1).

$$\frac{b_s}{t_s} = \frac{7}{\frac{3}{8}}$$

$$= 18.7 > \frac{3000}{\sqrt{\sigma_y}} \text{ or } 16$$

This ratio is too high, so *use a pair of 7″ x 7/16″ bearing stiffeners.*

9. Check this bearing stiffener area as a column; Figure 16.

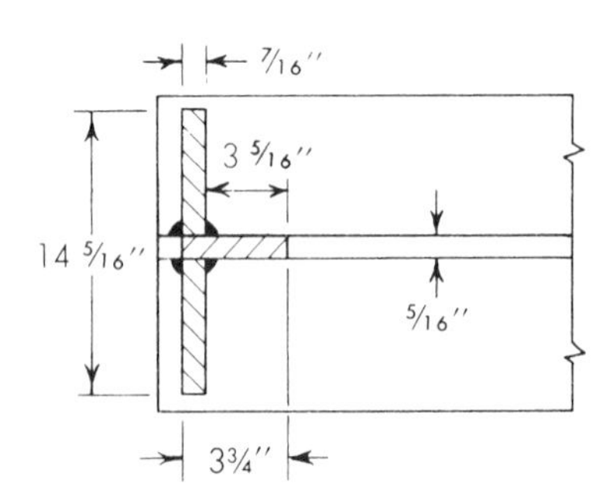

FIGURE 16

$$I_x = \frac{(7/16)(14\,5/16)^3}{12} + \frac{(3\,5/16)(5/16)^3}{12}$$

$$= 106.8 \text{ in.}^4$$

$$A = (7/16)(14\,5/16) + (3\,5/16)(5/16)$$

$$= 7.3 \text{ in.}^2$$

$$r_x = \sqrt{\frac{I_x}{A}}$$

$$= \sqrt{\frac{(106.8)}{(7.3)}}$$

$$= 4.6''$$

slenderness ratio

$$\frac{L_e}{r} = \frac{3/4(66'')}{(4.6'')}$$

$$= 10.6$$

allowable compressive stress

σ = 21,100 psi, from Table 6 in Section 3.1

and

$$R = \sigma A$$

$$= (21{,}100)(7.3)$$

$$= 154.0 \text{ kips} > 122.5 \text{ kips actual} \quad \underline{OK}$$

10. Determine the size of fillet weld joining bearing stiffeners to the girder web.

length of weld

$$L = 4\, d_w$$

$$= 4\,(66'')$$

$$= 264''$$

force on weld (treating weld as a line)

$$f = \frac{R}{L}$$

$$= \frac{(122.5 \text{ kips})}{(264'')}$$

$$= 464 \text{ lbs/in.}$$

leg size of fillet weld

$$\omega = \frac{(464)}{(11{,}200)}$$

$$= .042'' \text{ or } use\ 3/16''$$

11. Check bearing stress in these stiffeners.

bearing area of stiffener (less corner snipes)

$$(7'' - 1'')\ 7/16'' = 2.62 \text{ in.}^2 \text{ each}$$

bearing stress in stiffener

$$\sigma = \frac{R}{A}$$

$$= \frac{(122.5 \text{ kips})}{2(2.62)}$$

$$= 23{,}400 \text{ psi} < 27{,}000 \text{ psi or } .75\ \sigma_y \quad \underline{OK}$$

12. In a similar manner, check the bearing stiffener at centerline for resistance to 125-kip load. If using the same stiffener size as at ends, Figure 17:

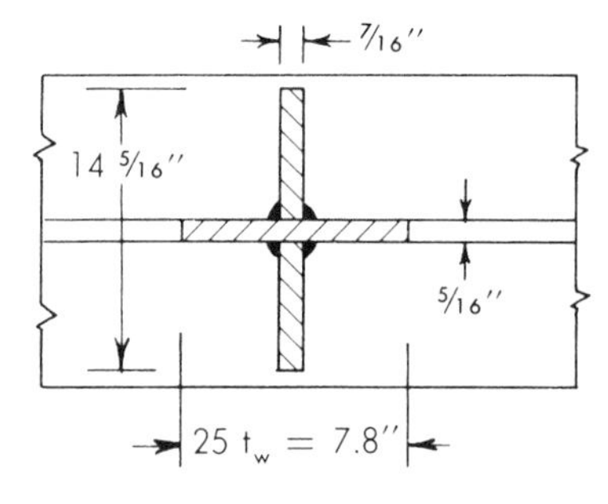

FIGURE 17

$$I_x = \frac{(7/16'')(14\,5/16'')^3}{12} + \frac{(7.8'' - 7/16'')(5/16'')^3}{12}$$

$$= 106.8 \text{ in.}^4$$

$$A = (7/16'')(14\,5/16'') + (7.8'' - 7/16'')(5/16'')$$

$$= 8.56 \text{ in.}^2$$

$$r_x = \sqrt{\frac{I_x}{A}}$$

$$= \sqrt{\frac{(106.8)}{(8.56)}}$$

$$= 3.92''$$

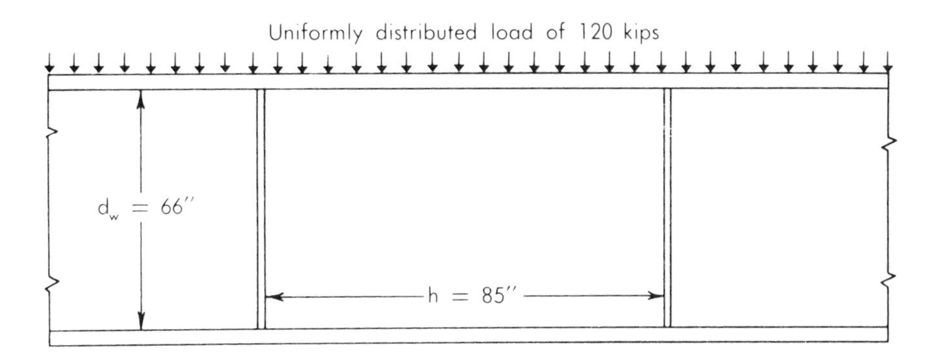

FIGURE 18

slenderness ratio

$$\frac{L_e}{r} = \frac{\frac{3}{4}(66'')}{(3.92'')}$$

$$= 12.5$$

allowable compressive stress

σ = 21,000 psi, from Table 6 in Section 3.1

and

$$F = \sigma A$$

$$= (21{,}000)(8.56)$$

$$= 179.5 \text{ kips} > 125.0 \text{ kips actual} \quad \underline{OK}$$

so use the same amount of fillet welding as before.

bearing stress in center stiffener

$$\sigma = \frac{F}{A}$$

$$= \frac{(125 \text{ kips})}{2(7'' - 1'')(\frac{7}{16}'')}$$

$$= 23{,}800 \text{ psi} < 27{,}000 \text{ psi or } .75\ \sigma_y \quad \underline{OK}$$

13. Check the compressive stresses from the uniformly distributed load of 120 kips on the compression edge of the web plate (AISC 1.10.10.2). See Figure 18.

allowable compressive stress against web edge assuming flange is not restrained against rotation

$$\sigma \leqq \left[2 + \frac{4}{(a/d_w)^2}\right] \frac{10{,}000{,}000}{(d_w/t_w)^2}$$

$$\leqq \left[2 + \frac{4}{(1.29)^2}\right] \frac{10{,}000{,}000}{(211)^2}$$

$$\leqq 990 \text{ psi}$$

actual pressure of uniform load against web edge

$$\sigma = \frac{(120 \text{ kips})}{(600'')(\frac{5}{16}'')}$$

$$= 640 \text{ psi} < 990 \text{ psi allowable} \quad \underline{OK}$$

14. Consolidate these findings into the final girder design, Figure 19.

As a matter of interest, reducing the web thickness to ¼″ would have saved about 143 lbs in steel. However, this would have required 13 pairs of stiffeners instead of 9 pairs, Figure 20. The additional cost in fitting and welding the extra 4 pairs of stiffeners probably would exceed any savings in steel.

Increasing the web thickness to ⅜″ would only reduce the number of stiffeners by 2 pair, Figure 21. However, this would increase the weight by 287 lbs.

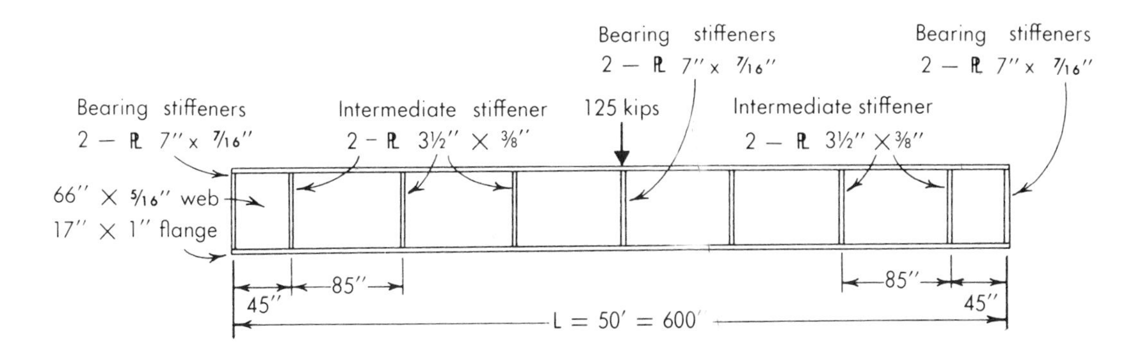

FIGURE 19

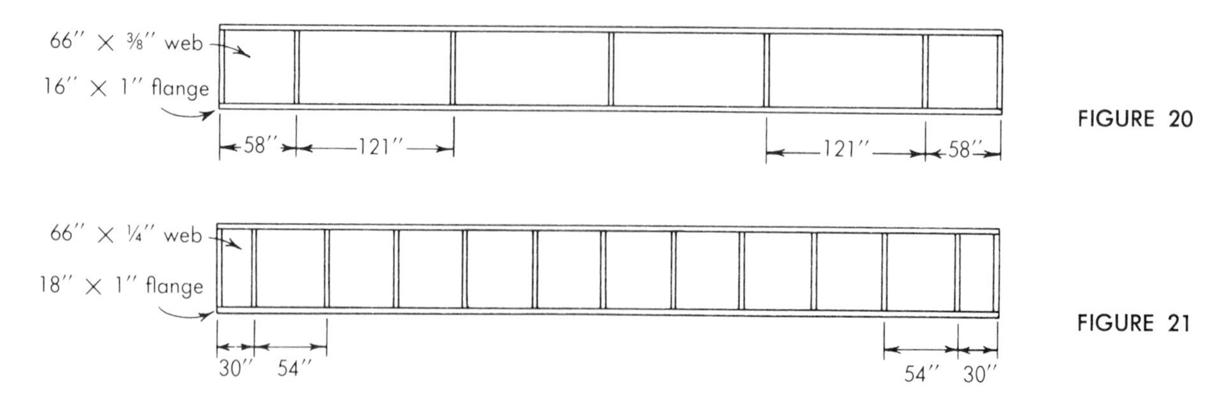

FIGURE 20

FIGURE 21

6. HOLES CUT INTO GIRDER WEB

Many times access holes must be cut into the webs of beams and girders for duct work, etc. If sufficiently large, they must be reinforced in some manner.

Since the flanges carry most of the bending forces, the loss of web area does not present much of a problem. However, since the shear (V) is carried for the most part by the web, any reduction of web area must be checked. See Figure 22.

If the hole is located at midspan (b), the shear is minimum and may have little effect on the strength of the girder. If the hole is located near the support in a region of high shear, the additional bending stresses produced by this shear must be added to the conventional bending stresses from the applied beam load. See Figure 23.

An inside horizontal flange may be added to the Tee section in order to give it sufficient bending strength, or sufficient compressive buckling strength.

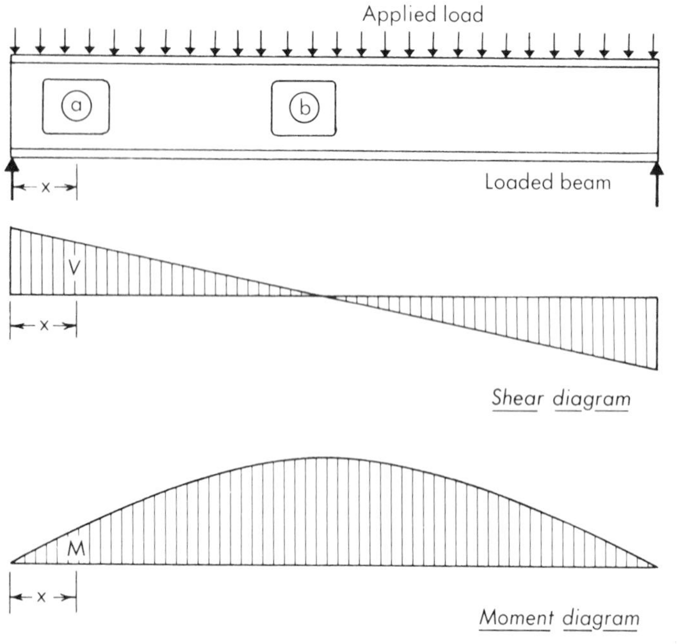

FIGURE 22

When this is done, it must be remembered that this flange becomes a part of the Tee area and is subjected to the same axial tension (F_b) and compression (F_t) force caused by the bending moment (M_x) from the external loading. Therefore, this flange must extend far enough beyond the web opening to effectively transfer this portion of the axial force back into the main web of the girder; see Figure 24. Of course in the region of low moment (M_x), this axial force may be low and not require this extra length of flange.

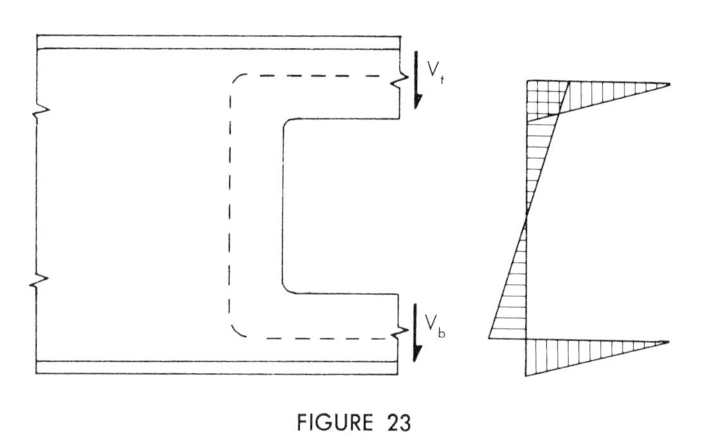

FIGURE 23

If these access holes in the web are close enough together, the portion of the web between the holes behaves in the same manner as the vertical members of a Vierendeel truss. See Figure 25.

Unless the bending stress at the corner of the access hole is rather low, reinforcement of this corner should be considered:

1. Because of the abrupt change in section, there is a stress concentration several times the average stress value. See Figure 26.

2. The Tee section at this inside corner behaves similar to a curved beam in that the neutral axis shifts in toward this inner corner, greatly increasing the bending stresses on this inward face. This increase is greater with a smaller radius of corner.

In the usual analysis of a Vierendeel truss, the horizontal shear (V_h) along the neutral axis of the

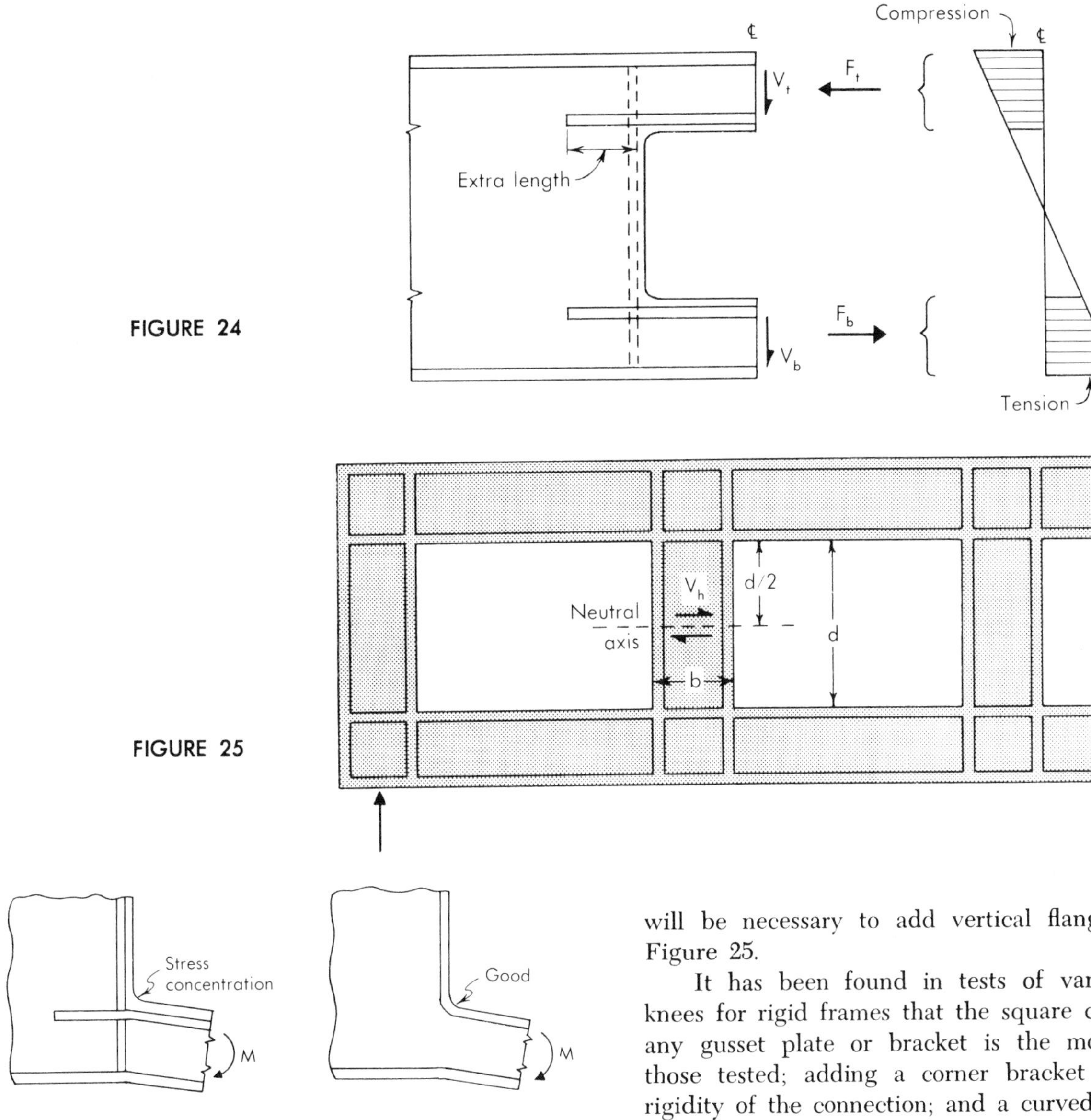

FIGURE 24

FIGURE 25

FIGURE 26

truss in the vertical member is assumed to cause a moment at the upper and lower ends of this vertical member. If the horizontal dimension of this member (b) is insufficient to resist this bending moment, it will be necessary to add vertical flange plates; see Figure 25.

It has been found in tests of various types of knees for rigid frames that the square corner without any gusset plate or bracket is the most flexible of those tested; adding a corner bracket increases the rigidity of the connection; and a curved knee has the greatest rigidity; see Figure 27.

If these holes in the web are a sufficient distance (b) apart, the bending resistance of this web portion may be developed without the additional vertical flange plates; see Figure 28.

The stem of the Tee section which is subject to

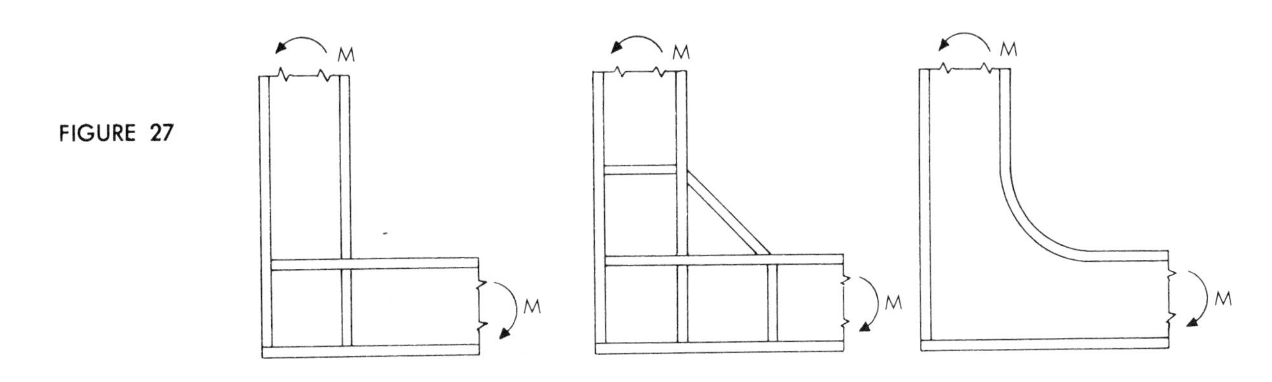

FIGURE 27

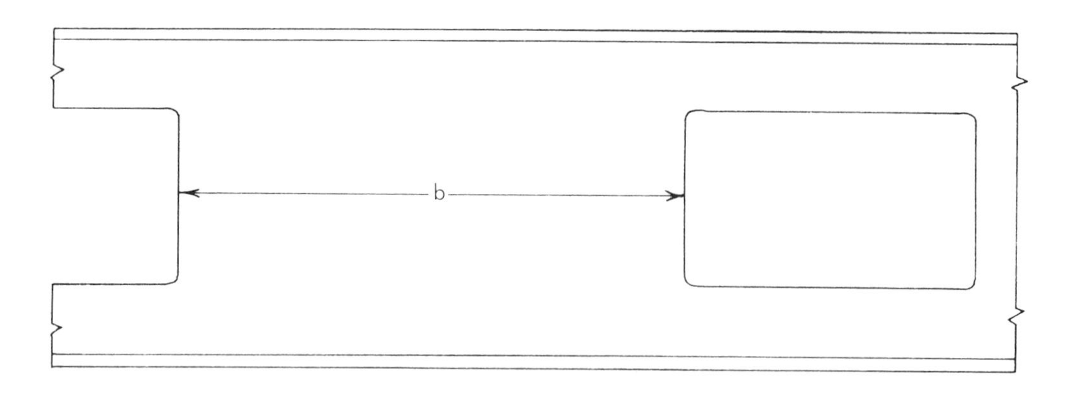

FIGURE 28

compression must be checked against buckling according to AISC 1.9.1:

$$\frac{b_f}{t_f} \geqq \frac{3000}{\sqrt{\sigma_y}}$$

$$\frac{b_s}{t_s} \geqq \frac{3000}{\sqrt{\sigma_y}}$$

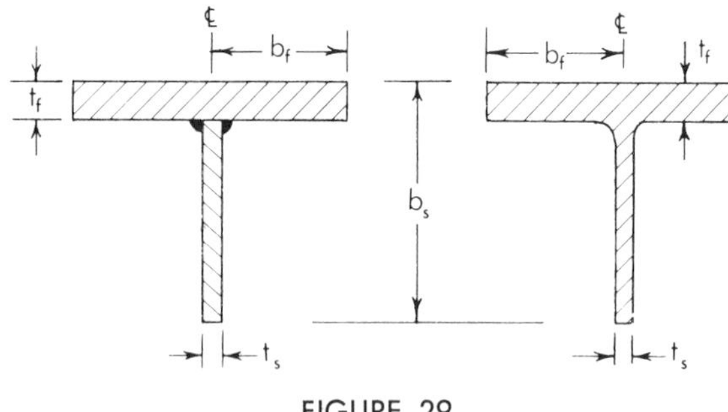

FIGURE 29

If the resulting bending stress in the stem is excessive, it must be reinforced by an inside flange or stiffener.

Corners of the hole should always be round and smooth. A minimum corner radius of 2″ is recommended when the hole is not stiffened.

Usually it is assumed the point of contraflexure of the moment in the top and bottom portions produced by the shear (V_t) and (V_b) is about midsection of the hole (℄). It is also assumed the total vertical shear is divided between these two sections in proportion to their depths. For Tees of equal depth, $V_t = V_b = ½\ V_x$.

The top and bottom Tee sections must be capable of withstanding this combined bending stress, and the vertical shear.

A flange may be added around the edge of the web opening to give the Tee section sufficient strength for the bending moment. An additional plate may be added to the web of the Tee to give it sufficient strength for the vertical shear (V).

7. COVER PLATES

It may be advantageous in some cases to use partial-length cover plates in the bearing regions of a beam or girder, to reduce the required thickness of the flange plate extending from end-to-end of the member.

Related discussion will be found further along in this text under Section 4.3 on Welded Plate Girders for Bridges (see Topic 12) and under Section 6.1 on Design of Rigid Frames (see Topic 3).

The termination of partial-length cover plates for buildings is governed by AISC Sec. 1.10.4. The following paragraphs summarize these requirements.

Partial-length cover plates shall extend beyond the theoretical cut-off point for a distance (a′), defined below. This extended portion (a′) shall be attached to the beam or girder with sufficient fillet welds to develop the cover plate's portion of the bending force

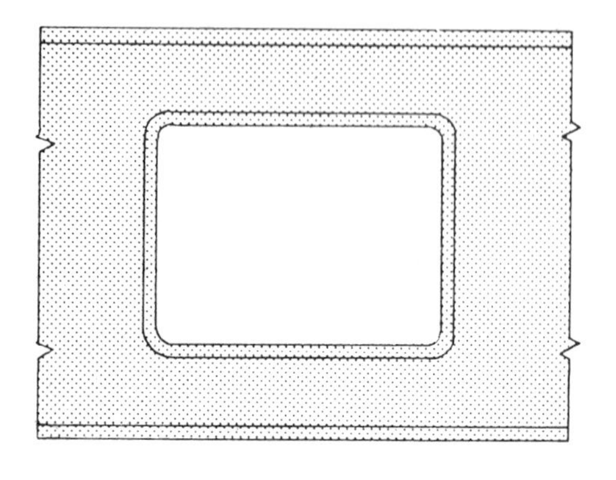

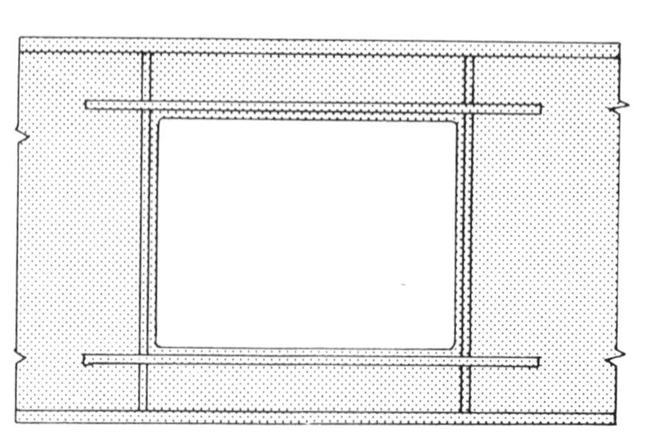

FIGURE 30

in the beam or girder at the theoretical cut-off point which is equal to—

$$F_{weld} = \frac{M\ Q}{I} \quad \text{.......................(14)}$$

where:

M = bending moment at section in question

Q = statical moment of cover plate area about neutral axis of cover-plated beam section

I = moment of inertia of cover-plated beam section

The moment, computed by equating $\frac{M\ Q}{I}$ to the capacity of the connecting fillet welds in this distance (a′) from the actual end of the cover plate, must equal or exceed the moment at the theoretical cut-off point. Otherwise, the size of the fillet welds in this terminal section (a′) must be increased, or the actual end of the cover plate must be extended to a point of lower moment.

The length (a′) measured from the actual end of the cover plate shall be:

1. A distance equal to the width of the cover plate when there is a continuous fillet weld equal to or larger than ¾ of the plate thickness across the end of the plate and continued welds along both edges of the cover plate in the length (a′).

2. A distance equal to 1½ times the width of the cover plate when there is a continuous fillet weld smaller than ¾ of the plate thickness across the end of the plate and continued welds along both edges of the cover plate in the length (a′).

3. A distance equal to 2 times the width of the cover plate when there is no weld across the end of the plate but continuous welds along both edges of the cover plate in the length (a′).

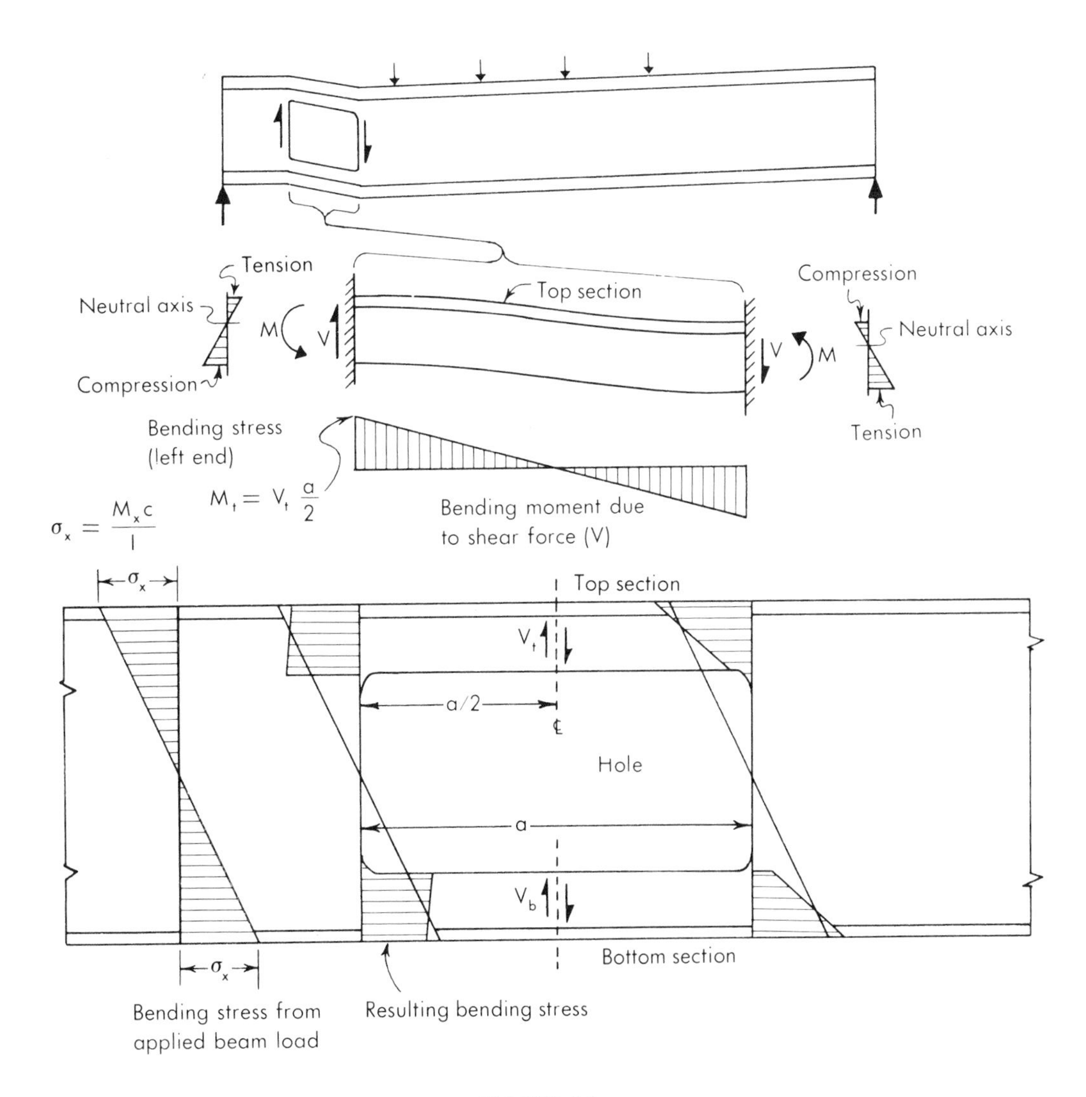

FIGURE 31

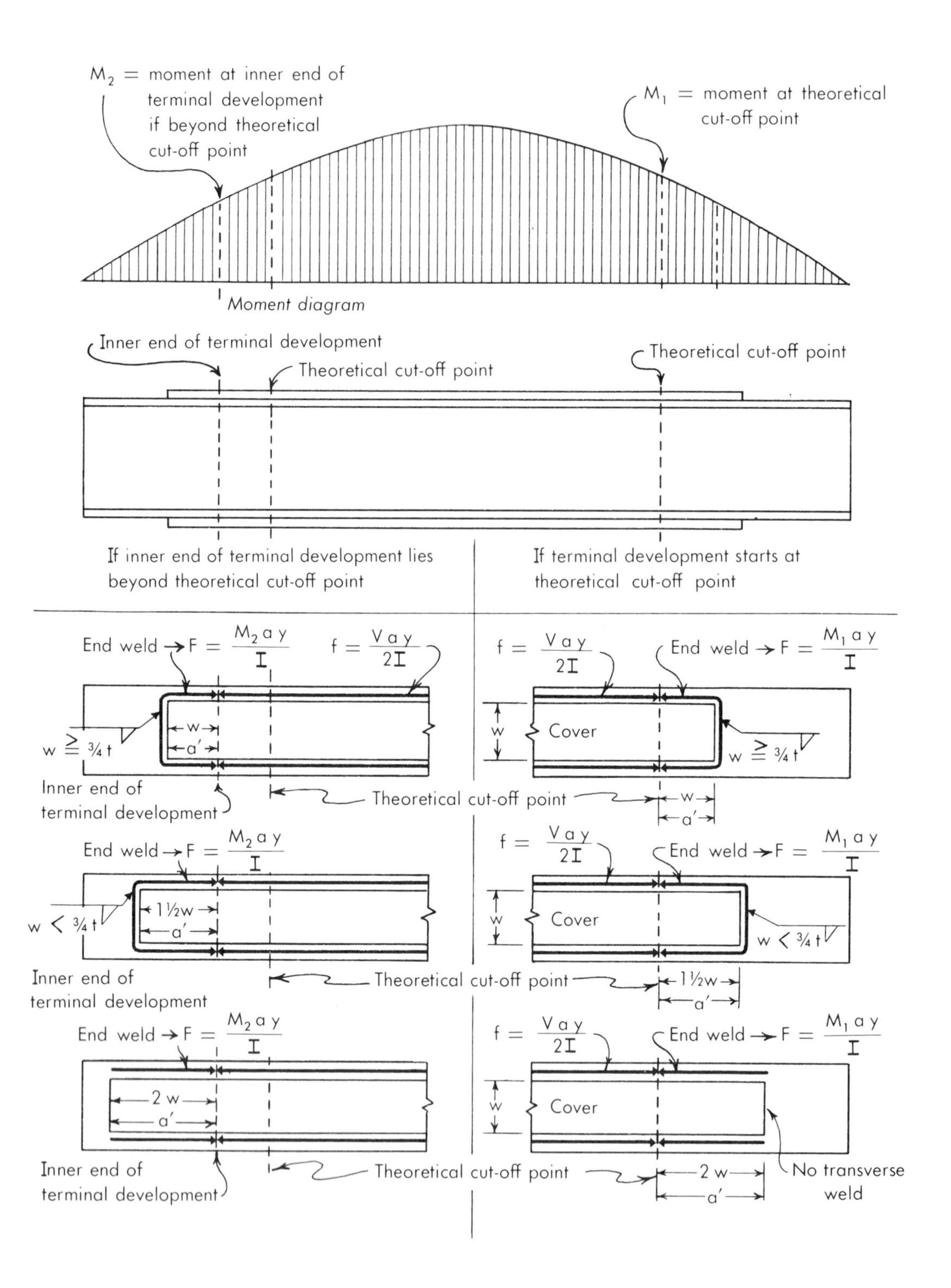

M2 = moment at inner end of terminal development if beyond theoretical cut-off point
M1 = moment at theoretical cut-off point
Moment diagram
Inner end of terminal development
Theoretical cut-off point
Theoretical cut-off point
If inner end of terminal development lies beyond theoretical cut-off point
If terminal development starts at theoretical cut-off point
End weld → F = M2 a y / I
f = V a y / 2I
f = V a y / 2I
End weld → F = M1 a y / I
w ≧ 3/4 t
w
a'
Cover
Inner end of terminal development
Theoretical cut-off point
w < 3/4 t
1 1/2w
2 w
No transverse weld

FIGURE 32

ALLOWABLE SHEAR STRESSES IN PLATE GIRDERS, KSI

And Required Gross Area of Pairs of Intermediate Stiffeners

AISC TABLE 3-33—Steel of 33 ksi Yield Point

Shear Stress, ksi (Shown on 1st line)
Stiffener Area, % of Web Area (In italics, on 2nd line)

Slenderness ratios h/t: web depth to web thickness	Aspect ratios a/h: stiffener spacing to web depth													
	0.5	0.6	0.7	0.8	0.9	1.0	1.2	1.4	1.6	1.8	2.0	2.5	3.0	over 3
70								13.0	13.0	13.0	13.0	13.0	13.0	12.6
80						13.0	13.0	12.9	12.5	12.2	12.0	11.6	11.5	11.0
90					13.0	12.9	12.1	11.5	11.3 *0.4*	11.1 *0.7*	11.0 *0.8*	10.7 *0.9*	10.6 *0.9*	9.8
100				13.0	12.4	11.6	11.2 *0.8*	11.0 *1.3*	10.7 *1.6*	10.5 *1.7*	10.4 *1.8*	10.0 *1.7*	9.8 *1.6*	8.4
110			13.0	12.2	11.4 *0.3*	11.2 *1.2*	10.8 *2.0*	10.5 *2.4*	10.2 *2.7*	9.8 *2.9*	9.5 *3.0*	9.0 *2.9*	8.6 *2.7*	6.9
120		13.0	12.3	11.4 *0.5*	11.1 *1.6*	10.8 *2.3*	10.4 *3.2*	9.8 *3.9*	9.4 *4.2*	9.0 *4.3*	8.7 *4.2*	8.2 *3.9*	7.8 *3.5*	5.8
130	13.0	12.7	11.5 *0.3*	11.1 *1.6*	10.8 *2.6*	10.4 *3.6*	9.8 *4.8*	9.2 *5.3*	8.8 *5.4*	8.4 *5.3*	8.1 *5.2*	7.5 *4.6*	7.1 *4.1*	5.0
140	13.0	11.8	11.2 *1.3*	10.9 *2.6*	10.5 *3.9*	10.0 *5.1*	9.3 *6.1*	8.8 *6.3*	8.3 *6.3*	7.9 *6.2*	7.6 *5.9*	7.0 *5.2*	6.5 *4.6*	4.3
150	12.8	11.4 *0.7*	11.0 *2.2*	10.6 *3.8*	10.1 *5.3*	9.6 *6.4*	8.9 *7.1*	8.4 *7.2*	7.9 *7.1*	7.5 *6.8*	7.2 *6.5*	6.6 *5.7*	6.1 *5.0*	3.7
160	12.0	11.2 *1.5*	10.9 *3.1*	10.3 *5.1*	9.8 *6.5*	9.3 *7.4*	8.6 *7.9*	8.1 *7.9*	7.6 *7.7*	7.2 *7.4*	6.9 *7.0*	6.2 *6.1*		3.2
170	11.5 *0.3*	11.1 *2.3*	10.6 *4.4*	10.0 *6.3*	9.5 *7.5*	9.1 *8.2*	8.4 *8.6*	7.8 *8.5*	7.3 *8.2*	6.9 *7.8*	6.6 *7.4*			2.9
180	11.3 *1.1*	10.9 *3.0*	10.3 *5.6*	9.8 *7.2*	9.3 *8.3*	8.8 *8.9*	8.2 *9.2*	7.6 *9.0*	7.1 *8.6*	6.7 *8.2*	6.4 *7.7*			2.6
200	11.1 *2.3*	10.5 *5.2*	9.9 *7.4*	9.4 *8.7*	8.9 *9.5*	8.5 *10.0*	7.8 *10.1*	7.3 *9.8*	6.8 *9.3*					2.1
220	10.8 *4.0*	10.2 *6.8*	9.6 *8.7*	9.1 *9.8*	8.7 *10.5*	8.3 *10.8*	7.6 *10.7*	7.0 *10.3*						1.7
240	10.5 *5.5*	9.9 *8.1*	9.4 *9.7*	8.9 *10.6*	8.5 *11.2*	8.1 *11.4*								1.4
260	10.3 *6.8*	9.7 *9.0*	9.2 *10.4*	8.8 *11.3*	8.3 *11.7*	7.9 *11.9*								1.2
280	10.1 *7.7*	9.6 *9.8*	9.1 *11.1*	8.6 *11.8*										
300	10.0 *8.5*	9.4 *10.4*	9.0 *11.6*											
320	9.8 *9.2*	9.3 *10.9*												
340	9.7 *9.7*													

Girders so proportioned that the computed shear is less than that given in right-hand column do not require intermediate stiffeners.
* For single angle stiffeners, multiply by 1.8; for single plate stiffeners, multiply by 2.4.

AISC TABLE 3-36—Steel of 36 ksi Yield Point

Shear Stress, ksi (Shown on 1st line)
Stiffener Area, % of Web Area (In italics, on 2nd line)

Slenderness ratios h/t: web depth to web thickness	Aspect ratios a/h: stiffener spacing to web depth													
	0.5	0.6	0.7	0.8	0.9	1.0	1.2	1.4	1.6	1.8	2.0	2.5	3.0	over 3
70							14.5	14.5	14.5	14.5	14.3	14.0	13.7	13.1
80					14.5	14.5	14.2	13.5	13.1	12.8	12.6 *0.7*	12.3 *0.3*	12.1 *0.4*	11.5
90				14.5	14.4	13.9	12.6	12.3 *0.6*	12.1 *0.9*	11.9 *1.1*	11.7 *1.2*	11.4 *1.3*	11.2 *1.2*	10.2
100			14.5	14.0	13.0	12.4 *0.5*	12.0 *1.4*	11.7 *1.8*	11.4 *2.1*	11.2 *2.1*	11.0 *2.2*	10.4 *2.3*	10.1 *2.1*	8.4
110		14.5	14.0	12.7	12.3 *1.0*	12.0 *1.8*	11.6 *2.5*	11.1 *3.1*	10.6 *3.5*	10.3 *3.6*	9.9 *3.6*	9.3 *3.4*	8.9 *3.1*	6.9
120	14.5	14.4	12.8	12.3 *1.1*	12.0 *2.1*	11.6 *2.9*	10.9 *4.1*	10.4 *4.7*	9.9 *4.9*	9.5 *4.9*	9.1 *4.8*	8.5 *4.3*	8.0 *3.8*	5.8
130	14.5	13.3	12.4 *0.9*	12.0 *2.2*	11.6 *3.2*	11.1 *4.3*	10.4 *5.6*	9.8 *5.9*	9.3 *6.0*	8.9 *5.8*	8.5 *5.6*	7.8 *5.0*	7.4 *4.4*	5.0
140	14.3	12.5 *0.3*	12.1 *1.9*	11.7 *3.2*	11.1 *4.8*	10.6 *5.9*	9.9 *6.7*	9.3 *6.9*	8.8 *6.8*	8.4 *6.6*	8.0 *6.3*	7.3 *5.5*	6.8 *4.9*	4.3
150	13.4	12.3 *1.2*	11.9 *2.8*	11.3 *4.7*	10.8 *6.1*	10.3 *7.1*	9.5 *7.6*	8.9 *7.7*	8.4 *7.5*	8.0 *7.2*	7.6 *6.8*	6.9 *6.0*	6.4 *5.2*	3.7
160	12.6 *0.1*	12.1 *2.1*	11.6 *4.1*	11.0 *6.0*	10.4 *7.2*	10.0 *8.0*	9.2 *8.4*	8.6 *8.3*	8.1 *8.1*	7.7 *7.7*	7.3 *7.3*	6.6 *6.3*		3.2
170	12.4 *0.9*	12.0 *2.8*	11.3 *5.3*	10.7 *7.0*	10.2 *8.1*	9.7 *8.7*	9.0 *9.0*	8.3 *8.9*	7.8 *8.5*	7.4 *8.1*	7.0 *7.7*			2.9
180	12.3 *1.6*	11.7 *4.0*	11.0 *6.4*	10.5 *7.9*	10.0 *8.8*	9.5 *9.4*	8.8 *9.6*	8.1 *9.3*	7.6 *8.9*	7.2 *8.5*	6.8 *8.0*			2.6
200	12.0 *2.9*	11.3 *6.0*	10.7 *8.0*	10.1 *9.2*	9.6 *10.0*	9.2 *10.4*	8.4 *10.4*	7.8 *10.0*	7.3 *9.5*					2.1
220	11.6 *4.8*	10.9 *7.5*	10.4 *9.2*	9.8 *10.2*	9.4 *10.8*	8.9 *11.1*	8.2 *11.0*	7.5 *10.6*						1.7
240	11.3 *6.2*	10.7 *8.6*	10.1 *10.1*	9.6 *11.0*	9.2 *11.5*	8.7 *11.7*								1.4
260	11.1 *7.3*	10.5 *9.5*	10.0 *10.8*	9.5 *11.6*	9.0 *12.0*	8.6 *12.1*								1.2
280	10.9 *8.2*	10.3 *10.2*	9.8 *11.4*	9.3 *12.1*										
300	10.8 *9.0*	10.2 *10.8*	9.7 *11.8*											
320	10.7 *9.5*	10.1 *11.2*												

Girders so proportioned that the computed shear is less than that given in right-hand column do not require intermediate stiffeners.
* For single angle stiffeners, multiply by 1.8; for single plate stiffeners, multiply by 2.4.

These tables simplify the design of intermediate stiffeners to AISC specifications, as discussed on pages 4.1-4, 5 and 7.

ALLOWABLE SHEAR STRESSES IN PLATE GIRDERS, KSI
And Required Gross Area of Pairs of Intermediate Stiffeners

AISC TABLE 3–42—Steel of 42 ksi Yield Point
Shear Stress, ksi (Shown on 1st line)
Stiffener Area, % of Web Area (In italics, on 2nd line)

Slenderness ratios h/t: web depth to web thickness	Aspect ratios a/h: stiffener spacing to web depth													
	0.5	0.6	0.7	0.8	0.9	1.0	1.2	1.4	1.6	1.8	2.0	2.5	3.0	over 3
70						17.0	17.0	16.7	16.1	15.7	15.5	15.0	14.8	14.2
80				17.0	17.0	16.4	15.3	14.6 *0.1*	14.4 *0.5*	14.2 *0.7*	14.0 *0.8*	13.6 *0.9*	13.4 *0.9*	12.4
90			17.0	16.8	15.5	14.7 *0.1*	14.2 *1.0*	13.8 *1.5*	13.5 *1.8*	13.3 *1.9*	13.1 *1.9*	12.6 *1.9*	12.2 *1.8*	10.4
100		17.0	16.6	15.1	14.4 *0.7*	14.1 *1.5*	13.6 *2.3*	13.2 *2.7*	12.6 *3.2*	12.2 *3.4*	11.8 *3.4*	11.1 *3.2*	10.6 *2.9*	8.4
110		17.0	15.1	14.4 *1.0*	14.0 *2.0*	13.6 *2.7*	12.9 *3.9*	12.2 *4.5*	11.6 *4.7*	11.1 *4.7*	10.7 *4.6*	10.0 *4.2*	9.5 *3.8*	6.9
120	17.0	15.5	14.4 *0.9*	14.0 *2.1*	13.6 *3.2*	13.0 *4.5*	12.1 *5.5*	11.4 *5.9*	10.8 *5.9*	10.4 *5.8*	9.9 *5.6*	9.2 *5.0*	8.6 *4.4*	5.8
130	16.6	14.6 *0.3*	14.1 *2.0*	13.6 *3.3*	13.0 *4.9*	12.4 *6.0*	11.5 *6.8*	10.8 *6.9*	10.2 *6.8*	9.7 *6.6*	9.3 *6.3*	8.5 *5.6*	7.9 *4.9*	5.0
140	15.5	14.3 *1.4*	13.9 *2.9*	13.2 *4.9*	12.5 *6.3*	11.9 *7.2*	11.1 *7.7*	10.4 *7.9*	9.8 *7.6*	9.3 *7.3*	8.8 *6.9*	8.0 *6.0*	7.4 *5.3*	4.3
150	14.6 *0.2*	14.1 *2.2*	13.5 *4.3*	12.7 *6.2*	12.1 *7.4*	11.5 *8.1*	10.7 *8.5*	10.0 *8.5*	9.4 *8.2*	8.9 *7.8*	8.4 *7.4*	7.6 *6.4*	7.0 *5.6*	3.7
160	14.4 *1.1*	13.9 *3.1*	13.1 *5.6*	12.4 *7.3*	11.8 *8.3*	11.2 *8.9*	10.4 *9.2*	9.7 *9.0*	9.1 *8.7*	8.5 *8.2*	8.1 *7.8*	7.2 *6.7*		3.2
170	14.3 *1.8*	13.6 *4.4*	12.8 *6.7*	12.1 *8.1*	11.5 *9.1*	11.0 *9.6*	10.3 *9.7*	9.4 *9.5*	8.8 *9.1*	8.3 *8.6*	7.8 *8.1*			2.9
180	14.1 *2.5*	13.3 *5.5*	12.5 *7.6*	11.9 *8.9*	11.3 *9.8*	10.8 *10.1*	9.9 *10.2*	9.2 *9.9*	8.6 *9.4*	8.0 *8.9*	7.6 *8.3*			2.6
200	13.6 *4.4*	12.8 *7.2*	12.1 *9.0*	11.5 *10.1*	11.0 *10.7*	10.4 *11.0*	9.6 *10.9*	8.9 *10.5*	8.2 *9.9*					2.1
220	13.3 *6.1*	12.5 *8.5*	11.9 *10.0*	11.3 *10.9*	10.7 *11.4*	10.2 *11.6*	9.3 *11.4*	8.6 *10.9*						1.7
240	13.0 *7.3*	12.3 *9.5*	11.6 *10.8*	11.1 *11.6*	10.5 *12.0*	10.0 *12.1*								1.4
260	12.7 *8.3*	12.1 *10.2*	11.5 *11.4*	10.9 *12.1*	10.4 *12.4*	9.9 *12.5*								1.2
280	12.6 *9.0*	11.9 *10.8*	11.3 *11.9*	10.8 *12.5*										

Girders so proportioned that the computed shear is less than that given in right-hand column do not require intermediate stiffeners.

* For single angle stiffeners, multiply by 1.8; for single plate stiffeners, multiply by 2.4.

AISC TABLE 3–46—Steel of 46 ksi Yield Point
Shear Stress, ksi (Shown on 1st line)
Stiffener Area, % of Web Area (In italics, on 2nd line)

Slenderness ratios h/t: web depth to web thickness	Aspect ratios a/h: stiffener spacing to web depth													
	0.5	0.6	0.7	0.8	0.9	1.0	1.2	1.4	1.6	1.8	2.0	2.5	3.0	over 3
60							18.5	18.5	18.5	18.5	18.5	18.3	18.0	17.3
70					18.5	18.5	18.3	17.5	16.9	16.5	16.2	15.8 *0.2*	15.3 *0.3*	14.9
80				18.5	18.3	17.2	16.1 *0.1*	15.7 *0.7*	15.4 *1.0*	15.1 *1.2*	14.9 *1.3*	14.5 *1.3*	14.2 *1.2*	13.0
90			18.5	17.6	16.3	15.8 *0.1*	15.3 *1.6*	14.8 *2.0*	14.5 *2.2*	14.2 *2.3*	13.8 *2.5*	13.1 *2.5*	12.6 *2.3*	10.4
100		18.5	17.4	16.0 *0.3*	15.6 *1.3*	15.2 *2.1*	14.6 *2.9*	13.9 *3.6*	13.3 *4.0*	12.8 *4.0*	12.4 *4.0*	11.6 *3.7*	11.0 *3.3*	8.4
110	18.5	17.8	16.0 *0.3*	15.5 *1.6*	15.1 *2.6*	14.6 *3.6*	13.6 *4.8*	12.9 *5.3*	12.3 *5.4*	11.7 *5.3*	11.3 *5.2*	10.5 *4.6*	9.9 *4.1*	6.9
120	18.5	16.3	15.6 *1.5*	15.1 *2.7*	14.5 *4.2*	13.8 *5.4*	12.9 *6.2*	12.1 *6.5*	11.5 *6.5*	10.9 *6.3*	10.5 *6.0*	9.6 *5.3*	9.0 *4.7*	5.8
130	17.4	15.8 *1.0*	15.3 *2.5*	14.6 *4.3*	13.9 *5.8*	13.2 *6.7*	12.3 *7.4*	11.5 *7.5*	10.9 *7.3*	10.3 *7.0*	9.9 *6.7*	9.0 *5.9*	8.3 *5.1*	5.0
140	16.2	15.5 *1.9*	14.9 *3.8*	14.1 *5.8*	13.4 *7.0*	12.8 *7.8*	11.8 *8.3*	11.1 *8.2*	10.4 *8.0*	9.8 *7.6*	9.4 *7.2*	8.4 *6.3*	7.8 *5.5*	4.3
150	15.9 *0.8*	15.3 *2.8*	14.5 *5.3*	13.7 *7.0*	13.0 *8.0*	12.4 *8.7*	11.5 *9.0*	10.7 *8.9*	10.0 *8.5*	9.4 *8.1*	9.0 *7.7*	8.0 *6.7*	7.4 *5.8*	3.7
160	15.7 *1.7*	14.9 *4.1*	14.1 *6.4*	13.4 *7.9*	12.7 *8.9*	12.1 *9.4*	11.2 *9.6*	10.4 *9.4*	9.7 *9.0*	9.1 *8.5*	8.6 *8.0*	7.7 *6.9*		3.2
170	15.5 *2.4*	14.6 *5.3*	13.8 *7.4*	13.1 *8.7*	12.4 *9.6*	11.8 *10.0*	10.9 *10.1*	10.1 *9.8*	9.4 *9.3*	8.9 *8.8*	8.4 *8.3*			2.9
180	15.2 *3.2*	14.3 *6.3*	13.5 *8.2*	12.8 *9.4*	12.2 *10.1*	11.6 *10.5*	10.7 *10.5*	9.9 *10.1*	9.2 *9.6*	8.6 *9.1*	8.1 *8.5*			2.6
200	14.7 *5.3*	13.9 *7.9*	13.1 *9.5*	12.5 *10.5*	11.9 *11.0*	11.3 *11.3*	10.4 *11.2*	9.6 *10.7*	8.9 *10.1*					2.1
220	14.3 *6.7*	13.6 *9.0*	12.9 *10.4*	12.2 *11.3*	11.6 *11.7*	11.1 *11.9*	10.1 *11.6*	9.3 *11.1*						1.7
240	14.0 *7.9*	13.3 *9.9*	12.6 *11.2*	12.0 *11.9*	11.4 *12.2*	10.9 *12.3*								1.4
260	13.8 *8.8*	13.1 *10.6*	12.5 *11.7*	11.8 *12.3*	11.3 *12.6*	10.7 *12.7*								1.2

Girders so proportioned that the computed shear is less than that given in right-hand column do not require intermediate stiffeners.

* For single angle stiffeners, multiply by 1.8; for single plate stiffeners, multiply by 2.4.

ALLOWABLE SHEAR STRESSES IN PLATE GIRDERS, KSI
And Required Gross Area of Pairs of Intermediate Stiffeners

AISC TABLE 3–50—Steel of 50 ksi Yield Point
Shear Stress, ksi (Shown on 1st line)
Stiffener Area, % of Web Area (In italics, on 2nd line)

Slenderness ratios h/t: web depth to web thickness	Aspect ratios a/h: stiffener spacing to web depth													
	0.5	0.6	0.7	0.8	0.9	1.0	1.2	1.4	1.6	1.8	2.0	2.5	3.0	over 3
60							20.0	20.0	20.0	20.0	19.7	19.1	18.8	18.1
70					20.0	20.0	19.1	18.2	17.6	17.3 *0.2*	17.1 *0.4*	16.7 *0.6*	16.5 *0.6*	15.5
80				20.0	19.1	17.9	17.1 *0.6*	16.7 *1.2*	16.4 *1.4*	16.1 *1.6*	15.8 *1.6*	15.4 *1.6*	15.0 *1.5*	13.1
90			20.0	18.3	17.3 *0.4*	16.9 *1.3*	16.3 *2.1*	15.8 *2.5*	15.3 *2.8*	14.8 *3.1*	14.3 *3.1*	13.5 *3.0*	13.0 *2.8*	10.4
100		20.0	18.1	17.2 *0.9*	16.7 *1.9*	16.3 *2.6*	15.4 *3.8*	14.6 *4.4*	13.9 *4.6*	13.4 *4.6*	12.9 *4.5*	12.0 *4.1*	11.4 *3.7*	8.4
110	20.0	18.5	17.2 *0.9*	16.7 *2.2*	16.2 *3.2*	15.4 *4.5*	14.4 *5.5*	13.6 *5.9*	12.9 *5.9*	12.3 *5.8*	11.8 *5.6*	10.9 *5.0*	10.3 *4.4*	6.9
120	19.7	17.4 *0.4*	16.8 *2.0*	16.2 *3.4*	15.4 *5.0*	14.7 *6.1*	13.7 *6.9*	12.8 *7.0*	12.1 *6.9*	11.5 *6.7*	11.0 *6.4*	10.1 *5.8*	9.4 *4.9*	5.8
130	18.2	17.0 *1.5*	16.4 *3.1*	15.6 *5.1*	14.8 *6.5*	14.1 *7.4*	13.1 *7.9*	12.2 *7.9*	11.5 *7.7*	10.9 *7.4*	10.4 *7.0*	9.4 *6.1*	8.7 *5.3*	5.0
140	17.3 *0.5*	16.7 *2.5*	15.9 *4.7*	15.1 *6.5*	14.3 *7.7*	13.6 *8.4*	12.6 *8.7*	11.8 *8.6*	11.0 *8.3*	10.4 *7.9*	9.9 *7.5*	8.9 *6.5*	8.2 *5.7*	4.3
150	17.1 *1.4*	16.4 *3.6*	15.5 *6.0*	14.6 *7.6*	13.9 *8.6*	13.3 *9.2*	12.2 *9.4*	11.4 *9.2*	10.7 *8.8*	10.0 *8.4*	9.5 *7.9*	8.5 *6.8*	7.7 *5.9*	3.7
160	16.9 *2.2*	16.0 *4.9*	15.1 *7.1*	14.3 *8.5*	13.6 *9.4*	13.0 *9.8*	11.9 *9.9*	11.1 *9.7*	10.3 *9.2*	9.7 *8.7*	9.2 *8.2*	8.1 *7.1*		3.2
170	16.7 *2.9*	15.6 *6.0*	14.8 *8.0*	14.0 *9.2*	13.3 *10.0*	12.7 *10.4*	11.7 *10.4*	10.8 *10.0*	10.1 *9.6*	9.5 *9.0*	8.9 *8.5*			2.9
180	16.3 *4.1*	15.4 *7.0*	14.5 *8.8*	13.8 *10.0*	13.1 *10.5*	12.5 *10.9*	11.5 *10.8*	10.6 *10.4*	9.9 *9.8*	9.2 *9.3*	8.7 *8.7*			2.6
200	15.8 *5.9*	14.9 *8.4*	14.1 *9.9*	13.4 *10.8*	12.8 *11.4*	12.2 *11.6*	11.1 *11.4*	10.3 *10.9*	9.5 *10.3*					2.1
220	15.4 *7.3*	14.6 *9.5*	13.8 *10.8*	13.2 *11.6*	12.5 *12.0*	11.9 *12.1*	10.9 *11.8*	10.0 *11.3*						1.7
240	15.1 *8.3*	14.3 *10.3*	13.6 *11.5*	13.0 *12.1*	12.3 *12.4*	11.7 *12.5*								1.4

Girders so proportioned that the computed shear is less than that given in right-hand column do not require intermediate stiffeners.

* For single angle stiffeners, multiply by 1.8; For single plate stiffeners, multiply by 2.4.

—This and preceding tables for the ASTM specification steels presented here by courtesy of American Institute of Steel Construction.

Bethlehem TABLE 3–45—Steel of 45 ksi Yield Point
See Notes Below

Slenderness ratios h/t: web depth to web thickness	Aspect ratios a/h: stiffener spacing to web depth															
h/t	0.5	0.6	0.7	0.8	0.9	1.0	1.2	1.3	1.4	1.5	1.6	1.8	2.0	2.5	3.0	over 3.0
60	18.00	18.00	18.00	18.00	18.00	18.00	18.00	18.00	18.00	18.00	18.00	18.00	18.00	17.95	17.65	16.96
70	18.00	18.00	18.00	18.00	18.00	18.00	17.93	17.47	17.09	16.79	16.53	16.13	15.84	15.45 0.1 0.1	15.25 0.2 0.3	14.54
80	18.00	18.00	18.00	18.00	17.92	16.82	15.69	15.44 0.2 0.3	15.27 0.5 0.6	15.11 0.7 0.9	14.97 0.9 1.1	14.73 1.1 1.3	14.53 1.2 1.4	14.14 1.2 1.5	13.88 1.2 1.4	12.72
90	18.00	18.00	18.00	17.19	15.93	15.33 0.6 0.7	14.85 1.5 1.8	14.64 1.7 2.1	14.45 1.9 2.4	14.27 2.0 2.5	14.11 2.1 2.6	13.82 2.2 2.7	13.50 2.3 2.9	12.81 2.3 2.9	12.34 2.2 2.8	10.27
100	18.00	18.00	17.00	15.54 0.1 0.1	15.13 1.2 1.5	14.76 2.0 2.5	14.23 2.7 3.4	13.89 3.1 3.9	13.55 3.4 4.3	13.25 3.6 4.5	12.97 3.8 4.7	12.49 3.9 4.8	12.09 3.9 4.8	11.33 3.6 4.5	10.81 3.2 4.1	8.31
110	18.00	17.38	15.54 0.1 0.1	15.09 1.5 1.8	14.67 2.4 3.0	14.20 3.3 4.2	13.30 4.6 5.7	12.91 4.9 6.1	12.57 5.1 6.4	12.25 5.2 6.5	11.96 5.2 6.5	11.46 5.2 6.5	11.04 5.0 6.3	10.24 4.5 5.7	9.68 4.0 5.0	6.87
120	18.00	15.93	15.17 1.3 1.7	14.71 2.6 3.2	14.11 3.9 4.9	13.46 5.1 6.4	12.56 6.1 7.6	12.17 6.3 7.8	11.82 6.4 7.9	11.49 6.4 8.0	11.20 6.3 7.9	10.68 6.2 7.7	10.24 5.9 7.4	9.41 5.2 6.5	8.82 4.6 5.8	5.77
130	17.06	15.35 0.8 1.0	14.85 2.4 3.0	14.22 4.0 5.1	13.52 5.6 6.9	12.89 6.6 8.2	11.98 7.2 9.0	11.59 7.3 9.2	11.23 7.3 9.2	10.91 7.3 9.1	10.60 7.2 9.0	10.08 6.9 8.6	9.63 6.6 8.2	8.76 5.8 7.2	8.15 5.1 6.3	4.92
140	15.84	15.08 1.8 2.2	14.50 3.6 4.5	13.72 5.6 6.9	13.04 6.8 8.6	12.43 7.7 9.6	11.53 8.1 10.2	11.13 8.2 10.2	10.77 8.1 10.2	10.44 8.0 10.0	10.13 7.9 9.8	9.59 7.5 9.4	9.13 7.1 8.9	8.25 6.2 7.8	7.61 5.4 6.8	4.24
150	15.40 0.7 0.9	14.85 2.6 3.3	14.06 5.0 6.3	13.31 6.8 8.5	12.66 7.9 9.9	12.06 8.6 10.7	11.16 8.9 11.1	10.76 8.9 11.1	10.40 8.8 11.0	10.06 8.6 10.8	9.75 8.4 10.5	9.20 8.0 10.0	8.74 7.6 9.5	7.83 6.6 8.2	7.18 5.7 7.1	3.70
160	15.19 1.5 1.9	14.52 3.8 4.8	13.70 6.2 7.8	12.98 7.8 9.7	12.34 8.7 10.9	11.76 9.3 11.6	10.86 9.5 11.9	10.46 9.4 11.8	10.09 9.3 11.6	9.75 9.1 11.4	9.44 8.9 11.1	8.89 8.4 10.5	8.41 7.9 9.9	7.49 6.9 8.6		3.25
170	15.01 2.2 2.8	14.19 5.1 6.3	13.40 7.2 9.0	12.71 8.6 10.8	12.08 9.4 11.8	11.51 9.9 12.4	10.61 10.0 12.5	10.21 9.9 12.4	9.84 9.7 12.1	9.50 9.5 11.9	9.18 9.3 11.6	8.62 8.7 10.9	8.14 8.2 10.3			2.88
180	14.82 3.0 3.8	13.91 6.1 7.6	13.15 8.1 10.1	12.48 9.3 11.6	11.86 10.0 12.5	11.30 10.4 13.0	10.40 10.4 13.0	10.00 10.3 12.8	9.62 10.1 12.6	9.28 9.8 12.3	8.96 9.6 12.0	8.40 9.0 11.3	7.92 8.5 10.6			2.57
200	14.30 5.1 6.3	13.48 7.7 9.6	12.76 9.4 11.7	12.12 10.4 13.0	11.52 11.0 13.7	10.97 11.2 14.0	10.07 11.1 13.9	9.66 10.9 13.6	9.29 10.6 13.3	8.94 10.4 12.9	8.62 10.1 12.6					2.08
220	13.92 6.6 8.2	13.15 8.9 11.1	12.47 10.3 12.9	11.85 11.2 14.0	11.27 11.6 14.5	10.73 11.8 14.8	9.83 11.6 14.5	9.42 11.3 14.2	9.04 11.1 13.8	8.70 10.7 13.4						1.72
240	13.63 7.7 9.7	12.91 9.8 12.3	12.25 11.1 13.8	11.64 11.8 14.7	11.08 12.2 15.2	10.55 12.3 15.3										1.44
260	13.41 8.6 10.8	12.71 10.5 13.1	12.08 11.6 14.5	11.49 12.3 15.3	10.93 12.6 15.7	10.40 12.6 15.8										1.23

Figures given in top horizontal line opposite each h/t value indicate allowable shear stresses F_v.

Figures given in second horizontal line indicate required gross area of pairs of intermediate stiffeners, as per cent of web area A_w, using 45 ksi yield-point steel for the stiffeners ($Y=1.00$; $D=1.00$).

Figures given in third horizontal line indicate required gross area of pairs of intermediate stiffeners, as per cent of web area A_w, using 36 ksi yield-point steel for the stiffeners ($Y=1.25$; $D=1.00$).

Girders so proportioned that the computed shear is less than that given in the extreme right-hand column do not require intermediate stiffeners.

For single angle stiffeners, multiply values in second and third horizontal lines by 1.8.

For single plate stiffeners, multiply values in second and third horizontal lines by 2.4.

—This and following tables for some of the proprietary steels presented here by courtesy of Bethlehem Steel Corp. (Similar tables have been developed by United States Steel Corp.)

ALLOWABLE SHEAR STRESSES IN PLATE GIRDERS, KSI
And Required Gross Area of Pairs of Intermediate Stiffeners

Bethlehem TABLE 3–50—Steel of 50 ksi Yield Point
See Notes Below

Slenderness ratios h/t: web depth to web thickness; Aspect ratios a/h: stiffener spacing to web depth

h/t	0.5	0.6	0.7	0.8	0.9	1.0	1.2	1.3	1.4	1.5	1.6	1.8	2.0	2.5	3.0	over 3.0
60	20.00	20.00	20.00	20.00	20.00	20.00	20.00	20.00	20.00	20.00	20.00	19.84	19.48	18.92	18.61	17.88
70	20.00	20.00	20.00	20.00	20.00	20.00	18.90	18.41	18.02	17.69	17.42	17.13 0.2 0.3	16.93 0.4 0.5	16.57 0.6 0.8	16.32 0.6 0.8	15.33
80	20.00	20.00	20.00	20.00	18.89	17.73	16.96 0.6 0.9	16.74 0.9 1.3	16.54 1.2 1.6	16.36 1.3 1.8	16.19 1.4 2.0	15.90 1.6 2.2	15.66 1.6 2.3	15.20 1.6 2.2	14.88 1.5 2.1	12.99
90	20.00	20.00	19.91	18.12	17.12 0.4 0.6	16.71 1.3 1.8	16.15 2.1 2.9	15.90 2.3 3.2	15.68 2.5 3.4	15.43 2.6 3.7	15.13 2.8 3.9	14.61 3.1 4.2	14.18 3.1 4.3	13.37 3.0 4.2	12.82 2.8 3.8	10.27
100	20.00	20.00	17.92	16.98 0.9 1.2	16.53 1.9 2.6	16.10 2.6 3.7	15.23 3.7 5.2	14.81 4.1 5.7	14.43 4.4 6.1	14.08 4.5 6.3	13.77 4.6 6.4	13.22 4.6 6.4	12.76 4.5 6.3	11.89 4.1 5.7	11.29 3.7 5.1	8.31
110	20.00	18.32	17.01 0.9 1.2	16.51 2.1 3.0	16.00 3.2 4.4	15.27 4.5 6.2	14.26 5.5 7.7	13.83 5.8 8.0	13.44 5.9 8.2	13.09 5.9 8.2	12.76 5.9 8.2	12.19 5.8 8.0	11.71 5.6 7.7	10.80 5.0 6.9	10.15 4.4 6.1	6.87
120	19.48	17.17 0.4 0.6	16.62 2.0 2.8	16.03 3.4 4.8	15.23 5.0 7.0	14.53 6.1 8.5	13.52 6.9 9.5	13.09 7.0 9.7	12.69 7.0 9.8	12.33 7.0 9.7	12.00 6.9 9.6	11.41 6.7 9.3	10.92 6.4 8.9	9.97 5.6 7.8	9.29 4.9 6.8	5.77
130	17.98	16.84 1.5 2.1	16.27 3.1 4.3	15.40 5.1 7.1	14.63 6.5 9.0	13.95 7.4 10.2	12.95 7.9 11.0	12.51 7.9 11.0	12.11 7.9 11.0	11.74 7.8 10.9	11.40 7.7 10.7	10.81 7.4 10.2	10.30 7.0 9.7	9.32 6.1 8.5	8.62 5.3 7.4	4.92
140	17.17 0.5 0.7	16.56 2.5 3.4	15.73 4.7 6.6	14.90 6.5 9.0	14.16 7.7 10.6	13.50 8.4 11.6	12.49 8.7 12.1	12.05 8.7 12.1	11.64 8.6 12.0	11.27 8.5 11.8	10.93 8.3 11.5	10.32 7.9 11.0	9.81 7.5 10.4	8.80 6.5 9.0	8.09 5.7 7.9	4.24
150	16.92 1.4 1.9	16.22 3.6 5.0	15.29 6.0 8.4	14.49 7.6 10.6	13.77 8.6 11.9	13.13 9.2 12.7	12.12 9.4 13.0	11.68 9.3 13.0	11.27 9.2 12.8	10.89 9.0 12.5	10.55 8.8 12.2	9.93 8.3 11.6	9.41 7.9 10.9	8.39 6.8 9.4	7.66 5.9 8.2	3.70
160	16.70 2.1 3.0	15.81 4.9 6.8	14.93 7.1 9.9	14.16 8.5 11.8	13.46 9.3 13.0	12.83 9.8 13.7	11.82 9.9 13.8	11.38 9.8 13.6	10.96 9.7 13.4	10.59 9.4 13.1	10.24 9.2 12.8	9.62 8.7 12.1	9.08 8.2 11.4	8.05 7.1 9.8		3.25
170	16.49 2.9 4.0	15.48 6.0 8.4	14.63 8.0 11.1	13.88 9.2 12.8	13.20 10.0 13.9	12.58 10.4 14.4	11.57 10.4 14.4	11.12 10.2 14.2	10.71 10.0 13.9	10.33 9.8 13.6	9.98 9.5 13.3	9.35 9.0 12.5	8.82 8.5 11.8			2.88
180	16.16 4.1 5.7	15.20 6.9 9.6	14.38 8.8 12.2	13.65 9.9 13.7	12.98 10.5 14.6	12.37 10.8 15.1	11.36 10.8 15.0	10.91 10.6 14.7	10.50 10.4 14.4	10.12 10.1 14.0	9.76 9.8 13.7	9.13 9.3 12.9	8.59 8.7 12.1			2.57
200	15.65 5.9 8.2	14.77 8.4 11.7	13.99 9.9 13.8	13.29 10.8 15.1	12.64 11.3 15.8	12.04 11.6 16.1	11.03 11.4 15.8	10.58 11.1 15.5	10.17 10.9 15.1	9.78 10.6 14.7	9.42 10.3 14.3					2.08
220	15.27 7.3 10.1	14.44 9.5 13.1	13.70 10.8 15.0	13.02 11.6 16.1	12.39 12.0 16.6	11.80 12.1 16.8	10.79 11.8 16.4	10.34 11.5 16.0	9.92 11.2 15.6	9.53 10.9 15.2						1.72
240	14.98 8.3 11.6	14.20 10.3 14.3	13.48 11.5 15.9	12.82 12.1 16.8	12.20 12.4 17.3	11.61 12.5 17.4										1.44

Figures given in top horizontal line opposite each h/t value indicate allowable shear stresses F_v.
Figures given in second horizontal line indicate required gross area of pairs of intermediate stiffeners, as per cent of web area A_w, using 50 ksi yield-point steel for the stiffeners ($Y=1.00$; $D=1.00$).
Figures given in third horizontal line indicate required gross area of pairs of intermediate stiffeners, as per cent of web area A_w, using 36 ksi yield-point steel for the stiffeners ($Y=1.39$; $D=1.00$).
Girders so proportioned that the computed shear is less than that given in the extreme right-hand column do not require intermediate stiffeners.
For single angle stiffeners, multiply values in second and third horizontal lines by 1.8.
For single plate stiffeners, multiply values in second and third horizontal lines by 2.4.

—Note that AISC and Bethlehem values for steel of 50 ksi yield vary only slightly. The Bethlehem table is included here for the additional values for area of stiffeners fabricated from A36 steel.

Bethlehem TABLE 3–55—Steel of 55 ksi Yield Point
See Notes Below

Slenderness ratios h/t: web depth to web thickness; Aspect ratios a/h: stiffener spacing to web depth

h/t	0.5	0.6	0.7	0.8	0.9	1.0	1.2	1.3	1.4	1.5	1.6	1.8	2.0	2.5	3.0	over 3.0
60	22.00	22.00	22.00	22.00	22.00	22.00	22.00	22.00	22.00	21.65	21.32	20.81	20.43	19.84	19.52	18.75
70	22.00	22.00	22.00	22.00	22.00	21.26	19.82	19.31	18.96 0.1 0.1	18.79 0.3 0.5	18.62 0.5 0.7	18.34 0.7 1.1	18.10 0.8 1.3	17.66 0.9 1.5	17.36 0.9 1.4	16.07
80	22.00	22.00	22.00	21.38	19.81	18.87 0.3 0.5	18.28 1.2 1.9	18.03 1.5 2.3	17.80 1.7 2.6	17.58 1.8 2.8	17.39 1.9 3.0	17.05 2.0 3.1	16.77 2.1 3.1	16.00 2.1 3.2	15.44 2.0 3.1	12.99
90	22.00	22.00	20.88	19.02	18.53 1.1 1.7	18.07 1.9 2.9	17.43 2.6 4.0	17.05 3.0 4.6	16.64 3.3 5.1	16.26 3.5 5.4	15.92 3.7 5.6	15.34 3.8 5.8	14.85 3.8 5.8	13.93 3.5 5.4	13.30 3.2 4.9	10.27
100	22.00	21.13	18.96 0.2 0.3	18.41 1.5 2.3	17.90 2.5 3.8	17.30 3.5 5.3	16.20 4.7 7.1	15.73 5.0 7.6	15.30 5.2 7.9	14.92 5.3 8.0	14.57 5.3 8.1	13.95 5.2 8.0	13.43 5.1 7.8	12.45 4.6 7.0	11.76 4.1 6.2	8.31
110	22.00	19.21	18.47 1.5 2.3	17.91 2.7 4.2	17.12 4.2 6.5	16.33 5.4 8.2	15.23 6.3 9.6	14.75 6.5 9.9	14.32 6.5 10.0	13.92 6.5 10.0	13.56 6.5 9.9	12.92 6.3 9.6	12.39 6.0 9.2	11.36 5.3 8.1	10.63 4.7 7.2	6.87
120	20.43	18.67 1.1 1.7	18.06 2.6 4.0	17.21 4.5 6.8	16.35 5.9 9.1	15.59 6.9 10.5	14.49 7.5 11.4	14.01 7.6 11.6	13.57 7.6 11.6	13.16 7.5 11.5	12.79 7.4 11.3	12.14 7.1 10.8	11.59 6.8 10.3	10.52 5.9 9.0	9.77 5.2 7.9	5.77
130	18.99 0.1 0.2	18.32 2.1 3.2	17.51 4.2 6.4	16.57 6.0 9.2	15.75 7.3 11.1	15.02 8.0 12.3	13.91 8.4 12.9	13.43 8.5 12.9	12.98 8.4 12.8	12.57 8.3 12.6	12.20 8.1 12.4	11.54 7.7 11.8	10.97 7.3 11.2	9.88 6.4 9.7	9.10 5.5 8.5	4.92
140	18.69 1.1 1.7	18.00 3.1 4.8	16.96 5.6 8.6	16.07 7.3 11.1	15.28 8.3 12.7	14.56 8.9 13.7	13.45 9.2 14.0	12.97 9.1 14.0	12.52 9.0 13.8	12.11 8.9 13.5	11.73 8.7 13.2	11.05 8.2 12.6	10.48 7.8 11.9	9.36 6.7 10.2	8.56 5.8 8.9	4.24
150	18.43 1.9 3.0	17.51 4.6 7.0	16.52 6.8 10.5	15.66 8.3 12.6	14.89 9.2 14.0	14.19 9.7 14.8	13.08 9.8 15.0	12.60 9.7 14.8	12.15 9.5 14.6	11.73 9.3 14.3	11.35 9.1 13.9	10.67 8.6 13.2	10.08 8.1 12.4	8.95 7.0 10.7	8.14 6.1 9.3	3.70
160	18.21 2.7 4.1	17.10 5.8 8.9	16.16 7.8 11.9	15.33 9.1 13.9	14.58 9.9 15.1	13.89 10.3 15.7	12.78 10.3 15.7	12.29 10.2 15.5	11.84 10.0 15.2	11.42 9.7 14.9	11.03 9.5 14.5	10.35 8.9 13.7	9.76 8.4 12.9	8.61 7.2 11.0		3.25
170	17.84 3.9 6.0	16.77 6.8 10.4	15.87 8.6 13.2	15.06 9.8 14.9	14.32 10.4 15.9	13.64 10.8 16.5	12.53 10.7 16.4	12.04 10.5 16.1	11.59 10.3 15.8	11.16 10.1 15.4	10.78 9.8 14.9	10.08 9.2 14.1	9.49 8.7 13.2			2.88
180	17.51 5.0 7.6	16.49 7.6 11.7	15.62 9.3 14.2	14.83 10.3 15.8	14.10 10.9 16.7	13.43 11.2 17.1	12.32 11.1 16.9	11.83 10.9 16.6	11.37 10.6 16.2	10.95 10.3 15.8	10.56 10.0 15.3	9.86 9.4 14.4	9.26 8.9 13.5			2.57
190	17.23 5.9 9.0	16.26 8.3 12.8	15.41 9.9 15.1	14.63 10.8 16.5	13.92 11.3 17.3	13.25 11.5 17.6	12.15 11.3 17.3	11.65 11.1 17.0	11.19 10.9 16.6	10.77 10.6 16.1	10.38 10.3 15.7	9.68 9.6 14.7				2.30
200	17.00 6.7 10.2	16.06 9.0 13.7	15.23 10.4 15.9	14.46 11.2 17.1	13.76 11.7 17.8	13.10 11.8 18.1	12.00 11.6 17.7	11.50 11.4 17.3	11.04 11.1 16.9	10.61 10.8 16.4	10.22 10.4 16.0					2.08
210	16.79 7.3 11.2	15.88 9.5 14.5	15.07 10.8 16.5	14.32 11.6 17.7	13.62 12.0 18.3	12.97 12.1 18.5	11.86 11.8 18.0	11.37 11.6 17.6	10.91 11.3 17.2	10.48 10.9 16.7						1.89
220	16.61 7.9 12.1	15.73 9.9 15.2	14.94 11.2 17.1	14.20 11.9 18.1	13.51 12.2 18.7	12.86 12.3 18.8	11.75 12.0 18.3	11.25 11.7 17.9	10.79 11.4 17.4	10.36 11.1 16.9						1.72

Figures given in top horizontal line opposite each h/t value indicate allowable shear stresses F_v.
Figures given in second horizontal line indicate required gross area of pairs of intermediate stiffeners, as per cent of web area A_w, using 55 ksi yield-point steel for the stiffeners ($Y=1.00$; $D=1.00$).
Figures given in third horizontal line indicate required gross area of pairs of intermediate stiffeners, as per cent of web area A_w, using 36 ksi yield-point steel for the stiffeners ($Y=1.53$; $D=1.00$).
Girders so proportioned that the computed shear is less than that given in the extreme right-hand column do not require intermediate stiffeners.
For single angle stiffeners, multiply values in second and third horizontal lines by 1.8.
For single plate stiffeners, multiply values in second and third horizontal lines by 2.4.

ALLOWABLE SHEAR STRESSES IN PLATE GIRDERS, KSI
And Required Gross Area of Pairs of Intermediate Stiffeners

Bethlehem TABLE 3–60—Steel of 60 ksi Yield Point
See Notes Below

Slenderness ratios h/t: web depth to web thickness	Aspect ratios a/h: stiffener spacing to web depth																
h/t	0.4	0.5	0.6	0.7	0.8	0.9	1.0	1.2	1.3	1.4	1.5	1.6	1.8	2.0	2.5	3.0	over 3.0
60	24.00	24.00	24.00	24.00	24.00	24.00	24.00	24.00	23.53	23.03	22.61	22.27	21.73	21.34	20.74	20.49 0.1 0.2	19.59
70	24.00	24.00	24.00	24.00	24.00	23.64	22.20	20.73	20.48 0.4 0.6	20.25 0.6 1.1	20.05 0.8 1.4	19.86 1.0 1.6	19.53 1.2 1.9	19.25 1.3 2.1	18.73 1.3 2.1	18.38 1.2 2.0	16.79
80	24.00	24.00	24.00	24.00	22.33	20.74 0.1 0.1	20.25 0.9 1.6	19.59 1.8 3.0	19.30 2.0 3.4	19.03 2.2 3.7	18.79 2.3 3.8	18.57 2.4 4.0	18.01 2.6 4.3	17.50 2.7 4.5	16.56 2.7 4.5	15.91 2.5 4.1	12.99
90	24.00	24.00	24.00	21.81	20.47 0.7 1.1	19.92 1.7 2.8	19.42 2.5 4.1	18.48 3.5 5.8	17.97 3.9 6.4	17.51 4.1 6.9	17.10 4.3 7.2	16.72 4.4 7.3	16.07 4.4 7.4	15.52 4.4 7.3	14.49 4.0 6.7	13.77 3.6 6.0	10.27
100	24.00	24.00	22.07	20.44 0.8 1.4	19.83 2.1 3.5	19.25 3.1 5.1	18.37 4.4 7.3	17.16 5.4 9.1	16.65 5.7 9.5	16.18 5.8 9.7	15.75 5.9 9.8	15.36 5.9 9.8	14.68 5.7 9.6	14.11 5.5 9.2	13.01 4.9 8.2	12.24 4.4 7.3	8.31
110	24.00	23.28	20.58 0.5 0.8	19.92 2.1 3.5	19.20 3.5 5.9	18.24 5.1 8.5	17.39 6.2 10.3	16.19 6.9 11.5	15.67 7.0 11.7	15.19 7.1 11.8	14.76 7.0 11.7	14.36 7.0 11.6	13.66 6.7 11.2	13.06 6.4 10.7	11.91 5.6 9.4	11.11 4.9 8.2	6.87
120	24.00	21.34	20.16 1.7 2.8	19.42 3.3 5.6	18.38 5.4 8.9	17.47 6.7 11.1	16.66 7.5 12.5	15.45 8.0 13.4	14.92 8.1 13.4	14.44 8.0 13.4	14.00 7.9 13.2	13.59 7.8 13.0	12.87 7.4 12.4	12.26 7.1 11.8	11.08 6.2 10.3	10.24 5.4 9.0	5.77
130	23.92	20.53 0.7 1.2	19.80 2.7 4.4	18.74 5.1 8.4	17.75 6.8 11.3	16.87 7.9 13.2	16.08 8.6 14.3	14.87 8.9 14.8	14.34 8.9 14.8	13.86 8.8 14.6	13.41 8.6 14.4	13.00 8.4 14.1	12.27 8.0 13.4	11.64 7.6 12.6	10.44 6.6 10.9	9.57 5.7 9.5	4.92
140	22.21	20.21 1.6 2.7	19.29 4.1 6.8	18.19 6.4 10.7	17.24 7.9 13.2	16.39 8.9 14.8	15.62 9.4 15.7	14.42 9.6 16.0	13.88 9.5 15.8	13.39 9.4 15.6	12.94 9.2 15.3	12.52 8.9 14.9	11.78 8.5 14.1	11.15 8.0 13.3	9.92 6.9 11.5	9.04 6.0 10.0	4.24
150	20.75	19.94 2.5 4.1	18.80 5.4 9.0	17.76 7.5 12.5	16.84 8.8 14.7	16.01 9.6 16.1	15.25 10.1 16.8	14.05 10.1 16.9	13.51 10.0 16.7	13.02 9.8 16.4	12.56 9.6 16.0	12.14 9.4 15.6	11.40 8.8 14.7	10.75 8.3 13.9	9.51 7.2 11.9	8.61 6.2 10.4	3.70
160	20.51 0.8 1.3	19.58 3.6 5.9	18.39 6.5 10.9	17.40 8.4 14.0	16.51 9.6 16.0	15.70 10.3 17.1	14.95 10.6 17.7	13.75 10.6 17.7	13.21 10.4 17.4	12.71 10.2 17.0	12.26 10.0 16.6	11.83 9.7 16.2	11.08 9.1 15.2	10.43 8.6 14.3	9.17 7.4 12.3		3.25
170	20.28 1.5 2.5	19.18 4.7 7.9	18.06 7.4 12.4	17.10 9.2 15.3	16.23 10.2 17.0	15.44 10.8 18.0	14.70 11.1 18.5	13.50 11.0 18.3	12.96 10.8 18.0	12.46 10.5 17.6	12.00 10.3 17.1	11.57 10.0 16.6	10.81 9.4 15.7	10.16 8.8 14.7			2.88
180	20.09 2.1 3.5	18.86 5.7 9.5	17.78 8.2 13.7	16.85 9.8 16.3	16.00 10.7 17.9	15.22 11.2 18.7	14.49 11.5 19.1	13.29 11.3 18.8	12.75 11.1 18.5	12.25 10.8 18.0	11.78 10.5 17.5	11.36 10.2 17.0	10.59 9.6 16.0	9.94 9.0 15.0			2.57
190	19.87 2.8 4.7	18.58 6.5 10.9	17.55 8.9 14.8	16.64 10.3 17.2	15.81 11.2 18.6	15.03 11.6 19.4	14.32 11.8 19.7	13.11 11.6 19.3	12.57 11.3 18.9	12.07 11.0 18.4	11.60 10.7 17.9	11.17 10.4 17.4	10.41 9.8 16.3	9.74 9.2 15.3			2.30
200	19.56 3.8 6.3	18.34 7.2 12.1	17.35 9.4 15.7	16.46 10.8 17.9	15.64 11.5 19.2	14.88 11.9 19.9	14.17 12.1 20.1	12.96 11.8 19.7	12.42 11.5 19.2	11.91 11.2 18.7	11.45 10.9 18.2	11.02 10.6 17.6					2.08

Figures given in top horizontal line opposite each h/t value indicate allowable shear stresses F_v.
Figures given in second horizontal line indicate required gross area of pairs of intermediate stiffeners, as per cent of web area A_w, using 60 ksi yield-point steel for the stiffeners ($Y = 1.00$; $D = 1.00$).
Figures given in third horizontal line indicate required gross area of pairs of intermediate stiffeners, as per cent of web area A_w, using 36 ksi yield-point steel for the stiffeners ($Y = 1.67$; $D = 1.00$).
Girders so proportioned that the computed shear is less than that given in the extreme right-hand column do not require intermediate stiffeners.
For single angle stiffeners, multiply values in second and third horizontal lines by 1.8.
For single plate stiffeners, multiply values in second and third horizontal lines by 2.4.

Bethlehem TABLE 3–65—Steel of 65 ksi Yield Point
See Notes Below

Slenderness ratios h/t: web depth to web thickness	Aspect ratios a/h: stiffener spacing to web depth																
h/t	0.4	0.5	0.6	0.7	0.8	0.9	1.0	1.2	1.3	1.4	1.5	1.6	1.8	2.0	2.5	3.0	over 3.0
50	26.00	26.00	26.00	26.00	26.00	26.00	26.00	26.00	26.00	26.00	26.00	26.00	26.00	26.00	25.89	25.46	24.46
60	26.00	26.00	26.00	26.00	26.00	26.00	26.00	25.13	24.49	23.97	23.54	23.18	22.62	22.32 0.1 0.2	21.87 0.4 0.7	21.57 0.4 0.8	20.39
70	26.00	26.00	26.00	26.00	26.00	24.61	23.11	22.07 0.6 1.1	21.79 0.9 1.6	21.53 1.1 2.0	21.29 1.3 2.3	21.08 1.4 2.6	20.70 1.6 2.8	20.38 1.6 2.9	19.78 1.6 2.9	19.37 1.5 2.7	16.97
80	26.00	26.00	26.00	25.54	23.25	22.15 0.6 1.1	21.62 1.5 2.7	20.88 2.3 4.1	20.55 2.5 4.5	20.25 2.6 4.7	19.81 2.9 5.2	19.42 3.1 5.6	18.74 3.3 5.9	18.17 3.3 6.0	17.11 3.2 5.7	16.39 2.9 5.2	12.99
90	26.00	26.00	25.52	22.70	21.90 1.2 2.2	21.31 2.2 4.0	20.74 3.0 5.3	19.44 4.3 7.7	18.88 4.6 8.3	18.38 4.8 8.7	17.93 4.9 8.9	17.52 5.0 9.0	16.80 5.0 9.0	16.19 4.8 8.7	15.05 4.4 7.9	14.25 3.9 7.0	10.27
100	26.00	26.00	22.97	21.90 1.4 2.5	21.24 2.6 4.7	20.37 4.0 7.2	19.43 5.2 9.3	18.12 6.1 11.0	17.56 6.3 11.4	17.05 6.4 11.5	16.59 6.4 11.5	16.16 6.3 11.5	15.41 6.2 11.1	14.78 5.9 10.7	13.57 5.2 9.5	12.71 4.6 8.3	8.31
110	26.00	24.23	22.08 1.0 1.9	21.36 2.6 4.7	20.37 4.4 8.0	19.36 5.9 10.6	18.46 6.8 12.3	17.15 7.4 13.4	16.58 7.5 13.6	16.07 7.5 13.6	15.59 7.5 13.5	15.15 7.4 13.3	14.39 7.1 12.8	13.73 6.7 12.1	12.47 5.9 10.6	11.58 5.1 9.3	6.87
120	26.00	22.43 0.2 0.3	21.64 2.2 3.9	20.66 4.2 7.6	19.56 6.1 11.0	18.59 7.3 13.2	17.72 8.1 14.6	16.41 8.5 15.3	15.84 8.5 15.3	15.31 8.4 15.2	14.83 8.3 15.0	14.39 8.1 14.7	13.61 7.7 14.0	12.94 7.3 13.3	11.64 6.4 11.5	10.72 5.6 10.0	5.77
130	24.89	22.05 1.2 2.2	21.18 3.3 6.0	19.97 5.8 10.5	18.92 7.4 13.4	17.99 8.4 15.2	17.14 9.0 16.3	15.84 9.3 16.8	15.26 9.2 16.7	14.73 9.1 16.4	14.24 8.9 16.1	13.79 8.7 15.7	13.00 8.3 14.9	12.32 7.8 14.1	10.99 6.8 12.2	10.05 5.9 10.6	4.92
140	23.11	21.72 2.1 3.8	20.58 4.9 8.8	19.43 7.1 12.8	18.42 8.5 15.3	17.51 9.3 16.8	16.69 9.8 17.7	15.38 9.9 17.9	14.80 9.8 17.7	14.27 9.6 17.4	13.78 9.4 17.0	13.32 9.2 16.6	12.52 8.7 15.7	11.82 8.2 14.8	10.48 7.1 12.7	9.52 6.1 11.1	4.24
150	22.31 0.5 0.9	21.39 3.0 5.5	20.09 6.1 11.1	18.99 8.1 14.6	18.01 9.3 16.8	17.13 10.0 18.1	16.32 10.4 18.8	15.01 10.4 18.8	14.43 10.3 18.6	13.89 10.1 18.2	13.40 9.8 17.8	12.94 9.6 17.3	12.13 9.0 16.3	11.43 8.5 15.3	10.07 7.3 13.2	9.09 6.3 11.4	3.70
160	22.05 1.3 2.3	20.92 4.3 7.8	19.68 7.1 12.9	18.63 8.9 16.1	17.68 10.0 18.1	16.82 10.6 19.2	16.02 10.9 19.8	14.71 10.9 19.6	14.13 10.7 19.3	13.59 10.4 18.8	13.09 10.2 18.4	12.63 9.9 17.9	11.81 9.3 16.8	11.10 8.7 15.8	9.73 7.5 13.5		3.25
170	21.83 1.9 3.5	20.53 5.4 9.8	19.35 8.0 14.4	18.33 9.6 17.3	17.41 10.6 19.1	16.56 11.1 20.1	15.77 11.4 20.5	14.46 11.2 20.2	13.88 11.0 19.8	13.33 10.7 19.4	12.83 10.4 18.9	12.37 10.1 18.3	11.54 9.5 17.2	10.83 9.0 16.2			2.88
180	21.62 2.5 4.6	20.20 6.3 11.4	19.07 8.7 15.7	18.08 10.2 18.4	17.18 11.1 20.0	16.34 11.5 20.8	15.56 11.7 21.2	14.25 11.5 20.8	13.66 11.3 20.3	13.12 11.0 19.8	12.62 10.7 19.3	12.15 10.4 18.7	11.32 9.7 17.6	10.61 9.1 16.5			2.57
190	21.26 3.6 6.4	19.92 7.1 12.8	18.84 9.3 16.8	17.87 10.7 19.3	16.98 11.5 20.7	16.15 11.9 21.4	15.38 12.0 21.7	14.07 11.7 21.2	13.49 11.5 20.7	12.94 11.2 20.2	12.44 10.9 19.6	11.97 10.6 19.0	11.14 9.9 17.9				2.30

Figures given in top horizontal line opposite each h/t value indicate allowable shear stresses F_v.
Figures given in second horizontal line indicate required gross area of pairs of intermediate stiffeners, as per cent of web area A_w, using 65 ksi yield-point steel for the stiffeners ($Y = 1.00$; $D = 1.00$).
Figures given in third horizontal line indicate required gross area of pairs of intermediate stiffeners, as per cent of web area A_w, using 36 ksi yield-point steel for the stiffeners ($Y = 1.81$; $D = 1.00$).
Girders so proportioned that the computed shear is less than that given in the extreme right-hand column do not require intermediate stiffeners.
For single angle stiffeners, multiply values in second and third horizontal lines by 1.8.
For single plate stiffeners, multiply values in second and third horizontal lines by 2.4.

Access holes cut in girder web must be reinforced. In regions of high bending moment, flanges must extend far enough beyond web opening to effectively transfer forces into main web of girder. Semi-automatic welding, with self-shielding cored electrode wire, is used here in attaching reinforcements at double the speed of manual welding.

Efficient Plate Girders

1. GENERAL REQUIREMENTS

Every plate girder must have several properties:

1. Sufficient strength, as measured by its section modulus (S).

2. Sufficient stiffness, as measured by its moment of inertia (I).

3. Ability to carry the shear forces applied to it, as measured by its web area (A_w).

4. Ability to withstand web buckling, as indicated by the empirical relationship of the web depth to web thickness—

$$K = \frac{d_w}{t_w} \quad \text{.........................(1)}$$

In some cases, the depth (d) must be held within a certain maximum value.

Also, the choice of flange and web plates should not result in any unusual fabricating difficulties.

An "efficient" girder will satisfy all of these requirements with the minimum weight.

An "economical" girder will satisfy these same requirements and in addition will be fabricated for the least cost for the whole structure. This may not necessarily be the lowest weight design.

Most structural texts suggest a method of girder design in which some assumption is made as to the depth, usually from 1/10 to 1/12 of the girder length (a minimum of 1/25). Knowing the web depth, the web thickness is then found. This is kept above the value required for web area (A_w) to satisfy the shear forces and also to insure that the ratio $K = d_w/t_w$ will be below the proper value.

Table 1 lists the AASHO (Bridge) limiting values of $K = d_w/t_w$ for common materials, with or without transverse stiffeners.

2. DESIGN APPROACH

It might be well to investigate the efficient girder design on the basis of minimum weight. If done simply, it would offer a good guide or starting point in any design of a girder. An estimate of weight that is obtained quickly would allow the designer to deviate from the efficient depth to a more shallow girder when necessary. He would then balance off the additional weight with any advantages of the altered design, such as increased head room, less fill at bridge approaches, etc.

In order to simplify the derivation of the efficient girder, it will be necessary to assume the depth of the web plate (d_w) is also the distance between the centers of gravity of the two flange plates as well as the overall depth of the girder. See Figure 1.

In the case of welded plate girders where the thickness of flange plates is very small compared to the girder's depth, this assumption doesn't introduce very much of an error while greatly simplifying the procedure and resulting formulas.

The moment of inertia of the girder section is—

$$I = 2\,A_f \left(\frac{d_w}{2}\right)^2 + \frac{t_w d_w^3}{12}$$

$$= \frac{A_f\,d_w^2}{2} + \frac{d_w^4}{12\,K} \text{ and}$$

$$S = \frac{I}{d/2} = A_f\,d_w + \frac{d_w^3}{6\,K} \text{ or}$$

$$A_f = \frac{S}{d_w} - \frac{d_w^2}{6\,K} \text{ also}$$

$$A_w = t_w\,d_w = \frac{d_w^2}{K}$$

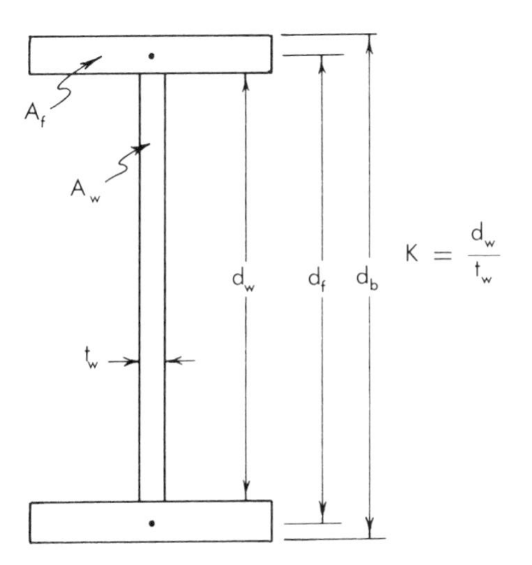

FIG. 1 Girder description.

TABLE 1—Limiting Ratios of Web Depth to Thickness

$K = \frac{d_w}{t_w} = \frac{\text{web depth}}{\text{web thickness}}$ AASHO (Bridges)

	Mild Steel A373, A36	Low Alloy Steel A441 or Weldable A242 46,000 psi yield	Low Alloy Steel A441 or Weldable A242 50,000 psi yield
No transverse stiffeners (1.6.80)	$K \leqq 60$	$K \leqq 52$	$K \leqq 50$
Transverse stiffeners (1.6.75)	$K \leqq 170$	$K \leqq 145$	$K \leqq 140$
Longitudinal stiffener with transverse stiffeners (1.6.75)	$K \leqq 340$	$K \leqq 290$	$K \leqq 280$

Therefore, the total girder area is—

$$A_t = 2\,A_f + A_w = \frac{2\,S}{d_w} - \frac{d_w^2}{3\,K} + \frac{d_w^2}{K}$$

$$= \frac{2\,S}{d_w} + \frac{2\,d_w^2}{3\,K}$$

Now differentiate with respect to the depth (d_w) and set equal to zero:

$$\frac{dA_t}{dd_w} = -\frac{2\,S}{d^2} + \frac{4\,d_w}{3\,K} = 0$$

$$\therefore \frac{2\,S}{d_w} = \frac{4\,d_w}{3\,K} \quad \text{or}$$

$$d_w^3 = \frac{3\,K\,S}{2} \quad \text{and}$$

$$\boxed{d_w = \sqrt[3]{\frac{3\,K\,S}{2}}} \qquad \text{(2)}$$

also

$$S = \frac{2\,d_w^3}{3\,K}$$

Since

$$A_f = \frac{S}{d_w} - \frac{d_w^2}{6\,K}$$

$$= \frac{2\,d_w^3}{3\,K\,d_w} - \frac{d_w^2}{6\,K}$$

$$\therefore \boxed{A_f = \frac{d_w^2}{2\,K}} \qquad \text{(3)}$$

Also, the total area of the girder is—

$$A_t = 2\,A_f + A_w$$

$$= \frac{d_w^2}{K} + \frac{d_w^2}{K}$$

$$= \frac{2\,d_w^2}{K}$$

$$\therefore \boxed{A_t = 4\,A_f} \qquad \text{(4)}$$

This indicates that the efficient girder has half its weight in the web and half in the flanges. Based on steel weighing 3.4 lbs/linear ft/sq in. of section area, the efficient girder's weight is—

$$\boxed{W_t = \frac{6.8\,d_w^2}{K} \text{ lbs/linear ft}} \qquad \text{(5)}$$

Figure 2 contains two curves showing the weights and depths of girders for a given set of requirements; in this case a section modulus of $S = 5{,}000$ in.^{3}

Curve A gives the weight (W_t, lbs/lin ft) and depth (d_w, inches) of the girder for any given value of K.

These two values come from Formulas 2 and 5:

$$d_w = \sqrt[3]{\frac{3\,K\,S}{2}} \quad \text{and} \quad W_t = \frac{6.8\,d_w^2}{K}$$

These combine to form—

$$\boxed{W_t = 8.91\,\sqrt[3]{\frac{S^2}{K}}} \qquad \text{(6)}$$

which is the weight of girder not including weight of

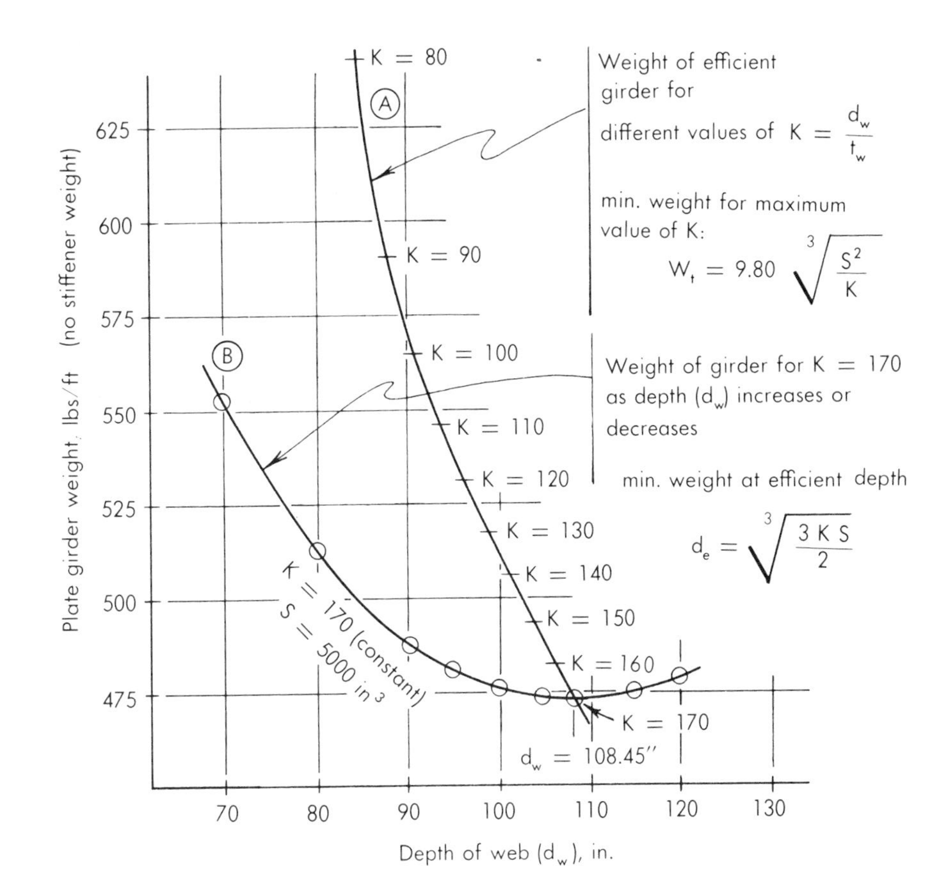

FIG. 2 Relationship of efficient girder weight and depth for given requirements (here, S=5,000 in.³).

stiffeners.

It is seen that larger values of K result in lower weight (W_t) and increased depth (d_w) of girder. Conversely, lower values of K will produce heavier and more shallow girders. This represents the lowest weight design for any given value of K.

Assuming the weight of stiffeners will be 20% of the web weight, and since in the efficient girder, the web represents half of the girder weight, the stiffeners would increase the girder weight by 10%, or—

$$W_t = 9.80 \sqrt[3]{\frac{S^2}{K}} \qquad \text{.......................}(7)$$

which is the weight of girder including weight of stiffeners.

Effect of Changing Dimensions

In an efficient girder the depth of which is determined by Formula 2—

$$d_w = \sqrt[3]{\frac{3\ K\ S}{2}}$$

the weight decreases as the ratio (K) increases; hence use as large a K ratio as is possible (see Table 1). Once the flange area (A_f) is determined, the actual profile of the flange (thickness to width) has almost no effect on the resulting girder weight (W_t).

Occasionally the girder depth may be restricted because of head room or some other reason. The shallow-depth web then must be thicker in order to make up the web area required for the shear forces; in this case, it may be possible to further increase the web thickness, very slightly, to arrive at 1/60 of its clear depth and thus eliminate the transverse stiffeners. If this is the case, the decision not to use stiffeners should be made at the start of the design rather than later. For example, See Figure 3.

Here on the left side, the efficient girder using stiffeners (K = 170) weighs 188 lbs/linear ft. Taking this same design and increasing the web thickness to 1/60 of its depth to eliminate the stiffeners, would increase its weight to 328 lbs/linear ft, or 1.74 times. On the other hand if the efficient depth is first determined using no stiffeners (K = 60), the weight is increased to only 243 lbs/linear ft, or 1.29 times. In this particular case, the design which eliminated the stiffeners at the start (right-hand girder) weighs only 74% as much as the design which eliminated the stiffeners after the depth was determined (center girder).

The graph in Figure 4 shows the direct effect of changing web depth. Changing the combination of flange dimensions, but using same depth of web (d_w)

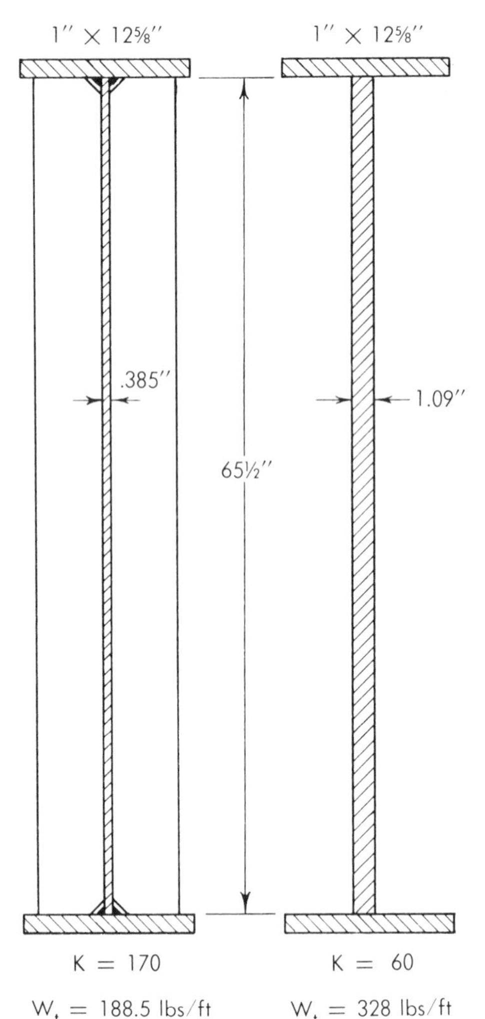

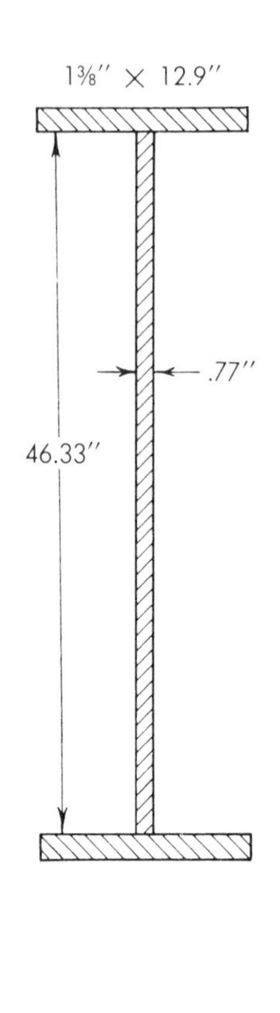

FIG. 3 Efficient girder with stiffeners (left) weighs less. Merely increasing the web thickness to eliminate stiffeners (center) results in greater weight than again designing on basis of efficient depth (right).

and required section modulus (S), does not change the girder weight very much. The thinner and wider flanges result in a very slight reduction in girder weight.

If at any time in the design, the web area (A_w) falls below the required shear-carrying capacity (V), the design becomes dictated by the shear requirements. In this case, a given web area (A_w) must be maintained and the value of K held as high as possible for minimum girder weight.

Weight of the efficient girder depends on:

1. Value of K used (the lower values produce heavier girders), and

2. How far the actual depth deviates from the efficient depth.

3. DESIGN OUTLINE

The following is a guide to the design of an efficient girder. This would represent a starting point for the final girder design.

Given these requirements:

$$S = \frac{M}{\sigma}$$

$$A_w = \frac{V}{\tau}$$

$$K \leqq \frac{d_w}{t_w} \qquad \text{(see Table 1)}$$

Start with Method A, and continue unless it is determined that the web area of the proposed girder does not equal or exceed the given required value. In this case, Method B represents a short detour to be taken in the design procedure.

Method A

1. As a starting point for web depth, use—

$$d_w = \sqrt[3]{\frac{3\ K\ S}{2}}$$

This may occasionally exceed the depth permitted by architectural considerations, in which case the latter

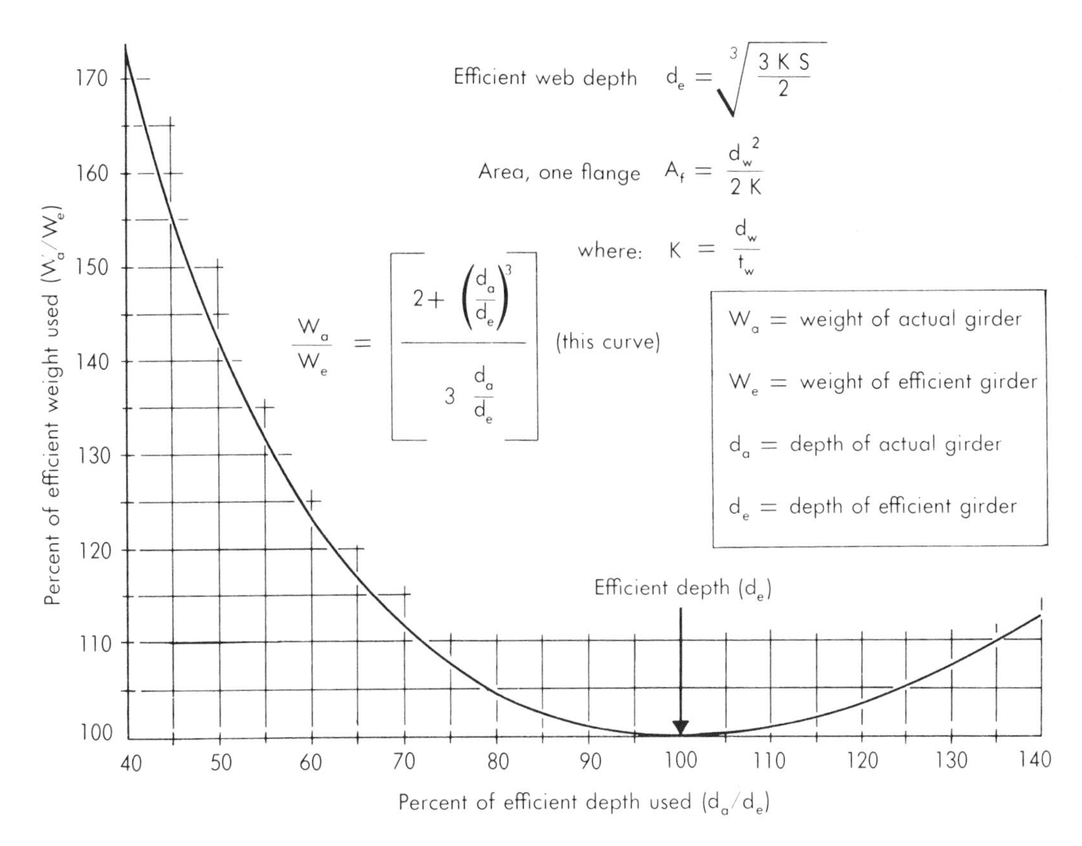

FIG. 4 Effect of changing web depth on girder weight.

must be used.

2. For web thickness, use

$$t_w = \frac{d_w}{K}$$

3. Check the resulting values for

$$K = \frac{d_w}{t_w}$$

$$A_w = d_w \ t_w$$

Try to use values of t_w and d_w that will provide the highest allowable value of K. If resulting A_w equals or exceeds the given required value, proceed to Step 4 of Method A; if not, jump to Step 3A of Method B.

Method A cont'd

4. Now compute the web's moment of inertia:

$$I_w = \frac{t_w \ d_w^3}{12}$$

5. Select a flange thickness and compute the distance from the entire section's neutral axis to the outer fiber (c), and then compute c_f:

$$c = \frac{d_w}{2} + t_f$$

$$c_f = \frac{d_w + t_f}{2}$$

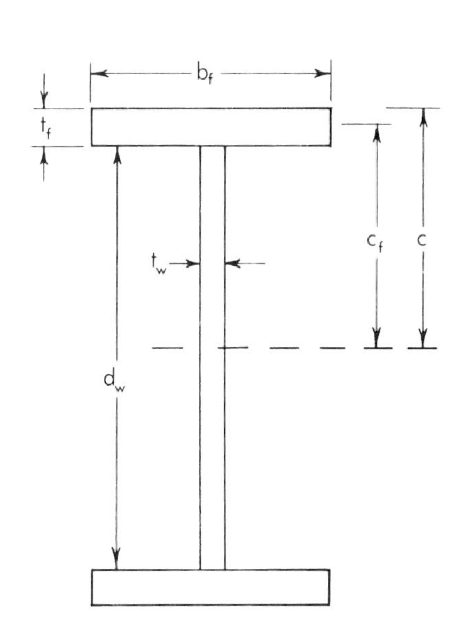

FIG. 5. Girder description.

FIG. 6 Efficient Web Depth and Approximate Weight of Plate Girder

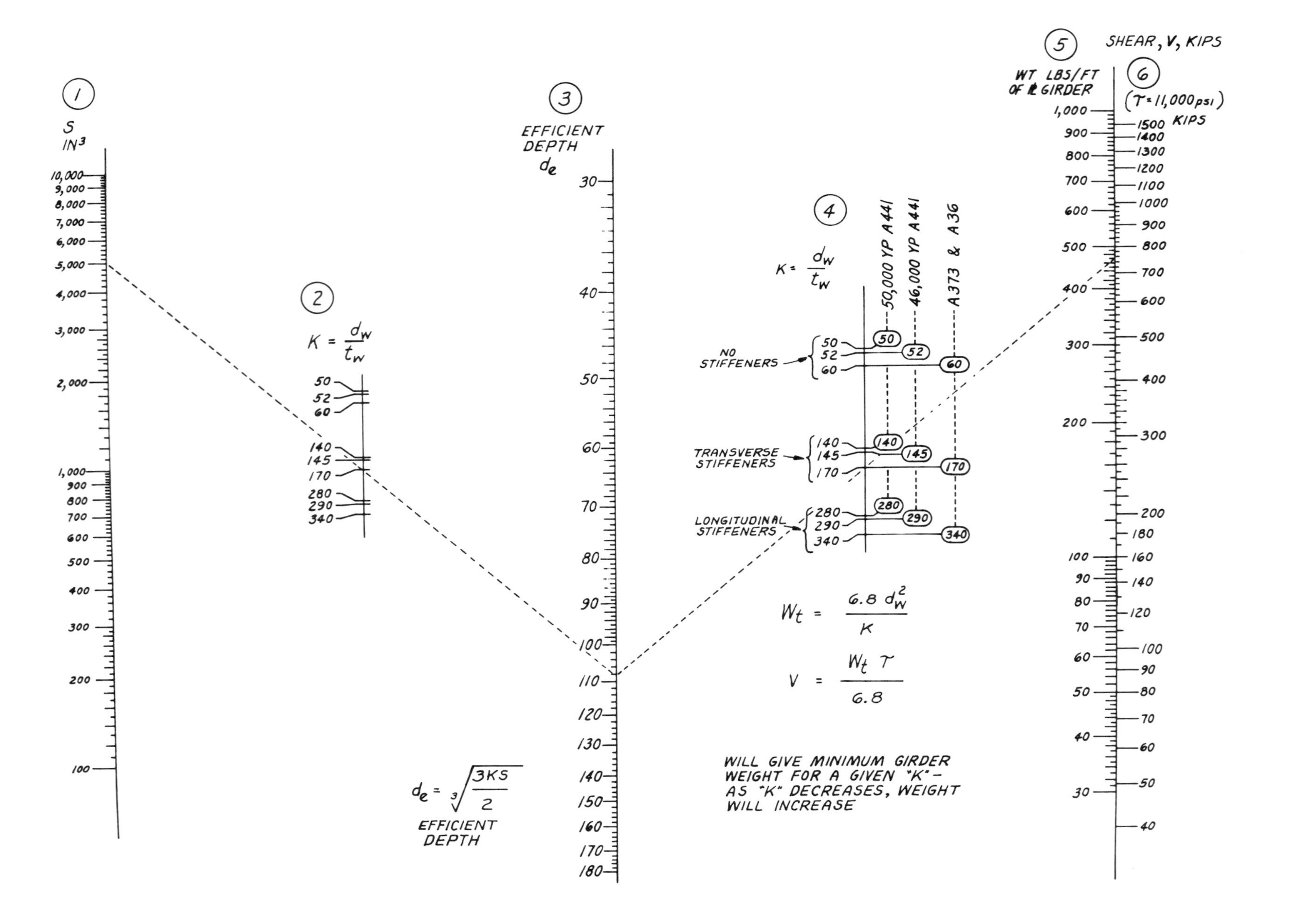

6. With this, compute the section's total required moment of inertia:

$$I_t = S\ c$$

7. Now select a flange width from the following:

$$b_f = \frac{I_t - I_w}{2\ t_f\ c_f^2}$$

Since:

$$I_f = 2\ b_f\ t_f\ c_f^2$$

and use the next larger convenient plate width for flange width (b_f).

8. Then check

$$I_f = 2\ b_f\ t_f\ c_f^2 \text{ and}$$

$$I_t = I_f + I_w \text{ and}$$

$$S = \frac{I_t}{c}$$

This final value of section modulus (S) must equal or exceed the value initially stated as a requirement to resist the bending moment.

Method B | When Shear Governs Design of Girder

If the web area (A_w) computed back in Step 3 does not equal or exceed the given required amount, take these additional steps before proceeding with Step 4 of Method A.

3A. Calculate the web thickness (t_w) and web depth (d_w) from the required web area (A_w) and required depth-to-thickness ratio (K), using the following formulas:

$$t_w \geq \sqrt{\frac{A_w}{K}}$$

and

$$d_w \leq t_w\ K$$

3B. Using this as a guide, adjust the thickness (t_w) and depth (d_w) of the web plate to satisfy the above conditions and also the following:

$$t_w\ d_w \geq A_w$$

which must equal or exceed the required value of A_w ($= V/\tau$); and

$$\frac{d_w}{t_w} \leq K$$

which must equal or be less than the maximum allowable value of K.

Having selected d_w and t_w, return to Step 4 of Method A and follow through to completion (Step 8).

Short-Cut Nomographs

The first nomograph, Figure 6, will quickly give the girder's efficient web depth as well as its estimated weight (lbs/lin ft).

On this nomograph:

Line 1 = required section modulus (S)
Line 2 = required ratio of web depth to web thickness (K)
Line 3 = (read:) efficient web depth (d_e)
Line 4 = required ratio of web depth to web thickness (K)
Line 5 = (read:) estimated weight of girder (W_t)
Line 6 = (read:) allowable shear carried by web (V) on the basis of τ = 11,000 psi (bridges)

If the right-hand line 6 should indicate an allowable shear value (V) for the efficient web which is less than the actual value, the girder design must be based on the shear-carrying capacity of the web. This is done by going to the second nomograph, Figure 7:

Here:

Line 1 = actual shear value which must be carried by the web (V)
Line 2 = required ratio of web depth to web thickness (K)
Line 3 = (read:) web thickness to be used (t_w)
Line 4 = required ratio of web depth to web thickness (K)
Line 5 = (read:) web depth to be used (d_w)

The weight of this shear design may be estimated by the third nomograph, Figure 8. Two values of weight are obtained; these must be added together.

Here, for first weight:

Line 1a = required section modulus (S)
Line 2a = web depth (d)
Line 3 = (read:) estimated weight (W_t)

For the second weight:

Line 1b = shear to be carried by web (V)
Line 2b = allowable shear stress (τ)
Line 3 = (read:) estimated weight (W_t)

The sum of these two weights still does not include the weights of stiffeners if required.

Problem 1

Design a bridge girder for the following loads:

M = 7500 ft-kips
V = 600 kips

FIG. 7 Required Thickness and Depth of Plate Girder Web Based on Shear-Carrying Capacity

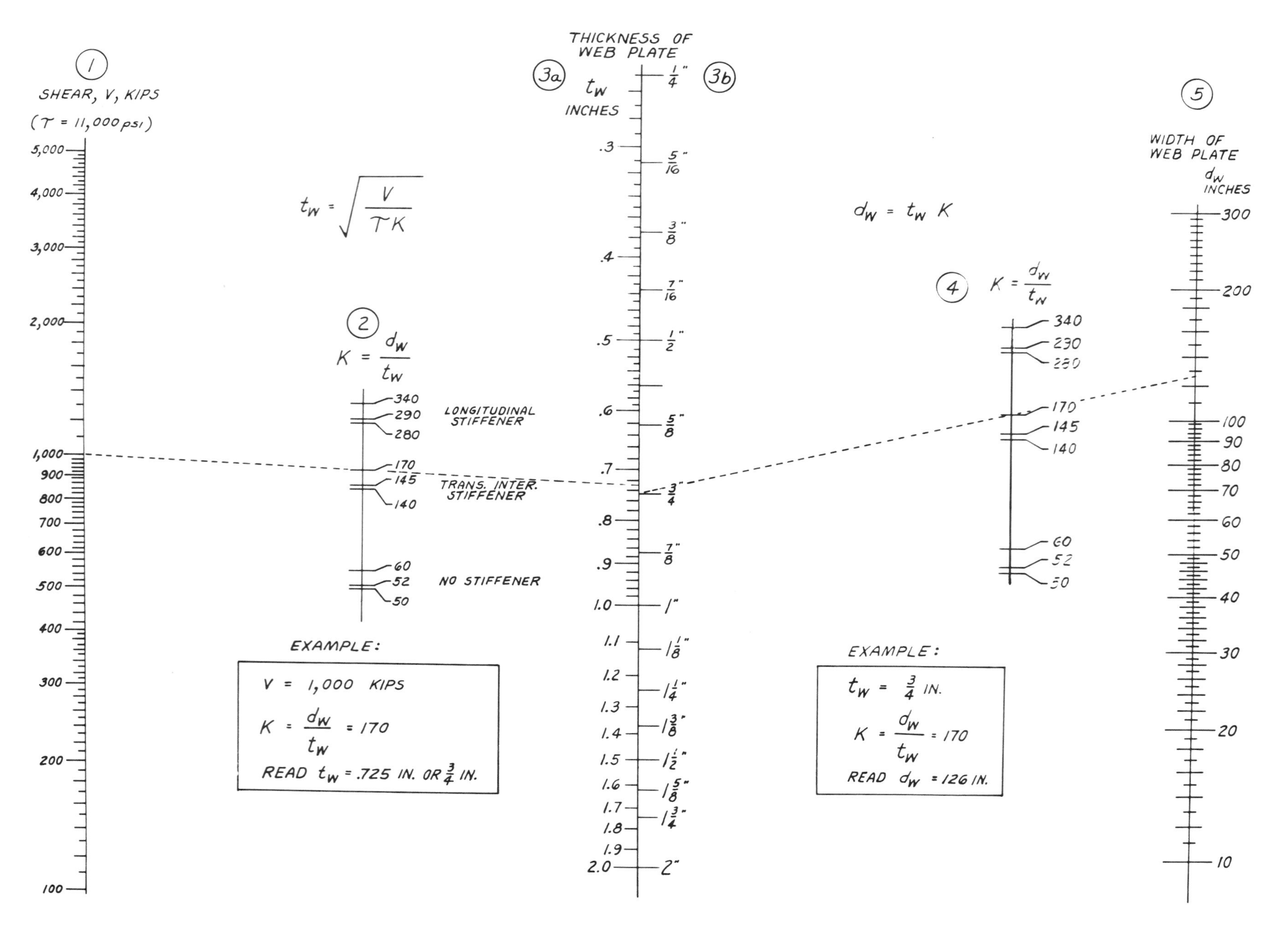

For A36 steel, AASHO Sec 1.6.75 (see Table 1) requires the K ratio of web depth to thickness (d_w/t_w) to be not more than K = 170 using transverse stiffeners.

Then:

$$S = \frac{M}{\sigma} = \frac{(7500)(12)}{(18 \text{ ksi})} = 5000 \text{ in.}^3$$

$$A_w = \frac{V}{\tau} = \frac{(600)}{(11 \text{ ksi})} = 54.5 \text{ in.}^2$$

Following the suggested outline for designing an efficient girder:

1. $$d_w = \sqrt[3]{\frac{3\,K\,S}{2}} = \sqrt[3]{\frac{3(170)(5000)}{2}} = 108.45''$$

2. $$t_w = \frac{d_w}{K} = \frac{(108.45)}{(170)} = .638''$$

or *use an 11/16" thick web, 110" deep.*

3. Check these proposed dimensions:

$$K = \frac{d_w}{t_w} = \frac{(110)}{(11/16)} = 160 < 170 \quad O.K.$$

$$A_w = t_w\, d_w = (11/16)(110) = 75.6 \text{ in.}^2 > 54.5 \text{ in.}^2 \quad O.K.$$

4. $$I_w = \frac{t_w\, d_w^3}{12} = \frac{(11/16)(110)^3}{12} = 76{,}255 \text{ in.}^4$$

5. Let flange thickness be $t_f = 2''$:

$$c = \frac{d_w}{2} + t_f = \frac{(110)}{2} + (2) = 57.0''$$

$$c_f = \frac{d_w + t_f}{2} = \frac{(110) + (2)}{2} = 56.0''$$

6. $$I_t = S\,c = (5000 \text{ in.}^3)(57'') = 285{,}000 \text{ in.}^4$$

7. $$b_f = \frac{I_t - I_w}{2\, t_f\, c_f^2} = \frac{(285{,}000) - (76{,}255)}{2\,(2)\,(56)^2} = 16.65''$$

or use 17.0" wide × 2" thick flange plates

8. Then, to find properties of the actual proposed section:

$$I_f = 2\, b_f\, t_f\, c_f^2 = 2\,(17)(2)(56)^2 = 213{,}250 \text{ in.}^4$$

$$I_t = I_f + I_w = (213{,}250) + (76{,}250) = 289{,}500 \text{ in.}^4$$

$$S = \frac{I_t}{c} = \frac{(289{,}500)}{(57)} = 5080 \text{ in.}^3 > 5000 \text{ in.}^3 \quad OK$$

Then, to find the weight of this designed girder:

$$2\,A_f = 2(2'')(17'') = 68.0$$

$$A_w = (11/16'')(110'') = \underline{75.6}$$

$$143.6 \text{ in.}^2$$

∴ W_t = *488 lbs/lin ft* of girder, on the basis of steel's weighing 3.4 lbs/lin ft/in.^{2} of cross section.

To show that this does result in the minimum girder weight, nine other combinations have been figured, from a web depth of 70" up to 120", as shown by Curve B in Figure 2. In the example just worked, the various dimensions were rounded off to the next

FIG. 8 Weight of Plate Girder When Design Is Governed by Shear

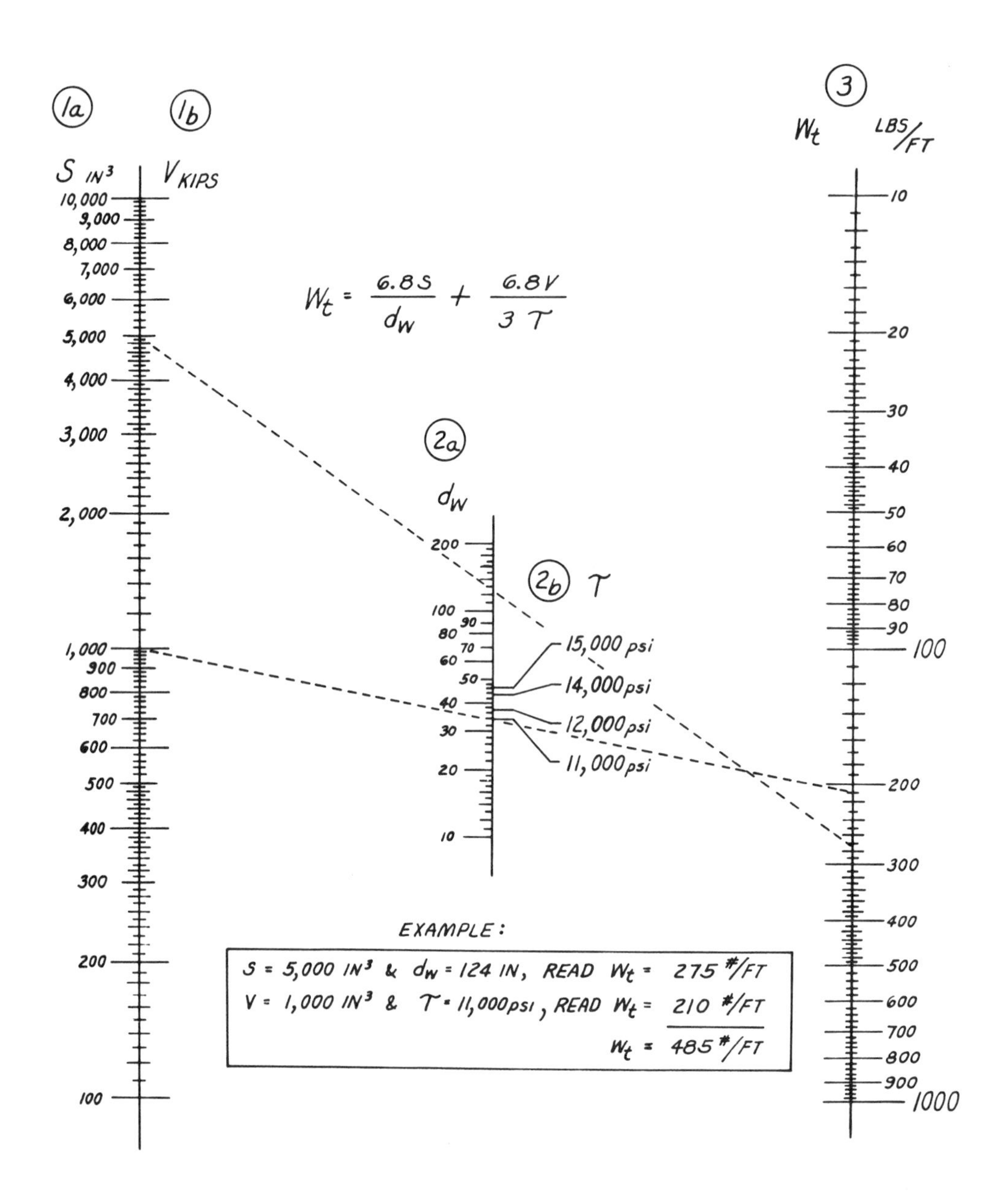

size fraction based on available plate. The actual plate girder example using a web depth of 110″ weighed 488 lbs/ft, yet the efficient girder for this same depth should weigh 473 lbs/ft.

Four other combinations of flange dimensions were figured, using the same web depth ($d_w = 108.45''$), but there was little difference in girder weight. The thinner and wider flanges result in a very slight reduction in weight.

Problem 2

Consider the same girder in which the shear load is increased to V = 1000 kips. This will illustrate the work to be done where shear (V) would govern the design.

Here:

$$A_w = \frac{V}{\tau}$$

$$= \frac{(1000)}{(11 \text{ ksi})}$$

$$= 90.9 \text{ in.}^2$$

Following the suggested outline:

1. $d_w = \sqrt[3]{\frac{3\ K\ S}{2}}$

$= \sqrt[3]{\frac{3(170)(5000)}{2}}$

$= 108.45''$

2. $t_w = \frac{d_w}{K}$

$= \frac{(108.45)}{(170)}$

$= .638''$

In the previous problem, this led to a web 11/16″ × 110″; however—

3. $A_w = t_w\ d_w$

$= (11/16)(110)$

$= 75.6 \text{ in.}^2 < 90.9 \text{ in.}^2$

In this case the 11/16″ × 110″ web plate has insufficient area to carry the shear load. So, switching to Method B:

3A. $t_w = \sqrt{\frac{A_w}{K}}$

$= \sqrt{\frac{(90.9)}{(170)}}$

$= .732''$

or *use a ¾″-thick web plate.*

$d_w = t_w\ K$

$= (3/4)(170)$

$= 127.5''$

or *use a 124″ deep web plate.*

3B. Check:

$K = \frac{d_w}{t_w}$

$= \frac{(124)}{(3/4)}$

$= 165.3 < 170$ *OK*

$A_w = t_w\ d_w$

$= (3/4)(124)$

$= 93.0 \text{ in.}^2 > 90.9 \text{ in.}^2$ *OK*

Now returning to the basic Method A outline:

4. $I_w = \frac{t_w\ d_w^3}{12}$

$= \frac{(3/4)(124)^3}{12}$

$= 119{,}164. \text{ in.}^4$

5. Let flange thickness be $t_f = 2''$:

$c = \frac{d_w}{2} + t_f$

$= \frac{(124)}{2} + (2)$

$= 64''$

$c_f = \frac{d_f + t_f}{2}$

$= \frac{(124) + (2)}{2}$

$= 63''$

6. $I_t = S\ c$

$= (5000 \text{ in.}^3)(64'')$

$= 320{,}000 \text{ in.}^4$

7. $b_f = \frac{I_t - I_w}{2\ t_f\ c_f^2}$

$= \frac{(320{,}000) - (119{,}164)}{2\ (2)(63)^2}$

$= 12.65''$

or *use 13″ wide x 2″ thick flange plates*

8. Then, to find properties of the actual proposed section:

$I_f = 2\ b_f\ t_f\ c_f^2$

$= 2(13)(2)(63)^2$

$= 206{,}388 \text{ in.}^4$

$I_t = I_f + I_w$

$= (206{,}388) + (119{,}164)$

$= 325{,}550 \text{ in.}^4$

$S = \frac{I_t}{c}$

$= \frac{(325{,}550)}{(64)}$

$= 5090 \text{ in.}^3 > 5000 \text{ in.}^3$ *OK*

Then, to find the weight of this designed plate girder:

$$2\,A_f = 2(2'')(13'') = 52.0$$
$$A_w = (\tfrac{3}{4}'')(120'') = 90.0$$
$$142.0 \text{ in.}^2$$

$\therefore$ W_t = *482.8 lbs/lin ft* of girder

Problem 3

Find the approximate web dimensions and weight for the same girder, using the nomographs, Figures 6, 7 and 8.

1st Nomograph

Given:

$$S = 5000 \text{ in.}^3$$

$$K = \frac{d_w}{t_w} = 170$$

read:

$$d = 108''$$

Given:

$$K = \frac{d_w}{t_w} = 170$$

read:

$$W_t = 470 \text{ lbs/ft}$$

and:

V = *750 kips* allowable

Using an actual depth of 110″ as in Figure 1 would increase this estimated weight to 483 lbs/ft as read on the nomograph. In Problem 1, the weight was computed to be 488 lbs/ft; this slight increase is due to the increase in web thickness from the required .638″ to the next fraction, 11/16″.

2nd Nomograph

If the shear value is increased to V = 1000 kips as in Problem 2, this exceeds the allowable value of 750 kips read from the first nomograph. Therefore, shear governs the design and the second nomograph must be used.

Given:

$$V = 1000 \text{ kips}$$

$$K = \frac{d_w}{t_w} = 170$$

read:

t_w = .725″ or *use ¾″*

Given:

$$K = \frac{d_w}{t_w} = 170$$

read:

d_w = 126″ or *use 124″*

3rd Nomograph

Given:

$$S = 5000 \text{ in.}^3$$
$$d = 124''$$

read:

W_t = ——————→ 275 lbs/ft

Given:

$$V = 1000 \text{ kips}$$
$$\tau = 11{,}000 \text{ psi}$$

read:

W_t = ——————→ + 210 lbs/ft

Total = 485 lbs/ft

In Problem 2, the weight was computed to be 482.8 lbs/ft.

Welded Plate Girders for Bridges

1. INTRODUCTION

Plate girders are fabricated for requirements which exceed those of a rolled beam, or a rolled beam with added cover plates. The usual welded plate girder is made of two flange plates fillet welded to a single web plate. Box girders are made of two flange plates and two web plates. They have extremely high torsional strength and rigidity.

Plate girders are proportioned by their moments of inertia. See preceding Section 4.2 on Efficient Plate Girders.

AASHO Specifications govern in the Bridge field, with AWS Specifications generally governing welded joint details. This particular section brings together these two Specifications, with interpretation and supplementary recommendations being added for the designer's guidance.

AASHO (1.6.11) limits the minimum ratio of the depth of beams and plate girders to 1/25 of their length. For continuous spans, the span length shall be considered as the distance between dead-load points of contraflexure.

2. PLATE GIRDER WEBS

AASHO Specifications (1.6.75 & 1.6.80) require that the thickness-to-depth ratio of girder webs be not less than the values indicated in Table 1.

The above ratio of web thickness to clear depth is based on predications of the plate buckling theory, the web plate being subjected to shear throughout its depth and to compressive bending stresses over a portion of its depth.

The plate buckling theory assumes the panel portion of the web to be an isolated plate; however, in the plate girder, the web is part of a built-up member. When the critical buckling stress in the web is reached, the girder does not collapse. The flange plates carry all of the bending moment, the buckled web serves as a tension diagonal, and the transverse stiffeners become the vertical compression members. This has the effect of making the girder act as a truss.

Research at Lehigh University tested, among other things, the effect of the web thickness on the ultimate carrying capacity of the girder; see Figure 1. It was found that the ultimate load carrying capacity of the girder, expressed as the ratio of the ultimate load (P_u) to load causing yield stress (P_y) was directly proportional to the restraint offered by the compression flange. The more torsionally flexible flange (wide and thin) resulted in the lower strengths, and the more torsionally rigid flange (tubular) resulted in higher strengths.

Differences in web slenderness ratio produced little effect on the ultimate load carrying capacity of the girder for the same compression flange.

Although the tubular type of compression flange was used to obtain a torsionally rigid flange, it is not recommended for actual bridge practice. However, the concrete floor slab directly on top of the usual compression flange offers a similarly high torsional restraint, as well as good lateral bracing.

Designers in Europe, as well as Canada, are not held to this (Table 1) fixed ratio of web thickness to web depth. One exception made in the United States is the Quinnipiac River Bridge in New Haven, Conn., which used thin longitudinally stiffened webs. Instead of using an arbitrary ratio of web thickness to depth, the design was based on the elastic stability of the web from information by Mosseiff and Lienhard*. The design also considered safety against yielding based on a yielding criterion obtained from the following Huber-Mises formula:

$$\boxed{\sigma_{cr} = \sqrt{\sigma_x^2 - \sigma_x \sigma_y + \sigma_y^2 + 3 \tau_{xy}^2}} \quad \ldots (1)$$

* "Theory of Elastic Stability Applied to Structural Design" ASCE paper 2120.

TABLE 1—Minimum Girder Web *Thickness-To-Depth Ratios* *(AASHO 1.6.80, 1.6.75)*

	A-7, A-373 & A-36 Steels	A-441 Steel 46,000 psi yield	A-441 Steel 50,000 psi yield
No stiffeners	1/60	1/52	1/50
Intermediate transverse stiffeners	1/170	1/145	1/140
Longitudinal stiffeners	1/340	1/290	1/280

If the value of σ_{cr} resulting from the above formula is equal to the yield point of the steel in uni-axial tension (what is commonly called the yield strength, σ_y), it is assumed this combination of stresses will just produce yielding in the material. Hence, the use of this formula will give some indication of the factor of safety against yielding.

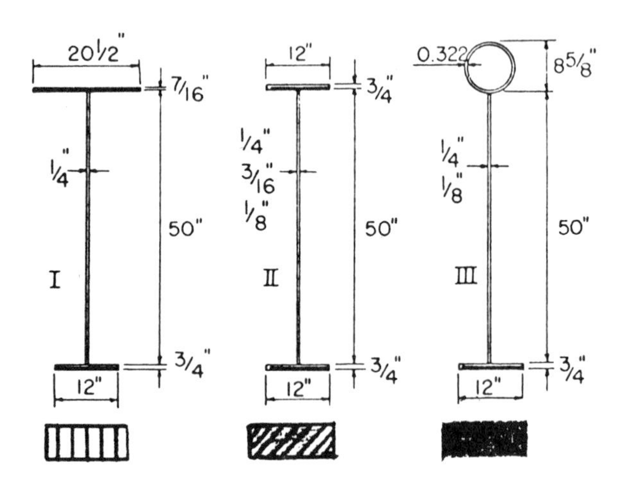

(a) Cross-sections of test specimens

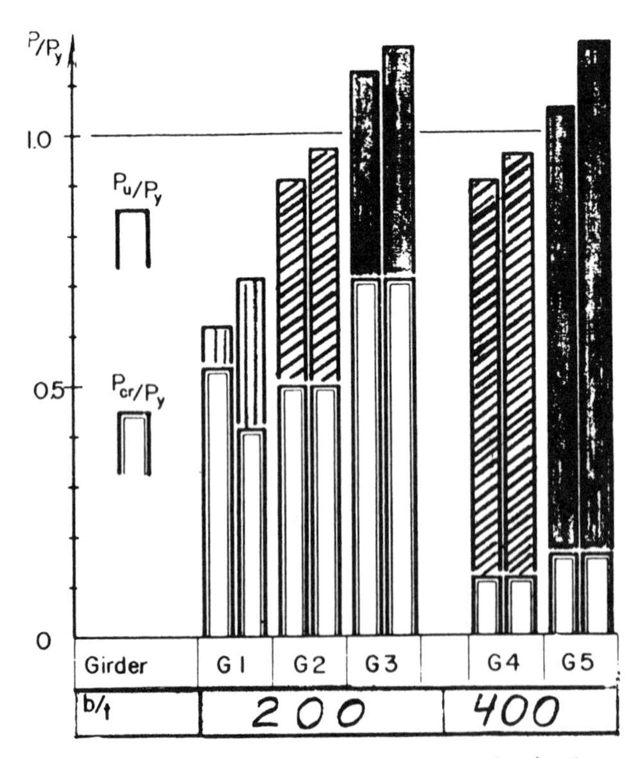

(b) Comparison: ultimate and critical loads of bending tests

FIG. 1 Effect of web thickness on ultimate carrying capacity of the girder.

3. TRANSVERSE INTERMEDIATE STIFFENERS (AASHO 1.6.80)

Transverse intermediate stiffeners shall preferably be in pairs. They may be either single or double, and be plates or inverted tees. When stiffeners are used on only one side of the web, they shall be welded to the compression flange to give it proper support.

The moment of inertia of the transverse stiffener shall not be less than—

$$I = \frac{a_a \, t_w^3 \, J}{10.92} \quad \text{.......................(2)}$$

where:

$$J = 25 \frac{d_w^2}{a_r} - 20 = 5 \quad \text{...............(3)}$$

I = minimum required moment of inertia of stiffener, in.[4]

a_r = required clear distance between transverse stiffeners, in.

a_a = actual clear distance between transverse stiffeners, in.

d_w = unsupported depth of web plate between flanges, in.

t_w = web thickness, in.

When transverse stiffeners are in pairs, the moment of inertia shall be taken about the centerline of the web plate. When single stiffeners are used, the moment of inertia shall be taken about the face in contact with the web plate.

The width of a plate stiffener shall not be less than 16 times its thickness, and not less than 2″ plus 1/30 of the girder depth.

The distance between transverse stiffeners shall not exceed—

1. 12 feet
2. the clear unsupported depth of the web (d_w)
3. $$a_r = \frac{12{,}000}{\sqrt{\tau}} t_w \quad \text{..................(4)}$$

where:

τ = average unit shear stress in the web's cross-section at the point considered, psi

4. LONGITUDINAL STIFFENERS (AASHO 1.6.81)

The longitudinal stiffener shall lie along a line 1/5 d_w

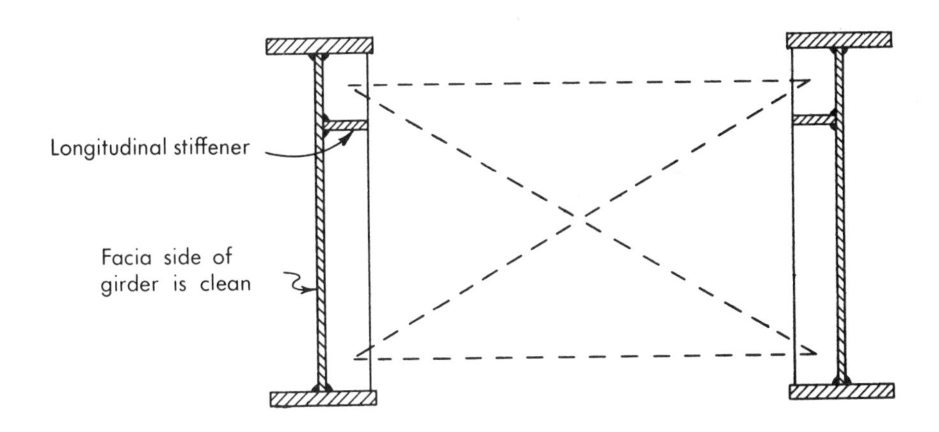

(a) Longitudinal stiffeners on inside of girder

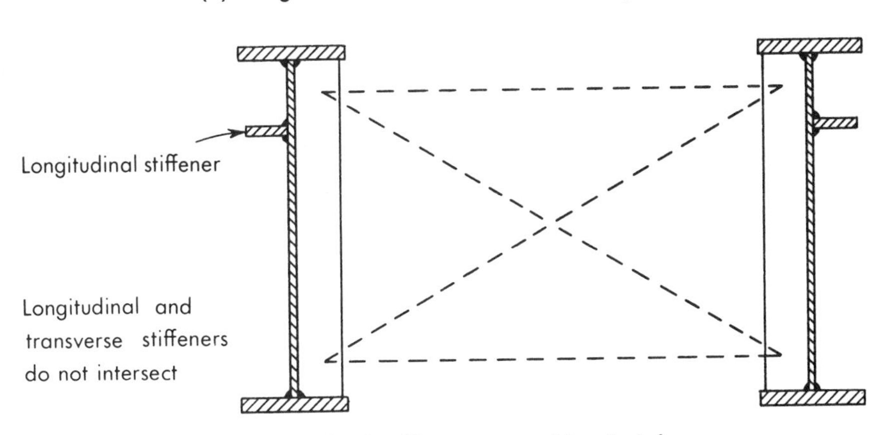

(b) Longitudinal stiffeners on outside of girder

FIG. 2 Placing longitudinal stiffeners on outside of girder and transverse stiffeners inside saves fabricating time.

from the compression flange. Its moment of inertia shall not be less than—

$$I = d_w \, t_w^3 \left(2.4 \frac{a_r^2}{d_w^2} - 0.13\right) \quad \cdots\cdots\cdots (5)$$

These stiffeners do not necessarily have to be continuous, but may be cut where they intersect transverse intermediate stiffeners if they lie on the same side of the web.

5. BEARING STIFFENERS

Transverse stiffeners shall be used over the end bearings or along the length of the girder where concentrated loads must be carried, and shall be designed to transmit the reactions to the web. They shall extend as nearly as practicable to the outer edge of the flange, but not to exceed 12 times their thickness. (AASHO 1.6.17)

Some bridges have longitudinal stiffeners on the inside of the girders, others on the outside. If the longitudinal stiffeners are on the inside, along with the transverse stiffeners, it leaves the outside of the girder smooth; Figure 2(a). This, of course, means the longitudinal stiffener must be cut into short lengths and then inserted between the transverse stiffeners. This results in increased welding time and production costs.

Some states have used longitudinal stiffeners on the outside and transverse on the inside; Figure 2(b). This method saves on fabricating time and also allows the use of automatic welding techniques to join the longitudinal stiffeners to the girder web, thereby substantially increasing welding speed.

6. WELDING OF STIFFENERS

AASHO (2.10.32) will allow the welding of stiffeners or attachments transverse to a tension flange if the bending stress is 75% or less than the allowable.

AWS Bridge (225 c) will allow the welding of stiffeners or attachments transverse to a tension flange if the bending stress in the flange is held to within those of the fatigue formulas (1), (3), or (5) for the welding of attachments by fillet welds; see Section 2.9, Table 1.

Figure 3 illustrates the effect of transverse attachments welded to a plate when tested from tension to an equal compression (K = —1).*

* "Fatigue Tests of Welded Joints in Structural Steel Plates", Bull. 327, University of Illinois, 1941.

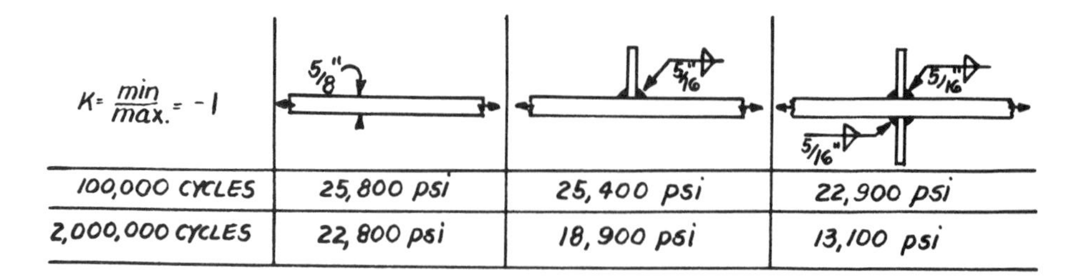

$K = \frac{min}{max.} = -1$	5/8"	5/16"	5/16", 5/16"
100,000 CYCLES	25,800 psi	25,400 psi	22,900 psi
2,000,000 CYCLES	22,800 psi	18,900 psi	13,100 psi

FIG. 3 Effect of transverse attachments on fatigue strength of member.

Some engineers have felt this reduction in fatigue strength is due to the transverse fillet welds; however, it is caused by the abrupt change in section due to the attachment. It is believed these plates would have failed at about the same value and location if they had been machined out of solid plate without any welding. This same problem exists in the machining of stepped shafts used in large high-speed turbines and similar equipment.

Figure 4 illustrates the effect of welding transverse stiffeners to tension flanges.* Tests, again at the University of Illinois, were made from tension to zero tension in bending (K = 0) and at 2 million cycles.

Eliminating the weld between the stiffener and the tension flange increased the fatigue strength of the beam. In addition, leaving the weld off the lower quarter portion of the web in the tension region gave a further increase in fatigue strength.

Later tests at the University of Illinois** took into consideration not only the bending stress in the flange, but also the resulting principal tensile stress in the web at critical locations, such as the termination of the connecting fillet weld of the stiffener. See Figure 5.

It was discovered that the fatigue failure in the stiffener area did not necessarily occur at the point of maximum bending stress of the beam. Failure started at the lower termination of the fillet weld connecting the stiffener to the web. When the bottom of the stiffener was also welded to the tension flange, failure started at the toe of the fillet weld connecting the stiffener to the beam flange. After the flange had failed, the crack would progress upward into the web. Here, the failures usually occurred in the maximum moment section of the beam.

This test indicated fairly good correlation when the results were considered in terms of the principal tensile stresses (including the effect of shear) rather than simply the bending stress. The angle of the fatigue failure in the web generally was found to be about

* "Flexural Strength of Steel Beams", Bull. 377, University of Illinois, 1948.

** "Fatigue in Welded Beams and Girders" W. H. Munse & J. E. Stallmeyer, Highway Research Board, Bull. 315, 1962, p 45.

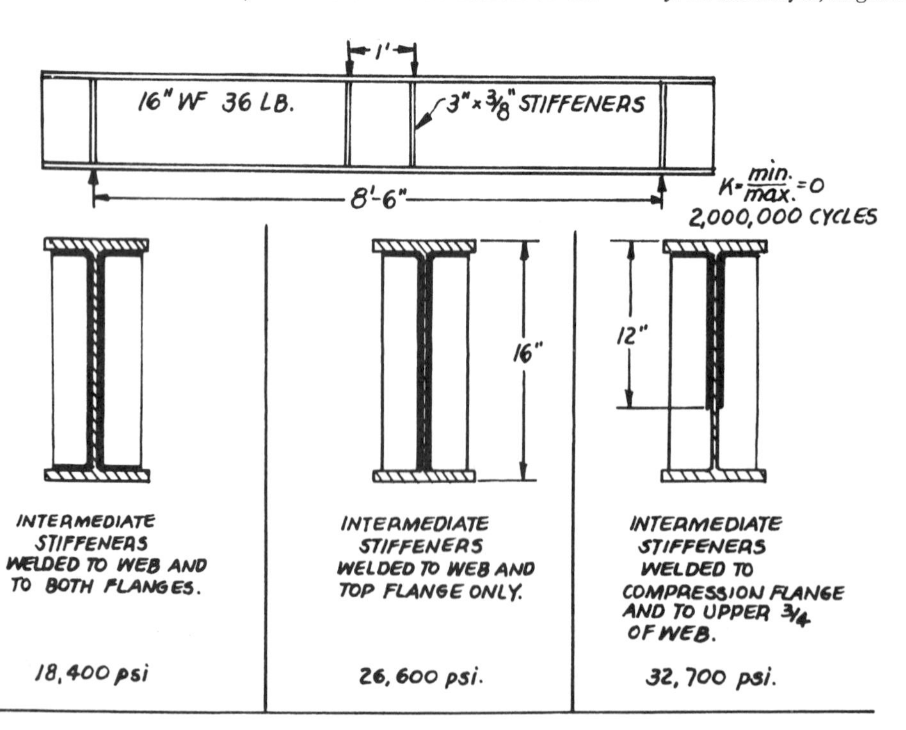

FIG. 4 Effect of welded intermediate stiffener on tension flange.

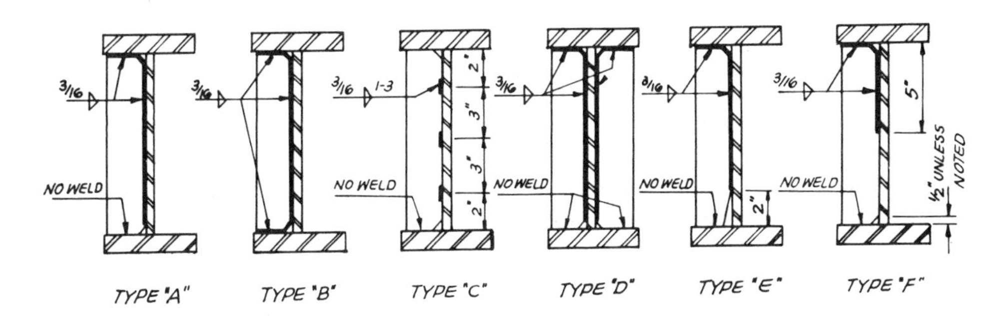

(a) Details of various stiffener types

FIG. 5 Effect of stiffener type on fatigue strength of member.

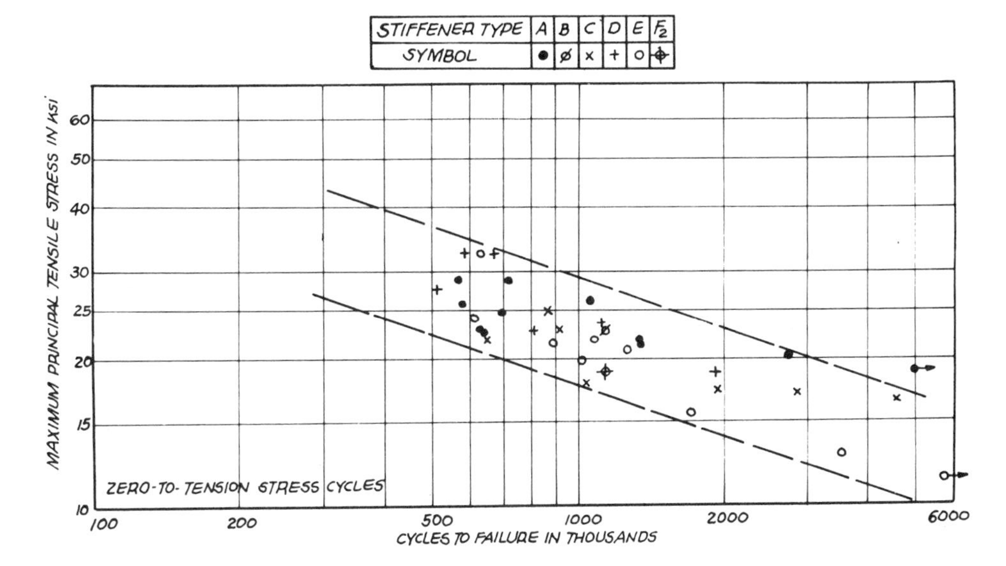

(b) Sigma-n diagram for maximum principal tensile stress at failure section.

20% less than the computed angle of the principal stress.

AASHO Specifications (2.10.32) state that transverse intermediate stiffeners shall fit sufficiently tight to exclude water after painting.

Some inspectors interpret a tight fit to be one in which the stiffeners must be forced into position. Many fabricators feel this is an unnecessary deterrent since it takes extra time to force the edges of the flanges apart to allow the stiffeners to be inserted.

There are two general methods of fitting these stiffeners to the plate girder (Fig. 6):

1. Use a stiffener that does not fit too tight. Push it tightly against the tension flange. Weld it to the girder web and to the compression flange.

With this method, the fitting of the stiffener will comply with the above AASHO specs; yet it is not welded to the tension flange, nor is it a problem to insert. An alternate method is to—

2. Use a stiffener which is cut short about 1″. Fit it against the compression flange and weld it to the web. If it is a single stiffener, also weld it to the compression flange. It is not welded to the tension flange. Experience indicates the 1″ gap at the lower tension

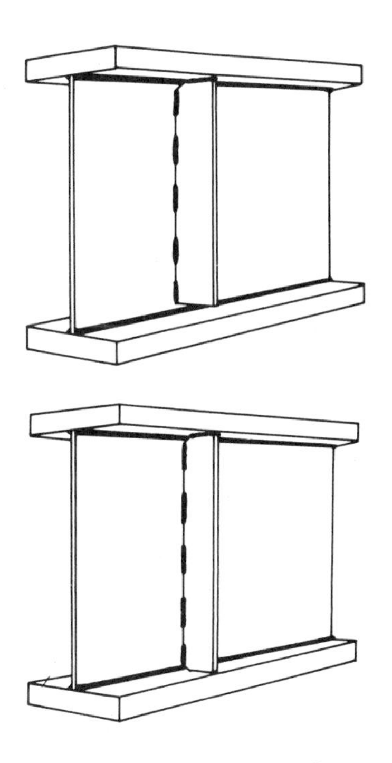

FIG. 6 Fit of stiffeners to girder.

flange will present no maintenance problem. Although this does not comply with the above AASHO requirement, many girders for highway bridges are fitted with stiffeners in this manner.

Plate girder research at Lehigh University* has indicated the stiffener does not have to contact the tension flange to develop the ultimate capacity of the girder. They recommended the stiffeners be cut short as described in the alternate method above (2). The distance between the lower and tension flange and the stiffener is set at 4 times the web thickness; see their recommendations in Figure 7.

There is no clear-cut answer as to whether continuous or intermittent fillet welds should be used to attach the stiffener to the web. The latest research at Illinois on stiffeners indicated that fatigue failures occurred at the terminations of fillet welds, regardless of whether they were continuous or intermittent. Naturally, a continuous weld will have fewer terminations, hence fewer areas for potential fatigue cracks.

Where large, intermittent fillet welds are specified, ⅜" for example, replacement with ¼" continuous fillet welds made by automatic welding equipment achieves a considerable saving in cost. Where small intermittent fillet welds are specified, ¼" possibly, savings from the introduction of continuous welds and automatic equipment become questionable.

With thin, deep web plates, a smaller size weld may tend to reduce distortion. In this case, automatic welding would be of benefit, provided this substitution of continuous welds for intermittent welds does not increase weld length to any major extent.

* "Strength of Plate Girders", Bruno Thurliman, AISC Proceedings 1958; "Plate Girder Research", Konrad Basler & Bruno Thurliman, AISC Proceedings, 1959.

7. FLANGE-TO-WEB WELDS

These welds hold the flanges to the web of the plate girder. They are located in areas of bending stresses and must transfer longitudinal shear forces between flanges and web. Some restraining action may develop with thick flange plates, but any resulting transverse residual stress should not reduce the weld's load-carrying capacity. This being parallel loading, the actual contour or shape of the fillet weld is not as critical as long as the minimum throat dimension is maintained.

Shop practice today usually calls for submerged-arc automatic welding equipment to make these welds. For the usual thickness of web plate, the two fillet welds penetrate deeply within the web and intersect as in Figure 8(b), giving complete fusion even though simple fillet welds are called for, as in (a). A few

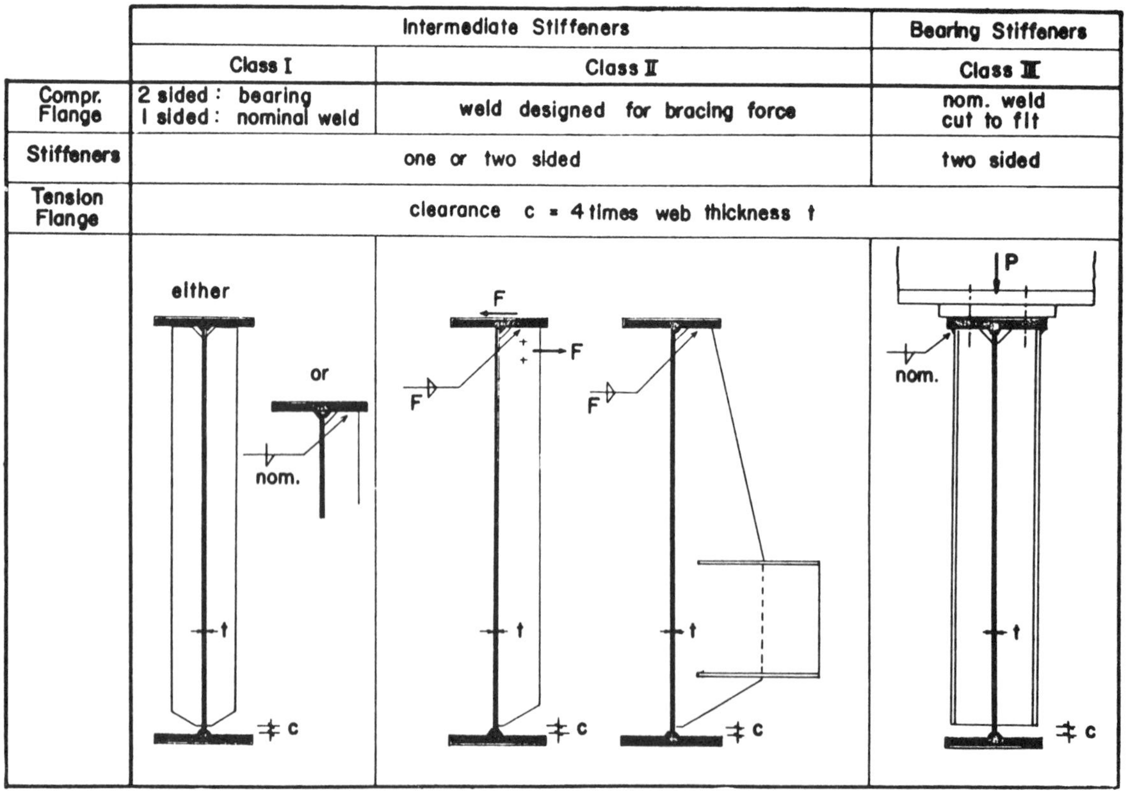

	Intermediate Stiffeners		Bearing Stiffeners
	Class I	Class II	Class III
Compr. Flange	2 sided: bearing 1 sided: nominal weld	weld designed for bracing force	nom. weld cut to fit
Stiffeners	one or two sided		two sided
Tension Flange	clearance c = 4 times web thickness t		

FIG. 7 Summary of design recommendations relative to girder stiffeners.

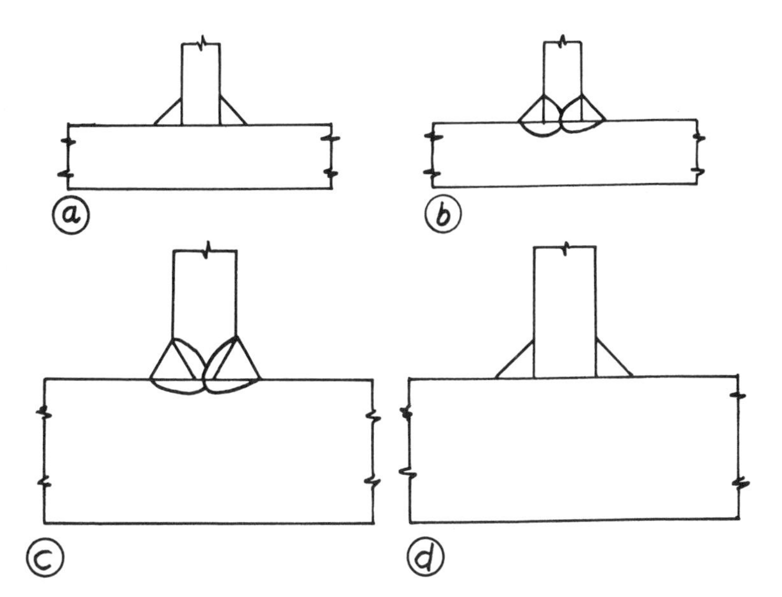

FIG. 8 Flange-to-web welds.

states recognize this penetration and are now detailing this weld with complete fusion. This proves no problem on the normal web thickness. In the future, however, if the same detail is shown on much thicker web plates, the fabricator will have to use a double-bevel edge preparation to obtain the intersection (c), even though detail (d) is sufficient.

It should not be necessary to detail groove welds for this joint from a design standpoint. Selection of a groove T-joint design should be based on a cost comparison with fillet welds. The grooved T-joint requires about ½ the amount of weld metal compared with fillet welds (assuming full-strength welds). However, the grooved joint has the extra cost of preparing the double bevel.

In respect to the physical performance of either the fillet or the grooved T-joint design, tests have been made, by A. Neumann, of these welds under fatigue bending from 0 to tension, $K = 0$, at 2 million cycles.*

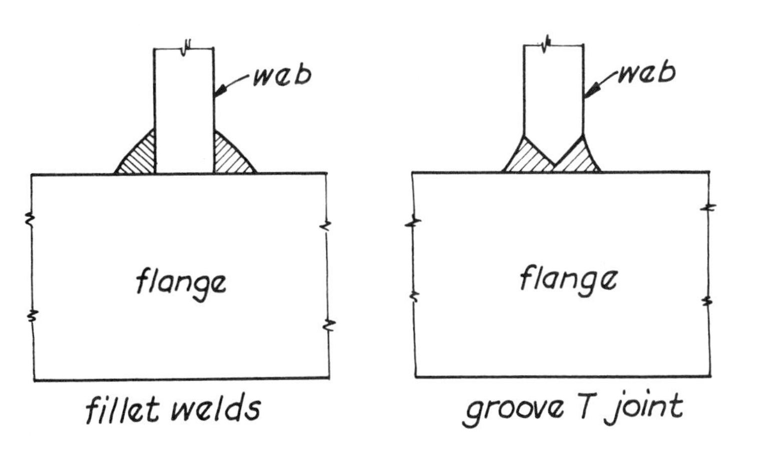

FIG. 9 Both weld types showed same fatigue strength.

No difference was indicated for the fatigue strength of the beam using either joint design, with both types demonstrating a fatigue strength in the beam of 22,000 to 24,000 psi (bending stress); Figure 9.

Fillet Weld Minimum Size

From a design standpoint, these welds may be quite small. Their actual size is usually established by the minimum allowable leg size for the thickness of the flange plate. Table 2 lists the minimum size of fillets for various plate thicknesses as established by AWS Specifications. Leg size increases to take care of the faster cooling rate and greater restraint that exists in thicker plates.

TABLE 2—Minimum Fillet Weld Sizes
For Various Plate Thicknesses (AWS)

THICKNESS OF THICKER PLATE TO BE JOINED	MINIMUM LEG SIZE OF FILLET WELD*
THRU 1/2 inch	3/16 in.
Over 1/2 in. thru 3/4 in.	1/4 in.
Over 3/4 in. thru 1 1/2 in.	5/16 in.
Over 1 1/2 in. thru 2 1/4 in.	3/8 in.
Over 2 1/4 in. thru 6 in.	1/2 in.
Over 6 in.	5/8 in.

* Need not exceed the thickness of the thinner plate

On thicker plates, with multiple pass welds, it is desirable to get as much heat input into the first pass as possible. This means higher welding currents and slower welding speeds. Low-hydrogen electrodes are better for manual welding in this work. The low-hydrogen characteristics of a submerged-arc welding deposit gives this welding method a similar advantage.

* "Discussion at the Symposium on Fatigue of Welded Structures" The British Welding Journal, August, 1960.

TABLE 3—Allowable Shear Forces On *Fillet Welds For Various Fatigue Loadings*

100,000 CYCLES	600,000 CYCLES	2,000,000 CYCLES
$f = \dfrac{8800\ \omega}{1 - \dfrac{K}{2}}$ lb/in.	$f = \dfrac{7070\ \omega}{1 - \dfrac{K}{2}}$ lb/in.	$f = \dfrac{5090\ \omega}{1 - \dfrac{K}{2}}$ lb/in.

but shall not exceed $f = 8{,}800\ \omega$ (E60 or SAW 1 welds)
$f = 10{,}400\ \omega$ (E70 or SAW 2 welds)

Where:

$K = \dfrac{\text{MINIMUM}}{\text{MAXIMUM}}$ (shear (V) applied to girder)

ω = leg size of fillet

Determination of Combined Stress

The combined stresses in a fillet weld between the girder web and flanges is seldom considered for the following reasons:

1. The maximum bending stress for a simply supported girder does not occur at the same region as the maximum shear force. For a continuous girder, however, the negative moment and shear force are high in the same region near the support, and perhaps the combined forces in this fillet weld should be checked.

2. The maximum bending stress in the outer surface of flange is always designed for something less than the allowable (Bridge code = 18,000 psi). The weld lies inside of the flange and is stressed at a lower value. Ex: If the weld is in an area of 15,000 psi bending stress, this additional normal stress would reduce, theoretically, the allowable shear force for the weld from $f = 8800\ \omega$ to $f = 7070\ \omega$, or about 80% of what it would be if just horizontal shear were considered (E60 or SAW-1 welds).

3. Usually these welds must be larger than design requirements because of the minimum weld size specifications listed above.

Nevertheless, if desirable to determine the combined stresses, it can be theoretically shown that the axial normal stress from the bending, applied to the fillet weld, would increase the maximum shear stress applied to the throat. For a given applied normal stress (σ), the resulting maximum value for the allowable force (f) which may be applied to the fillet weld of a given leg size (ω) under parallel loading is expressed by the formula:—

$$f = \omega \sqrt{8800^2 - \frac{\sigma^2}{8}} \qquad \text{(E60 or SAW-1 welds)} \quad \ldots\ldots (6a)$$

$$f = \omega \sqrt{10{,}400^2 - \frac{\sigma^2}{8}} \qquad \text{(E70 or SAW-2 welds)} \quad \ldots\ldots (6b)$$

This formulation still permits the maximum shear stress resulting from the combined shear stresses to be held within the allowable of $\tau = 12{,}400$ psi (E60 or SAW-1 welds) or 14,700 psi (E70 or SAW-2 welds).

Allowable Fatigue Strength

Table 3 contains the formulas for establishing the allowable shear force that may be applied to fillet welds under various conditions of fatigue loading.

8. FLANGE BUTT JOINTS

In nearly all welded plate girders, the flange is a single plate. These plates are stepped down as less area is required. A smooth transition is made between the two, by reducing either the thickness or width of the larger flange to correspond to that of the smaller.

When this transition is made in thickness, the end of the larger flange is beveled by a flame-cutting torch. There is a practical limit to the angle of bevel, but this slope, according to AWS Bridge Specifications, should not be greater than 1″ in 2½″ (an angle of 23°). On the Calcasieu River bridge, this slope was decreased to about 1″ in 6″ (an angle of about 9½°). Transitions also can be made by varying the surface contour of

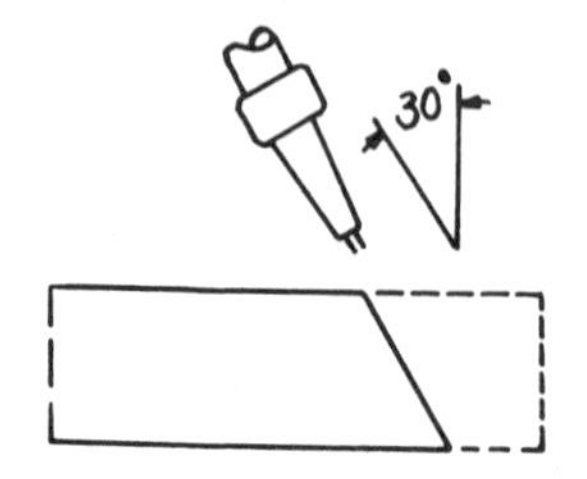

(a) Beveling end of flange plate for groove butt weld

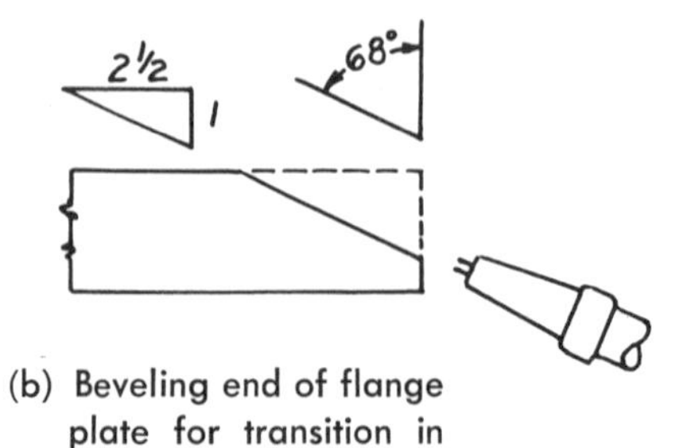

(b) Beveling end of flange plate for transition in thickness.

FIG. 10 Plate bevels made by flame cutting.

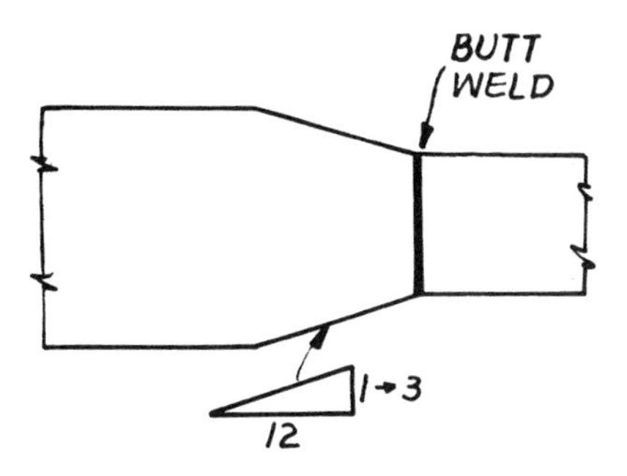

(a) Straight-line transition in width

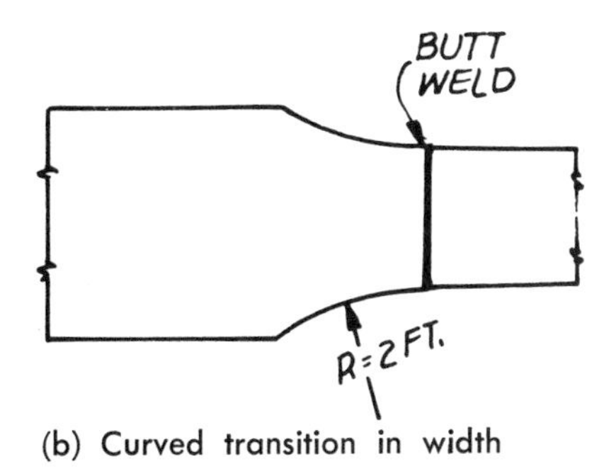

(b) Curved transition in width

FIG. 11 Method of transition in width affects weld's allowable fatigue values.

TABLE 4—Allowable Fatigue Strengths *Of Groove Welds in Butt Joints*

	100,000 CYCLES	600,000 CYCLES	2,000,000 CYCLES
BUTT WELD IN TENSION (not to exceed 18,000 psi)	$\sigma = \dfrac{18{,}000 \text{ psi}}{1 - \dfrac{K}{2}}$	$\sigma = \dfrac{17{,}000 \text{ psi}}{1 - .7\,K}$	$\sigma = \dfrac{16{,}000 \text{ psi}}{1 - .8\,K}$
BUTT WELD IN COMPRESSION (not to exceed p)	$\sigma = \dfrac{18{,}000 \text{ psi}}{1 - \dfrac{K}{2}}$	$\sigma = \dfrac{18{,}000 \text{ psi}}{1 - 0.8\,K}$	$\sigma = \dfrac{18{,}000 \text{ psi}}{1 - K}$

Where:

(p) is the allowable compressive stress for the member involved.

$K = \dfrac{\text{MINIMUM}}{\text{MAXIMUM}}$ (bending stress or bending moment)

the groove welds.

The usual method of flame cutting a bevel in the preparation of a welded joint is to cut down through the surface of the plate at the proper angle. Because of the wide angle needed for this transition in thickness, it is often better to flame-cut back from the edge of the plate after the flange plate has been cut to length. See Figure 10.

When the transition is made in width, the end of the wider flange is cut back at an angle, again with the flame-cutting torch. There is no problem in cutting in this manner, and any slope may be used; many times 1 in 12, but usually a maximum slope of 1 in 4. Often this taper may extend back for several feet.

Generally, it is felt that the straight-line transition in width is sufficient, and in the case of fatigue loading the allowable fatigue values for butt groove welds in tension or compression are used. See Figure 11. If a curve tangent to the edge of the narrow flange at the point of termination is used, it may be assumed the flanges have equal widths. Thus, for equal plate thicknesses and with the weld reinforcement removed, the butt groove weld may be assigned the same allowable stress as the flange plate, under any condition of fatigue loading.

Studies at the University of Illinois have indicated a slight advantage in making a transition in width rather than in thickness. This advantage undoubtedly would be greater if the transition in width were made more gradual; however, both methods are sound and acceptable. Fatigue values for these transitions are found in Figure 12.

Allowable Fatigue Strengths

Groove welds in butt joints of equal plate thickness, if the reinforcement is finished smooth with the surface, may be allowed the same fatigue strength under any type of fatigue loading as the base metal. For plates of unequal thickness where the transition slope is not greater than 1 in 2½, the formulas found in Table 4 may be used.

Type of transition of flange section	K=0 N=100,000 ~	K=0 N=2,000,000~
1 : 2½ transition in thickness	34,600 psi	18,500 psi
1 : 2½ transition in width	34,900	19,500

FIG. 12 Making a transition in flange width rather than thickness has a slight advantage in fatigue strength.

FIG. 13—Summary of Bridge Plate-Girder Specifications AWS & AASHO

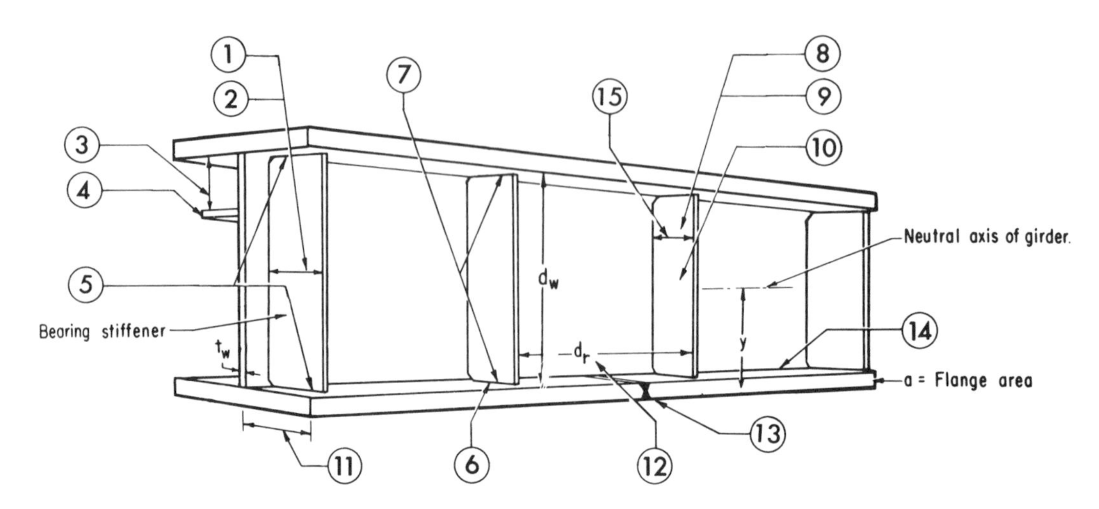

9. SUMMARY OF BRIDGE SPECIFICATIONS

In order to aid the bridge engineer in designing a welded plate girder, the pertinent AWS and AASHO Specifications have been brought together into a single drawing, Figure 13, and related text, below. The corresponding numbers are included so the engineer may refer back to the original specifications.

This summary can also serve as a checkoff list, so that nothing will be inadvertently omitted.

The following requirements apply:

1. Extend bearing stiffener as near as practical to outer edge of flange. Proportion for bearing. Welds to web must transmit end reaction. (1.6.79)

2. Width of bearing stiffener must not exceed 12 times stiffener thickness (1.6.17).

3. Space (horizontal) longitudinal stiffener ⅕ d_w from compression flange (1.6.81).

4. Dimension longitudinal stiffener for required moment of inertia, using—

$$I = d_w\, t_w{}^3 \left(2.4\, \frac{d_r{}^2}{d_w{}^2} - 0.13 \right)$$

about edge of stiffener (1.6.81).

5. Mill or grind bearing stiffener ends for even bearing to flange. Stiffener may be welded without milling to compression flange, or to tension flange if less than 75% tensile strength (2.10.32).

6. Do not weld transverse intermediate stiffener to tension flange if stressed over 75% (2.10.32) or unless stress is within that of fatigue formulas 1, 3 or 5 of Art. 228 (225c).

7. Fit intermediate stiffener tight to flanges to exclude water after painting (2.10.32).

8. Consider placing intermediate stiffeners at points of concentrated load to transmit reactions to the web (1.6.80).

9. Use transverse intermediate stiffener preferably in pairs on opposite sides of web. If only one side of web, weld ends to compression flange and intermittent weld to web (1.6.80, 225c).

10. The minimum moment of inertia of transverse intermediate stiffener shall be (1.6.80)—

$$I = \frac{d_a\, t_w{}^3\, J}{10.92}$$

where:

$$J = 25\, \frac{d_w{}^2}{d_r} - 20 \geqq 5$$

d_a = actual distance between stiffeners, in.

d_r = required distance between stiffeners, in.

d_w = web depth, in.

t_w = web thickness, in.

τ = average shear stress in web

11. Girder flange shall not extend beyond 12 times its thickness (1.6.17).

12. Distance between stiffeners must not exceed 12′, d_w, or $\dfrac{12{,}000\ t_w}{\sqrt{\tau}}$ (1.6.80)

13. All shop groove butt welds in flange and web plates shall be made before final fitting and welding into girder (404f).

14. Web-to-flange fillet weld leg size $= \dfrac{V\ a\ y}{17{,}600\ I}$.

15. Width of transverse intermediate stiffeners must not exceed 16 times stiffener thickness, or 2″ plus 1/30 of girder depth.

Also, deflection due to live load plus impact shall not exceed 1/800 of the span; for cantilever arms, 1/300 of the span (1.6.10).

MINIMUM WEB THICKNESS (t_w)

	A-7, A-373 A-36	A-441 Low Alloy 46,000 YP	50,000 YP
If no stiffeners (1.6.80)	$t_w = \frac{1}{60} d_w$	$t_w = \frac{1}{52} d_w$	$t_w = \frac{1}{50} d_w$
If trans. int. stiffeners (1.6.75)	$t_w = \frac{1}{170} d_w$	$t_w = \frac{1}{145} d_w$	$t_w = \frac{1}{140} d_w$
If long. and trans. stiffeners	$t_w = \frac{1}{340} d_w$	$t_w = \frac{1}{290} d_w$	$t_w = \frac{1}{280} d_w$

Also, ratio of depth to length of span shall preferably not be less than 1/25; for lower depth the section shall be increased so that the maximum deflection will not be greater than if this ratio had not been exceeded (1.6.11).

Also, web thickness shall meet requirements given in the above table for the more common steels.

10. DIMENSIONAL TOLERANCES

The dimensional tolerances in Figure 14 have been set up for welded plate girders by the AWS Bridge Specifications.

FIG. 14—Maximum Dimensional Tolerances AWS 407

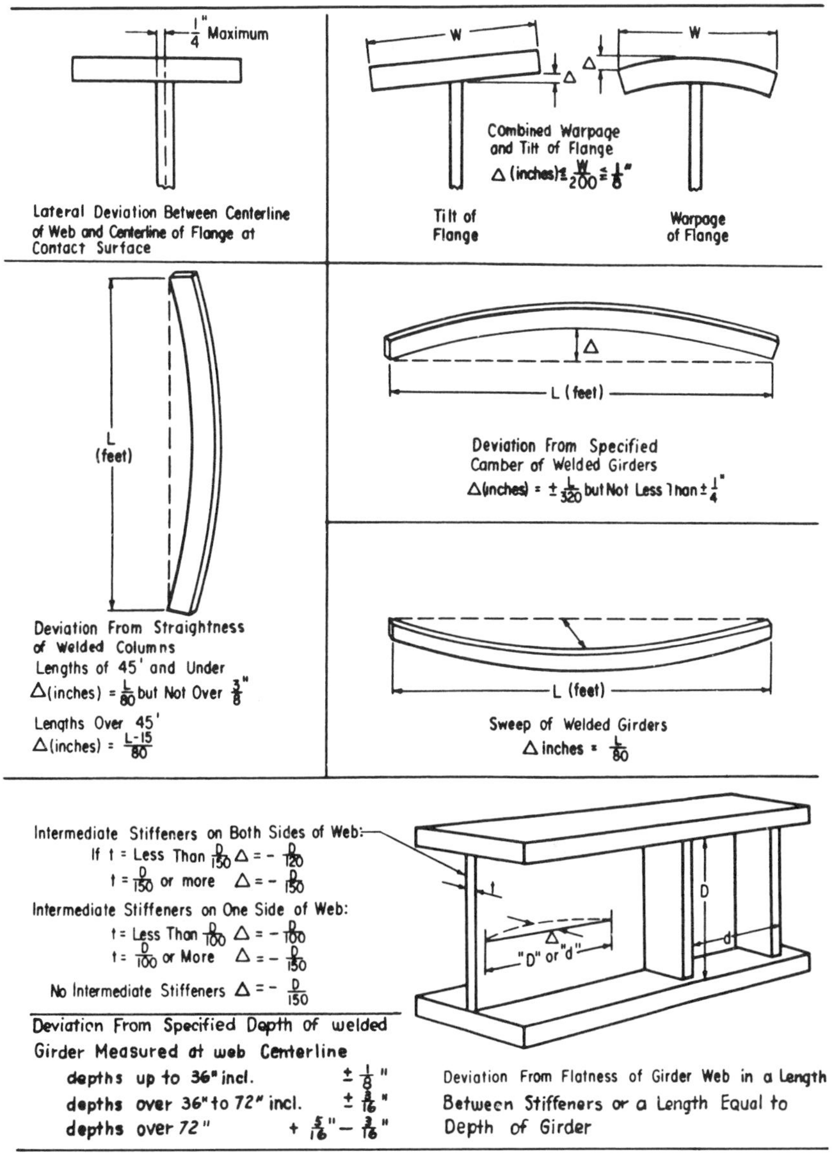

$\frac{1}{4}$" Maximum

Lateral Deviation Between Centerline of Web and Centerline of Flange at Contact Surface

W

Δ

Combined Warpage and Tilt of Flange

Δ (inches) $\leq \frac{W}{200} \geq \frac{1}{8}$"

Tilt of Flange

Warpage of Flange

L (feet)

Deviation From Straightness of Welded Columns

Lengths of 45' and Under

Δ(inches) $= \frac{L}{80}$ but Not Over $\frac{3}{8}$"

Lengths Over 45'

Δ(inches) $= \frac{L-15}{80}$

L (feet)

Deviation From Specified Camber of Welded Girders

Δ(inches) $= \pm \frac{L}{320}$ but Not Less Than $\pm \frac{1}{4}$"

L (feet)

Sweep of Welded Girders

Δ inches $= \frac{L}{80}$

Intermediate Stiffeners on Both Sides of Web:

If t = Less Than $\frac{D}{150}$ $\Delta = -\frac{D}{120}$

t = $\frac{D}{150}$ or more $\Delta = -\frac{D}{150}$

Intermediate Stiffeners on One Side of Web:

t = Less Than $\frac{D}{100}$ $\Delta = -\frac{D}{100}$

t = $\frac{D}{100}$ or More $\Delta = -\frac{D}{150}$

No Intermediate Stiffeners $\Delta = -\frac{D}{150}$

t

D

d

"D" or "d"

Deviation From Specified Depth of welded Girder Measured at web Centerline

depths up to 36" incl. $\pm \frac{1}{8}$"

depths over 36" to 72" incl. $\pm \frac{3}{16}$"

depths over 72" $+ \frac{5}{16}$" $- \frac{3}{16}$"

Deviation From Flatness of Girder Web in a Length Between Stiffeners or a Length Equal to Depth of Girder

11. DIAPHRAGMS

Figure 15 illustrates several types of diaphragms used, and represent the extremes in designs and fabrication. Diaphragm (a), although so simple in design that no shop welding is required, must be fitted and welded in the field. Diaphragm (b), although much more complicated, may be mass-produced in the shop: The angles are sheared to length, and the plates are sheared and punched. These are placed into a simple fixture and welded together at low cost. The field erection is simpler, since the diaphragms are put into position, held by an erection bolt, and then welded into place.

12. COVER PLATES

Using A-441 steel (previously A-242), it may be advantageous in some cases to use two plates, a flange plate and a cover plate, to make up the flange. This will permit use of thinner plates and take advantage of the higher allowable stresses. This steel has the following allowable tension in members subject to bending:

THICKNESS	ALLOWABLE
3/4" and under	27,000 psi
over 3/4" to 1 1/2"	24,000 psi
over 1 1/2" to 4"	22,000 psi

Many methods have been suggested for termination of cover plates. The existence of at least four conditions which affect this makes it impossible to recommend one specific cover plate end which will best meet all conditions.

First, the tensile forces, assumed to be uniformly distributed across the width of the cover plate, should be transferred simply and directly into the corresponding flange of the rolled beam without causing any stress concentration in the beam flange. In general, a large transverse fillet weld across the end of the cover plate does this in the simplest manner.

Second, there must be a very gradual change in the beam section at the end of the cover plate, in order to develop a similar gradual change in bending stress of the beam. Any abrupt change in beam section

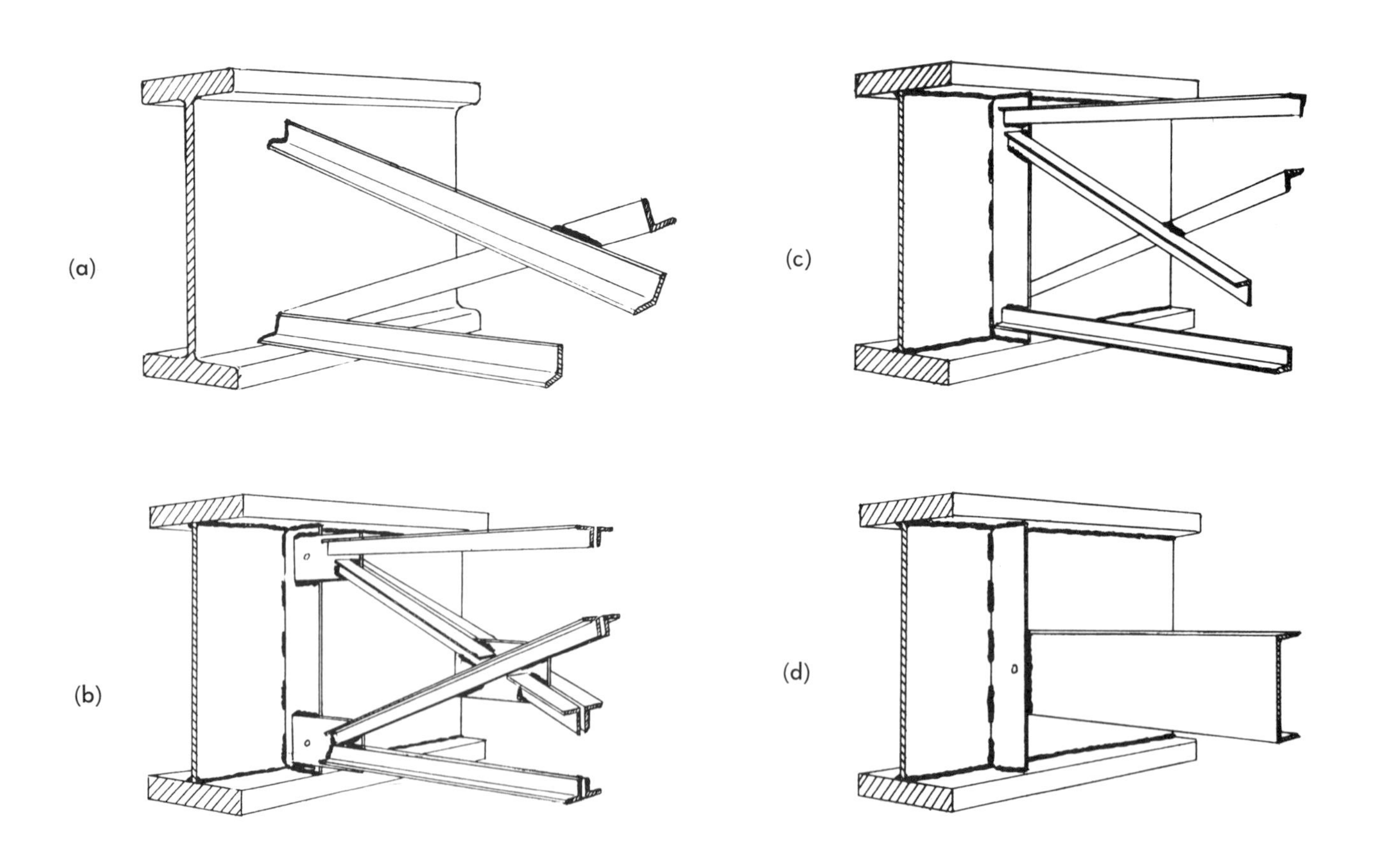

FIG. 15 Diaphragms used in modern bridges: (a) angles cut to length and dropped into place; (b) Shop welded diaphragm, field welded to girder stiffener; (c) angles attached to stiffeners; and (d) channel welded to web and stiffeners.

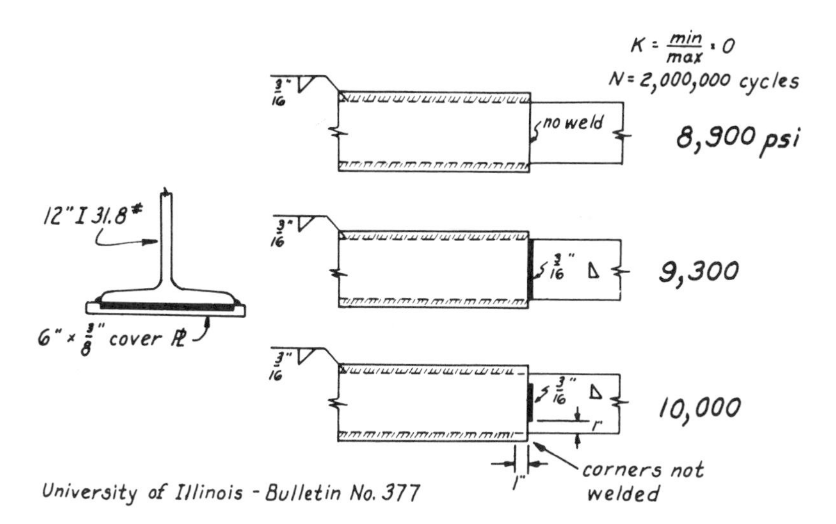

FIG. 16 Cover plates extending beyond width of beam flange.

will reduce the beam's fatigue strength. This would tend to favor a gradual tapered width at the end of the cover plate.

Third, some caution should be exercised relative to terminating the cover plate in the narrow zone of the flange that is in direct line of the beam web. This is a rigid portion with little chance for localized yielding to prevent the build-up of possible high stress concentration.

Fourth, the selected joint should be economically practical to make and answer functional requirements. For example:

1. Continuous welds may be needed to provide a positive seal and prevent moisture from entering underneath the plate and causing connection deterioration.

2. Minimum appearance standards may eliminate some joint designs.

Early fatigue testing at the University of Illinois* on rolled beams with cover plates indicated that:

1. In general, continuous fillet welds were better than intermittent fillet welds for joining cover plates to the beam flange.

2. On cover plates extending beyond the width of the beam flange and connected with longitudinal 3/16" continuous fillet welds, adding a 3/16" fillet weld across the end of the cover plate produced a slight increase in fatigue strength (from 8900 psi to 9300 psi at 2 million cycles). Omitting the welds for a distance at each corner of the cover plate increased this value up to 11,000 psi; see Figure 16.

The intersection of the longitudinal and transverse fillet welds could present a point of weakness if not properly made. This "cross-over" usually results in a very shallow concave weld. By eliminating this weld for 1" back from each corner, the fatigue strength is increased. This does not apply if the cover plate lies within the beam flange, since the weld does not have to "crossover."

* Bull. No. 377, Jan. 1948.

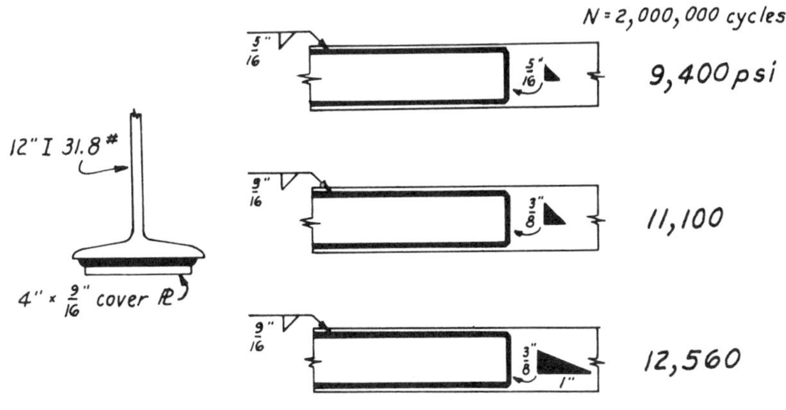

no tests made with the transverse fillet weld left off
University of Illinois - Bulletin No. 377

FIG. 17 Cover plates lying within width of beam flange.

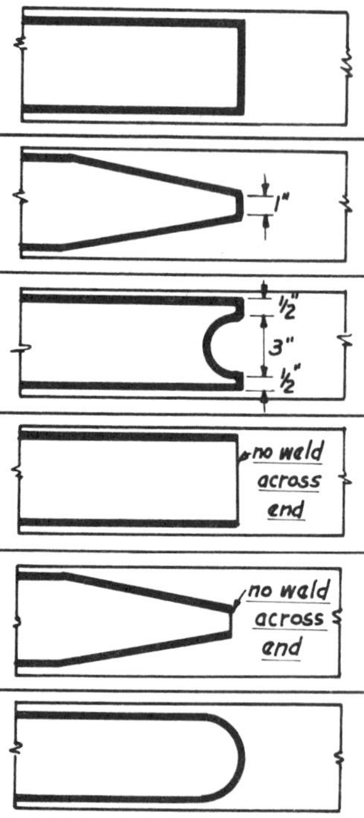

Type of termination of cover plate	K=0 N=100,000~	K=0 N=2,000,000~
(a)	26,500 psi	11,300 psi
(b) 1"	33,000	11,500
(c) ½" 3" ½"	30,700	14,500
(d) no weld across end	34,700	12,500
(e) no weld across end	36,500	13,700
(f)	29,000	11,700

FIG. 18 Effect of cover plate termination on fatigue strength. Calculations based on 4" x ½" cover plate and ¼" fillet weld.

3. For cover plates lying within the width of the beam flange, increased fillet weld size across the end of the cover plate produced a gradual increase in fatigue strength. A $\frac{5}{16}$" fillet weld had a strength of 9400 psi at 2 million cycles, a ⅜" fillet weld 11,000 psi, and a ⅜" × 1" fillet weld up to 12,600 psi. This particular size of cover plate was not tested with the transverse fillet weld omitted; see Figure 17.

The latest work reported at the University of Florida on steady loading of 18" WF 70# beams with 5" × ⅝" cover plates showed that the beam flange within the cover-plated region was stressed lower when a ⅝" fillet weld was placed across the end of the cover plate as compared to that with no transverse weld. The transverse weld also produced a more uniform distribution of stress across the cover plate as well as the beam flange, and allowed the plate to pick up its share of the beam force in a shorter distance. However, all of these factors occur within the cover-plated region of greater section modulus and lower bending stress, so this is not very serious.

What is more important is the effect the transverse weld and shape of the cover plate's end has on the stress in the beam flange adjacent to where the cover plate is attached. This is the region of lower section modulus and higher bending stress and is much more critical than any region within the cover plate.

The drawing, Figure 18, illustrates variations of cover plate terminations.* The data summarizes recent tests on the fatigue strength of beams with partial cover plates, conducted at the University of Illinois. Although the common method of terminating the cover plate directly across the flange with a transverse fillet weld is satisfactory and acceptable by the AWS Bridge Specifications, this data would seem to indicate that tapering the end of the cover plate and eliminating transverse welds across the end slightly increases the fatigue strength.

* "Fatigue in Welded Beams and Girders", W. H. Munse and J. E. Stallmeyer, Highway Research Board, Bull. 315, 1962, p. 45.

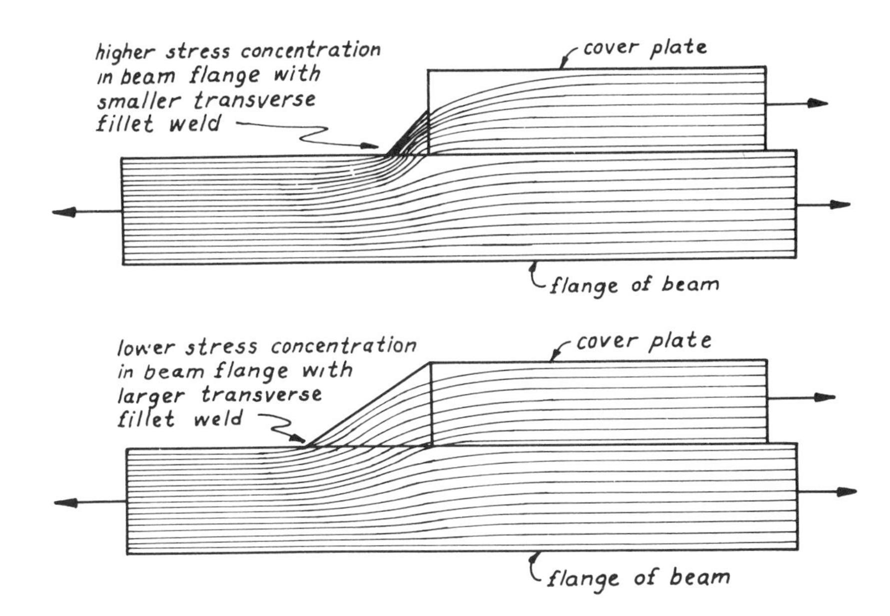

FIG. 19 Effect of transverse fillet weld size on fatigue strength.

It should be noted that a small ¼″ fillet weld was used across the end of the ½″ thick cover plate. The results might have been different if a larger transverse weld had been used. Most states require continuous welds on cover plates and across their ends, thereby limiting the selection to termination types *a* or *b*. Since the data indicates that tapering has little effect, final selection between *a* or *b* would have to be made on the basis of some other factor such as appearance, or lower dead weight.

In summary, it would appear that the short section of the transverse weld across the end of the cover plate directly over the web of the beam (1) is restrained and (2) when tested under severe fatigue loading may reduce the fatigue strength of the connection unless it is made large. A large transverse fillet weld, especially in this central section, would more uniformly transfer this force through the surface of the beam flange into the end of the cover plate. See Figure 19.

Summary of Cover Plate Specifications (AWS Art. 225)

The AWS Bridge Specifications limit the thickness of cover plates to 1½ times the thickness of the flange to which it is attached (225 e 1).

For partial-length cover plates, their end shall extend beyond the "theoretical end" (theoretical cut-off point) which is determined by the allowable stresses from fatigue formulas (1), (3), or (5) of Section 2.9, Table 1.

The ends of the cover plate shall extend beyond this "theoretical end" a sufficient distance to allow "terminal development" (transfer of cover plate bending force into the beam flange) by either of the following two methods:

A. With *square ends* and a continuous transverse fillet weld across the end and along both edges of the cover plate, the minimum terminal development length measured from the actual end of the cover plate to the theoretical end or cut-off point shall be 1½ times the width of the cover plate.

B. With *tapered ends* having no transverse weld across the end but welds along both tapered edges, tapered beyond the terminal end to a width not greater than ⅓ the width, but not less than 3", the terminal development length shall be 2 times the width of the cover plate.

Normally the inner end of the terminal development length will lie at the theoretical cut-off point; see Figure 20, (A) and (B). However, the cover plate may be extended farther so that the distance between the actual and the theoretical cut-off point exceeds the required terminal development length. In this case only the required terminal development length shown in (A) and (B) shall be used for the length of connecting weld when determining weld size, rather than the actual length between the actual and theoretical cut-off point; see (A′) and (B′).

Fillet welds between terminal developments along the cover plated length, shall be continuous and be designed to transfer the horizontal shear forces:

$$f = \frac{V\,a\,y}{2\,I} \qquad \text{.......................... (7)}$$

(for each weld, there are 2 welds along the edge of the cover plate)

Fillet welds within the terminal development zone (between the inner end of the terminal development and the actual end of the cover plate) shall be continuous and be designed to transfer the cover plate portion of the bending force in the beam at the inner

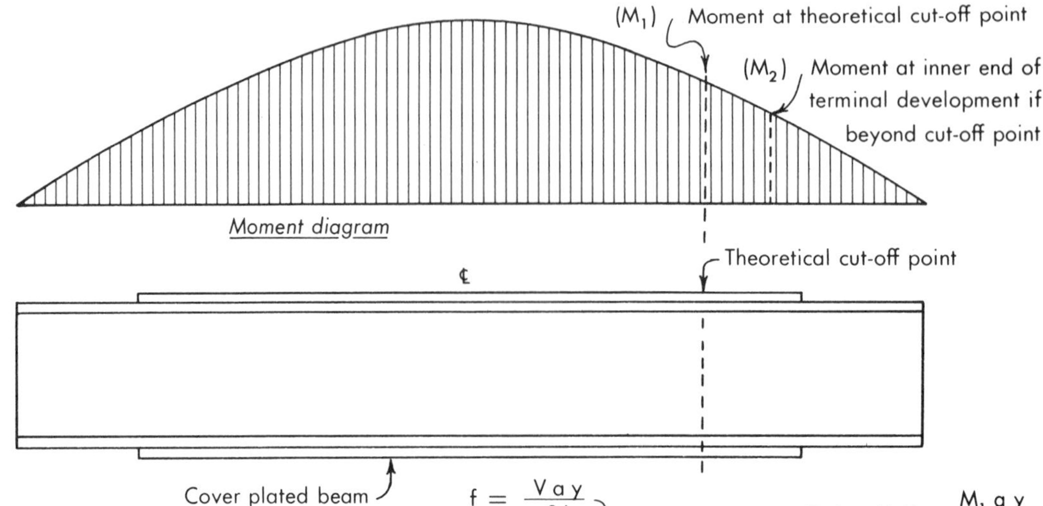

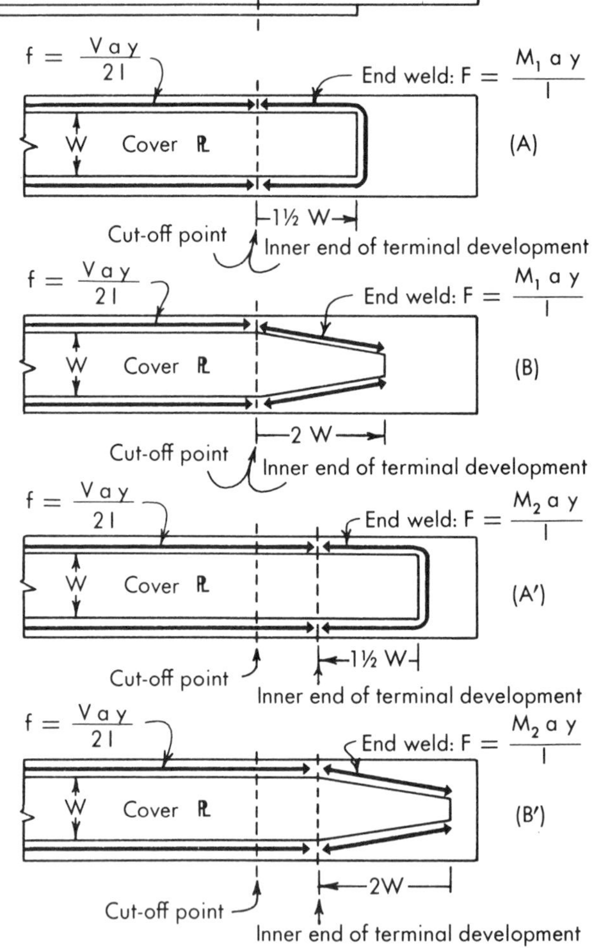

FIG. 20 Relationship of terminal development to weld size. Required terminal development length (A and B) is used rather than actual length (A′ and B′) between actual and theoretical cut-off points.

end of the terminal development length (usually the theoretical cut-off point):

$$\boxed{F = \sigma A_{P\ell}} \quad \cdots\cdots (8)$$

$$\sigma = \frac{M\ y}{I}$$

$$\therefore \boxed{F = \frac{M\ a\ y}{I}} \quad \cdots\cdots (9)$$

where:

V = vertical shear at section of beam under consideration

a = area of cover plate connected by the 2 fillet welds

y = distance between C. G. of cover plate and the N.A. of the total section

I = moment of inertia of the total section

M_1 = moment applied to beam at the section of the theoretical cut-off point

M_2 = moment applied to beam at the section of the inner end of the terminal development

The allowable to be used for these fillet welds would come from formulas (10), (14), or (18) of Table 1, Section 2.9, and shall conform to the minimum fillet weld size of Table 2.

AASHO (1.6.74) specifies that the length of any cover plate added to a rolled beam shall not be less than—

$$(2d + 3) \text{ feet}$$

where

d = depth of beam (feet)

Bridge Plate Girders With Variable Depth

1. TYPES OF HAUNCHED GIRDERS

It has been pointed out* that the sloping bottom flange of the parabolic haunch has a vertical component of its compressive force and this will reduce the shear stress (τ_{xy}) in the girder web in this region. In addition, the concave compression flange produces a radial compressive stress (σ_y) in the web depending on the radius of curvature of the flange.

In contrast, the fish belly haunch provides no appreciable reduction in shear in the critical portion of the web near the support. This is because the slope of the bottom flange is small in that area. Also, the convex compressive flange produces a radial tensile stress (σ_y) in the web, which is greater than the radial compressive stress in the parabolic haunch. This is because of the sharper curvature of the fish belly haunch.

It is seen by observation of the Huber-Mises formula that both of these factors will result in the yield criterion (σ_{cr}) having a lower value in the case of the parabolic haunch. This result compared with the yield strength of the steel (in uniaxial tension) would indicate a higher factor safety.

(Huber-Mises Formula)

$$\sigma_{cr} = \sqrt{\sigma_x^2 - \sigma_x \sigma_y + \sigma_y^2 + 3\tau_{xy}^2}$$

Haunched girders do not present much increase in cost for welded construction for longer spans. The web plates are normally trimmed by flame cutting, so that a gradual curve would add little to the cost. In most cases the curved flange plates can be added without prior forming; the flat flange plates are simply pulled into place against the curved web. Although the transverse stiffeners would vary in length, this should be no problem. The flange can still be automatically fillet welded to the web by placing the web in the horizontal position. The portable automatic welder would then ride against the curved flange.

* "Design of the Bridge Over the Quinnipiac River" by Roman Wolchuk.

2. NEED FOR MODIFIED SHEAR FORCE VALUE

The horizontal force (F_h) in the sloping flange is equal to the bending moment at that section divided by the vertical distance between the two flanges:

$$F_h = \frac{M}{d}$$

Or, this force may be found by multiplying the flange area by the bending stress in the flange using the section modulus of the girder. This method will produce a more accurate value.

From this value, the actual force in the flange (F_x) may be found, as well as the vertical component (F_v) of this force:

$$F_x = \frac{F_h}{\cos \theta} = \frac{M}{d \cos \theta} \text{ and}$$

$$F_v = F_h \tan \theta = \frac{M}{d} \tan \theta$$

This vertical component (F_v) acting along with the shear force in the web resists the external shear (V) at this section.

Modified shear is the resulting shear force in the web after the vertical component of the flange force (F_v) is substracted or added, depending upon whether it acts in the same direction or opposite direction as the shear in the web.

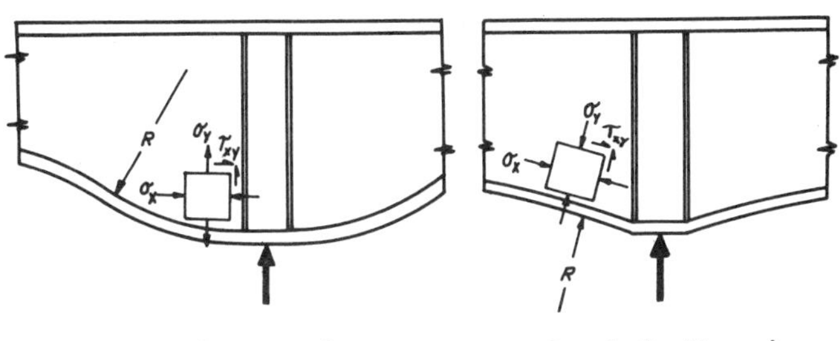

FIGURE 1

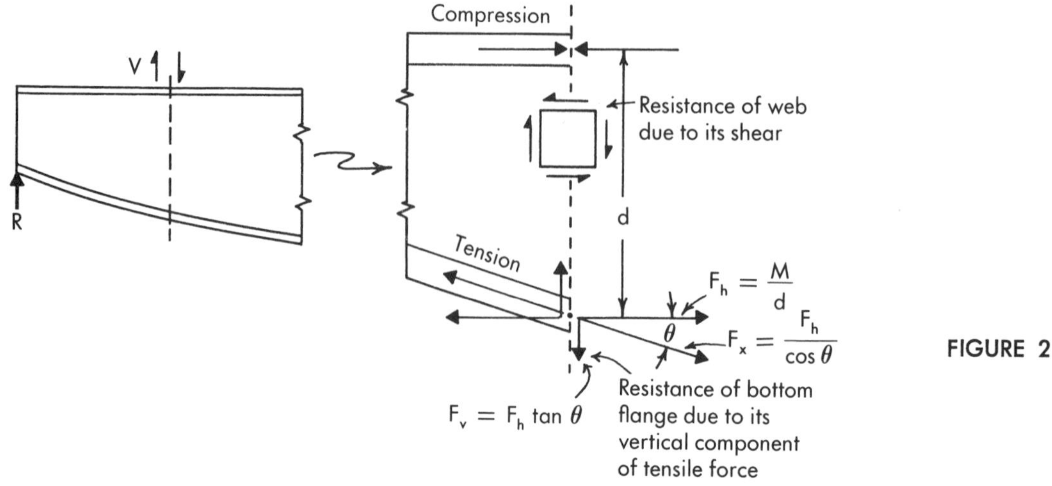

FIGURE 2

Simply Supported Girder Straight or Curved Bottom Flange

See Figure 2.

Here the external shear is—

$$V = A_w \tau_W + \frac{M}{d} \tan\theta$$

and the modified shear is—

$$V' = A_w \tau_W$$

$$= V - \frac{M}{d} \tan\theta$$

In this case the vertical component is subtracted from the web shear.

Continuous Parabolic Haunched Girder

See Figure 3.

Here the external shear is—

$$V = A_w \tau_W + \frac{M}{d} \tan\theta$$

and the modified shear is—

$$V' = A_w \tau_W$$

$$= V - \frac{M}{d} \tan\theta$$

In this case the vertical component is subtracted from the web shear.

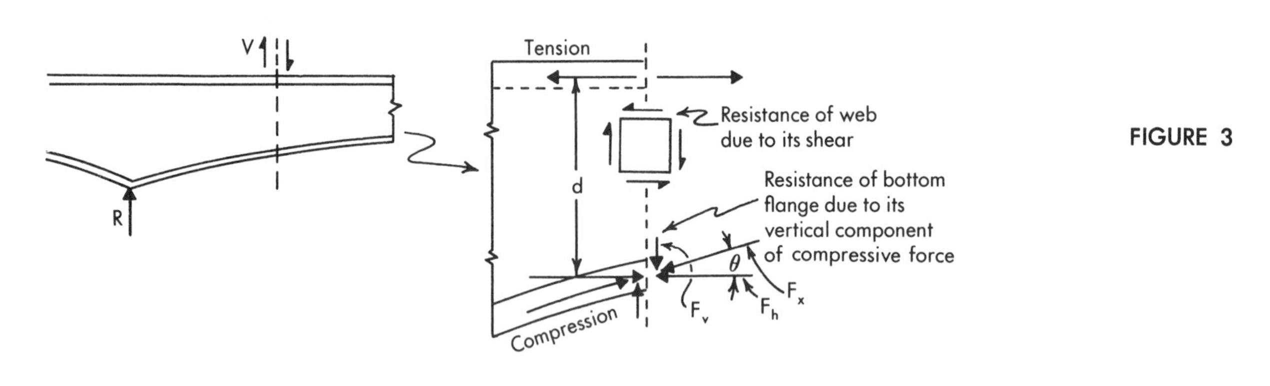

FIGURE 3

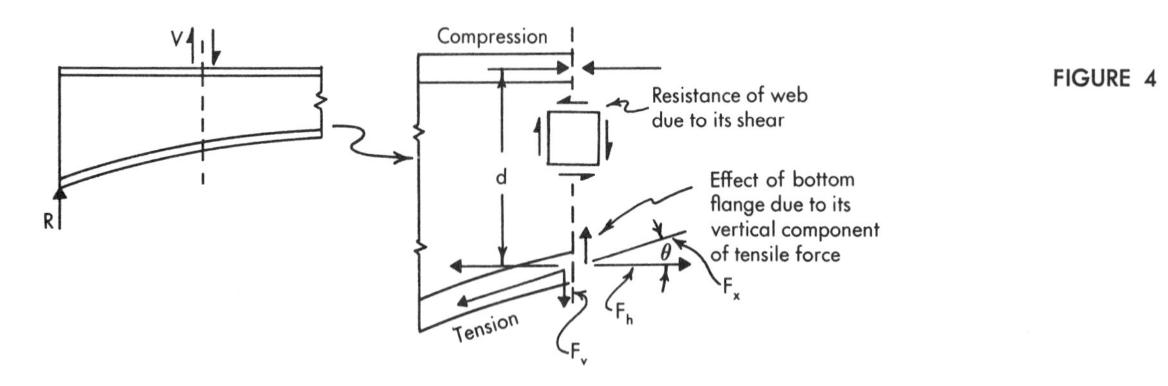

FIGURE 4

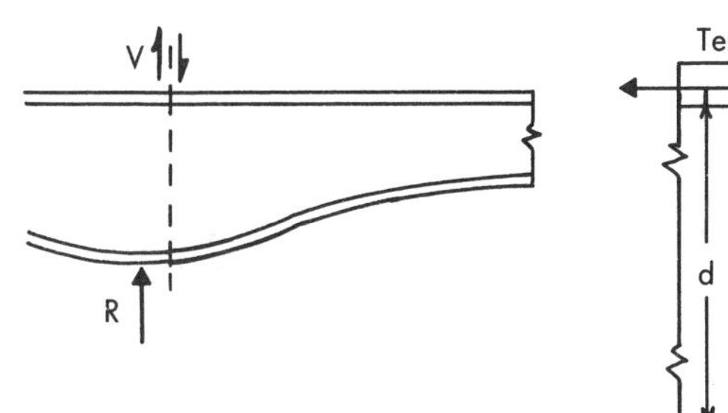

FIGURE 5

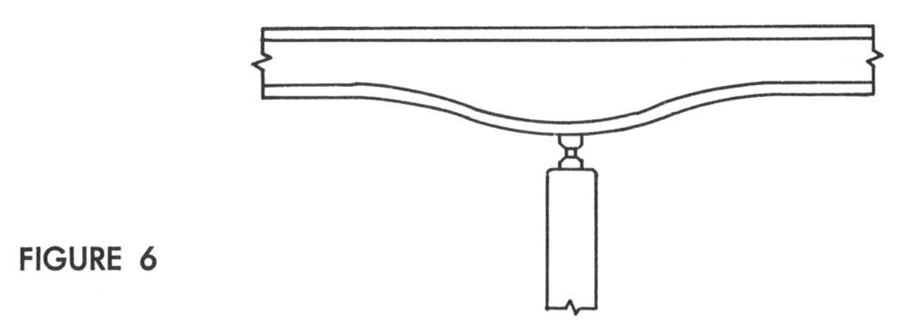

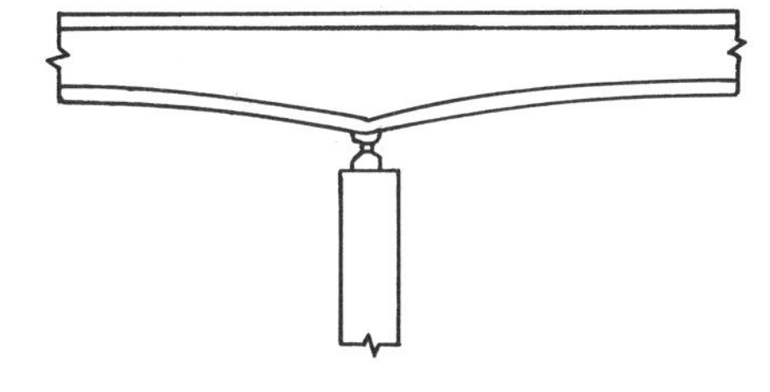

FIGURE 6

Simply Supported Haunched Girder

See Figure 4.

Here the external shear is—

$$V = A_W \tau_W - \frac{M}{d} \tan \theta$$

and the modified shear is—

$$V' = A_W \tau_W$$

$$= V + \frac{M}{d} \tan \theta$$

In this case the vertical component is added to the web shear.

Continuous Fish Belly Haunched Girder

See Figure 5.

Here the external shear is—

$$V = A_W \tau$$

In this case the flange force has no vertical component; hence, there is no reduction of shear in the web.

Problem 1

Check the haunched girder section (at point of support) shown in Figure 7, to determine the difference between the fish belly haunch and the parabolic haunch in the area of the compression flange near the support.

See Figure 6.

Conditions include the following:

Use of A441 steel

$M = 55{,}000$ ft-kips

$V = 1200$ kips

$I_x = 3{,}979{,}000$ in.^{4}

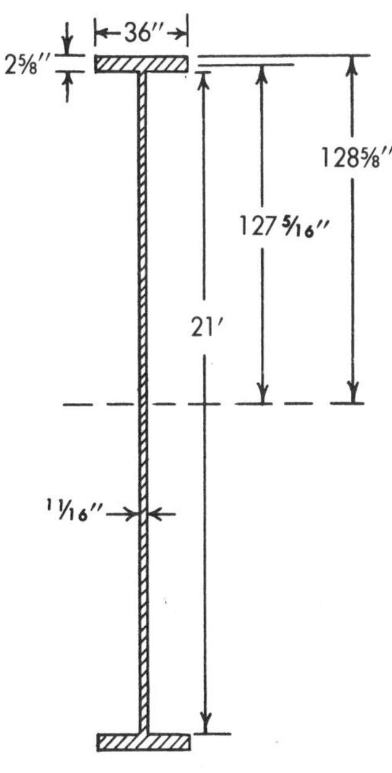

FIGURE 7

Analysis of Parabolic Haunch

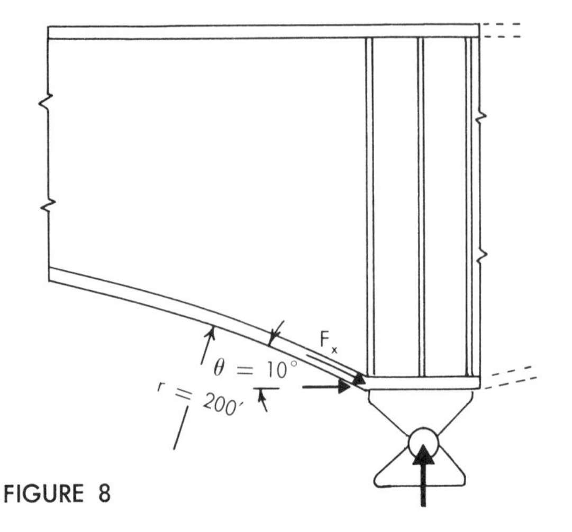

FIGURE 8

average bending stress in lower flange

$$\sigma_f = \frac{Mc}{I}$$

$$= \frac{(55{,}000'^k \times 12)(127\tfrac{5}{16}'')}{3{,}979{,}000}$$

$$= 21{,}150 \text{ psi compression}$$

flange forces

$$F_h = \sigma_f\, A_f$$

$$= (21{,}150)(2\tfrac{5}{8} \times 36)$$

$$= 2{,}000 \text{ kips}$$

$$F_v = F_h \tan\theta$$

$$= (2000)(.1763)$$

$$= 353 \text{ kips}$$

$$F_x = \frac{F_h}{\cos\theta}$$

$$= \frac{2000}{.9848}$$

$$= 2030 \text{ kips}$$

shear stress in web

Since the external shear is—

$$V = A_W\, \tau_W + F_v \text{ or}$$

$$A_W\, \tau_W = V - F_v \text{ and}$$

$$\tau_W = \frac{V - F_v}{A_W}$$

$$= \frac{1200 - 353}{(252 \times \tfrac{11}{16})}$$

$$= 4890 \text{ psi}$$

stress in web at lower flange at support

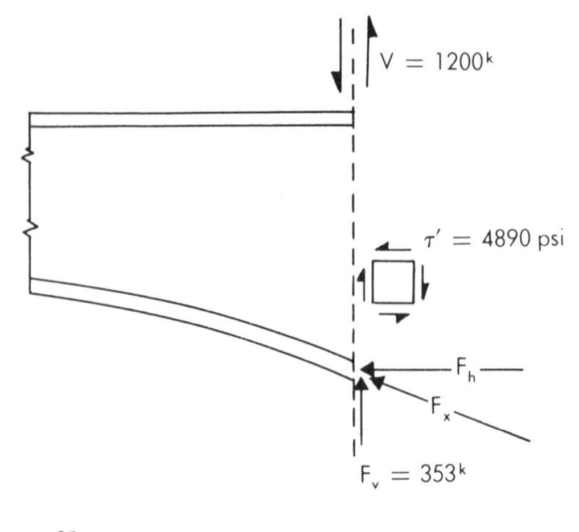

or:

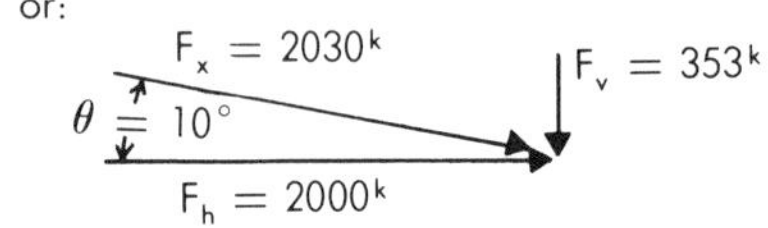

FIGURE 9

$$\sigma_h = \frac{M\,c}{I}$$

$$= \frac{(55{,}000 \times 12)(126)}{(3{,}979{,}000)}$$

$$= 20{,}900 \text{ psi, compression}$$

These stresses in Figure 10, left-hand side, must now be rotated 10° to line up with the sloping flange in order that the radial compressive stress may be added. This is shown on the right-hand side of Figure 10. This may be analyzed by one of two methods:

1. Graphically, using Mohr's circle of stress: (Fig. 11)
a) Draw the given stresses (σ_x', σ_y', and τ') at the two points (a′) and (b′)
b) Construct a circle through these two points
c) Rotate clockwise through an angle of 2θ or 20°
d) Read the new stresses (σ_x, σ_y, and τ)

2. Analytically; work is performed as follows:

$$k = \frac{\sigma_x' + \sigma_y'}{2}$$

$$= \frac{20{,}900}{2}$$

$$= 10{,}450$$

$$\tan\alpha = \frac{\tau'}{\tfrac{1}{2}(\sigma_x' + \sigma_y')}$$

$$= \frac{4890}{\tfrac{1}{2}(20{,}900)}$$

$$= .4680$$

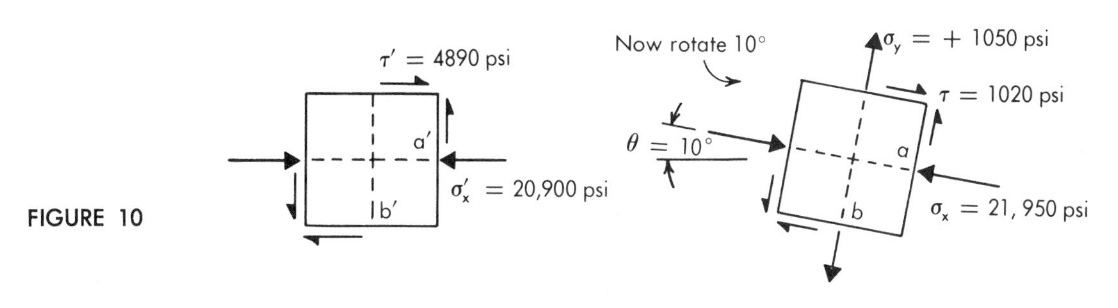

FIGURE 10

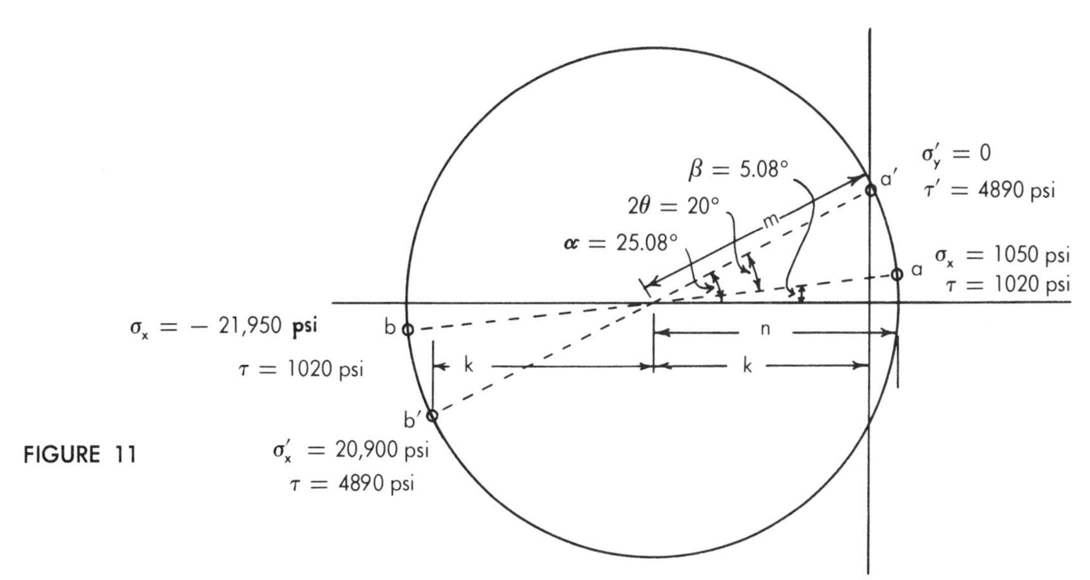

FIGURE 11

$$\alpha = 25.08°$$

$$\beta = 25.08° - 20°$$
$$= 5.08°$$

$$\sin \beta = .0886$$

$$\cos \beta = .9961$$

$$m = \sqrt{k^2 + (\tau')^2}$$
$$= \sqrt{(10{,}450)^2 + 4890^2}$$
$$= 11{,}540$$

$$\tau = m \sin \beta$$
$$= (11{,}540)(.0886)$$
$$= 1020 \text{ psi}$$

$$n = m \cos \beta$$
$$= (11{,}540)(.9961)$$
$$= 11{,}500 \text{ psi}$$

$$\sigma_x = k + n$$
$$= (10{,}450) + (11{,}500)$$
$$= 21{,}950 \text{ psi, compression}$$

$$\sigma_y = k - n$$
$$= (10{,}450) - (11{,}500)$$
$$= 1050 \text{ psi, tension}$$

radial force of lower compression flange against web

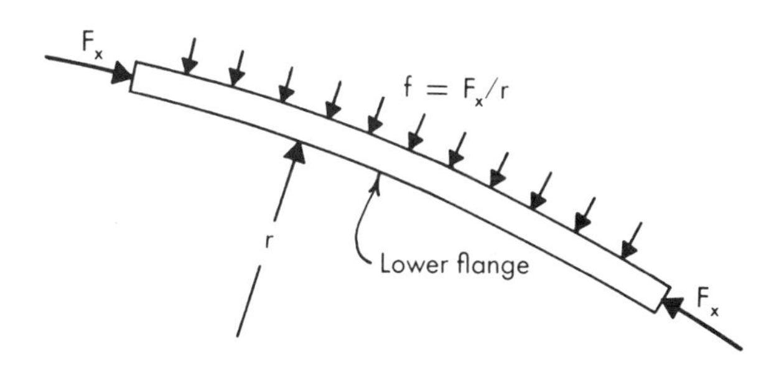

FIGURE 12

$$f = \frac{F_x}{r}$$
$$= \frac{(2030)}{(200 \times 12)}$$
$$= 846 \text{ lbs/linear in.}$$

resultant radial compressive stress in web

$$\sigma_y = \frac{(846)}{(1 \times 1\tfrac{1}{16})}$$
$$= 1230 \text{ psi, compression}$$

Web

1″

$1\tfrac{1}{16}$″

$\sigma_y = 1230$ psi

$\theta = 10°$

This produces the final stress condition of:

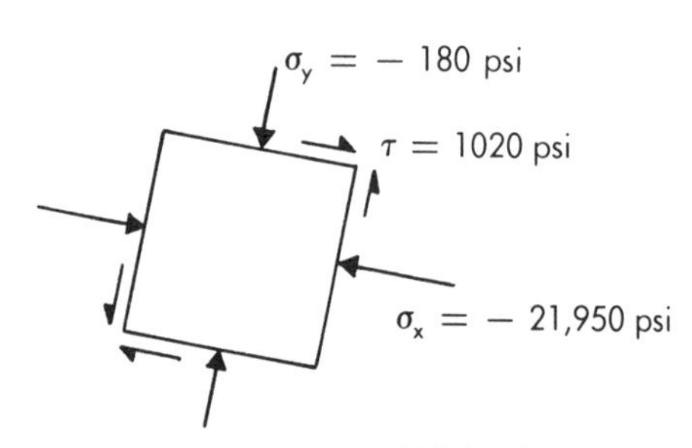

FIGURE 13

critical stress

Using the Huber-Mises formula:

$$\sigma_{cr} = \sqrt{\sigma_x^2 - \sigma_x \, \sigma_y + \sigma_y^2 + 3\, \tau_{xy}^2}$$
$$= \sqrt{(-21{,}950)^2 - (-21{,}950)(-180) + (-180)^2 + 3(1020)^2}$$
$$= \underline{22{,}000 \text{ psi}}$$

This results in an indicated factor of safety against yielding of—

$$FS = \frac{\sigma_y}{\sigma_{cr}}$$
$$= \frac{(42{,}000)}{(22{,}000)}$$
$$= \underline{1.90}$$

Analysis of Fish Belly Haunch

Now using the same load conditions on the fish belly haunch with the same web and flange dimensions:

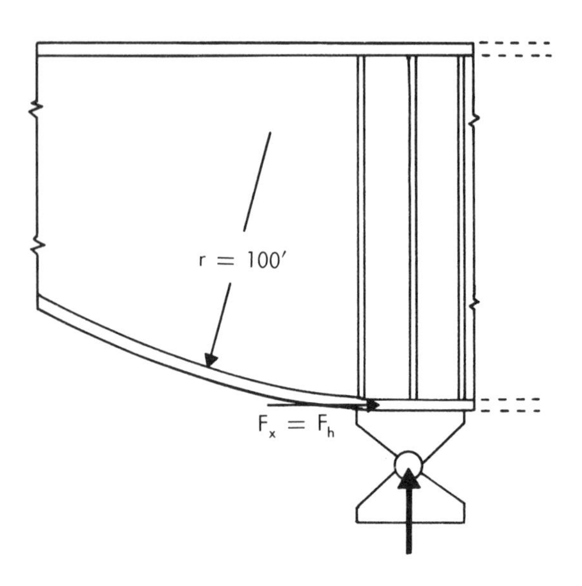

FIGURE 14

At this point: $\sigma_x = \sigma_h$ & $F_x = F_h$

stress in web or lower flange from bending moment

$$\sigma_x = \frac{M\ c}{I}$$
$$= \frac{(55{,}000'^{k} \times 12)(126)}{3{,}979{,}000}$$
$$= 20{,}900 \text{ psi, compression}$$

average stress in lower flange from bending moment

$$\sigma_f = \frac{M\ c}{I}$$
$$= \frac{(55{,}000'^{k} \times 12)(127\tfrac{5}{16})}{3{,}979{,}000}$$
$$= 21{,}150 \text{ psi}$$

force in lower flange from bending moment

$$F_x = \sigma_f \, A_f$$
$$= (21{,}150)(2\tfrac{5}{8} \times 36)$$
$$= 2000 \text{ kips}$$

radial tensile force of lower compression flange against web

$$f = \frac{F_x}{r}$$
$$= \frac{(2000)}{(100 \times 12)}$$
$$= 1670 \text{ lbs/linear in.}$$

resultant radial tensile stress in web

$$\sigma_y = \frac{f}{t_w}$$

$$= \frac{(1670)}{(1 \times 1\tfrac{1}{16})}$$

$$= 2420 \text{ psi}$$

shear stress in web

$$\tau = \frac{V}{A_w}$$

$$= \frac{(1200)}{(252 \times 1\tfrac{1}{16})}$$

$$= 6930 \text{ psi}$$

combining stresses to find the critical stress

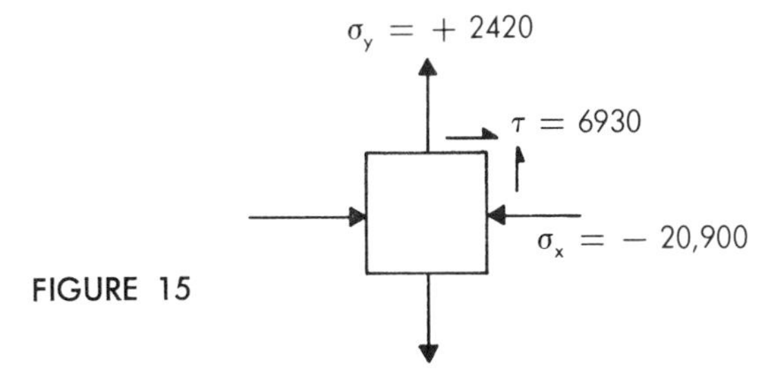

FIGURE 15

Using the Huber-Mises formula:

$$\sigma_{cr} = \sqrt{\sigma_x{}^2 - \sigma_x\,\sigma_y + \sigma_y{}^2 + 3\,\tau_{xy}}$$

$$= \sqrt{(20{,}900)^2 - (-20{,}900)(+2460) + (+2460)^2 + 3(6{,}930)^2}$$

$$= \underline{25{,}100 \text{ psi}}$$

This results in an indicated factor of safety against yielding of—

$$\text{F.S.} = \frac{\sigma_y}{\sigma_{cr}}$$

$$= \frac{(42{,}000)}{(25{,}100)}$$

$$= \underline{1.67}$$

It is apparent from this that the parabolic haunch has a slightly lower critical stress and, therefore, a slightly higher factor of safety.

3. WELDS CONNECTING SLOPING FLANGE TO WEB

In any girder, the horizontal shear force in the connecting weld between the web and the horizontal flange is found from the following formula:

$$f = \frac{V\ a\ y}{I\ n} \text{ lbs/in.}$$

Approximate value:

$$f_h = \frac{V}{d\ n} \text{ lbs/in.}$$

Where the flange slopes, the modified vertical shear (V′) must be used. The shear component along the slope will be—

$$f_x = \frac{f_h}{\cos\,\theta}$$

but the distance along this slope for every horizontal inch is—

$$s_x = \frac{1''}{\cos\,\theta}$$

so that the shear force on the weld along this sloping flange is obtained from the above formula for the horizontal flange, using the modified value of V′:

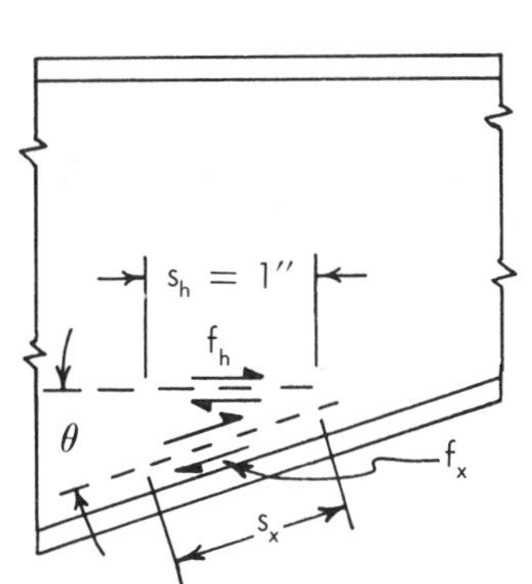

FIGURE 16

$$f = \frac{f_x}{s_x} = \frac{\dfrac{f_h}{\cos\,\theta}}{\dfrac{s_h}{\cos\,\theta}} = \frac{f_h}{s_h}$$

$$\therefore \boxed{f = \frac{V'\ a\ y}{I\ n} \text{ lbs/in.}}$$

or the approximate:

$$\boxed{f = \frac{V'}{d\ n} \text{ lbs/in.}}$$

where:

- f = shear force on weld, lbs/linear in.
- V = external shear on the section, lbs.
- V′ = modified shear on section if sloping flange, lbs
- a = area of flange held by weld, $in.^2$
- y = vertical distance between center of gravity of flange held by weld, and neutral axis of section, in.
- I = moment of inertia of section, $in.^4$
- n = number of welds connecting web to flange
- d = distance between C.J. of flanges, in.

Erection view of New York State Thruway bridge shows haunched girders. Straightness and true camber of the lower flanges are apparent. Note vertical stiffeners and suspended (235′) span bearing surfaces at girder junctions.

Portion of 295′ span of bridge on Connecticut Turnpike being settled onto supporting piers. Note continuous parabolic haunched girder construction.

Girders on a Horizontal Curve

1. RECENT PROJECTS

Today, it is accepted practice to design and fabricate plate girders with horizontal curves when necessary. Several such bridges or freeway overpasses have been built within the past several years.

- A series of 4 lines of curved welded plate girders with 90′ spans are a part of the Pasadena-Golden State Freeway's interchange in the Los Angeles area, Figure 1. These have a curve radius of 400′. They were fabricated in Kaiser Steel's plant at Montebello.
- One of Milwaukee's new expressways has a section of 4 continuous spans with a total length of 345′ in which the two outer girders have a 9° horizontal curve and the 2 inner girders are straight.
- Bristol Steel & Iron Works, Bristol, Tennessee, recently fabricated several curved girders for the Southwest Freeway-Inner Loop in Washington, D. C.

2. DESIGN AND FABRICATION

Although there are torsional stresses within the curved girder, usually the degree of curvature is not overly high and these additional stresses are offset by the diaphragms connecting the girders. The number of diaphragms has occasionally been increased for this reason, and sometimes the allowable stresses have been reduced slightly.

Curved flange plates are laid out by offsets and flame cut from plate. By cutting both edges at the same time, there is no bowing from any unbalanced shrinkage effect of the flame cutting. The web plates do not have to be preformed, usually being easily pulled into alignment along the centerline of the flanges.

Caution must be used in placing attaching plates for the diaphragms to the webs and flanges. The proper angle for these plates may vary along the length of the girder. Shear attachments are added mainly to accomplish composite action between the concrete deck and steel girder, and thereby increase torsional rigidity. During erection, a pair of curved girders is usually attached together by means of the diaphragms and then hoisted into position as a unit.

FIG. 1 Welded plate girders, having a 400′ radius of curvature, dominate the interest in Los Angeles interchange of Pasadena-Golden State Freeway. Curving girders permit economies in deck system by keeping overhangs uniform from end to end of curve.

FIG. 2 Bridge plate girders being weld fabricated. With flanges flame-cut on a curve, weight of the rolled web is utilized in making it conform to desired radius.

FIG. 3 A two-span continuous box girder and curved ramp construction provided the answer to space limitations in reaching elevated parking area at busy New York terminal complex. Smooth, clean lines, without outside stiffeners, demonstrate aesthetic possibilities inherent in welded design.

Tapered Girders

1. FABRICATION AND USE

The use of tapered girders has become widespread, especially in the framing of roofs over large areas where it is desirable to minimize the number of interior columns or to eliminate them altogether. They permit placing maximum girder depth where it is needed, while reducing the depth considerably at points where it is not needed.

Tapered girders are fabricated either 1) by welding two flange plates to a tapered web plate, or 2) by cutting a rolled WF beam lengthwise along its web at an angle, turning one half end for end, and then welding the two halves back together again along the web. See Figure 1.

Camber When Required

Camber can be built into the tapered girder when required. When the girder is made from WF beams, each half is clamped into the proper camber during assembly. Then the butt joint along the web is groove welded while the girder is held in this shape. Since the weld along the beam web lies along the neutral axis, no bending or distortion will result from welding, and the girder will retain the shape in which it is held during welding.

When the girder is made of two flange plates and a tapered web, the proper camber can be obtained by simply cutting the web to the proper camber outline. The flange plates during assembly are then pulled tightly against the web, into the proper camber. The four fillet welds joining the flanges to the web are balanced about the neutral axis of the girder and as a result there should be no distortion problem.

Application of Tapered Girders

When the tapered girders are used with the sloping flange at the top, their taper in both directions from the ridge will provide the slope needed for drainage. By varying the depth at the ends of successive girders, the deck can be canted to drain toward roof boxes in the valleys between adjacent gabled spans and at flanking parapet walls.

For flat roofs, the girders are inverted, with their tapered flange down. There are many combinations of roof framing systems possible. For example, on a three-span design, the central span can use the tapered flange up, forming the slope of the roof; the two adjacent spans use the tapered flange down to provide a flat roof, but tilted to continue the same slope as the central section.

The problem of lateral support for the top compression flange of tapered girders is no different than with other beams and girders. Generally the roof deck is sufficiently rigid to function as a diaphragm, and it's only necessary to attach the deck to the top flange. There's apparently no advantage in designing with a reduced stress allowable, in accordance with AISC Formulas 4 or 5, in order to permit a greater distance between bracing points at the top flange.

Where tapered girders are critical, Section 5.11 on Rigid Frame Knees goes into more detail relative to stresses (elastic design).

Because of the reduced depth at the ends of the

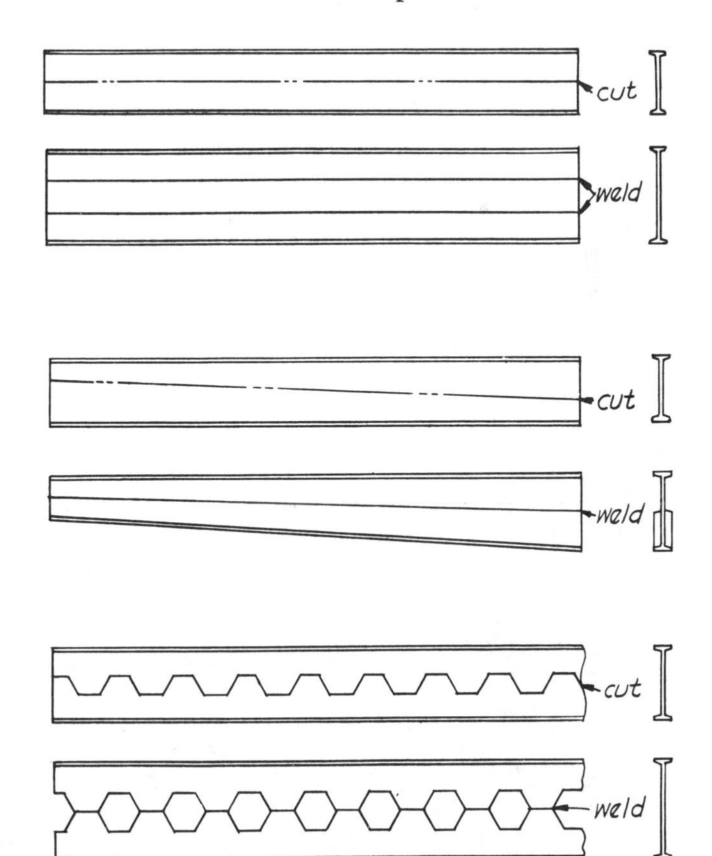

FIGURE 1

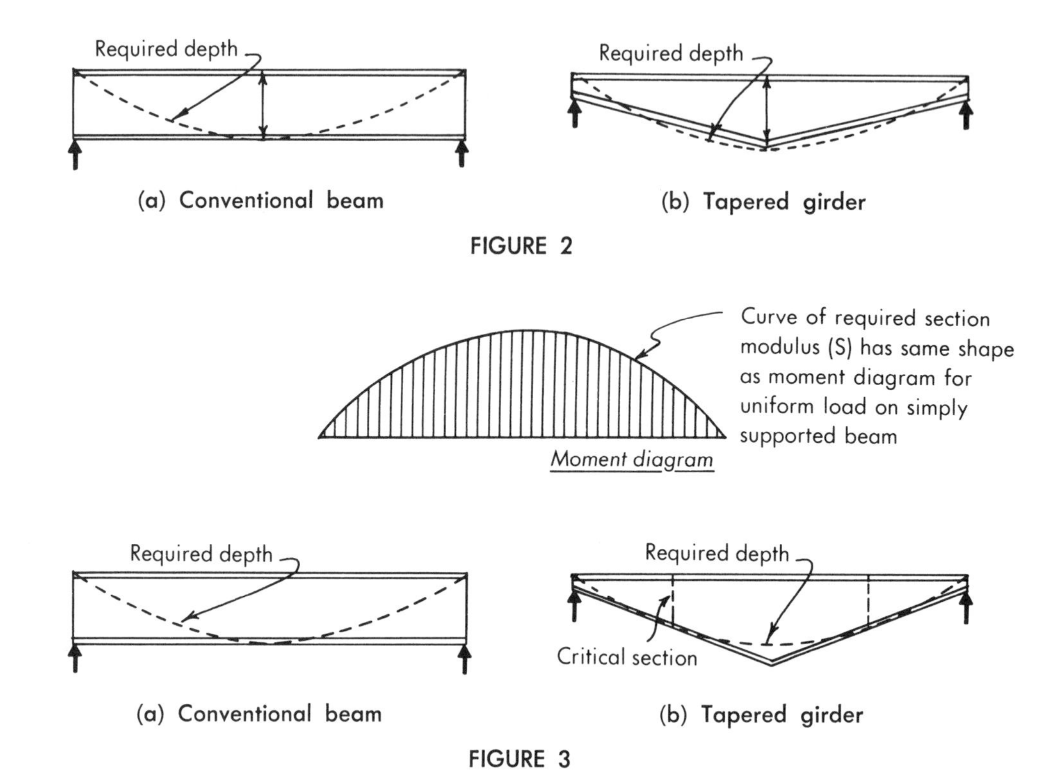

FIGURE 2

FIGURE 3

tapered girders, their connection to supporting columns may offer little resistance to horizontal forces. For this reason, some knee braces may be required unless the roof deck or a positive system of bracing in the plane of the roof is stiff enough to transmit these forces to adequately braced walls.

At first glance, there appears to be quite a weight saving in tapered girder; however, this is not always as great as it might seem:

First, the flange area remains the same; the only weight saving is in the web. See Figure 2.

Second, the depth of the tapered girder at midspan must be increased over that of the conventional straight beam to be sufficient at the critical section (about ¼ span). This is necessary to develop the required section modulus along the full length of the tapered girder.

This will slightly offset the initial weight saving in the web. See Figure 3.

FIG. 4 For flat roofs, tapered girders are used inverted, with tapered flange downward. Frequently the girder is tilted to provide a slope to the roof or roof section.

2. DETERMINING CRITICAL DEPTH AND SLOPE

The critical depth section of a tapered girder is that section in which the actual depth of the girder just equals the minimum depth required for the moment. It would be the highest stressed section of the girder in bending.

In the case of a uniformly loaded, simply supported girder, its sloping flange must be tangent to the required-depth curve at this point in order for the beam to have sufficient depth along its length.

Setting the slope of the tapered girder flange so that the critical section is located at the ¼ span will result in about the minimum web weight. See Figure 5.

The properties of this critical section are—

$$I = 2\,A_f\left(\frac{d_f}{2}\right) + \frac{t_w\,d_w}{12}$$

$$S = \frac{I}{d_b{}^2} = \frac{A_f\,d_f{}^2}{d_b} - \frac{t_w\,d_w}{6\,d_b}$$

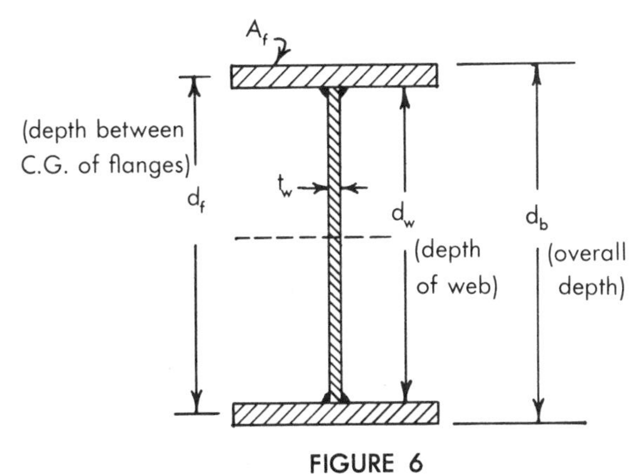

FIGURE 6

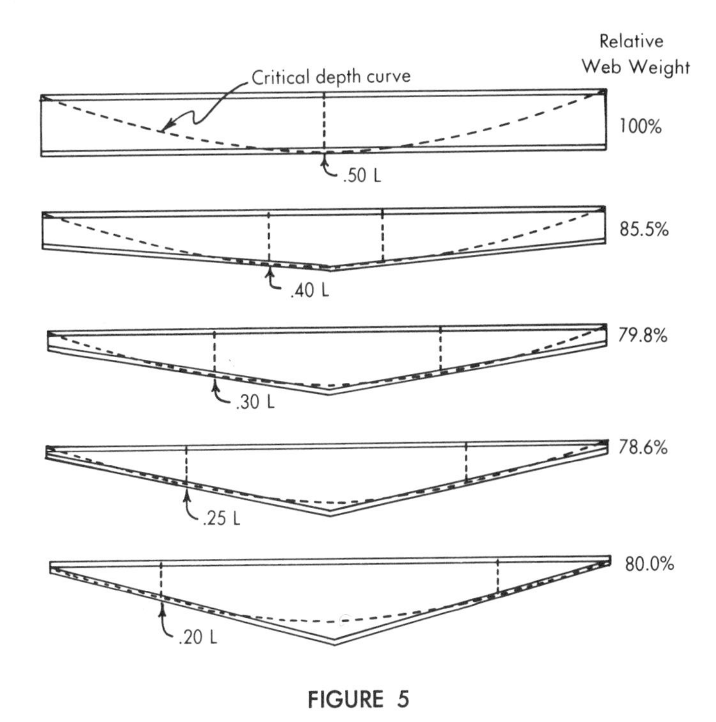

FIGURE 5

This formula for section modulus can be simplified with little loss in accuracy, by letting—

$$d_W = d_f = d_b$$

$$\therefore \boxed{S = A_f\,d_W + \frac{t_w\,d_w{}^2}{6}} \quad \ldots\ldots\ldots\ldots\ldots\ldots(1)$$

If the section modulus required to resist the bending moment is known, the required beam depth (d) is solved for:

$$d_w{}^2 + \frac{6\,A_f\,d_w}{t_w} - \frac{6\,S}{t_w} = 0$$

FIG. 7 Tapered girders used with the tapered flange at the top provide for roof drainage in both directions from the ridge. Multi-span designs often call for combinations of girders having tapered flange up and others having tapered flange down.

TABLE 1

	1 conc. load	2 conc. loads	3 conc. loads	4 conc. loads	5 conc. loads	uniform load
critical depth at	at $\frac{1}{2}$ L	at load $\frac{1}{3}$ L	at 1st loads $\frac{1}{4}$ L	at 1st loads $\frac{1}{5}$ L	at $\frac{1}{4}$ span $\frac{1}{4}$ L	at $\frac{1}{4}$ span $\frac{1}{4}$ L
critical depth d_w	$\sqrt{\left(\frac{3A_f}{t_w}\right)^2 + \frac{3\ PL}{2t_w\sigma}} - \frac{3A_f}{t_w}$	$\sqrt{\left(\frac{3A_f}{t_w}\right)^2 + \frac{2\ PL}{t_w\sigma}} - \frac{3A_f}{t_w}$	$\sqrt{\left(\frac{3A_f}{t_w}\right)^2 + \frac{9\ PL}{4t_w\sigma}} - \frac{3A_f}{t_w}$	$\sqrt{\left(\frac{3A_f}{t_w}\right)^2 + \frac{2.4\ PL}{t_w\sigma}} - \frac{3A_f}{t_w}$	$\sqrt{\left(\frac{3A_f}{t_w}\right)^2 + \frac{13\ PL}{4t_w\sigma}} - \frac{3A_f}{t_w}$	$\sqrt{\left(\frac{3A_f}{t_w}\right)^2 + \frac{9\ wL^2}{16t_w\sigma}} - \frac{3A_f}{t_w}$
slope θ	$\frac{1.5\ P}{\sigma(t_w d_w + 3A_f)}$	$\frac{3\ P}{\sigma(t_w d_w + 3A_f)}$	$\frac{1.5\ P}{\sigma(t_w d_w + 3A_f)}$	$\frac{3\ P}{\sigma(t_w d_w + 3A_f)}$	$\frac{4.5\ P}{\sigma(t_w d_w + 3A_f)}$	$\frac{.75\ wL}{\sigma(t_w d_w + 3A_f)}$
depth at center line $d_{℄}$	$d_{℄} = d_w$	$d_{℄} = d_w + \frac{1}{6} \tan \theta$	$d_{℄} = d_w + \frac{1}{4} \tan \theta$	$d_{℄} = d_w + .3\ L \tan \theta$	$d_{℄} = d_w + \frac{1}{4} \tan \theta$	$d_{℄} = d_w + \frac{1}{4} \tan \theta$
depth at end d_e	$d_e = d_w - \frac{1}{2} \tan \theta$	$d_e = d_w - \frac{1}{3} \tan \theta$	$d_e = d_w - \frac{1}{4} \tan \theta$	$d_e = d_w - .2\ L \tan \theta$	$d_e = d_w - \frac{1}{4} \tan \theta$	$d_e = d_w - \frac{1}{4} \tan \theta$

$$\text{or} \quad d_w = \sqrt{\left(\frac{3\ A_f}{t_w}\right)^2 + \frac{6\ S}{t_w}} - \frac{3\ A_f}{t_w} \qquad \text{(2)}$$

For a simply supported, uniformly loaded, tapered girder—

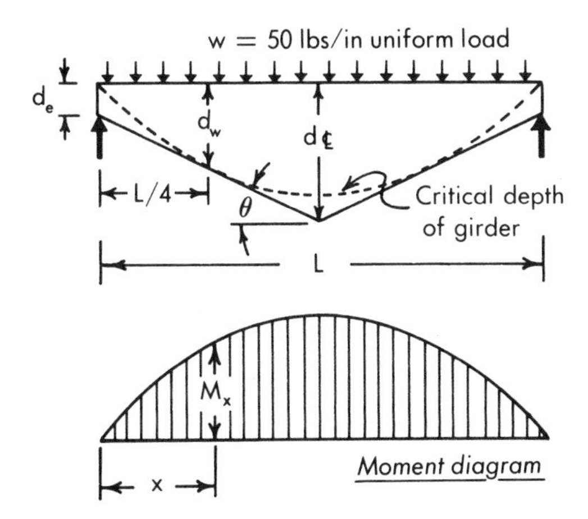

FIGURE 8

$$M_x = \frac{w\ x}{2}\ (L - x)$$

$$S_x = \frac{M_x}{\sigma}$$

$$d_x = \sqrt{\left(\frac{3\ A_f}{t_w}\right)^2 + \frac{6\ S}{t_w}} - \frac{3\ A_f}{t_w}$$

or to find the depth in one step—

$$d_x = \sqrt{\left(\frac{3\ A_f}{t_w}\right)^2 + \frac{3\ w\ x}{t_w\ \sigma}\ (L - x)} - \frac{3\ A_f}{t_w}$$

To find the slope of the critical-depth curve formed by points d_x along the girder length, this expression for depth (d_x) is differentiated with respect to the distances (x):

$$\theta = \frac{dd_x}{dx} = \frac{\frac{3\ w}{2\ t_w\ \sigma}\ (L - 2_x)}{\sqrt{\left(\frac{3\ A_f}{t_w}\right)^2 + \frac{3\ w\ x}{t_w\ \sigma}\ (L - x)}}$$

It is simpler to find the slope at ¼ span, letting x = L/4:

$$\theta = \frac{\frac{3\ w\ L}{4\ t_w\ \sigma}}{\sqrt{\left(\frac{3\ A_f}{t_w}\right)^2 + \frac{9\ w\ L^2}{16\ t_w\ \sigma}}}$$

Also, at x = L/4:

$$d_w = \sqrt{\frac{3\ A_f}{t_w} + \frac{9\ w\ L^2}{16\ t_w\ \sigma}} - \frac{3\ A_f}{t_w} \qquad \text{(3)}$$

$$\theta = \frac{.75\ w\ L}{\sigma\ (t_w\ d_w + 3\ A_f)} \qquad \text{(4)}$$

and:

$$d_{℄} = d_w + \frac{L}{4}\ \tan\theta \qquad \text{(5)}$$

$$d_e = d_w - \frac{L}{4}\ \tan\theta \qquad \text{(6)}$$

Since loading on the girder is not always uniform, the above formulas do not always apply. Table 1 summarizes the working formulas to use for various conditions of loading, as well as locating the critical depth.

3. CONCENTRATED LOADS

Figure 9 shows the effects of placing multiple loads upon a simply-supported tapered girder. These effects on the bending moment and the critical depth of the girder can be explained as follows:

- In the case of the single concentrated load at midspan, the critical depth section is at midspan, and the maximum slope is θ.
- In the case of 2 equal concentrated loads applied at ⅓ points, the critical depth section is at the points of load application and the maximum slope is θ. Assuming the slope were to pivot about this critical depth section, any slope less than this value would cause the depth at the end to increase at twice the rate at which the depth at centerline is decreasing. Since such a shift would increase the web weight, this maximum slope value of θ should be used initially.

If more depth is needed at the end because of higher vertical shear, do this by pivoting about this critical depth section. This will result in the least increase in web weight. It can be shown that, under this condition, the resulting depth at centerline will be—

$$d_{℄} = \frac{3\ d_w - d_e}{2} \qquad \text{(7)}$$

- In the case of 3 equal concentrated loads applied at ¼ points, the critical depth section will be chosen at ¼ span. The slope of the girder must lie somewhere between θ and ϕ. For any angle between these two values, the weight of the web will remain the same

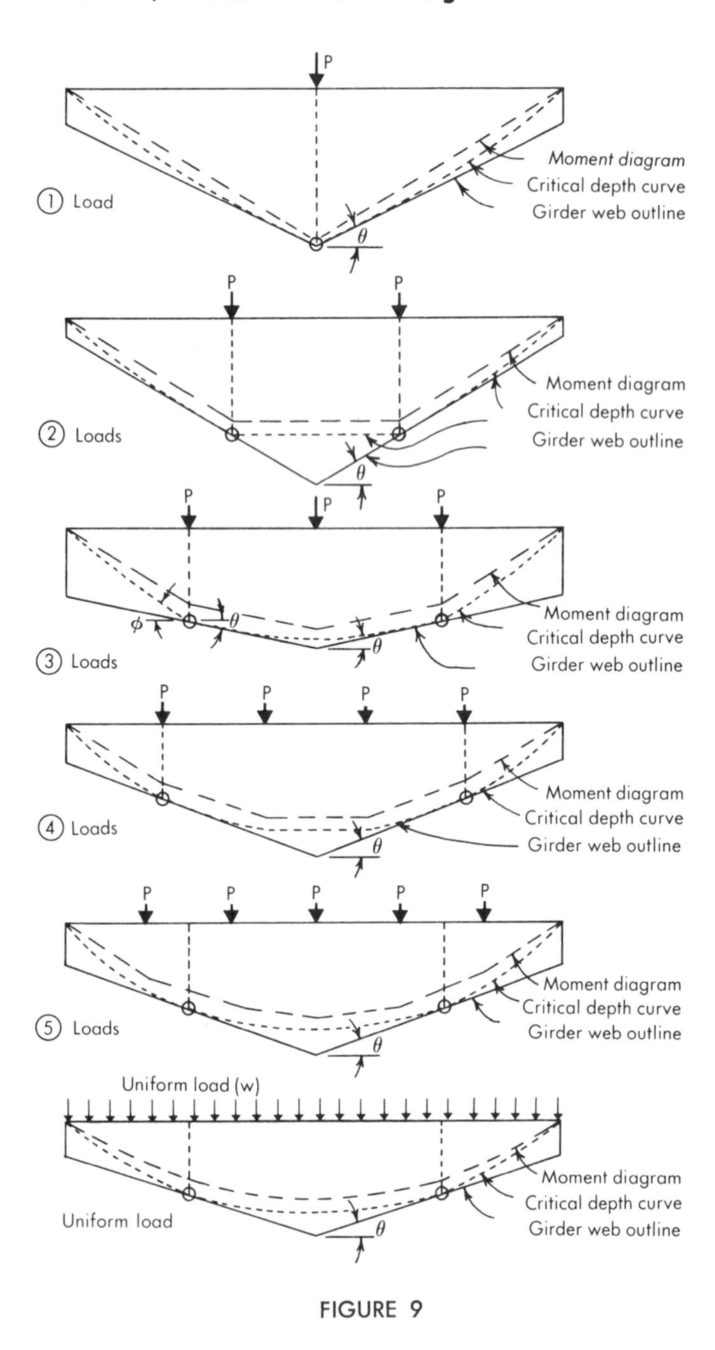

FIGURE 9

because this is pivoting halfway between the end and the centerline. Any change in the web depth at the centerline will change the depth at the end at the same rate, but inversely.

Of the two extreme conditions, it would be better to use the angle θ since this will give a larger value for the depth at the end, which may be needed because of the higher vertical shear value. There would be no advantage in using ϕ.

- In the case of 4 equal concentrated loads applied at $1/5$ points, use the critical depth section at the first load. The section chosen lies closer to the end of the girder and further from the centerline. Because of this, the depth at centerline will change at a faster rate than the depth at the end as the slope is varied. Therefore, for the lowest web weight, keep the depth at centerline as small as possible, hence use the angle θ.

- In the case of 5 equal concentrated loads applied at $1/6$ points, the critical depth section will be taken at the $1/4$ span for convenience. The slope of the girder will be θ.

Problem 1

Design a welded tapered girder, with a uniformly-distributed load of 600 lbs/ft; Figure 10. The girder has a length of 50′ and is simply supported. Use A36 steel and E70 welds.

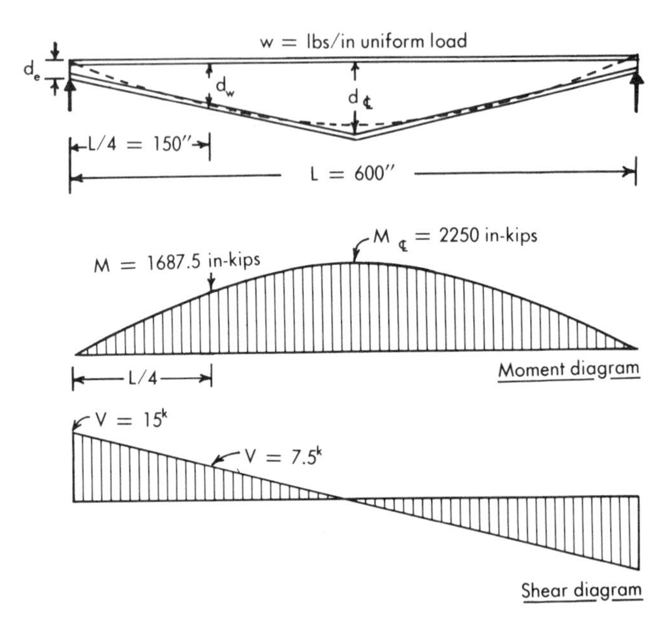

FIGURE 10

The top compression flange of the girder has suitable support.

Design for critical section at $1/4$ span; check moment at centerline; and check shear stress at centerline and end.

From Section 8.1, Beam Diagrams:

$$M_x = \frac{w\ L}{2}\ (L - x)$$

at $x = L/4$

$$M = \frac{3\ w\ L^2}{32}$$

$$= \frac{3(50)(600)^2}{32}$$

$$= 1687.5 \text{ in.-kips}$$

and:

$$S = \frac{M}{\sigma}$$

$$= \frac{(1687.5)}{(22{,}000)}$$

$$= 76.7 \text{ in.}^3$$

To use an "efficient" section (Sect. 4.2, Topic 2), the efficient depth would be—

$$d = \sqrt[3]{\frac{3\ K\ S}{2}}$$

It would be preferable not to have to use transverse intermittent stiffeners. Looking in Section 4.1 on Plate Girders for Buildings, Topic 2, it is seen that these stiffeners are not required if:

a) The ratio $K = \frac{d_w}{t_w}$ is less than 260

b) The shear stress (τ) does not exceed that of AISC Formula 9.

This means the values of K and shear stress (τ) shall fall within the values of the right-hand column of AISC Table 3-36, in Section 4.1, page 25.

Assume a value of K = 70 at the end of the girder; here the shear (V) is highest. Assume a value of K = 170 at midspan; here the shear (V) is very low. This means at ¼ span (the critical section under consideration) K would fall halfway between these two values, or K = 120.

therefore, the efficient depth

$$d = \sqrt[3]{\frac{3\ K\ S}{2}}$$

$$= \sqrt[3]{\frac{3(120)(76.7)}{2}}$$

$$= 24.0''$$

required flange area (efficient section)

$$A_f = \frac{d^2}{2\ K}$$

$$= \frac{(24)^2}{2(120)}$$

$= 2.4$ in.^{2} or *use ½″ × 5″ flange,* the area of which is $A_f = 2.5$ in.^{2}

web thickness

$$t_w = \frac{d_w}{K}$$

$$= \frac{(24)}{(120)}$$

$= .20''$ or *use a 3/16″ thick plate.* Then—

ratio of web's depth to thickness

$$K = \frac{d_w}{t_w}$$

$$= \frac{(24)}{(3/16)}$$

$$= 128$$

And from Table 3-36 in Sect. 4.1; since with no stiffeners $a/d_w = \infty$ (over 3), allowable shear is $\tau = 5000$ psi.

actual shear stress

$$\tau = \frac{V}{A_w}$$

$$= \frac{(7.5 \text{ kips})}{(3/16)\ (24)}$$

$= 1670$ psi < 5000 psi *OK*

required slope of tapered girder

$$\theta = \frac{.75\ w\ L}{\sigma\ (t_w d_w + 3\ A_f)}$$

$$= \frac{.75(50)(600)}{(22{,}000)\ (3/16 \times 24 + 3 \times 2.5)}$$

$= .0852$ radians, or *4.88°*

required depth of web

$$d_{℄} = d_w + \frac{L}{4} \tan \theta$$

tan 4.88° = .08538

$$= (24.0) + \frac{(600)}{4}\ (.08538)$$

$$= 24.0 + 12.8$$

$$= 36.8''$$

$$d_e = d_w - \frac{L}{4} \tan \theta$$

$$= (24.0) - (12.8)$$

$= $ *11.2″*

Check Shear Stress at End

$$A_w = 3/16\ (11.2)$$

$$= 2.1 \text{ in.}^2$$

$$\tau = \frac{V}{A_w}$$

$$= \frac{(15 \text{ kips})}{(2.1)}$$

$$= 7140 \text{ psi}$$

Here:

$$K = \frac{d_w}{t_w} = \frac{(11.2)}{(3/16)}$$

= 60, and from Table AISC 3-36 in Section 4.1, page 25 it is determined that no stiffeners are required.

Check Section at Midspan

$$K = \frac{d_w}{t_w} = \frac{(36.8)}{(3/16)} = 196 < 260 \quad OK$$

Also, practically no shear here.

$$M_{℄} = \frac{w\ L^2}{8} = \frac{(50)\ (600)^2}{8} = 2250 \text{ in.-kips}$$

$$S_{℄} = A_f\ d_w + \frac{t_w\ d_w^2}{6} = (2.5)\ (36.8) + \frac{(3/16)\ (36.8)^2}{6} = 134.4 \text{ in.}^3$$

$$\sigma_{℄} = \frac{M_{℄}}{S_{℄}} = \frac{(2250 \text{ in.-kips})}{(134.4 \text{ in.}^3)} = 16{,}750 \text{ psi} < 22{,}000 \text{ psi} \quad OK$$

Problem 2 Alternate Design

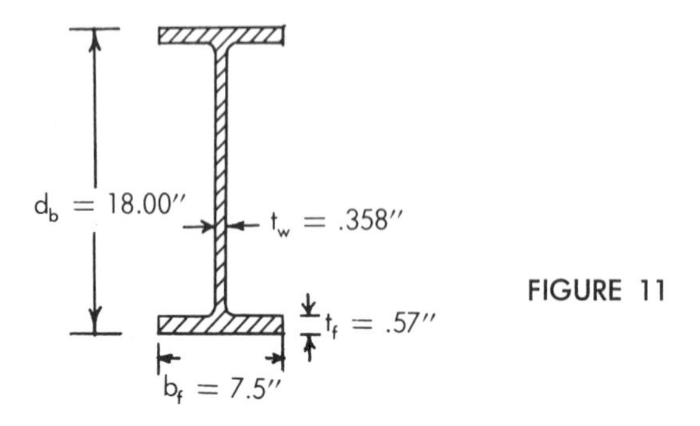

FIGURE 11

To make this tapered girder by splitting a WF rolled beam, and welding back together after reversing one-half end for end.

Since the required section modulus of the critical section at ¼ span is—

$$S = 76.7 \text{ in.}^3$$

an 18″ WF 50-lb beam could be used.

properties of this rolled beam

$$A_f = (.57)(7.5) = 4.27 \text{ in.}^2$$

$$d_w = 18.00 - 2(.57) = 16.86''$$

$$S = 89.0 \text{ in.}^3$$

shear stress at ¼ span

$$\tau = \frac{V}{A_w} = \frac{(7.5 \text{ kips})}{(.358)(16.86)} = 1240 \text{ psi} \quad OK$$

slope of tapered girder

$$\theta = \frac{.75\ w\ L}{\sigma(t_w\ d_w + 3A_f)} = \frac{(.75)(50)(600)}{(22{,}000)(.358 \times 16.96 + 3 \times 4.27)} = .05415 \text{ radians or } 3.10°$$

$\tan\theta = .05416$
$\cos\theta = .99854$

depth of web

$$d_{℄} = d_w + \frac{L}{4}\tan\theta = (16.96) + \frac{(600)}{4}(.05416) = 16.96 + 8.12 = 25.08$$

$$d_e = d_w - \frac{L}{4}\tan\theta = (16.96) - (8.12) = 8.84$$

Before going further, check the *shear stress at the end of beam*—

$$A_w = t_w\ d_w = (.358)(8.84) = 3.17 \text{ in.}^2$$

$$\tau = \frac{V}{A_w}$$

$$= \frac{(15^k)}{(3.17)}$$

$$= 4730 \text{ psi} \quad OK$$

depth of beam

$$d_{\mathfrak{C}} = d_w + 2(t_f)$$

$$= (25.08) + 2(.57)$$

$$= 26.12''$$

$$d_e = d_w + 2\ (t_f)$$

$$= (8.84) + 2(.57)$$

$$= 9.88''$$

starting point of cut

$$d_{\mathfrak{C}} = a + d = a + \frac{a}{\cos\theta}$$

$$= a\left(1 + \frac{1}{\cos\theta}\right)$$

$$= a\left(1 + \frac{1}{.99854}\right)$$

$$= 2.0014\ a \text{ and}$$

$$a = \frac{26.12}{2.0014}$$

$$= 13.06''$$

or use the dimension ($a = 130''$) to determine the starting point for flame cutting the WF beam to prepare a tapered girder.

Check Girder Section at Midspan

$$K = \frac{d_w}{t_w}$$

$$= \frac{(25.08)}{(.358)}$$

$$= 78 \quad OK$$

Also, practically no shear here.

$$M_{\mathfrak{C}} = 2250 \text{ in.-kips}$$

$$S_{\mathfrak{C}} = A_f\ d_w + \frac{t_w\ d_w^2}{6}$$

$$= (.427)(25.08) + \frac{(.358)(25.08)^2}{6}$$

$$= 166.8 \text{ in.}^3$$

$$\sigma_{\mathfrak{C}} = \frac{M_{\mathfrak{C}}}{S_{\mathfrak{C}}}$$

$$= \frac{(2250)}{(166.8)}$$

$$= 13{,}500 \text{ psi} \quad OK$$

4. DEFLECTION OF TAPERED GIRDERS

The area-moment method may be used with good results to find the deflection of tapered girders, where no portion of the member has a constant moment of

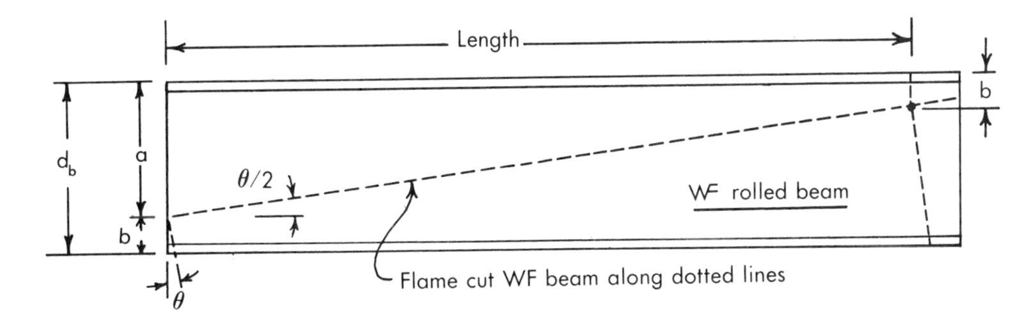

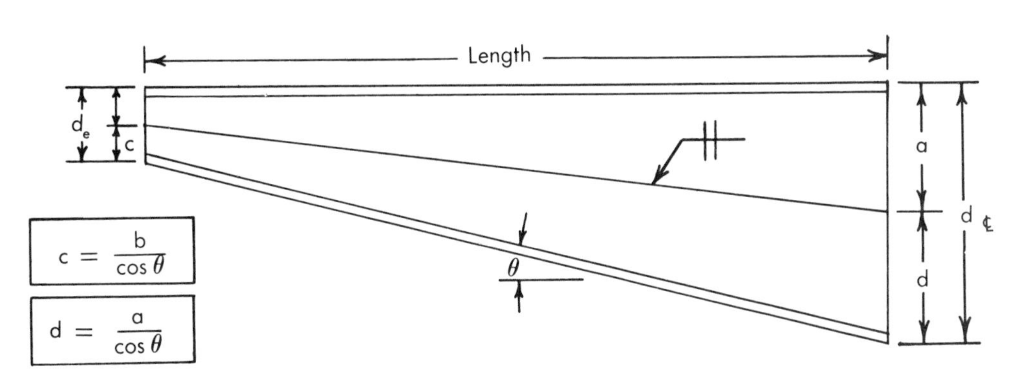

FIG. 12 Turn one-half end for end, and submerged-arc weld this web joint without special edge preparation. Trim ends.

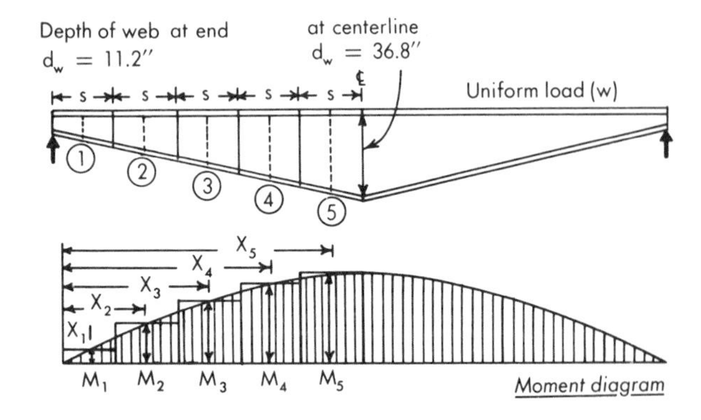

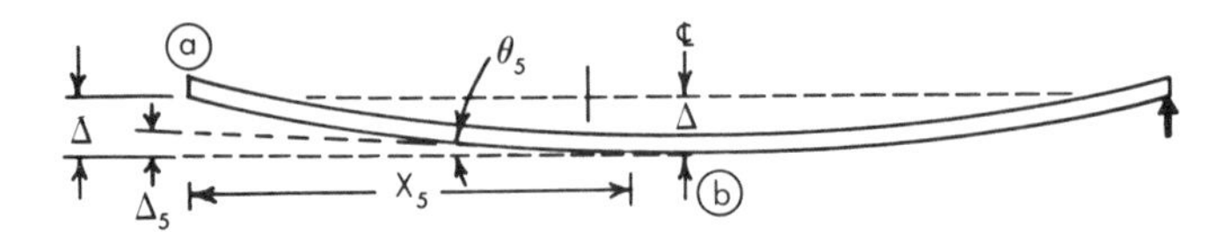

FIGURE 13

For each division, the moment of inertia (I_n), moment (M_n), and distance to the end (x) are determined and listed in table form.

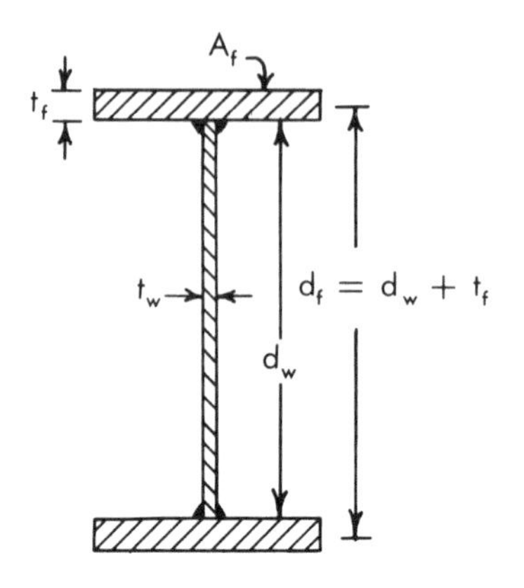

FIGURE 14

inertia. This method is described under Topics 5 and 7 of Section 2.5 on Deflection by Bending.

Problem 3

To compute the deflection of the tapered girder shown in Figure 13. This girder has a uniform load of 50 lbs/in., and a length of 50′ or 600″.

Using the area-moment method, the distance of point ⓐ from the tangent to point ⓑ equals the moment of the area under the moment diagram taken about point ⓐ, divided by the EI of the section.

Divide the girder into 10 equal lengths (s = 60″ long). The greater the number of divisions, the more accurate the answer will be.

	x	d_w	d_f	I_x	M_x	$\frac{M_x X}{I_x}$
①	30″	13,76″	14.26″	346.in.⁴	427.5 in.-k	37.2
②	90″	18.88″	19.38″	669.in.⁴	1147.5 in.-k	154.6
③	150″	24.00″	24.50″	1117.in.⁴	1687.5 in.-k	226.7
④	210″	29.12″	29.62″	1702.in.⁴	2047.5 in.-k	253.2
⑤	270″	34.24″	34.74″	2439.in.⁴	2227.5 in.-k	246.7
					Total →	918.4

Here, for each segment:

$$I_n = \frac{A_f \; d_f^2}{2} + \frac{t_w \; d_w^3}{12} \qquad \text{.................. (8)}$$

Since:

$$A_f = 3.0 \text{ in.}^2$$

$$t_w = 3/16''$$

The above formula, in this problem, reduces to:

$$I_n = 1.5 \; d_f^2 + \frac{d_w^3}{64}$$

Since:

$$\Delta_n = \frac{M_n \; s \; X_n}{E \; I_n}$$

$$\Delta = \frac{s}{E} \; \Sigma \; \frac{M_n \; X}{I_n} \qquad \text{...................... (9)}$$

and:

$$\Delta = \frac{(60)}{(30 \times 10^6)} \; 918.4$$

$$= 1.84''$$

Open-Web Expanded Beams and Girders

1. DESIGN CONCEPT

Dramatic savings can be obtained from an often forgotten design concept. The open-web expanded beam has already paid substantial dividends for various engineering firms. It should be considered on many more projects.

The opening up of a rolled beam increases its section modulus and moment of inertia, results in greater strength and rigidity. The reduction in beam weight has a chain effect on savings throughout the structure.

The open-web expanded beam is made economically by flame cutting a rolled beam's web in a zig-zag pattern along its centerline. See Figure 1. One of the two equal halves is then turned end for end and arc welded to the other half. The result is a deeper beam, stronger and stiffer than the original.

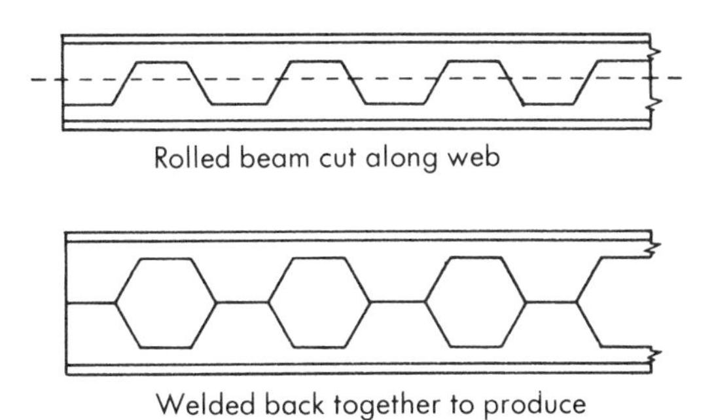

FIG. 1 Result: a deeper beam, stronger and stiffer than the original. Design starts with a lighter beam for immediate savings in material and handling costs. It often eliminates need for heavy built-up beam.

Starting the design with a lighter rolled beam realizes immediate savings in material and handling costs. There is no waste material with this method. It often eliminates the need for a heavy built-up beam.

In the design of buildings, the web opening is frequently used for duct work, piping, etc. which conventionally are suspended below the beam. See Figure 2. On this basis for equivalent strength, open-web expanded beams usually permit a reduction in the distance between ceiling below and floor above and thus provides savings in building height.

Oxygen flame cutting of the light beam web is

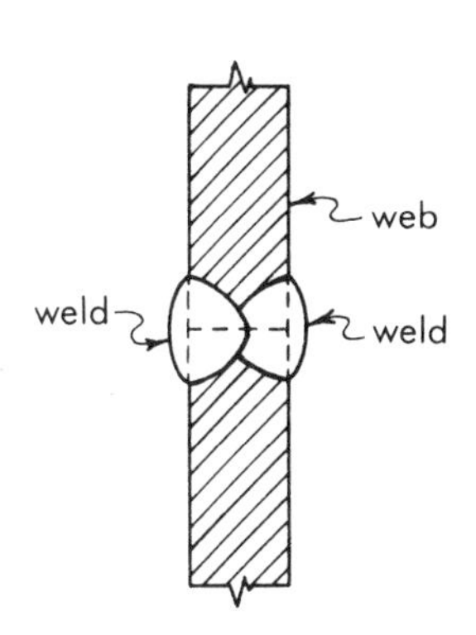

FIG. 2 Use semi-automatic arc welding to rejoin the two halves. A 100% fully penetrated butt weld can often be made with a single pass on each side of web without beveling.

relatively easy on a template-equipped machine.

The use of semi-automatic arc welding to rejoin the two halves enables good, sound welds to be made faster, more economically. Welding is confined to a portion of the web's total length. A 100% fully penetrated butt weld can usually be made with a single pass on each side of the web, without prior beveling of the edges. See Figure 2.

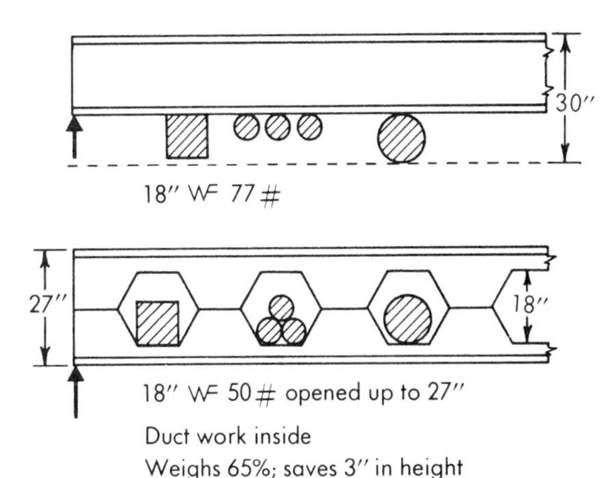

FIG. 3 Opening in web used for duct work, piping, etc., normally suspended below beam. For equivalent strength, open-web expanded beam usually reduces distance between ceiling below and floor above.

Cutting the zig-zag pattern along a slight angle to the beam axis results in a tapered open-web expanded beam. See Figure 4. This has many applications in roof framing, etc.

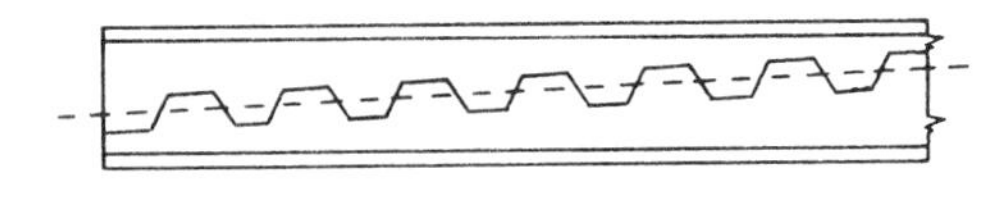

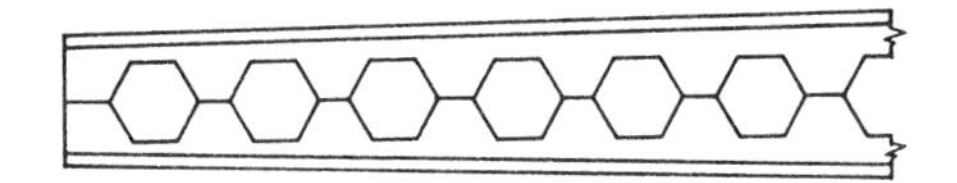

FIG. 4 Cutting the zig-zag pattern along an axis at slight angle to the beam results in tapered open-web expanded beam. This has many applications in roof framing, etc.

Two open-web expanded beams can sometimes be nested together to form a column having a high moment of inertia about both its x-x and y-y axes. See Figure 5.

2. GEOMETRY OF CUTTING PATTERN

The zig-zag cutting pattern and the resulting geometry of the web cut-out help determine properties of the section.

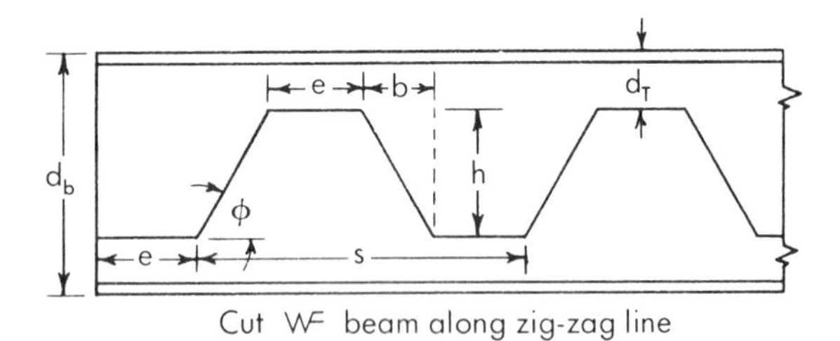

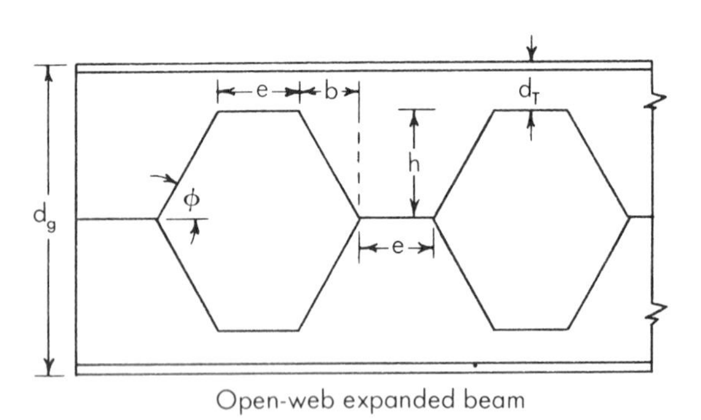

FIGURE 6

$$\tan \phi = \frac{h}{b} \qquad \text{or} \qquad b = \frac{h}{\tan \phi}$$

$$d_g = d_b + h \qquad \text{or} \qquad d_T = \frac{d_b - h}{2}$$

$$s = 2(b + e)$$

In general, the angle (ϕ) will be within about 45° minimum and about 70° maximum, with 45° and 60° being most commonly used. This angle must be

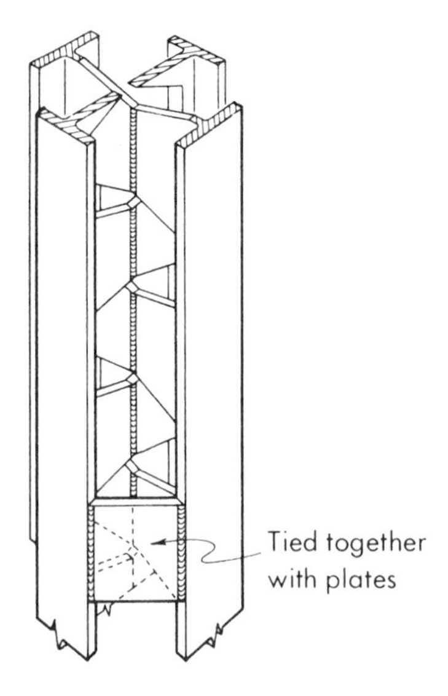

FIG. 5 Two open-web expanded beams can sometimes be nested together to form a column having a high moment of inertia about both its x-x and y-y axes.

sufficient to keep the horizontal shear stress along the web's neutral axis from exceeding the allowable; see Figure 7.

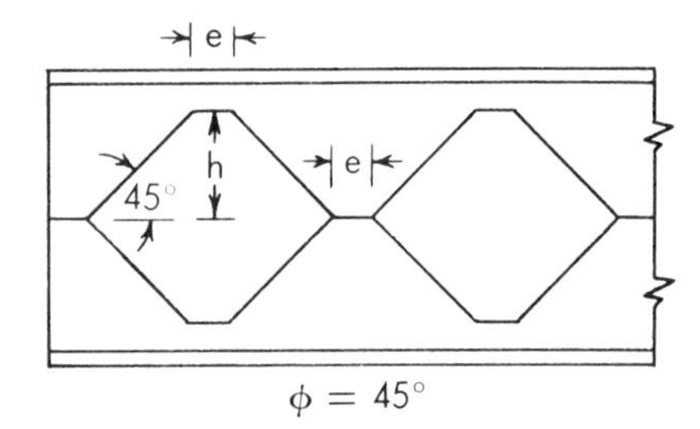

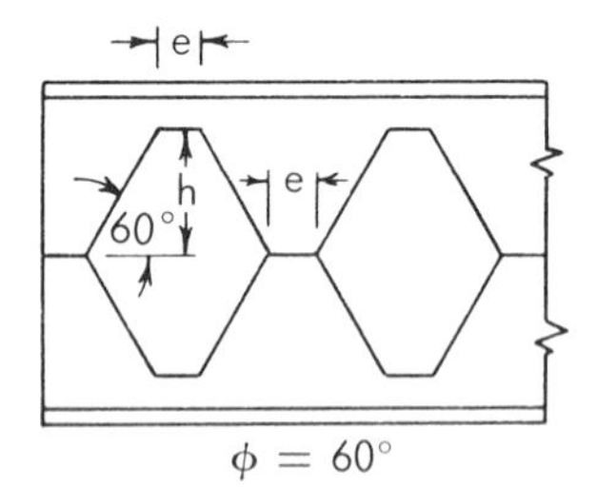

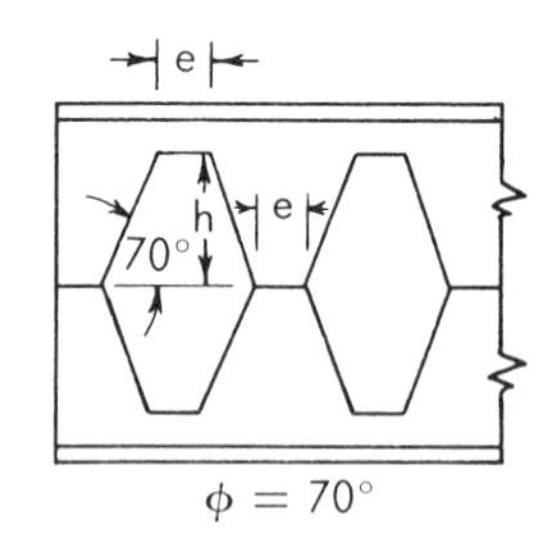

FIGURE 7

The distance (e) may be varied to provide the proper web opening for duct work, etc., and/or the proper distance for welding between openings. See Figure 8. However, as this distance (e) increases, the bending stress within the Tee section due to the applied shear force (V) increases. Thus, there is a limit to how large (e) may be.

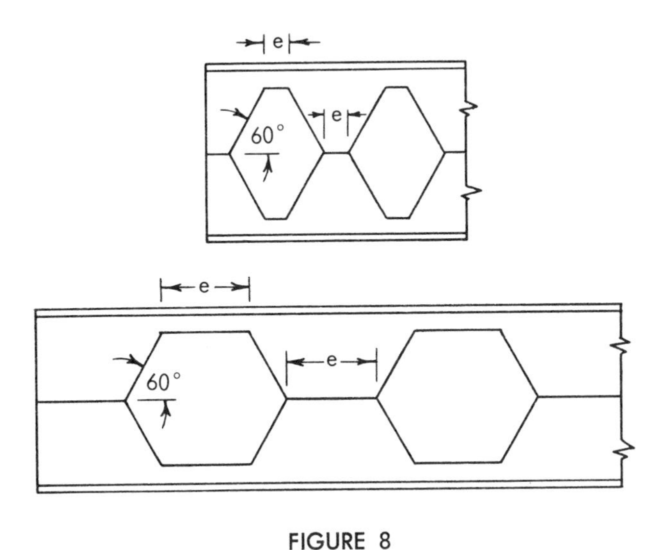

FIGURE 8

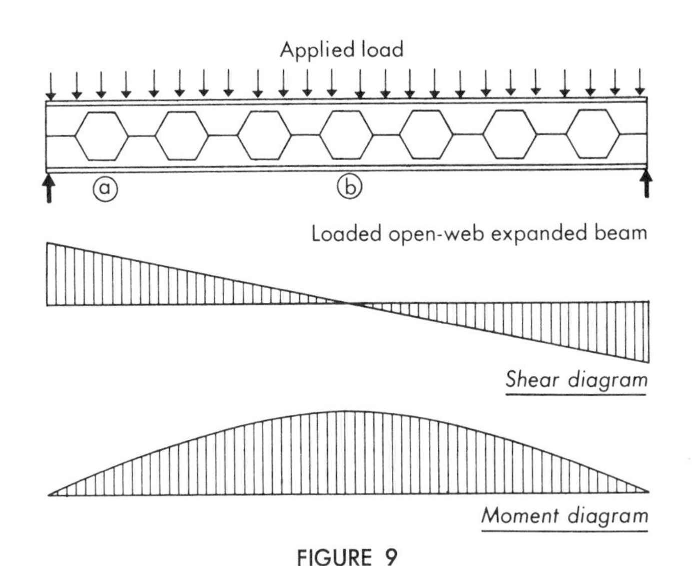

FIGURE 9

3. RESISTANCE TO APPLIED FORCES

Since the beam flanges carry most of the bending load, the loss of web area is not much of a problem as far as moment is concerned. However, shear (V) is carried by the web, and must be considered.

At each web opening, two Tee sections act as members of a frame in resisting vertical shear forces.

At midspan b , Figure 9, the shear (V) is minimum and may have little effect on the beam's strength. Approaching the support in the region of high shear a , the bending stress produced by this shear on the shallow Tee section must be added to the conventional bending stress from the applied beam load.

The bending moment due to shear is diagrammed in Figure 10. Usually, the point of inflection in top and bottom Tee sections due to the moment produced by shear, is assumed to be at mid-section of the opening (e/2). It is further assumed that the total vertical shear (V) at this point is divided equally between these two Tee sections, since they are of equal depth.

Actually, the design and stress behavior of an open-web expanded beam or girder is very similar to that of a Vierendeel truss. The primary design considerations are as follows:

1. The top and bottom portions of the girder are subjected to compression and tension bending stresses from the main bending moment, $\sigma_b = M/S_b$. There must be a continuity of these sections throughout the girder length to transfer these stresses. In addition, the compression portion must be checked for lateral sup-

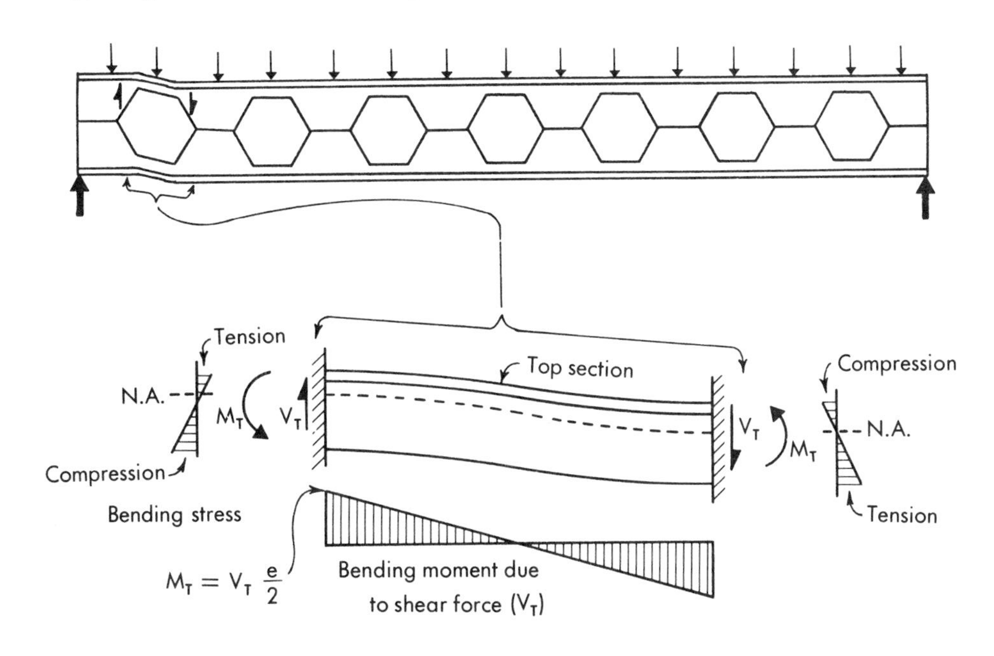

FIGURE 10

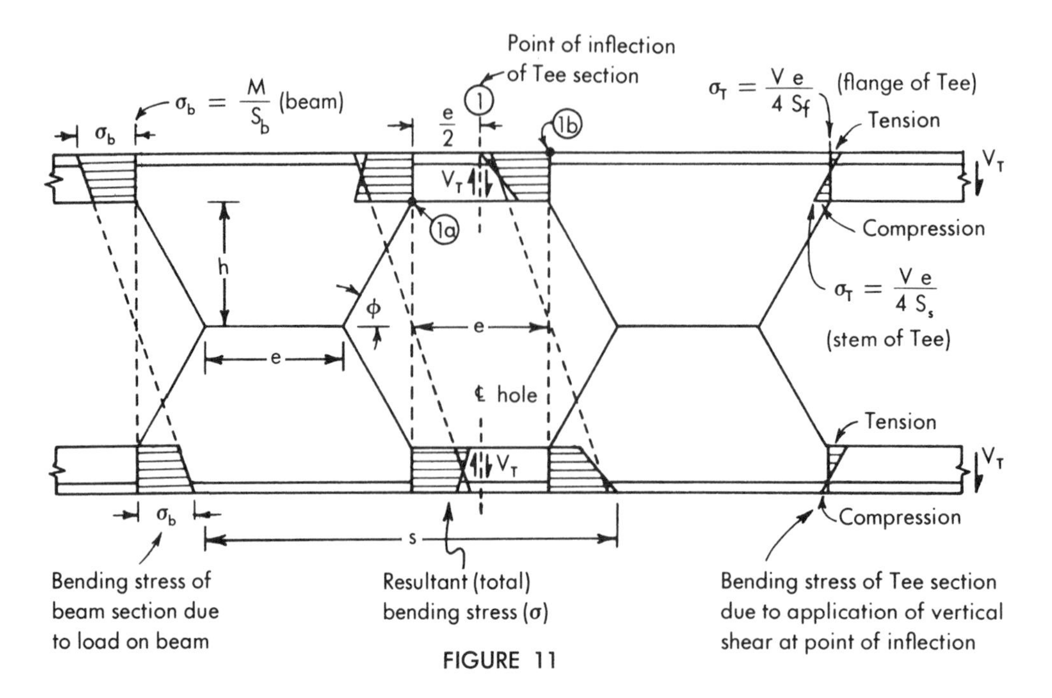

FIGURE 11

port, minimum width-to-thickness ratio, and allowable compressive stress; see the left end of Figure 11.

2. The vertical shear (V) in the girder is carried by the web, and produces vertical shear stresses in the web section, both in the solid portion of the web, and in the stem of the Tee section of the open portion.

3. In the open portion of the web, the vertical shear (V) is divided equally between the top and bottom Tee sections (assuming same depth of Tee sections). Assuming the shear is applied at the mid-opening, it will produce a bending moment on the cantilevered Tee section; see the right-hand end of Figure 11. The resulting secondary bending stresses

$$\sigma_T = \frac{V\ e}{4\ S}$$

must be added to those of the main bending moment, Item 1. If needed, a flange may be added around the inside of the web opening to give the Tee sections added strength.

4. The horizontal shear force (V_h) applied at the solid portion of the web along the girder's neutral axis may subject this portion to buckling. See Figure 20. The resulting compressive bending stress on this un-reinforced web section is important because of the possibility of this web section buckling under this stress.

5. The solid portion of the web may transfer a vertical axial force (compressive or tensile) equal to one-half of the difference between the applied vertical shears (V_1) and (V_2) at the end of any given unit panel of the girder. See Figure 27.

6. There should be 100% web depth at the points of support. Bearing stiffeners may be needed at the ends of the girder where reactions are applied.

4. TOTAL BENDING STRESS IN THE GIRDER

The main bending stress (σ_b) Item 1, acting on a section where the open Tee section starts, is assumed to increase linearly to a maximum at the outer fiber. To this stress must be added or subtracted, depending upon signs, the secondary bending stress (σ_T), Item 3. See central portion of Figure 11.

At point (1a)

Secondary bending stress at stem of Tee due to vertical shear (V) at Section (1), added to main bending stress at stem of Tee due to main moment (M) at Section (1a):

$$\sigma_{1a} = \frac{M_{1a}\ h}{I_g} + \frac{V_1\ e}{4\ S_s} \quad \text{.................. (1a)}$$

At point (1b)

Secondary bending stress at flange of Tee due to vertical shear (V) at Section (1), added to the main bending stress at flange of Tee due to main moment (M) at Section (1b):

$$\sigma_{1b} = \frac{M_{1b}\ d_g}{I_g\ 2} + \frac{V_1\ e}{4\ S_f} \quad \text{.................. (1b)}$$

Research at the University of Texas* indicated these main bending stresses in the Tee section do not increase linearly to a maximum at the outer fiber of the flange, but in some cases the reverse is true; the stress along the stem of the Tee section is higher than that at the outer fiber of the flange. For this reason, in their analysis, they calculated the bending force $F = M/d$ using the moment (M) on the girder at Section (1),

---

* "Experimental Investigations of Expanded Steel Beams", by M. D. Altfillisch; Thesis; Aug. 1952.

"Stress Distribution in Expanded Steel Beams", by R. W. Ludwig; Thesis; Jan. 1957.

"An Investigation of Welded Open Web Expanded Beams", by Altfillisch, Cooke, and Toprac; AWS Journal, Feb. 1957, p 77-s.

DEFINITIONS OF SYMBOLS

d = Distance between neutral axes of Tee section
d_b = Depth of original beam
d_g = Depth of expanded girder
e = Length of Tee section, also length of solid web section along neutral axis of girder.
h = Height of cut, or distance of expansion
A_T = Cross-sectional area of Tee section
I_g = Moment of inertia of open section of expanded girder
S_f = Section modulus of flange of Tee section
S_s = Section modulus of stem of Tee section

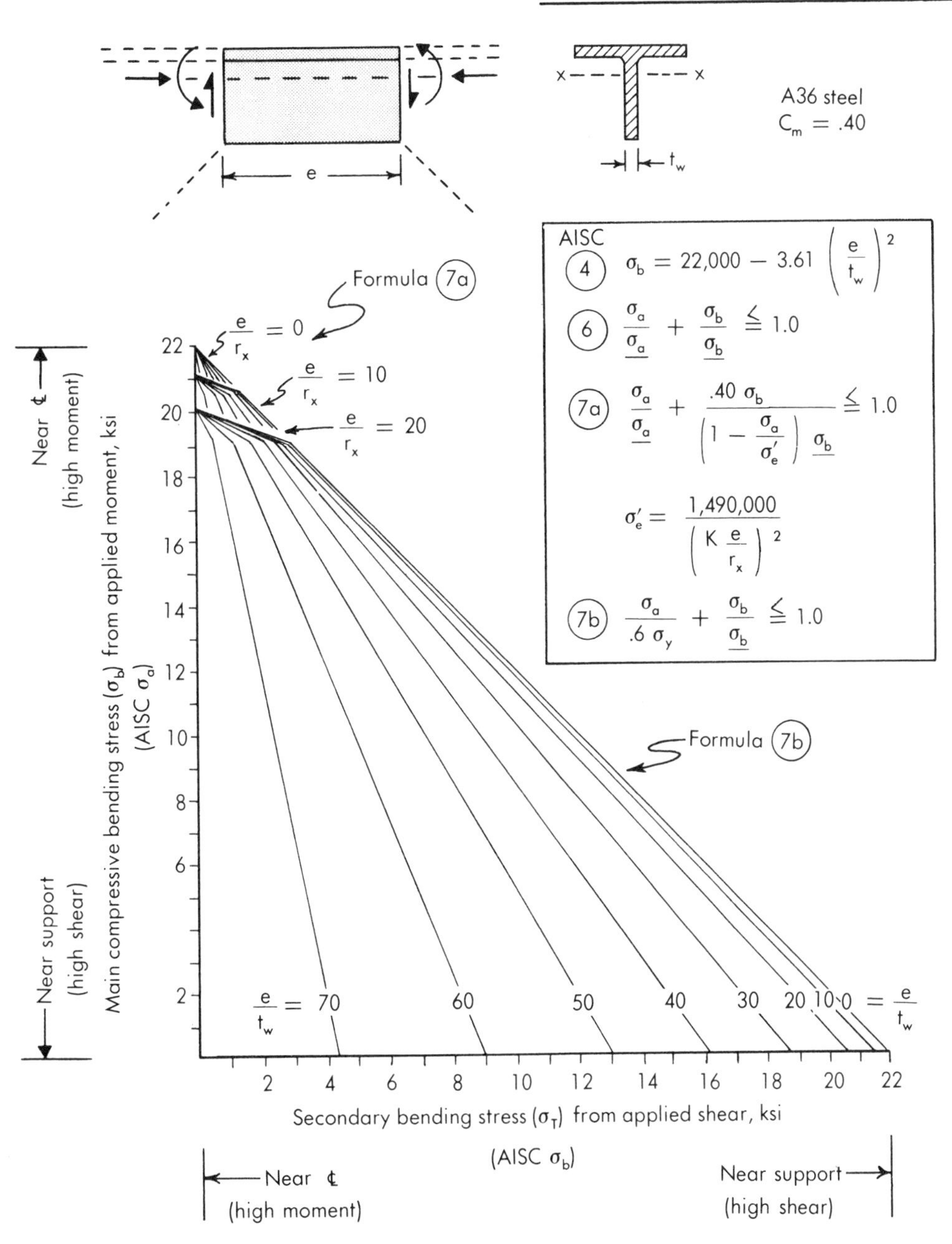

FIGURE 12

the point of inflection of the Tee section. This is convenient because it is the same section at which we assume the vertical shear (V) is applied for the secondary bending stress. They also assume this force (F) is uniformly distributed across the Tee section.

This simplifies the calculations, since for a given unit panel only one section must be considered for both the applied moment (M) and the applied shear (V). This is Section (1) at the point of inflection of the Tee section. Also, only one total bending stress is required for this section—the maximum secondary bending stress at the stem added to the average main bending stress. It does not require calculating at two different points—the stem at Section (1a) and the flange at Section (1b)

$$\boxed{\sigma_1 = \frac{M_1}{d\ A_T} + \frac{V_1\ e}{4\ S_s}} \quad \cdots\cdots (2)$$

since $F = \frac{M_1}{d}$ and

$$\sigma = \frac{F}{A_T} \quad \text{or} = \frac{M_1}{d\ A_T}$$

The main bending stress (σ_b) and secondary bending stress (σ_T) may be considered according to AISC Interaction Formulas 6, 7a, and 7b. These are shown graphically in Figure 12. (Note that AISC refers to main bending stress as σ_a and to secondary bending stress as σ_b.)

Buckling Due to Axial Compression

The Tee section, because it is subjected to axial compression, also must be checked against buckling according to AISC Sec 1.9.1. See Figure 13, and see Table 1 of limiting ratios for steels of various yield strengths.

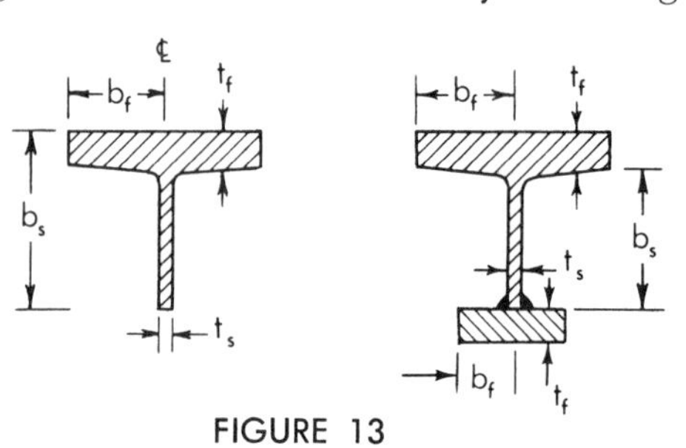

FIGURE 13

Tee Section Unstiffened	Tee Section Stiffened by Flange Welded Around Web Opening
$\frac{b_f}{t_f} \leq \frac{3000}{\sqrt{\sigma_y}}$	$\frac{b_f}{t_f} \leq \frac{3000}{\sqrt{\sigma_y}}$
$\frac{b_s}{t_s} \leq \frac{4000}{\sqrt{\sigma_y}}$	$\frac{b_s}{t_s} \leq \frac{8000}{\sqrt{\sigma_y}}$

Number of Points to Check Along Girder's Length

It will be desirable to check the proposed design at only a limited number of points to determine initially whether it will work.

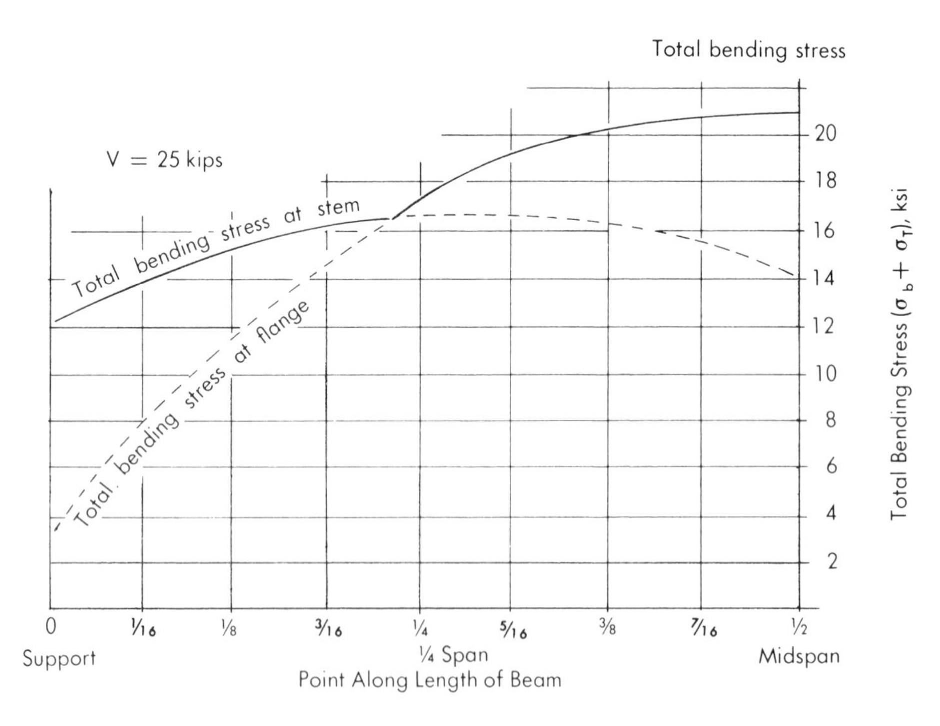

FIGURE 14

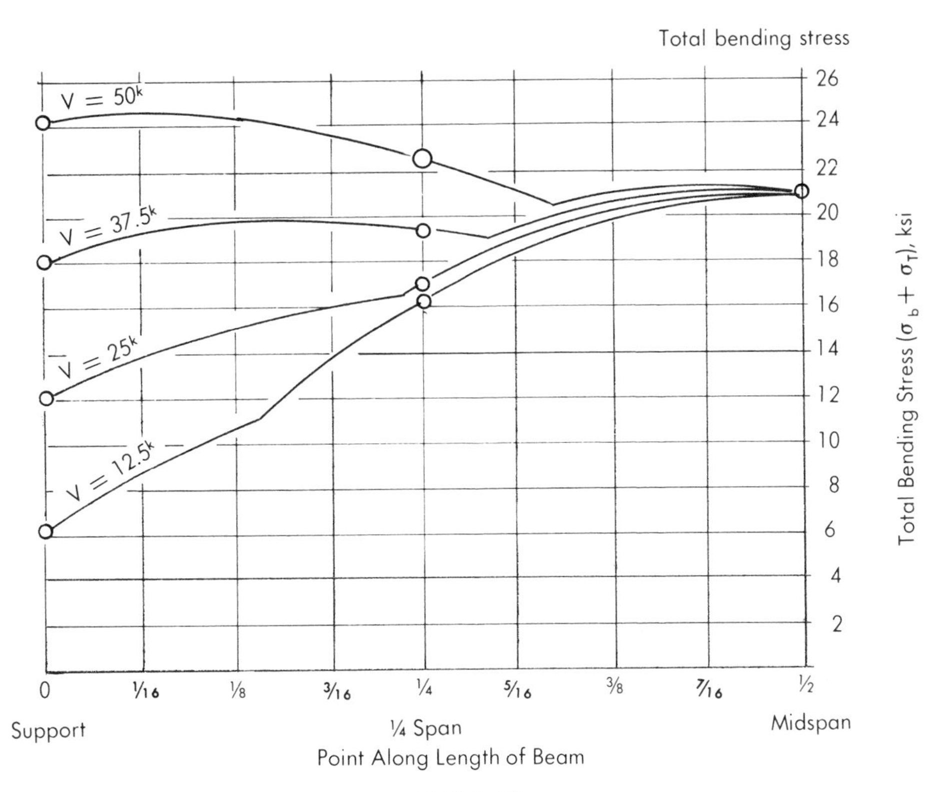

FIGURE 15

Referring to Figure 11, notice the bending stress (σ_b) from the applied moment is assumed to be maximum at the outer fibers of the flange. The bending stress (σ_T) from the applied shear is greatest at the stem of the Tee because its section modulus (S_s) is less than the section modulus at the outer flange (S_f). For this reason, combinations of bending stresses must be considered at the outer fibers of the flange as well as the stem of the Tee.

In Figure 14, the total bending stresses at the outer fiber of the flange as well as at the stem of the Tee section are plotted along the length of the beam. This data is from a typical design problem. In this case, the vertical shear at the support is V = 25 kips.

In Figure 15, the example has been reworked with different span lengths, and with different applied uniform loading so that the bending moment (and the bending stress due to this moment) remains the same. The shorter spans require an increased load, hence increased shear (V). The longer spans require a lower load, hence decreased shear (V).

Notice in Figure 15, that for short beams with higher shear force relative to bending moment, this curve for the total bending stress (moment and shear) will rise on the left-hand side, and the point of maximum stress will move to the left, or near the support. Of course there is a limit to how short and how high the vertical shear (V) may be, because this type of open web construction does weaken the web for shear. For very high shear loads, the opening in the expanded web would defeat its purpose, and a standard solid web beam or girder should be used. For longer spans, with relatively lower shear force to bending moment, this curve will lower, shifting the point of maximum stress to the right, or near the midspan.

An alternate method to finding the bending stress directly from the applied moment (M) is to convert the moment (M) into a concentrated force (F) applied at the center of gravity of the Tee section and assume it to be uniformly distributed across the section. See Figure 16.

TABLE 1—Limiting Ratios of Section Elements Under Compression

	$\frac{3{,}000}{\sqrt{\sigma_y}}$	$\frac{4{,}000}{\sqrt{\sigma_y}}$	$\frac{8{,}000}{\sqrt{\sigma_y}}$
33,000	16	22	44
36,000	16	21	42
42,000	15	20	39
45,000	14	19	38
46,000	14	19	37
50,000	13	18	36
55,000	13	17	34
60,000	12	16	33
65,000	12	16	31

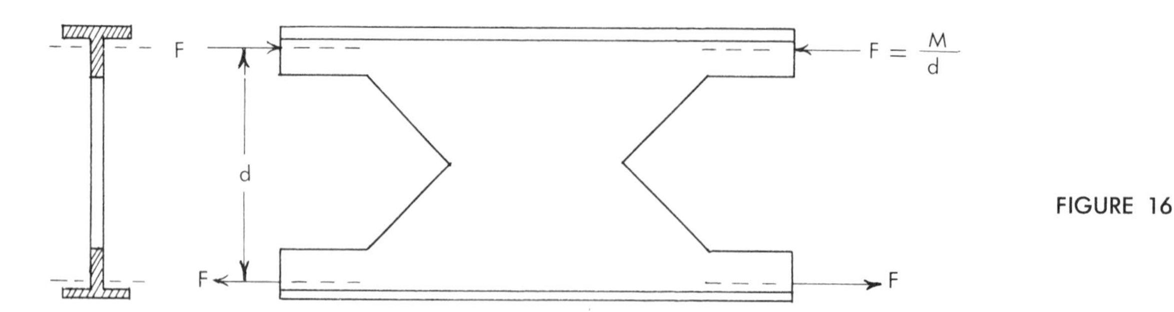

FIGURE 16

Then:

$$\sigma_b = \frac{F}{A_T} = \frac{M}{A_T\,d} \quad \text{......................} (3)$$

This bending stress is the same at the outer flange of the Tee section as well as the inner stem. It is now only necessary to add the greater bending stress from the applied shear (V) of the Tee section. Therefore, the smaller section modulus at the stem of the Tee section will be used, and only one set of total stress values will be considered.

In Figure 17, the applied moment (M) has been converted into a concentrated force (F) applied at the center of gravity of the Tee section and assumed to be uniformly distributed across the section.

This illustrates that the point of maximum combination of bending stresses due to applied shear and applied moment lies somewhere between 1) the support (region of high vertical shear) and 2) the midspan (region of high bending moment). This point of maximum stress is indicated in Figure 17 by an arrow.

Unless the beam is examined as in Figure 17 for the maximum stress all the way between the support and midspan, it would be well to check a third point in addition to the support and midspan. A convenient point would be at ¼ span.

5. HORIZONTAL SHEAR STRESS

There are three methods of checking the horizontal shear stress along the beam's neutral axis (N.A.):

1. Use the conventional formula for shear stress,

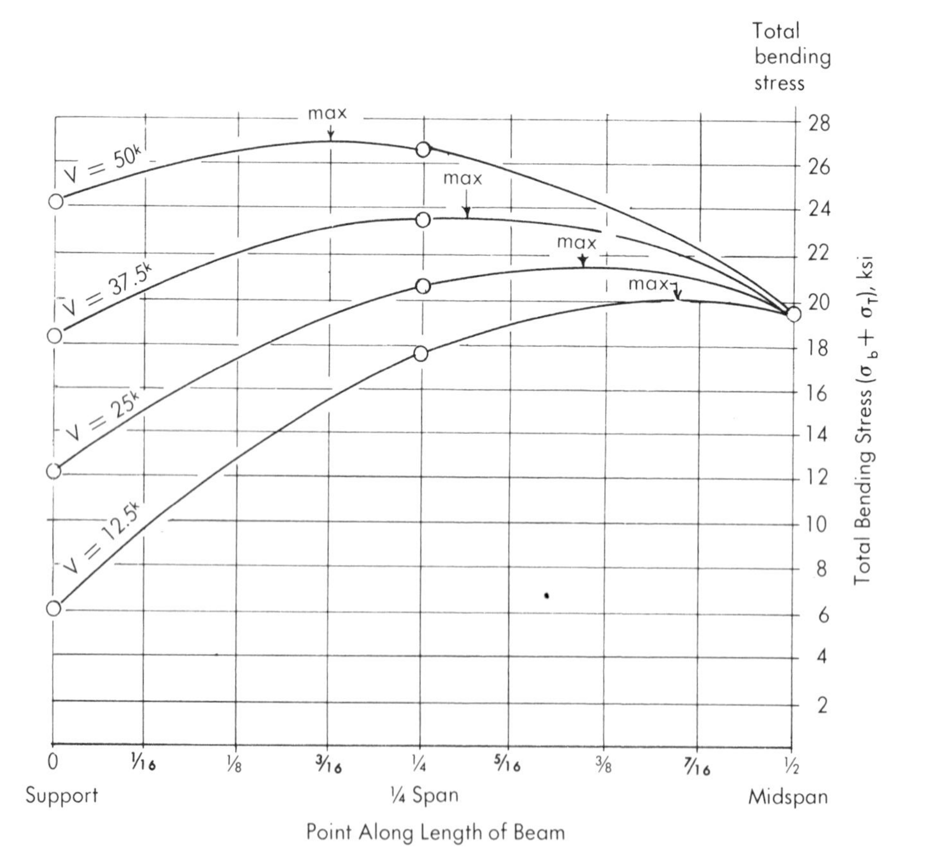

FIGURE 17

assuming the web to be solid $\left(\tau = \frac{V\,a\,y}{I\,t} \right)$. Then increase this stress by the ratio of overall web segment to net web segment (s/e) to account for only a portion (e/s) of the web along the neutral axis being solid.

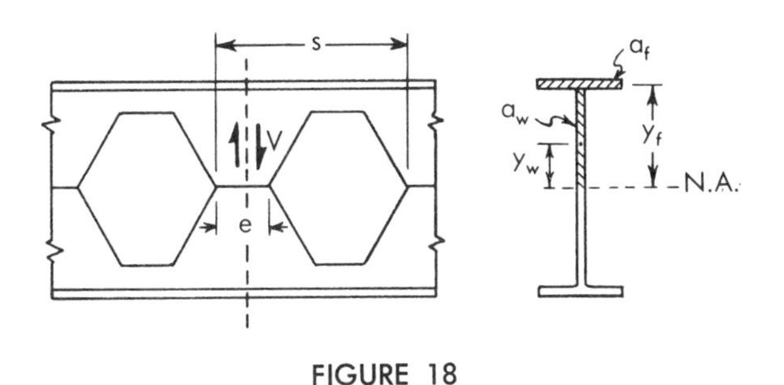

FIGURE 18

$$\boxed{\tau_h = \frac{V\,a\,y}{I\,t}\left(\frac{s}{e}\right) = \frac{V(a_f y_f + a_w y_w)}{I\,t_w}\left(\frac{s}{e}\right)} \quad \cdots (4)$$

2. Treat a top segment of the beam as a free body acted upon by the bending moment force. The difference in this force from one end of the segment to the other is transferred out as horizontal shear along the neutral axis into the similar section below. This horizontal shear force is then divided by the net area of the solid portion of the web section along the neutral axis. See Figure 19.

By substitution:

$V_h = \frac{M_2 - M_1}{d}$ which acts along distance (e).

This horizontal shear force is then divided by the net area of the solid web section ($e\,t_w$) to give the shear stress:

$$\boxed{\tau_h = \frac{M_2 - M_1}{d\,e\,t_w}} \quad \cdots\cdots\cdots\cdots (5)$$

3. Using the same free body, Figure 19, take moments about point (y):

$$\frac{V_1}{2}\left(\frac{s}{2}\right) + \frac{V_2}{2}\left(\frac{s}{2}\right) - V_h\,\frac{d}{2} = 0$$

$$\text{or } V_h = (V_1 + V_2)\left(\frac{s}{2\,d}\right)$$

Assuming that $\frac{V_1 + V_2}{2} = V_x$, the average vertical shear at this point, this becomes—

$$V_h = V_x\left(\frac{s}{d}\right)$$

and

$$\boxed{\tau_h = \frac{V_h}{t_w\,e}} \quad \cdots\cdots\cdots\cdots (6)$$

6. WEB BUCKLING DUE TO HORIZONTAL SHEAR FORCE

The web of a *conventional plate girder* may have to have transverse intermediate stiffeners to keep it from buckling due to the diagonal compressive stresses resulting from the applied shear stresses. If stiffeners are used, the girder will have a higher carrying capacity. This is because the web, even though at the point of buckling, is still able to carry the diagonal tensile stresses, while the stiffener will transfer the compressive forces. The web of the girder then functions as the web of a truss.

However, in the *open-web expanded girder,* treated as a Vierendeel truss, the open portion prevents any tension acting in the web. Therefore, a transverse stiffener on the solid web section will not function as the vertical compression member for truss-like action.

Since this solid portion of the web is isolated to some extent, the horizontal shear force (V_h) applied along the neutral axis of the beam will stress this web portion in bending.

The simplest method of analysis would be to consider a straight section (n), Figure 20. However, the resulting bending stress acting vertically would somehow have to be resolved about an axis parallel to the

FIGURE 19

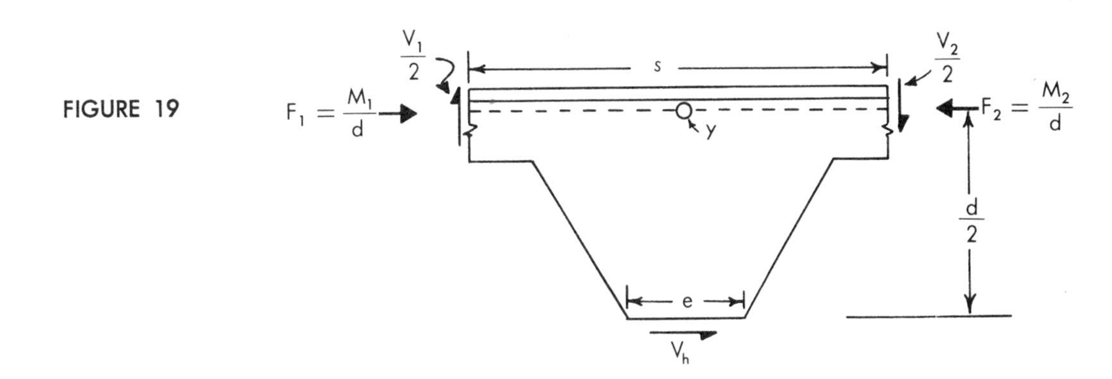

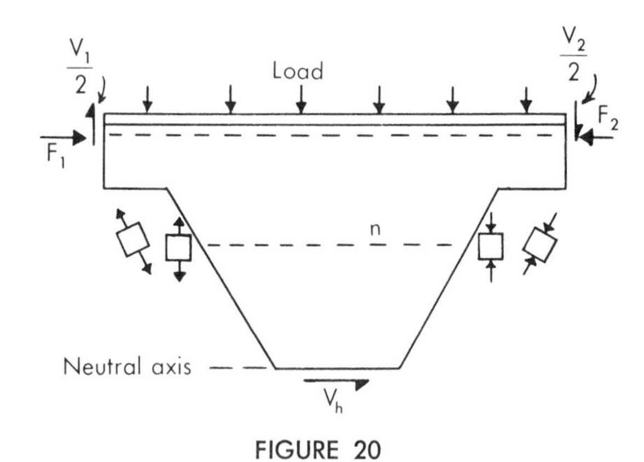

FIGURE 20

sloping edge of this tapered web section.

One method by which tapered beams and knees are analyzed is the Wedge Method, originally proposed by W. R. Osgood and later modified by H. C. Olander (ASCE Transaction paper 2698, 1954). With this method, Figure 21, the non-parallel sides are extended out to where they intersect; this becomes point 0. From this point as a center, an arc is drawn through the wedge section representing the section (a) to be considered. The section modulus of this curved section is determined.

The actual forces and moments applied to the member are then transferred out to point 0. The horizontal force (V_h) will cause a moment at point 0.

It can be shown that these forces and moments acting at point 0 cause the bending stresses on the curved section (a) of the wedge; see Figure 22.

Moment acting on curved section (a):

$$M = V_h\, \rho - M_o$$
$$= V_h\, \rho - V_o\, f$$
$$= V_h\, (\rho - f)$$

Radial bending stress on this curved section (a):

$$\boxed{\sigma_r = \frac{M}{S} = \frac{V_h\,(\rho - f)}{S}} \qquad (7)$$

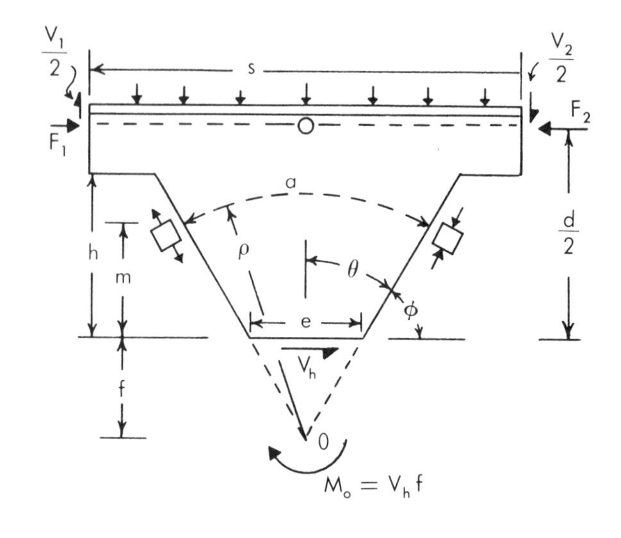

FIGURE 21

where

$$\boxed{f = \frac{e}{2\,\tan\,\theta}} \qquad (8)$$

Since:

$$\rho = \frac{m + f}{\cos\,\theta} \text{ or}$$

$$\boxed{\rho = \frac{m}{\cos\,\theta} + \frac{e}{2\,\sin\,\theta}} \qquad (9)$$

Since:

$$a = 2\,\pi\,\rho\,\frac{2\,\theta}{2\,\pi}$$
$$= 2\,\rho\,\theta \text{ and}$$
$$S = \frac{t_w\, a^2}{6}$$

$$\boxed{S = \frac{2}{3}\, t_w\, \rho^2\, \theta^2}$$

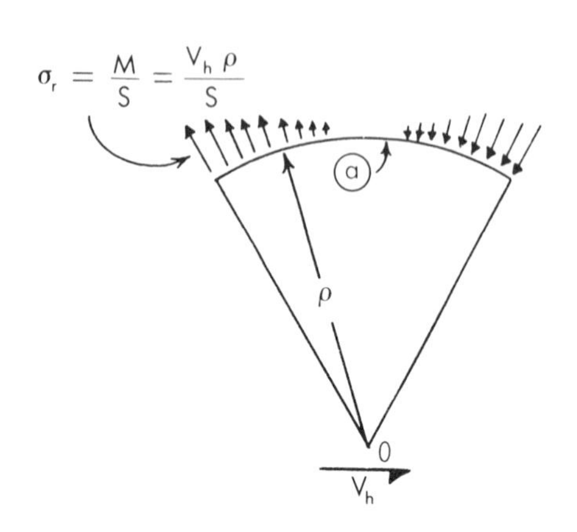

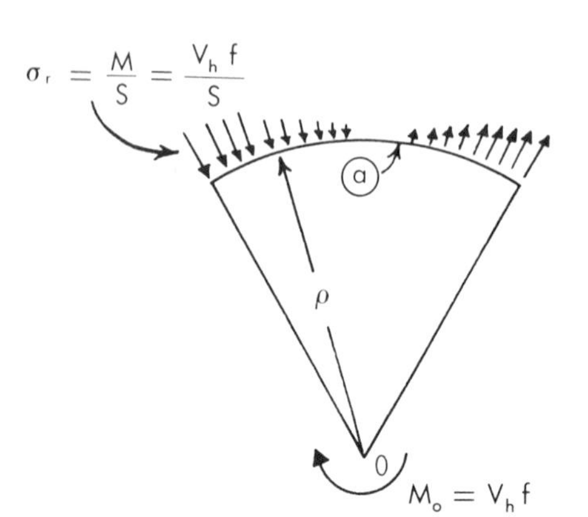

FIGURE 22

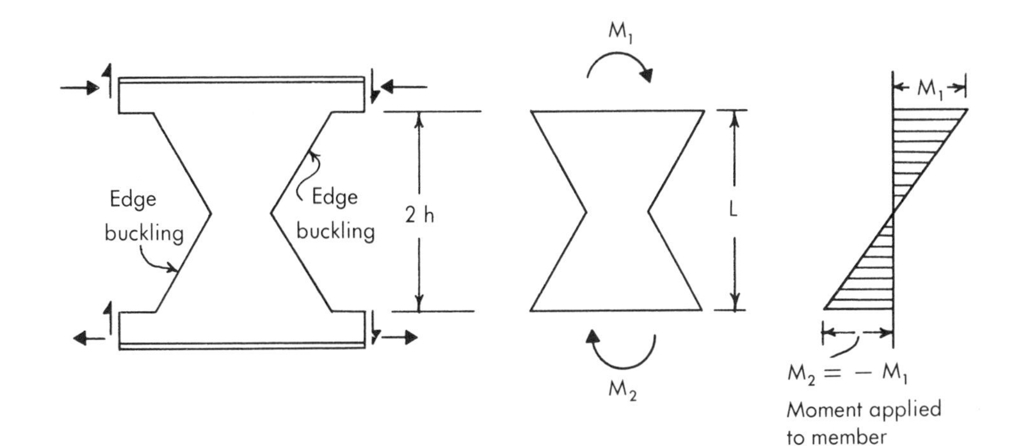

FIGURE 23

Therefore, the radial bending stress along curved section (a):

$$\sigma_r = \frac{3\ V_h\ (\rho - f)}{2\ t_w\ \rho^2\ \theta^2} \quad \dots\dots\dots\dots\dots\dots\dots (10)$$

It can be shown that the curved section (a) having the greatest bending stress (σ_r) occurs at a distance of:

$$m = \frac{e}{\tan\theta}\left(\cos\theta - \frac{1}{2}\right) \leqq h \quad \dots\dots\dots (11)$$

This value of (m) will be less than (h) and may be used in the following Formula 12 if (e) does not exceed these values—

for $\theta = 45°$, $e \leqq 4.83\ h$
for $\theta = 30°$, $e \leqq 1.58\ h$

For most designs, this would be true and Formula 12 could be used directly without first solving for (m) in Formula 11.

This value of (m) for the position of the greatest bending stress may be inserted back into Formula 10, and the following will give the greatest bending stress along (a):

$$\underset{(max)}{\sigma_r} = \frac{3\ V_h\ \tan\theta}{4\ t_w\ e\ \theta^2} \quad \dots\dots\dots\dots\dots\dots\dots (12)$$

The next step is to determine the allowable compressive bending stress ($\underline{\sigma}$). If the above bending stress in the solid portion of the web (σ_r) is excessive, it might be possible to increase the distance (e). However, this will also increase the length of the Tee section, resulting in increase of the secondary bending stress in the Tee section (σ_T). As an alternative to increasing distance (e), it would be possible to stiffen the outer edge of this wedge portion of the web by adding a flange around the edge of the hole in the web in the particular panel which is overstressed.

Allowable Compressive Bending Stress

There are two suggestions for determining the allowable compressive bending stress along the sloping edge of the wedge section of the web:

1. Treat this section as a prismatic member and apply AISC Sec. 1.5.1.4.5 Formula 4; see Figure 23. AISC Formula (4) for allowable compressive stress:

$$\underline{\sigma} = \left[1.0 - \frac{(L/r)^2}{2\ C_c^2\ C_b}\right] .60\ \sigma_y$$

where

$$C_b = 1.75 - 1.05\left(\frac{M_1}{M_2}\right) + .3\left(\frac{M_1}{M_2}\right)^2 \leqq 2.3$$

and

$$C_c = \sqrt{\frac{2\ \pi^2\ E}{\sigma_y}}$$

See additional notes, Section 3.1.

Since $M_1 = -M_2$ in the above formula, $C_b = 2.83$; but since it cannot exceed 2.3 therefore $C_b = 2.3$ and AISC Formula (4) becomes—

$$\underline{\sigma} = \left[1.0 - \frac{10.434}{C_c^2}\left(\frac{h}{t_w}\right)^2\right] .60\ \sigma_y \quad \dots . (13)$$

See Table 2 for values of Formula 13 for various steels.

2. As an alternate method, treat this as a canti-

TABLE 2—Allowable Compressive Stress On Wedge Section of Open-Web Girder *For Various Steels*

Steel's Yield Strength σ_y	Allowable Compresive Stress $\underline{\sigma}$
36,000	$22{,}000 - 14.44 \left(\frac{h}{t_w}\right)^2$
42,000	$25{,}000 - 19.15 \left(\frac{h}{t_w}\right)^2$
45,000	$27{,}000 - 22.14 \left(\frac{h}{t_w}\right)^2$
46,000	$27{,}500 - 23.04 \left(\frac{h}{t_w}\right)^2$
50,000	$30{,}000 - 27.34 \left(\frac{h}{t_w}\right)^2$
55,000	$33{,}000 - 33.10 \left(\frac{h}{t_w}\right)^2$
60,000	$36{,}000 - 39.35 \left(\frac{h}{t_w}\right)^2$
65,000	$39{,}000 - 46.27 \left(\frac{h}{t_w}\right)^2$

lever beam, and measure its unsupported length (L) from the point of inflection (e) to the support; see Figure 24.

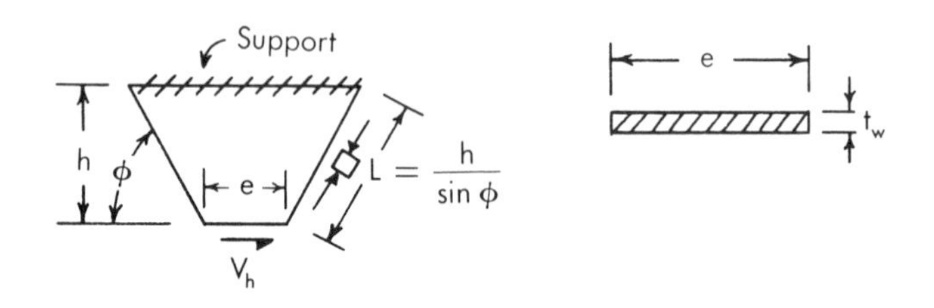

FIGURE 24

where:

$$r = \frac{t_w}{\sqrt{12}} = .29\ t_w$$

Consider the outer fiber of this cantilever as an element in compression. Using the resulting (L/r) ratio, determine the allowable compressive stress from the AISC tables.

Allowable Shear Stress

From either Formula 13 or the above Method 2, we obtain the allowable compressive bending stress ($\underline{\sigma}$). Since $V_h = \tau\ t_w\ e$ and holding the maximum bending stress (σ_r) of Formula 12 to the allowable ($\underline{\sigma}$), we obtain the following—

$$\sigma_r = \frac{3\ V_h \tan\theta}{4\ t_w\ e\ \theta^2}$$

$$= \frac{3\ \tau_a\ t_w\ e \tan\theta}{4\ t_w\ e\ \theta^2} \leq \underline{\sigma}$$

or:

$$\boxed{\underline{\tau} \leq \frac{4\ \theta^2}{3\ \tan\theta}\ \underline{\sigma} \leq .40\ \sigma_y} \quad \text{.............}(14)$$

Formula 14 for allowable shear stress ($\underline{\tau}$) has been simplified for various angles of cut (θ); see Table 3.

If the allowable shear stress ($\underline{\tau}$) in this web section is held within the value shown in Formula 14, no further check of web buckling due to the compressive bending stress will have to be made, nor will this edge have to be reinforced with a flange.

To keep the resulting shear stress within this allowable, either (t_w) or (e) may have to be increased; see Figure 25.

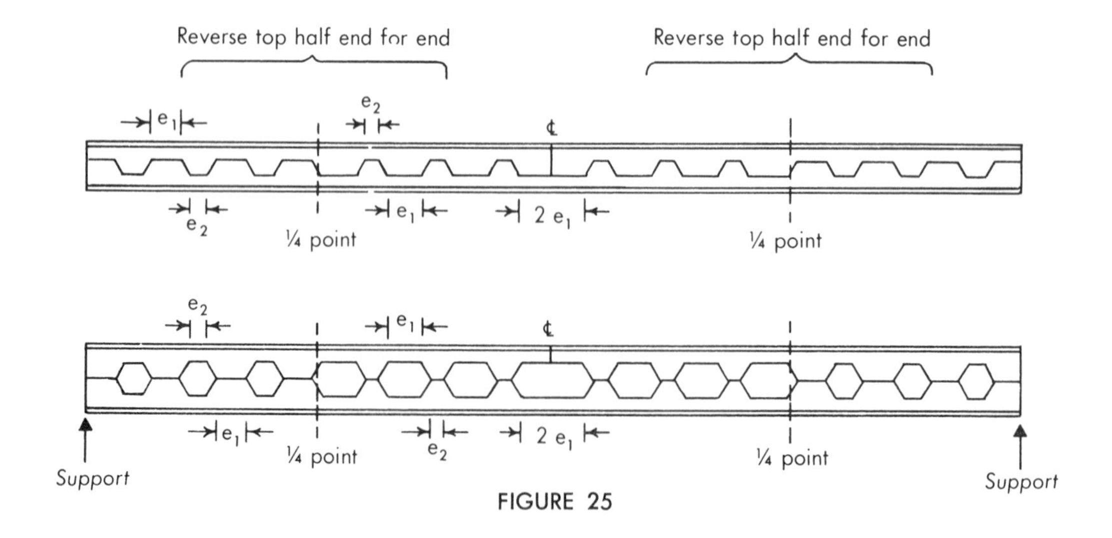

FIGURE 25

Adjusting the Distance of Cut (e)

The distance (e) may be varied to provide the proper strength of the web, or the proper opening for duct work; see Figure 8. However, as this distance (e) increases, the secondary bending stress within the Tee section due to the applied shear force (V) also increases.

In other words, (e) must be sufficiently large to provide proper strength in the web section, yet must be small enough to provide proper bending strength in the Tee section. In both cases, these stresses are caused directly by the applied vertical shear (V) on the member. This becomes more critical near the supports where the shear is the highest. Larger trial WF beam sections are chosen until the value of (e) will satisfy both conditions.

It would be possible to gradually vary the size of the openings from the support to the centerline; however, this would be difficult to fabricate. If this is desired, it might be better to use two dimensions of horizontal cut (e_1) and (e_2), alternating them and reversing their order at the ¼ point. See Figure 25. This would allow a larger value of (e_1) for the strength of the web and a smaller value of (e_2) for the strength of the Tee section, near the support in the region of high shear (V). In the central region of the girder between the ¼ points where the shear (V) is one-half of this value or less, these values will reverse, resulting in the smaller value of (e_2) for the web and the larger value of (e_1) for the Tee.

The top portion of the cut WF beam would be cut in half and each half turned end for end. This will require a butt groove weld. However, this top section is in compression and the requirement for the weld will not be as severe as though it were in the bottom tensile chord. It might be possible to make this compression butt joint by fillet welding splice bars on each side of the Tee section. This lap joint would transfer the compressive force; the splice bars would apply additional stiffness and therefore a higher allowable compressive stress for this Tee section at midspan.

TABLE 3—Allowable Shear Stress For Various Angles of Cut

$\phi = 45°$	$\theta = 45°$	$\tau_a \leqq .8225\ \sigma_a$
$\phi = 50°$	$\theta = 40°$	$\tau_a \leqq .7745\ \sigma_a$
$\phi = 55°$	$\theta = 35°$	$\tau_a \leqq .7106\ \sigma_a$
$\phi = 60°$	$\theta = 30°$	$\tau_a \leqq .6332\ \sigma_a$

This cutting pattern results in the hole at the centerline having twice the length as the others. However, this is the region of only high moment (M); there is almost no shear (V). This section should be sufficient if it can develop the required compression from the main bending load.

Stiffening Edge of Wedge Section

The edge of the wedge section of the web may be strengthened against buckling due to the horizontal shear force, by adding a flange around the web opening. See Figure 26.

Here:

$$S = A_f\, a + \frac{t_w\, a^2}{6}$$

$$= 2\, A_f\, \rho\, \theta + \frac{2}{3}\, t_w\, \rho^2\, \theta^2$$

Inserting this into Formula 7, we get—

$$\sigma_r = \frac{V_h\, (\rho - f)}{2\, A_f\, \rho\, \theta + ⅔\, t_w\, \rho^2\, \theta^2} \quad \text{...........(15)}$$

It can be shown that the value of (m) for the position of the greatest bending stress is—

$$m = \left(\cos\theta\left[1 + \sqrt{1 + \frac{3\, A_f}{f\, t_w\, \theta}}\right] - 1\right) \leqq h \quad .(16)$$

FIGURE 26

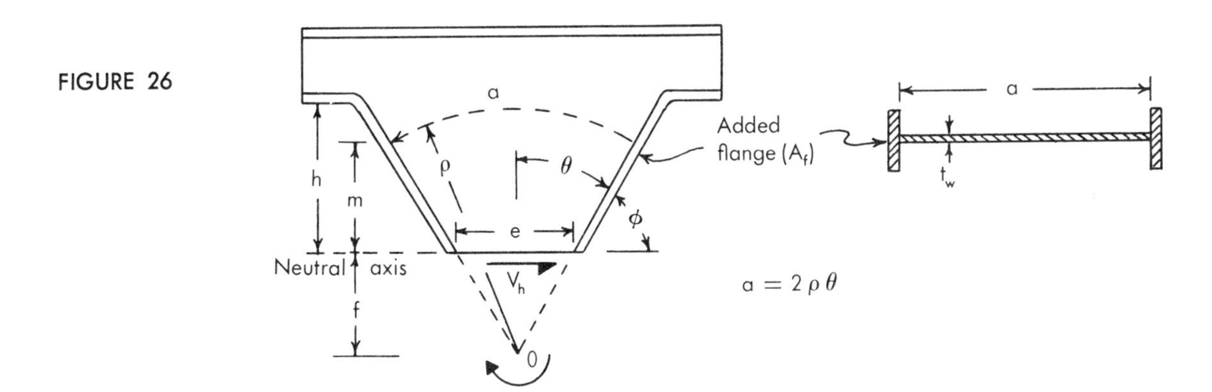

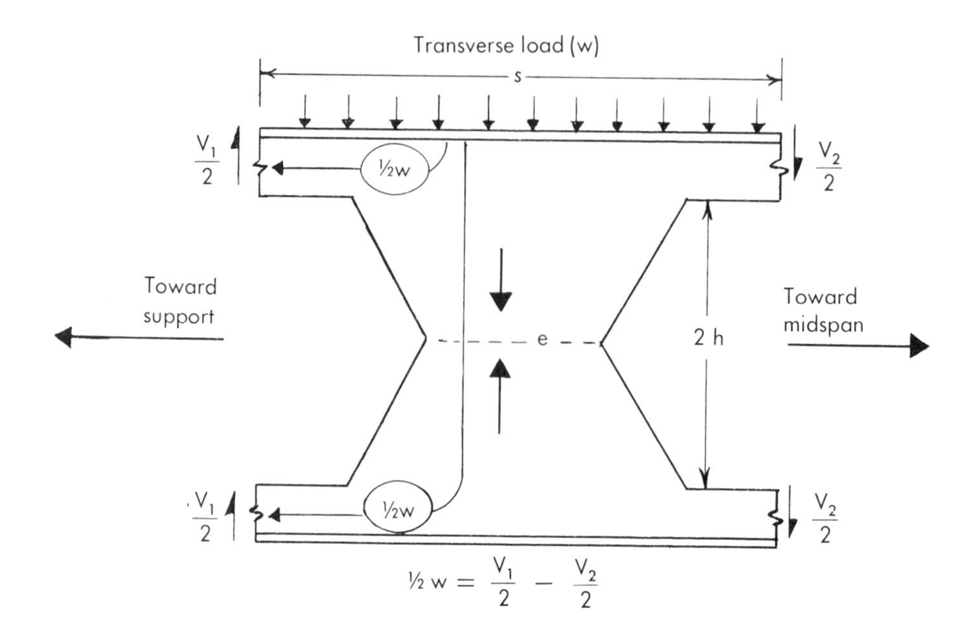

FIGURE 27

This value of (m) could then be used in Formula 12 for the bending stress. This would give the following formula for the greatest bending stress:

$$\sigma_r = \frac{\frac{V_h}{2\,\theta}\sqrt{1 + \frac{2\,A_f}{K}}}{K + 2\,A_f + (K + A_f)\sqrt{1 + \frac{2\,A_f}{K}}} \qquad (17)$$

where:

$$K = \frac{2\,t_w\,\theta}{3\,f}$$

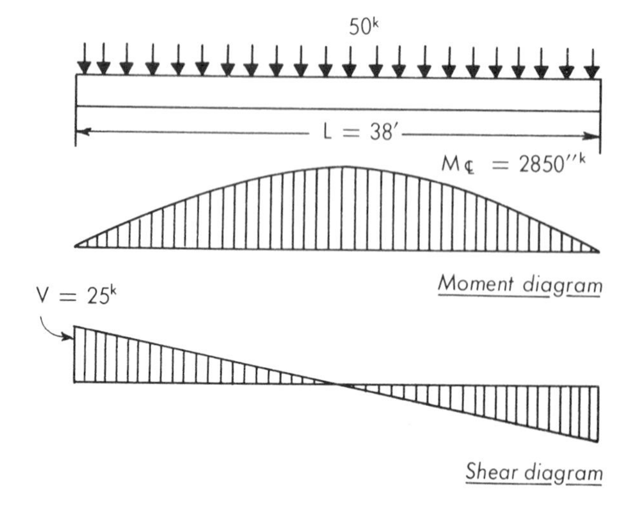

FIGURE 28

7. WEB BUCKLING DUE TO COMPRESSION

Any direct transverse load applied to the upper flange of the open-web girder is carried as vertical shear on the web. See Figure 27. Since this resisting shear is equally divided between the top and bottom Tee section chords, half of this transverse load applied to a unit panel segment of the girder (distance s) must be transferred as compression down through the solid portion (e) of the web into the bottom chord.

If it is felt that this solid web section, acting as a column, cannot handle this force, it could be reinforced with a transverse (vertical) stiffener. Usually this force, one-half of the applied transverse load with the segment (s), is small. Thus, the resulting compressive stress within this web section (e) is low, and stiffening is not usually required.

Compressive stress in web section (e):

$$\sigma = \frac{w}{2\,e\,t_w} = \frac{V_1 - V_2}{2\,e\,t_w} \qquad \ldots\ldots\ldots\ldots\ldots (18)$$

The allowable compressive stress would be found in the AISC tables, using —

$$L = 2\,h$$

$$r = \frac{t_w}{\sqrt{12}} = .29\,t_w$$

8. GENERAL OUTLINE FOR DESIGN OF OPEN-WEB EXPANDED GIRDER

Design of an open-web expanded girder will be facilitated by following the design outline below. Its application is demonstrated by working a typical design problem: Design an open-web expanded girder with a span of 38 ft to support a uniformly-distributed load of 50 kip. Design on the basis of using A36 steel and E70 welds, and angle of cut $\phi = 45°$. See Figure 28.

STEP 1. Determine the expanded girder's required section modulus (S_g) at midspan for the main bending moment:

$$\boxed{S_g = \frac{M_{\text{℄}}}{\sigma}}$$

$$S_g = \frac{2850''^{k}}{22{,}000 \text{ psi}} = 130 \text{ in.}^3$$

STEP 2. For the relationship of the expanded girder's depth to that of the original beam, let—

$$\boxed{K_1 = \frac{d_g}{d_b}}$$

Assume it = about 1.5

STEP 3. Select a trial WF beam having a section modulus of—

$$\boxed{S_b = \frac{S_g}{K_1}}$$

$$S_b = \frac{130}{1.5} = 86.4 \text{ in.}^3 \text{ (use this as a guide)}$$

Try an *18″ WF 50#/ft beam,* having $S_b = 89.0$ in.^{3}

Now, refigure K_1 using the S_b of the actual selected beam:

$$\boxed{K_1 = \frac{S_g}{S_b}}$$

$$K_1 = \frac{130}{89} = 1.46$$

STEP 4. Determine the height of cut (h) and round off to the nearest inch or fraction of an inch:

$$\boxed{h = d_b\,(K_1 - 1)}$$

$$h = 18.0\,(1.46 - 1) = 8.3'' \textit{ or use } 8''$$

However, (h) cannot exceed the following value in order to keep the vertical shear stress in the stem of the Tee section within the allowable:

$$\boxed{d_T \geqq \frac{V^*}{2\, t_w\, \tau}} \quad \text{where } \tau = .40\, \sigma_y$$

$$d_T = \frac{25^k}{2(.358)(14{,}500)} = 2.41''$$

$$\boxed{h \leqq d_b - 2\, d_T}$$

$$h = 18 - 2(2.41) = 13.18'' > 8'' \qquad OK$$

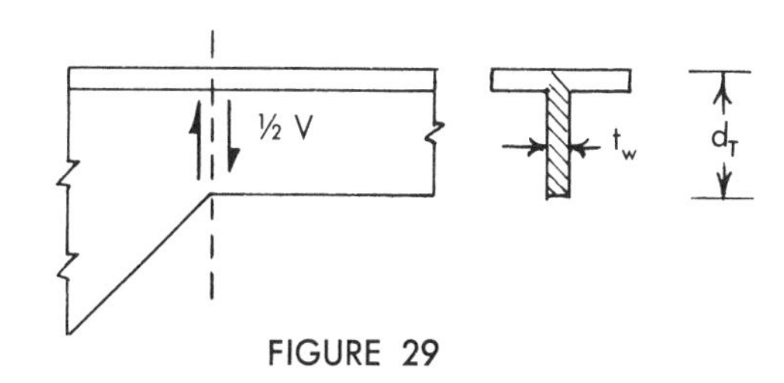

FIGURE 29

STEP 5. Then

$$\boxed{d_g = d_b + h}$$

$$d_g = 18 + 8 = 26''$$

$$\boxed{d_T = \frac{d_g}{2} - h}$$

$$d_T = \frac{26}{2} - 8 = 5''$$

$$\boxed{d_s = d_T - t_f}$$

$$d_s = 5 - .57 = 4.43''$$

STEP 6. Determine the allowable compressive bending stress on wedge section of web, using modified AISC Sec 1.5.1.4.5 Formula (4):

$$\boxed{\sigma = \left[1.0 - \frac{10.434}{C_c^2}\left(\frac{h}{t_w}\right)^2\right] .60\, \sigma_y} \qquad (13)$$

where:

$$C_c = \sqrt{\frac{2\, \pi^2\, E}{\sigma_y}}$$

---

* Could assume shear (V) is about 95% of maximum shear (at the support) because first panel will be away from the point of support. However, because we are not at the support, there will be some main bending stresses to be added to these secondary bending stresses in the Tee section from applied shear (V). Hence, it would be better to use full value of shear (V).

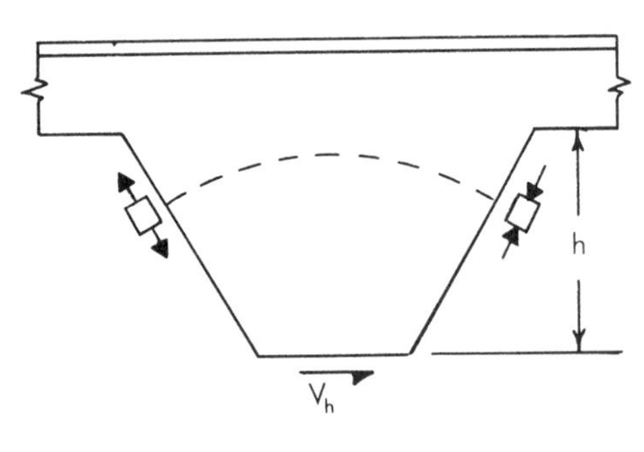

FIGURE 30

or from Table 2 (values for different steels):

$$\underline{\sigma} = 22{,}000 - 14.44 \left(\frac{h}{t_w}\right)^2$$

$$\underline{\sigma} = 22{,}000 - 14.44 \left(\frac{8}{.358}\right)^2 = 14{,}810 \text{ psi}$$

The compressive bending stress can be kept within the above allowable value, if the shear stress in this wedge web section is held to—

$$\underline{\tau} = \frac{4\ \theta^2}{3 \tan \theta}\ \underline{\sigma} \leqq .40\ \sigma_y \qquad (14)$$

$$\underline{\tau} = \frac{4(.7854)^2(14{,}810)}{3\ (1.00)} = 12{,}180 \text{ psi which}$$

is less than $.40\ \sigma_y = 14{,}400$ psi, so is *OK*

STEP 7. Estimate the maximum shear stress along the neutral axis of the girder's web section, assuming the web to be solid the full length of the girder:

$$\tau_{max} = 1.16\ \tau_{av} = 1.16\ \frac{V^*}{t_w\ d_g}$$

$$\tau_{max} = 1.16\ \frac{95\%\ (25^k)}{(.358)(26)} = 2960 \text{ psi}$$

* Where (V) is the shear at the first wedge section, assume about 95% of the maximum shear (at the support) because the first panel will be away from the point of support. This is all right here because we are working with just one stress (shear); there is *no main* bending stress to be considered.

The maximum shear stress is equal to about 1.16 times the average shear stress.

STEP 8. Knowing the maximum shear on a solid web section, and the allowable shear for the open web section, we now have the ratio—

$$\frac{e}{s} = \frac{\tau_{max}}{\underline{\tau}} = K_2$$

Since:

$$\underline{\tau} = \tau_{max}\ \frac{s}{e}$$

Then

$$\frac{e}{s} = \frac{\tau_{max}}{\underline{\tau}} = \frac{2960}{12{,}180} = .243 = K_2$$

If this ratio (K_2) is reasonably low (up to about ⅜″), there is a good chance this trial WF beam may be used.

Since

$$s = 2\ (e + h \tan \theta), \text{ then}$$

$$e \geqq \frac{2\ h \tan \theta}{\frac{1}{K_2} - 2}$$

$$e = \frac{2(8)(1.00)}{\frac{1}{.243} - 2} = 7.56'' \text{ or use } 8''$$

Distance (e) is usually constant along the full length of the girder. However, it is possible to vary this distance; in this case there will be two dimensions (e_1) and (e_2). Near the support, (e_1) lies along the neutral axis of the girder determining the width of the solid web section and (e_2) determines the width of the Tee section. See left end of Figure 31.

At the ¼ point, the details are reversed, and dimension (e_1) rather than (e_2) will control the secondary bending stress (σ_T). See right end of Figure 31. Since

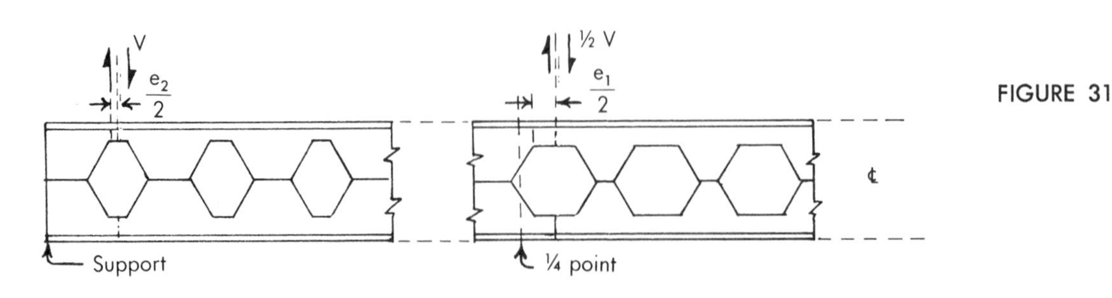

FIGURE 31

the shear (V) at this ¼ point is reduced to about half of that at the support, the distance (e_1) may be double that of (e_2) and still not increase the resulting secondary bending stress (σ_T). Therefore, $K_3 = e_2/e_1$ should not be less than ½.

Using the two dimensions (e_1) and (e_2), the above formulas become:

$$\frac{e_1}{s} = \frac{\tau_{max}}{\tau} = K_2$$

Let

$$K_3 = \frac{e_2}{e_1}$$

Since

$$s = e_1 + e_2 + 2\ h \tan \theta$$

then

$$e_1 \geqq \frac{2\ h \tan \theta}{\frac{1}{K_2} - 1 - K_3}$$

STEP 9. Now determine the properties of expanded girder:

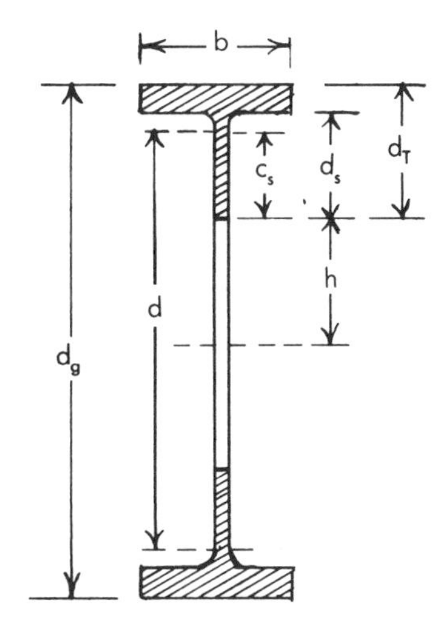

FIGURE 32

$$A_T = A_f + A_s = b\ t_f + d_s\ t_w = 5.861 \text{ in.}^2$$

$$M_y = A_f\left(d_s + \frac{t_f}{2}\right) + A_s\frac{d_s}{2} = 23.67 \text{ in.}^3$$

$$I_y = A_f\left(d_s^2 + d_s\ t_f + \frac{t_f^2}{3}\right) + A_s\frac{d_s^2}{3}$$

$$= 105.53 \text{ in.}^4$$

From this we get—

$$c_s = \frac{M_y}{A_T} = \frac{23.67}{5.861} = 4.039''$$

$$I_T = I_y - c_s\ M_y$$

$$I_T = 105.53 - (4.039)(23.67) = 9.93 \text{ in.}^4$$

$$S_s = \frac{I_T}{c_s}$$

$$S_s = \frac{9.93}{4.039} = 2.46 \text{ in.}^3$$

$$d = 2\ (h + c_s)$$

$$d = 2\ (8 + 4.039) = 24.077''$$

$$I_g = 2\ I_T + \frac{A_T\ d^2}{2}$$

$$I_g = 2(9.33) + \frac{(5.861)(24.077)^2}{2} = 1719.1 \text{ in.}^4$$

$$S_g = \frac{2\ I_g}{d_g}$$

$$S_g = \frac{2(1719.1)}{26} = 132.2 \text{ in.}^3$$

STEP 10. *At the support,* check the secondary bending stress:

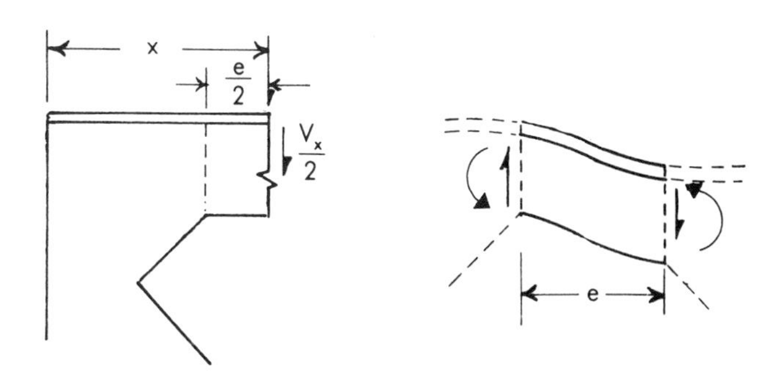

FIGURE 33

$$\sigma_T = \frac{V_x\ e}{4\ S_s}$$

$$\sigma_T = \frac{(25^k)(8)}{4(2.46)} = 20{,}300 \text{ psi}$$

The allowable compressive bending stress may be found in a similar manner to that of Step 6, except the unsupported length here is (e).

At the support, there is no main bending moment,

TABLE 4—For Various Steels

$\sigma_y = 36{,}000$	$\sigma = 22{,}000 - 14.44\left(\frac{h}{t_w}\right)^2$	$\sigma = 22{,}000 - 3.61\left(\frac{e}{t_w}\right)^2$
$\sigma_y = 42{,}000$	$\sigma = 25{,}000 - 19.15\left(\frac{h}{t_w}\right)^2$	$\sigma = 25{,}000 - 4.79\left(\frac{e}{t_w}\right)^2$
$\sigma_y = 45{,}000$	$\sigma = 27{,}000 - 22.14\left(\frac{h}{t_w}\right)^2$	$\sigma = 27{,}000 - 4.85\left(\frac{e}{t_w}\right)^2$
$\sigma_y = 46{,}000$	$\sigma = 27{,}500 - 23.04\left(\frac{h}{t_w}\right)^2$	$\sigma = 27{,}500 - 5.76\left(\frac{e}{t_w}\right)^2$
$\sigma_y = 50{,}000$	$\sigma = 30{,}000 - 27.34\left(\frac{h}{t_w}\right)^2$	$\sigma = 30{,}000 - 6.84\left(\frac{e}{t_w}\right)^2$
$\sigma_y = 55{,}000$	$\sigma = 33{,}000 - 33.10\left(\frac{h}{t_w}\right)^2$	$\sigma = 33{,}000 - 8.28\left(\frac{e}{t_w}\right)^2$
$\sigma_y = 60{,}000$	$\sigma = 36{,}000 - 39.35\left(\frac{h}{t_w}\right)^2$	$\sigma = 36{,}000 - 9.84\left(\frac{e}{t_w}\right)^2$
$\sigma_y = 65{,}000$	$\sigma = 39{,}000 - 46.27\left(\frac{h}{t_w}\right)^2$	$\sigma = 39{,}000 - 11.57\left(\frac{e}{t_w}\right)^2$

hence no axial compressive force acting on this Tee section. The allowable stress here is—

$$\underline{\sigma} = \left[1.0 - \frac{2.609}{C_c^2}\left(\frac{e}{t_w}\right)^2\right] .60\ \sigma_y$$

or, from Table 4 of values for different steels—

$$\underline{\sigma} = 22{,}000 - 3.61\left(\frac{e}{t_w}\right)^2$$

$$\underline{\sigma} = 22{,}000 - 3.61\left(\frac{8}{.358}\right)^2 = 20{,}200 \text{ psi}$$

STEP 11. *At midspan of girder,* check the main bending stress:

(as a compressive or tensile stress)

$$\sigma_b = \frac{F}{A_T} = \frac{M_{℄}}{d\ A_T} \tag{3}$$

$$\sigma_b = \frac{2850''^k}{(24.08)(5.861)} = 20{,}200 \text{ psi}$$

or

(as a bending stress)

$$\sigma_b = \frac{M_{℄}}{S_g}$$

$$\sigma_b = \frac{2850''^k}{132.2} = 21{,}600 \text{ psi}$$

STEP 12. If the main bending stress (σ_b) in Step 11 is excessive, it may be reduced slightly with a higher value of (h); however, this will greatly increase the secondary bending stress (σ_T) of Step 10, since it reduces the depth (d_t) of the Tee section. In this case undoubtedly, the WF beam selected cannot be used and a larger WF beam must be tried.

If the main bending stress (σ_b) is within the allowable, but the secondary bending stress (σ_T) in Step 10 exceeds the allowable, (σ_T) may be greatly reduced by decreasing (h) with just a slight increase in (σ_b).

Stresses (σ_b) and (σ_T) may be considered according to AISC interaction formulas (6), (7a) and (7b), shown graphically in Figure 12.

As a matter of interest, Table 5 shows that decreasing (h) results in a large decrease in the secondary bending stress (σ_T) and a slight increase in the main bending stress (σ_b).

If (h) cannot be reduced because (σ_b) is close to the allowable, use two different size holes, (e_1) and (e_2). Provide a larger value of distance (e_1) for the compressive bending stress in the wedge section of the web, but a lower value of (e_2) for the cantilevered Tee section.

TABLE 5

$h = 7''$	$h = 8''$	$h = 9''$	$h = 10''$
$A_T = 6.040$	$A_T = 5.861$	$A_T = 5.682$	$A_T = 5.503$
$d_T = 5.5$	$d_T = 5.0$	$d_T = 4.5$	$d_T = 4.0$
$S_s = 2.98$	$S_s = 2.46$	$S_s = 1.97$	$S_s = 1.57$
$S_g = 127.96$	$S_g = 132.22$	$S_g = 136.53$	$S_g = 139.17$
$d = 22.82$	$d = 24.08$	$d = 25.32$	$d = 26.54$
$e = 6.0$	$e = 9.0$	$e = 10.5$	$e = 16.5$
$\sigma_T = 12{,}600$	$\sigma_T = 20{,}300$	$\sigma_T = 33{,}300$	$\sigma_T = 65{,}700$
$\sigma_b = 22{,}230$	$\sigma_b = 21{,}600$	$\sigma_b = 21{,}000$	$\sigma_b = 20{,}250$

STEP 13. Make any adjustments necessary to facilitate fabrication. See the text immediately following this design outline.

STEP 14. After the girder is detailed, the stresses may be rechecked in view of more exact values of (V_x) and (M_x) since the exact positions of the panels are not known. Also, it may be well to check additional points between the point of support and midspan. See Figure 34 and Table 6.

9. DESIGN MODIFICATION TO FACILITATE FABRICATION

The practical aspects of structural fabrication may mean some adjustment of original girder design is required.

If Same Size Holes Are to be Used

If openings in the web are to be of uniform size for the full length of the girder, that is $e_1 = e_2$, and the open-web expanded *girder is to be symmetrical* about its centerline, let n = number of unit panels and use as a starting point in measuring a unit panel either:

(a) Centerline of wedge web section. Figure 35, or

(b) Centerline of open Tee section, Figure 36

Divide the length of the required girder (L_g) by the length of one unit panel (s) to get the number of units (n). Then reduce (n) to the nearest whole number. The distance left over (z) on each side is—

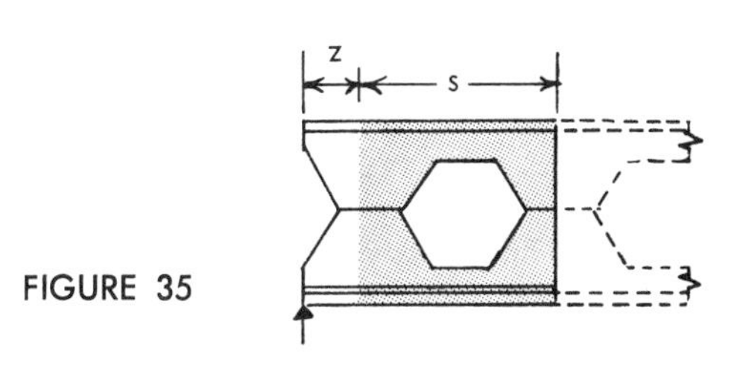

FIGURE 35

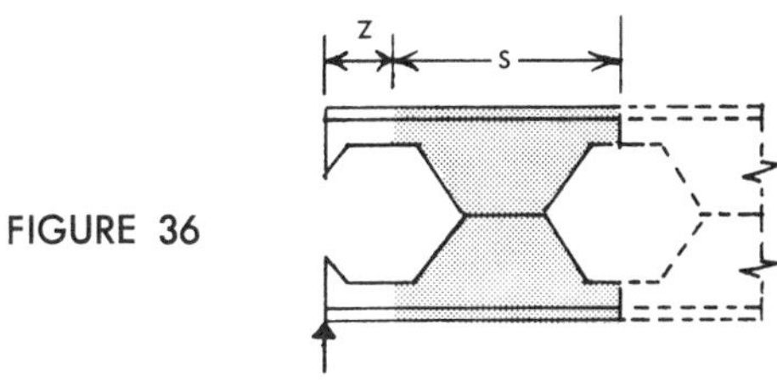

FIGURE 36

$$z = \frac{L_g - n\,s}{2}$$

Since the length of the open-web expanded girder is—

$$L_g = n\,s + 2\,z$$

the length of the WF beam to be cut is—

$$L_b = (n + \tfrac{1}{2})\,s + 2\,z$$

The extra length of WF beam required is—

$$L_g - L_b = \tfrac{1}{2}\,s$$

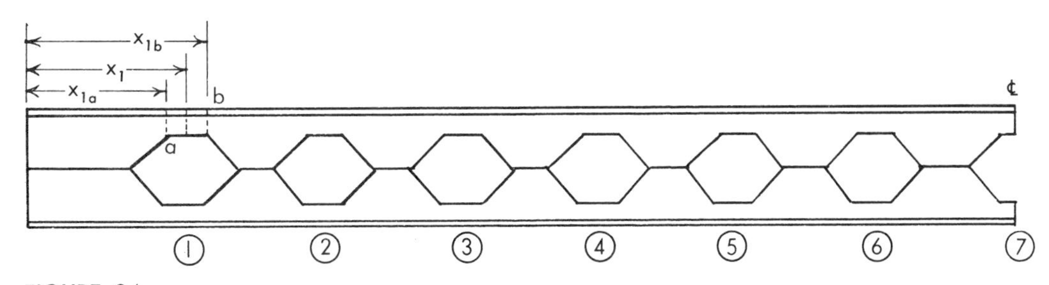

FIGURE 34

TABLE 6

	X_a	X	X_b	V_x	M_a	M_b	SECONDARY σ_1 @ stem a	SECONDARY σ_1 @ flange b	MAIN σ_2 @ stem a	MAIN σ_2 @ flange b	TOTAL $\sigma = \sigma_1 + \sigma_2$ stem a	TOTAL $\sigma = \sigma_1 + \sigma_2$ flange b
1	32″	36″	40″	21.05^K	744″ ^K	911″ ^K	−17,100	−4,065	− 3,460	− 6,880	−20,560	−10,945
2	64″	68″	72″	17.55	1372	1515	−14,270	−3,390	− 6,380	−11,450	−20,650	−14,840
3	96″	100″	104″	14.04	1892	2200	−11,420	−2,715	− 8,800	−16,620	−20,220	−19,335
4	128″	132″	136″	10.53	2300	2385	− 8,560	−2,035	−10,700	−18,030	−19,260	−20,065
5	160″	164″	168″	7.02	2595	2650	− 5,710	−1,360	−11,600	−20,000	−17,310	−21,360
6	192″	196″	200″	3.51	2778	2807	− 2,860	− 680	−12,920	−21,200	−15,780	−21,880
7	224″	228″		0	2849		0	0	−13,250	−21,550	−13,250	−21,550

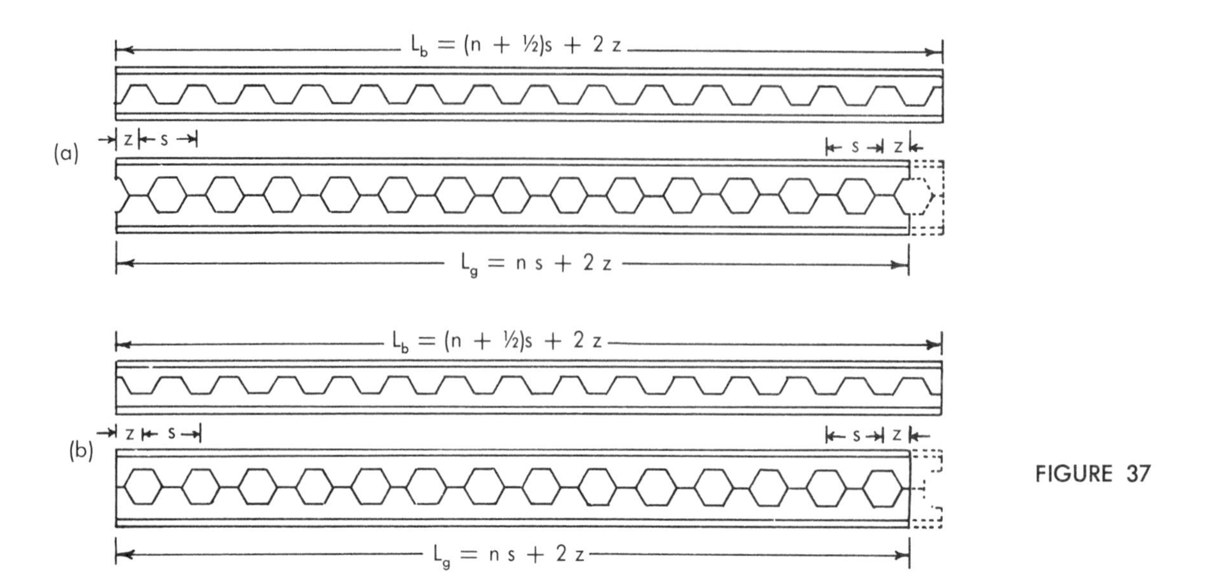

FIGURE 37

In either case (a) or (b), there probably will be a small hole left in the girder at the ends which must be filled. The simplest method is to add one or a pair of web doubling bars or plates at each end to cover and lap over the holes. See Figure 38.

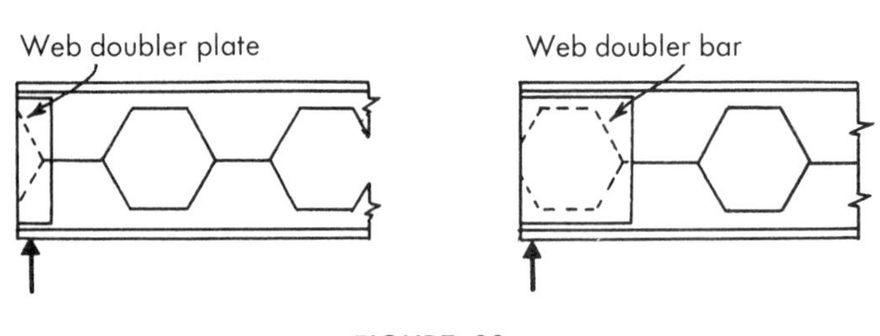

FIGURE 38

If the same size holes are to be used, that is $e_1 = e_2$, and the *girder is not to be symmetrical* about its centerline, then start a unit panel right at one end of the girder. The other end may have a partial hole in the web which will have to be covered. The only advantage to this method is that just one end will have a hole in the web to be covered. See Figure 39.

It might be possible to adjust the value of (e) so that the panels will fit exactly into the length of the girder (L_g). See Figure 40.

Here:

$$L_g = n\,s + e$$
$$= e\,(2\,n + 1) + 2\,n\,h\,\tan\phi$$

First, determine the number of holes (n) from the following formula and round off to the nearest whole number—

$$n = \frac{L_g - e}{s} = \frac{L_g - e}{2\,e + 2\,h\,\tan\phi} \quad \text{.......(19)}$$

Second, find the required value of (e) from the following formula—

$$e = \frac{L_g - 2\,n\,h\,\tan\phi}{2\,n + 1} \quad \text{................(20)}$$

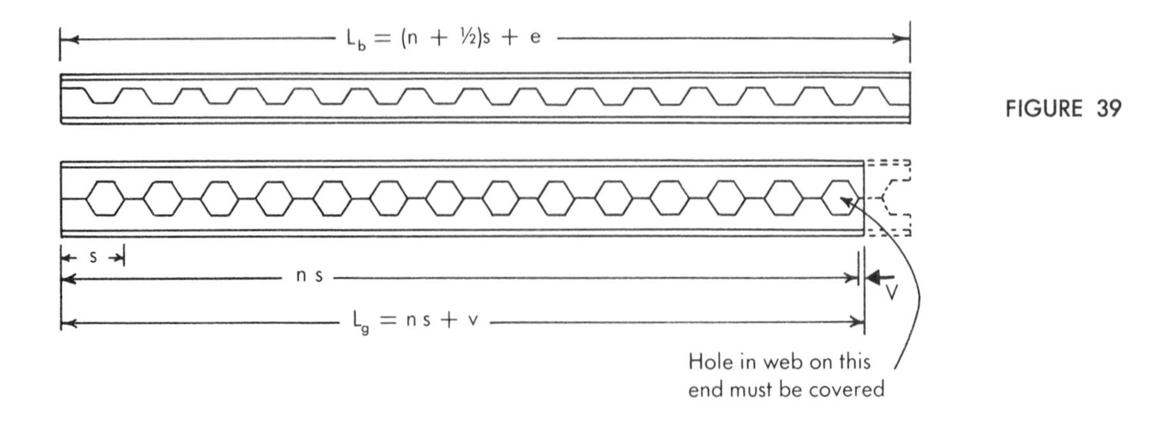

FIGURE 39

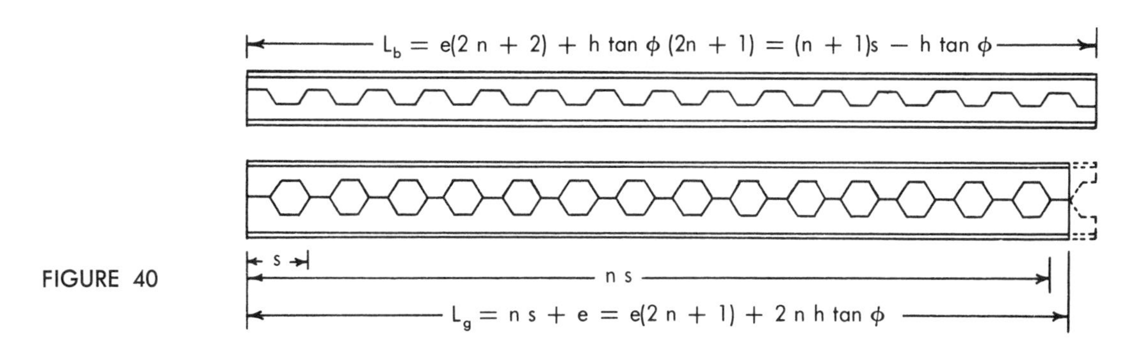

FIGURE 40

This adjusted value of (e) cannot be less than that of Step 8 in the design outline, nor exceed the value which would result in an excessive secondary bending stress (σ_T) in Step 10.

If Different Size Holes Are to be Used

If distances (e_1) and (e_2) are not to be the same, and the girder is symmetrical about its centerline, then the following method may be employed.

In order to easily fabricate this type of open-web girder, it is necessary to be able to rotate each top half about the ¼ point. This presents two possibilities—case (a) rotation at the ¼ point about the larger dimension (e_1), and case (b) rotation at the ¼ point about the smaller dimension (e_2). See Figure 41.

Let (n) = number of holes in the web, counting the centerline hole as two holes.

Determine the approximate number of holes from—

$$n = \frac{L}{e_1 (1 + K_3) + h \tan \phi} \qquad \text{..........(21)}$$

Case (a). There are an odd number of holes in each half, therefore:

Adjust (n) so it is a multiple of 2 only, and solve for (e_1) from the following—

$$e_1 = \frac{L - (n - 1) h \tan \phi}{n(1 + K_3) + 2(1 - K_3)} \qquad \text{.......(22a)}$$

Case (b). There are an even number of holes in each half, therefore:

Adjust (n) so it is a multiple of 4, and solve for (e_1) from the following—

$$e_1 = \frac{L - (n - 1) h \tan \phi}{n (1 + K_3)} \qquad \text{..........(22b)}$$

In both case (a) and case (b) this resulting value of (e_1) should not be less than that obtained in Step 8 and that just used in Formula 21 to find (n).

10. TAPERED OPEN-WEB EXPANDED GIRDERS

Cutting the zig-zag pattern along an axis at a slight angle to the axis of the beam results in a tapered girder. See Figure 42.

In order to have the deeper section at the mid-span, it is necessary to cut the top portion in half and reverse these two top halves. The cut could be made in the lower portion; however this is in tension, and a simpler weld could be made in the compression or top portion.

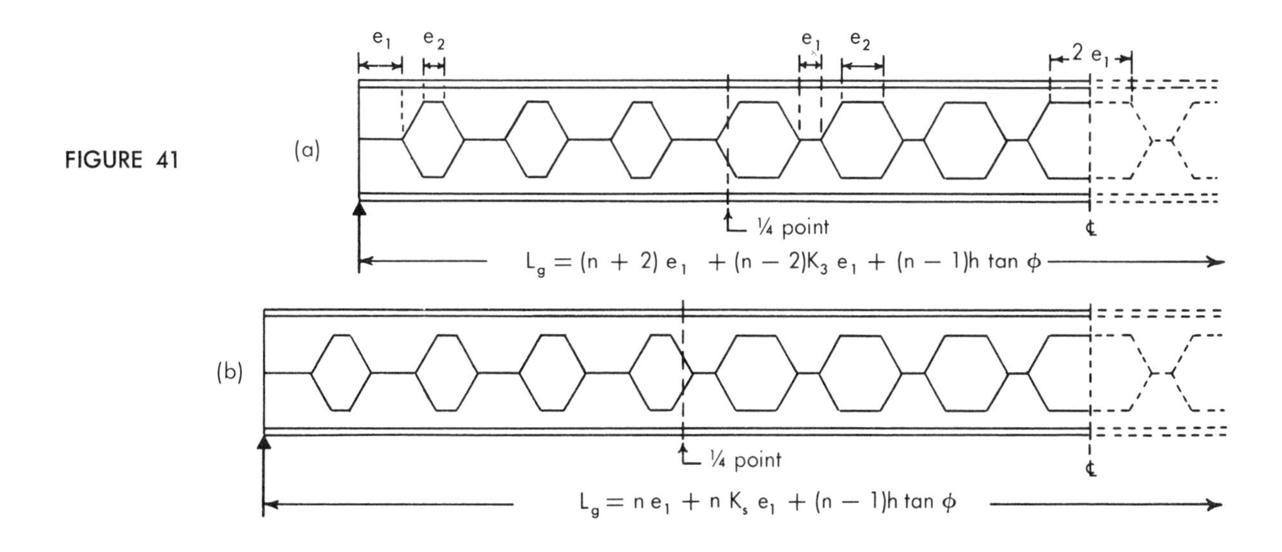

FIGURE 41

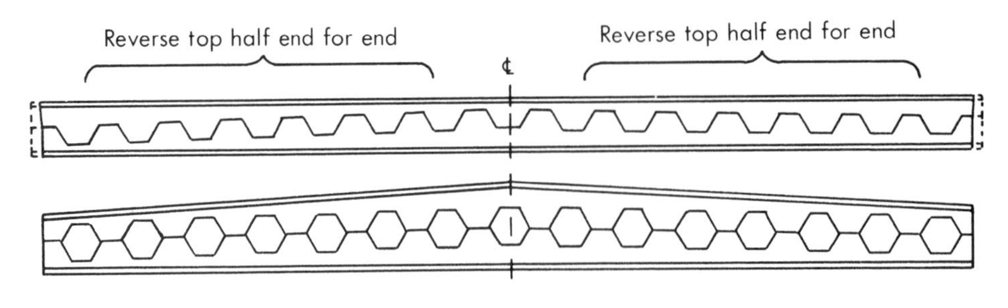

FIGURE 42

In tapered open-web expanded girders, the axial force in the chord which slopes has a vertical component ($F_v = F_h \tan \alpha$); here ($F_h = M/d$).

Whenever this chord changes direction, for example at the midspan of the girder, this vertical component must be considered. It will be carried as shear in the web members back to the support, and in this case has a sign opposite to that of the main shear (V). Hence, its effect is to reduce the shear over most of the girder's length, but to increase it in the midspan region.

The modified shear becomes—

$$V' = A_w \tau = V - F_v = V - \frac{M_{\text{℄}}}{d} \tan \alpha$$

This means there is a vertical shift of the initial shear diagram on each half of the girder, so that the central portion to be checked which initially had zero shear ($V = 0$) now has a shear value ($V' = F_v$) as well as the maximum bending moment. See Figure 43.

A transverse stiffener at the point where the sloping flange changes direction would transfer the vertical component of the flange efficiently into the web. The greater the change in slope, the more important this would become.

If there is a panel opening at this point, the Tee section must resist this vertical component in bending (in this example, the top Tee section). This is similar to the analysis of the secondary bending stress (σ_T) due to the shear applied to the Tee section at midopening where each half behaved as a cantilever beam. See Figure 44. However, in this case, the cantilever beams have fixed ends (at the centerline of the girder); resulting in one-half the bending moment and stress. (This half length Tee section is treated as a beam fixed at one end and guided at the other end, with a concentrated load.)

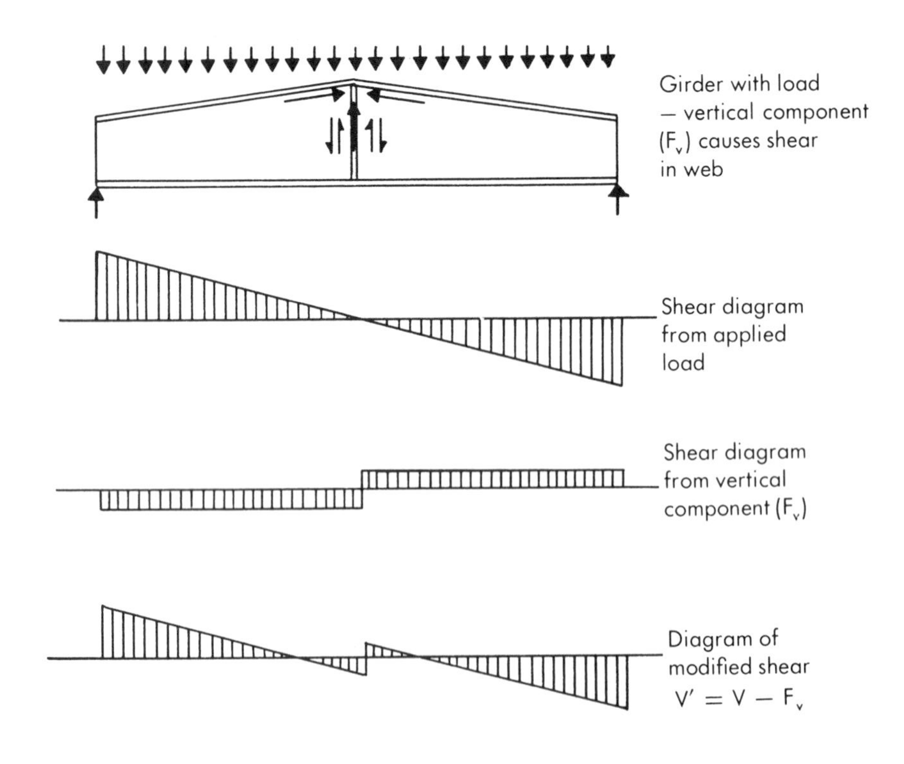

FIGURE 43

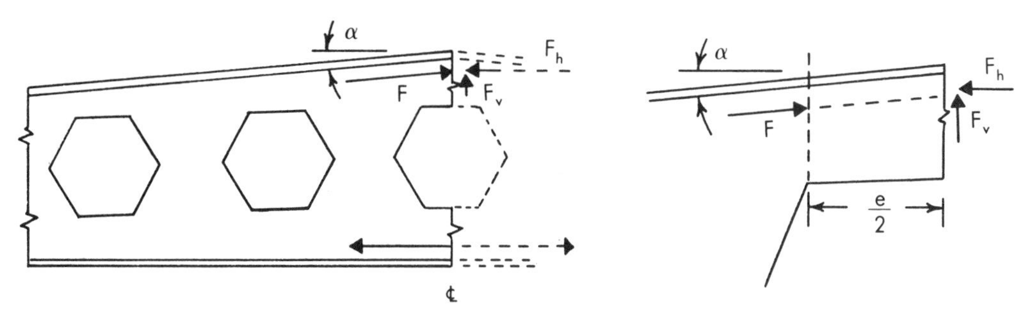

FIGURE 44

The open-web expanded rolled beam is sometimes an economical substitute for a heavy built-up plate girder.

In the 21-story Washington Bldg., open-web expanded beams led to significant savings in construction costs.

Open-web expanded beam serves as longitudinal roof girder in the Tulsa Exposition Center. It provides the needed high moment of inertia, at minimum weight, and eliminates lateral wind bracing. Below, weldor is shown making connections of beam to the tapered box columns.

Shear Attachments for Composite Construction—Building

1. BASIC REQUIREMENTS

The concrete floor may be attached to the top flanges of the steel girders or beams by the use of suitable shear connectors. These allow the slab to act with the steel and form a composite beam having greater strength and rigidity.

The concrete slab becomes part of the compression flange of this composite element. As a result, the neutral axis of the section will shift upward, making the bottom flange of the beam more effective in tension. By such an arrangement, beam cross-sections and weight can be reduced. Since the concrete already serves as part of the floor, the the only additional cost will be the shear connectors.

The types of shear connectors in use today take various shapes and sizes. Some typical ones are shown in Figure 1.

In addition to transmitting the horizontal shear forces from the slab into the steel beam making both beam and slab act as a unit, the shear connector provides anchorage for the slab. This prevents any tendency for it to separate from the beam. While providing for these functions, connector placement must not present difficulty in the subsequent placing of reinforcing rods for the concrete slab.

Because of lower shop costs and better conditions, it is more economical to install these connectors in the shop. However, this may be offset by the possibility of damage to them during shipping, and by the difficulty presented to walking along the top flanges during erection before the slab is poured. For the latter reasons, there is a growing trend toward field installation of connectors.

The previous AISC Specifications had no information on the use of shear attachments for use in composite construction. If shear attachments were to be used, AASHO allowables were followed. These require the use of rather long formulas to determine the individual factor of safety to be used on the connector. It also made a difference whether the beam was to be shored or not shored during the placing of the concrete floor.

Factor of Safety

The new AISC Specifications recognize the use of shear attachments and, as a result of recent research on this subject, has taken a more liberal stand on this. The design work has been greatly reduced, and no longer is it necessary to compute the factor of safety. A more liberal factor of safety is now included in the shear connection formulas. The use of shoring is no longer a factor in the design calculations of the connector, since it has been found that the ultimate load carrying

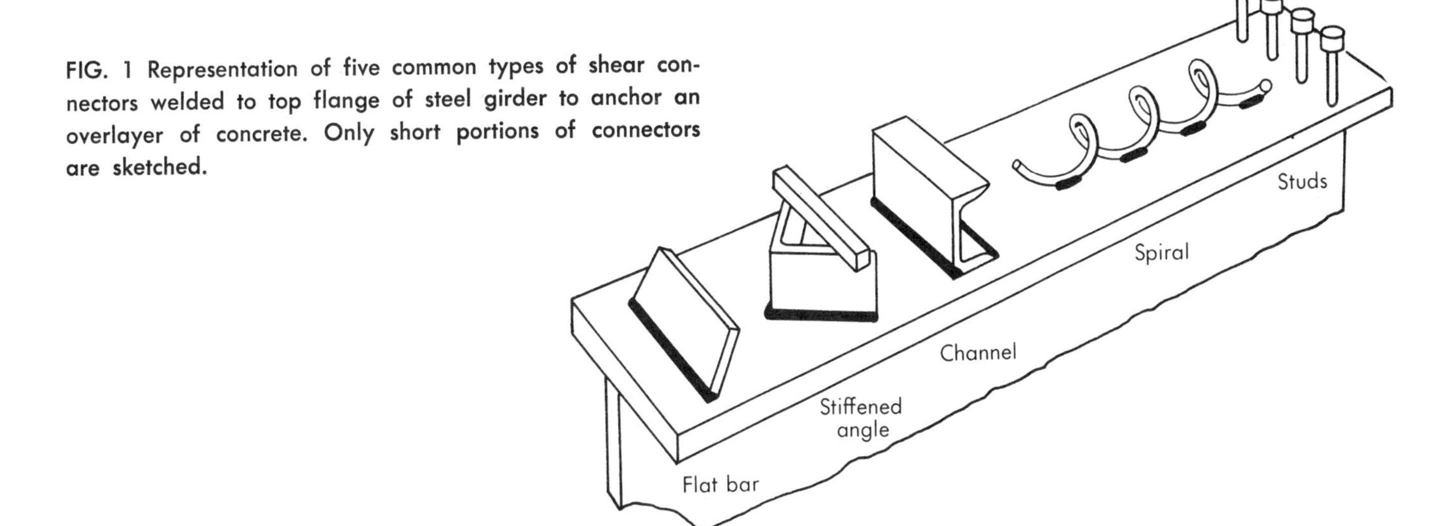

FIG. 1 Representation of five common types of shear connectors welded to top flange of steel girder to anchor an overlayer of concrete. Only short portions of connectors are sketched.

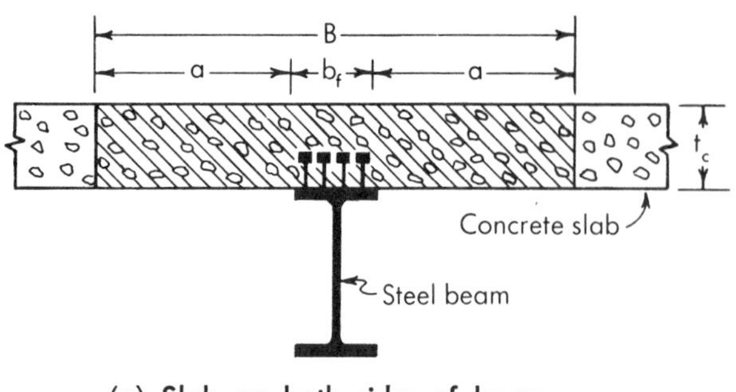

(a) Slab on both sides of beam

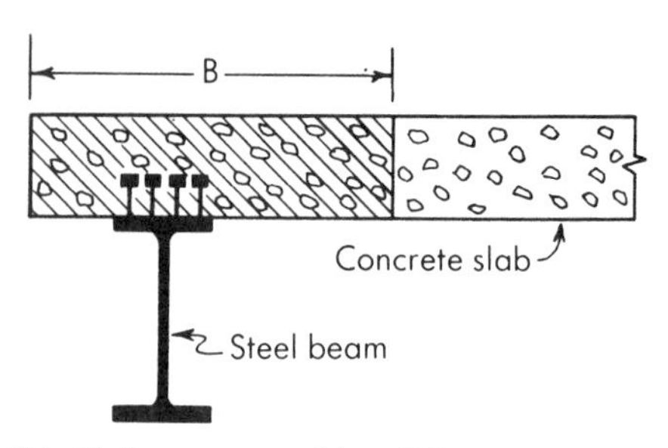

(b) Slab on one side of beam

FIGURE 2

capacity of the composite beam is unaffected whether shores have or have not been used.

Shear Connector Spacing

AASHO requires the determination of shear connector spacing, which may vary along the length of the beam. Now AISC requires just one determination of spacing, and this value is used throughout the length of the beam, greatly simplifying the work. This is because the allowables are such that at ultimate loading of the composite beam, some of the connectors will yield before the others. This movement provides a redistribution of shear transfer so that all connections are ultimately loaded uniformly, hence uniform spacing is allowed.

Composite Section Properties

A further help is a series of tables listing properties of possible combinations of rolled beams with typical concrete slab sections, similar to tables in wide use for available rolled beam sections.

These new tables have been published in the AISC "Manual of Steel Construction," Sixth Edition, 1963, and in Bethlehem Steel Co.'s "Properties of Composite Sections for Bridges and Buildings."

The new tables eliminate the various calculations for composite sections. A simple calculation will indicate the required section modulus of the composite section, and a quick reference to the tables will indicate possible combinations of rolled beam and concrete slab.

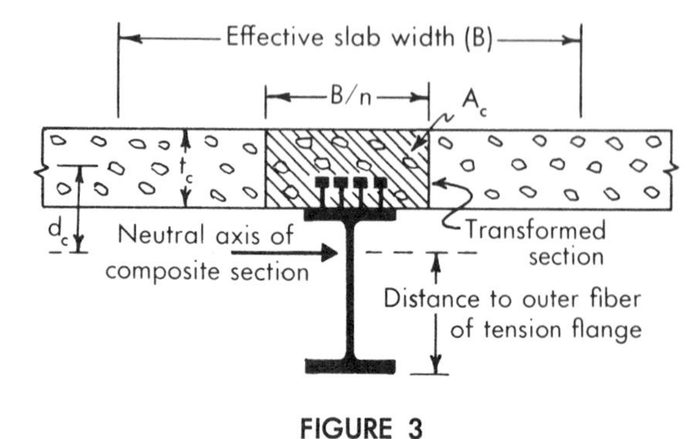

FIGURE 3

2. DESIGN OF CONNECTORS

In order to get the transformed area of the concrete floor, it is necessary to decide how large a width of the concrete acts along with the steel beam to form the composite section. This is known as the effective width (B) of the slab. AISC (1.11.1) requires the following:

slab on both sides of beam, Figure 2(a)

$B \leqq$ ¼ beam span

$a \leqq$ ½ distance to adjacent beam

$a \leqq$ 8 times least thickness of slab (t_c)

slab on one side of beam, Figure 2(b)

$B \leqq$ 1⁄12 beam span

$B \leqq$ ½ distance to adjacent beam

$B \leqq$ 6 times least thickness of slab (t_c)

This effective width of concrete is now transformed into an equivalent steel section, having the same thickness as the concrete (t_c), but having a width equal to 1/n that of the concrete. See Figure 3. Here n, the modular ratio, is the ratio of the modulus of elasticity of the steel to that of the concrete.

From this transformed section, the various properties of the section may be determined.

I = moment of inertia of transformed section, $in.^4$

S = section modulus for the extreme tension fibers of the steel beam (bottom flange), $in.^3$

Beams may be totally encased within the floor slab as a Tee section in which the top of the beam is at least 1½″ below the top and 2″ above the bottom of the slab, and encased with at least 2″ of concrete around the sides of the beam. With these conditions, shear attachments are not used (AISC 1.11.1).

If no temporary shores are used, the total bending stress in the tension flange of the encased steel beam is figured under two conditions:

1. The steel beam acting alone for any dead loads applied prior to hardening of the concrete.

2. The steel beam acting with the concrete for any live loads and additional dead loads applied after hardening of the concrete.

The beam shall be so proportioned that the above stress under either condition does not exceed .66 σ_y* (AISC 1.11.2.1).

If temporary shores are used, the tension steel flange of the encased beam acting with the concrete slab to form the composite section shall be designed at $\sigma = .66\ \sigma_y$* to carry all dead and live loads applied after hardening of the concrete.

If shear attachments are used, encasement is not needed and it does not matter in the design whether temporary shores are used or not used. In either case, the steel tension flange acting with the concrete slab to form the composite section shall be designed at $\sigma = .66\ \sigma_y$* to carry all of the loads (AISC 1.11.2.2). If no temporary shoring is used, the section modulus of the composite section (S_c) in regard to the tension flange of the beam shall not exceed the following:

$$S_c \leqq \left(1.35 + 0.35 \frac{M_L}{M_D}\right) S_s \qquad \text{(AISC Formula 17)} \quad \ldots\ldots\ldots (1)$$

where:

S_c = section modulus of composite section (relative to its tension steel flange)

* If steel section is not compact: $\sigma = .60\ \sigma_y$.

TABLE 1—Design of Section for Composite Construction

	Encased Beams (1.11.2.1) (no shear attachments) — 1½" min; 2" min; Encasement around side 2" min		With Shear Attachments (1.11.2.2)	
	Section Modulus Used	Loads Used *	Section Modulus Used	Loads Used*
With Shoring	composite section with	all loads after hardening of concrete	composite section with	all loads
	$\sigma_S = \frac{M_D + M_L}{S_c} \leqq .66\ \sigma_y \leqq .60\ \sigma_y$		$\sigma_S = \frac{M_D + M_L}{S_c} \leqq .66\ \sigma_y \leqq .60\ \sigma_y$	
Without Shoring	steel beam with	all loads prior to hardening of concrete	composite section with	all loads
	and			
	composite section with	all loads after hardening of concrete		
	$\sigma_S = \frac{M_D}{S_s} + \frac{M_L}{S_c} \leqq .66\ \sigma_y \leqq .60\ \sigma_y$		$\sigma_S = \frac{M_D + M_L}{S_c} \leqq .66\ \sigma_y \leqq .60\ \sigma_y$	
	or		also	
	steel beam with	all loads	$S_c \leqq \left(1.35 + 0.35 \frac{M_L}{M_D}\right) S_s$ (AISC formula 17)	
	$\sigma_S = \frac{M_D + M_L}{S_s} \leqq .76\ \sigma_y$			

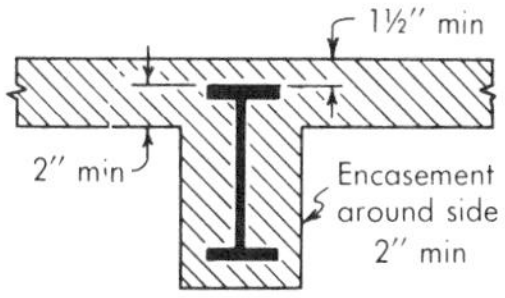

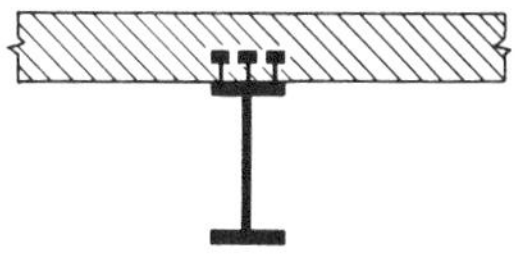

* $\sigma = .66\ \sigma_y$ for "compact" beams; otherwise $\sigma = .60\ \sigma_y$

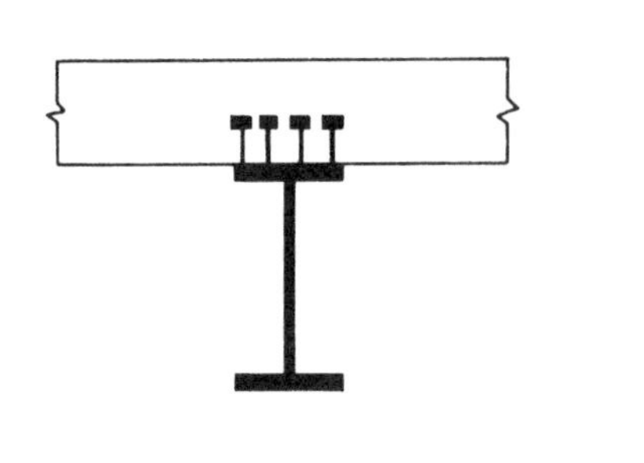

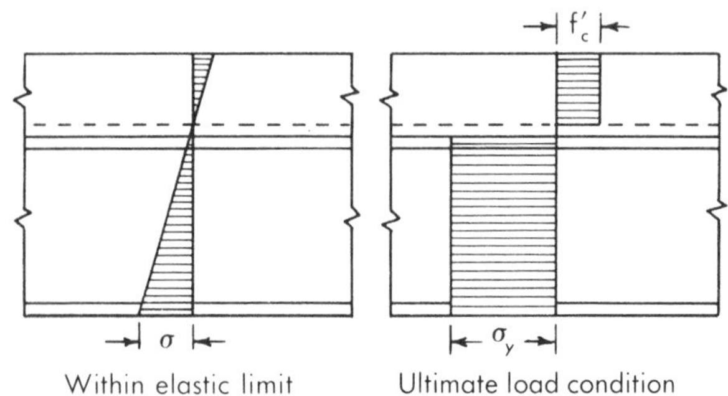

Within elastic limit   Ultimate load condition

FIGURE 4

S_s = section modulus of steel beam (relative to its tension flange)

M_D = dead-load moment prior to hardening of concrete

M_L = moment due to live and additional dead load after hardening of concrete

Table 1 summarizes these requirements for encased beams without shear attachments and for composite beams with shear attachments.

Forces Carried by Connectors

For elastic design, the horizontal unit shear force is obtained from the well-known formula:

$$f = \frac{V\ a\ y}{I}$$

However in the new AISC Specification for building applications, the design is based on the shear connectors allowing the composite beam to reach ultimate load. In the usual composite beam, the ultimate load is reached after the full depth of the steel beam reaches yield stress in tension. This force is resisted by the compressive area of the concrete slab. See Figure 4.

The total horizontal shear (V_h) at ultimate load to be transferred from concrete slab to steel beam between section of maximum moment and ends of the beam, is equal to the total horizontal forces (F_h) from bending acting on either the slab or the beam. See Figure 5.

where:

B = effective width of slab

t_c = thickness of slab

f'_c = compressive strength of concrete

A_s = cross-sectional area of steel beam

A_c = cross-sectional area of effective concrete slab

σ_y = yield strength of steel

Figure 6 diagrams the bending moment that results in horizontal forces; compression in the concrete slab and tension in the steel beam.

These horizontal ultimate forces are then reduced by a factor of safety of 2, and concrete is taken at 85% of its strength. These formulas become:

$$V_h = \frac{.85\ f'_c\ A_c}{2} \quad \text{(AISC Formula 18)} \qquad \ldots\ldots (2)$$

(a) Neutral axis lies within steel beam

$V_h = F_h = b\ t_c\ f'_c$

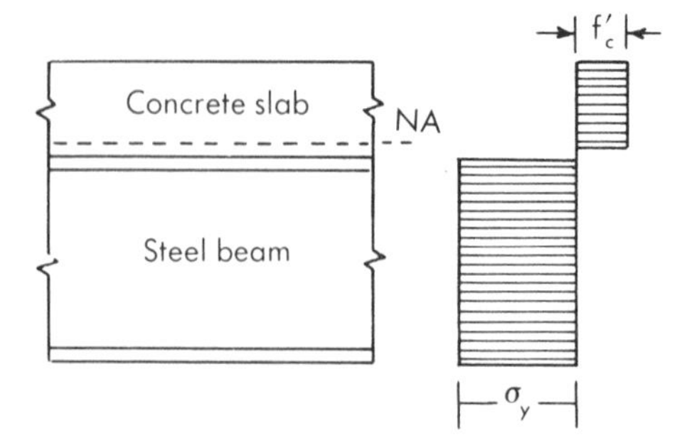

(b) Neutral axis lies within concrete slab

$V_h = F_h = A_s\ \sigma_y$

FIGURE 5

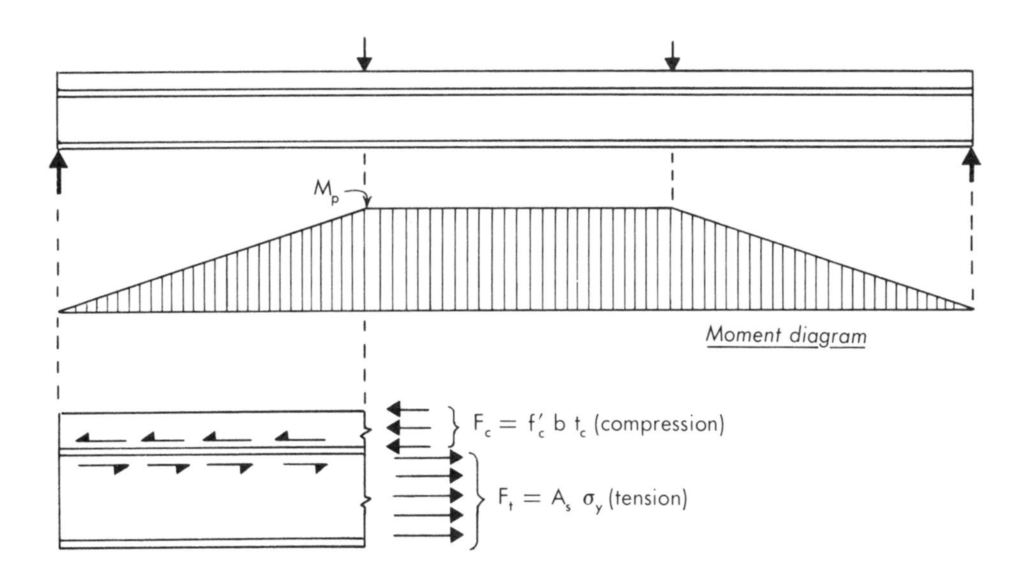

FIGURE 6

$$V_h = \frac{A_s\ \sigma_y}{2} \quad \text{(AISC Formula 19)} \qquad \ldots\ldots\ldots\ldots\ldots\ldots\ldots (3)$$

The smaller of the two values above (V_h) is taken as the total horizontal shear force to be carried by all of the connectors between the point of maximum moment and the ends of the beam, or between the point of maximum moment and a point of contraflexure in continuous beams.

The number of shear connectors needed within this region is found by dividing the above force (V_h) by the allowable (q) for the type of connector used.

Allowable Loads

Formulas have been established to give the useful capacity of three types of shear connections. These are used by AASHO in the bridge field with the proper values of (K):

stud

$$q = K_1\ d_s^2\ \sqrt{f'_c} \qquad \text{(lbs/stud)}$$

channel

$$q = K_2\ (h + \tfrac{1}{2}\ t)w\ \sqrt{f'_c} \qquad \text{(lbs/channel)}$$

where:

w = channel length in inches

spiral

$$q = K_3\ d_b\ \sqrt[4]{f'_c} \qquad \text{(lbs/turn of spiral)}$$

Later the Joint ASCE-ACI Committee on Composite Construction recommended these same basic formulas, but applied a factor of safety of 2 and these became allowable loads for the connectors.

In the meantime additional testing has indicated the connectors to have greater strength than previously thought. Although AISC did not publish these final formulas with their constants (K), they did produce Table 1.11.4 of values for allowable loads on some of the typical standard shear connectors. See Table 2.

Working back from this table, the basic formulas for allowable loads on shear connectors would be the following:

$$q = 372\ d^2\ \sqrt{f'_c} \quad \text{(when } h/d = 4.2\text{)} \qquad \ldots\ldots\ldots (4)$$

TABLE 2—Allowable Horizontal Shear Load (q), Kips *(Applicable Only to Stone Concrete)*

Connector	$f'_c = 3{,}000$	$f'_c = 3{,}500$	$f'_c = 4{,}000$
½″ diam. × 2″ hooked or headed stud	5.1	5.5	5.9
⅝″ diam. × 2½″ hooked or headed stud	8.0	8.6	9.2
¾″ diam. × 3″ hooked or headed stud	11.5	12.5	13.3
⅞″ diam. × 3½″ hooked or headed stud	15.6	16.8	18.0
3″ channel, 4.1 lb.	4.3ω	4.7ω	5.0ω
4″ channel, 5.4 lb.	4.6ω	5.0ω	5.3ω
5″ channel, 6.7 lb.	4.9ω	5.3ω	5.6ω
½″ diam. spiral bar	11.9	12.4	12.8
⅝″ diam. spiral bar	14.8	15.4	15.9
¾″ diam. spiral bar	17.8	18.5	19.1

ω = length of channel in inches.

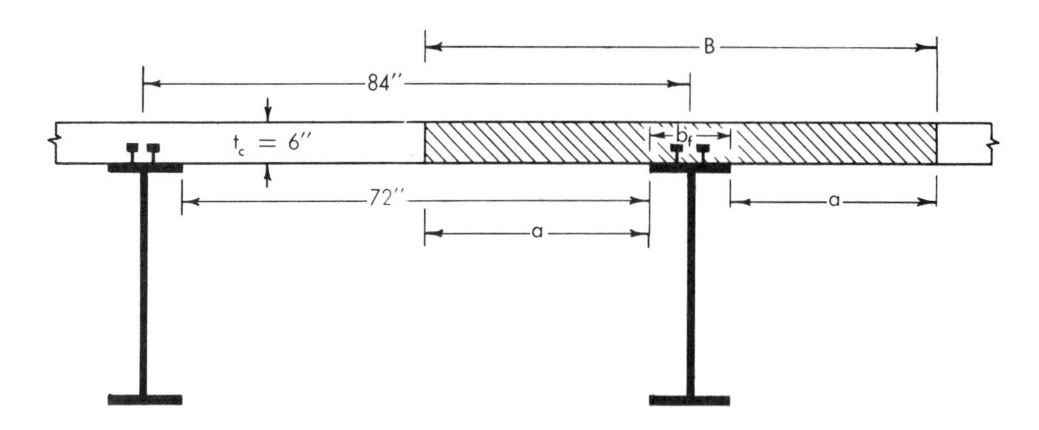

FIGURE 7

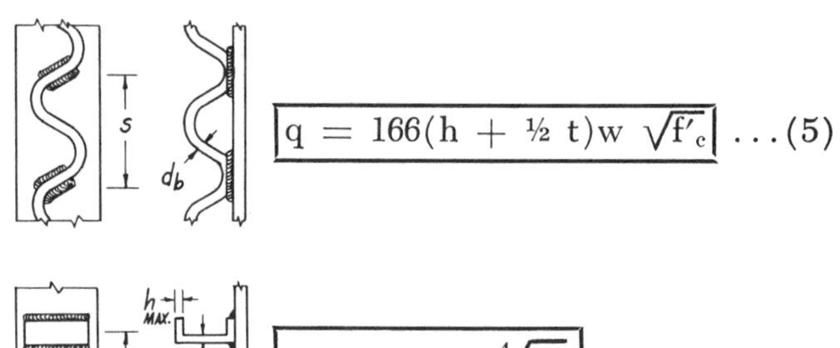

s
d_b
$q = 166(h + ½\ t)w\ \sqrt{f'_c}$ . . . (5)
h
MAX.
t
s
W
$q = 3200\ d\ \sqrt[4]{f'_c}$ . . . . (6)

These will enable the engineer to compute the value for a shear connector not covered in the AISC table.

The connectors may be spaced evenly along this region and shall have at least 1″ of concrete cover in all directions.

Problem 1

Check the composite beam of Figure 7, and its shear connectors. The following are given conditions:

36″ WF 150-lb beams on 7′ centers, with a 6″ thick concrete slab

A36 steel, E70 welds, and 3000 psi concrete

A uniformly distributed live load of 240 kips

Span of 40′ between supports

$$n = \frac{E_s}{E_c} = 10 \text{ (modular ratio)}$$

dead load moment

Steel beam	=	6,000 lbs
Concrete slab	=	20,160 lbs
Total W_D	=	26,160 lbs

$$M_D = \frac{W_D\ L}{8} = \frac{(26{,}160)(480)}{8} = 1570 \text{ in.-kips}$$

live load moment

$$M_L = \frac{W_L\ L}{8} = \frac{(240{,}000)(480)}{8} = 14{,}400 \text{ in.-kips}$$

projection of concrete slab

$$a \leqq 8\ t_c \leqq 8(6'') \leqq 48''$$

$$a \leqq ½ \text{ distance to adjacent beam} \leqq ½(84 - 12) \leqq 36'' < 48'' \qquad OK$$

effective width of concrete flange acting with beam

$$B \leqq ¼ \text{ beam span} \leqq ¼(40) \leqq 10' \text{ or } 120''$$

$$B = 2a + b_f = 2(36) + (12) = 84'' < 120'' \qquad OK$$

and width of transformed concrete area is

$$B/n = \frac{84''}{10} = 8.4''$$

properties of steel beam section

36″ WF 150-lb beam

$I = 9012.1$ in.^{4}

$S = 502.9$ in.^{2}

$A_s = 44.15$ in.^{2}

$d_b = 35.84''$

$b_f = 11.972''$

$t_f = .940''$

$t_w = .625''$

properties of composite section

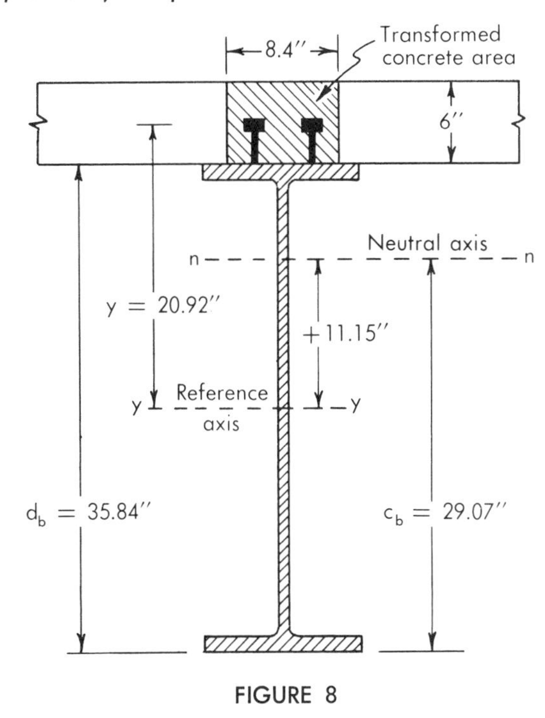

FIGURE 8

Taking reference section (y-y) through the beam's center of gravity:

Area	A	y	M = A y	I_y = M y	$I_g = \frac{(B/n)t^3}{12}$
Transformed slab	50.40	+ 20.92	1054.37	22,057.4	151.2
36″ WF 150 lb. beam	44.16	0	0	0	9,012.1
Total →	94.56		1054.37	31,220.7	

$$I_n = (I_y + I_g) - \frac{M^2}{A}$$

$$= (31{,}220.7) - \frac{(1054.37)^2}{(94.56)}$$

$$= 19{,}462 \text{ in.}^4$$

$$N.A. = \frac{M}{A} \text{ (distance from reference axis to neutral axis)}$$

$$= \frac{(1054.37)}{(94.56)}$$

$$= 11.15''$$

$$c_b = (11.15) + (17.92)$$

$$= 29.07''$$

$$S = \frac{I_n}{c_b}$$

$$= \frac{(19{,}462)}{(29.07)}$$

$$= 670 \text{ in.}^3 \text{ (relative to bottom tension flange in steel beam)}$$

check bending stress in beam

Check the tensile bending stress in bottom flange of steel beam. From Table 1—

$$\sigma_s = \frac{M_D + M_L}{S_c}$$

$$= \frac{(1570 + (14{,}400)}{(670)}$$

$$= 23{,}800 \text{ psi} < .66\ \sigma_y$$

check section modulus

Since no shores are to be used, a further requirement is that the section modulus of the composite section shall not exceed—

$$S_{c(max)} \leqq \left[1.35 + 0.35 \frac{M_L}{M_D}\right] S_s$$

$$\leqq \left[1.135 + 0.35 \frac{(14{,}400)}{(1570)}\right] (502.9)$$

$$\leqq 2290 \text{ in.}^3$$

$$S_{c(actual)} = 670 \text{ in.}^3 < 2290 \text{ in.}^3 \quad \textit{OK}$$

horizontal shear

The horizontal shear to be transferred by connectors will be the smaller of the following two values:

$$V_h = \frac{.85\ f'_c\ A_c}{2}$$

$$= \frac{.85\ (3000)(6 \times 84)}{2}$$

$$= 642.6 \text{ kips}$$

$$V_h = \frac{A_s\ \sigma_y}{2}$$

$$= \frac{(44.16)(36{,}000)}{2}$$

$$= 794.9 \text{ kips}$$

So, use V_h = 642.6 kips

Stud Connectors

Use ¾″ x 4″ studs. From Table 2, q = 11.5 kips per stud.

number of studs

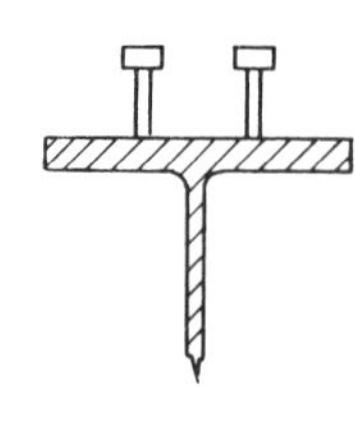

$$n = \frac{V_h}{q} = \frac{(642.6)}{(11.5)} = 55.9$$

or 60 studs from centerline to each end of beam.

If using 2 rows of studs, use 28 lines on each end of girder.

approximate spacing

$$s = \frac{240'' \text{ (half length)}}{28 \text{ (studs)}} = 8.57'' \text{ or } 8\tfrac{9}{16}''$$

Place first line of studs at ½ of this space (or 4¼″) from end of beam; from there on give all studs full spacing (8⁹⁄₁₆″).

Channel Connectors

Use 4″ 5.4-lb channel of 10″ length. From Table 2,

$$q = 4.6 \text{ w} = 4.6 \text{ (10)} = 4.6 \text{ kips per channel}$$

number of channels

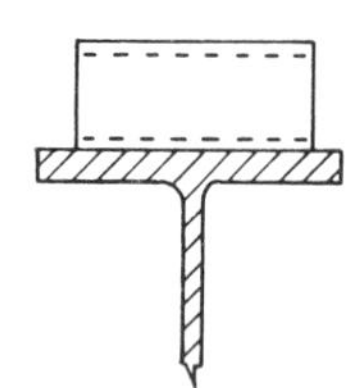

$$n = \frac{V_h}{q} = \frac{(642.6)}{(4.6)} = 14 \text{ channels}$$

from centerline to each end of beam, or 28 channels per beam.

approximate spacing

$$s = \frac{240'' \text{ (half length)}}{14 \text{ (channels)}} = 17.15'' \text{ or } 17\tfrac{3}{16}''$$

and use ½ of this or 8½″ for spacing first channel from end of beam.

To compute the required size of connecting weld:

F = 46 kips, each channel

length of fillet weld

$$L = 2 \times 10'' = 20''$$

force on weld

$$f = \frac{F}{L} = \frac{(46)}{(20)} = 2300 \text{ lbs/in.}$$

leg size of weld (E70)

$$\omega = \frac{2300}{11{,}200} = .205'' \text{ or use } \tfrac{1}{4}''$$

Check: Welding to .94″ thick flange calls for minimum weld size of ⁵⁄₁₆″, but the weld need not exceed thickness of the thinner part joined, which is the flange of the channel. Hence, use ⁵⁄₁₆″ at the heel and ³⁄₁₆″ at the toe.

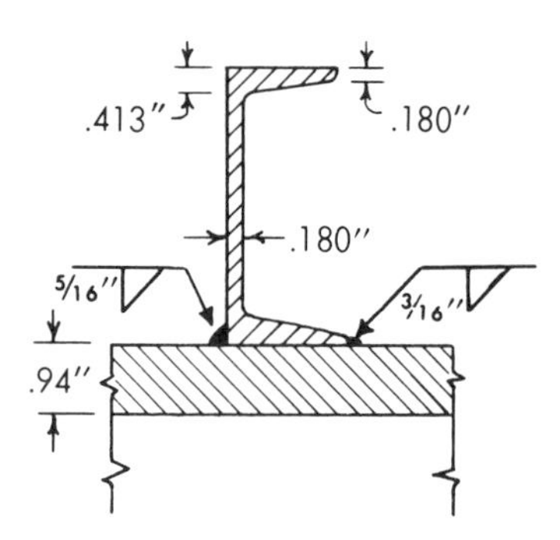

Spiral Connector

Use ¾″ diameter bar. From Table 2, q = 17.8 kips per turn.

number of turns

$$n = \frac{V_h}{q} = \frac{(642.6)}{(17.8)}$$

= 36.1 from end to end or 37 turns from centerline to each end of beam.

approximate pitch

$$s = \frac{240'' \text{ (half length)}}{37 \text{ (turns)}} = 6.49'' \text{ or use } 6\tfrac{7}{16}''$$

To compute the required connecting welds (E70), assume weld size is equivalent to a ⅜″ fillet weld (has same throat). Force on the weld is—

$$f = 11{,}200\ \omega$$
$$= 11{,}200\ (3/8)$$
$$= 4200 \text{ lbs/in.}$$

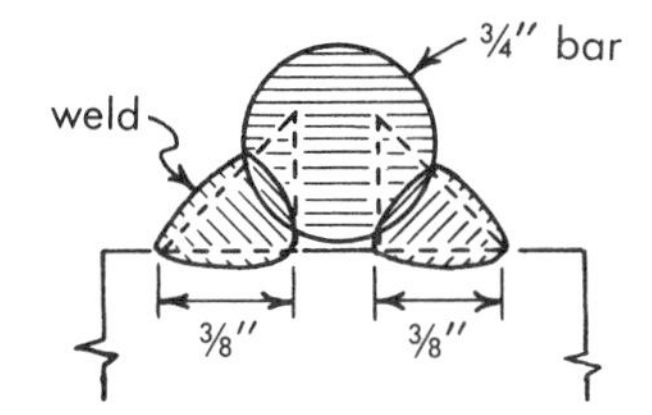

length of weld at each turn of spiral

$$L = \frac{q}{f}$$
$$= \frac{(17.8 \text{ kips})}{(4200 \text{ lbs/in.})}$$
$$= 3.18'' \text{ or } \underline{1\tfrac{5}{8}'' \text{ on each side}} \qquad \underline{OK}$$

Application of one type of proprietary shear connector for composite construction, providing equivalent strength with less steel tonnage. Connectors welded to beams makes concrete slab integral with supporting member.

Lightweight stud welders permit shear connectors to be attached to girder flanges at high speed. Studs are the most popular form of attachment for anchoring concrete floor slab to the steel girders, permitting steel and concrete to act together for greater strength and rigidity.

Shear Connections for Composite Construction—Bridges

1. BASIC REQUIREMENTS

Concrete roadway decks may be attached to the top flanges of steel girders or beams by the use of suitable shear connectors. These connectors allow the slabs to act with the steel and form a composite beam having greater strength and rigidity.

The concrete slab becomes part of the compression flange of this composite element. As a result, the neutral axis of the section will shift upward, making the bottom flange of the beam more effective in tension. By such an arrangement, beam cross-section and weight can be reduced. Since the concrete already serves as part of the floor, the only additional cost will be the shear connectors.

The types of shear connectors in use today take various shapes and sizes. Some typical ones are shown in Figure 1.

In addition to transmitting the horizontal shear forces from the slab into the steel beam making both beam and slab act as a unit, the shear connector provides anchorage for the slab. This prevents any tendency for it to separate from the beam. While providing for these functions, connector placement must not present difficulty in the subsequent placing of reinforcing rods for the concrete slab.

Because of lower shop costs and better conditions, it is more economical to install these connectors in the shop. However, this may be offset by the possibility of damage to them during shipping, and by the difficulty presented to walking along the top flanges during erection before the slab is poured. For the latter reasons, there is a growing trend toward field installation of connectors.

Erection procedures influence the design of the composite beam. If the girder or beam has proper temporary support during construction, its design can be based on the dead loads plus live loads being carried by the composite section after the concrete has attained 75% of its 28-day strength.

If the girder is not shored, then the steel alone must be designed to support the entire dead load during the curing period, and the composite section designed for any live, impact, and additional dead loads. This usually requires greater steel cross-section than is required for the composite design using temporary shoring. However, in bridge construction this savings in steel usually cannot offset the high shoring costs for the long spans involved. As a result, most bridges are designed without shoring.

In the negative moment regions at the supports of continuous beams, the concrete slab would be stressed in tension and cannot be considered effective in the design. Some bridge designers assume the reinforcing

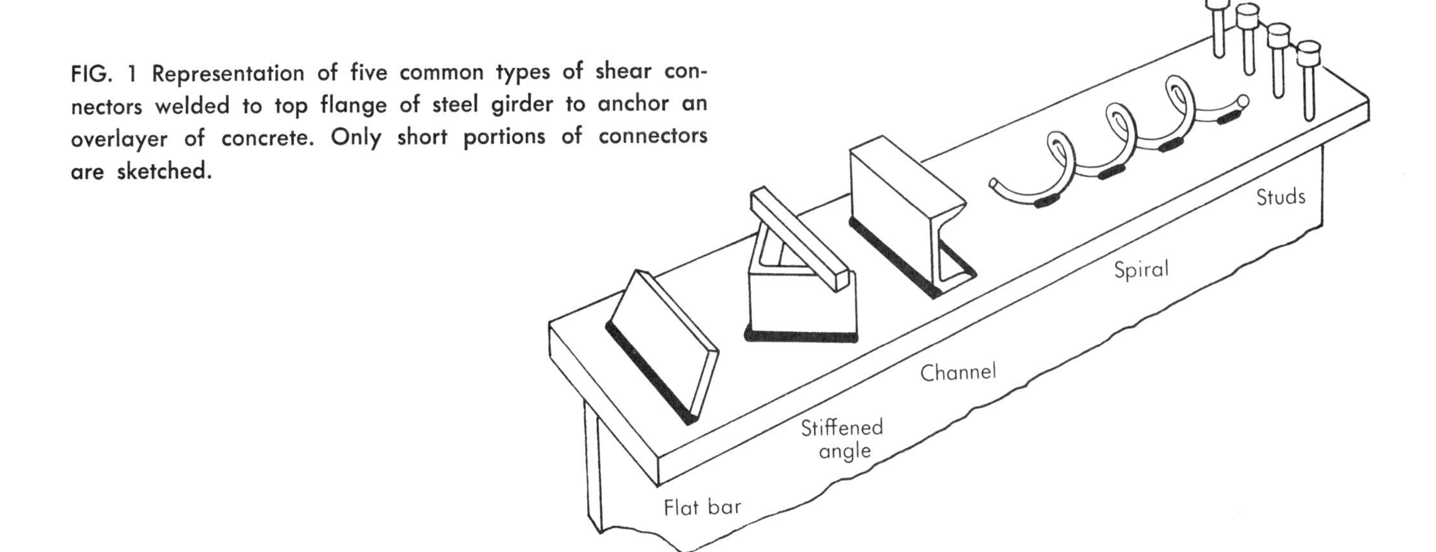

FIG. 1 Representation of five common types of shear connectors welded to top flange of steel girder to anchor an overlayer of concrete. Only short portions of connectors are sketched.

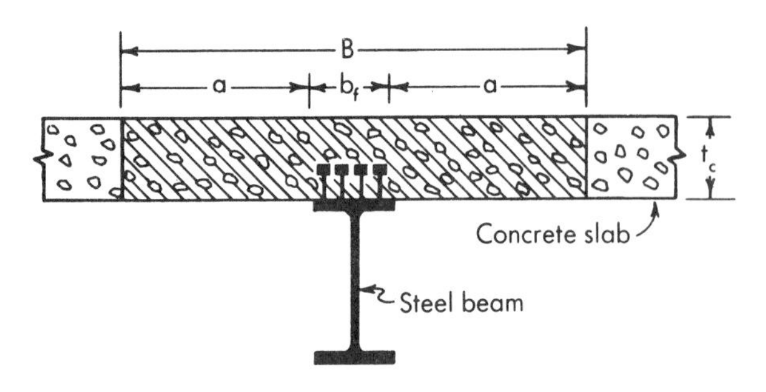

(a) Slab on both sides of beam

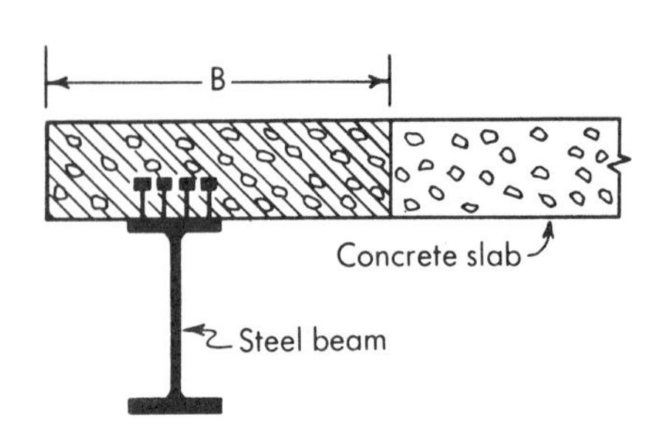

(b) Slab on one side of beam

FIGURE 2

steel in this area to be effective in tension when proper shear attachments are continued throughout the area. This approach slightly reduces the beam's cross-sectional area.

2. DESIGN OF CONNECTORS

Shear connectors should have at least 1″ of concrete cover in all directions. They should be designed for only the portion of the load carried by the composite section.

horizontal shear

$$V_h = \frac{V_c\, m}{I_c} \qquad (1)$$

where:

V_h = horizontal shear of steel flange, at junction of slab and beam, lbs/linear in.

V_c = total external shear acting on composite section after concrete has attained 75% of its 28-day strength, lbs

m = statical moment of transformed concrete area about neutral axis of composite section, or the statical moment of the area of reinforcement embedded in slab for negative moment, $in.^3$

I_c = moment of inertia of transformed composite section

transformed area

In order to get the transformed area of the concrete deck, it is necessary to decide how large a width of the concrete acts along with the steel beam to form the composite section. This is known as the effective width (B) of the slab (AASHO 1.9.3).

This effective width of concrete is now transformed into an equivalent steel section, having the same thickness as the concrete (t_c), but having a width equal to 1/n that of the concrete. See Figure 3. Here n, the modular ratio, is the ratio of the modulus of elasticity of the steel to concrete.

From this transformed section, the various section properties may be determined:

m = statical moment = $A_c\, d_c$ of concrete about neutral axis of composite section

I_c = moment of inertia of transformed composite section, $in.^4$

S = section modulus for the extreme tension fibers of the steel beam (bottom flange), $in.^3$

The moment of inertia of the transformed concrete section (I_c) may be read directly from Table 1, the section modulus (S) from Table 2, and the coefficient value of m/I_c for horizontal shear (V_h) from Table 3. Tables 1, 2 and 3 are from "Composite Construction in Steel and Concrete" by Viest, Fountain and Singleton; McGraw-Hill.

where:

$n = E_s/E_c = 10$, the modular ratio

B = effective slab width

t = slab thickness

design load (working value) for one shear connector

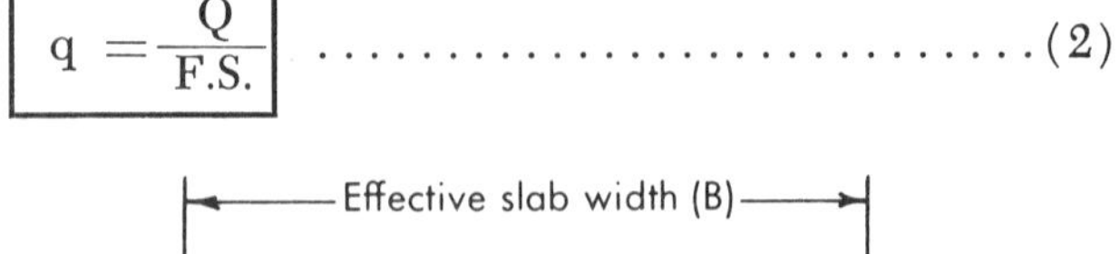

$$q = \frac{Q}{F.S.} \qquad (2)$$

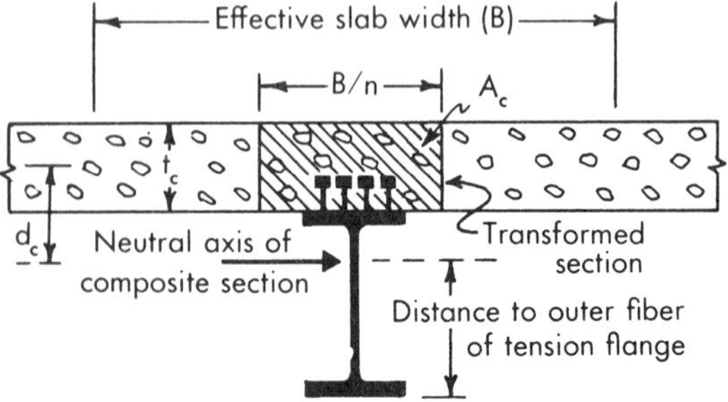

FIGURE 3

where:

Q = useful capacity of one shear connector, beyond which the connector permits an appreciable slip between concrete slab and steel beam, lbs

F.S. = factor of safety

useful capacity of one shear connector

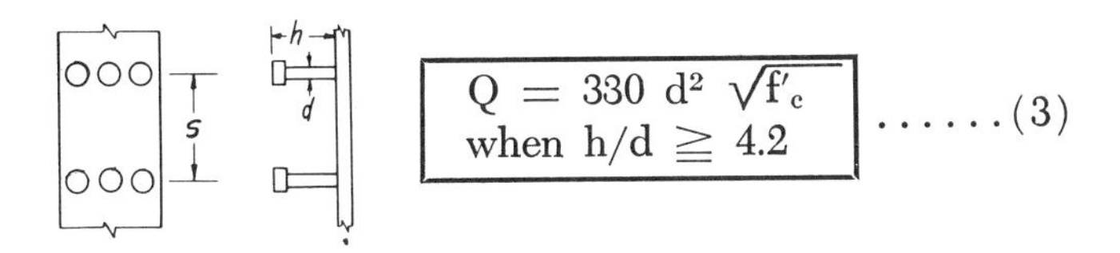

$$Q = 330\ d^2 \sqrt{f'_c} \quad \text{when } h/d \geqq 4.2 \qquad \ldots\ldots(3)$$

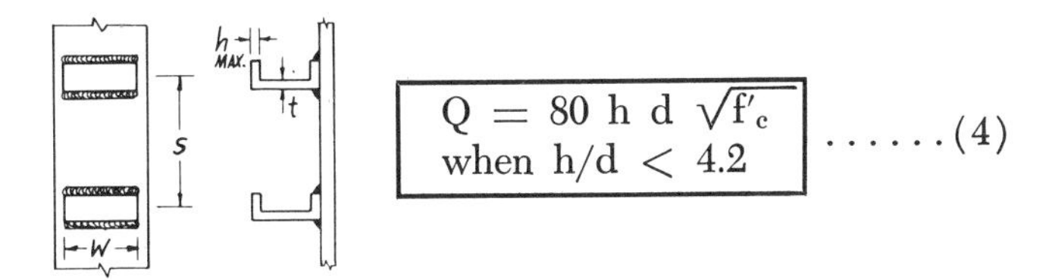

$$Q = 80\ h\ d \sqrt{f'_c} \quad \text{when } h/d < 4.2 \qquad \ldots\ldots(4)$$

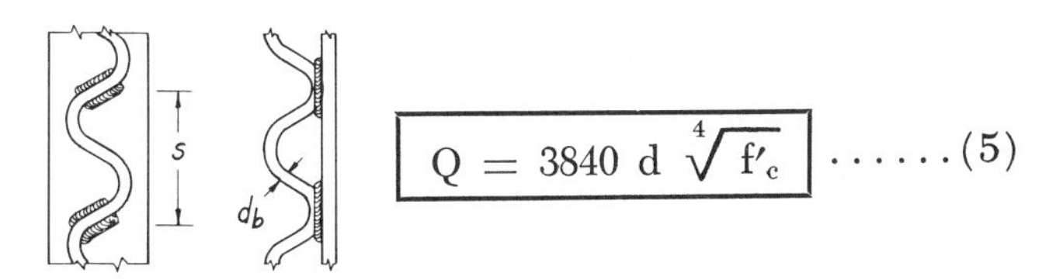

$$Q = 3840\ d \sqrt[4]{f'_c} \qquad \ldots\ldots(5)$$

$$Q = 180 \left(h + \frac{t}{2} \right) w \sqrt{f'_c} \qquad \ldots\ldots\ldots(6)$$

Note: f'_c = 28-day compressive strength of concrete

For most conditions, the useful capacity (Q) of the shear connector may be read directly from Table 4, 5, or 6 which make it unnecessary to work the above formulas.

factor of safety

The factor of safety to be used in computing the allowable design load for one shear connector, is obtained from the following formula*:

$$F.S. = \frac{2.7(1 + C_{mc} + C_{mi}\,C_s) - (C_{mc} + C_{mi}) + C_v}{1 + C_v} \qquad \ldots\ldots\ldots\ldots\ldots\ldots\ldots\ldots(7)$$

* AASHO (1.95) now allows as an alternate, a factor safety of 4 in lieu of calculating it with the above formula.

TABLE 1—Moment of Inertia, Transformed Composite Section

Modular ratio n = 10, b = effective slab width, t = slab thickness

Steel beam		Moment of inertia I_c of composite beams, in.^{4}							
		b = 5 ft			b = 6 ft			b = 7 ft	
Shape	I_B, in.^{4}	t = 6 in.	t = 7 in.	t = 8 in.	t = 6 in.	t = 7 in.	t = 8 in.	t = 7 in.	t = 8 in.
36 WF 300	20,290	32,062	34,056	36,085	33,648	35,820	38,017	37,386	39,715
36 WF 280	18,819	30,237	32,147	34,086	31,743	33,813	35,903	35,285	37,494
36 WF 260	17,234	28,265	30,083	31,926	29,682	31,646	33,624	33,019	35,104
36 WF 245	16,092	26,816	28,561	30,328	28,164	30,043	31,932	31,338	33,323
36 WF 230	14,988	25,403	27,076	28,766	26,683	28,477	30,279	29,696	31,583
36 WF 194	12,103	22,172	23,713	25,259	23,328	24,963	26,594	26,036	27,732
36 WF 182	11,282	21,028	22,496	23,967	22,116	23,668	25,215	24,670	26,274
36 WF 170	10,470	19,880	21,270	22,663	20,896	22,363	23,823	23,292	24,802
36 WF 160	9,739	18,845	20,172	21,500	19,805	21,198	22,586	22,066	23,498
36 WF 150	9,012	17,800	19,060	20,319	18,699	20,017	21,330	20,823	22,174
33 WF 220	12,312	21,334	22,806	24,298	22,425	24,001	25,591	25,038	26,703
33 WF 200	11,048	19,646	21,019	22,409	20,647	22,108	23,582	23,047	24,584
33 WF 141	7,442	15,002	16,099	17,200	15,754	16,899	18,047	17,572	18,753
33 WF 130	6,699	13,896	14,919	16,046	14,584	15,648	16,715	16,257	17,353
30 WF 124	5,347	11,376	12,255	13,145	11,939	12,855	13,781	13,355	14,309
30 WF 116	4,919	10,704	11,535	12,376	11,226	12,090	12,963	12,550	13,449
30 WF 108	4,461	9,983	10,763	11,553	10,463	11,271	12,090	11,692	12,533
27 WF 102	3,604	8,187	8,858	9,541	8,578	9,271	9,981	9,614	10,345
27 WF 94	3,267	7,612	8,234	8,871	7,964	8,608	9,269	8,916	9,597
24 WF 100	2,987	6,739	7,316	7,914	7,056	7,657	8,281	7,940	8,585
24 WF 94	2,683	6,379	6,936	7,512	6,681	7,260	7,861	7,527	8,148
24 WF 84	2,364	5,791	6,298	6,822	6,054	6,579	7,126	6,811	7,377
24 WF 76	2,096	5,292	5,757	6,239	5,524	6,005	6,508	6,210	6,730
21 WF 73	1,600	4,202	4,603	5,026	4,390	4,807	5,250	4,975	5,435
21 WF 68	1,478	3,955	4,334	4,733	4,127	4,521	4,939	4,675	5,111
21 WF 62	1,327	3,640	3,990	4,361	3,793	4,157	4,545	4,294	4,700
18 WF 60	984	2,834	3,137	3,464	2,957	3,274	3,619	3,389	3,751
18 WF 55	890	2,622	2,905	3,211	2,732	3,029	3,353	3,133	3,474
18 WF 50	801	2,412	2,674	2,959	2,510	2,786	3,088	2,879	3,199
16 WF 50	655	2,056	2,300	2,567	2,144	2,401	2,686	2,486	2,789
16 WF 45	583	1,876	2,100	2,349	1,953	2,190	2,456	2,268	2,551
16 WF 40	516	1,697	1,903	2,133	1,764	1,983	2,230	2,053	2,316
16 WF 36	446	1,532	1,723	1,937	1,592	1,795	2,027	1,859	2,107
14 WF 34	339	1,230	1,401	1,597	1,281	1,465	1,677	1,522	1,751
14 WF 30	290	1,096	1,253	1,435	1,141	1,311	1,510	1,363	1,579

TABLE 2—Section Modulus, Bottom Flange of I Beam

Modular ratio n = 10, b = effective slab width, t = slab thickness

Steel beam			Section modulus S_{bc} of composite beam, in.^{3}							
			b = 5 ft			b = 6 ft			b = 7 ft	
Shape	S_s, in.^{3}	S_s/A_B, in.	t = 6 in.	t = 7 in.	t = 8 in.	t = 6 in.	t = 7 in.	t = 8 in.	t = 7 in.	t = 8 in.
36 WF 300	1,105.1	12.5	1,306.0	1,340.3	1,375.2	1,325.8	1,361.5	1,397.7	1,379.0	1,416.9
36 WF 280	1,031.2	12.5	1,223.2	1,255.2	1,288.7	1,241.9	1,275.5	1,309.9	1,292.0	1,327.2
36 WF 260	951.1	12.4	1,136.1	1,166.9	1,198.4	1,153.1	1,185.2	1,217.4	1,200.3	1,233.5
36 WF 245	892.5	12.4	1,070.9	1,100.2	1,130.0	1,087.0	1,117.3	1,147.8	1,130.9	1,162.7
36 WF 230	835.5	12.3	1,007.7	1,035.4	1,063.8	1,022.7	1,051.2	1,080.6	1,064.4	1,094.0
36 WF 194	663.6	11.6	838.3	863.9	889.4	851.7	878.1	904.3	889.5	916.5
36 WF 182	621.2	11.6	788.5	812.7	836.8	801.0	825.8	850.7	836.3	861.7
36 WF 170	579.1	11.6	739.0	761.5	784.2	750.3	773.3	796.8	783.2	806.8
36 WF 160	541.0	11.5	695.4	716.8	738.6	706.1	728.2	750.4	737.0	759.5
36 WF 150	502.9	11.4	651.5	672.1	692.5	661.4	682.2	703.3	690.6	711.8
33 WF 220	740.6	11.4	902.5	929.3	956.6	916.1	943.8	971.9	955.6	984.3
33 WF 200	669.6	11.4	821.7	846.5	871.6	833.9	859.2	885.2	869.7	896.2
33 WF 141	446.8	10.8	581.9	600.9	620.3	590.5	609.9	629.7	617.2	637.4
33 WF 130	404.8	10.6	533.8	551.7	573.5	541.8	559.9	578.4	566.4	585.5
30 WF 124	354.6	9.7	472.8	489.6	507.1	479.7	497.1	515.0	503.0	521.3
30 WF 116	327.9	9.6	441.6	457.6	474.2	448.0	464.5	481.4	469.9	487.3
30 WF 108	299.2	9.4	408.8	423.9	439.4	414.7	430.2	446.1	435.3	451.6
27 WF 102	266.3	8.9	363.1	377.4	392.3	368.3	383.0	398.3	387.5	403.2
27 WF 94	242.8	8.8	334.4	347.7	361.6	339.0	352.8	367.1	356.8	371.7
24 WF 100	248.9	8.5	332.8	346.6	361.0	337.3	351.4	366.6	355.6	371.2
24 WF 94	220.9	8.0	308.0	321.4	335.5	312.5	326.3	341.0	330.3	345.6
24 WF 84	196.3	7.9	276.3	288.5	301.3	280.1	292.8	306.2	296.3	310.2
24 WF 76	175.4	7.8	249.9	261.2	273.2	253.3	265.0	277.5	268.3	281.3
21 WF 73	150.7	7.0	219.4	230.5	242.6	222.6	234.3	246.7	237.4	250.5
21 WF 68	139.9	7.0	205.1	215.7	227.1	208.1	219.1	231.1	222.0	234.6
21 WF 62	126.4	6.9	187.1	197.0	207.7	189.8	200.1	211.4	202.7	214.6
18 WF 60	107.8	6.1	164.2	174.2	185.0	166.8	177.2	188.8	179.9	192.3
18 WF 55	98.2	6.1	150.9	160.2	170.5	153.2	163.1	174.2	165.7	177.4
18 WF 50	89.0	6.1	137.7	146.5	156.1	139.8	149.1	159.6	151.5	162.7
16 WF 50	80.7	5.5	128.3	137.4	147.4	130.5	140.2	151.1	142.7	154.3
16 WF 45	72.4	5.5	116.2	124.6	134.2	118.1	127.3	137.5	129.6	140.6
16 WF 40	64.4	5.5	104.2	112.1	120.9	106.0	114.5	124.2	116.8	127.2
16 WF 36	56.3	5.3	93.6	101.0	109.5	95.3	103.4	112.6	105.6	115.6
14 WF 34	48.5	4.9	82.9	90.5	99.2	84.7	93.0	102.5	95.3	105.6
14 WF 30	41.8	4.7	73.5	80.6	88.7	75.2	82.9	92.0	85.2	95.2

where:

$$C_{mc} = \frac{M_{Dc}}{M_L}$$

$$C_{ml} = \frac{M_{Ds}}{M_L}$$

$$C_s = \frac{S_c}{S_s}$$

$$C_v = \frac{V_D}{V_L}$$

where:

M_{Dc} = max. moment caused by dead loads acting on composite section

M_{Ds} = max. moment caused by dead loads acting on steel beam alone

M_L = max. moment caused by live load

S_c = section modulus of composite beam for extreme tension fibers

S_s = section modulus of steel beam for extreme tension fibers

TABLE 3—Coefficient m/I_c for Horizontal Shear

Modular ratio n = 10, b = effective slab width, t = slab thickness

Steel beam	Coefficient $\frac{m}{I_c}$ of composite beam, 1/in.							
Shape	b = 5 ft			b = 6 ft			b = 7 ft	
	t = 6 in.	t = 7 in.	t = 8 in.	t = 6 in.	t = 7 in.	t = 8 in.	t = 7 in.	t = 8 in.
36 WF 300	0.0170	0.0183	0.0193	0.0184	0.0196	0.0205	0.0206	0.0215
36 WF 280	0.0176	0.0188	0.0198	0.0190	0.0201	0.0210	0.0211	0.0220
36 WF 260	0.0183	0.0195	0.0204	0.0196	0.0208	0.0216	0.0218	0.0226
36 WF 245	0.0188	0.0200	0.0209	0.0202	0.0213	0.0221	0.0222	0.0230
36 WF 230	0.0194	0.0205	0.0214	0.0207	0.0218	0.0226	0.0227	0.0234
36 WF 194	0.0212	0.0222	0.0230	0.0224	0.0233	0.0240	0.0242	0.0248
36 WF 182	0.0217	0.0227	0.0234	0.0229	0.0238	0.0244	0.0246	0.0251
36 WF 170	0.0222	0.0232	0.0238	0.0234	0.0242	0.0248	0.0250	0.0255
36 WF 160	0.0227	0.0237	0.0243	0.0239	0.0247	0.0252	0.0255	0.0259
36 WF 150	0.0233	0.0242	0.0248	0.0244	0.0252	0.0257	0.0260	0.0263
33 WF 220	0.0213	0.0225	0.0234	0.0227	0.0238	0.0246	0.0248	0.0255
33 WF 200	0.0222	0.0233	0.0242	0.0235	0.0246	0.0253	0.0255	0.0262
33 WF 141	0.0253	0.0261	0.0267	0.0264	0.0271	0.0276	0.0279	0.0283
33 WF 130	0.0261	0.0269	0.0273	0.0272	0.0279	0.0283	0.0286	0.0289
30 WF 124	0.0288	0.0296	0.0301	0.0299	0.0306	0.0309	0.0313	0.0315
30 WF 116	0.0295	0.0302	0.0306	0.0306	0.0311	0.0314	0.0318	0.0320
30 WF 108	0.0303	0.0309	0.0313	0.0313	0.0318	0.0320	0.0325	0.0325
27 WF 102	0.0331	0.0337	0.0340	0.0341	0.0346	0.0347	0.0352	0.0351
27 WF 94	0.0338	0.0343	0.0345	0.0348	0.0352	0.0352	0.0357	0.0356
24 WF 100	0.0361	0.0367	0.0369	0.0372	0.0376	0.0376	0.0383	0.0381
24 WF 94	0.0371	0.0376	0.0377	0.0382	0.0385	0.0384	0.0391	0.0388
24 WF 84	0.0381	0.0384	0.0383	0.0391	0.0392	0.0390	0.0397	0.0393
24 WF 76	0.0390	0.0392	0.0390	0.0399	0.0399	0.0395	0.0403	0.0398
21 WF 73	0.0436	0.0435	0.0432	0.0445	0.0442	0.0435	0.0447	0.0438
21 WF 68	0.0441	0.0440	0.0435	0.0450	0.0446	0.0438	0.0449	0.0439
21 WF 62	0.0449	0.0446	0.0439	0.0457	0.0451	0.0442	0.0453	0.0442
18 WF 60	0.0507	0.0501	0.0489	0.0514	0.0503	0.0490	0.0505	0.0489
18 WF 55	0.0514	0.0505	0.0492	0.0520	0.0508	0.0493	0.0509	0.0491
18 WF 50	0.0519	0.0509	0.0495	0.0525	0.0510	0.0494	0.0511	0.0492
16 WF 50	0.0566	0.0550	0.0531	0.0568	0.0552	0.0530	0.0551	0.0525
16 WF 45	0.0570	0.0554	0.0532	0.0573	0.0554	0.0528	0.0550	0.0522
16 WF 40	0.0575	0.0556	0.0532	0.0578	0.0554	0.0527	0.0550	0.0519
16 WF 36	0.0583	0.0561	0.0535	0.0583	0.0556	0.0526	0.0550	0.0517
14 WF 34	0.0635	0.0605	0.0571	0.0634	0.0599	0.0560	0.0591	0.0545
14 WF 30	0.0641	0.0607	0.0565	0.0636	0.0596	0.0553	0.0587	0.0541

From "Composite Construction in Steel and Concrete" by Viest, Fountain & Singleton.

TABLE 4—Useful Capacity, Q, of One Stud Connector, lbs. (h/d > 4.2)

Stud dia., d, in.	CONCRETE STRENGTH, f'c psi			
	2,500	3,000	3,500	4,000
5/8	6,500	7,100	7,600	8,200
3/4	9,300	10,200	11,000	11,700
7/8	12,600	13,800	15,000	16,000

Note: A factor of safety must be applied to the above useful capacity, Q, to arrive at the working value, q.

TABLE 5—Useful Capacity, Q, Per Turn of Spiral Connector

Spiral wire dia, in.	CONCRETE STRENGTH, f'c, psi.			
	2500	3000	3500	4000
1/2	13,580	14,210	14,770	15,270
5/8	16,970	17,760	18,460	19,000
3/4	20,360	21,310	22,150	22,900
7/8	23,760	24,870	25,840	26,720

Note: A factor of safety must be applied to the above useful capacity, Q, to arrive at the working value, q.

V_D = vertical shear caused by dead load acting on composite section

V_L = vertical shear caused by live load

spacing of sheer connectors

$$\boxed{s = \frac{n\,q}{V_h}} \qquad (8)$$

where:

s = spacing or pitch of shear connectors in the direction of beam axis, in.

n = number of shear connectors at one transverse beam cross-section

q = capacity of one connector, lbs

V_h = horizontal shear to be transferred, lbs

The spacing of shear connectors should not exceed 24".

3. DESIGN OF CONNECTING WELDS

Welds joining shear connectors to beams should be designed to the allowable fatigue force (f_w), for the range (K) of shear stress and the working load (q) of the connector. See Table 7.

where:

$$K = \frac{\text{min. shear (V)}}{\text{max. shear (V)}}$$

ω = leg size of fillet weld, in.

f_w = allowable force on fillet weld, lbs/lin. in.

TABLE 6—Useful Capacity Q, Per 1 In. of Channel (Lbs)

Channel type and size	FLANGE THICKNESS, IN.		Web thickness t, in.	CONCRETE STRENGTH f'_c (psi)			
	Max, h	Min.		2,500	3,000	3,500	4,000
American Standard:							
3-in:							
4.1-lb	0.377	0.170	0.170	4,160	4,560	4,920	5,260
5.0-lb	0.377	0.170	0.258	4,560	4,980	5,380	5,750
6.0-lb	0.377	0.170	0.356	4,990	5,460	5,910	6,310
4-in:							
5.4-lb	0.413	0.180	0.180	4,520	4,960	5,360	5,710
7.25-lb	0.413	0.180	0.320	5,160	5,640	6,100	6,510
5-in.:							
6.7-lb	0.450	0.190	0.190	4,910	5,370	5,810	6,200
9.0-lb	0.450	0.190	0.325	5,510	6,030	6,520	6,960
6-in.:							
8.2-lb	0.487	0.200	0.200	5,870	5,780	6,260	6,680
10.5-lb	0.487	0.200	0.314	5,790	6,350	6,860	7,330
13.0-lb	0.487	0.200	0.437	6,350	6,950	7,510	8,020
7-in.:							
9.8-lb	0.523	0.210	0.210	5,650	6,180	6,690	7,140
12.25-lb	0.523	0.210	0.314	6,110	6,700	7,240	7,740
14.75-lb	0.523	0.210	0.419	6,590	7,210	7,810	8,330
Car building:							
3-in.:							
7.1-lb	0.390	0.313	0.312	4,910	5,370	5,810	6,210
9.0-lb	0.390	0.313	0.500	5,760	6,310	6,810	7,280
4-in.:							
13.8-lb	0.531	0.469	0.500	7,250	7,690	8,310	7,870
Shipbuilding							
6-in.:							
12.0-lb	0.413	0.337	0.313	5,130	5,610	6,060	6,480
15.1-lb	0.521	0.429	0.313	6,070	6,680	7,210	7,810
15.3-lb	0.440	0.330	0.340	5,490	6,010	6,500	6,940
16.3-lb	0.521	0.429	0.375	6,380	6,980	7,550	8,060
18.0-lb	0.530	0.420	0.375	6,460	7,070	7,640	8,160
7-in.:							
17.6-lb	0.521	0.429	0.375	6,380	6,980	7,550	8,060
19.1-lb	0.554	0.446	0.350	6,560	7,190	7,760	8,300
22.7-lb	0.554	0.446	0.500	7,240	7,920	8,560	9,150

Note: A factor of safety must be applied to the above useful capacity (Q) to arrive at the working value (q).

4. COMPOSITE CONSTRUCTION SUMMARY

1.a. Without shoring, dead load carried by steel and live load is carried by the composite section.

b. With shoring, dead loads and live loads are carried by the composite section.

2. With shoring, there is reduction in steel but added cost of shoring.

3. Type and cost of shear connector must be balanced against installation cost.

4. In taking advantage of composite action, effort should be made to reduce weight and depth of steel beams.

5. Savings in steel from use of bottom cover plates must be evaluated against additional fabricating cost.

6. Composite construction has the advantage of greater rigidity.

7. Studs may also serve as "high chairs" to support steel reinforcing mesh for the concrete.

8. Future connector designs may be more efficient and reduce the number required.

TABLE 7—Allowable Fatigue Force on Fillet Welds

Cycles	Allowable force on weld, lbs/linear in.	Formula No. in AWS Bridge Spec.
N = 2,000,000	$f_\omega = \dfrac{5090\omega}{1 - \frac{k}{2}}$	No. 10
N = 600,000	$f_\omega = \dfrac{7070\omega}{1 - \frac{k}{2}}$	No. 14
N = 100,000	$f_\omega = \dfrac{8484\omega}{1 - \frac{k}{2}}$	No. 18

Note: But not to exceed 8800 ω lb/linear in

Problem 1

To determine the working load (q), spacing (s), and weld length (L_w) for each of several types of shear connectors, for a typical composite section.

In the building field, the total horizontal shear force to be carried by the shear connectors is based on the total bending force in either the concrete or the steel section resulting from the maximum positive moment on the beam. It is assumed this force will be transferred from the concrete slab into the steel beam by the connectors along a distance from the point of maximum positive moment out to the end of the beam, for simply supported beams; or from the point of maximum positive moment out to the point of contraflexure, for continuous beams.

In the bridge field, this shear transfer is based on the vertical shear applied to the beam. In most cases this value will vary along the beam's length. For this reason, more than one section may have to be checked when the size and number of shear connectors are determined.

This example considers just one point of application, the section near the pier supports, and assumes certain conditions:

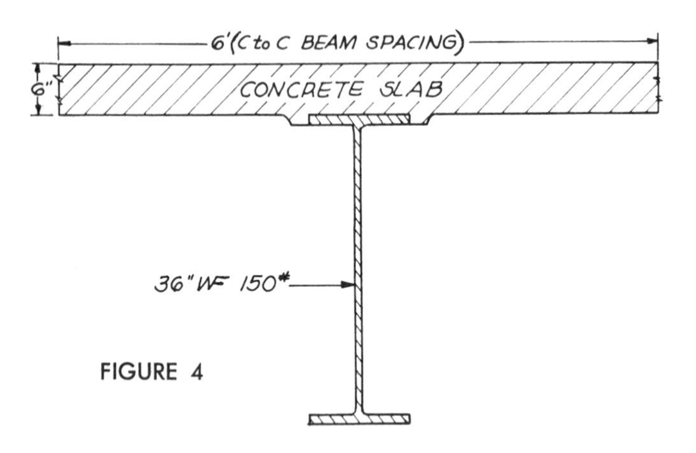

FIGURE 4

$f_c' = 3000$ psi (concrete)

$\dfrac{m}{I_c} = .0244$/in. (See Table 3)

F.S. = 3.81

$V_{max} = 49.6$ kips

$V_{min} = 5.06$ kips

calculating for horizontal shear

$$V_h = \frac{V_c\ m}{I_c}$$

$$= (49.6)(.0244)$$

$$= 1.21 \text{ kips/in.}$$

Stud Connectors

Use ¾" dia. x 4" studs. From Table 4, Q = 10.2 kips/stud.

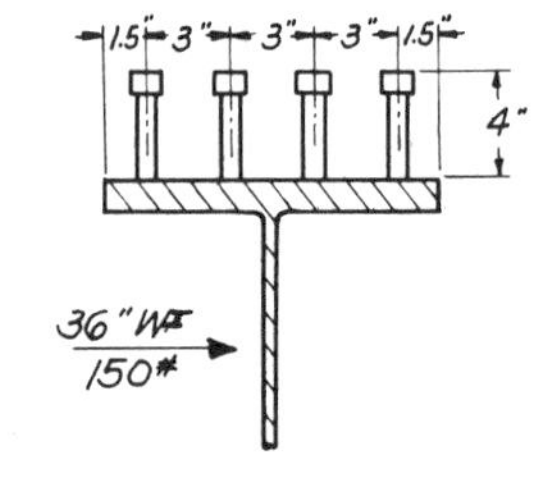

working load

$$q = \frac{Q}{F.S.}$$

$$= \frac{(10.2)}{(3.81)}$$

$$= 2.68 \text{ kips/stud}$$

spacing of connectors (use 4 studs per transverse section)

$$s = \frac{n\ q}{V_h}$$

$$= \frac{(4)(2.68)}{(1.21)}$$

$$= 8.85'' \text{ or use } 8\tfrac{1}{2}''$$

weld length

Complete contact surface of stud is joined to beam. No calculation of weld length is necessary.

Channel Connectors

Use a 4" 5.4-lb channel of 10" length. From Table 6, Q = 49.6 kips/channel.

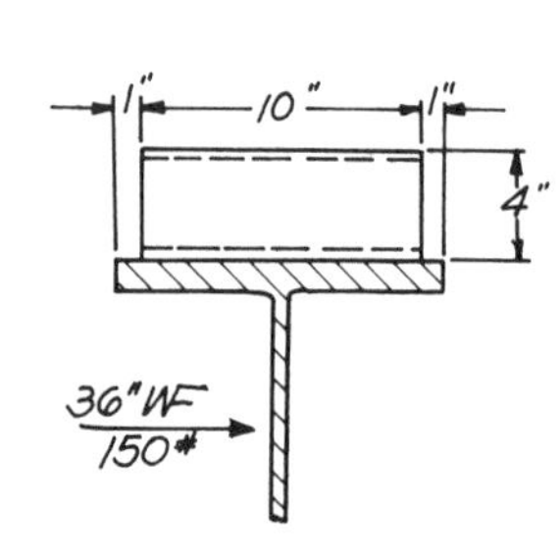

working load

$$q = \frac{F.S.}{Q}$$

$$= \frac{(49.6)}{(3.81)}$$

$$= 13.0 \text{ kips/channel}$$

spacing of connectors

$$s = \frac{n\ q}{V_h}$$

$$= \frac{(1)(13.0)}{(1.21)}$$

$$= 10.75'' \text{ or use } 10\tfrac{1}{2}''$$

allowable force on weld

Assume fillet leg size of $\omega = \frac{3}{16}''$ and N = 600,000 cycles:

$$K = \frac{V_{min}}{V_{max}}$$

$$= \frac{(+5.06 \text{ kips})}{(+46.6 \text{ kips})}$$

$$= +0.102$$

$$f_w = \frac{7070\ \omega}{1 - \frac{K}{2}} \qquad \text{(See Table 7)}$$

$$= \frac{7070(3/16)}{1 - (.051)}$$

$$= 1.4 \text{ kips/in. of weld}$$

required weld length

$$L_w = \frac{q}{f_w}$$

$$= \frac{(13.0)}{(1.4)}$$

$$= 9.3'' < 20'' \text{ actually used} \qquad \underline{OK}$$

This indicates most channels are overwelded.

Spiral Connectors

Use ¾″ dia rod. From Table 5, Q = 21.31 kips/turn.

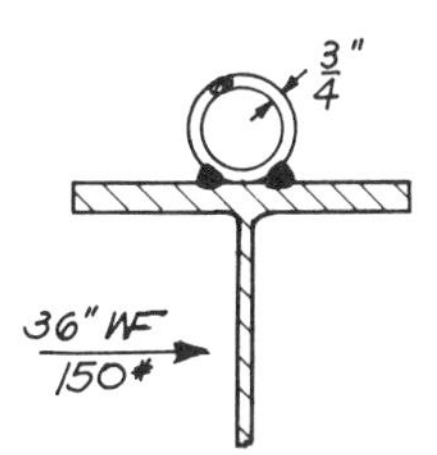

working load

$$q = \frac{Q}{F.S.}$$

$$= \frac{(21.31)}{(3.81)}$$

$$= 5.6 \text{ kips/turn}$$

pitch

$$s = \frac{n\ q}{V_h}$$

$$= \frac{(1)(5.6)}{(1.21)}$$

$$= 4.61'' \text{ or } \underline{\text{use } 4\tfrac{1}{2}''\text{/turn}}$$

force on weld

Assume fillet leg size of ω = ⅜″ and N = 600,000 cycles:

$$K = \frac{V_{min}}{V_{max}}$$

$$= \frac{(+5.06 \text{ kips})}{(+49.6 \text{ kips})}$$

$$= +.102$$

$$f_w = \frac{7070\ \omega}{1 - \frac{K}{2}} \qquad \text{(From Table 7)}$$

$$= \frac{7070(3/8)}{1 - (.051)}$$

$$= 2.8 \text{ kips/in. of weld}$$

length of weld

$$L_w = \frac{q}{f_w}$$

$$= \frac{(5.6)}{(2.8)}$$

$$= 2.0'' \text{ or } \underline{1'' \text{ each side in contact area}}$$

Studs are widely used in both building and bridge work as shear connectors for composite construction. Quickly attached by efficient arc-welding equipment, studs serve to anchor the concrete slab to the steel beams. The composite beam provides high strength at lower cost.

Typical scenes of modern bridge work featuring composite construction. Prior to pouring the concrete deck, studs are attached to girder flanges by specialized arc-welding equipment. Connectors allow the concrete slab to act with the steel.

Floor Systems for Bridges

1. REINFORCED CONCRETE

Many bridge designs use reinforced concrete slabs for floors. These may be supported by stringers and floor beams of the bridge. When no floor beams are present, the concrete floor is supported directly on top of the primary longitudinal members.

On deck-type bridges, with the concrete floor resting on the top flange or top chord of the longitudinal member, the concrete slab may be anchored to the steel by means of shear attachments. In this manner, the concrete floor becomes an integral part of the steel member in compression.

This composite construction is recognized by most structural authorities as an effective means of insuring economy (particularly in steel tonnage); of promoting shallow depth and more graceful structural lines, and of improving the rigidity of bridges. Typical savings produced with composite construction alone are in the range of 8 to 30% by weight of steel. To be effective, of course, the concrete must always be in compression to prevent cracks in the pavement.

Some types of shear attachments are shown in Figure 1. See Section 4.9 on Shear Attachments for Bridges.

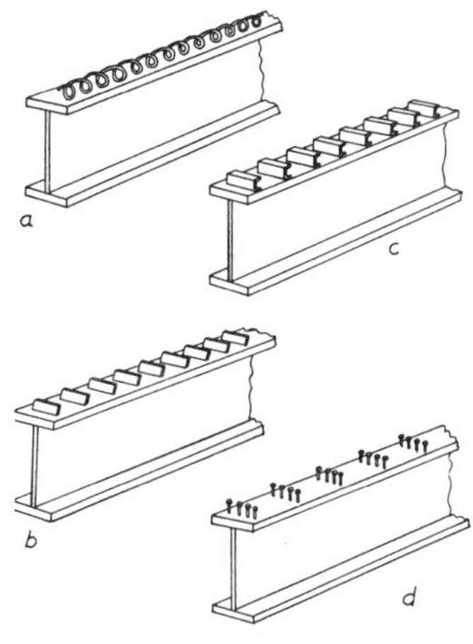

FIGURE 1

2. STEEL GRID

Steel grids may be used for floors for the following reasons:

1. Reduced dead weight of flooring. This reduces the required size of stringers, floor beams, and girders and results in a savings in the amount of steel and cost of the bridge.

2. Snow does not remain on the grid floor; hence, grids greatly lower snow removal cost during the winter.

3. Since snow and rain do not remain on the grid floor, there is no reason for a crown for drainage purposes. This simplifies construction costs.

4. For the same reason, scuppers and drains are not required.

5. The grid flooring can be installed easily and quickly.

Sometimes a light concrete layer is applied to the steel grid.

FIGURE 2

3. STEEL PLATE

Steel plate welded to the bridge structure and properly stiffened has been used for flooring. By welding a comparatively thin steel plate to the top flange of longi-

FIGURE 3

tudinal members, a built-up section is produced which greatly increases the strength and stiffness of the member. This has sometimes been called "battledeck flooring".

4. TYPICAL FLOOR SYSTEMS

The design in Figure 4(a) utilizes a steel grid floor in order to reduce the dead weight of the structure. The steel grid rests on the main girders and the longitudinal stringers. The floor beams are set lower so that the stringers, when placed on top, will be flush with the top of the girder. Brackets are shop welded to the girders to receive the floor beams. The top bracket plate is slightly narrower than the flange of the floor beam, and the bottom bracket plate is slightly wider than the flange of the floor beam. This is so that downhand fillet welds may be used in the field connection of the floor beams to the girders.

With a little extra care in shipping and erecting, it would be possible to shop weld the railing and like attachments to the girders and further reduce the field welding.

The floor system in Figure 4(b) is made up of two longitudinal steel girders with a concrete floor attached to the girders by means of shear connections. Although spiral shear connections are shown here, this composite beam could be made by using any type of shear attachments. Shear attachments can also be used on the floor beams.

In the design in Figure 5(a), the top portion of the girders helps to form the curb. For this reason, the floor beams must be lowered, so as to get the bridge floor below the top flange of the girders. To keep this floor level down, the stringers run between the floor beams and their top flanges are flush with the top flanges of the floor beams. Although this produces a very compact and efficient design, it does involve a little more fitting and welding than the previous floor designs.

A very popular design today is the continuous girder deck bridge, Figure 5(b). Several plate girders are placed side-by-side with sufficient cross bracing. A composite concrete floor is attached to the top of the girders by means of shear connectors. For short spans, rolled beams are used with cover plates added

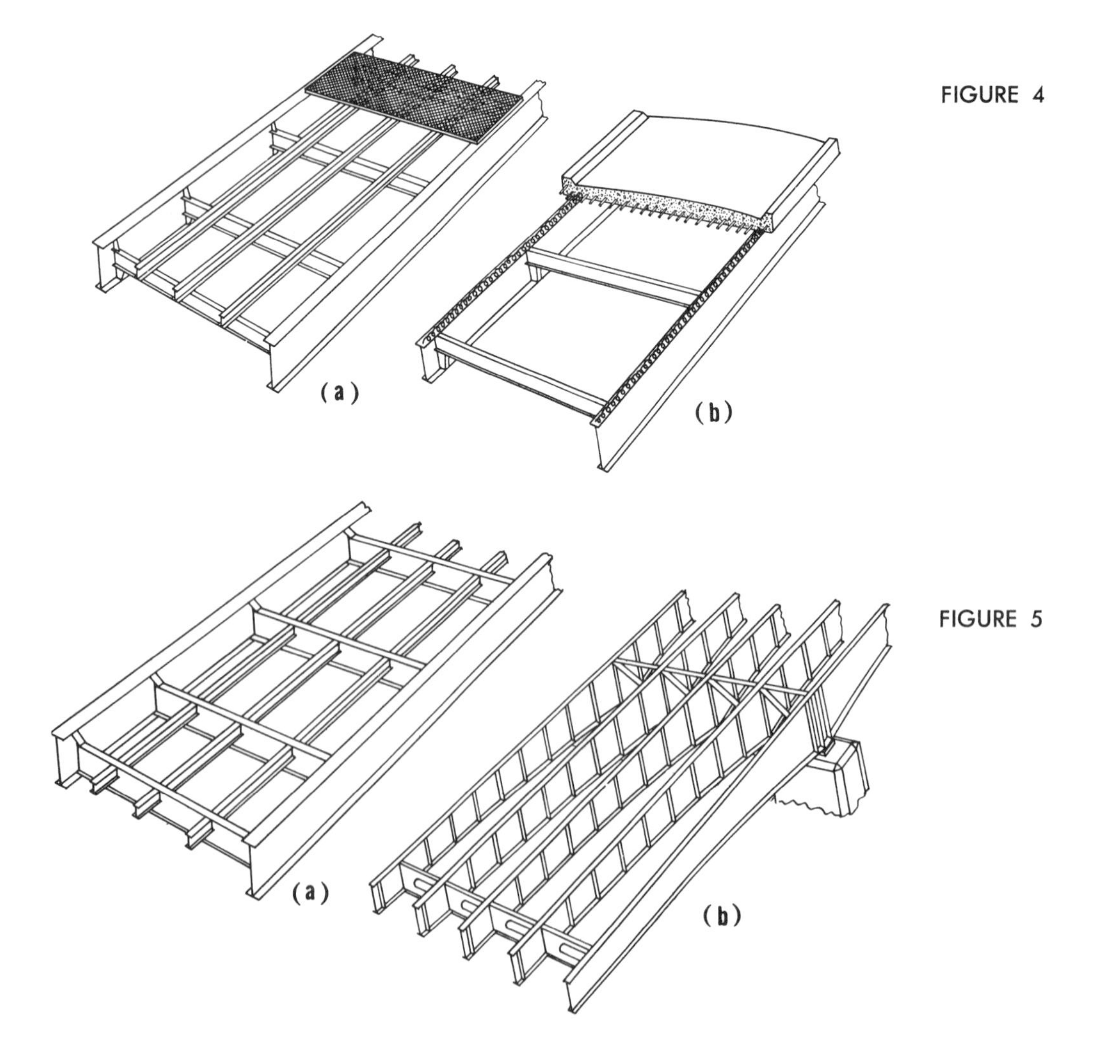

FIGURE 4

FIGURE 5

at points of high moment. For longer spans, deeper plate girders are fabricated. For a more efficient design, these girders are deeper at points of high moment. The outside girders usually have their intermediate stiffeners placed on one side only, the inboard side, so that they have a more pleasing appearance.

Box girders have been used for bridges; usually two or more are used. They may be joined by several methods. The example in Figure 6(a) uses floor beams flush with the top of the box girder, on which is placed a concrete floor attached with shear connectors.

with floor beams extending outward to support the bridge floor. In Figure 6(b), longitudinal stringers are supported on the floor beams, and the floor rests on these. It has even been suggested that a similar design could be made from a large diameter fabricated pipe section.

5. TORSIONAL RESISTANCE

Designers are coming to realize the importance of designing bridge floors, etc., with more inherent lateral stability and torsional resistance.

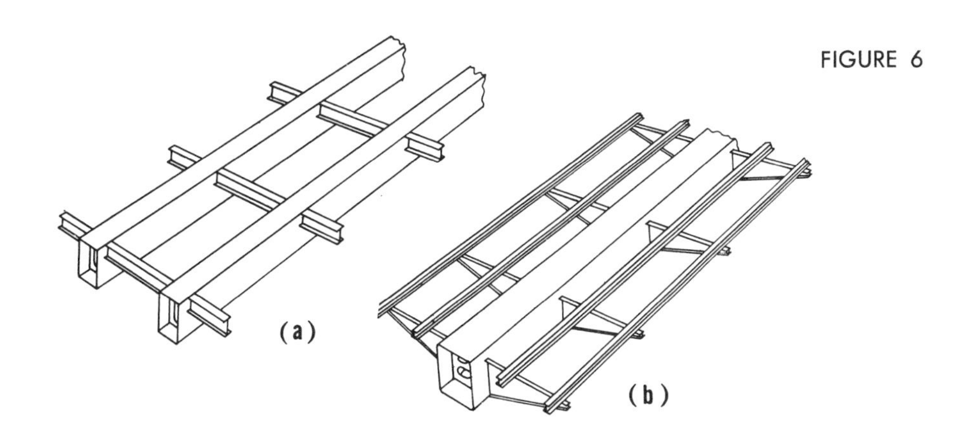

FIGURE 6

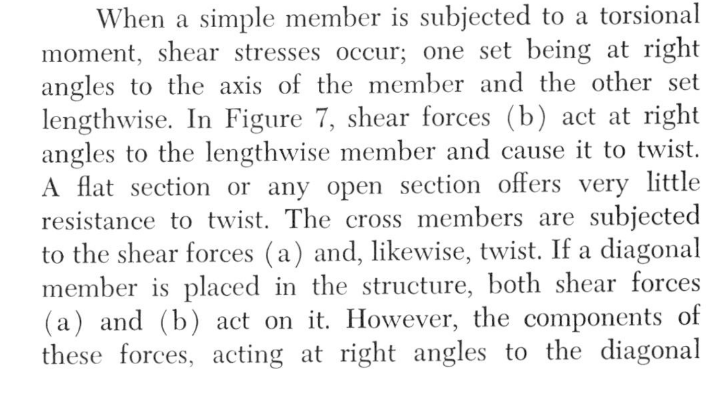

Box girder construction has several advantages. It presents a flat surface for other attachments; hence, the floor beams do not have to be coped when they are welded to the girder. There is less of a corrosion problem because of the flat surfaces. Also, since the box girder ends may be sealed off, the inside is protected. Perhaps the greatest advantage is the tremendous increase in torsional resistance offered by the closed box section. It also has good lateral stability. These torsional and lateral stability properties are becoming recognized advantages, and more bridge engineers are making use of them.

Some designs have made use of a single box girder,

When a simple member is subjected to a torsional moment, shear stresses occur; one set being at right angles to the axis of the member and the other set lengthwise. In Figure 7, shear forces (b) act at right angles to the lengthwise member and cause it to twist. A flat section or any open section offers very little resistance to twist. The cross members are subjected to the shear forces (a) and, likewise, twist. If a diagonal member is placed in the structure, both shear forces (a) and (b) act on it. However, the components of these forces, acting at right angles to the diagonal

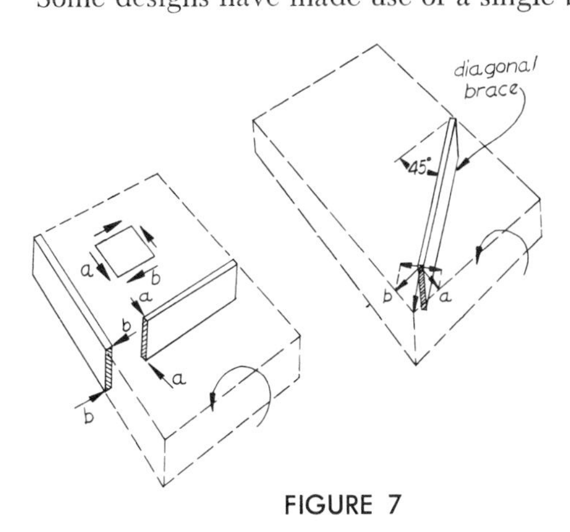

FIGURE 7

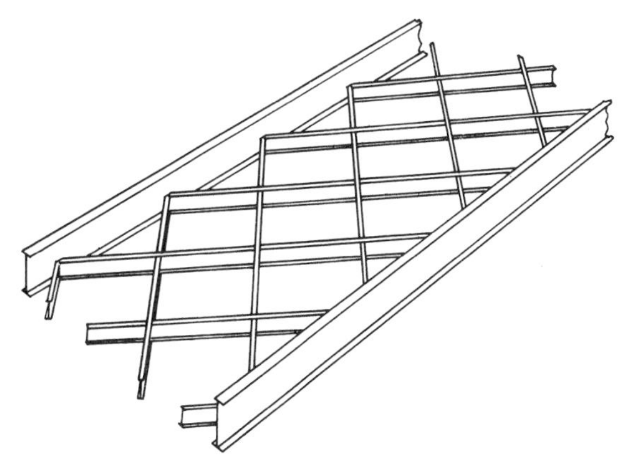

FIGURE 8

member, cancel each other out, so there is no twisting action applied to the member. These forces do combine to place tension and compression in line with the member, thus placing the diagonal member in bending for which it is very rigid. Welding can be used to very good advantage in diagonal bracing.

Figure 8 is from a bridge designed by Camilo Piccone and erected over the Rio Blanco River in Mexico. It is based on an earlier design of Thomas C. Kavanagh. The floor makes use of diagonal members which produce a grid type structure, extremely resistant to twisting and lateral movement.

6. EXPANSION JOINTS

Thermal changes in temperature cause certain physical changes in the size and shape of all construction materials and in their completed structures. The changes are in proportion to the dimensions of the structure, the coefficients of expansion for the materials, and the number of degrees of temperature change.

The structure contracts with the cold and expands with the heat, so a typical bridge might be approximately 1″ longer per 100 linear feet in the summer than in the winter. It will also have daily and short-time changes of a lesser degree in proportion to every change in temperature and it will have additional movements from the elastic deflections of the structure.

These changes in length can be compensated for by corresponding deformations within the structure itself. This is because changing the stress in the structure will also cause it to change in length in proportion to its modulus of elasticity. However, it is usually more economical to use expansion joints since the forces that are required to deform a structure are very large.

Masonry materials such as stone and concrete compress elastically but will not stretch. Therefore, they are likely to crack when subjected to the stresses of temperature contraction.

For these reasons and others, most structures are designed with provision for expansion joints at intervals to take care of the normal movements of expansion and contraction and to relieve the thermal forces. Many types of joints in common use have been designed to do this, varying from open joints, simple planes of weakness, and elastite joints such as are commonly used in pavements, to the long interlocking fingered castings and sliding bar joints used in bridge work.

One Example

The all-welded expansion joint shown in Figure 9 is similar to those in the deck of a large bridge built in recent years. This joint is made entirely from rolled structural plates and angles at a great saving in cost by welding.

It is typical of many cases wherein welding has

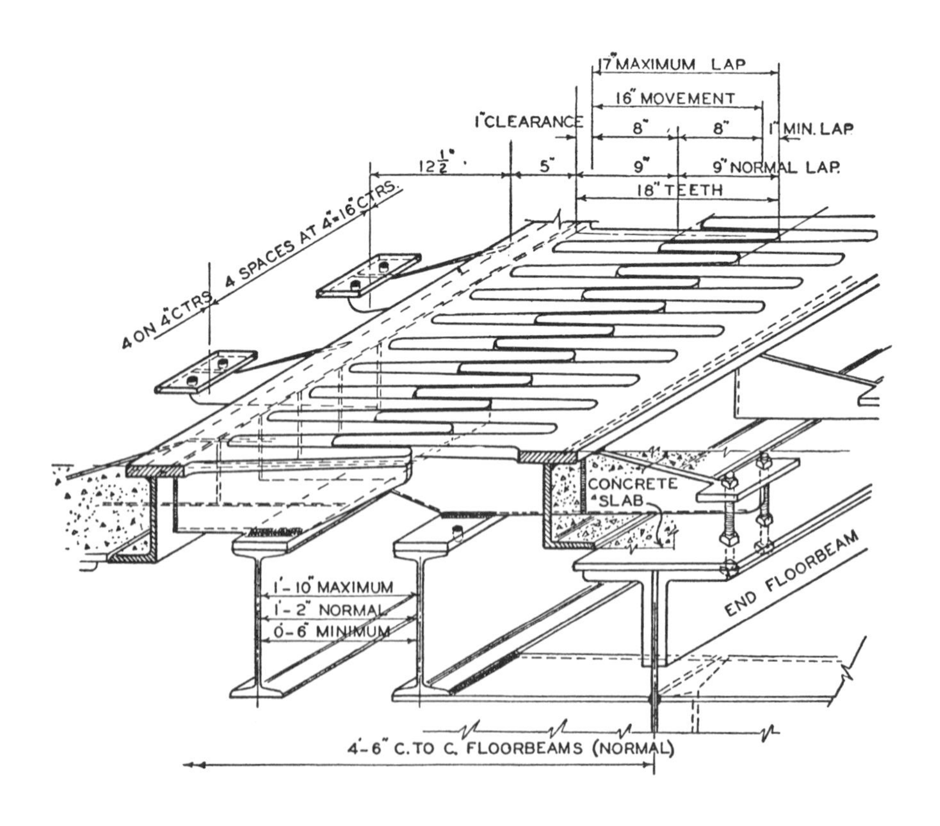

FIGURE 9

not only simplified and improved bridge deck designs but has also reduced the cost of the installation to considerably less than half the estimated cost of conventional type of segmental cast steel fingered joints.

The joint as shown provides for 16″ of movement computed at the rate of 1¼″ per 100′ for the 1200′ length of structure.

The joint (Fig. 9) is made in two halves, each half being symmetrical by rotating 180° with respect to the other half. The joint integral with the curbs, extends the full width of the 24′ roadway in one piece. This is fabricated to fit the curvature of the roadway crown.

The interlocking teeth which form the top surfaces on both sides of the joint are flame-cut in a single operation from a common 28″ x 1″ x 24′ plate as shown in the layout of Figure 10. The cut is made just wide enough to insure finish on both edges of the cut and to give proper clearance for the final meshing of the teeth. The slight side taper of ½″ in the length of the tooth adds to the clearance as the teeth are pulled apart. The 18″ length of tooth is determined by adding 1″ clearance at extreme expansion movements, plus a minimum lap of 1″ when the bridge is fully contracted to the 16″ of required movement.

The teeth are spaced on 4″ centers. This spacing is as small as practical in order to distribute the loads from the roadway surface over as many teeth as possible. It is also desirable in order to avoid having large holes between the teeth when the joint is open. The upper surfaces of the ends of the teeth are ground down and rounded slightly to insure a smooth transition of the loads from one side of the joint to the other.

The joint shown in Figure 9 is designed to support 16,000-lb H-20 truck wheel loads with 100% impact. This load is distributed equally to each of five adjacent

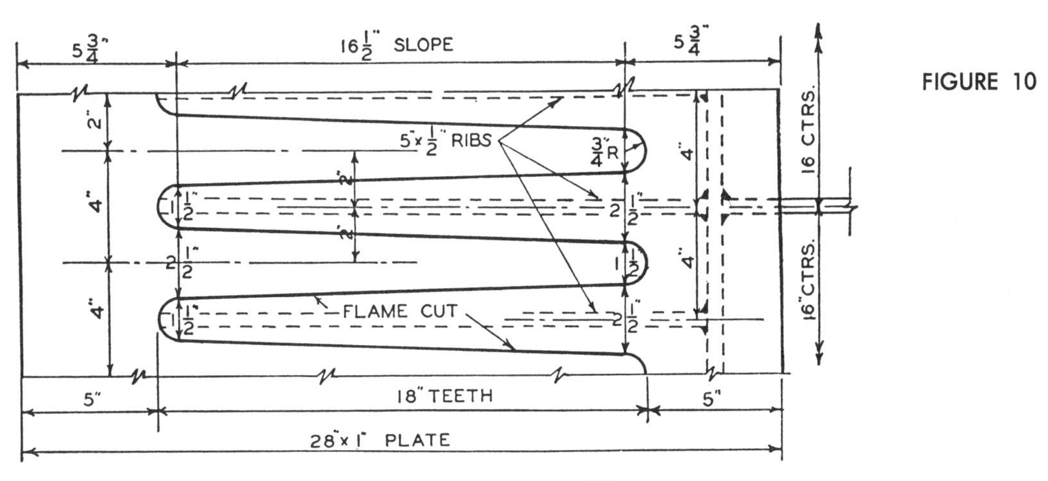

FIGURE 10

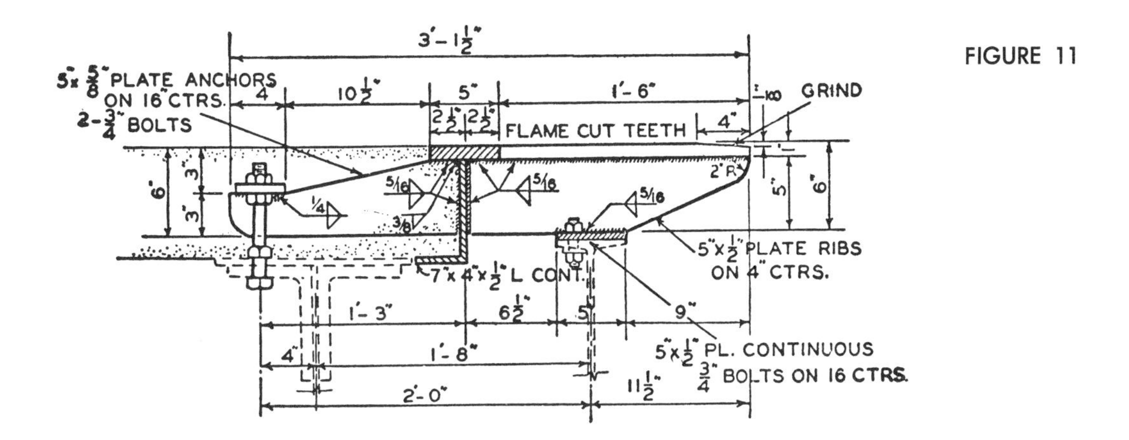

FIGURE 11

teeth and is assumed to be applied on a contact area 3″ long, centered 1½″ from the end of the teeth. While in this extreme position, the teeth on only one side of the joint support the entire load. On this basis the depth of the web, the thickness of the plates, and other proportions are determined to support these load requirements.

The unusually long cantilevered projection of the teeth is reduced by supporting the teeth directly on an auxiliary end cross beam. The cross beams in turn are supported from the end floor beams at 10′-3″ intervals by means of cantilevered stringer brackets. The floor beams span 35′ center-to-center of trusses, and the trusses are supported on expansion rocker or roller bridge shoes.

The strength of the teeth in this case is obtained by continuously groove or fillet welding 5″ x ½″ x 1′-8½″ vertical web plate ribs to the underside of each tooth, as shown in Figure 11. The rear ends of these ribs are anchored for uplift by groove welding to the back of the 7″ x 4″ x ½″ slab closure angle. This angle is continuously welded to the 1″ surface plate, and serves also as a lateral distribution beam between the plate anchors.

Plate anchors composed of 5″ x ⅝″ x 1′-5″ web plates are welded to the rear of the joint opposite the web of every fourth tooth. These plates are spaced at 16″ centers, and each plate engages two ¾″ jacking bolts to the flange of the floor beam. These bolts serve both as erection bolts for setting the joint to elevation and grade, and as anchor bolts to hold down the rear of the joint against uplift caused by traffic. The plate anchors lap with the main longitudinal reinforcement bars in the slab for continuity, and the end of the concrete casts into the pocket formed by the surface plate and the 7″ x 4″ x ½″ angle.

The vertical leg of the 7″ x 4″ angle is flame cut to fit the curve of the roadway crown before welding to the 1″ plate. This helps to hold the joint in proper shape. The ribs are all held together at the bottom by welding to the 5″ x ½″ continuous plate bolted to the auxiliary cross beam.

The entire joint should be assembled in the shop with the cross beams and the field holes drilled to insure a proper fit in the field.

Field erection consists simply of setting the bridge shoes the proper distances apart, shimming the end cross beams to proper grade, and a final adjustment of the jacking bolts and the bolts to the cross beams. The concrete slab is then cast up to the joint around the anchors and cured, and the joint is ready for traffic.

One complete 24′ joint as shown in Figure 9 weighs 6250 lbs. This compares to an estimated weight of 8500 lbs for a conventional cast steel fingered joint.

This comparison indicates that the welded detail accomplishes a saving in metal weight of 26%, in addition to replacing expensive cast steel metal with rolled structural material. The relative cost of rolled metal is much less per pound.

7. ORTHOTROPIC DECKS

A very important type of floor construction is the orthotropic deck, in which all elements of the structure work together. Having principal application in the bridge field, orthotropic construction will be covered separately in the following Section 4.11.

Orthotropic Bridge Decks

1. THE ORTHOTROPIC DESIGN CONCEPT

There is a growing interest in this country in the use of orthotropic bridge design and construction, a system now commonly used in Europe.

With conventional bridge structures, the three main elements—longitudinal main girders, transverse floor beam, and lighter longitudinal stringers or stiffeners—all act independently of each other. Usually an 8″ thick concrete floor distributes the applied loads; see Figure 1(A).

In contrast, all elements of the orthotropic structure work together; see Figure 1(B). This new system uses a thin steel deck plate across the entire width and length of the bridge, and this serves as the top flange plate of the (1) longitudinal main girders, (2) transverse floor beams, and (3) lighter longitudinal stiffeners. The deck plate also contributes to the torsional resistance of the stiffeners when it forms a closed section.

Having a common top flange member, all three elements act and load up together in the most efficient manner. The steel deck plate is topped with a light 1½″ thick asphalt wearing surface for complete elimination of the heavy concrete floor.

The combined orthotropic deck structure acts as a single plate or membrane with three separate sectional properties: bending resistance about the x-x axis (transverse to the length of the bridge), bending resistance about the y-y axis (parallel to the bridge), and torsional resistance about the y-y axis. A concentrated load placed upon the deck plate is distributed over a wide area to several adjacent floor beams. The longitudinal stiffeners below this load act as beams on elastic supports. With increasing load, the rather flexible deck and stiffeners spread the load over a greater area. This action has been confirmed by many tests on models as well as actual bridges.

In the tests of the model of one bridge, the computed test load corresponding to maximum allowable design stress was 2.06 tons. The computed ultimate load was 5.6 tons. During testing, measurements indicated there was perfect elastic behavior up to an actual load of 4.1 tons. When loaded above the elastic limit, there was no rapid and unrestrained increase in deflection as is customary in the usual bending of beams; rather the deflections increased linearly just a little faster than the applied load. At a load of 48 tons, a crack started to appear in the stiffener region, and at 56 tons this had spread over the entire depth of the stiffener. This test indicated an apparent factor of safety of 27 to 1.

With optimum use of welding, orthotropic construc-

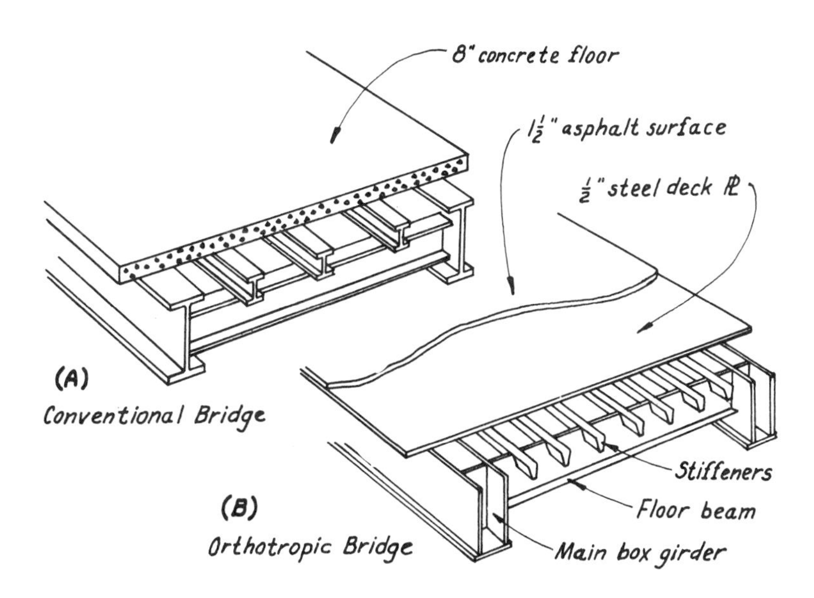

FIGURE 1

tion results in the bridge superstructure usually weighing only half as much as would result from any other design system. This weight saving is such a tremendous advantage on long span bridges, that orthotropic design is rapidly replacing truss design on all European bridges having spans of 400′ or more, and should do the same in this country.

AISC has published an excellent design manual on "Orthotropic Steel Plate Deck Bridges" by Roman Wolchuk (1963). It contains theory, methods of design, and suggested details of orthotropic bridges.

This type of bridge design would be impractical without the extensive use of welding. The miles of welded joints afford a good opportunity to subassemble the sections for automatic downhand welding and modern fabricating methods. Since numerous identical deck sections are required, they may be set up in a jig and automatically submerged-arc welded with minimum time and cost.

2. JOINING LONGITUDINAL STIFFENERS TO DECK PLATE

In European orthotropic bridge design, longitudinal stiffeners are commonly of trapezoidal cross-section for torsional rigidity. American design interest appears to favor this approach; see Figure 2. Although not too clear on the sketch of the Port Mann bridge, the edge

FIG. 2—Typical Hollow Trapezoidal Ribs and Connecting Welds

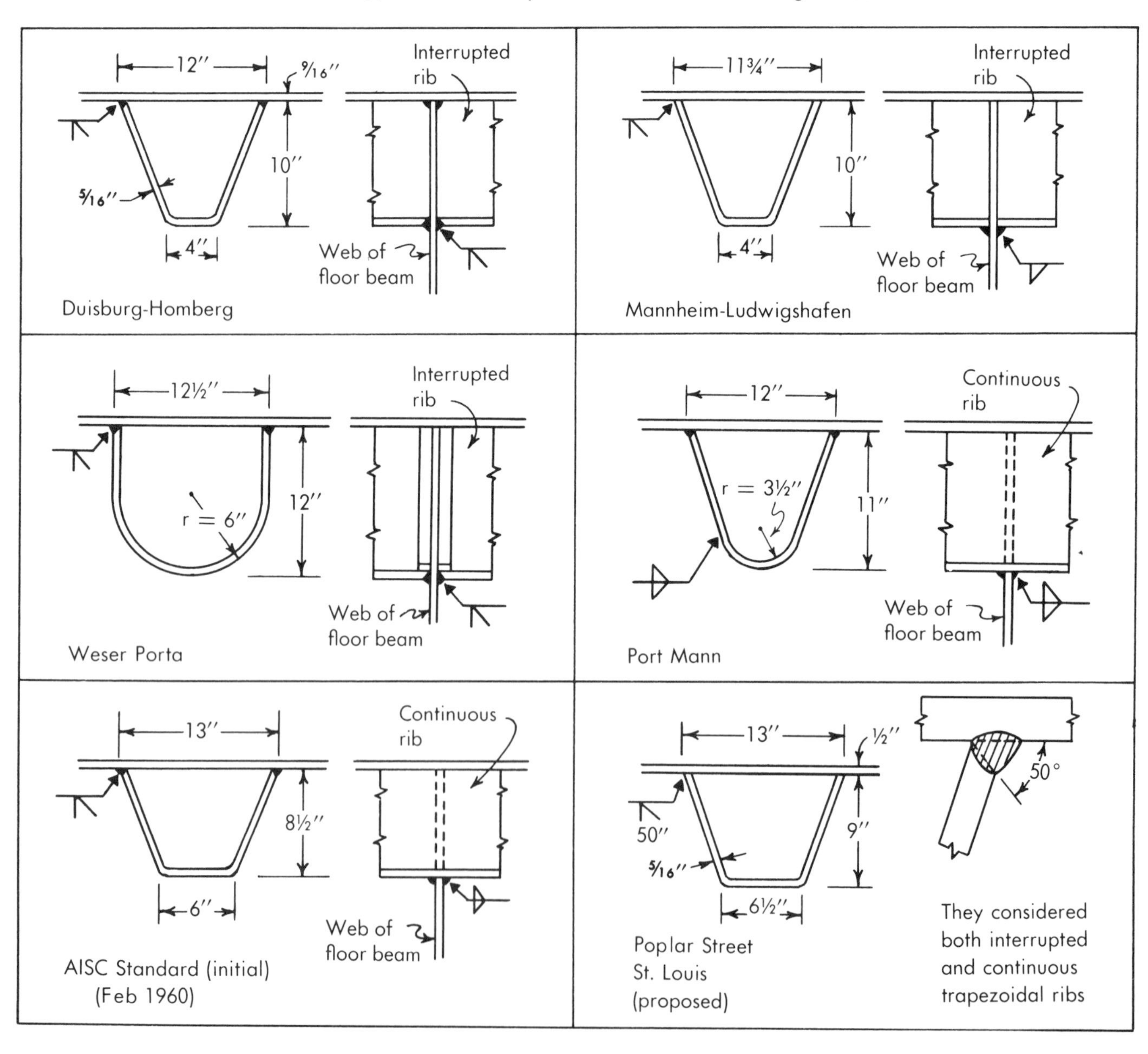

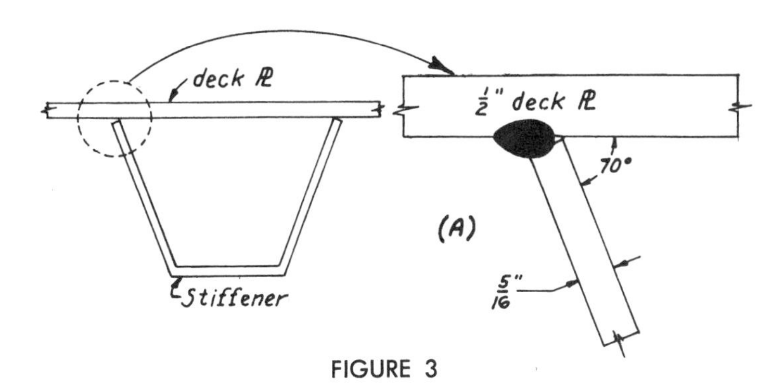

FIGURE 3

of the stiffener was cut square without any bevel. It was shown in tests by the fabricator that a single pass made with the automatic submerged-arc welder would produce a sound weld with throat greater than stiffener thickness; see Figure 3.

The torsional resistance of any closed tubular section, as indicated by Figure 4, is:

$$R = \frac{4\,[A]}{\int \frac{dt}{ds}} = \frac{4\,[A]}{\frac{t_{℞}}{b_{℞}} + \frac{t_s}{b_s}}$$

where:

[A] = area enclosed by the trapezoid
$t_{℞}$ = thickness of deck plate
t_s = thickness of stiffener
$b_{℞}$ = width of deck plate within region of stiffener
b_s = undeveloped width of stiffener

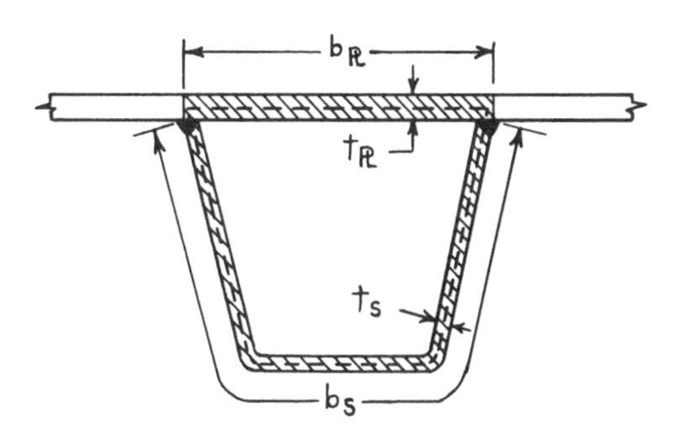

FIGURE 4

The Design Manual for Orthotropic Steel Plate Deck Bridges multiplies this torsional resistance (R) by a reduction factor (μ) which has been determined by testing of various shapes of stiffeners. This factor is affected by the shape of the stiffener.

Stiffeners can be readily formed to the trapezoidal shape on a press brake. Because of the tonnage required, it might be more economical to purchase a special mill-rolled section for the stiffeners; see Figure 5. Thus the outer portions of the plate width which become webs of the built-up trapezoid section are rolled thinner, and the central portion is left thicker for the lower flange. This places the material where required, further reducing the bridge weight and tonnage of steel required. The plate could be rolled to the final trapezoid section, thus eliminating the braking operation Lengths of this section would nest and present no problem in shipping.

Another refinement would be to provide slightly greater thickness at web extremities so as to give more bearing against the deck plate and greater throat to the connecting weld.

In designing the Port Mann Bridge in British Columbia, Canada, engineers specified orthotropic deck construction for maximum weight reduction and dollar economy. Deck plate is stiffened by longitudinal trough-shaped stringers formed by press-brake. Welding of stringers to transverse beams is done by a progressive assembly technique . . . for near continuous-flow production.

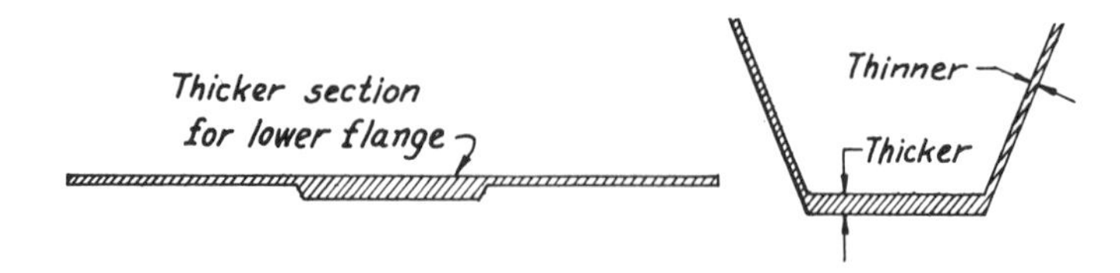

FIGURE 5

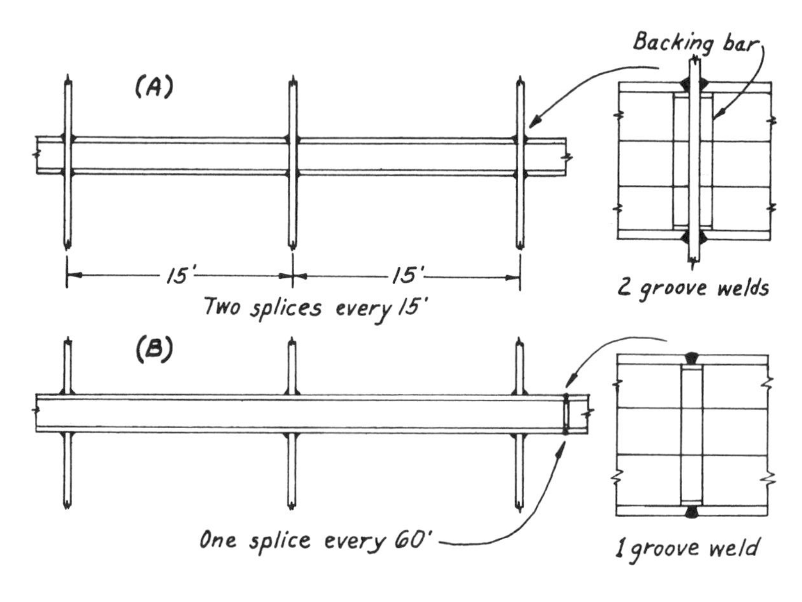

FIGURE 6

3. FIELD SPLICE OF LONGITUDINAL STIFFENERS

There are two basic methods for detailing the intersection of longitudinal stiffeners and transverse floor beams; see Figure 6.

(A) Following the common European practice, the floor beam webs run continuous and stiffeners are cut to fit between the beams. The stiffeners are thus limited to about 15′ in length, and the main bending stresses of the structure in the stiffeners must be transferred transversely through the web of each floor beam by means of groove welds (T joint). There might be a question of the possibility of a lamination in the web opening up because of the transverse force applied through it. This method requires a large number of field groove welds to be made in the vertical and overhead position. There are 2 welds at each beam per stiffener.

(B) An alternate method would be to have the trapezoid stiffeners run continuous throughout the length of the structure, with webs of the floor beams cut out to fit around the stiffeners. This would eliminate any questions as to the safe transfer of main bending stresses.

This method would greatly reduce the required field welding. For example, the stiffeners could be shop fabricated into 60′ lengths; this would require just a single groove weld in the field every 60′. This would be a single groove butt joint in contrast to the 2 groove welds at each floor beam required by Method A. The critical field welding thus would be only ⅛ of that required by Method A.

In a translation of a German paper, "Fatigue Tests on Hollow Rib Connections" by H. Hansch and G. Muller, results of fatigue testing three different details of longitudinal stiffeners were summarized:

1. The longitudinal stiffeners were interrupted at the transverse floor beam webs and joined by fillet welds to the webs of the floor beam.

2. The longitudinal stiffeners were interrupted at the floor beam webs, but were welded with single bevel groove welds to the webs of the floor beams.

3. The longitudinal stiffeners ran continuously through the floor beam webs.

The results showed the continuous stiffener (1) to have the highest fatigue strength, $\sigma = 28{,}000$ psi, when tested with a stress range of

$$K = \frac{\text{min}}{\text{max}} = +\ .2$$

The shape of the closed tubular longitudinal stiffener tested had no appreciable effect upon the test results. Cold forming of the stiffeners had no effect. They recommend that the designer place the field splice of the stiffeners in low-stressed regions.

4. SHOP FABRICATED SUBASSEMBLIES

It is possible to fabricate nearly the entire deck of the bridge, in sections, under optimum shop conditions and thereby minimize the amount of field welding. This includes deck sections lying between the main box girders, and any sections to be cantilevered out from the box girder.

The deck unit which is to rest between the main box girders can be made initially in three sections. For an average bridge, each of these prefabricated sections, 9′ wide by 60′ long, would weigh about 8¾ tons; see Figure 7.

Three of these sections would be laid out, still upside down, and tack welded together; see Figure 8(A). This work would preferably be done on the final means of transport, in some cases a barge. Each longitudinal joint of the top deck plate can be made with a two-pass weld; one pass on each side using a submerged-arc automatic welder. This joint is a simple square-butt joint without any backing bar, and requires no beveling of plate edges. After making the first pass, the four floor beams are manually welded in place. Each beam consists of a bottom flange plate and a web plate having trapezoidal cutouts along the top edge to fit around each stiffener.

With the transverse floor beam welded in place,

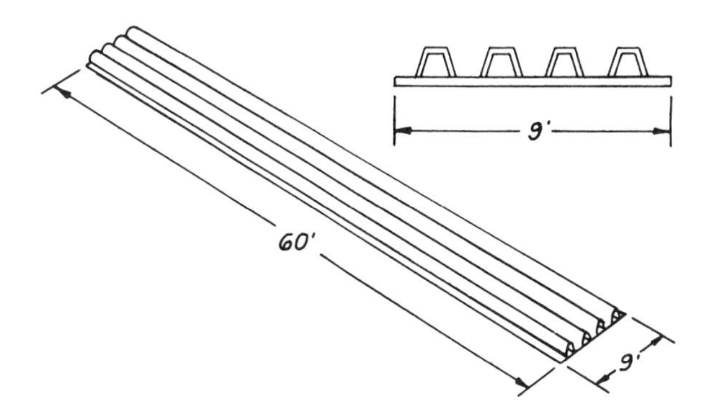

FIGURE 7

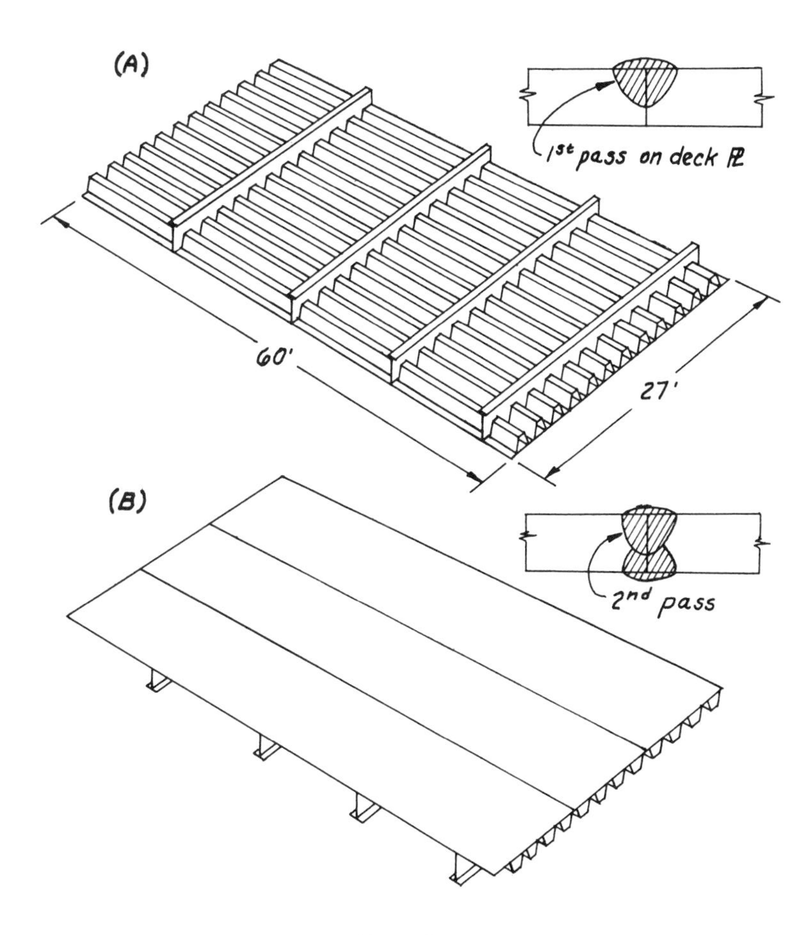

FIGURE 8

the entire unit can be turned over without undue strain on the incomplete butt weld. A second pass is taken to complete the automatic welding of the longitudinal joints, all in the downhand position; see Figure 8(B). The result is a complete deck unit, 27′ × 60′, weighing about 29 tons, to be hoisted from the barge into position between the two main box girders.

The Port Mann bridge deck panels were fabricated and welded in the shop as units 65′ wide, the width of the deck lying in between the main longitudinal girders, and 25′ long, the distance between the transverse floor beams. These panels weighed between 32 and 36 tons, depending upon the deck plate thickness. In Europe, panels up to 58′ × 18′ have been fabricated and transported by barges to the site. The Save River bridge had prefabricated panels weighing 27.5 tons. The Mannheim-Ludwigshafen bridge was erected in panels 18.5′ wide and 60′ long. The Severin bridge in Cologne was erected in panels 62.8′ wide and 47 to 54′ long.

5. FIELD ERECTION

The entire superstructure probably would be erected in units, starting from a pier support and cantilevering out. A traveling crane could place the individual units. For any given segment of the span, the main longitudinal box girders would be put into position first. The field splice of the top flange deck plate should be welded because the 1½″ thick asphalt floor to be applied leaves little room for splice plates and bolts. The erection bolts probably should be on the girder webs. The girder's bottom flange may vary from ¾″ to 3 or 4″ thick plate, and could be spliced by field welding because field bolting of this thick plate would be costly.

Transverse shrinkage of the weld on the ½″ deck plate within this box girder is estimatel at about .03″, and shrinkage of the groove weld of a 3″ bottom flange plate at about .10″. Under this condition, a suggested procedure is to weld the bottom flange to about ⅔ completion, then weld the top deck simultaneous with welding the remaining ⅓ of the bottom flange. In this manner, both flanges should pull in together evenly.

The next step would be erection of the subassembled deck unit between these two main box girders.

6. FIELD WELDING

With a deck unit raised into place, the ends of each floor beam would be field welded to the main box girders. The two longitudinal joints and one transverse joint of the ½″ deck plate should be welded in a single pass with a submerged-arc tractor. Plates should be partially beveled at the top and a backing bar used so that full-penetration welds can be made in the downhand position; see Figure 9.

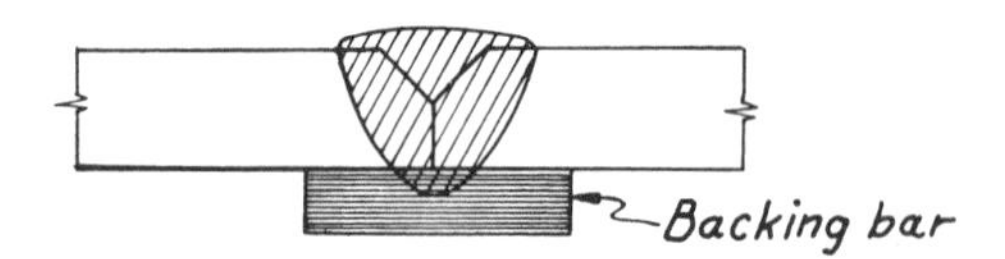

FIGURE 9

Longitudinal stiffeners would be field spliced by manually groove welding the butt joint using a light backing bar placed on the inside of the trapezoid, very similar to pipe welding. The upper edge of the stiffener could be notched at this joint so a backing bar can run continuously across the deck to facilitate automatic welding of the deck plate transverse joint. Under these conditions, the joints of deck plate and stiffeners should be offset at least 2″, as shown in Figure 10, so each deck unit can be lowered down without interference of the backing bars.

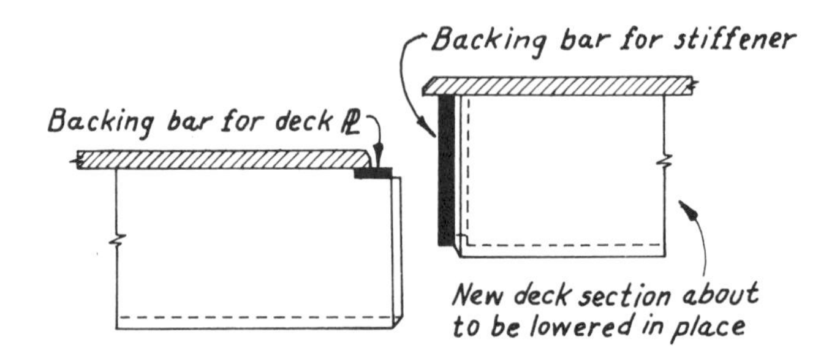

FIGURE 10

If there is any doubt about the fit-up of multiple stiffeners for field splicing, ends of the stiffeners can be left unwelded to the deck plate for about a foot. This will permit them to be individually aligned horizontally for welding.

If specific dimensions of the stiffener indicates a possible problem in acessibility for the weldor in making the field splices, the deck plate can be left short by about 10″ from each end of the section; see Figure 11. This would also allow the back of the joints on the inside of the trapezoid stiffener to be root gouged and a root or back pass made. A 20″ wide deck plate section would then be inserted, and two transverse groove welds made. This would double the length of transverse welds for splicing the deck plates; however, all of this welding would be automatic, single pass work. Ends of the stiffeners would then be overhead welded to this deck insert; as shown in Figure 11.

An alternate way to field splice the trapezoidal stiffeners is to place the bevel on the inside and a backing bar on the outside; the weldor then makes all the splices while working from the top of the deck.

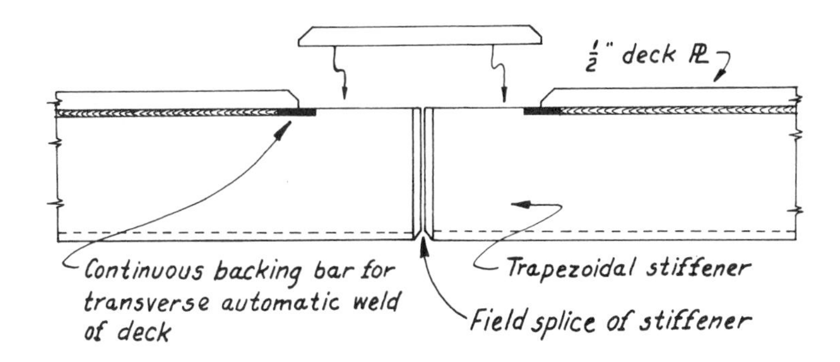

FIGURE 11

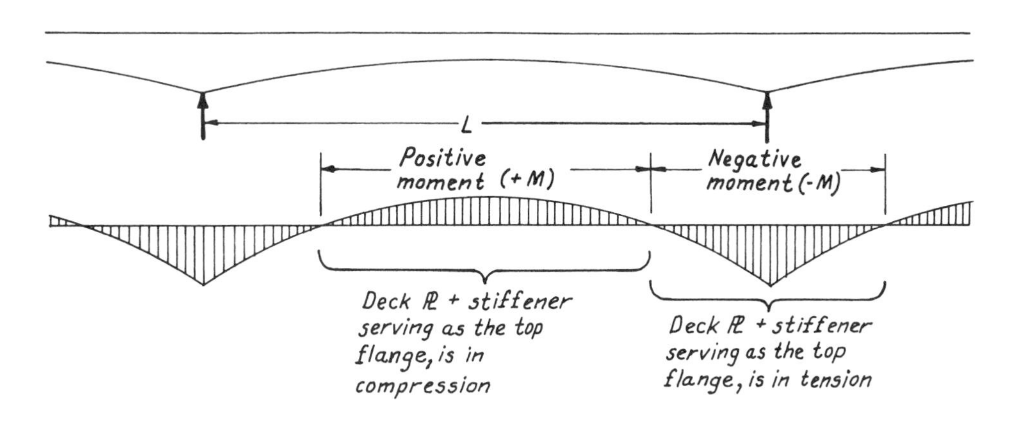

FIGURE 12

7. RADIOGRAPHIC INSPECTION

This type of inspection should be limited to critical joints which the Engineer should select. Fatigue conditions that reduce the allowable stress in design may indicate such a need; for example, groove welded butt joints subject to tension, a wide range of stress, a high stress, and a large number of cycles. As the factors that produce fatigue loading are reduced, the necessity for radiographic inspection is likewise reduced.

If all of the groove welds in the deck plate are made by the submerged-arc automatic process, proper procedures can be established to insure good welding. This should eliminate the need for costly radiographic inspection of these welds, although limited spot checks could be made.

Any field splice in the lower flange of the main box girders in a region of positive moment, might be inspected by radiography.

Field splices in the longitudinal stiffeners must be considered from the type of loading:

1. The stiffener serves along with the deck plate as the top flange of the main structure, and as such is subjected to tension in the negative moment region near the pier supports. However, this comes from the dead load of the structure and any live load spread over a rather large area, thus the range of stress variation and the number of stress cycles would be relatively small; see Figure 12.

2. The stiffener serves along with the deck plate as a short beam between floor beams, and any localized wheel load would produce a wide range in stress and the number of applications could be very high. However, by using Method B to detail the network of floor beams and stiffeners the only critical welds would occur at about every 60′ of bridge length. The influence lines, see Figure 13, show the moment due to concentrated wheel load at given points as the load progresses along the span between floor beams. By locating the field splice of the stiffener at a point about $\frac{1}{10}$ L along the span between supporting floor beams, the bending stress on the weld is rather low and without much fluctuation.

Spot checks of the stiffener field splices by gamma ray inspection, if required, could be made by drilling a small hole in the ½″ deck plate and lowering the capsule down halfway into the interior of the trapezoidal area, with the film wrapped around the outside

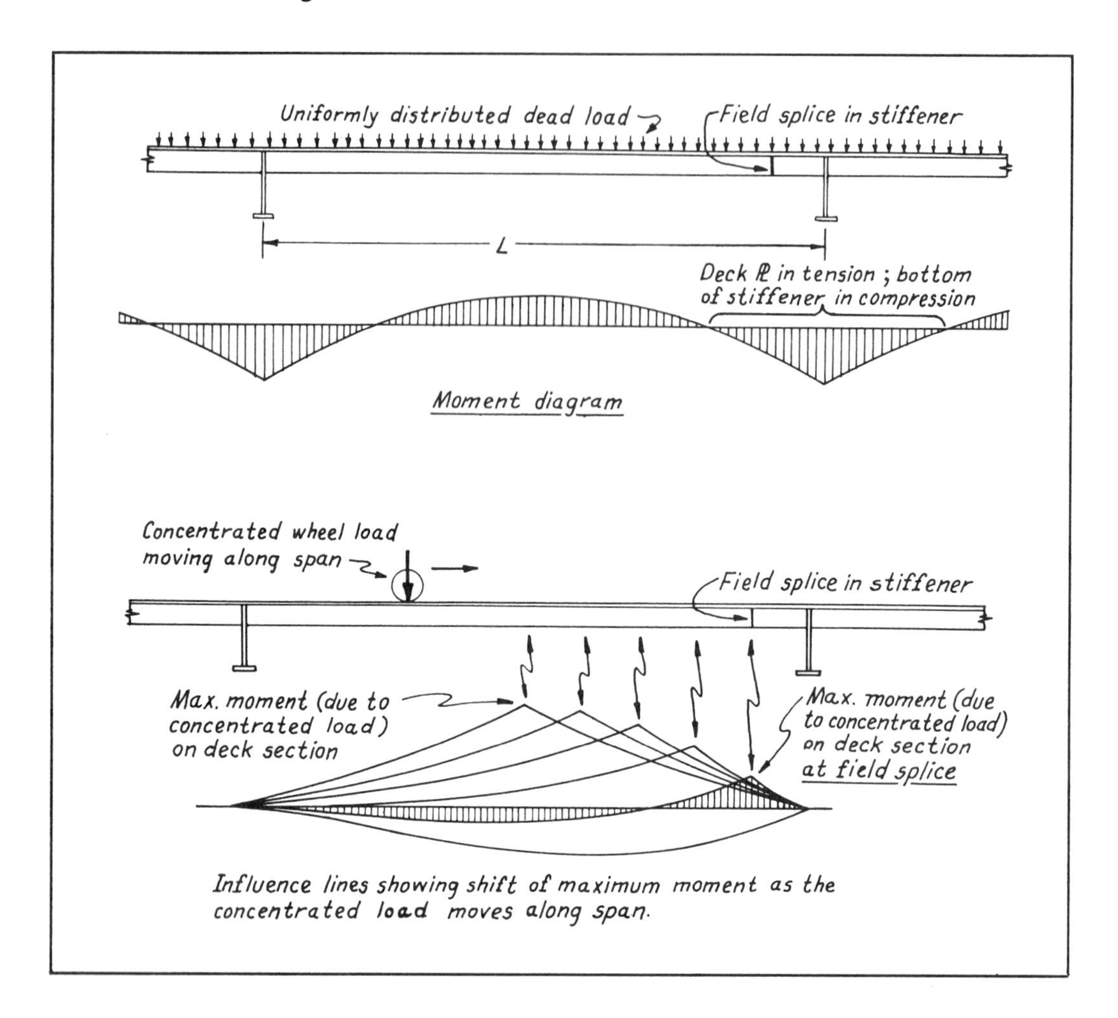

FIGURE 13

of the stiffener. This hole can be filled later by welding, or by tapping it and screwing a pipe plug into it.

8. WELDOR QUALIFICATION

In addition to the standard AWS weldor qualification test, it would be well for those men assigned to field weld the stiffeners to first weld a test joint of this splice in position. This can be given a visual inspection, including sawing of the joint at one or more points and etching to determine if proper fusion was obtained. It might be well to consider weldors who have had some experience in pipe welding.

Problem 1

An orthotropic deck is to be fabricated in units 104″ wide containing 4 trapezoidal stiffeners each 13″ wide and on 11″ centers. The stiffeners are welded to the ⅜″ deck plate along their edges. If these units are 30′ long, estimate the amount of bending or camber due to the shrinkage of the welds; see Figure 14.

To find the properties of this section, select reference axis (x-x) along underneath surface of deck plate. This is almost through the center of gravity of the 2 welds, and the resulting distance to the neutral axis (n) will also be the distance between the neutral axis and the center of gravity of welds (d).

$$I_{NA} = I_x + I_g - \frac{M^2}{A}$$

$$= (279.87) - \frac{(-35.412)^2}{(16.179)} \quad \text{(From Table A)}$$

$$= 279.87 - 77.51$$

$$= 202.36 \text{ in.}^4$$

$$n = \frac{M}{A}$$

$$= \frac{(-35.412)}{(16.179)}$$

$$= -2.19'' \text{ also } = d$$

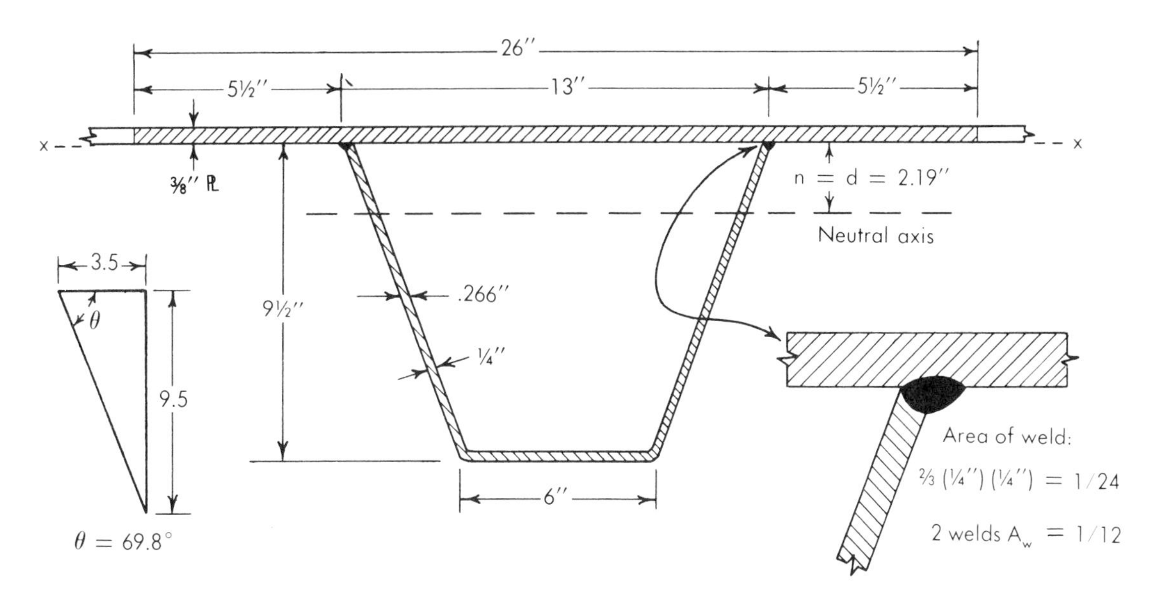

FIGURE 14

TABLE A

	Plate	A	y	M = A y	I_x = M y	I_g
(A)	26" x ⅜"	9.750	+ 3/16"	+ 1.828	+ .34	.11
(B)	.532" x 9½"	5.054	− 4.75"	− 24.007	+114.03	38.00
(C)	5½ x ¼"	1.375	− 9.625"	−13.233	+127.38	.007
	Total →	16.179		−35.412	279.87	

bending or camber L = 30′ = 360″

$$\Delta = \frac{.005\ A_w\ d\ L^2}{I}$$

$$= \frac{.005\ (1/12)\ (2.19)\ (360)^2}{(203.36)}$$

$$= .585''$$ (ends would go up this amount)

This means when the 30′ long unit is upside down for welding, the fixture should be curved sufficiently to pull the central section of the unit down by this amount (.585″).

Problem 2

The orthotropic deck used in the Port Mann bridge in British Columbia consists of trapezoidal stiffeners with rounded bottoms spaced on 24″ centers and welded to a ½″ to 7/16″ deck plate. These deck sections are shop welded into panels about 65′ wide, the width of the bridge in between the main longitudinal girders, and 25′ long; as shown in Figure 15. Estimate the amount of bending or camber due to the shrinkage of the welds.

In order to find the property of this built-up section, it is necessary to know the properties of the arc of a circle which forms the round bottom portion.

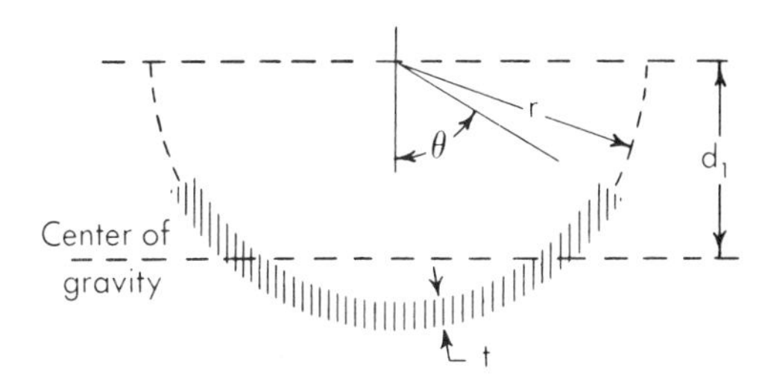

FIGURE 16

It can be shown that the following is true:

$$A = 2\ t\ r\ \theta$$

$$d_1 = \frac{r \sin \theta}{\theta}$$

$$I_g = t\ r^3 \left[\theta + \tfrac{1}{2} \sin 2\theta - \frac{2 \sin^2 \theta}{\theta} \right]$$

(about center of gravity)

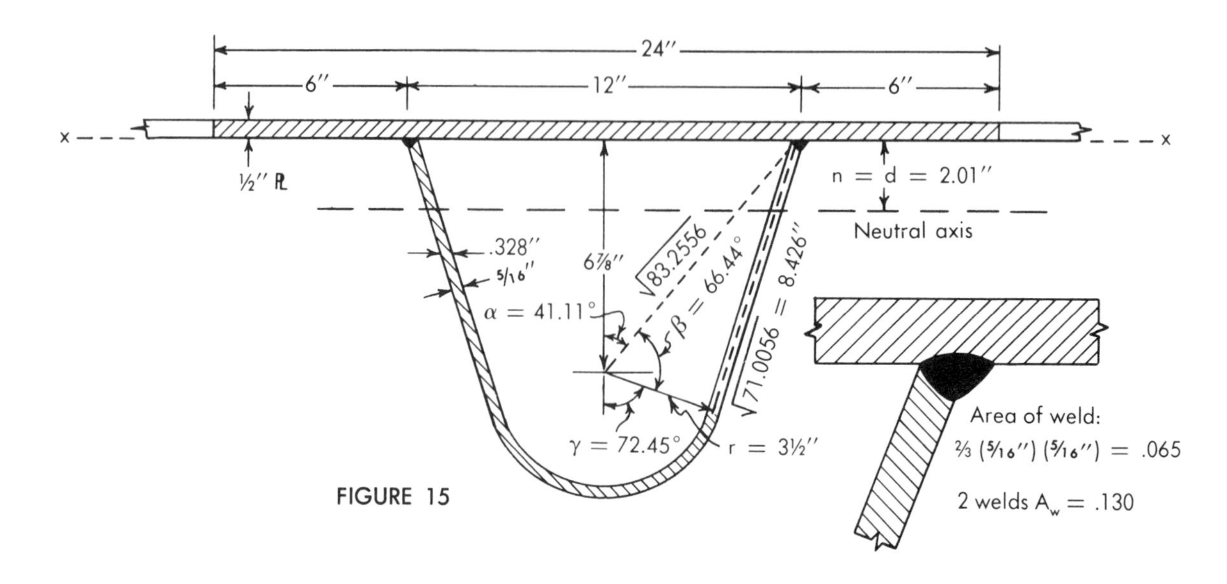

FIGURE 15

TABLE B

	Plate	A	y	M = A y	I_x = M y	I_g
(A)	24″ x ½″	12.00	+ .25	+ 3.00	+ .75	.25
(B)	.656″ x 6⅞″	4 51	−3.4375	−15.50	+ 53.29	17.73
(C)	round bottom	2.76	−9.515	−26.26	+249.87	1.46
	Total →	19.27		−38.76	323.35	

In this example:

$$t = 5/16''$$

$$r = 3\tfrac{1}{2}''$$

$$\theta = 72.45^\circ \text{ or } 1.263 \text{ radians}$$

$$A = 2\,(5/16)(3\tfrac{1}{2})(1.263)$$

$$= 2.76 \text{ in.}^2$$

$$d_1 = \frac{(3\tfrac{1}{2})(.9535)}{1.263}$$

$$= 2.64''$$

$$I_g = (5/16)(3\tfrac{1}{2})\left[1.263 + \tfrac{1}{2}(.575) - \frac{2(.9535)^2}{1.263}\right]$$

$$= 1.46 \text{ in.}^4$$

These values will now be used in finding the properties of the built-up section. To find these properties, select reference axis (x-x) along the underneath surface of the deck plate. This is almost through the center of gravity of the 2 welds, and the resulting distance to the neutral axis (n) will also be the distance between the neutral axis and the center of gravity of welds (d).

$$I_{NA} = I_x + I_g - \frac{M^2}{A}$$

$$= (323.35) - \frac{(-38.76)^2}{(19.27)} \quad \text{(From Table B)}$$

$$= 323.35 - 77.96$$

$$= 245.39 \text{ in.}^4$$

$$n = \frac{M}{A}$$

$$= \frac{(-38.76)}{(19.27}$$

$$= -2.01'' = d$$

bending or camber $\qquad L = 25' = 300''$

$$\Delta = \frac{.005\, A_w\, d\, L^2}{I}$$

$$= \frac{.005(.130)(2.01)(300)^2}{(245.39)}$$

$$= .48'' \text{ (ends would go up this amount)}$$

This means when the 25′ long unit is upside down for welding, the fixture should be curved sufficiently to pull the central section of the unit down by this amount or about ½″.

Fabrication of Plate Girders And Cover-Plated Beams

FIG. 1 Multiple burning torches cut heavy steel plate to be used in fabricated bridge girders.

FIGURE 2

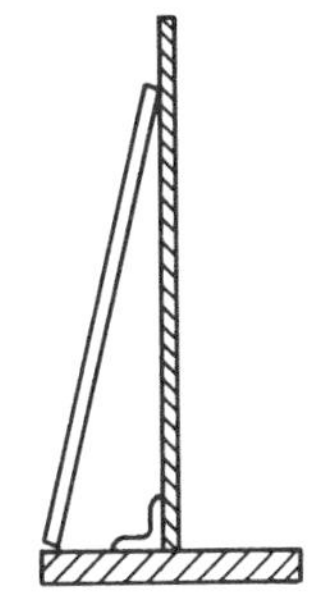

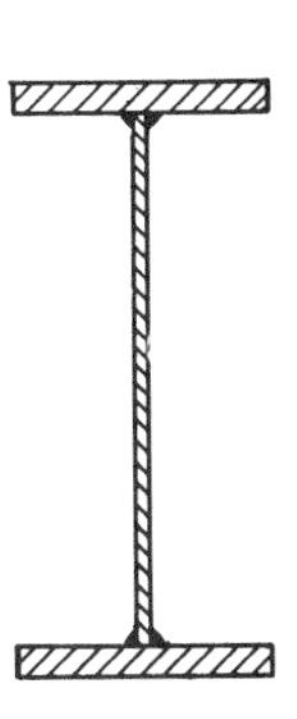

1. PLATE PREPARATION

Flange plates may be ordered as bars rolled to the proper width and thickness. No further preparation is required except cutting to proper length and beveling the ends for the butt joint.

Some fabricators will flame cut the flange plates from wide plates; Figure 1. Since there is some shrinkage due to the flame cutting operation, the flange will have a sweep or bend if it is cut along just one side. For this reason the flange is made by cutting along both sides, usually with a cutting unit having multiple torches which are cut at the same time.

For girders with a horizontal curve, the flange plates are flame cut to the proper curve.

2. FIT-UP AND ASSEMBLY

Fabricators having full-automatic, submerged-arc welding heads usually fit the flanges to the web and then complete the fillet welding.

Plate girders may be fitted and assembled by one of the following procedures:

First, one flange is laid flat on the floor. A chalk line is marked along the centerline of the flange and small right-angle clips tack welded at intervals along the length of the flange near this centerline. See Figure 2. Next, the web is placed vertically on the flange and temporarily supported with angles or bars tack welded between the web and the flange. The clips along the flange align the web along the centerline of the flange. The top flange plate may then be placed on top of the web. This method may be used for straight girders if they are not too deep.

The plate girder may be assembled by placing the web down on a fixture in the horizontal position; Figure 3. The flange plates are put in position and some

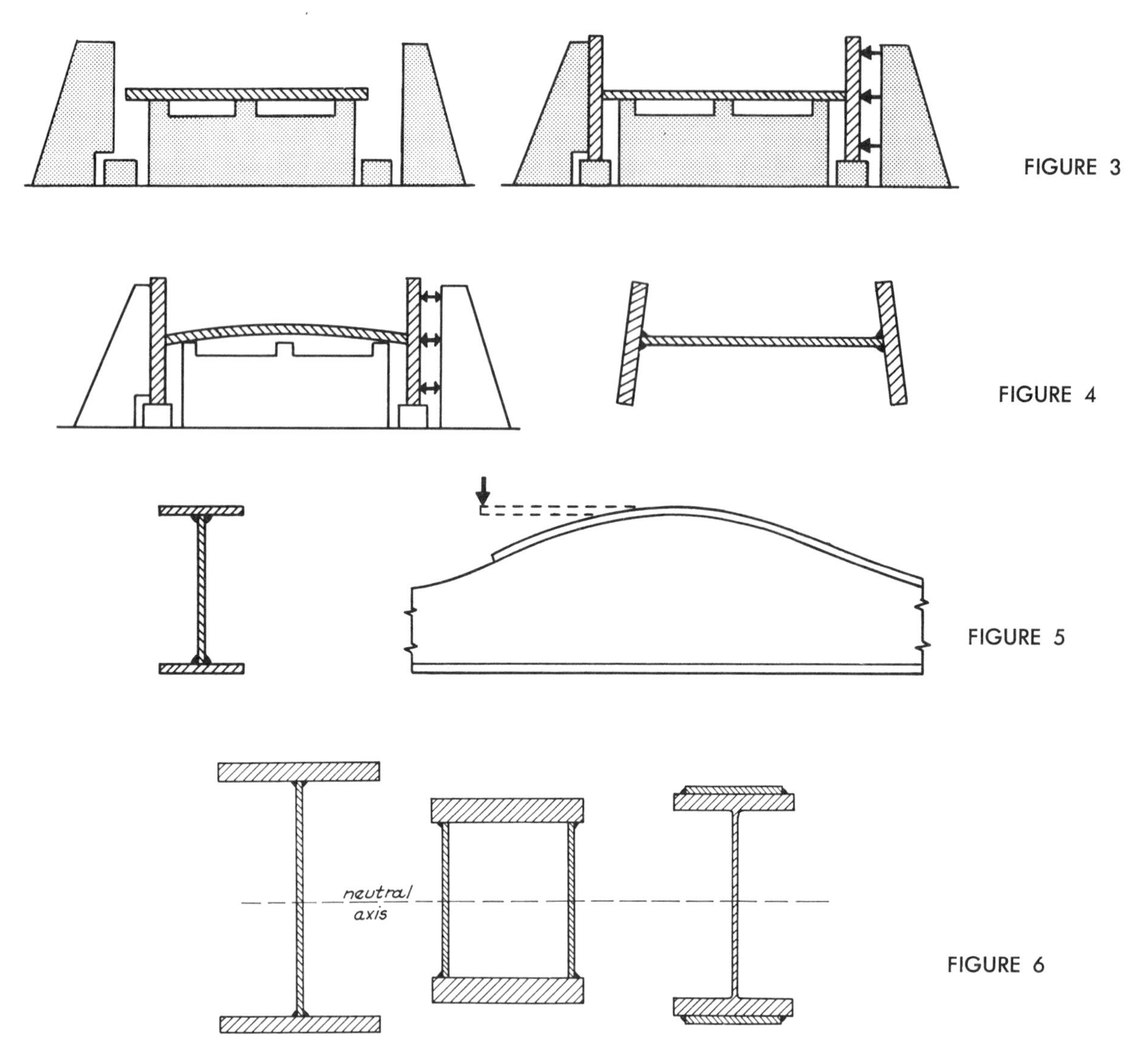

FIGURE 3

FIGURE 4

FIGURE 5

FIGURE 6

clamping method (such as wedges, screws, jacks, or in some cases compressed air) is used to force the flange tight against the edge of the web. These fixtures automatically hold the flange in proper vertical alignment.

If the web is thin and very deep, caution must be used so that excessive pressure is not used against the flanges because this may bow the web upward. See Figure 4. Since the flanges are vertical in the fixture, when the pressure is released and the web straightens out, the flanges may rotate and not be parallel.

Haunched or fishbelly girders are usually assembled with the web horizontal in this manner. However, some fishbelly girders that are not too deep have been assembled upside down with the web vertical. See Figure 5. What would be the straight top flange is placed on the bottom of the fixture, and the web is positioned vertically. What would be the bottom flange is assembled on top, and its own weight is usually sufficient to pull it down against the curved edge of the web with little additional force or heating.

3. CONTINUOUS WELDING

If rolled beams with cover plates, plate girders, and/or box girders are symmetrical, the four fillet welds will be well balanced about the neutral axis of the section. Because of this, there should be very little distortion or bowing of the girder. See Figure 6. The sequence for automatic welding to produce the four fillet welds can be varied without major effect on distortion.

In most cases the welding sequence is based on the type of fixture used and the method of moving the girder from one welding position to another in the shop.

In Figure 7, the fabricator has two fixtures to hold the girder assembly at an inclined angle. These fixtures lie on each side of the automatic welder which runs lengthwise on a track. Since it is more difficult to completely turn the girder over, the sequence must be designed to do this as few times as possible.

In Figure 7, the girder assembly is first placed

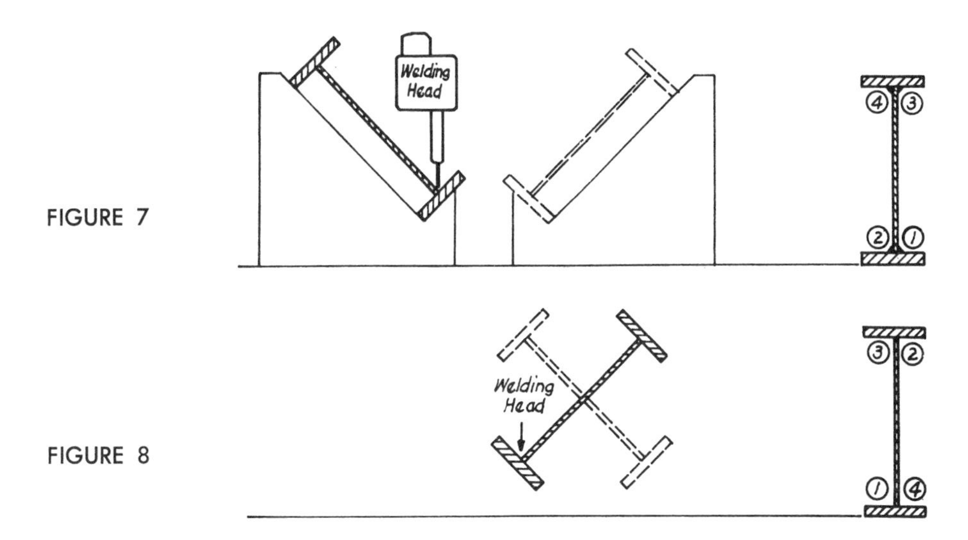

FIGURE 7

FIGURE 8

in the left fixture and weld (1) is made. The next easiest step is to pick up the girder with the crane hooked to the upper flange and swing it over to the right fixture. Here weld (2) is made on the same flange but opposite side of the web. Now the girder must be picked up, laid down on the floor, turned over, and placed back into one of the fixtures where weld (3) is made in the flat position. Finally the girder is picked up and swung over to the other fixture where weld (4) is made.

In Figure 8, the fabricator uses a set of trunnions on the end of the girder assembly, or places the girder within a series of circular hoops, so that the girder may be revolved. After weld (1) is completed, the girder is turned completely over and weld (2) is made. Now the welding head must be moved over to the back side of the girder and weld (3) is made. Finally the girder is turned completely over and weld (4) is made.

The difference in the above sequence of welding passes depends entirely on the fixturing and methods used rather than any effect on distortion.

4. ANGULAR DISTORTION AND TRANSVERSE STIFFENERS

Usually after the flange-to-web fillet welds have been completed, the transverse stiffeners are fitted and welded into the girder; Figure 9.

If the flanges are thin and wide, the girders may exhibit some angular distortion of the flange plates. If this has occurred, the flanges may have to be forced

FIGURE 9

apart before the stiffeners can be inserted between them.

The following formula will help in estimating the amount of angular distortion of the flanges:

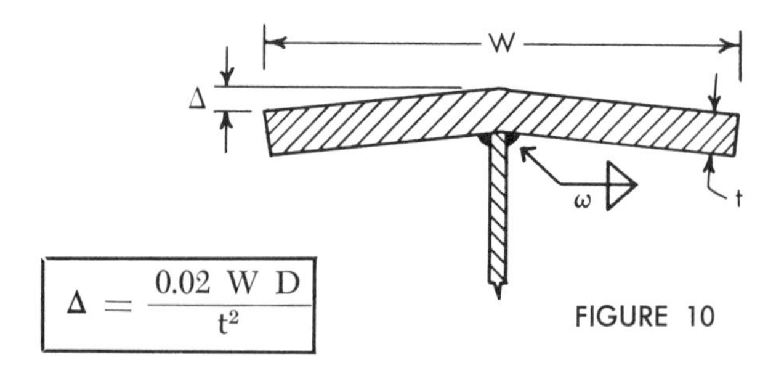

$$\Delta = \frac{0.02\ W\ D}{t^2}$$

FIGURE 10

where:

$D = \omega^{1.3}$

See Table A for value of D corresponding to actual leg of weld (ω).

TABLE A

ω	D
3/16	.113
1/4	.164
5/16	.220
3/8	228
7/16	.342
1/2	.406
5/8	.543
3/4	.688
1	1.000

AASHO bridge specifications (2.10.32) state that these stiffeners shall fit sufficiently tight after painting that they will exclude water. In addition, no attachments should be welded to the tension flange if it is stressed above 75% of the allowable.

Some interpret the AASHO specification to mean a force fit; this is costly and not necessary. The following procedure will comply with this:

1. Use a loose stiffener so it may be fitted easily.
2. Push this tight against the tension flange.
3. Weld this to the web of the girder.
4. Weld this to the compression flange.

Some states have not been concerned with this tight fit and have cut the stiffeners short by about 1″; these have been pushed tight against the compression flange and welded to the web. If just a single stiffener is used, it is also welded to the compression flange. The recent plate girder research at Lehigh University found that the stiffeners do not have to be against the tension flange in order to develop the full capacity of the girder. The new AISC specifications follow this in allowing transverse intermediate stiffeners to be cut short at the tension flange by a distance equal to 4 times the web thickness.

Fabricators having semi-automatic welding equipment sometimes insert the transverse stiffeners into the girder before welding the flanges to the web. This is easily done since the unwelded flanges are flat (not distorted). With the girder web in the horizontal position, the semi-automatic welders are used to make the fillet welds between the flange and web as well as the stiffeners in the same set-up.

The corners of the stiffeners are snipped so that the flange-to-web fillet weld may be continued in back of the stiffeners. Quite often all of this welding is completed in a single panel area before moving to the next. The girder is then turned over and the welding completed on the other side.

5. POSITION OF WELDING

The girder may be positioned with the web at an angle between 30° and 45° with the horizon, permitting the welds to be deposited in the flat position. This position is desirable, since it makes welding easier and slightly faster. It also permits better control of bead shape and the production of larger welds in a single pass when necessary.

For example, the largest single-pass fillet weld made in the horizontal position is about 5/16″ with a single wire, and ½″ with tandem arc; whereas in the flat position this single-pass weld may be about ¾″ with either process.

For a ¼″ or 5/16″ fillet weld, the position in which the weld is made, whether horizontal or flat, would not make much difference.

If a ⅜″ or ½″ fillet weld is required, the fabricator has several choices.

If the girder may be positioned with the web vertical, this will allow both welds on the same flange to be completed without moving the girder. See Figure 11(a). If the fabricator has two welding heads, these two welds may be made simultaneously, thus reducing the overall welding time. However, this horizontal position does limit the maximum size of the weld which may be made in a single pass.

If the fabricator has a single-wire automatic head, he must make this fillet weld in two passes. If he has a tandem setup, this weld can be made in a single pass with less welding time.

By tilting the girder at an angle, either a single wire or tandem heads can make this weld in a single pass; however, only one of the welds can be made at one time. See Figure 11(b). It would be necessary to rotate the girder for each weld with increased handling time.

A fabricating shop with two automatic welding heads can make two fillet welds on the girder simultaneously. To do this, the shop must decide between two methods of positioning the girder; Figure 12.

It might be argued that method (a) should be used

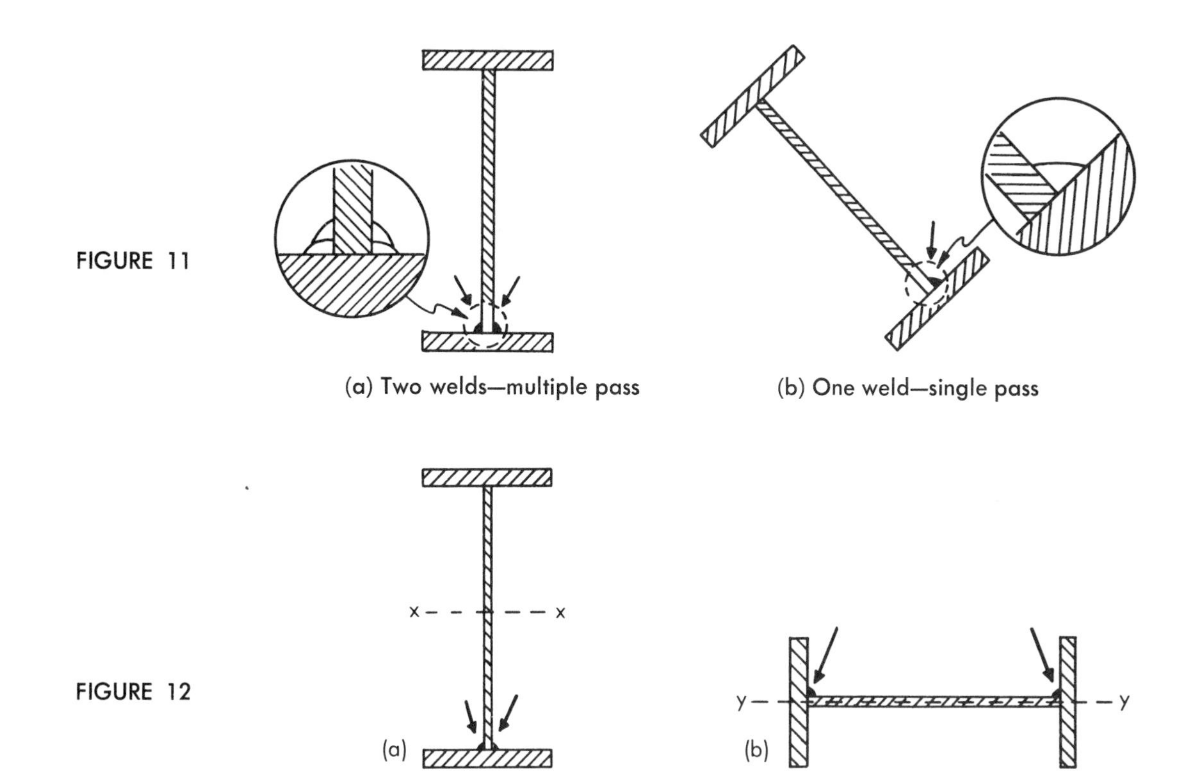

FIGURE 11

(a) Two welds—multiple pass

(b) One weld—single pass

FIGURE 12

because the girder is much more rigid about this axis (x-x) and therefore would deflect less as a result of the first two welds on the bottom flange.

However in method (b) the weld is next to the neutral axis (y-y) of the girder. Its distance to this axis is much less than that in (a), and therefore it would have very little bending effect on the girder.

Since this is a thick flange, there may be concern about getting a large enough fillet weld to provide enough welding heat for the mass of flange plate. Therefore, it might also be argued that method (a) would provide double the amount of heat input on the flange.

Actually there should be little difference between these methods in the effect of weld shrinkage after all of the welds have been made.

6. COVER PLATES FOR BEAMS

Many times, rolled beams must have cover plates added to their flanges for increased strength. Usually two cover plates are added, keeping the section symmetrical about the horizontal axis. For composite beams having shear attachments on the top flange so that the concrete floor acts compositely with the beam, a cover plate may be added to the bottom flange for increased strength. All of these beams must have a certain amount of camber.

The welds connecting the cover plates to the beam flange tend to shrink upon cooling. With a cover plate on each flange, this shrinkage on top and bottom flanges of the beam will balance and the beam will not distort. However, if there is a cover plate on just the bottom flange, the unbalanced shrinkage will cause the center of the beam to bow upward; in other words, it will increase the camber of the beam.

The cambering that results from this unbalanced welding can be estimated by the following formula:

$$\Delta = \frac{0.005\ A\ d\ L^2}{I}$$

where:

A = total cross-sectional area of welds, sq. in.

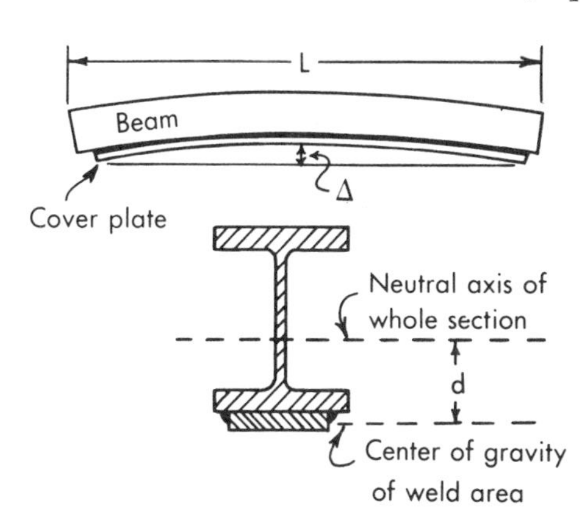

FIGURE 13

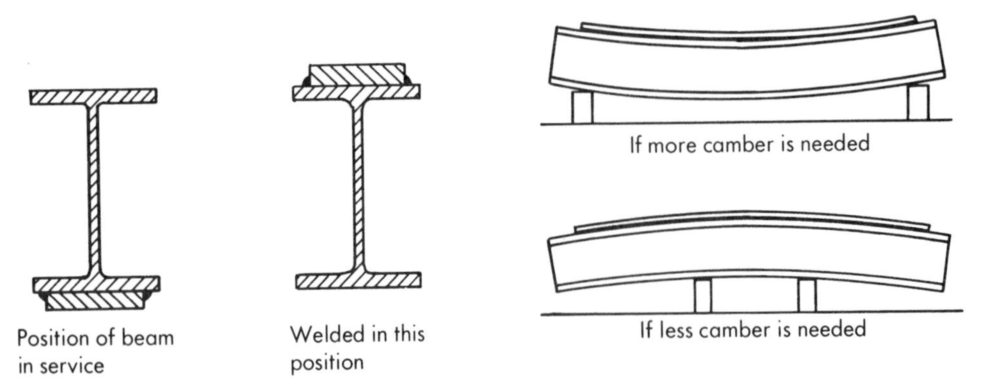

(a) When cover plate is less than flange width

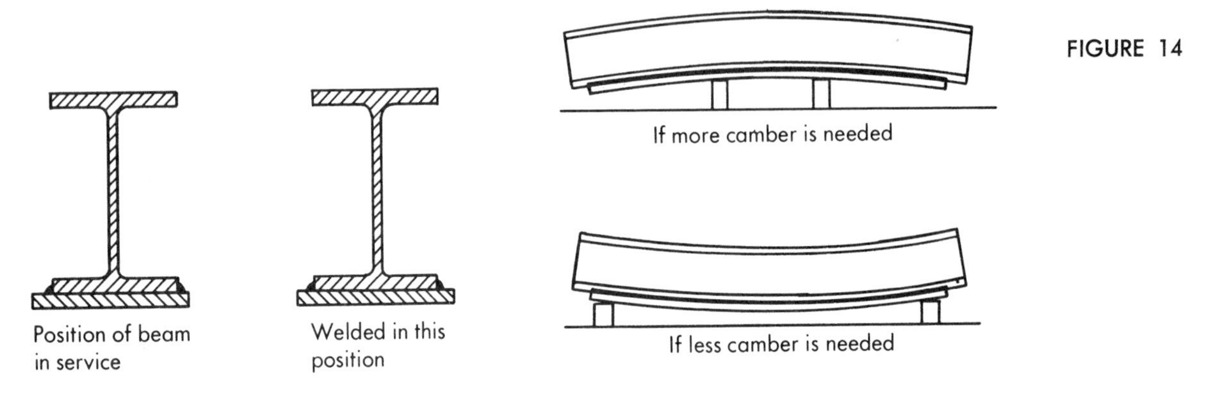

FIGURE 14

(b) When cover plate is greater than flange width

d = distance from the center of gravity of welds to the neutral axis of the section, inches

L = length of the beam, inches

I = moment of inertia of the section, in.^{4}

This may be more or less than the final desired camber, Figure 14. If this camber due to welding is excessive, the beam must be supported in such a manner that it tends to sag in the opposite direction before welding. If the camber due to welding is not enough, then the beam must sag in the same direction before welding.

A good experienced shop man will support the beam either near its ends or near its midpoint so as to control the direction and extent to which the beam bends before it is welded.

If the cover plate does not extend to the full width of bottom flange, it must be welded with the beam upside down, Figure 14(a). Supporting this beam near its ends will increase the final camber, and supporting the beam near its midpoint will decrease the final camber. If the cover plate extends beyond the bottom flange, it must be welded in this position and just the opposite technique must be used in supporting it; Figure 14(b).

The fillet welds holding this cover plate to the beam should be interrupted at the corner, if it is wider than the beam flange, as shown in Figure 15.

7. SHOP WELDING VS FIELD WELDING

It is practical to do as much welding in the shop as possible and to make only those welds in the field that can't be made in the shop. The following two sections on the Field Welding of Buildings (Sect. 4.13) and of Bridges (Sect. 4.14) include some recommendations on shop welding specific connection joints.

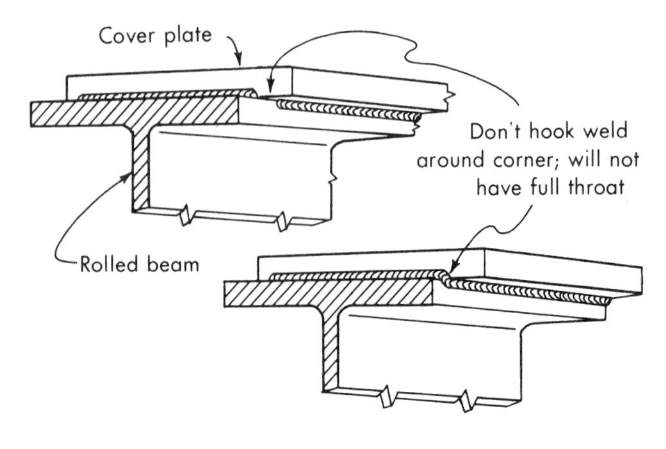

FIGURE 15

Field Welding of Buildings

1. ERECTION PRACTICES

The main cost in fabrication and erection of any steel structure is labor. It is important to get in quickly on a job and to come out in as short a time as possible.

In some cases, steel is brought in by rail and unloaded near the tracks at the job site; otherwise it is brought in by trucks. In the case of a multi-story building, storage space is at a premium, and there must be an even flow of steel to the job as it is needed. The steel is stored in the proper order so that the first steel to be used comes off the top of the pile.

The usual method of erecting a multi-story building is to set up a derrick in the center of the building area. The columns are erected at the periphery of the building and plumbed. The beams are then connected between the columns. This erection progresses toward the center of the building where the derrick is located. Finally, the central section is closed in.

These column sections may come in one or two story heights, although higher sections have been used. When the last beam is closed in at each elevation, it is important that full strength is immediately obtained in these final joints so that the derrick may be jumped to the next elevation without any loss of time. This can be done by placing these beams upon seat brackets which have previously been shop welded to the columns. The flanges of the beam can then be welded to the columns in the flat position for maximum speed.

This erection sequence is repeated for each level until the entire structure is completed. With the exception of the immediate area supporting the derrick, the field welding usually follows the erection by about one floor.

FIGURE 1

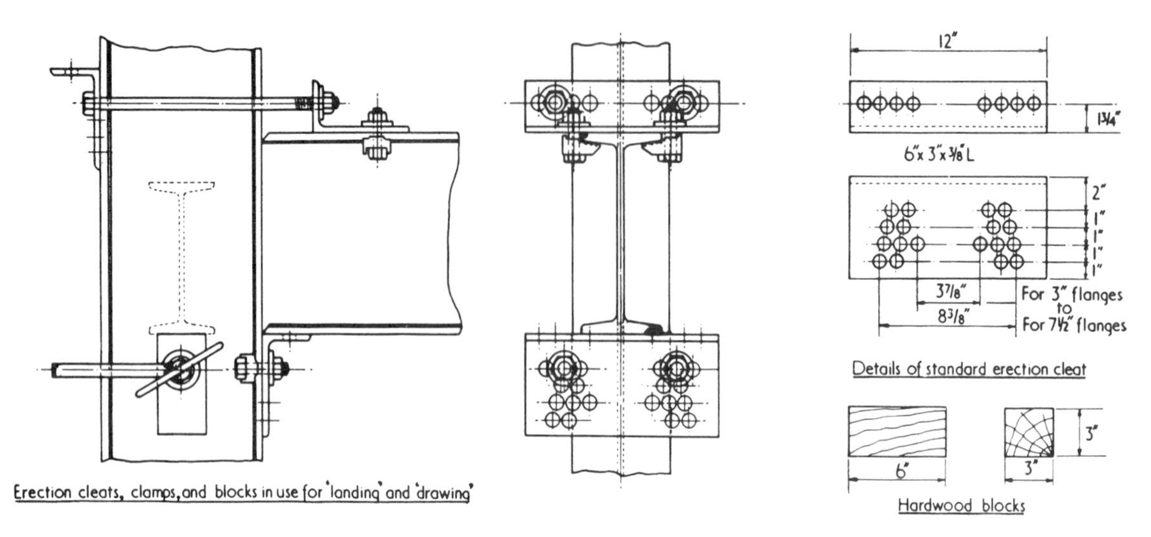

FIGURE 2

2. ERECTION HELPS

Several methods of temporarily fastening these connections have been used. Tack welding alone may be unsatisfactory because it does not make allowance for plumbing the building before final welding.

Clamping the beams to the column seat is not always safe, although this has been used for "site erection" of lighter structures; see Figure 2.

The steel is ordered cut to length and delivered to the site of erection. Temporary seat angles are clamped onto the column at the proper position, and a temporary lug clamped onto the top flange of the beam. The beam is hoisted into position and set upon the temporary seat angle of the column. A tie bolt is then screwed on to hold the beam in proper alignment with the column. Next, the beam is welded directly to the column, and any temporary lugs then disconnected and used over again.

Saxe erection clips, which are welded to the beam ends and the column, have been used with success; see Figures 3 and 4. These units consist of a forged steel clip and seat. The clip is shop welded to the end of the beam, and the seat is shop welded at the proper position on the column. During erection, the beam is placed in position so that the clips drop down into the seat. An adjustable clip has been developed to take care of possible poor fit-up between the beam

FIGURE 3

FIGURE 4

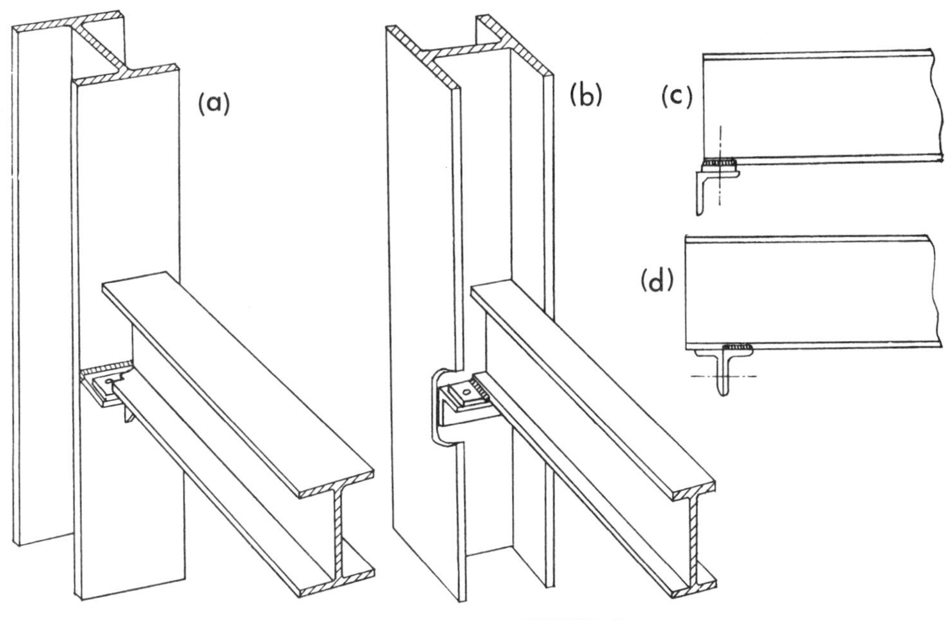

FIGURE 5

and the column.

It is recommended that the working load on any one seat should not exceed 20,000 lbs. If a greater erection load is to be carried, such as a heavy plate girder or truss, it is recommended that two or more seats be used, side by side.

The use of a few erection bolts has been found to be a satisfactory means of temporarily fastening before welding. Bolting may be done directly to main members. It is less costly to punch small attachments for erection bolts than to move heavy main members into the punch shop for punching. Many times, holes are flame cut in the ends of beams for erection bolts.

In Figure 5(a), a small connection plate is shop welded to the bottom beam flange at the end. A seat is also shop welded to the column flange at the proper height. During erection, the beam is placed upon the seat and two erection bolts are used to hold them in place.

In Figure 5(b), the beam is connected to the column web. A seat angle is shop welded to the inside faces of the column flanges and/or to the column web. A flat plate is shop welded at the end of the lower beam flange; see Figure 5(c). During erection, the beam is held in place by two erection bolts. All punching has been done on small attaching plates or angles. No punching has been necessary on the heavy main members. Any of several methods may be used to tie in the top beam flange.

Figure 5(d) indicates that when the beam flange is too wide for easy access to bolts applied as at Figure 5(c), the angle welded between the column flanges may be reversed. In this case, another angle of same size is welded to the underside of the lower beam flange. The erection bolts are run through the vertical legs of the two angles.

Welded studs may be used for erection. In Figure 6, two studs are placed on the beam web and serve the same purpose as erection bolts. The welding of the studs would be done at the same time the beams are laid out. Since the studs are placed on the beam web, it would be difficult to damage them in transit or erection since the overhang of the beam flanges would protect them.

The attaching plate on the column is designed for

FIGURE 6

FIGURE 7

FIGURE 8

the shear reaction and is shop welded in the flat position for minimum cost. No punching or drilling of the main member is necessary. Since the attaching plate would be punched with a template having the same distance between holes as the punch marks for the welded studs, there should be no difficulty in fitting the beam in place during erection.

The small attaching plate may be punched with a slot in the horizontal direction of the beam. This will allow some adjustment, to take care of dimensional tolerance on the column size or beam length and yet give a positive location for the height of the beam.

With this arrangement, the only field welding would be the top and bottom flange butt joints and whatever vertical welding would be required for the shear reaction to the beam web. The flange butt welds would have the proper root opening and use a light backing strap, about ⅛″ x 1″. This backing strap could extend slightly beyond the joint so as to form a shelf or run-off tab to insure proper build-up at the end of the joint.

By welding a seat plate to the column flange, as in Figure 7, any vertical welding in the field would be eliminated. The plate would have sufficient size and attaching weld to transmit the shear reaction of the beam. Here, two short welding studs are placed one on each side of the bottom flange's centerline at the beam ends. They are spaced to the thickness of the seat plate, and after erection, will keep the beams securely positioned over the seat. A third welding stud is placed on the underside of the top beam flange and engages a small attaching plate shop welded to the column. This plate has a slot punched in it, the slot being lengthwise with the beam.

With this arrangement, the beam can be simply lowered down into position, with the studs dropping into place and locating the beam squarely and tightly for field welding.

A possible improvement of this method would be to have the two welding studs on the bottom flange so they would engage into the holes first. This third stud just under the top flange could be threaded and when tightened with a nut would hold the beam from accidentally being knocked upward and out of the connection.

A slight modification can be made by placing this third stud on the beam web, near the top; see Figure 8. The small attaching plate has a hole larger, perhaps by ⅛″, than the stud diameter. In erection, the beam is lowered into position as before, but must be rolled slightly to engage the web stud. A nut is drawn up tightly on this stud for firm holding.

A further variation could use a T-shaped stiffened seat bracket with the horizontal plate punched accurately to receive the two studs on the bottom flange of the beam. The third stud could be placed on the underside of the top beam flange to provide horizontal stability.

It is true that with this method of using welding studs to avoid making holes in the main members, there would be no provision for using the tapered end of a structural offset or spud wrench to bring the beam end into proper alignment with the connection. However, with the accuracy of placing the welding studs and laying out the corresponding slotted holes so as to allow for some horizontal adjustment, there should be little difficulty.

3. FIELD WELDING

Plumbing of a building usually starts around an elevator shaft or service core. This is usually centrally located and has greater bracing. The butt welds of the beam and girder flanges to the supporting column will have some transverse shrinkage. It is necessary that this shrinkage be estimated and the joint opened up by this amount before welding. Otherwise, this shrinkage will accumulate along the length or width of the building and build up to a sizable amount. See Figure 9.

A good estimate of this transverse shrinkage is—

$$\Delta = .10 \frac{A_w}{t_{℄}}$$

$$\Delta = .10\, W_{av}$$

where:

A_w = cross-sectional area of weld

$t_{℄}$ = thickness of plate

W_{av} = average width of weld

The cross-sectional area of the weld may be computed by breaking it down into standard areas; that is, rectangles for root opening, triangles for included angle of bevel, and parabolas for weld reinforcement. This calculation can be greatly shortened by making use of standard table giving the weight of weld metal for various joints; use Table 6 in Section 7.5. It is only necessary to divide these values by 3.4 to arrive at the area of the weld. This value is then placed into one of the above formulas for shrinkage.

Problem 1

To determine the shrinkage effects in making the welds indicated in Figure 9. The girder with a 1½″ flange is to be welded to a column. The joint has a ¼″ root opening, an included angle of 45°, and uses a backing bar.

From Table 6 in Section 7.5, the weight of weld metal is 5.93 lbs/ft. and has an area of—

$$A_w = \frac{5.93}{3.4} = 1.74 \text{ in.}^2$$

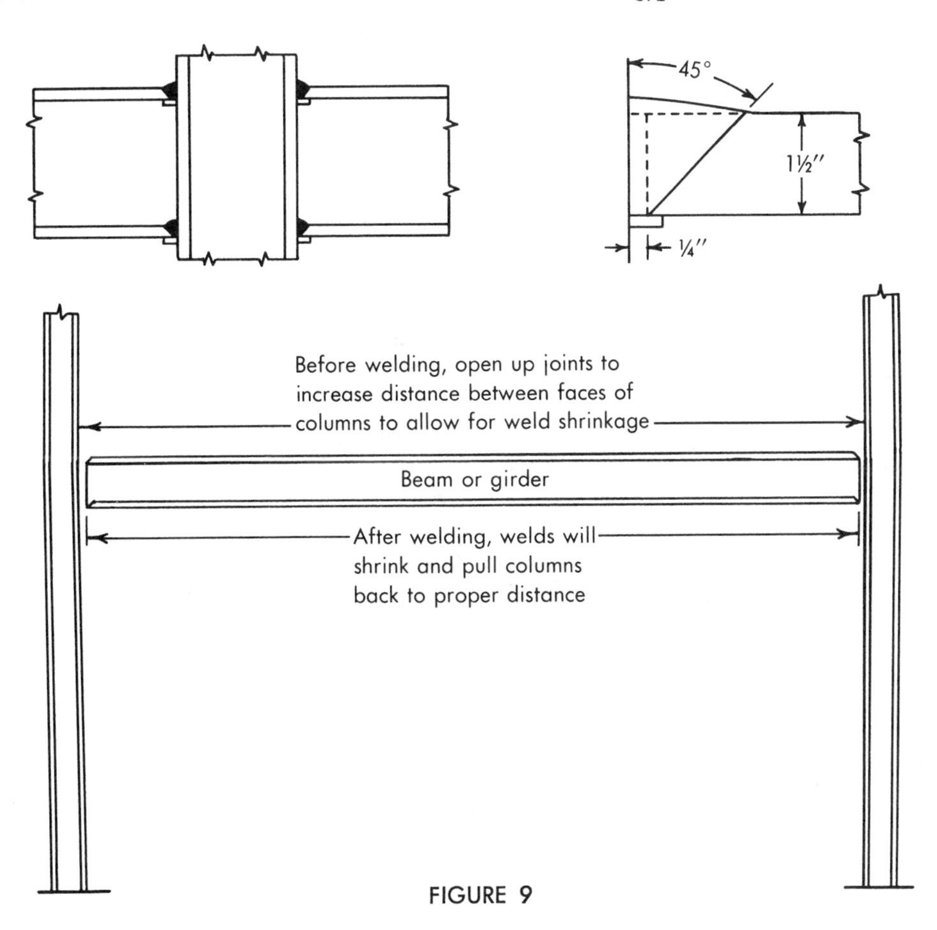

FIGURE 9

FIGURE 10

FIGURE 11

The transverse shrinkage is—

$$\Delta = .10 \left(\frac{1.74}{1\frac{1}{2}} \right)$$

$$= .116'' \text{ or about } \tfrac{1}{8}''$$

Using ¼″ fillet welds on the web will result in very little transverse shrinkage. The average width of a ¼″ fillet weld is ⅛″, and 10% of this is .012″ or about 10% of the shrinkage of the flange butt welds.

In this example, the joint of the girder flanges would be opened up an extra ⅛″ on each end of the girder so that the distance between the faces of the two columns is ¼″ greater than the detail calls for. After welding, the two joints should shrink sufficient to bring the two columns back to the desired spacing. This shrinkage could be checked after welding and this value adjusted.

* * *

The box columns in the building shown in Figure

FIGURE 12

FIGURE 13

FIGURE 14

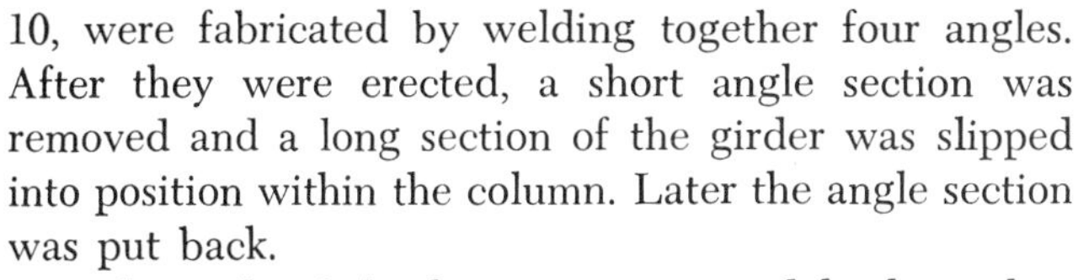

10, were fabricated by welding together four angles. After they were erected, a short angle section was removed and a long section of the girder was slipped into position within the column. Later the angle section was put back.

The ends of the beams were coped back so they could be slipped into place with their top flange resting on the top flange of the girders; Figure 11. A short seat angle shop welded to the girder web supported the lower beam flange. This resulted in a very fast erection procedure without the use of erection bolts. Later the bottom beam flange was field welded to the girder web, using the seat angle as a backing strap.

A plate was placed between the top beam flanges and the girder. The top flanges of the beams were butt groove welded together, using the plate as a backing strap. The plate was then fillet welded to the beam flanges. A long cover plate was then welded to the beam flanges to take care of the increased negative moment of the beam at this support point. Notice that this type of welded connection makes the beam continuous, thereby reducing its required size. At the same time, it does not tie the top flanges of the beam to the girder, which might produce some biaxial stresses. All of the field welding shown here was done in the flat position, greatly speeding up the erection welding.

FIGURE 15

FIGURE 16

Welding is used quite extensively on rigid frames. Figure 12 shows the shop fabrication and welding of sections of a large rigid frame. For small structures, the entire frame is fabricated and erected in one piece.

For larger structures, the frame may be divided into two or more sections and assembled at the job site and erected. Figures 13 and 14 show the construction of a rigid-frame freight terminal area, and the upright portions of the frame being unloaded from the railcar and hoisted into position by the rail crane. Later the central portions of the arch were put into position. Welding machines, also on flat cars, were brought in and the field joints welded.

Frames for the Long Beach Harbor Shed were assembled on the ground, Figure 15. The sections were laid out on wood blocks and jacked up to proper position and checked with a transit. The field joints were then welded. Three crawler cranes picked the entire frame up and placed it in position. Some of the field welding which was inaccessible when on the ground, such as the back side of the web butt joint, was completed in the air.

FIGURE 17

4. WELDING OF JOISTS AND FLOORING

Welding is used universally in the attachment of open-web joist to beams. This becomes a simple matter of laying the joist on the beam at the proper place and later welding in the flat position. A considerable amount of light-gauge steel roof decking is used on top of joists or beams. This is easily and quickly attached by means of welding in the flat position. The use of both open-web joist and steel decking is shown in Figure 16.

Floor decking of heavier gauge has been used as a support for any of several floor materials. Welding is used in the flat position to fasten this steel deck to beams of the steel structure. Many times this deck is designed to take the horizontal forces on the structure caused by wind or earthquake.

5. WELDOR PLATFORMS

It does not take much in the scaffolding to support a weldor and his equipment. Many of the joints can be reached without any platform; the weldor simply works off of the beam or works from a ladder.

For welds below the beam, it may be necessary to put up a platform. Figure 17 shows a rectangular wooden platform with four ropes attached to it. The platform is fastened to the steel structure at the proper level by the ropes. Although this type of platform is self-contained, it is rather heavy, especially for one man.

Figure 18 shows a simpler scaffold for a similar position in the steel structure. It is lighter and easier for one man to set up. Two wood planks have ropes fastened at their ends; the ropes are tied to steel grab hooks. The hooks, supporting the wood planks, are dropped over the top flange of the beam, and the other two planks are put into place. This platform can be used on all beams having approximately the same depth without any further adjustment in the rope length. It can be used in almost any condition. Usually a weldor's helper or one from the erecting crew will set up the necessary scaffolding ahead of time, so there will be no delay in welding.

On large structures which have connections requiring quite a bit of welding at the connections, it may help to use a weldor's cage which hooks over the top flange of the beams and is put in place by the derrick. This is shown in Figure 19. These cages can be covered on three sides to form a windbreak when used on the outside of the steel structure. The weldor is not aware he is working at a great height when he is inside this shielded cage.

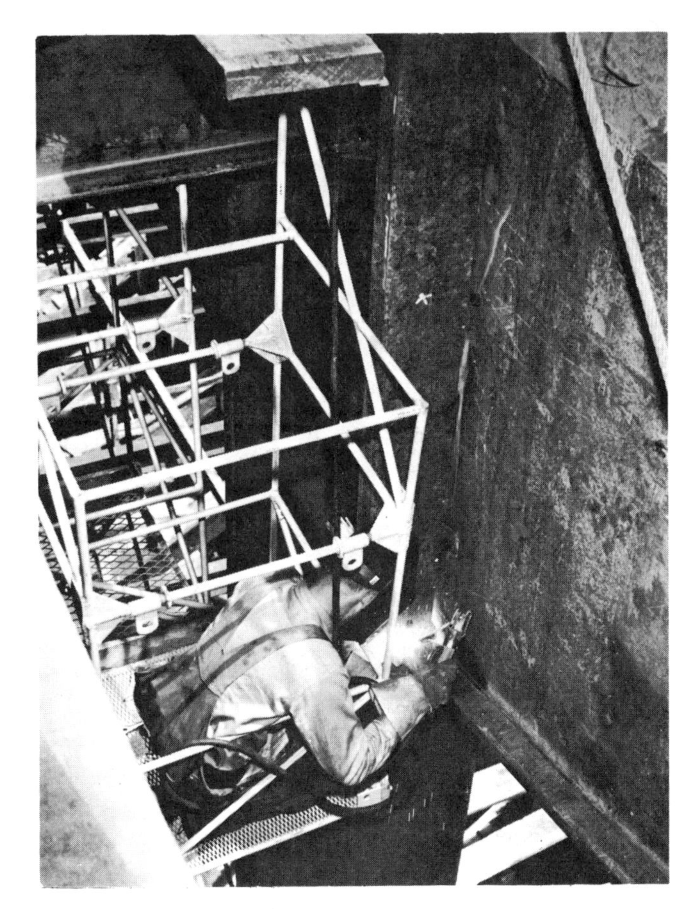

FIGURE 19

FIGURE 18

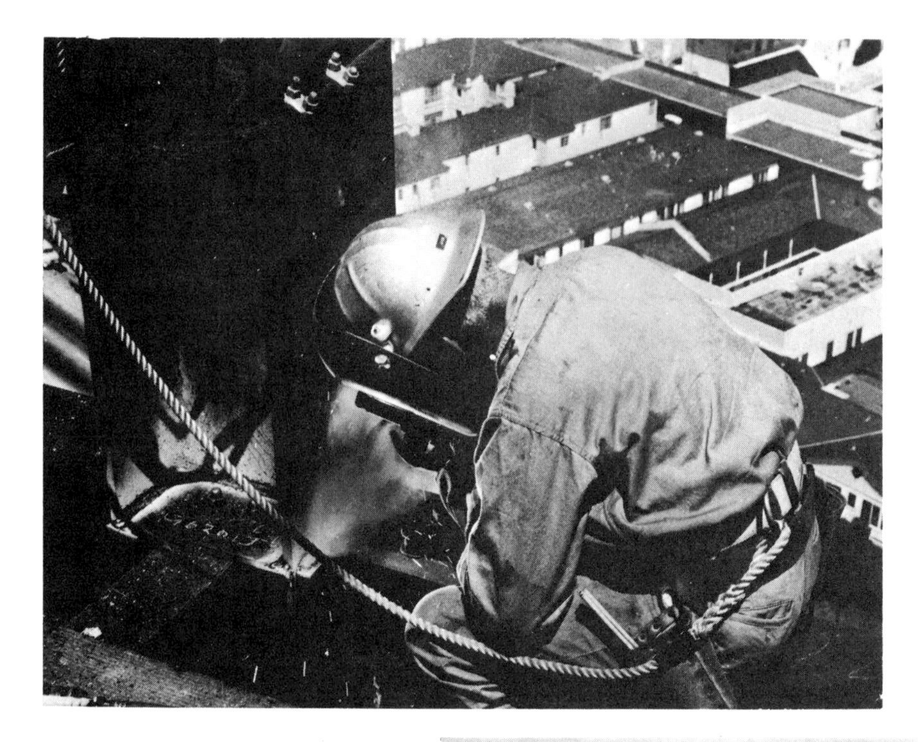

Semi-automatic welding, using self-shielding cored electrode, being employed in making beam-to-column connections on Wilshire-Ardmore Building in Los Angeles.

Semi-automatic welding speeding erection of 32-story Commerce Towers in Kansas City, Missouri. Making welded girder connections in the open was facilitated by use of lightweight compact gun and continuously-fed, self-shielding cored electrode.

Field Welding of Bridges

1. BUTT JOINTS

In butt groove welding the ends of flange plates, some thought should be given to the proper type of joint. J and U joints require the least amount of weld metal; however, these joint types generally require the plates to be prepared by planing or milling which is impractical in most structural fabricating shops. This limits the preparation to flame beveling, giving a V joint.

In the V joint, less weld metal is necessary as the included angle is decreased. However, as this angle decreases, the root opening must be increased in order to get the electrode down into the joint and produce a sound weld at the root of the joint. Obviously, the one tends to offset the other slightly in respect to the amount of weld metal needed. On thicker plates, the joint with the smaller included angle and larger root opening, requires the least weld metal.

If a backing strap is used, any amount of root opening within reason can be tolerated, and all of the welding must be done on the same side; in other words, a single-V joint. If a backing strap is not employed, this root opening must be held to about ⅛″. This enables the root pass to bridge the gap and not fall through. The welding may be done on one side only, single-V; or it may be done on both sides, double V. In either case, the joint is back-gouged from the opposite side to the root before depositing additional weld metal on the other side. This will insure sound metal throughout the entire joint.

Single-V joints may be acceptable if the plates are not too thick; for thicker plates, double-V joints are preferred since they require less weld metal. Remember that a single-V joint will produce more angular distortion. This increases rapidly as the flange thickness increases.

Shop Splicing

Shop splices in flange and web plates should be made before the girder is fitted together and welded, providing the resulting sections are not too long or heavy to handle. These shop splices do not have to be in a single plane, but are placed where they are most convenient, or where a transition in section is desired.

In the shop, flange plates can be turned over easily as welding progresses, so that on thicker plates double-V joints would be used. They require the least amount of weld metal and the welding is balanced so there should be no angular distortion. On wider plates, perhaps 2′ to 3′, semi-automatic and full automatic submerged-arc welding equipment is frequently used.

Field Splicing

Field splices usually are located on a single plane. Staggering the butt welds of flanges and webs will not improve performance of the girder. It is much easier to prepare the joints and maintain proper fit-up by flame-cutting and beveling when all are located in the same plane. See Figure 2. There is an advantage to having extended the fillet welds of flanges to the web all the way to the very end of the girder. This provides better support when the flanges are clamped together for temporary support during erection.

Most welding sequences for field splices of beams and girders are based on the following general outline

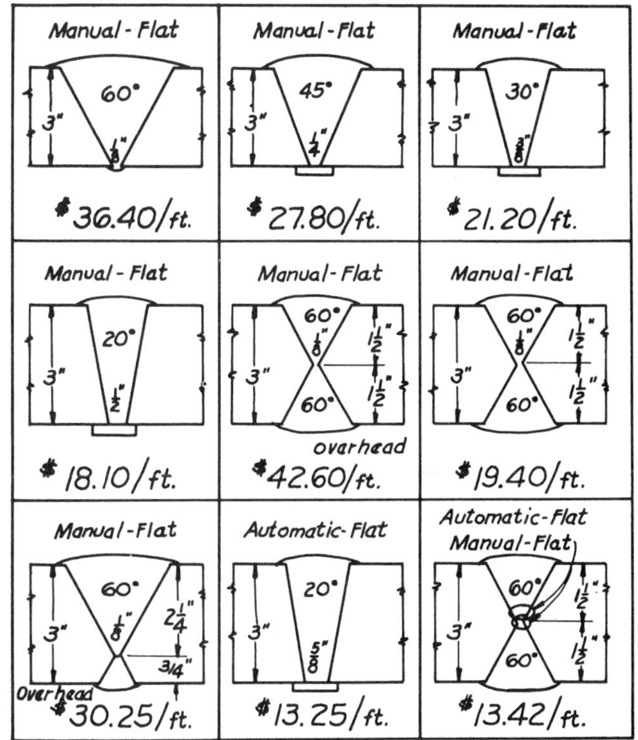

FIG. 1 Relative cost of flange butt welds.

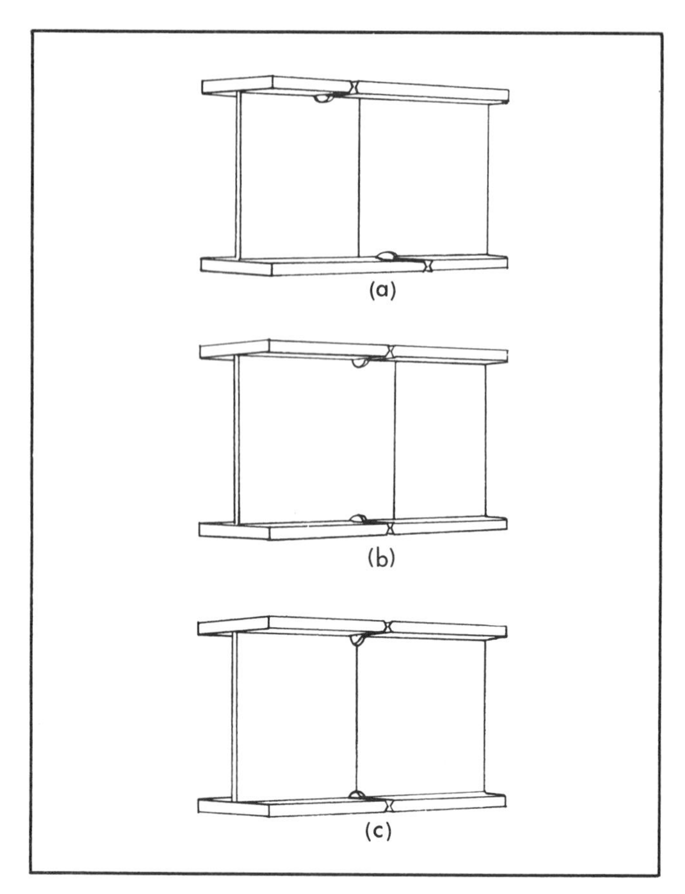

FIG. 2 Three methods of preparing edges of girders for field welding. Placing the three welds in three different planes makes it difficult to get close fit. It is easier to lay out all three butt welds in same plane. Placing two flange welds in the same plane and slightly offsetting the weld in the web offers a method of supporting one girder on the other during erection.

in which both flanges and web are alternately welded to a portion of their depth, after securing with sufficient tack welds; see Figure 3.

1. Weld a portion of the thickness of both flanges (about ⅓ to ½), full width.
2. Weld a portion of the thickness of the web (about ½), full width.
3. Complete the welding of the flanges.
4. Complete the welding of the web.

For deep webs, the vertical welding is sometimes divided into two or more sections, and a backstep method is used; Figure 4. This will result in a more uniform transverse shrinkage of this joint.

Most butt joints used in field splicing the webs are of the single-V type. For thicker webs, perhaps above ½″, a double-V joint is used in order to reduce the amount of welding required and to balance the welding about both sides to eliminate any angular distortion.

Most flange butt joints to be field welded are either the single-V or double-V type, depending on the flange thickness and the method of welding used. For higher welding speeds, such as when using iron powdered manual electrodes, or semi-automatic, or fully-automatic submerged-arc welding, more of the welding would be done in the flat position, with less in the overhead position.

It must be remembered that a single-V joint will result in more angular distortion, and this increases

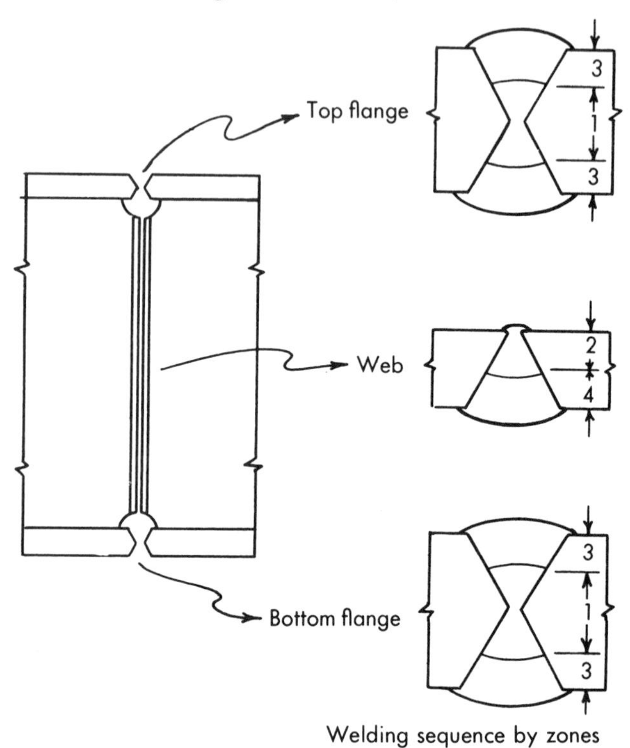

FIG. 3 Both flanges and web are alternately welded.

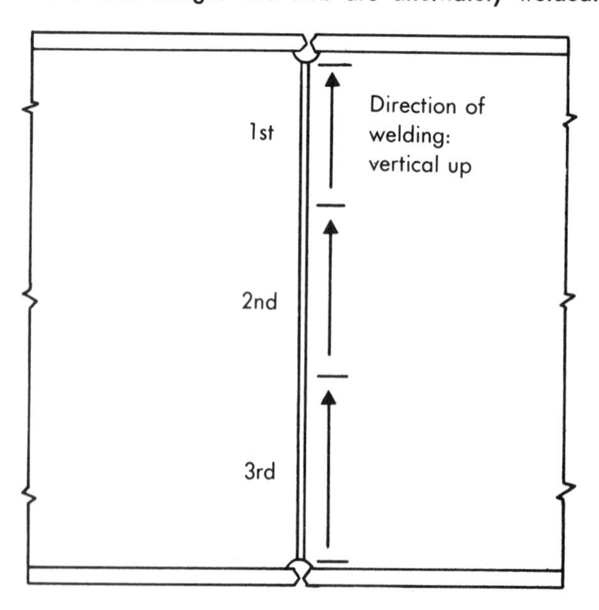

FIG. 4 For deep webs, use back-step sequence.

rapidly as flange thickness increases. A double-V joint with half of the welding on both the top and bottom of the joint is best as far as distortion is concerned, but it may require a considerable amount of overhead welding. For this reason the AWS Prequalified Joints allow the double-V joint to be prepared so that a maximum weld of ¾ of the flange thickness is on top, and the remaining ¼ on the bottom; Figure 5. This will give some reduction in the overall amount of weld metal, and yet reduce the amount of overhead welding.

Table 6 in Section 7.5 gives the amount of weld metal required (lbs/ft of joint) for the various AWS Prequalified Joints. This will aid in making a better choice of the actual details for the best overall joint.

For the double-V butt joint for the flange, the State of Texas allows the field weldor to place the overhead pass in the bottom side of the joint first, and then after cleaning the top side to place the next pass in the flat position. Their thinking is that while some overhead welding is needed regardless of the sequence used, this procedure eliminates all of the back chipping or back gouging in the overhead position. If the welding is done properly, there should be less clean-up required.

2. COPED HOLES IN WEB AT SPLICE

Considerable questioning has been directed toward whether the web should have coped holes to aid in field welding butt joints in the flange. The disadvantage of the coped holes must be carefully weighed against the advantages of making a sounder weld in the flange.

Tests on 12″ deep girders at the University of Illinois* have shown that the field splice having welds

* "Fatigue in Welded Beams and Girders", W. H. Munse & J. E. Stallmeyer; Highway Research Board, Bulletin 315, 1962, p 45.

(a) Single-V groove joint. Simplest preparation. Tendency for angular distortion.

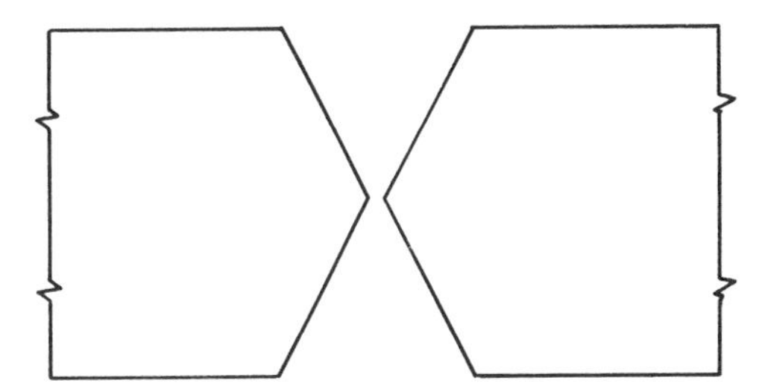

(b) Double-V groove joint. For thicker plate, reduces amount of weld metal. If welds alternate between top and bottom, there's no angular distortion. Unless plate is turned over, will require overhead welding on the bottom.

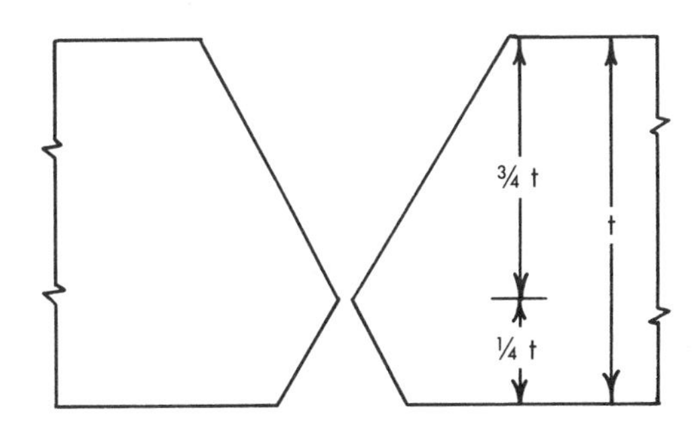

(c) When plates cannot be turned over, the amount of overhead welding can be reduced by extending the top portion of the double V to a maximum of ¾ plate thickness.

FIGURE 5

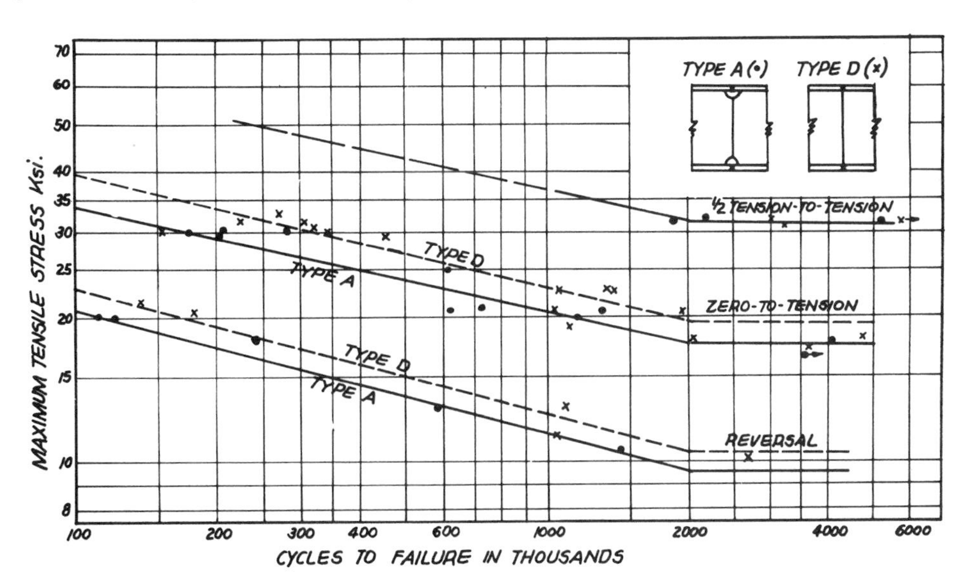

FIG. 6 Results of fatigue tests on welded beams with splices.

in a single plane and using coped holes has a fatigue strength of about 84% of the corresponding splice with no coped holes at 100,000 cycles, and about 90% at 2,000,000 cycles. See Figure 6.

Knowing these figures represent the maximum reduction in fatigue strength because of the coped holes, it is felt these holes will do more good than harm since they insure the best possible weld in the butt joint of the flanges. The reduction in fatigue strength due to coped holes on much deeper plate girders would seem to be less, since the reduction in section modulus ascribable to the coped hole would be much less. Of course, any notch effect of the coped hole would still be present. If necessary, this hole can be filled by welding after the butt joint of the flanges is completed.

3. PROPER FIT-UP

Good fit-up is essential to the development of efficient welding procedures. This means proper alignment and correct root opening. Placement of flange and web butt splices in the same plane greatly increases the ability to achieve correct root opening when the girder is pulled into alignment.

Figure 7 illustrates a misaligned double-V butt joint in a girder flange at the point of transition. Note the offset of the joint preparation makes it difficult to reach the root of the joint and deposit a sound weld

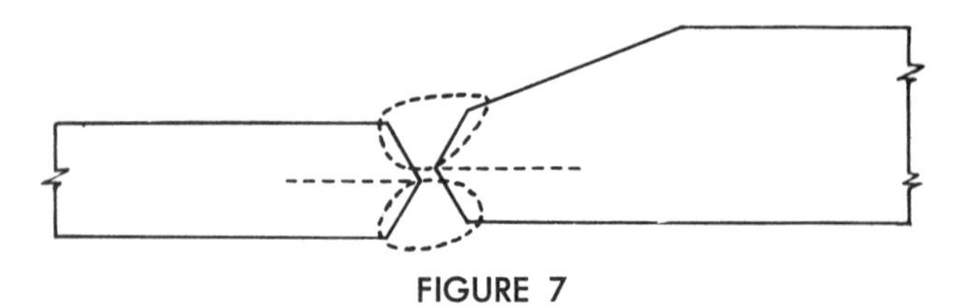

FIGURE 7

throughout the entire joint. The flange joints should be checked for alignment throughout their entire length before welding.

This illustrated condition can exist at the flange extremities even though perfect alignment exists in the web area. Accidental tilt of the flanges during fabrication, mishandling during movement to the job site, or even a difference in warpage of the two flanges can cause this condition. The warpage problem increases with the size of web-to-flange fillet weld and decreases as the flange thickness increases.

Various methods exist for correcting this condition. Figure 8 illustrates one such method. When the plates are not too thick, small clips can be welded to the edge of one plate. Driving a steel wedge between each clip and the other plate will bring both edges into alignment. Welding the clips on just one side greatly simplifies their removal.

Figure 9 illustrates still another method which is used commonly when problems develop in respect to misaligned thicker flanges. Here (top sketch) a heavy

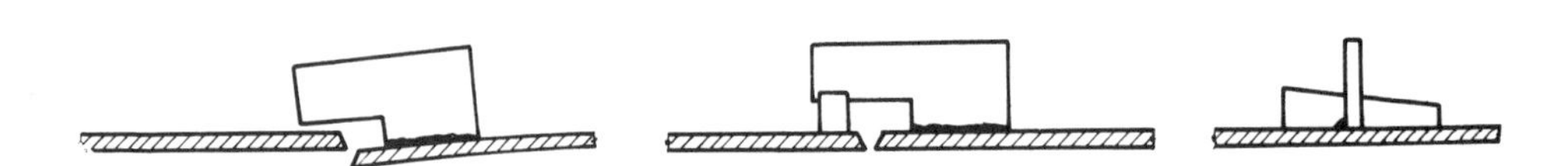

FIG. 8 Weld clip along one edge only, so it may be removed easily with a hammer. Drive steel wedge below clip until plate edges are in alignment.

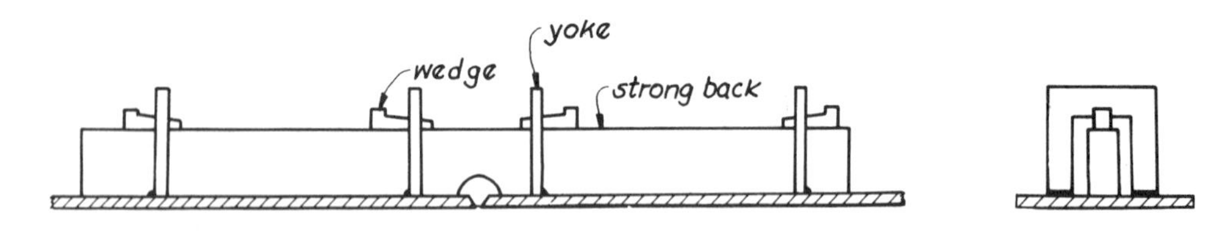

(a) Plates forced into alignment and held there by means of strongbacks. Pressure is applied by means of wedge driven between yoke and strongback.

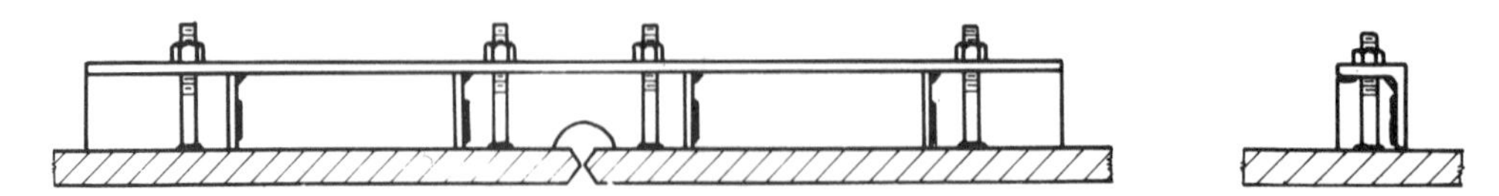

(b) For heavier plates, pressure may be applied by means of bolts temporarily welded to the plate. Strongback is then pulled tightly against the plate.

FIGURE 9

bar or strongback is pulled up against the misaligned plates by driving steel wedges between the bar and attached yokes. An alternate method (lower sketch) involves the welding of bolts to the misaligned plate and then drawing the plate up against the strongback by tightening up on the bolts.

4. RUN-OFF TABS OR EXTENSION BARS

Butt joints of stress carrying members should, where possible, be welded with some type of run-off bar attached to the ends of the joint to make it easier to obtain good quality weld metal at the ends.

In general the bar should have a similar joint preparation to that being welded; gouging or chipping may be used to provide the depth of groove. For automatic welding, the bars should have sufficient width to support the flux used during welding. These bars are usually removed after welding.

A flat run-off bar may not give proper support for weld metal to keep the top corners of the plate from melting back at the ends; Figure 10(a). If the bars were placed high enough for this, they would be above the groove of the joint and would interfere with proper welding at the ends; the welding wire (if automatic welding) would have to drop down into the groove at the start and climb out at the other end very quickly, undoubtedly sticking; Figure 10(b).

The flat run-off bar in Figure 10(c) for manual welding does not give proper support or maintain the sides of the welded joint at the ends as welding progresses and requires special effort on the part of the welding operator to build these ends up.

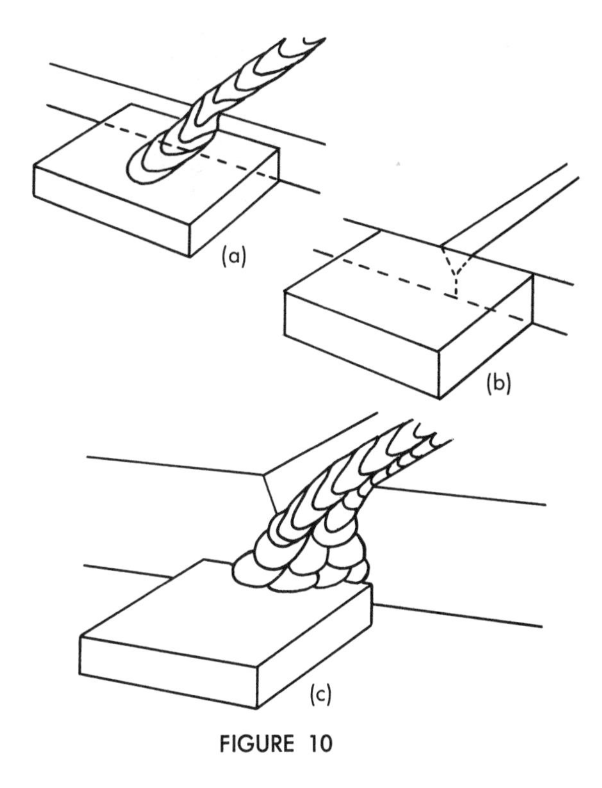

FIGURE 10

The types of run-off bars illustrated in Figure 11 would give the proper equivalent joint detail at the ends.

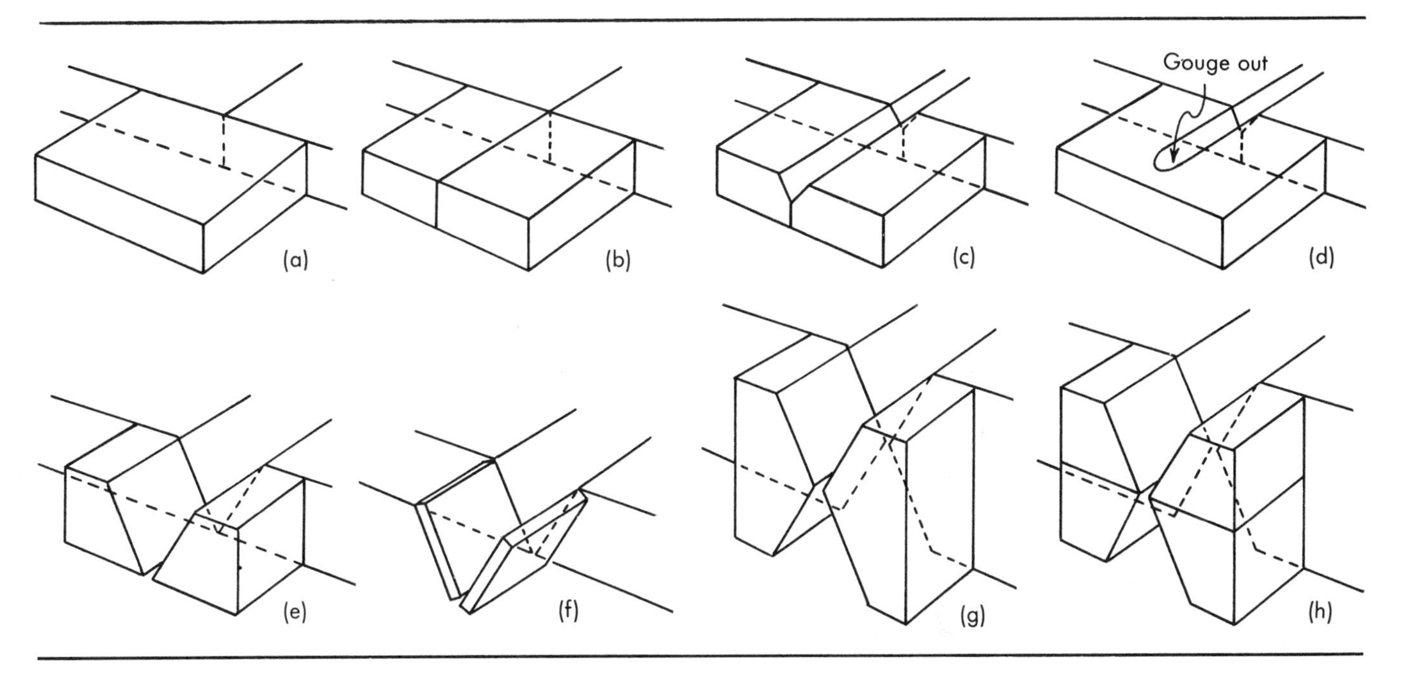

FIGURE 11

Steel sulky seat aids weldors on bridge construction. Float at left lacks stability in windy weather, while sulky at right enables operator to sit comfortably and safely.

Shop weld-fabricated girders of variable depth provided important economies and facilitated erection of Thompson's Bridge near Gainesville, Georgia.

Beam-to-Column Connections

1. TYPES OF DESIGN

AISC Specifications permit four types of design and design assumptions in steel construction. Beam-to-column connections can be categorized accordingly; see Figure 1. The four types of design:

		Restraint (R)
(a) simple frame	AISC Type 2	below approx. 20%
(b) fully rigid frame	AISC Type 1	above approx. 90%
(c) semi-rigid frame	AISC Type 3	approx. 20 to approx. 90%
(d) plastic design	AISC Plastic Design	

Here the degree of restraint (R) is the ratio of the actual end moment (assuming no column rotation) to the end moment in a fully fixed end beam.

These various connections are discussed comparatively here in Section 5.1, but details of their design are presented more comprehensively in later sections.

2. SIMPLE BEAM CONNECTIONS

The most common types of simple beam connections use web framing angles, or a top connecting angle with the beam supported on a seat.

The connection is designed to transfer the vertical shear reaction only, it being assumed there is no bending moment present at the connection. However the simple beam, under load, will deflect, causing the ends to rotate slightly. The connection must be designed to rotate this amount without failure, and to flex enough to keep the end moment from building up to any appreciable amount. This is sometimes referred to as a "flexible connection."

A top connecting plate is sometimes used for simple beams. In this case the end of the plate is beveled and butt welded to the column, the plate and connecting weld being designed to develop about 25% of the resisting moment of the beam at the standard allowable bending stress. Just beyond this weld, the plate is reduced in cross-section to produce yield stress at this load. The length of the reduced section should be about 1.2 times its width to allow the plate to yield plastically without failure. This plate is attached to the beam flange with a continuous fillet weld across the end and returning for a sufficient length on both sides to develop the strength of the butt weld at standard allowables.

Wind moments applied to these connections present an additional problem. Some means to transfer these wind moments must be provided in a connection that is supposed to be flexible. Any additional restraint in the connection will increase the end moment resulting from the beam load. AISC (Sec. 1.2) provides for two approximate solutions:

Method 1. Designing the top plate for the force resulting from the moment caused by the combination of gravity and wind loads at a ⅓ increase in the stress allowables. This same ⅓ increase may also be applied to the connecting welds (AISC Sec. 1.5.3 and 1.5.6).

Method 2. Designing the top plate to carry the force resulting from the calculated wind moment at a ⅓ increase in the allowable stress. The top plate should be capable of safely yielding plastically within the unwelded length for any combination of gravity and wind loads causing it to be stressed above its yield point, thus relieving these additional moments. The connecting welds are designed for standard allowables when plate is at yield stress.

This type of connection may necessitate some non-elastic but self-limiting deformation of the connecting plate, but under forces which do not overstress the weld (AISC Sec. 1.2).

3. SEMI-RIGID CONNECTIONS

Semi-rigid connections are very intriguing, but unfortunately are many times misleading.

The disadvantage of a simply supported beam is that the entire moment requirement is at one portion of the beam, its central section having the greatest moment: $M = \frac{1}{8} W L$ (if uniformly loaded).

A rigid, fixed-end connection reduces the moment at the central portion of the beam, with a corresponding increase in the moment at the ends. The moment reduction at the center is added to the ends. As the degree of restraint or rigidity of the connection increases, the center moment decreases, and the end moments increase. Fully rigid connections for uniformly loaded beams result in a center moment of $M = \frac{1}{24}$

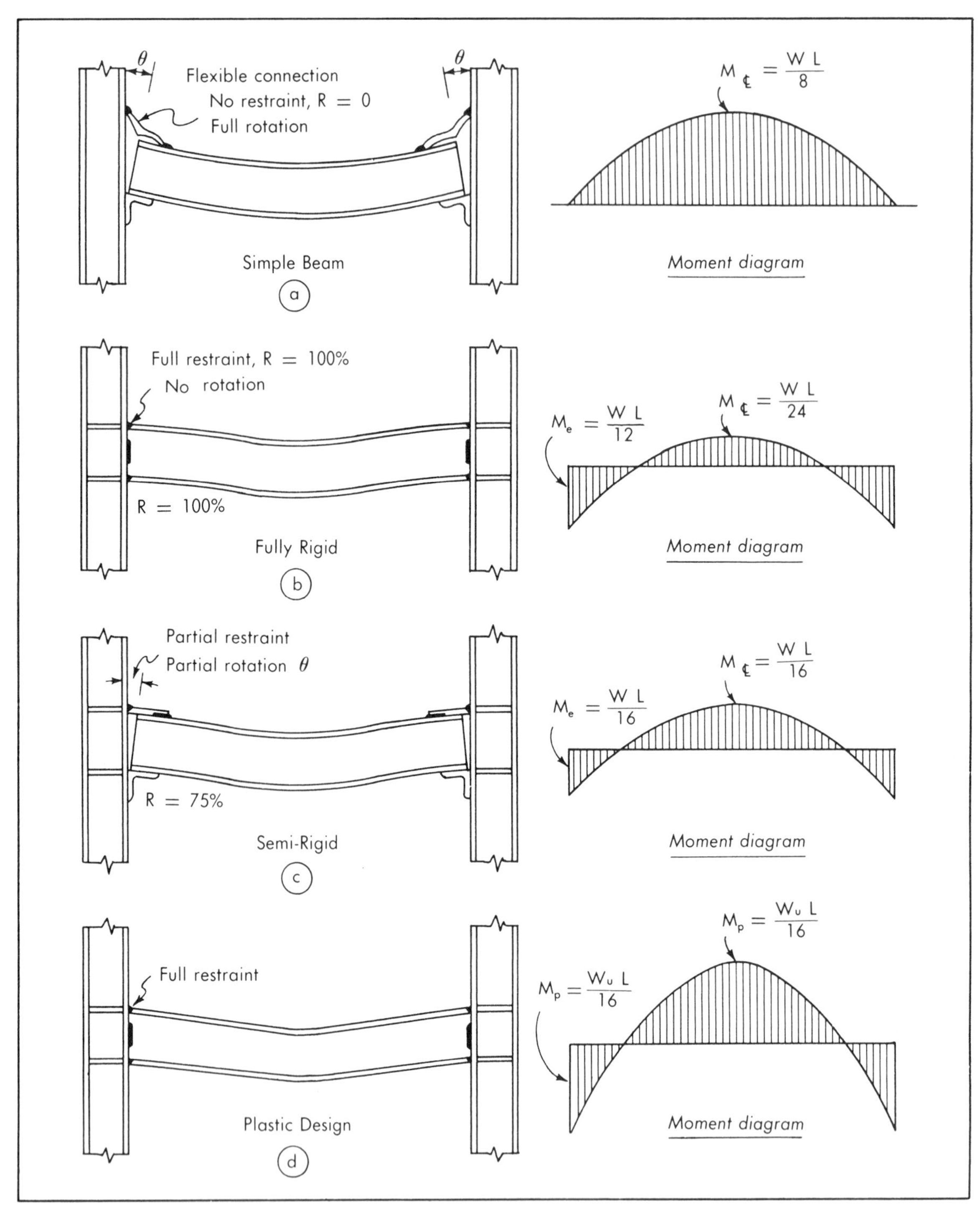

FIGURE 1

W L, and the end moment of M = $\frac{1}{12}$ W L. Thus, the beam needs a section modulus just $\frac{2}{3}$ of that required for a simply supported beam using flexible connections.

Advocates of semi-rigid connections point out that the above redistribution of moment has been carried a little too far. They advise that if a semi-rigid connection is used instead, having an end restraint of R = 75%, both the center moment and the end moments would be equal, or M = $\frac{1}{16}$ W L. This would produce the least requirement for section modulus, being ½ of that needed for the original simply supported beam. This is true, but this ideal condition depends on two requirements:

1. The supports to which the connection joins the beam must be unyielding, i.e. absolutely rigid.

2. The beam must not be influenced by adjacent

spans from which additional moments might be carried over through the connection.

This condition of R = 75% restraint does produce the minimum section modulus for the uniformly loaded beam, but it does not offer any leeway or range of connection rigidity. If the resulting connection should be a little too rigid (anything over 75%), the end moment increases above the allowable; if the connection is a little too flexible (anything below 75%), the center moment increases above the allowable. To take care of this, it is usually suggested that the beam be designed for an end restraint of R = 50% (center moment of $\frac{1}{12}$ W L), and the connection for a restraint of R = 75% (end moment of $\frac{1}{16}$ W L). This appears to be good until it is remembered that this resulting design moment of $\frac{1}{12}$ W L is no lower than if fully rigid welded connections were used; so, there is no saving in beam requirements by using the semi-rigid connections.

It could be argued that this semi-rigid connection results in a slight reduction in the amount of connecting weld. This might be true if the fully rigid connection used a top connecting plate (groove weld to the column and fillet weld to the beam), but would not be true if the beam flanges for the rigid connection were groove welded directly to the supporting column without the additional fillet welds.

Although perhaps not intended, most structural texts, and other literature on the subject, imply that the engineer simply takes each span one at a time and designs the beam for an end restraint of R = 50% and the connection for a restraint of R = 75%. It wouldn't be difficult to calculate the cross-sectional area and the length of reduced section of the proper top connecting plate for this semi-rigid connection to arrive at the actual required restraint.

Those who voice the apparent advantages of semi-rigid connections seldom discuss how to apply them to actual frames of several spans and stories and different span loadings.

In frames using fully rigid, welded connections, the resulting moments must be found. For example, if the moment distribution method is used, the end moments must be determined for each span, treating each as an isolated, fixed-end beam. A distribution factor is required for each member so that the unbalanced moment at each joint may be properly distributed about the various members connecting at a given joint. Carry-over factors are needed to determine the amount of the unbalanced moment to be carried over to the opposite end of the member.

For a frame using semi-rigid connections, all of these factors (end moments, distribution factors, and carry-over factors) will be affected by the connection's degree of rigidity. This would make the analysis more complicated.

AISC allows semi-rigid connections only upon evidence that they are capable of resisting definite moments without overstressing the welds. Design of the members so connected shall be based on no greater degree of end restraint than the minimum known to be effective.

This type of connection may necessitate some non-elastic but self-limiting deformation, but under forces which do not overstress the weld (AISC Sec. 1.2).

4. RIGID CONNECTIONS (Elastic Design)

For fully rigid connections the actual moments must be found by one of several methods, and the beams and their connections designed for the proper moments and shear forces. The connections must have sufficient rigidity to hold virtually unchanged the original angles between connecting members.

The rigidity of a connection is also influenced by the rigidity of its support. For beams framing into column flanges, a decrease in rigidity will occur if the column flanges are too thin, or if stiffeners are not used between the column flanges in line with the beam flanges. For a single beam framing into a column web, a decrease in rigidity may occur unless the beam flange is also welded directly to the column flanges or attached with suitable connecting plates.

5. PLASTIC-DESIGN CONNECTIONS

The use of welded connections based on plastic design has several advantages:

1. A more accurate indication of the true carrying capacity of the structure.
2. Requires less steel than conventional simple beam construction. In many cases, there is a slight saving over conventional elastic design of rigid frames.
3. Requires less design time than does elastic design of rigid frames.
4. Tested by several years of research on full-scale structures.
5. Backed by the AISC.

So far, plastic design connections have been largely restricted to one-story structures, and to applications where fatigue or repeat loading is not a problem. See separate Sect. 5.12 in this manual for a full discussion of Welded Connections for Plastic Design.

6. BEHAVIOR OF WELDED CONNECTIONS

One way to better understand the behavior of a beam-to-column connection under load, and its load-carrying capacity, is to plot it on a moment-rotation chart; see Figure 2.

The vertical axis is the end moment of the beam,

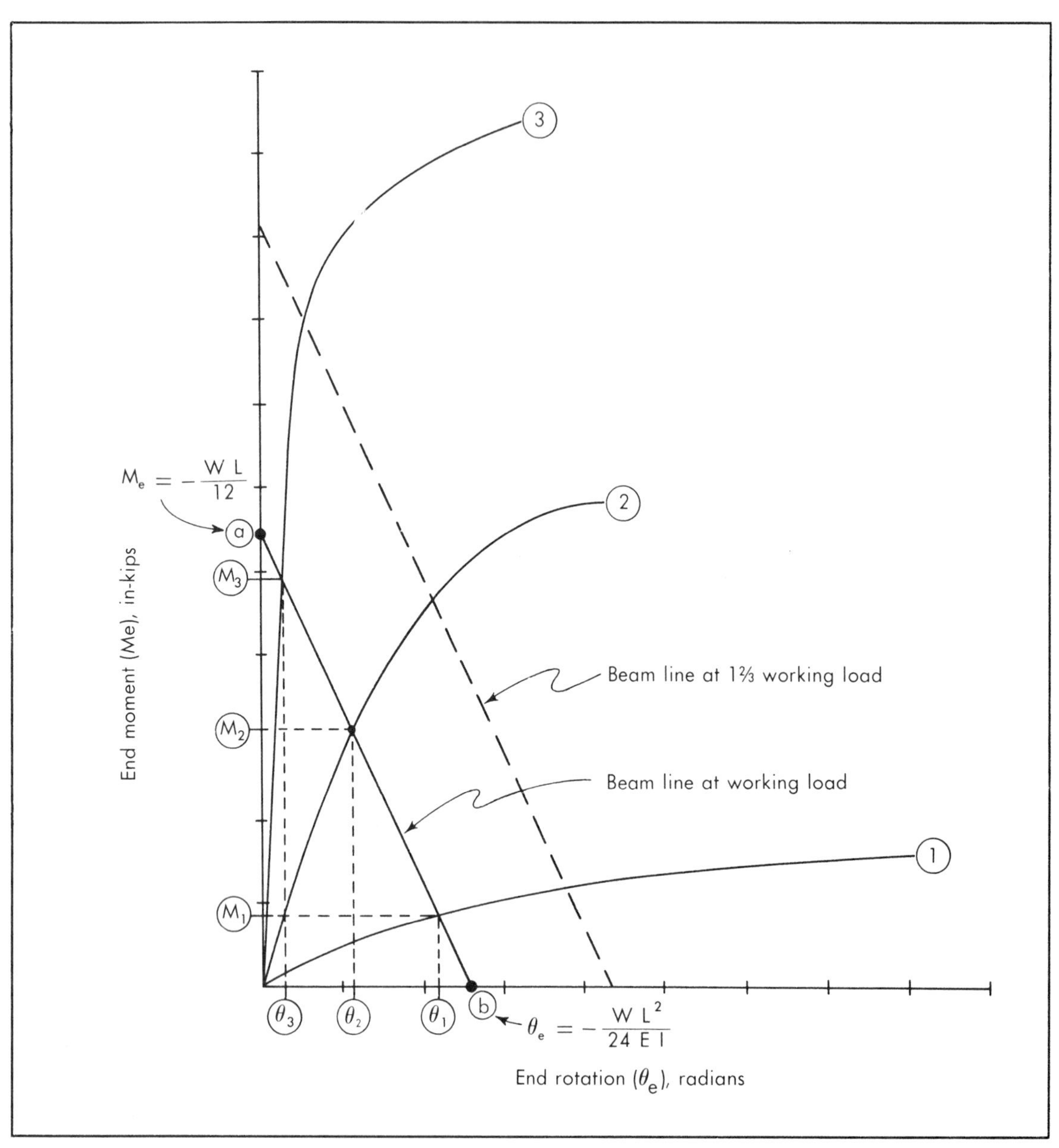

FIGURE 2

which is applied to the connection. The horizontal axis is the resulting rotation in radians. Basically this is another type of stress-strain diagram.

Superimposed upon this is the beam diagram. The equation expressing the resulting end moment (M_e) and end rotation (θ_e), for a uniformly loaded beam and any end restraint from complete rigid to simply supported, is:

$$M_e = -\frac{2 E I \theta}{L} - \frac{W L}{12}$$

This is a straight line, having points *a* and *b* on the chart.

Point *a* is the end moment when the connection is completely restrained ($\theta_e = 0$), in other words a fixed-end beam, and is equal to—

$$(a)\ M_e = -\frac{W L}{12}$$

Point *b* is the end rotation when the connection has no restraint ($M_e = 0$), in other words a simple beam, and is equal to—

$$(b)\ \theta_e = -\frac{W L^2}{24 E I}$$

For increased loads on the beam, the beam line moves out parallel to the first line, with correspondingly increased values of end moment (M_e) and the end rotation (θ_e). This (dashed) second beam line on the chart represents the addition of a safety factor, and is usually 1.67 to 2 times that of the first which is based on the working load.

The point at which the connection's curve intersects the beam line, gives the resulting end moment and rotation under the given load. From this it is seen how the beam's behavior depends on its connection.

It is assumed, in this case, the beam is symmetrically loaded and the two end connections are the same. In this way both ends will react similarly.

Curve 1 represents a flexible connection. At a very low moment it safely yields (M_1) and allows the connection to rotate (θ_1). This is typical of top angle connections, web framing angles, and top plate connections small enough to yield. Notice, even with these so-called flexible connections, some end moment does set up.

Curve 2 represents a semi-rigid connection. One type is the top connecting plate so detailed that under working load it elastically yields sufficiently to provide the necessary rotation of the connection, and yet has sufficient resistance to develop the proper end moment. Although thick top angles have been suggested for service as semi-rigid connections, they are impractical to design and fabricate with the desired built-in restraint.

Curve 3 represents a rigid connection, using a top connecting plate detailed to develop the full end moment. Since no elastic yielding is needed or desired, the plate is made as short as practical.

All three of these connections have ample reserve carrying capacity, as shown by where their curves intersect the beam line at 1⅔ load relative to their crossing of the beam line at working load.

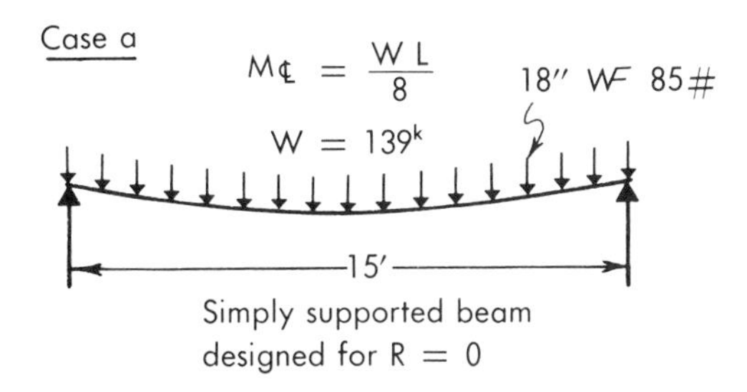

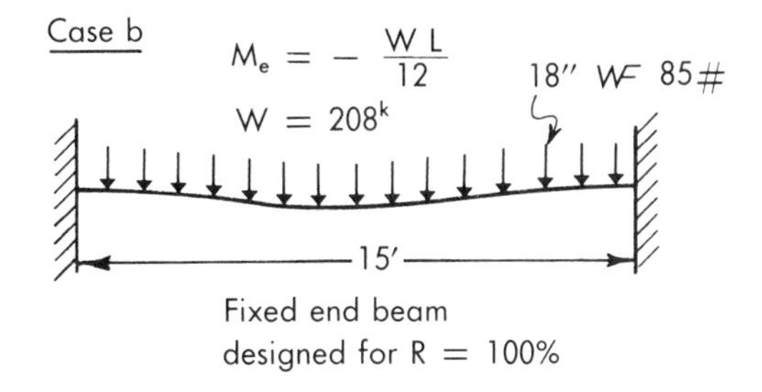

FIGURE 3

The actual results of testing three top plate connections on an 18″ WF 85# beam are shown in Figure 4. Two conditions are considered, as shown by the load diagrams, Figure 3.

Beam line a (in Figure 4) is based on a design moment of ⅛ W L at centerline, i.e. simply supported. Beam line a_1 is for a load 1⅔ times that of the working load.

Beam line b is based on a design moment of $1/12$ W L at the ends, i.e. fixed ends, and will support a 50% greater load. Beam line b_1 is for a load 1⅔ times that of the working load. Both of these two beam lines stop at R = 50%, because at this restraint the center of the beam now has this moment of $1/12$ W L and a restraint lower than this would overstress the central portion of the beam.

Top plate #1 is a $5/16$″ thick plate, 3″ wide at the reduced section, and has a cross-sectional area of A_p = .94 in.² It is widened to 6″ at the butt-welded connection. This connection should reach yield at about $M = A_p \sigma_y d_b = (.94)(33{,}000)(18) = 558$ in.-kip. The actual value from the test is about M = 600 in.-kip. Above this moment, the plate yields and due to strain hardening will have increased resistance. The ultimate moment should be about twice this yield value, or about M = 1200 in.-kip. The resulting restraint is about R = 34.5%, a little too high for the beam to be classed as simply supported.

Top plate #2 has the same $5/16$″ thickness, but has a 6″ width throughout its length. It has double the cross-sectional area, A_p = 1.88 in.² As expected, it is twice as rigid. It should reach yield at about M = 1110 in.-kip. The actual is about M = 1000 in.-kip. The restraint is about R = 58%. Notice if the beam had been designed for a moment of $1/12$ W L, i.e. a restraint of R = 100%, the connection's curve would have intersected the beam line b just short of the R = 50% value. There would then be a slight overstress of the beam at centerline.

Top plate #3 is ⅞″ thick and 7½″ wide, having a cross-sectional area of A_p = 6.56 in.² This greater area produces a more rigid connection with greater restraint. The actual connection curve (solid) shows slightly more flexibility than the calculated curve (dotted). The extra flexibility probably comes from some movement of the lower portion of the connection which has just short parallel fillet welds joining the lower flange of the beam to the seat. A butt weld placed directly across the end of this lower flange to the column, undoubtedly would bring the rigidity of the connection curve up almost to that of the calculated curve.

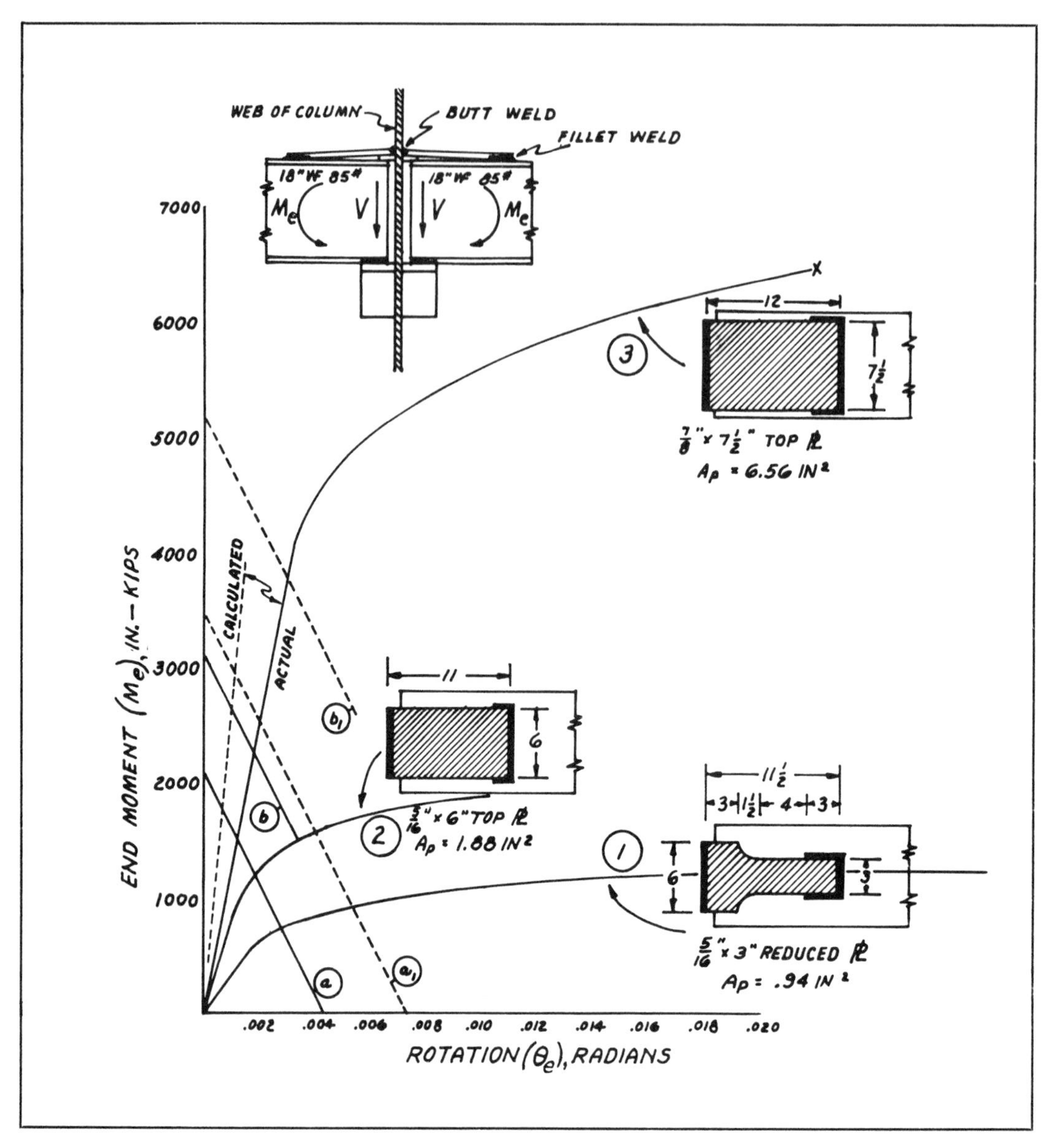

FIGURE 4

Figure 4 from: "Tests of Miscellaneous Welded Building Connections"; Johnston & Diets; AWS Welding Journal Jan. 1942 and "Report of Tests of Welded Top Plate and Seat Building Connections"; Brandes & Mains; AWS Welding Journal Mar. 1944

Figure 5 illustrates the additional restraining action provided by column flange stiffeners. Both connections use 5/16" x 6" top plates.

Connection #1 has column stiffeners. In the case of the beam designed for a moment of 1/12 W L (R = 100% down to R = 50%), it would supply a restraint of about R = 70.2%.

Connection #2 has no column stiffeners and loses sufficient rigidity so that the beam designed for a moment of 1/12 W L (R = 100% down to R = 50%) will be overstressed. This is because the connection restraint would be only about R = 45%.

This shows the importance of proper stiffening.

7. FACTORS IN CONNECTION DESIGN

The following items greatly affect the cost of welded structural steel and cannot be overlooked. In order to take full advantage of welded construction, they must be considered.

Moment Transfer

The bending forces from the end moment lie almost entirely within the flanges of the beam. The most effective and direct method to transfer these forces is some type of flange weld. The relative merits of three types are discussed here.

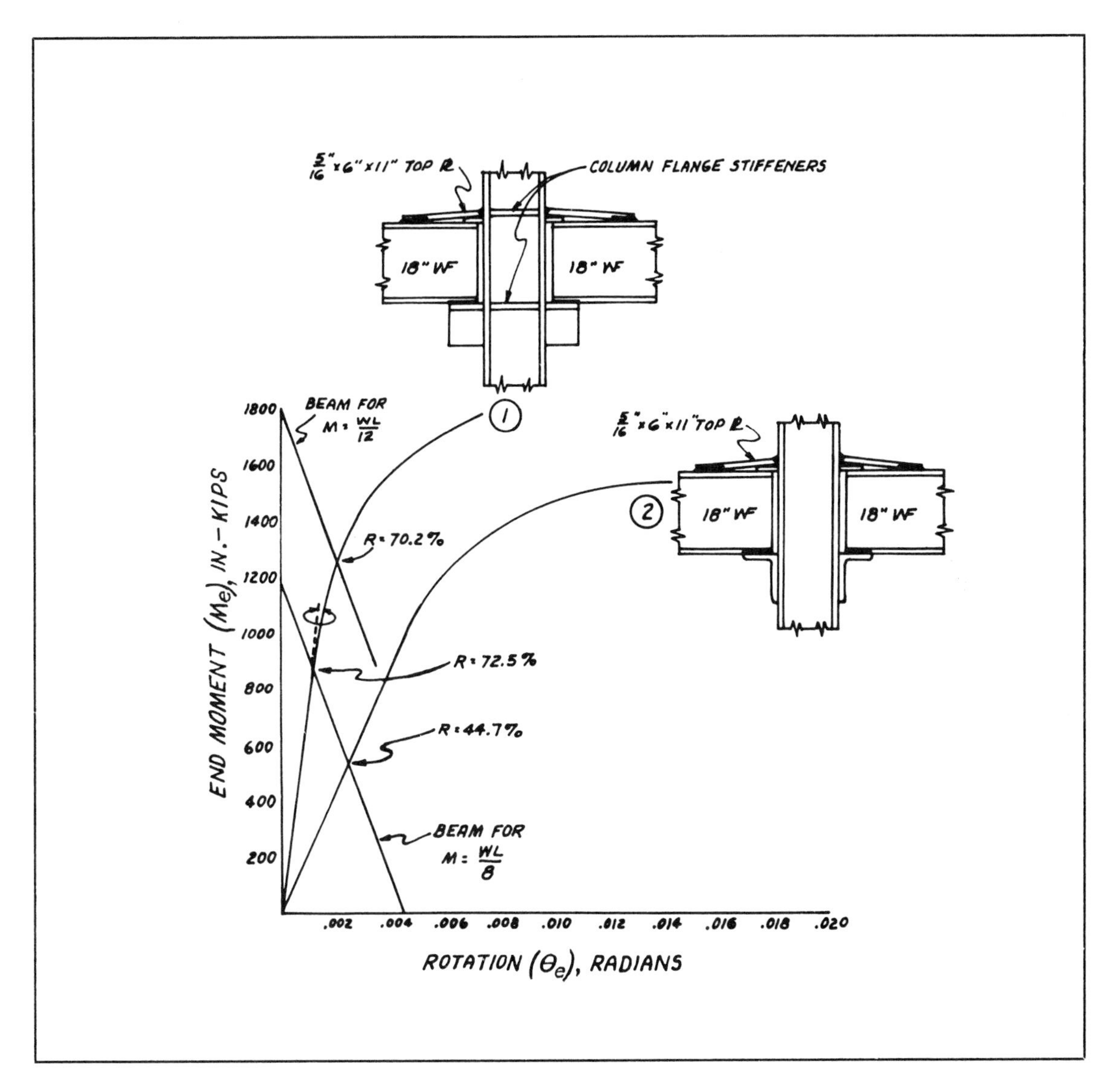

FIGURE 5

Figure 5: From "Tests of Miscellaneous Welded Building Connections"; Johnston & Deits; AWS Welding Journal, Jan. 1942

In Figure 6, the flanges are directly connected to the column by means of groove welds. This is the most direct method of transferring forces and requires the least amount of welding.

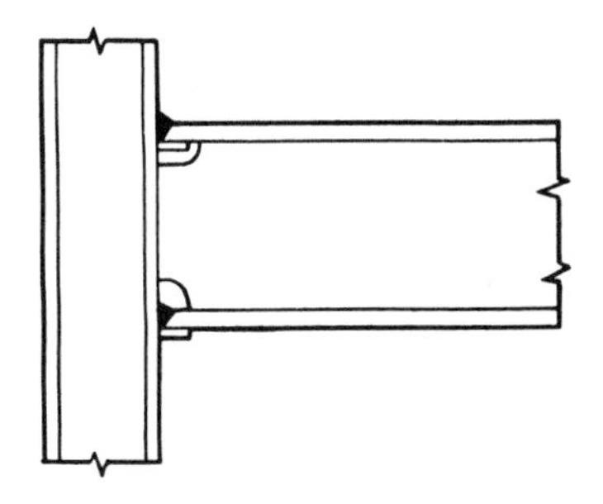

FIGURE 6

The backing strip just below each of the flanges allows the weld to be made within reasonable fit-up, as long as there is a proper root opening.

There is little provision for over-run of the column dimensions which may be as much as ± ⅛". For excessive over-run, the flanges of the beam may have to be flame-cut back, in the field, in order to provide the minimum root opening. For under-run, the excessive root opening will increase the amount of welding required, but the joint is still possible.

It is usually more costly to cut the beam to exact length; in addition there is the cost of beveling the flanges. Milling the beam to length is costly and not recommended because the over-run or under-run of the column having a tolerance of ± ⅛" would reduce this accuracy in fit-up.

In Figure 7, a top connecting plate is shipped loose and, for proper fit-up, is put in place by the weldor after the beam is erected. A greater tolerance can be allowed in cutting the beam to length, and any method can be used (circular cutoff saw, flame-cutting,

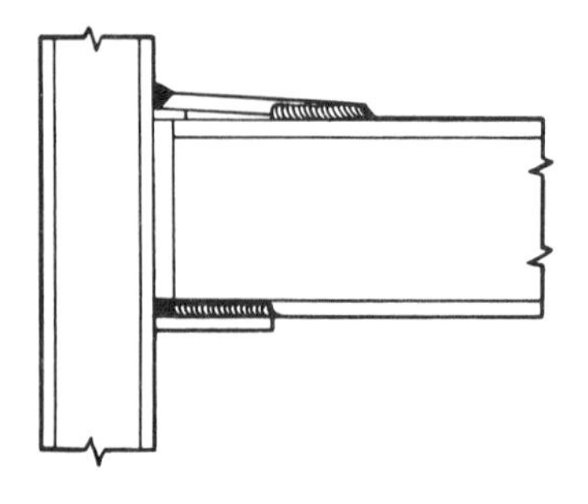

FIGURE 7

etc.) without subsequent beveling of the flanges. The beams frequently are ordered from the steel supplier cut shorter than required: ¾″ ± ¼″. Sometimes beams are ordered still shorter, allowing a cutting tolerance of ± ⅜″. This greatly reduces the cost of cutting and preparation.

This type of connection requires the extra connecting plate, which must be cut to size and beveled. It doubles the amount of field welding on the top flange. It also can interfere with metal decks placed on top of the beam. Occasionally, the top plate is shop welded to the top flange on one or both ends of the beam. This decreases the amount of field welding but eliminates the fit-up advantage.

The beam's bottom flange may be groove welded directly to the column if sufficient root spacing is obtained, even though the edge of the flange is not beveled. Although this is not an AWS Prequalified Joint, it is widely used, perhaps because the bottom flange weld is in compression. One disadvantage is that the beam length must be held accurately. As the beam flange increases in thickness, the required root spacing must increase. The bottom seat also serves as a backing strip. Sometimes for additional strength, the flange is fillet welded to this plate for a short distance along its

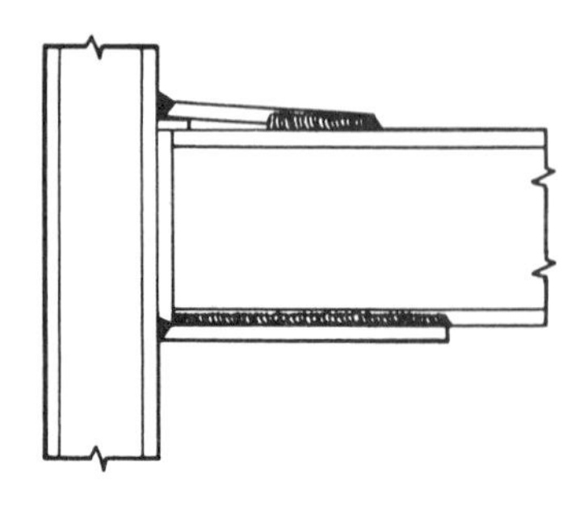

FIGURE 8

length. All of this field welding is done in the flat position.

In Figure 8, the lower flange is not groove welded directly to the column; instead, the bottom seat plate is extended farther along the beam, and is fillet welded to the beam flange. These welds are designed to transfer the compressive force of the flange back into the column. All of the field welding is done in the flat position. This connection requires a little more care in handling and shipping so that these longer plates are not damaged. This also requires a little more weight of connecting material.

A beam that is "compact" (AISC Sec. 2.6) permits a 10% higher bending stress, $\sigma_b = 0.66\ \sigma_y$. However, to take advantage of this higher bending allowable in the connection, it is necessary that the web be welded almost its full depth to the support. Thus, it might be possible to stress the entire depth of the web to yield (σ_y) in bending to develop the plastic moment (M_p), (AISC Sec. 1.5.1.4.1). These same beams if continuous over supports or rigidly framed to columns, may be proportioned for 90% of the negative moment provided the maximum positive moment is increased by 10% of the average of the two negative moments (AISC Sec 1.5.1.4.1).

Check to see if stiffeners between the column flanges are necessary. Recent research indicates web crippling is the deciding factor and if the column web has sufficient thickness, stiffeners are not required.

If flange stiffeners are required, consider whether they can be fillet welded to the column. Usually the groove type of T joint is detailed, i.e. the stiffener has a single 45° bevel all the way around three sides. If the fillet weld has a leg size of about ¾ the stiffener thickness, it will develop full plate strength. Both of these joints would require about the same amount of weld metal. The single bevel joint requires extra fitting, a lower welding current and smaller electrodes for the first few passes. The groove joint in this case is not very accessible for the weldor and presents an additional problem because it is difficult to get down in between the column flanges to do this welding. On this basis, fillet welds would probably cost less and be easier to use.

Double bevel joints require about half as much welding as the fillet welded joint; but unless the stiffeners are extremely thick, perhaps above 1½″, fillet welds would still be the lowest in cost and trouble.

Consider the use of iron powder manual electrodes or the semi-automatic submerged-arc process for flat welding in the field as well as in the shop.

Shear Transfer

The shear forces lie almost entirely within the web of the beam and must be 1) transferred directly out to the supporting column by means of a connection on the web, or 2) directly down to a supporting seat.

The web connection must have sufficient vertical weld length so as not to overstress the beam web in shear. The seat connection must have sufficient horizontal length so as not to overstress the beam web in compression or bearing.

In Figure 9, the vertical reaction of the beam is carried by a weld connecting the beam web to an attaching plate. This plate, which was shop welded to the column, is used also for the erection bolts. This method of shear transfer not only requires a field weld, but the weld must be made in the vertical position at lower speeds.

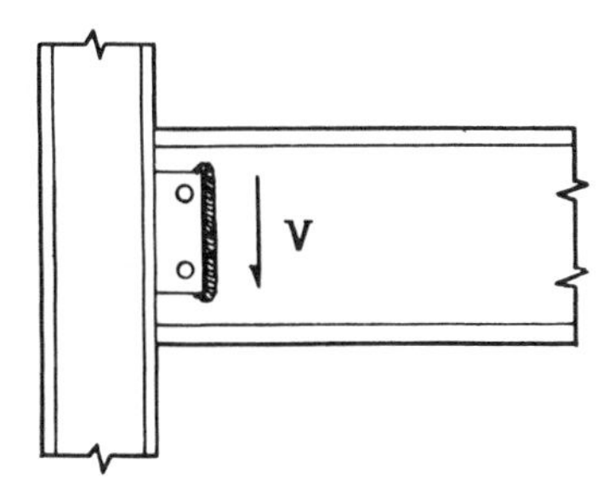

FIGURE 9

In Figure 10, the beam fits close enough for its web to be fillet welded on both sides directly to the column. The length of these welds is determined by the shear reaction to be transferred. This method of transfer also requires a field weld in the vertical position at lower welding speeds.

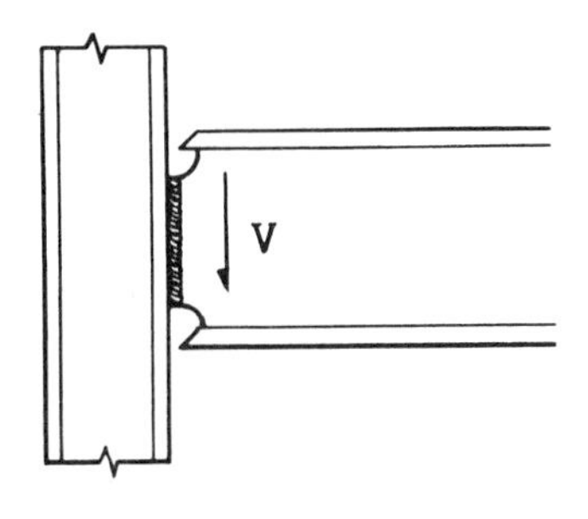

FIGURE 10

Vertical welding in the field increases the cost of the joint and should be eliminated if possible.

In Figure 11, the stiffened seat bracket has sufficient welding to transfer the shear reaction back into the column. This welding on the column is done in the shop in the flat position for the fastest welding speeds. It eliminates any out-of-position, more costly, welding in the field. The seat bracket serves as a support for the beam during erection, a place for the erection bolts through the bottom flange, and a means to carry the shear reaction. This bracket should not extend out too far, or it will interfere with any fireproofing or wall construction. The web of the beam sometimes is reinforced with an additional plate on the end to give it the necessary thickness for this reduced bearing length.

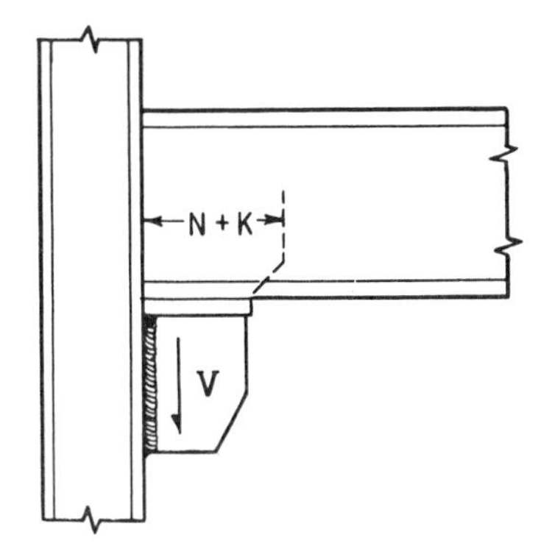

FIGURE 11

If some vertical welding in the field is still required, consider having one or more welding operators do this and other operators do the flat welding with the higher currents. This eliminates changing welding current and electrode size for the various positions of welding.

Erection Ease

The connection must allow rapid erection and fitting in place of the beam. It must provide temporary support for the dead load and some horizontal stability until the connection can be completed by welding.

If erection bolts are used, holes must be punched or drilled in the member. For beams and columns with thick flanges which exceed the capacity of the punch, these holes must be drilled; this is costly. It might be well to place these holes in the thinner web of the beam.

Where possible, use small attaching plates which may be punched while separate and then shop welded to the beam or column. This eliminates any need to move heavy members into another area for punching or drilling.

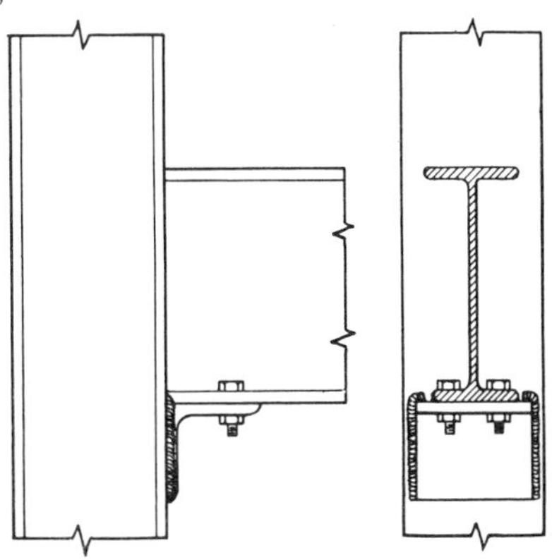

FIGURE 12

In Figure 12, a shop-welded seat provides support for the dead load of the beam. The beam is held in place by means of erection bolts through the bottom flange.

In Figure 13, a shop-welded plate on the column provides temporary support for the beam. Erection bolts through the beam web hold the beam in position. An angle could be used instead of the plate. Although this would increase the material cost slightly, it would be easier to install and hold in proper alignment during welding. Sometimes a small seat is shop welded to the column, as shown, to give support while the erection bolts are being installed.

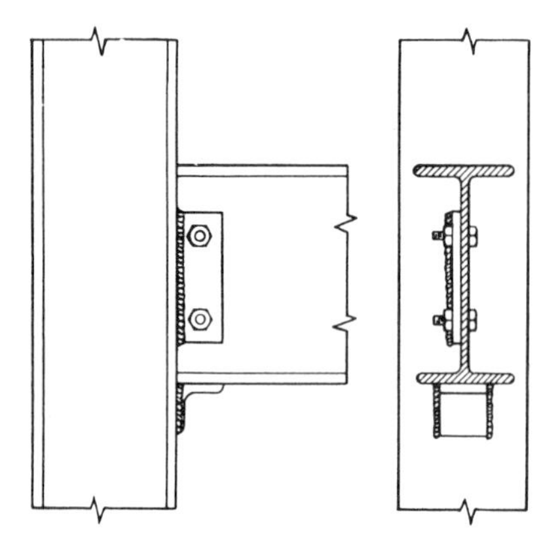

FIGURE 13

If the beam is supported on a seat, the elevation at the top of the beam may vary because of possible over-run or under-run of the beam. If the beam is supported by a web connection, this may be laid out from the top of the beam so as to eliminate this problem.

Saxe erection clips, Figure 14, are made of forged steel and are readily weldable. The clip is shop welded to the under side of the beam flange and the seat is shop welded in the proper position on the column. This allows the beam to slip easily into place during erection. One type of Saxe clip is adjustable and allows a movement of $3/16''$ as well as some rotation.

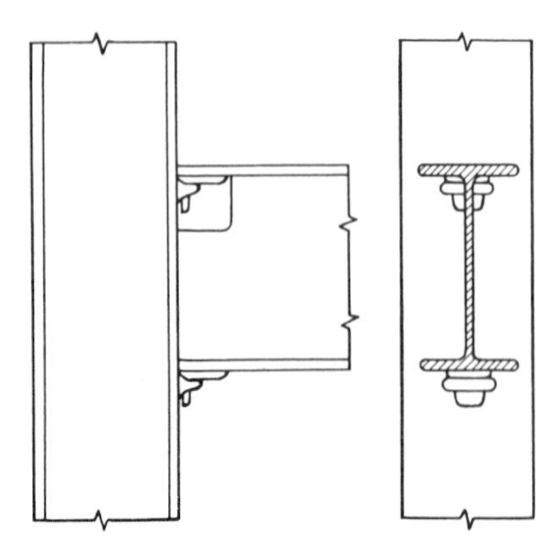

FIGURE 14

Consider the use of welded studs on main members in place of erection bolts; this will eliminate the punching of main members. These have already been accepted in the building and bridge fields for use as shear attachments, and an increasing number of fabricating shops have this equipment. See Figures 15, 16 and 17.

FIGURE 15

FIGURE 16

FIGURE 17

FIGURE 18

Between the time the beam is erected and the joint welded, the columns are pulled into proper alignment by cables. Careful layout in the fabricating shop and a positive location in the connection will facilitate this.

Any over-run or under-run of the column requires some adjustment of the connection. Otherwise the column would be pulled out of line in order to get the beam in place and the connection lined up.

General

Use the newer A36 steel for a 10% higher stress allowable and about 5 to 7% savings in steel at little additional unit price in steel. E70 welds have 16% higher allowable for fillet welds.

Use a 10% higher allowable bending stress for "compact beams", $\sigma = .66\ \sigma_y$ instead of $.60\ \sigma_y$, and for negative moment region at supports use only 90% of the moment (AISC Sec 1.5.1.4.1).

Many connections provide a direct and effective transfer of forces and yet are too costly in preparation, fitting and welding.

Maximum economy is obtained when a joint is designed for welding. It is not sufficient to apply welding to a riveted or bolted design.

Use rigid, continuous connections for a more efficient structure. This will reduce the beam weight and usually reduces the overall weight of the complete structure.

Use plastic design to reduce steel weight below that of simple framing, and reduce the design time below that of conventional elastic rigid design.

The greatest portion of welding on a connection should be done in the shop and in the flat position. As much as possible, miscellaneous plates used in connections, such as seat angles, stiffeners on columns, etc., should be assembled, fitted, and welded in the shop in the flat position.

The connection must offer proper accessibility for welding, whether done in shop or field. This is especially true of beams framing into the webs of columns.

Proper fit-up must be obtained for best welding. Care must be used in layout of the connection, flame cutting the beam to the proper length, preparation of the joint, and erecting the member to the proper position and alignment. Good workmanship, resulting in good fit-up pays off.

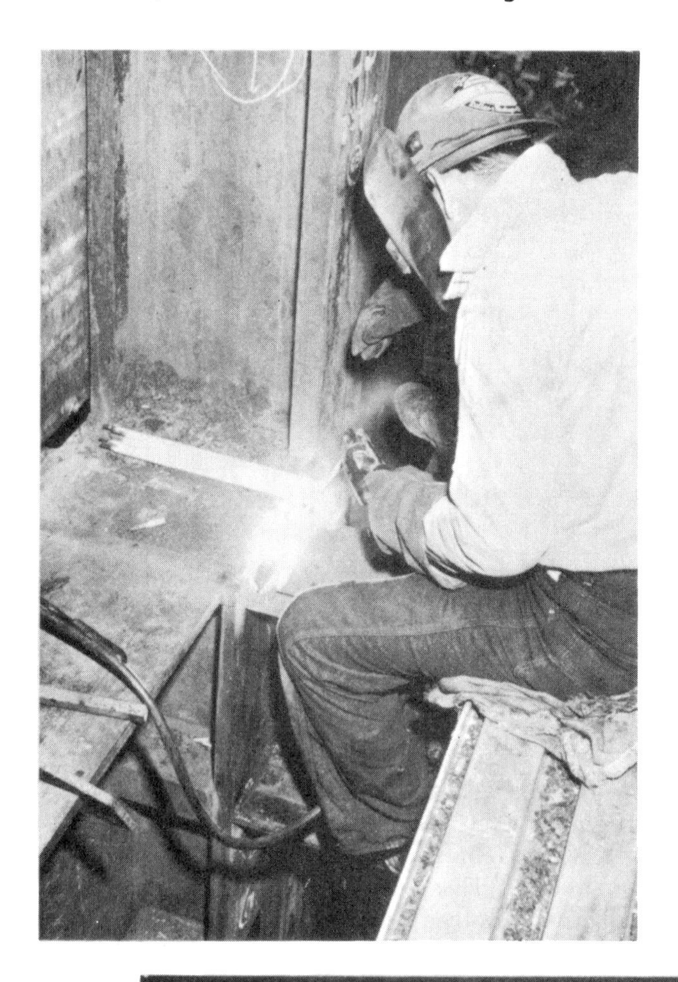

Weldor makes continuous beam-to-column connection on Inland Steel Co.'s office building in Chicago. At this level, the column cross-section is reduced, the upper column being stepped back. Spandrel beam is here joined to column by groove welds. The weldor, using low-hydrogen electrodes, welds into a backing bar. Run-off tabs are used to assure full throat size from side to side of flange.

For New York's 21-story 1180 Avenue of the Americas Building, welded construction offered important weight reductions and economy, quiet and fast erection. Maximum use of shop welding on connections minimized erection time.

Flexible Seat Angles

1. BEHAVIOR UNDER LOAD

When designing a flexible seat angle, it is important to understand how it is loaded, and how it reacts to its load. See Figure 1.

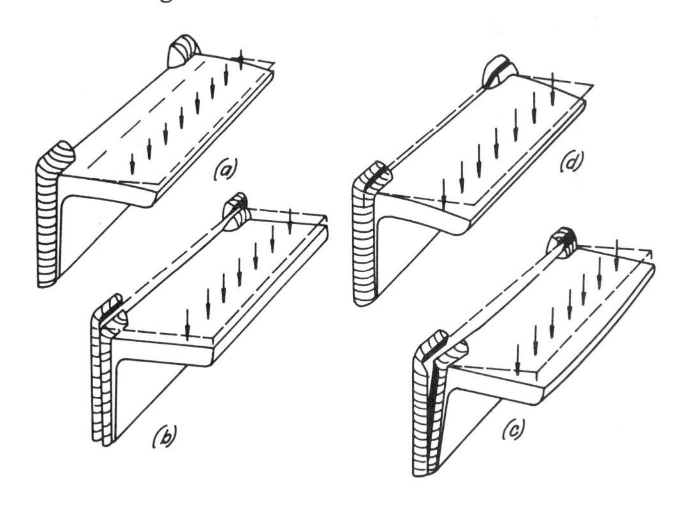

FIGURE 1

The outstanding (top) leg of the seat angle is subject to bending stresses, and will deflect downward (1,a). The vertical reaction (R) on the connecting weld of the angle results in direct shear (1,b) and in bending forces (1,c).

If the seat angle is too thin, the top of the connecting weld tends to tear, because only this portion of the weld resists the bending action. With thicker angles, the whole length of the connecting weld would carry this bending load (Fig. 1,d).

The top leg of the seat angle is stressed in bending by the reaction (R) on the end of the beam which it supports. It is necessary to determine the point at which this force is applied on the leg in order to get the moment arm of the force. See Figure 2.

A simply supported beam is placed on the seat angle (2,a). Because of the loading on the beam, the beam deflects and its ends rotate (2,b). Consequently the point of contact of the reaction (R) tends to move outward. This increase in moment arm increases the bending moment on the seat, causing the leg of the angle to deflect downward. As the deflected leg takes the same slope as the loaded beam, the point of contact moves back (2,c).

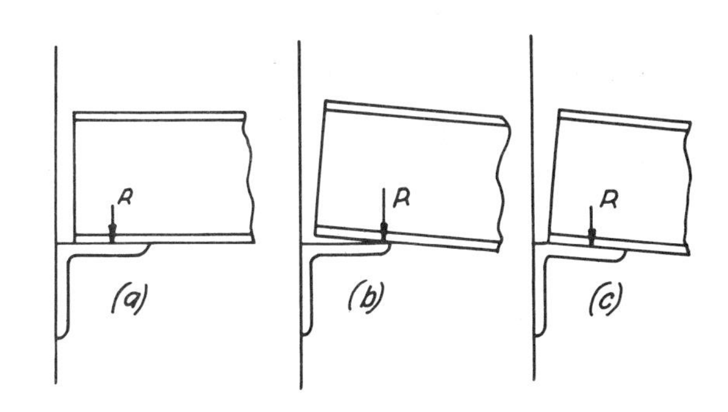

FIGURE 2

If the leg of the angle were made thicker, it would deflect less. Consequently, the point of contact would extend farther out along the leg, thus increasing the bending moment.

If the angle were made too thick, this bearing reaction would be concentrated and might overstress the beam web in bearing.

If the angle were made too thin, it would deflect too easily and the point of contact would shift to the end of the beam, thereby not producing sufficient length of contact for proper support of the beam web.

Definitions of Symbols

ω = leg size of fillet weld, inches
σ_y = yield strength of material used, psi
a = clearance between column and end of beam, usually ½″
b = width of seat angle, inches
e = moment arm of reaction (R) to critical section of horizontal leg of seat angle, inches
e_f = distance of reaction (R) to back of flexible seat angle, inches
t = thickness of seat angle, inches
t_w = thickness of beam web, inches
K = vertical distance from bottom of beam flange to top of fillet of beam web, obtained from steel handbook, inches
L_h = horizontal leg of seat angle, inches
L_v = vertical leg of seat angle, also length of vertical connecting weld, inches
N = minimum bearing length
R = vertical bearing reaction at end of beam, kips

---

2. ALLOWABLE STRESS IN BEAM

AISC (Sec. 1.10.10) specifies that the compressive stress at the web toe of the fillet of a beam without bearing stiffeners shall not exceed $\sigma = .75\ \sigma_y$ psi. This stress is located at distance K up from bottom face of flange. See Figure 3.

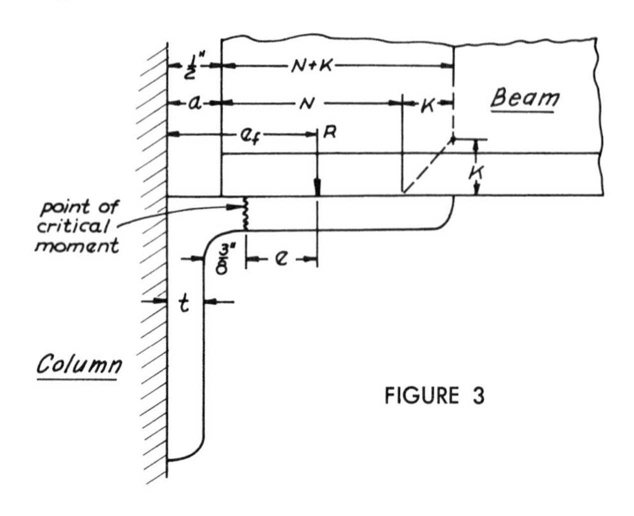

FIGURE 3

For end reactions, the following formula is given:

$$\frac{R}{t_w\ (N + K)} = \text{not over } .75\ \sigma_y \text{ psi (AISC Sec 1.10.10)} \quad \ldots\ldots(1)$$

	A7, A373	A36	A441 or weldable A242		
yield (σ_y)	33,000	36,000	42,000	46,000	50,000
75% allowable	25,000	27,000	31,500	34,500	37,500

This means that the web section (N + K) may be stressed to $\sigma = .75\ \sigma_y$ psi. This plane lies at the top of the toe of the fillet of the beam web, or at height K. This can be projected down at 45° to the base of the beam flange to get the minimum bearing length (N). It is assumed the bearing reaction (R) may be centered midway along this length (N).

3. SEAT ANGLE DIMENSIONS

AISC (Steel Construction Manual), recommends the following method for finding the required size of the seat angle. The point of critical bending moment in the angle leg is assumed to be at the tangent of the fillet of the outstanding leg of the angle. This is approximately 3/8" in from the inside face of the vertical leg, for most angles used as seat angles.

Step 1: Determine the point where the beam reaction is applied to the angle, so that the eccentricity or moment arm (e) of the load may be known.

$$N = \frac{R}{t_w\ (.75\ \sigma_y)} - K \quad \ldots\ldots(2)$$

$$e_f = a + \frac{N}{2} \quad \ldots\ldots(3)$$

$$e = e_f - t - 3/8'' \quad \ldots\ldots(4)$$

Nomograph No. 1 (Fig. 4) for A 36 steel will give the value of e_f for flexible seats or e_s for stiffened seats. (Stiffened seat brackets are discussed further in the following section.) Known values needed for use of this nomograph are the end reaction (R) of the beam in kips, the thickness of the beam web (t_w), and the distance from the bottom of the beam flange to the top of the fillet (K), obtained from any steel handbook.

Step 2: Determine the required thickness of the angle (t) to provide sufficient bending resistance for the given beam reaction (R).

$$M = R\ e \quad \ldots\ldots(5)$$

$$M = \sigma\ S \quad \ldots\ldots(6)$$

$$S = \frac{b\ t^2}{6} \quad \ldots\ldots(7)$$

From this we get—

$$R\ e = M = \sigma\ S = \frac{\sigma\ b\ t^2}{6}$$

$$\therefore \frac{R}{b} = \frac{\sigma\ t^2}{6\ e} \quad \ldots\ldots(8)$$

Since the outstanding leg of the angle acts as a beam with partially restrained ends, the AISC Manual (1956, p 263) allows a bending stress of $\sigma = 24{,}000$ psi for A7 or A373 steel. For A36 steel, a value of $\sigma = 26{,}000$ psi will be used. This then becomes:

A7 or A373 Steel	A36 Steel
$\frac{R}{b} = \frac{4.0\ t^2}{e_f - t - 3/8}$	$\frac{R}{b} = \frac{4\frac{1}{3}\ t^2}{e_f - t - 3/8}$

$\ldots(9)$

FIGURE 4—Eccentricity of Load on Flexible or Stiffened Seats For A36 Steel

NOMOGRAPH NO. 1

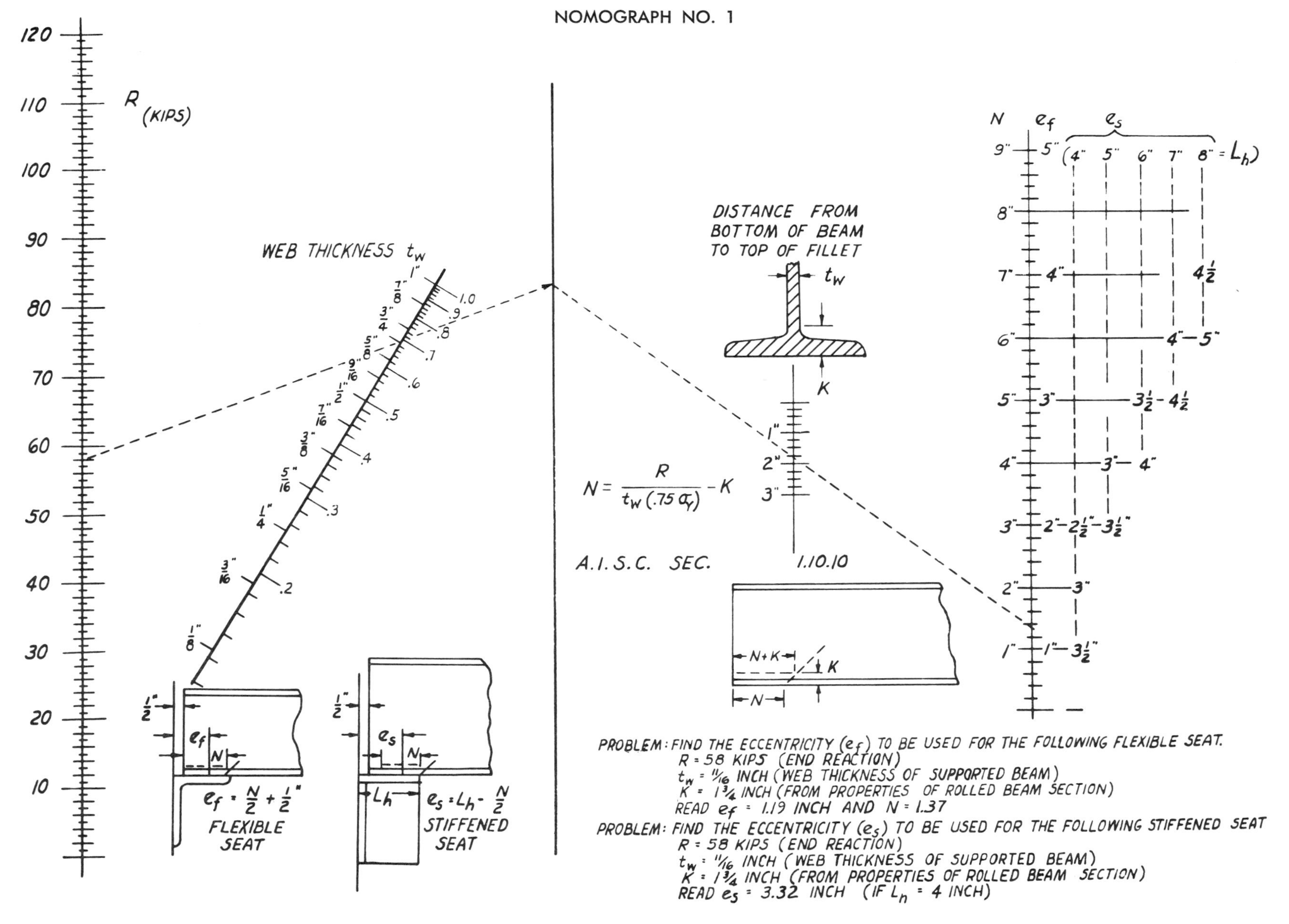
R (KIPS)
120
110
100
90
80
70
60
50
40
30
20
10
WEB THICKNESS t_w
DISTANCE FROM BOTTOM OF BEAM TO TOP OF FILLET
t_w
K
$N = \frac{R}{t_w(.75\sigma_y)} - K$
A.I.S.C. SEC. 1.10.10
N+K
N
N
e_f
e_s
($4''$ $5''$ $6''$ $7''$ $8'' = L_h$)
$e_f = \frac{N}{2} + \frac{1}{2}''$
FLEXIBLE SEAT
$e_s = L_h - \frac{N}{2}$
STIFFENED SEAT
PROBLEM: FIND THE ECCENTRICITY (e_f) TO BE USED FOR THE FOLLOWING FLEXIBLE SEAT.
R = 58 KIPS (END REACTION)
t_w = 11/16 INCH (WEB THICKNESS OF SUPPORTED BEAM)
K = 1 3/4 INCH (FROM PROPERTIES OF ROLLED BEAM SECTION)
READ e_f = 1.19 INCH AND N = 1.37
PROBLEM: FIND THE ECCENTRICITY (e_s) TO BE USED FOR THE FOLLOWING STIFFENED SEAT
R = 58 KIPS (END REACTION)
t_w = 11/16 INCH (WEB THICKNESS OF SUPPORTED BEAM)
K = 1 3/4 INCH (FROM PROPERTIES OF ROLLED BEAM SECTION)
READ e_s = 3.32 INCH (IF L_h = 4 INCH)

FIGURE 5—Thickness of Flexible Seat For A36 Steel

NOMOGRAPH NO. 2

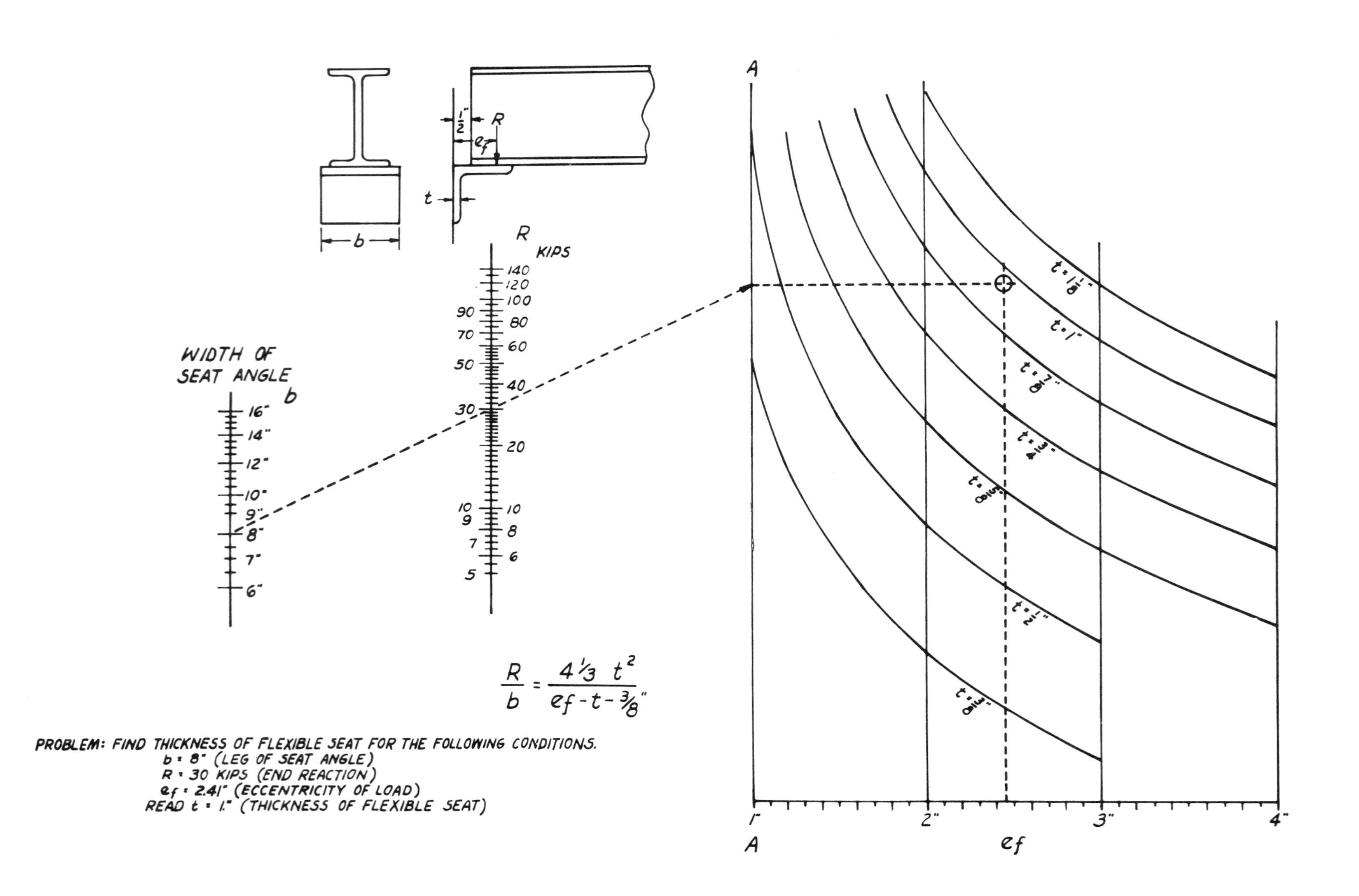

$$\frac{R}{b} = \frac{4\frac{1}{3}\, t^2}{e_f - t - \frac{3}{8}"}$$

PROBLEM: FIND THICKNESS OF FLEXIBLE SEAT FOR THE FOLLOWING CONDITIONS.
b = 8" (LEG OF SEAT ANGLE)
R = 30 KIPS (END REACTION)
e_f = 2.41" (ECCENTRICITY OF LOAD)
READ t = 1" (THICKNESS OF FLEXIBLE SEAT)

To solve directly for (t), the formula #9 may be put into the following form:

$$t = \sqrt{\tfrac{1}{4} A^2 + A\,(e_f - \tfrac{3}{8})} - \tfrac{1}{2} A \quad \text{..(10)}$$

where:

A7 or A373 Steel	A36 Steel
$A = \dfrac{R}{4.0\ b}$	$A = \dfrac{R}{4\tfrac{1}{3}\ b}$

.....(11)

Knowing the values of A and e_f, the thickness of the seat angle (t) may be found from the above formula.

Nomograph No. 2 (Fig. 5) for A36 steel makes use of formula #9 and will give values of seat angle thickness (t). The width of the seat angle (b) is known since it is usually made to extend at least ½″ on each side of the beam flange. A line is drawn from this value of (b) through the value of (R) to the vertical axis A-A. The required thickness of the angle (t) is found at the intersection of a horizontal line through A-A and a vertical line through the given value of (e_f). In case these lines intersect between two values of angle thickness, the larger value is used as the answer.

Table 1 will give values of R/b in terms of seat angle thickness (t) and eccentricity (e_f). Table 1 is for A36 steel.

Step 3: Determine the horizontal length of the seat angle leg (L_h). This must be sufficient to permit easy erection and provide ample distance for the connecting welds and erection bolts on the bottom flange of the beam.

This minimum length is:

$$L_h = a + N \quad \text{.......................(12)}$$

Step 4: Determine the vertical length (L_v) of the connecting fillet weld, for a given leg size of weld (ω). This will determine the required length of the seat

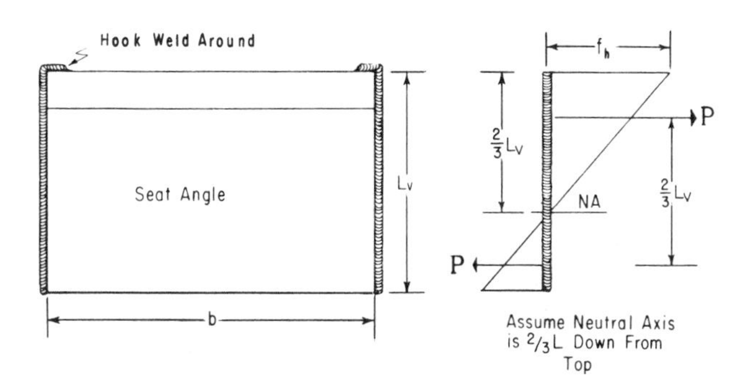

FIGURE 6

TABLE 1—Values of R/b
For A36 Steel

$$\frac{R}{b} = \frac{\text{Reaction, kips}}{\text{Width of seat, inches}} \qquad \frac{R}{b} = \frac{4\tfrac{1}{3}\ t^2}{e_f - t - \tfrac{3}{8}}$$

e_f \ t	3/8″	7/16″	1/2″	9/16″	5/8″	3/4″	7/8″	1″	1 1/8″
1.0	2.44	4.41	8.66	21.9					
1.1	1.74	2.88	4.81	8.44					
1.2	1.35	2.13	3.34	5.21	8.45				
1.3	1.10	1.70	2.54	3.78	5.63				
1.4	.937	1.41	2.07	2.97	4.23	7.86			
1.5	.812	1.20	1.73	2.44	3.39	6.50			
1.6	.717	1.05	1.49	2.07	2.82	5.14	9.48		
1.7	.631	.934	1.31	1.80	2.42	4.24	7.37		
1.8	.579	.840	1.17	1.59	2.11	3.62	6.04	10.20	
1.9	.530	.763	1.05	1.42	1.88	3.14	5.10	8.26	
2.0	.487	.697	.964	1.29	1.69	2.78	4.44	6.93	10.96
2.1	.451	.644	.883	1.17	1.54	2.50	3.90	5.98	9.15
2.2	.420	.596	.818	1.08	1.41	2.28	3.47	5.26	7.83
2.3	.393	.557	.761	1.01	1.30	2.08	3.16	4.68	6.85
2.4	.369	.521	.710	.936	1.21	1.92	2.88	4.22	6.09
2.5	.349	.490	.666	.877	1.13	1.78	2.65	3.85	5.47
2.6	.329	.463	.628	.824	1.06	1.66	2.46	3.53	4.98
2.7	.312	.438	.593	.777	.996	1.55	2.30	3.27	4.57
2.8	.297	.416	.562	.736	.940	1.45	2.14	3.04	4.21
2.9	.284	.396	.536	.698	.891	1.37	2.02	2.84	3.91
3.0	.271	.379	.510	.663	.845	1.30	1.89	2.66	3.66
3.1			.486	.631	.806	1.23	1.80	2.52	3.42
3.2			.466	.604	.769	1.17	1.70	2.37	3.23
3.3			.446	.579	.736	1.12	1.62	2.25	3.04
3.4			.428	.555	.705	1.07	1.55	2.14	2.88
3.5			.412	.533	.677	1.03	1.47	2.05	2.74
3.6					.650	.986	1.41	1.95	2.61
3.7					.628	.947	1.35	1.86	2.49
3.8					.604	.912	1.30	1.79	2.38
3.9					.584	.878	1.26	1.71	2.29
4.0					.564	.848	1.20	1.65	2.19

angle's vertical leg, being assumed equal.

horizontal force on weld

$$\text{Moment (each weld)} = \frac{R}{2}\,(e_f) = P\,(\tfrac{2}{3}\,L_v)$$

also:

$$P = \tfrac{1}{2}\,(f_h)\,(\tfrac{2}{3}\,L_v)$$

From this:

$$f_h = \frac{2.25\ R\ e_f}{L_v^2}$$

vertical force on weld

$$f_v = \frac{R}{2\ L_v}$$

resultant force on weld

$$f_r = \sqrt{f_v^2 + f_h^2} = \sqrt{\left(\frac{R}{2\ L_v}\right)^2 + \left(\frac{2.25\ R\ e_f}{L_v^2}\right)^2}$$

or

$$\boxed{f_r = \frac{R}{2\ L_v^2}\sqrt{L_v^2 + 20.25\ e_f^2}} \quad \ldots\ldots\ldots(13)$$

leg size of fillet weld

$$\omega = \frac{\text{actual force}}{\text{allowable force}}$$

A7, A373 Steel; E60 Welds	A36 Steel; E70 Welds
$\frac{R}{\omega} = \frac{19.2\ L_v^2}{\sqrt{L_v^2 + 20.25\ e_f^2}}$	$\frac{R}{\omega} = \frac{22.4\ L_v^2}{\sqrt{L_v^2 + 20.25\ e_f^2}}$

....(14)

Since there are a limited number of rolled angles available (for example, L = 9″, 8″, 7″, 6″, 5″, 4″, etc.) it might be well to select a vertical leg length (L_v) = vertical weld length, and solve for the required leg size of fillet weld (ω).

Nomograph No. 3 is based on formula #14 and will give the required length of the vertical connecting weld (L_v) and its leg size (ω) if the other values (R and e_f) are known. (The weld length is assumed equal to the seat's leg length.) Nomograph No. 3 is for A36 steel and E70 welds.

Table 2 will give values of R/ω in terms of vertical leg length of the seat angle (L_v) and eccentricity (e_f). Table 2 is for A36 steel, and E70 welds.

TABLE 2—Values of R/ω
For A36 Steel & E70 Welds

$$\frac{R}{\omega} = \frac{\text{Reaction, kips}}{\text{Leg size fillet weld}} \qquad \boxed{\frac{R}{\omega} = \frac{22.4\ L_v^2}{\sqrt{L_v^2 + 20.25\ e_f^2}}}$$

e_f \ L_v	VERTICAL LEG LENGTH OF SEAT ANGLE (L_v)							
	3″	3½″	4″	5″	6″	7″	8″	9″
1.0	37.3	48.1	59.5	83.3	107.3	137.7	156.2	180.8
1.1	35.0	45.5	56.6	79.3	103.6	128.2	151.7	177.2
1.2	33.0	42.9	53.6	75.8	99.7	124.8	148.2	172.7
1.3	31.2	40.6	51.1	72.4	96.3	120.2	144.7	169.2
1.4	29.2	38.3	48.4	69.2	93.1	116.2	140.0	165.7
1.5	27.6	36.4	45.8	66.3	89.5	112.6	136.5	161.0
1.6	26.0	34.6	43.9	63.6	86.3	109.2	133.0	157.5
1.7	24.7	32.8	41.8	60.7	83.4	105.6	129.5	154.0
1.8	23.4	31.2	39.9	58.3	80.5	102.3	126.0	149.3
1.9	22.4	29.8	38.3	56.2	77.9	99.1	122.5	145.8
2.0	21.2	28.5	36.4	54.3	74.6	96.2	119.0	142.2
2.1	20.4	27.3	35.0	52.2	72.6	93.3	115.8	138.8
2.2	19.5	26.2	33.6	50.4	70.0	90.6	112.8	135.2
2.3	18.7	25.4	32.4	48.7	67.9	87.8	109.7	131.8
2.4	18.0	24.2	31.2	47.0	65.6	85.1	107.0	129.5
2.5	17.3	23.2	30.0	45.5	63.6	82.8	104.2	126.0
2.6	16.7	22.4	28.9	44.1	61.5	80.5	101.5	122.5
2.7	15.9	21.6	28.0	42.6	59.6	78.4	98.8	120.2
2.8	15.5	21.0	27.1	41.4	58.0	76.4	96.2	116.7
2.9	15.0	20.3	26.2	40.2	56.3	74.4	93.6	114.6
3.0	14.6	19.7	25.4	39.0	54.5	72.2	91.3	112.0
3.1	14.2	19.1	24.7	37.9	53.1	70.6	89.2	109.2
3.2	13.8	18.5	24.0	37.0	51.8	68.8	87.2	107.7
3.3	13.3	18.1	23.3	35.9	50.6	67.1	85.2	104.3
3.4	13.1	17.6	22.6	35.0	49.3	65.3	82.2	102.2
3.5	12.6	17.1	22.0	34.1	47.9	63.8	81.4	100.0
3.6	12.4	16.7	21.5	33.2	46.6	62.3	79.6	98.0
3.7	12.0	16.2	21.0	32.3	45.6	60.7	77.8	95.7
3.8	11.7	15.8	20.4	31.5	44.6	59.5	76.3	93.8
3.9	11.3	15.4	19.9	30.7	43.5	58.1	74.6	92.1
4.0	11.1	14.9	19.4	30.0	41.3	56.9	72.8	90.4

4. APPLYING CONNECTING WELDS

The two vertical fillet welds should be "hooked" around the top portion of the seat angle for a distance of about twice the leg size of the fillet weld, or about ½″, provided the width of column flange exceeds the width of seat angle.

A horizontal fillet weld across the top of the seat angle would greatly increase its strength; however, it might interfere with the end of the beam during erection if the beam were too long or the column too deep in section.

When width of the seat angle exceeds the width of the column flange, connecting fillet welds are placed along the toes of the flange on the back side of the angle.

These seats may line up on opposite sides of a supporting web, either web of column or web of girder, if the leg size of the fillet weld is held to ¾ of the web thickness when determining the length (L_v) of the weld. This will prevent the web within this length of connection from being stressed in shear in excess of a value equivalent to ¾ of the allowable tension.

FIGURE 7—Leg Length of Flexible Seat and Weld Size For A36 Steel & E70 Welds

NOMOGRAPH NO. 3

PROBLEM: FIND LEG SIZE OF FLEXIBLE SEAT FOR THE FOLLOWING CONDITIONS.
ω = 5/16" (WELD SIZE - SINCE SEAT ANGLE THICKNESS IS 5/8 INCH)
R = 30 KIPS (END REACTION)
e_f = 2.41" (ECCENTRICITY OF LOAD)
READ L = 8 INCH (LENGTH OF SEAT ANGLE'S VERTICAL LEG)

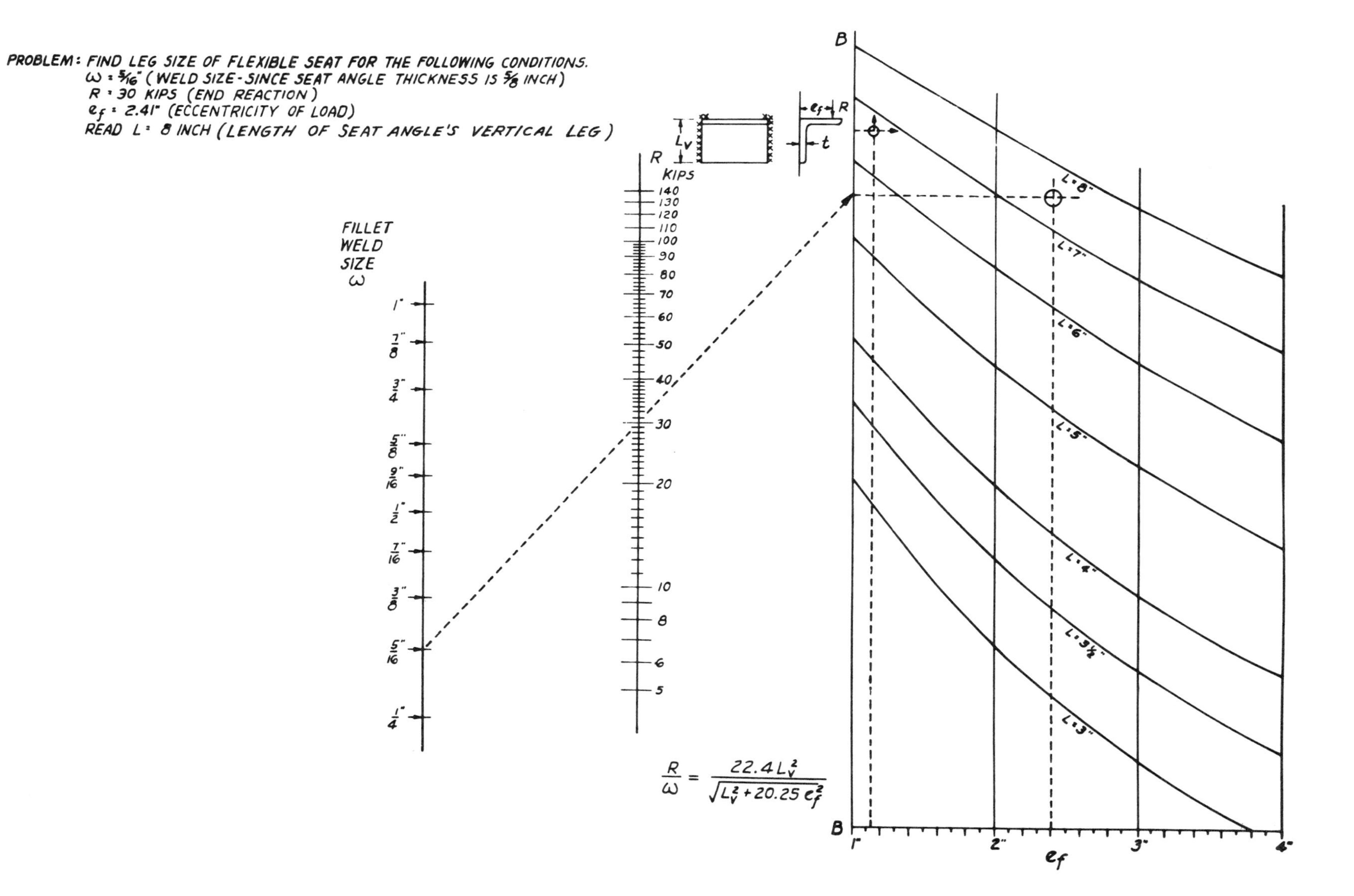

$$\frac{R}{\omega} = \frac{22.4 L_v^2}{\sqrt{L_v^2 + 20.25 e_f^2}}$$

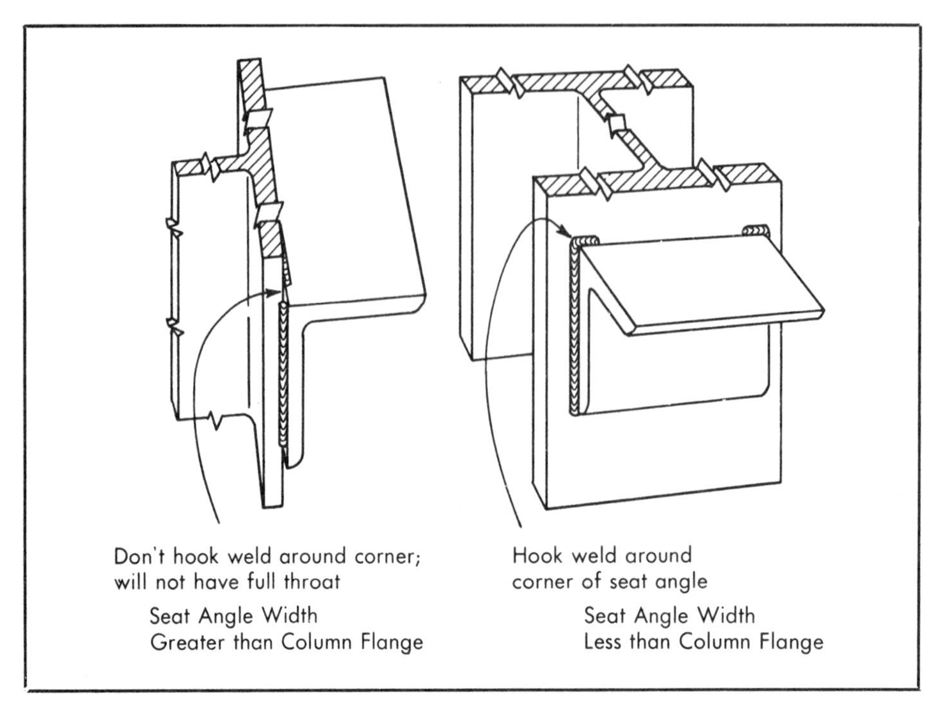

FIGURE 8

5. HORIZONTAL STABILITY

A flexible top angle is usually used to give sufficient horizontal stability to the beam. It is not assumed to carry any of the beam reaction. The most common is a 4″ x 4″ x ¼″ angle, which will not restrain the beam end from rotating under load. After the beam is erected, this top angle is field welded only along its two toes. For beam flanges 4″ and less in width, the top angle is usually cut 4″ long; for beam flanges over 4″ in width, the angle is usually cut 6″ long.

In straight tension tests of top connecting angles at Lehigh University, the 4″ x 4″ x ¼″ angle pulled out as much as 1.98″ before failure, which is about 20 times greater than usually required under normal load conditions.

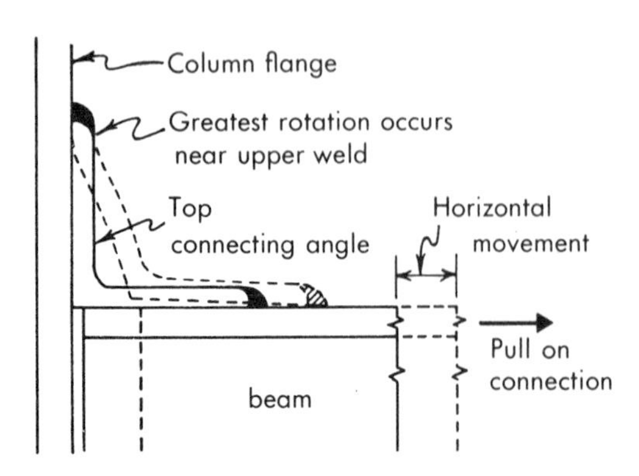

FIGURE 9

Notice in the following figure, that the greatest movement or rotation occurs in the fillet weld connecting the upper leg of the angle to the column. It is important that this weld be made full size.

This test also indicated that a return of the fillet weld around the ends of the angle at the column equal to about ¼ of the leg length resulted in the greatest strength and movement before failure.

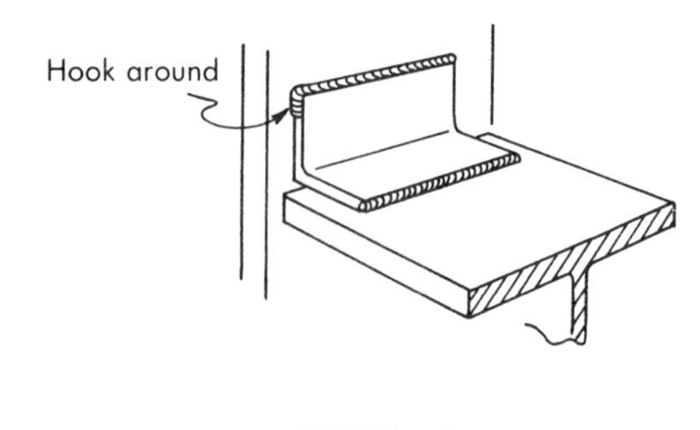

FIGURE 10

Problem 1

Design a flexible seat angle to support a 12″ WF 27# beam, having an end reaction of R = 30 kips. Use A36 steel, E70 welds.

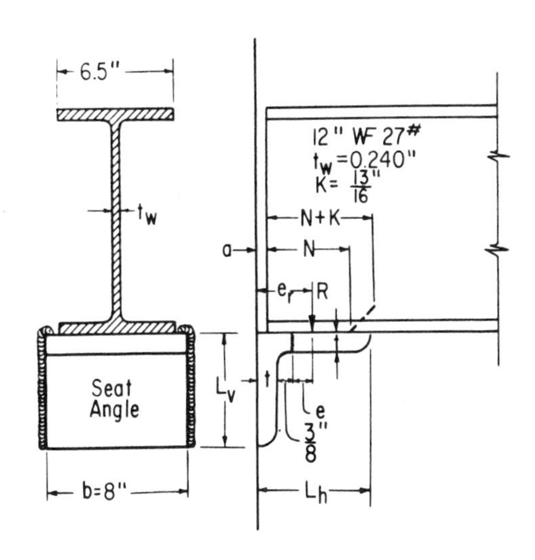

FIGURE 11

thickness of seat angle

$$(2)\quad N = \frac{R}{t_w\ (.75\ \sigma_y)} - K$$

$$= \frac{(30)}{(.240)(27)} - \frac{13}{16}$$

$$= 3.82''$$

$$(3)\quad e_f = a + \frac{N}{2}$$

$$= \tfrac{1}{2} + \frac{3.82}{2}$$

$$= 2.41''$$

$$(10)\quad t = \sqrt{\tfrac{1}{4}A^2 + A(e_f - \tfrac{3}{8})} - \tfrac{1}{2}A$$

where $A = \frac{R}{4\tfrac{1}{3}b} = \frac{(30)}{4\tfrac{1}{3}(8)} = .909$

$$t = \sqrt{\tfrac{1}{4}(.909)^2 + (.909)(2.41 - \tfrac{3}{8})} - \frac{(.909)}{2}$$

$$= .979'' \text{ or } \underline{1''}$$

horizontal leg of seat angle

$$(12)\ L_h = a + N$$

$$= (\tfrac{1}{2}) + (3.82)$$

$$= 4.32'' \text{ or } \underline{4\tfrac{1}{2}'' \text{ min.}}$$

vertical weld size and length

A 5″ angle, 1″ thick, is not rolled. The only 7″ and 9″ angles rolled have a 4″ horizontal leg which is not sufficient. This leaves just the 6″ and 8″ angles.

a) Using a 6″ x 6″ x 1″ seat angle $L_v = 6''$

$$(14)\quad \omega = \frac{R}{22.4\ L_v^2}\sqrt{L_v^2 + 20.25\ e_f^2}$$

$$= \frac{(30)}{(22.4)(6)^2}\sqrt{(6)^2 + 20.25\ (2.41)^2}$$

$$= .461 \text{ or } \underline{\text{use } \tfrac{1}{2}''}$$

b) Using a 8″ x 6″ x 1″ seat angle $L_v = 8''$

$$(14)\quad \omega = \frac{R}{22.4\ L_v^2}\sqrt{L_v^2 + 20.25\ e_f^2}$$

$$= \frac{(30)}{(22.4)(8)^2}\sqrt{(8)^2 + 20.25\ (2.41)^2}$$

$$= .282'' \text{ or } \underline{\text{use } \tfrac{5}{16}''}$$

The structural designer might be inclined to select the 6″ x 6″ x 1″ angle because of the obvious saving in weight. The shop man knowing that the 5⁄16″ fillet weld in (b) is a single-pass weld and can be made very fast, whereas the ½″ fillet weld in (a) is a three-pass

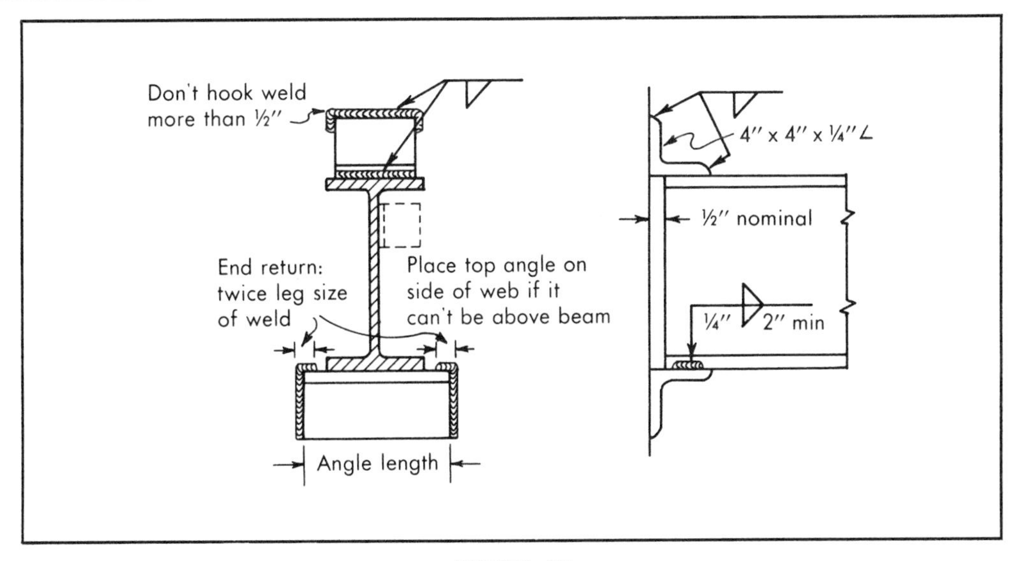

FIGURE 12

weld, would select the 8″ x 6″ x 1″ angle (b). He knows that the cross-sectional area of a fillet weld, and therefore its weight, varies as the square of the leg size. He figures the ratio of the leg sizes for (a) and for (b) to be 8 to 5. This ratio squared produces 64 to 25, or as far as he is concerned 2½ times the amount of weld metal.

Alternate Method Using Tables

From Table 1, $R/b = 30/8 = 3.75$. Using $e_f = 2.4''$ would give this value if $t = 1''$. (Here $R/b = 4.22$)

From Table 2, using $e_f = 2.4''$

a) If $L_v = 6''$, $R/\omega = 65.2$

or leg size of fillet weld,

$$\omega = \frac{30}{65.2} = .460'' \text{ or use } \underline{\tfrac{1}{2}''}$$

b) If $L_v = 8''$, $R/\omega = 107.0$

or leg size of fillet weld,

$$\omega = \frac{30}{107.0} = .280 \text{ or use } \underline{\tfrac{5}{16}''}$$

6. STANDARD SEAT ANGLE CONNECTIONS

(From American Institute of Steel Construction)

SEATED BEAM CONNECTIONS

Welded—E60XX & E70XX electrodes

TABLE VIII

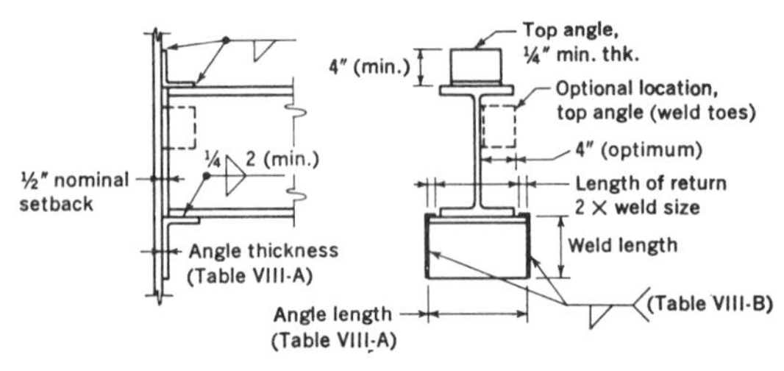

Seated connections are to be used only when the beam is supported by a top angle placed as shown above, or in the optional location as indicated.

Welds attaching beams to seat or top angles may be replaced by bolts or rivets, providing the limitations on the use of ASTM A307 bolts, stipulated in AISC Specification, Sect. 1.15.12, are observed.

In addition to the welds shown, temporary erection bolts may be used to attach beams to seats (optional).

Nominal beam setback is ½″. Allowable loads in Table VIII-A are based on ¾″ setback, which provides for possible mill underrun in beam length.

Allowable loads in Table VIII-A are based on ASTM A36 material in both beam and seat angle. These values will be conservative when used with beams, or seat angles of ASTM A242 or A441 material.

Weld capacities in Table VIII-B for E60XX and E70XX are applicable when supporting steel is ASTM A36, A242 or A441. When supporting steel is ASTM A7 or A373, use capacities shown for E60XX, regardless of the electrode used.

Should combinations of material thickness and weld size selected from Tables VIII-A and VIII-B, or shown in the sketch above, exceed the limits set by AISC Specification, Sections 1.17.4 and 1.17.5, increase the weld size or material thickness as required.

No reduction of the tabulated weld capacities is required when unstiffened seats line up on opposite sides of a supporting web.

If the reaction values of a beam are not shown on contract drawings, the connections shall be selected to support half the total uniform load capacity shown in the tables for Allowable Loads on Beams for the given shape, span and steel specification of the beam in question. The effect of concentrated loads near an end connection shall also be considered.

TABLE VIII-A Outstanding Leg Capacity, kips (based on OSL = 3½ or 4 inches)

Angle Length		6 inches						8 inches					
Angle Thickness		⅜	½	⅝	¾	⅞	1	⅜	½	⅝	¾	⅞	1
Beam Web Thickness	3/16	7.2	10.0	12.8	15.6	18.4	18.4	8.2	11.3	14.4	17.4	18.4	18.4
	¼	9.0	12.4	15.8	19.1	22.5	25.3	10.1	13.8	17.6	21.3	25.0	25.3
	5/16	11.3	15.9	19.8	23.7	27.6	31.6	13.1	17.4	21.7	26.0	30.4	34.0
	⅜	12.4	19.3	24.3	28.7	33.2	37.6	14.3	21.5	26.3	31.2	36.0	40.9
	7/16	13.4	21.1	28.8	33.7	38.7	43.6	15.5	23.8	30.9	36.3	41.7	47.1
	½	14.3	22.8	31.6	39.2	44.6	50.0	16.5	25.7	35.1	41.8	47.7	53.6
	9/16	15.2	24.4	34.0	43.8	51.0	56.9	17.5	27.5	37.8	47.8	54.1	60.5

Note: Values above heavy lines apply only for 4 inch outstanding legs.

TABLE VIII-B Weld Capacity, kips

Weld Size	E60XX Electrodes, Seat angle size (long leg vertical)						E70XX Electrodes, Seat angle size (long leg vertical)						Weld Size
	4 × 3½	5 × 3½	6 × 4	7 × 4	8 × 4	9 × 4	4 × 3½	5 × 3½	6 × 4	7 × 4	8 × 4	9 × 4	
¼	7.4	11.1	14.1	18.4	23.0	27.8	8.6	13.0	16.4	21.5	26.8	32.5	¼
5/16	9.3	13.9	17.6	23.0	28.8	34.8	10.8	16.2	20.6	26.8	33.6	40.6	5/16
⅜	11.1	16.7	21.1	27.6	35.4	41.7	13.0	19.5	24.7	32.2	40.3	48.7	⅜
7/16	13.0	19.5	24.7	32.2	40.3	48.7	15.1	22.7	28.8	37.6	47.0	56.8	7/16
½	14.8	22.2	28.2	36.8	46.0	55.7	17.3	25.9	32.9	43.0	53.7	64.9	½
⅝	...	27.8	35.2	46.0	57.5	69.6	...	32.4	41.1	53.7	67.1	...	⅝
Range of available seat angle thicknesses													
Min.	⅜	⅜	⅜	⅜	½	½	⅜	⅜	⅜	⅜	½	½	Min.
Max.	⅝	¾	⅞	⅞	1	1	⅝	¾	⅞	⅞	1	1	Max.

Stiffened Seat Brackets

1. ANALYSIS OF STIFFENER AT RIGHT ANGLES TO BEAM WEB

When the reaction load (R) requires a thickness of angle greater than the available sections, a stiffened seat bracket may be used. There are two analyses: (A) in which the seat stiffener is at right angles to the web of the beam, and (B) in which the seat stiffener is in line with the web of the beam.

For analysis, the stiffener of Type (A) is considered an eccentrically loaded column with the reaction load applied at a fixed point. The maximum stress is the sum of the direct load and bending effects. The line of action of the compressive load is approximately parallel to the outer edge of the stiffener. The critical cross-section of the stiffener (to be used for the area and section modulus) is at right angles to the line of action of the load.

The area and section modulus are—

$$A = t\ X = t\ L_h \sin \phi$$

$$S = \frac{t\ X^2}{6} = \frac{t\ L_h{}^2 \sin^2 \phi}{6}$$

$$a = \left(e_s - \frac{L_h}{2} \right) \sin \phi$$

$$X = L_h \sin \phi$$

Since the maximum stress,

$$\sigma = \frac{F}{A} + \frac{M}{S} = \frac{F}{A} + \frac{F\ a}{S}$$

$$= \frac{R}{t\ L_h{}^2 \sin^2 \phi} + \frac{6R\left(e_s - \frac{L_h}{2} \right) \sin \phi}{t\ L_h{}^2 \sin^3 \phi}$$

$$= \frac{R(6e_s - 2L_h)}{t\ L_h \sin^2 \phi}$$

the required thickness of the bracket web is—

$$t = \frac{R(6e_s - 2L_h)}{\sigma\ L_h{}^2 \sin^2 \phi} \quad \cdots\cdots\cdots (1)$$

The thickness of the bracket web can be determined quickly from Nomograph No. 4 (Fig. 2) for A36 steel; this is based on formula #1. The vertical line at the left is for values of load eccentricity (e_s) and length of outstanding bracket leg (L_h). The next line is for the angle between the side of the bracket web and the horizontal. A line is drawn through these two values to the pivot line (C). From this pivot point, a line is drawn through the reaction value (R) and the required thickness of bracket web (t) is read on the extreme right-hand line.

* The above analysis of bracket web thickness requirement is based upon "Welded Structural Brackets", Cyril D. Jensen, AWS Welding Journal, Oct. 1936.

FIGURE 1

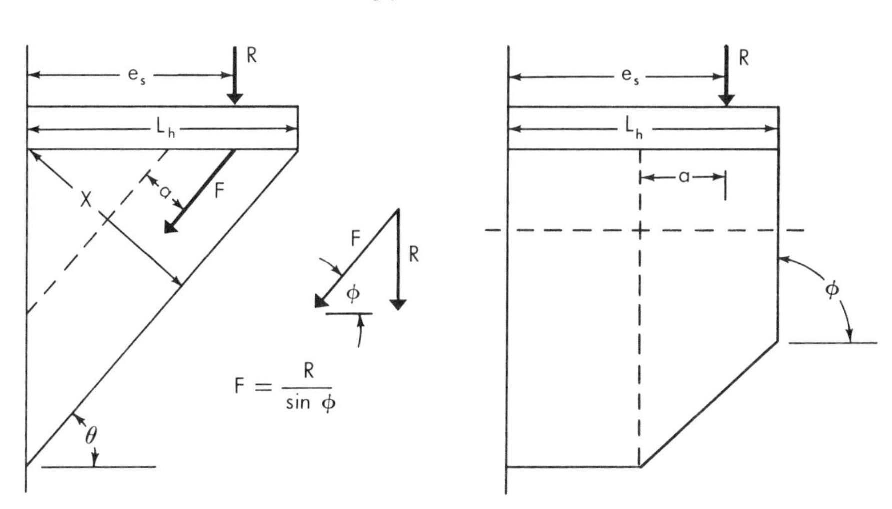

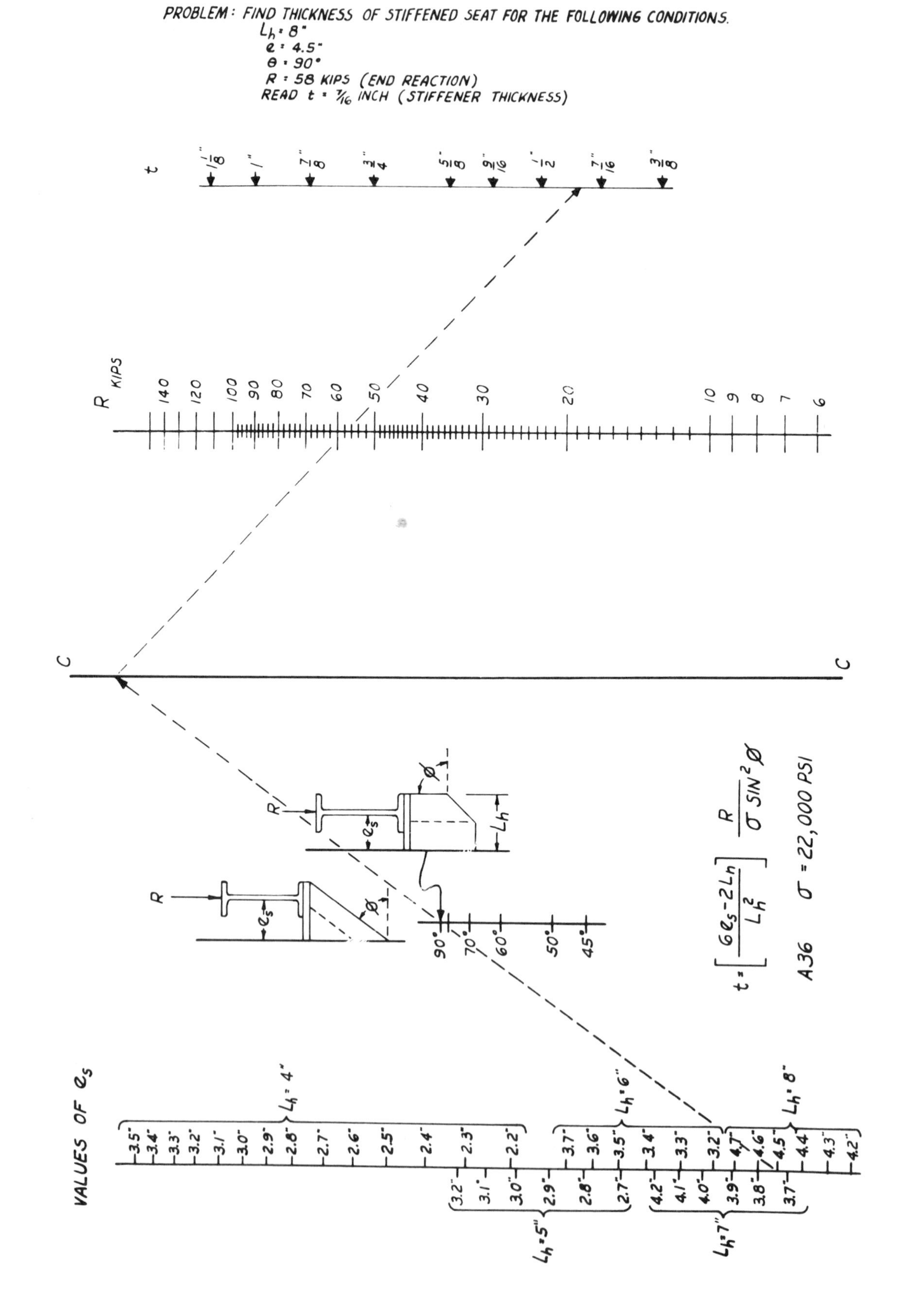

FIGURE 2—Thickness of Stiffened Seat For A36 Steel

NOMOGRAPH NO. 4

2. ANALYSIS OF STIFFENER IN LINE WITH BEAM WEB

If the beam rests in line with the bracket stiffener, Type B, Figure 3, the bearing length (N) of the beam (AISC Sec 1.10.10) is—

$$N = \frac{R}{t_w\ (.75\ \sigma_y)} - K \qquad (2)$$

and this would be the minimum value allowed.

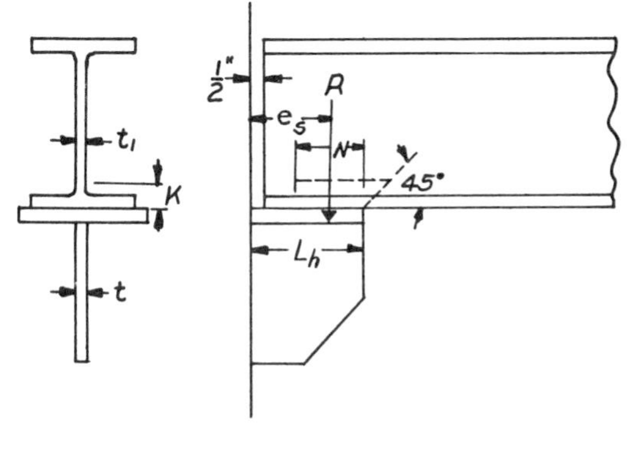

FIGURE 3

The eccentricity (e_s) of the reaction load is—

$$e_s = L_h - \frac{N}{2} \qquad (3)$$

This value of load eccentricity (e_s) can be quickly found by using Nomograph No. 1 (Fig. 4 in previous Sect. 5.2). Sometimes it is figured as 80% of the bracket's outstanding leg length (L_h).

The eccentrically loaded column formula (#1) is seldom used in this case because it will result in an excessively thick bracket web or stiffener. This is because the formula is based upon stress only and does not take into consideration some yielding of the bracket which will cause the point of application of the load to shift in toward the support, thus reducing the moment arm and bending stress.

AISC Manual, page 4-39 recommends for A36 bracket material that the bracket web's thickness be at least equal to 1.33 times the required fillet weld size (E70 welds). Also it should not be less than the supported beam web thickness for A7, A373 and A36 beams, and not less than 1.4 times the beam web thickness for A242 and A441 beams.

For stiffened seats in line on opposite sides of the column web, the fillet weld size should not exceed ¾ the column web thickness when determining its length (L_v).

3. WELDING OF BRACKETS

If the bracket is made up of plates, AISC recommends that the welds connecting the top plate to the web of the stiffener should have strength equivalent to the horizontal welds between the bracket and the column support.

The depth of the stiffener is determined by the vertical length of weld (L_v) required to connect the bracket.

The length of the bracket top plate (L_h) should be sufficient for it to extend at least beyond the bearing length of the beam (N).

The stiffened seat bracket is shop welded to the supporting member in the flat or downhand position. Usually the top portion of the bracket is welded on the underside only, and the web of the stiffener is welded both sides, full length. By placing the weld on the underside of the bracket, it does not interfere in any way with the beam which it supports.

Some engineers do not like the notch effect of this fillet weld's root to be at the outer fiber of the connection, and would prefer to place this fillet weld on top of the bracket; this can be done.

4. WELD SIZE AND LENGTH

The following method is used to determine the leg size of the connecting fillet weld (ω). For simplicity the length of the horizontal top weld is assumed to be a certain percentage of the vertical weld length (L_v). The top weld length is usually less than the bracket width, and the vertical weld length is assumed equal to the vertical length of the bracket.

This analysis uses the value of 0.4 L_v for the top weld as it is a more commonly used value, although any reasonable value might be used, Figure 4.

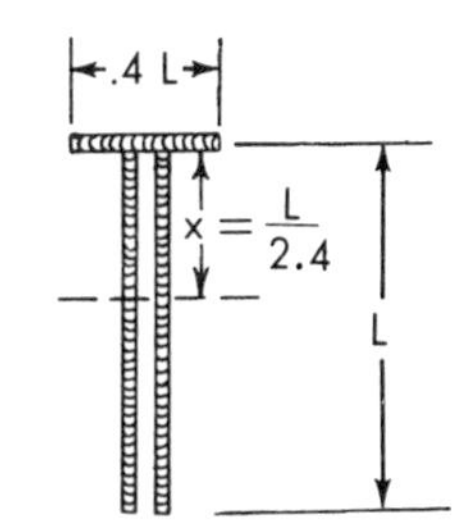

FIGURE 4

Thus it can be shown that:
neutral axis of connecting weld

$$x = \frac{L_v}{2.4}$$

section modulus of connecting weld

$$S_w = 0.6\ L_v^2$$
(top)

FIGURE 5—Length of Stiffener and Size of Weld for Stiffened Seat
For A36 Steel & E70 Welds

NOMOGRAPH NO. 5

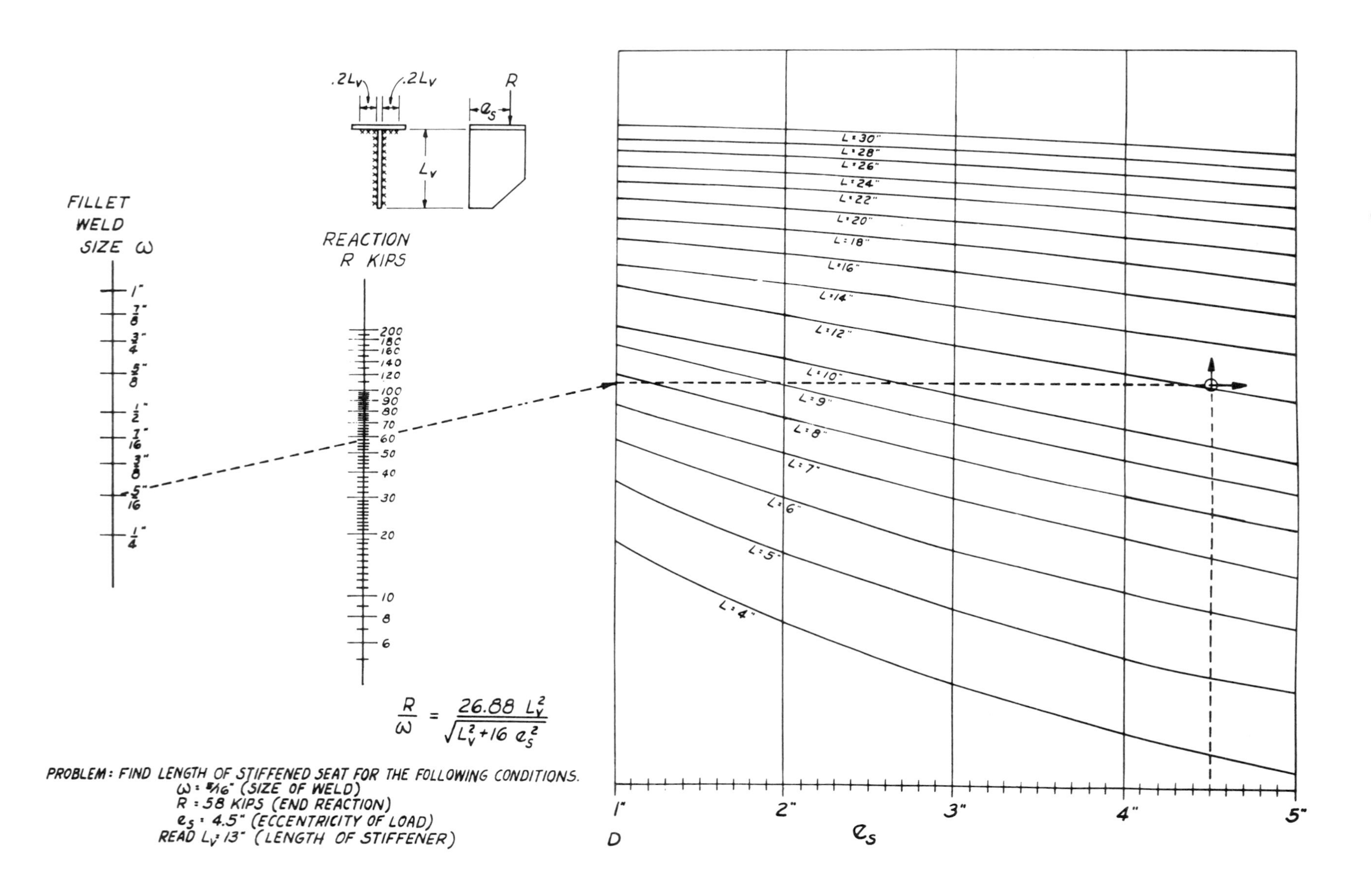

length of connecting weld

$$A_w = 2.4\ L_v$$

bending force on weld

$$f_b = \frac{M}{S_w} = \frac{R\ e_s}{.6\ L_v^2}$$

vertical shear on weld

$$f_s = \frac{R}{A_w} = \frac{R}{2.4\ L_v}$$

resultant force on weld

$$f_r = \sqrt{f_b^2 + f_s^2} = \sqrt{\left(\frac{R\ e_s}{.6\ L_v^2}\right)^2 + \left(\frac{R}{2.4\ L_v}\right)^2}$$

or

$$f_r = \frac{R}{2.4\ L_v^2}\sqrt{L_v^2 + 16\ e_s^2} \quad \ldots\ldots\ldots\ldots (4)$$

leg size of fillet weld

$$\omega = \frac{\text{actual force}}{\text{allowable force}} \quad \text{or}$$

A7, A373 Steel; E60 Welds	A36 Steel; E70 Welds
$\frac{R}{\omega} = \frac{23.04\ L_v^2}{\sqrt{L_v^2 + 16\ e_s^2}}$	$\frac{R}{\omega} = \frac{26.88\ L_v^2}{\sqrt{L_v^2 + 16\ e_s^2}}$

vertical weld length (L_v)

$$L_v = \sqrt{\frac{B}{2}\left[B + \sqrt{B^2 + 64\ e_s^2}\right]} \quad \ldots\ldots\ldots (6)$$

where:

A7, A373 Steel; E60 Welds	A36 Steel; E70 Welds
$B = \frac{R}{23.04\ \omega}$	$B = \frac{R}{26.88\ \omega}$

By knowing the value of B and e_s, the engineer may solve directly for L_v.

The length of connecting vertical weld (L_v) may be determined quickly from Nomograph No. 5 (Fig. 5) for A36 steel and E70 welds; this is based on formula #7. The welded connection is assumed to extend horizontally 0.2 L on each side of the bracket web. The maximum leg size of fillet weld (ω) is held to ¾ of the stiffener thickness. Draw a line from weld size (ω) through the reaction (R) to the vertical line (D). The required length of weld (L_v), = vertical length of stiffener (L), is found at the intersection of a horizontal line through (D) and a vertical line through the given value of (e_s).

For stiffener brackets which have a top width (b) other than 40% of the depth (L_v), the Table I formulas may be used.

Problem 1

Design a bracket to support a beam with an end reaction of 58 kips. The beam lies at right angles to the bracket. Use A36 steel and E70 welds. See Figure 6.

Using Nomograph No. 4:

$L_h = 8''$

$e_s = 4.5''$

$\theta = 90°$

$R = 58$ kips

TABLE 1—Fillet Weld Leg Sizes

Bracket Width	A7, A373 Steel & E60 Welds	A36 Steel & E70 Welds
$b = 0.4\ L_v$	$\omega = \frac{R}{23.04\ L^2_v}\sqrt{L^2_v + 16.00\ e^2_s}$	$\omega = \frac{R}{26.88}\sqrt{L^2_v + 16.00 + e^2_s}$
$b = 0.5\ L_v$	$\omega = \frac{R}{24.00\ L^2_v}\sqrt{L^2_v + 14.06\ e^2_s}$	$\omega = \frac{R}{28.00}\sqrt{L^2_v + 14.06 + e^2_s}$
$b = 0.6\ L_v$	$\omega = \frac{R}{24.96\ L^2_v}\sqrt{L^2_v + 12.57\ e^2_s}$	$\omega = \frac{R}{29.12}\sqrt{L^2_v + 12.57 + e^2_s}$
$b = 0.7\ L_v$	$\omega = \frac{R}{25.92\ L^2_v}\sqrt{L^2_v + 11.37\ e^2_s}$	$\omega = \frac{R}{30.24}\sqrt{L^2_v + 11.37 + e^2_s}$
$b = 0.8\ L_v$	$\omega = \frac{R}{26.88\ L^2_v}\sqrt{L^2_v + 10.44\ e^2_s}$	$\omega = \frac{R}{31.36}\sqrt{L^2_v + 10.44 + e^2_s}$
$b = 0.9\ L_v$	$\omega = \frac{R}{27.84\ L^2_v}\sqrt{L^2_v + 9.65\ e^2_s}$	$\omega = \frac{R}{32.48}\sqrt{L^2_v + 9.65 + e^2_s}$
$b = 1.0\ L_v$	$\omega = \frac{R}{28.80\ L^2_v}\sqrt{L^2_v + 9.00\ e^2_s}$	$\omega = \frac{R}{33.60}\sqrt{L^2_v + 9.00 + e^2_s}$

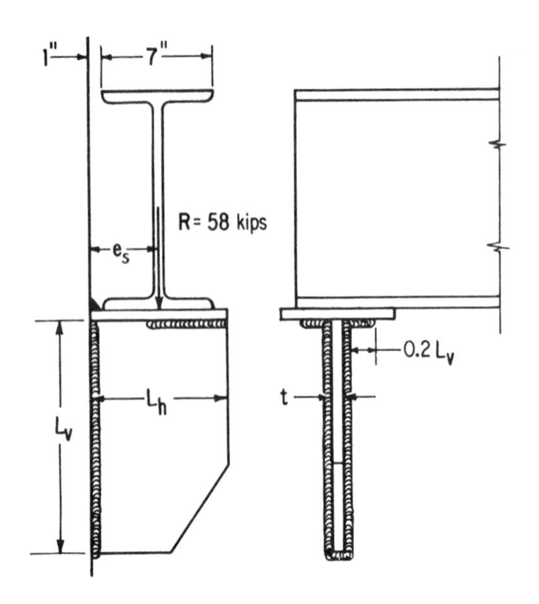

FIGURE 6

read the required stiffener thickness as—

$t = \frac{7}{16}''$

Using Nomograph No. 5:

$\omega = \frac{5}{16}''$ $(t = \frac{7}{16}'')$

$R = 58$ kips

$e_s = 4.5''$

read the required vertical length of the stiffener as—

$L_v = \underline{13''}$

Problem 2

Design a bracket to support a 20″, 85# I-beam with an end reaction of 58 kips. The beam lies in line with the bracket. Use A36 steel and E70 welds.

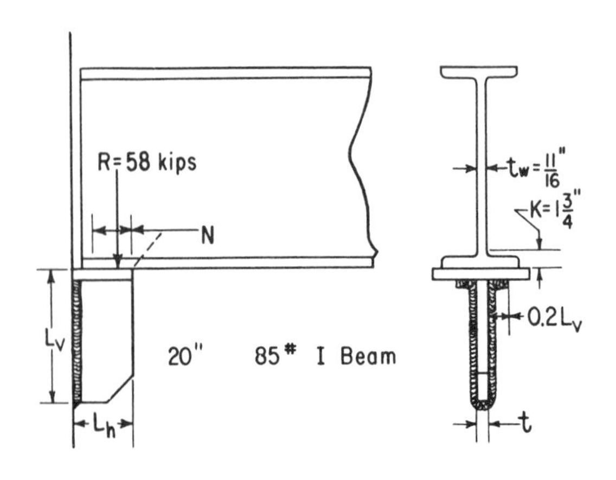

FIGURE 7

Using Nomograph No. 1 (Fig. 4, Sect. 5.2):

$R = 58$ kips

$t = \frac{11}{16}''$

$K = 1\frac{3}{4}''$

read the bearing length and load eccentricity as—

$\left.\begin{matrix} N = 1.54'' \\ e_s = 3.23'' \end{matrix}\right\}$ (if $L_h = 4''$)

Since $t = \frac{11}{16}''$, use $t = \underline{\frac{3}{4}''\text{ plate}}$.

Using Nomograph No. 5:

$R = 58$ kips

$e_s = 3.37''$

for $\omega = \frac{3}{8}''$, read $L_v = 10''$

for $\omega = \frac{5}{16}''$, read $L_v = 11''$

Use the $\frac{5}{16}''$ fillet weld with a length of 11″.

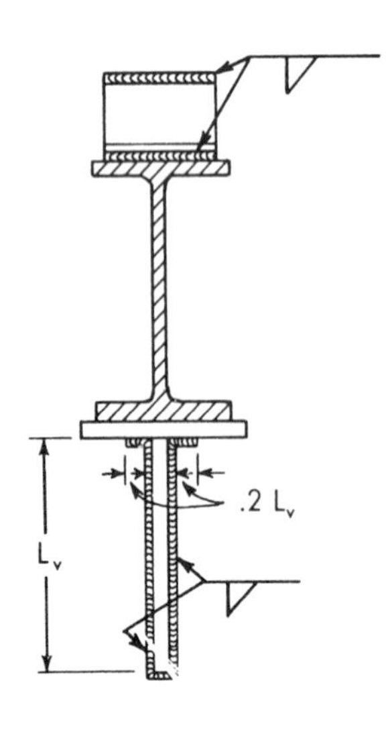

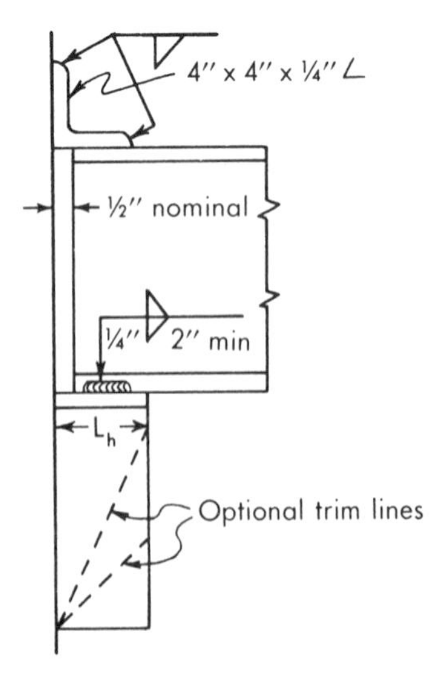

FIGURE 8

5. STANDARD SEAT BRACKET CONNECTIONS

(From American Institute of Steel Construction)

STIFFENED SEATED BEAM CONNECTIONS

Welded—E60XX or E70XX electrodes

TABLE X

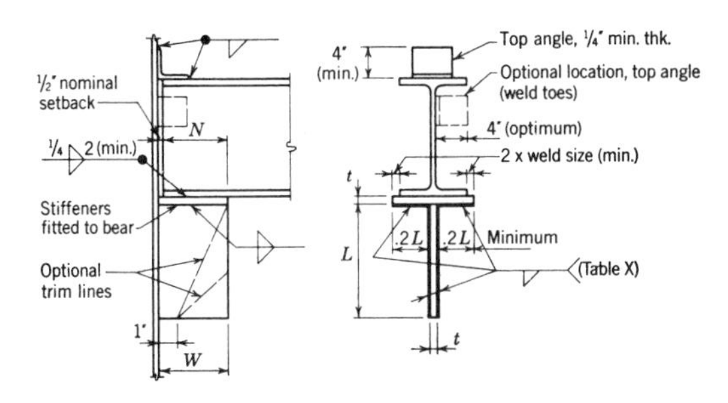

Allowable loads in Table X are based on the use of E60XX electrodes. For E70XX electrodes, multiply tabular loads by 1.16, or enter the table with 86% of the given reaction. Note: Advantage may be taken of the higher allowable unit stress of E70XX electrodes only if both bracket and supporting members are ASTM A36, A242 or A441 material.

Based on ASTM A36 bracket material, minimum stiffener plate thickness, t, shall not be less than the supported beam web thickness for ASTM A7, A373 and A36 beams, and not less than 1.4 times the beam web thickness for ASTM A242 and A441 beams. Based on ASTM A242 or A441 bracket material, t shall not be less than the beam web thickness, regardless of beam material. Minimum stiffener plate thickness, t, shall be at least 1.33 times the required weld size.

Thickness, t, of the horizontal seat plate, or flange of tee, shall not be less than the thickness of the stiffener.

If seat and stiffener are separate plates, fit stiffener to bear against seat. Welds connecting the two plates shall have a strength equal to or greater than the horizontal welds to the support under the seat plate.

Welds attaching beam to seat may be replaced by bolts or rivets, providing the limitations on the use of ASTM A307 bolts, stipulated in AISC Specification, Sect. 1.15.12, are observed.

For stiffened seats in line on opposite sides of a column web, select a weld size no greater than ¾ of the column web thickness.

Should combinations of material thickness and weld size selected from Table X, or shown in the sketch above, exceed the limits set by AISC Specification, Sect. 1.17.4 and 1.17.5, increase the weld size or material thickness as required.

In addition to the welds shown, temporary erection bolts may be used to attach beams to seats (optional).

Seated connections are to be used only when the beam is supported by a top angle placed as sketched above, or in the optional location, as indicated.

If the reaction values of a beam are not shown on contract drawings, the connections shall be selected to support half the total uniform load capacity tabulated in the beam load tables for the given shape, span and steel specification of the beam in question. The effect of concentrated loads near an end connection shall also be considered.

L In.	Width of Seat, W, Inches											
	4				5				6			
	Weld Size, Inches				Weld Size, Inches				Weld Size, Inches			
	¼	5/16	⅜	7/16	5/16	⅜	7/16	½	5/16	⅜	7/16	½
6	14.7	18.4	22.0	25.7	15.2	18.2	21.2	24.2				20.6
7	19.4	24.2	29.0	33.9	20.2	24.2	28.3	32.3		20.7	24.2	27.6
8	24.4	30.6	36.7	42.8	25.8	30.9	36.1	41.2	22.2	26.6	31.0	35.4
9	29.8	37.3	44.7	52.2	31.8	38.1	44.5	50.8	27.5	33.0	38.5	44.0
10	35.5	44.4	53.2	62.1	38.2	45.8	53.4	61.0	33.3	39.9	46.6	53.2
11	41.3	51.6	61.9	72.2	44.9	53.8	62.8	71.8	39.4	47.2	55.1	63.0
12	47.3	59.1	70.9	82.7	51.9	62.2	72.6	83.0	45.8	55.0	64.1	73.3
13		66.7	80.0	93.4	59.0	70.8	82.6	94.4	52.5	63.0	73.5	84.0
14		74.4	89.3	104.	66.4	79.7	93.0	106.	59.4	71.3	83.2	95.0
15		82.2	98.6	115.	73.9	88.6	103.	118.	66.5	79.8	93.1	106.
16		90.0	108.	126.	81.5	97.7	114.	130.	73.8	88.5	103.	118.
17		97.8	117.	137.	89.2	107.	125.	143.	81.2	97.4	114.	130.
18		106.	127.	148.	96.9	116.	136.	155.	88.7	106.	124.	142.
19		113.	136.	159.	105.	126.	147.	167.	96.2	115.	135.	154.
20		121.	146.	170.	112.	135.	157.	180.	104.	125.	145.	166.
21		129.	155.	181.	120.	144.	168.	192.	112.	134.	156.	179.
22		137.	164.	192.	128.	154.	179.	205.	119.	143.	167.	191.
23		145.	174.	203.	136.	163.	190.	218.	127.	153.	178.	203.
24		152.	183.	213.	144.	173.	201.	230.	135.	162.	189.	216.
25		160.	192.	224.	152.	182.	212.	243.	143.	171.	200.	228.
26		168.	202.	235.	159.	191.	223.	255.	151.	181.	211.	241.
27		176.	211.	246.	167.	201.	234.	268.	158.	190.	222.	254.

Note 1: Loads shown above apply to welds made with E60XX electrodes. For E70XX electrodes, multiply tabular loads by 1.16, or enter the table with 86% of the given reaction. Increased values are applicable only when E70XX electrodes are used with ASTM A36, A242 or A441 material.

L In.	Width of Seat, W, Inches											
	7				8				9			
	Weld Size, Inches				Weld Size, Inches				Weld Size, Inches			
	5/16	⅜	7/16	½	5/16	⅜	½	⅝	5/16	⅜	½	⅝
11	34.9	41.9	48.9	55.8				62.5				
12	40.8	49.0	57.1	65.3			58.6	73.3				
13	47.0	56.4	65.8	75.2			67.8	84.8				77.0
14	53.4	64.1	74.8	85.4		58.0	77.4	96.7				88.1
15	60.1	72.1	84.1	96.2	54.6	65.5	87.4	109.			79.8	99.8
16	67.0	80.3	93.7	107.	61.1	73.3	97.7	122.			89.5	112.
17	74.0	88.8	104.	118.	67.7	81.2	108.	135.		74.6	99.5	124.
18	81.2	97.4	114.	130.	74.6	89.5	119.	149.		82.4	110.	137.
19	88.5	106.	124.	142.	81.6	97.9	130.	163.	75.4	90.4	121.	151.
20	95.9	115.	134.	153.	88.7	106.	142.	177.	82.2	98.6	131.	164.
21	103.	124.	145.	165.	95.9	115.	153.	192.	89.1	107.	143.	178.
22	111.	133.	155.	178.	103.	124.	165.	207.	96.2	115.	154.	192.
23	119.	142.	166.	190.	111.	133.	177.	221.	103.	124.	165.	207.
24	126.	152.	177.	202.	118.	142.	189.	236.	111.	133.	177.	221.
25	134.	161.	188.	214.	126.	151.	201.	252.	118.	142.	189.	236.
26	142.	170.	199.	227.	133.	160.	213.	267.	125.	151.	201.	251.
27	150.	180.	209.	239.	141.	169.	226.	282.	133.	160.	213.	266.
28	157.	189.	220.	252.	149.	179.	238.	298.	141.	169.	225.	281.
29	165.	198.	231.	264.	157.	188.	250.	313.	148.	178.	237.	296.
30	173.	208.	242.	277.	164.	197.	263.	329.	156.	187.	249.	312.
31	181.	217.	253.	289.	172.	207.	275.	344.	164.	196.	262.	327.
32	189.	227.	264.	302.	180.	216.	288.	360.	171.	206.	274.	343.

Note 1: Loads shown above apply to welds made with E60XX electrodes. For E70XX electrodes, multiply tabular loads by 1.16, or enter the table with 86% of the given reaction. Increased values are applicable only when E70XX electrodes are used with ASTM A36, A242 or A441 material.

Beam-to-column connection being made on the Colorado State Services Building in Denver. Operator is anchoring the beam to a stiffened seat bracket by downhand welding, using iron powder electrode.

Extensive use of modern structural techniques and welding processes speeded erection of Detroit Bank & Trust Co. Building. Stiffened seat bracket can be seen at upper left. Angle clip to facilitate field splicing of column lengths shows immediately above.

Web Framing Angles

1. GENERAL REQUIREMENTS

Web framing angles are usually shop welded to the web of the beam, extending about ½″ beyond the end of the beam, and field welded to the supporting member.

Erection bolts are usually placed near the bottom of the angle, so they do not restrain the beam end from rotating under load. For deeper girders, the erection bolts may be placed near the top of the angle for better stability during erection. If there is concern about any restraining action, the bolts may be removed after field welding.

The thickness of the framing angles must be limited to that which will allow sufficient flexibility, otherwise the connection would restrain the end of the simply supported beam from rotating and thus would load up in end moment. AISC has a table of typical framing angle connections. It lists 3″ and 4″ angles of 5⁄16″ to 7⁄16″ thickness. When thicker angles are used the leg against the supporting member must be increased in about the same proportion as the thickness in order to maintain the same order of flexibility.

The analysis of this type of connection is divided into two parts: a) the field weld of the angle to the supporting member and b) the shop weld of the angle to the web of the beam.

2. ANALYSIS OF FIELD WELDS TO THE SUPPORT

When the reaction (R) is applied, the framing angles tend to twist or rotate, pressing against each other at the top, and swinging away from each other at the bottom.

It is assumed the two angles bear against each other for a vertical distance equal to ⅙ of their length. The remaining ⅚ of the length is resisted by the connecting welds. It is assumed also that these forces on the welds increase linearly, reaching a maximum (f_h) at the bottom of the connection, Figure 1.

horizontal force on weld

Applied moment from load = Resisting moment of weld

$$\frac{R}{2} L_h = \frac{2}{3} P L_v$$

where L_h = leg length of angle

$$\text{or } P = \frac{.75 R L_h}{L_v}$$

From force triangle, find—

$$P = \tfrac{1}{2} (f_h)(\tfrac{5}{6} L_v)$$

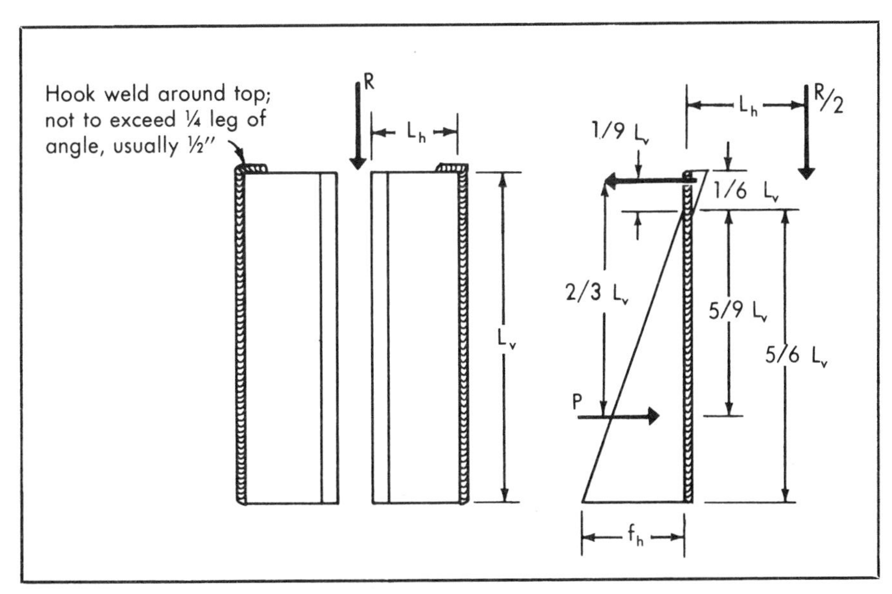

FIGURE 1

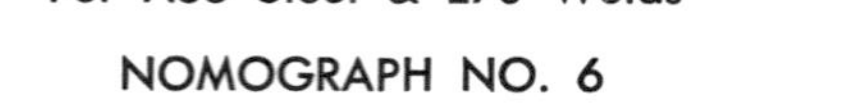

FIGURE 2—Framing Angles and Size of Field Welds
For A36 Steel & E70 Welds

NOMOGRAPH NO. 6

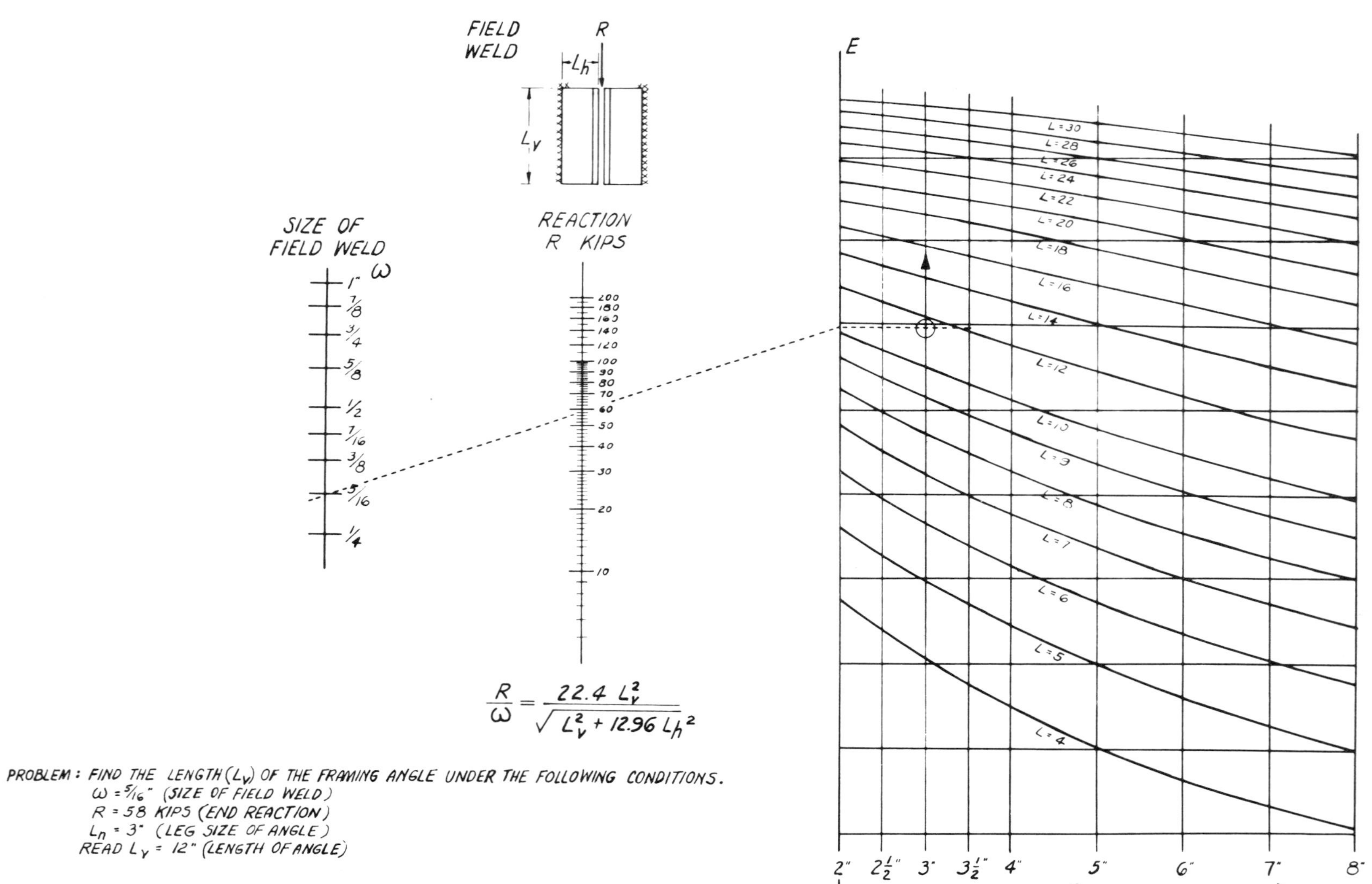

$$\frac{R}{\omega} = \frac{22.4\, L_v^2}{\sqrt{L_v^2 + 12.96\, L_h^2}}$$

PROBLEM: FIND THE LENGTH (L_v) OF THE FRAMING ANGLE UNDER THE FOLLOWING CONDITIONS.
$\omega = 5/16$" (SIZE OF FIELD WELD)
$R = 58$ KIPS (END REACTION)
$L_n = 3$" (LEG SIZE OF ANGLE)
READ $L_v = 12$" (LENGTH OF ANGLE)

From these two equations, determine—

$$f_h = \frac{9\ R\ L_h}{5\ L_v^2}$$

vertical force on weld

$$f_v = \frac{R}{2L_v}$$

resultant force on weld

$$f_r = \sqrt{f_h^2 + f_v^2} = \sqrt{\left(\frac{9\ RL_h}{5\ L_v^2}\right)^2 + \left(\frac{R}{2L_v}\right)^2}$$

or:

$$f_r = \frac{R}{2L_v^2}\sqrt{L_v^2 + 12.96\ L_h^2} \quad \text{.........(1)}$$

leg size of fillet weld

$$\omega = \frac{\text{actual force on weld}}{\text{allowable force}} \quad \text{and:}$$

A7, A373 Steel; E60 Welds	A36 Steel; E70 Welds
$\frac{R}{\omega} = \frac{19.2\ L_v^2}{\sqrt{L_v^2 + 12.96\ L_h^2}}$	$\frac{R}{\omega} = \frac{22.4\ L_v^2}{\sqrt{L_v^2 + 12.96\ L_h^2}}$

.(2)

Be sure the supporting plate is thick enough for this resulting weld size (ω).

The two vertical welds connecting framing angles to supporting member should be "hooked" around the top of the angles for a distance of about twice the leg size of the weld, or about ½". (Original tests indicated that a distance not to exceed ¼ of the angle's leg length helped the carrying capacity of the connection.)

Nomograph No. 6 (Fig. 2) may be used for the field welding. This nomograph is for A36 steel and E70 welds. In the chart on the right-hand side, from the point of intersection of the angle's leg size (L_h) and the length of the angle (L_v), draw a horizontal line to the vertical axis E-E. From this point, draw a line through the reaction (R) to the left-hand axis. Read the leg size (ω) of the field weld on this axis.

Table 1, for A36 steel and E70 welds, gives values of R/ω in terms of leg size of angle (L_h) and length of angle (L_v).

AISC, Sect 1.17.5 specifies that the leg size of a fillet weld used in calculating its length (L_v) should not cause the web of the supporting member to be overstressed in shear.

For a single pair of framing angles on just one side of the supporting web, assume the leg size of the fillet weld not to exceed 1.3 t_w.

TABLE 1—Values of R/ω
For Field Weld of Framing Angle to Support For A36 Steel & E70 Welds

$$\frac{R}{\omega} = \frac{\text{Reaction, kips}}{\text{Leg size of fillet weld}} \qquad \frac{R}{\omega} = \frac{22.4\ L_v^2}{\sqrt{L_v^2 + 12.96\ L_h^2}}$$

Length of framing angle (L_v)	Leg of Angle (L_h)						
	2″	3″	4″	5″	6″	7″	8″
4″	43	30	22	19	16	14	12
5″	63	46	37	29	25	21	19
6″	84	64	51	41	35	30	27
7″	108	84	67	55	47	41	36
8″	131	105	85	71	61	53	47
9″	156	127	105	88	76	66	59
10″	180	150	125	106	92	81	72
12″	229	197	169	146	128	113	101
14″	277	246	215	189	167	149	122
16″	321	294	262	234	209	188	170
18″	372	343	312	281	254	219	209
20″	416	392	360	328	300	274	251
22″	466	440	409	385	347	319	294
24″	514	487	457	426	394	365	338
26″	560	536	505	476	443	413	384
28″	607	583	547	523	491	461	425
30″	654	630	603	571	540	509	480

For two pairs of framing angles, one on each side of the supporting web, assume the leg size of the fillet weld not to exceed ⅔ t_w.

These factors of (⅔) and (1.3 = 2 x ⅔) may be adjusted for the exact type of steel used by referring to Table 2.

3. ANALYSIS OF SHOP WELDS TO THE BEAM

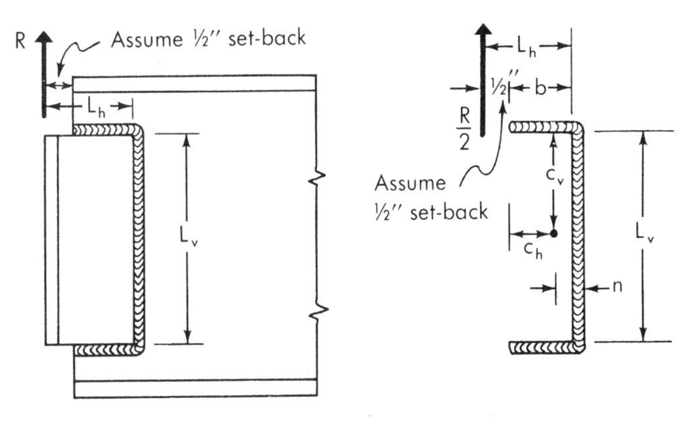

FIGURE 3

In Figure 3, analysis of the shop weld shows—

$$n = \frac{b^2}{2b + L_v}$$

$$c_h = L_h - n - ½''$$

$$c_v = \frac{L_v}{2}$$

$$b = L_h - ½''$$

$$J_w = \frac{(2b + L_v)^3}{12} - \frac{b^2(b + L_v)^2}{2b + L_v}$$

twisting (horizontal)

$$f_h = \frac{T\,c_v}{J_w} = \frac{R}{2}\,\frac{(L_h - n)c_v}{J_w} \quad \text{...............(3)}$$

twisting (vertical)

$$f_{v1} = \frac{T\,c_h}{J_w} = \frac{R}{2}\,\frac{(L_h - n)c_h}{J_w} \quad \text{...............(4)}$$

shear (vertical)

$$f_{v2} = \frac{R/2}{2b + L_v} \quad \text{...............(5)}$$

resultant force on outer end of connecting weld

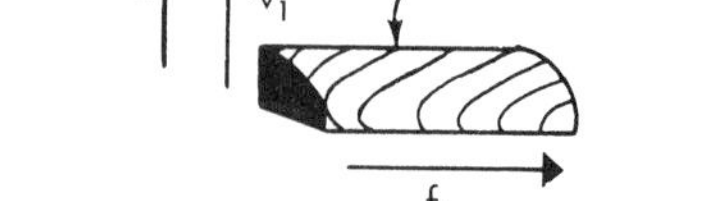

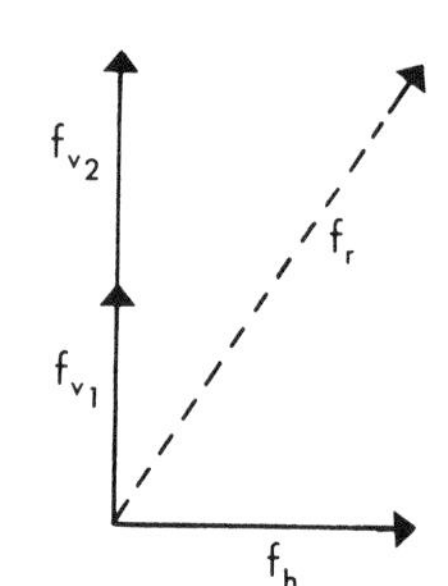

FIGURE 4

$$f_r = \sqrt{f_h^2 + (f_{v1} + f_{v2})^2} \quad \text{...............(6)}$$

leg size of fillet weld

$$\omega = \frac{\text{actual force on welds}}{\text{allowable force}}$$

A7, A373 Steel; E60 Welds	A36 Steel; E70 Welds
$\omega = \frac{f_r}{9600}$	$\omega = \frac{f_r}{11{,}200}$

(7)

Unfortunately there is no way to simplify these

TABLE 2—Maximum Leg Size to Use in Calculating Vertical Length of Weld

FOR VARIOUS COMBINATIONS OF WELD METALS AND STEEL

Given these conditions:

Steel	A7 A373	A36	A242, A441		
thickness			Over 1½″ To 4″	Over ¾″ To 1½″	¾″ or less
σ_y	33,000	36,000	42,000	46,000	50,000
τ	13,000	14,500	17,000	18,500	20,000
weld	E60 or SAW-1	E70 or SAW-2	E70 or SAW-2	E70 or SAW-2	E70 or SAW-2
f	9,600 ω	11,200 ω	11,200 ω	11,200 ω	11,200 ω
$\omega/t \leqq$	.667	.648	.759	.826	.893

Then: Maximum leg size of fillet weld to use in calculating vertical length

leg size ω	Web thickness (t_w) over —				
¼″	.375	.386	.329	.325	.280
5/16″	.468	.482	.412	.378	.350
⅜″	.562	.579	.494	.454	.420
7/16″	.656	.676	.576	.529	.490
½″	.750	.772	.659	.605	.560
9/16″	.844	.868	.741	.681	.630
⅝″	.937	.964	.824	.756	.700

FIGURE 5—Size of Shop Weld of Framing Angles
For A36 Steel & E70 Welds

NOMOGRAPH NO. 7

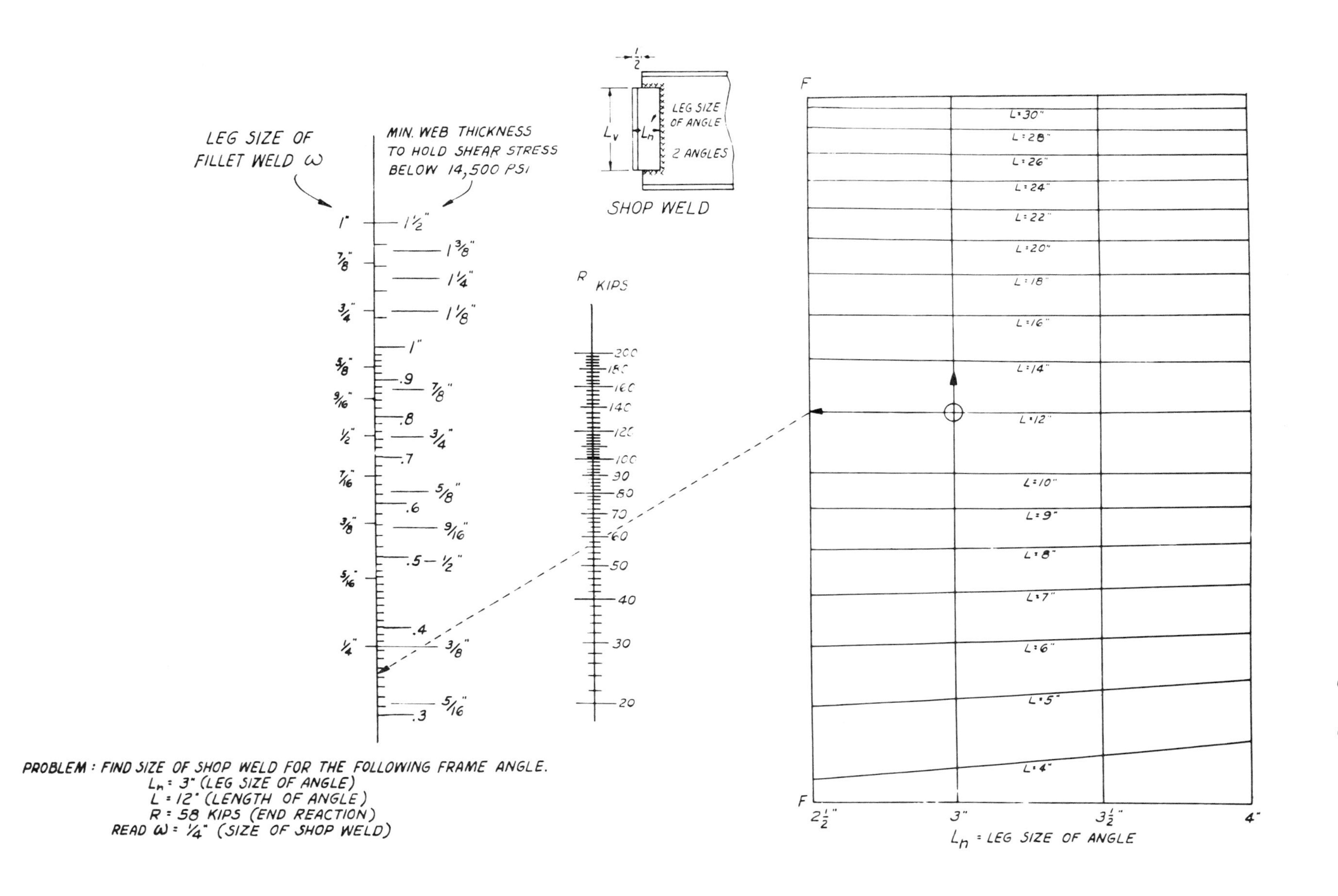

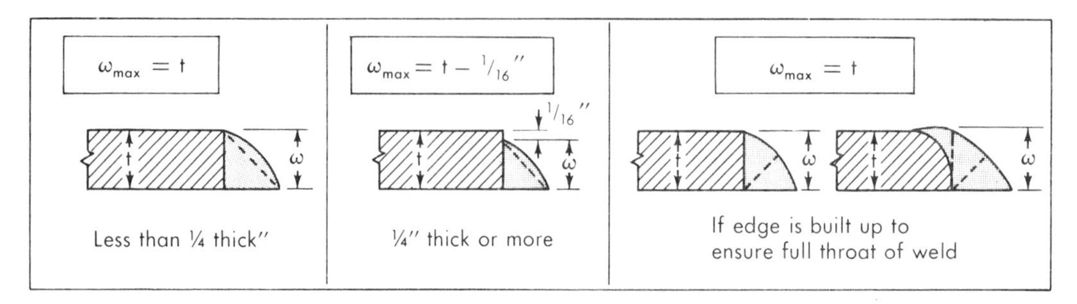

FIGURE 6

formulas into one workable formula. It is necessary to work out each step until the final result is obtained.

The leg size of this shop weld may be determined quickly by means of Nomograph No. 7 (Fig. 5), for A36 steel and E70 welds. In the chart on the right-hand side, from the point of intersection of the angle's horizontal leg length (L_h) and its vertical length (L_v) draw a horizontal line to the vertical axis F-F. From this point, draw a line through the reaction (R) to the left-hand axis. Read the leg size (ω) of the shop weld along the left-hand scale of this axis.

If the nomograph is used from left to right to establish an angle size, be sure that the leg size of the fillet weld does not exceed a value which would overstress the web of the beam in shear (AISC Sec 1.17.5) by producing too short a length of connecting weld (L_v).

The following limits apply to the fillet weld leg size (ω) relative to the thickness of the beam web (as used in calculating the vertical length of connecting weld):

A7, A373 Steel and E60 Weld

$(\tau = 13{,}000 \text{ psi}) \; (f_w = 9600\ \omega \text{ lbs/in.})$

$$\omega \leqq t_w \frac{13{,}000}{2 \times 9600} \leqq .676\ t_w \text{ or } < \tfrac{2}{3}\ t_w$$

A36 Steel and E70 Weld

$(\tau = 14{,}500 \text{ psi}) \; (f_w = 11{,}200\ \omega \text{ lbs/in.})$

$$\omega \leqq t_w \frac{14{,}500}{2 \times 11{,}200} \leqq .648\ t_w \text{ or } < \tfrac{2}{3}\ t_w$$

or $\omega \leqq \tfrac{2}{3}\ t_w$ .... (8)

However, the actual leg size of the fillet weld used may exceed this value.

Table 2 reflects the limiting value of $\omega = \tfrac{2}{3}\ t_w$. AISC holds to this limit for shop weld of the angle to the beam (AISC Manual, pages 4-25).

Notice the left-hand axis of Nomograph No. 7 also gives the minimum web thickness of the beam in order to hold its shear stress (τ) within 14,500 psi. Just be sure the actual web thickness of the supported beam is equal to or exceeds this value found just opposite the resulting leg size of the weld.

Some engineers feel this limiting shear value (A36 steel, $\tau = 14{,}500$ psi) is to insure that the web of the beam does not buckle, and that a higher allowable value might be used here, perhaps ¾ of the allowable tensile strength. In this case the maximum leg size of the weld would be held to ¾ of the web thickness.

$\omega = \tfrac{3}{4}\ t_w$ .... (9)

AISC (Sec 1.17.5) specifies the maximum leg size of fillet weld relative to angle plate thickness to be as shown in Figure 6.

Table 3 will give values of R/ω in terms of leg size of angle (L_h) and length of angle (L_v). Table 3 is for direct use with A36 steel, and E70 welds.

TABLE 3—Values of R/ω
For Shop Weld of Framing Angle To Beam Web For A36 Steel & E70 Welds

$$\frac{R}{\omega} = \frac{\text{Reaction, kips}}{\text{Leg size of fillet weld}}$$

Length of framing angle (L_v)	Leg of Angle (L_h)			
	2½"	3"	3½"	4"
4"	75.8	78.6	81.6	86.1
6"	116.7	119.3	120.2	122.8
8"	160.3	160.3	162.2	163.2
10"	205.3	204.6	204.7	205.2
12"	251.7	250.7	249.7	249.5
14"	298.5	295.5	296.3	294.4
16"	347.0	345.2	343.0	340.5
18"	395.0	393.0	390.7	389.0
20"	443.0	439.0	436.5	434.5
22"	490.5	487.0	484.0	481.5
24"	537.0	535.5	533.5	530.0
26"	586.0	583.5	580.5	576.7
28"	635.0	631.0	628.5	625.0
30"	681.0	680.0	676.5	673.5

As indicated by Figure 3 and the related weld analysis, the fillet welds connecting angle to beam web should be hooked around the ends of the angle, top and bottom, for the distance (b) to the end of the beam web. They should not be continued around the end of the web, Figure 7.

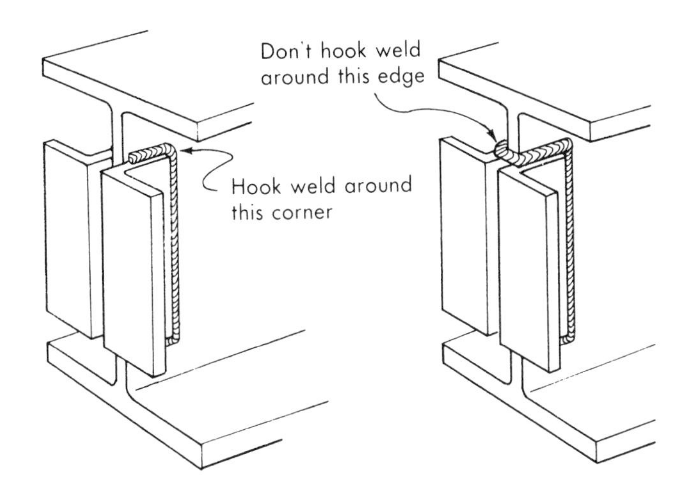

FIGURE 7

Problem 1

To design a web framing angle connection to support a 20″ 85# I beam, having an end reaction of R = 58 kips. Use A36 steel and E70 welds.

See Figure 8.

Field Weld of Framing Angle to Column

Nomograph No. 6 shows that for a ⅜″ fillet weld (ω), a reaction (R) of 58 kips and an angle with a leg (L_h) of 3″, its length (L_v) should be 10½″. However, for a 5⁄16″ fillet weld (ω) the angle length (L_v) would only have to be increased to 12″.

Shop Weld of Framing Angle to Beam Web

Nomograph No. 7 shows that for a reaction (R) of 58 kips, an angle leg (L_h) of 3″ and length (L_v) of 12″, a ¼″ fillet weld (ω) would be required. Hence use 3″ × 3″ × ⅜″ framing angles, 12″ long, 5⁄16″ field weld to column and ¼″ shop weld to beam web.

4. STANDARD WEB FRAMING ANGLE CONNECTIONS

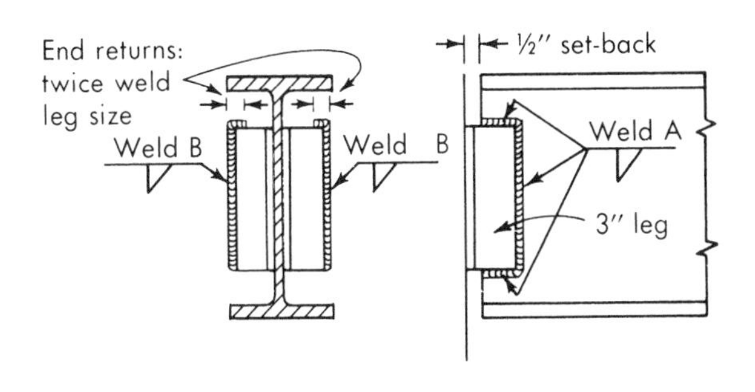

FIGURE 9

Table 4 gives the AISC allowable loads (kips) on web framing angle connections, using A36, A242 and A441 steels and E70 welds. The table gives the capacity and size of (Shop) Weld A connecting the framing angle to the beam web, and of (Field) Weld B connecting the framing angle to the beam support.

Problem 2

To select a web framing angle connection for a 16″ B 26# beam (0.25″ web thickness and T = 14″) of A441 steel, with end reaction of R = 35 kips. Use E70 welds. Allowable shear is 20 ksi.

This beam would take an angle with length L_v = 10″ or 12″. In Table 4, the (Shop) Weld A capacity

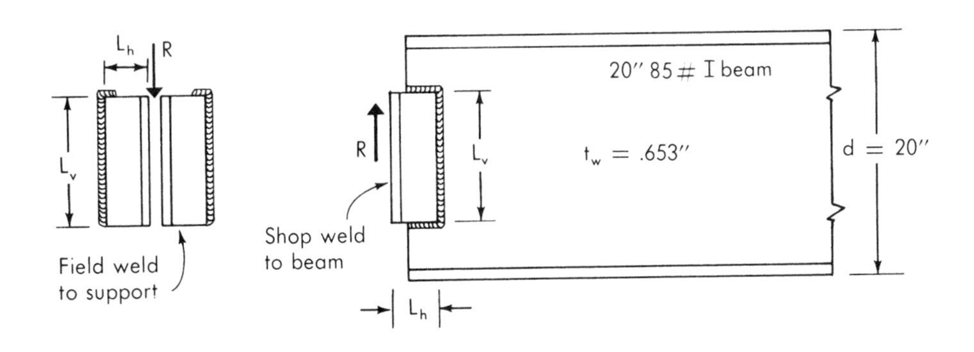

FIGURE 8

TABLE 4—Standard Web Framing Angle Connections

From American Institute of Steel Construction

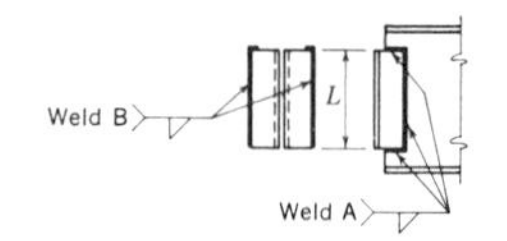

FRAMED BEAM CONNECTIONS
Welded—E60XX electrodes
TABLE V

Weld A Capacity Kips	Weld A [c]Size In.	Weld B [d]Capacity Kips	Weld B [c]Size In.	L In.	Angle Size (ASTM A36)	[a,b]Minimum Web Thickness for Welds A: A36 F_v=14.5	A242 and A441 F_v=18.5	A242 and A441 F_v=20.0
195	5/16	210	3/8	32	4×3×7/16	.41	.32	.30
156	1/4	175	5/16	32	4×3×3/8	.33	.26	.24
117	3/16	140	1/4	32	4×3×5/16	.25	.19	.18
182	5/16	195	3/8	30	4×3×7/16	.41	.32	.30
146	1/4	162	5/16	30	4×3×3/8	.33	.26	.24
109	3/16	130	1/4	30	4×3×5/16	.25	.19	.18
169	5/16	179	3/8	28	4×3×7/16	.41	.32	.30
135	1/4	149	5/16	28	4×3×3/8	.33	.26	.24
101	3/16	120	1/4	28	4×3×5/16	.25	.19	.18
156	5/16	164	3/8	26	4×3×7/16	.41	.32	.30
125	1/4	136	5/16	26	4×3×3/8	.33	.26	.24
93.8	3/16	109	1/4	26	4×3×5/16	.25	.19	.18
143	5/16	148	3/8	24	4×3×7/16	.41	.32	.30
115	1/4	124	5/16	24	4×3×3/8	.33	.26	.24
86.1	3/16	98.8	1/4	24	4×3×5/16	.25	.19	.18
131	5/16	133	3/8	22	4×3×7/16	.41	.32	.30
104	1/4	110	5/16	22	4×3×3/8	.33	.26	.24
78.4	3/16	88.4	1/4	22	4×3×5/16	.25	.19	.18
118	5/16	117	3/8	20	4×3×7/16	.41	.32	.30
94.2	1/4	97.4	5/16	20	4×3×3/8	.33	.26	.24
70.7	3/16	77.9	1/4	20	4×3×5/16	.25	.19	.18
105	5/16	101	3/8	18	4×3×7/16	.41	.32	.30
84.0	1/4	84.4	5/16	18	4×3×3/8	.33	.26	.24
63.0	3/16	67.5	1/4	18	4×3×5/16	.25	.19	.18
92.2	5/16	95.5	3/8	16	3×3×7/16	.41	.32	.30
73.8	1/4	79.6	5/16	16	3×3×3/8	.33	.26	.24
55.3	3/16	63.6	1/4	16	3×3×5/16	.25	.19	.18
79.6	5/16	79.8	3/8	14	3×3×7/16	.41	.32	.30
63.6	1/4	66.5	5/16	14	3×3×3/8	.33	.26	.24
47.7	3/16	53.2	1/4	14	3×3×5/16	.25	.19	.18
67.1	5/16	64.2	3/8	12	3×3×7/16	.41	.32	.30
53.7	1/4	53.5	5/16	12	3×3×3/8	.33	.26	.24
40.3	3/16	42.8	1/4	12	3×3×5/16	.25	.19	.18
54.9	5/16	48.9	3/8	10	3×3×7/16	.41	.32	.30
43.9	1/4	40.8	5/16	10	3×3×3/8	.33	.26	.24
32.9	3/16	32.6	1/4	10	3×3×5/16	.25	.19	.18
48.9	5/16	41.5	3/8	9	3×3×7/16	.41	.32	.30
39.1	1/4	34.6	5/16	9	3×3×3/8	.33	.26	.24
29.3	3/16	27.6	1/4	9	3×3×5/16	.25	.19	.18
43.0	5/16	34.3	3/8	8	3×3×7/16	.41	.32	.30
34.4	1/4	28.6	5/16	8	3×3×3/8	.33	.26	.24
25.8	3/16	22.8	1/4	8	3×3×5/16	.25	.19	.18
37.3	5/16	27.4	3/8	7	3×3×7/16	.41	.32	.30
29.8	1/4	22.9	5/16	7	3×3×3/8	.33	.26	.24
22.4	3/16	18.3	1/4	7	3×3×5/16	.25	.19	.18
31.7	5/16	21.0	3/8	6	3×3×7/16	.41	.32	.30
25.3	1/4	17.5	5/16	6	3×3×3/8	.33	.26	.24
19.0	3/16	14.0	1/4	6	3×3×5/16	.25	.19	.18
26.3	5/16	15.1	3/8	5	3×3×7/16	.41	.32	.30
21.0	1/4	12.6	5/16	5	3×3×3/8	.33	.26	.24
15.8	3/16	10.1	1/4	5	3×3×5/16	.25	.19	.18
21.1	5/16	10.0	3/8	4	3×3×7/16	.41	.32	.30
16.9	1/4	8.4	5/16	4	3×3×3/8	.33	.26	.24
12.7	3/16	6.7	1/4	4	3×3×5/16	.25	.19	.18

[a]When a beam web is less than the minimum, multiply the connection capacity furnished by welds **A** by the ratio of the actual thickness to the tabulated minimum thickness. Thus, if 5/16" weld **A**, with a connection capacity of 54.9 kips and a 10" long angle, is being considered for a beam of web thickness .270", ASTM A36, the connection capacity must be multiplied by .270/.41, giving 36.2 kips.

[b]When beam material is ASTM A7 or A373, with F_v = 13.0 ksi, minimum web thicknesses to develop 5/16", 1/4" and 3/16" welds A are .46", .37" and .28" respectively.

[c]Should the thickness of material to which connection angles are welded exceed the limits set by AISC Specification, Sect. 1.17.4, for weld sizes specified, increase the weld size as required, but not to exceed the angle thickness.

[d]For welds on outstanding legs, connection capacity may be limited by the shear capacity of the supporting member as stipulated by AISC Specification, Sect. 1.17.5. See examples (d) and (e), pages 4-26, 4-27.

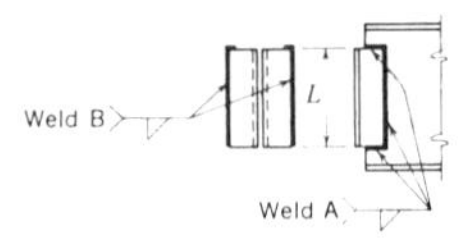

FRAMED BEAM CONNECTIONS
Welded—E70XX electrodes
TABLE VI

Weld A Capacity Kips	Weld A [b]Size In.	Weld B [c]Capacity Kips	Weld B [b]Size In.	L In.	Angle Size (ASTM A36)	[a]Minimum Web Thickness for Welds A: A36 F_v=14.5	A242 and A441 F_v=18.5	A242 and A441 F_v=20.0
227	5/16	245	3/8	32	4×3×7/16	.48	.38	.35
182	1/4	204	5/16	32	4×3×3/8	.39	.30	.28
136	3/16	163	1/4	32	4×3×5/16	.29	.23	.21
212	5/16	227	3/8	30	4×3×7/16	.48	.38	.35
170	1/4	189	5/16	30	4×3×3/8	.39	.30	.28
127	3/16	151	1/4	30	4×3×5/16	.29	.23	.21
197	5/16	209	3/8	28	4×3×7/16	.48	.38	.35
158	1/4	174	5/16	28	4×3×3/8	.39	.30	.28
118	3/16	139	1/4	28	4×3×5/16	.29	.23	.21
182	5/16	191	3/8	26	4×3×7/16	.48	.38	.35
146	1/4	159	5/16	26	4×3×3/8	.39	.30	.28
109	3/16	127	1/4	26	4×3×5/16	.29	.23	.21
167	5/16	173	3/8	24	4×3×7/16	.48	.38	.35
134	1/4	144	5/16	24	4×3×3/8	.39	.30	.28
100	3/16	115	1/4	24	4×3×5/16	.29	.23	.21
152	5/16	155	3/8	22	4×3×7/16	.48	.38	.35
122	1/4	129	5/16	22	4×3×3/8	.39	.30	.28
91.4	3/16	103	1/4	22	4×3×5/16	.29	.23	.21
137	5/16	136	3/8	20	4×3×7/16	.48	.38	.35
110	1/4	114	5/16	20	4×3×3/8	.39	.30	.28
82.4	3/16	90.9	1/4	20	4×3×5/16	.29	.23	.21
122	5/16	118	3/8	18	4×3×7/16	.48	.38	.35
98.0	1/4	98.4	5/16	18	4×3×3/8	.39	.30	.28
73.5	3/16	78.7	1/4	18	4×3×5/16	.29	.23	.21
108	5/16	111	3/8	16	3×3×7/16	.48	.38	.35
86.1	1/4	92.9	5/16	16	3×3×3/8	.39	.30	.28
64.6	3/16	74.3	1/4	16	3×3×5/16	.29	.23	.21
92.9	5/16	93.1	3/8	14	3×3×7/16	.48	.38	.35
74.3	1/4	77.6	5/16	14	3×3×3/8	.39	.30	.28
55.7	3/16	62.1	1/4	14	3×3×5/16	.29	.23	.21
78.3	5/16	74.9	3/8	12	3×3×7/16	.48	.38	.35
62.6	1/4	62.5	5/16	12	3×3×3/8	.39	.30	.28
47.0	3/16	50.0	1/4	12	3×3×5/16	.29	.23	.21
64.0	5/16	57.1	3/8	10	3×3×7/16	.48	.38	.35
51.2	1/4	47.6	5/16	10	3×3×3/8	.39	.30	.28
38.4	3/16	38.0	1/4	10	3×3×5/16	.29	.23	.21
57.1	5/16	48.4	3/8	9	3×3×7/16	.48	.38	.35
45.6	1/4	40.4	5/16	9	3×3×3/8	.39	.30	.28
34.2	3/16	32.3	1/4	9	3×3×5/16	.29	.23	.21
50.2	5/16	40.0	3/8	8	3×3×7/16	.48	.38	.35
40.1	1/4	33.4	5/16	8	3×3×3/8	.39	.30	.28
30.1	3/16	26.7	1/4	8	3×3×5/16	.29	.23	.21
43.5	5/16	32.0	3/8	7	3×3×7/16	.48	.38	.35
34.8	1/4	26.7	5/16	7	3×3×3/8	.39	.30	.28
26.1	3/16	21.3	1/4	7	3×3×5/16	.29	.23	.21
37.0	5/16	24.5	3/8	6	3×3×7/16	.48	.38	.35
29.6	1/4	20.4	5/16	6	3×3×3/8	.39	.30	.28
22.2	3/16	16.3	1/4	6	3×3×5/16	.29	.23	.21
30.7	5/16	17.6	3/8	5	3×3×7/16	.48	.38	.35
24.5	1/4	14.7	5/16	5	3×3×3/8	.39	.30	.28
18.4	3/16	11.8	1/4	5	3×3×5/16	.29	.23	.21
24.6	5/16	11.6	3/8	4	3×3×7/16	.48	.38	.35
19.7	1/4	9.7	5/16	4	3×3×3/8	.39	.30	.28
14.8	3/16	7.8	1/4	4	3×3×5/16	.29	.23	.21

[a]When a beam web is less than the minimum, multiply the connection capacity furnished by welds **A** by the ratio of the actual thickness to the tabulated minimum thickness. Thus, if 5/16" weld **A**, with a connection capacity of 50.2 kips and an 8" long angle, is being considered for a beam of web thickness .305", ASTM A36, the connection capacity must be multiplied by .305/.48, giving 31.9 kips.

[b]Should the thickness of material to which connection angles are welded exceed the limits set by AISC Specification, Sect. 1.17.4, for weld sizes specified, increase the weld size as required, but not to exceed the angle thickness.

[c]For welds on outstanding legs, connection capacity may be limited by the shear capacity of the supporting members as stipulated by AISC Specification, Sect. 1.17.5. See examples (d) and (e), pages 4-26, 4-27.

Note 1: Capacities shown in this table apply only when material welded is ASTM A36, A242 or A441. Use appropriate capacities from Table V when beam or supporting material is ASTM A7 or A373.

of 38.4 kips for a weld size of $\omega = 3/16''$ and angle length of $L_v = 10''$ slightly exceeds the reaction. The corresponding (Field) Weld B, using $\omega = 1/4''$, also is satisfactory. Since the beam's required web thickness is 0.21″ while the actual web thickness is 0.25″, the indicated 3″ x 3″ x 5/16″ is all right.

If the beam is made of A36 steel, this connection's capacity will be reduced in the ratio of 0.25/0.29 of actual to required web thickness. The resulting capacity of 33.1 kips is less than the reaction. The next larger connection with apparently sufficient capacity shows that (Shop) Weld A's capacity is 47 kips, using same angle section but an angle length of $L_v = 12''$. Applying the multiplier of 0.25/0.29 reduces the capacity of the connection to 40.5 kips, which exceeds the end reaction.

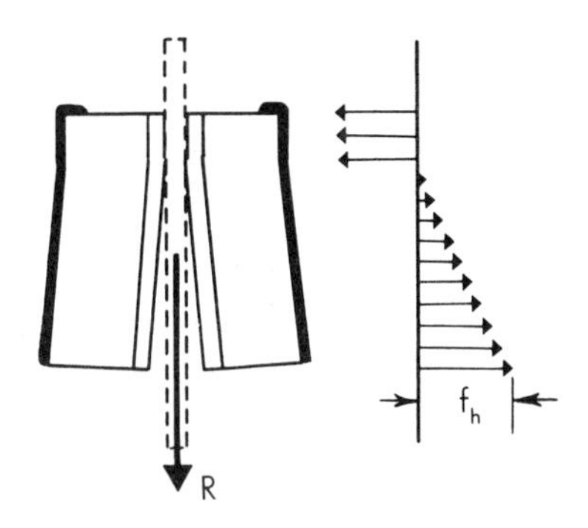

FIG. 10—Double-web framing angle.

5. SINGLE-PLATE OR TEE CONNECTION ON BEAM WEB

In the previous design of the field weld, connecting a pair of web framing angles to the supporting column or girder, it was assumed that the reaction (R) applied eccentric to each angle, resulted in a tendency for the angles to twist or rotate. In doing so, they would press together at the top and swing away from each other at the bottom, this being resisted by the welds. These forces are in addition to the vertical forces caused by the reaction (R); see Figure 10.

However, in both the single-plate web connection and the Tee-section type, this portion of the connection welded to the column is solid. Thus, there is no tendency for this spreading action which must be resisted by the welds. These vertical field welds to the column would be designed then for just the vertical reaction (R); see Figure 11.

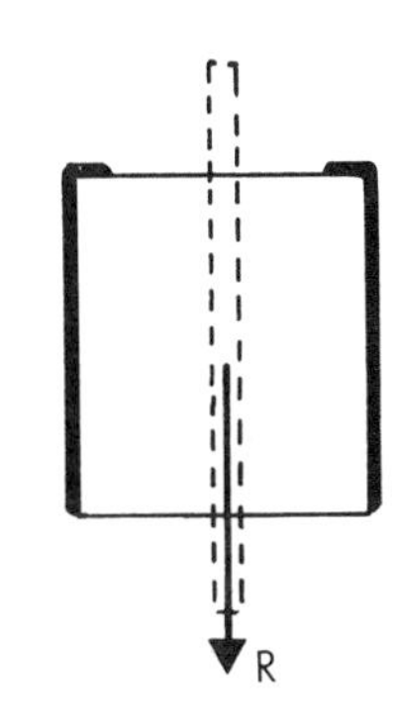

FIG. 11—Single plate or Tee.

In the shop weld of the single plate to the web of the beam, Figure 12, this double vertical weld would be designed for just the vertical reaction (R). There is not enough eccentricity to consider any bending action.

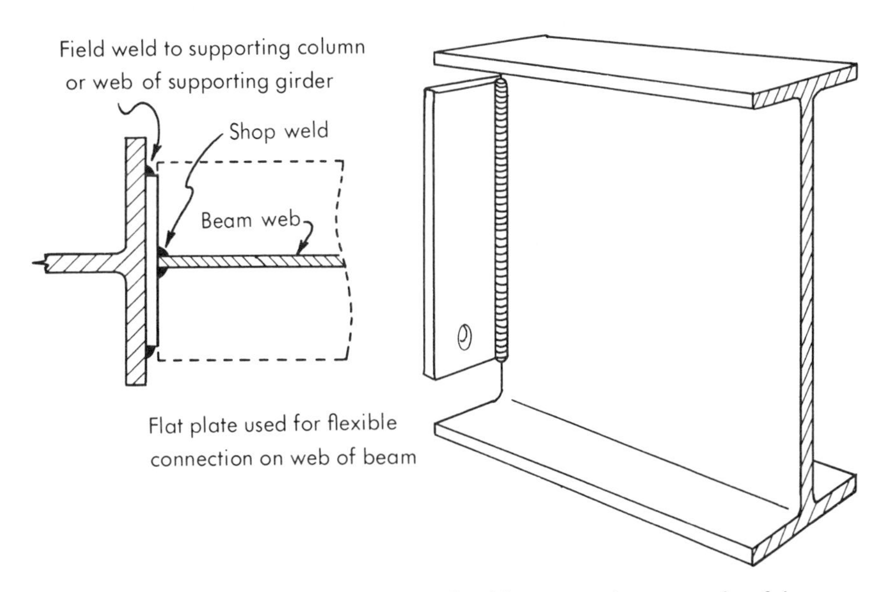

FIG. 12—Flat plate used for flexible connection on web of beam.

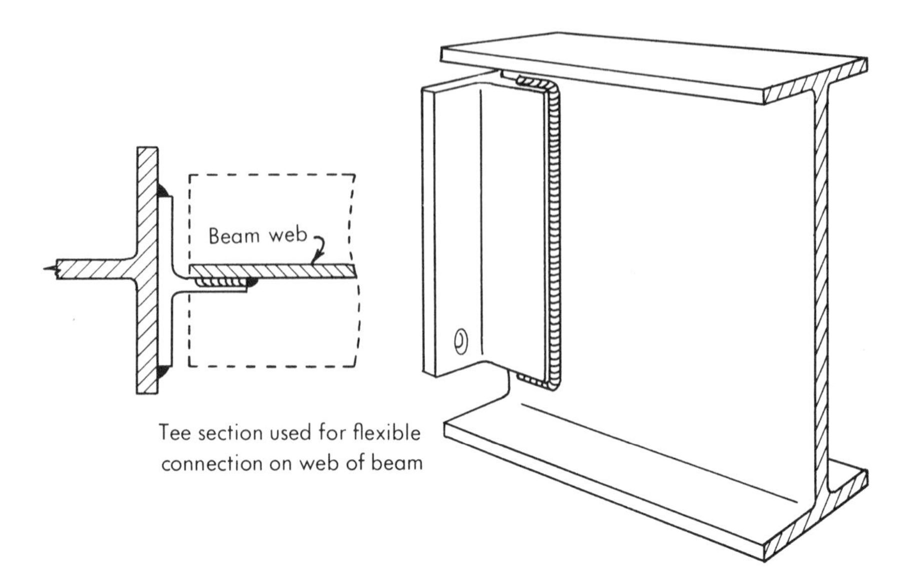

FIG. 13—Tee section used for flexible connection on web of beam.

In the shop weld of the Tee connection to the web of the beam, Figure 13, the size and length of the fillet weld would be determined just as in the case of the double-web framing angles, except there is just a single fillet weld in this case rather than two; so, for a given connection, this would carry just half of the reaction of the corresponding double-angle connection.

6. DIRECTLY-WELDED WEB CONNECTION

To see how this type of connection behaves, consider the following 18″ WF 85# beam, simply supported, 15′ span, with a uniformly distributed load of 139 kips, the same beam and load used in the general discussion on behavior of connections in Sect. 5.1, Topic 6.

If only the web is to be welded to the column, the weld must have sufficient length (L_v) so that the adjacent web of the beam will not be overstressed in shear.

For A373 steel

$$\tau = .40\ \sigma_y = 13{,}000 \text{ psi}$$

$$L_v = \frac{R}{t_w\ \tau} \qquad t_w = .526''$$

$$= \frac{(69.5^k)}{(.526'')(13 \text{ ksi})}$$

$$= 10.2'', \text{ or } \textit{use } 11''$$

The leg size of this fillet weld must be equal to the web thickness, based upon standard allowables, if it is to match the allowable strength of this web section in shear as well as tension.

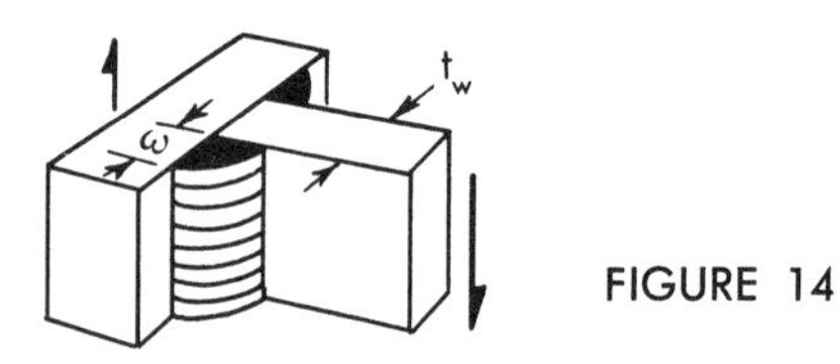

FIGURE 14

fillet weld in shear; parallel load

$$2(9600\omega)L = t_w\ 13{,}000\ L$$

$$\boxed{\omega = \tfrac{2}{3}\ t_w}$$

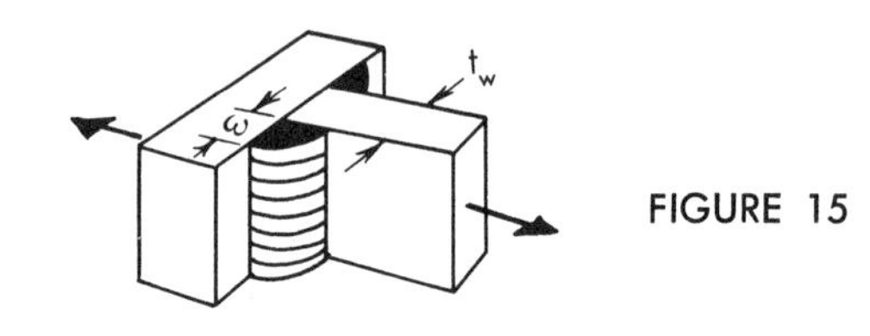

FIGURE 15

fillet weld in tension; transverse load

$$2(9600\omega)L = t_w\ 20{,}000\ L$$

$$* \quad \boxed{\omega = t_w}$$

* Actually, transverse fillet welds are about ⅓ stronger than parallel fillet welds; this can be proved by theory as well as testing. This means for transverse loads, the leg size would be ⅔ of the plate thickness, just as in parallel loads. However, welding codes do not as yet recognize this; and for code work, fillet welds for transverse loads would be made equal to the plate thickness.

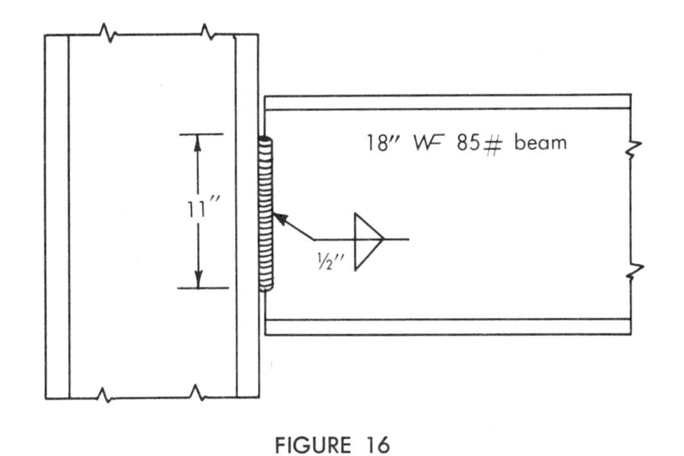

FIGURE 16

If there is a gap between the beam and the column, the leg size of this fillet weld is increased by this amount.

The moment-rotation chart, Figure 17, shows the beam line for this particular beam length and load, and the actual connection curve taken from test data at Lehigh University.

In testing this connection, the beam web showed initial signs of yielding adjacent to the lower ends of the weld at a moment of 360 in.-kips. At a moment of 660 in.-kips, point (a), there were indications that the beam web along the full length of the weld had yielded. At a moment of 870 in.-kips, both welds cracked slightly at the top; this point is marked with an "X" on the curve. With further cracking of the weld and yielding in the beam web, the lower flange of the beam contacted the column, point (b), and this resulted in increased stiffness. The moment built up to a maximum of 1918 in.-kips, and then gradually fell off as the weld continued to tear.

Notice in this particular example, the web would have yielded the full length of the weld at design load.

The weld started to crack when the connection had rotated about .011 radians; this would correspond to a horizontal movement of .06″ at the top portion of the weld. Compare this small amount of movement with that obtained in the top connecting plate example of Figure 4 which had the ability to pull out 1.6″ before failing.

This directly welded web connection (Fig. 18)

FIGURE 18

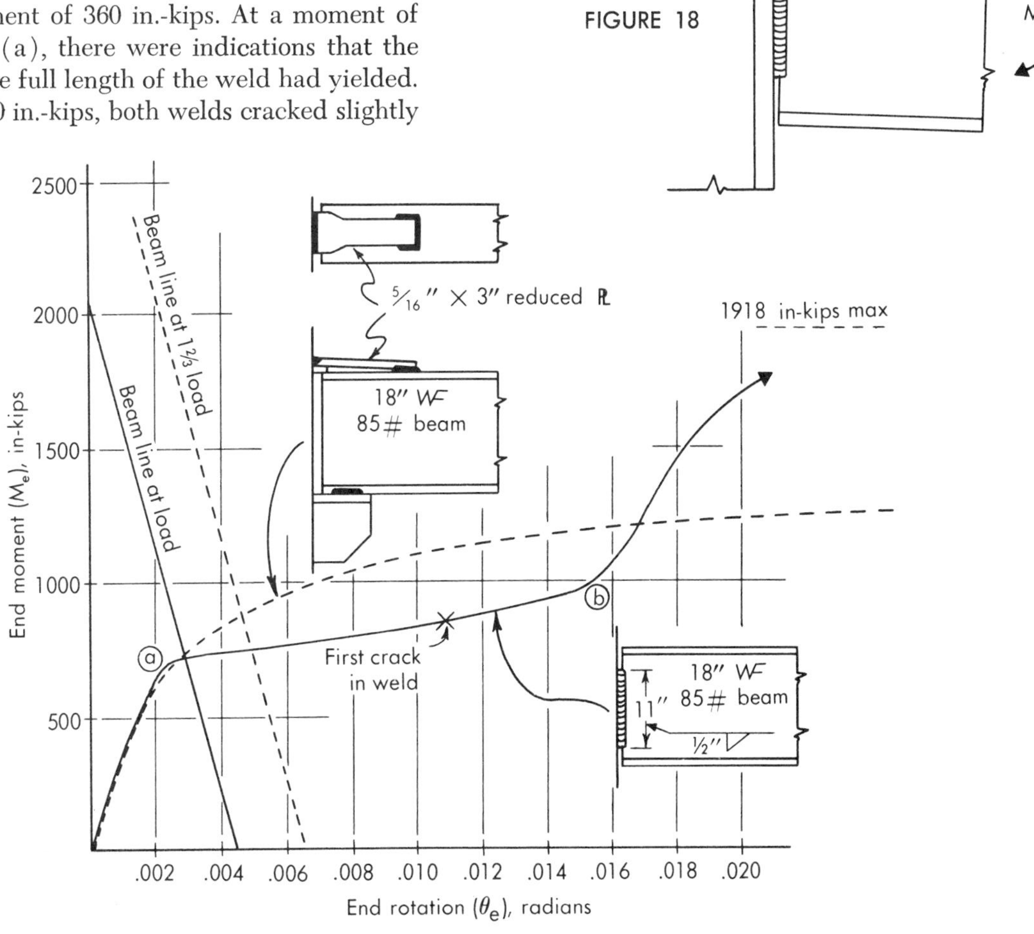

FIGURE 17

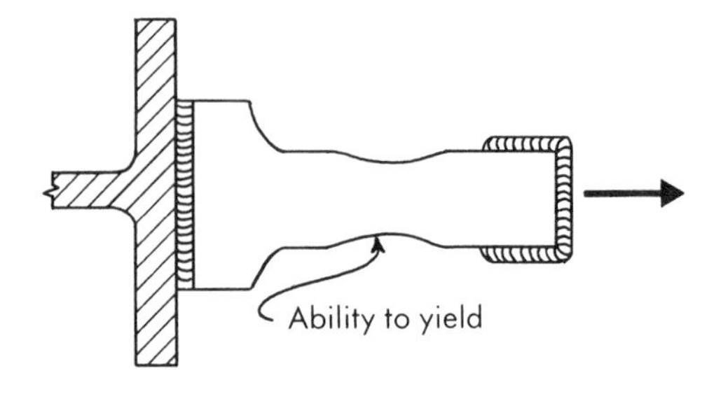

FIGURE 19

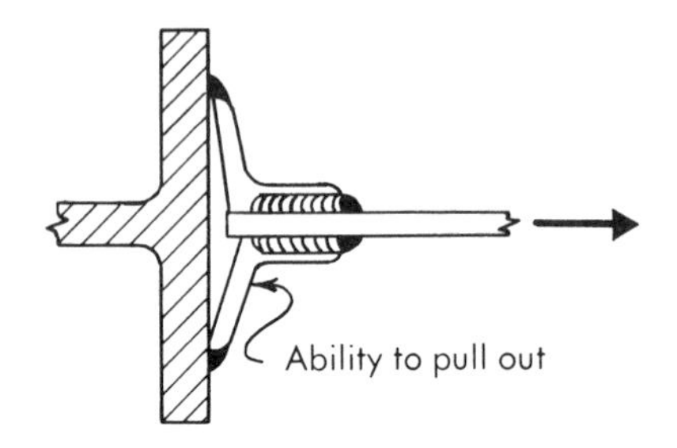

FIGURE 20

is not as dependable as a top connecting plate designed to yield at working load (Fig. 19) or either flexible web framing angles (Fig. 20) or flexible top angle.

Also remember this highly yielded web section, in the case of the directly welded web connection, must still support or carry the vertical reaction (R) of the beam, whereas in the top plate connection, the support of the beam at the bottom seat is still sound no matter what happens to the top plate.

Figure 17 would indicate the directly welded web connection results in an end moment of $M_e = 720$ in.-kips, or an end restraint of—

$$R = \frac{720 \text{ in.-kips}}{2016 \text{ in.-kips}}$$
$$= 35.8\%$$

This restraint is a little high to be classed as simply supported.

The same top plate connection is shown in dotted lines on Figure 17; it has about the same stiffness, but many times the rotational ability.

The use of side plates, Figure 21, would allow a wide variation in fit-up, but in general they are no better than the directly welded web connection. Unless the plates are as thick as the beam web, the resulting connecting fillet welds will be smaller and will reduce the strength of the connection.

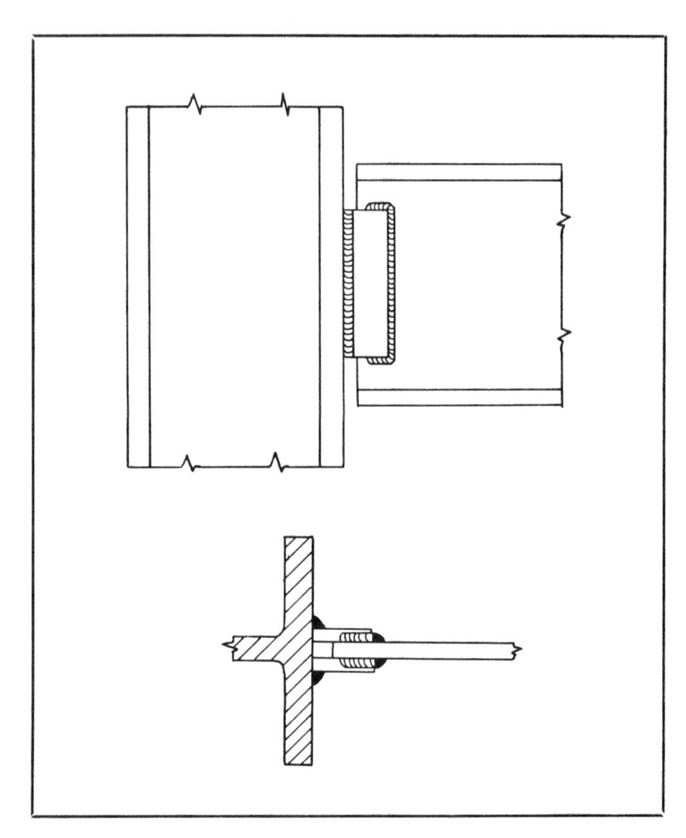

FIGURE 21

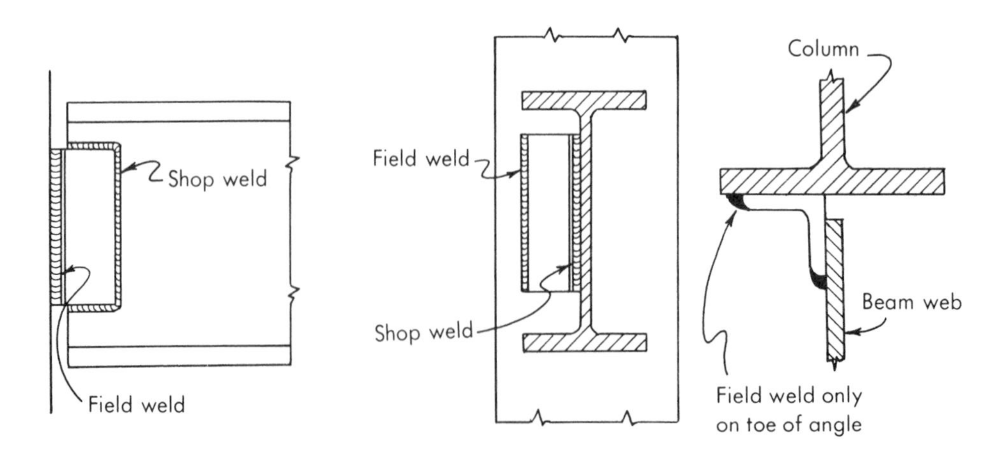

FIGURE 22

In the tests at Lehigh University, the corresponding connection on the 18″ WF 85# beam (.526″-thick web) used 5/16″ thick side plates with 5/16″ fillet welds. They failed at a lower load.

If ½″ thick side plates with ½″ fillet welds had been used, they undoubtedly would have been as strong as the directly welded web connection.

7. ONE-SIDED WEB CONNECTIONS

A single web framing angle used by itself is not recommended; see Figure 22.

Use of only a single vertical fillet weld to join the angle to the supporting member imposes a greater eccentricity upon the connection. This results in a maximum force on the weld of about 4 times that of the double-angle connection; see Figures 23 and 24.

It might be argued that in the conventional double-angle connection, the field weld is subject only to vertical shear because the stiffness of the angles largely prevents any twisting action on the connection even though the analysis is based upon this twist as shown in Figure 23. However, there is no doubt that the single-angle connection has this twisting action which would greatly decrease its strength.

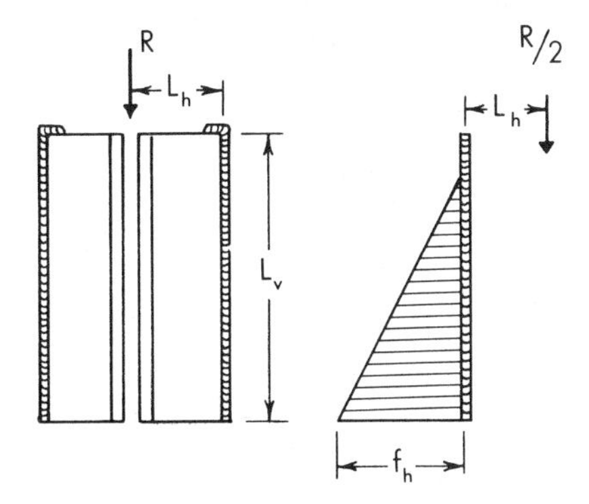

FIGURE 23

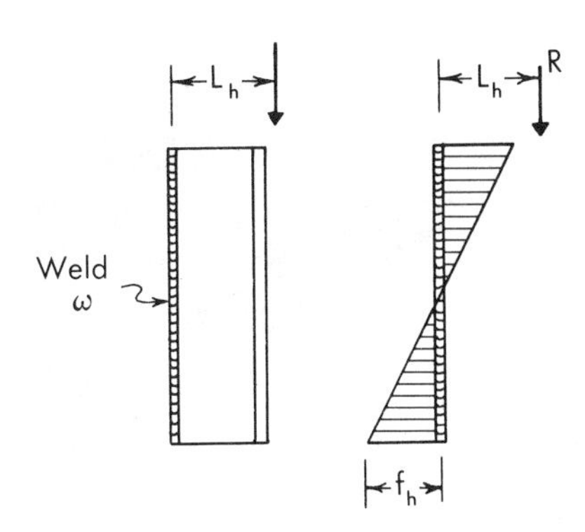

FIGURE 24

Any additional welding on the single angle, such as vertically along its heel or horizontally across the top and bottom edges, would make it rigid and prevent it from moving under load. This would cause the end moment to build up and greatly overstress the connection.

In the original research at Lehigh University on welded connections, this single-angle connection with a single vertical weld was never tested. Single angle connections welded both along the sides and along the ends were tested, but as already mentioned, they did not have enough flexibility, and the end moment built up above the strength of the connection.

Web framing angles are commonly shop welded to the supported beam. To facilitate erection, bolts are used in joining the other member until the web framing angle can be permanently welded to it. The erection bolts can be left in, or removed if there is any concern that they will offer restraint. Note the use of box section column, in this case it being hot rolled square structural tubing.

Top Connecting Plates For Simple Beams and Wind Bracing

1. DESIGN PLATE TO BE STRESSED AT YIELD

A top connecting plate if designed to be stressed at its yield will provide a flexible connection, suitable for a simple beam and easily adapted to carry the additional moment due to wind.

Since this flexibility is due to plastic yielding of the plate, the portion of its length which is to yield should be at least 1.2 times its width.

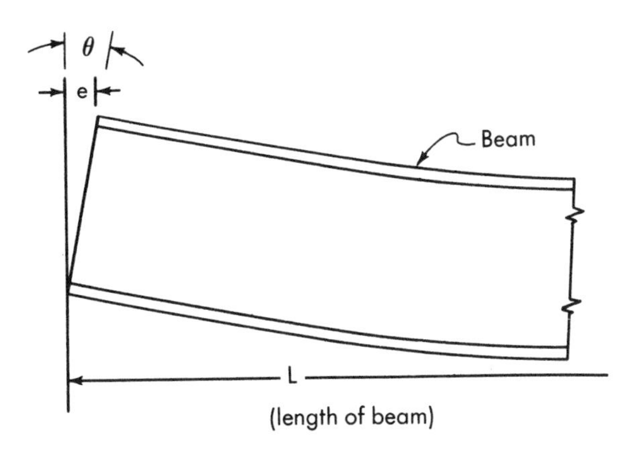

FIGURE 1

The plate should be capable of plastically yielding a distance equivalent to the movement of the end of the top beam flange as it rotates under load if the connection were to offer no restraining action (AISC Sec. 1.15.4); see Figure 1. For a simply supported beam, uniformly loaded, this maximum movement (e) would be:

$$e = \frac{2\,\sigma\,(12\,L)}{3\,E} = \frac{\sigma\,L}{3{,}600{,}000} \qquad (1)$$

where:

e = movement, in inches

L = length of beam, feet

The graph in Figure 2 illustrates what this movement would be as a function of beam length, under various load conditions.

There is no problem in detailing a top plate to safely yield this much, providing there are no notches which might act as stress risers and decrease the plate's strength. Any widening of the plate for the connecting welds must be done with a smooth transition in width.

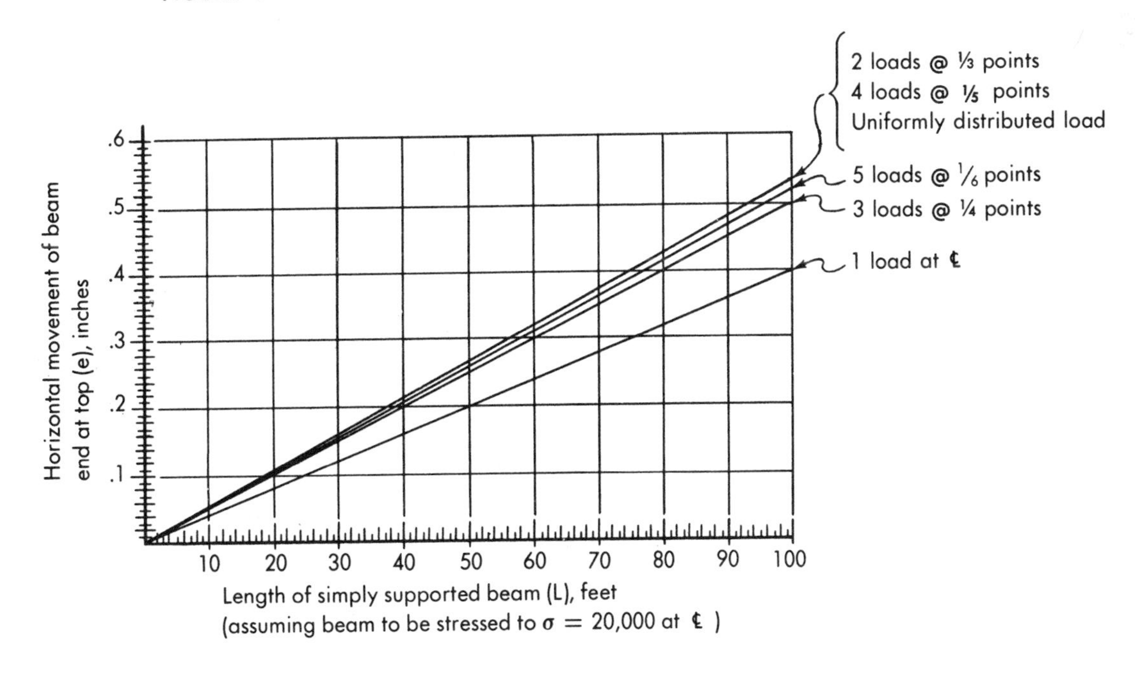

FIGURE 2

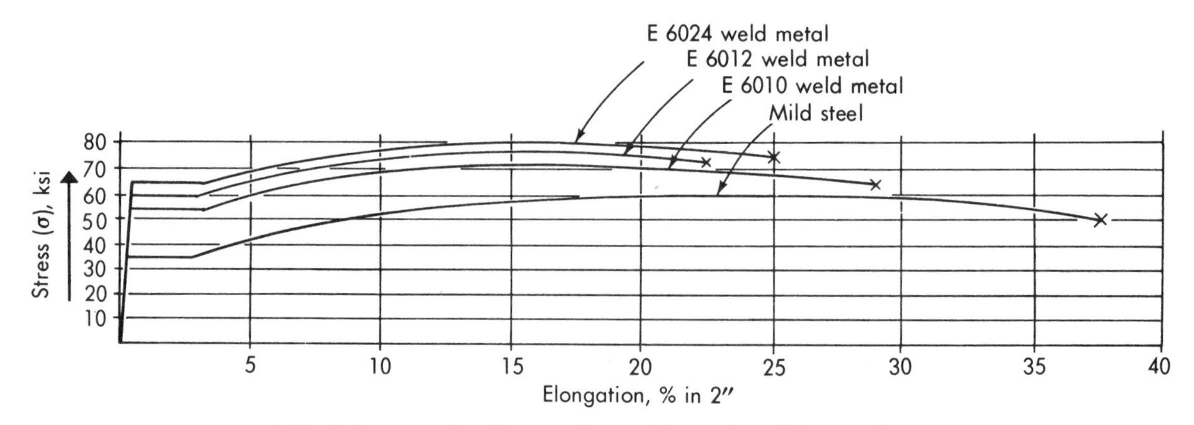

FIG. 3 Stress-strain diagram for weld metal and beam plate.

ASTM specifies the following minimum percent of elongation as measured in an 8″ gage length for structural steels:

A7	21%
A373	21%
A36	20%
A242	18%
A441	18%

This minimum value of 20% for A36 steel would represent a total elongation of 20% × 8″ = 1.6″ within the 8″ length.

Notice in Figure 2 that a simply supported beam, uniformly loaded, with a span of 20 feet would rotate inward about .106″, so that this particular beam would utilize only $1/15$ of the capacity of this top plate to yield.

Figure 3, a stress-strain diagram, shows that a mild steel base plate will yield and reach maximum elongation before its welds reach this yield point.

The test specimen in Figure 4 shows that ample plastic elongation results from the steel tensile specimen necking down and yielding. This is similar to the behavior of a top connecting plate which yields plastically under load.

2. TOP PLATE FOR SIMPLE BEAMS

There is some question as to what value should be used for the end moment in the design of the top plate for simple beams. Any top plate will offer some restraint, and this will produce some end moment. Lehigh researchers originally suggested assuming simple beam construction (AISC Type 2) to have an end restraint of about 20%. On this basis, the end moment for a uniformly loaded beam would be:

$$M_e = (.20)\,\frac{W\,L}{12} = \frac{W\,L}{60}$$

and this is 13.3% of the beam's resisting moment.

Heath Lawson ("Standard Details for Welded Building Construction", AWS Journal, Oct. 1944, p. 916) suggests designing the top plate (simple beam construction) for an end moment of about 25% of the beam's resisting moment. This would correspond to an end restraint of about 37.5%, which approaches the range of "semi-rigid" connections.

In Figure 5 the end of the top connecting plate is beveled and groove welded directly to the column, the groove weld and adjacent plate being designed to develop about 25% of the restraining moment of the

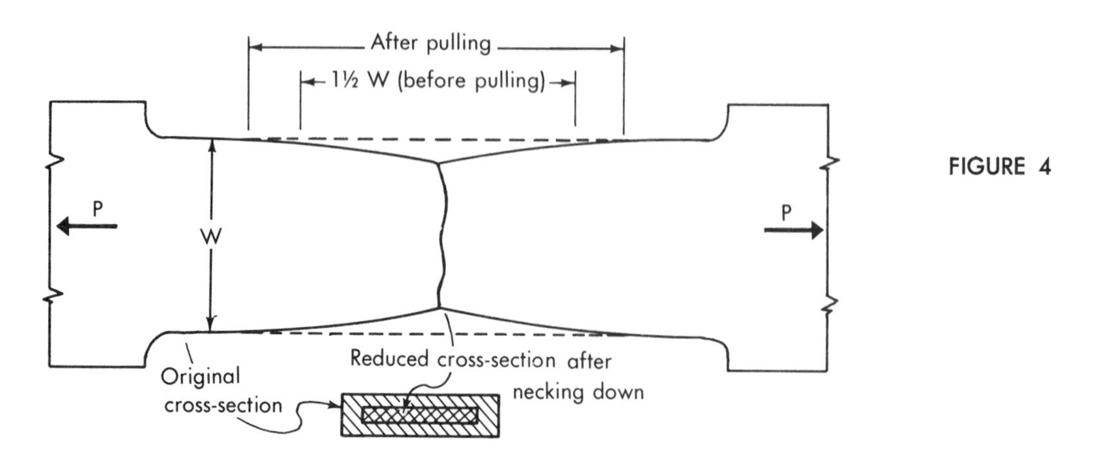

FIGURE 4

beam using the standard allowable bending stress. The standard bending stress allowed here would be limited to $\sigma = .60\ \sigma_y$. (Type 2, simple framing).

Just beyond the groove weld section, the plate is reduced in width so that the same load will produce a localized yield stress (σ_y). The length of this reduced section should be at least 1.2 times its width to assure ductile yielding.

This plate is attached to the beam flange by means of a continuous fillet weld across the end and returning a sufficient distance on both sides of the plate to develop the strength of the groove weld at standard allowables:

A7, A373 Steels; E60 Welds	
$f = 9600\ \omega$ lbs/linear in.	...(2)
A36, A441 Steels; E70 Weld	
$f = 11{,}200\ \omega$ lbs/linear in.	

3. TOP PLATE FOR WIND BRACING

Wind moments applied to simple beam connections present an additional problem. Some means to transfer these wind moments must be provided in a connection which is designed to be flexible. Any additional restraint in the connection will increase the end moment resulting from the gravity load. AISC Sec 1.2 provides for two approximate solutions, referred to hereafter as Method 1 and Method 2.

In tier buildings, designed in general as Type 2 construction, that is with beam-to-column connections (other than wind connections) flexible, the distribution of the wind moments between the several joints of the frame may be made by a recognized empirical method provided that either:

Method 1. The wind connections, designed to resist the assumed moments, are adequate to resist the moments induced by the gravity loading and the wind loading at the increased unit stresses allowable, or

Method 2. The wind connections, if welded and if designed to resist the assumed wind moments, are so designed that larger moments induced by the gravity loading under the actual condition of restraint will be relieved by deformation of the connection material without over-stress in the welds.

AISC Sec. 1.5.6 permits allowable stresses to be increased ⅓ above the values provided in Sec 1.5.1 (steel), and 1.5.3 (welds), when produced by wind or seismic loading acting alone or in combination with the design dead and live loads, on condition that the required section computed on this basis is not less than that required for the design dead and live load and impact, if any, computed without the ⅓ stress increase, nor less than that required by Sec. 1.7, (repeated loading) if it is applicable. Since we are discussing Type 2 construction (simple framing) the initial basic allowable stress is $.60\ \sigma_y$, not $.66\ \sigma_y$.

Method 1

The top plate (Fig. 6) is designed to carry the force resulting from the end moment caused by the combination of the gravity and wind moments, and at a ⅓ increase in the standard stress allowable (or $\sigma = .80\ \sigma_y$). This ⅓ increase may also be applied to the connecting welds (AISC Sec. 1.5.3, & 1.5.6). The fillet welds connecting the lower flange of the beam to the seat angle must be sufficient to transfer this same load.

The top plate must have the ability to yield plastically if overloaded (last paragraph of AISC Sec. 1.2).

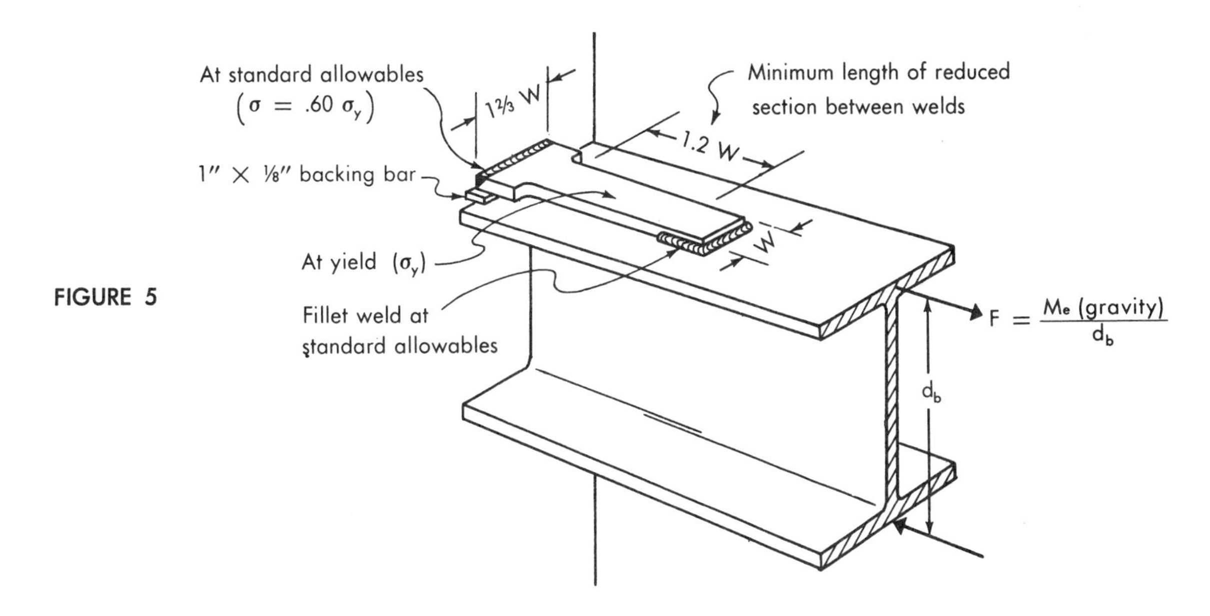

FIGURE 5

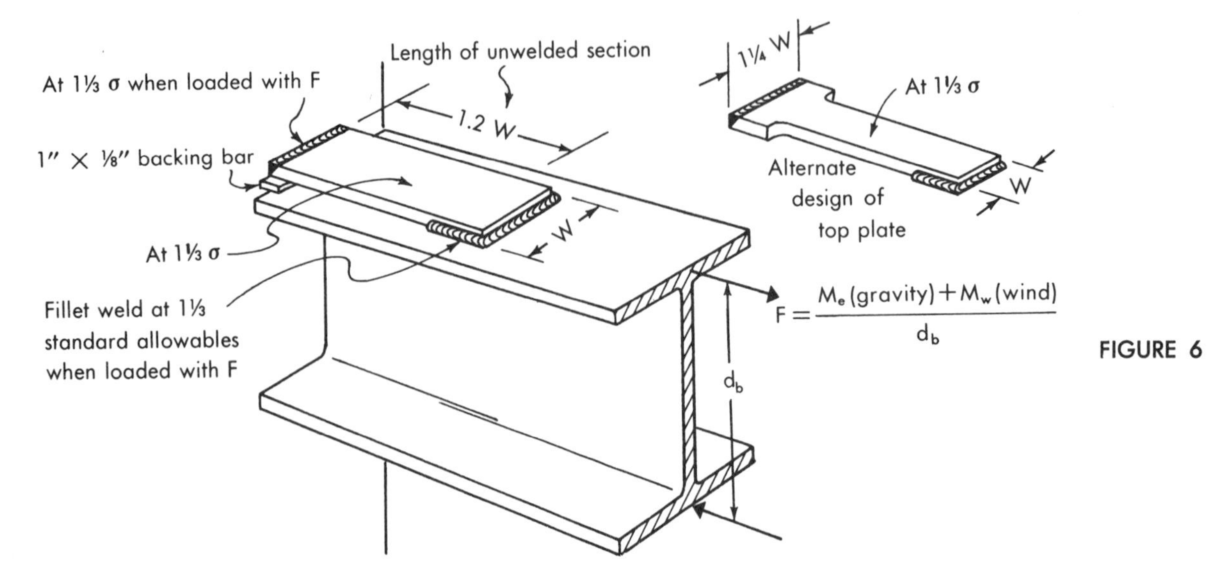

FIGURE 6

In the alternate design of the top plate shown at upper right in Figure 6, the reduced section (W) is designed for the force resulting from the end moment caused by the combination of the gravity and wind moments at a ⅓ increase in the standard allowables. It will reach yield at a 25% increase in load (F). The wider section at the groove weld (1¼ W) will reach 1⅓ σ or .80 σ_y when the reduced section has reached this yield value.

Method 2

The top plate (Fig. 7) is designed to carry the force resulting from the wind moment (M_w) using a ⅓ increase in the standard allowables:

$$\sigma = (1⅓)\ .60\ \sigma_y = .80\ \sigma_y.$$

The top plate must be capable of yielding plastically to relieve larger moments induced by gravity loading, figuring the connecting welds at standard allowables.* This is the same method for figuring the connecting welds of top connecting plates for simply supported beams without wind loads.

The reduced section will reach yield stress (σ_y) at a 25% increase in load (F). The wider section at the groove weld (1⅔ W) will reach standard allowables (.60 σ_y) at this time.

In case there should be a reversal in wind moment, the top plate must be thick enough to safely withstand any compressive load without buckling.

It is recommended that the top plate's thickness be held to at least 1/24 of its length (L) between welds. This will provide a slenderness ratio (L/r) of 83; and corresponds to about 80% of the allowable compressive strength for a short column (L/r ratio of 1).

* This weld allowable by AISC is not clear; AISC simply says welds shall not be overstressed when plate is at yield.

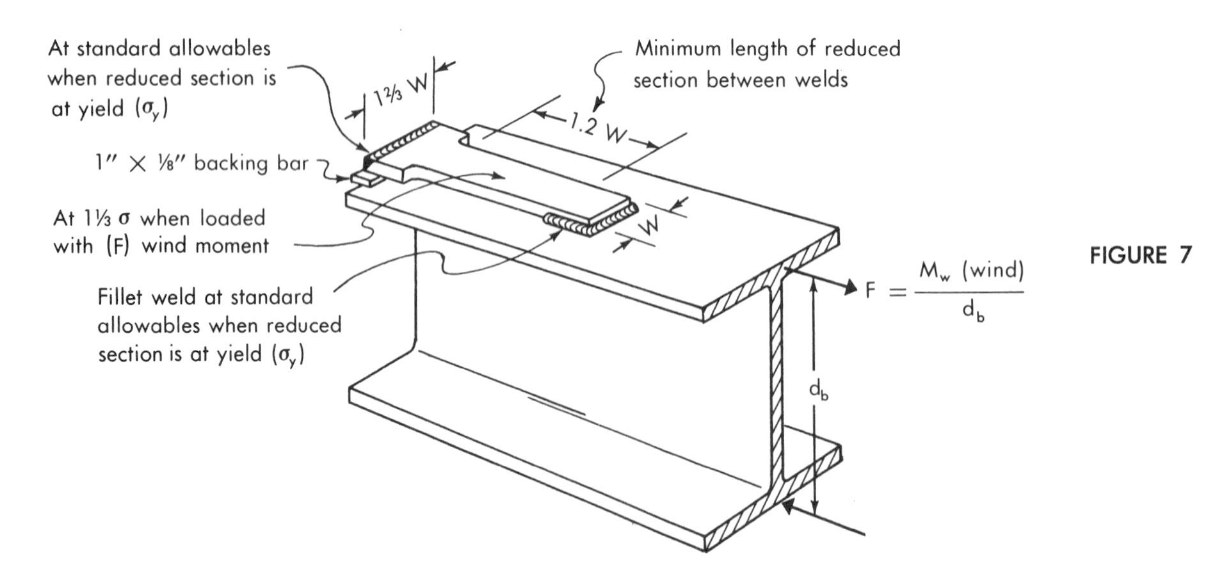

FIGURE 7

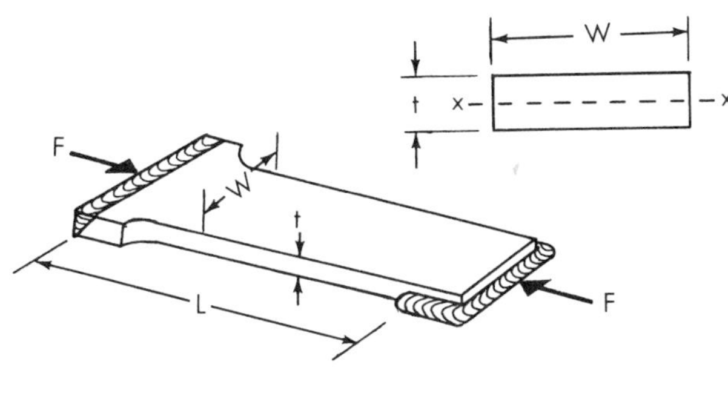

FIGURE 8

Where:

$$I_x = \frac{W\,t^3}{12} \text{ and}$$

$$A = W\,t$$

radius of gyration

$$r = \sqrt{\frac{I}{A}}$$

$$= \sqrt{\frac{W\,t^3}{12\,W\,t}} = \frac{t}{2\sqrt{3}}$$

$$= .289\ t$$

slenderness ratio

$$\frac{L}{r} = \frac{(24\ t)}{(.289\ t)}$$

$$= 83$$

$$\therefore \boxed{t > \frac{L}{24}}$$

4. EXAMPLE OF TOP PLATE DESIGN—WITH WIND MOMENT

A 14″ WF 38# beam is simply supported and loaded uniformly with 296 lbs/in. on a 15-ft span. Based on these beam-load conditions, the maximum bending moment at center is M = 1200 in.-kips. Use A36 steel and E70 welds. Wind moment on each end is M_w = 600 in.-kips.

Beam conditions here: (See Figure 9.)

14″ WF 38# beam

$b = 6.776''$

$d_b = 14.12''$

$t_f = .513''$

$S = 54.6 \text{ in.}^3$

If there were no wind load, the above connection might be designed for about 25% of the present (gravity) moment as a simply supported beam:

$$M_g = .25\ M_{℄}$$

$$= .25\ (1200)$$

$$= 300 \text{ in.-kips on connection at each end}$$

$$F = \frac{M_g}{d_b}$$

$$= \frac{(300)}{(14.12)}$$

$$= 21.3 \text{ kips}$$

The reduced section of the top plate is designed to carry this force at yield stress (σ_y):

$$A_p = \frac{F}{\sigma_y}$$

$$= \frac{(21.3 \text{ kips})}{(36{,}000 \text{ psi})}$$

$$= .59 \text{ in.}^2$$

or use a 1¾″ x ⅜″ plate

$A_p = .656 \text{ in.}^2 > .59 \text{ in.}^2$ OK

Connecting Welds at Standard Allowables

For the groove weld to the column flange, this plate is widened to 1⅔W, or—

width = 1⅔ (1¾)

= 2.9″ or use 3.0″

For the fillet welds to the beam flange, use $\frac{5}{16}''$ fillets at an allowable force of—

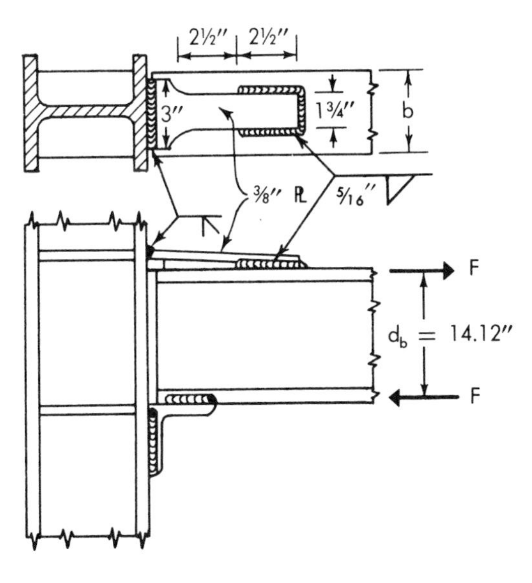

FIGURE 9

$$f_w = 11{,}200\ \omega$$
$$= 11{,}200\ (5/16)$$
$$= 3500 \text{ lbs per linear inch}$$

The length of this weld is—

$$L_w = \frac{F}{f_w}$$
$$= \frac{(.656 \text{ in.}^2)(36{,}000 \text{ psi})}{(3500 \text{ lbs/in.})}$$
$$= \underline{6.74''}$$

This would be 1¾″ across the end, and 2½″ along the sides.

Applying Method 1 for Additional Wind Moment

This connection will now be designed for the additional wind moment of M_w = 600 in.-kips, using Method 1.

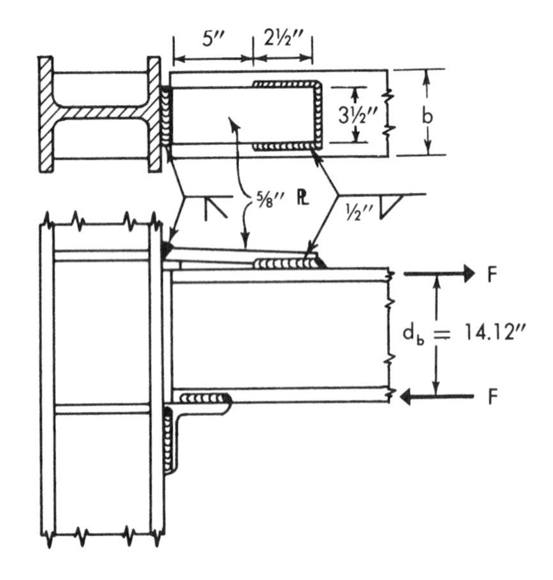

FIGURE 10

Beam conditions here:

14″ WF 38# beam

$$b = 6.776''$$
$$d_b = 14.12''$$
$$t_f = .513''$$
$$S = 54.6 \text{ in.}^3$$

Total moment on the connection is—

$$M = M_g + M_w$$
$$= 300 \text{ in.-kips} + 600 \text{ in.-kips}$$
$$= 900 \text{ in.-kips}$$

Force on top plate is—

$$F = \frac{M}{d_b}$$
$$= \frac{(900 \text{ in.-kips})}{(14.12'')}$$
$$= 63.8 \text{ kips}$$

The top plate is designed for this force at ⅓ higher allowables:

$$A_p = \frac{F}{1\tfrac{1}{3}\ \sigma}$$
$$= \frac{(63.8 \text{ kips})}{1\tfrac{1}{3}\ (22{,}000 \text{ psi})}$$
$$= 2.18 \text{ in.}^2$$

or <u>use a 3½″ x ⅝″ plate</u>

$$A_p = 2.19 \text{ in.}^2 > 2.18 \text{ in.}^2 \qquad \underline{OK}$$

The connecting welds are figured at ⅓ higher allowables:

For the fillet welds at the beam flange, use ½″ fillets. The standard allowable force is $f_w = 11{,}200\ \omega = 11{,}200\ (½) = 5600$ lbs per linear inch.

The length of this weld is—

$$L_w = \frac{F}{1\tfrac{1}{3}\ f_w}$$
$$= \frac{(63.8 \text{ kips})}{1\tfrac{1}{3}\ (5600)}$$
$$= \underline{8.54''}$$

This weld length would be distributed 3½″ across the end, and 2½″ along the side edges of the top plate.

The above connection may be cut from bar stock without the necessity of flame cutting any reduced section in it. This is a good connection and is in widespread use. The connecting groove weld and fillet welds are strong enough to develop the plate to yield plastically if necessary due to any accidental overload of the connection.

Some engineers prefer to widen this plate at the groove weld so that if the plate should have to reach yield stress, the connecting welds would be stressed only up to the wind allowable or ⅓ higher, hence $\sigma = .80\ \sigma_y$.

Accordingly, the plate is widened here to 1¼W = 1¼ (3½) = 4⅜″.

(See Figure 11.)

The length of the fillet weld, using ½″ fillet welds and allowable of f_w = 5600 lbs/in., would be—

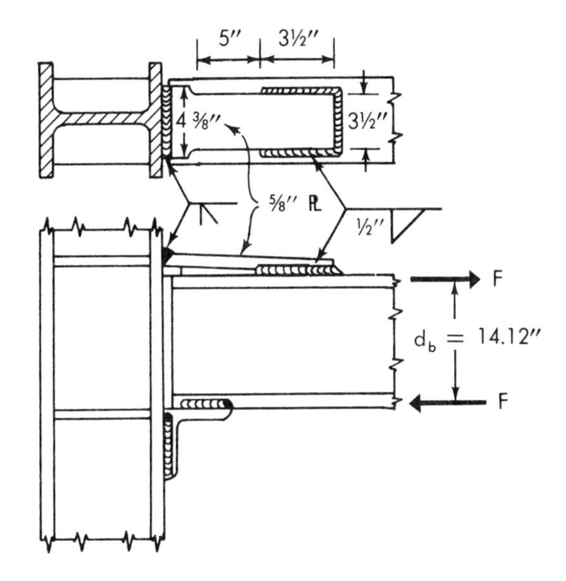

FIGURE 11

$$L_w = \frac{F}{1\frac{1}{3}\, f_w}$$ reduced section at yield (σ_y) and fillet weld at ⅓ higher allowable

$$= \frac{(2.19 \text{ in.}^2)(36{,}000 \text{ psi})}{1\frac{1}{3}\,(5600)}$$

$$= \underline{10.55''}$$

This would be 3½″ across the end, and 3½″ along the side edges of the plate.

Applying Method 2 for Additional Wind Moment

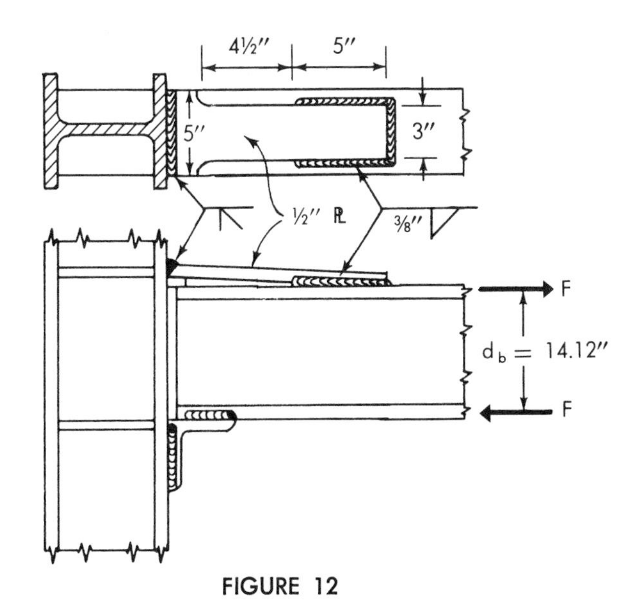

FIGURE 12

Temporarily ignoring the gravity load, the top plate is designed to carry the wind load, M_w = 600 in.-kip on each end.

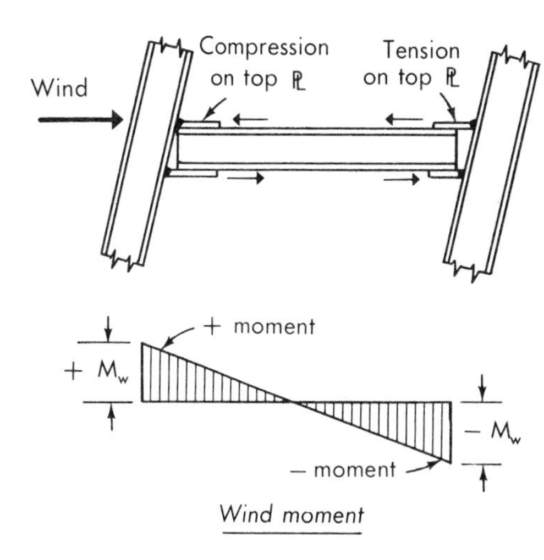

FIGURE 13

$$F = \frac{M_w}{d_b}$$

$$= \frac{(600 \text{ in.-kips})}{(14.12'')}$$

$$= 42.5 \text{ kips}$$

The reduced section of the plate is designed to carry this at ⅓ higher allowable:

$$A_p = \frac{F}{1\frac{1}{3}\,\sigma}$$

$$= \frac{(42.5 \text{ kips})}{1\frac{1}{3}\,(22{,}000)}$$

$$= 1.45 \text{ in.}^2$$

or <u>use 3″ by ½″ plate</u>

$$A_p = 1.50 \text{ in.}^2 > 1.45 \text{ in.}^2 \qquad \underline{OK}$$

The plate must now be modified so that larger moments induced by the gravity loading can be relieved by plastic yielding of the top plate, designing the connecting welds at standard allowables.

The plate is widened at the groove weld to 1⅔ W = 1⅔ (3) = 5.0″.

For the connecting fillet welds to the beam flange, use ⅜″ fillets:

$$f_w = 11{,}200\ \omega$$

$$= 11{,}200\ (⅜)$$

$$= 4200 \text{ lbs per linear inch}$$

The length of this weld is—

$$L_w = \frac{F}{f_w} = \frac{(1.5 \text{ in.}^2)(36{,}000 \text{ psi})}{(4200)}$$

$$= \underline{12.9''}$$

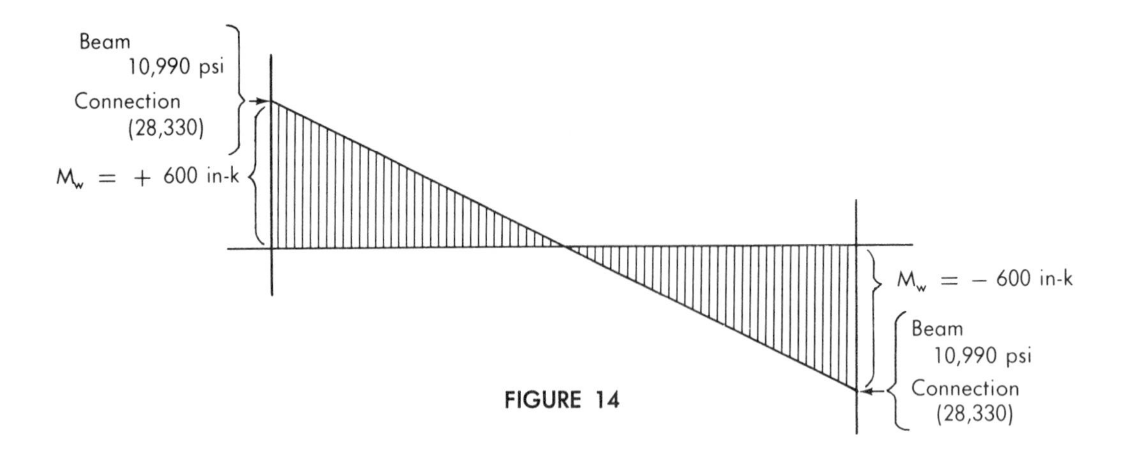

FIGURE 14

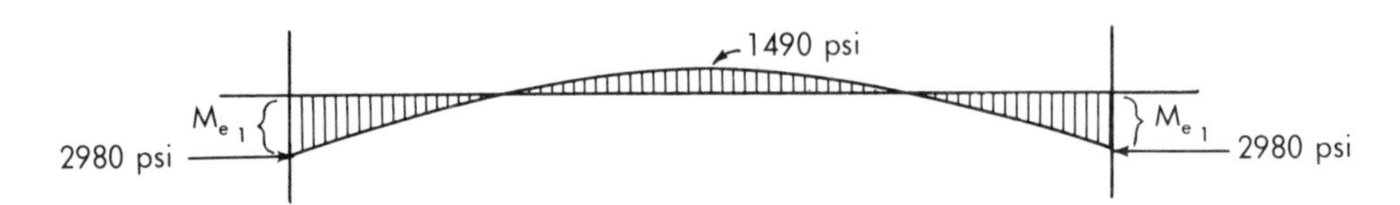

FIGURE 15

This would be 3″ of weld across the end, and 5″ along each side.

5. EXAMINING THIS EXAMPLE

To better understand how this wind connection operates, this example will be examined, using Method 2.

1. The connection is first designed for the wind moment of $M_w = 600$ in.-kip at ⅓ increase in the standard allowables applied to each end of the beam.

The wind moment will cause a bending stress in the beam of—

$$\sigma_b = \frac{M_w}{S_b}$$

$$= \frac{(600 \text{ in.-kips})}{(54.6 \text{ in.}^3)}$$

$$= 10{,}990 \text{ psi}$$

(See Figure 14.)

The corresponding stress in the top connecting plate is—

$$\sigma_p = \frac{M}{d_b\ A_p}$$

$$= \frac{(600 \text{ in.-kips})}{(14.12)(1.5)}$$

$$= 28{,}330 \text{ psi}$$

Note that the connection will not yield until a stress of 36,000 psi is reached.

$$\text{Let } K = \frac{S_p}{S_b} = \frac{\sigma_b}{\sigma_p}$$

$$= \frac{10{,}990}{28{,}330}$$

$$= .388$$

2. Now the gravity load can be gradually added, treating the beam as having fixed ends, until the right-hand connection reaches yield stress. This would be an additional stress in the connecting plate of: 36,000 − 28,330 = 7670 psi. This would correspond to a stress in the beam end of: (.388)(7670 psi) = 2980 psi.

(See Figure 15.)

Since the allowable moment on this end connection resulting from gravity load is (treated as a fixed end beam)—

$$M_{e1} = \frac{w_1\ L^2}{12} \text{ also } = \sigma_p\ A_p\ d$$

the portion of the gravity load to be added here is—

$$w_1 = \frac{12\ \sigma_p\ A_p\ d}{L^2}$$

$$= \frac{12(7670)(1.5)(14.12)}{(180)^2}$$

$$= 60.2 \text{ lbs/in.}$$

The stress in this beam end due to gravity load is then added to the initial wind moment diagram:

(See Figure 16.)

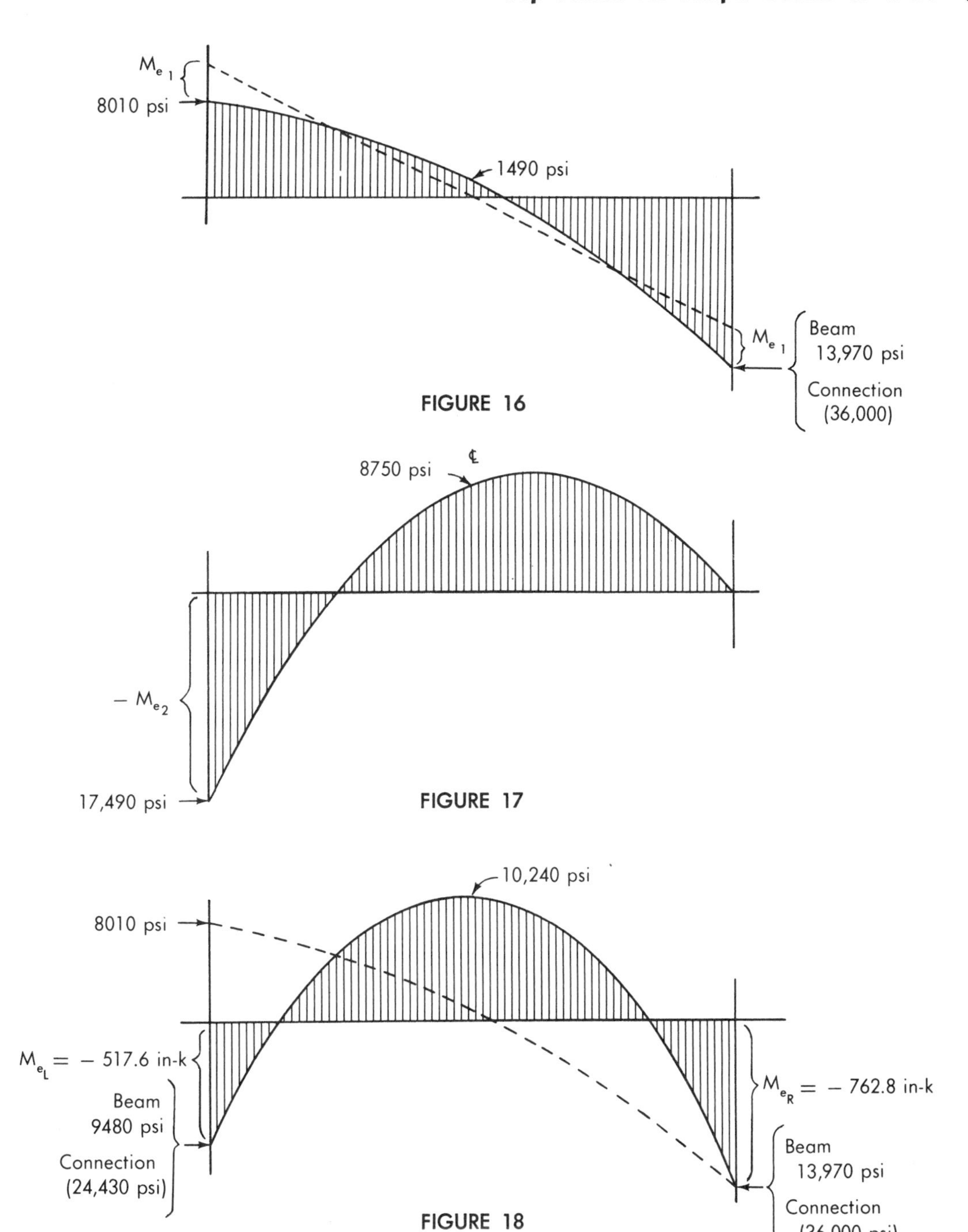

FIGURE 16

FIGURE 17

FIGURE 18

At this point, the right-hand connection reaches yield stress ($\sigma_y = 36{,}000$ psi) even though the beam end is stressed to only $\sigma = 13{,}970$ psi.

3. The remainder of the gravity load ($w_2 = w - w_1 = 296 - 60.2 = 235.8$ lbs/in.) can now be applied, treating the beam as having one fixed end on the left and simply supported on the right. See Figure 17.

The resulting end moment here is—

$$M_{e2} = \frac{w_2\ L^2}{8} = \frac{(235.8)(180)^2}{8}$$

$$= 955 \text{ in.-kip}$$

or a bending stress of

$$\sigma_{b2} = \frac{M_{e2}}{S_b} = \frac{(955 \text{ in.-kips})}{(54.6 \text{ in.}^3)}$$

$$= 17{,}490 \text{ psi}$$

Also since $M_{℄} = \dfrac{w_2\ L^2}{16}$

$$\sigma_b \text{ at } ℄ = \tfrac{1}{2}\ (17{,}490) = 8750 \text{ psi}$$

These stresses are then added to the previous moment diagram; Figure 18.

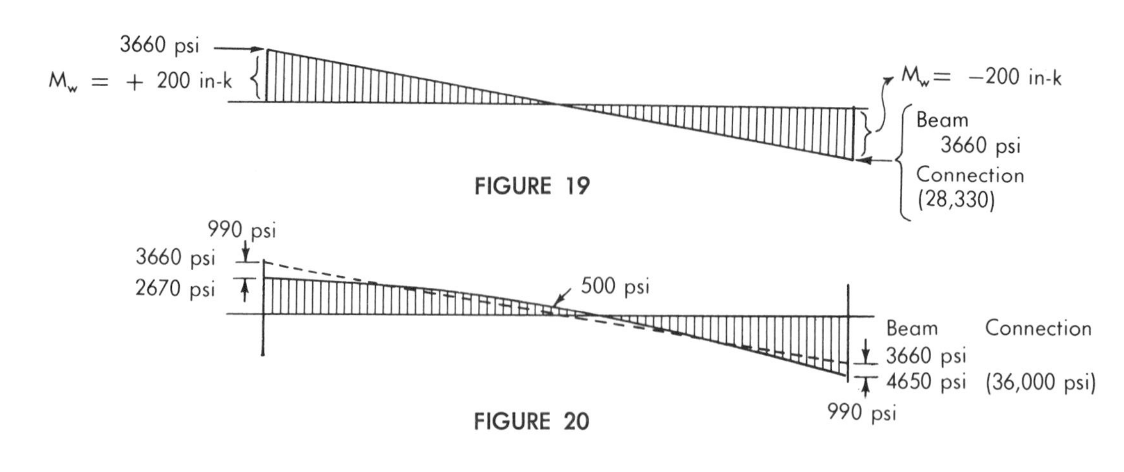

FIGURE 19

FIGURE 20

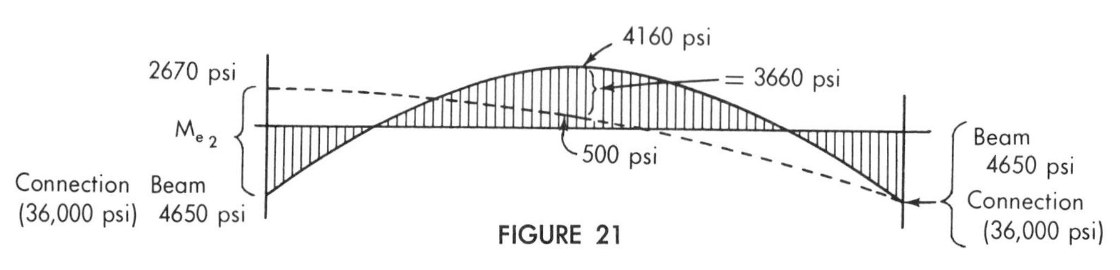

FIGURE 21

6. SMALL WIND MOMENT

A lower design wind moment will not require as large a top connecting plate. The smaller plate will yield sooner and it is possible that the final gravity load would cause both end connections to yield.

Consider the same problem as previously but with the wind moment reduced to $M_w = 200$ in.-kip, applied to each end of the beam.

The required top plate is designed for this wind moment:

$$A_p = \frac{M_w}{d_b \; 1\tfrac{1}{3} \; \sigma}$$

$$= \frac{(200 \text{ in.-kips})}{(14.12) \; 1\tfrac{1}{3} \; (22{,}000)}$$

$$= .48 \text{ in.}^2$$

or <u>use a 1″ x ½″ plate</u>

(This very small top plate is used here only for illustrative purposes.)

$$A_p = .50 \text{ in.}^2 > .48 \text{ in.}^2$$

This moment will cause a bending stress in the beam of—

$$\sigma_b = \frac{M_w}{S_b}$$

$$= \frac{(200 \text{ in.-kips})}{(54.6 \text{ in.}^3)}$$

$$= 3660 \text{ psi}$$

See Figure 19.

The corresponding stress in the top plate is—

$$\sigma_p = \frac{M_w}{d \; A_p} = \frac{(200 \text{ in.-kips})}{(14.12) \; (.50)}$$

$$= 28{,}330 \text{ psi}$$

$$\text{Let } K = \frac{S_b}{S_p} = \frac{\sigma_b}{\sigma_p}$$

$$= \frac{(3660)}{(28{,}330)}$$

$$= .129$$

A portion of the gravity load is added, treating the beam as having fixed ends, until the right hand connection reaches yield stress. This would be an additional stress in the connection plate of: 36,000 — 28,330 = 7670 psi. This would correspond to a stress in the beam of: (.129) (7670 psi) = 990 psi. See Figure 20.

Since the allowable moment on this end connection resulting from gravity load is—

$$M_{e1} = \frac{w_1 \; L^2}{12}$$

$$= \sigma_p \; A_p \; d_b$$

the portion of the gravity load to be added here is—

$$W_1 = \frac{12 \; \sigma_p \; A_p \; d_b}{L^2} = \frac{12 \; (7670)(.50)(14.12)}{(180)^2}$$

$$= 20.1 \text{ lbs/in.}$$

At this point, the right-hand connection reaches yield stress ($\sigma_y = 36{,}000$ psi) even though the end of the beam is stressed to only $\sigma = 4650$ psi.

In this example, if the remainder of the gravity load were applied, the left-hand connection would go over the yield point. For this reason only enough of the gravity load will be added to bring the left-hand connection just to yield, treating the beam as having one fixed end on the left and simply supported on the right. See Figure 21.

To reach yield stress in the left connection, the stress in the beam must increase from 2670 psi compression in upper flange to 4650 psi tension, or 7320 psi.

This would correspond to an applied gravity load of:

$$M_{e2} = \frac{w_2 \, L^2}{8}$$

$$= \sigma_b \, S_b$$

$$w_2 = \frac{8 \, \sigma_b \, S_b}{L^2}$$

$$= \frac{8(7320 \text{ psi})(54.6 \text{ in.}^3)}{(180)^2}$$

$$= 98.6 \text{ lbs/in.}$$

$$\text{And } M_{\text{℄}} = \frac{w_2 \, L^2}{16}$$

$$\text{so } \sigma_{\text{℄}} = \tfrac{1}{2}(7320)$$

$$= 3660 \text{ psi}$$

This now leaves a gravity load of w_3 to be applied, treating the beam as having simply supported ends since their connections have both reached yield stress.

The remaining gravity load:

$$w_3 = w - w_1 - w_2$$

$$= 296.0 - 20.1 - 98.6$$

$$= 177.3 \text{ lbs/in.}$$

Since:

$$M_{\text{℄}} = \frac{w_3 \, L^2}{8}$$

$$= \frac{(177.3)(180)^2}{8}$$

$$= 718 \text{ in.-kips}$$

$$\therefore \sigma_{\text{℄}} = \frac{718}{54.6}$$

$$= 13{,}150 \text{ psi}$$

This stress in the beam is added to the preceding moment diagram; see Figure 22:

The total $\sigma_{\text{℄}} = 17{,}310 \text{ psi} < 22{,}000 \text{ psi}$ <u>OK</u>

7. GRAVITY LOAD APPLIED FIRST, THEN WIND LOAD

In the preceding examination of the wind connection, the wind was applied first and then the gravity load. This is the sequence of design followed in Method 2. The cross-sectional area of the top plate is determined by wind only, and then the connecting welds are designed so that larger moments induced by the gravity loading under actual conditions of restraint may cause the plate to yield plastically.

Of course in actual practice, the gravity load is applied first and then the wind may be encountered secondly. The same problem will now be examined in this order of loading.

The beam with the gravity load is considered as simply supported; however, the top plate which must resist the wind moment does restrain the end of the beam to some extent. The larger the plate, the greater the restraint, this will also increase the end moment resulting from the gravity load. It is necessary to get some indication of the restraining action of the connection so that the end moment from the gravity load may be known.

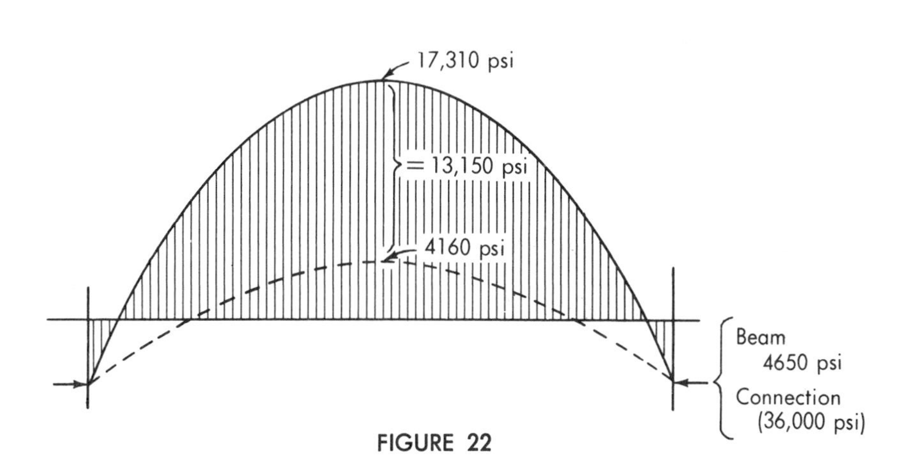

FIGURE 22

To do this, a simple moment-rotation diagram is constructed for both the loaded beam and the connection. The resulting conditions are represented by the point of intersection of these two lines or curves.

In the Lehigh research of connections, the actual test results of moment-rotation of the connections were plotted on this type of diagram; in this example the properties of this top plate connection are computed, and will be fairly accurate since practically all of the movement will occur in the reduced portion of the top plate.

Connection Line

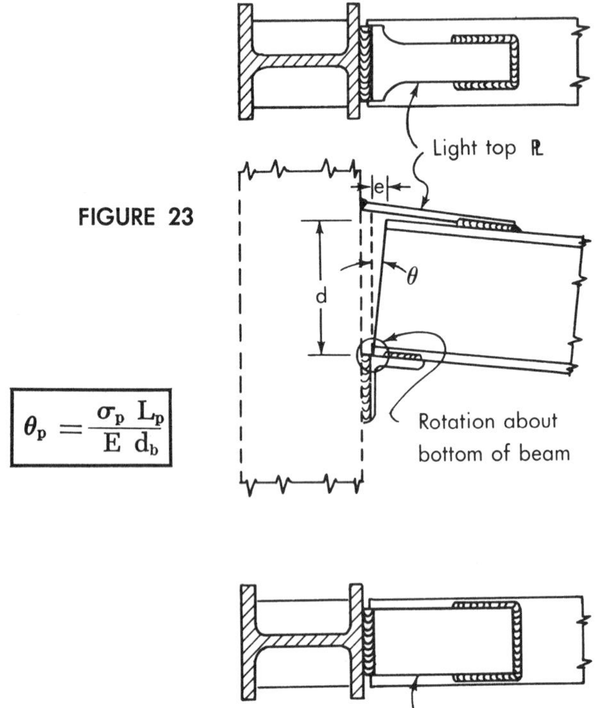

FIGURE 23

$$\theta_p = \frac{\sigma_p \, L_p}{E \, d_b}$$

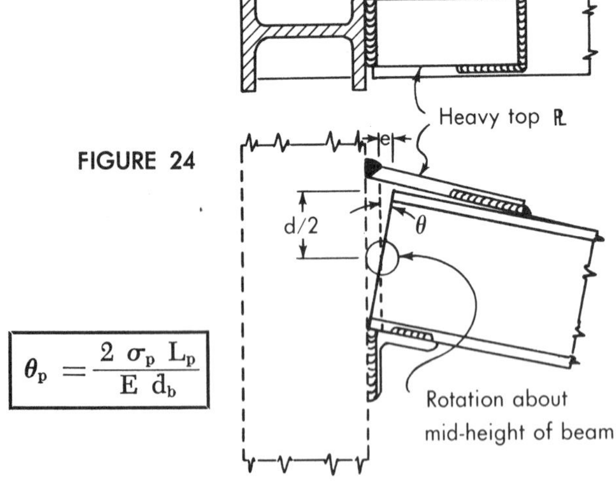

FIGURE 24

$$\theta_p = \frac{2 \, \sigma_p \, L_p}{E \, d_b}$$

where L_p = length of plate section between welds, inches

Since $\theta = \dfrac{e}{d_b}$ and $e = \epsilon \, L_p$

$$\epsilon = \frac{\sigma}{E}$$

also $\boxed{M_p = \sigma_p \, A_p \, d_b}$

If the bottom of the beam is securely anchored and the top plate is relatively small, Figure 23, rotation may be assumed to occur about a point near the bottom of the beam. As the top plate becomes larger, offering more restraint, this point of rotation moves up. If the top plate has the same size as the beam flange, Figure 24, rotation may be assumed to be at mid-height of the beam.

Since movement (e) depends upon the over-all elastic elongation of the top plate, and for simplicity length (L_p) is shown only as the length of the reduced portion, there is some elongation in the widened section as well as in the reduced section within the fillet welded zone. For this reason the value of the calculated rotation (θ) in this example will be doubled.

Two points will determine the connection line. Since this line passes through the origin or zero load, it is only necessary to have a second point; for simplicity this second point will be a yield conditions.

At yield:

$$\theta_p = \frac{\sigma_p \, L_p}{E \, d_b}$$

$$= \frac{(36{,}000 \text{ psi})(4.5'')}{(30 \times 10^6)(14.12'')}$$

$$= .382 \times 10^{-3} \text{ radians}$$

This value will be doubled because of elastic elongation of other portions of the plate:

$$\theta_p = .764 \times 10^{-3} \text{ radians}$$

and:

$$M_p = \sigma_p \, A_p \, d_b$$

$$= (36{,}000 \text{ psi})(1.5 \text{ in.}^2)(14.12'')$$

$$= 762 \text{ in.-kips}$$

Beam Line—Gravity load, uniformly loaded

It is necessary to have two points to determine this beam line on the moment-rotation chart:

(a) the end moment (M_e) if fully restrained

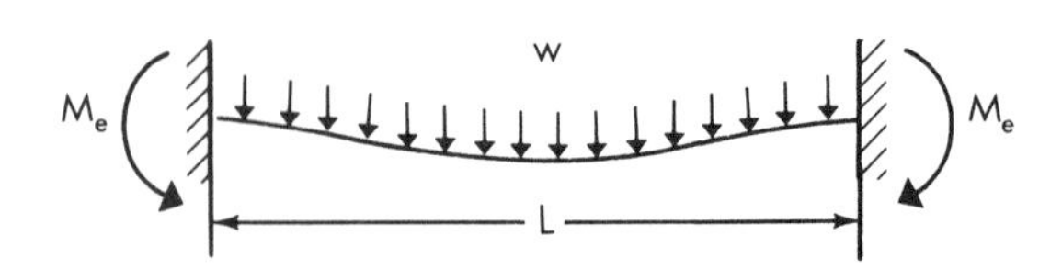

$$\boxed{M_e = \frac{w \, L^2}{12} = \frac{2 \, M_{℄}}{3}}$$

$$\therefore M_e = \frac{2\ M_{\mathfrak{L}}}{3}$$

$$= \frac{2(1200)}{3}$$

$$= 800 \text{ in.-kips}$$

(b) the end rotation (θ_e) if simply supported

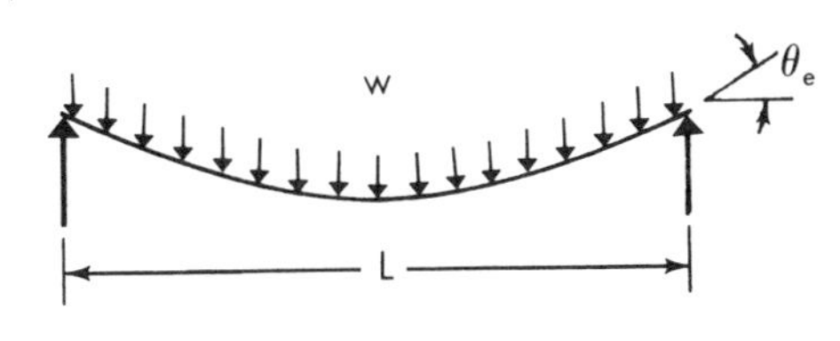

$$\boxed{\theta_e = \frac{w\ L^3}{24\ E\ I} = \frac{M_e\ L}{2\ E\ I}}$$

where L = length of beam in inches

$$\therefore \theta_e = \frac{M_e\ L}{2\ E\ I}$$

$$= \frac{(800)(180)}{2(30 \times 10^6)(385.3)}$$

$$= 6.24 \times 10^{-3} \text{ radians}$$

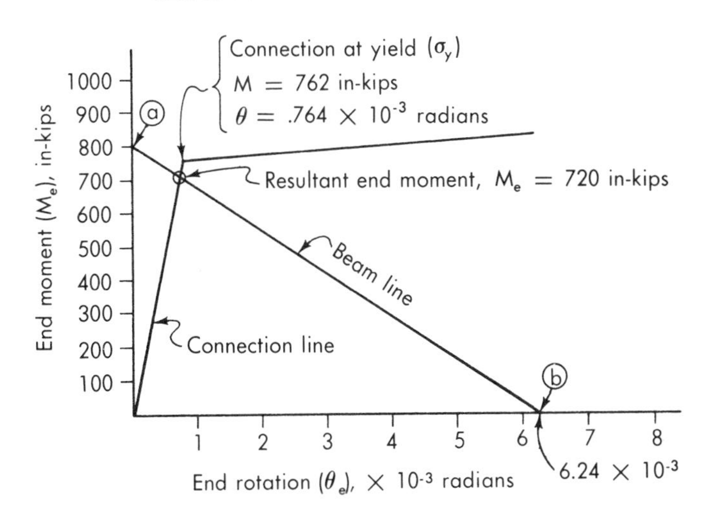

FIGURE 25

With the gravity load only on the beam, this would indicate that the end moments would be M_e = 720 in.-kip. This would leave:

$$M_{\mathfrak{L}} = 1200 - 720$$

$$= 480 \text{ in.-kips}$$

This would correspond to a bending stress at the end of the beam of—

$$\sigma = \frac{M_e}{S_b}$$

$$= \frac{(720 \text{ in.-kips})}{(54.6'')}$$

$$= 13{,}200 \text{ psi}$$ See Figure 26.

The stress at centerline of the beam would be—

$$\sigma = \frac{M_{\mathfrak{L}}}{S_b}$$

$$= \frac{(480 \text{ in.-kips})}{(54.6'')}$$

$$= 8800 \text{ psi}$$

As before $K = \frac{\sigma_b}{\sigma_p} = .388$ so that the stress in the connecting plate would be—

$$\sigma_p = \frac{13{,}200 \text{ psi}}{.388}$$

$$= 34{,}020 \text{ psi}$$

Now the wind load is gradually applied equally to both ends until the right-hand connection reaches yield. This would occur when the stress in the connecting plate is increased from 34,020 psi to 36,000 psi, or an increase of 1980 psi. This would correspond to a wind moment of—

$$M_{w1} = \sigma_p\ A_p\ d_b = (1980 \text{ psi})(1.5 \text{ in.}^2)(14.12'')$$

$$= 42.0 \text{ in.-kips}$$

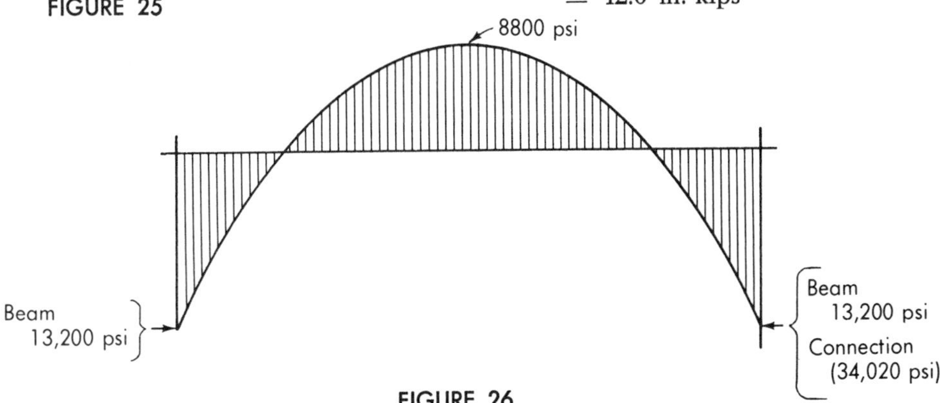

FIGURE 26

FIGURE 27

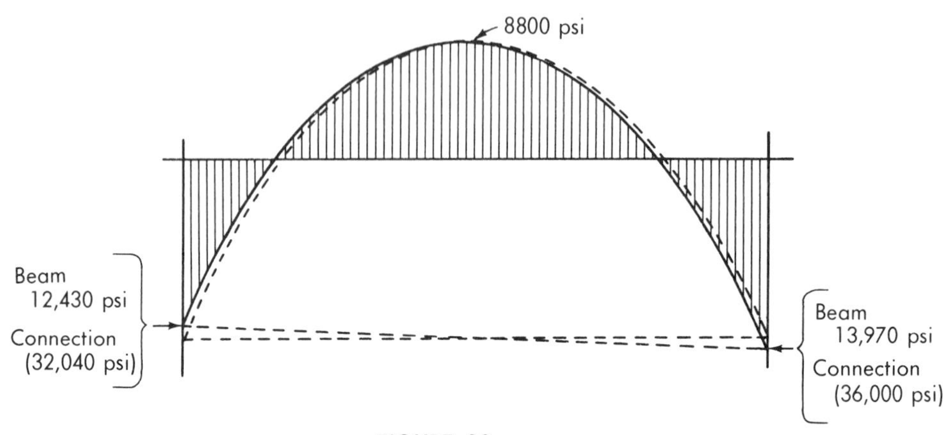

FIGURE 28

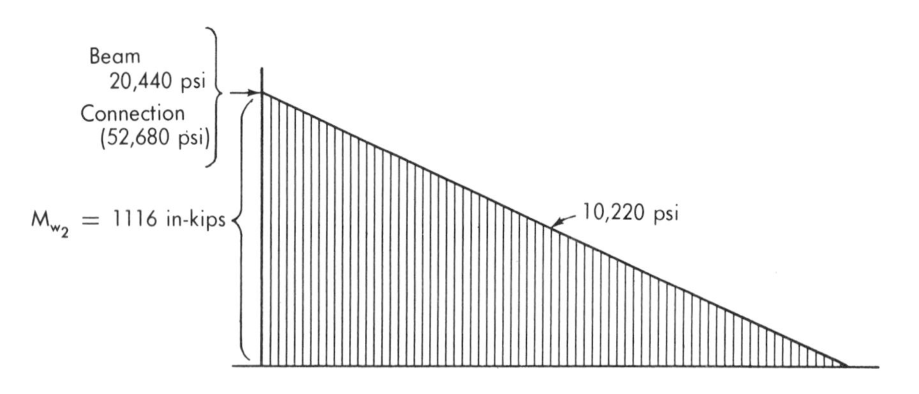

FIGURE 29

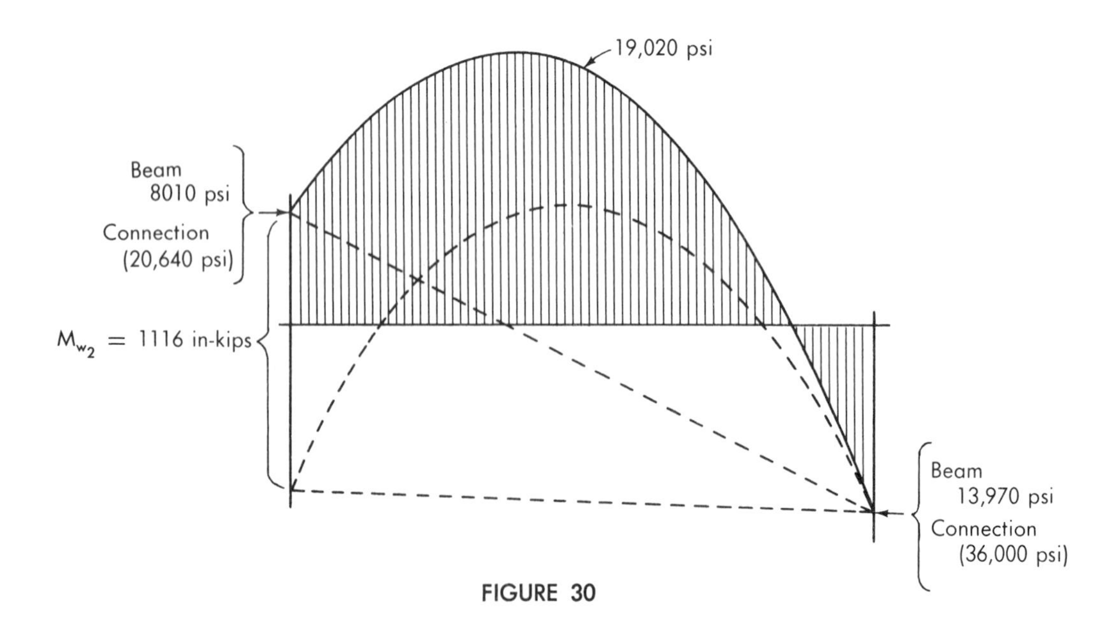

FIGURE 30

And stress in the beam is—

$$\sigma_b = (.388)(1980)$$
$$= 770 \text{ psi} \qquad \text{See Figure 27.}$$

Adding this wind moment diagram to the initial gravity moment diagram gives Figure 28.

There now is left a wind moment of 600 — 42 = 558 in.-kip to be applied to each end, but since the right-hand connection has reached yield stress, the remaining moment of 2 x 558 = 1116 in.-kip must be added to the left end of the beam.

$$\sigma_b = \frac{M}{S_b}$$
$$= \frac{1116 \text{ in.-kips}}{54.6}$$
$$= 20{,}440 \text{ psi}$$

$$\text{and } \sigma_p = \frac{20{,}440}{.388}$$

= 52,680 psi (compression) to be added to the 32,040 psi in tension already in the left-hand connecting plate

Adding this last wind moment diagram to the diagram in Figure 28 gives the final diagram, Figure 30.

8. ALTERNATE GRAPHICAL SOLUTION

This same example can be illustrated in a slightly different manner. The right-hand connection and beam end is on the right of Figure 31; the left-hand connection and its beam end is on the left.

As before, the beam line with gravity load only is constructed for both ends. This beam line represents the moment at the end caused by the gravity load, the actual value of the moment depends on the effect of the connection.

A wind moment would be represented by a horizontal line through the actual value of the moment. It would not be influenced by the connection unless it exceeds the yield of the connection; then the portion of the wind moment carried would be limited by the yield of the connection. Any wind moment superimposed on the gravity load will shift the beam line vertically up or down depending on the sign of the wind moment.

By observation, the right-hand connection can be

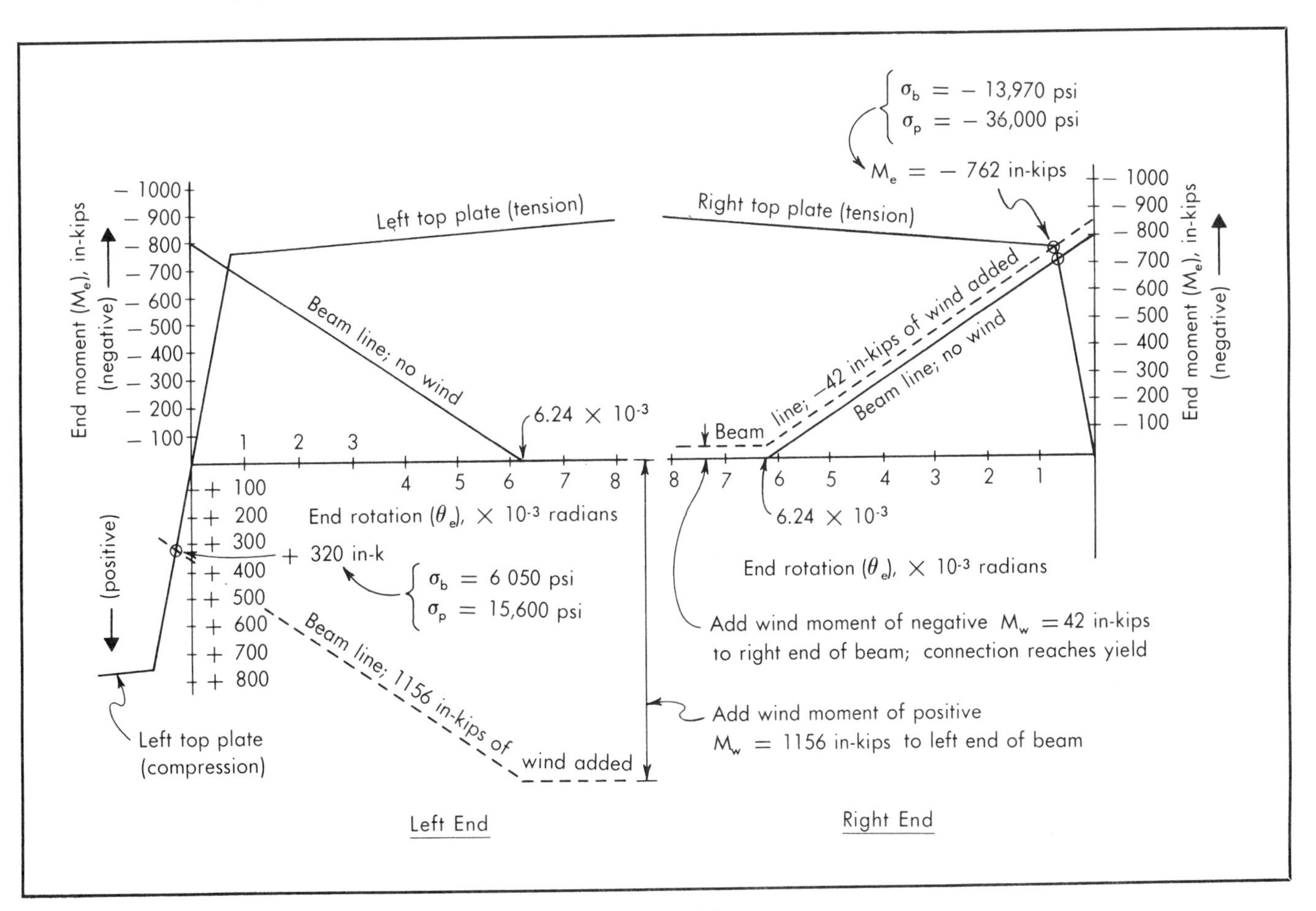

FIGURE 31

increased another 42.0 in.-kip from wind, then it will reach yield and no further moment can be applied. Since the applied wind moment was 600 in.-kip on each end, this will leave a balance of 2 x 600 in.-kip — 42 in.-kip = 1156 in.-kip to be carried entirely by the left-hand connection.

To do this, the beam line on the left of Figure 31 will be lowered vertically + 1156 in.-kip; see the dotted line. This will intersect the connection curve (extended into the positive moment region) at an end moment of M_e = 320 in.-kip.

This will correspond to a bending stress in the beam end of 6050 psi, and in the connection plate of 15,600 psi. In this case, the connection curve had to be extended downward into the positive moment region in order to intersect the new beam line. This indicates a + moment and reverses the stress in the plate, now compression, and the bottom of the beam connection is now in tension.

The previous examination of this problem indicated a bending stress in the left end of the beam of σ_b = 8010 psi; this examination indicates a stress of σ_b = 6050 psi. Why should there be a difference? The previous examination stopped after the first end moment due to gravity load was determined and then for simplicity from then on considered the connection as perfectly rigid, whereas this examination considered the elastic properties of the connecting plate all the way through the problem. This last approach would be a little more accurate.

This same problem was previously worked with a reduced wind moment of M_w = 200 in.-kip applied to each end. Figure 32 shows how this can be worked graphically. This is an interesting problem since the lower wind moment requires a smaller top plate, with ⅓ the cross-sectional area, hence ⅓ the strength, and the gravity load caused the plate to yield plastically at both ends even before any wind load is applied. This is represented by the black dot where the beam line (without wind) intersects with the connection curve.

When the wind moment is added, the right connection is already at yield and can carry no additional moment, therefore the entire wind moment of 2 x 200 in.-kip = 400 in-kip must be carried by the left-hand connection. Accordingly the beam line is lowered vertically a distance of 400 in.-kip; see the dashed line. As this is lowered, the resulting moment (M_e) and rotation (θ_e) of the connection (black dot) slide down parallel to the elastic portion of the connection line until it intersects with this new beam line (white dot).

In Figure 33 these final conditions representing the beam with gravity load and wind load are represented with black dots. If the wind were now removed, the left beam line moves upward 200 in.-kip and the right beam line moves down 200 in.-kip, the new conditions being represented by the white dots. For a complete reversal of wind, this operation is again repeated and is represented by the broken lines.

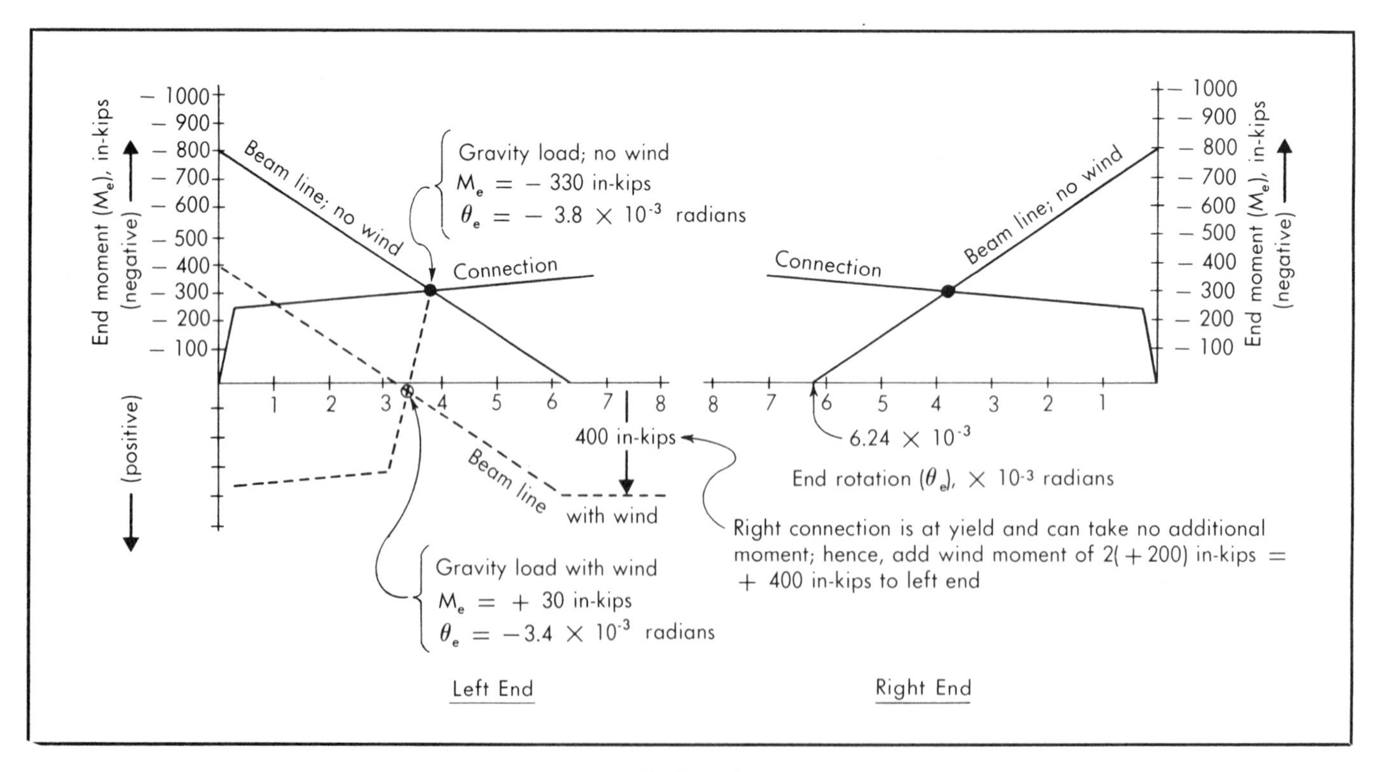

FIGURE 32

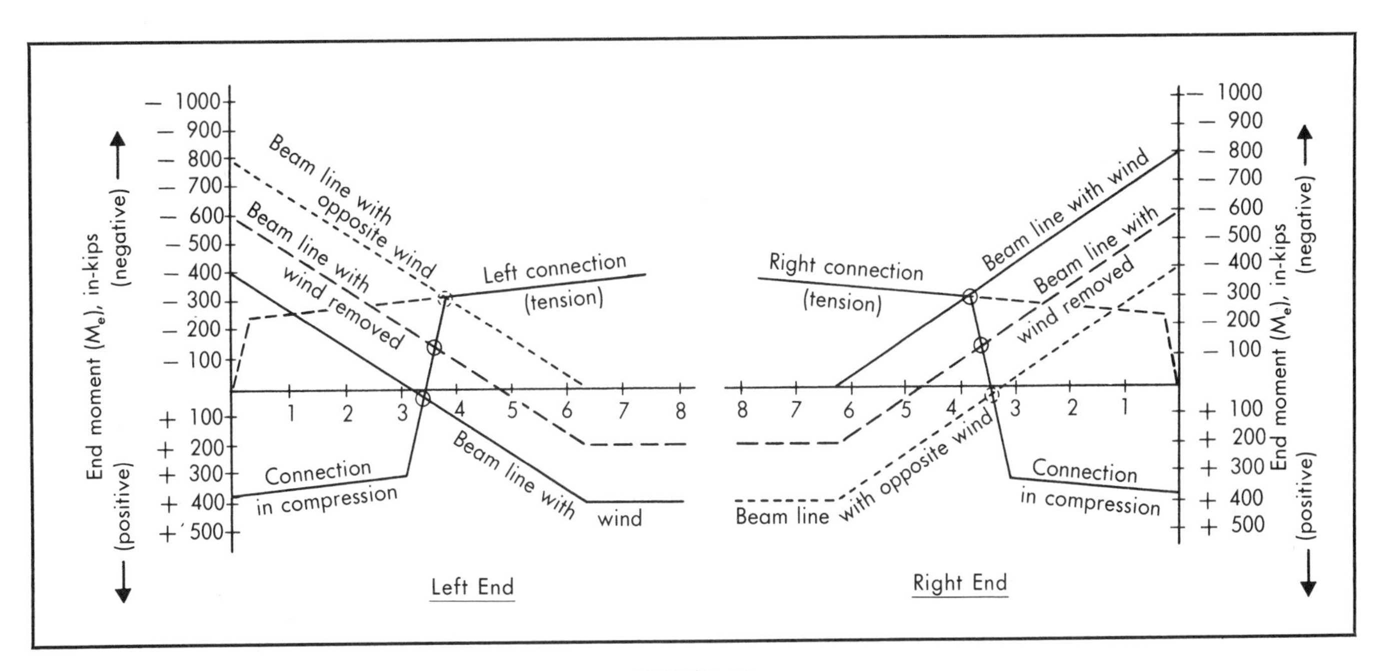

FIGURE 33

Typical scene in structural shop with weldors attaching stiffeners in place on curved knees. Proper use of welding results in significant savings in structural steel weight and in fabricating costs.

Welded continuous connections were used extensively in the Hartford Building in San Francisco. Photo shows the use of short Tee sections welded in place under ends of girders to provide deeper section at the point of maximum negative moment. Note that columns are weld fabricated. The small angle supports steel roof decking.

Top Connecting Plates For Semi-Rigid Connections

1. ANALYSIS OF CONNECTION

A top connecting plate designed to be stressed only below its yield point may be used as a semi-rigid connection. The reduced portion of the plate is detailed to have sufficient length (L) for elastic elongation of this section to provide the proper amount of joint rotation. See Figure 1.

Analysis of this type of connection requires locating the center of rotation. This depends on the relative stiffness of the top and bottom portions of the connection.

For the more flexible type of semi-rigid connection, rotation will occur closer to the bottom of the beam; see Figure 2. For the more rigid connection, rotation will occur closer to the midheight of the beam; see Figure 3.

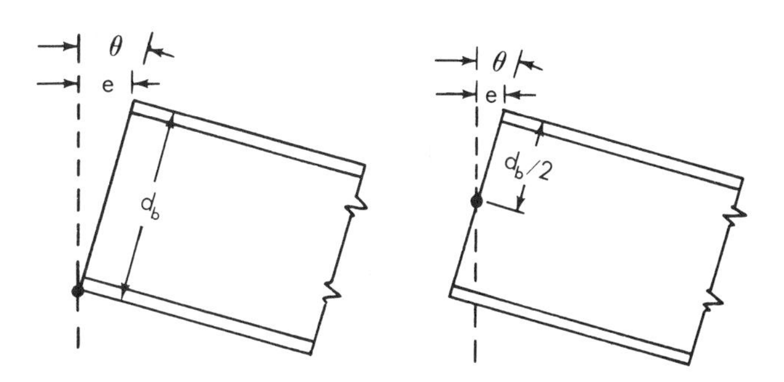

Rotation about bottom of beam

FIGURE 2

Rotation about mid-height of beam

FIGURE 3

The resisting moment of the connection is—

$$M_c = A_p \, \sigma \, d_b \quad \text{.......................(1)}$$

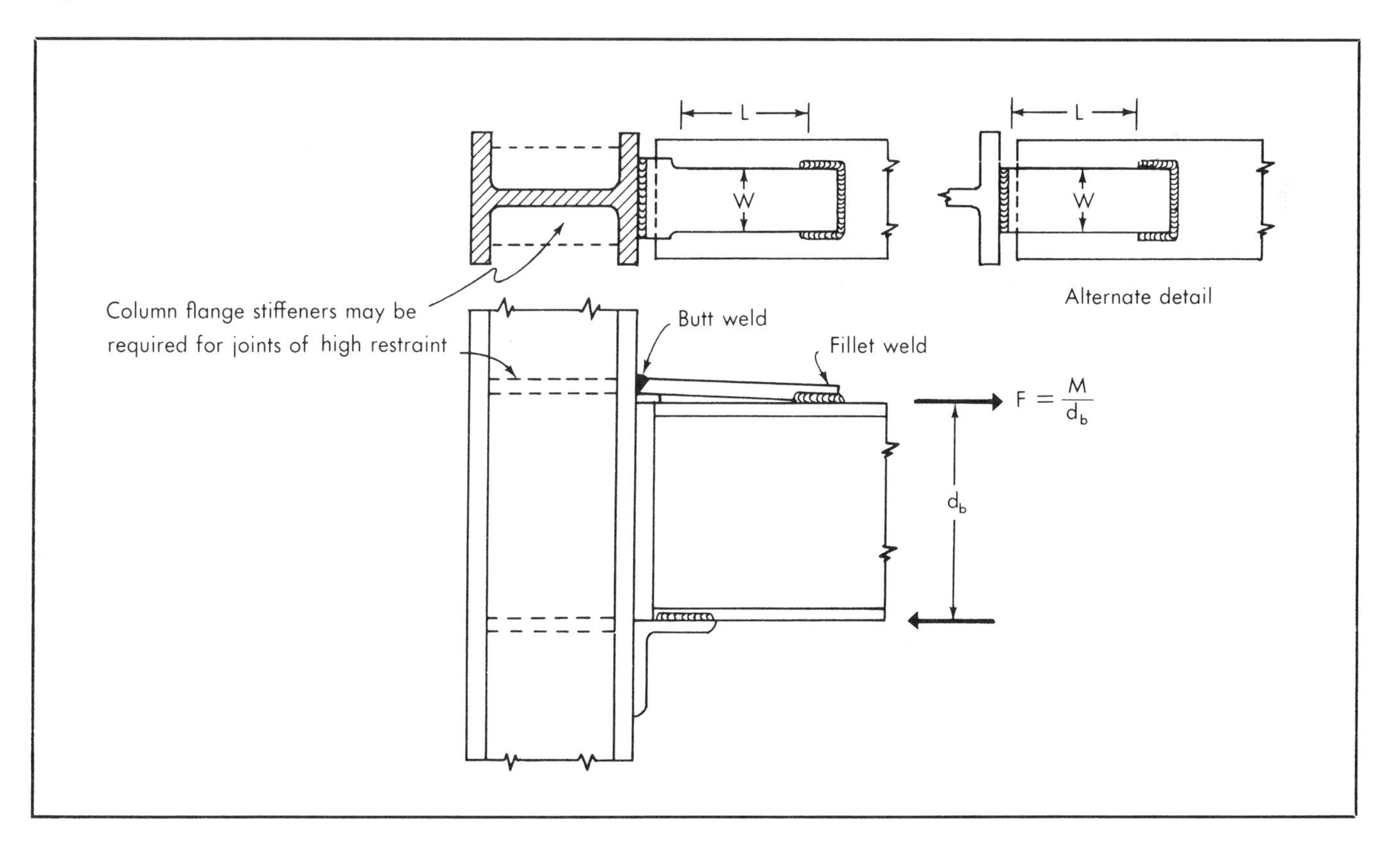

FIGURE 1

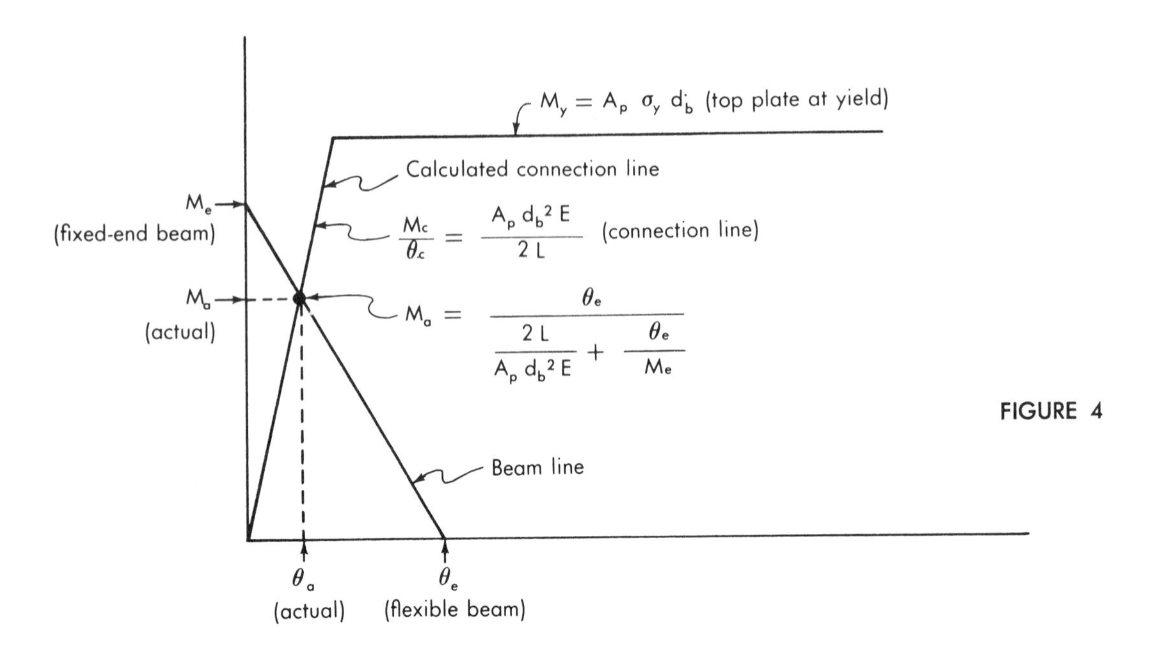

FIGURE 4

and the required cross-sectional area of the top plate is—

$$A_p = \frac{M}{\sigma\ d_b} \quad \text{.......... (2)}$$

The rotation of the connection, assuming rotation about midheight of the beam is—

$$\theta_c = \frac{2\ e}{d_b} \quad \text{and}$$

$$e = \epsilon\ L = \frac{\sigma\ L}{E} \quad \text{or}$$

$$\sigma_c = \frac{2\ \sigma\ L}{d_b\ E} \quad \text{.......... (3)}$$

The slope of this connection line is—

$$\frac{M_c}{\theta_c} = \frac{A_p\ d_b^2\ E}{2\ L} \quad \text{.......... (4)}$$

This connection line breaks at the yield point, or becomes horizontal at:

$$M_y = A_p\ \sigma_y\ d_b \quad \text{.......... (5)}$$

The actual conditions of moment (M_a) and rotation (θ_a) are found at the intersection of the beam line and the connection line; see Figure 4.

Table 1 shows the moments (M) and end rotation (θ) for various load and beam conditions.

The total centerline moment ($\Sigma M_{℄}$) and total end moment (ΣM_e) of a beam with any combination of the Table 1 loads equals the sum of the individual values resulting from each type of load.

When designing a beam for a given end restraint (R), the resulting maximum moment at centerline for which the beam is designed (M_b) equals the difference between the maximum centerline moment ($M_{℄}$) when R = 0 and the actual end moment (R M_e) for the given value of R. See Figure 5.

$$M_b = \Sigma M_{℄} - R\ \Sigma M_e$$

This can also be found by totaling the individual

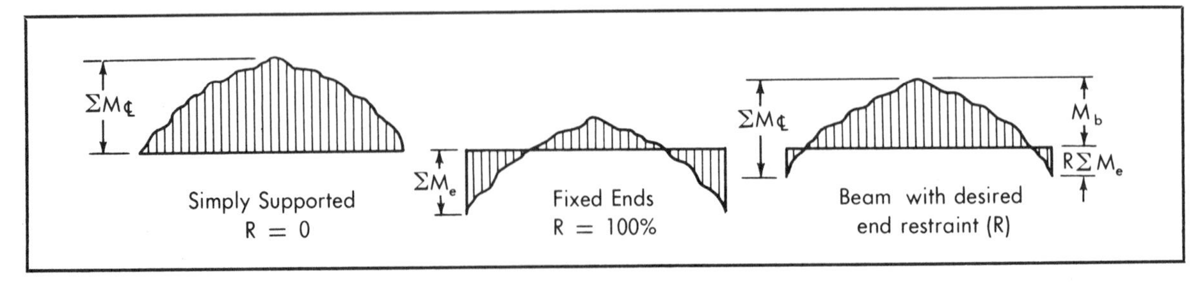

FIG. 5 Moment diagrams for different restraints (R).

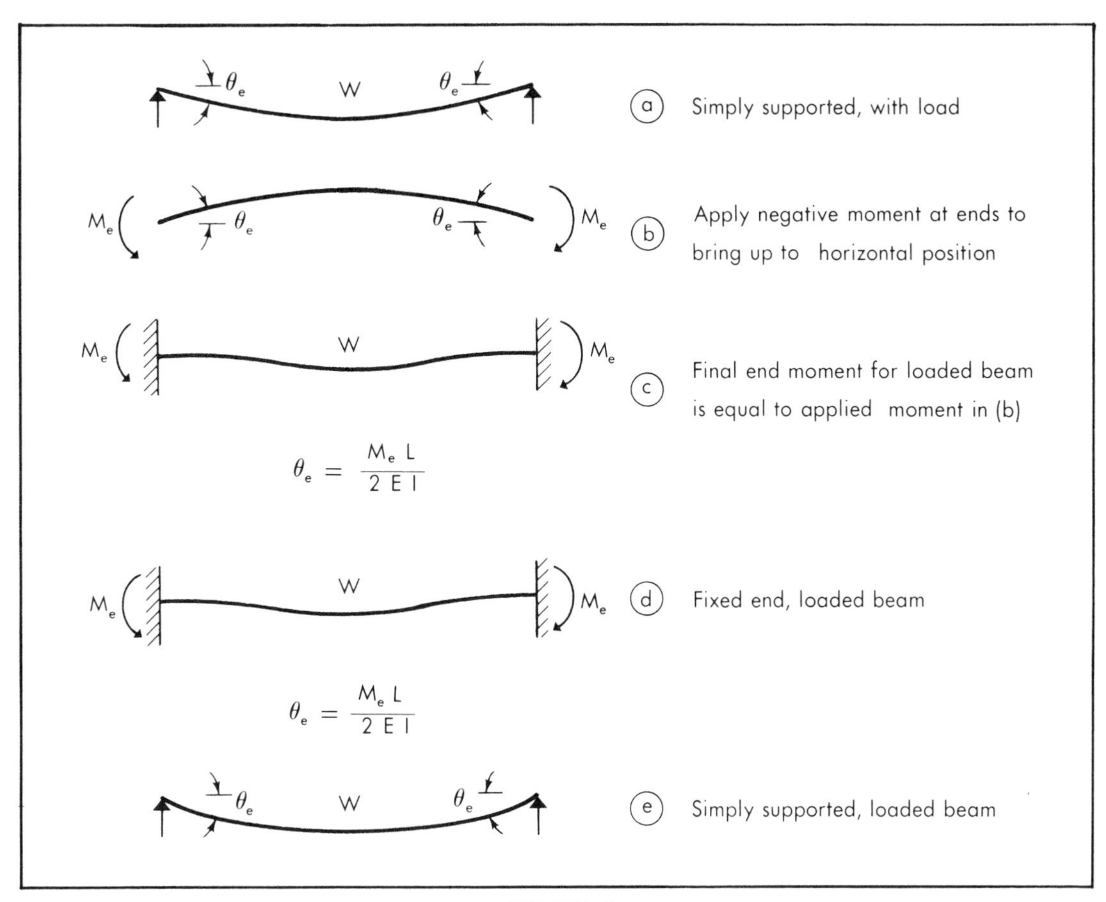

FIGURE 6

TABLE 1—Moments and End Rotation for Various Load/Beam Conditions

	1 Force W	2 Forces W	3 Forces W	4 Forces W	5 Forces W	Uniform Load W
Moment Diagram Simply Supported						
Center Moment $M_{℄}$ Simply Supported	$+\frac{WL}{4}$	$+\frac{WL}{6}$	$+\frac{WL}{6}$	$+\frac{3WL}{20}$	$+\frac{3WL}{20}$	$+\frac{WL}{8}$
End Rotation θ_e Simply Supported (R = 0)	$\frac{WL^2}{16EI}$	$\frac{WL^2}{18EI}$	$\frac{5WL^2}{96EI}$	$\frac{WL^2}{20EI}$	$\frac{7WL^2}{144EI}$	$\frac{WL^2}{24EI}$
End Moment M_e Fixed Ends (R = 100%)	$-\frac{WL}{8}$	$-\frac{WL}{9}$	$-\frac{5WL}{48}$	$-\frac{WL}{10}$	$-\frac{7WL}{92}$	$-\frac{WL}{12}$
Beam Moment M_b at ℄ For Given Value of R	$\frac{WL}{8}(2 - R)$	$\frac{WL}{18}(3 - 2R)$	$\frac{WL}{48}(8 - 5R)$	$\frac{WL}{20}(3 - 2R)$	$\frac{WL}{360}(54 - 35R)$	$\frac{WL}{24}(3 - 2R)$

values of M_b for a given value of R resulting from each of the types of loads; see Table 1.

We must now obtain the two points for the beam line with all of its loads (W): the total end moment (M_e) when beam ends are fixed and the angle rotation (θ_e) when beam ends are simply supported.

The fixed moments (M_e) from all the loads are totaled, and the angle rotation (θ_e) may be found from this total fixed end moment (M_e):

$$\theta_e = \frac{M_e\ L}{2\ E\ I}$$

This relationship may be found by determining the end moment required to rotate the end of a simply supported beam back to a horizontal position; see Figure 6a, b and c.

It will be easier then, to total the individual end moments for all of the types of applied loads; this becomes the final end moment when treated as a fixed-end beam, Figure 6d. Use this formula to determine the final end rotation (θ_e) of this beam with all of its applied loads when simply supported, Figure 6e.

Problem 1

Design a beam of A373 steel and detail the connection to support a uniformly distributed load of 22 kips (Fig. 7) and four concentrated loads of 6 kips each on L/5 centers along a 15-ft span (Fig. 8). The beam's design will be based on an end restraint of R = 50%, and the connection's design for R = 75%.

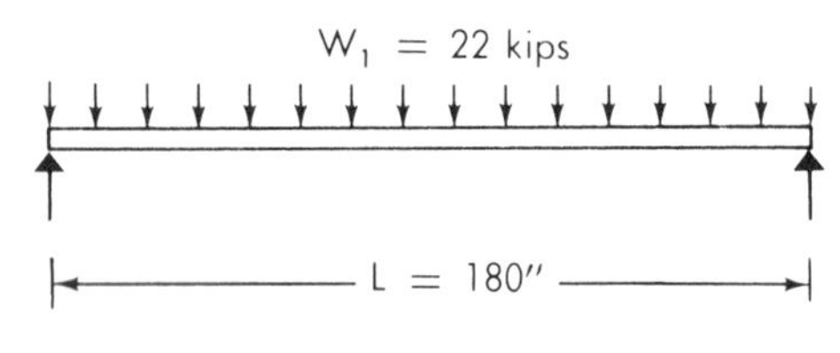

FIGURE 7

Here, the beam moment at centerline:

$$M_{b1} = \frac{W\ L}{24}\ (3 - 2\ R)$$

$$= \frac{(22{,}000)(180)}{24}\ [3 - 2\ (.50)]$$

$$= 330 \text{ in.-kips}$$

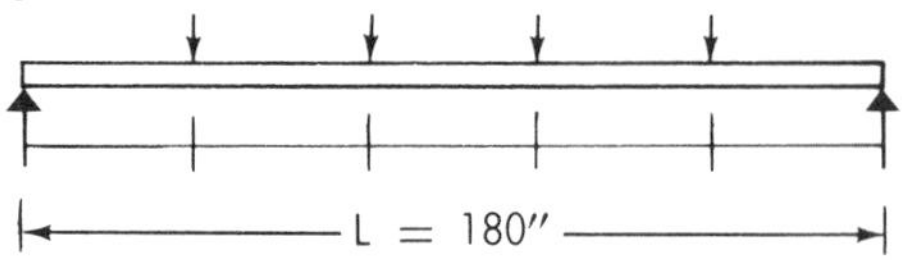

W_2 = 24 kips

L = 180″

FIGURE 8

Here, the beam moment at centerline:

$$M_{b2} = \frac{W\ L}{20}\ (3 - 2\ R)$$

$$= \frac{(24{,}000)(180)}{20}\ [3 - 2\ (.50)]$$

$$= 432 \text{ in.-kips}$$

Thus the total moment on the beam at its centerline is—

$$M_b = 330 + 432 \qquad (R = 50\%)$$

$$= 762 \text{ in.-kips}$$

The beam's required section modulus is—

$$S = \frac{M_b}{\sigma}$$

$$= \frac{(762)}{(20{,}000)}$$

$$= \underline{38.1 \text{ in.}^3}$$

A 14″ WF 30# beam could be used, since it has—

$$S = 41.8 \text{ in.}^3 \qquad \underline{\text{OK}}$$

In order to plot this as a beam line, it is necessary to know 1) the end rotation (θ_e) of the beam under the total load when simply supported, and 2) the end moment (M_e) on the beam under the total load considering the beam as having fixed ends.

$$M_{e1} = \frac{W\ L}{12}$$

$$= \frac{(22{,}000)(180)}{12}$$

$$= 330 \text{ in.-kips}$$

$$M_{e2} = \frac{W\ L}{10}$$

$$= \frac{(24{,}000)(180)}{10}$$

$$= 432 \text{ in.-kips}$$

Total end moment (R = 100%):

$$M_e = M_{e1} + M_{e2}$$

$$= 330 + 432$$

$$= \underline{762 \text{ in.-kips.}}$$

Resulting end rotation of beam, with combined loads, simply supported (R = 0):

$$\theta_e = \frac{M_e\ L}{2\ E\ I}$$

$$= \frac{(762)\ (180)}{2(30 \times 10^6)(289.6)}$$

$$= 7.9 \times 10^{-3} \text{ radians}$$

Design top plate for an end moment of 75% M_e = .75 (762 in.-kips) = 571 in.-kips.

Cross-sectional area of top plate:

$$A_p = \frac{M}{\sigma\ d_b}$$

$$= \frac{(571{,}000)}{(20{,}000)(13.86)}$$

$$= 2.06 \text{ in.}^2$$

or use a ⅜" x 5½" plate, having A_p = 2.06 in.²

The length of the reduced portion of the top plate will be made L = 7".

The slope of the connection line:

$$\frac{M_c}{\theta_c} = \frac{A_p\ d_b^2\ E}{2\ L}$$

$$= \frac{(2.06)(13.86)^2(30 \times 10^6)}{2\ (7)}$$

$$= 8.47 \times 10^5 \text{ in.-lbs/radian}$$

This connection line can also be constructed by solving for end moment (M_c) and end rotation (θ_c) when stressed to yield, σ_y = 33,000 psi:

$$M_c = A_p\ \sigma_y\ d_b$$

$$= (2.06)(33{,}000)(13.86)$$

$$= 943 \text{ in.-kips}$$

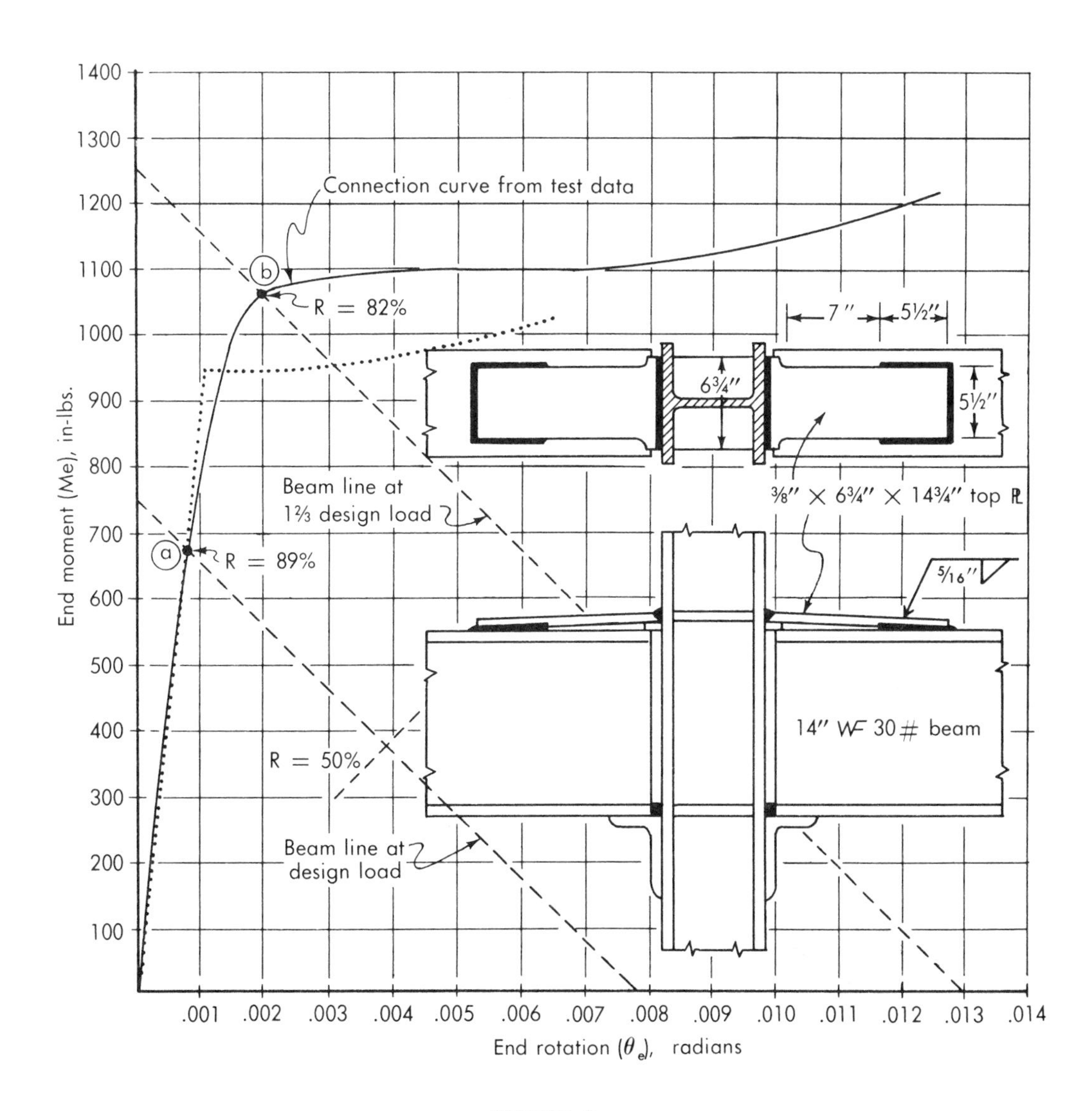

FIGURE 9

FIG. 10. Moment Capacity of Top Plate Connection.

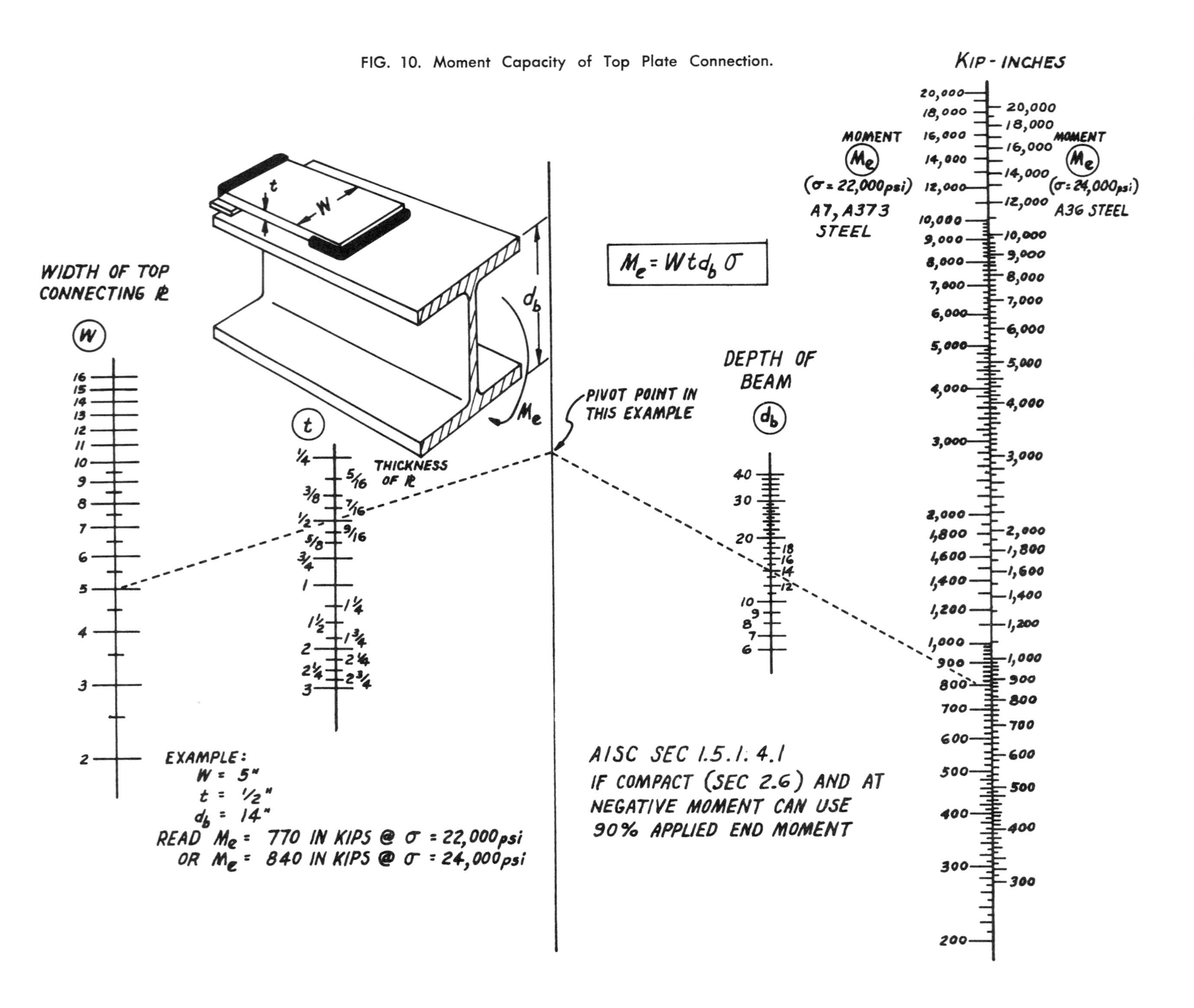

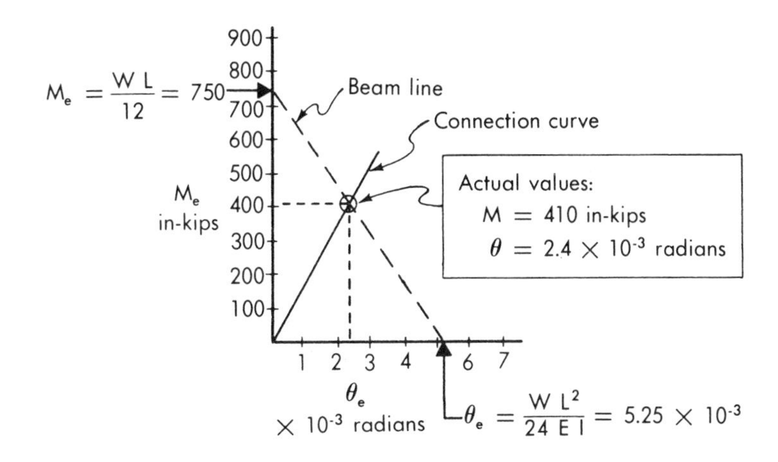

FIGURE 11

$$\theta_c = \frac{2\ \sigma_y\ L}{d_b\ E}$$

$$= \frac{2(33{,}000)(7)}{(13.86)(30 \times 10^6)}$$

$$= 1.11 \times 10^{-3} \text{ radians}$$

This calculated connection line is shown as a dotted line in Figure 9. It rises to a moment of M = 943 in.-kips at which time the top plate should reach yield stress. From there on, this plate will yield plastically and build up a higher resistance as it work hardens. It would finally reach the ultimate tensile strength of the plate unless some other portion of the connection would fail first.

Superimposed upon this graph in solid lines are the actual test results of this particular connection, from the paper "Welded Top Plate Beam-Column Connections" by Pray and Jensen, AWS Welding Journal, July 1956, p 338-s.

The beam lines of the particular example are shown as broken lines in the figure. Notice that the beam line at working load intersects the connection curve (point a) well within the capacity of the connection.

The second beam line at 1⅔ working load also is well within the ultimate capacity of the connection (point b).

Holding the length of the reduced portion of the top plate to L = 7″ has resulted in an end moment of M = 680 in.-kips instead of the 75% value or M = 571 in.-kips as originally planned. This is a restraint of R = 89.3% instead of R = 75%.

A lower restraint could be obtained by increasing the length of the reduced portion (L) of the top plate. However with the present connection the top plate has sufficient strength:

$$\sigma = \frac{.9\ M}{A_p\ d_b}$$ 90% M used at negative moment; (AISC Sec 1.5.1.4.1)

$$= \frac{.9(680{,}000)}{(2.06)(13.86)}$$

$$= 21{,}400 \text{ psi} < 22{,}000 \text{ psi} \quad \underline{\text{OK}}$$

(AISC Sec 1.5.1.4.1)

Notice also that the connection curve lies quite a distance above the R = 50% point of the beam line. Since the beam is designed on the basis of R = 50%, the connection could drop down to this value before the beam would be overstressed.

The moment capacity of a proposed top plate connection can be readily obtained from the nomograph, Figure 10.

2. CONNECTION BEHAVIOR UNDER ASYMMETRICAL CONDITIONS

In the usual analysis of a connection made by superimposing a beam line on a connection curve, it is assumed that the beam is symmetrically loaded and has identical connections on both ends.

This is illustrated in Figure 11, where the member is a 14″ WF 43# beam, and:

W = 50 kips
L = 15 ft
I = 429 in.^{4}

When these conditions of symmetrical loading and identical connections do not exist, the following method may be used to better understand the behavior of the connection under a given load. The above beam and load value will be used.

Step 1. Start at the left end (a) of the beam with the right end (b) held fixed. The left end (a) is first held fixed ($\theta_a = 0$) and the end moment (M_a) determined; the left end is then released and simply supported ($M_a = 0$) and the end rotation (θ_a) determined. See Figure 12.

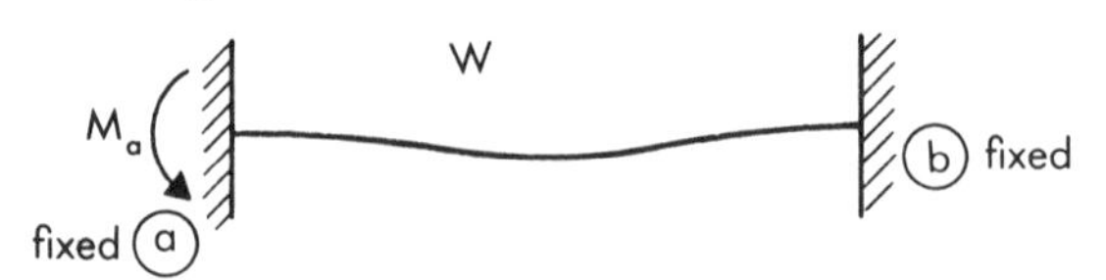

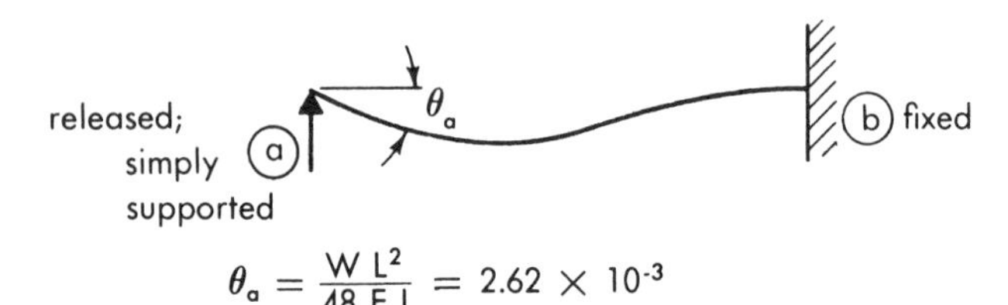

$$\theta_a = \frac{W\ L^2}{48\ E\ I} = 2.62 \times 10^{-3}$$

FIGURE 12

From these two points ($M_a = 750$ in.-kips and $\theta_a = 2.62 \times 10^{-3}$ radians), the beam line for the left end (a) is drawn, Figure 13. Upon this is superimposed the connection line, and the point at which it intersects the beam line represents the actual end moment and end rotation after the connection has allowed the beam end to move.

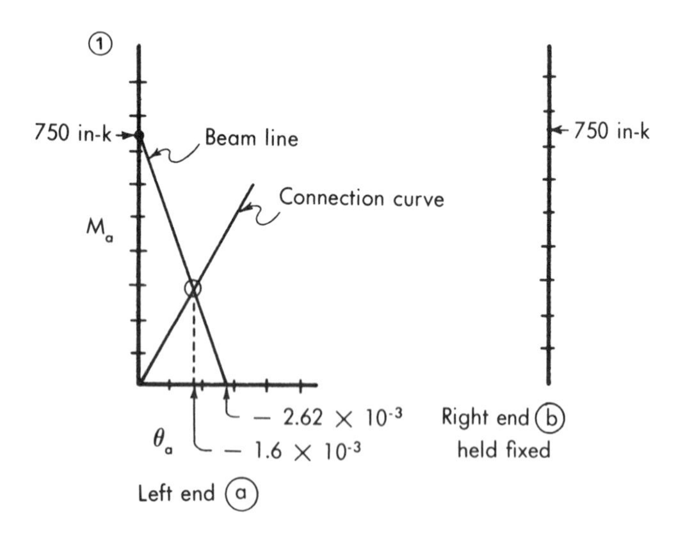

FIGURE 13

This relaxing or movement of the left end (a), from $\theta_a = 0$ to $\theta_a = 1.6 \times 10^{-3}$ radians, causes the fixed opposite end (b) to increase in end moment (M_b). This increase may be found by the following:

If a uniformly loaded beam is supported by fixed ends which have previously rotated (θ_a and θ_b), the two end moments (M_a and M_b) are—

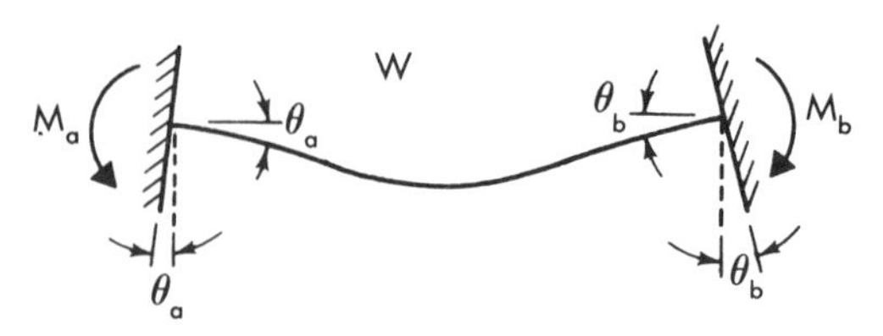

FIGURE 14

$$M_a = -\frac{4\ E\ I}{L}\ \theta_a - \frac{2\ E\ I}{L}\ \theta_b - \frac{W\ L}{12}$$

$$M_b = +\frac{2\ E\ I}{L}\ \theta_a + \frac{4\ E\ I}{L}\ \theta_b - \frac{W\ L}{12}$$

Step 2. Thus with the right end held fixed ($\sigma_b = 0$), the resulting moment at the right end (b) consisting of the initial moment and the additional moment due to movement of the left end (a), is—

where:
$\theta_a = -\ 1.6 \times 10^{-3}$
$\theta_b = 0$

$$M_b = \frac{2\ E\ I}{L}\ \theta_a + \frac{4\ E\ I}{L}\ \theta_b - \frac{W\ L}{12}$$

$$= -979 \text{ in.-kips}$$

Now the left end (a) of the beam is held fixed at $\theta_a = -1.6 \times 10^{-3}$ while the right end (b) is released and simply supported ($M_b = 0$) and the end rotation (θ_b) determined. See Figure 15.

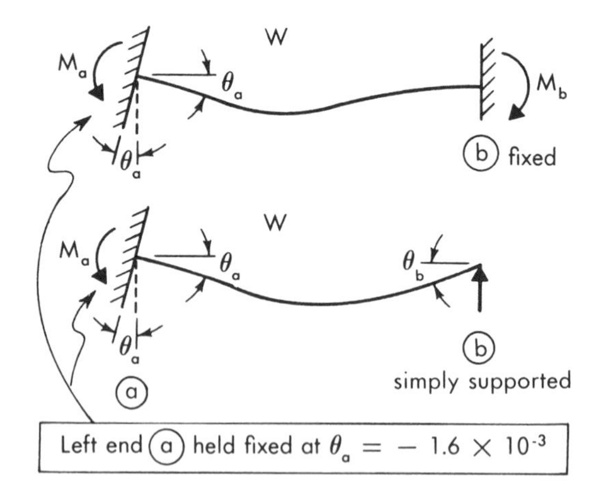

FIGURE 15

From:

$$M_b = +\frac{2\ E\ I}{L}\ \theta_a + \frac{4\ E\ I}{L}\ \theta_b - \frac{W\ L}{12}$$

when:

$$M_b = 0 \text{ and } \theta_a = -1.6 \times 10^{-3}$$

the rotation of the beam at the right end (b), if simply supported and no restraint from the connection, would be:

$$\theta_b = +3.42 \times 10^{-3}$$

These two points (M_b = —979 and θ_b = +3.42 x 10^{-3}) determine the beam line for the right end (b); Figure 16. Its intersection with the connection curve represents the actual end moment and end rotation after the connection has allowed the end to move.

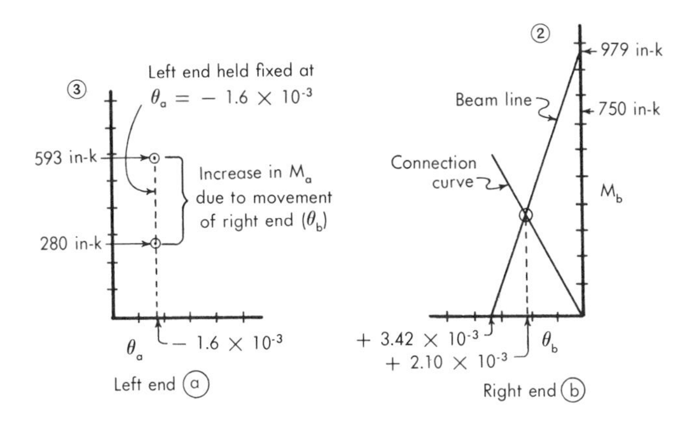

FIGURE 16

Step 3. As before, this movement of the right end (b) from θ_b = 0 to θ_b = +2.1 x 10^{-3} causes an increase in the moment on the left end (a); Figure 16, left.

From:

$$M_a = -\frac{4\,E\,I}{L}\,\theta_a - \frac{2\,E\,I}{L}\,\theta_b - \frac{W\,L}{12}$$

when:

$$\theta_a = -1.6 \times 10^{-3} \text{ and } \theta_b = +2.1 \times 10^{-3}$$

the moment on the left end (a) is found to be

$$M_a = -593 \text{ in.-kips}$$

This entire procedure is repeated until the corrections become very small, Figures 17 and 18.

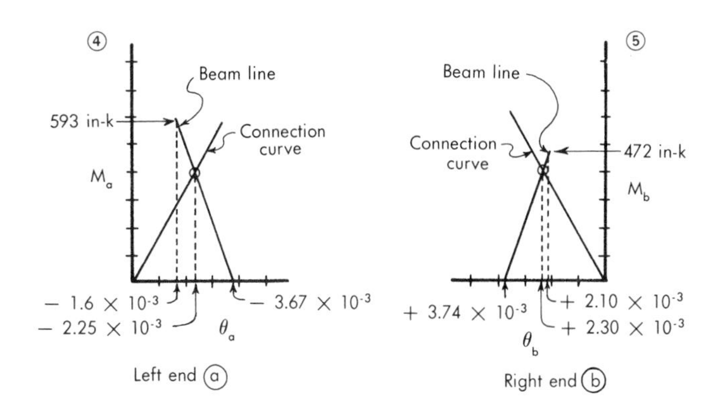

FIGURE 17

Step 4. When the left end (a) is simply supported (M_a = 0), the end rotation would be θ_a = —3.67 x 10^{-3}. Releasing the left end (a) allows it to rotate to θ_a = —2.25 x 10^{-3}.

Step 5. This movement θ_a from —1.6 x 10^{-3} to —2.25 x 10^{-3} on the left end causes the right moment to increase to M_b = —472 in.-kips. When the right end (b) is simply supported (M_b = 0), the end rotation would be θ_b = +3.74 x 10^{-3}. Releasing the right end (b) allows it to rotate to θ_b = +2.3 x 10^{-3}.

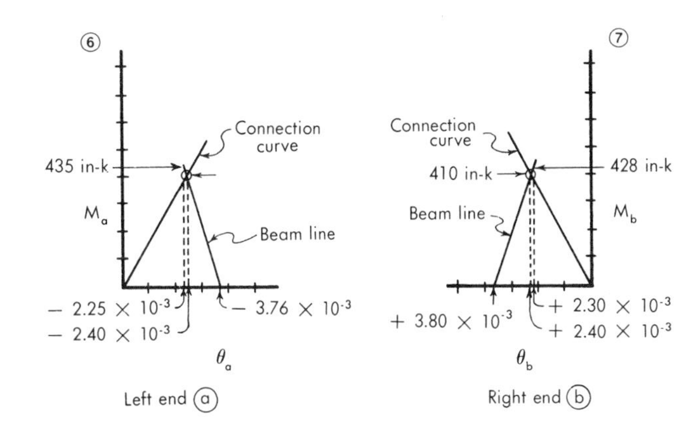

FIGURE 18

Step 6. This movement of θ_b from +2.1 x 10^{-3} to

$+2.3 \times 10^{-3}$ on the right end causes the left moment to increase to $M_a = -435$ in.-kips. When the left end (a) is simply supported ($M_a = 0$), the end rotation would be $\theta_a = -3.76 \times 10^{-3}$. Releasing the left end (a) allows it to rotate to $\theta_a = -2.40 \times 10^{-3}$.

Step 7. This movement of θ_a from -2.25×10^{-3} to -2.40×10^{-3} on the left end causes the right moment to increase to $M_b = -428$ in.-kips. When the right end (b) is simply supported ($M_b = 0$), the end rotation would be $\theta_b = +3.80 \times 10^{-3}$. Releasing the right end (b) allows it to rotate to: $\theta_b = +2.40 \times 10^{-3}$.

Conclusion: The final end conditions resulting from this sequential handling of the given connection and beam loading are—

$$M_e = -410 \text{ in.-kips}$$

$$\theta_e = 2.40 \times 10^{-3} \text{ radians}$$

Reference to Figure 11 shows that these are the same values as obtained when the beam was considered to be symmetrically loaded with identical conditions on both ends.

3. BEHAVIOR OF CONNECTIONS STRESSED ABOVE YIELD

The same method used previously may also be applied to connections that are stressed above their yield points and thus yield plastically. See Figure 19, using same beam as before.

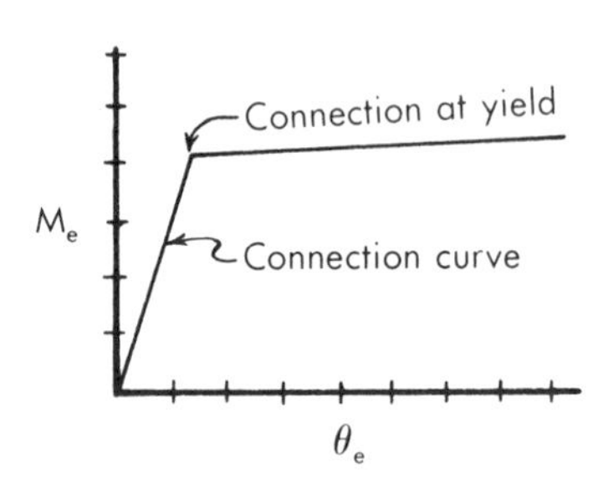

FIGURE 19

To simplify this analysis, two changes will be made.

First. In computing the two points of the beam line (M_e) for fixed ends and (θ_e) for this end simply supported, it is noticed that these same values can be obtained by considering the beam as fixed at one end and supported at the other, with no gravity load. A moment (M_e) is applied at the supported end and the resulting end rotation (θ_e) is found at this same end, Figure 20.

FIGURE 20

Here:

$$\theta_e = \frac{M_e\, L}{4\, E\, I} \quad \text{or} \quad \frac{M_e}{\theta_e} = \frac{4\, E\, I}{L}$$

In this particular example:

$$\frac{M_e}{\theta_e} = \frac{4\, E\, I}{L}$$

$$= \frac{4(30 \times 10^6)(429)}{(180)}$$

$$= 286 \times 10^6$$

With the particular scale used in the original construction of Figure 19,

$1'' = 4 \times 10^{-3}$ radians

or 1 radian $= \frac{1}{4} \times 10^3$ inch

and $1'' = 400$ in-kips $= 400{,}000$ in.-lbs

or 1 in.-lb $= \frac{1}{4} \times 10^{-5}$ inch

The slope of this beam line is—

$$\frac{M_e}{\theta_e} = 286 \times 10^6 \frac{\text{inch-lbs}}{\text{radians}} = \frac{286 \times 10^6 (\frac{1}{4} \times 10^{-5})}{(\frac{1}{4} \times 10^3)}$$

$$= 2.86$$

or an angle of 70.7°, Figure 21.

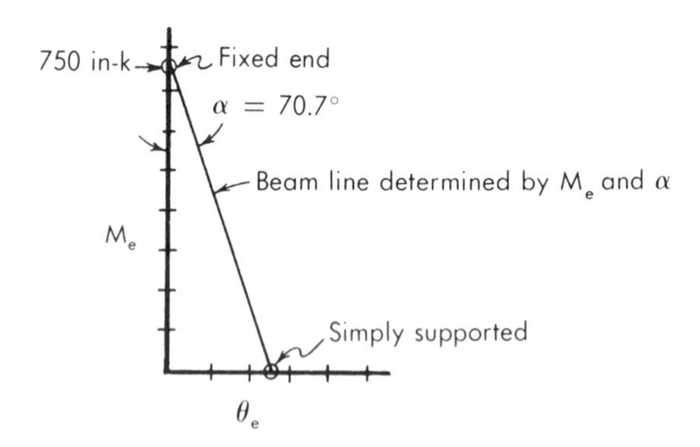

FIGURE 21

Another method of constructing this slope is to use a convenient value of θ_e; for example, $\theta_e = 5 \times 10^{-3}$. The corresponding end moment would be—

$$M_e = (286 \times 10^6)\ \theta_e$$

$$= (286 \times 10^6)(5 \times 10^{-3})$$

$$= 1430 \text{ in.-kips}$$

These two values are plotted on the figure and the slope determined by protractor; Figure 22.

Since the slope of the beam line remains constant, it won't be necessary to compute the value of θ_e for the simply supported end for each step.

Second. Instead of computing the end moment after it has been increased by the angle movement on the other end of the beam, it is seen that the actual increase in moment is—

$$M_x = \frac{2\ E\ I}{L}\ \theta_x$$

This may be drawn on the figure from any convenient value of θ_e and M_e. Any given increase in θ_x is laid off horizontally on this line, and the increase in moment (M_x) is measured off as the vertical distance and added to the moment on the opposite end of the beam. See Figure 23.

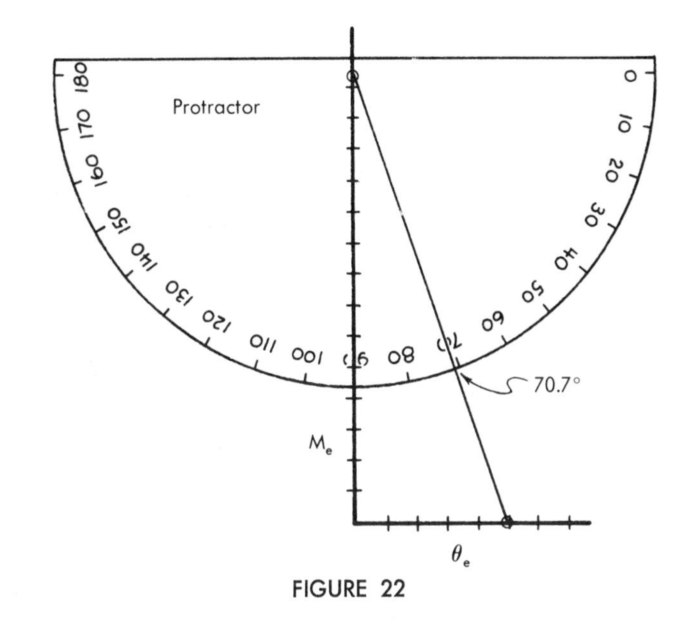

FIGURE 22

Application of Method

This method is now used on the same 14" WF 43# beam, uniformly loaded with 50 kips on a 15-ft span; Figure 24. The connection is made with a top connecting plate, 5/16" x 3", which is stressed to yield (σ = 33,000 psi) at a moment of 423 in.-kips.

With additional movement, the plate will strain harden and its resisting moment will very gradually increase. This accounts for the slight rise in the connection line above the point of initial yield.

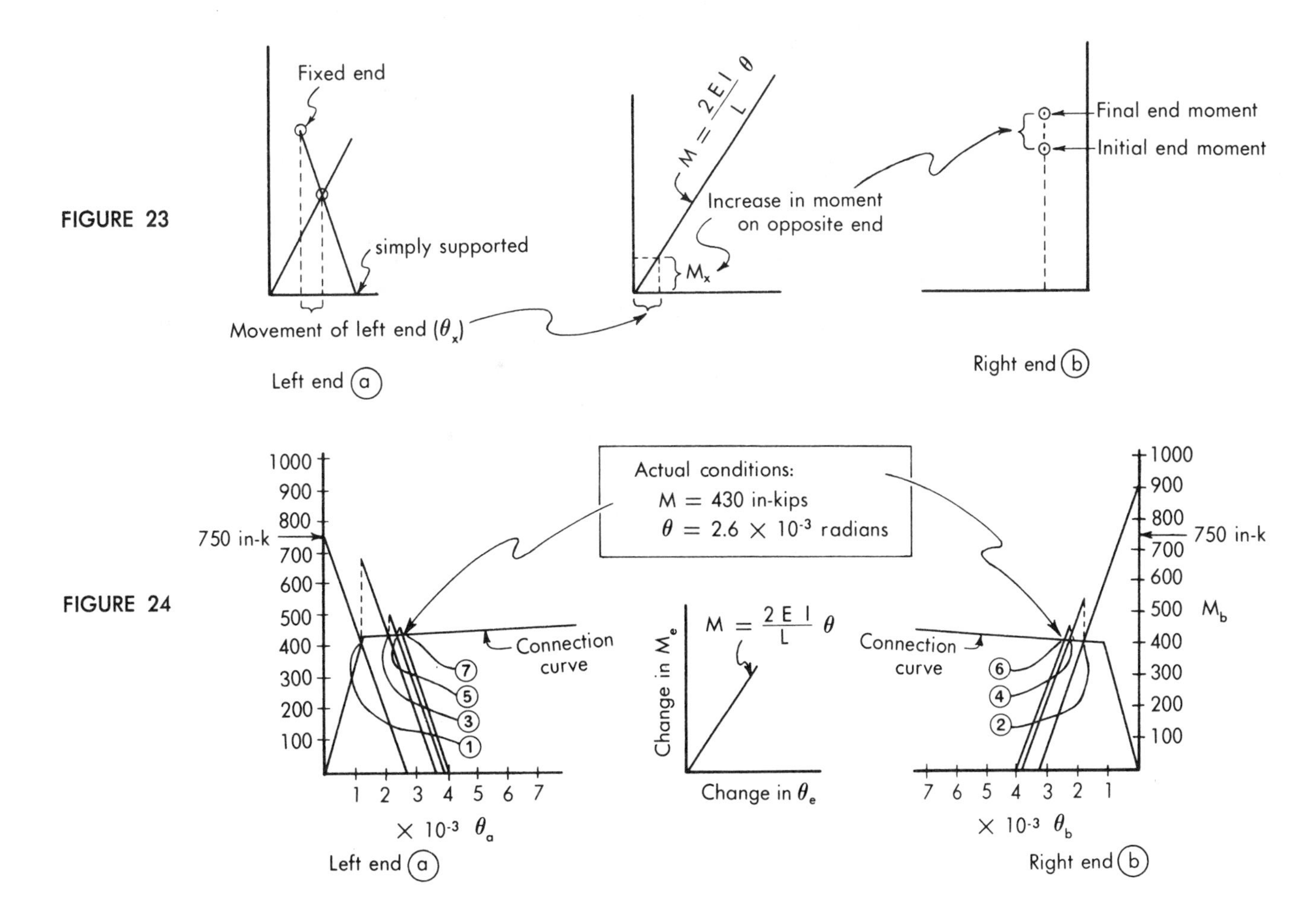

On the Ainsley Building in Miami, weldor is completing fillet weld on top connecting plate, leaving an unwelded length 1.2 times the plate width. Plate is beveled and groove welded to the column.

Beam-to-Column Continuous Connections

1. INTRODUCTION

Welding is most efficient in structures designed for full continuity. This type of design builds into the structure the inherent strength which comes from continuous action of all members. Loads are easily redistributed when overloading occurs on certain members.

This type of design realizes a weight saving in the beams since a negative moment acts at the supports, thus reducing the positive moment at the center of the span by the same amount.

Continuous connections also take advantage of what used to be a 20% increase in the allowable bending stress in the negative moment region near the support. This is accomplished through a 10% increase in bending allowables for "compact" sections, and using a 10% reduction in the negative moment. This reduction in negative moment is allowed for "compact" sections, provided the section modulus here is not less than that required for the positive moments in the same beam and provided the compression flange is regarded as unsupported from the point of support to the point of contraflexure.

Examples of Continuous Connections

In Figure 1, a beam frames into the web of a column. A seat, made of a plate with a stiffener, is shop welded to the column. This stiffener carries the beam reaction. A pair of flange connecting plates are field welded to the column and the beam. By using two plates instead of one, fillet welds on the flange can be of greater length to transmit the required load.

In Figure 2, flange and web plates are shop welded into the column. Usually these plates are of the same thickness as the corresponding part of the beam which they connect. An additional plate, fastened to the lower flange plates, serves as a seat plate. The flanges of the beam are beveled for downhand groove welding in the field. The web plate laps the web of the beam and is connected by a fillet weld.

In Figure 3, the beam frames to the column flange. The erection seat, with stiffener, and the web connecting plate are shop welded to the column flange. Also, column flange stiffeners if needed are shop welded. A flange connecting plate is field welded in place, being groove welded to the column flange and fillet welded to the upper beam flange. Usually a backing strip is

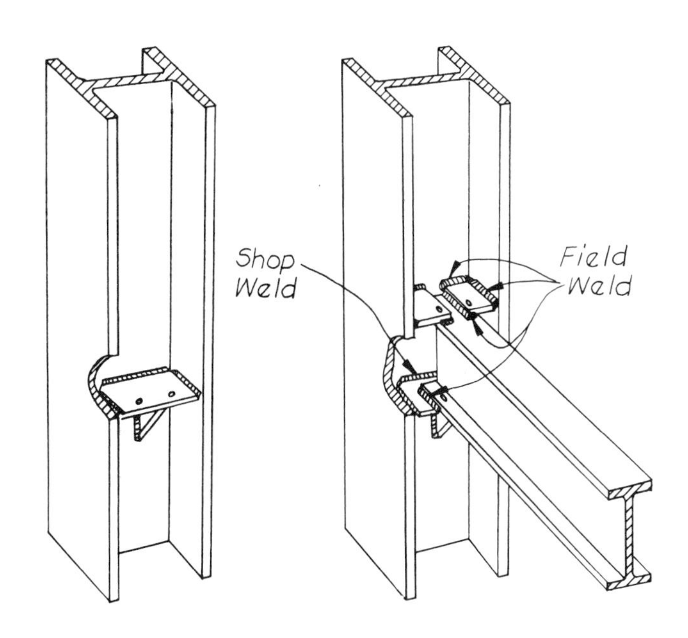

FIGURE 1

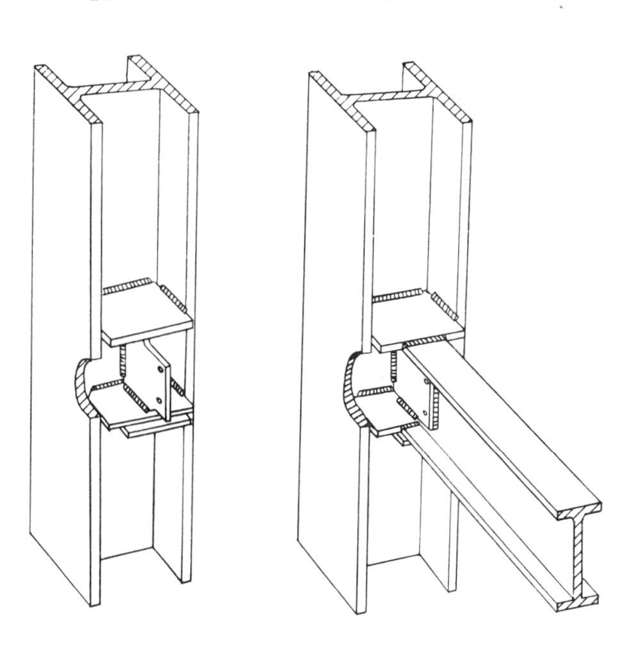

FIGURE 2

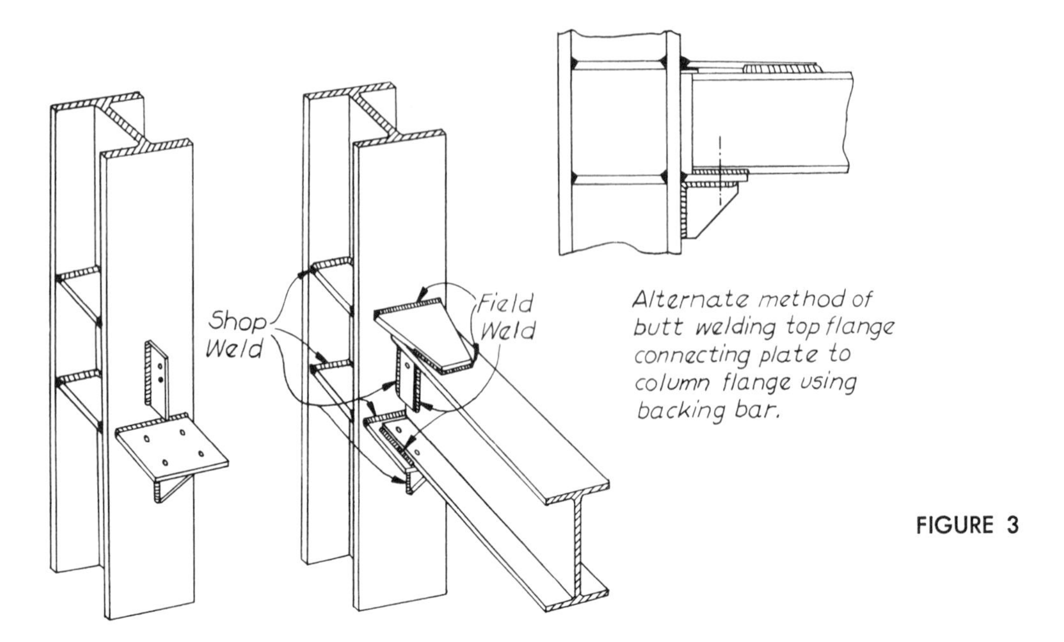
Shop Weld
Field Weld
Alternate method of butt welding top flange connecting plate to column flange using backing bar.

FIGURE 3

placed between the connecting plate and the beam flange to ensure a complete-penetration groove weld to the column. This eliminates back gouging and welding an overhead pass on the other side.

Reducing Welding Requirements

It is possible to design the seat stiffener to carry all of the end reaction, eliminating any vertical welding in the field. This reduces the field welding to just downhand groove welding of the beam flanges to the column.

Where good fit-up can be assured, the beam flanges are beveled from the top side and groove welded in the field directly to the column flange. The beam web is cut back about 1″ and fillet welded to the web connecting plate.

Some fabricating shops have jigs so that columns can be elevated into a vertical position. This allows much of the shop welding on the connecting plates to be made in the downhand position.

Cover Plates

When added at ends of beams to carry the extra negative moment, cover plates must be welded to the column for continuity; Figure 4.

Shop welding the cover plates to the beam, with the lower beam flange and the upper cover plate left

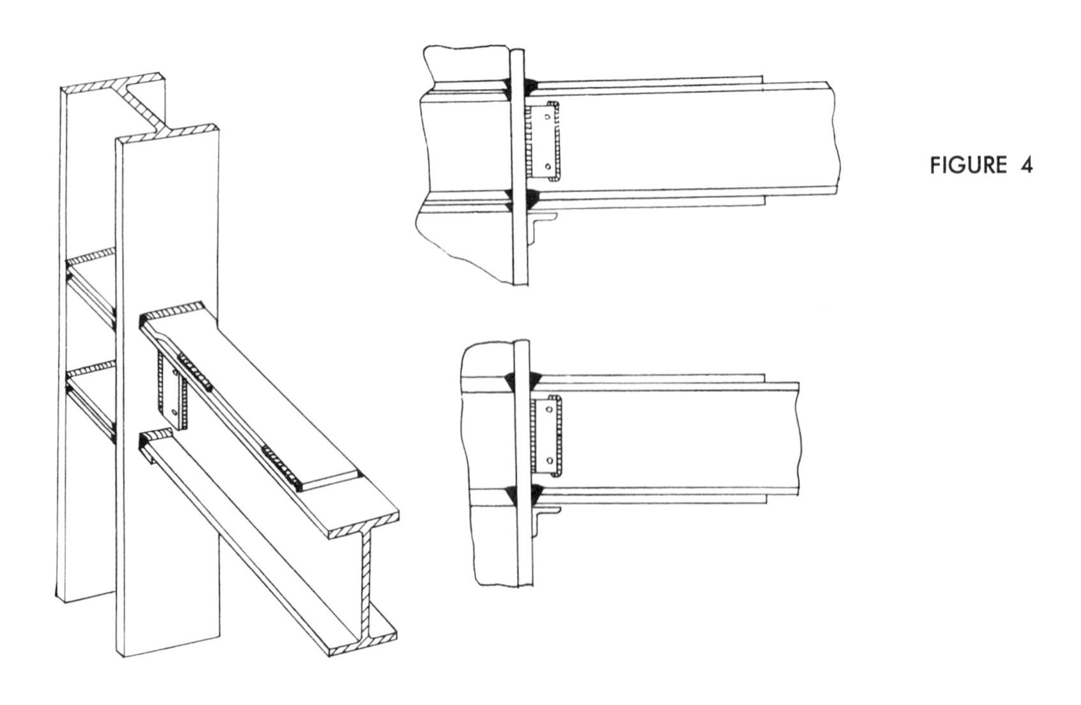

FIGURE 4

unbeveled, produces a type of "J" groove for the weld connecting them to the column flange.

If column-flange stiffener plates are needed in this case, they should be of about the same thickness as the beam flange and cover plate combined. The usual single thick stiffener in line with each beam flange can be replaced with two plates, each having half the required thickness. This means working with lighter connecting material and using two groove welds, each being half the size of the original single groove weld, which reduces the amount of welding on the stiffeners by half.

2. ANALYZING NEED FOR COLUMN STIFFENERS

If the flange of the supporting column is too flexible, the forces transmitted by the connecting flanges will load the outstanding portion of the column flange as a cantilever beam and cause it to deflect slightly; Figure 5. As this deflection takes place it reduces the stress in the outer ends of the beam-to-column connecting weld, thereby loading up the center portion of the weld in line with the column web.

It was previously thought that unless the column flange is extremely rigid (thick), flange stiffeners must be added to the column in line with the beam's top and bottom flanges (or their connecting plates). Such stiffeners keep the column flange from deflecting and load the weld uniformly.

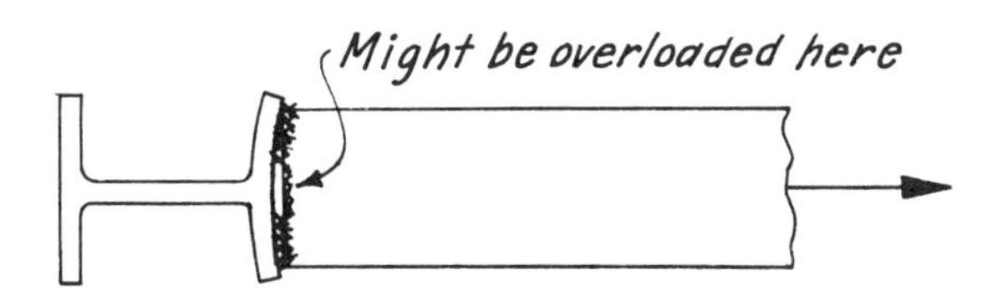

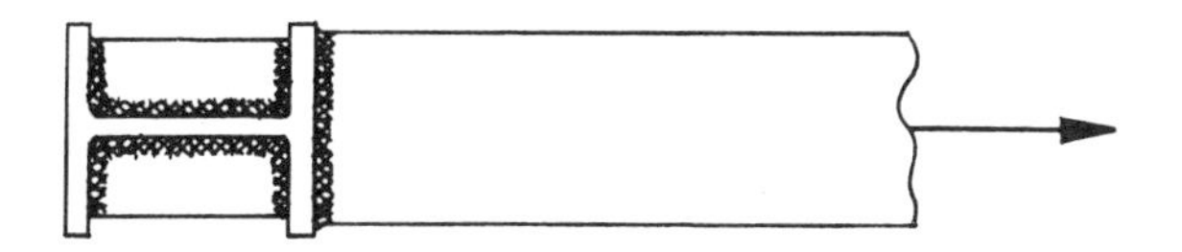

FIGURE 5

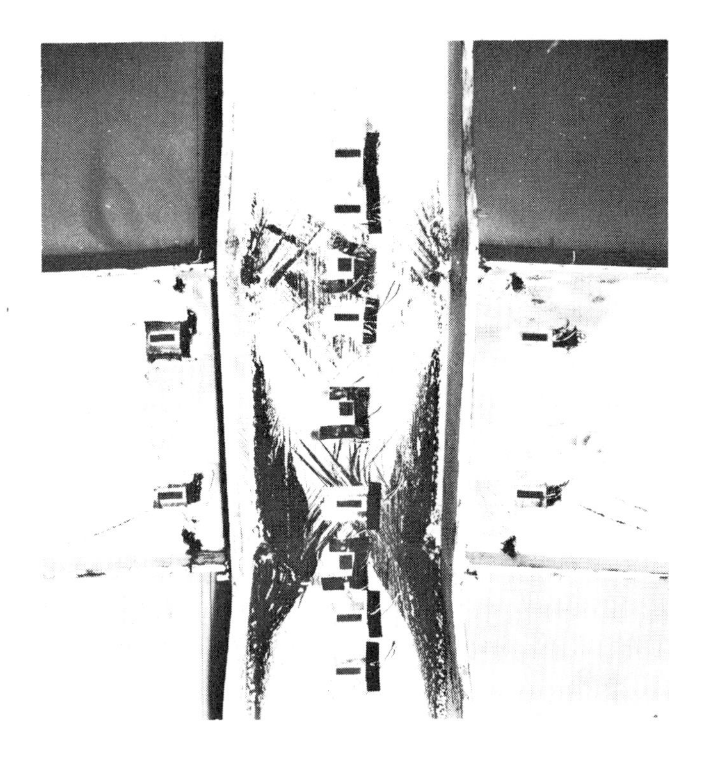

FIGURE 6

However, recent research at Lehigh University indicates that in most cases the deciding factor is a crippling of the column web; Figure 6. If the column web is thick enough, stiffeners are not required.

Buckling of Column Web Due to Compressive Force of Lower Beam Flange

A test was set up, Figure 7, to evaluate effects of the lower flange of the beam in compression against the column. Two bars, one on each side of the column, represented the cross-section of the beam flange. The test member was placed in a testing machine and loaded under compression.

In all cases, yielding began in the fillet of the

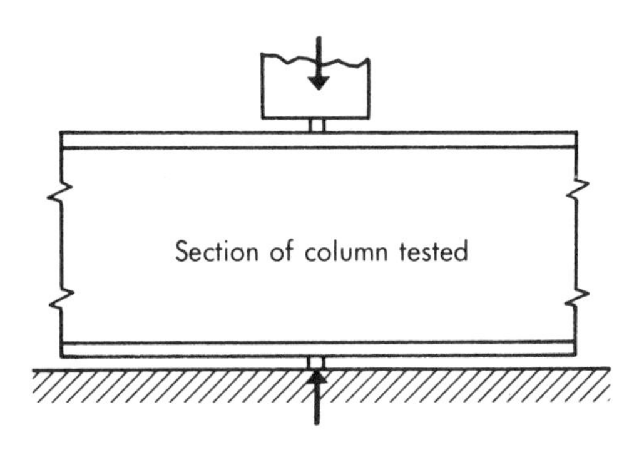

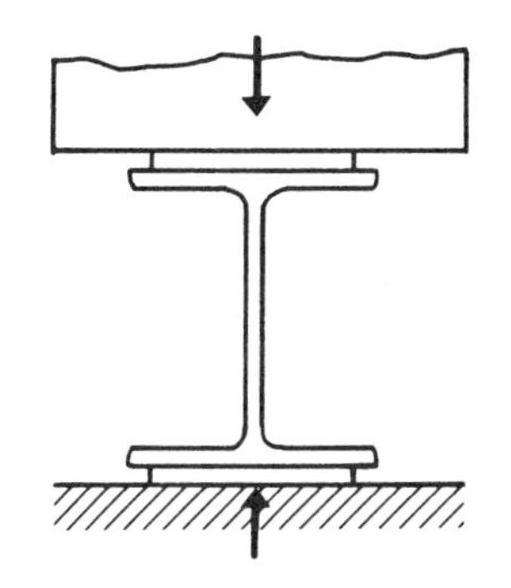

FIGURE 7

column just inside the column flange, and directly beneath the bars. Yielding progressed into the column web by means of lines radiating from this point to the column "K" line, at a maximum slope of 1 to 2½. This progressed for some distance. A slight bending of the column flanges was noticed at about 80% of the failure load. Figure 8 shows an analysis of this.

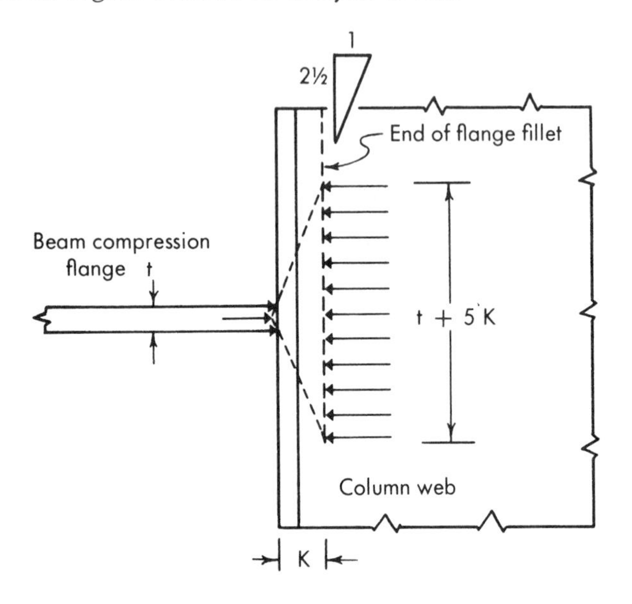

FIGURE 8

Overloading of Column Flange Due to Tension Force of Upper Beam Flange

A test was set up, Figure 9, to evaluate effects of the upper flange of the beam in tension against the column. Two plates, one on each side of the column and welded to it, represented the cross-section of the beam flange. The member was pulled in a tensile testing machine.

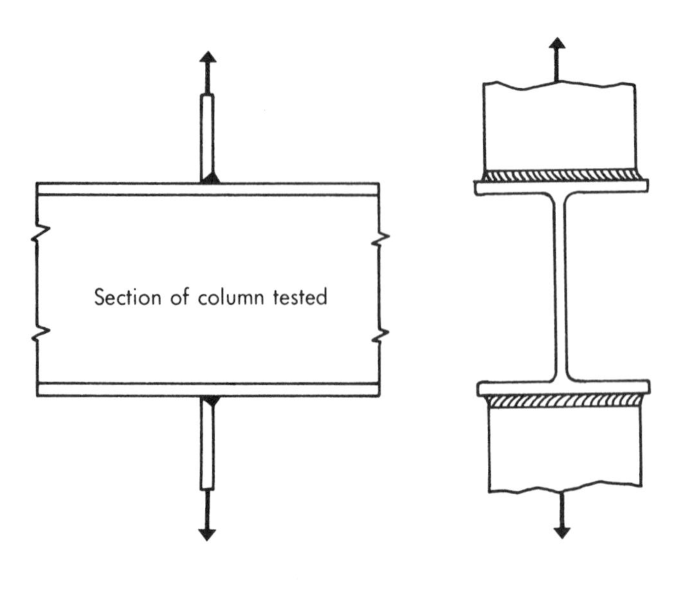

FIGURE 9

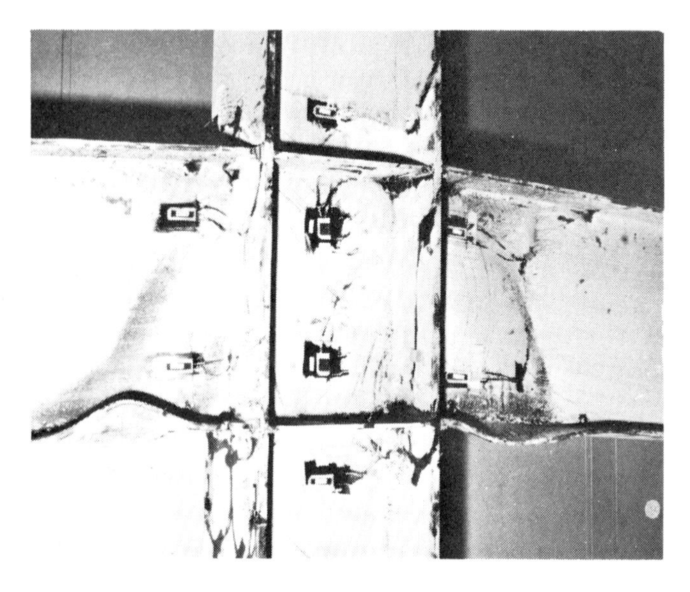

FIGURE 10

Dimensions of both the column flange and the connecting plates were varied in order to study the effect of different combinations of columns and beams.

First yielding was noticed in the fillet of the column just inside the column flange, and directly beneath the attaching plates, at about 40% of the ultimate load. With further loading, yielding proceeded into the column web, underneath the column flange parallel to the attaching plate, and into the column flange from the center of the connecting welds, and parallel to the column web. After ultimate loading, some members failed by cracking of the central portion of the connecting weld directly over the column web, some by cracking in the inside fillet of the column, and some by cracking in the inside fillet of the column, and some by a tearing out of material in the column flange.

FIGURE 11

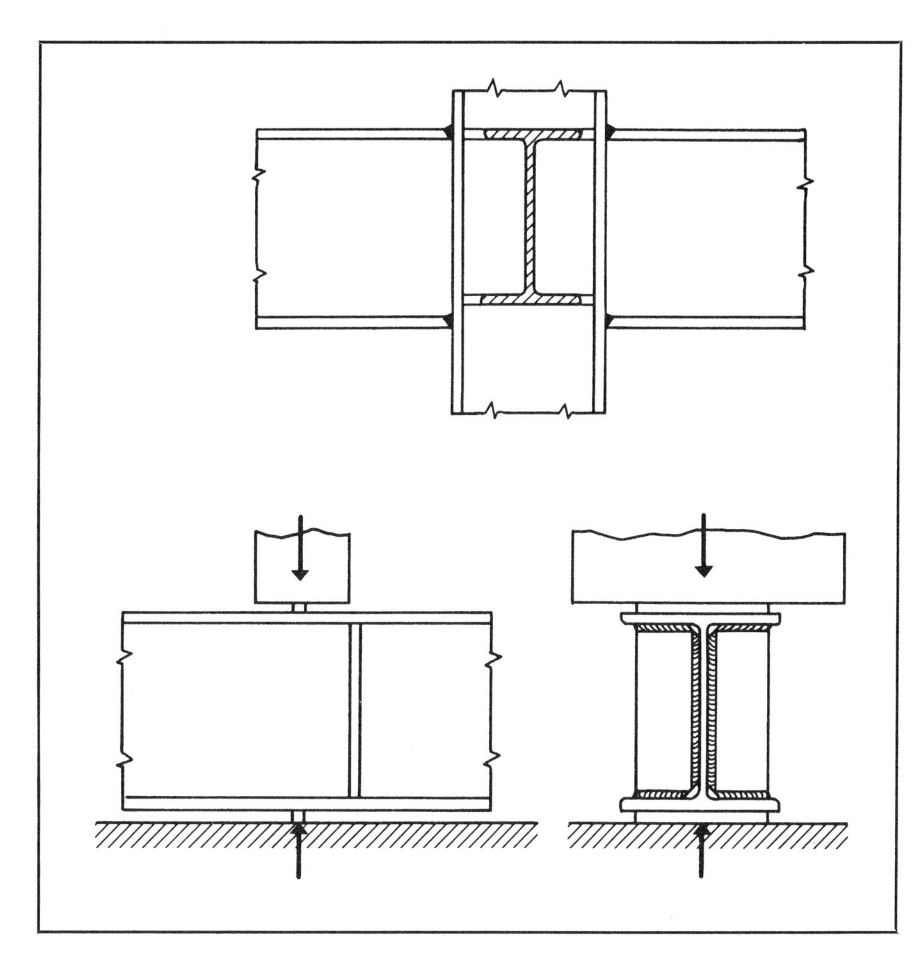

FIGURE 12

Standard Stiffeners

When some type of web stiffening is required, the standard horizontal flange stiffeners are an efficient way to stiffen the column web. Figure 10 shows this type under test.

A Tee section flame cut from a standard wide-flange section may be used for stiffening, Figure 11. The stem of the Tee section is welded to the column web for a short distance in from the ends. This could be entirely shop welded, all of it being done in the flat position, possibly using a semi-automatic welder. This type stiffener would have numerous advantages in four-way beam connections. The beams normally framing into the column web would now butt against this flat surface with good accessibility. The flanges of the beam could be beveled 45° and then easily groove welded in the field to this surface, using backing straps. There would be no other connecting or attaching plates to be used. In effect this part of the connection would be identical to the connection used for beams framing to column flanges.

See Figures 28, 29 and 30 and related text for specifications of stiffeners applicable to elastic design.

Effect of Eccentric Stiffeners

In a four-way beam-to-column connection, the column flanges may be stiffened by the connecting plates of the beam framing into the column web. It may be that the beam framing to the column flange is of a different depth. This in effect will provide eccentric stiffeners, Figure 12.

The lower part of Figure 12 shows how this was tested. It was found that an eccentricity of 2″ provided only about 65% of the stiffening provided by concentric stiffeners, and an eccentricity of 4″ provided less than 20%.

Three methods of framing beams of different depths on opposite flanges of columns are shown in Figure 13.

3. TEST COMPARISON OF STIFFENER TYPES

The following is adapted from "Welded Interior Beam-To-Column Connections", AISC 1959, which summarized tests on various connections.

Figure 14 represents a direct beam-to-column connection. Here the column has no stiffening and is not as stiff against rotation as the 16″ WF 36# beams which frame to the column.

This arrangement showed high stress concentrations at the center of the beam tension flanges, and therefore at the center of the connecting groove weld.

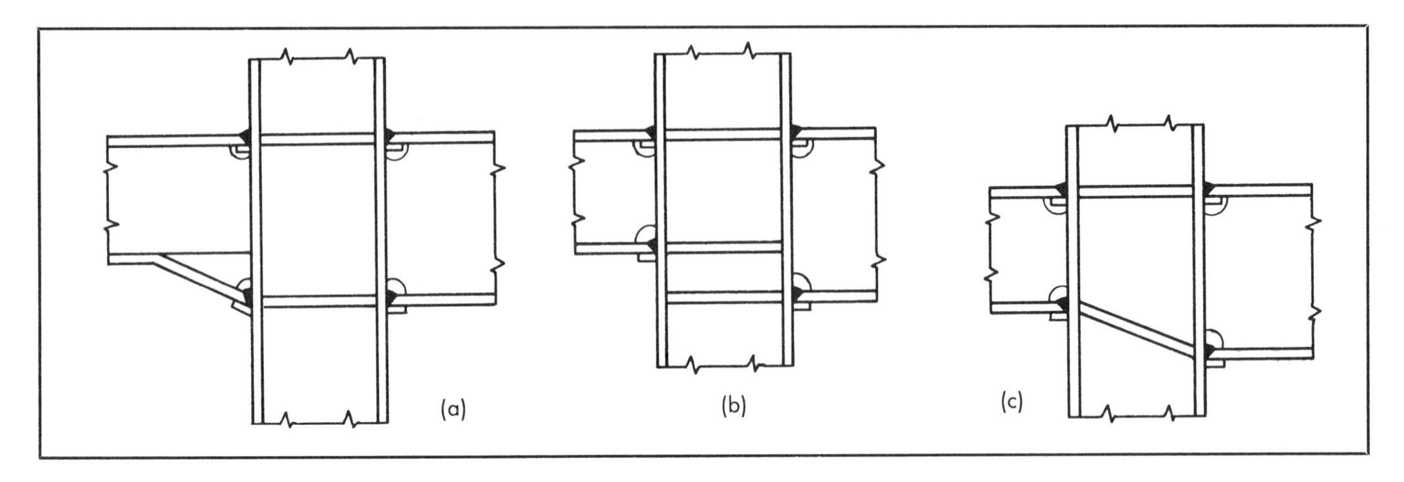

FIGURE 13

However, it was noted that no weld failures occurred until after excessive rotation had taken place.

The stiffeners here in Figure 15 provide the equivalent of beam flanges to the columns, and the columns become as stiff against rotation as the beams framing to the column.

The stress distribution on the compression flanges were uniform on the whole, while in the tension areas the stresses were somewhat higher in the center.

In Figure 16 the column is shown stiffened by a pair of wide-flange Tee sections. As a result the columns are as stiff against rotation as the beams framing into the columns.

From strain gage readings it was calculated that each of the vertical plate stiffeners in the elastic range transmitted only about $\frac{3}{16}$ of the forces coming from the beam flanges and the column web transmitted $\frac{5}{8}$ of the forces.

Placing these stiffener plates closer to the column web might have improved the distribution. However, since the prime purpose of this type of connection is to afford a convenient four-way connection, the plate usually needs to be positioned flush with the edge of the column flange.

The stress distribution was uniform in both flanges at the working load. At 1.5 of the working load, high

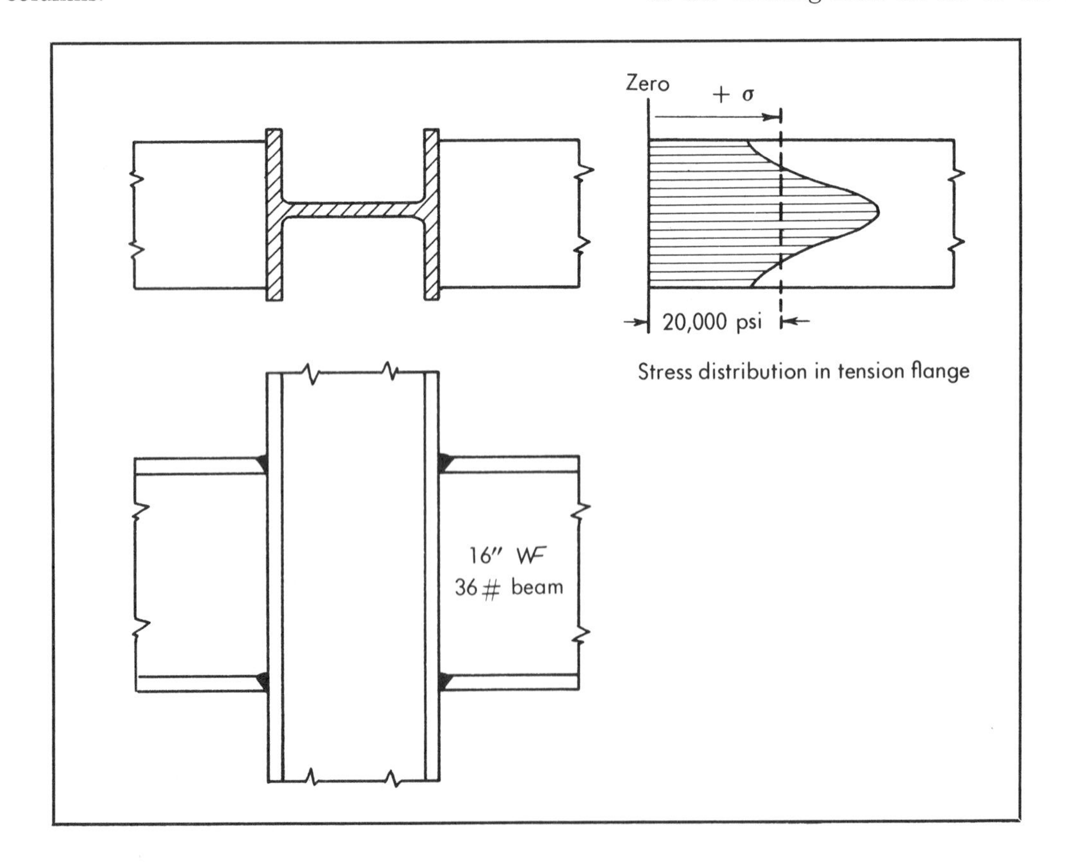

FIGURE 14

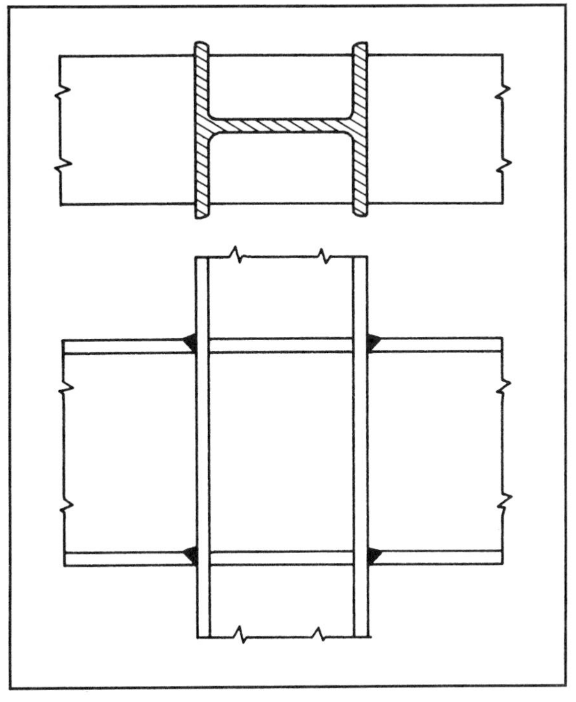

FIGURE 15

FIGURE 16

tensile stresses occurred at midflange.

The connection in Figure 17 was stronger than its two-way counterpart. This evidently shows that the stiffening action provided by two beams framing into the column web strengthens the connection more than it is weakened by the triaxial stresses.

The connections of Figure 18 involving (East-West) beams welded directly to the column flanges proved stiffer than the connection of (North-South) beams to the Tee stiffeners.

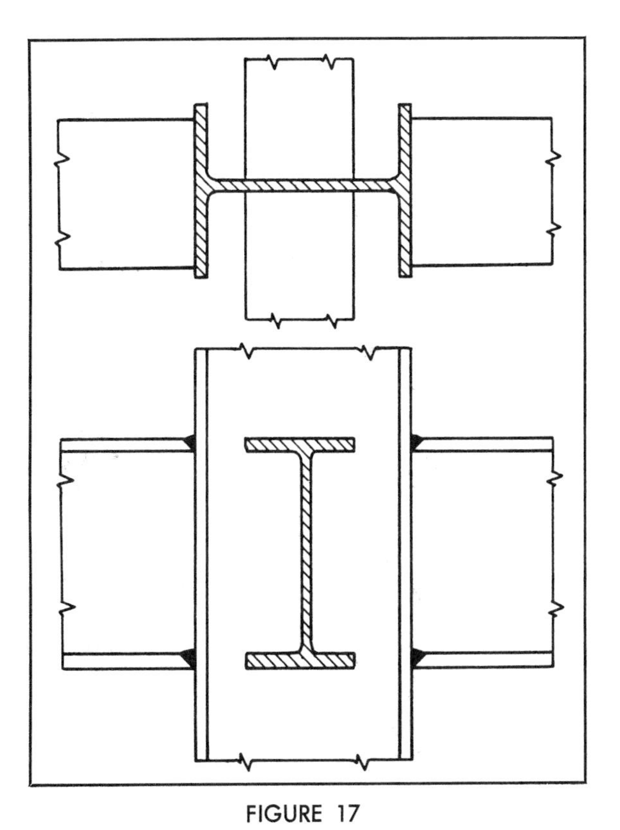

FIGURE 17

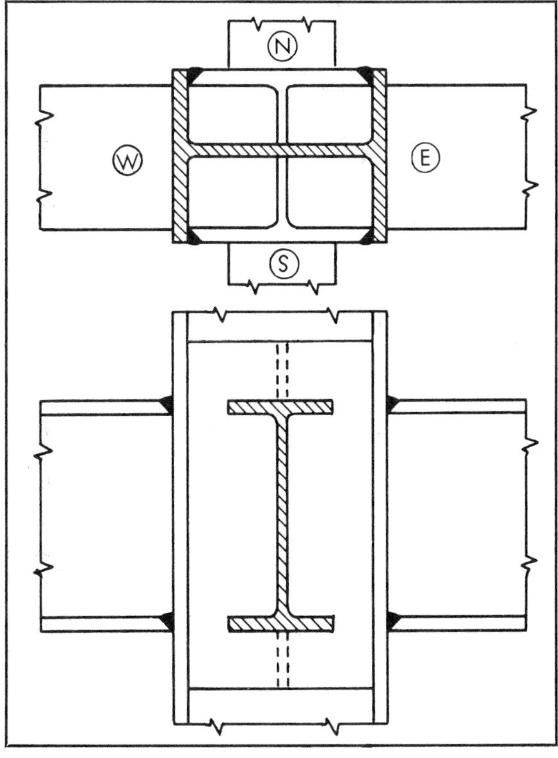

FIGURE 18

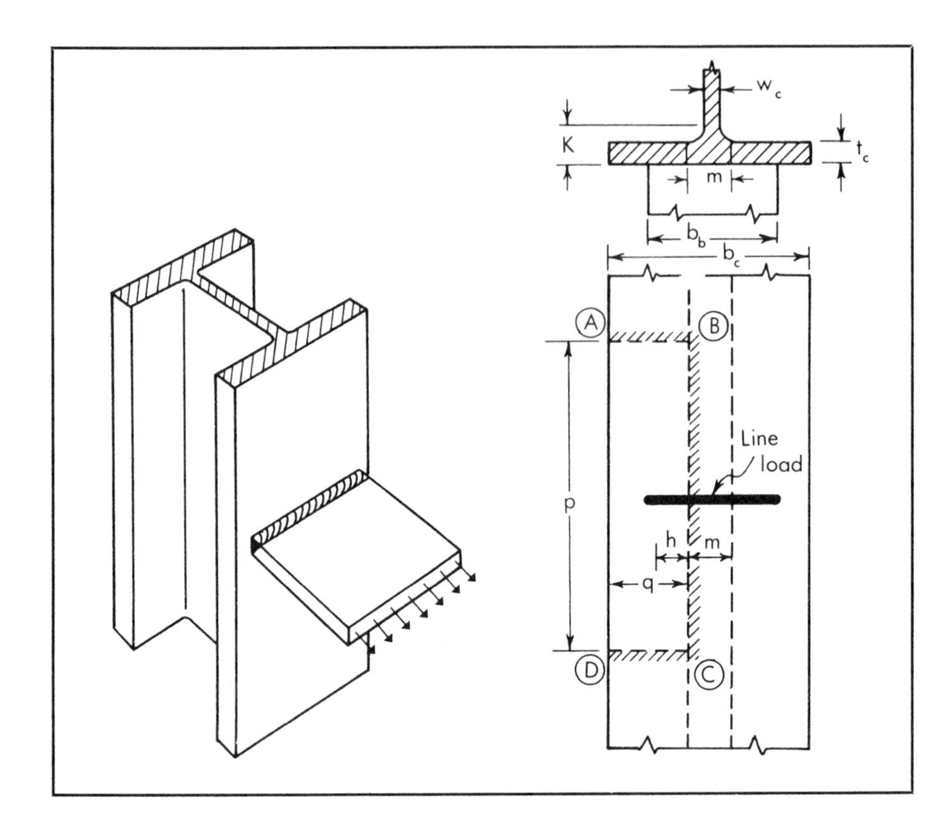

FIGURE 19

The stiffening of the latter connection is mainly dependent on the thickness of the stem of the Tee stiffener, the flanges of the column being too far away to offer much resistance.

The column web is ably assisted in preventing rotation at the connection by the flanges of the split-beam Tee stiffeners.

4. ANALYSIS OF STIFFENER REQUIREMENTS IN TENSION REGION OF CONNECTION (Elastic Design)

The following is adapted from "Welded Interior Beam-to-Column Connections", AISC 1959.

The column flange can be considered as acting as two plates, both of type ABCD; see Figure 19. The beam flange is assumed to place a line load on each of these plates. The effective length of the plates (p) is assumed to be 12 t_c and the plates are assumed to be fixed at the ends of this length. The plate is also assumed to be fixed adjacent to the column web.

where:

$$m = w_c + 2\,(K - t_c)$$

$$q = \frac{b_c - m}{2}$$

$$h = \frac{b_b - m}{2}$$

$$p = 12\ t_c$$

Analysis of this plate by means of yield line theory leads to the ultimate capacity of this plate being—

$$P_u = c_1\ \sigma_y\ t_c^2$$

where:

$$c_1 = \frac{\dfrac{4}{\beta} + \dfrac{\beta}{\eta}}{2 - \dfrac{\eta}{\lambda}}$$

Let:

$$\eta = \frac{\beta}{4}\left[\sqrt{\beta^2 + 8\lambda} - \beta\right]$$

$$\beta = \frac{p}{q}$$

$$\lambda = \frac{h}{q}$$

For the wide-flange columns and beams used in practical connections, it has been found that c_1 varies within the range of 3.5 to 5. A conservative figure would be—

$$P_u = 3.5\ \sigma_y\ t_c^2$$

The force carried by the central rigid portion of the column in line with the web is—

$$\sigma_y\ t_b\ m$$

Setting this total force equal to that of the beam's tension flange:

$$\sigma_y \ t_b \ m + 7 \ \sigma_y \ t_c^2 = \sigma_y \ b_b \ t_b = \sigma_y \ A_f$$

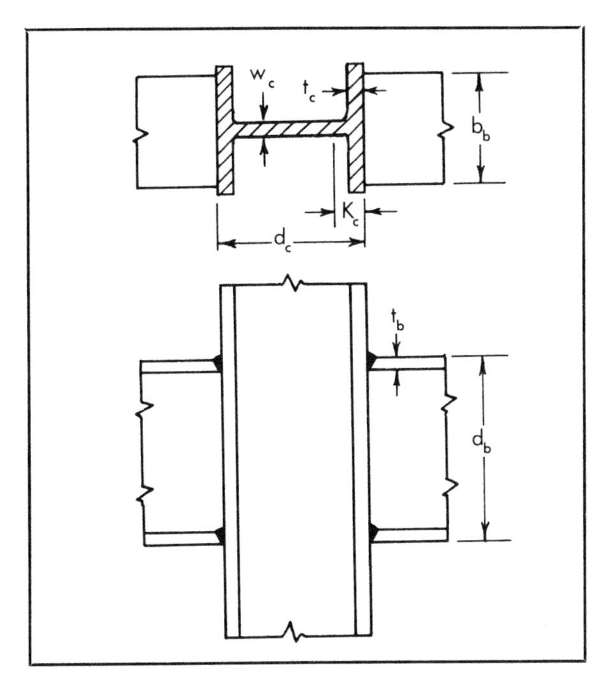

FIGURE 20

Reducing the strength of this column region by 20% and making the conservative assumption that $m/b_b = .15$, this reduces to the following:

$$\boxed{t_c \geqq 0.4 \sqrt{A_f}}$$

If the thickness of the column flange (t_c) meets the above requirement, column stiffeners are not needed in line with the tension flanges of the beam.

If the actual thickness of the column flange (t_c) is less than this value, stiffeners are needed.

5. ANALYSIS OF STIFFENER REQUIREMENTS IN COMPRESSION REGION OF CONNECTION (Elastic Design)

It is assumed the concentrated compression force from the beam flange spreads out into the column web at a slope of 1 in 2½ until it reaches the K line or web toe of the fillet; see Figure 8.

Equating the resisting force of the column web to the applied force of the beam flange, assuming yield stress—

$$w_c \ (t_b + 5 \ K_c) \ \sigma_y \geqq A_f \ \sigma_y \qquad \text{or}$$

$$\boxed{w_c \geqq \frac{A_f}{t_b + 5 \ K_c}}$$

If the thickness of the column web (w_c) meets the above requirement, column stiffeners are not needed in line with the compression flanges of the beam.

If the actual thickness of the column web (w_c) is less than this value, the web must be stiffened in some manner.

6. HORIZONTAL STIFFENERS

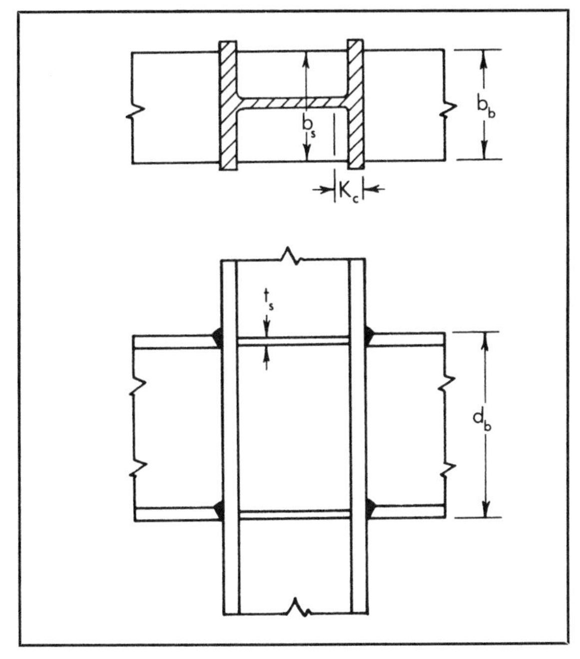

FIGURE 21

Equating the resisting force of the column web and a pair of horizontal plate stiffeners to the applied force of the beam flange at yield stress—

$$w_c \ (t_b + 5 \ K_c) \ \sigma_y + A_s \ \sigma_y \geqq A_f \ \sigma_y \qquad \text{or}$$

$$\boxed{A_s \geqq A_f - w_c \ (t_b + 5 \ K_c)}$$

where:

A_s = total cross-sectional area of pair of stiffeners

To prevent buckling of the stiffener—

$$\boxed{\frac{b_s}{t_s} \leqq 16}$$

where:

b_s = total width of pair of stiffeners

If the stiffener is displaced not more than 2″ from alignment with the adjacent beam flange (as in Fig. 12), it may still be used if considered about 60% as effective as when in direct line. The stiffener thickness (t_s) found from the above formula should then be multiplied by 1.70 to give the actual required value.

7. VERTICAL STIFFENERS

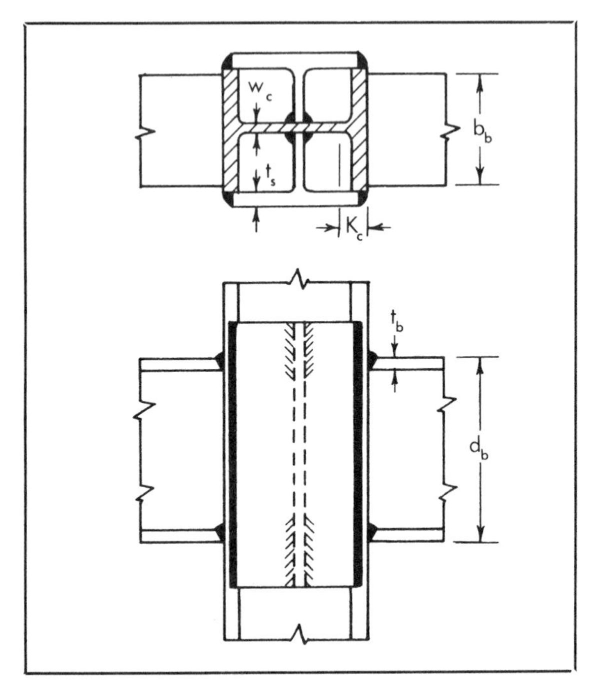

FIGURE 22

Because the vertical stiffeners (usually Tees) are placed at the outer edges of the column flange, they are assumed to be half as effective as though placed near the column web. It is assumed the concentrated beam flange force spreads out into the vertical stiffener in the same manner as the column web.

Equating the resisting force of the column web and a pair of vertical Tee stiffeners to the applied force of the beam flange at yield stress—

$$w_c\ (t_b + 5\ K_c)\ \sigma_y + 2 \times \tfrac{1}{2}\ t_s\ (t_b + 5\ K_c)\ \sigma_y = A_f\ \sigma_y \quad \text{or}$$

$$\boxed{t_s \geqq \frac{A_f}{t_b + 5\ K_c} - w_c}$$

To prevent buckling of the stiffener—

$$\boxed{\frac{d_c}{t_s} \geqq 30}$$

Problem 1

As an example of applying the preceding analysis of the tension region of a connection, we will analyze a connection which, when tested to failure, performed well; see Figure 23.

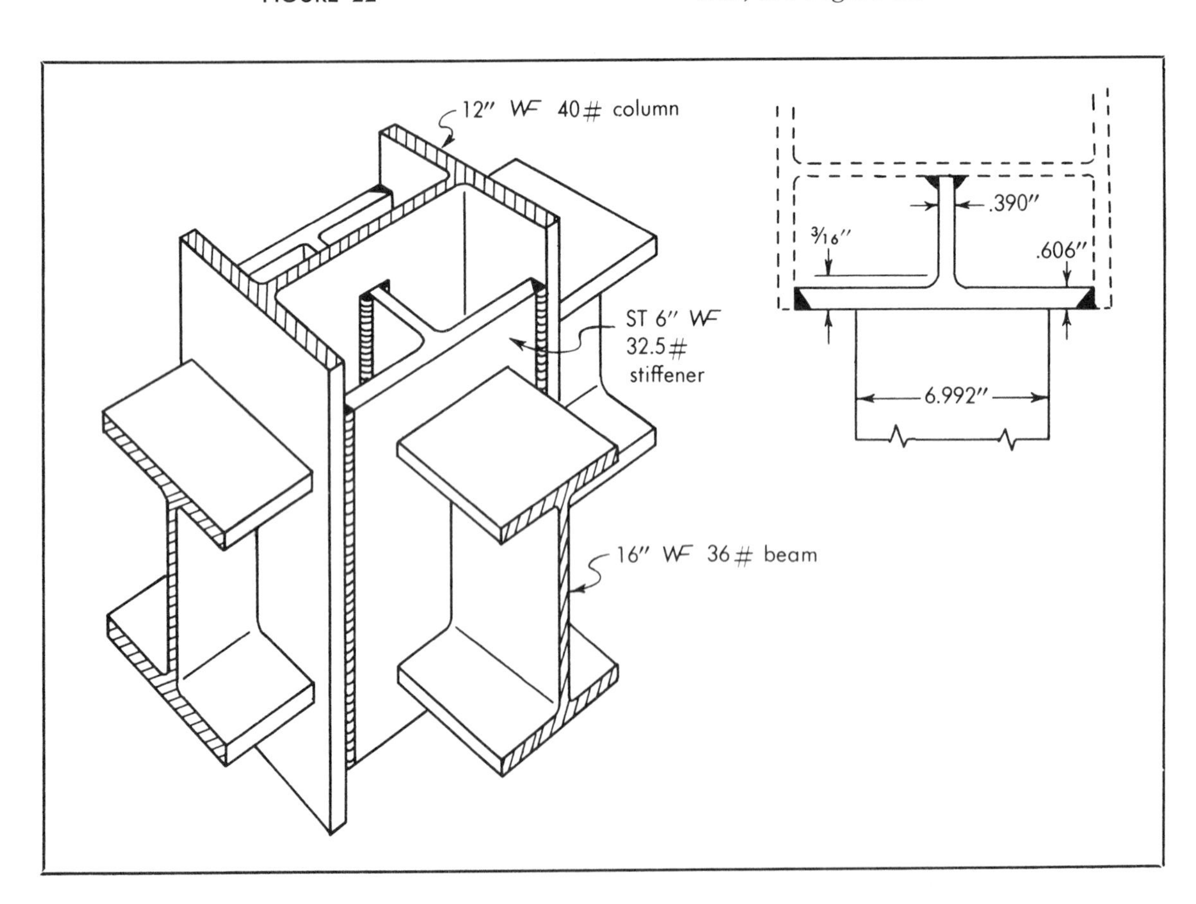

FIGURE 23

where:

$$m = w_c + 2\ (K - t_c)$$
$$= (.390) + 2\ [(1\ \tfrac{3}{16}) - (.606)]$$
$$= 1.553''$$

$$q = \frac{b_c - m}{2}$$
$$= \frac{(10.92) - (1.55)}{2}$$
$$= 4.69''$$

$$h = \frac{b_b - m}{2}$$
$$= \frac{(6.99) - (1.55)}{2}$$
$$= 2.72''$$

$$p = 12\ t_c$$
$$= 12\ (.606)$$
$$= 7.27''$$

Since:

$$\lambda = \frac{h}{q}$$
$$= \frac{(2.72)}{(4.69)}$$
$$= .58$$

$$\beta = \frac{p}{q}$$
$$= \frac{(7.27)}{(4.69)}$$
$$= 1.55$$

and:

$$\eta = \frac{\beta}{4}\left[\sqrt{\beta^2 + 8\ \lambda} - \beta\right]$$
$$= \frac{(1.55)}{4}\left[\sqrt{(1.55)^2 + 8\ (.58)} - (1.55)\right]$$
$$= .387$$

$$\therefore\ c_1 = \frac{\dfrac{4}{\beta} + \dfrac{\beta}{\eta}}{2 - \dfrac{\eta}{\lambda}}$$
$$= \frac{\dfrac{4}{(1.55)} + \dfrac{(1.55)}{(.387)}}{2 - \dfrac{(.387)}{(.58)}}$$
$$= 4.94$$

The total force which can be carried by the tension region of the column stiffener's flange must equal or exceed the force of the beam's tension flange, or:

$$\sigma_y\ t_b\ m + 2\ c_1\ \sigma_y\ t_c^2 \geqq \sigma_y\ A_f$$

Provided both column stiffener and beam have same yield strength:

$$(.428)(1.553) + 2\ (4.94)(.606)^2 \geqq (6.992)(.428)$$
$$4.28 \geqq 3.00 \qquad \text{O.K.}$$

If we used the conservative formula:

$$t_s \geqq 0.4\ \sqrt{A_f}$$
$$\geqq .40\ \sqrt{(6.992)(.428)}$$
$$\geqq .692''$$

but the initial design called for $t_c = .606''$ and the connection tested O.K.

8. CONNECTIONS THROUGH VERTICAL TEE STIFFENERS

Tests have shown that when the beam flange extends the full width of the connecting plate, Figure 24, about ⅝ of the flange force is carried by the central portion of the plate. Each of the two outer edges carry about $\frac{3}{16}$ of this force.

Figure 25 comes from test data of Lehigh University. Notice in the East-West beams, the flange of which extends almost the full width of the column

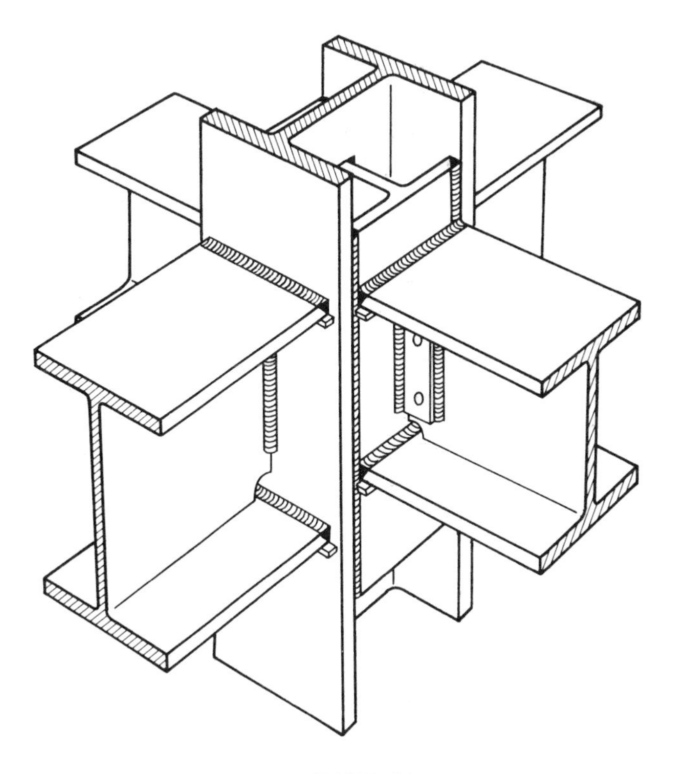

FIGURE 24

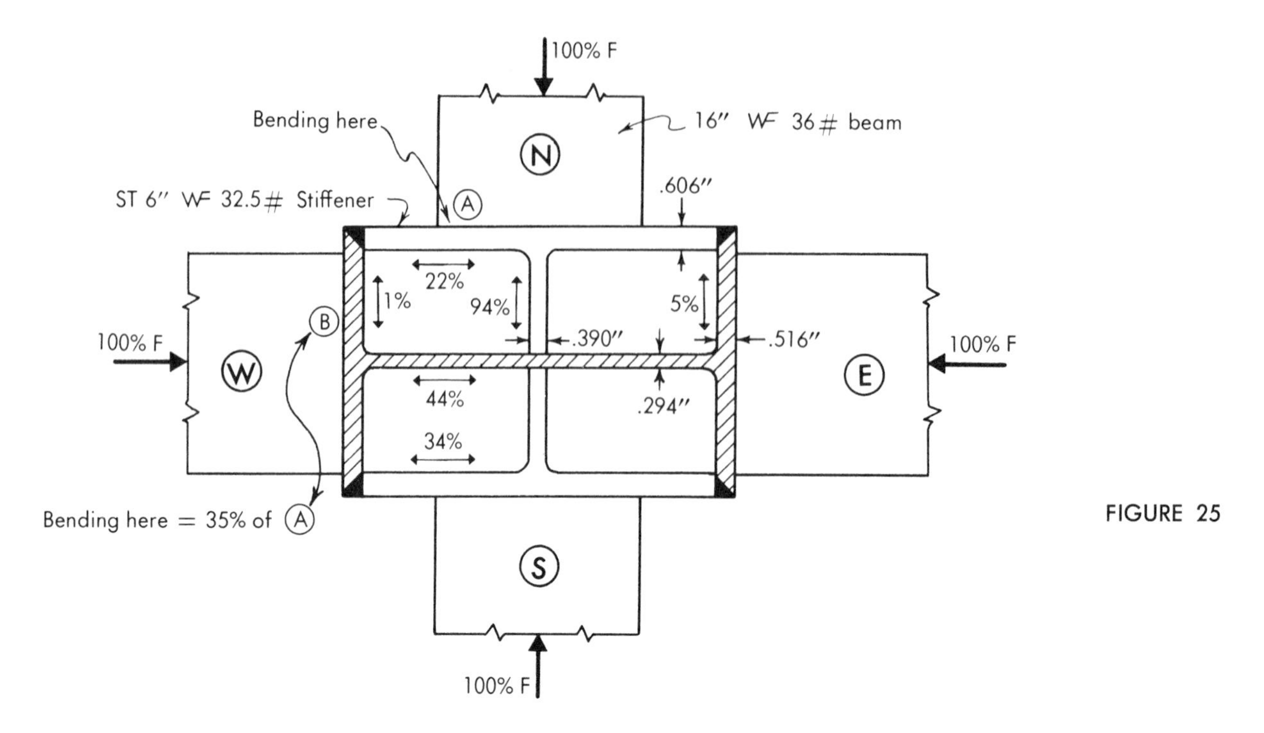

FIGURE 25

flange, 44% of the force is transferred through the web of the connection even though it is only about half as thick as the stiffener plates. This corresponds well with the idea that the flange of the column in this region is similar to a two-span beam on three supports with a uniform load; in this case the center reaction is ⅝ of the total load, and the two outer supports each carry $\frac{3}{16}$ of the load.

The report "Welded Interior Beam-To-Column Connections", AISC 1959, mentions that "from strain gage readings it was calculated that the vertical plate stiffeners in the elastic range each transmitted only about $\frac{3}{16}$ths of the forces coming from the beam flanges and the web transmitted ⅝ths."

Of course, the same would not be true in the North-South beams because they do not extend the full width of the flange of the Tee stiffener. As a result, most of this force must be transferred into the web or stem of the Tee stiffener since any portion of this force reaching the outer edges of the column flange must be transferred as bending out along the flange of the Tee section.

Weld Size: Stiffener Stem to Column Web

On the basis of these tests at Lehigh University, on connections where the beam flange extends the full

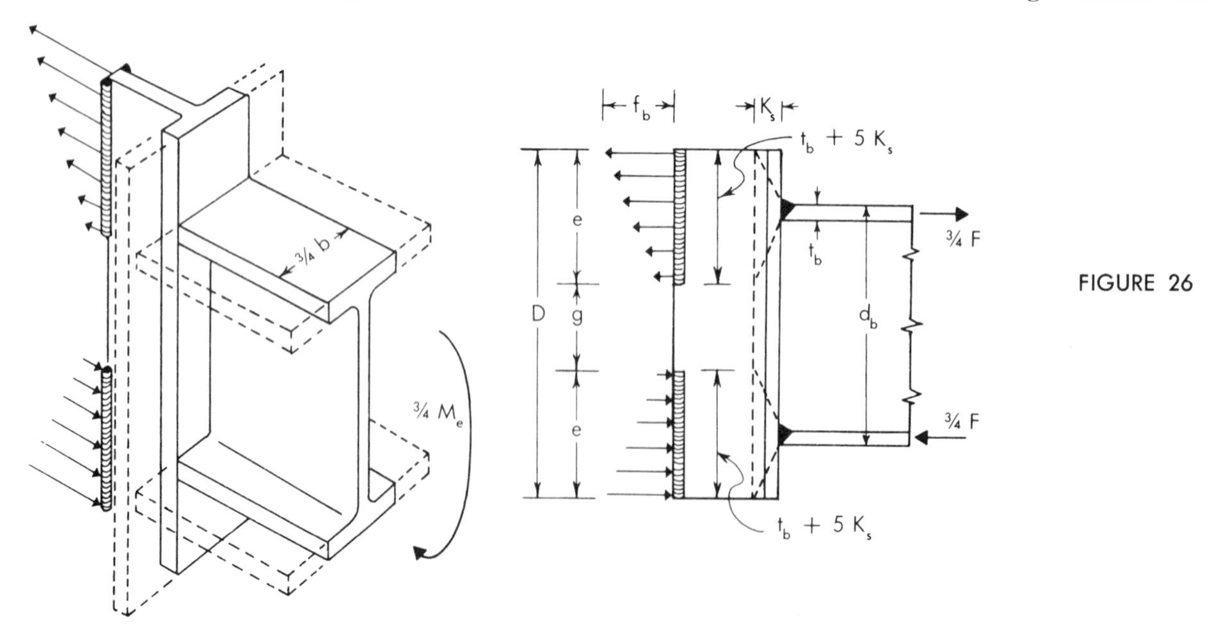

FIGURE 26

width of the stiffener flange, we will assume that ¾ of the beam flange force is carried by the stem portion of the connection. See Figure 26.

Because of the stiffening effect of the beam web and the stem of the connecting plate, this central (stem) portion of the connection will load up in bending. This assumes it rotates as a unit about a point at mid-height. The bending force on the weld is zero at this neutral axis and increases linearly to a maximum value at the upper and lower edges of the connection.

Treating the weld group as a line, the section modulus is equal to—

$$S_w = \frac{(D^3 - g^3)}{3\ D}$$

The resulting maximum unit bending force at the top portion of the weld on the stem is—

$$f_b = \frac{M}{S_w} = \frac{\frac{3}{4}\ M\ D\ 3}{(D^3 - g^3)}$$

The leg size of this weld would be found by dividing this value by the allowable for the particular weld metal.

A7, A373 Steel; E60 Welds
$f = 9600\ \omega$
A36, A441 Steel; E70 Welds
$f = 11{,}200\ \omega$

Here:

$$D = d_b + 5\ K_s$$

$$g = d_b - 2\ t_b - 5\ K_s$$

Weld Size: Stiffener Flange to Column Flange

The Tee stiffeners may be joined to the column flanges by a) fillet welds, b) groove welds, or c) corner welds. The groove welds (b) were used in the Lehigh Research of this connection.

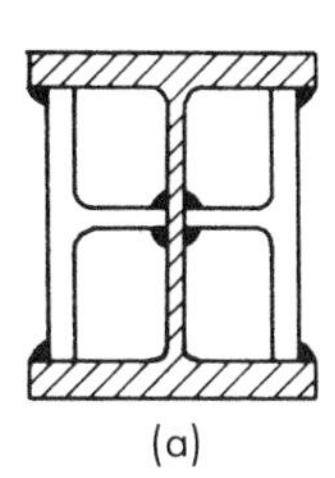
(a)

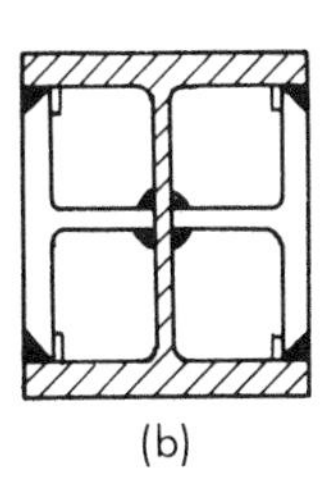
(b)

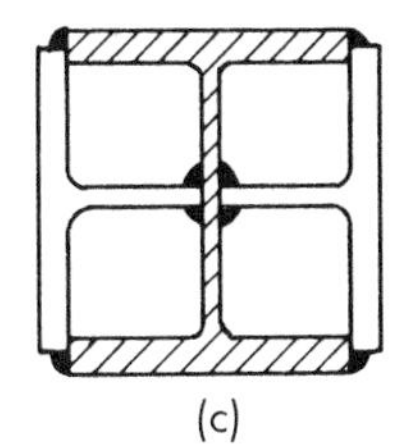
(c)

FIGURE 27

Since tests on full-width flanges showed that the two outer edges of the connection carry about $\frac{3}{16}$ of the flange force, we will assume that each outer weld must carry ⅓ of the flange force. See Figure 28.

These welds will be pulled with an axial force of ⅓ F. We may assume the same distribution of force through the connecting plate at a slope of 1 to 2½ into the connecting welds. This will provide an effective length of weld of $t_b + 5\ t_s$ to carry this force.

The unit force on this weld is—

$$f_a = \frac{M_e}{3(d_b - t_b)(t_b + 5\ t_s)}$$

The leg size of the fillet weld, or throat of groove weld, is determined by dividing this unit force by the suitable allowable.

The effect of the vertical shear load (V) on these

FIGURE 28

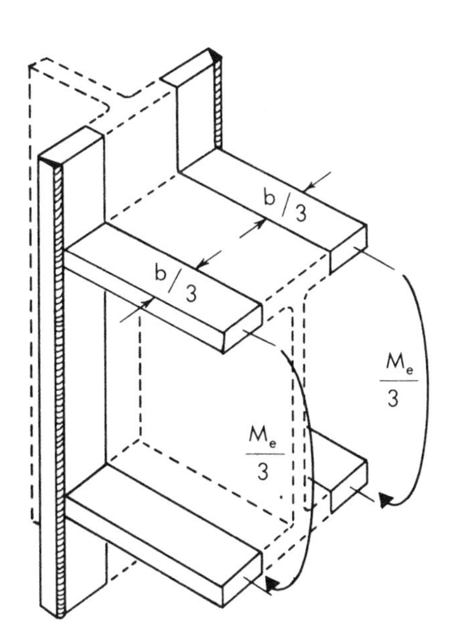

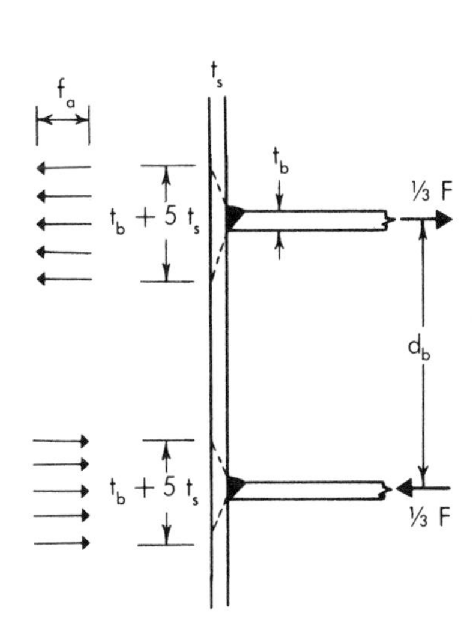

welds could be checked by using the entire length of the welds. However, this would represent little additional force on these welds.

Proportioning the Tee Stiffener

The following will be helpful in selecting a Tee stiffener section for this type of connection, where the beam flange equals the full width of the stiffener flange:

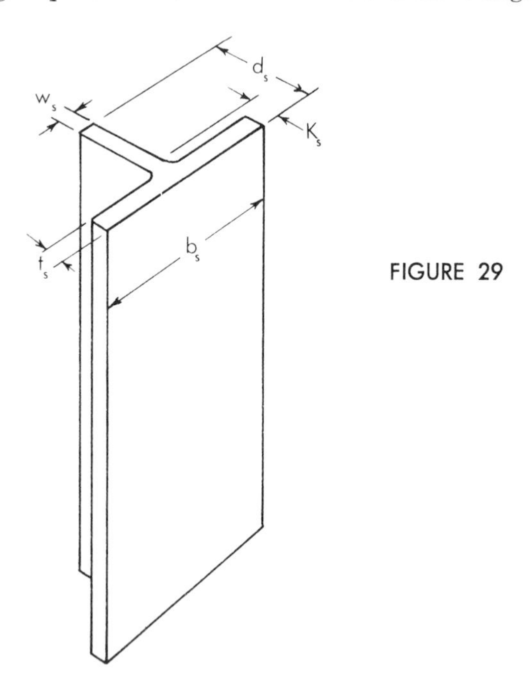

FIGURE 29

1. The thickness of the stiffener flange (t_s) must be sufficient to transfer the tensile force of the beam flange. In this case ¾ of the beam flange will be used.

$$t_s \geqq .40 \sqrt{3/4\ b_b\ t_b}$$

2. The width of the stiffener flange (b_s) must be sufficient for it to reach to the column flanges.

$$b_s \geqq d_c - 2\ t_c$$

3. The thickness of the stiffener stem (w_s) should be about the same as the beam flange thickness (t_b).

$$w_s \geqq t_b$$

4. The depth of the stiffener (d_s), as measured through the stem portion, must be sufficient for it to extend from the face of the column web to the outer edge of the column flange.

$$d_s \geqq \frac{b_c - w_c}{2}$$

5. As a guide, the stiffener should satisfy this condition:

$$w_s\ (t_b + 5\ K_s) \geqq 3/4\ b_b\ t_b$$

or an approximation on the conservative side:

$$w_s\ K_s = \frac{3/4\ b_b\ t_b}{5}$$

Where Beam Flange Width < Stiffener Flange Width

Where the beam flange does not extend the full width of the connecting plate, the stem portion of the connection is assumed to carry the entire moment. Therefore the maximum bending force on the top portion of this weld will be—

$$f_b = \frac{3\ M\ D}{(D^3 - g^3)}$$

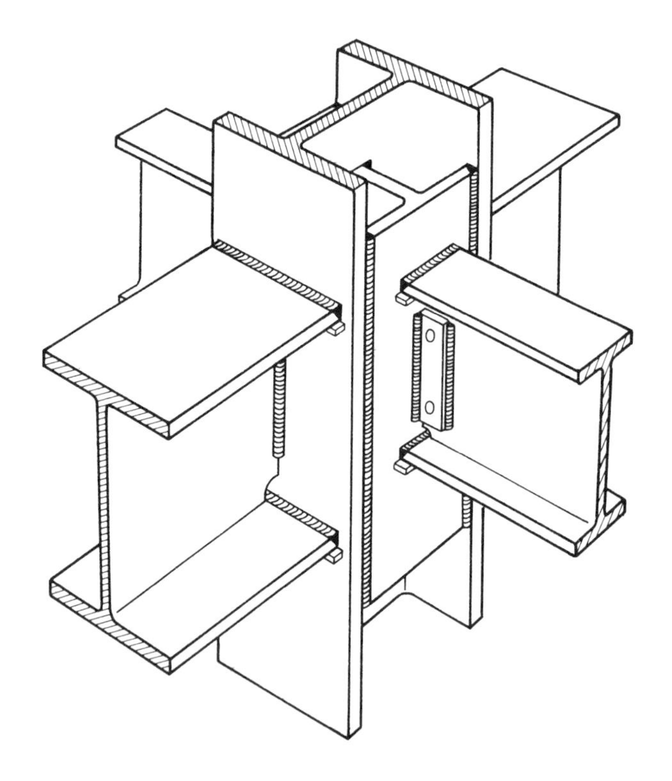

FIGURE 30

The same items as before are used to proportion the Tee stiffener, except in items 1 and 5 where the full value of the beam flange's section area is used instead of ¾ of this value. These formulas become—

1. $$t_s \geqq .40 \sqrt{b_b\ t_b}$$

5. $w_s \, K_s \geqq \dfrac{b_b \, t_b}{5}$

Problem 2

To design a fully welded beam-to-column connection for a 14″ WF beam to an 8″ WF column to transfer an end moment of M = 1100 in.-kips and a vertical shear of V = 20 kips. The solution of this problem will be considered with seven variations. Use A36 steel and E70 welds.

(1)

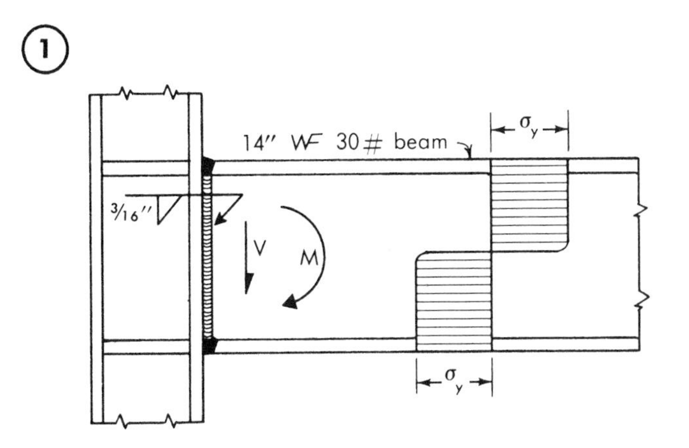

FIGURE 31

Here:

$$M = 1100 \text{ in.-kips}$$
$$V = 20 \text{ kips}$$

The welding of both the flanges and the web along its full depth enables the beam to develop its full plastic moment, thus allowing the "compact" beam to be stressed 10% higher in bending, or $\sigma = .66 \, \sigma_y$. This also allows the end of the beam, and its welded connection, to be designed for 90% of the end moment due to gravity loading. (AISC Sec 1.5.1.4.1 and Sec 2.6)

$$\sigma = \frac{.9 \, M}{S}$$
$$= \frac{.9(1100 \text{ in.-kips})}{(41.8 \text{ in.}^3)}$$
$$= 23{,}700 \text{ psi} < .66 \, \sigma_y < 24{,}000 \text{ psi} \qquad \underline{\text{OK}}$$

TABLE 1—Properties of Beams Used in Problem 2

	b	d_b	t_f	t_w	S	K
14″ WF 30# beam	6.733″	13.86″	.383″	.270″	41.8 in.^{3}	
14″ WF 34# beam	6.75″	14.00″	.453″	.287″	48.5 in.^{3}	
14″ WF 38# beam	6.776″	14.12″	.513″	.313″	54.6 in.^{3}	1.0″

The weld on the beam's web must be able to stress the web in bending to yield (σ_y) throughout its entire depth; see the bending stress distribution in Figure 25. The weld must also be able to transfer the vertical shear.

unit force on this weld from the vertical shear

$$f_w = \frac{V}{2 \, L_v}$$
$$= \frac{(20 \text{ kips})}{2(13.86 - 2 \times .387)}$$
$$= 770 \text{ lbs/in.}$$

leg size of fillet weld

$$\omega = \frac{\text{actual force}}{\text{allowable force}}$$
$$= \frac{(770)}{(11{,}200)}$$
$$= .069''$$

However, since the beam web is welded to a .433″ thick flange of the column, the minimum size for this fillet weld would be 3/16″; see Section 7.4, Table 3.

WELD SIZE TO DEVELOP ULTIMATE LOAD

The next question is what size fillet weld would be required to develop the beam web to yield stress. The force in question results from bending, so it is transverse to the weld.

The AWS allowables for fillet welds are based on parallel loading, AWS has not set up any allowable values for transverse loading.

weld vs *web plate*

(parallel load) (transverse load-tension)

$$2(11{,}200 \, \omega) \geqq t_w \, (.60 \, \sigma_y) = t_w \, 22{,}000$$
$$\omega \geqq .982 \, t_w$$

or $\boxed{\omega \geqq t_w}$ (AWS Code)

However it has been known for several years through testing and theory that a fillet weld loaded transversely is ⅓ stronger than when loaded parallel. Accordingly this ratio would become—

weld vs *web plate*

(transverse load) (transverse load-tension)

$$2(11{,}200 \, \omega) \, 1\tfrac{1}{3} \geqq t_w \, (.60 \, \sigma_y) = t_w \, 22{,}000$$
$$\omega \geqq .736 \, t_w$$

or $\boxed{\omega \geqq \tfrac{3}{4} \, t_w}$

For plastic design concepts, based on ultimate loading, the allowable for the fillet weld would be increased by the factor 1.67 (AISC Sec 2.7). This is the same increase used for the member (.60 σ_y up to σ_y), hence the same relationship between weld size and plate thickness will still hold.

Based on AWS Code allowables (for parallel loading), this fillet weld on the web of the beam would have to be equal to the web thickness.

$t_w = .270''$ or use $\omega = \frac{1}{4}''$

However since it is known a fillet weld ($\omega = \frac{3}{4}\ t_w$) will outpull the web, a $\frac{3}{16}''$ fillet weld will be used here.

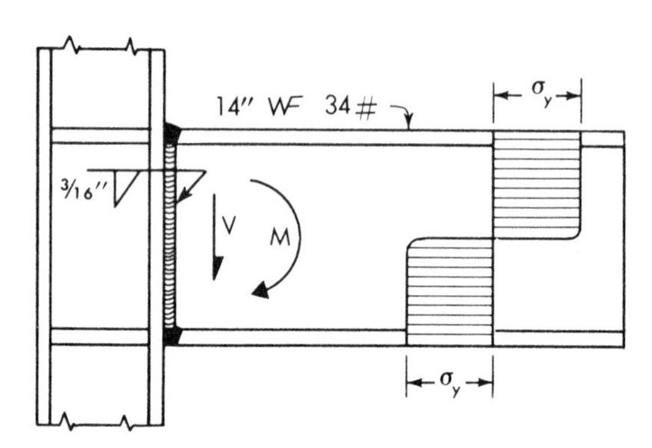

FIGURE 32

Here:

$M = 1100$ in.-kips

$V = 20$ kips

The welding of the flanges and full depth of the web enables the beam to develop its full plastic moment, allowing the "compact" beam to be stressed 10% higher in bending, or $\sigma = .66\ \sigma_y$. In this case the beam cantilevers out from the support so that no 10% reduction in the negative moment can be made.

$$\sigma = \frac{M}{S}$$

$$= \frac{(1100 \text{ in.-kips})}{(48.5 \text{ in.}^3)}$$

$$= 22{,}700 \text{ psi} < .66\ \sigma_y < 24{,}000 \text{ psi} \qquad \underline{\text{OK}}$$

The fillet weld on the web of the beam is figured as in method (1.)

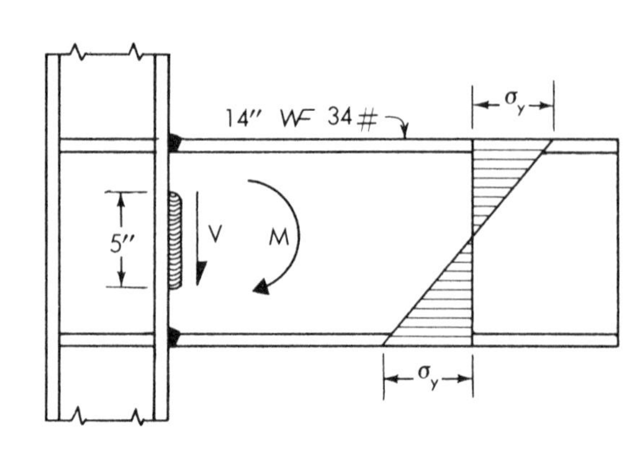

FIGURE 33

Here:

$M = 1050$ in.-kips

$V = 20$ kips

If this cantilever beam had an end moment of M = 1050 in.-kips instead of the previous 1100 in.-kips:

$$\sigma = \frac{M}{S}$$

$$= \frac{(1050 \text{ in.-kips})}{(48.5 \text{ in.}^3)}$$

$$= 21{,}600 \text{ psi} < .60\ \sigma_y < 22{,}000 \text{ psi} \qquad \underline{\text{OK}}$$

In this case the bending stress is within .60 σ_y, and the beam and connection must be able to develop a bending resistance equal to the product of the beam's section modulus and yield point stress (see Fig. 27) rather than the full plastic moment. As a result it is not necessary to weld the web for its full depth.

For determining the minimum length of the fillet weld on the web, assume the leg size to not exceed ⅔ t_w = ⅔ (.287") = .192". This will provide sufficient length of weld so the beam web at the connection will not be overstressed in shear. (AISC Sec 1.17.5)

The minimum length of fillet weld on each side of the web is—

$$L_v = \frac{V}{2\ f_w}$$

$$= \frac{(20 \text{ kips})}{2(11{,}200\ \omega)} = \frac{20 \text{ kips}}{2(11{,}200)(.192)}$$

$$= 4.65''$$

If $\frac{3}{16}''$ fillet welds are used (next size smaller than .192"), their length would be—

$$L_v = \frac{V}{2\ f_w}$$

$$= \frac{(20\ \text{kips})}{2(11{,}200)(3/16)}$$

$$= 4.75''$$

Hence use $3/16''$ ◺ 5″ long on both sides < 4.65″. OK

Since the size of this weld used in determining its length was held to ⅔ of the web thickness, it is unnecessary to check the resulting shear stress in the web at this connection. However, to illustrate this, it will be checked here:

$$\tau_{web} = \frac{V}{A_w}$$

$$= \frac{(20\ \text{kips})}{(5)\ (.287)}$$

$$= 14{,}000\ \text{psi} < .40\ \sigma_y < 14{,}500\ \text{psi} \quad \text{OK}$$

(4)

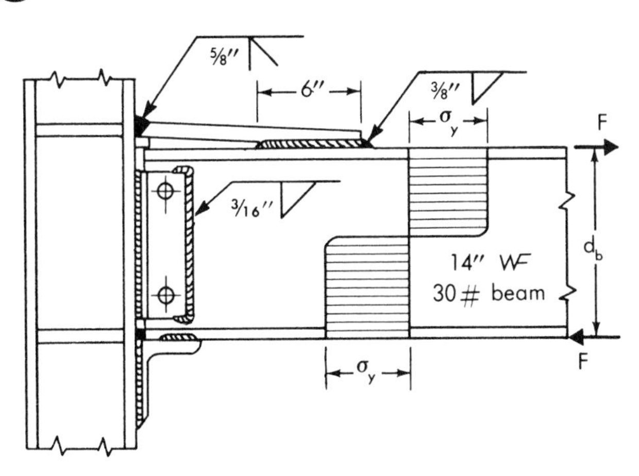

FIGURE 34

Here:

$$M = 1100\ \text{in.-kips}$$
$$V = 20\ \text{kips}$$

The welding of the flanges and full depth of the web enables the beam to develop its full plastic moment, allowing the "compact" beam to be stressed 10% higher in bending, or $\sigma = .66\ \sigma_y$. This also allows the end of the beam, and its welded connection, to be designed for 90% of the end moment due to gravity loading. (AISC Sec 1.5.1.4.1 and Sec 2.6)

bending stress in beam

$$\sigma = \frac{.9\ M}{S}$$

$$= \frac{.9\ (1100\ \text{in.-kips})}{(41.8\ \text{in.}^3)}$$

$$= 23{,}700\ \text{psi} < .66\ \sigma_y < 24{,}000\ \text{psi} \quad \text{OK}$$

bending force on top connecting plate

$$F = \frac{.9\ M}{d_b}$$

$$= \frac{.9\ (1100\ \text{in-kips})}{13.86''}$$

$$= 71.5\ \text{kips}$$

section area of top connecting plate

$$A_p = \frac{F}{\sigma}$$

$$= \frac{(71.5\ \text{kips})}{(24{,}000\ \text{psi})}$$

$$= 2.98\ \text{in.}^2$$

or use a 5½″ x ⅝″ plate, the section area of which is—

$$A_p = 3.44\ \text{in.}^2 > 2.98\ \text{in.}^2 \quad \text{OK}$$

If ⅜″ fillet welds are used to connect top plate to upper flange of beam:

$$f_w = 11{,}200\ (3/8)$$
$$= 4200\ \text{lbs/linear inch}$$

length of fillet weld

$$L = \frac{F}{f_w}$$

$$= \frac{(71.5\ \text{kips})}{(4200\ \text{lbs/in.})}$$

$$= 17''$$

or use 5½″ of weld across the end, and return 6″ along each side, for a total weld length of 17½″.

The lower flange of the beam is groove butt welded directly to the column flange; and, since the web framing angle carries the shear reaction, no further work is required on this lower portion of the connection. The seat angle simply serves to provide temporary support for the beam during erection and a backing for the flange groove weld.

The fillet weld on the web of the beam is figured as in method (1).

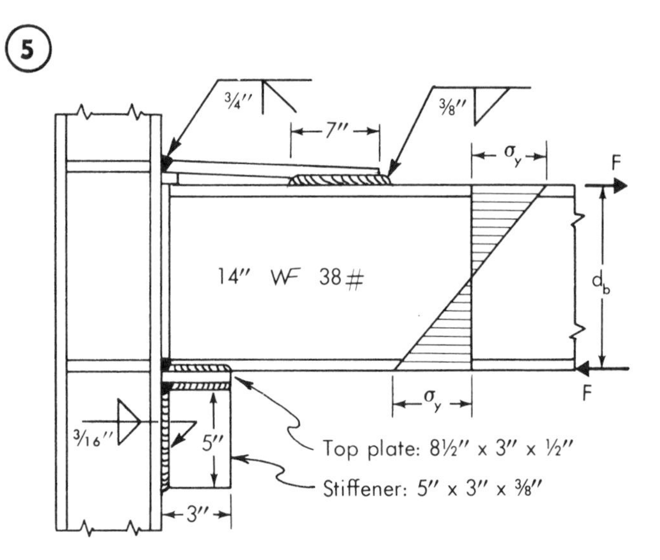

FIGURE 35

Here:

$$M = 1100 \text{ in.-kips}$$
$$V = 20 \text{ kips}$$

In this particular connection, the shear reaction is taken as bearing through the lower flange of the beam.

There is no welding directly on the web. For this reason it cannot be assumed that the web can be stressed (in bending) to yield through its full depth. Since full plastic moment cannot be assumed, the bending stress allowable is held to $\sigma = .60\ \sigma_y$ or $\sigma = 22{,}000$ psi for A36 steel. (AISC Sec 1.5.1.4.1)

bending stress in beam

$$\sigma = \frac{M}{S} = \frac{(1100 \text{ in.-kips})}{(54.6 \text{ in.}^3)} = 20{,}200 \text{ psi} < .60\ \sigma_y < 22{,}000 \text{ pso} \quad \underline{\text{OK}}$$

bending force in top connecting plate

$$F = \frac{M}{d} = \frac{(1100 \text{ in.-kips})}{(14.12'')} = 78.0 \text{ kips}$$

section area of top connecting plate

$$A_p = \frac{F}{\sigma} = \frac{(78.0 \text{ kips})}{(22{,}000 \text{ psi})} = 3.54 \text{ in.}^2$$

or use a 5″ x ¾″ plate, the section area of which is—

$$A_p = 3.75 \text{ in.}^2 > 3.54 \text{ in.}^2 \quad \underline{\text{OK}}$$

If ⅜″ fillet welds are used to connect the top plate to the upper flange of the beam:

$$f_w = 11{,}200\ (3/8) = 4200 \text{ lbs/linear inch}$$

length of fillet weld

$$L = \frac{F}{f_w} = \frac{(78.0 \text{ kips})}{(4200 \text{ lbs/in.})} = 18.6''$$

or use 5″ of weld across the plate end and return 7″ along each side, to give a total weld length of 19″ > 18.6″ <u>OK</u>

DESIGN OF BOTTOM SEAT

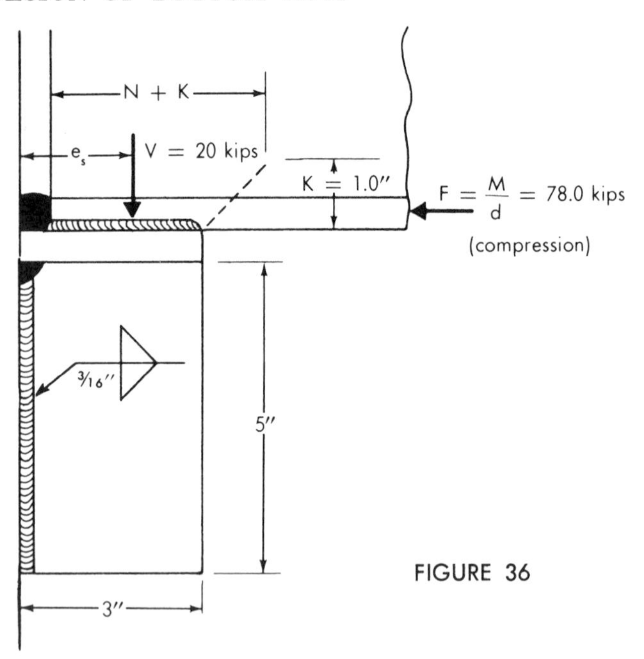

FIGURE 36

The shear reaction (V) by itself, applied to the bracket, produces a bending moment in the seat. This causes a tensile force in the seat bracket's top plate and connecting welds.

In the usual simple beam type construction, this moment must be considered in addition to the shear reaction when determining the required size of connecting weld on the seat.

In a continuous beam, the negative moment produces a compressive force in the lower flange which, in most cases, will offset the tensile force mentioned above.

As a result, the welds connecting the seat bracket will be designed only to resist the vertical shear force (V).

web crippling from end reactions

$$\frac{R}{t_w\ (N + K)} = .75\ \sigma_y \qquad \text{(AISC Sec 1.10.10)}$$

or:

$$N = \frac{R}{.75\ \sigma_y\ t_w} - K$$

$$= \frac{(20\ \text{kips})}{.75(36{,}000\ \text{psi})(.313'')} - 1.0''$$

$$= 1.37''$$

Hence the top plate of the seat must extend to at least ½″ gap + 1.37″ = 1.87″ and have a width at least 1″ greater than the beam's flange width (b) = 1″ + 6.776″ = 7.776″; or use an 8½″ x 3″ x ½″ plate. The 3″ dimension would allow room for erection bolt.

seat stiffener

The thickness of the seat stiffener (t_s) should be slightly greater than that of the beam web (t_w = .313″), or use a ⅜″ plate.

For determining the minimum length of the fillet weld on the stiffener, assume the leg size to not exceed ⅔ t_s = ⅔ (⅜) = ¼″. This keeps the stiffener at the connection from being overstressed in shear. (AISC Sec 1.17.5)

Thus, the minimum length of fillet weld on each side of the stiffener is—

$$L = \frac{V}{2\ f_w}$$

$$= \frac{(20\ \text{kips})}{2(11{,}200)(\frac{1}{4})}$$

$$= 3.57''$$

Because the column flange to which this weld is placed is .433″ thick, the minimum fillet weld size would be $\frac{3}{16}$″.

Hence, use:

$$L = \frac{V}{2\ f_w}$$

$$= \frac{20\ \text{kips}}{2(11{,}200)(\frac{3}{16})}$$

$$= 4.76'' > 3.57'' \qquad \underline{\text{OK}}$$

or use welds of $\frac{3}{16}$″ leg size and 5″ long, and of course the stiffener must be 5″ deep.

In this case, the lower flange of the beam will not

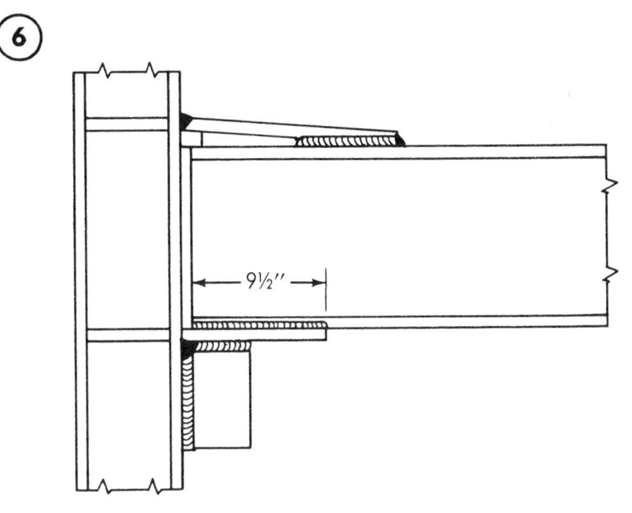

FIGURE 37

be groove welded to the column flange. Instead, the top plate of the seat bracket will be extended to provide sufficient length of fillet weld.

If ⅜″ fillet welds are used along the edge of the .513″ thick beam flange:

$$L = \frac{F}{2\ f_w}$$

$$= \frac{(78.0\ \text{kips})}{2(11{,}200)(\frac{3}{8})}$$

$$= 9.3''\ \text{or use}\ 9\tfrac{1}{2}''$$

Therefore, allowing for ½″ fit-up gap, use a 10″ x 8½″ x ½″ top plate for the seat.

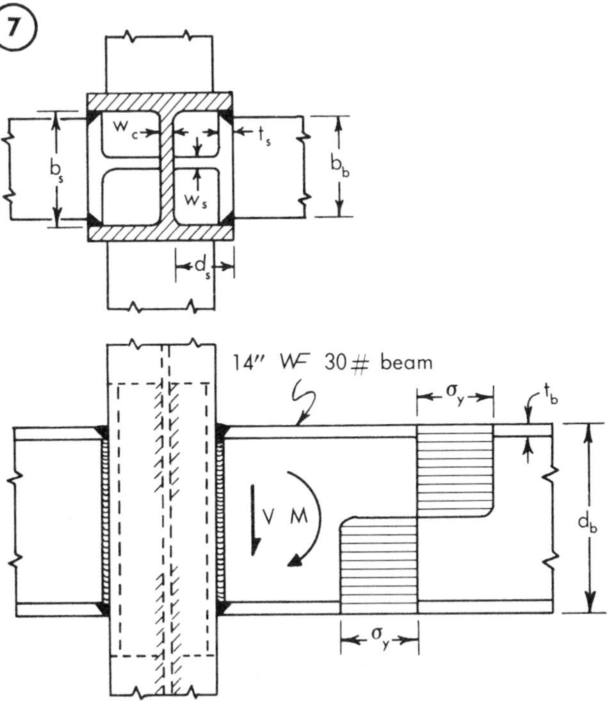

FIGURE 38

In this case the connection is made through the Tee stiffeners of the column. Since the beam flange is nearly as wide as the stiffener flange, the central stem portion of the stiffener is designed for ¾ of the moment and each outer edge of the stiffener flange for ⅓ of the moment.

The welding of the upper and lower portions of the stem to the column web is sufficient to stress the beam web up to yield (in bending) through its full depth. Thus, the beam may develop its full plastic moment. This allows the "compact" beam to be stressed at $\sigma = .66\ \sigma_y$, and also to be designed for only 90% of the end moment. (AISC Sec 1.5.1.4.1 and Sec 2.6)

DETAIL THE TEE STIFFENER

1. $t_s \geqq .40 \sqrt{¾\ b_b\ t_b}$

$\geqq .40 \sqrt{¾\ (6.733)(.387)}$

$\geqq .56''$

2. $b_s \geqq d_c - 2\ t_c$

$\geqq (8.0) - 2\ (.433)$

$\geqq 7.13''$

3. $w_s \geqq t_b$

$\geqq .433''$

4. $d_s \geqq \dfrac{b_c - w_c}{2}$

$\geqq \dfrac{(8.0) - (.288)}{2}$

$\geqq 3.86''$

5.* $w_s K_s \geqq \dfrac{¾\ b_b\ t_b}{5}$

$\geqq \dfrac{¾(6.733)(.387)}{5}$

$\geqq .39$

---

* $w_s\ (t_b + 5\ K_s) = ¾$ beam flange area $= ¾\ b_b\ t_b$

For simplicity,
use a conservative value:

$w_s\ 5\ K_s = ¾\ b_b\ t_b$ or:

$w_s\ K_s = \dfrac{¾\ b_b\ t_b}{5}$

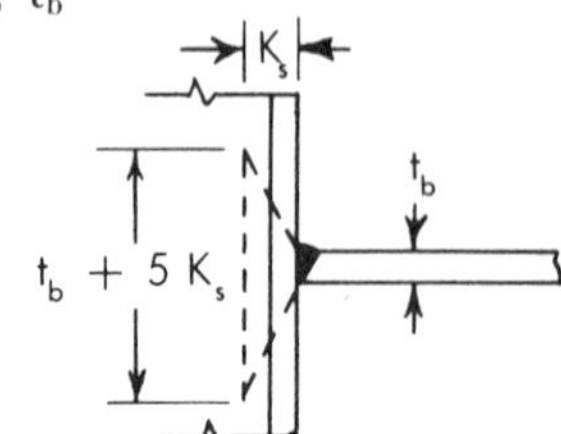

On this basis use Tee section cut from an 8″ WF 48# beam; see Figure 39.

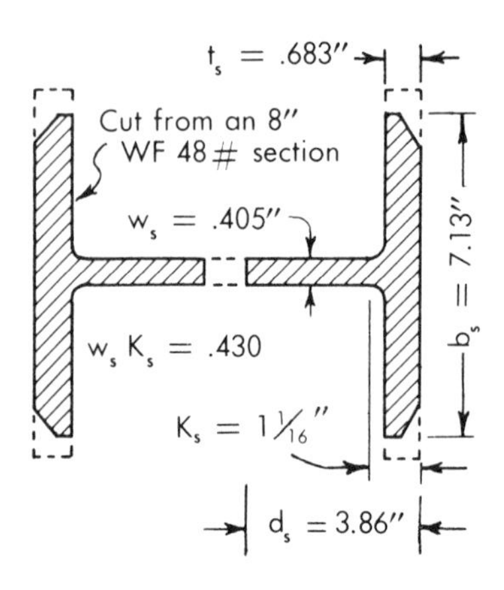

FIGURE 39

CHECK SIZE OF WELDS ON STIFFENER STEM

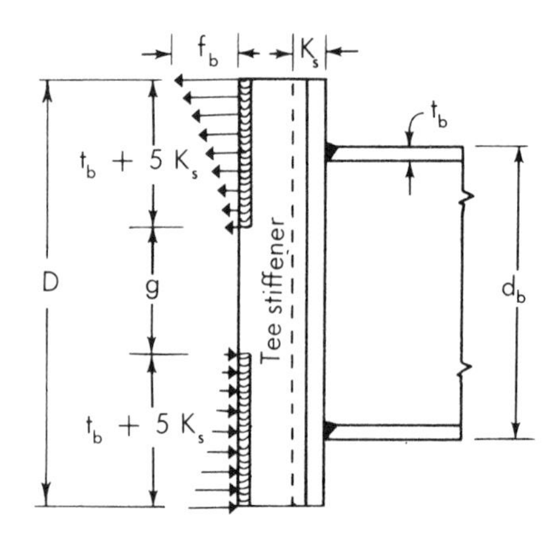

$D = d_b + 5\ K_s$

$= (13.86) + 5\ (1\tfrac{1}{16})$

$= 19.18''$

$g = d_b - 2\ t_b - 5\ K_s$

$= (13.86) - 2\ (.387) - 5\ (1\tfrac{1}{16})$

$= 7.77''$

maximum bending force

At top of weld on stem. Use ¾ of the moment (M).

$f_b = \dfrac{¾\ M\ 3\ D}{D^3 - g^3}$

$= \dfrac{¾\ (.90 \times 1100)\ 3\ (19.18)}{(19.18)^3 - (7.77)^3}$

$= 6500$ lbs/linear inch

leg size of fillet weld

$$\omega = \frac{\text{actual force}}{\text{allowable force}}$$

$$= \frac{(6500)}{(11{,}200)}$$

$$= .58'' \text{ or use } \tfrac{9}{16}''$$

CHECK WELDS AT OUTER EDGES OF STIFFENER

Use ⅓ of the moment (M).

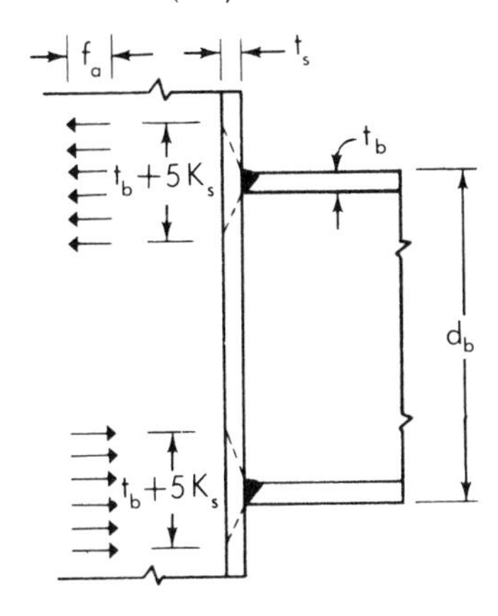

force on weld

$$f_a = \frac{\tfrac{1}{3}\ M}{(d_b - t_b)(t_b + 5\ t_s)}$$

$$= \frac{\tfrac{1}{3}\ (.90 \times 1100)}{(13.86 - .387)(.387 + 5 \times .683)}$$

$$= 6270 \text{ lbs/linear in.}$$

if fillet welds, leg size

$$\omega = \frac{\text{actual force}}{\text{allowable force}}$$

$$= \frac{6270}{11{,}200}$$

$$= .56'' \text{ or use } \tfrac{9}{16}''$$

if partial-penetration single-bevel groove welds, throat size

$$t_e = \frac{\text{actual force}}{\text{allowable force}}$$

$$= \frac{6270}{15{,}800}$$

$$= .397''$$

actual throat is—

$$t = t_e + \tfrac{1}{4}''$$

$$= .397'' + \tfrac{1}{4}''$$

$$= .647'' \text{ or use } \tfrac{11}{16}''$$

CHECK EFFECT OF SHEAR

The vertical shear of 20 kips was not considered on the welds because of the great length of welding. This could be checked out.

assumed total length of welding

$$L = 2\ D + 4\ (t_b + 5\ K_s)$$

$$= 2\ (19.18) + 4\ (.387 + 5 \times 1\tfrac{1}{16})$$

$$= 61.2''$$

unit shear force on weld

$$f_s = \frac{V}{L}$$

$$= \frac{(20)}{(61.2)}$$

$$= 327 \text{ lbs/linear inch}$$

For fillet welds, this would represent an additional leg size of—

$$\omega = \frac{327}{11{,}200}$$

$$= .029''$$

For partial-penetration groove welds, this would represent an additional throat of—

$$t = \frac{327}{15{,}800}$$

$$= .021''$$

These additional weld sizes are neglected in this example. If they had been appreciably larger, they would have been added to the weld sizes already obtained for bending.

9. LARGE HEAVILY LOADED BEAM-TO-COLUMN CONNECTION

It might be well to consider the basic transfer of forces through a beam-to-column connection.

A force applied transverse or at right angles to a member is transferred almost wholly into the portions of that member which lie parallel to this force. See Figure 40.

In the design of some connections, the portion of this force (F) transferred into any given element of the built-up member has been assumed to be proportionate to the stiffness or moment of inertia of this element compared to the total. See Figure 41.

An axial force in a member can transfer out at one end either as an axial force (normal stress, either tensile or compressive) or out sideways into an adjacent member as shear.

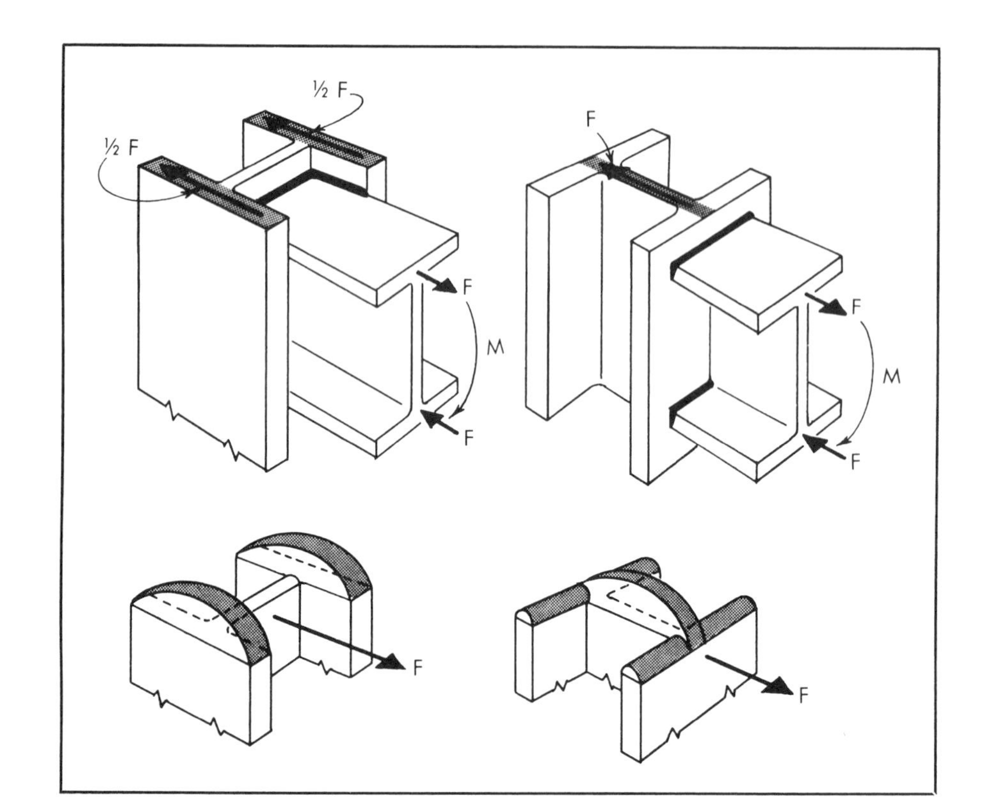

FIGURE 40

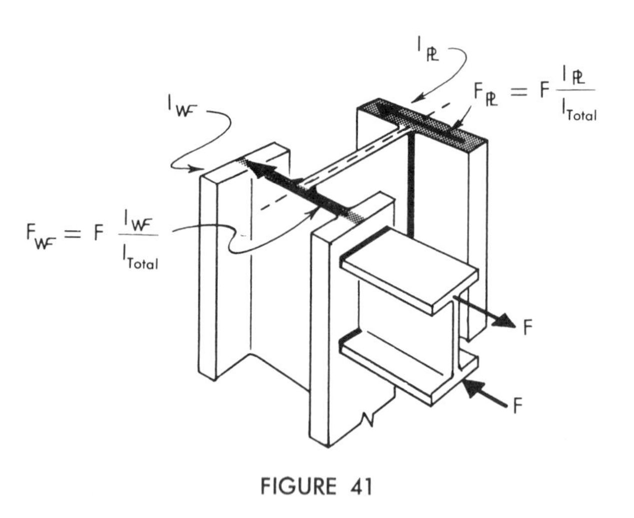

FIGURE 41

Tensile Transfer

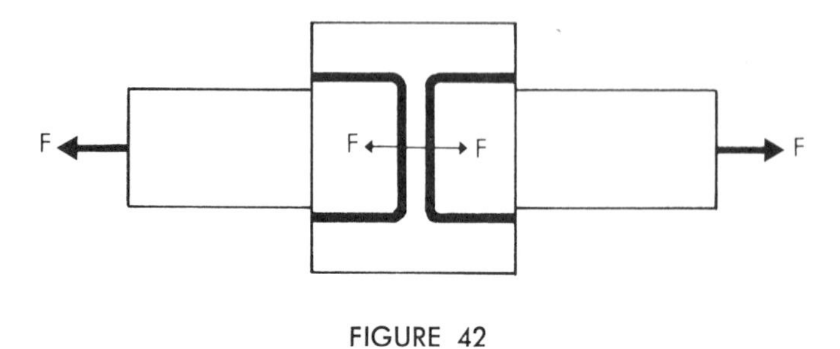

FIGURE 42

Tensile force from right-hand beam flange transfers directly as tension through the right-hand stiffener, column web, left-hand stiffener, and into flange of opposing beam.

Welds to column web and flange must be designed for this force. Although the total length of welding on the stiffener would be figured for this force, actually most of the force would be carried by the transverse weld between the stiffener and the column web. Under ultimate loading, we can assume the transverse portion will have yielded and the force will be uniformly distributed.

Shear Transfer

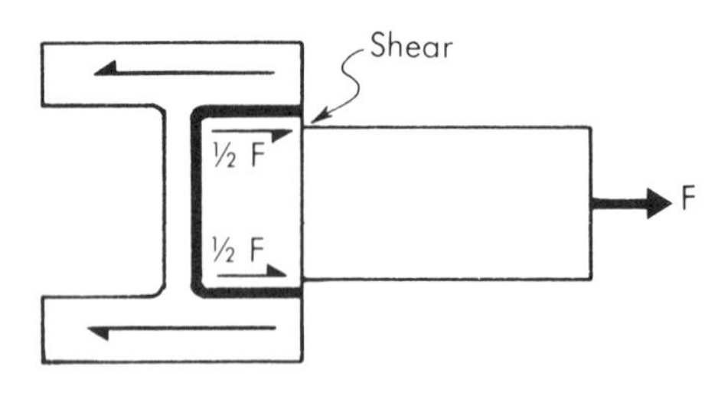

FIGURE 43

Tensile force from beam flange transfers directly as tension into stiffener and then out as shear into the column flanges.

Parallel welds to column flanges must be designed for this force, unless another stiffener is placed on the opposite side of the column web to back up this stiffener.

Tensile Transfer

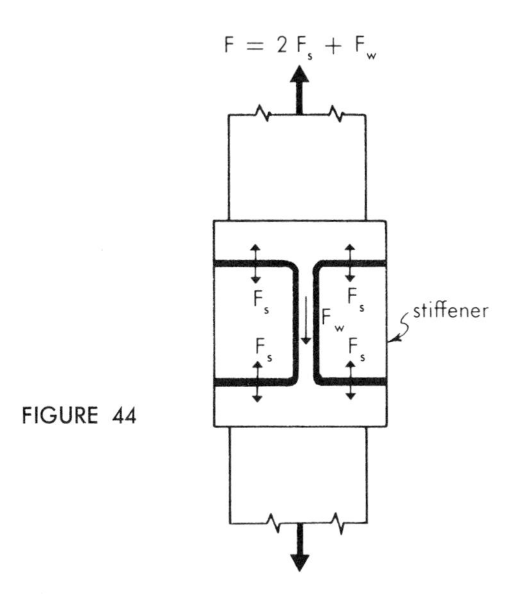

FIGURE 44

Tensile force from beam flange transfers directly as tension through both stiffeners and web of column into other beam flange.

Transverse welds between column flanges and stiffeners must be designed for this force (F) less that which passes directly into the web from the flange.

Parallel welds between stiffeners and column web transfer no force. Compression portion of beam connection would keep stiffener from buckling.

Shear Transfer

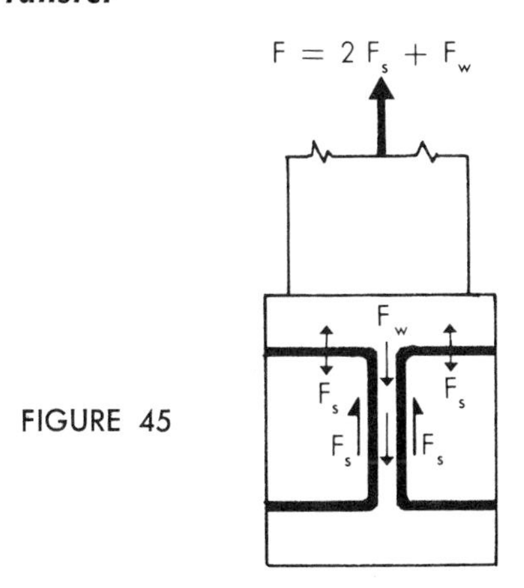

FIGURE 45

Tensile force from beam flange transfers directly as tension into stiffeners and column web. The tensile force in the stiffeners then transfers out as shear through the parallel welds into column web.

Transverse welds between column flanges on the beam side and stiffeners must be designed for this force (F) less that which passes directly into the web from the flange. Parallel welds to column web must be designed for this same force.

Any unbalanced moment ($M = M_1 - M_2$) entering the column must be transferred into the column flanges as a shear transfer. Assume $M_1 > M_2$.

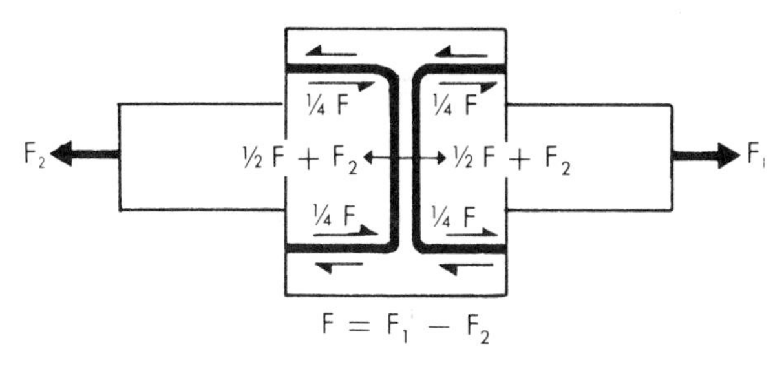

FIGURE 46

The tensile force F_2 of the flange of the left-hand beam will transfer as tension into the stiffener, then through the transverse welds along the column web into the other stiffener, and into the flange of the other beam.

The unbalanced tensile force ($F_1 - F_2$) of the flange of the right-hand beam will transfer as tension into the right-hand stiffener, and half of this through the transverse welds of the column web into the left-hand stiffener. This unbalanced tensile force in these stiffeners now transfers through the parallel welds as shown into the flanges of the columns.

Welds to column web must be designed for the balanced force, or $\frac{1}{2}\ F + F_2 = \dfrac{F_1 + F_2}{2}$.

Welds to column flange must be designed for the unbalanced force or $F_1 - F_2$.

Distribution of Tensile Force

There is some problem in estimating the portion of the tensile force in the beam flange transferring directly into the web of the column and into the column stiffeners.

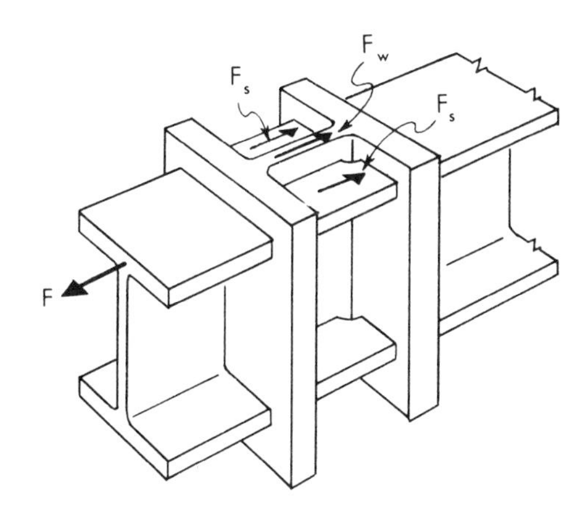

FIGURE 47

At first glance it would seem reasonable to assume this force would be divided according to the width of the stiffeners (b_s) and thickness of column web (t_w).

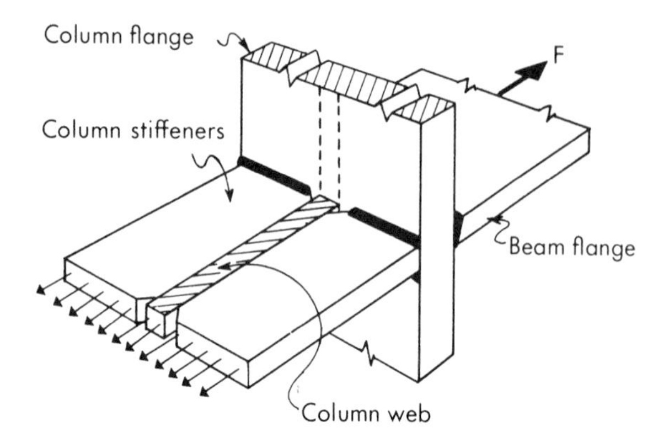

FIGURE 48

However, this column web section is not limited to the thickness of the beam flange since there is some spreading out of this force in the web. This might be assumed to occur at a slope of 1 to 2½.

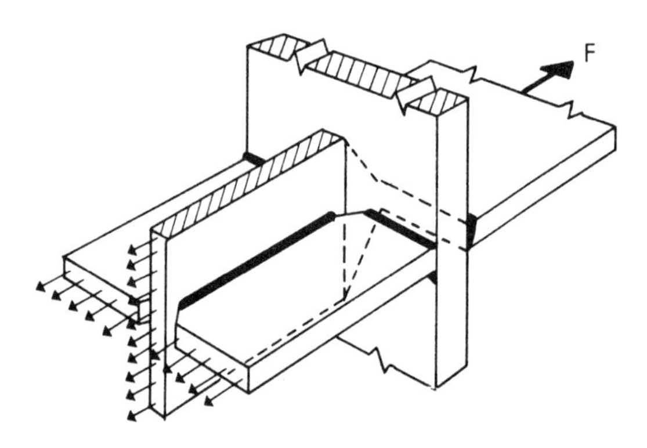

FIGURE 49

The effective depth of the column web through which force is distributed, is obtained as follows:

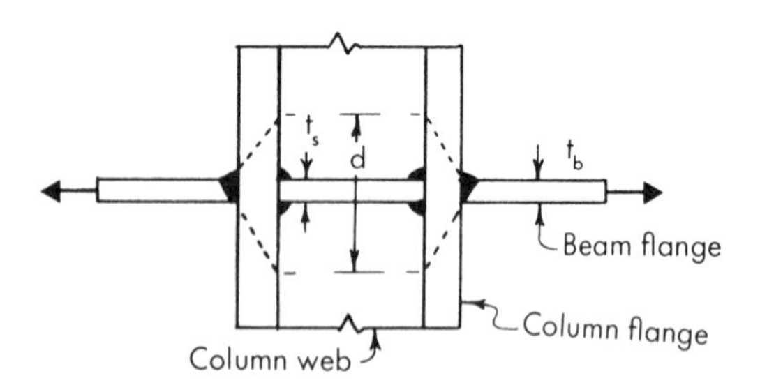

FIGURE 50

rolled column

$$d = t_b + 5\ K_c$$

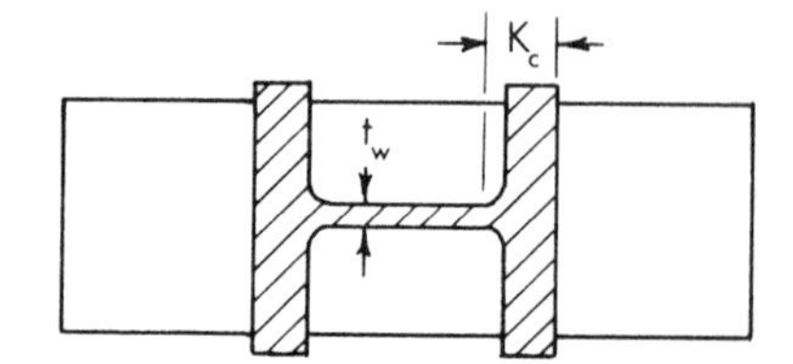

fabricated column

$$d = t_b + 5\ K_c$$

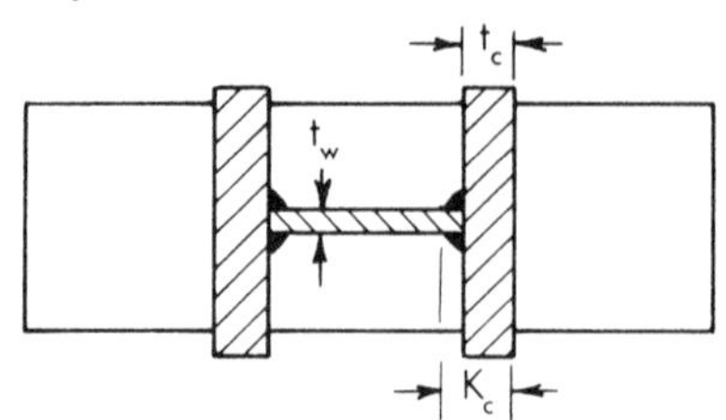

Since:

A_w = area of column web over which force is distributed = $d\ t_w$

A_s = area of one stiffener (there is a pair)

$$\text{(web)}\ F_w = F\left(\frac{A_w}{A_w + 2\ A_s}\right)$$

$$\text{(stiffener)}\ F_s = F\left(\frac{A_s}{A_w + 2\ A_s}\right)$$

Combined Stress in Stiffener (See Figure 51.)

On the left-hand figure, the shear stress (τ_{xy}) results from the unbalanced East-West moments. This causes the difference in tensile beam flange force (F_1-F_2) to be transferred as shear in the stiffeners into the column flanges.

Although conservative in this particular analysis, it is assumed the small section in the stiffener to be checked lies outside of the path which the East-West tensile flange force will travel; hence $\sigma_x = 0$. Actually some of this tensile force will spread out into this region, and this would result in lower principal stress. In either case, it would be checked by the following formula:

$$\sigma_{max} = \frac{\sigma_x + \sigma_y}{2} + \sqrt{\left(\frac{\sigma_x - \sigma_y}{2}\right)^2 + \tau_{xy}^2}$$

or

$$\boxed{\sigma_{max} = \frac{\sigma_y}{2} + \sqrt{\left(\frac{\sigma_y}{2}\right)^2 + \tau_{xy}^2}}$$

On the right-hand figure, it is assumed the small section to be checked is not subjected to any shear stress, just biaxial tensile stress. In this case, the use of the formula results in the principal stresses being equal to the applied tensile stresses. This does not result in any higher stress.

$$\sigma_{max} = \frac{\sigma_x + \sigma_y}{2} + \sqrt{\left(\frac{\sigma_x - \sigma_y}{2}\right)^2 + \tau_{xy}^2}$$

or

$$\boxed{\sigma_{max} = \sigma_x \text{ or } \sigma_y}$$

FIGURE 51

Problem 3

To check beam-to-column connection shown in Figure 52 (next page) for weld sizes.

flange force: 24″ WF 160# beam

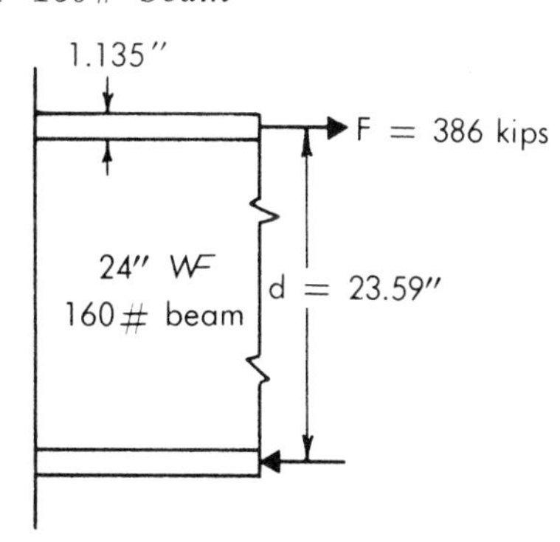

$$M = \sigma S$$
$$= (22{,}000 \text{ psi})(413.5 \text{ in.}^3)$$
$$= 9097 \text{ in.-kips}$$
$$d = 24.72'' - 1.135''$$
$$= 23.59''$$

$$F = \frac{M}{d}$$
$$= \frac{(9097 \text{ in-kips})}{(23.59'')}$$
$$= 386 \text{ kips}$$

flange force: 21″ WF 73# beam

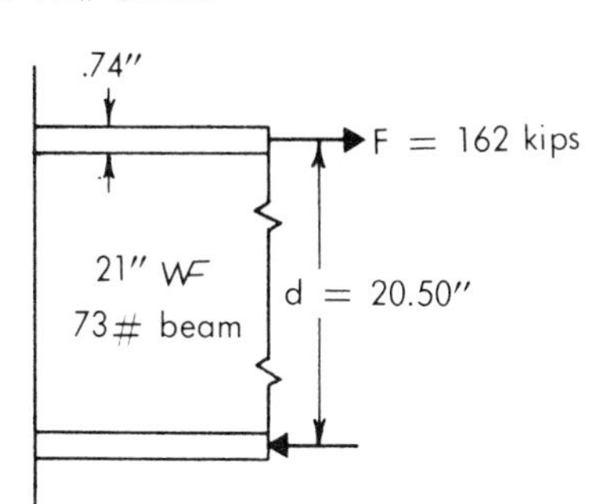

$$M = \sigma S$$
$$= (22{,}000 \text{ psi})(150.7 \text{ in.}^3)$$
$$= 3315 \text{ in.-kips}$$
$$d = 21.24'' - .74''$$
$$= 20.50''$$

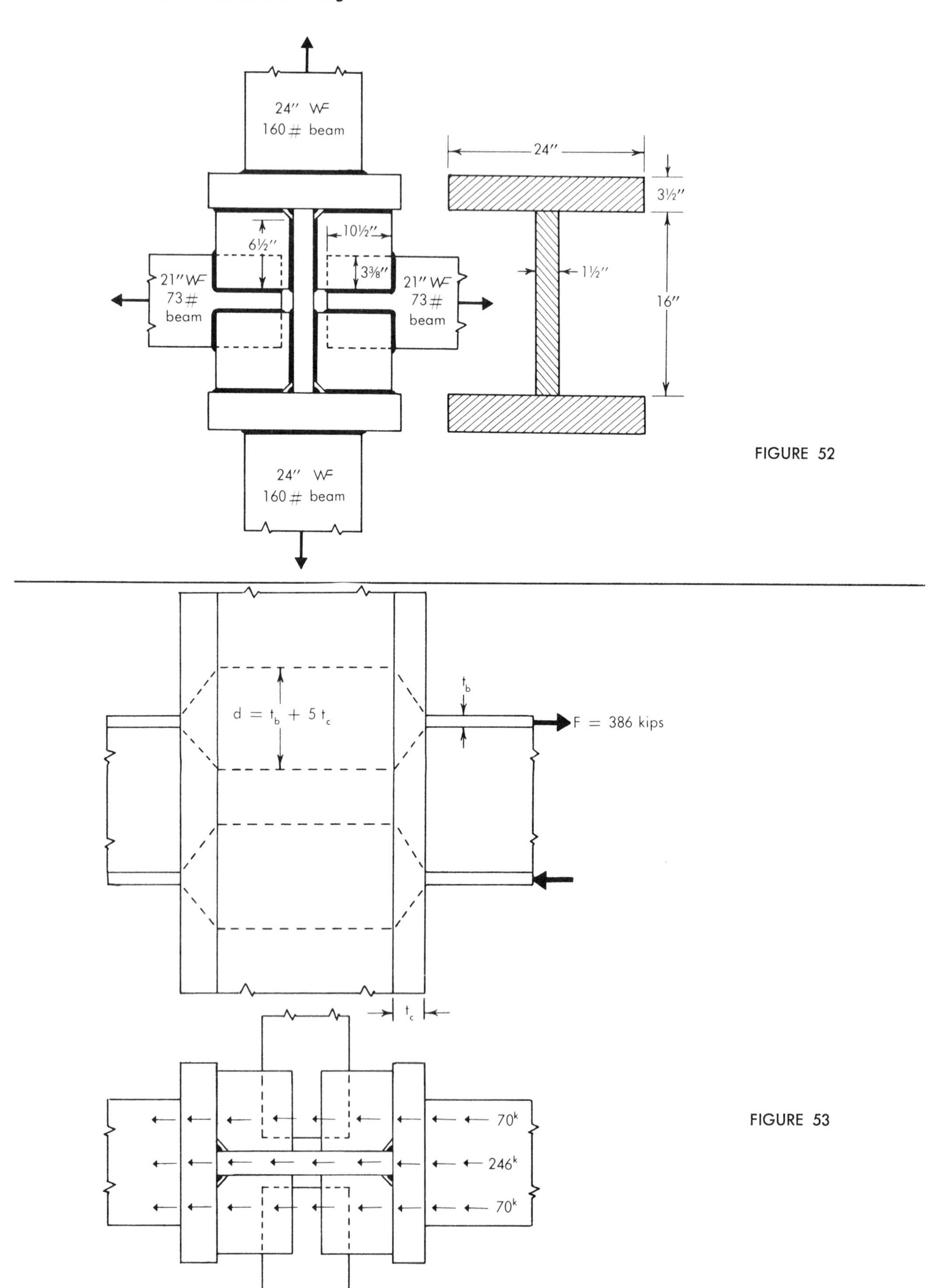

FIGURE 52

FIGURE 53

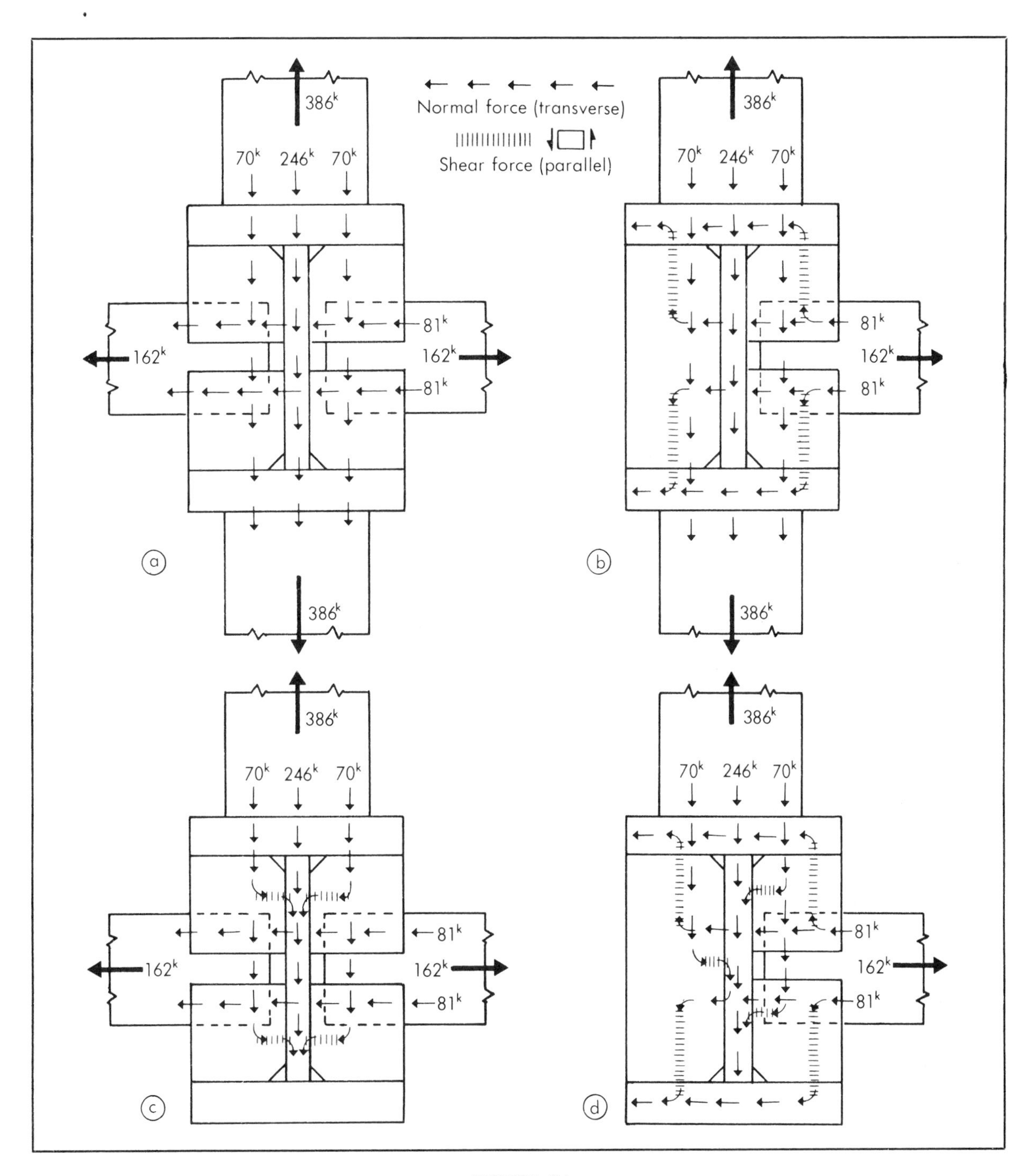

FIGURE 54

$$F = \frac{M}{d}$$

$$= \frac{(3315 \text{ in.-kips})}{(20.50'')}$$

$$= 162 \text{ kips}$$

distribution of beam force (See Figure 53.)

Depth of column web through which beam force is transferred is—

$$d = t_b + 5\ t_c$$

$$= (1.135'') + 5\ (3\tfrac{1}{2}'')$$

$$= 18.64''$$

If 1″ horizontal plate stiffeners are used—

$$A_s = (10\tfrac{1}{2})(1)$$

$$= 10.5 \text{ in.}^2$$

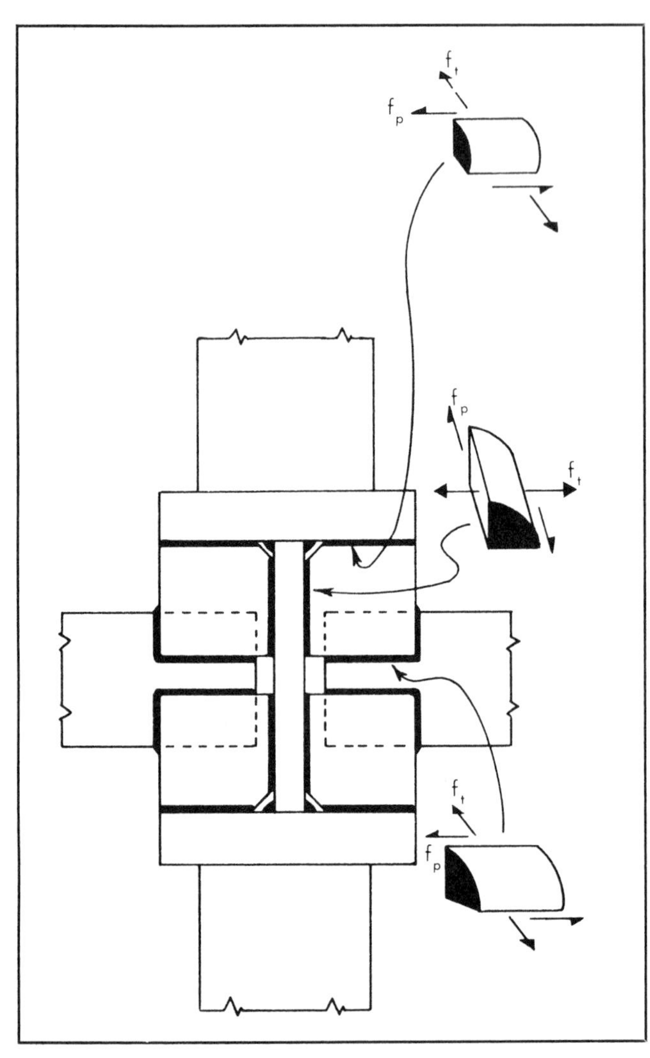

FIGURE 55

$$A_w = (18.64)(2)$$
$$= 37.28 \text{ in.}^2$$
$$F_w = F\left(\frac{A_w}{A_w + 2\ A_s}\right)$$
$$= 386\left(\frac{37.28}{37.28 + 21}\right)$$
$$= 246 \text{ kips}$$
$$F_s = F\left(\frac{A_s}{A_w + 2\ A_s}\right)$$
$$= 386\left(\frac{10.5}{37.28 + 21}\right)$$
$$= 70 \text{ kips}$$

Figure 54 diagrams this distribution of beam force for four situations. Only one need be considered for any one problem. However, in this example we will detail the welds so they can carry any combination of forces from any of these four situations.

Figure 55 shows the forces on the various welds for which size must be determined.

weld size: stiffener to column flange; case (b) and (d)

$$f_t = \frac{70^k}{2\ (10\tfrac{1}{2}'')}$$
$$= 3.33 \text{ kips/in.}$$
$$f_p = \frac{81^k}{4\ (10\tfrac{1}{2}'')}$$
$$= 1.93 \text{ kips/in.}$$
$$f_r = \sqrt{f_t^2 + f_p^2}$$
$$= \sqrt{3.33^2 + 1.93^2}$$
$$= 3.87 \text{ kips/in.}$$
$$\omega = \frac{3.87}{11.2}$$

= .344″ or ⅜″ if shop weld,

but 3¾″ plate would need ½″

In the shop, fillet welds would be used, because they can be made on both sides of the stiffener.

For field welding, use 45° single bevel groove weld because it would be difficult to weld underside overhead.

weld size: stiffener to column web; case c and d

$$f_t = \frac{81^k}{2(6\tfrac{1}{2}'')}$$
$$= 6.23 \text{ kips/in.}$$
$$f_p = \frac{70^k}{4(6\tfrac{1}{2}'')}$$
$$= 2.69 \text{ kips/in.}$$
$$f_r = \sqrt{f_t^2 + f_p^2}$$
$$= \sqrt{6.23^2 + 2.69^2}$$
$$= 6.78 \text{ kips/in.}$$
$$\omega = \frac{6.78}{11.2}$$

= .605″ or ⅝″ if shop weld

(2″ plate needs min. of ⅜″).

For field weld, use 45° single bevel groove weld.

weld size: beam flange to stiffener; case (a) and (b)

$$f_t = \frac{70^k}{(10\tfrac{1}{2}'') + (3\tfrac{3}{8}'')}$$
$$= 5.04 \text{ kips/in.}$$
$$f_p = \frac{81^k}{(10\tfrac{1}{2}'') + (3\tfrac{3}{8}'')} = 5.84 \text{ kips/in.}$$

$$f_r = \sqrt{f_t^2 + f_p^2}$$

$$= \sqrt{5.04^2 + 5.84}$$

$$= 7.72 \text{ kips/in.}$$

$$\omega = \frac{7.72}{11.2}$$

$$= .69'' \text{ or } 3/4''$$

check combined stress in stiffener; case (d)

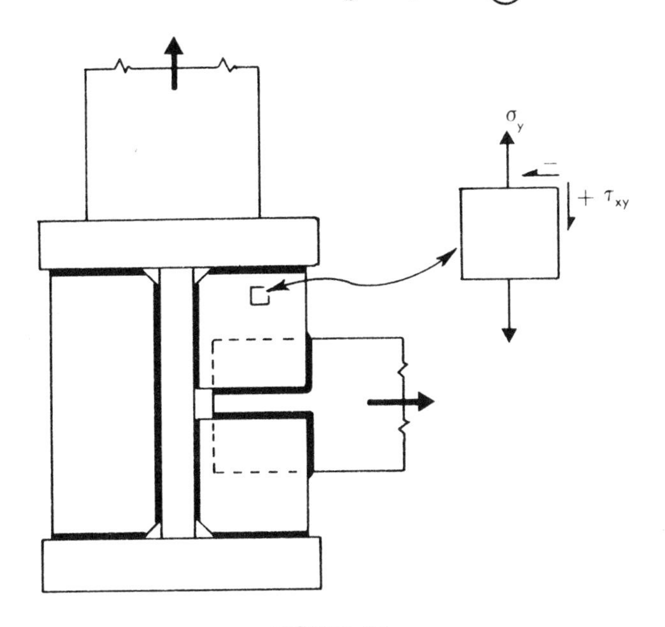

FIGURE 56

$$\sigma_y = \frac{70^k}{1''(10\tfrac{1}{2}'')}$$

$$= 6660 \text{ psi}$$

$$\tau_{xy} = \frac{81^k}{1''(2 \times 10\tfrac{1}{2}'')}$$

$$= 3860 \text{ psi}$$

$$\sigma_{max} = \frac{\sigma_y}{2} + \sqrt{\left(\frac{\sigma_y}{2}\right)^2 + \tau_{xy}^2}$$

$$= \frac{6660}{2} + \sqrt{\left(\frac{6660}{2}\right) + 3860^2}$$

$$= 8430 \text{ psi} \quad \underline{\text{OK}}$$

$$\tau_{max} = \sqrt{\left(\frac{\sigma_y}{2}\right)^2 + \tau_{xy}^2}$$

$$= \sqrt{\left(\frac{6600}{2}\right)^2 + 3860^2}$$

$$= 5100 \text{ psi} \quad \underline{\text{OK}}$$

Problem 4

To check the weld size joining the flange and web of the built-up welded column in Figures 57 and 58.

(1) *weld on column between floors*

$$f_1 = \frac{V_1 \, a \, y}{I \, n}$$

$$= \frac{(54^k)(84)(9\tfrac{3}{4})}{(16{,}815)(2)}$$

$$= 1310 \text{ lbs/in. longitudinal shear on weld}$$

$$\omega = \frac{1310}{11{,}200}$$

$$= .10''$$

but because of 3½″ plate, use ½″

(2) *weld on column within beam connection*

$$f_2 = \frac{V_2 \, a \, y}{I \, n}$$

$$= \frac{(332^k)(84)(9\tfrac{3}{4})}{(16{,}815)(2)}$$

$$= 8090 \text{ lbs/in. longitudinal shear on weld}$$

FIGURE 57

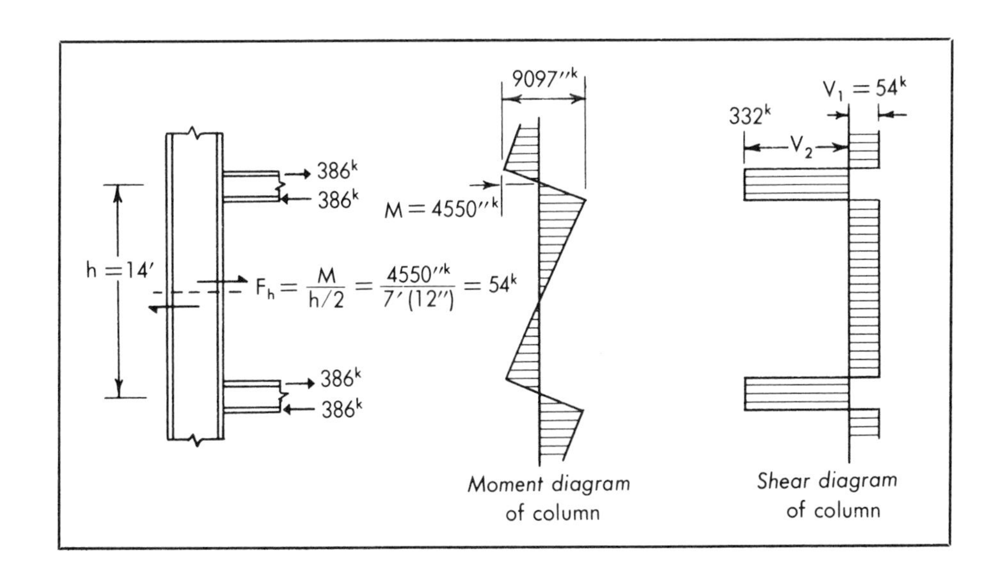

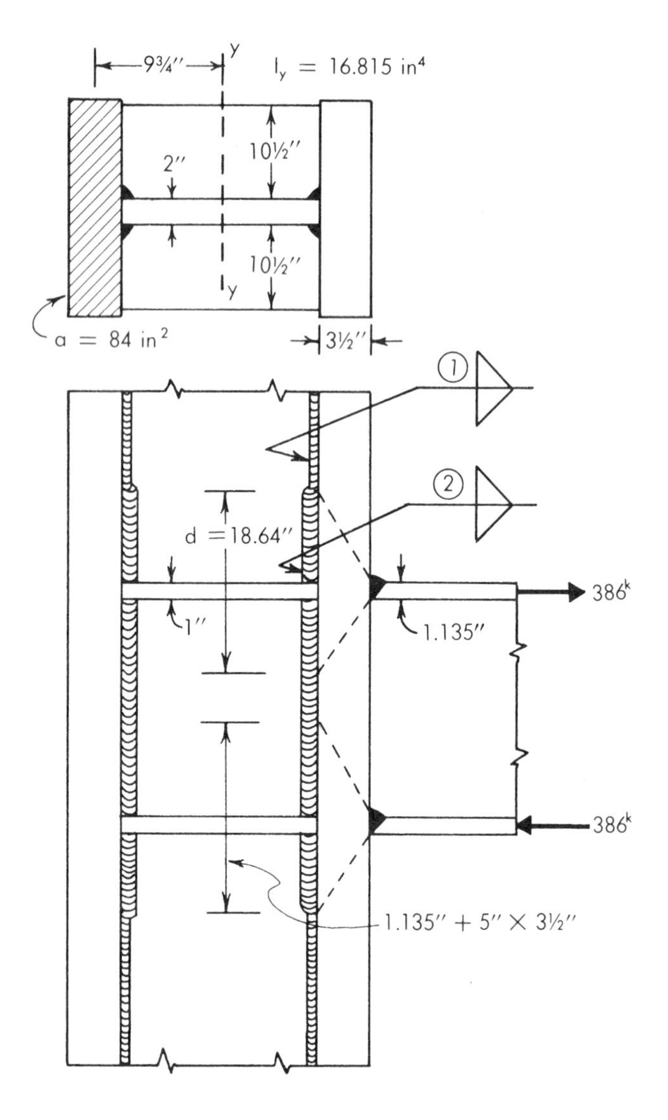

FIGURE 58

The transverse force must be added to this. A portion of the beam flange force must be transferred through this flange-to-web weld within the distance d $= t_b + 5\ K_s = 18.64''$; the remainder of this force is transferred directly through the horizontal stiffeners:

$$F_{web} = F\left(\frac{A_w}{A_w + A_s}\right)$$

$$= 386^k\left(\frac{(18.64 \times 2)}{(18.64 \times 2) + 2(10\tfrac{1}{2} \times 1)}\right)$$

$$= 247 \text{ kips}$$

This is a unit force on the weld of—

$$f_t = \frac{F_w}{2\ d}$$

$$= \frac{(247^k)}{2(18.64)}$$

$$= 6630 \text{ lbs/in.}$$

The resultant force on the weld is—

$$f_r = \sqrt{f_2^2 + f_t^2}$$

$$= \sqrt{8.09^2 + 6.63^2}$$

$$= 10{,}460 \text{ lbs/in.}$$

(a) If fillet welds are used, the required leg size is—

$$\omega = \frac{10{,}460}{11{,}200}$$

$$= .933'' \text{ or use } 1''$$

(a)

(b) If partial penetration J-groove welds are used, the required throat is—

$$t = \frac{10{,}460}{15{,}800}$$

$$= .622''$$

(b) ⅝″ root face

and the root face is—

$$2'' - 2(.662'') = .676'' \text{ or } \tfrac{5}{8}''$$

(c) If partial penetration bevel groove welds are used, the required throat is —

$$t_e = \frac{10{,}460}{15{,}800}$$

$$= .662''$$

$$t = t_e + \tfrac{1}{8}''$$

$$= .787''$$

(c) ⅜″ root face

and the root face is—

$$2'' - 2(.787'') = .426'' \text{ or } \tfrac{3}{8}''$$

10. ADDITIONAL STIFFENING OF WEB WITHIN BEAM-TO-COLUMN CONNECTION

In cases of unusually high unbalance of applied moments to a column, it might be well to check the resulting shear stresses in the web within the connection. See Figures 59 and 60.

Here the end moments (M_1 and M_2) of the beam due to a combination of the gravity load and wind, are resisted by the moments (M_3 and M_4) in the column. A good example of this occurs in multi-story buildings having no interior columns.

The forces in the beam flanges (F_1) resulting from the end moment (M_1), are transferred into the web of the connection as shear.

There are similar forces in the column flange (F_3 and F_4) from the same resisting moment. These forces

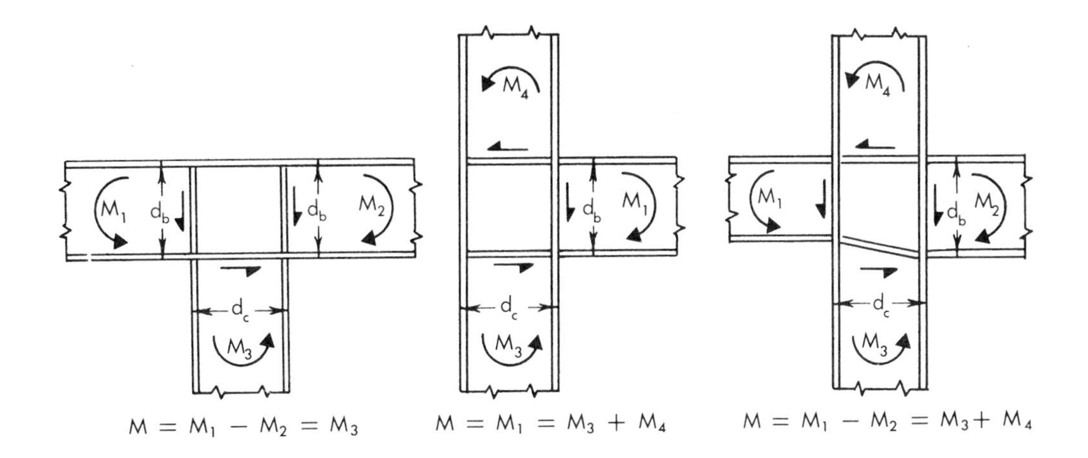

FIGURE 59

are transferred into the column web within the connection region as shear.

It can be assumed that most of the vertical shear force (V_1) of the beam web is transferred directly into the flange of the supporting column and does not enter the web of the connection.

The horizontal shear force (V_4) of the upper column will be transferred through the web of the connection into the lower column if caused by wind; or out across the beam to the adjacent column if caused by gravity load.

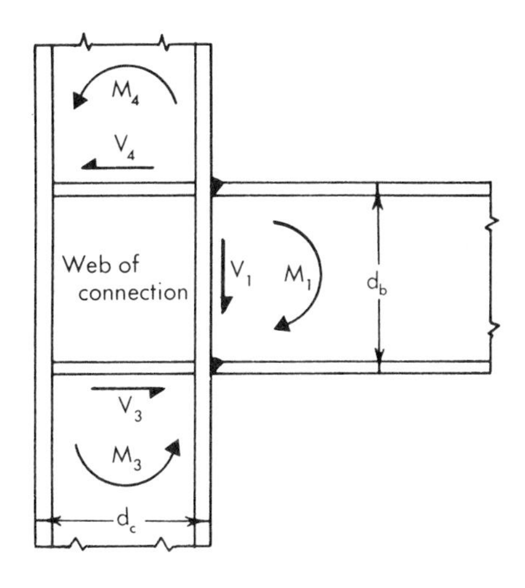

FIGURE 60

These resulting vertical and horizontal shear forces cause a diagonal compressive force to act on the web of the connection; and, if the web is too thin compared to its width or depth, it may suffer some buckling action. See Figure 61.

The following analysis, based on plastic design concepts, may be used to check this condition.

Analysis of Required Web Thickness

The unit shear force applied to the web of the connection is—

$$\nu = \frac{V}{d} = \frac{F_1 - V_4}{d_c} = \frac{M_1}{d_b d_c} - \frac{V_4}{d_c}$$

The resulting unit shear stress in the web of the connection is—

$$\tau = \frac{\nu}{w_1} = \frac{1}{w_c}\left(\frac{M_1}{d_b d_c} - \frac{V_4}{d_c}\right)$$

Using plastic design concepts, the applied moment (M_1) will become the plastic moment. For this value, the allowable shear stress (τ) will be based on the yield strength of the steel. The value for the shear

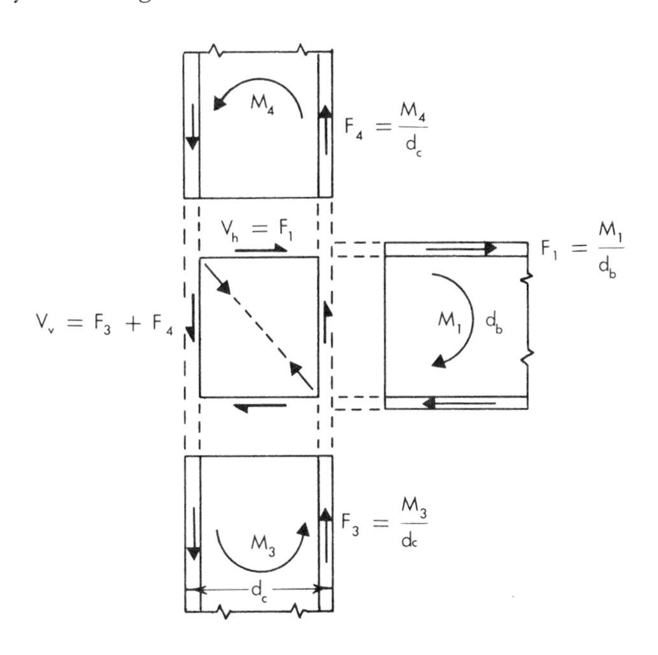

FIGURE 61

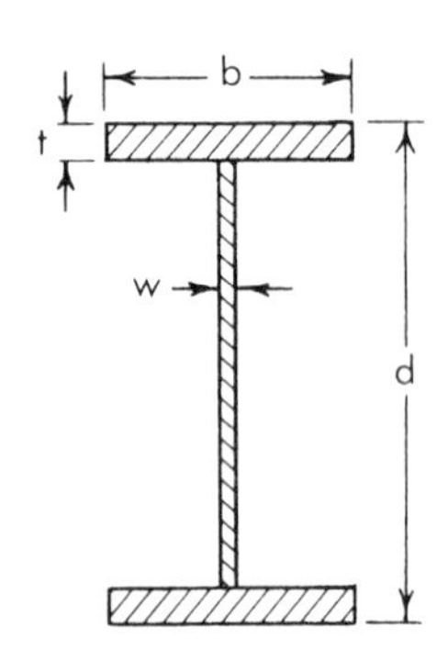

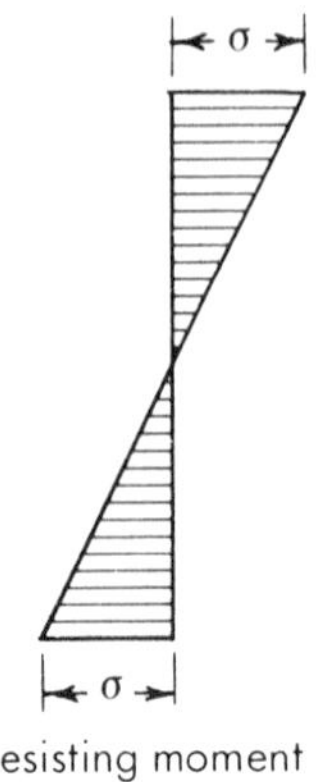

Resisting moment at allowable (σ)

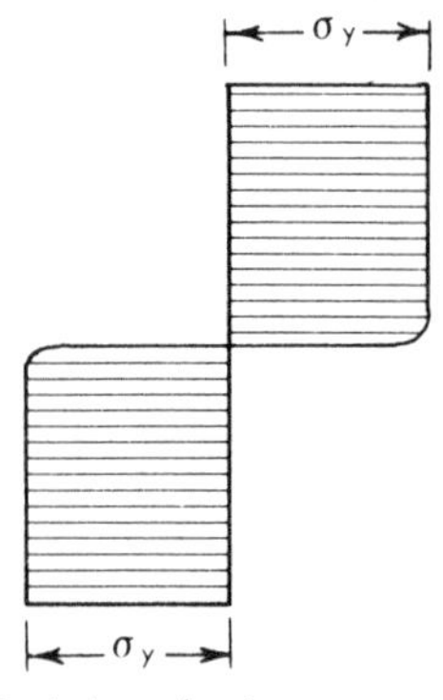

Resisting plastic moment

FIGURE 62

stress at yield (τ_y) may be found by using the Mises yield criterion:

$$\sigma_{cr} = \sqrt{\sigma_x^2 - \sigma_x\,\sigma_y + \sigma_y^2 + 3\,\tau_{xy}}$$

In this application of pure shear, σ_x and $\sigma_y = 0$, and setting the critical value (σ_{cr}) equal to yield (σ_y), we obtain:

$$\sigma_y = \sqrt{3\,\tau_{xy}} \qquad \text{or} \qquad \tau = \frac{\sigma_y}{\sqrt{3}}$$

hence:

$$\tau = \frac{\sigma_y}{\sqrt{3}} = \frac{1}{w_1}\left(\frac{M_1}{d_b d_c} - \frac{V_4}{d_c}\right)$$

or

$$\boxed{w_1 = \frac{\sqrt{3}}{\sigma_y}\left(\frac{M_1}{d_b d_c} - \frac{V_4}{d_c}\right)} \quad \ldots\ldots\ldots\ldots (1)$$

The horizontal shear force (V_4) of the upper column acts in the opposite direction to (F_1) and thus reduces the shear value in the web of the connection; so this portion could be neglected for simplicity. This formula then becomes:

$$\boxed{w_1 = \frac{\sqrt{3}\;\;M_1}{d_b d_c\;\;\sigma_y}} \quad \ldots\ldots\ldots\ldots\ldots\ldots\ldots\ldots (2)$$

The plastic moment (M_1) is obtained by multiplying the plastic section modulus (Z) of the beam by the yield strength (σ_y) of the steel.

The plastic section modulus for all rolled sections is available in several steel manuals.

The plastic section modulus of a welded plate girder (Fig. 62) is obtained from the following formula:

$$\boxed{Z = b\,t\,(d - t) + \frac{w}{4}\,(d - 2t)^2} \quad \ldots .(3)$$

Or assuming that a conservative shape factor,

$$f = \frac{M_p}{M_y} = \frac{Z}{S} = 1.12$$

$$M_p = 1.12\,M_y \qquad \text{and } M_y = \sigma_y\,S$$

Formula 2 may be reduced to—

$$\boxed{w_1 = \frac{1.94\;S}{d_b\;\;d_c}} \quad \ldots\ldots\ldots\ldots\ldots\ldots\ldots\ldots (4)$$

If the actual thickness of the web in the connection (w_z) is equal to or greater than this required value (w_1), no additional stiffening of the web would be necessary.

If the web thickness is less than this value, it must be stiffened by some method.

Methods of Stiffening Web in Connection

A web doubler plate could be added to make up this difference between actual and required values of web thickness.

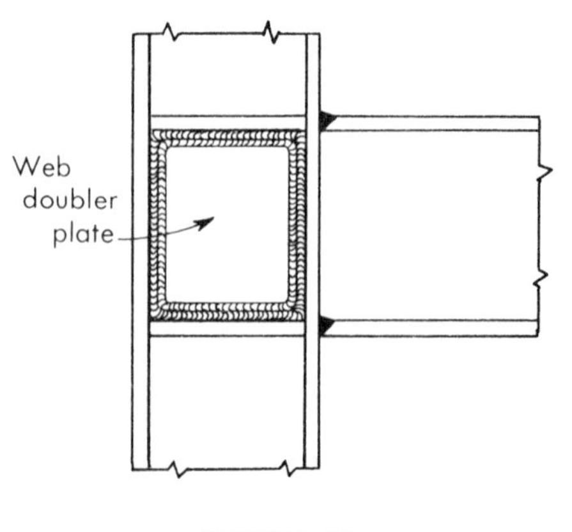

FIGURE 63

The most common solution is to use a pair of diagonal stiffeners. Their cross-sectional area would

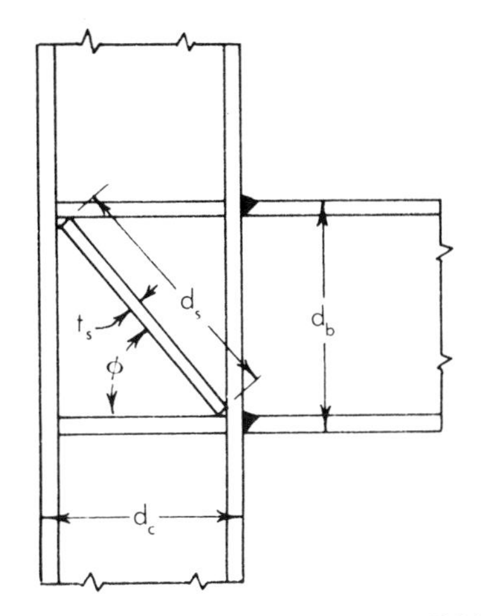

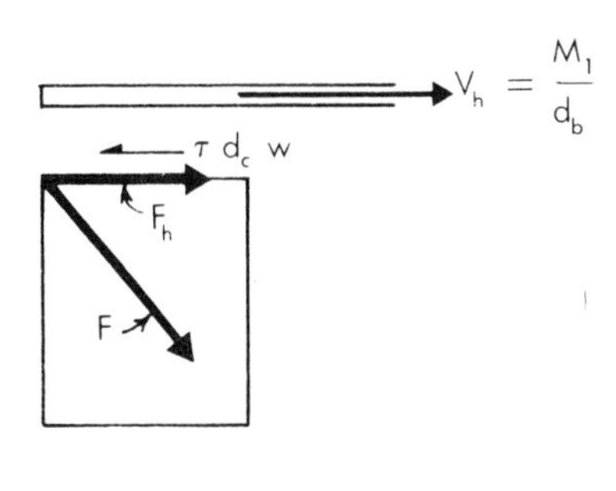

FIGURE 64

depend on the compressive force they must carry, over and above that carried by the web. See Figure 64.

The horizontal force applied to the connection is—

$$V_h = F_1 = \frac{M_1}{d_b}$$

The horizontal shear force resisted by the web is—

$$\tau\ d_c\ w_2 = \frac{\sigma_y}{\sqrt{3}}\ d_c\ w_2$$

The resulting horizontal component applied to the diagonal stiffener is—

$$F_h = \frac{M_1}{d_b} - \frac{\sigma_y}{\sqrt{3}} d_c\ w_2$$

The force on the diagonal stiffener is—

$$F = \frac{F_h}{\cos\theta} = \frac{1}{\cos\theta}\left(\frac{M_1}{d_b} \frac{\sigma_y}{\sqrt{3}} d_b\ w_2\right)$$

and the required total area of both stiffeners is—

$$A_s = \frac{F}{\sigma_y} = \frac{1}{\cos\phi}\left(\frac{M_1}{\sigma_y d_b} - \frac{w_2 d_c}{\sqrt{3}}\right) \quad \ldots\ldots(5)$$

also

$$A_s = \sqrt{d_b^2 + d_c^2}\left(\frac{M_1}{\sigma_y\ d_b d_c} - \frac{w_2}{\sqrt{3}}\right) \quad .(6)$$

also

$$A_s = \frac{\sqrt{d_b^2 + d_c^2}}{\sqrt{3}}(w_1 - w_2) = \frac{d_s\ (w_1 - w_2)}{3}$$

................................(7)

where:

w_1 = minimum required web thickness, from Formula 2 or 4

w_2 = actual web thickness of connection

d_s = length of diagonal of connection area

11. COPE HOLES

When beam flanges will be field (groove) welded to the column, cope holes are quite often provided in the beam web to aid the welding operator in making the best possible groove weld across the flange where the web intersects it. See Figure 65.

This design decision is more important in bridge construction because of the possibility of fatigue or repeated loading. For steady loads, or even fatigue loads if the range of stress fluctuation is not very much, the requirement for a perfect groove weld is less important. This does not mean we should not try to get a good sound weld.

Although a cope hole in the web should provide a better groove weld, there is some concern with the notch effect of the hole when subjected to fatigue loading. In some fatigue testing of groove welds of beam flanges, with and without cope holes, it was found that the hole reduced the fatigue strength about 10% between the ranges of 100,000 cycles and 2,000,000 cycles. This was for a fatigue stress range of

$$K = \frac{\sigma_{min}}{\sigma_{max}} = 0$$

in other words going from a given stress down to zero, etc. For a more narrow range of stress, for example K = ½, going from a given stress down to just one-half, etc., there was almost no difference with or without cope holes.

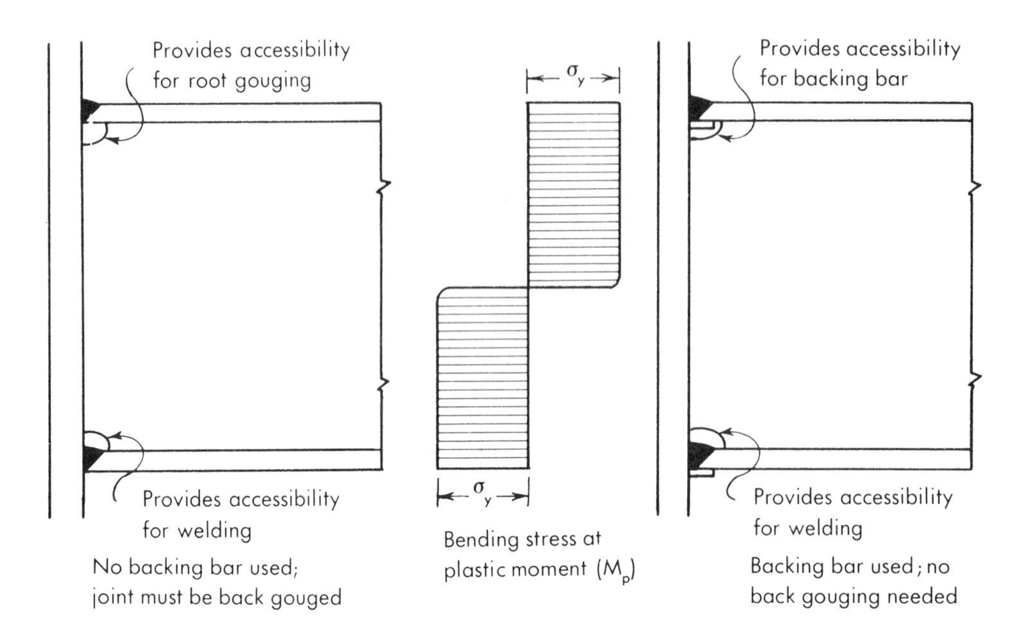

FIGURE 65

Plastic design is not used under fatigue loading conditions, so there should be less concern here about the need for cope holes and their resulting effect on the connection's strength. Cope holes would probably not result in any appreciable loss in plastic strength. The additional moment brought about by allowing the web to be stressed to yield strength after the outer fibers once reach yield is about 10%, and the cope hole represents a very small portion of this web section. Hence, the reduction in strength caused by the cope hole should be only a small fraction of the 10%.

Along the same line of thought, any minor lack of weld penetration due to this lack of accessibility with no cope hole would not be as critical.

In going through the original test reports of welded connections for plastic design, there are many beam-to-column connections or knees in which no cope holes were used. In the AISC report, "Welded Interior Beam-To-Column Connections" cope holes were used and a detail of these shown; see Figure 66. Notice that backing bars were used and the holes were not later filled with weld metal.

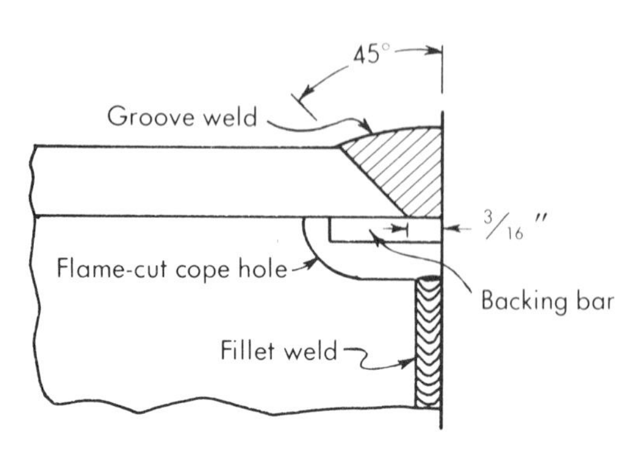

FIGURE 66

In plastic design, cope holes are not required to provide the weld quality required, although they would make it easier for the welding operator. And, if they are used, they won't have a detrimental effect on the strength of the connection if left unfilled.

The cope hole helps more for accessibility of the groove weld on the lower flange if welded in position. In most cases this would be an area of negative moment and this weld would be under compression, so this should not be as critical as the tension weld on the upper flange.

If the member could be turned over for shop welding, both flanges could be beveled from the outside and cope holes would not be needed; see Figure 67.

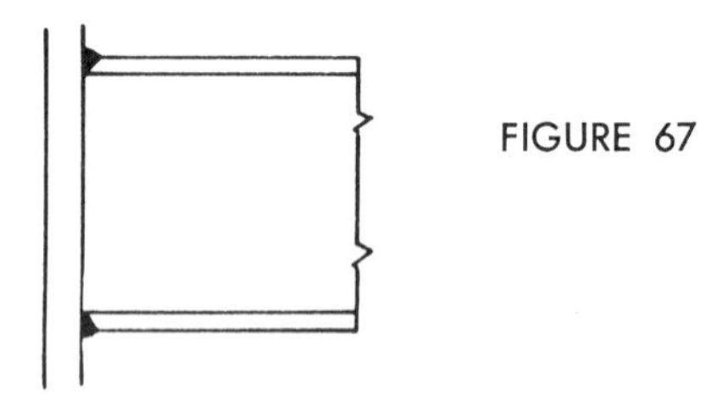

FIGURE 67

12. BEAMS CONTINUOUS THROUGH COLUMN (COLUMN CUT OFF)

On one-story construction, it is quite common to obtain continuity of the beam by allowing it to run continuously over the top of the column for two or more spans. Frequently the splice in the beam is carried out to the point of contraflexure.

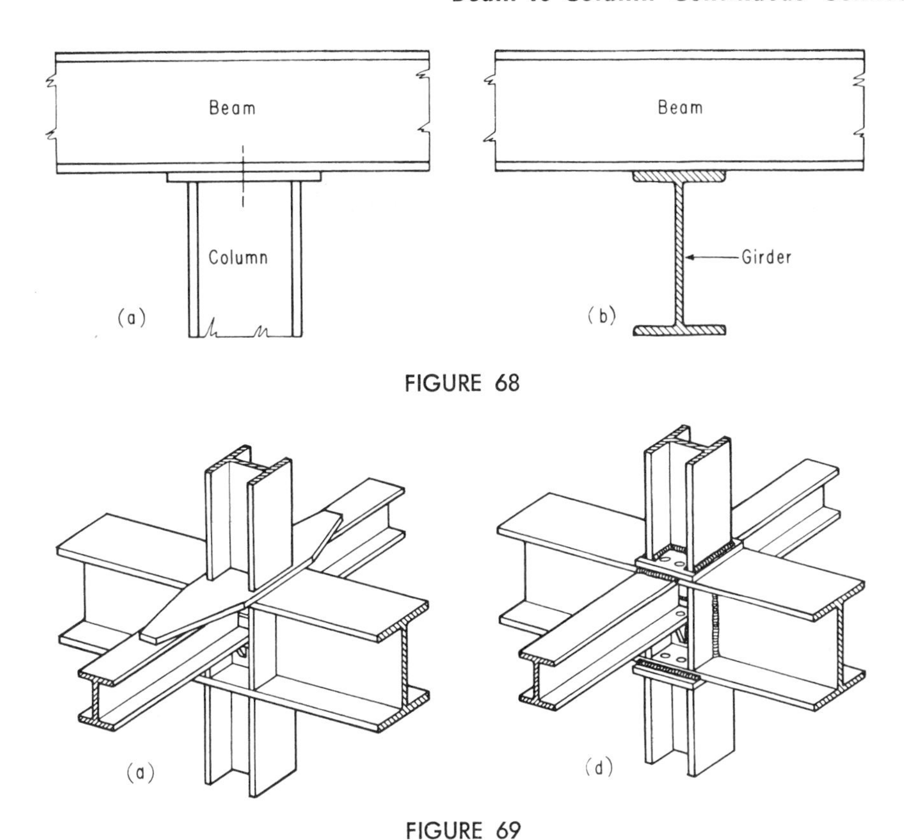

FIGURE 68

FIGURE 69

Figure 68 (a) shows the beam resting on a plate shop welded to the top of the column. In most cases fillet welds made in the downhand or flat position will be sufficient, since there is usually very little moment which must be transferred from the beam into the column.

Figure 68 (b) shows a similar connection made in the beam and the girder which supports it.

Figures 69 (a) and (b) show this method extended to multi-story construction. In both cases, stiffening plates are shop welded in between the flanges of the beam, in line with the column flanges, so that the compressive load may be transferred directly from one column flange to the other.

13. COVER PLATES FOR CONTINUOUS FRAMING

Cover plates are sometimes used in connection with rolled beams in order to increase the strength (S) or stiffness (I) properties of the beam.

Unless minimum weight is a real factor, the use of cover plates on simply supported beams might not be justified in building construction since the savings in steel might not offset the additional cost of fabricating and welding the cover plate to the beam. This is because the cover plate must extend quite a distance to both sides of the beam centerline. Notice in the example shown for uniform loading, Figure 70 (a), that the cover plate must extend 70.7% of the beam's length (c). Because of this great length, the weight reduction is only 8.7%.

On continuous girders and beams, however, there is a real advantage in using cover plates since the increased section produced needs to extend only a very short distance in from each end of the beam, Figure 70 (d). In the example shown, the total length of cover plate is just 18.3% of the length of the beam (f). Here weight reduction in applying cover plates to the continuous beam is 29.8%.

Additional weight reduction is achieved in going from the simply supported beam to the continuous beam with fixed ends. When considering this in the example below, of going from a simply supported beam to the continuous beam with cover plates, the over-all weight reduction in the beam becomes 35.8%.

Constants to Help Calculate Final Moments

Charts have been developed by which the designer can readily find constants to use in determining stiffness factors, carry-over factors, and fixed-end moments for beams in which there are abrupt changes in moment of inertia due to welded cover plates.

Sources include:

(1) Bull. 176, R. A. Caughy and R. S. Cebula: Iowa Engineering Experiment Sta., Iowa State College, Ames, Iowa. 36 charts for beams with cover plates at ends. Also reprinted as Structural Study 1302.150, The Lincoln Electric Co.

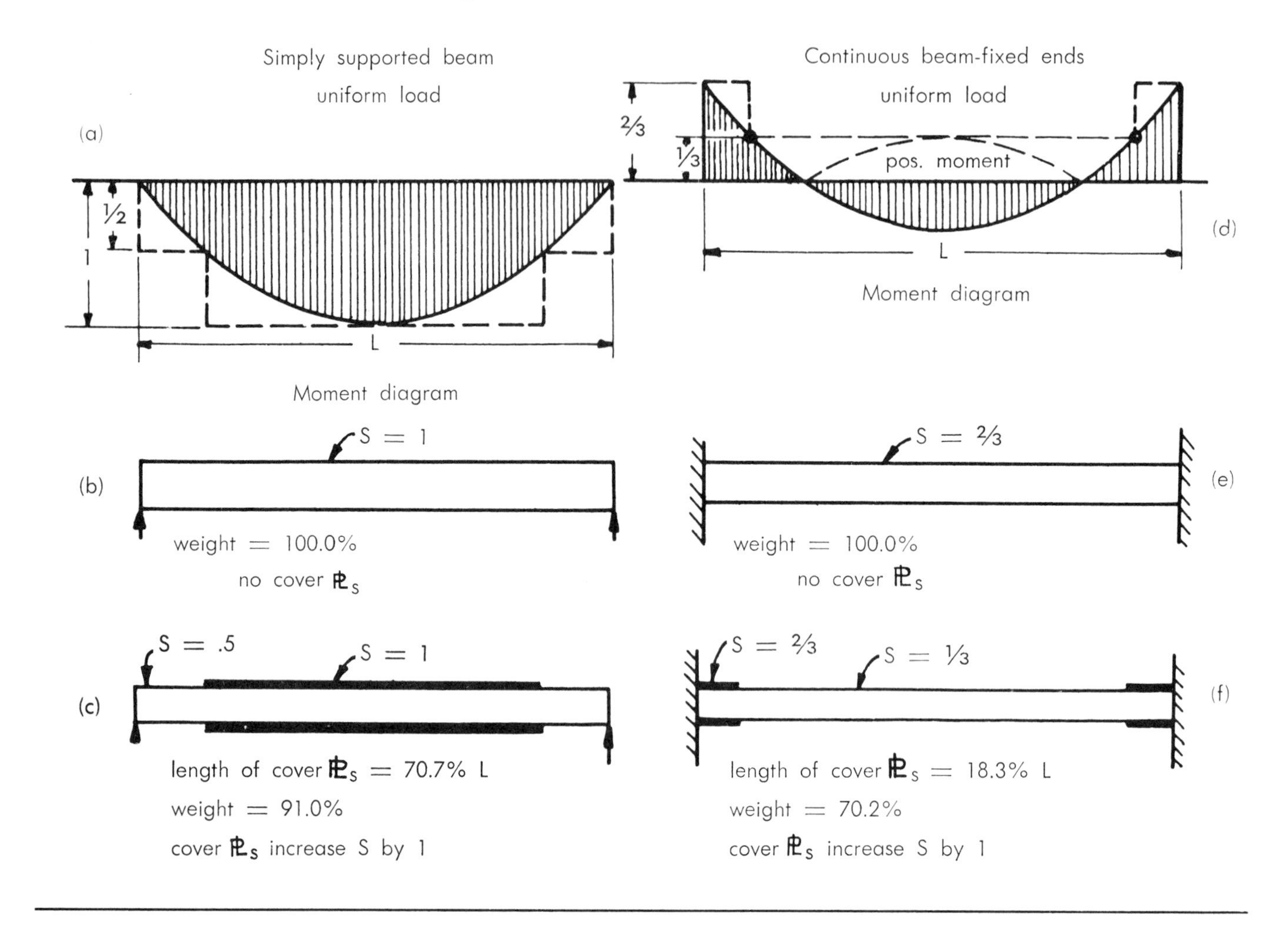

FIGURE 70

(2) "Moment Distribution", J. M. Gere, 1963; D. Van Nostrand Co. 29 charts for beams with cover plates at ends; 42 charts for tapered beams.

For methods of calculating these design factors, see Section 6.1, on Design of Rigid Frames.

Example

A frame is to be designed to support a uniform load of 2.4 kips/ft. Three spans of 20′ each are supported by four columns, 12′ high. The beams are 12″ WF 27# beams, reinforced with ⅜″ x 5″ cover plates for a distance of 2′ on each side of the interior supports. The columns are 8″ WF 31# sections. See Figure 71.

The section properties of the rolled beam, Figure 72, without and with cover plates are as follows:

beam only

$$I_1 = 204.1 \text{ in.}^4$$

$$S_1 = 34.1 \text{ in.}^3$$

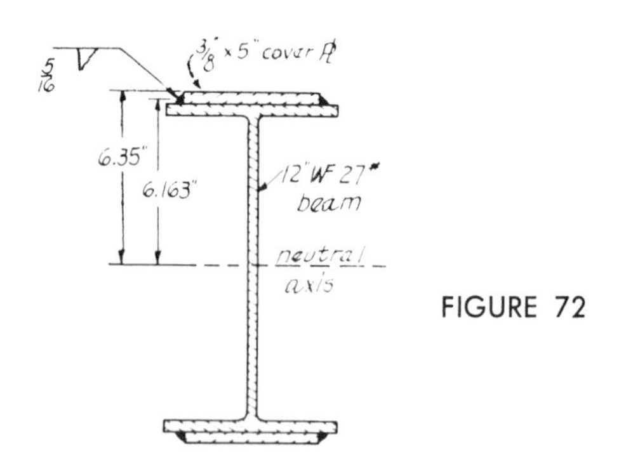

FIGURE 72

beam with cover plates

$$I_2 = 204.1 + 2\,(\tfrac{3}{8} \times 5)(6.163)^2$$

$$= 346 \text{ in.}^4$$

$$S_2 = \frac{I_2}{c_2}$$

$$= \frac{346}{6.35}$$

$$= 56 \text{ in.}^3$$

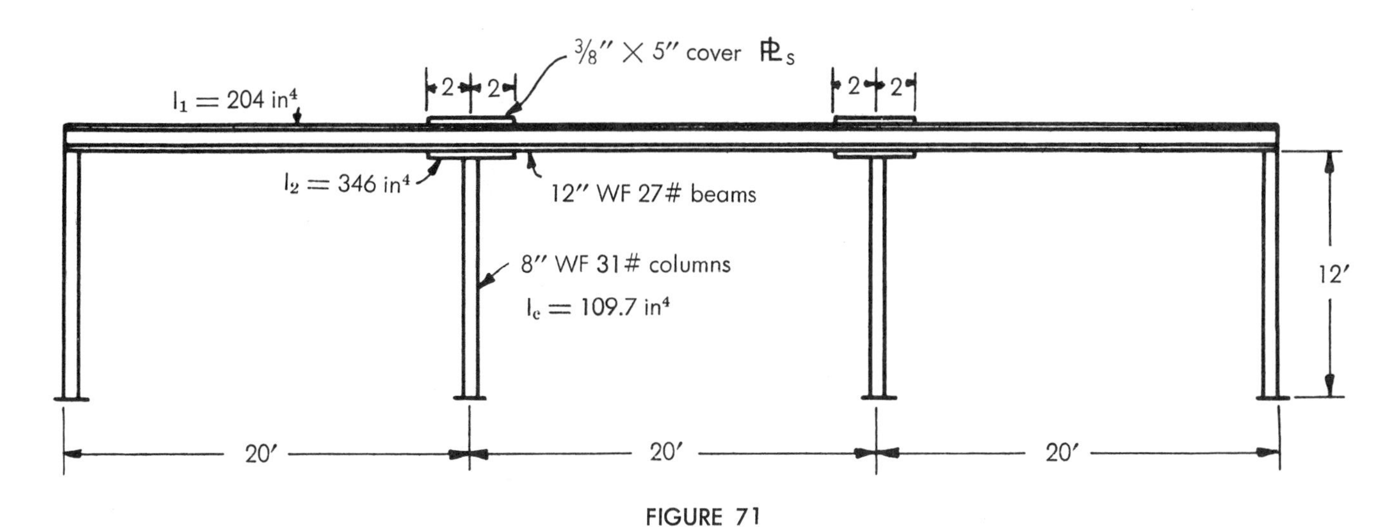

FIGURE 71

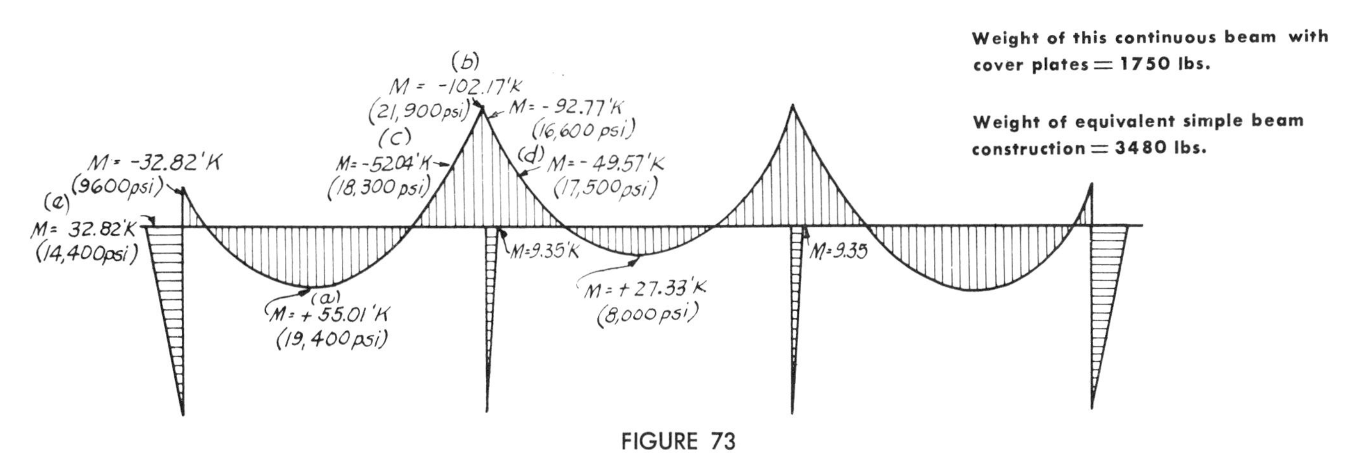

FIGURE 73

14. EXAMPLES OF CONTINUOUS CONNECTIONS

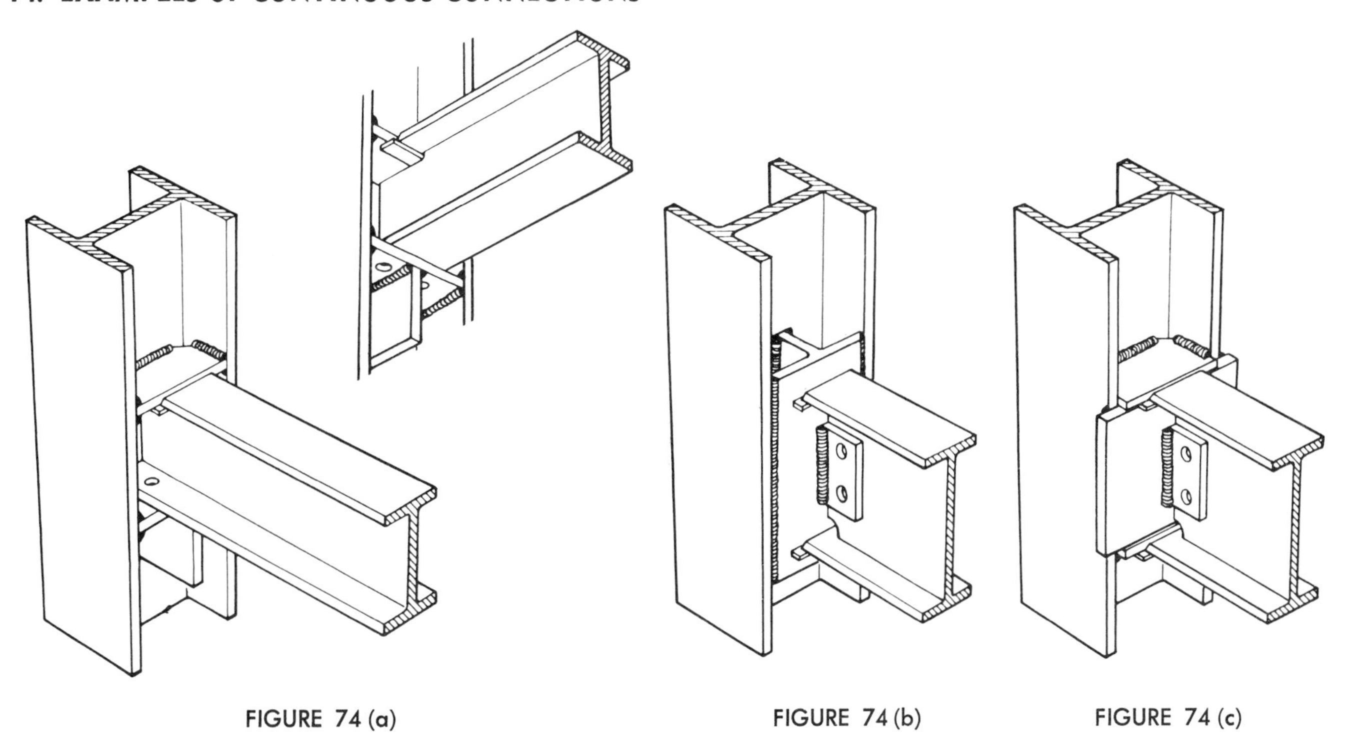

FIGURE 74 (a) FIGURE 74 (b) FIGURE 74 (c)

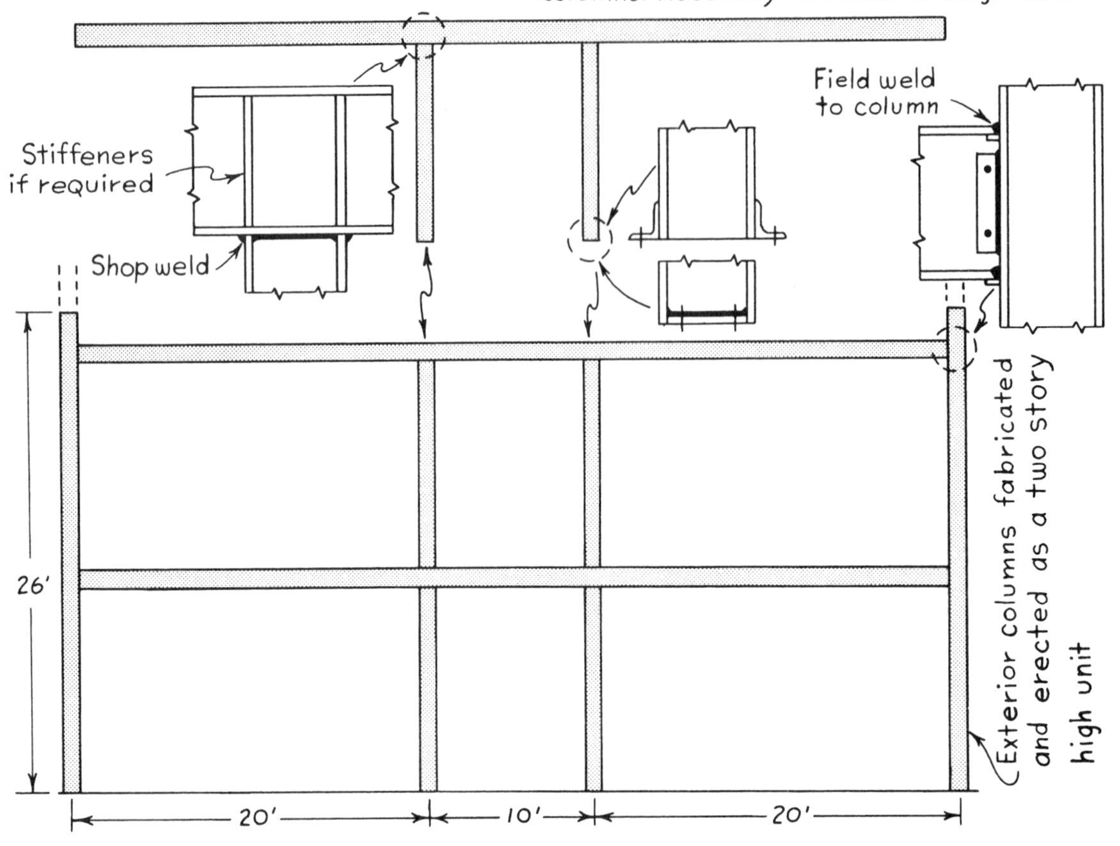
Multi-Story Dormitory Building
Shop fabricated and welded continuous beam with two interior columns. Assembly erected as single unit.
Field weld to column
Stiffeners if required
Shop weld
26'
Exterior columns fabricated and erected as a two story high unit
20'
10'
20'

FIGURE 75

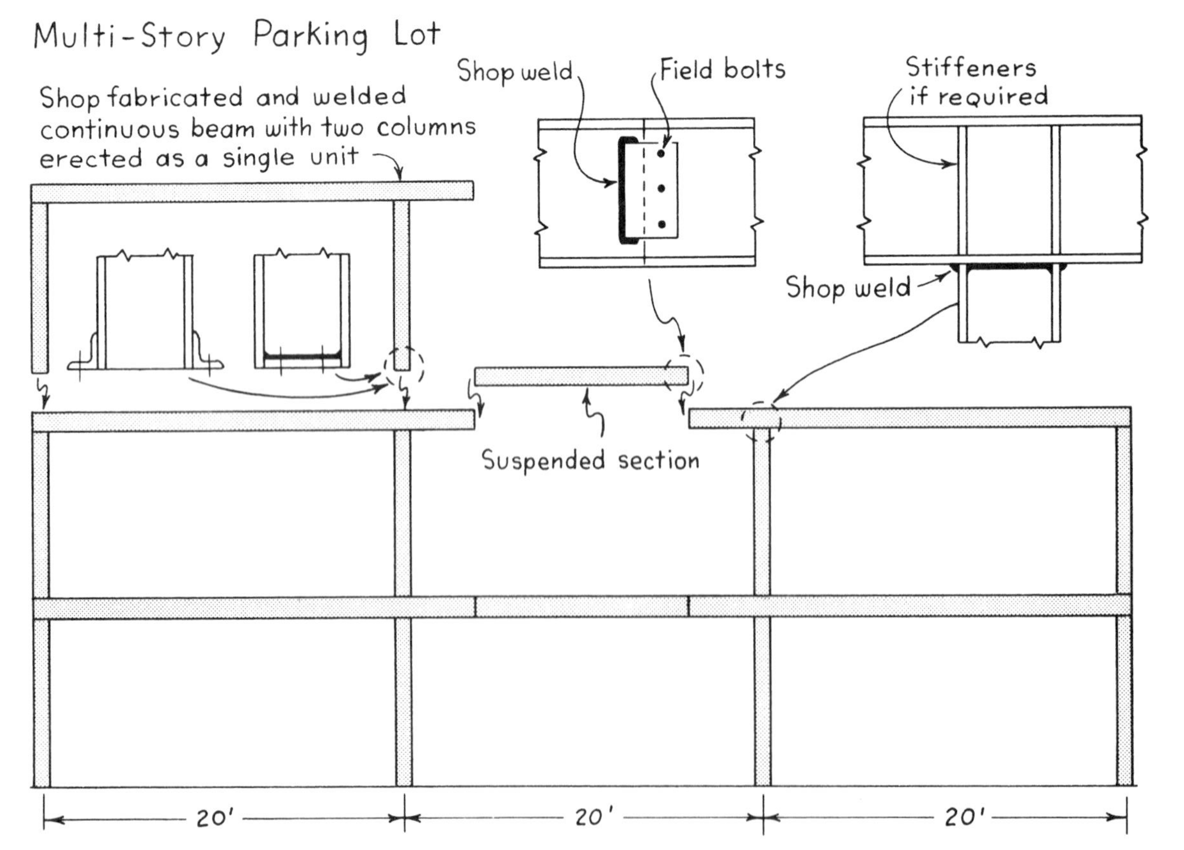
Multi-Story Parking Lot
Shop fabricated and welded continuous beam with two columns erected as a single unit
Shop weld
Field bolts
Stiffeners if required
Shop weld
Suspended section
20'
20'
20'

FIGURE 76

Girder terminating at a column and not continuing through loads the column web in shear in the region of the beam connection. This causes high diagonal compressive stresses, and diagonal stiffeners are used to resist the tendency of the web to buckle.

Typical column joint to develop continuity in both directions. The column is cut off at this point. The main girder (left to right) has 100% continuity, no joint; column stiffeners on girder webs are shop welded. The cross beams are provided continuity by the use of a welded top plate extending right across the upper girder flange. The column for the floor above is positioned on top of this connecting plate, temporarily held by angles shop-welded to the column web, and then permanently field welded along the flanges to the connecting plate.

Actual service conditions on beam-to-column continuous connections were simulated in this experimental setup at Lehigh University's Fritz Engineering Laboratories. Here, the column is subjected to compressive axial load by the main press ram while the beam stubs are loaded individually by means of hydraulic cylinders.

Beam-to-Girder Continuous Connections

1. INTRODUCTION

Beams may be made continuous through their girder supports by any of the methods illustrated in Figure 1.

In Figure 1 (a), the beam flange and part of the web below are cut back so that this flange can be butt welded directly to the edge of the girder flange, with top surfaces of both members on the same level.

In (b), (c) and (d), the beam web is cut back just below the top flange so that this top flange rests on the top flange of the girder. This allows a very easy method of erection.

Additional plates are used in (c) along the top after the top beam flanges have been welded to the girder. This gives the necessary increased area for the negative moment over the support, and reduces the beam size for the remainder of the span.

Sometimes a small seat is placed below the beam; as in (e) and (f). This facilitates erection and also serves as a backing strip for the groove weld on the lower beam flange.

Top connecting plates are used in (e) and (f). These also serve as cover plates to increase the stiffness (I) or strength (S) properties at ends of the beam.

If beams are offset, Figure 2, the top connecting plate can be adjusted to tie both together with the girder.

At exterior columns, Figure 3, the top connecting plate is cut in the shape of a Tee so as to tie in spandrel beams, girder and column.

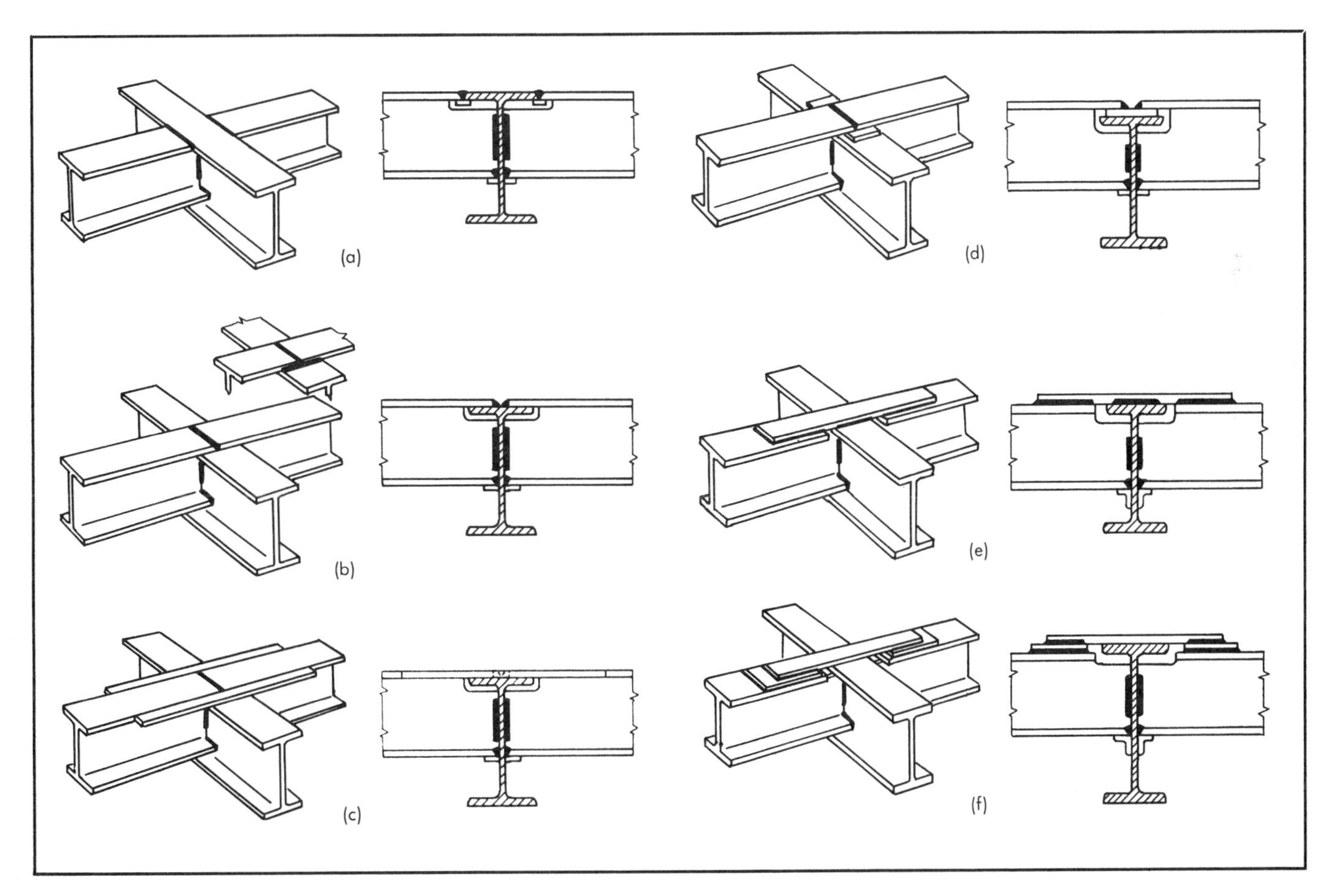

FIGURE 1

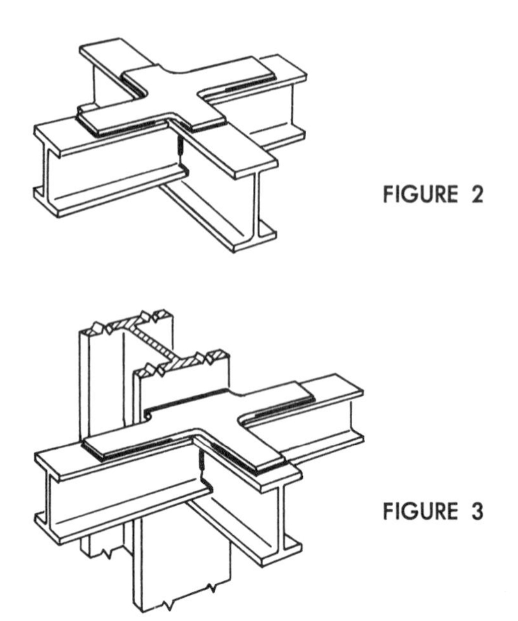

FIGURE 2

FIGURE 3

2. BUTT WELDING OF INTERSECTING FLANGES VS ISOLATING THEM

Should the intersecting flanges of beams and girders be isolated or may they be welded directly together?

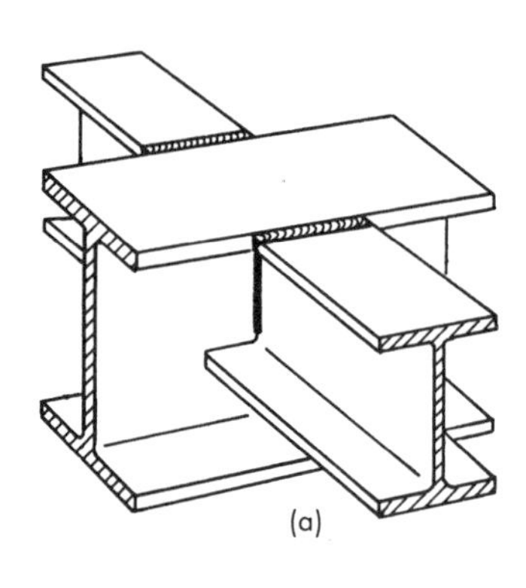

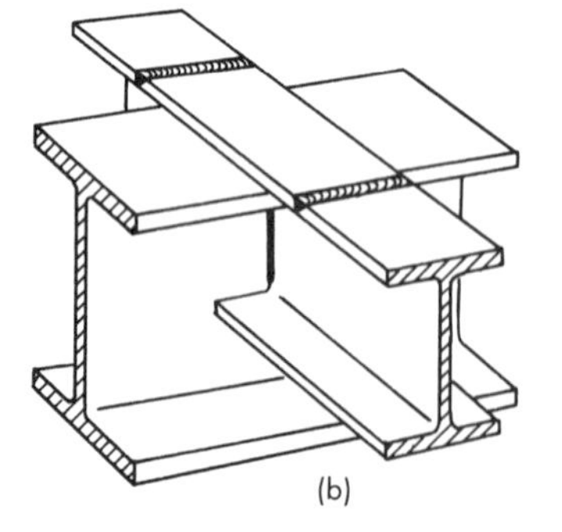

FIGURE 4

Consider the bay, Figure 5, with a dead — live load of 200 lbs/ft². On this basis each beam would have a 20-kip load uniformly distributed; each main girder would have three concentrated forces of 20 kips applied at quarter points.

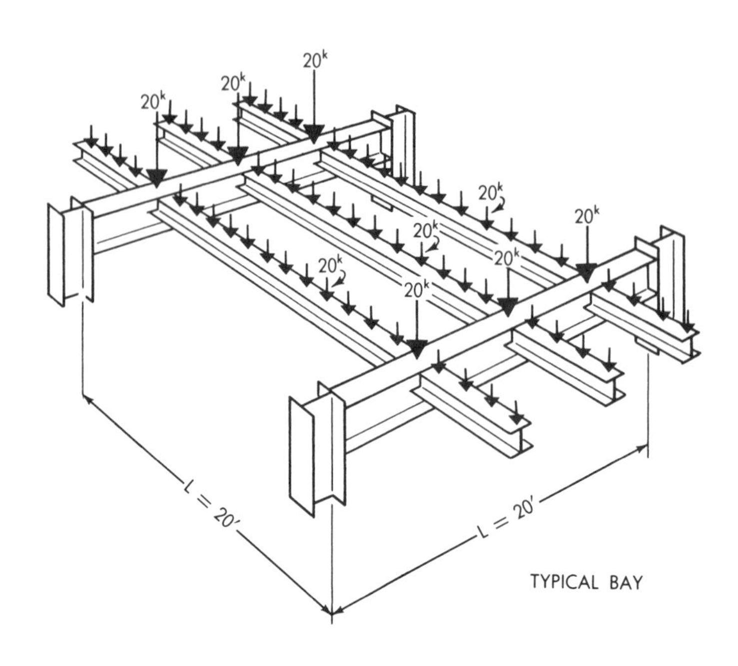

FIGURE 5

(1) For example, assume the girder to be simply supported, and the beams welded for continuity to the girders.

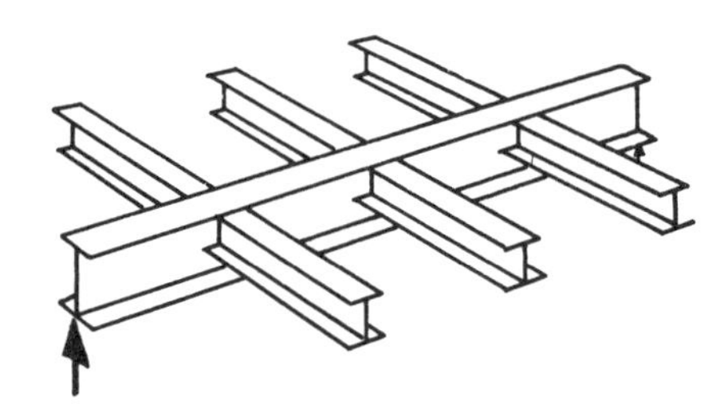

FIGURE 6

Design the girder as simply supported. Use 14″ WF 68# beam having S = 103.0 in.³

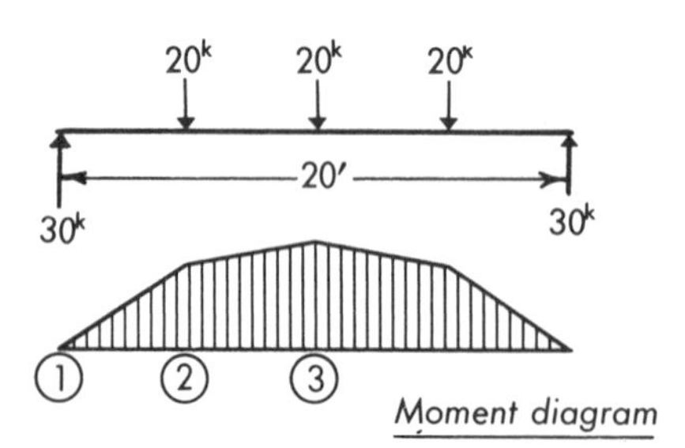

$$M_3 = \frac{W_1 \ L}{6}$$

$$= \frac{(60^k)(240'')}{6}$$

$$= 2400 \text{ in.-kips}$$

$$\sigma_3 = \frac{M}{S}$$

$$= \frac{(2400 \text{ in.-kips})}{(103.0 \text{ in.}^3)}$$

$$= 23{,}300 \text{ psi compression}$$

Since the girder in itself provides very little end restraint for the intersecting beams which it supports, the beams will be designed as simply supported even though their flanges are welded to the girder. Use a 10″ WF 25# beam having S = 26.4 in.[3]

However, if two beams framing on opposite sides of a girder are loaded, their ends will be restrained and their end moments must be considered.

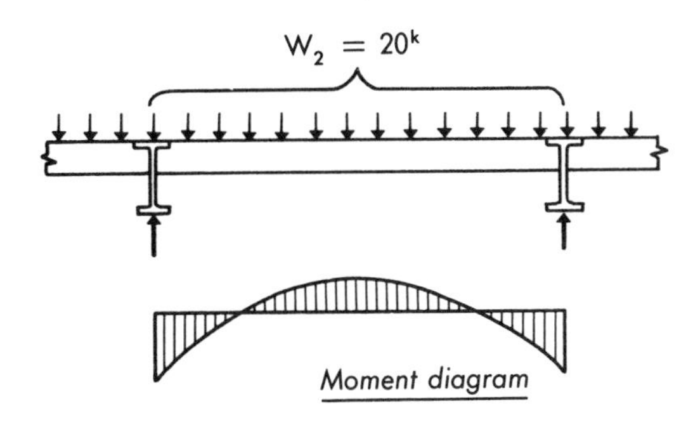

$$M_e = \frac{W_2 \; L}{12}$$

$$= \frac{(20^k)(240'')}{12}$$

$$= -\; 400 \text{ in.-kips}$$

The resulting flange forces and stresses can be diagrammed as in Figure 7.

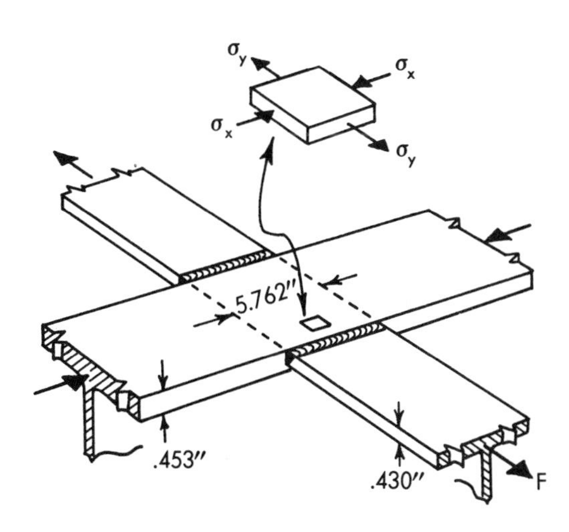

FIGURE 7

Here:

$$F = \frac{M}{d}$$

$$= \frac{(400 \text{ in.-kips})}{(10.08'' - .43'')}$$

$$= 41.5 \text{ kips}$$

$$\sigma_y = \frac{(41.5^k)}{(5.762'')(.453'')}$$

$$= 15{,}900 \text{ psi}$$

These two biaxial stresses, $\sigma_x = -\ 23{,}300$ psi and $\sigma_y = +\ 15{,}900$ psi, will affect the yield properties of the girder's top flange within the region where the beam flange is attached.

A plate subjected to uniaxial tensile stress, or stress in one direction only, will have a certain critical stress (σ_{cr}) above which the plate will yield plastically.

In this case, this stress point is referred to as the yield strength.

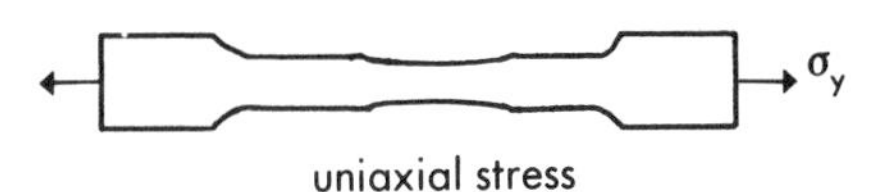

However, if in addition, there is a compressive stress applied at right angles, this will allow the plate to yield easier and at a lower load.

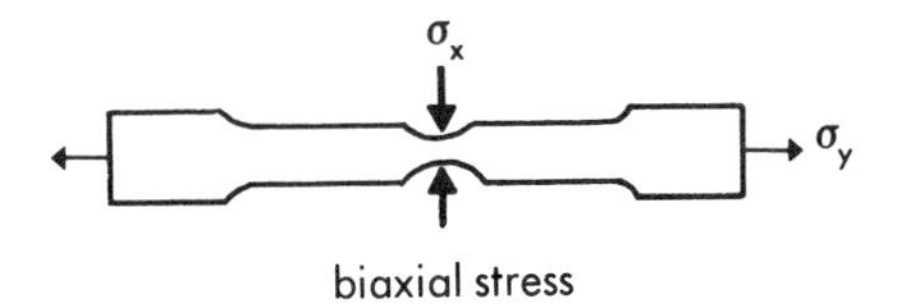

A convenient method to check the effect of the applied stresses upon the yielding of the plate is the Huber-Mises formula. If for a certain combination of normal stress (σ_x) and (σ_y) and shear stress (τ_{xy}), the resulting value of critical stress (σ_{cr}) is equal to the yield strength of the steel when tested in uniaxial tension, this combination of stresses is assumed to just produce yielding in the steel.

$$\sigma_{cr} = \sqrt{\sigma_x^2 - \sigma_x \, \sigma_y + \sigma_y^2 + 3 \; \tau_{xy}}$$

$$= \sqrt{23{,}300^2 - (-23{,}300)(15{,}900) + 15{,}900^2 + 0}$$

$$= 36{,}600 \text{ psi}$$

This would indicate the top flange of the girder is on the verge of yielding, and the tensile flange of the beam should be isolated from the biaxial compressive

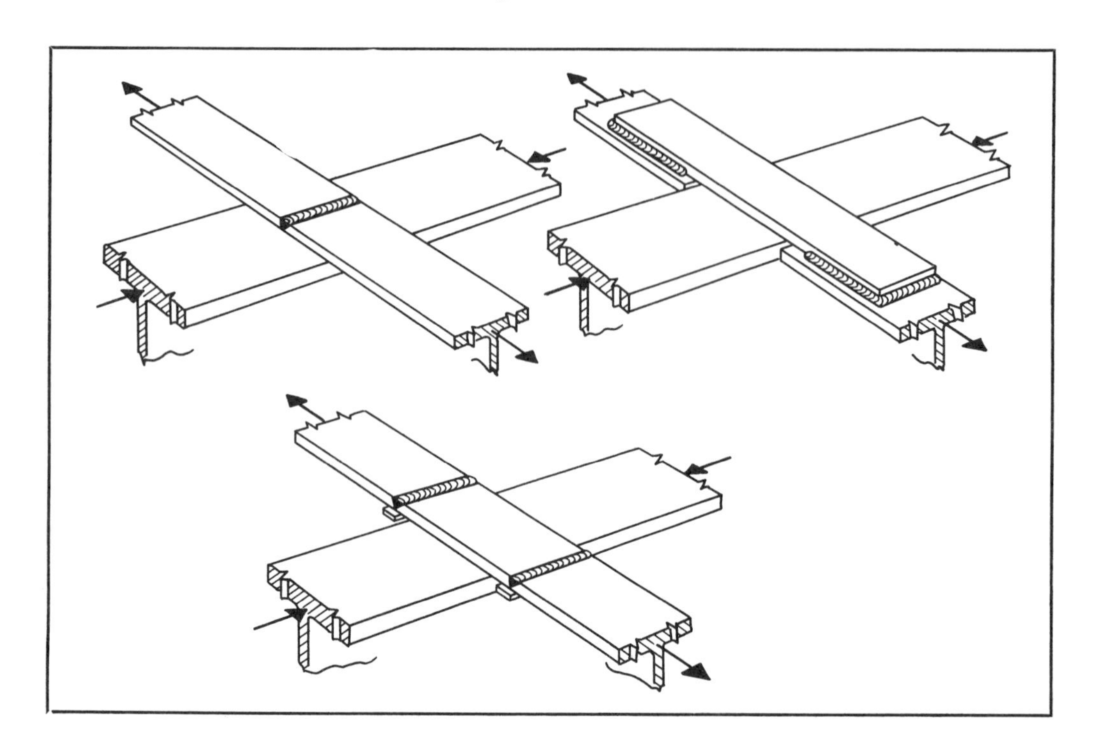

FIGURE 8

stress. This may be done by one of several methods, Figure 8.

(2) Now assume the girder to be fixed at the ends and the beams welded for continuity to the girders.

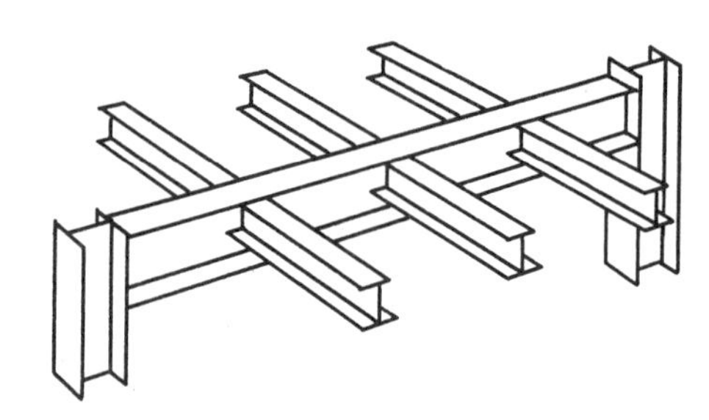

FIGURE 9

Design the girder as having fixed ends. Use 14″ WF 43# beam having $S = 62.7$ in.^{3}

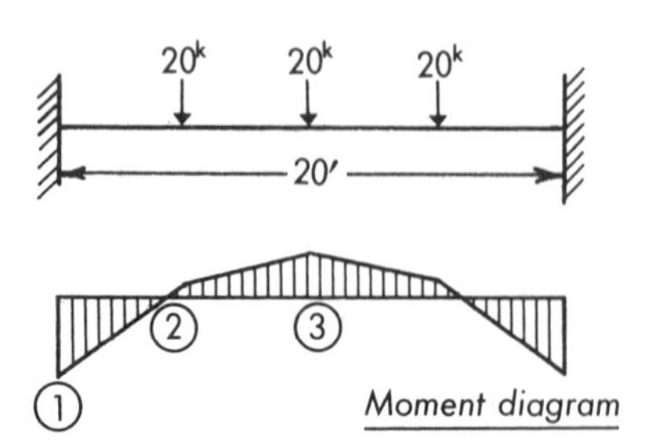

$$M_1 = -\frac{5\ W_1\ L}{48} = -\frac{5(60^k)(240'')}{48}$$

$$= -\ 1500 \text{ in.-kips}$$

$$\sigma_1 = \frac{.90\ M}{S}$$

$$= \frac{.90\ (1500 \text{ in.-kips})}{(62.7 \text{ in.}^3)}$$

$$= 21{,}500 \text{ psi}$$

(Only need $S = 56.2$ in.^{3}, but this is the lightest 14″ WF section.)

$$M_2 = +\frac{M_1\ L}{48}$$

$$= +\frac{(60^k)(240'')}{48}$$

$$= +\ 300 \text{ in.-kips}$$

$$\sigma_2 = \frac{M_2}{S}$$

$$= \frac{(300 \text{ in.-kips})}{(62.7 \text{ in.}^3)}$$

$$= 4780 \text{ psi}$$

$$M_3 = +\frac{W\ L}{16}$$

$$= +\frac{(60^k)(240'')}{16}$$

$$= +\ 900 \text{ in.-kips}$$

$$\sigma_3 = \frac{M_3}{S}$$

$$= \frac{(900 \text{ in.-kips})}{(62.7 \text{ in.}^3)}$$

$$= 14{,}350 \text{ psi}$$

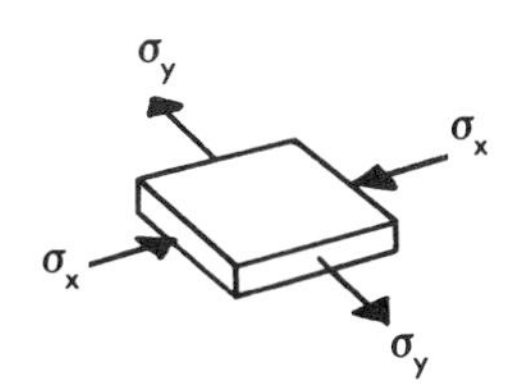
σy
σx
σx
σy

$$\sigma_x = -\ 14{,}350 \text{ psi}$$

$$\sigma_y = +\ 15{,}900 \text{ psi}$$

$$\sigma_{cr} = \sqrt{\sigma_x{}^2 - \sigma_x\ \sigma_y + \sigma_y{}^2 + 3\ \tau_{xy}}$$

$$= \sqrt{(-14{,}350)^2 - (-14{,}350)(15{,}900) + 15{,}900^2}$$

$$= 21{,}600 \text{ psi}$$

The apparent factor of yielding is—

$$r = \frac{\sigma_y}{\sigma_{cr}} = \frac{36{,}000}{21{,}600} = 1.67$$

This seems reasonable, and under these conditions the beam flange could be butt welded directly to the edge of the girder flange without trying to isolate the two intersecting flanges.

3. WELDING OF TAPERED FLANGES

Figure 10 shows the method for butt welding wide-flange rolled beams which have a slightly tapered flange to the edge of a girder flange.

By using a light ⅛" x 1" backing bar, it may be hammered as it is tack welded so that it will be tight against the joint.

Figure 11 shows the method for butt welding wide-flange rolled beams with a slightly tapered flange to a flat plate.

By using a light ⅛" x 1" backing bar, it may be hammered as it is tack welded so that it will be tight against the joint.

If there is any criticism in doing this, the following should be remembered. This type of butt welded joint on the wide-flange beams with a slightly tapered flange presents a smoother transition in section and transfer of beam flange force, than the widely used type of (beam-to-column) top connecting plate shown in Figure 12 which is accepted.

In this case (Fig. 12) the flange force must work

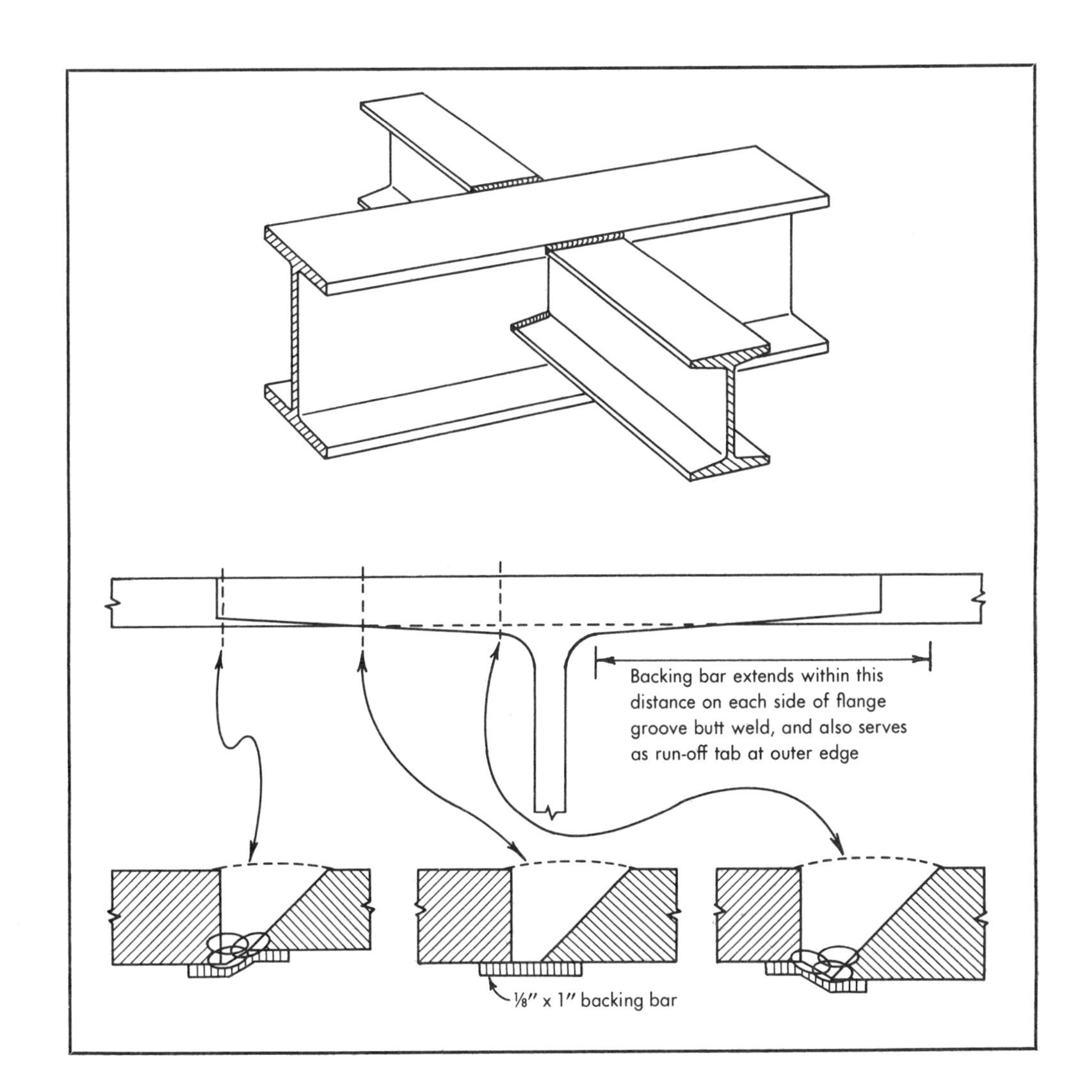
Backing bar extends within this distance on each side of flange groove butt weld, and also serves as run-off tab at outer edge
⅛" x 1" backing bar

FIGURE 10

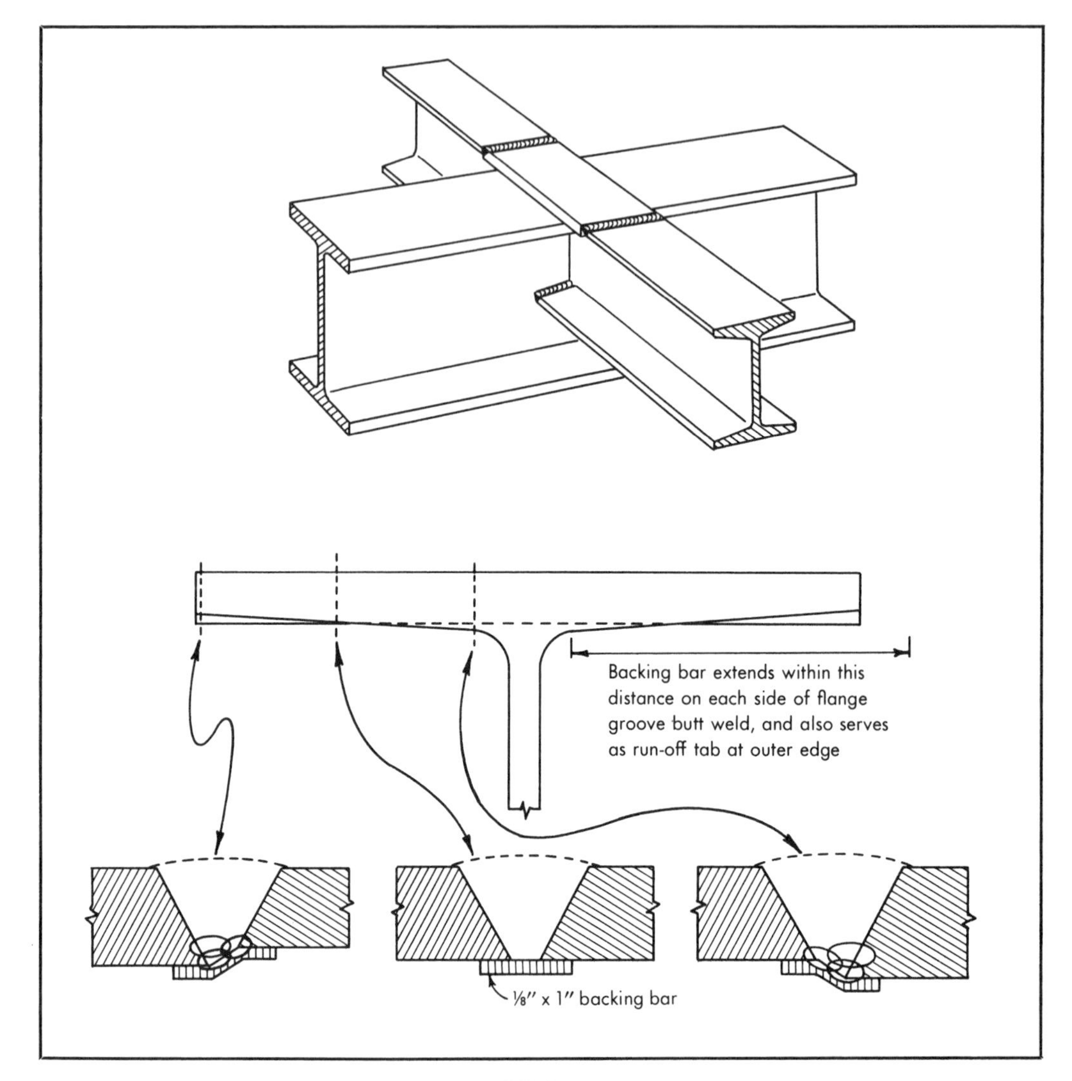
Backing bar extends within this distance on each side of flange groove butt weld, and also serves as run-off tab at outer edge
⅛" x 1" backing bar

FIGURE 11

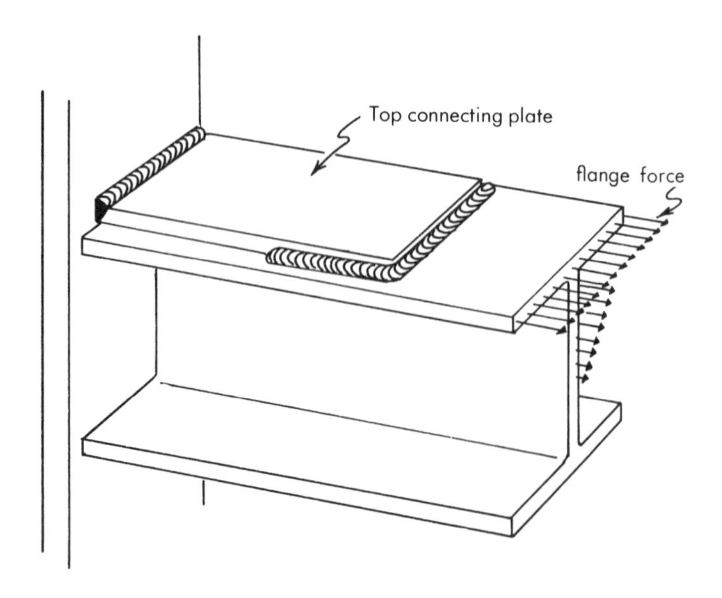
Top connecting plate
flange force

FIGURE 12

itself up through the connecting fillet welds into the top plate, and then out through the groove butt weld into the supporting member. Although there is a transverse fillet weld across the end of the top plate, much of the flange force must spread out along the edge in order to enter the fillet welds along the side of the plate. These connections stood up very well under testing and showed they could develop the full plastic moment of the beam.

4. EXAMPLES OF CONTINUOUS CONNECTIONS

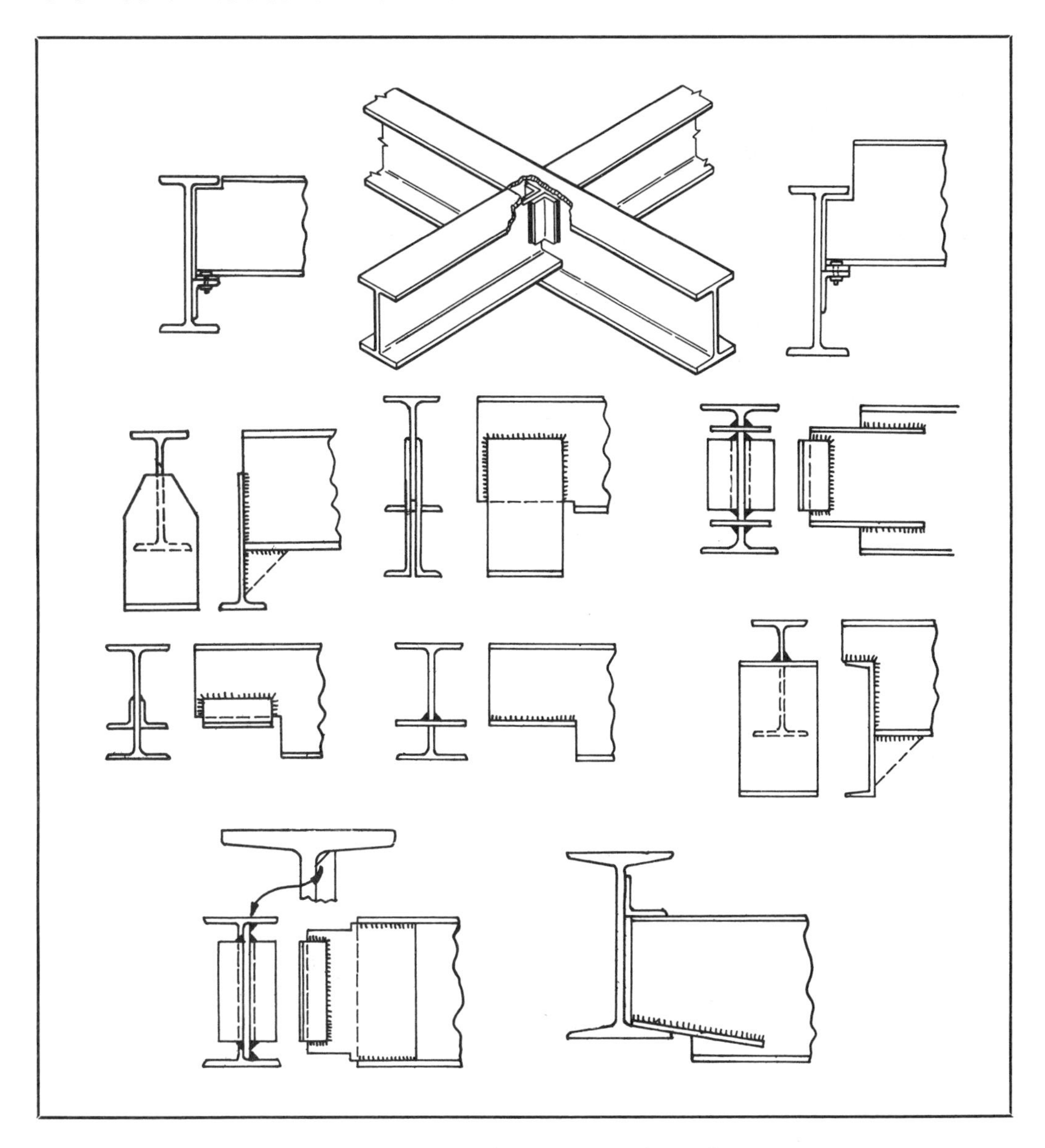

FIG. 13 Beams framing to girder web.

Welded connections are used throughout the Ainsley Building in Miami. Here, the beams are given continuity by connecting top flanges, using strap plates reaching across the girder. Lower flanges are butt welded to the web on both sides.

Continuous welded connections were used extensively in building the 7-story Harvey's Department Store in Nashville, Tenn. Here cross beams are given continuity through the main floor girders by means of a 1" thick cover plate and a bottom support plate, wider than the beam flange. This type of connection eliminates any need for beveling plates and laying groove welds.

Design of Trusses

1. INTRODUCTION

In trusses of proper arc welded design, gusset plates are generally eliminated. Tension members in the welded design are lighter because the entire cross-section is effective, and the amount of extraneous detail metal is reduced to a minimum.

Welded trusses may be designed in various ways, using T shapes, H and WF sections, etc. for chords. The diagonal members are usually angles. Various types of welded truss designs are illustrated in the following:

1. Perhaps the simplest type of truss construction is made of angle shapes and Tee's. In this example, the bottom and top chords are made of T sections, with angle sections for the diagonals. This is easy to fabricate and weld because the sections lap each other and fillet welds are used, Figure 1.

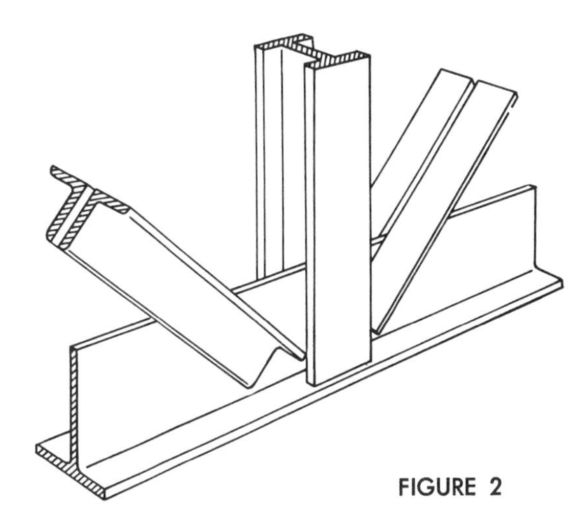

FIGURE 2

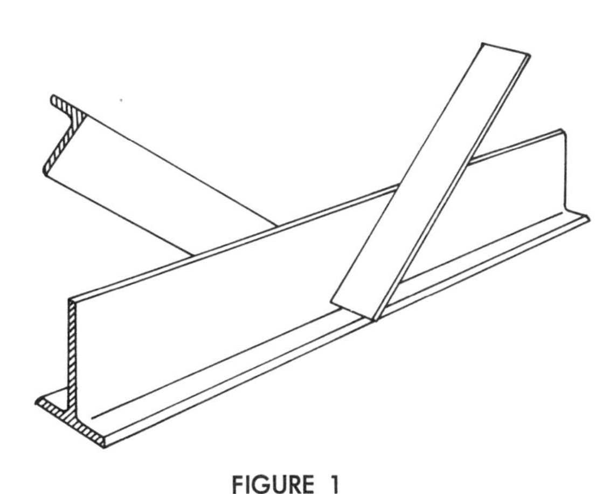

FIGURE 1

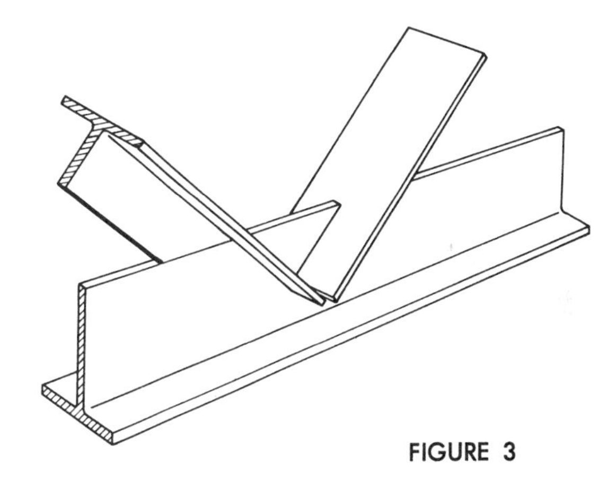

FIGURE 3

2. For a heavier truss, the vertical member can be an I or WF section. The web of this member, in the example illustrated, is slotted to fit over the stem of the T section. The T section is used for both the top and bottom chord members. The diagonal members are made of a double set of angles, Figure 2.

3. Some trusses make use of T sections for their diagonal members. The flanges of the diagonal members must be slotted to fit over the stem of the T section used for the top and bottom chords. The stem of the diagonal is also cut back and butt welded to the stem of the top and bottom chords, Figure 3.

4. Quite a few trusses are made of WF sections completely: both top and bottom chords as well as

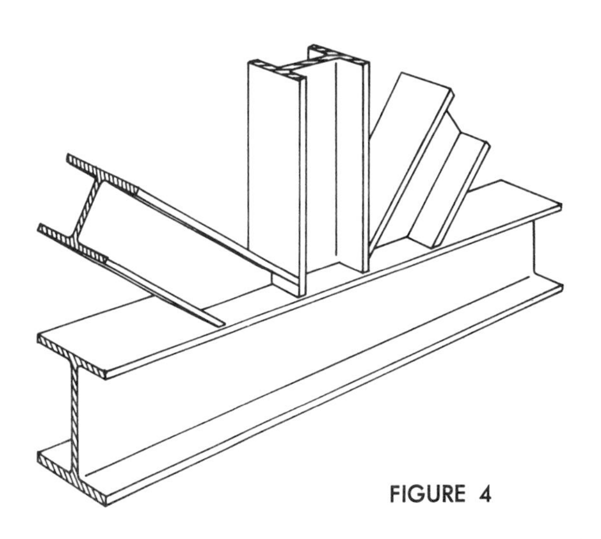

FIGURE 4

diagonal and vertical members. This allows loads to be placed anywhere along the top and bottom chords because of their high bending strength. (With the conventional truss design, loads must be placed only at points where diagonal or vertical members connect to the chord members.) Almost all of the welds are on the flanges of the top and bottom chords, and since these are flat surfaces, there is no difficult fitting of the members to make these connections, Figure 4.

5. Where longer lengths of connecting fillet welds are required, a simple flat plate may be butt welded directly to the stem of the horizontal T chord, without any joint preparation. This weld is then chipped or ground flush in the area where web members will connect, Figure 5.

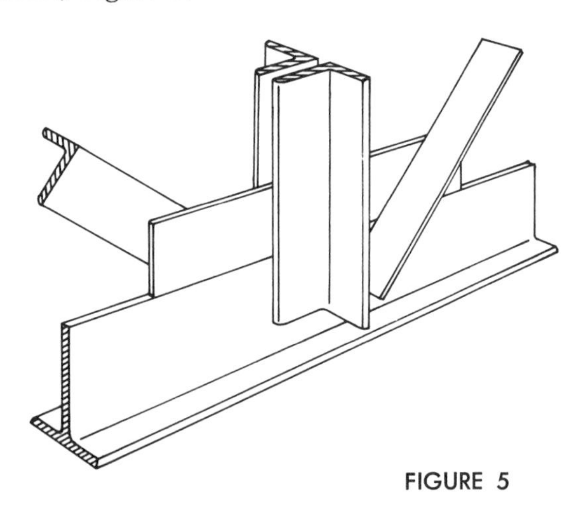

FIGURE 5

6. Sometimes heavier trusses are made of WF sections with the web of the top and bottom chords in the horizontal position. The welding of these members would consist mainly of butt welding the flanges together. Under severe loading, gusset plates may be added to strengthen the joint and reduce the possibility of concentrated stresses, Figure 6.

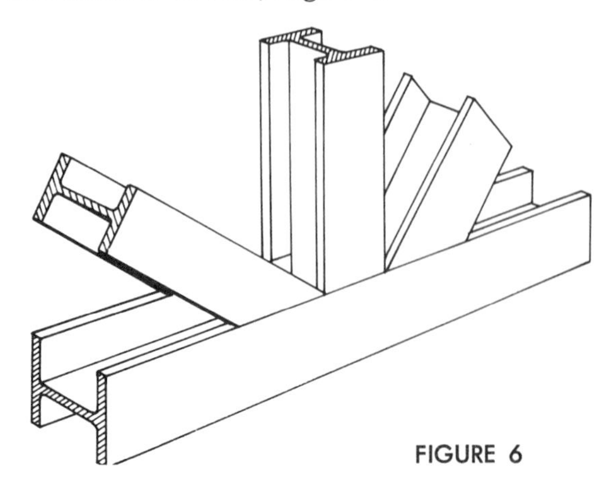

FIGURE 6

7. It is now possible to obtain hot-rolled square and rectangular tubular sections in A36 steel at about the same price as other hot-rolled sections. This type of section has many advantages. It has good resistance to bending, and has high moment of inertia and section modulus in both directions. It offers good strength in compression because of high radius of gyration in both directions. It is very easy to join by welding to other similar sections because of its flat sides. For lighter loads, fillet welds are sufficient. These sections offer good torsional resistance; this in turn provides greater lateral stability under compression, Figure 7.

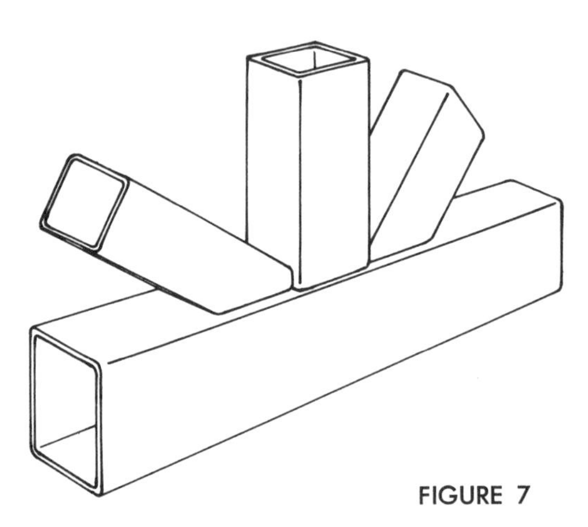

FIGURE 7

8. Round tubular sections or pipe have certain advantages in truss construction: good bending resistance, good compressive strength, and good torsional resistance. There is no rusting problem on the inside if they are sealed at the ends by welding, hence only the outside must be painted. Although it is more difficult to cut, fit, and weld the pipe sections together, this is not a problem for fitters and weldors experienced in pipe fabrication and welding. Pipe is used extensively in Europe for trusses. In this country it has been used for some mill buildings, special trusses for material handling bridges, extremely large dragline booms, off-shore drilling rigs, etc., Figure 8.

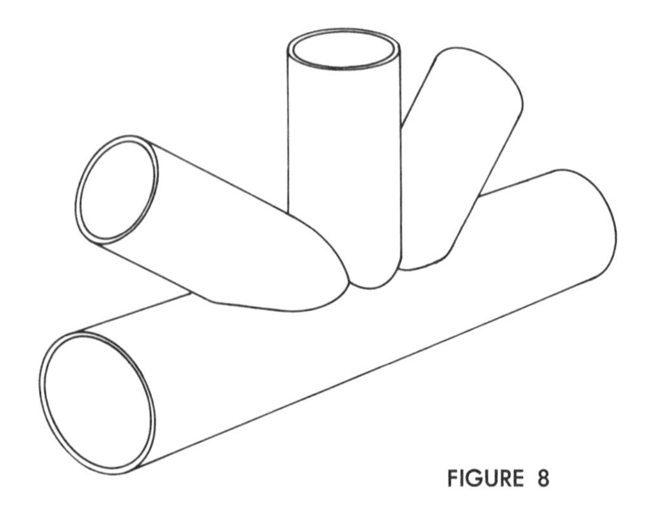

FIGURE 8

TABLE 1—Effect of Eccentric Loading

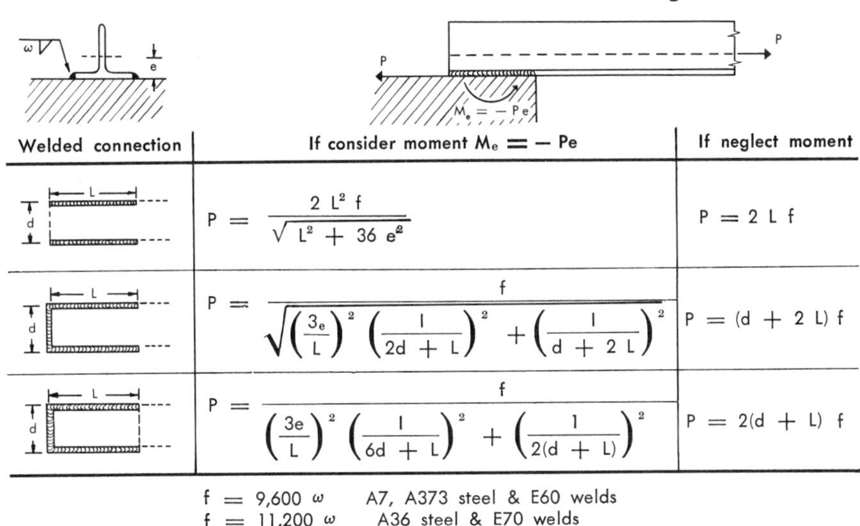

Welded connection	If consider moment $M_e = -Pe$	If neglect moment
	$P = \dfrac{2\,L^2\,f}{\sqrt{L^2 + 36\,e^2}}$	$P = 2\,L\,f$
	$P = \dfrac{f}{\sqrt{\left(\frac{3e}{L}\right)^2 \left(\frac{1}{2d + L}\right)^2 + \left(\frac{1}{d + 2\,L}\right)^2}}$	$P = (d + 2\,L)\,f$
	$P = \dfrac{f}{\left(\frac{3e}{L}\right)^2 \left(\frac{1}{6d + L}\right)^2 + \left(\frac{1}{2(d + L)}\right)^2}$	$P = 2(d + L)\,f$

$f = 9{,}600\ \omega$ A7, A373 steel & E60 welds
$f = 11{,}200\ \omega$ A36 steel & E70 welds

There are many methods by which to join the various pipe sections together in a truss. In this case, the pipe is cut back and a gusset plate is used to tie them together. A gusset plate also provides additional stiffness to the pipe within the connection area. However, they tend to cause an uneven stress distribution within the pipe, with rather high stresses in line with the gusset plate. See Figure 9.

These closed sections, with less surface area exposed to the elements, are less subject to corrosion than are open sections; in practically all cases they are left unpainted on the inside. It is only necessary to see that the ends are sealed by welding.

2. EFFECT OF ECCENTRIC LOADING

It can be shown that, with members back to back, or separated with a gusset plate, the connections will supply a restraining end moment:

$$M_e = -\,P\,e$$

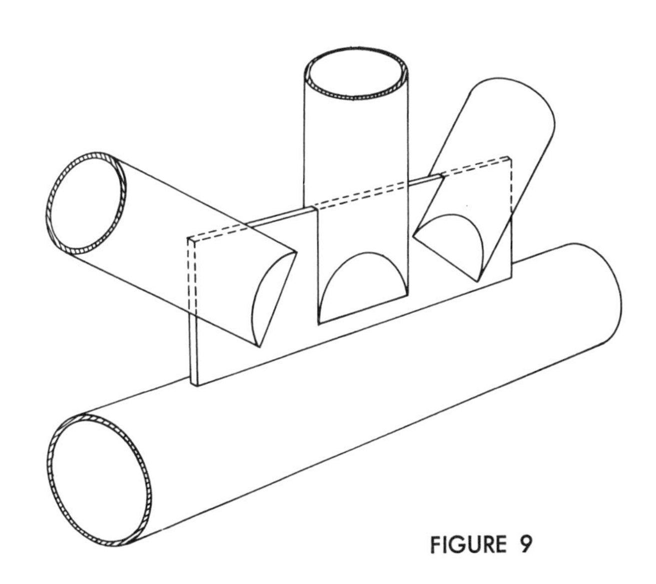

FIGURE 9

Since this moment is equal and opposite to the moment due to the eccentric loading ($M = P\,e$), they will cancel. As a result there will be no moment through-

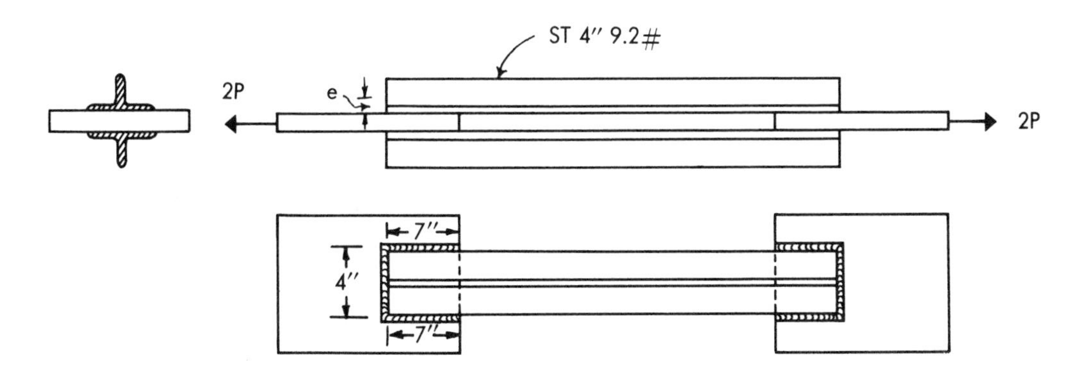

FIGURE 10

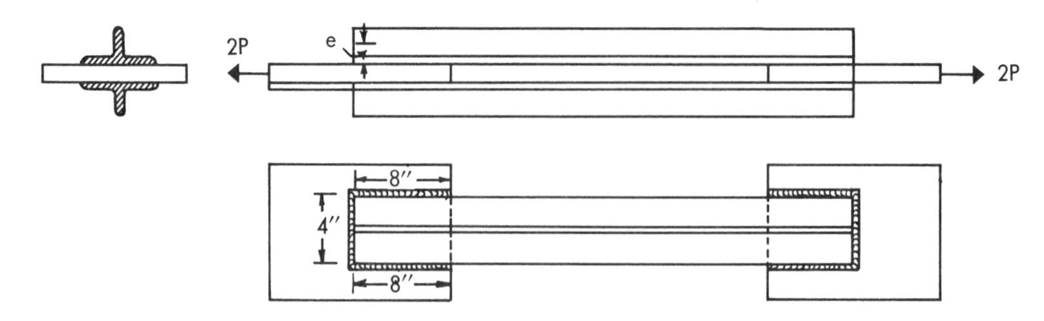

FIGURE 11

out the length of the member and it will remain straight.

However, this moment (M_e) is carried by the connecting welds in addition to their axial load (P). This moment is usually neglected in the design of the welded connection, because of the difficulty in determining the length of weld (L) when it is considered. Further, there usually is not much difference in the actual length of the required weld whether it is considered or not.

(a) *If the moment (M_e) is neglected:*

(See Figure 10.)

Assuming A373 steel and E60 welds,

$$A_T = 2.67 \text{ in.}^2$$

$$P = \sigma\ A_T$$
$$= (20{,}000)(2.67)$$
$$= 53.4 \text{ kips}$$

leg size of fillet weld

$$\omega = \tfrac{3}{4}\ t_f$$
$$= \tfrac{3}{4}\ (.425)$$
$$= .3185'' \text{ or } \tfrac{5}{16}''$$ ◺

total length of weld

$$L_T = \frac{P \text{ kips}}{\tfrac{5}{16}\ (9.6) \text{ kips/in.}}$$
$$= \frac{(53.4)}{(3)}$$
$$= 17.8''$$

This would be distributed 4″ across the end, returning 6.9″ on the sides, or use 7″ long on each side. This would give a total length of 18″ of 5/16″ ◺ weld.

(b) *If the moment (M_e) is considered:*

(See Figure 11.)

Here:

$$e = y = .94''$$
$$d = 4''$$
$$\omega = \tfrac{5}{16}''$$
$$P = 53.4 \text{ kips}$$

since:

$$P = \frac{f}{\sqrt{\left(\frac{3e}{L}\right)^2\left(\frac{1}{2d + L}\right)^2 + \left(\frac{1}{d + 2L}\right)^2}}$$

$$= \frac{9600\ (\tfrac{5}{16})}{\sqrt{\left(\frac{3 \text{ x } .94}{L}\right)^2\left(\frac{1}{8 + L}\right)^2 + \left(\frac{1}{4 + 2L}\right)^2}}$$

$$= 53.4 \text{ kips}$$

and from this we find L = 8″. (This value was found by plotting several values of L on graph paper and selecting that L value which gave the closest value of P = 53.4 kips.) This would give a total length of 20″ of 5/16″ ◺ weld.

In this case, the extra work involved in considering the moment did not pay for the very slight overstress in the weld when the moment was neglected.

If only one member is used, and the plate to which it is attached is not very rigid, this restraining end moment will not be set up. The member will then have a moment due to the eccentric load (M = P e), in addition to its axial load (P). See Figure 12.

axial tensile stress in member

$$\sigma = \frac{P}{A}$$

bending stress

$$\sigma = \frac{M\ c}{I} = \frac{P\ y^2}{I}$$

Since the distance to the outer tensile fiber (c) and the distance of the section's center of gravity from the base line (y) are equal, and since the eccentricity of

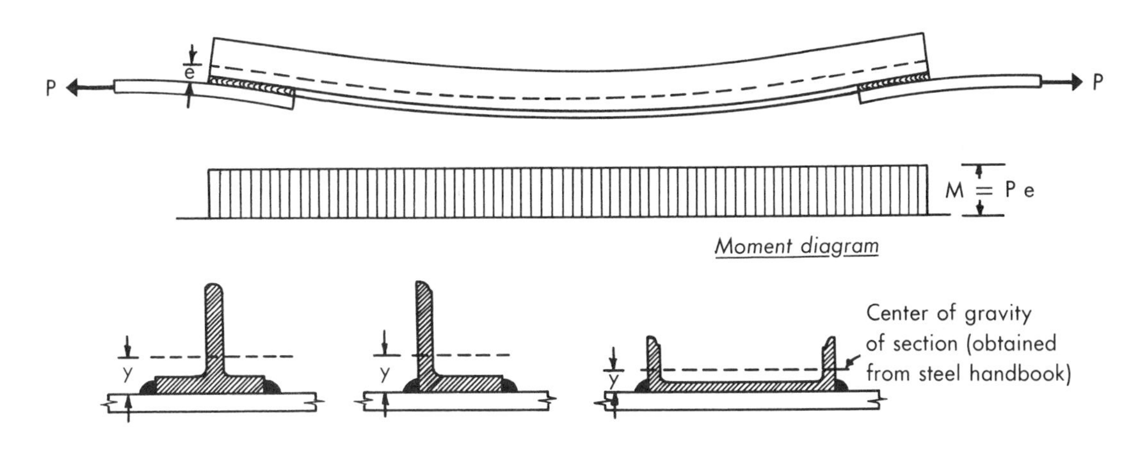

FIGURE 12

loading (e) is nearly equal to these, it is assumed for simplicity that c = e = y. Therefore, the total (maximum) stress is—

$$\sigma = \frac{P}{A} + \frac{P\ y^2}{I} \qquad (1)$$

or the maximum axial load (P) for a given allowable stress (σ) is—

$$P = \frac{\sigma}{\frac{1}{A} + \frac{y^2}{I}} \qquad (2)$$

For the ST 4″ I 9.2# member used in the previous example, Figure 10, this additional moment due to eccentricity of loading would reduce the member's allowable axial tensile force to:

$$P = \frac{\sigma}{\frac{1}{A} + \frac{y^2}{I}} = \frac{(20{,}000)}{\frac{1}{2.67} + \frac{(.94)^2}{(3.50)}}$$

$$= 32 \text{ kips}$$

In this particular case, the additional moment due to the eccentrically applied axial load reduces the member's allowable load carrying capacity by 40%. This far exceeds any reduction in the strength of the welded connection due to this moment. Thus, the connection will be on the conservative side.

Conclusions:

(a) If the attaching plate is very flexible and offers no restraining action at the end of the member, the full moment (M = P e) must be added to the member and no moment added to the connection. In other words, the connection is designed for the transfer of the axial force only.

(b) If the attaching plate is rigid enough so there is no end rotation of the member, this moment is not added to the member, but must be added to the connection.

Even in this example, if the moment were also figured to be added to the connection, at the reduced load of P = 32 kips, it would not require as much weld as in the previous case:

Here:

$\omega = 5/16''$ $\qquad$ $d = 4''$

$e = .94''$ $\qquad$ $P = 32$ kips

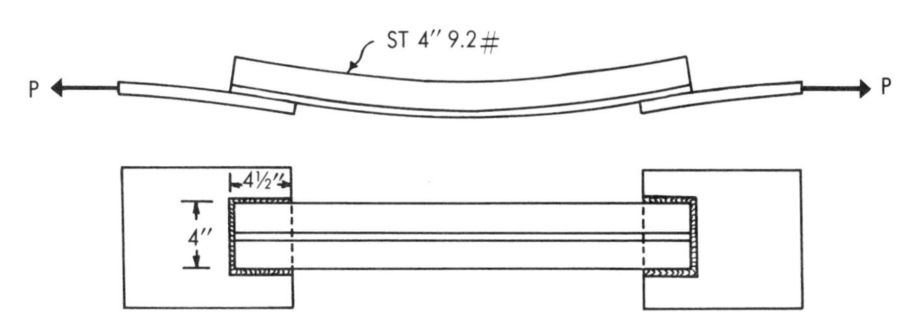

FIGURE 13

since:

$$P = \frac{f}{\sqrt{\left(\frac{3e}{L}\right)^2 \left(\frac{1}{2d + L}\right)^2 + \left(\frac{1}{d + 2L}\right)^2}}$$

$$= \frac{9600\ (5/16)}{\sqrt{\left(\frac{3 \times .94}{L}\right)^2 \left(\frac{1}{8 + L}\right)^2 + \left(\frac{1}{4 + 2L}\right)^2}}$$

$$= 32 \text{ kips}$$

From this we find L = 4.4″ or = 4½″. (This value was found by plotting several values of L on graph paper and selecting that which gave the closest value of P = 32 kips.) This would give a total length of 13″ of 5/16″ ◺ weld.

This is another case where theory would indicate a much higher reduction in the carrying capacity of a connection than actual testing shows. The following lap joints were welded and pulled to failure.

(a) *calculated allowable load:*

$$P = \frac{2\ L^2\ f}{\sqrt{L^2 + 36\ e^2}}$$

$$= \frac{19{,}200\ (2)^2\ (1/4)}{\sqrt{2^2 + 36\ (1/4)^2}}$$

$$= 7500 \text{ lbs}$$

(b) *calculated allowable load:*

$$P = \frac{2\ L^2\ f}{\sqrt{L^2 + 36\ e^2}}$$

$$= \frac{19{,}200\ (2)^2\ (1/4)}{\sqrt{2^2 + 36\ (1)^2}}$$

$$= 3040 \text{ lbs}$$

Theory would indicate that, in the above samples, increasing the eccentricity (e) from ¼″ up to 1″ would decrease the strength of the welds by 60%.

Yet, the actual test results showed:

(a) f = 11,260 lbs/in.

(b) f = 10,280 lbs/in.

or that this large increase in eccentricity (e), from ¼″ to 1″, only decreased the strength by 8.7%.

The reasons for neglecting this eccentricity in the detailing of most connections may be summarized as follows:

1. In the usual welded connection, the eccentricity is not very large, and in these cases the theoretical reduction in strength due to the additional moment induced by the eccentricity is not very much.

2. Actual test results indicate a much smaller decrease in strength due to this eccentricity than theory would indicate. Also these test pieces were very short; the usual member would be much longer and, if any-

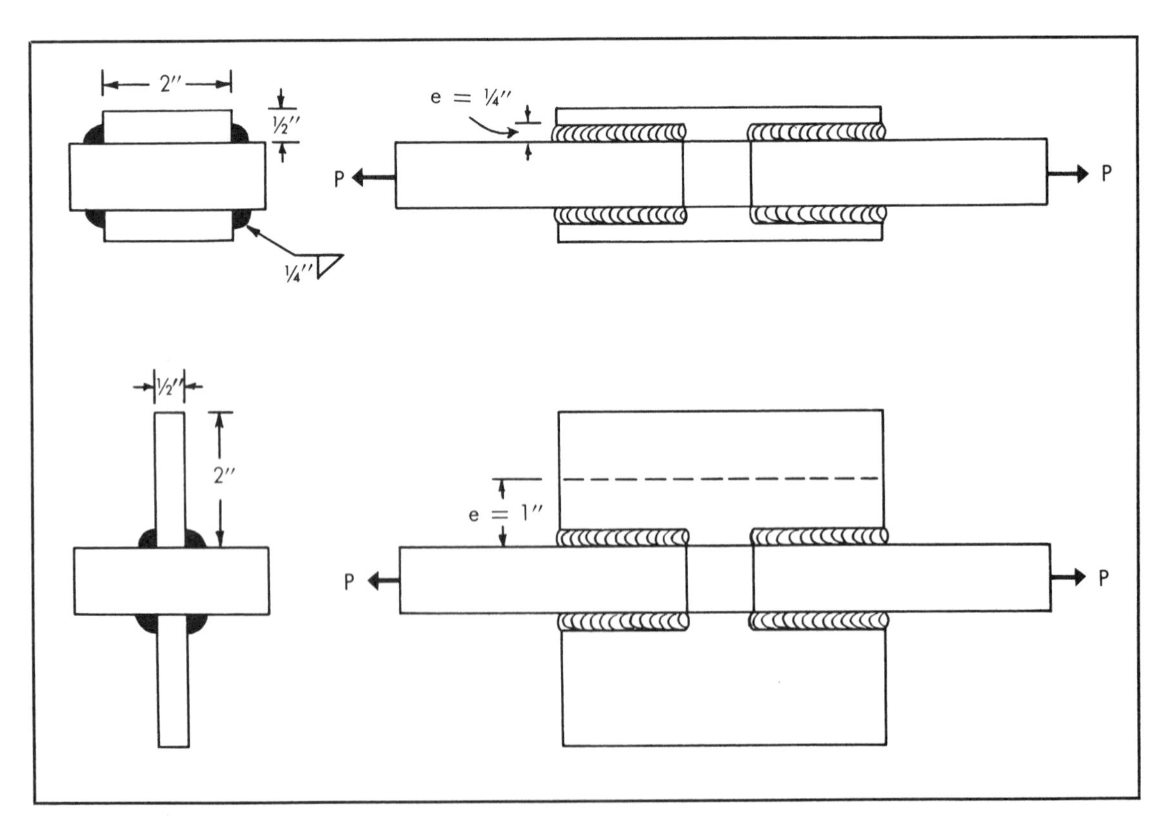

FIGURE 14

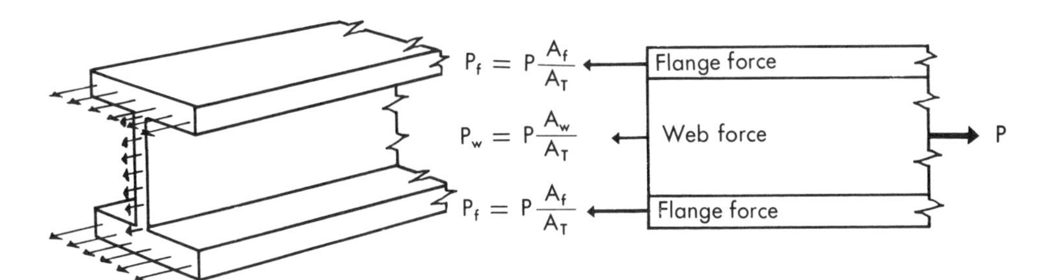

FIGURE 15

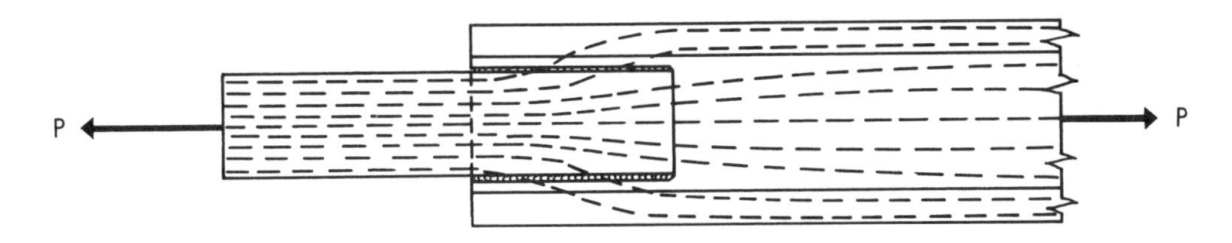

FIGURE 16

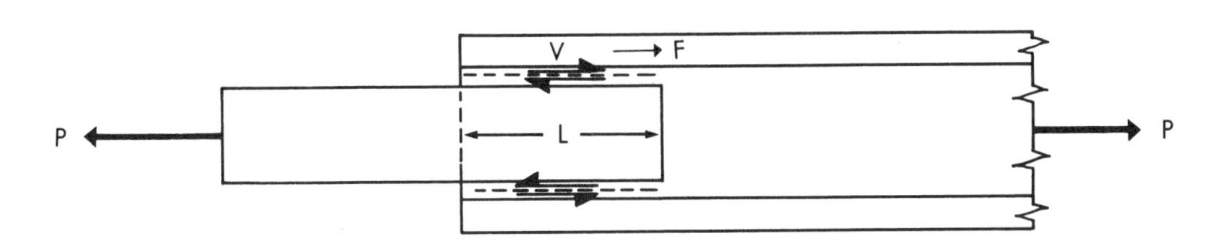

FIGURE 17

thing, would minimize this problem.

3. The eccentric loading would effect a reduction in strength of the member several times greater than any reduction in the strength of the welded connection.

4. It is very time-consuming to include this moment in consideration of the connection.

AISC Sec 1.15.3 requires that welds at the ends of any member transmitting axial force into that member shall have their center of gravity line up with the gravity axis of the member unless provision is made for the effect of the resulting eccentricity. However, except for fatigue loading conditions, fillet welds connecting the ends of single angles, double angles, and similar types of members (i.e. having low center of gravity or neutral axis, relative to attaching surface) need not be balanced about the neutral axis of the member.

3. DISTRIBUTION AND TRANSFER OF FORCES

It is assumed that the axial forces in a member are uniformly distributed throughout the various elements of the cross-section.

See Figure 15, where:

A_f = area of flange

A_w = area of web

A_T = total area of section

If the force in some element of a member cannot be transferred directly through the connection, this portion of the force must work its way around into another element of the member which can provide this transfer. See Figure 16.

This decrease in axial force (F) of one element of a member is accomplished through a transfer in shear (V) into another element. See Figure 17.

The length of this shear transfer (L) must be sufficient so that the resulting shear stress (τ) within this area does not exceed the allowable. This area may also have to be reinforced with doubler plates so it can safely carry this increased axial force.

If we assume uniform distribution of axial stress through the cross-section of the following member, then the web area has a force of P_w.

(See Figure 18.)

Shear transfer from web:

$V_w = P_w = \sigma\, A_w$ and

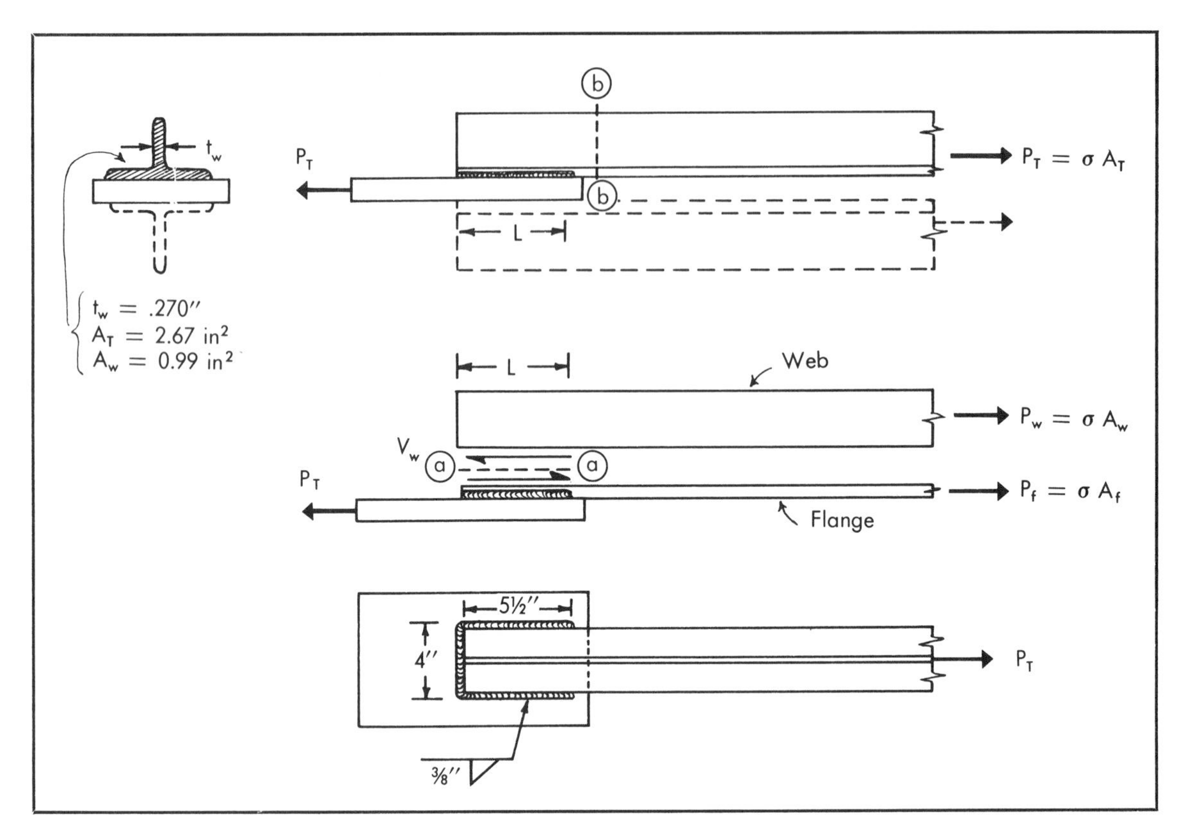

FIGURE 18

$$P_w = \sigma A_w$$
$$= (20{,}000)(.99)$$
$$= 19.8 \text{ kips}$$

This force in the web area (P_w = 19.8 kips) must be transferred down into the flange by shear (V_w), and out into the connection.

Theoretically, if the section is not to be stressed above its allowable, this shear transfer (V_w) must take place within a length bounded by the connecting welds.

If this is true, then this 19.8-kip force in the web, transferred as shear through a length of 5½″ where the flange joins the web, causes a shear stress in the section (a-a) of:

$$\tau = \frac{P_w}{A_w}$$
$$= \frac{(19.8 \text{ kips})}{(.270)(5\tfrac{1}{2})}$$
$$= 13{,}330 \text{ psi} > 13{,}000 \text{ psi (A373 steel)}$$

This is close enough. However, if it were higher, it would indicate that one of the following conditions exists:

a. The shear transfer takes place over a greater distance and, beyond the welds, must travel this short distance in the flange as additional tension until the weld is reached. It thus slightly overstresses the section (b-b) in tension.

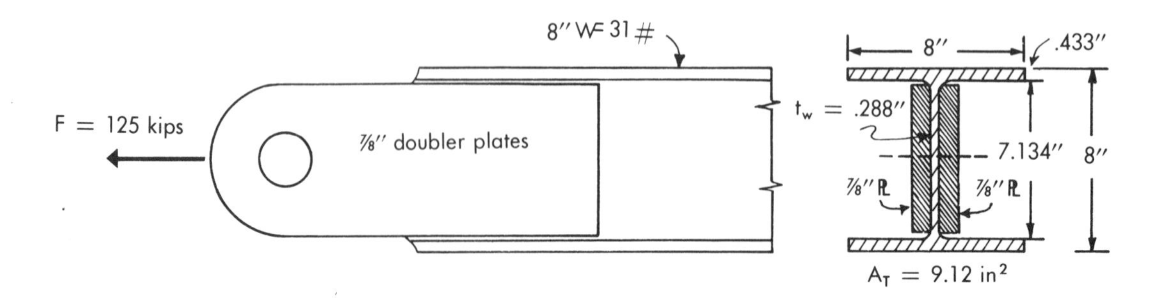

FIGURE 19

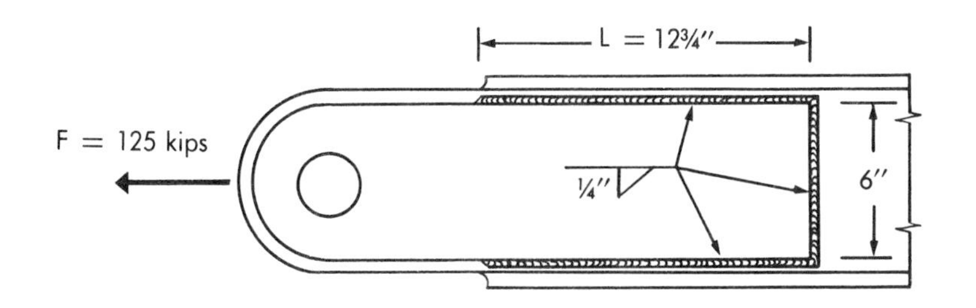

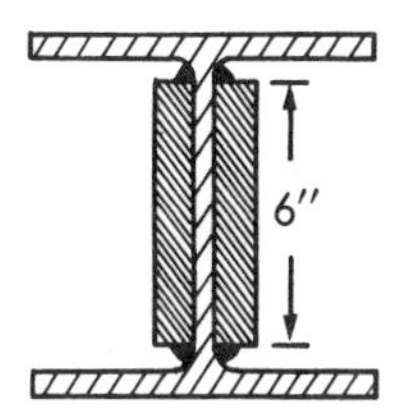

FIGURE 20

b. The shear transfer does take place within this 5½″ length, and slightly overstresses this section (a-a) in shear.

In most cases the welded connection will provide sufficient length (a-a) for the proper transfer of these forces from one portion of the member to another.

Problem 1

To detail an attachment to the tension member shown in Figure 19.

If we assume the total axial tensile force (F = 125 kips) is divided among the two flanges and web of the beam by the ratio of their areas to the total area, then the force in the flange which must be transferred out is—

$$F_f = F \frac{A_f}{A_T}$$

$$= (125) \frac{(.433 \text{ x } 8)}{(9.12)}$$

$$= 47.5 \text{ kips}$$

(a) If the doubler plates are 6″ wide, this flange force (F_f = 47.5 kips) must first transfer into the beam web along the length (L) as shear, V = 47.5 kips.

This length (L) must be—

$$L = \frac{V}{t_w \, \tau} \qquad \text{(See Figure 20.)}$$

$$= \frac{(47.5 \text{ kips})}{(.288)\ (13{,}000)}$$

$$= 12.7'' \text{ or } \underline{12\tfrac{3}{4}''}$$

The leg size of these parallel welds would be based upon the force on the weld:

$$f = \frac{V}{2\ L}$$

$$= \frac{(47.5 \text{ kips})}{2(12\tfrac{3}{4})}$$

$$= 1865 \text{ lbs/in.}$$

$$\omega = \frac{\text{actual force}}{\text{allowable force}}$$

$$= \frac{(1865)}{(9600)}$$

$$= .194'' \text{ or } \underline{\text{use } \tfrac{1}{4}''} \text{ (A373 steel; E60 weld)}$$

(b) If the doubler plates are 7″ wide and are welded directly to the inside of the flanges of the WF section, the flange force (F_f = 47.5 kips) will transfer directly through the parallel welds. See Figure 21.

If the leg size of these parallel fillet welds is ω = ½″, the length of these welds would be—

$$L = \frac{F_f}{2(9600\ \omega)}$$

$$= \frac{(47.5 \text{ kips})}{2(9600)(\tfrac{1}{2})}$$

$$= 4.95'' \text{ or } \underline{\text{use } 5''}$$

Transverse Forces

Any transverse component of a force applied to a member is carried by those elements of the member which lie parallel to this force. In other words, a vertical force applied to an I beam with the web vertical is carried as

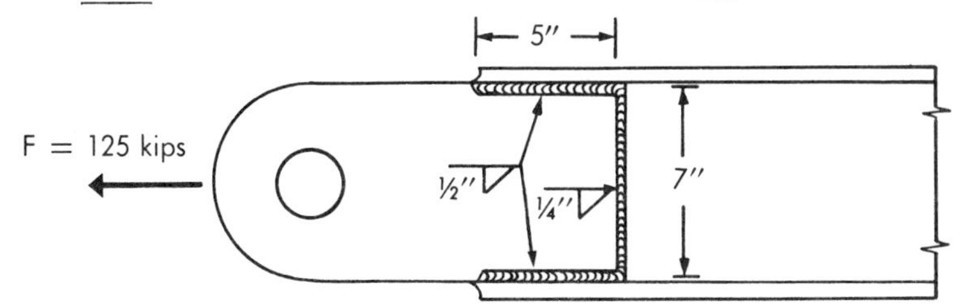

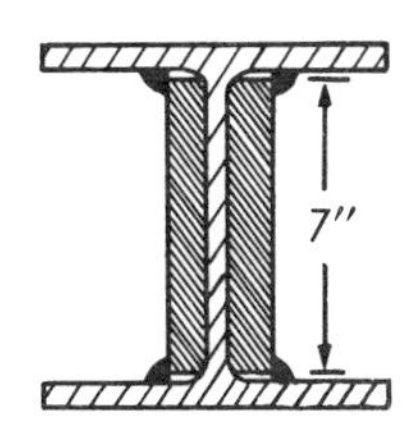

FIGURE 21

shear almost entirely by the web. If the web is horizontal, this force is carried as shear almost entirely by the two flanges. See Figure 22.

In a truss connection subject to a moment (for example, a Vierendeel Truss), the applied moments, if unbalanced, cause shear forces (V) around the periphery of the connection web. The resulting diagonal compression from these shear forces can buckle the web if it is not thick enough. See Figure 23.

The Law of Force and Reaction states that in a member constrained by its supports, an applied force at any point sets up at this point an equal, collinear. opposite reaction. This of course assumes the member to be a rigid body, that is one which does not change its shape or dimensions.

In the following member which is supported, the applied force (F) has two components: horizontal (F_h) and vertical (F_v). The result is two reactions in the member: vertical (R_v) in the web stiffener, and horizontal (R_h) for the most part in the lower flange. See Figure 24.

In order for one of these components of the applied force to be transferred into another member, it is necessary for the other component to be transferred also.

Figure 25 illustrates this. If either one of the force components cannot be carried (F_v in this example, because there is no stiffener), there will be little or no transfer of the other component (here F_h) even though there is a member or element present to do this. In other words the amount of a force component (here F_h) which may be transferred into the member depends on the ability of the connection to transfer the

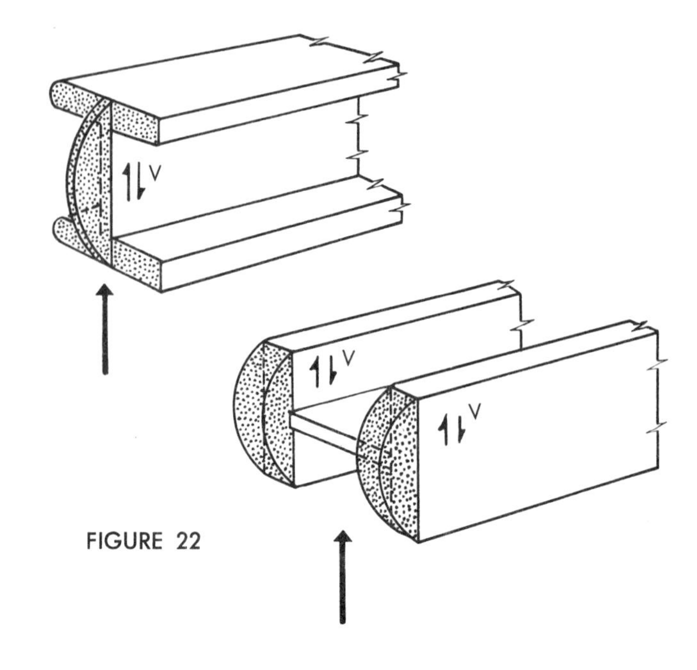

FIGURE 22

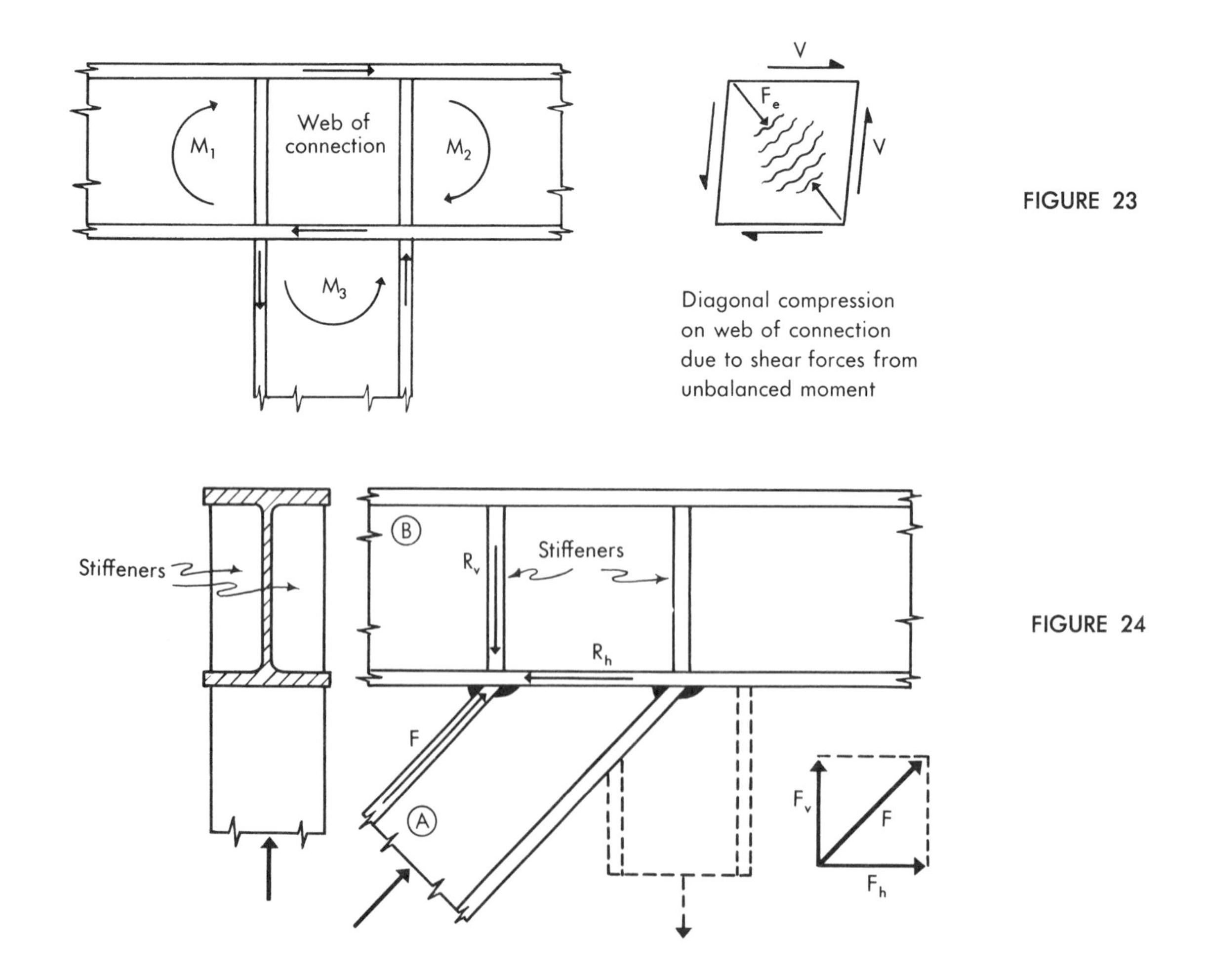

FIGURE 23

FIGURE 24

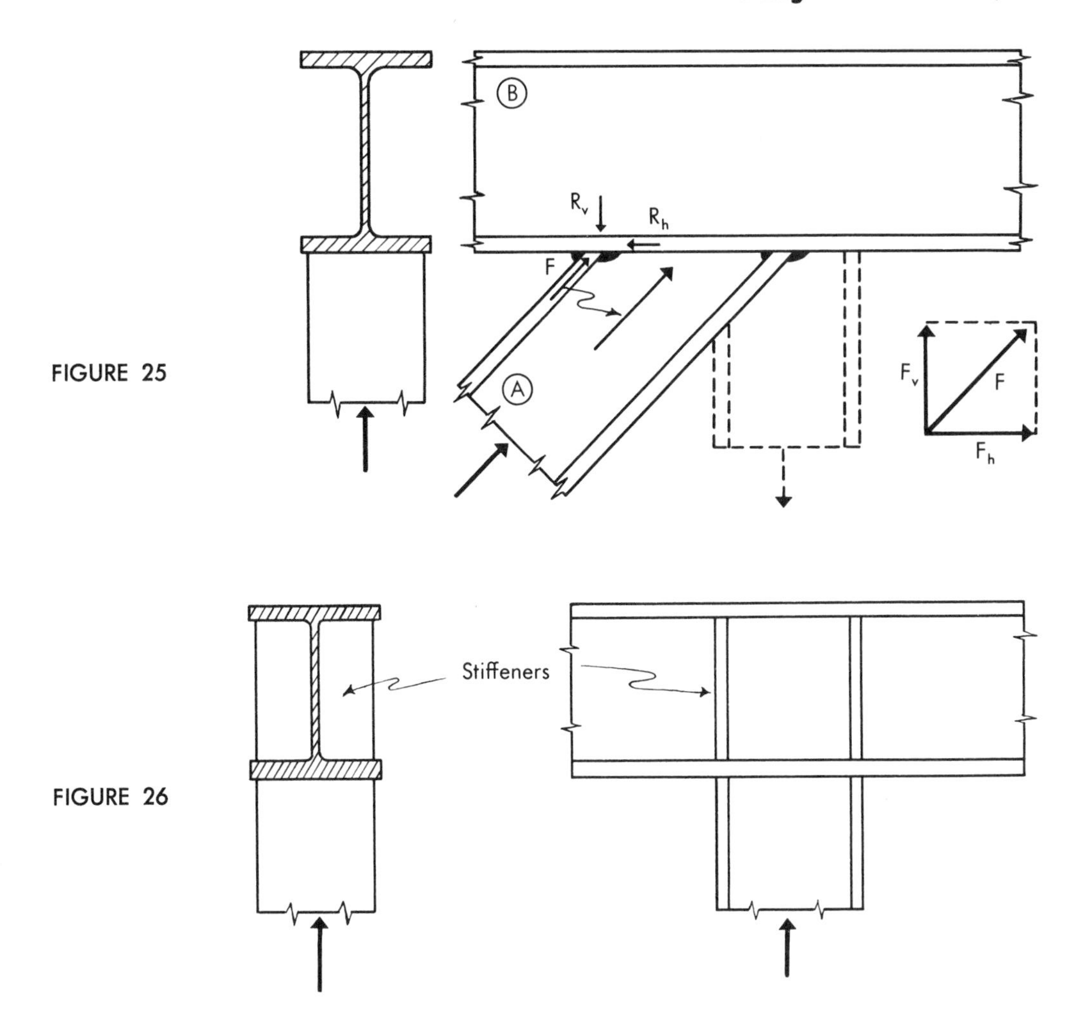

FIGURE 25

FIGURE 26

other component (here F_v). Of course the applied force (F) will be reduced also, and under these conditions some other portion of this member must transfer it. In this case the web of member A will transfer the balance of the force (F).

Determining Need for Stiffeners

Normally stiffeners would be added to a member in which large concentrated transverse forces are applied.

However, for smaller members with lower forces, these stiffeners are sometimes left off in truss connections. It is difficult to know under what conditions this might have to be stiffened.

In recent research at Lehigh University on "Welded Interior Beam-to-Column Connections", short sections were tested under transverse compression as well as tension, with and without stiffeners. See Figure 27.

It was found that the compressive force applied over a narrow section (t_f) of member's flange spread out over a wide section of the web by the time the net web thickness was reached. A conservative value for this distance is given as:

$$(t_f + 5K)$$

where K = the distance from the outer face of the flange to the web toe of the fillet. This value for all rolled sections may be found in any steel handbook.

t_f = thickness of the flange of the connecting member which supplies the compressive force.

Although there was no axial compression applied to the member in this test, on subsequent work involving actual beam-to-column connections, axial compression was simultaneously applied. See Figure 28.

It was found that an axial compressive stress of about 1.65 times the working stress (14,500 psi), or $\sigma = 24{,}000$ psi, had little effect on the strength of the connection. At the end of each test with the final loads left on the beams, this axial compressive stress was increased to twice the working stress or $\sigma = 29{,}000$ psi with no indication of trouble in the connection.

From this, they concluded that the minimum web thickness of the column for which stiffeners are not required is found from the following:

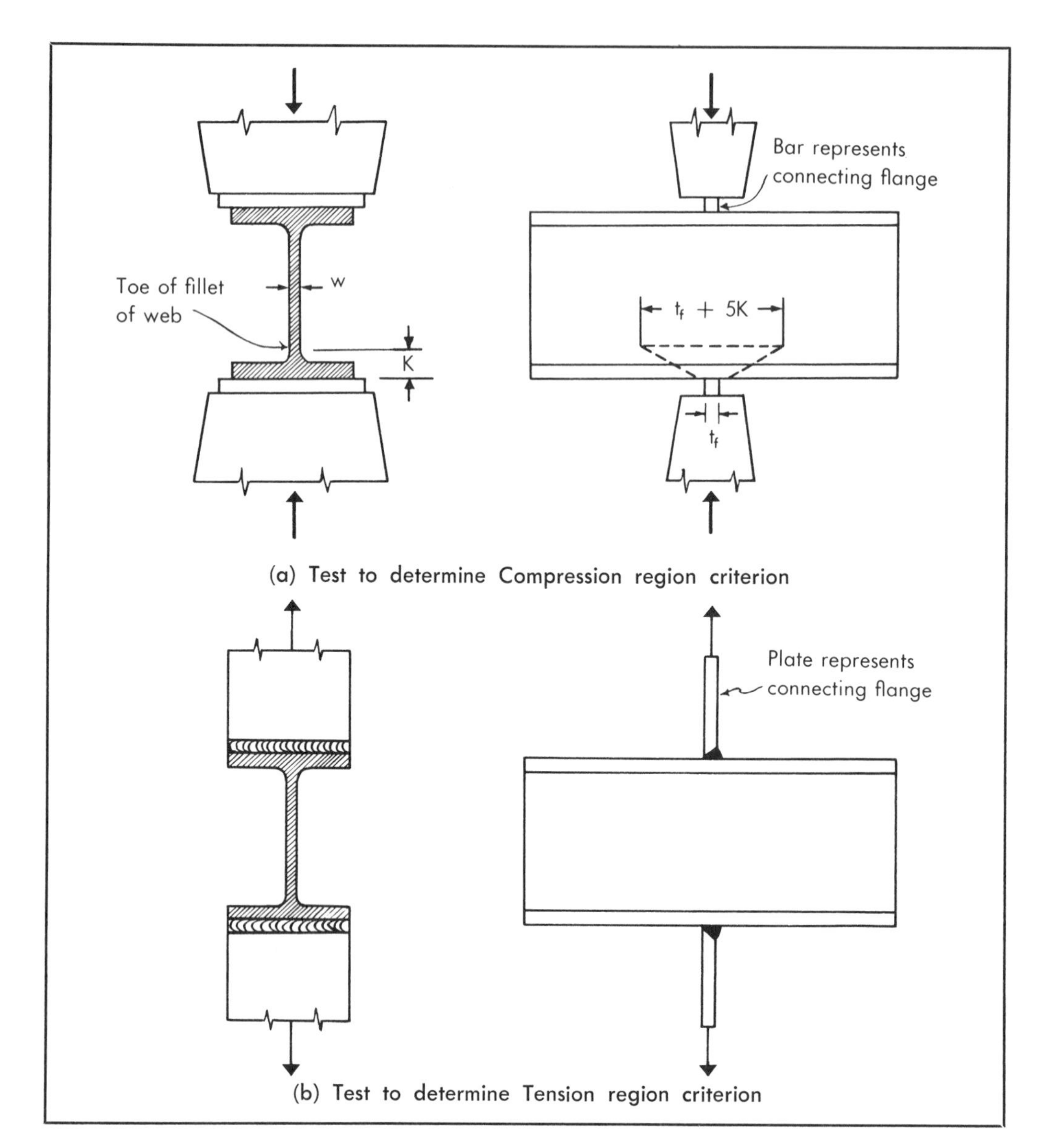

(a) Test to determine Compression region criterion

(b) Test to determine Tension region criterion

FIGURE 27

$$w \geqq \frac{t_f \, b_b}{t_f + 5K}$$

This research, concerned with the application of concentrated flange forces applied to flanges of WF members, was directed toward beam-to-column connections. However, it does seem reasonable to use this as a guide for the distribution of flange forces in truss connections. This will then provide an indication of the stresses in the chord resulting from the flange force of the connecting member.

In the test of the tension area, they found that the thickness of the column flange (t_c) determined whether stiffeners were required. On the basis of their tests, they made the following analysis.

Analysis of Tension Region of Connection

The following is adapted from "Welded Interior Beam-to-Column Connections", AISC 1959.

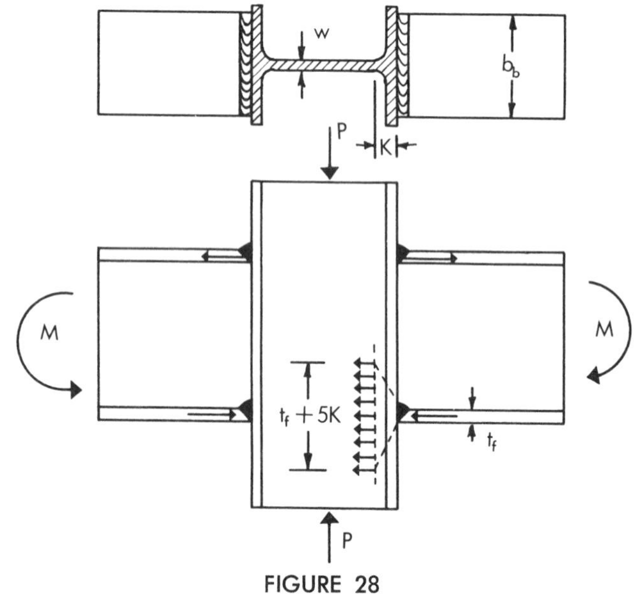

FIGURE 28

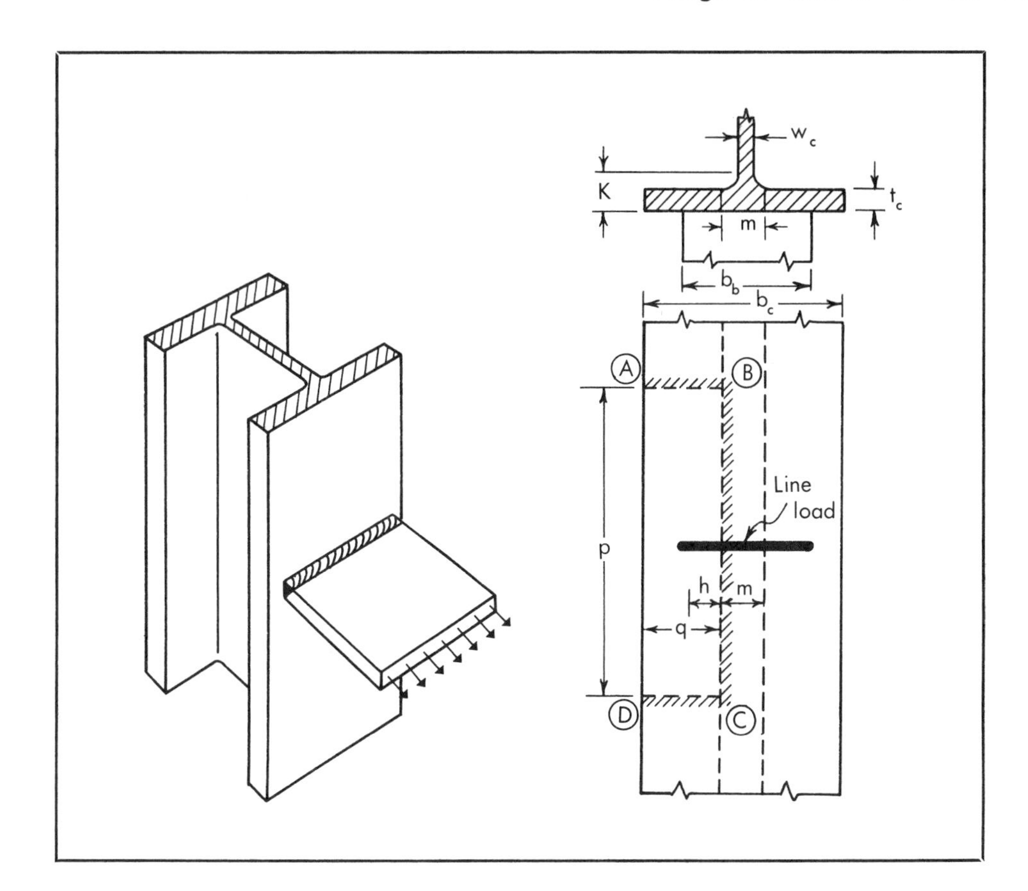

FIGURE 29

The column flange can be considered as acting as two plates, both of type ABCD; see Figure 19. The beam flange is assumed to place a line load on each of these plates. The effective length of the plates (p) is assumed to be 12 t_c and the plates are assumed to be fixed at the ends of this length. The plate is also assumed to be fixed adjacent to the column web.

See Figure 29, where:

$$m = w_c + 2(K - t_c)$$

$$q = \frac{b_c - m}{2}$$

$$h = \frac{b_b - m}{2}$$

$$p = 12\ t_c$$

Analysis of this plate by means of yield line theory leads to the ultimate capacity of this plate being—

$$Pu = c_1\ \sigma_y\ t_c^2$$

where:

$$c_1 = \frac{\dfrac{4}{\beta} + \dfrac{\beta}{\eta}}{2 - \dfrac{\eta}{\lambda}}$$

$$\eta = \frac{\beta}{4}\left[\sqrt{\beta^2 + 8\lambda} - \beta\right]$$

$$\beta = \frac{p}{q}$$

$$\lambda = \frac{h}{q}$$

For the wide-flange columns and beams used in practical connections, it has been found that c_1 varies within the range of 3.5 to 5. A conservative figure would be—

$$P_u = 3.5\ \sigma_y\ t_c^2$$

The force carried by the central rigid portion of the column in line with the web is—

$$\sigma_y\ t_b\ m$$

Setting this total force equal to that of the beam's tension flange:

$$\sigma_y\ t_b\ m + 7\ \sigma_y\ t_c^2 = \sigma_y\ b_b\ t_b$$

Reducing the strength of this column region by 20% and making the conservative assumption that $m/b_b = .15$, this reduces to the following:

$$(.80)\ \sigma_y\ t_b\ (.15\ b_b) + (.80)\ 7\ \sigma_y\ t_c^2 = \sigma_y\ b_b\ t_b$$

$$t_c^2 = \frac{b_b\ t_b - .12\ b_b\ t_b}{5.6}$$

or $\boxed{t_c \geqq .40\ \sqrt{b_b\ t_b}}$ ....(3)

If the column flange has this thickness, stiffeners are not required as far as the tension area is concerned.

We might carry this thought one step further and apply it to a tension flange which connects to the member at an angle other than 90°, such as in a truss connection. See Figure 30.

resistance of supporting flange (t_c)

$$P = (.80)\ \sigma_y\ t_b\ (.15\ b_b) + (.180)\ 7\ \sigma_y\ t_c^2$$

pull of tension flange (t_b)

$$P_1 = b_b\ t_b\ \sigma_y$$

$$\therefore\ (.80)\ \sigma_y\ t_b\ (.15\ b_b) + (.80)\ 7\ \sigma_y\ t_c^2 = b_b\ t_b\ \sigma_y\ \sin \alpha$$

or $\boxed{t_c \geqq \sqrt{\frac{b_b\ t_b\ (\sin \alpha - .12)}{5.6}}}$ ....(4)

Application to Truss Connections

This Lehigh work for beam-to-column connections will now be applied as a guide for determining the distribution of compressive forces in a truss connection.

It is assumed that this transfer of the flange force of Ⓐ occurs in the web of member Ⓑ within distance of ($t + 5K$). See Figure 31.

Here:

$$t = \frac{t_b}{\sin \phi}$$

The vertical component of the web force of member Ⓐ transfers directly into the web of member Ⓑ within the distance of $\dfrac{d}{\sin \phi}$

Within the region b–c, these compressive stresses in the web of member Ⓑ overlap and would be added.

$$\sigma = \frac{F_f\ \sin \phi}{\left(\dfrac{t_b}{\sin \phi} + 5K\right) w} + \frac{F_w\ \sin \phi}{\left(\dfrac{d}{\sin \phi}\right) w}$$

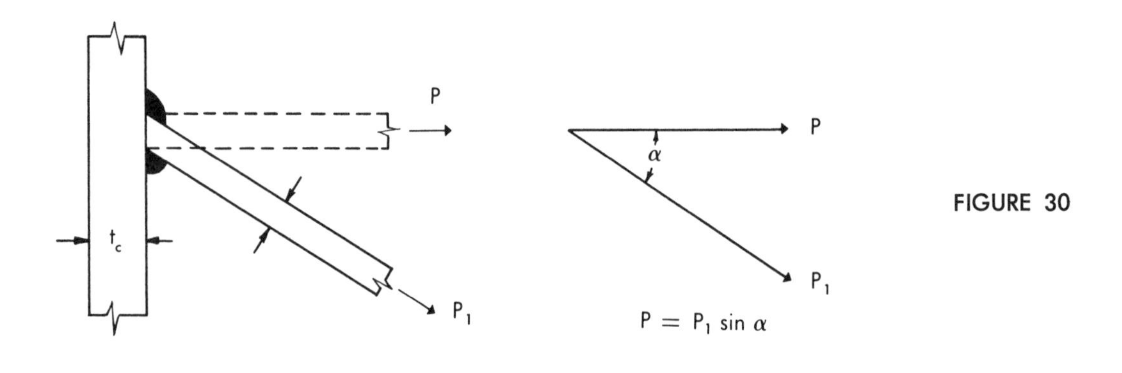

FIGURE 30

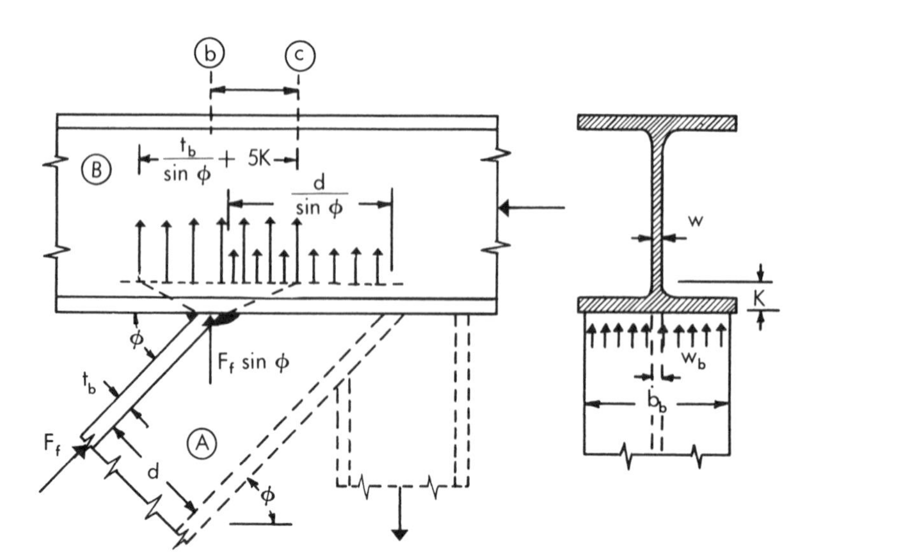

FIGURE 31

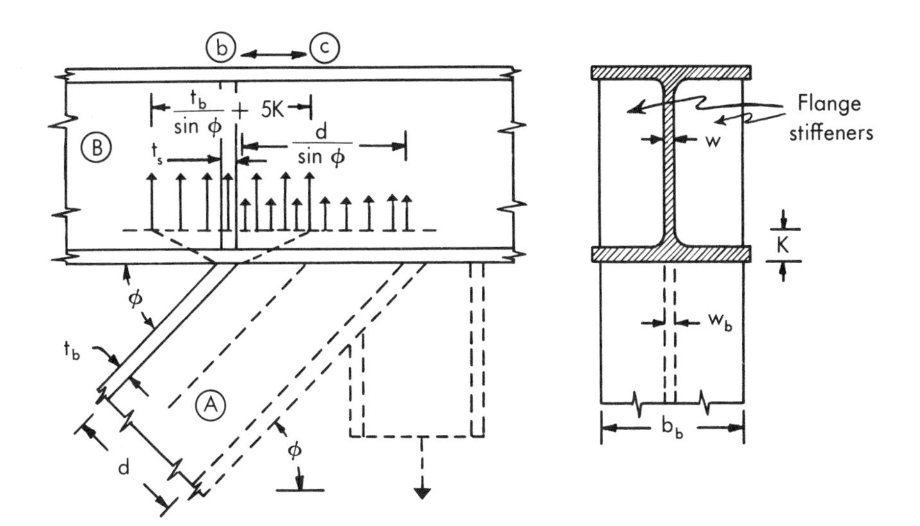

FIGURE 32

or $$\boxed{\sigma = \frac{\sin^2\phi}{w}\left[\frac{F_f}{t_b + 5K\sin\phi} + \frac{F_w}{d}\right]} \quad \ldots\ldots(5)$$

Another method would be to assume ultimate load conditions, with all parts involved, stressed to yield. Using the previous formula (5):

where:

$$F_f = b_b\, t_b\, \sigma_y$$

$$F_w = d\, w_b\, \sigma_y$$

$$\sigma_y = \frac{\sin^2\phi}{w}\left[\frac{b_b\, t_b\, \sigma_y}{t_b + 5K\sin\phi} + \frac{d\, w_b\, \sigma_y}{d}\right]$$

or $$\boxed{w \geqq \sin^2\phi\left[\frac{b_b\, t_b}{t_b + 5K\sin\phi} + w_b\right]} \quad \ldots\ldots(6)$$

If the thickness of the web (w) of member (B) satisfies this formula, stiffeners are not required. Normally, member (A) will not be stressed up to its allowable in compression, so that this shorter method of checking stiffener requirements is on the conservative side.

4. VERTICAL STIFFENERS

If Formula 6 should indicate that stiffeners are required, the same method of analysis may be extended to get an expression for the cross-sectional area of the vertical stiffeners. See Figure 32.

It is assumed the transfer of the flange force of member (A) occurs in the web of member (B) within the distance (t + 5K) as well as in the flange stiffeners. The compressive stress within this section would be—

$$\sigma_1 = \frac{\text{force}}{\text{area}} = \frac{F_f \sin\phi}{\left(\frac{t_f}{\sin\phi} + 5K\right)w + b_s\, t_s}$$

The vertical component of the web force of member (A) transfers directly into the web of member (B) within the distance $\frac{d}{\sin\phi}$.

The compressive stress within this section would be—

$$\sigma_2 = \frac{\text{force}}{\text{area}} = \frac{F_w \sin\phi}{\frac{d}{\sin\phi}\, w}.$$

Within the region (b–c), these compressive stresses in the member (B) overlap and would be added:

$$\boxed{\sigma = \frac{F_f \sin\phi}{\left(\frac{t_f}{\sin\phi} + 5K\right)w + b_s\, t_s} + \frac{F_w \sin^2\phi}{d\, w}} \quad (7)$$

Now if ultimate load conditions are assumed, that is all parts involved are stressed to yield:

where:

$$F_f = b_b\, t_b\, \sigma_y$$

$$F_w = d\, w_b\, \sigma_y$$

$$\sigma_y = \frac{b_b\, t_b\, \sigma_y \sin\phi}{\left(\frac{t_f}{\sin\phi} + 5K\right)w + b_s\, t_s} + \frac{d\, w_b\, \sigma_y\, \sin^2\phi}{d\, w}$$

and the required cross-sectional area of a pair of stiffeners becomes:

$$\boxed{b_s\, t_s \geqq \frac{w\, b_b\, t_b \sin\phi}{w - w_b \sin^2\phi} - \left(\frac{t_f}{\sin\phi} + 5K\right)w} \quad (8)$$

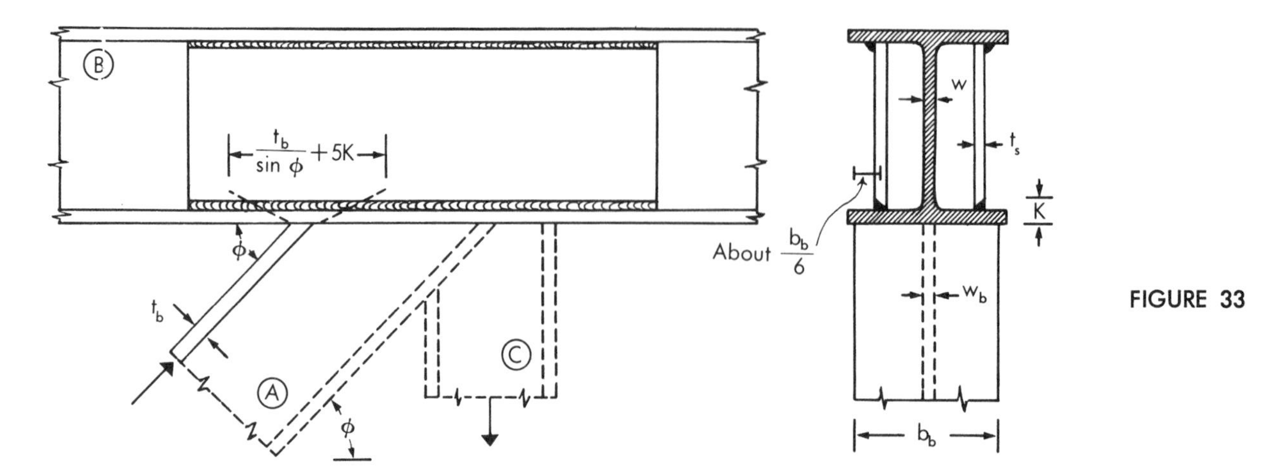

FIGURE 33

5. LONGITUDINAL STIFFENERS

The type of connection shown here may be reinforced with two stiffeners placed parallel to the web, and welded to the flanges of member (B). See Figure 33.

In the Lehigh test of this type of stiffening for beam-to-column connections, these plates were added along the outer edges of the flange so that beams framing in the other direction could be attached directly to them without extending within the column section. It was found that these plates each carried about 3/16 of the applied compression, while the central web section loaded up and carried the remaining 5/8. For this reason the recommendation was made to assume these plates to be about half as effective.

It is interesting to remember that when a beam is supported at three points, the two ends and the center, the two outer supports each will carry only 3/16 of the load and at center 5/8 of the load. If the outer supports are pushed in for 1/6 of the beam length toward the center, all three reactions will be equal.

By setting the stiffening plates about 1/6 b_b in from the edge of the flange of member (A), as shown above, it seems reasonable to assume they will carry a greater load and can be considered as effective as the web.

Although the K value applies only to the distribution in the web of member (B) and has nothing to do with these side plates, the Lehigh researchers for simplicity assumed the same distribution in the plates. The compressive stress in the web (B) and the two side stiffeners due to the vertical component of the flange force of member (A) is:

$$\sigma_1 = \frac{\text{force}}{\text{area}}$$

$$= \frac{F_f \sin\phi}{\left(\frac{t_b}{\sin\phi} + 5K\right) w + 2\left(\frac{t_b}{\sin\phi} + 5K\right) t_s}$$

$$= \frac{F_f \sin\phi}{\left(\frac{t_b}{\sin\phi} + 5K\right)\left(w + 2\, t_s\right)}$$

The compressive stress in the web of member (B) due to the vertical component of the web force of member (A) is:

$$\sigma_2 = \frac{\text{force}}{\text{area}} = \frac{F_w \sin\phi}{\frac{d}{\sin\phi}\, w}$$

$$= \frac{F_w \sin^2\phi}{d\, w}$$

These stresses are added together.

$$\sigma = \frac{F_f \sin\phi}{\left(\frac{t_b}{\sin\phi} + 5K\right)\left(w + 2\, t_s\right)} + \frac{F_w \sin^2\phi}{d\, w} \quad \ldots(9)$$

Now if ultimate load conditions are assumed, that is all parts involved are stressed to yield:

where:

$F_f = b_b\, t_b\, \sigma_y$
$F_w = d\, w_b\, \sigma_y$

$$\sigma_y = \frac{b_b\, t_b\, \sigma_y \sin\phi}{\left(\frac{t_b}{\sin\phi} + 5K\right)\left(w + 2\, t_s\right)} + \frac{d\, w_b\, \sigma_y \sin^2\phi}{d\, w}$$

and the required thickness of the two vertical plate stiffeners becomes:

$$t_s \geq \frac{w\, b_b\, t_b \sin\phi}{2\left(\frac{t_b}{\sin\phi} + 5K\right)\left(w - w_b \sin^2\phi\right)} - \frac{w}{2} \quad .(10)$$

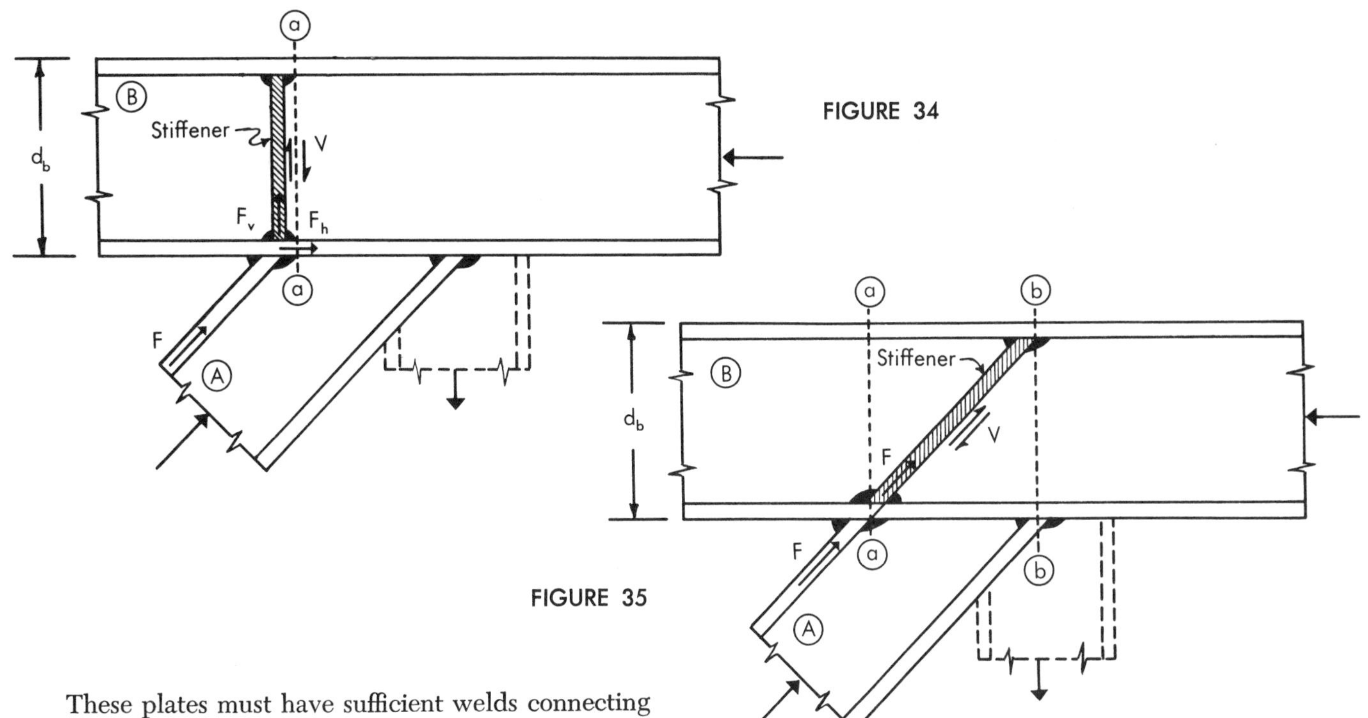

FIGURE 34

FIGURE 35

These plates must have sufficient welds connecting them to the lower flange because the compressive force of member (A) enters here. Since fillet welds cannot be placed on the inside, this would mean a rather large fillet weld on the outside. It may be more economical to bevel the plate and use a groove weld. In this example, the vertical compressive force is transferred from the plate down into the vertical member (C); thus a simple fillet weld along the top edge of the plate to the upper flange would be sufficient.

This discussion and resulting formulas will allow the connection to be detailed without computing the actual stresses. It is based on providing a connection as strong as the members.

Since member (A) will normally not be stressed to its full allowable compression, a more efficient connection would probably result if the actual stresses were computed, using these guides on distribution. Instead of providing full-strength welds, their size would then be determined from these computed forces.

These ideas will now be applied to various parts of a truss connection.

6. STIFFENING ACTUAL TRUSS CONNECTIONS

The vertical component (F_v) from the flange of (A) enters the stiffener and passes into the web of (B) as shear, $V = F_v$, along section a-a. The horizontal component (F_h) from the flange of (A) enters the lower flange of (B). The weld between stiffener and web of member (B) would be designed to transfer this shear force (V), Figure 34.

The force (F) from the flange of (A) transfers directly into the stiffener, leaving no horizontal component to enter the lower flange of (B). This force (F), now in the stiffener, gradually transfers into the web of (B) as shear, from section a-a to section b-b. This unit shear force is equivalent to $\nu = \frac{F_v}{d_b}$ The weld between stiffeners and web of member (B) would be designed to transfer this shear force (V), Figure 35.

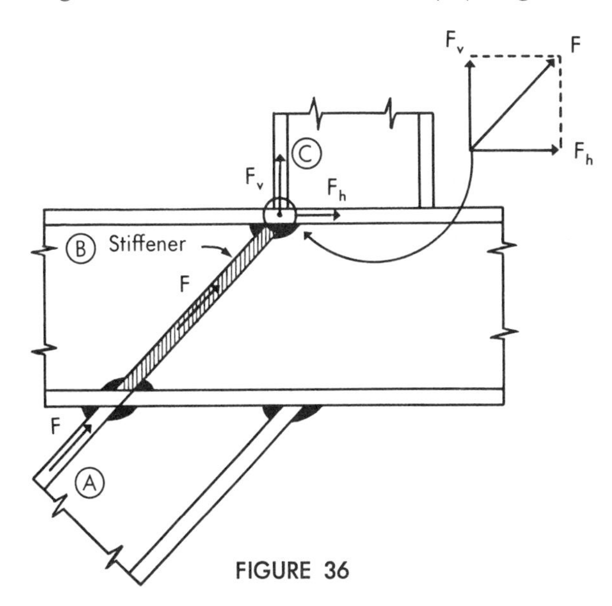

FIGURE 36

The force (F) from the flange of (A) enters the stiffener, and is transferred through to the opposite end. The vertical component (F_v) enters the flange of (C), and the horizontal component (F_h) enters the upper flange of (B) . No shear force is transferred through the weld between stiffener and web of member (B) . Only enough weld is required near midsection of stiffener to keep it from buckling, Figure 36.

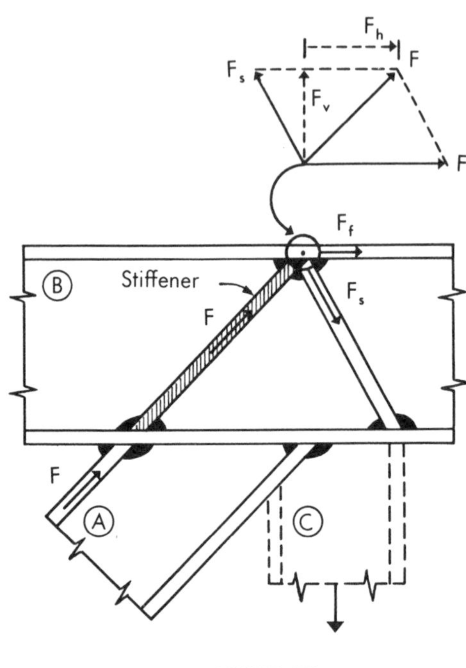

FIGURE 37

The force (F) from the flange of (A) enters the stiffener, and is transferred through to the opposite end. The vertical component (F_v) is taken by the second stiffener as (F_s), and the horizontal component (F_h) is taken by the upper flange of (B) , Figure 37.

In these last two cases, it is assumed that no portion of the force (F) in the stiffener is transferred into the web of (B) . The welding of the stiffener would be similar to the previous case, that is Figure 37.

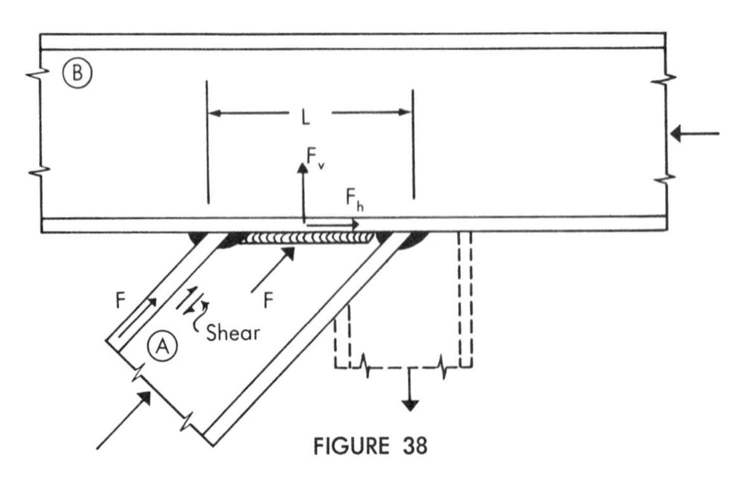

FIGURE 38

If there are no flange stiffeners on member B and no advantage of the preceeding distribution of the concentrated force into the web is to be taken, then the conservative method may be used. Thus, it is assumed that the flange force must first be transferred as shear into the web of the same member before it is transferred through the connecting weld into member (B) . This weld may have to be made larger because of this additional force, Figure 38.

If this flange force (F) is high, a web doubler plate might have to be used so that these forces can be effectively distributed into the web of (A) without overstressing it.

Problem 2A

Consider the connection of Figure 39, using A373 steel and E60 welds.

In this case a portion of the vertical component of (A) is transferred directly into (C) . It will be assumed that the vertical component of the left flange of (A) and the vertical force in the right flange of (C) will be transferred around through the web of (B) by means of two vertical stiffeners. See Figure 40.

(a) Check the size of the connecting welds on the flanges of (A) .

unit force on flange fillet welds

$$f_f = \frac{F}{L}$$

$$= \frac{(138 \text{ kips})}{2(10)}$$

$$= 6.9 \text{ kips/linear inch}$$

leg size of flange fillet welds

$$\omega_f = \frac{6.9}{9.6}$$

$$= .72'' \text{ or use } \underline{3/4''} \text{ (or use a groove weld)}$$

(b) Check the size of the connecting welds on the web of (A) , which has a force of 74 kips.

unit force on web fillet welds

$$f_w = \frac{F}{L}$$

$$= \frac{(74 \text{ kips})}{2(17.5)}$$

$$= 2.11 \text{ kips/linear inch}$$

leg size of web fillet welds

$$\omega_w = \frac{2.11}{9.6}$$

$$= .22''$$

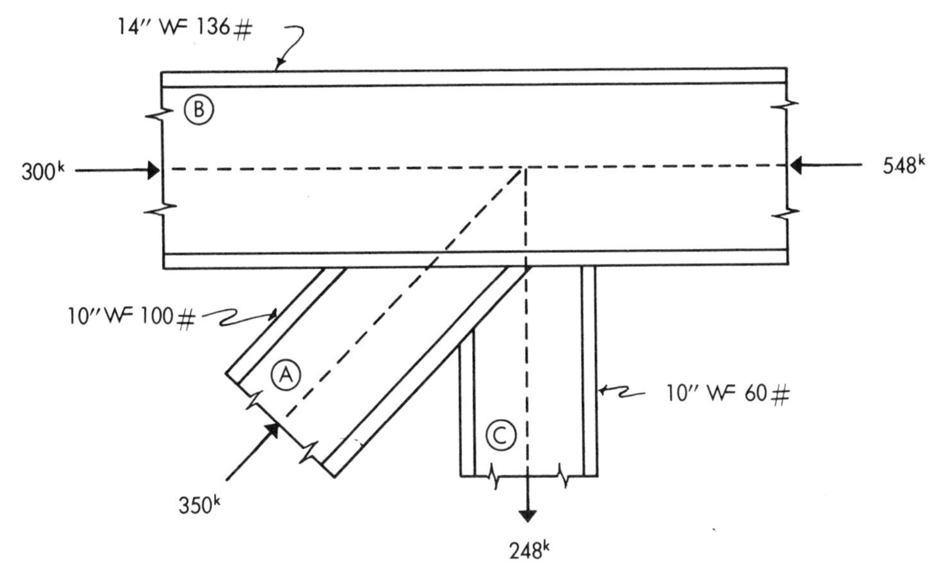

FIGURE 39

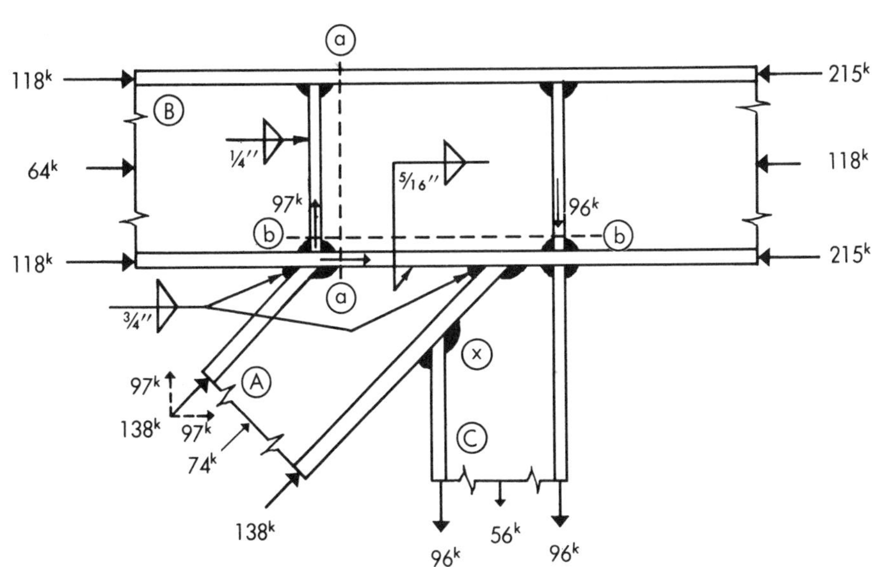

FIGURE 40

However, the minimum fillet weld to be attached to the 1.063"-thick flange would be $\omega_w = \frac{5}{16}''$. (AISC Sec 1.17.4)

(c) Determine required sectional area of vertical stiffeners.

$$A_s = \frac{F_v}{.90\ \sigma_y}$$

$$= \frac{(97 \text{ kips})}{(29.7 \text{ ksi})} \qquad \text{(AISC Sec 1.5.1.5.2)}$$

$= 3.27$ in.^{2}, or use two 3/8" x 5" stiffeners

Their $A_s = 3.75$ in.$^2 > 3.27$ in.^{2} OK

(d) Check the size of connecting welds to transfer this force (F_v) as shear into the web of B.

unit force on stiffener-to-web fillet welds

$$f = \frac{97 \text{ kips}}{4(12.6)}$$

$= 1.92$ kips/linear inch

leg size of fillet welds

$$\omega = \frac{1.92}{9.6}$$

$= .20''$ or use 1/4" ◺

(e) Check the vertical shear stress along a-a.

$$\tau = \frac{V}{A_w} \qquad \text{See Figure 41.}$$

$$= \frac{(97 \text{ kips})}{(.660)(12.62)}$$

$= 11{,}650$ psi $< 13{,}000$ psi $< .40\ \sigma_y$ OK (AISC Sec 1.5.1.2)

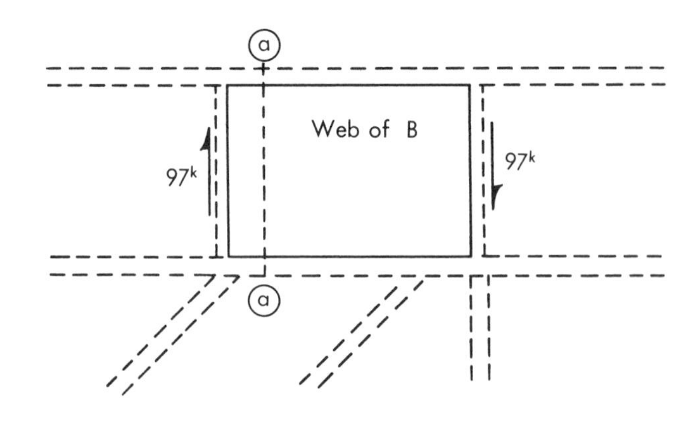

FIGURE 41

(f) Check the horizontal shear stress along b-b in the web of (B) parallel to the welded connection between (A) and (B). This length is about 20″.

The total horizontal component from (A) to be transferred into (B) is 248 kips. The lower flange of (B) has a compressive force of 215 kips on the right end and 118 kips on the left end. This means it will pick up 215 — 118 = 97 kips from (A).

Hence, a force of 248 — 97 = 151 kips is to be transferred into the web of (B) over a distance of 20″.

$$\tau = \frac{V}{A_w}$$

$$= \frac{(151 \text{ kips})}{(.660)(20)}$$

$$= 11{,}430 \text{ psi} < 13{,}000 \text{ psi} < .40\, \sigma_y \quad \underline{\text{OK}}$$

(AISC Sec 1.5.1.2)

As a result no stiffening of the web of (B) is required as far as shear is concerned. If these shear stresses exceed the allowable, the web of the connection could be reinforced with a doubler plate, either on the web itself, or separated slightly and welded to the edges of the upper and lower flanges of (B).

(g) There is one more item to check; consider point (x) in the figure below. It is necessary that the vertical component of the right flange of (A) be transferred into the left flange of (C), and yet its horizontal component be transferred into the lower flange of (B).

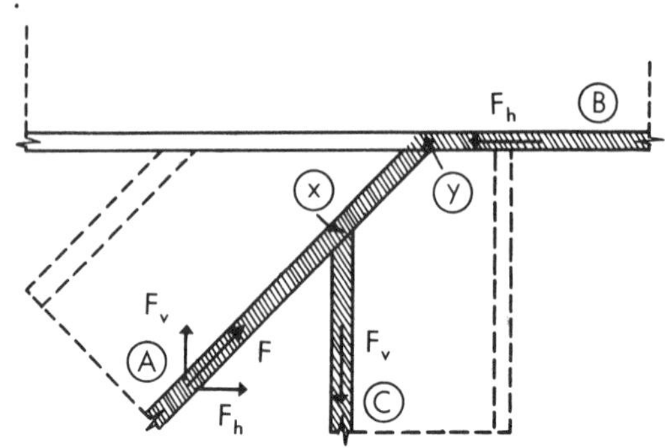

FIGURE 43

Theoretically, the flange of (A) can only transmit an axial force (F) between points (x) and (y). There would be no problem if these 3 flanges met at a common point.

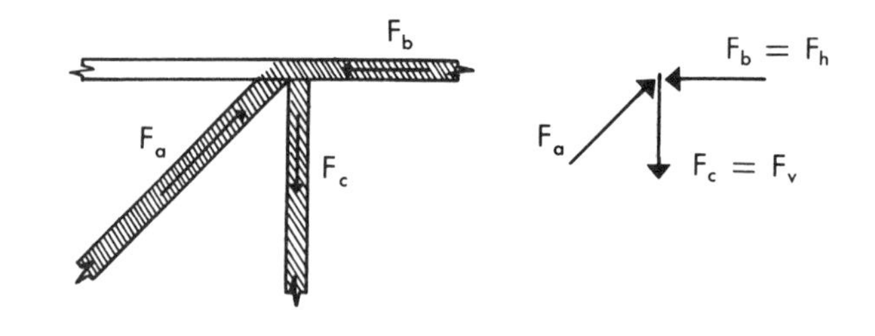

FIGURE 44

In order for the flange of (C) to take the vertical component (F_v) from the flange of (A) at (x), it is necessary that the horizontal component (F_h) also

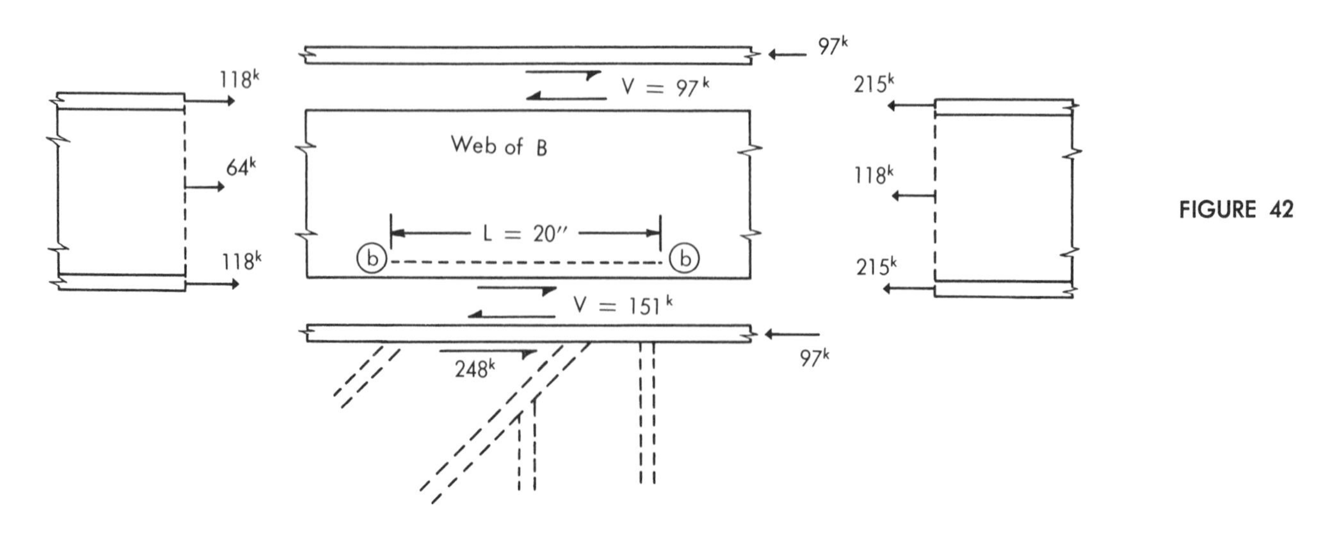

FIGURE 42

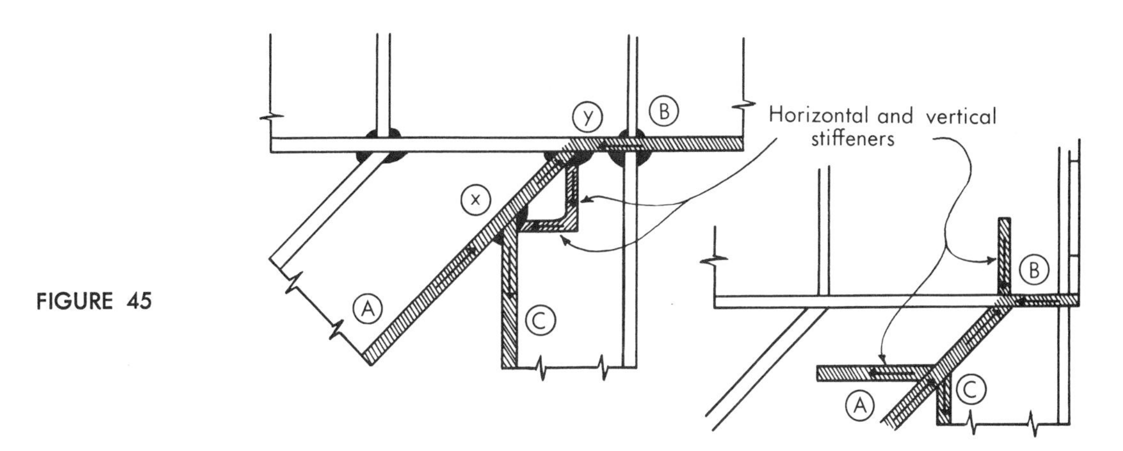

FIGURE 45

be taken at this point and somehow carried up into the lower flange of (B).

Likewise, in order for the flange of (B) to take the horizontal component (F_h) at (y), it is necessary that the vertical component (F_v) also be taken at this point and carried into the flange of (C). There are several methods by which this may be done.

(1) This could be accomplished with a vertical stiffener at (y) and a horizontal stiffener at (x). These would transfer the components into the web of (C) from where they could work their way back into the flange of (B) and the flange of (C). Two methods of using this are shown in Figure 45.

(2) This also could be accomplished with two sets of vertical stiffeners; see Figure 46. The left stiffener would transfer the vertical force of the flange of (C) up into the web of (B), where it would work its way over to the right stiffener through shear (V). The right stiffener would transfer the vertical component (F_v) of the flange of (A) into the web of (B) so that the horizontal component (F_h) could be transferred into the flange of (B).

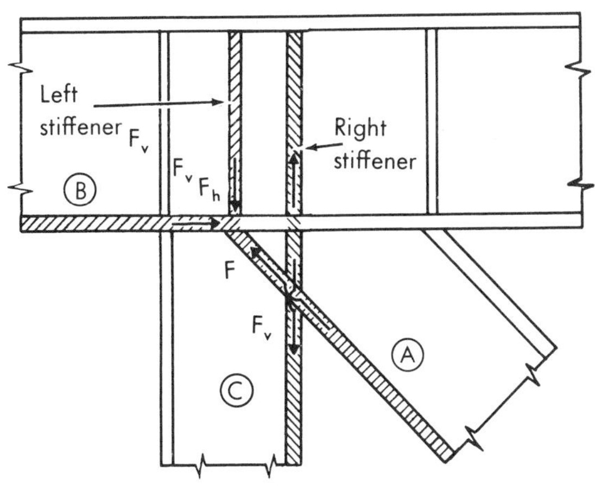

FIGURE 46

If the shear transfer (V) between these two stiffeners exceeds the allowable of the web of (B), a doubler plate may be added to the web; or a plate may be set out on each side to box in this area.

In this substructure for an offshore drilling rig, the truss connections carry large concentrated transverse forces. Vertical flange stiffeners are required to prevent web buckling. The triangular "gusset" is welded in to enclose the area for greater protection against corrosion in addition to stiffening.

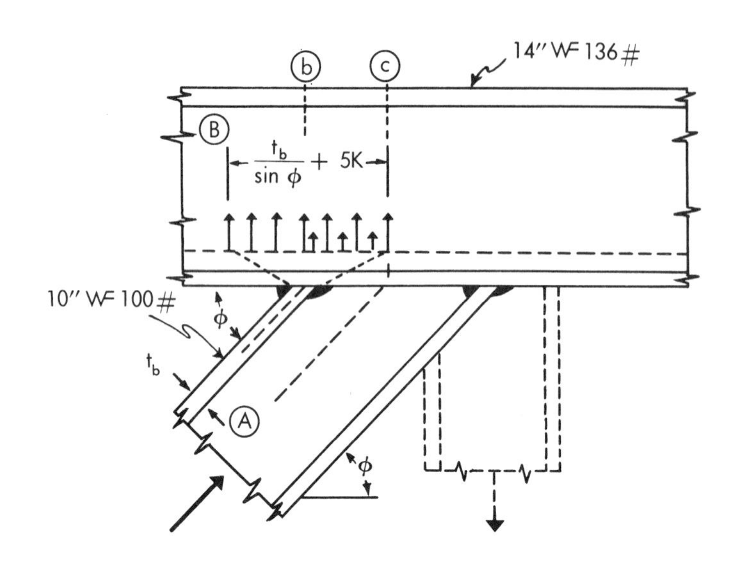

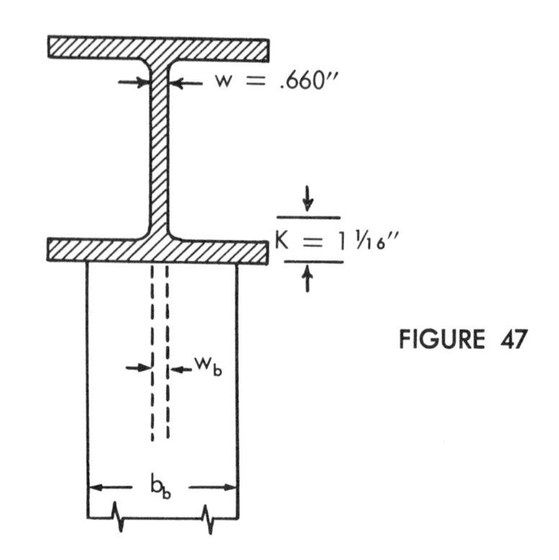

FIGURE 47

Problem 2B

Another solution of the same problem would be to check the stiffener requirements using the Lehigh research for beam-to-column connections as a guide for the distribution of the forces through the connection.

(a) See if the web thickness (w) of Ⓑ is sufficient for stiffeners not to be required; Figure 47.

$$w \geqq \sin^2\phi \left[\frac{b_b\ t_b}{t_b + 5K\ \sin\phi} + w_b \right]$$

$$\geqq (.707)^2 \left[\frac{(10.345)(1.118)}{1.118 + 5(1^{11}/_{16})(.707)} + .685 \right]$$

$$w \geqq 1.16'' \text{ required} > .660'' \text{ actual}$$

On this basis some stiffeners would be required.

FIGURE 48

(b) Check the tension flange of Ⓒ where it joins the flange of Ⓑ, as to the necessity of stiffeners to transfer the flange force; Figure 48.

$$t_c = .40\ \sqrt{b_b\ t_b}$$

$$= .40\ \sqrt{(10.075)(.683)}$$

$$= 1.05'' < 1.063'' \quad \underline{\text{OK}}$$

On this basis, stiffeners would not be needed opposite this flange of Ⓒ where it joins the bottom flange of Ⓑ.

(c) Check the tension flange of Ⓒ where it joins the flange of member Ⓐ; Figure 49.

$$t_c = \sqrt{\frac{b_b\ t_b\ (\sin\alpha - .12)}{5.6}}$$

$$= \sqrt{\frac{(.683)(10.075)(.707 - .12)}{5.6}}$$

$$= .85'' < 1.118'' \quad \underline{\text{OK}}$$

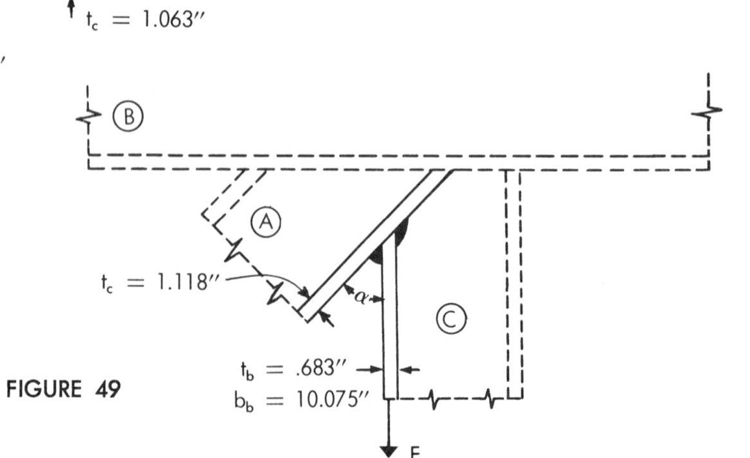

FIGURE 49

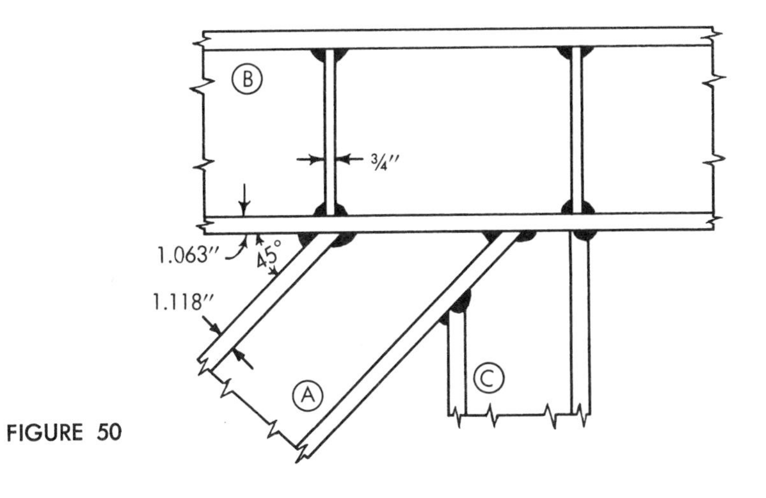

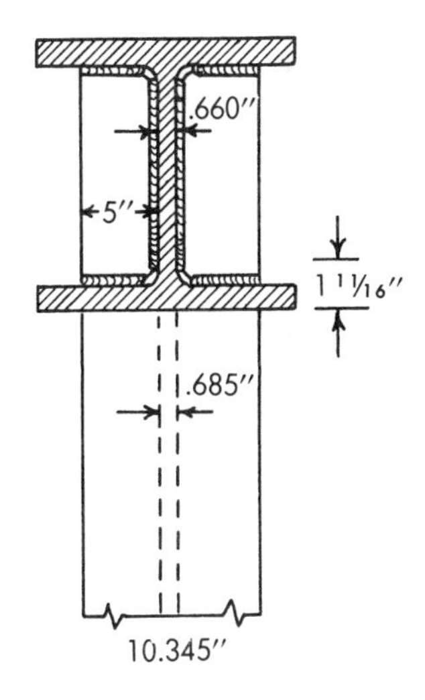

FIGURE 50

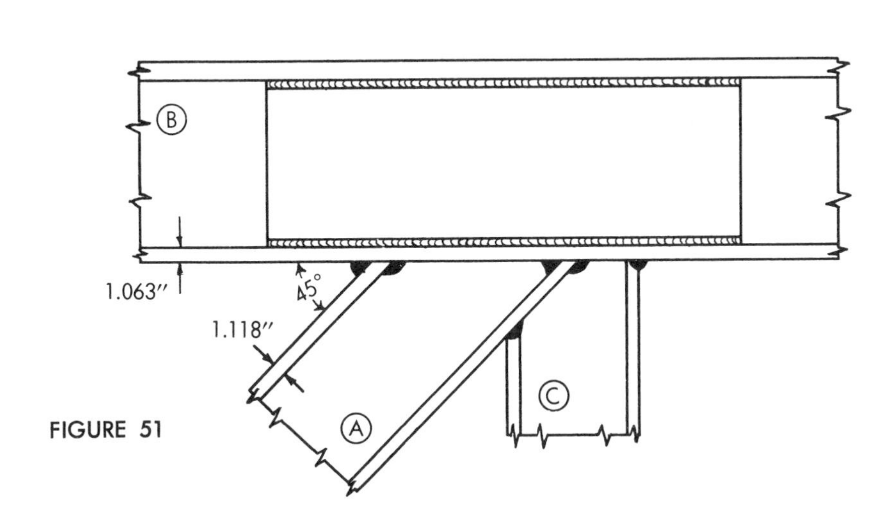

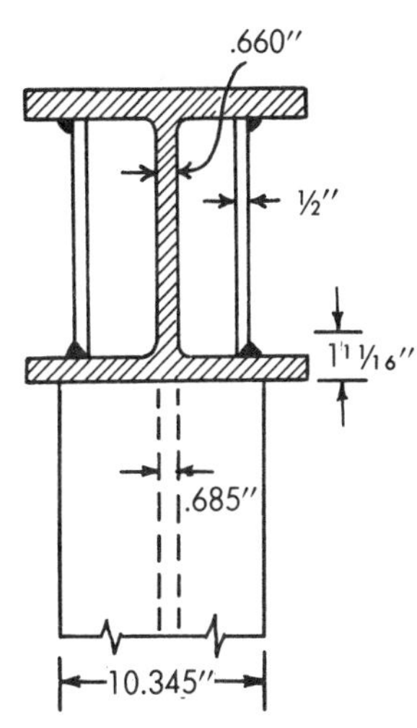

FIGURE 51

On this basis, stiffeners would not be required on Ⓐ opposite this flange of member Ⓒ .

Either vertical flange stiffeners or longitudinal flange stiffeners can be used to provide added stiffness for the compressive force of Ⓐ .

vertical flange stiffeners

$$b_b t_s \geqq \left(\frac{w \ b_b t_b \ \sin \phi}{w - w_b \ \sin^2 \phi} \right) - \left(\frac{t_b}{\sin \phi} + 5K \right)$$

$$\geqq \frac{(.660)(10.345)(1.118)(.707)}{(.660) - (.685)(.707)^2} - \left(\frac{1.118}{.707} + 5 \text{ x } 1\frac{11}{16} \right)$$

$$\geqq 7.03 \text{ in.}^2$$

so use two pairs of ¾″ x 5″ stiffeners.

longitudinal flange stiffeners

$$t_s \geqq \frac{w \ b_b t_b \ \sin \phi}{2\left(\frac{t_b}{\sin \phi} + 5K \right)(w - w_b \ \sin^2 \phi)} - \frac{w}{2}$$

$$\geqq \frac{(.660)(10.345)(1.118)(.707)}{2\left(\frac{1.118}{.707} + 5 \text{ x } 1\frac{11}{16} \right)\left[.660 - .685(.707)^2 \right]} - \frac{.660}{2}$$

$$\geqq .53''$$

or use a pair of ½″ x 12⅝″ x 36″ stiffeners.

7. TYPICAL TRUSS PROBLEMS

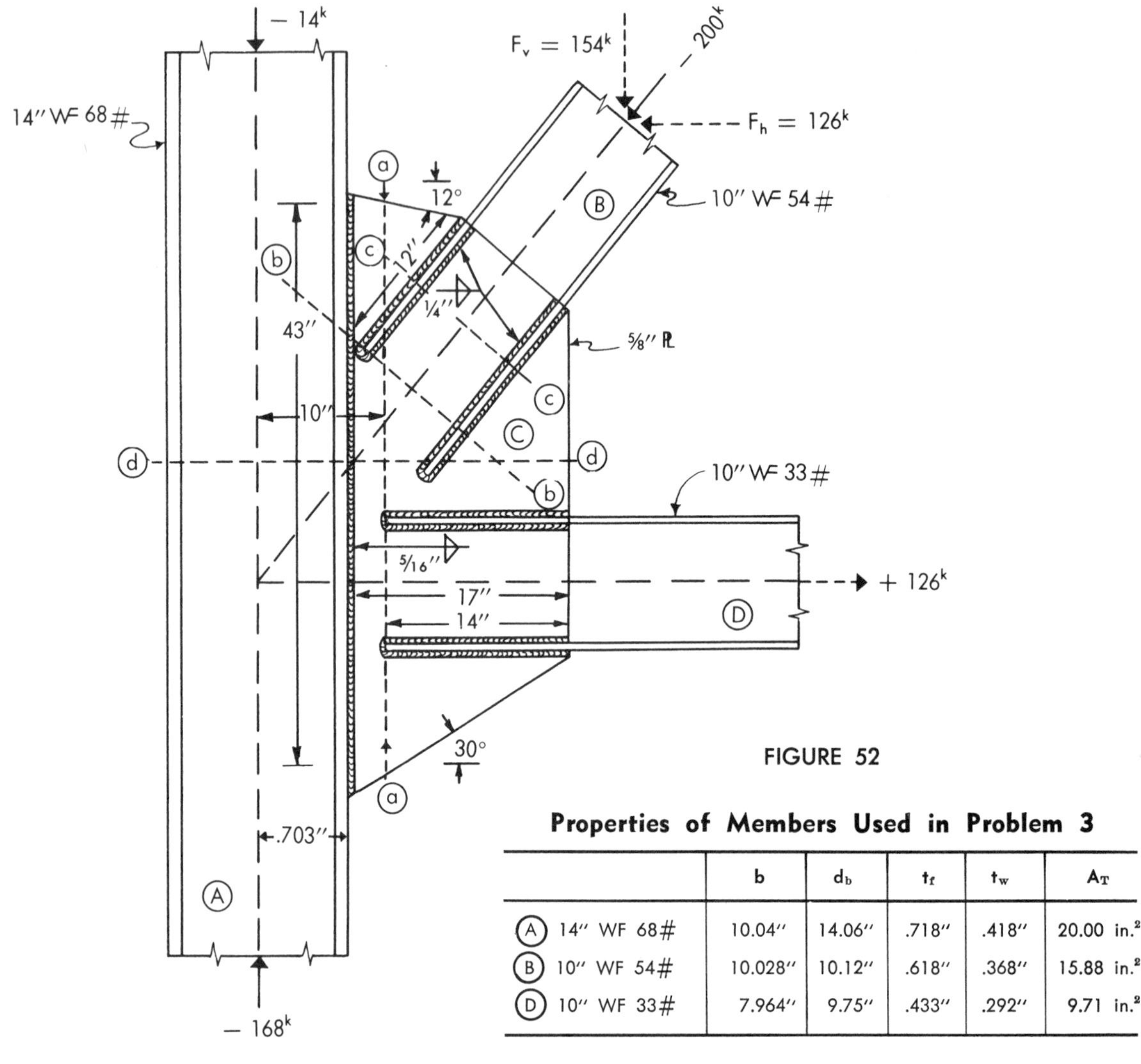

FIGURE 52

Properties of Members Used in Problem 3

	b	d_b	t_f	t_w	A_T
(A) 14″ WF 68#	10.04″	14.06″	.718″	.418″	20.00 in.^{2}
(B) 10″ WF 54#	10.028″	10.12″	.618″	.368″	15.88 in.^{2}
(D) 10″ WF 33#	7.964″	9.75″	.433″	.292″	9.71 in.^{2}

Problem 3

Check the details of this connection, using A373 steel and E60 welds.

(a) Consider the moment and vertical shear on section a-a.

$$M = F\ d = (168^k - 14^k)(10'') = 1540 \text{ in-kips}$$

$$V = 154 \text{ kips}$$

section modulus of section a-a

$$S = \frac{(5/8)(43)^2}{6} = 192.5 \text{ in.}^3$$

bending

$$\sigma = \frac{M}{S} = \frac{(1540)}{(192.5)} = 8{,}000 \text{ psi}$$

shear

$$\tau = \frac{V}{A} = \frac{(154^k)}{(5/8)(43)} = 5{,}730 \text{ psi}$$

resulting maximum normal stress (See Figure 53.)

$$\sigma_{max} = \frac{\sigma}{2} \pm \sqrt{\left(\frac{\sigma}{2}\right)^2 + \tau^2}$$

$$= \frac{(8000)}{2} \pm \sqrt{\left(\frac{8000}{2}\right)^2 + 5730^2}$$

$$= 10{,}980 \text{ psi}$$

The resulting bending stress of $\sigma = 8{,}000$ psi at the outer fiber is for a horizontal edge. If this edge slopes (ϕ), the resulting fiber stress along this edge may be found from the following:

so: $$\sigma_\phi = \frac{\sigma_h}{\cos^2\phi}$$ (See Figure 54.)

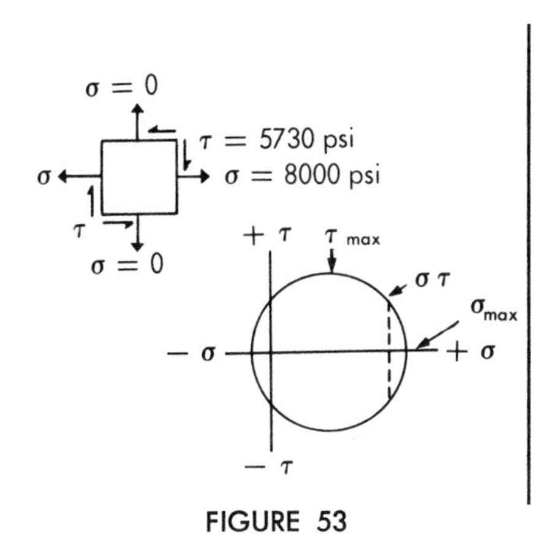

FIGURE 53

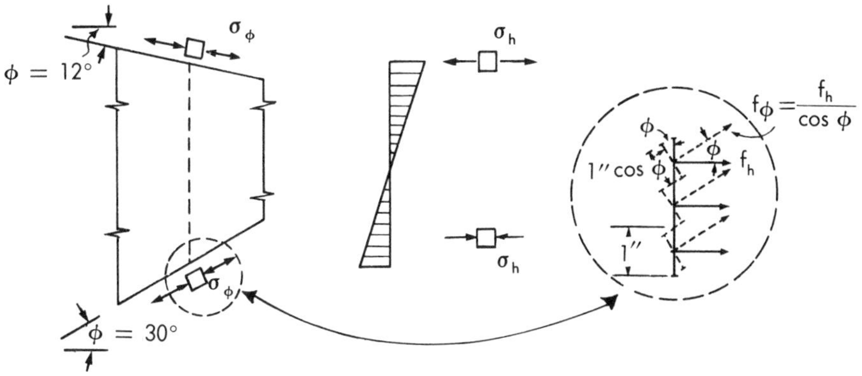

FIGURE 54

at top edge of gusset plate

$$\phi = 12^\circ \qquad \cos 12^\circ = .977$$

$$\sigma = \frac{8{,}000}{.977^2} = 8{,}390 \text{ psi (compression)}$$

at bottom edge of gusset plate

$$\phi = 30^\circ \qquad \cos 30^\circ = .865$$

$$\sigma = \frac{8{,}000}{.865^2} = 10{,}700 \text{ psi (tension)}$$

(b) Consider the transfer of the vertical component (F_v) of the truss members Ⓑ and Ⓓ through gusset plate Ⓒ and into the web of column Ⓐ within the connection length of 43″ as shear. From this vertical component (F_v), deduct the portion to be carried by the right flange of Ⓐ. (This does not have to enter the web of column Ⓐ.) This portion carried by the right flange can be determined by the ratio of the flange area to the total section area.

The force taken by this flange is—

$$F = 154 \frac{(10.04)(.718)}{(20.00)}$$

$$= 55.5 \text{ kips}$$

This leaves 154 − 55.5 = 98.5 kips to pass into the web (some of which will enter into the left flange). The resulting shear stress within this 43″ length of web is:

$$\tau = \frac{(98.5)}{(43)(.418)}$$

$$= 5{,}490 \text{ psi} < 15{,}000 \text{ psi} < .40\, \sigma_y \quad \underline{\text{OK}}$$

(AISC Sec 1.5.1.2)

This transfer can be made while still keeping the flange compressive stress within the uniform stress of—

$$\sigma = \frac{(168 \text{ kips})}{(20.00 \text{ in.}^2)} = 8400 \text{ psi}$$

(c) Consider the vertical weld between connection plate Ⓒ and member Ⓐ. The forces applied on the left side of this weld are—

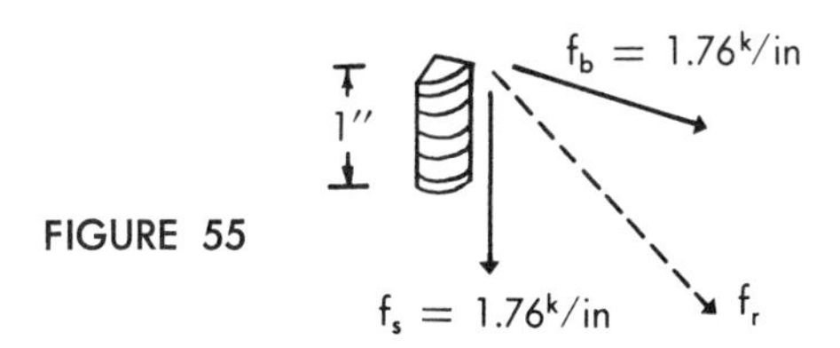

FIGURE 55

$$M = (168^k - 14^k)(7.03'') = 1082\text{-in.-kips}$$

$$V = 154 \text{ kips}$$

section modulus of weld connection

$$S_w = \frac{2\ d^2}{6} = \frac{43^2}{3} = 616.3 \text{ in.}^2$$

bending force on weld

$$f_b = \frac{M}{S_w} = \frac{(1082)}{(616.3)} = 1.76 \text{ kips/in.}$$

shear force on weld

$$f_s = \frac{V}{A_w} = \frac{(154)}{(2)(43)} = 1.79 \text{ kips/in.}$$

resultant force on weld

$$f_r = \sqrt{f_b^2 + f_s^2} = \sqrt{(1.76)^2 + (1.79)^2}$$

$$= 2.51 \text{ kips/in.}$$

leg size of fillet weld

$$\omega = \frac{(2.51)}{(9.6)} = .261'' \text{ or use } 5/16''$$

(d) Flange plates, ⅝″ by 4¾″, are welded onto Ⓒ to extend the flange of Ⓑ back a sufficient distance. The compressive force in the flange of Ⓑ is—

$$F = 200^k \frac{(10.028)(.618)}{(15.88)} = 78.0 \text{ kips}$$

On this basis, the stress in each of these flange plates is:

$$\sigma = \frac{(78 \text{ kips})}{(2'')(5/8'')(4\tfrac{3}{4}'')}$$
$$= 13{,}100 \text{ psi} \quad \underline{\text{OK}}$$

The force from an adjacent pair of these plates is transferred into Ⓒ as double shear.

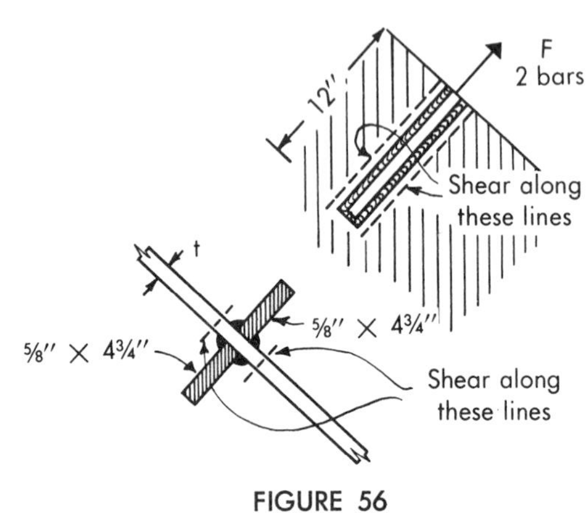

FIGURE 56

This shear stress in Ⓒ is—

$$\tau = \frac{F}{4 \text{ L t}}$$
$$= \frac{(78.0 \text{ kips})}{4(12'')(5/8'')}$$
$$= 2600 \text{ psi} < 13{,}000 \text{ psi} \quad \underline{\text{OK}}$$

size of connecting welds

$$f = \frac{(37.4 \text{ kips})}{(2)(12'')} = 1.56 \text{ kips/in.}$$

$$\omega = \frac{(1.56 \text{ k/in.})}{(9.6 \text{ k/in.})} = .163'' \text{ or } \underline{\text{use } 3/16''}$$

However, the AWS as well as the AISC would require a ¼" fillet weld because of the ⅝" plate.

(e) At section b-b at the termination of the flange plates, we will assume the 200-kip compressive force must be taken by Ⓒ alone. The cross-sectional area of Ⓑ is A = 15.88 in².

For the same stress in Ⓒ , this would require the same cross-sectional area, or 15.88 in.², and a net width of

$$W = \frac{15.88}{5/8} = 25.4''$$

There is sufficient width; see Figure 52.

(f) At section c-c halfway along the flange plates, it is assumed that half of the flange force of Ⓑ has been transferred out into Ⓒ :

$$\tfrac{1}{2}\,(200^k)\,\frac{(10.028)(.618)}{(15.88)} = 39.0 \text{ kips}$$

For the two flange plates, this reduction would leave—

$(200^k) - 2\,(39.1^k) - 122.0$ kips to be taken by Ⓒ .

For the same stress, this would require an area of—

$$A = \frac{(122.0^k)}{(12.52 \text{ ksi})} = 9.74 \text{ in.}^2$$

and a net width of—

$$W = \frac{(9.74)}{(5/8)} = 15.6''$$

There is sufficient width; see Figure 52.

(g) Another section which might be checked is along d-d. The loads on this section are the direct compressive load of the column Ⓐ , a shearing force from the tension in the lower chord member Ⓓ , and a bending moment from the eccentricity of both the column Ⓐ and the bottom chord Ⓓ . This critical section (d-d) is placed as high as possible above the lower chord Ⓓ without intercepting the stiffening elements of the connection. In this case it is placed 9" above the centerline of member Ⓓ .

The properties of this built-up cross-section are

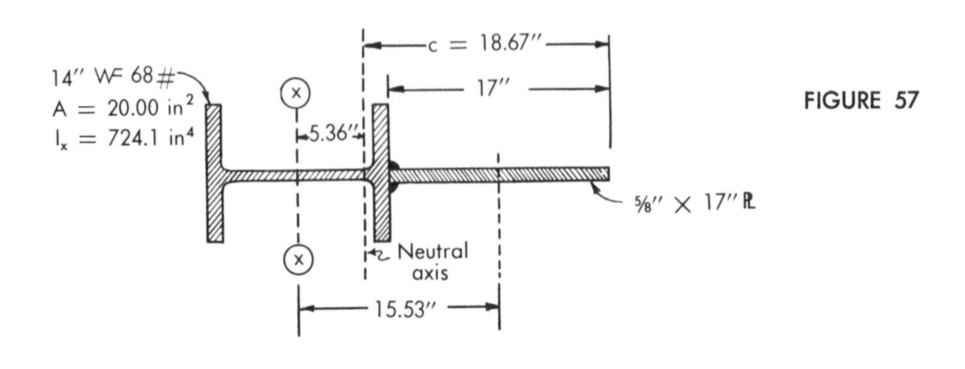

FIGURE 57

computed and the eccentricities determined. For simplicity in this computation, the reference axis (x-x) is placed along the centerline of the column Ⓐ.

Member	A	d	M = A d	I = M d	I_g
14″ WF 68#	20.00	0	0	0	724.1
⅝ x 17″ ℄	10.52	+15.53	+163.5	+2675.	255.9
Total ⟶	30.52		163.5	3655.0	

$$I_{NA} = I_x - \frac{M^2}{A} = (3655) - \frac{(163.5)^2}{(30.52)} = 2380 \text{ in.}^4$$

$$NA = \frac{M}{A} = \frac{(163.5)}{(30.52)} = 5.36''$$

From this:

$$c = (14.06 + 17) - (7.03 + 5.36) = 18.67''$$

$$S = \frac{I}{c} = \frac{(2380)}{(18.67)} = 127.5 \text{ in.}^3$$

Applied Loads

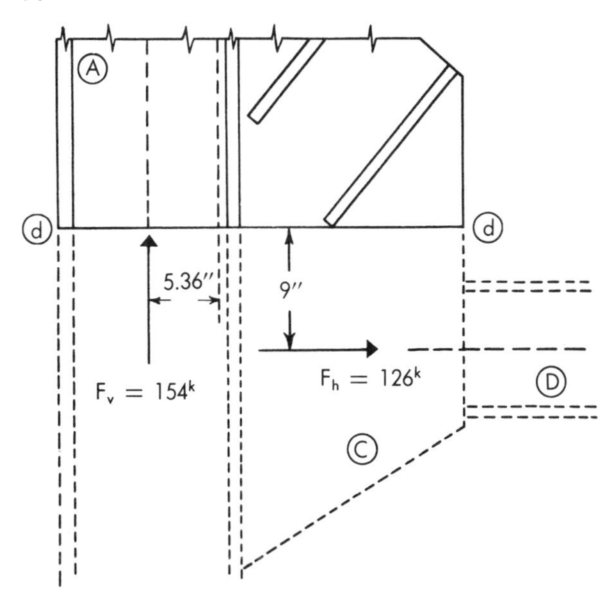

FIGURE 58

compression

$$F_v = 168^k - 14^k = 154 \text{ kips}$$

$$\sigma = \frac{F_v}{A} = 5050 \text{ psi (compression)}$$

shear

$$F_h = 126^k$$

$$= \frac{(126^k)}{(14.06)(.418) + (17)(5/8)} = 7640 \text{ psi}$$

bending

$$M = (126^k)(9'') - (154^k)(5.36) = 233.0 \text{ in.-kips}$$

$$\sigma = \frac{(233.0)}{(127.5)} = 2420 \text{ psi (compression)}$$

This is a total compressive stress of 5050 + 2420 = 7470 psi, and a shear stress of 7640 psi at the outer edge of the connection plate Ⓒ.

The resultant maximum normal (compressive) stress at the edge of the plate is—

$$\sigma_{max} = \frac{\sigma}{2} \pm \sqrt{\left(\frac{\sigma}{2}\right)^2 + \tau^2}$$

$$= \frac{(7470)}{2} + \sqrt{\frac{7470^2}{2} + 7640^2}$$

$$= 12{,}800 \text{ psi}$$

Check the outer edge of this plate Ⓒ as a column.

radius of gyration

$$r = .289\ t = (.289)(5/8) = .181''$$

The unbraced length of this edge is L = 15″, and

$$\frac{L}{r} = \frac{15}{.181} = 83$$

and the corresponding allowable compressive stress is—

$$\sigma = 14{,}130 \text{ psi} > 12{,}285 \text{ psi} \quad \underline{\text{OK}}$$

(AISC Sec 1.5.1.3.1)

If the calculated compressive stress had exceeded this allowable, a flange could have been added along this one outer edge to give it sufficient stiffness against buckling.

Plate Ⓒ will have 7/16″ by 4″ flange plates to extend the flanges of member Ⓓ along a distance of 12″. ¼″ fillet welds will be sufficient to attach these plates, this size being required because of the ⅝″ plate. No further checking is necessary because, by observation, the 126-kip force is much less than the 200-kip force of member Ⓑ and the same amount of plate Ⓒ is available.

Problem 4

Determine the leg size of the four fillet welds connecting the two ¾″ gusset plates to the vertical leg of a tower. A373 steel, E60 welds. See Figure 59.

The horizontal component of the 350-kip force of the diagonal member (10″ WF 100#) is transferred back to the horizontal member (248 kips) through the

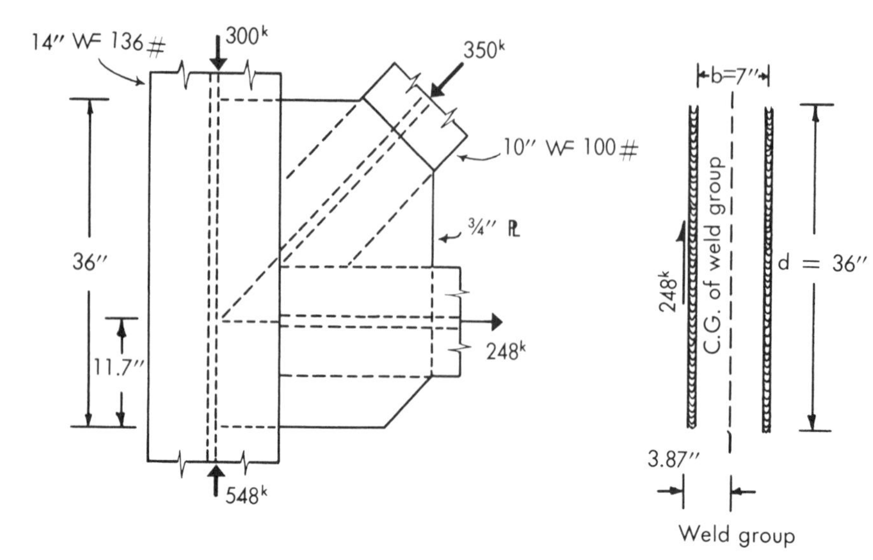

FIGURE 59

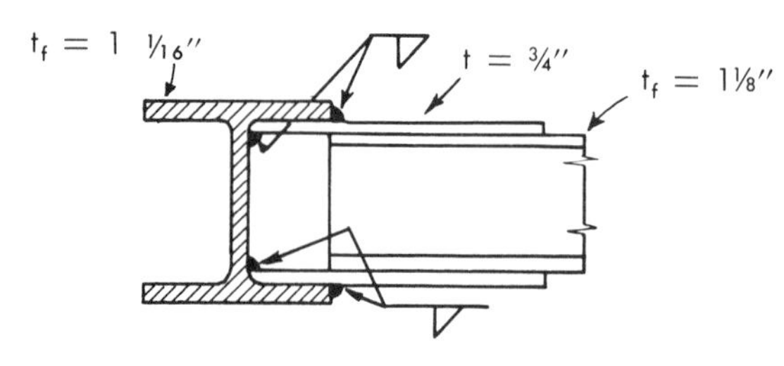

gusset plate. The only force transferred through this connecting weld to the vertical member (14" WF 136#) connecting weld to the vertical member (14" WF 136#) is the 248-kip vertical force acting 3½" away from the center of gravity of the welded connection.

Treat the weld group as a line:

$$J_w = 2\,\frac{d(3b^2 + d^2)}{6}$$

$$= 2\,\frac{36}{6}\,(3 \text{ x } 7^2 + 36^2)$$

$$= 18.516 \text{ in.}^3$$

twisting action

vertical force:

$$f_v = \frac{T\ c}{J_w}$$

$$= \frac{(248 \text{ x } 3.87)(3\tfrac{1}{2})}{(18{,}516)}$$

$$= 181 \text{ lbs/in.}$$

horizontal force

$$f_h = \frac{T\ c}{J_w}$$

$$= \frac{(248 \text{ x } 3.87)(18)}{(18{,}516)}$$

$$= 933 \text{ lbs/in.}$$

vertical shear

$$f_{v1} = \frac{F}{L_w}$$

$$= \frac{(248)}{(4 \text{ x } 36)}$$

$$= 1720 \text{ lbs/in.}$$

resultant

$$f_r = \sqrt{f_h^2 + (f_v + f_{v1})^2}$$

$$= \sqrt{(933)^2 + (181 + 1720)^2}$$

$$= 2120 \text{ lbs/in.}$$

leg size of weld

$$\omega = \frac{\text{actual force}}{\text{allowable force}}$$

$$= \frac{(2120)}{(9600)}$$

$$= .220'' \text{ or } \underline{1/4''}$$

However, AWS and AISC would require $\underline{5/16''}$ because of $1\tfrac{1}{16}''$ flange.

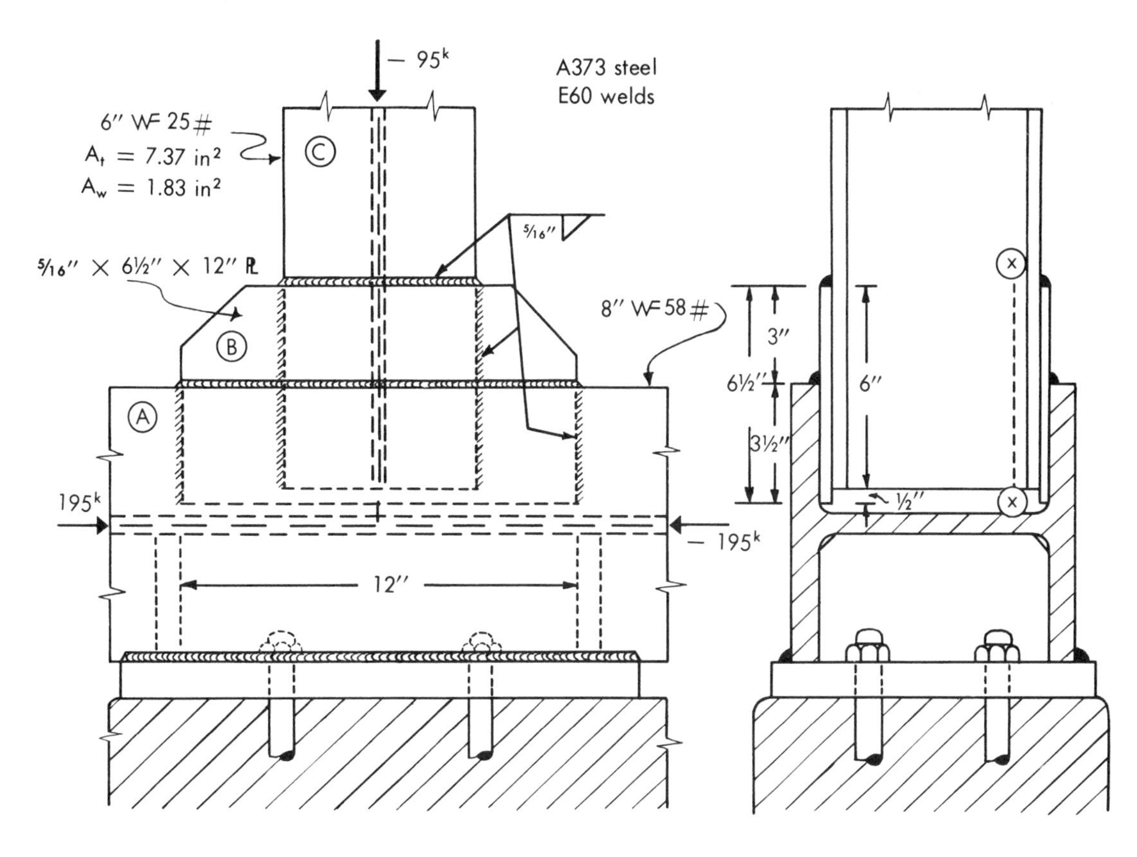

FIGURE 60

Problem 5

Determine the weld sizes on this connection. A373 steel, E60 welds.

(a) Find the required size of fillet weld between member Ⓒ and connecting plates Ⓑ The total length of connecting weld is—

$$L = 4(6'') + 2(6.08'') = 36.0''$$

force of weld

$$f = \frac{F}{L} = \frac{(95 \text{ kips})}{(36'')} = 2.64 \text{ kips/in.}$$

weld leg size

$$\omega = \frac{(2.64 \text{ k/in.})}{(9.6 \text{ k/in.})} = .275'' \text{ or } \underline{\text{use } 5/16''}$$

Check the length of web Ⓒ within the connection along section x-x, required to transfer the force of the web Ⓒ out into the flanges of Ⓒ as shear.

force in web

$$F_w = 95^k \frac{(1.83)}{(7.37)} = 23.6 \text{ kips}$$

shear stress

$$\tau = \frac{F}{A_w} = \frac{\frac{1}{2}(23.6 \text{ kips})}{(.320)(L)} = 13{,}000 \text{ psi}$$

minimum weld length

$$L = \frac{\frac{1}{2}(23.6 \text{ kips})}{(.320)(13 \text{ k/in.}^2)} = 2.84'' < 6'', \text{ so is } \underline{\text{OK}}$$

(b) Find the required size of fillet weld between flanges of Ⓐ and plates Ⓑ. The total length of connecting weld is—

$$L = 4(3\tfrac{1}{2}'') + 2(12'') = 38.0''$$

force on weld

$$f = \frac{(95 \text{ kips})}{(38'')} = 2.5 \text{ kips/in.}$$

weld leg size

$$\omega = \frac{2.5}{9.6} = .260'' \text{ or } \underline{\text{use } 5/16''}$$

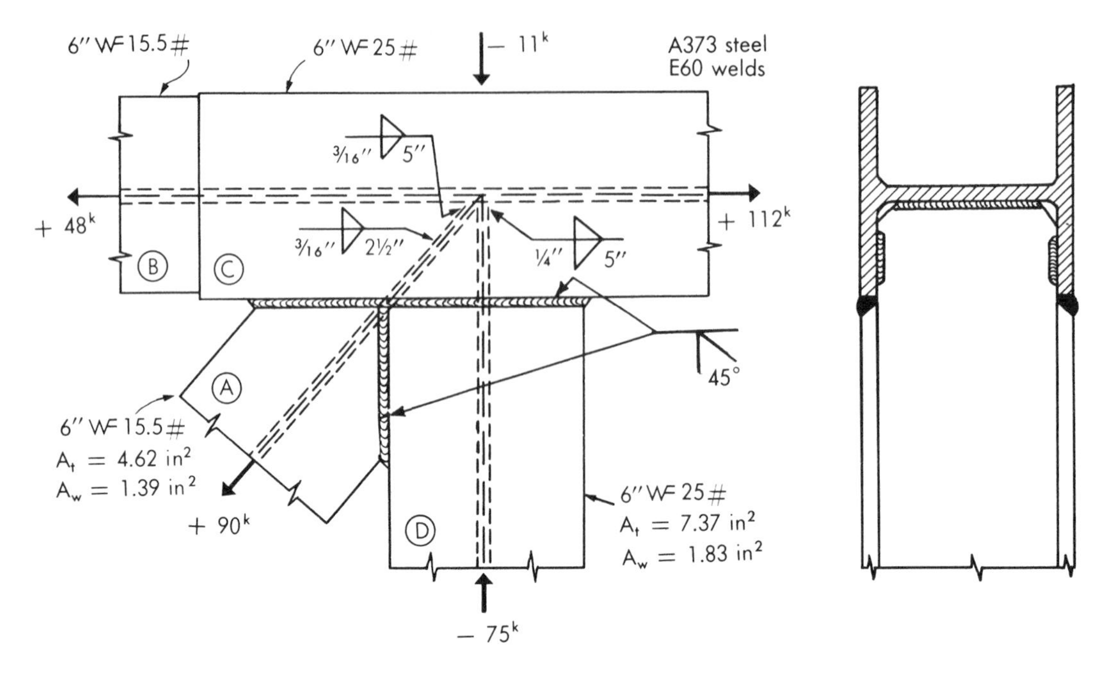

FIGURE 61

Problem 6

Check the weld sizes on this truss connection. A373 steel, E60 welds.

No calculations are required for the flange groove welds, since they will develop the full strength of the flanges.

The force in the web of diagonal member (A) is—

$$F_w = 90^k \frac{(1.39)}{(4.62)} = 27.1 \text{ kips}$$

The effective fillet weld size for this web (A) is—

$$\omega = \tfrac{3}{4}\, t_w = \tfrac{3}{4}(.240) = .180'' \text{ or } \tfrac{3}{16}''$$

The total length of this weld is—

$$L = \frac{(27.1 \text{ kips})}{(1.8 \text{ k/in.})} = 15.0''$$

If there is 5″ of 3/16″ fillet weld on each side of web (A) to web (C), this leaves 15″ − 2(5″) = 5″ or 2½″ on web of (A) to each flange of (C).

The force in the web of member (D) is—

$$F_w = 75^k \frac{(1.83)}{(7.37)} = 18.6 \text{ kips}$$

If there is 5″ of ¼″ fillet weld on each side of the web of (D) to the webs of (A) and (C), this will develop:

F = 2 × 5″(2.4 k/in.) = 24.0 kips > 18.6 kips, so is <u>OK</u>

* * *

The solution of some truss connection problems can be arrived at by an approach often used in connection with the design of hangers and supports. See Section 6.8, Problem 3.

8. SECONDARY STRESSES IN TRUSSES

So-called "Secondary Stresses" may result from bending moments applied to the various chord members as the result of the truss deflecting under load. With the exception of large bridge trusses, these secondary stresses are usually ignored and only the primary or direct stresses are considered. If these must be determined, it would be possible to compute the actual deflection of the truss under load and from this condition to then compute the secondary stresses.

In Grinter's "Modern Steel Structures", Volume 1, page 51, he mentions that experiments have shown that these secondary stresses ordinarily do not exceed 30% of the primary stresses for a given member. If the engineer is concerned about this, he may reduce the working stress to allow for an assumed secondary stress of about ⅓ of the primary stress. This method will of course require additional steel, but it is easy to use and is reasonably safe.

In order to take full advantage of possible economy in the design of large important structures, the secondary moments should be calculated and used in the design with increased working stresses.

Trusses were essential to the all welded framing of the steel and glass Phillis Wheatley Elementary School in New Orleans. The school was erected off the ground on two rows of concrete piers, plus exposed steel supporting columns under end trusses of the cantilevered classroom wings. This provides both open and sheltered play area beneath the structure.

The roof supporting space frame that tops the Upjohn Co.'s Kalamazoo office building is of welded angle construction. A system of subassembly jigs facilitated the holding of alignment during fabrication of the giant frame sections. Nearly all joints are welded downhand.

Main load-carrying element in the world's largest ore reclaimer, at Kaiser's Eagle Mountain mine in California, is a 170′ long welded truss of triangular cross-section. Tubular construction is used where practical for extra strength and torsional resistance, and in order to keep weight to a minimum. Closeup below shows welded cluster where vertical and diagonal members meet the top chord.

Connections for Tubular Construction

1. INTRODUCTION

Tubular construction is beginning to be used to a greater extent in this country, although for many years it has been an accepted method in Europe where it is used extensively. Although the advantages of the tube have been known for a long time, it was the introduction of welding to the connections which made its extensive use possible.

The tube represents an efficient section, having good properties in all directions. There is no problem in maintaining the inside of the tube against corrosion and in most cases this is left unpainted. The welded connections seal the tube against any moisture entering and prevents the circulation of air, hence any rusting very soon stops and equilibrium is reached.

The joints represent the intersections of curved surfaces, and therefore extra care and time is involved in cutting the pipe to prepare the joints. Usually these are flame-cut, although there are abrasive cut-off saws which make a series of straight cuts and provide good fit-up and there are shears with special tools which allow the end of the tube to be sheared. Fully automatic flame-cutting machines have been built which may be preset for the inner diameter of the tube to be cut, the outside diameter of the tube which it intersects, and the angle of intersection. This will very quickly provide the proper cut, at the proper bevel, and results in close fit-up of the joint.

Recently steel mills have introduced square and rectangular tubing; these of course, are much easier to connect because of their flat surfaces.

2. GUSSET PLATES

Gusset plates have been used in pipe connections for at least 3 reasons:

(1) Provides additional length of fillet welding to the pipe. Most pipe is not very thick. For example, 4″ standard pipe has a ¼″ thick wall. Unless extra care is used in cutting, beveling, and fitting, it is easier to use fillet welds rather than try to make 100% penetration groove welds on thin-wall pipe.

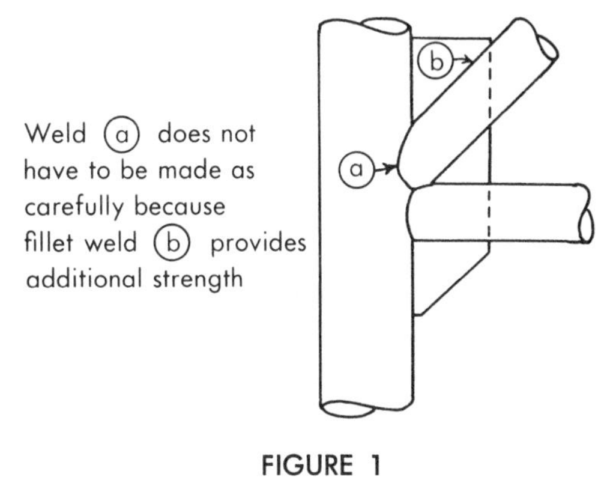
Weld (a) does not
have to be made as
carefully because
fillet weld (b) provides
additional strength
(a)
(b)

FIGURE 1

(2) Allows the intersecting pipe members to be cut short and the gusset plate carries the entire load back to the main member.

In some cases, the web members are shop fabricated and welded into assemblies. This facilitates field erection and welding because only vertical welds between the main pipe member and gusset plate are still required.

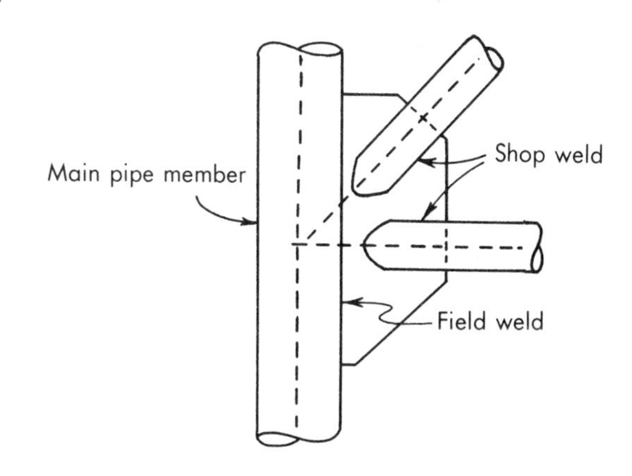
Main pipe member
Shop weld
Field weld

FIGURE 2

(3) Provides a direct transfer of force through a main pipe member when other members connect on opposite sides of the member. This may be done if it is felt that the main member has too low a thickness (t) to diameter (d) ratio and would need additional stiffness.

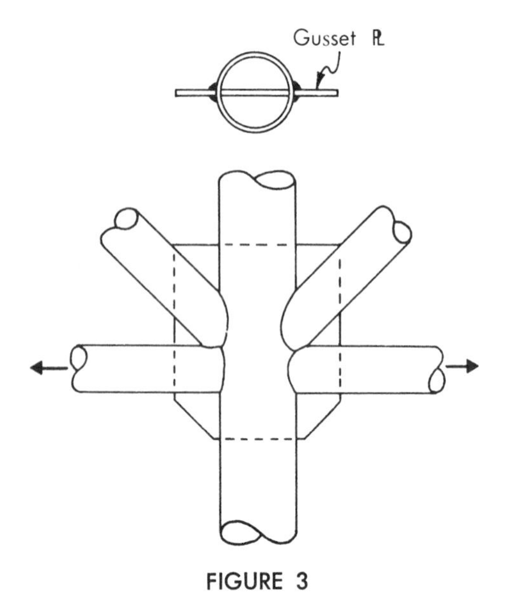

FIGURE 3

Another solution to this problem would be to add a "sleeve" or "collar" around the main member within this connection zone so that it would have the required thickness. It would be possible to insert by welding, a short length of thicker tubing within this zone. Usually the main pipe members must be butt welded together somewhere to provide the required length, and this weld could be located at this position. See Figure 4.

If the wall thickness, bevel, and fit-up of the pipe are sufficient for 100% penetration groove welds to be made, there should be no reason for gusset plates. In most cases, with proper care, groove welds could be made easily.

Although gusset plates are used in pipe connections, they tend to stiffen the pipe and, as a result, concentrate the stress in the pipe at the end of the plate. See Figure 5.

It has been suggested that, if gusset plates are to be used, they be tapered at their ends so as to have less stiffening effect on the pipe and thus provide a more even distribution of stress within the pipe at this connection.

Under static loads, any reasonable stress concentration in the pipe near the termination of the gusset plate would probably be reduced by some localized plastic yielding; so, this would not be a problem. However, gusset plates should be avoided for connections subject to fatigue loading.

3. ORDER OF ASSEMBLY

When web members intersect at a connection, normally the tensile member is first welded completely all the way around to the main member. Then the compression member is cut back to overlap the tensile member, and

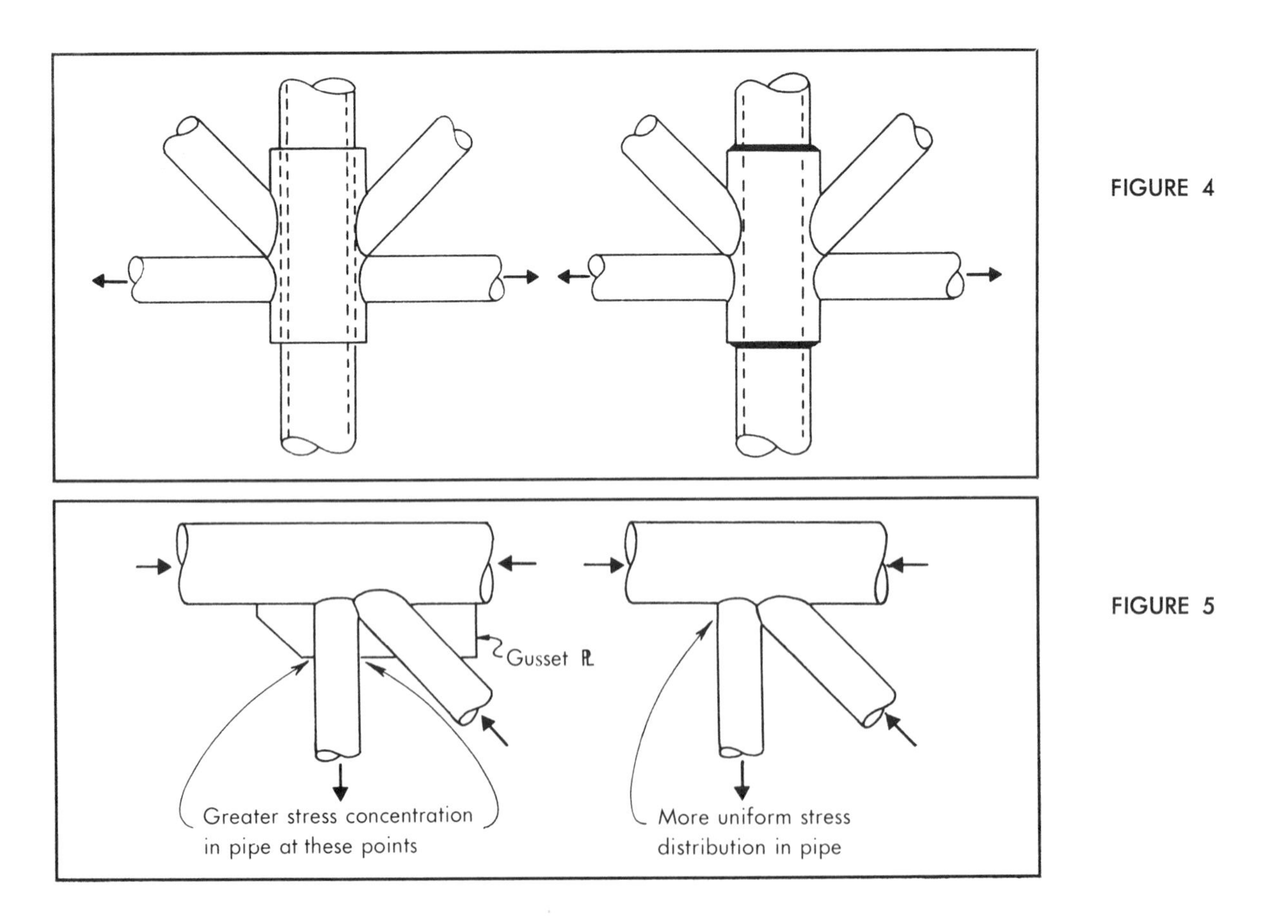

FIGURE 4

FIGURE 5

FIGURE 6

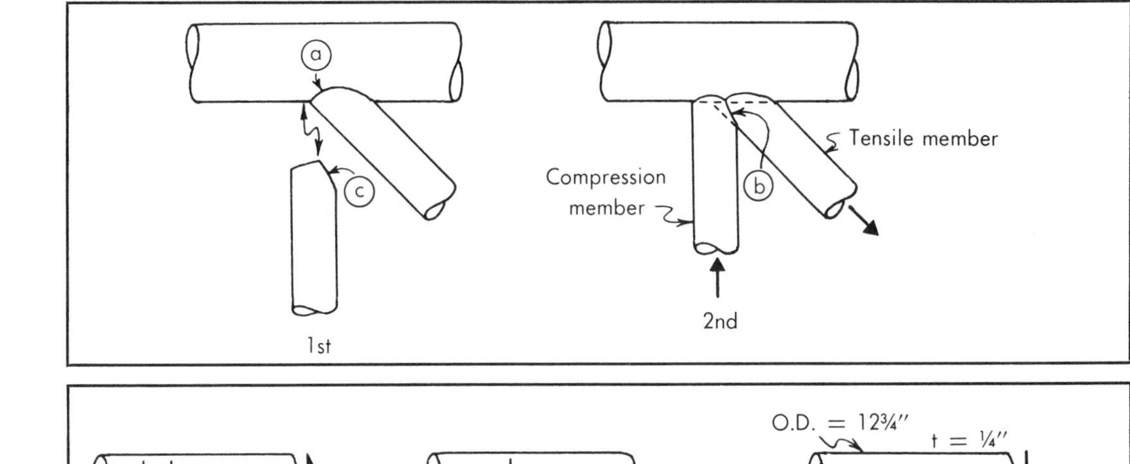

FIGURE 7

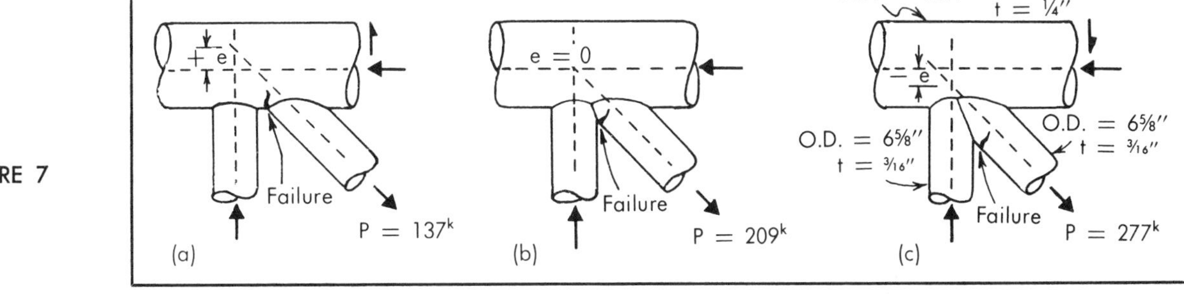

this is welded to both of these members. Every effort is made to obtain the best tensile connection; Figure 6.

This is not quite as important as it first sounds since most of the vertical component in the tension member is transferred directly into the compression member through the welds of this overlapping portion (b) without ever passing through the weld connecting the tension member to the main horizontal member (a).

The portion of the weld (a) in the overlapped area connecting the tension member to the main member is subjected to two forces: tension from the tensile member, and compression from the compression member since it pushes against this overlapped portion of the tensile member. One force offsets the other, so that very little of any vertical force must be carried by this portion of the weld at (a), just the horizontal force into the top member.

Figures 7 and 8 describe a test conducted at the University of California, "Research on Tubular Connections in Structural Work" J. G. Bouwkamp, WRC #71, Aug. 1961. This test shows the effect that overlapping the intersecting web members has on the strength of the joint.

It is seen that a more negative eccentricity of the connection (c) results in more overlapping of the web members and greater stiffness of the main member. With this great overlapping of the web members, the transfer of the vertical component of the diagonal web member into the vertical web member will occur before it enters the main horizontal chord member. The above test shows this connection to have the highest strength, actually slightly higher than the tube itself, which in a separate test pulled at an average of 260 kips. Notice all three of the above tests failed in the tube wall adjacent to the connecting weld.

4. APPLICABLE BRITISH SPECIFICATIONS

The following is taken from Addition No. 1 (Nov 1953) to B.S. 449 (1948), British Standards Institution:

Sealed tubes or sealed box sections, for exposed structures shall not be thinner than .160″; for non-exposed structures this limit is .128″, and not less than—

$$t = .10 \sqrt[3]{D}$$

D = outside diameter of pipe

t = thickness of pipe

The angle between intersecting pipe shall not be less than 30°; otherwise the strength of the connection shall be demonstrated.

A complete penetration groove weld may be used regardless of the ratio of the diameters of the intersecting pipes.

If the ratio of the diameter of the pipes is less than ⅓, fillet welds may be used.

If this ratio is ⅓ or greater, a combination of fillet welds for a portion of the joint and groove welds for the remainder may be used.

Pipes connected end to end shall be groove welded.

In a fillet weld or a combination of fillet and groove

FIG. 8a This pipe connection (Fig. 7a) had a positive eccentricity of 1/4 the diameter of the larger pipe. Its ultimate load was 137 kips.

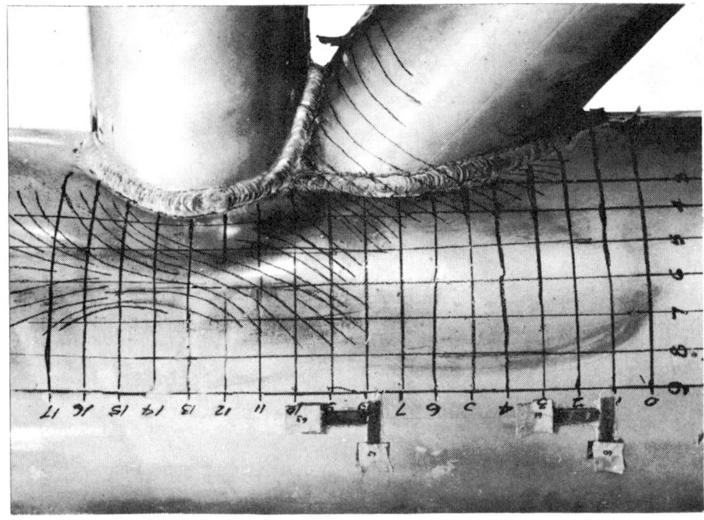

FIG. 8b This pipe connection (Fig. 7b) had no eccentricity. There's a slight overlapping of the connection. Its ultimate load was 209 kips.

FIG. 8c This pipe connection (Fig. 7c) had a negative eccentricity of 1/4 the diameter of the larger pipe. Because of larger amount of overlapping, its ultimate load was 277 kips.

weld, the allowable stress on the throat shall not exceed the allowable shear stress of the pipe.

In a groove weld, the allowable tensile, compressive, or shear stress on the throat shall not exceed that of the pipe.

5. DESIGN OF TUBULAR TRUSS CONNECTIONS

The application of tubular construction to a truss arrangement is typified by the following problem. Here the loading is similar to that on the connection which was the subject of Problem 3, in the preceding Section 5.9.

Problem 1

To design an efficient connection on this tubular truss, Figure 9.

(a) First check the allowable loads on the various selected pipe sections against the actual loading.

Member Ⓐ

$$\frac{L}{r} = \frac{(432)}{(4.38)}$$

$$= 98.7$$

and the allowable is $\sigma = 12{,}520$ psi

$$P = \sigma A$$

$$= (12{,}520)(14.58)$$

$$= 182 \text{ kips} > 168 \text{ kips} \qquad \underline{\text{OK}}$$

Member Ⓑ

$$\frac{L}{r} = \frac{(238)}{(4.38)}$$

$$= 54.3$$

and the allowable is $\sigma = 16{,}660$ psi

$$P = \sigma A$$

$$= (16{,}660)(14.58)$$

$$= 243 \text{ kips} > 200 \text{ kips} \qquad \underline{\text{OK}}$$

Member Ⓓ

$$P = \sigma A$$

$$= (20{,}000)(7.265)$$

$$= 145.3 \text{ kips} > 126 \text{ kips} \qquad \underline{\text{OK}}$$

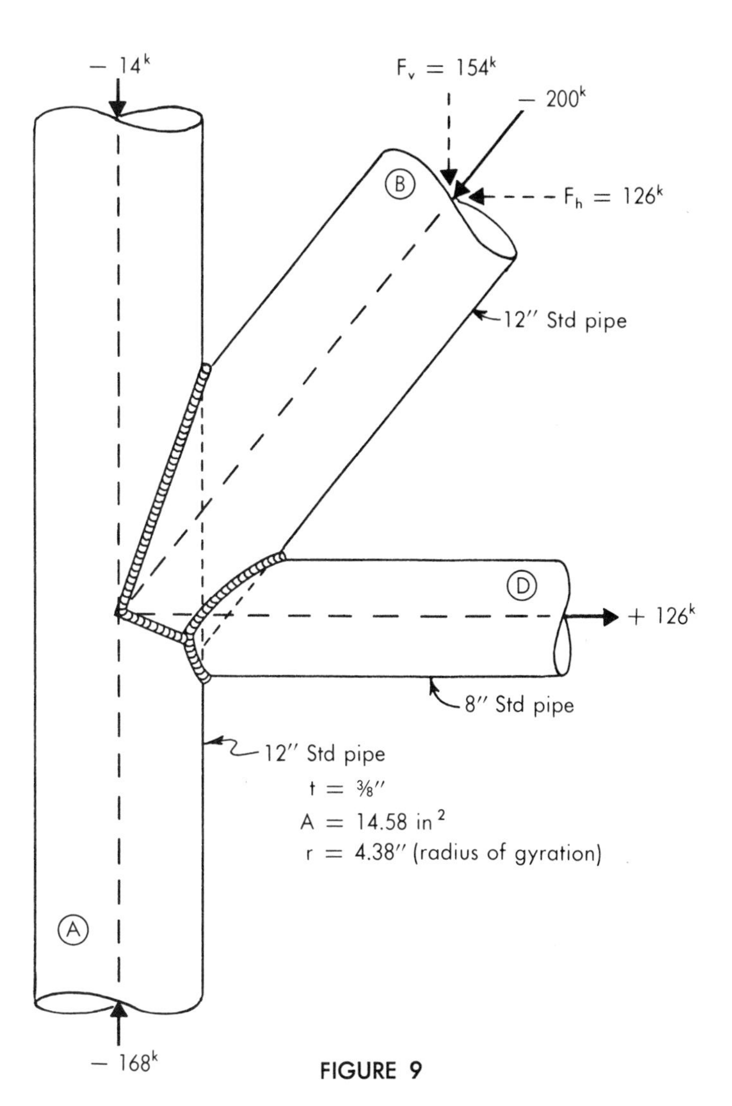

FIGURE 9

(b) Use a ⅝″ gusset plate on this connection, resulting in Figure 10.

moment applied to pipe

$$M_h = (126^k)(7.86'')$$

$$= 990 \text{ in.-kips}$$

also

$$M_h = (154^k)(6\tfrac{5}{8}'')$$

$$= 982 \text{ in.-kips}$$

assumed value of e

$$e = 12\ t$$

$$= 12\ (\tfrac{3}{8})$$

$$= 4\tfrac{1}{2}''$$

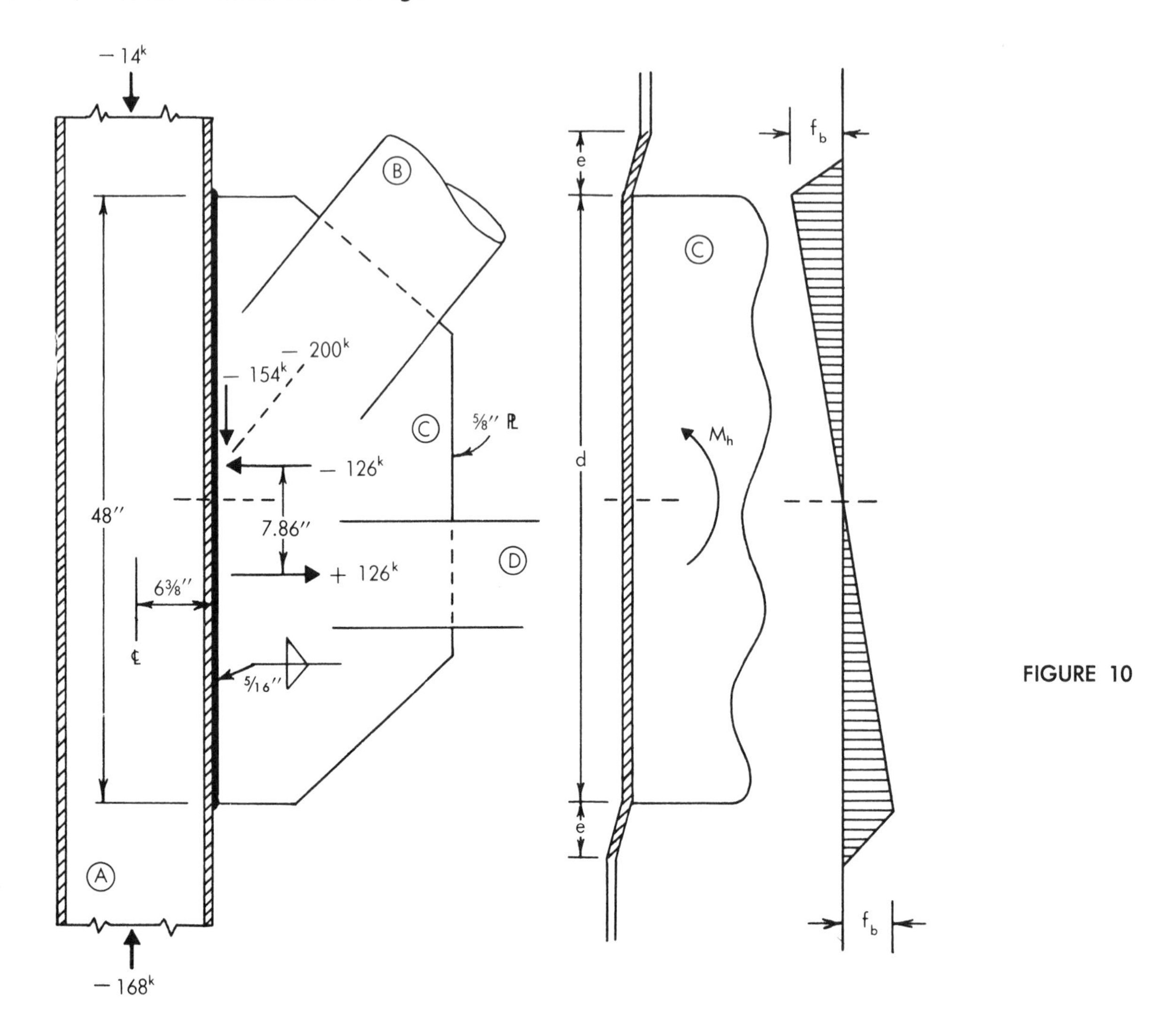

FIGURE 10

maximum unit force (radial) applied to 1″ ring section of pipe (A)

$$f_b = \frac{6\ M_h}{(d + e)(d + 2e)}$$

$$= \frac{6(990)}{(48 + 4\tfrac{1}{2})(48 + 9)}$$

$$= 1.98 \text{ kips}$$

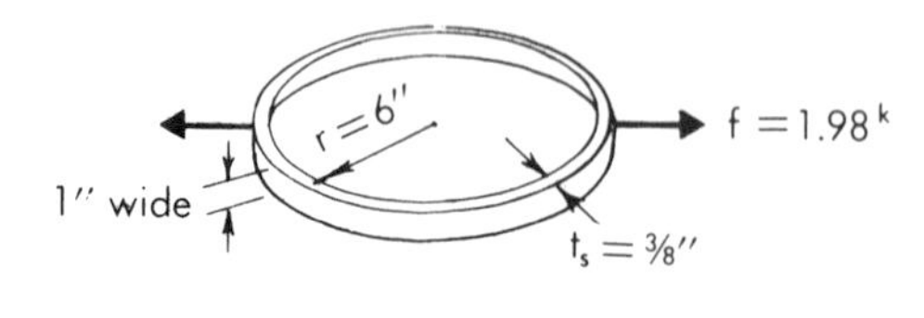

FIGURE 11

Although there is just a single radial force (f) acting on the pipe shell, assume there is an equal force on the opposite side of the shell, resisting this force. This represents a worse condition than actually exists.

$$S = \frac{t^2}{6}$$

$$= \frac{(\tfrac{3}{8})^2}{6}$$

$$= .023 \text{ in.}^3$$

$$M_{max} \text{ (at force f)} = k\ f\ r$$

$$= (.318)(1.98(6)$$

$$= 3.78 \text{ in.-kips}$$

$$\sigma = \frac{M}{S}$$

$$= \frac{(3.78)}{(.023)}$$

$$= 164{,}000 \text{ psi} \quad \underline{\text{Excessive}}$$

Because of these excessive bending stresses within the pipe shell resulting from the moment applied by the connecting plate, some means of stiffening the pipe within this area must be used. There are several possibilities.

(1) One possible solution is to put a casing around the pipe so as to increase its wall thickness. This will provide sufficient section modulus so that the resulting bending stress is reduced to an allowable value. (Assume $\sigma = 18{,}000$ psi.)

$$S = \frac{M}{\sigma}$$

$$= \frac{(3.78)}{(18{,}000)}$$

$$= .210 \text{ in.}^3$$

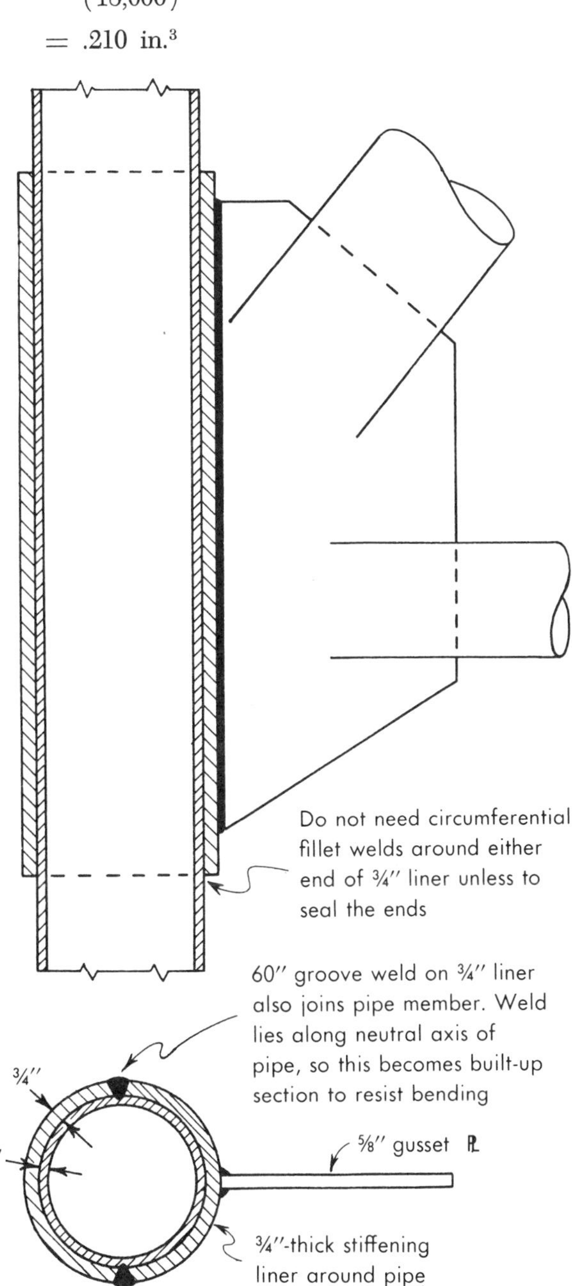
Do not need circumferential fillet welds around either end of ¾″ liner unless to seal the ends
60″ groove weld on ¾″ liner also joins pipe member. Weld lies along neutral axis of pipe, so this becomes built-up section to resist bending
¾″
⅜″
⅝″ gusset ℞
¾″-thick stiffening liner around pipe

FIGURE 12

$$S = \frac{t^2}{6} \quad \text{or}$$

$$t = \sqrt{6\ S}$$

$$= \sqrt{6\ (.210)}$$

$$= 1.12'' \text{ required wall thickness}$$

Since 1.12″ — ⅜″ (present thickness of Ⓐ) = .745″ required additional thickness, or add a ¾″-thick wrap-around sheet around this pipe Ⓐ in the area of the connection. See Figure 12.

(2) Another possible solution would be to add to the wall thickness at top and bottom of the connection.

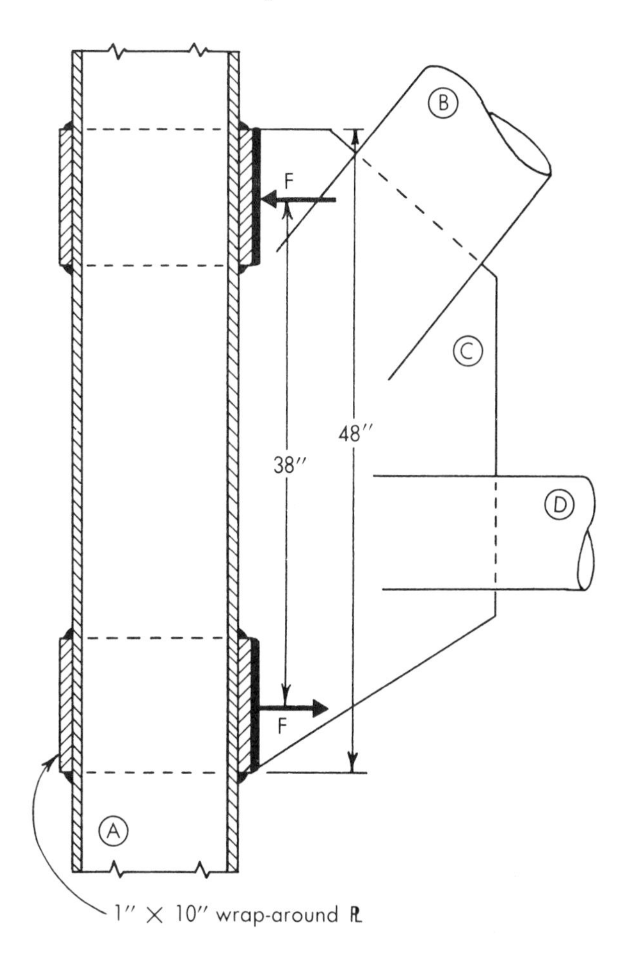
B
F
C
48″
38″
D
F
A
1″ × 10″ wrap-around ℞

FIGURE 13

$$F = \frac{M_h}{d}$$

$$= \frac{(990 \text{ in.-kips})}{(38'')}$$

$$= 26.1 \text{ kips}$$

$$M = k\ F\ r_c$$

$$= (.318)(26.1^k)(6'')$$

$$= 49.8 \text{ in.-kips}$$

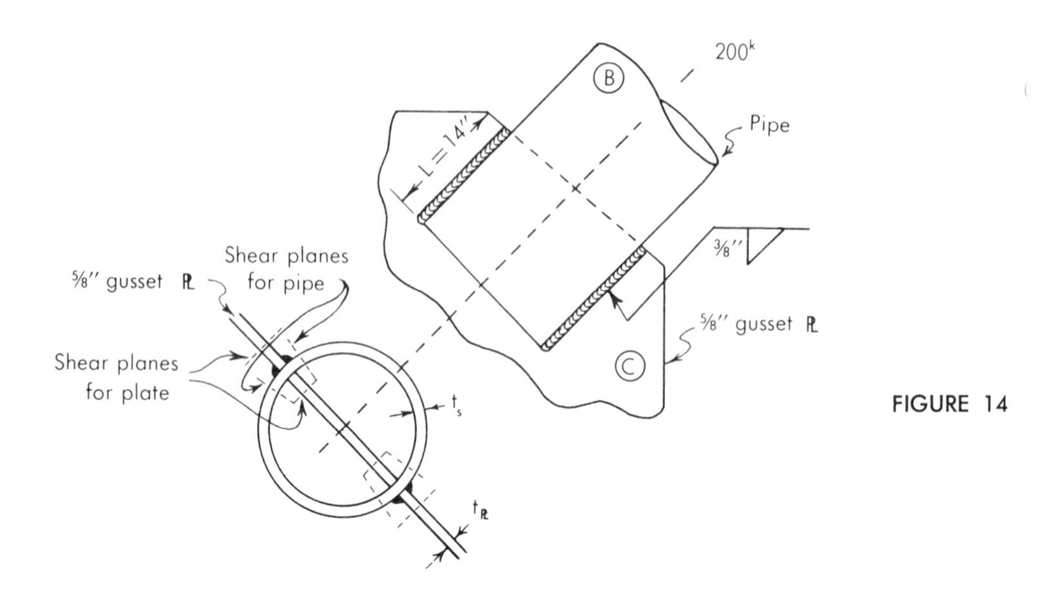

FIGURE 14

$$S = \frac{M}{\sigma}$$

$$= \frac{(49.8 \text{ in.-kips})}{(18{,}000 \text{ psi})}$$

$$= 2.77 \text{ in.}^3$$

$$S = \frac{w\ t^2}{6}$$

where: w = width of stiffening ring

$$\text{or} \quad t = \sqrt{\frac{6\ S}{w}}$$

$$= \sqrt{\frac{(6)(2.77)}{10}}$$

= 1.29″ required, and since 1.29″ — ⅜″ = .915″, add a 1″ x 10″ plate wrapped around the pipe Ⓐ at the top and bottom of the connection.

(c) Determine the amount of required connecting weld between pipe Ⓑ and gusset plate Ⓒ

For determining the minimum length of connection (L) to hold shear stress (τ) within the allowable, use the following maximum leg size of weld:

plate

$$4\ L\ 9600\ \omega = 4\ t_{PL}\ L\ \tau$$

$$\omega = \frac{13{,}000\ t_{PL}}{9600} = 1.355\ t_{PL}$$

pipe

$$4\ L\ 9600\ \omega = 4\ t_s\ L\ \tau$$

$$\omega = \frac{13{,}000\ t_s}{9600} = 1.355\ t_s$$

$$\therefore\ \omega \leqq 1.355\ t_s$$

$$\leqq 1.355\ (⅜)$$

$\leqq$ .509″; so we'll use ⅜″ ◺

Since:

$$F = 4\ L\ 9600\ \omega$$

$$L = \frac{F}{4 \times 9600\ \omega}$$

$$= \frac{200^k}{4 \times 9600\ (⅜)}$$

$$= 13.9'' \text{ or } 14''$$

An alternate method would be to use ⅜″ fillet weld all the way around the end of the pipe Ⓑ :

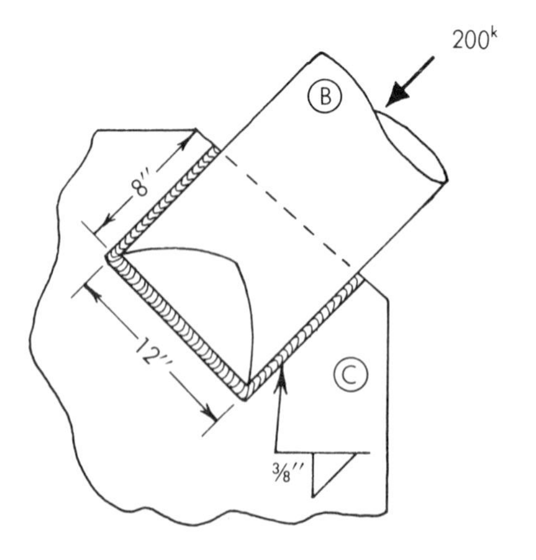

FIGURE 15

The total length of weld would be—

$$L = \frac{200^k}{3.6^k/in.}$$

$= 55.6''$, or $27.8''$ on each side of the ⅝″ gusset plate.

If the transverse weld is 12″ long, this leaves 27.8 — 12 = 15.8″, or 8″ on each side.

6. TEMPLATES FOR PIPE CONNECTIONS

Although pipe fabricating shops have shop men who are experienced in laying out and preparing these joints by making their own templates, this is something new for most structural shops. It may be necessary to supply templates for the more critical pipe joints where a gusset plate is not specified.

There are tables of ordinates available for most standard pipe sizes and given angles of intersection (15°, 30°, 45°, 60°, and 90°). However, these may be of little value because other round tubular sections may be used which are not standard pipe sizes, and in structural work the angle of intersection will not necessarily be one of the above.

For good fit-up, it is necessary that the inner radius (r_1) of the smaller pipe (A) and the outer radius (r_2) of the larger pipe (B) intersect along a curve which forms the root of the joint.

Following is a suggested method for making templates which will cover all possible connections at any angle of intersection, any amount of offset, and any possible combination of pipe sizes. This template will allow the end of the smaller pipe to be cut for proper fit-up against the surface of the larger pipe. In structural work, it is not necessary to cut a hole into the side of the larger pipe at the connection, as is done in pressure piping so a second template is not needed for this cut.

The inner radius (r_1) of the smaller pipe (A) and the outer radius (r_2) of the larger pipe (B) are used to make the template. This is done graphically or analytically, as explained a few paragraphs further.

The template is made of some type of heavy paper. It is wrapped around the pipe to be cut, at the proper location. The center of this template edge is transferred onto the pipe with chalk. The chalked curve on the pipe is then marked with a series of centerpunch marks. The pipe is then flame-cut along this curve, keeping the torch tip normal or at right angles to the surface of the pipe. This will produce the proper curve for the joint as far as the inside of the pipe is concerned.

It is then necessary to bevel the edge of this pipe back from the outside, just touching this inside cut to provide the required included angle for the groove weld. A good experienced flame-cutting operator will do this without any difficulty.

If fillet welds are to be used instead of groove welds, this second cut or bevel is only needed at reentrant corners of the joint or where the angle between the surfaces of the intersecting pipes is less than 90°.

TABLE 1—Properties of Polar Angles

position	a	12 POSITIONS sin a	sin² a	or (B) 1-cos a
1	0	0	0.0000	0
2	30°	+ .50000	+ .2500	+ .1340
3	60°	+ .8660	+ .7500	+ .5000
4	90°	+1.0000	+1.0000	+1.0000
5	120°	+ .8660	+ .7500	+1.5000
6	150°	+ .5000	+ .2500	+1.8660
7	180°	0	0	+2.0000
8	210°	— .50000	+ .2500	+1.8660
9	240°	— .8660	+ .7500	+1.5000
10	270°	—1.0000	+1.0000	+1.0000
11	300°	— .8660	+ .7500	+ .5000
12	330°	— .5000	+ .2500	+ .1340
1	360°	0	0	0

TABLE 2—Properties of Polar Angles

position	a	16 POSITIONS sin a	sin² a	or (B) 1-cos a
1	0	0	0	0
2	22.5°	+ .3827	+ .1465	+ .0761
3	45.0°	+ .7071	+ .5000	+ .2929
4	67.5°	+ .9239	+ .8536	+ .6173
5	90.8°	+1.0000	+1.0000	+1.0000
6	112.5°	+ .9239	+ .8536	+1.3827
7	135.0°	+ .7071	+ .5000	+1.7071
8	157.5°	+ .3827	+ .1465	+1.9239
9	180.0°	0	0	+2.0000
10	202.5°	— .3827	+ .1465	+1.9239
11	225.0°	— .7071	+ .5000	+1.7071
12	247.5°	— .9239	+ .8536	+1.3827
13	270.0°	—1.0000	+1.0000	+1.0000
14	292.5°	— .9239	+ .8536	+ .6173
15	315.0°	— .7071	+ .5000	+ .2929
16	337.5°	— .3827	+ .1465	+ .7061
1	360.0°	0	0	0

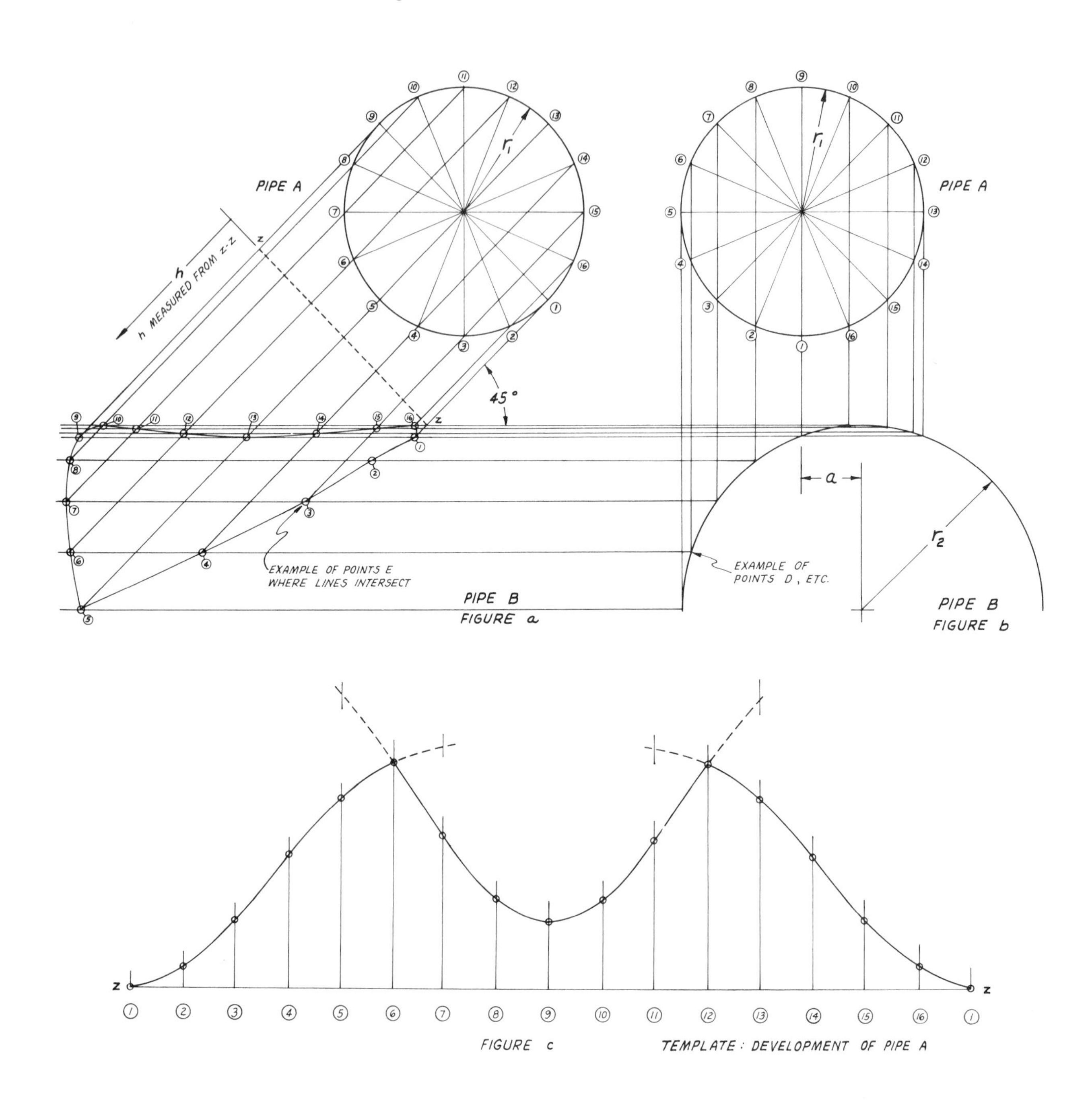

FIGURE 16

Graphical Method of Making Template

References are to views (a), (b), and (c) of Figure 16.

1. Draw a side view of the connection, figure (a). Draw an end view of the connection, figure (b).

2. Lay off pipe Ⓐ into a given number of equal sections, for example 16, and number these 1, 2, 3, etc. through to 16. Draw lines through these points parallel to the axis of pipe Ⓐ in both figures.

3. Where these parallel lines of pipe Ⓐ intersect pipe Ⓑ, in figure (b), make points (D).

4. Through points (D), draw lines parallel to the axis of the large pipe Ⓑ, extending them into figure (a).

5. Where these parallel lines of pipe Ⓑ intersect corresponding parallel lines of pipe Ⓐ, in figure (a), mark points (E). Number these points in accordance with the original division of the pipe Ⓐ.

6. In figure (c), lay off line z-z, equal to the outer circumference of pipe Ⓐ, and divide into 16 equal segments.

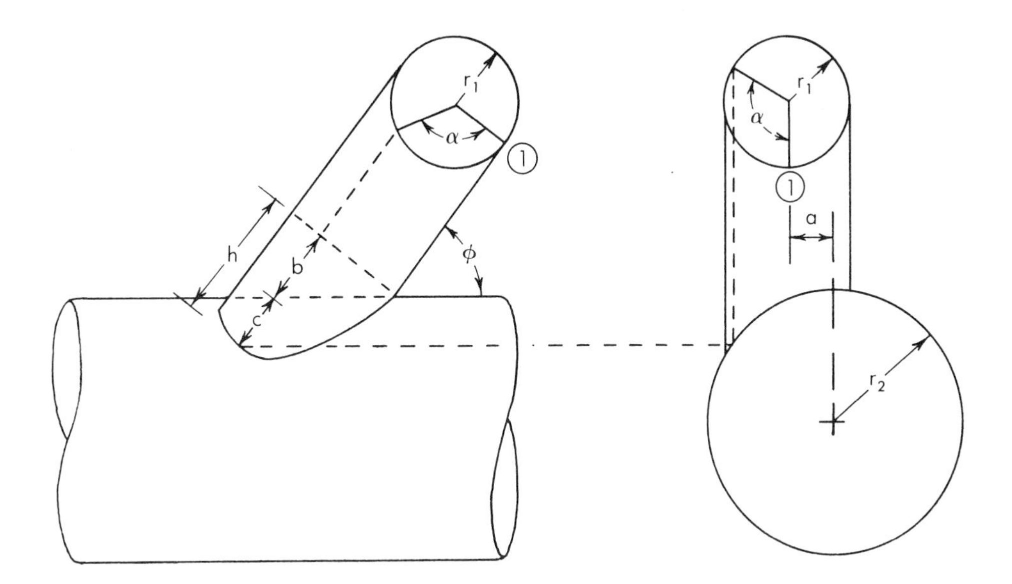

FIGURE 17

7. In figure (a), draw reference line Z-Z at right angles to the axis of pipe (A) and through the vertex of the connection angle. From this line Z-Z measure the ordinate distance (h) to the various intersecting points (E). Lay these distances (h) off vertically from line Z-Z in figure (c). Do this for all the points and draw a curve through the upper extremities of these vertical lines. This becomes the template for cutting pipe (A), figure (c).

Analytical Method

The following formula will give the value of the ordinate (h) for any polar position (α) along the smaller pipe. This method of finding ordinates by formula eliminates the mapping of figures (a) and (b) in the graphical method of Figure 16.

$$h = \frac{r_2 - \sqrt{r_2^2 - (a - r_1 \sin \alpha)^2}}{\sin \phi} + \frac{r_1}{\tan \phi}(1 - \cos \alpha) \qquad (1)$$

Practically all structural pipe connections will have no offset, a = 0, and this becomes—

$$h = \frac{r_2 - \sqrt{r_2^2 - r_1^2 \sin^2 \alpha}}{\sin \phi} + \frac{r_1}{\tan \phi}(1 - \cos \alpha) \qquad (2)$$

or:

$$h = \frac{r_2}{\sin \phi}[A] + \frac{r_1}{\tan \phi}[B] \qquad \ldots\ldots\ldots\ldots (3)$$

where:

$[A] = 1 - \sqrt{1 - K^2 \sin^2 \alpha}$ $\qquad K = \frac{r_1}{r_2}$

$[B] = 1 - \cos \alpha$

r_1 = inner radius of smaller intersecting pipe

r_2 = outer radius of larger intersecting pipe

ϕ = angle of intersection between axes of pipes

h = ordinate of the template for the smaller pipe for any position (α)

α = position along the smaller pipe

Tables 1 and 2 will give the necessary values for $\sin \alpha$, $\sin^2 \alpha$, and $1 - \cos \alpha$ for the various polar angles (α) for either 12 positions or 16 positions of the pipe.

If Formula 3 is to be used, the following nomograph, Figure 18, will give values of [A]. Values of [B] may be found in Tables 1 and 2.

Problem 2

For the tubular connection represented in Figure 16, the smaller pipe (A), inside radius $r_1 = 2''$, intersects the larger pipe (B), outside radius $r_2 = 3''$, at an angle of 45°, and with an offset of a = 2″.

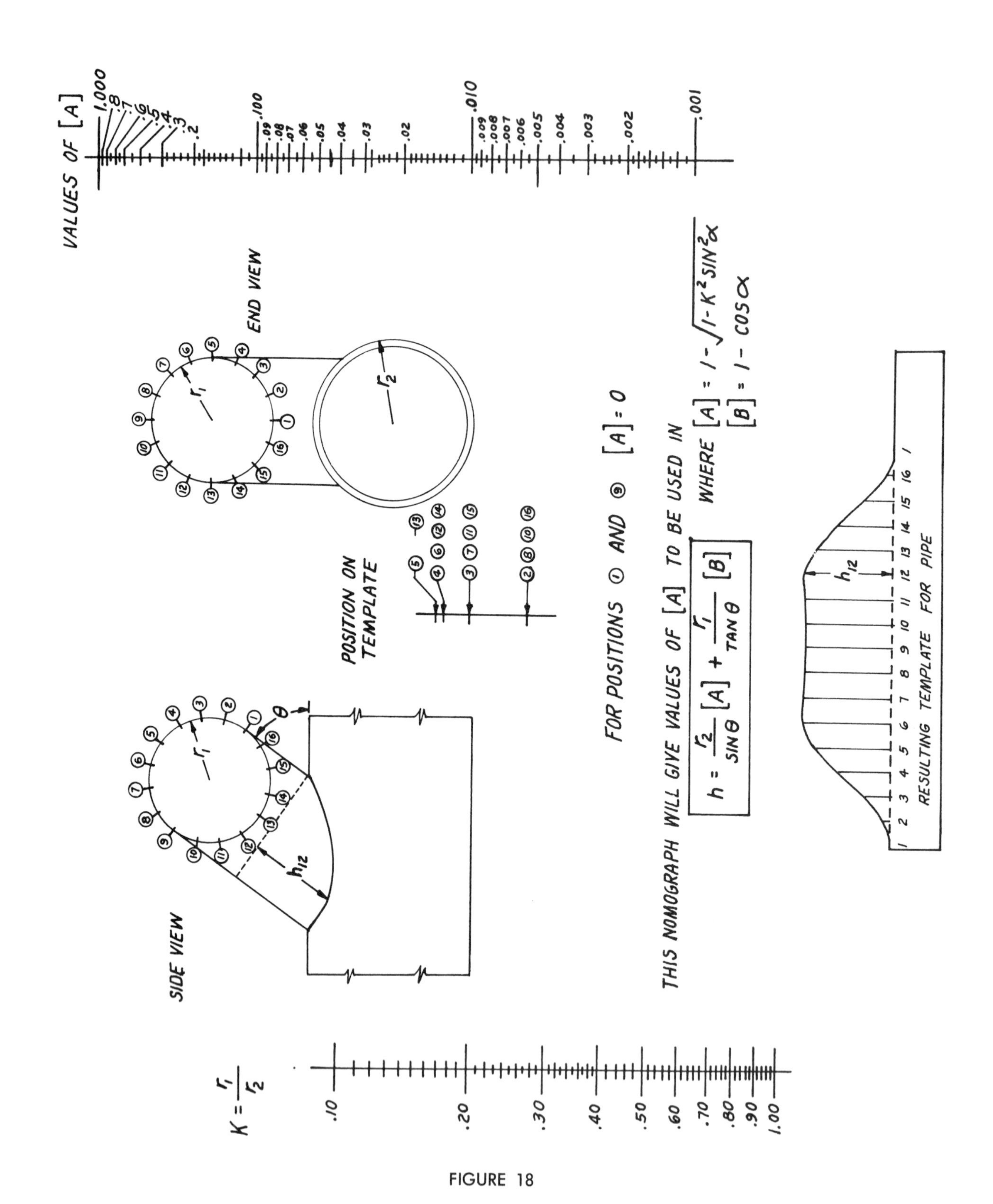
VALUES OF [A]
1.000
.8
.7
.6
.5
.4
.3
.2
.100
.09
.08
.07
.06
.05
.04
.03
.02
.010
.009
.008
.007
.006
.005
.004
.003
.002
.001
END VIEW
r_1
r_2
SIDE VIEW
θ
h_{12}
POSITION ON TEMPLATE
FOR POSITIONS ① AND ⑨ [A] = 0
THIS NOMOGRAPH WILL GIVE VALUES OF [A] TO BE USED IN
$h = \frac{r_2}{\sin\theta}[A] + \frac{r_1}{\tan\theta}[B]$
WHERE $[A] = 1 - \sqrt{1 - K^2 \sin^2\alpha}$
$[B] = 1 - \cos\alpha$
RESULTING TEMPLATE FOR PIPE
$K = \frac{r_1}{r_2}$
.10
.20
.30
.40
.50
.60
.70
.80
.90
1.00

FIGURE 18

Following are the ordinates (h) for the various positions figured both graphically (see Figure 16) and analytically (with Formula 1). This table shows close agreement between the two sets of values.

position	graphical	analytical
1	.26″	.242″
2	1.03″	.965″
3	2.31″	2.308″
4	4.14″	4.145″
5	6.25″	6.242″
6	5.70″	5.675″
7	5.17″	5.136″
8	4.65″	4.660″
9	4.29″	4.242″
10	3.87″	3.861″
11	3.52″	3.455″
12	3.00″	2.938″
13	2.30″	2.242″
14	1.40″	1.408″
15	.62″	.627″
16	.15″	.165″

A sheet of paper is laid out. A straight line X-X is drawn across the paper, parallel to the long edge and 2″ or 3″ from this edge. Starting from the left edge of the paper, measure off a distance on this line equal to the outer circumference of the smaller pipe A and mark this on the line. This can be done in two ways; the circumference of the pipe may be figured by knowing the outside diameter of the pipe, or this paper may be wrapped around the outside of the pipe and marked where this edge of the paper overlaps.

The easiest way to divide this line (which represents the circumference) into equal segments is to fold the left edge of the paper back toward the right until it lies directly on top of this mark, then fold this flat upon itself. This divides the circumference into two equal parts. Now fold this edge back toward the left until it lies directly over this fold, and fold down. Do the same for the similar portion on the bottom. This now divides the circumference into four equal parts. Open the paper and divide each of these quarter sections into three equal parts and number each of these vertical lines from 1 to 12. If 16 positions are to be used, divide each of these quarter sections into four equal parts and number from 1 to 16.

Lay off the corresponding ordinates (h) on these lines. Draw a curve through these points and cut along this curve; the lower portion of the paper is the template.

Problem 3

In the connection represented in Figure 19, the axes of these three intersecting pipes lie on a common plane; there is no offset ($a = 0$).

A template is required to cut pipe Ⓐ which intersects both pipes Ⓑ and Ⓒ . The inner radius of pipe Ⓐ is 2″, the outer radius of pipe Ⓑ is 3″, and the outer radius of pipe Ⓒ is 2¼″. The graphical work is shown in Figure 19.

Notice that the finished template is made of two portions, that due to the intersection with pipe Ⓑ , and that due to intersecting pipe Ⓒ .

Problem 4

In this example, the nomograph (Fig. 18) will be used to find the ordinates (h) for a template to be used in cutting the smaller pipe of a two-pipe connection. The smaller pipe Ⓐ has an inside radius of $r_1 = 2''$, the larger pipe Ⓑ has an outside radius of $r_2 = 3''$, and the angle of their intersection is $\phi = 60°$.

$$K = \frac{r_1}{r_2} = \frac{2''}{3''} = .67$$

$$\sin 60° = .8660$$

$$\tan 60° = 1.7321$$

Formula (3)

$$h = \frac{r_2}{\sin \phi}[A] + \frac{r_1}{\tan \phi}[B]$$

$$= \frac{3}{.8660}[A] + \frac{2}{1.7321}[B]$$

$$= 3.464\,[A] + 1.155\,[B]$$

The results are shown below in table form. As a matter of interest, the values computed by Formula (2) are listed on the extreme right and indicate the reasonable accuracy of the nomograph.

position	Values of [A] from nomograph	Values of [B] from table 2	Value of h = 3.464[A] + 1.155[B]	Value of h from formula (2)
1	0	0	0	0
2, 16	.032	.0761	.20	.202
3, 15	.115	.2929	.74	.747
4, 14	.21	.6173	1.44	1.448
5, 13	.26	1.0000	2.06	2.037
6, 12	.21	1.3827	2.33	2.332
7, 11	.115	1.7071	2.37	2.380
8, 10	.032	1.9239	2.42	2.336
9	0	2.0000	2.31	2.309

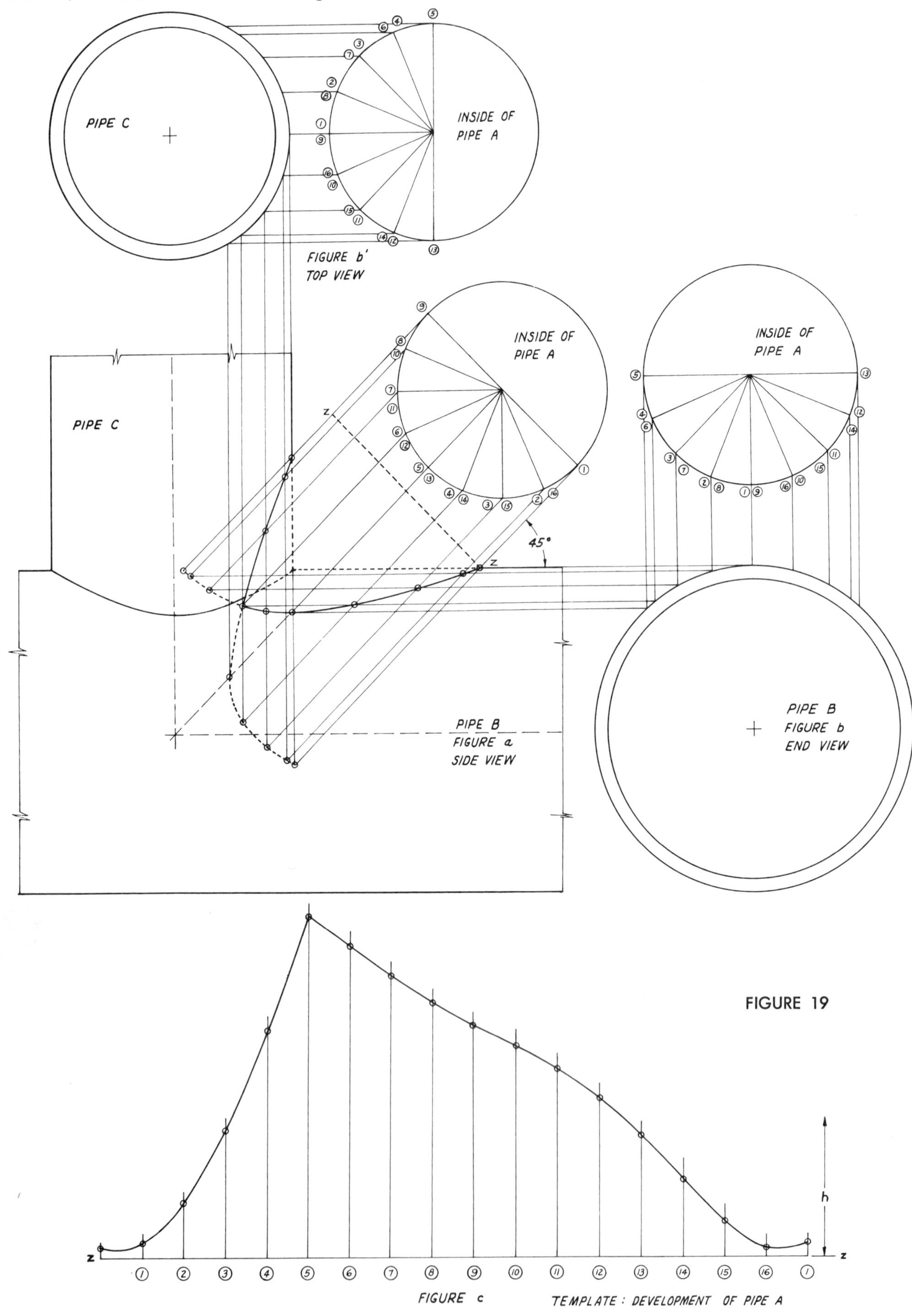

PIPE C
INSIDE OF PIPE A
FIGURE b'
TOP VIEW
INSIDE OF PIPE A
INSIDE OF PIPE A
PIPE C
45°
z
PIPE B
FIGURE a
SIDE VIEW
PIPE B
FIGURE b
END VIEW
h
z
1 2 3 4 5 6 7 8 9 10 11 12 13 14 15 16 1
FIGURE c
TEMPLATE : DEVELOPMENT OF PIPE A

FIGURE 19

7. BOX SECTIONS

The square and rectangular box sections, in which tubing has more recently become available at competitive prices, eliminate the problem of fit-up that is associated with the round sections. With box sections, the end of the smaller tube can be simply sawed with a single cut at the required angle.

Field erection of box sections is easily simplified by the use of Saxe clips, Figure 20. The clip and its seat are shop welded to the two intersecting members. Usually the clip is welded to the inside of the box beam where it is less vulnerable to damage during shipment to the project site. The clip also functions as a seat to help in support of the beam. This allows the joint to be made without any attachments on the outside, and produces a pleasing appearance.

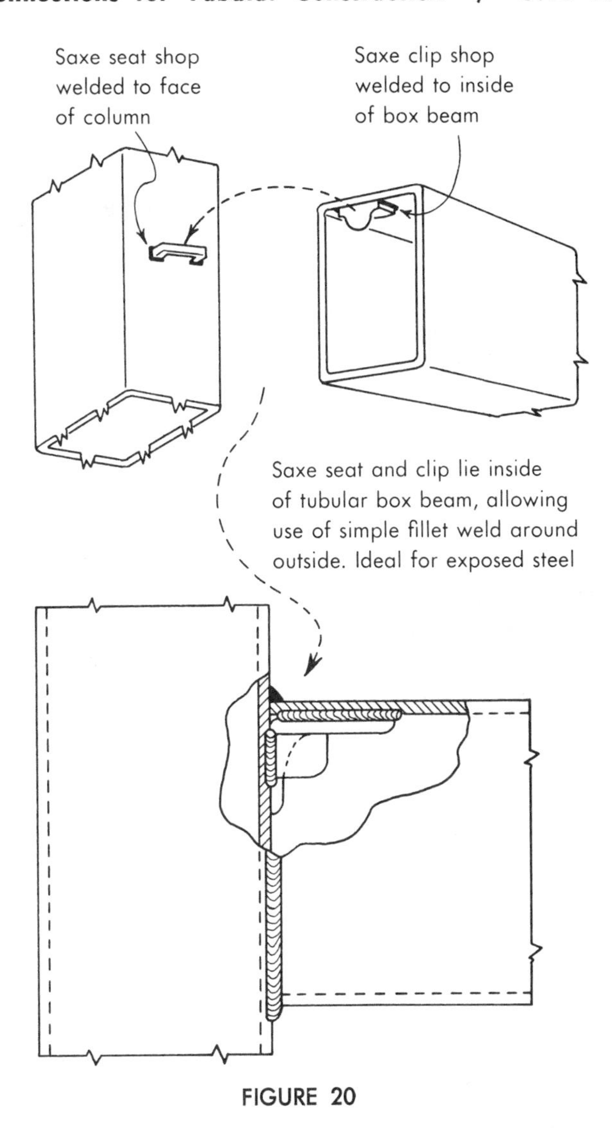
Saxe seat shop welded to face of column
Saxe clip shop welded to inside of box beam
Saxe seat and clip lie inside of tubular box beam, allowing use of simple fillet weld around outside. Ideal for exposed steel

FIGURE 20

Square and rectangular structural tubing, now available in many standard sizes, tends to simplify design and facilitate erection. Both shop and field connections are generally more easily made than when using round tubing.

Space frame roof on the combined warehouse and machine shop in Bethlehem Steel Co.'s research complex offers an interesting silhouette (at top). Roof frame is formed by eleven 96′-span welded pipe trusses braced apart by inclined pipe struts and arched structural members. The result is a very rigid structure, although temporary stiffening with steel channels was required during erection.

Typical connections to facilitate erection of structure using square tubing for columns. Columns have equally high strength in both x and y directions, plus excellent torsional resistance. Connections combine welding and erection bolting.

Unique roof suspension system combines with "tubular" design of members and weld fabrication to provide vast unobstructed area and light airy atmosphere to the Tulsa (Oklahoma) Exposition Center. In photo above, slag is being chipped from root pass on splice of built up box-section roof girder, preparatory to making main fill passes.

Rigid-Frame Knees (Elastic Design)

1. GENERAL REQUIREMENTS

The knee is an important part of a rigid frame and some thought should be given to its design.

The knee of any rigid frame must be capable of—

1. Transferring the end moment from the beam into the column.

2. Transferring the vertical shear at the end of the beam into the column.

3. Transferring the horizontal shear of the column into the beam.

A knee differs from the usual straight beam in these respects:

1. The neutral axis shifts toward the inner flange, causing an increase in the usual bending forces at this point.

2. Axial flange forces must change direction, causing radial forces to be set up.

2. EVALUATION OF KNEE TYPES

Figure 1 illustrates the five principal types of knees for rigid frames.

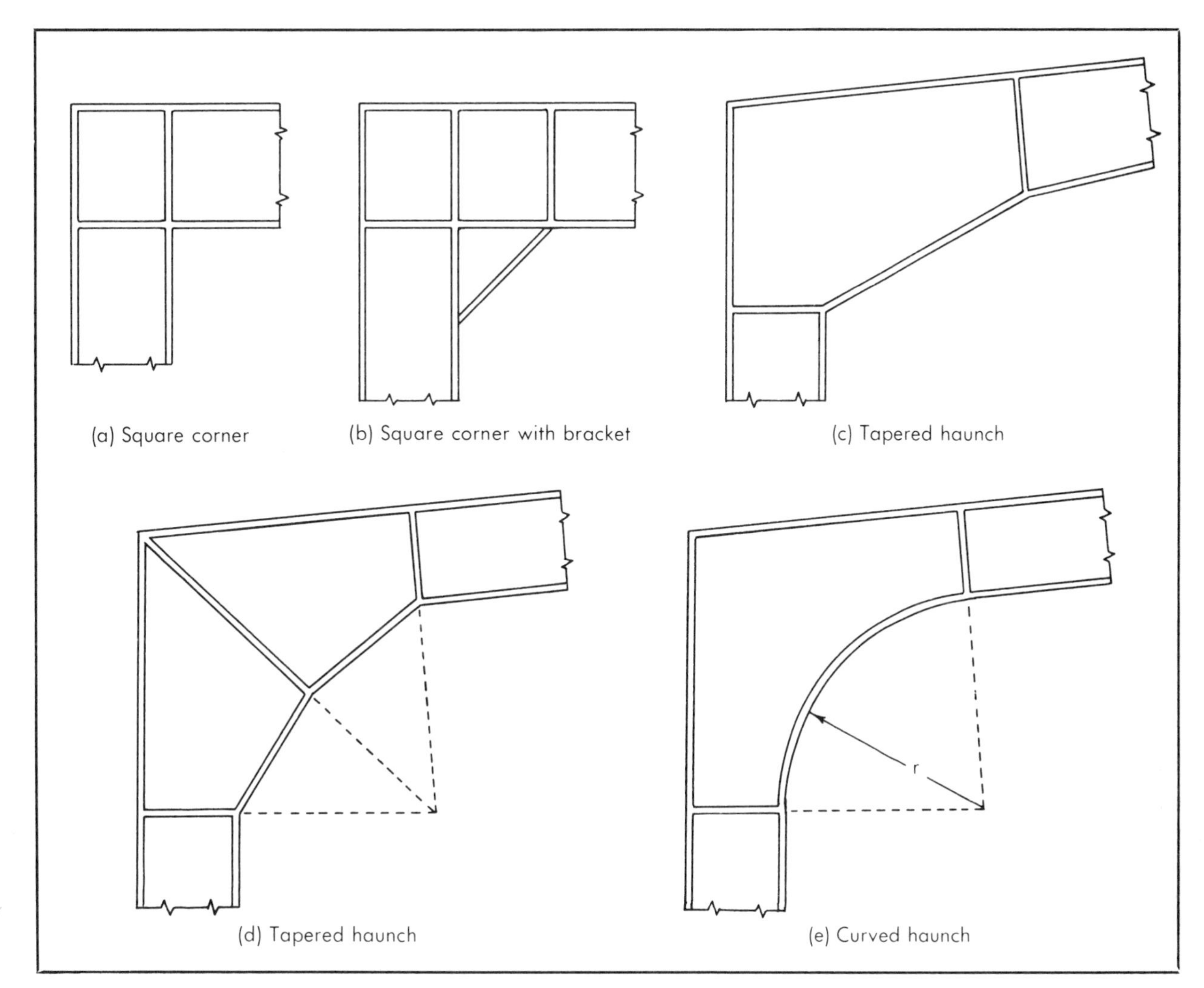

FIGURE 1

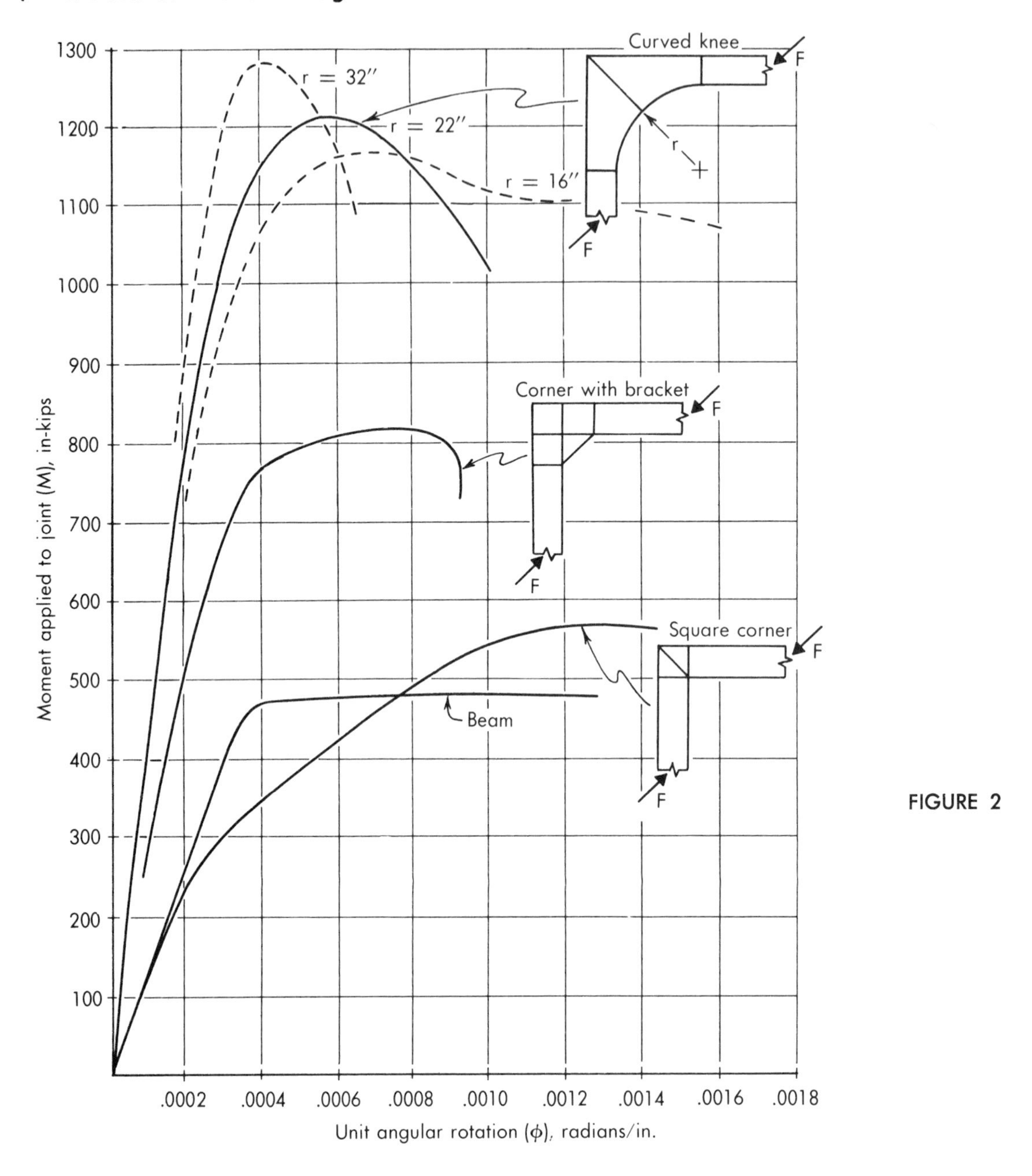

FIGURE 2

It might be thought that the simple square type of knee connection would naturally be as rigid as the connecting members, since it is a continuation of the same section. In many cases, this is true. However, stress causes strain, and the accumulation of strain over a distance results in a movement of some kind: deflection, angular movement, etc. This means that the sharp corner of this joint increases the stress in this region by several times. This stress concentration results in a higher strain and, therefore, greater movement in this local region.

With the square type of knee in which just flange stiffeners are added, it is difficult to exceed the stiffness of the member. In most cases it will just equal the member, and in some cases it will be less.

Figure 2 shows moment-rotation curves of various knee connections.* The vertical axis is the applied moment; the horizontal axis is the resulting rotation of the connection. The vertical height of the curve represents the maximum or ultimate strength of the connection. The slope of the straight portion of the curve represents the stiffness of the connection, with the more nearly vertical curves being the stiffer. The right-hand extremity of the curve represents the rota-

* Figure 2 adapted from "Connections for Welded Continuous Portal Frames", Beedle, Topractsoglon, and Johnston; AWS Journal; Part I July 1951, Part II August 1951, and Part III November 1952.

FIGURE 3

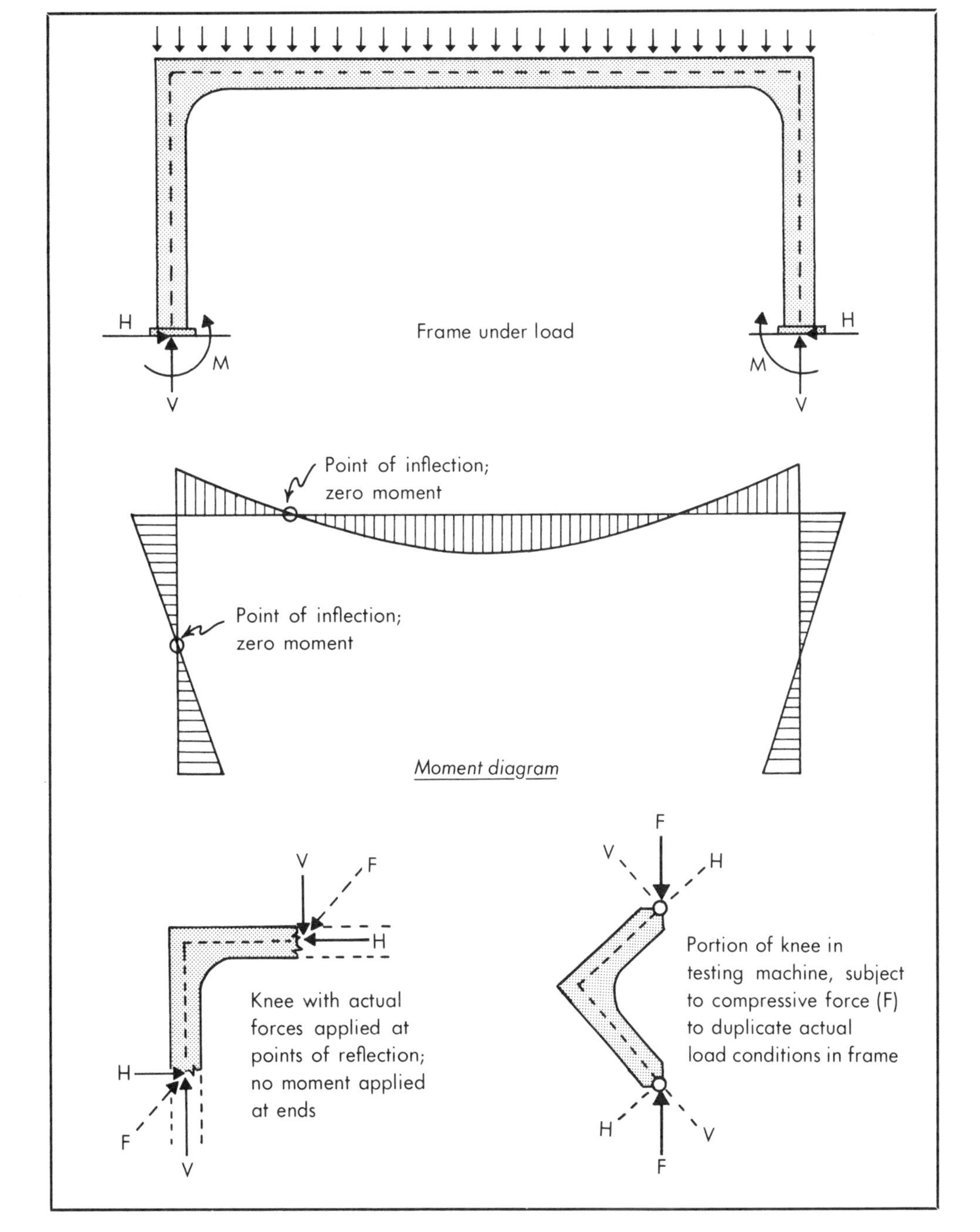

tional capacity of the connection.

Notice that the square-corner knee is the most flexible. It falls slightly short of the beam itself, but it does have the greatest rotational capacity. Tapered haunch knees (not shown here) and those with the additional bracket have greater stiffness and higher moment capacity, but less rotational capacity. The curved knees are the most rigid, have the highest moment capacity, and have a rotational capacity somewhere between the simple square corner and the haunched knee. As the radius of curvature of this inner flange is increased, the stiffness and moment capacity increase slightly, with slightly lower rotational capacity. Another purpose of the haunched and curved knees is to move the connection to the beam back into a region of lower moment so that the beam will not be overstressed in bending.

The dimensions of the test knee are so chosen that they extend out to the point of inflection (zero moment) of an actual frame; Figure 3.

In this manner, the testing machine applies a compressive force (F) which becomes the component of the two forces V (vertical) and H (horizontal) which would actually be applied to the knee at the frame's point of inflection.

3. SHEAR IN CONNECTION WEB

An axial force (tensile or compressive) can transfer sideways out of one element of a member as shear. For example, the tensile force from the beam flange will transfer down through the connection web as shear into the supporting column; Figure 4.

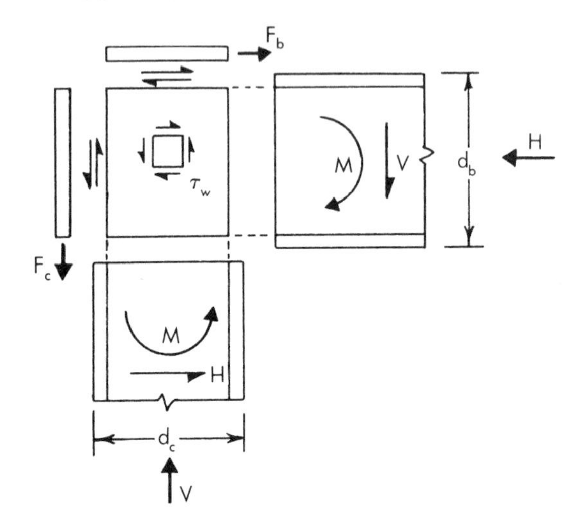

FIGURE 4

where the flange force in the beam is—

$$F_b = \frac{M}{d_b}$$

and the flange force in the column is—

$$F_c = \frac{M}{d_c}$$

Assuming this flange force (F) is transferred as shear into the connection web within the distance equal to the depth of the connecting member, the resulting shear stress within this connection web is—

$$\boxed{\tau = \frac{F_b}{t_w\ d_c} = \frac{F_c}{t_w\ d_b}} \quad \ldots\ldots\ldots\ldots\ldots\ldots (1)$$

If this shear stress exceeds the allowable for the web, it must be reduced by increasing the web thickness within the connection area. Or, a pair of diagonal stiffeners must be added to transfer some of this flange force as a diagonal component.

One method of detailing this connection is to calculate the portion of the flange force which may be transferred as shear within the web by stressing it to the allowable. Then, diagonal stiffeners are detailed to transfer whatever flange force remains.

Another method is to assume that the shortening of the diagonal stiffener under the compression component is equal to the diagonal shortening of the web due to the shear stress. From this, the resulting shear stress (τ_w) in the web and the compressive stress (σ_s) in the diagonal stiffener may be found for any given set of conditions.

Derivation of Stress Values

The final diagonal dimension (d_1) of the web, due to shear action on the web, will be—

$$d_1^2 = d_b^2 + d_c^2 - 2\ d_b\ d_c \cos(90° - \gamma)$$

but

$$\cos(90° - \gamma) = \cos 90° \cos(\gamma) + \sin 90° \sin(\gamma)$$

$$= \sin \gamma$$

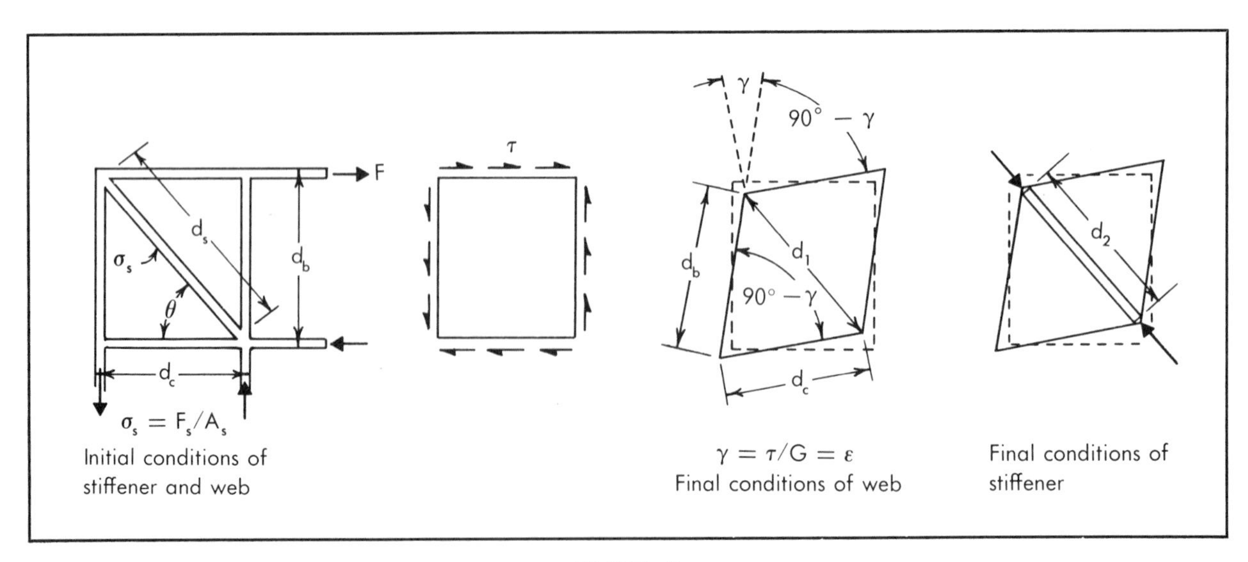

FIGURE 5

For small strains (ϵ_s) and angles (γ)—

$$\sin(\gamma) = \tan(\gamma) = \epsilon_s$$

Hence:

$$d_1^2 = d_b^2 + d_c^2 - 2\, d_b\, d_c \frac{\tau}{E_s} \quad \text{and}$$

$$d_1 = \sqrt{d_b^2 + d_c^2 - 2\, d_b\, d_c \frac{\tau}{E_s}} \quad \text{but}$$

$$d_b = d_c \tan\theta = d_c \frac{\sin\theta}{\cos\theta}$$

$$\therefore\ d_1 = \sqrt{d_c^2 \frac{\sin^2\theta}{\cos^2\theta} + d_c^2 - 2\, d_c^2 \frac{\tau}{E_s} \frac{\sin\theta}{\cos\theta}}$$

$$= \frac{d_c}{\cos\theta} \sqrt{1 - 2\frac{\tau}{E_s} \sin\theta\cos\theta}$$

The final dimension of the diagonal stiffener (d_2), due to compression, will be—

$$\epsilon = \frac{\sigma_s}{E}$$

Since the movement—

$$\Delta = \epsilon\, d_s$$

$$\text{so} \quad \Delta = \frac{\sigma_s\, d_s}{E}$$

$$\therefore\ d_2 = d_s - \Delta = d_s - \frac{\sigma_s\, d_s}{E}$$

$$= d_s\left(1 - \frac{\sigma_s}{E}\right) = \frac{d_c}{\cos\theta}\left(1 - \frac{\sigma_s}{E}\right)$$

Since diagonal stiffener and web are attached, the final dimension of diagonals in each case must be equal:

$$d_1 = d_2 \quad \text{or}$$

$$\frac{d_c}{\cos\theta}\sqrt{1 - 2\frac{\tau}{E_s}\sin\theta\cos\theta} = \frac{d_c}{\cos\theta}\left(1 - \frac{\sigma_s}{E}\right)$$

Squaring both sides:

$$1 - 2\frac{\tau}{E_s}\sin\theta\cos\theta = 1 - 2\frac{\sigma_s}{E} + \frac{\sigma_s^2}{E^2}$$ could neglect this last term

or

$$\frac{\tau}{E_s}\sin\theta\cos\theta = \frac{\sigma_s}{E}$$

Since for steel:

$$E = 30{,}000{,}000 \text{ psi}$$
$$E_s = 12{,}000{,}000 \text{ psi}$$
$$\therefore\ E = 2.5\, E_s$$

and the compressive stress in the diagonal stiffener is—

$$\boxed{\sigma_s = 2.5\,\tau\sin\theta\cos\theta} \quad \ldots\ldots\ldots\ldots (2)$$

Now we go back to the flange force (F) since it causes this load on the connection region.

The flange force of the beam is equal to the shear force carried by the web plus the horizontal component of the compressive force carried by the diagonal stiffener.

$$F = \tau\, t_w\, d_c + \sigma_s\, A_s \frac{d_c}{d_n} \quad \text{or}$$

$$\boxed{F = \tau\, t_w\, d_c + \sigma_s\, A_s \cos\theta} \quad \ldots\ldots\ldots (3)$$

Substituting (2) into (3) gives—

$$F = \tau\, t_w\, d_c + (2.5\,\tau\sin\theta\cos\theta)\, A_s\cos\theta$$
$$= \tau\,[t_w\, d_c + 2.5\, A_s\sin\theta\cos^2\theta]$$

or, the shear stress in the connection web is—

$$\boxed{\tau = \frac{F}{t_w\, d_c + 2.5\, A_s\sin\theta\cos^2\theta}} \quad \ldots\ldots\ldots (4)$$

Also, from (2)—

$$\tau = \frac{\sigma_s}{2.5\sin\theta\cos\theta}$$

Substituting this into (3)—

$$F = \left(\frac{\sigma_s}{2.5\sin\theta\cos\theta}\right) t_w\, d_c + \sigma_s\, A_s\cos\theta$$

$$= \sigma_s\left(\frac{t_w\, d_c}{2.5\sin\theta\cos\theta} + A_s\cos\theta\right)$$

or, the compressive stress in the diagonal stiffener is—

$$\boxed{\sigma_s = \frac{F}{\dfrac{t_w\, d_c}{2.5\sin\theta\cos\theta} + A_s\cos\theta}} \quad \ldots\ldots\ldots (5)$$

Some knees are more complex than those described here and analysis must consider factors that are covered more adequately in Section 2.12, Buckling of Plates.

Problem 1

To check stiffener requirements on the square knee connection shown in Figure 6, for the loads indicated. A36 steel and E70 welds are used.

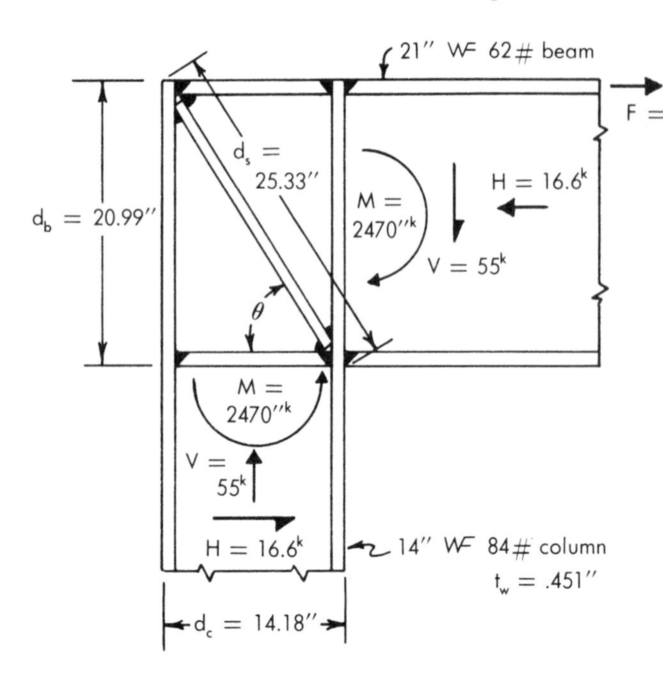

FIGURE 6

Here:

$$\sin \theta = \frac{20.99}{25.33} = .829$$

$$\cos \theta = \frac{14.18}{25.33} = .561$$

$$\tan \theta = \frac{20.99}{14.18} = 1.480$$

flange force on the beam

$$F = \frac{M}{d_b}$$

$$= \frac{(2470)}{(20.99)}$$

$$= 117.6 \text{ kips}$$

Method 1

horizontal component carried by web in shear

$$F_w = \tau\ t_w\ d_c$$

$$= (14{,}500)(.451)(14.18)$$

$$= 92.8 \text{ kips}$$

This leaves (117.6 — 92.8 =) 14.8 kips to be carried by the horizontal component of the compressive force on the diagonal stiffener.

compressive force on stiffener

$$F_s = 14.8 \left(\frac{25.83}{14.18} \right)$$

$$= 26.4 \text{ kips}$$

required sectional area of stiffeners

$$A_s = \frac{F_s}{\sigma_s}$$

$$= \frac{(26.4)}{(22.0)}$$

$$= 1.2 \text{ in.}^2 \text{ (pair)}$$

Also required:

$$b_s/t_s = 17$$

Hence, use a pair of ½″ x 3″ diagonal stiffeners.

Checking this size against the requirements:

$$A_s = 2 \text{ x } ½″ \text{ x } 3″$$

$$= 3.0 \text{ in.}^2 > 1.2 \text{ in.}^2 \quad \text{OK}$$

$$b_s/t_s = \frac{2 \text{ x } 3″}{½″}$$

$$= 12 < 17 \quad \text{OK}$$

Method 2 Plastic Design (See Sect. 5.12)

required thickness of connection web

$$w_r = \frac{\sqrt{3}\ M_p}{\sigma_y\ d_b\ d_c}$$

$$= \frac{\sqrt{3}\ \sigma_y\ Z}{\sigma_y\ d_b\ d_c}$$

$$= \frac{\sqrt{3}\ (144.1)}{(20.99)(14.18)}$$

$$= .837″$$

This exceeds the actual web thickness of t_w = .451″, so stiffening is required.

required area of diagonal stiffeners

$$A_s = \frac{d_s}{\sqrt{3}} (w_r - w_c)$$

$$= \frac{(25.33)}{\sqrt{3}} (.837) - .451)$$

$$= 5.64 \text{ in.}^2 \text{ (pair)}$$

Use a pair of ¾″ x 4″ diagonal stiffeners.

Checking this size against the requirements:

$$A_s = 2 \text{ x } ¾″ \text{ x } 4″$$

$$= 6.0 \text{ in.}^2 > 5.64 \text{ in.}^2 \quad \text{OK}$$

$$b_s/t_s = \frac{2 \text{ x } 4″}{¾″}$$

$$= 10.7 < 17 \quad \text{OK}$$

Method 3 Start with a pair of ½" x 3" diagonal stiffeners and, assuming both diagonals contract the same amount under load, check stresses in web and stiffener.

shear stress in web

$$\tau = \frac{F}{t_w\ d_c + 2.5\ A_s \sin\theta \cos^2\theta}$$

$$= \frac{117.6}{(.451)(14.18) + 2.5\ (3.0)(.829)(.561)^2}$$

$$= \underline{14{,}080 \text{ psi}}$$

compressive stress in diagonal

$$\sigma_s = \frac{F}{\dfrac{t_w\ d_c}{2.5 \sin\theta \cos\theta} + A_s \cos\theta}$$

$$= \frac{117.6}{\dfrac{(.451)(14.18)}{2.5\ (.829)(.561)} + (3.0)(.561)}$$

$$= \underline{14{,}200 \text{ psi}}$$

As a matter of interest, increasing the size of the diagonal stiffener to ¾" x 4" would decrease these stresses to—

$$\tau = 11{,}400 \text{ psi}$$

$$\sigma_s = 13{,}250 \text{ psi}$$

4. COMPRESSIVE FORCES IN CONNECTION WEB

An axial force is able to change its direction if suitable resisting components of force are available.

In the square or tapered haunch, this abrupt change in direction of the compressive flange force is accomplished by means of a diagonal stiffener; Figure 7(b).

In the curved haunch, this change in direction of the axial force is uniform along the curved edge of the flange and results from radial compressive forces in the web; Figure 7(a).

The force in the inner flange of the knee is greater than the force in the outer flange because it has a smaller radius of curvature. Usually this inner flange is the compression flange; therefore, this is the region to be checked for stiffening requirements using the following formula for radial compressive forces in the web.

$$\boxed{f_r = \frac{F_c}{r_i} \text{ lbs/linear in. of web}} \qquad \ldots\ldots\ldots\ldots(6)$$

In this case, the unit radial force (f_r) is a function of the compressive force (F_c) in the flange and the radius of curvature (r_i) of the flange.

This action is similar to the radial pressure applied to the rim of a pulley by the tensile forces in the belt.

As the radius of curvature decreases, these forces increase.

As this change in direction of the flange becomes more abrupt, as in a square or tapered haunch, these radial forces are concentrated into a single force. And, they must be resisted by a diagonal stiffener; Figure 5(b).

The axial force in the flange is assumed to be uniformly distributed across the width, therefore the radial pressure or stress is—

$$\boxed{\sigma_r = \frac{F_c}{r_i\ b_f} = \frac{\sigma\ t_f}{r_i} = \frac{f_r}{b_f}} \qquad \ldots\ldots\ldots\ldots(7)$$

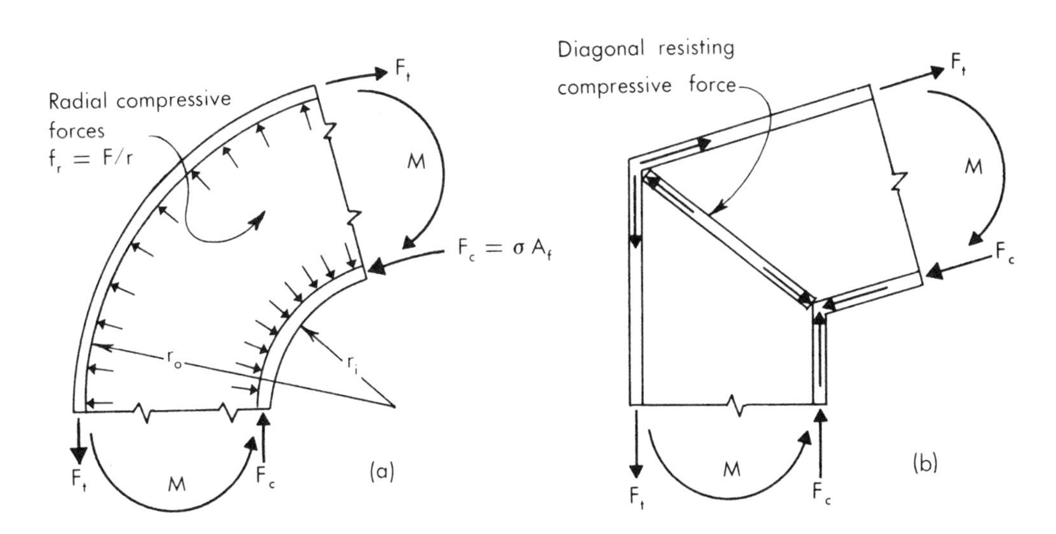

FIGURE 7

When applied to the flange, this radial stress will load any cross-section as a cantilever beam, since it is supported only along its centerline by the web; Figure 8.

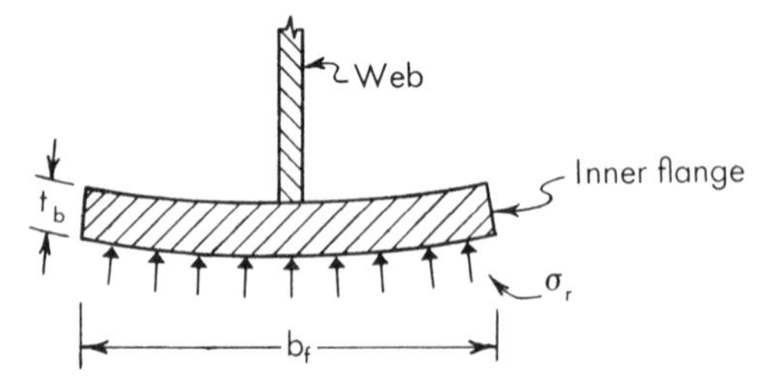

FIG. 8 Cross-section of lower flange and web.

The bending moment along the centerline of the beam flange due to this radial load will be:

$$M = \frac{\sigma_r}{2}\left(\frac{b_f}{2}\right)^2 = \frac{\sigma_r\ b_f^2}{8}$$

$$= \frac{\sigma\ t_f\ b_f^2}{r_i\ 8}$$

Also:

$$M = \sigma_t\ S$$

$$= \frac{\sigma_t\ t_f^2}{6} \quad \text{or}$$

Where:

$$S = \frac{1''\ t_f^2}{6}$$

$$\frac{\sigma_t\ t_f^2}{6} = \frac{\sigma\ t_f\ b_f^2}{8\ r_i} \quad \text{and}$$

$$\sigma_t = \frac{3}{4}\ \frac{\sigma\ b_f^2}{r_i\ t_f}$$

From this relationship, it is seen that in order to hold the transverse tensile stress (σ_t) to a value not exceeding the axial compressive stress of the flange (σ), the following must be held:

$$\frac{b_f^2}{r_i\ t_f} \leqq \frac{4}{3} \text{ or } 1\tfrac{1}{3} \qquad \ldots\ldots\ldots\ldots\ldots\ldots\ldots (8)$$

If this value is exceeded, stiffeners would be used between the inner compressive curved flange and web.

b_f = width of flange
t_f = thickness of flange
r_i = radius of curvature of inner flange
σ_t = transverse tensile stress in flange
σ = axial compressive stress in flange

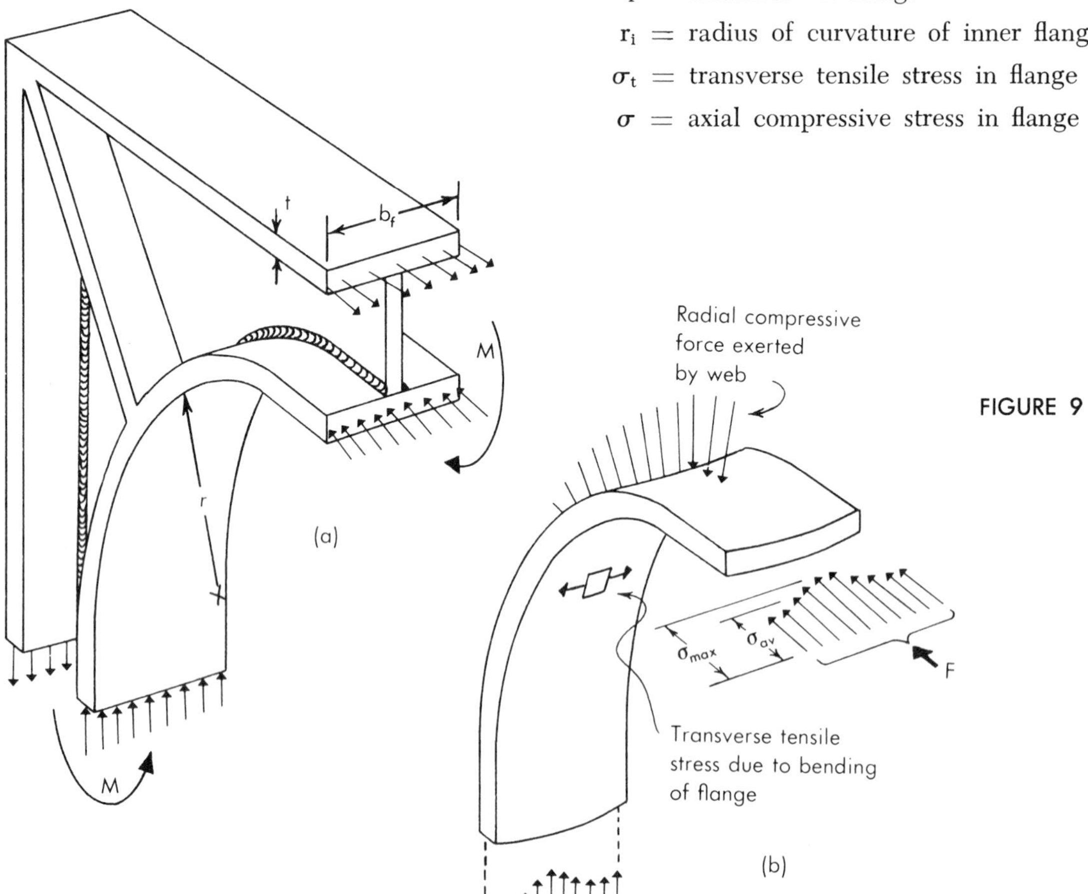

FIGURE 9

FIGURE 10

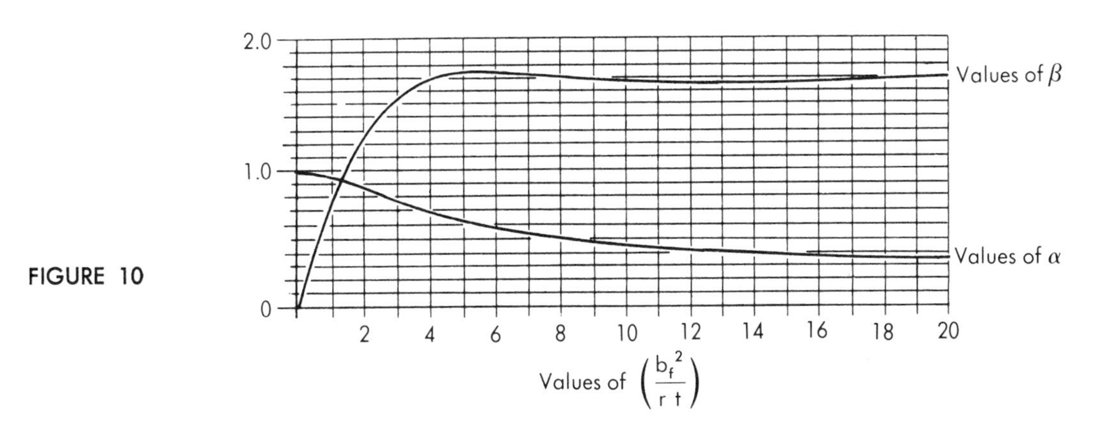

This analysis assumes a uniform distribution of stress across the cross-section of the flange.

If this is based on plastic design, the plastic section modulus (Z) is used instead of section modulus (S), where

$$Z = \frac{1'' \; t_f^2}{4} \qquad S = \frac{1'' \; t_f^2}{6}$$

Then (7) becomes the following:

$$\boxed{\frac{b_b^2}{r_i \; t_b} \leqq 2} \quad \cdots\cdots (9)$$

Bleich has carried this analysis a little further; see Figure 9.*

Because of the slight yielding of the flange's outer edge, there is a non-uniform distribution of flange stress (σ). This compressive stress is maximum in line with the web. In the following formula, the value of $\propto$ comes from the graph, Figure 10.

$$\boxed{\sigma_{max} = \frac{\sigma}{\propto}}^{\,*} \quad \cdots\cdots (10)$$

The transverse tensile bending stress (σ_t) in the curved flange is found in the following formula; the value of β comes from the graph, Figure 10.

$$\boxed{\sigma_t = \beta \; \sigma_{max}}^{\,*} \quad \cdots\cdots (11)$$

If this value is too high, stiffeners should be welded between this flange and the web. These keep the flange from bending. These stiffeners usually need not extend all the way between flanges, but may be a series of short triangular plates connecting with the curved flange.

The unit radial compressive force (f_r) which acts transverse to the connecting fillet welds between the curved flange and the web is found from—

* From "Design of Rigid Frame Knees" F. Bleich, AISC.

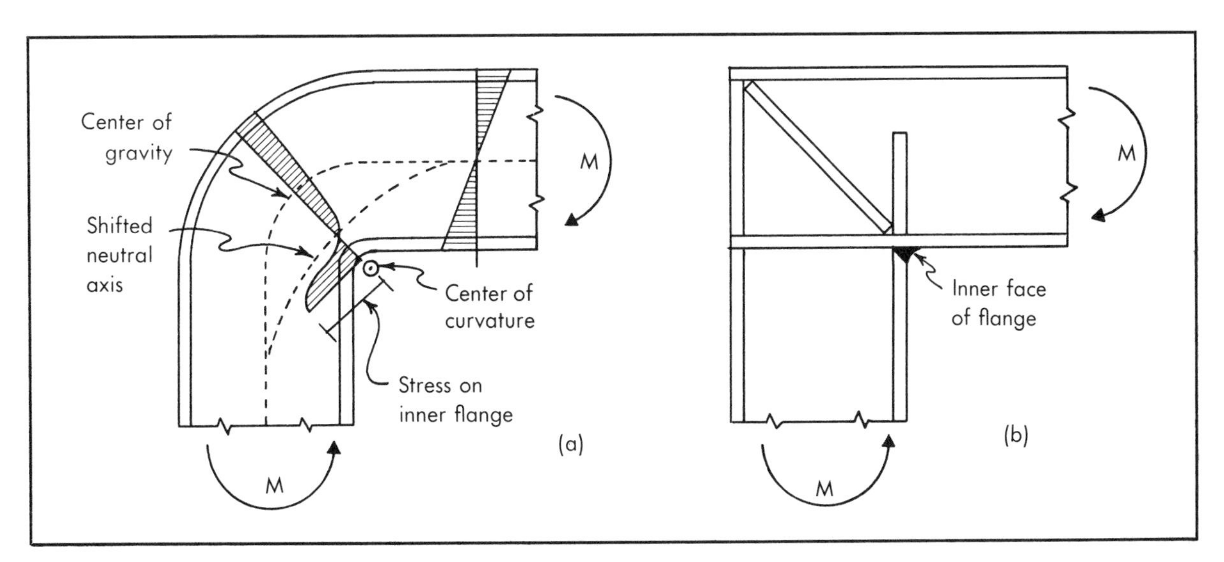

FIGURE 11

$$f_r = \frac{F}{r} \text{ lbs/linear in. (2 welds)} \qquad (12)$$

5. EFFECT OF RADIUS OF CURVATURE ON STRESS IN INNER CORNER

A straight beam has an infinite radius of curvature ($r = \infty$). As the beam becomes curved, this radius decreases, and the neutral axis no longer coincides with the center of gravity, but shifts toward the inner face. See Figure 11 (a).

Because of the shift of the neutral axis, the bending stress in the inner flange increases greatly while the bending stress in the outer flange decreases. This increase at the inner flange becomes more severe as the radius of curvature decreases.

In a square-knee connection, this radius of curvature is provided by only the reinforcement of the bevel groove weld or fillet weld on this inside corner; Figure 11 (b). For this reason, the square knee may not quite develop the full plastic moment of the connecting member unless it is somehow reinforced.

If for some reason a reversal in moment should be applied to the knee and the inner face of the knee is subjected to tension instead of the usual compression, it is important that this be a good sound weld. This is especially true at the surface of the weld. If the knee is loaded up to its plastic moment, the metal within the section below the weld is stressed up to its yield strength. During this time, the weld undergoes a considerable amount of plastic yielding and some strain hardening. The weld metal does have the ability to elongate about 28% as measured in 2″ before failure. However, this zone in which the yielding is confined is very narrow, being the width of the weld. Consequently, the overall movement of the connection due to plastic yielding of the weld is very low, although sufficient.

In this case almost all of the weld's ability to elongate may be used in developing the plastic moment of the connection. Any defect in the weld which would lower its ductility would probably prevent the connection from reaching its plastic moment. The knee could have greater strength and rotational capacity if this inner face were changed to a haunched or curved knee section. In testing these square knees in tension, plastic moment was reached when this weld was of good quality. Fortunately most knees are stressed in compression at this inner corner, without any tendency for this weld to fail.

6. LOCATING SECTION OF HAUNCH TO CHECK

Most theories concerning the strength of knees differ only in the placing of the neutral axis, and in locating the resulting section for determining the section modulus.

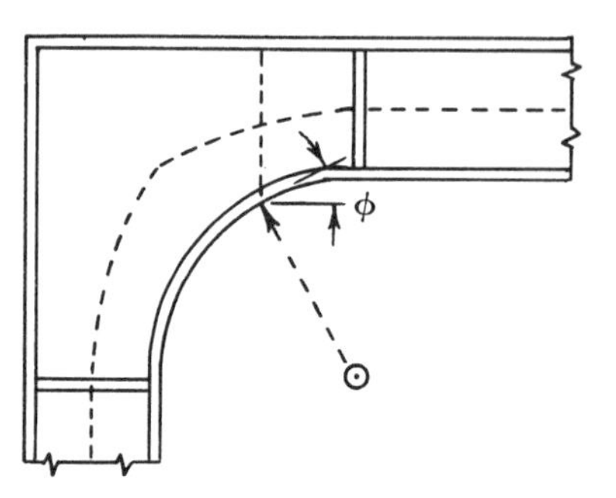

FIGURE 12

One method, Figure 12, uses straight sections normal to the axis of either the beam or column. The section modulus is determined about an axis through the center of gravity of the section. The resulting stress in the inner flange is increased by the factor

$$\frac{1}{\cos^2 \phi}$$

where ϕ is the slope of the flange. Although this method is easy, it might indicate excessively high stresses when the flange has a rather steep slope.

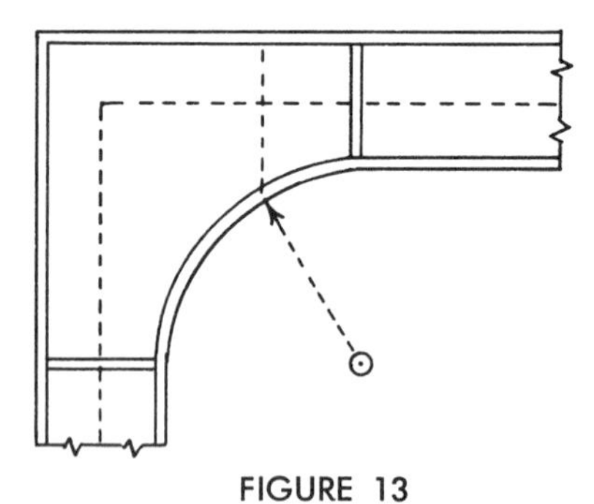

FIGURE 13

Another method, Figure 13, is to extend the centerlines of the beam and column to intersect in the knee. Straight sections are used, and the section modulus is determined about an axis lying on this centerline. This will give conservative values for the stress in the sloping flange. Because of this, no factor is used for the stress on the sloping flange.

A more accurate but longer method, Figure 14, is based on a curved section forming a wedge beam by

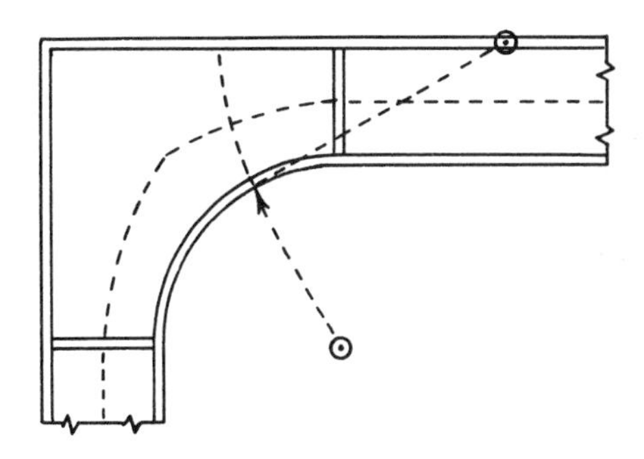

FIGURE 14

W. R. Osgood* and modified by H. C. Olander.**

* "Theory of Flexure for Beams with Nonparallel Extreme Fibers" by W. R. Osgood, ASME Vol. 61, 1939.
** "Stresses in the Corners of Rigid Frames" by H. O. Olander, ASCE Transactions Paper 2698, 1953.

Method of Using a Straight Cross-Section

Dimension of Straight Section
The dimensions of a straight section (A-B) of the haunch may be found from the following:

Here:

$$\boxed{v = r \sin (2 \alpha)} \quad \ldots\ldots\ldots\ldots (13)$$

$$\boxed{d_h = d + r (1 - \cos 2 \alpha)} \quad \ldots\ldots\ldots\ldots (14)$$

Bending Stress in Curved Flange (See Figure 16.)

Here:

$$b = a \cos \phi$$

$$f_b = \frac{f_a}{\cos \phi}$$

$$\sigma_a = \frac{f_a}{a \text{ x } 1''} \quad \text{or} \quad a = \frac{f_a}{\sigma_a \; 1''}$$

$$\sigma_b = \frac{f_b}{b \text{ x } 1''}$$

$$= \frac{f_a}{\cos \phi} \text{ x } \frac{1}{a \cos \phi}$$

$$= \frac{f_a}{\cos \phi} \text{ x } \frac{\sigma_a \text{ x } 1''}{f_a \cos \phi} \quad \text{or}$$

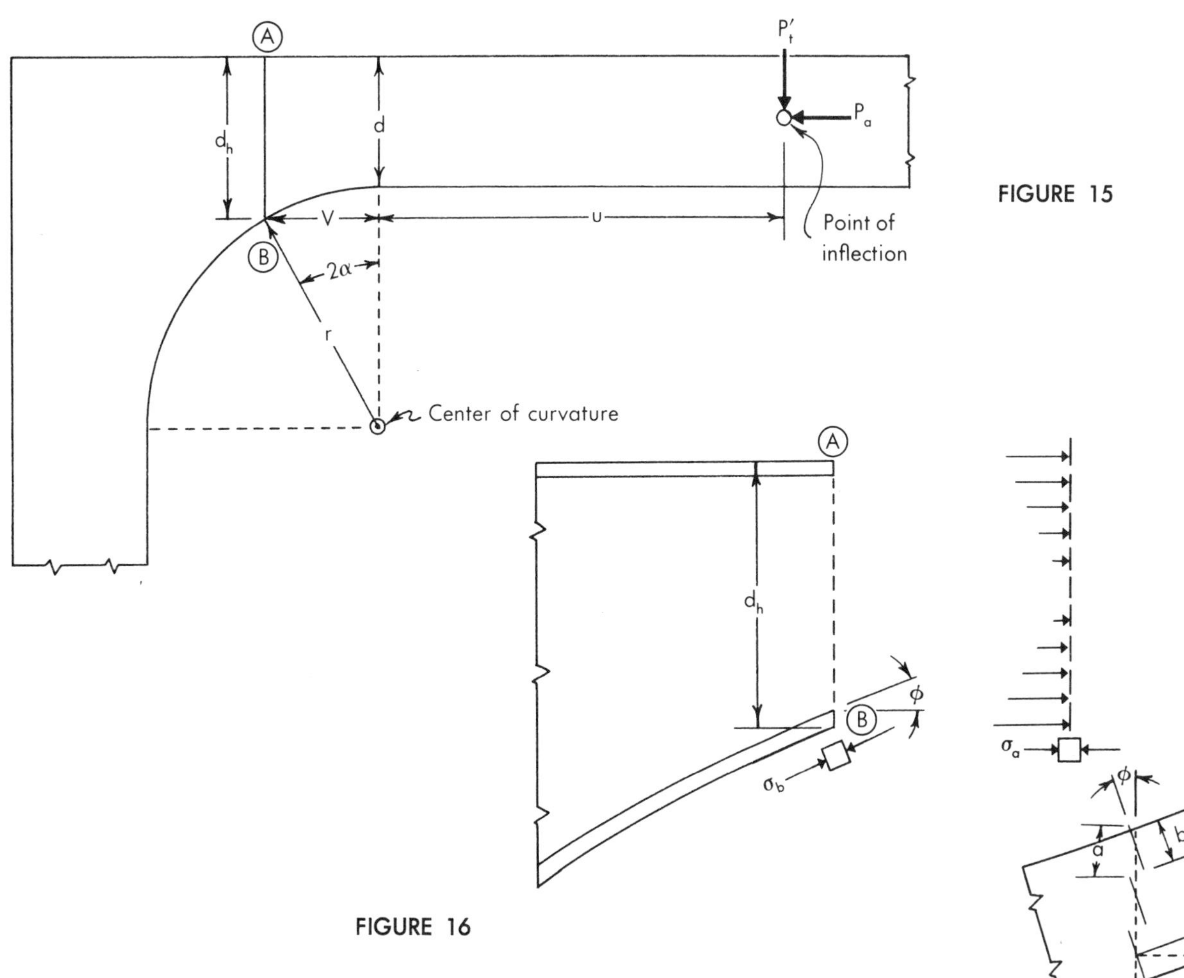

FIGURE 15

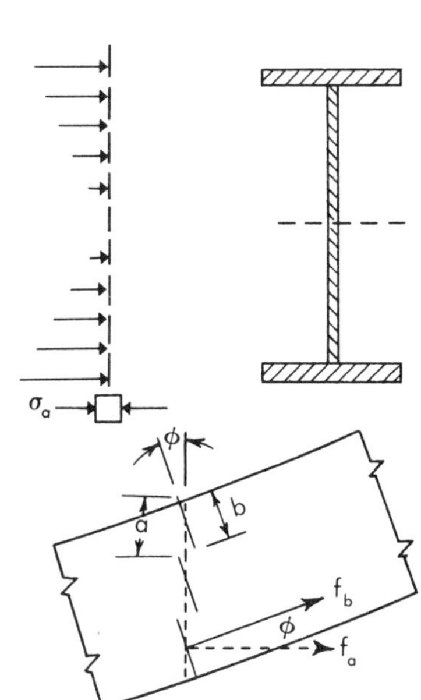

FIGURE 16

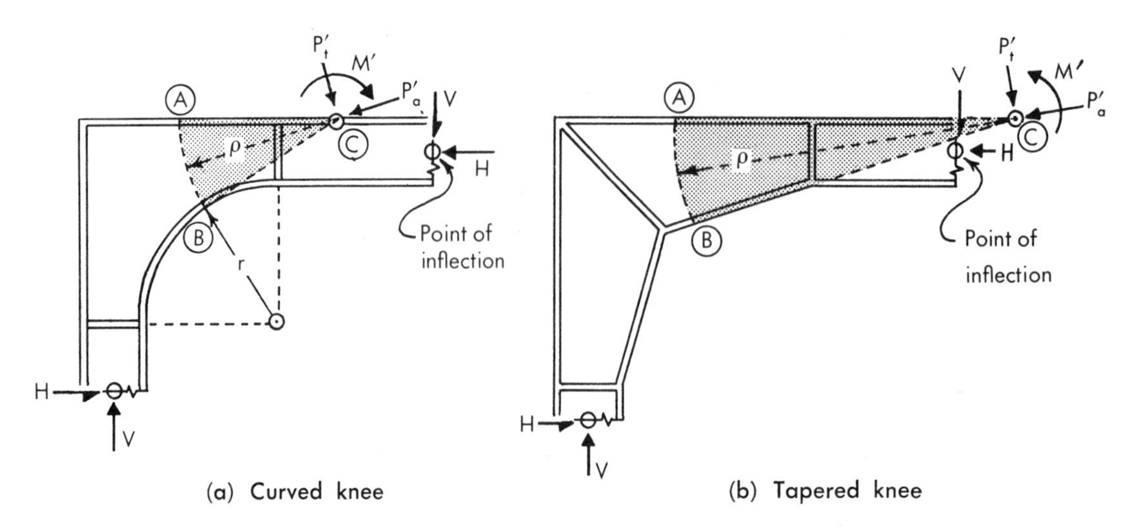

FIGURE 17

$$\sigma_b = \frac{\sigma_a}{\cos^2 \theta} \qquad \text{.....(15)}$$

Wedge Method of Determining Section

The wedge method may be used on any beam section whose flanges are not parallel.

A curved section (A-B) is constructed where the stresses are to be checked. This is normal to both flanges and has a radius (ρ) the center of which lies on the straight flange. See Figure 17.

The transverse force (P_t'), axial force (P_a'), and moment (M') acting at the apex (C) of the wedge are found. See Figure 18.

Here:

$$\rho = \frac{d}{\sin(2\alpha)} + \frac{r[1 - \cos(2\alpha)]}{\sin(2\alpha)} \qquad \text{.....(16)}$$

$$n = \frac{d}{\tan(2\alpha)} - \frac{r[1 - \cos(2\alpha)]}{\sin(2\alpha)} \qquad \text{.....(17)}$$

$$m = u - n \qquad \text{.....(18)}$$

$$d_h = \rho\, 2\alpha \qquad \text{.....(19)}$$

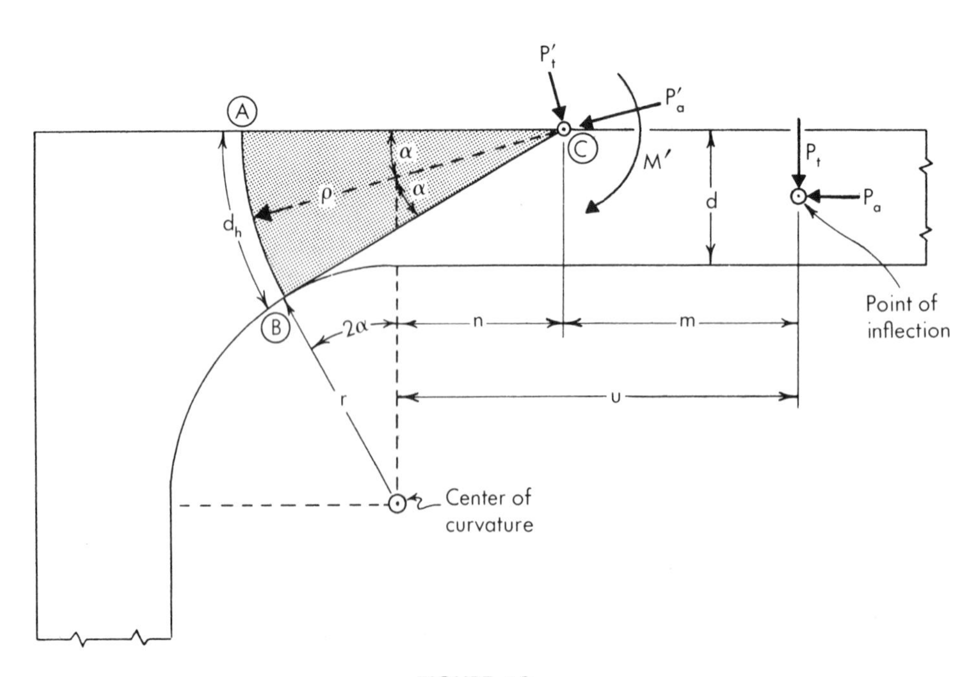

FIGURE 18

transverse force applied to wedge at point C

$$P_t' = P_t \cos \alpha - P_a \sin \alpha \quad \text{.............(20)}$$

axial force applied to wedge at point C

$$P_a' = P_a \cos \alpha + P_t \sin \alpha \quad \text{.............(21)}$$

moment about point C

$$M' = + P_t\, m + P_a \frac{d}{2} \quad \text{.................(22)}$$

These applied forces result in various stresses on the curved haunch section, as described in following paragraphs.

Moment (M') Applied to Wedge Member

The horizontal bending stresses (σ_h) resulting from the applied moment (M'), Figure 19(a), may be replaced with its two components: radial bending stress (σ_r) and tangential shear stress (τ), Figure 19(b). In Figure 19(c) are shown the resulting stresses.

It is seen in taking moments about the apex (C) of the wedge that all of the radial bending stresses pass through this point and cannot contribute to any moment. The tangential shear stresses along the curved section (A-B) acting normal to, and at a distance (ρ)

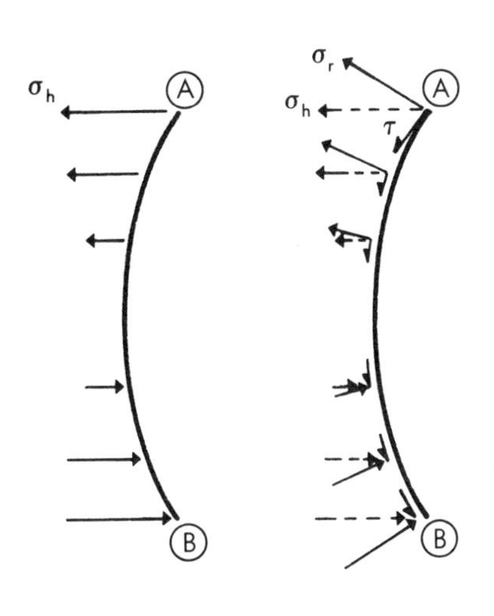

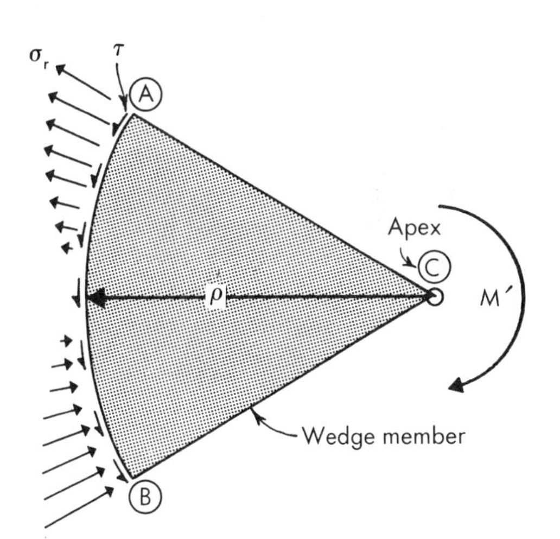

(a) Resisting horizontal bending stress

(b) Components of bending stress

(c) Resisting radial bending stress (σ_r) normal to curved section (A—B); also tangential shear stress (τ)

FIGURE 19

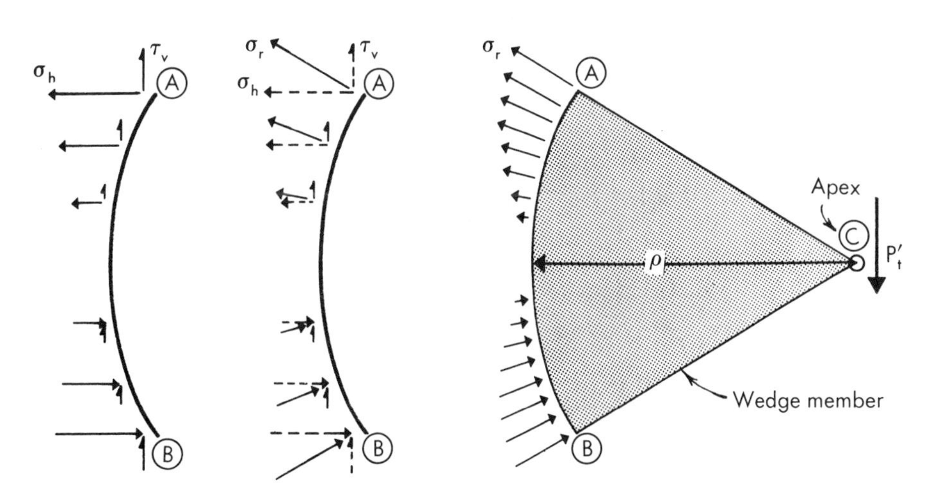

(a) Resisting horizontal bending stress and vertical shear stress

(b) Components of these two stresses

(c) Resisting radial bending stress (σ_r) normal to curved section (A—B)

FIGURE 20

will produce an equal and opposite moment. The value of this tangential shear force (V) acting on this curved section (A-B) may be found from the following:

$$V = \frac{M'}{\rho} \quad \text{.......... (23)}$$

Transverse Force (P_t') Applied to Wedge Member

The applied transverse force (P_t') results in horizontal bending stresses (σ_h) as well as vertical shear stresses; Figure 20(a).

These two stresses may be completely replaced with a single component, radial bending stress (σ_r); Figure 20(b). The results are shown in Figure 20(c). Notice that no tangential shear stresses are present.

Axial Force (P_a') Applied to Wedge Member

The axial force (P_a') applied at the apex of the wedge member, causes radial stresses to occur along the curved section (A-B); Figure 21. There are no tangential shear stresses from this force, because they cancel out.

Summary

The effects of all these forces applied to the wedge member may be summarized as follows:

shear stress on section A-B

$$V = \frac{M'}{\rho}$$

$$\tau = \frac{V\,Q}{I\,t} = \frac{V(A_f y_f + A_w y_w)}{I\,t} \quad \text{.......... (24)}$$

moment applied to section A-B

$$M = M' + P_t'\,\rho \quad \text{.......... (25)}$$

normal stress on inner flange

$$\sigma_r = + \frac{P'_a}{A} + \frac{M\,c_i}{I} \quad \text{.......... (26)}$$

normal stress on outer flange

$$\sigma_r = - \frac{P'_a}{A} + \frac{M\,c_o}{I} \quad \text{.......... (27)}$$

Problem 2

To check stresses and stiffener requirements on the knee connection shown in Figure 22, for the loads indicated. A36 steel and E70 welds are used.

STEP 1: Check Lower Curved Flange (Figure 23)

properties of haunch section (1-1)

Use reference axis (y-y) through centerline of web plate.

Plate	A	y	$M = A \cdot y$	$I_y = M \cdot y$	I_g
¾" x 10"	7.50	+24.500	+183.75	+4502.	—
½" x 48.25"	24.125	0	0	0	4681
1" x 10"	10.000	−24.625	−246.25	+6064	—
Total	41.625		− 62.50	15.247	

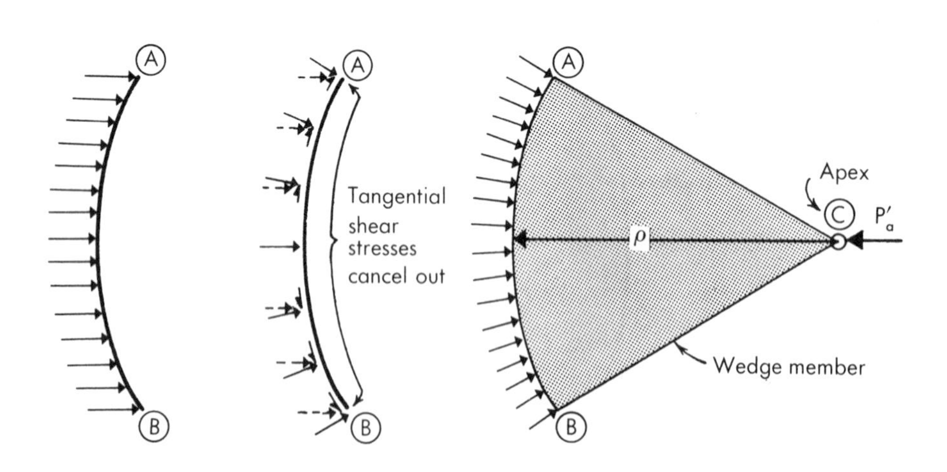

(a) Resulting axial stress

(b) Components of axial stress

(c) Resisting radial stresses (σ_r)

FIGURE 21

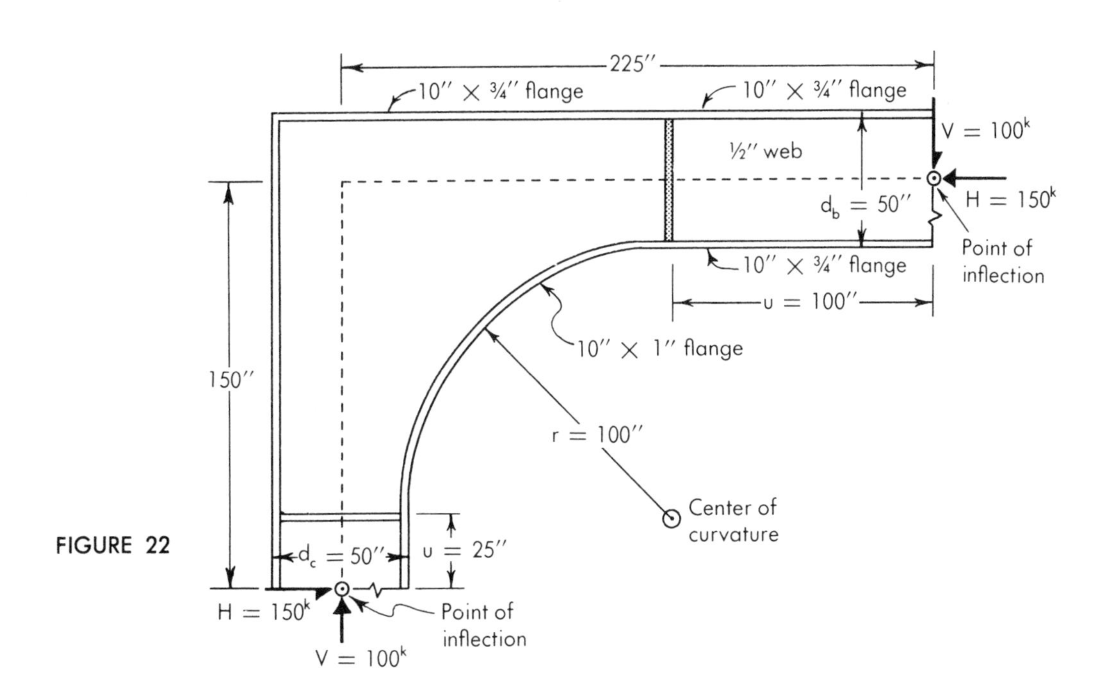

FIGURE 22

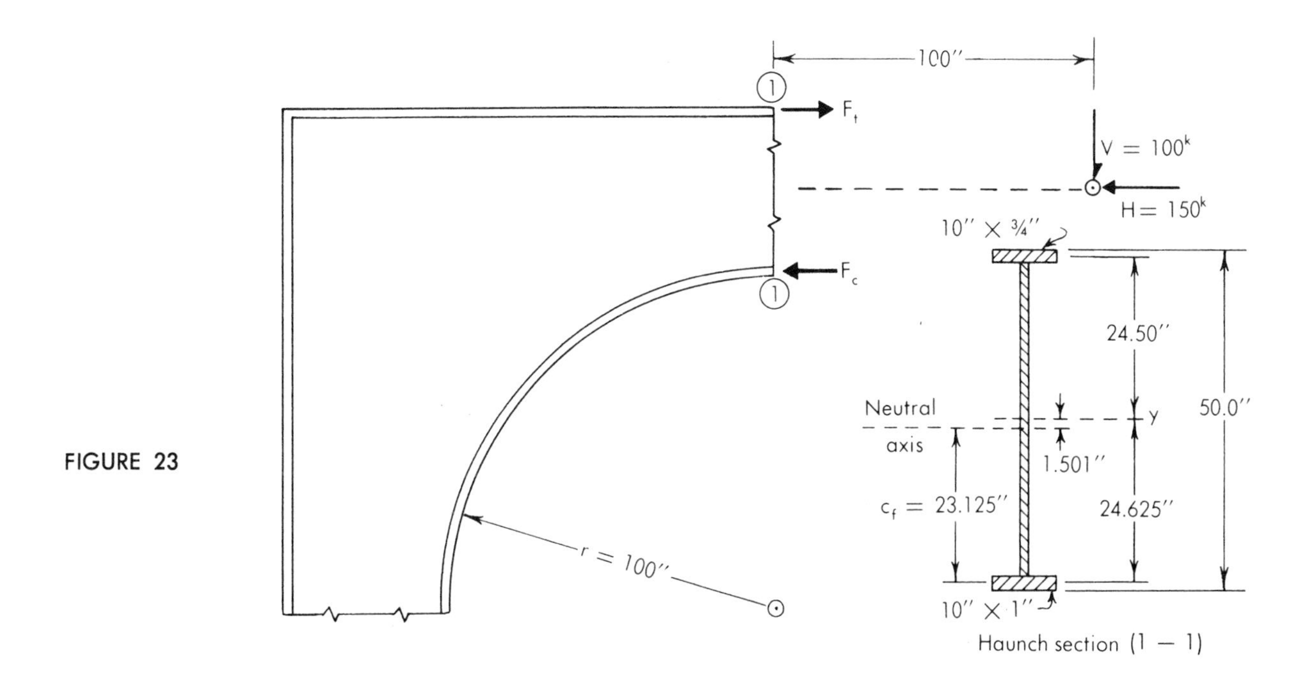

FIGURE 23

$$I_{NA} = I_y + I_g - \frac{M^2}{A}$$

$$= (15{,}247) - \frac{(-62.50)^2}{(41.625)}$$

$$= 15{,}153 \text{ in.}^4$$

$$NA = \frac{M}{A}$$

$$= \frac{(-62.50)}{(41.625)}$$

$$= -1.501$$

$$c_f = 23.125$$

average stress in lower curved flange at (1-1)

$$\sigma_f = \frac{P}{A} + \frac{M\ c_f}{I}$$

$$= \frac{(150\ \text{kips})}{(41.625)} + \frac{(100'' \times 100\ \text{kips})(23.125'')}{(15{,}153\ \text{in.}^3)}$$

$$= \underline{18{,}870\ \text{psi (compression)}}$$

force in flange

$$F_c = \sigma_f\ A_f$$

$$= (18{,}870)(10)$$

$$= 188.7\ \text{kips}$$

radial pressure of flange against web

$$f_r = \frac{F_c}{r}$$

$$= \frac{(188.7)}{(100)}$$

$$= 1.887\ \text{kips/in.}$$

radial compressive stress in web

$$\sigma = \frac{f_r}{t_w}$$

$$= \frac{(1887\ \text{lbs/in.})}{(\tfrac{1}{2}'')}$$

$$= \underline{3774\ \text{psi}}$$

The outer edges of the lower curved flange will tend to bend away from the center of curvature under this radial pressure, and will cause an uneven distribution of flange stress.

The maximum flange stress will be—

$$\sigma_{max} = \frac{\sigma_{ay}}{\propto}$$

and the transverse bending stress in the flange will be—

$$\sigma_t = \beta\ \sigma_{max}$$

The values of $\propto$ and β are obtained from Figure 10. In this case,

$$\frac{b_f^2}{r\ t} = \frac{(10)^2}{(100)(1)} = 1$$

and we find—

$$\propto = .96 \qquad \beta = .70$$

Hence:

maximum flange stress

$$\sigma_{max} = \frac{18{,}870}{.96}$$

$$= \underline{19{,}660\ \text{psi}}$$

transverse bending stress in flange

$$\sigma_t = \beta\ \sigma_{max}$$

$$= (.70)(19{,}600)$$

$$= \underline{13{,}760\ \text{psi}}$$

These stresses are a little high, so radial stiffeners will be added between the lower curved flange and the web.

STEP 2: Check Haunch Section for Bending Stress Using Olander's wedge method and curved section (A-B) (See Figure 24.)

Here:

$\sin 18° = .30902$

$\cos 18° = .95106$

$\tan 18° = .32492$

$\sin 9° = .15643$

$\cos 9° = .98769$

$18° = .31417$ radians

dimensions of wedge section (ABC)

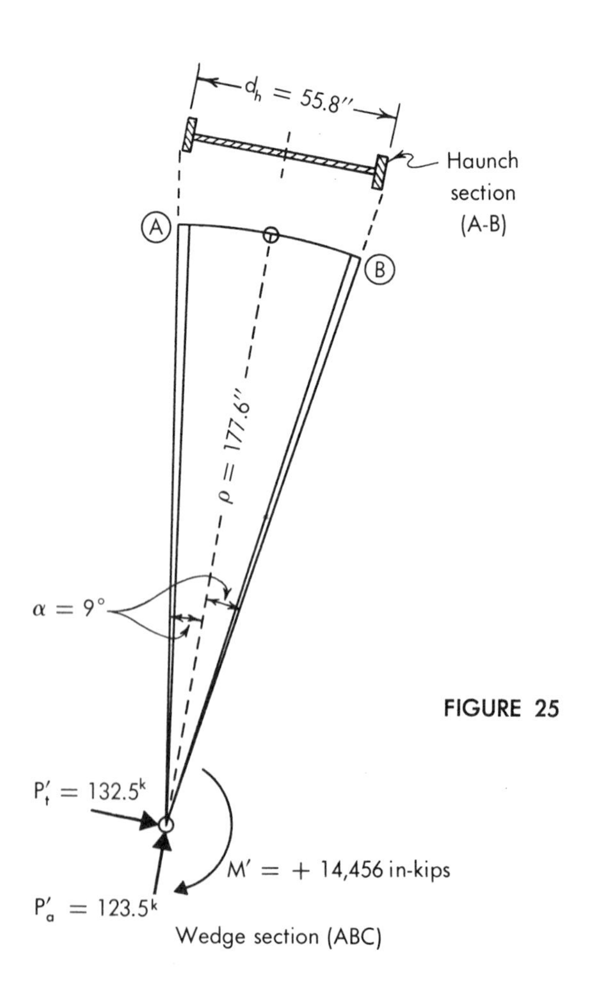

FIGURE 25

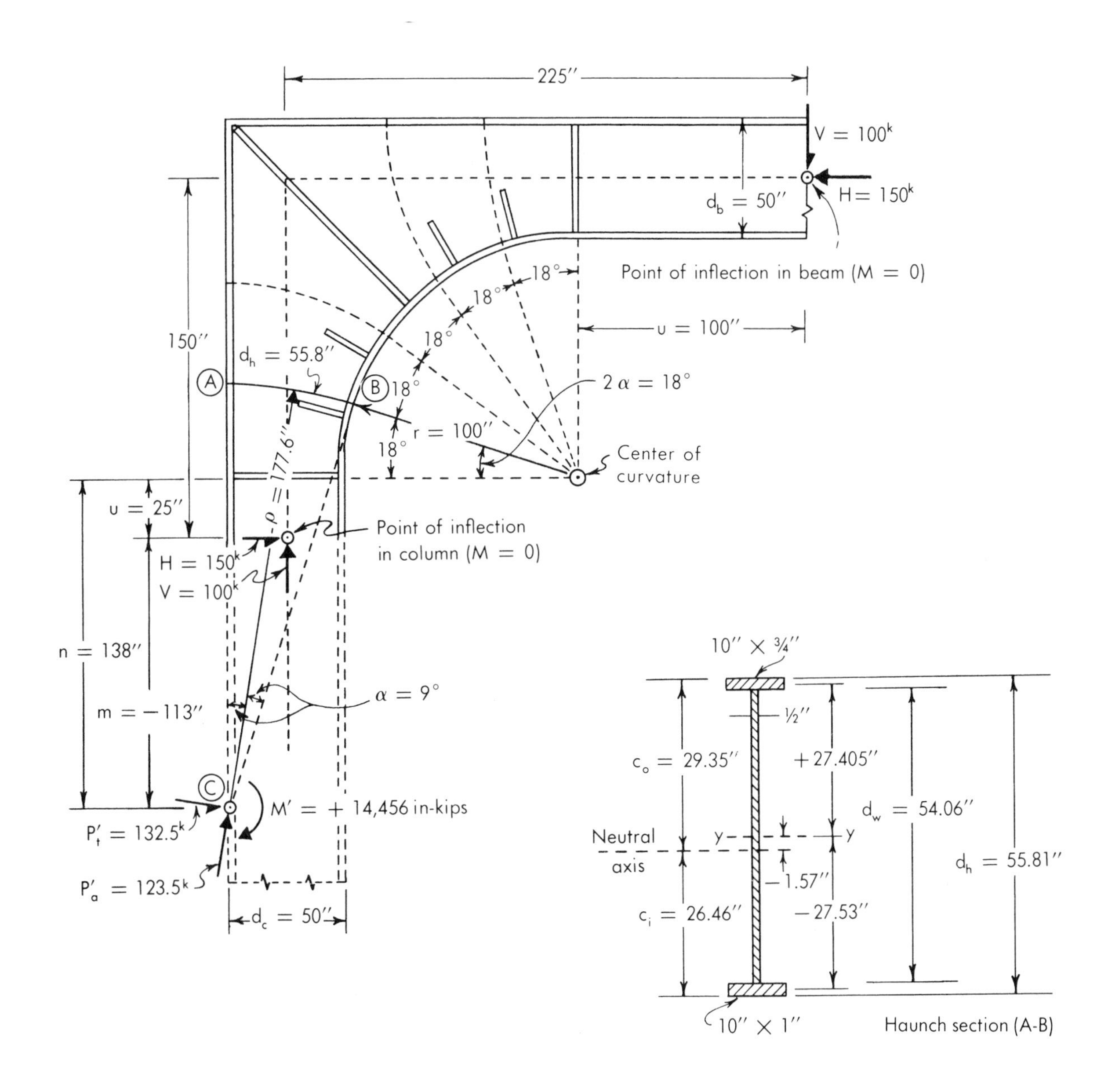

FIGURE 24

$$\rho = \frac{d}{\sin 2\alpha} + \frac{r}{\sin 2\alpha}(1 - \cos 2\alpha)$$

$$= \frac{(50)}{(.30902)} + \frac{(100)}{(.30902)}(.04894)$$

$$= 161.79 + 15.84$$

$$= 177.63''$$

$$d_n = \rho\, 2\alpha$$

$$= (177.63)(.31417 \text{ radians})$$

$$= 55.81''$$

$$d_w = 55.81'' - \tfrac{3}{4}'' - 1''$$

$$= 54.06''$$

$$n = \frac{d}{\tan 2\alpha} - \frac{r}{\sin 2\alpha}(1 - \cos 2\alpha)$$

$$= \frac{(50)}{(.32492)} - (15.84)$$

$$= 138.04''$$

$$u = 25''$$

$$m = u - n$$
$$= 25'' - 138.04''$$
$$= -113.04''$$

properties of haunch section (A-B)

Use reference axis (y-y) through centerline of web plate.

Plate	A	y	M = A•y	I_y = M•y	I_g
¾″ x 10″	7.50	+27.405	+205.54	+5,633	—
½″ x 54.06″	27.03	0	0	0	+6583
1″ x 10″	10.00	−27.53	−275.30	+7,579	—
Total	44.53		− 69.76	+19,795	

$$I_{NA} = I_y + I_g - \frac{M^2}{A}$$
$$= (19{,}795) - \frac{(-69.76)^2}{(44.53)}$$
$$= 19{,}686 \text{ in.}^4$$

$$NA = \frac{M}{A}$$
$$= \frac{(-69.76)}{(44.53)}$$
$$= -1.567''$$

$$c_o = 29.35'' \qquad c_i = 26.46''$$

Find forces applied at apex (C) of wedge section (ABC):

transverse force at C

$$P_t' = P_t \cos \alpha - P_a \sin \alpha$$
$$= (150)(.98769) - (100)(.15643)$$
$$= 132.5 \text{ kips}$$

axial force at C

$$P_a' = P_a \cos \alpha + P_t \sin \alpha$$
$$= (100)(.98769) + (150)(.15643)$$
$$= 123.5 \text{ kips}$$

moment about C

$$M' = -P_t\, m - P_a \frac{d}{2}$$
$$= (-150)(-113.04'') - (100)\frac{(50)}{2}$$
$$= +14{,}456 \text{ in.-kips}$$

These forces result in the following stresses on the haunch section (A-B) of the wedge (see Figure 26):

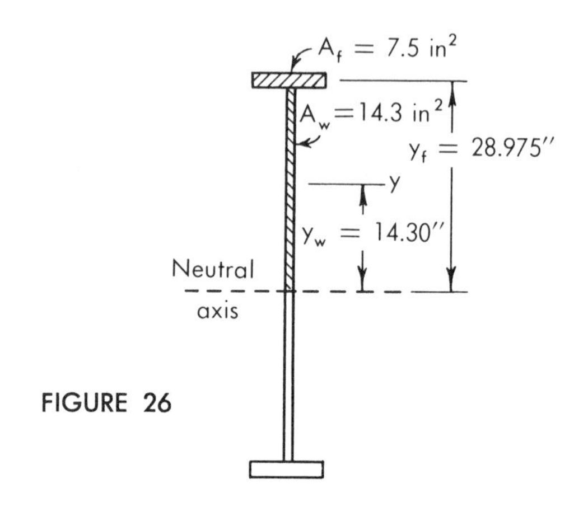

FIGURE 26

shear stresses in section (A-B)

$$V = \frac{M'}{\rho}$$
$$= \frac{(14{,}456)}{(177.63)}$$
$$= 81.35 \text{ kips}$$

$$\tau = \frac{V\,Q}{I\,t_w} = \frac{V[A_f y_f + A_w y_w]}{I\,t_w}$$
$$= \frac{(81.35)(7.5 \times 28.975 + 14.3 \times 14.3)}{(19{,}686)(\frac{1}{2})}$$
$$= 1800 \text{ psi}$$

moment applied to section (A-B)

$$M = M' - P_t'\,\rho$$
$$= (+14{,}456) - (132.5)(177.6)$$
$$= -9082 \text{ in.-kips}$$

normal stress on inner flange

$$\sigma_r = -\frac{P'_a}{A} + \frac{M\,c_i}{I}$$
$$= -\frac{(123.5)}{(44.53)} + \frac{(-9082)(26.46)}{(19{,}686)}$$
$$= -15{,}000 \text{ psi}$$

normal stress on outer flange

$$r = -\frac{P'_o}{A} - \frac{M\,c_o}{I}$$
$$= -\frac{(123.5)}{(44.53)} - \frac{(-9082)(29.35)}{(19{,}686)}$$
$$= +10{,}800 \text{ psi}$$

As an alternate method *Check Haunch Section for Bending Stress Using Conventional Straight Section (A-B)*

(See Figure 27.)

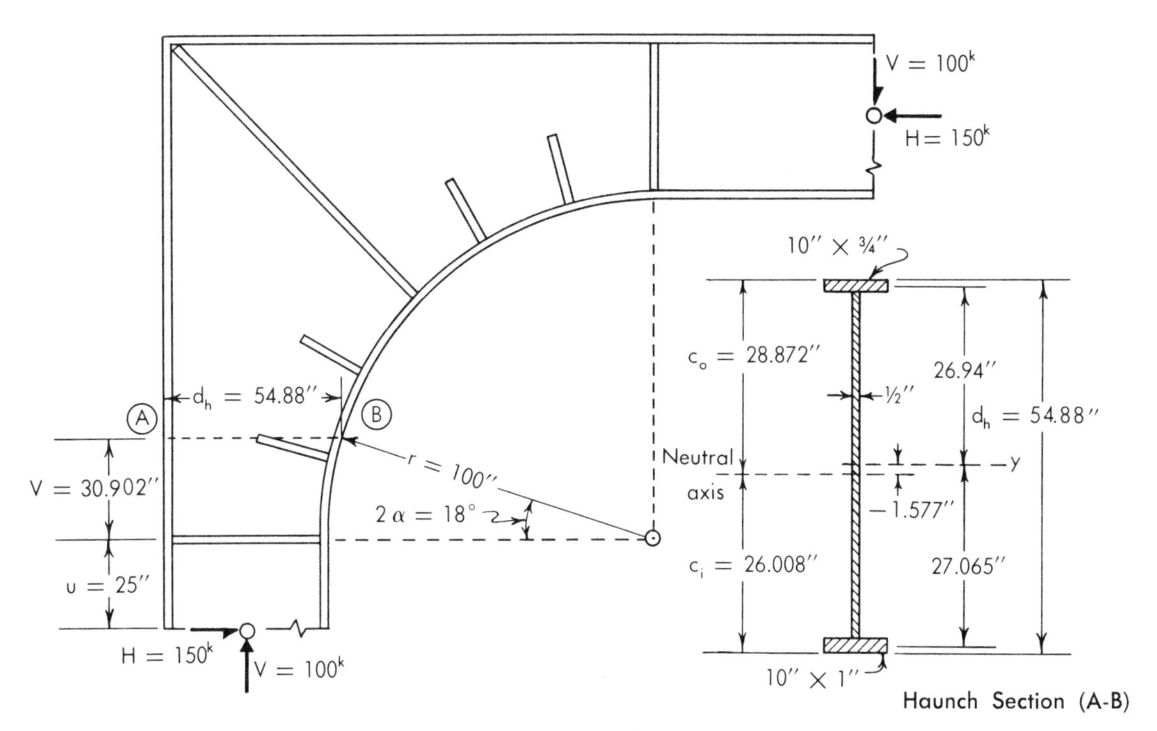

FIGURE 27

Here:

$$v = r \sin (2 \alpha)$$
$$= (100)(.30902)$$
$$= 30.902''$$

$$d_h = d + r (1 - \cos 2 \alpha)$$
$$= (50) + (100)(.0488)$$
$$= 54.88''$$

properties of haunch section (A-B)

Use reference axis (y-y) through centerline of web.

Plate	A	y	M = A•y	I_y = M•y	I_g
¾″ x 10″	7.50	+26.94	+202.05	+5443.2	—
½″ x 53.13″	26.565	0	0	0	+6249
1″ x 10″	10.000	−27.065	−270.65	+7325.3	—
Total	44.065		− 68.60	19,018	

$$I_{NA} = I_y + I_g - \frac{M^2}{A}$$
$$= (19{,}018) - \frac{(-68.60)^2}{(44{,}065)}$$
$$= 18{,}911 \text{ in.}^4$$

$$NA = \frac{M}{A}$$
$$= \frac{(-68.60)}{(44.065)}$$
$$= -1.557''$$

$c_o = 28.872''$ $c_i = 26.008''$

moment applied to section

$$M = (150)(55.902) = 8385.3 \text{ in.-kips}$$

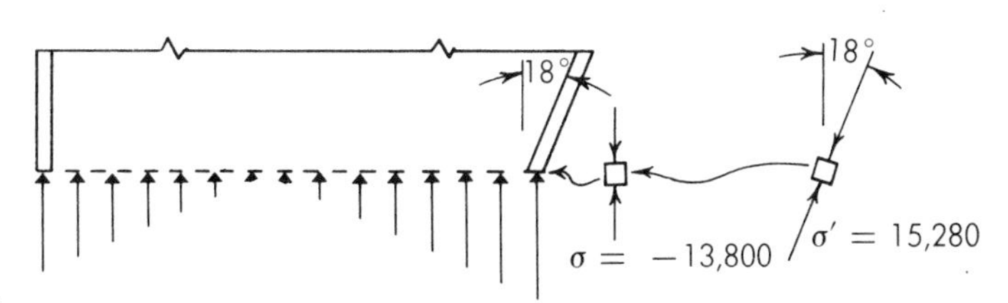

FIGURE 28

tensile bending and axial stress in outer flange

$$\sigma = -\frac{P}{A} + \frac{M\, c_o}{I}$$
$$= -\frac{(100)}{(44.065)} + \frac{(8385.3)(28.872)}{(18{,}911)}$$
$$= +10{,}550 \text{ psi, tension}$$

compressive bending and axial stress normal to section in inner flange

$$\sigma = -\frac{P}{A} - \frac{M\, c_i}{I}$$
$$= -\frac{(100)}{(44.065)} - \frac{(8385.3)(26.008)}{(18{,}911)}$$
$$= -\underline{13{,}800 \text{ psi, compression}}$$

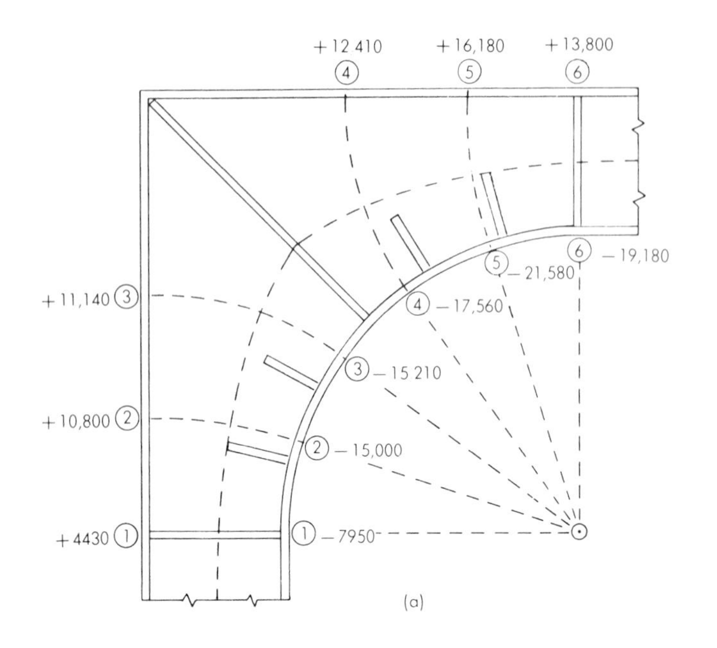

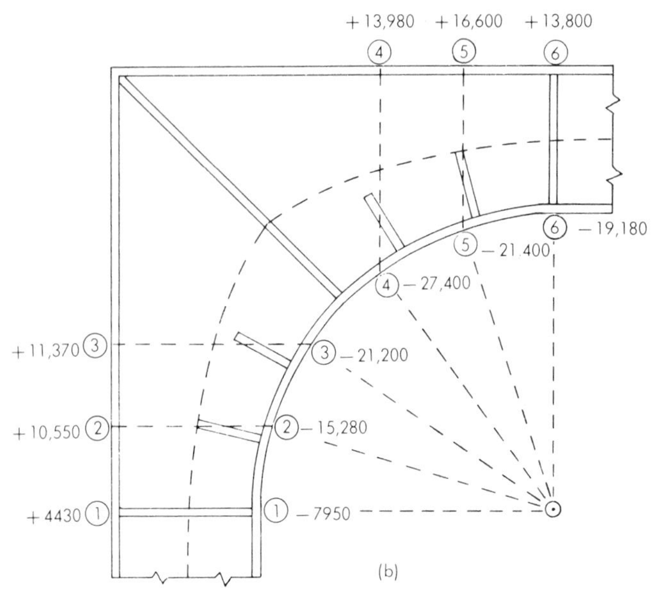

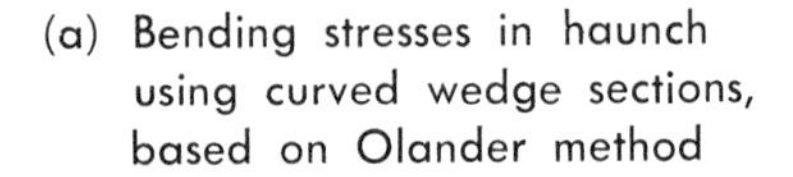
(a) Bending stresses in haunch using curved wedge sections, based on Olander method

(b) Bending stresses in haunch using conventional straight sections

FIGURE 29

stress normal to axis of curved flange

$$\sigma' = \frac{\sigma}{\cos^2 2\,\alpha}$$

$$= \frac{13{,}800}{(.95106)^2}$$

$$= \underline{15{,}280 \text{ psi, compression}}$$

STEP 4: Summary

Figure 29 summarizes the stresses at several sections of the haunch for both the wedge method and the conventional method using straight sections.

The wedge method gives results that check close with experimental results, although it does require more time. The conventional method using straight sections in which the stress on the inward curved flange is increased to account for the sloping flange is easier. However, note that it does give higher values for the steeper slope.

Welded Connections for Plastic Design

1. INTRODUCTION TO PLASTIC DESIGN

The allowable stress used on steel structures in bending is .60 σ_y, a percentage of the steel's yield strength (AISC Sec 1.5.1.4). A steel structure designed on this basis may carry an overload as great as 1.67 times the designed load before the most stressed fiber reaches the yield point. Naturally, this does not represent the maximum load-carrying capacity of the structure, nor does it indicate the reserve strength still in the structure.

Plastic design does not make use of the conventional allowable stresses, but rather the calculated ultimate load-carrying capacity of the structure.

With this method, the given load is increased by 1.70 times the given live and dead load for simple and continuous beams, 1.85 times the given live and dead load for continuous frames, and 1.40 times these loads when acting in conjunction with 1.40 times any specified wind or earthquake forces. Then the members are designed to carry this load at their ultimate or plastic strength. Some yielding must take place before this ultimate load is reached; however, under normal working loads, yielding will seldom occur.

For the past 25 years, a considerable amount of research, both in Europe and the United States, has been devoted to the ultimate load-carrying capacity of steel structures.

For about 15 years, extensive work on full-scale structures has been going on at Lehigh University under the joint sponsorship of the Structural Committee of the Welding Research Council and the American Institute of Steel Construction. Much has been learned as a result of this work.

Major Conclusions

The ultimate load-carrying capacity of a beam section is much greater than the load at yield point. For many years, it has been known that a beam stressed at its outer fibers to the yield point still had a considerable amount of reserve strength before final rupture or collapse. Consider Figure 1.

In this graph for A36 steel, the vertical axis is the applied moment (M), the horizontal axis is the resulting angle of rotation (ϕ). Within the elastic limit (B), there is a straight-line relationship. It is assumed that the bending stresses are zero along the neutral axis of the beam and increase linearly until they are maximum at the outer fibers. This is illustrated at the top of the figure. At point (A), the maximum outer fiber bending stress has reached 22,000 psi. At point (B), this stress has reached the yield point, or 36,000 psi, and yielding at the outer fiber starts to take place. In conventional design, this point is assumed to be the ultimate load on the member; however, this curve shows there is still some more reserve strength left in the beam. As the beam is still further loaded, as at (C), the outer fibers are not stressed higher, but the fibers down inside the beam start to load to the yield point, as in (D). At this point, the beam becomes a plastic hinge; in other words, it will undergo a considerable amount of angle change with very little further increase in load.

M_y is the moment yield point (B), and M_p is the

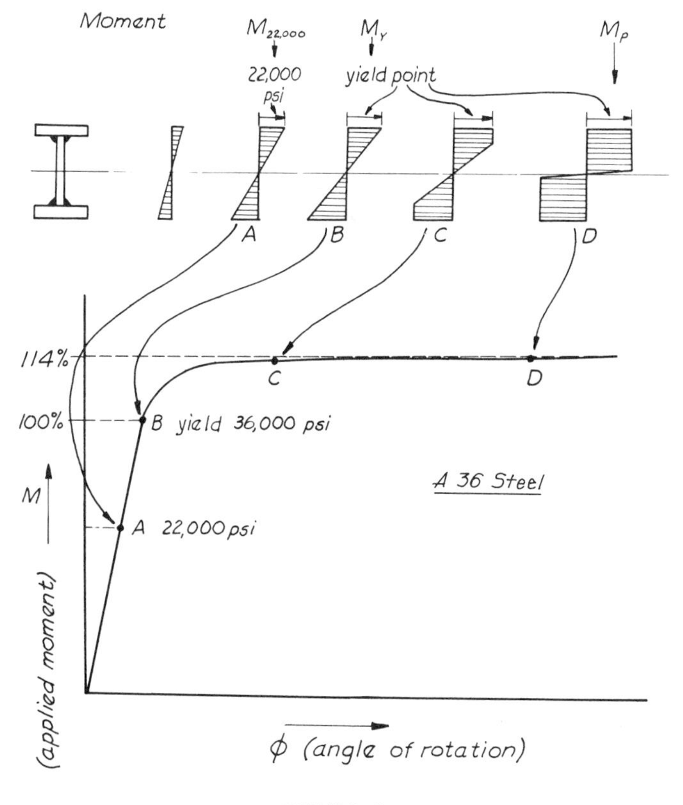

FIGURE 1

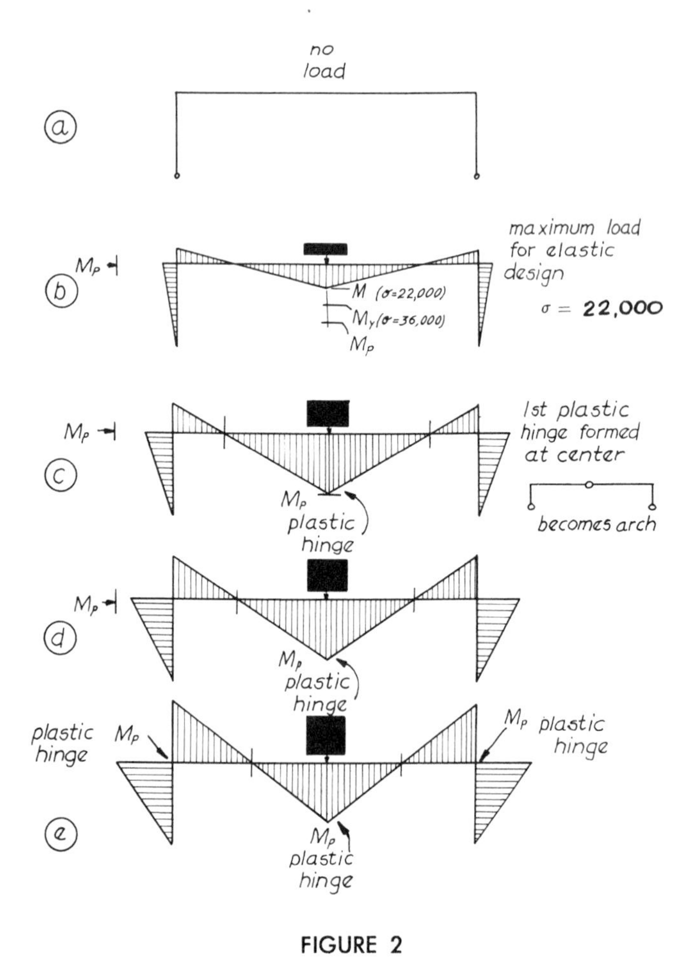

FIGURE 2

plastic moment which causes the beam at point (D) to act as a plastic hinge. For a rectangular cross-section, the plastic moment (M_p) is 1.5 times the moment at yield point (M_y). For the standard rolled WF sections, this plastic moment (M_p) is usually taken as 1.12 times the moment at yield point (M_y). The multiplier varies for other sectional configurations.

Redistribution of moments causes other plastic hinges to form. In Figure 2, a rigid frame with pinned ends is loaded with a concentrated load at midspan. The frame with no load is shown in (a). The frame is loaded in (b) so that its maximum bending stress is 22,000 psi, the allowable. Notice from the bending diagram that the moment at midspan is greater than the moments at the ends or knees of the frame. The three marks at midspan show the moment M where $\sigma = 22{,}000$ psi, or allowable; M_y where $\sigma = 36{,}000$ psi, or yield point; and M_p at plastic hinge. Notice at the left knee how much more the moment can be increased before a plastic hinge is formed.

In (c) the load has been increased until a plastic hinge has been formed at midspan. The knees of the frame in this example have only reached about half of this value. Even though, with conventional thinking, this beam has served its usefulness, it still will not fail because the two knees are still intact and the frame now becomes a three-hinged arch, the other two hinges being the original pinned ends.

Further loading of the frame may be continued, as in (d), with the knees loading up until they become plastic hinges, as in (e). Only when this point is reached would the whole frame fail. This condition is referred to as mechanism; that is, the structure would deform appreciably with only the slightest increase in load.

This entire hinge action takes place in a small portion of the available elongation of the member. In the lower portion of Figure 3 is a stress-strain curve showing the amount of movement which may be used in the plastic range. This may seem large, but it is a very small portion of the whole curve, as shown in the upper portion of the figure, which is carried out to 25% elongation.

The working load is multiplied by a factor of safety (1.85) to give the ultimate load. The design of the structure is based on this ultimate load. In order to establish a proper factor of safety to use in connection with the ultimate load, as found in the plastic method of design, it would be well to consider the loading of a simply supported beam with a concentrated load applied at its midpoint. This is shown in Figure 4. The moment diagrams for this beam are shown for the three loads: the moment M causing a bending stress of 22,000 psi; the moment M_y causing 36,000 psi or yield point; and the moment M_p causing a plastic hinge.

Here, for A36 steel:

Ⓐ Allowable bending stress = 22,000 psi
Ⓑ Yield stress = 36,000 psi = 67% above Ⓐ
Ⓒ Plastic hinge occurs 12% above Ⓑ

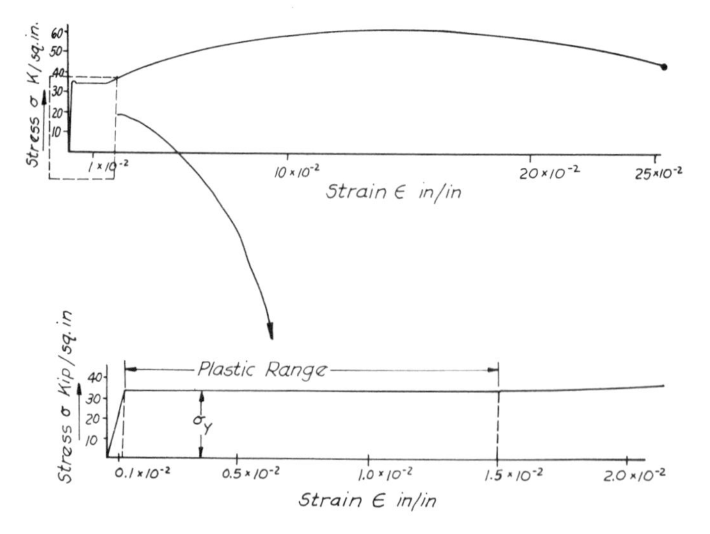

FIGURE 3

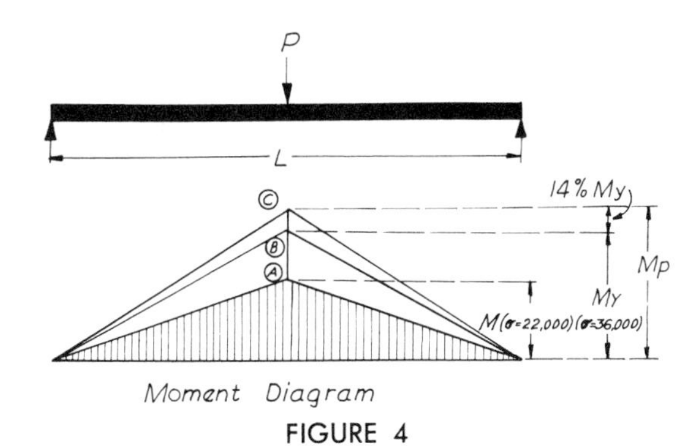

FIGURE 4

Hence:

Ⓒ = (1.67)(1.12) = 1.88 of Ⓐ

Thus, the true load factor of safety of the simple beam is 1.88.

In conventional design, it is assumed that the ultimate load is the value which causes the beam to be stressed to its yield point at the point of maximum stress. This would be represented in the figure by the moment at Ⓑ.

In conventional design, if the allowable bending stress is 22,000 psi and the yield point of the (A36) steel is assumed to be 36,000 psi, the designer is actually using a factor of safety of 1.67.

By means of plastic design, the ultimate load is approximately 12% higher (in the case of a WF beam) than the load which causes the yield point to be reached. Therefore, the factor of safety for plastic design on the same basis would be (1.67)(1.12) = 1.88.

Example

To illustrate plastic design, a beam will be designed using three different methods: (a) simple beam, (b) elastic design, rigid frame, and (c) plastic design, rigid frame. The beam will have a span of 80′ and carry a concentrated load of 55 kips at midspan. For simplicity the dead load will be neglected.

(a) The simply supported beam is shown in Figure 5 with its moment diagram. The maximum moment formula is found in any beam table. From this, the required section modulus (S) is found to be 600.0 in.^{3}, using an allowable load of 22,000 psi in bending. This beam may be made of a 36″ WF beam which weighs 182 lbs/ft.

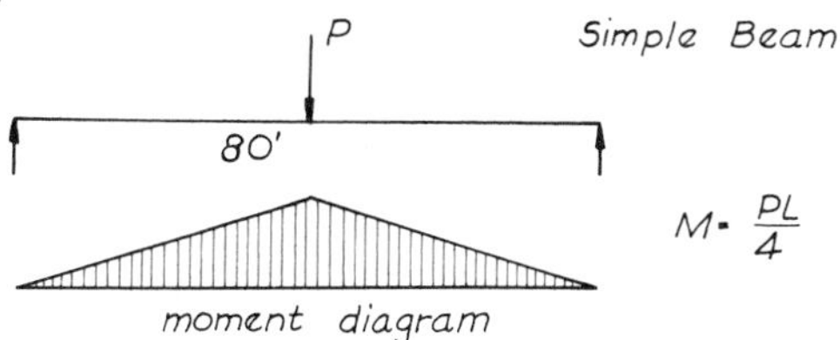

FIGURE 5

Here:

$$M = \frac{P\ L}{4} = \sigma\ S$$

$$S = \frac{P\ L}{4\ \sigma}$$

$$= \frac{(55{,}000)(80 \times 12)}{4(22{,}000)}$$

$$= 600 \text{ in.}^3$$

So, use 36″ WF 182# beam with S = 621 in.^{3}

(b) The elastic design, rigid frame is shown in Figure 6. Its span is 80′ and its height is 20′. There are several ways to solve for the bending moments on this frame.

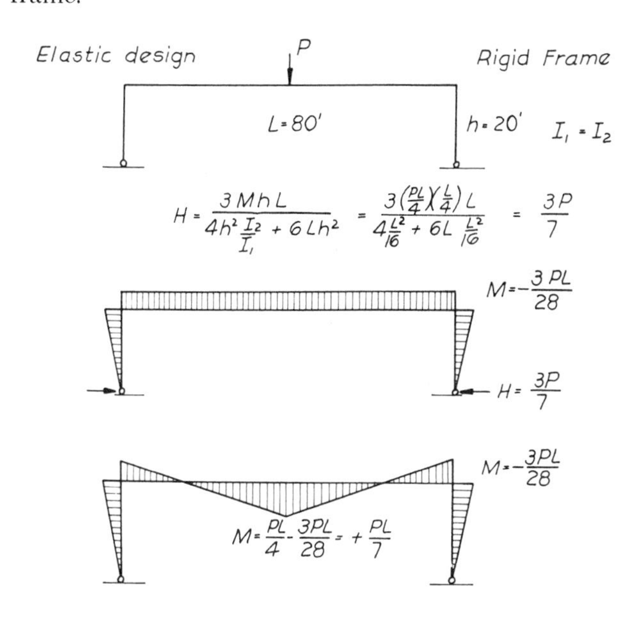

FIGURE 6

In this example the moment at midspan would be—

$$M = \frac{P\ L}{7} = \sigma\ S$$

$$S = \frac{P\ L}{7\ \sigma}$$

$$= \frac{(55{,}000)(80 \times 12)}{7(22{,}000)}$$

$$= 343 \text{ in.}^3$$

So, use a 30″ WF 124# beam with S = 354.6 in.^{3}

The redundant or unknown horizontal force at the pinned end of the frame is first found. Then, from this, the moment diagram is drawn and the maximum moment found. The required section modulus (S) of the frame is determined from this maximum moment.

This is found to be 343 in.^{3}, which is 55% of that required for the single beam. This beam could be made of a 30″ WF beam having a weight of 124 lbs/ft.

(c) The plastic design, rigid frame is shown in Figure 7. With this method, the possible plastic hinges are found which could cause a mechanism or the condition whereby the structure beyond a certain stress point would deform appreciably with only the slightest increase in load. These points of plastic hinge, in this example, are at the midpoint and the two ends, and are assigned the value of M_p. An expression is needed from which this value M_p can be found.

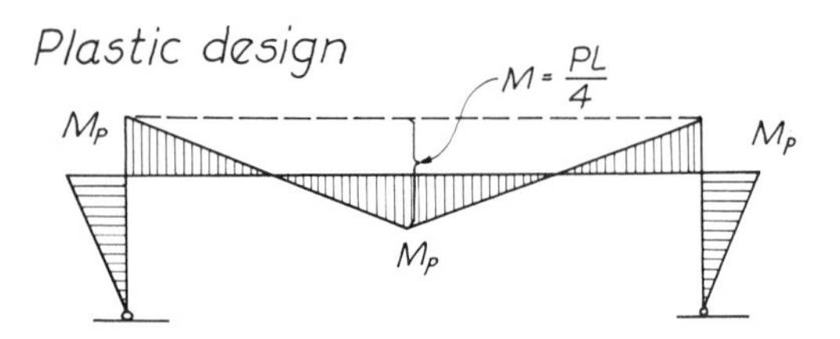

FIGURE 7

Here:

$$M_p + M_p = \frac{P\ L}{4}$$

$$\text{or } M_p = \frac{P_u\ L}{8}$$

$$= \frac{1.85\ P\ L}{8}$$

$$= \frac{1.85(55^k)(80')}{8}$$

$$= 1017.5 \text{ ft-kips}$$

So, use a 27″ WF 114# beam, with plastic moment (M_p) of 1029 ft-kips. (See AISC Manual of Steel Construction, Plastic Section Modulus Table.)

In this case, it is noticed that the altitude of the overall triangle in the moment diagram, which is M_p plus M_p, is also the same as that of the moment diagram of a simply supported beam with a concentrated load at its midspan, Figure 5. This can be found in any beam table. Hence, M_p plus M_p is set equal to $\frac{P\ L}{4}$ using for P the ultimate load which is the working load times 1.85. This works out to $M_p = 1017.5$ ft-kips as the ultimate load plastic moment, at centerline and at the two beam ends.

* * *

Summary of Advantages

As a summary, here are some of the advantages of plastic design:

1. More accurately indicates the true carrying capacity of the structure.
2. Requires less steel than conventional simple beam construction and, in most cases, results in a saving over the use of conventional elastic design of rigid frames.
3. Requires less design time than does elastic design of rigid framing.
4. Result of years of research and testing of full-scale structures.
5. Has the backing of the American Institute of Steel Construction.

2. DESIGN REQUIREMENTS OF THE MEMBER

Loads (AISC Sec. 2.1)

The applied loads shall be increased by the following factor:

1.70 live and dead loads on simple and continuous beams
1.85 live and dead loads on continuous frames
1.40 loads acting in conjunction with 1.40 times any wind and earthquake forces

Columns (AISC Sec. 2.3)

Columns in continuous frames where side-sway is not prevented shall be proportioned so that:

$$\frac{2\ P}{P_y} + \frac{L}{70\ r} \leqq 1.0 \quad \text{(AISC formula 20)} \qquad \cdots\cdots(1)$$

or

$$\frac{L}{r} \leqq 70 - 140\ \frac{P}{P_y} \qquad \cdots\cdots(2)$$

where:

L = unbraced length of column in the plane normal to that of the continuous frame

r = radius of gyration of column about an axis normal to the plane of the continuous frame

See the nomograph, Figure 8, for convenience in reading the limiting value of L/r directly from the values of P and P_y.

The AISC formulas (21), (22), and (23) give the effective moment (M_o), which a given shape is capable of resisting in terms of its full plastic moment (M_p) when it supports an axial force (P) in addition to its moment. See Table 1.

The maximum axial load (P) shall not exceed .60 P_y or .60 σ_y A_c, where A_c = cross-sectional area of the column.

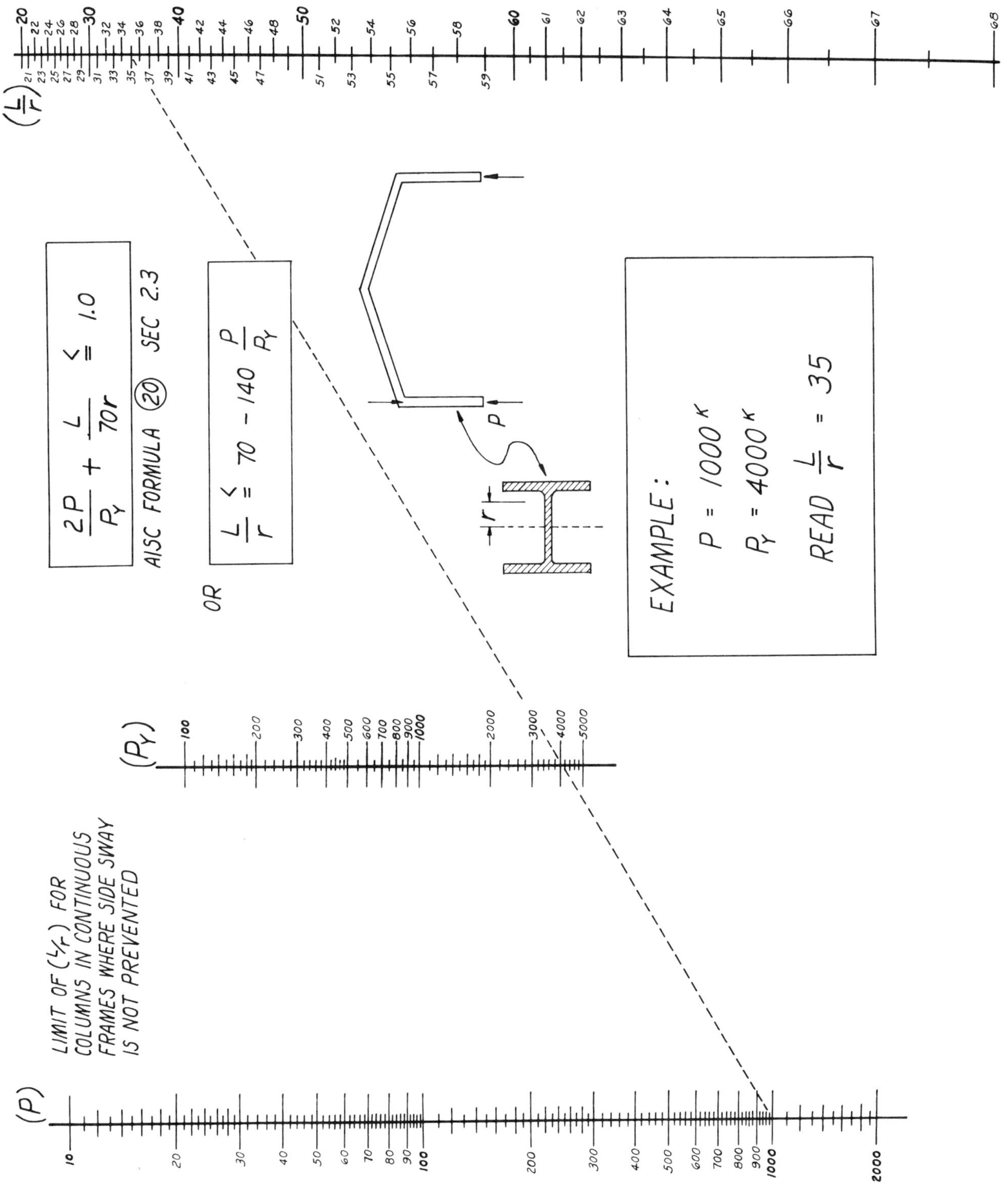

FIGURE 8—Limiting Slenderness Ratio of Columns in Continuous Frames (Plastic Design), Sidesway Permitted.

(P)

10 20 30 40 50 60 70 80 90 100 200 300 400 500 600 700 800 900 1000 2000

LIMIT OF (L/r) FOR COLUMNS IN CONTINUOUS FRAMES WHERE SIDE SWAY IS NOT PREVENTED

(P_Y)

100 200 300 400 500 600 700 800 900 1000 2000 3000 4000 5000

$$\frac{2P}{P_Y} + \frac{L}{70r} \leq 1.0$$

AISC FORMULA (20) SEC 2.3

OR

$$\frac{L}{r} \leq 70 - 140\,\frac{P}{P_Y}$$

P

r

EXAMPLE:

$P = 1000^K$

$P_Y = 4000^K$

READ $\frac{L}{r} = 35$

(L/r)

20 21 22 23 24 25 26 27 28 29 30 31 32 33 34 35 36 37 38 39 40 41 42 43 44 45 46 47 48 50 51 52 53 54 55 56 57 58 59 60 61 62 63 64 65 66 67 68

TABLE 1—Allowable End Moments Relative To Full Plastic Moment of Axially-Loaded Members

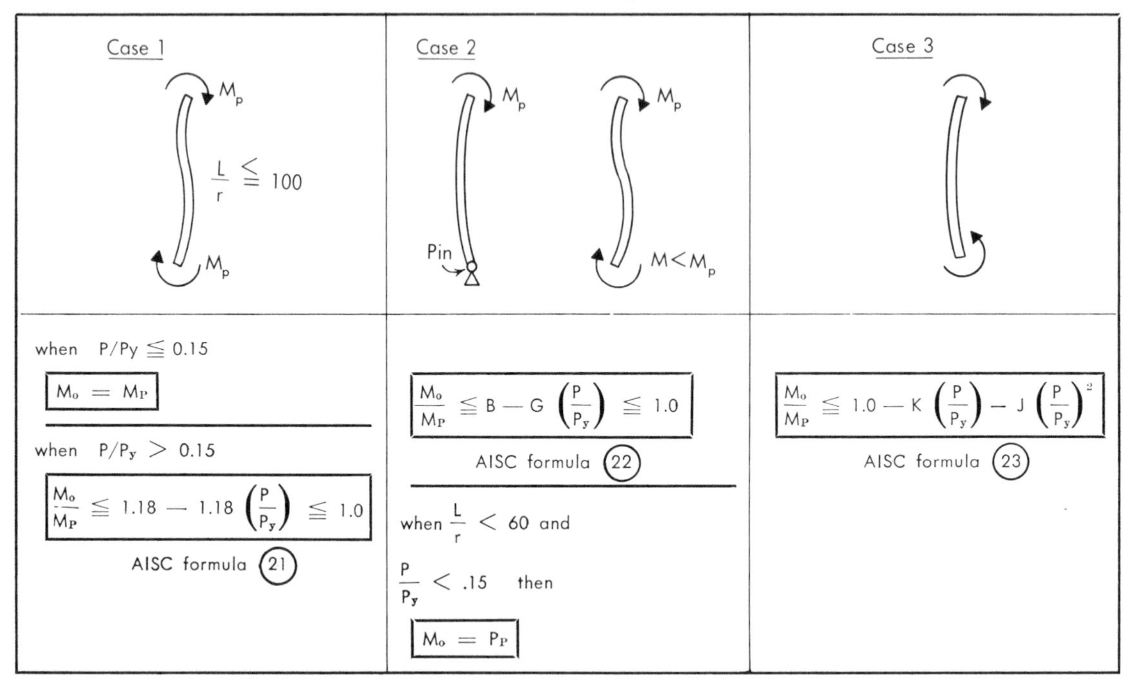

Case 1
M_p
$\frac{L}{r} \leqq 100$
M_p
Case 2
M_p
Pin
M_p
$M<M_p$
Case 3
when $P/P_y \leqq 0.15$
$M_o = M_P$
when $P/P_y > 0.15$
$\frac{M_o}{M_P} \leqq 1.18 - 1.18 \left(\frac{P}{P_y}\right) \leqq 1.0$
AISC formula (21)
$\frac{M_o}{M_P} \leqq B - G \left(\frac{P}{P_y}\right) \leqq 1.0$
AISC formula (22)
when $\frac{L}{r} < 60$ and
$\frac{P}{P_y} < .15$ then
$M_o = P_P$
$\frac{M_o}{M_P} \leqq 1.0 - K \left(\frac{P}{P_y}\right) - J \left(\frac{P}{P_y}\right)^2$
AISC formula (23)

Notes: See Tables 2-33, 3-33, 2-36 and 3-36 for values of B, G, K and J

TABLE 2-33 (AISC Table 4-33)

FOR 33 KSI SPECIFIED YIELD POINT STEEL

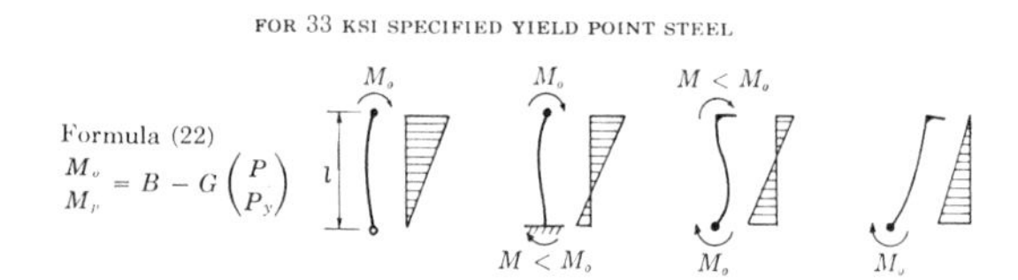

l/r	B	G	l/r	B	G	l/r	B	G
16	1.140	1.172	51	1.164	1.271	86	1.201	1.616
17	1.140	1.174	52	1.165	1.276	87	1.202	1.633
18	1.141	1.177	53	1.165	1.281	88	1.204	1.651
19	1.141	1.179	54	1.166	1.286	89	1.205	1.669
20	1.142	1.182	55	1.167	1.292	90	1.206	1.688
21	1.142	1.184	56	1.168	1.297	91	1.207	1.707
22	1.143	1.187	57	1.169	1.303	92	1.209	1.726
23	1.143	1.189	58	1.170	1.310	93	1.210	1.746
24	1.144	1.191	59	1.171	1.316	94	1.211	1.767
25	1.145	1.194	60	1.172	1.323	95	1.213	1.788
26	1.145	1.196	61	1.173	1.330	96	1.214	1.810
27	1.146	1.198	62	1.174	1.337	97	1.215	1.832
28	1.146	1.200	63	1.175	1.344	98	1.217	1.855
29	1.147	1.203	64	1.176	1.352	99	1.218	1.879
30	1.148	1.205	65	1.177	1.360	100	1.220	1.903
31	1.148	1.207	66	1.178	1.369	101	1.221	1.928
32	1.149	1.209	67	1.179	1.377	102	1.222	1.953
33	1.150	1.212	68	1.180	1.386	103	1.224	1.979
34	1.150	1.215	69	1.181	1.396	104	1.225	2.006
35	1.151	1.217	70	1.182	1.406	105	1.227	2.033
36	1.152	1.220	71	1.183	1.416	106	1.228	2.061
37	1.152	1.222	72	1.184	1.426	107	1.230	2.090
38	1.153	1.225	73	1.186	1.437	108	1.231	2.119
39	1.154	1.228	74	1.187	1.448	109	1.233	2.149
40	1.155	1.231	75	1.188	1.460	110	1.234	2.179
41	1.155	1.234	76	1.189	1.472	111	1.236	2.211
42	1.156	1.237	77	1.190	1.485	112	1.237	2.243
43	1.157	1.240	78	1.191	1.497	113	1.239	2.275
44	1.158	1.243	79	1.192	1.511	114	1.240	2.309
45	1.159	1.247	80	1.194	1.524	115	1.242	2.343
46	1.159	1.251	81	1.195	1.539	116	1.243	2.378
47	1.160	1.254	82	1.196	1.553	117	1.245	2.414
48	1.161	1.258	83	1.197	1.568	118	1.247	2.450
49	1.162	1.263	84	1.198	1.584	119	1.248	2.487
50	1.163	1.267	85	1.200	1.600	120	1.250	2.525

TABLE 3-33 (AISC Table 5-33)

FOR 33 KSI SPECIFIED YIELD POINT STEEL

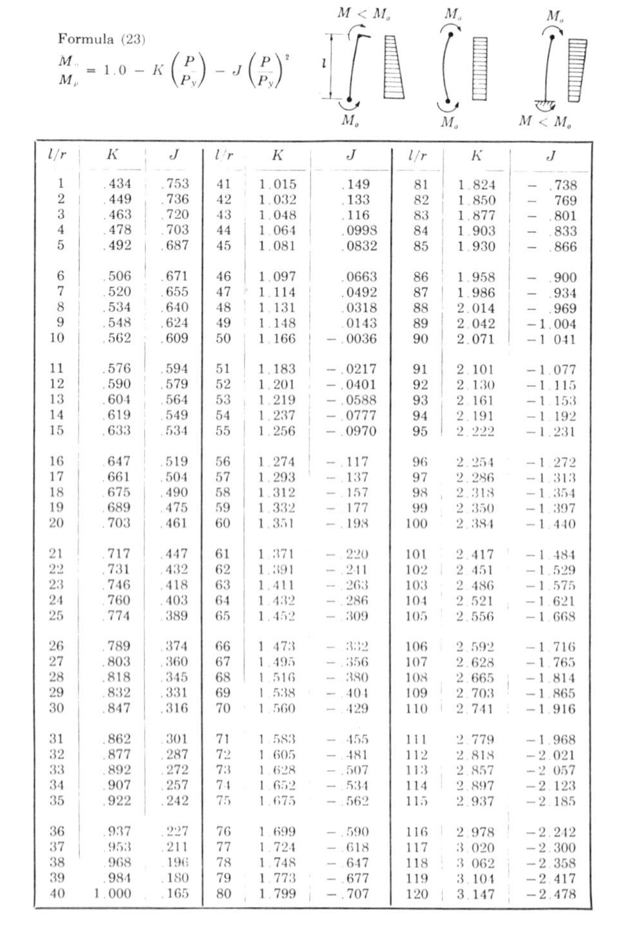

l/r	K	J	l/r	K	J	l/r	K	J
1	.434	.753	41	1.015	.149	81	1.824	− .738
2	.449	.736	42	1.032	.133	82	1.850	− .769
3	.463	.720	43	1.048	.116	83	1.877	− .801
4	.478	.703	44	1.064	.0998	84	1.903	− .833
5	.492	.687	45	1.081	.0832	85	1.930	− .866
6	.506	.671	46	1.097	.0663	86	1.958	− .900
7	.520	.655	47	1.114	.0492	87	1.986	− .934
8	.534	.640	48	1.131	.0318	88	2.014	− .969
9	.548	.624	49	1.148	.0143	89	2.042	−1.004
10	.562	.609	50	1.166	−.0036	90	2.071	−1.041
11	.576	.594	51	1.183	−.0217	91	2.101	−1.077
12	.590	.579	52	1.201	−.0401	92	2.130	−1.115
13	.604	.564	53	1.219	−.0588	93	2.161	−1.153
14	.619	.549	54	1.237	−.0777	94	2.191	−1.192
15	.633	.534	55	1.256	−.0970	95	2.222	−1.231
16	.647	.519	56	1.274	−.117	96	2.254	−1.272
17	.661	.504	57	1.293	−.137	97	2.286	−1.313
18	.675	.490	58	1.312	−.157	98	2.318	−1.354
19	.689	.475	59	1.332	−.177	99	2.350	−1.397
20	.703	.461	60	1.351	−.198	100	2.384	−1.440
21	.717	.447	61	1.371	−.220	101	2.417	−1.484
22	.731	.432	62	1.391	−.241	102	2.451	−1.529
23	.746	.418	63	1.411	−.263	103	2.486	−1.575
24	.760	.403	64	1.432	−.286	104	2.521	−1.621
25	.774	.389	65	1.452	−.309	105	2.556	−1.668
26	.789	.374	66	1.473	−.332	106	2.592	−1.716
27	.803	.360	67	1.495	−.356	107	2.628	−1.765
28	.818	.345	68	1.516	−.380	108	2.665	−1.814
29	.832	.331	69	1.538	−.404	109	2.703	−1.865
30	.847	.316	70	1.560	−.429	110	2.741	−1.916
31	.862	.301	71	1.583	−.455	111	2.779	−1.968
32	.877	.287	72	1.605	−.481	112	2.818	−2.021
33	.892	.272	73	1.628	−.507	113	2.857	−2.057
34	.907	.257	74	1.652	−.534	114	2.897	−2.123
35	.922	.242	75	1.675	−.562	115	2.937	−2.185
36	.937	.227	76	1.699	−.590	116	2.978	−2.242
37	.953	.211	77	1.724	−.618	117	3.020	−2.300
38	.968	.196	78	1.748	−.647	118	3.062	−2.358
39	.984	.180	79	1.773	−.677	119	3.104	−2.417
40	1.000	.165	80	1.799	−.707	120	3.147	−2.478

TABLE 2-36 (AISC Table 4-36)

FOR 36 KSI SPECIFIED YIELD POINT STEEL

Formula (22)

$$\frac{M_o}{M_p} = B - G\left(\frac{P}{P_y}\right)$$

l/r	B	G	l/r	B	G	l/r	B	G
16	1.137	1.173	51	1.163	1.285	86	1.203	1.693
17	1.137	1.176	52	1.164	1.291	87	1.204	1.713
18	1.138	1.179	53	1.165	1.296	88	1.206	1.734
19	1.139	1.182	54	1.166	1.303	89	1.207	1.755
20	1.139	1.184	55	1.166	1.309	90	1.208	1.777
21	1.140	1.187	56	1.167	1.316	91	1.210	1.799
22	1.140	1.189	57	1.168	1.323	92	1.211	1.822
23	1.141	1.192	58	1.170	1.330	93	1.213	1.846
24	1.142	1.194	59	1.171	1.337	94	1.214	1.870
25	1.142	1.196	60	1.172	1.345	95	1.215	1.895
26	1.143	1.199	61	1.173	1.354	96	1.217	1.921
27	1.143	1.201	62	1.174	1.362	97	1.218	1.947
28	1.144	1.204	63	1.175	1.371	98	1.220	1.974
29	1.145	1.206	64	1.176	1.380	99	1.221	2.002
30	1.145	1.209	65	1.177	1.390	100	1.223	2.030
31	1.146	1.211	66	1.178	1.400	101	1.224	2.059
32	1.147	1.214	67	1.179	1.410	102	1.226	2.089
33	1.148	1.216	68	1.180	1.421	103	1.227	2.120
34	1.148	1.219	69	1.181	1.432	104	1.229	2.151
35	1.149	1.222	70	1.183	1.444	105	1.231	2.183
36	1.150	1.225	71	1.184	1.456	106	1.232	2.216
37	1.151	1.228	72	1.185	1.468	107	1.234	2.249
38	1.151	1.231	73	1.186	1.481	108	1.235	2.283
39	1.152	1.234	74	1.187	1.494	109	1.237	2.318
40	1.153	1.237	75	1.189	1.508	110	1.239	2.354
41	1.154	1.241	76	1.190	1.522	111	1.240	2.391
42	1.155	1.244	77	1.191	1.537	112	1.242	2.429
43	1.155	1.248	78	1.192	1.552	113	1.244	2.467
44	1.156	1.252	79	1.194	1.568	114	1.245	2.506
45	1.157	1.256	80	1.195	1.584	115	1.247	2.546
46	1.158	1.260	81	1.196	1.601	116	1.249	2.587
47	1.159	1.265	82	1.197	1.618	117	1.250	2.628
48	1.160	1.270	83	1.199	1.636	118	1.252	2.671
49	1.161	1.275	84	1.200	1.654	119	1.254	2.714
50	1.162	1.280	85	1.201	1.673	120	1.256	2.759

If L/r > 120, the ratio of axial load (P) to plastic load (P_y) shall be—

$$\frac{P}{P_y} \leqq \frac{8700}{(L/r)^2} \quad \text{(AISC formula 24)} \qquad \ldots\ldots\ldots\ldots\ldots\ldots (3)$$

Shear (AISC Sec. 2.4)

Webs of columns, beams, and girders not reinforced by a web doubler plate or diagonal stiffeners shall be so proportioned that:

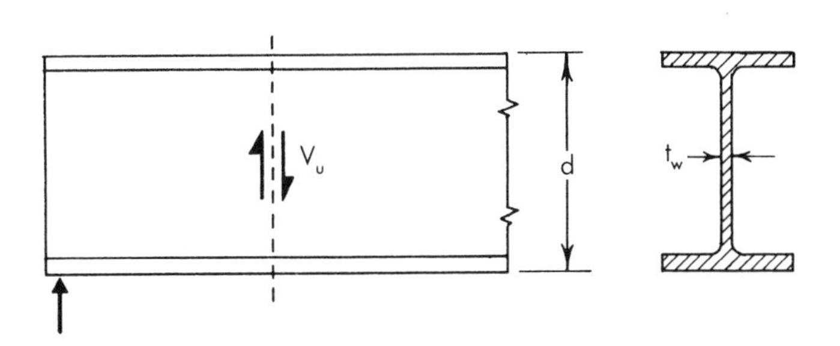

FIGURE 9

TABLE 3-36 (AISC Table 5-36)

FOR 36 KSI SPECIFIED YIELD POINT STEEL

Formula (23)

$$\frac{M_o}{M_p} = 1.0 - K\left(\frac{P}{P_y}\right) - J\left(\frac{P}{P_y}\right)^2$$

l/r	K	J	l/r	K	J	l/r	K	J
1	.435	.753	41	1.036	.137	81	1.904	− .817
2	.450	.736	42	1.053	.121	82	1.932	− .851
3	.464	.719	43	1.070	.104	83	1.961	− .886
4	.479	.702	44	1.087	.0867	84	1.990	− .922
5	.494	.686	45	1.105	.0692	85	2.020	− .958
6	.508	.670	46	1.122	.0516	86	2.050	− .996
7	.523	.654	47	1.140	.0336	87	2.080	−1.034
8	.537	.638	48	1.158	.0154	88	2.111	−1.072
9	.552	.622	49	1.176	−.0031	89	2.142	−1.112
10	.566	.607	50	1.195	−.0219	90	2.174	−1.152
11	.581	.591	51	1.213	−.0411	91	2.206	−1.193
12	.595	.576	52	1.232	−.0605	92	2.239	−1.234
13	.610	.561	53	1.251	−.0803	93	2.272	−1.277
14	.624	.546	54	1.271	−.100	94	2.306	−1.320
15	.639	.531	55	1.290	−.121	95	2.340	−1.364
16	.653	.516	56	1.310	−.142	96	2.375	−1.409
17	.668	.501	57	1.330	−.163	97	2.410	−1.455
18	.682	.486	58	1.351	−.185	98	2.445	−1.501
19	.697	.472	59	1.371	−.207	99	2.482	−1.549
20	.711	.457	60	1.392	−.229	100	2.518	−1.597
21	.726	.442	61	1.413	−.252	101	2.555	−1.646
22	.741	.428	62	1.435	−.275	102	2.593	−1.696
23	.755	.413	63	1.456	−.299	103	2.631	−1.747
24	.770	.398	64	1.478	−.323	104	2.670	−1.799
25	.785	.384	65	1.501	−.348	105	2.709	−1.852
26	.800	.369	66	1.523	−.373	106	2.749	−1.906
27	.815	.354	67	1.546	−.399	107	2.789	−1.960
28	.830	.340	68	1.570	−.425	108	2.830	−2.016
29	.845	.325	69	1.593	−.452	109	2.871	−2.073
30	.860	.310	70	1.617	−.479	110	2.914	−2.130
31	.876	.295	71	1.641	−.507	111	2.956	−2.189
32	.891	.280	72	1.666	−.535	112	2.999	−2.248
33	.907	.265	73	1.691	−.564	113	3.043	−2.309
34	.922	.249	74	1.716	−.593	114	3.087	−2.371
35	.938	.234	75	1.742	−.623	115	3.132	−2.433
36	.954	.218	76	1.768	−.654	116	3.178	−2.497
37	.970	.202	77	1.794	−.685	117	3.224	−2.562
38	.987	.186	78	1.821	−.717	118	3.271	−2.627
39	1.003	.170	79	1.848	−.750	119	3.318	−2.694
40	1.020	.154	80	1.876	−.783	120	3.366	−2.762

Assuming depth of web = .95 d (depth of member), the shear on web section at ultimate load is—

$$V_u = t_w(.95\ d)\ \sigma_y$$

$$= t_w(.95\ d)\ \frac{\sigma_y}{\sqrt{3}}$$

or

$$V_u \leqq .55\ \sigma_y\ t_w\ d \qquad \ldots\ldots\ldots\ldots\ldots\ldots (4)$$

Minimum Width-to-Thickness Ratios (AISC Sec. 2.6)

When subjected to compression involving plastic hinge rotation under ultimate loading, section elements shall be so proportioned that:

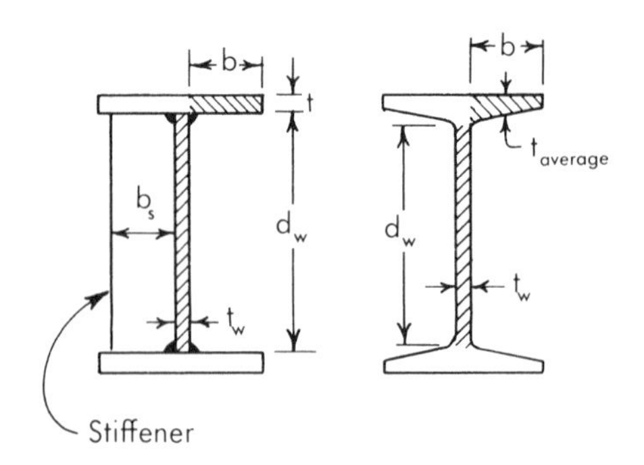

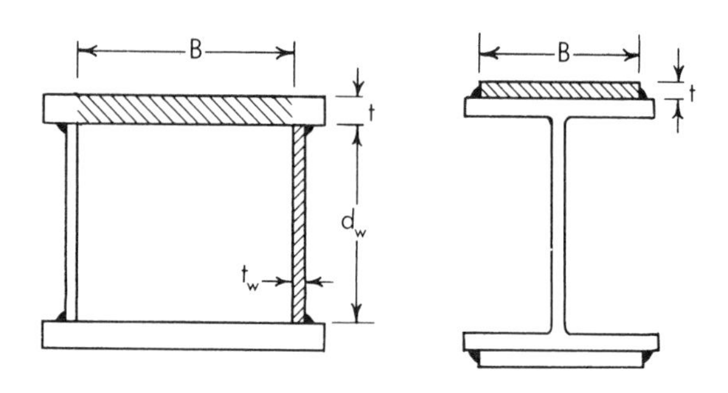

FIGURE 10

$$\frac{b}{t} \text{ or } \frac{b_s}{t_s} \leqq 8\tfrac{1}{2} \qquad (5)$$

$$\frac{B}{t} \leqq 32 \qquad (6)$$

$$\frac{d_w}{t_w} \leqq 70 \qquad (7)$$
If $P = 0$

and when beam or girder is subjected to axial force (P) and plastic bending moment (P_y) at ultimate load,

$$\frac{d_w}{t_w} \leqq 70 - 100\frac{P}{P_y} \geqq 43 \qquad (8)$$
(AISC formula 25)

See nomograph, Figure 11, for convenient direct reading of d_w/t_w ratio from values of P and P_y.

Lateral Bracing (AISC Sec. 2.8)

Plastic hinge locations associated with all but the last failure mechanism shall be adequately braced to resist lateral and torsional displacement.

Laterally unsupported distance (L_{cr}) from such braced hinged locations to the nearest adjacent point on the frame similarly braced shall be—

$$L_{cr} \leqq \left[60 - 40\frac{M}{M_p}\right] r_y \qquad (9)$$
(AISC formula 26)

but need not be less than $35\ r_y$

where:

r_y = radius of gyration of member about its weak axis

M = the lesser of the moments at the ends of the unbraced segment

$\frac{M}{M_p}$ = the end moment ratio, positive when the segment is bent in single curvature and negative when bent in double curvature

In the usual square frame, plastic hinges would ultimately form at maximum negative moments at the corners, and at the maximum positive moment near the center of the span. However, a tapered haunch may develop a plastic hinge at the corner and also at the point where the haunch connects to the straight portions of the rafter or column because of the reduced depth of the member. These also become points where lateral bracing must be provided.

3. BASIC REQUIREMENTS OF WELDED CONNECTIONS

Connections are an important part of any steel structure designed according to plastic design concepts. The connection must allow the members to reach their full plastic moments with sufficient strength, adequate rotational ability, and proper stiffness. They must be capable of resisting moments, shear forces, and axial loads to which they would be subjected by the ultimate loading. Stiffeners may be required to preserve the flange continuity of interrupted members at their junction with other members in a continuous frame.

A basic requirement is that the web of the resulting connection must provide adequate resistance against buckling from (a) *Shear*—the diagonal compressive force resulting from shear forces applied to the web from the connecting flanges, which in turn are stressed by the end moment of the member, and (b) *Thrust*—any concentrated compressive force applied at the edge of the web from an intersecting flange of a member, this force resulting from the end moment of that member. See Figure 12.

In addition to meeting the above requirements, the connection should be so designed that it may be economically fabricated and welded.

Groove welds and fillet welds shall be proportioned

FIGURE 11—Proportioning Web of Beam or Girder Under Axial Load and Plastic Moment.

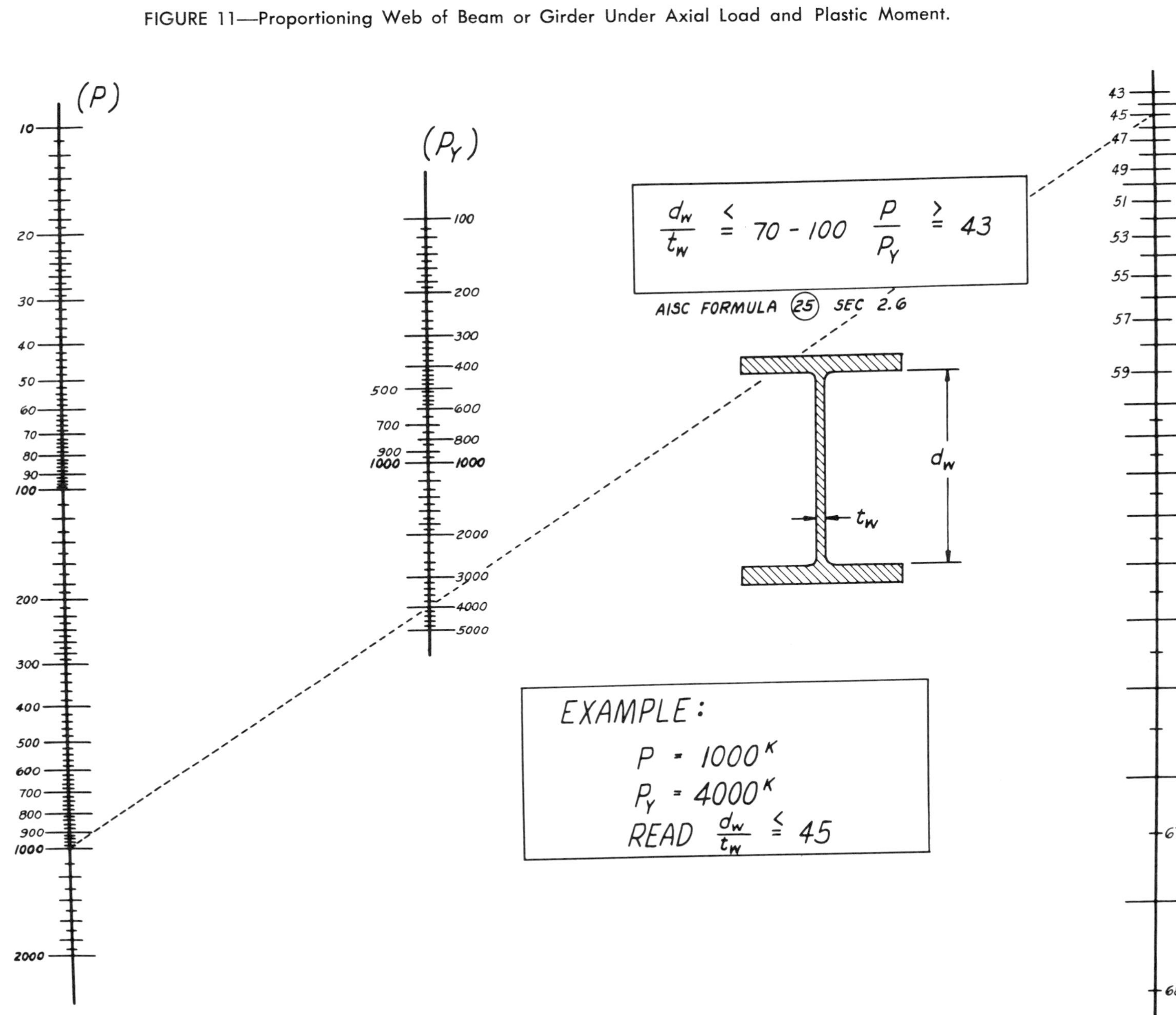

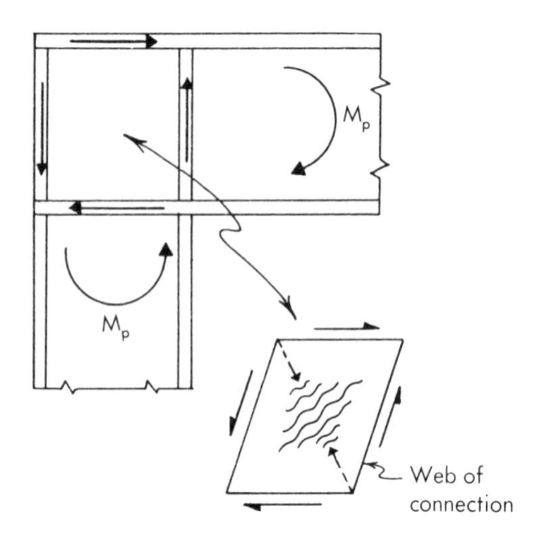

(a) Web resisting shear

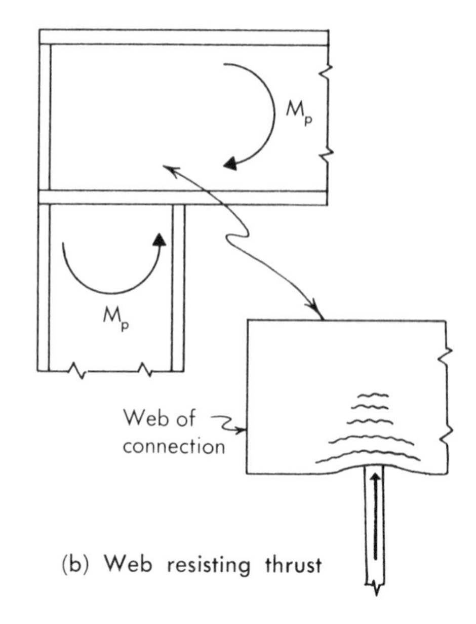

(b) Web resisting thrust

FIGURE 12

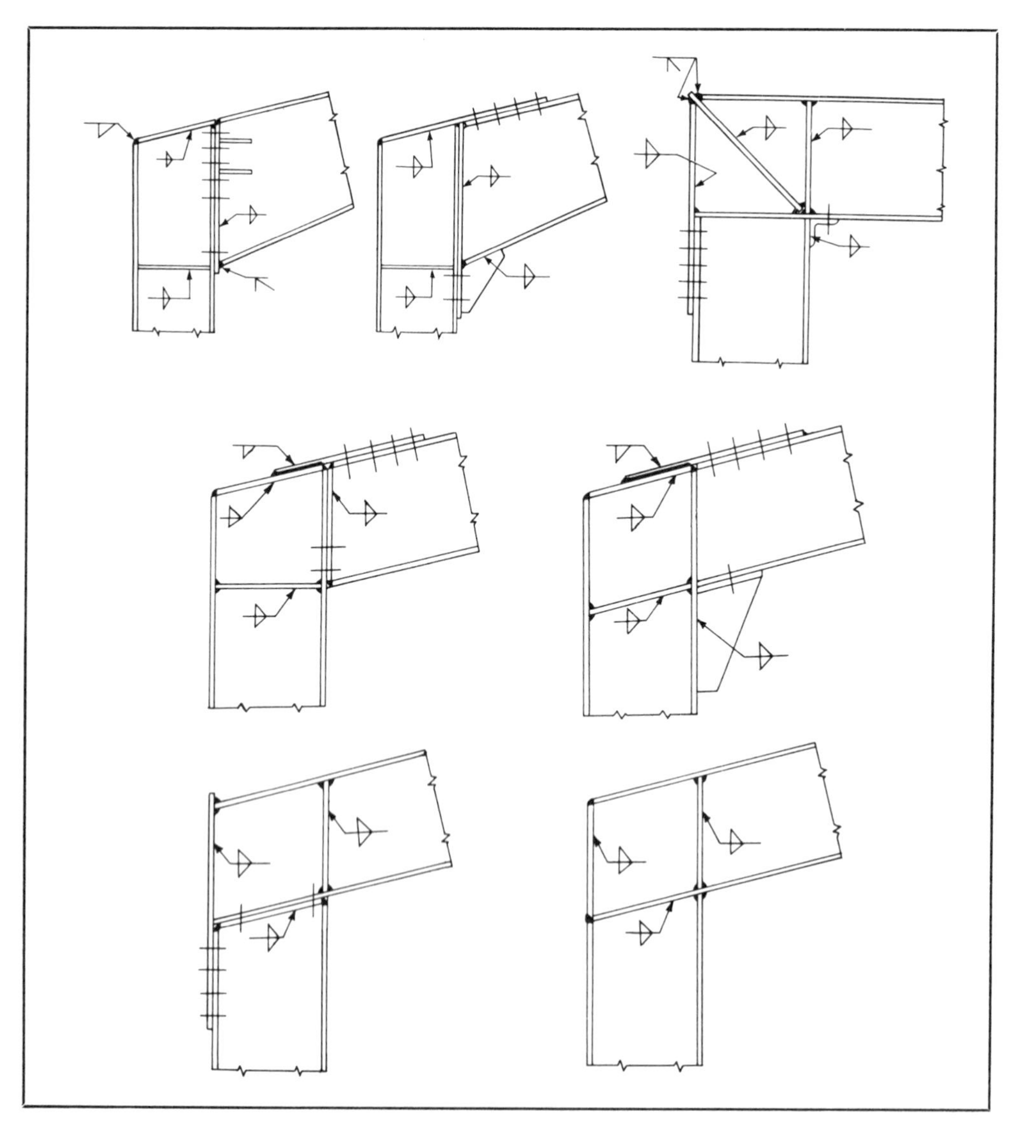

FIGURE 13

to resist the forces produced at ultimate load, using an increase of 1.67 over the standard allowables (AISC Sec. 2.7).

Following pages cover first the design of simple two-way rectangular corner connections, tapered haunches, and curved haunches. Next, the design of beam-to-column connections, whether three-way or four-way, is dealt with.

Analysis and design of a particular connection may not always be as simple as those illustrated on these pages. Figure 13 shows some other typical welded connections.

4. STRAIGHT CORNER CONNECTIONS

Web Resisting Shear

The forces in the flanges of both members at the connection resulting from the moment (M_p) are transferred into the connection web as shear (V).

Some of the vertical shear in the beam (V_b) and the horizontal shear in the column (V_c) will also be transferred into the connection web. However, in most cases these values are small compared to those resulting from the applied moment. Also, in a simple corner connection, these are of opposite sign and tend to reduce the actual shear value in the connection.

In this analysis, only the shear resulting from the applied moment is considered in the web of the connection.

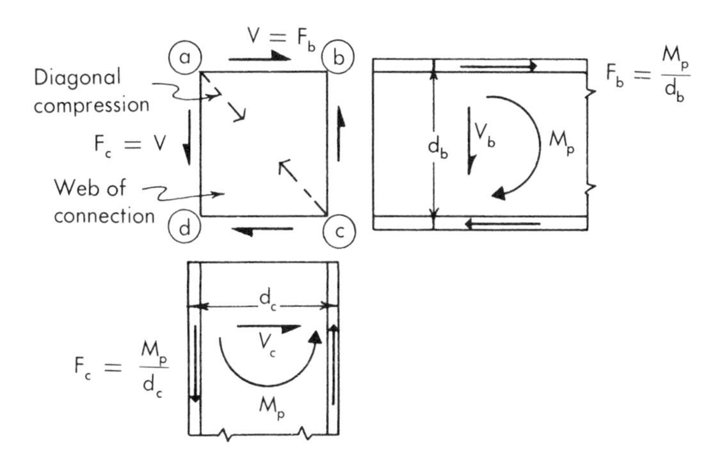

FIGURE 14

The minimum web thickness required to assure that the web of the connection does not buckle from the shear forces set up by the moment applied to the connection (M_p), may be found from the following:

unit shear force applied to connection web

$$\nu = \frac{V}{d} = \frac{F_b}{d_c}\left(\text{also} = \frac{F_c}{d_b}\right) = \frac{M_p}{d_b\ d_c}$$

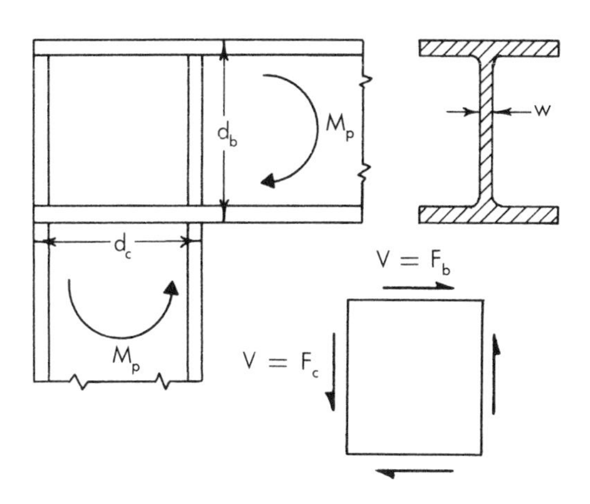

FIGURE 15

resulting shear stress in connection web

$$\tau = \frac{\nu}{w} = \frac{M_p}{w\ d_b\ d_c}$$

The values for the shear stress at yield (τ_y) may be found by using the Mises criterion for yielding—

$$\sigma_{cr} = \sqrt{\sigma_x{}^2 - \sigma_x\ \sigma_y + \sigma_y{}^2 + 3\ \tau_{xy}{}^2}$$

In this application of pure shear, σ_x and $\sigma_y = 0$ and setting the critical value (σ_{cr}) equal to yield (σ_y), we obtain—

$$\sigma_y = \sqrt{3\ \tau_{xy}{}^2} \qquad \text{or}$$

$$\tau_{xy} = \frac{\sigma_y}{\sqrt{3}}$$

Hence,

$$\tau = \frac{M_p}{w\ d_b\ d_c} = \frac{\sigma_y}{\sqrt{3}}$$

or

$$\boxed{w_r \geq \frac{\sqrt{3}\ M_p}{d_b\ d_c\ \sigma_y}} \qquad \ldots\ldots\ldots\ldots\ldots\ldots\ldots (10)$$

The nomograph, Figure 16, will facilitate finding this required web thickness.

In the above:

M_p = plastic moment at connection, in.-lbs

d_b = depth of beam, in.

d_c = depth of column, in.-lbs

w = actual web thickness in connection area, in.

w_r = required web thickness in connection area, in.

σ_y = yield strength of steel, psi

FIGURE 16—Thickness of Connection Web to Resist Shear From Unbalanced Plastic Moment.

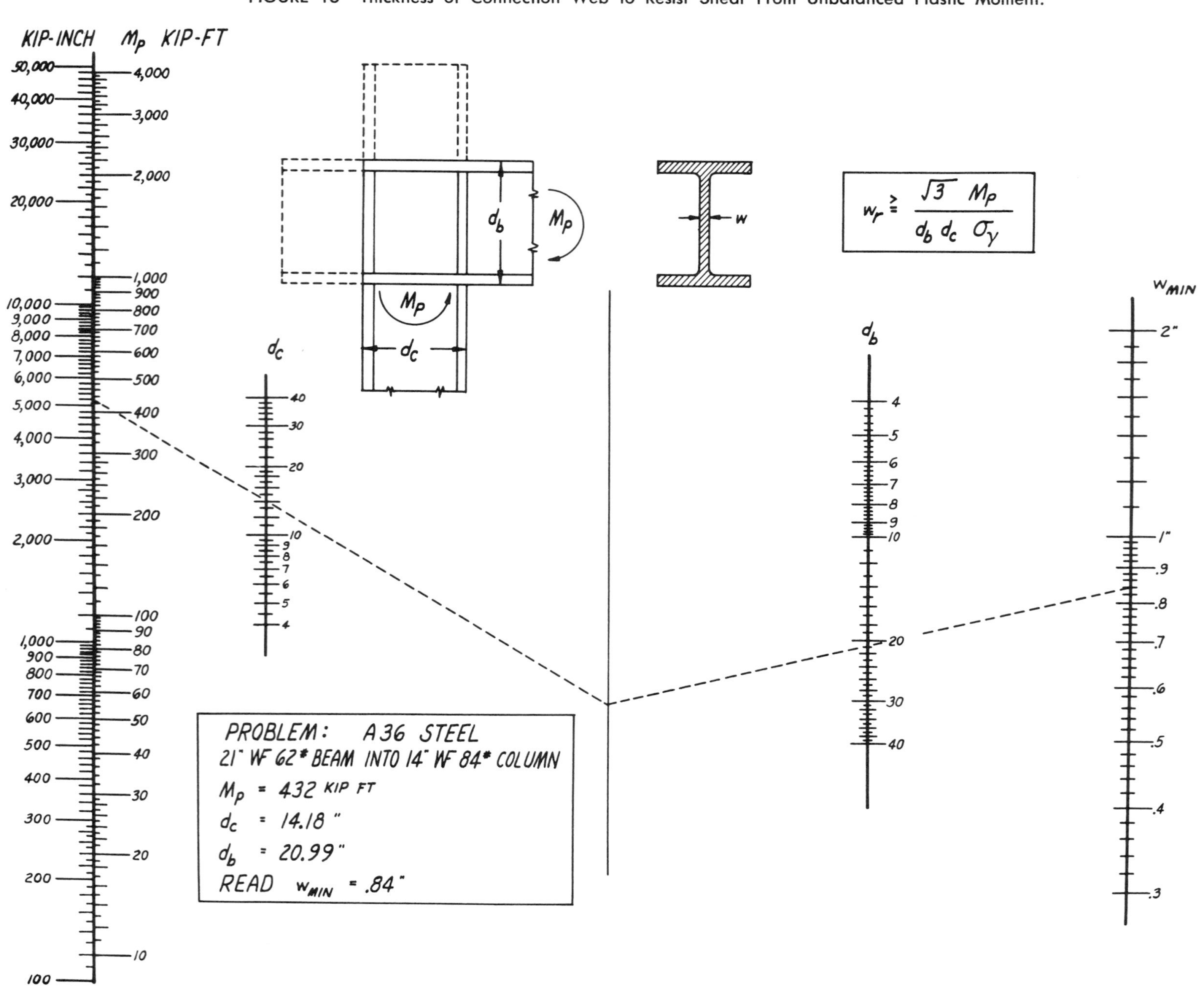

AISC uses an effective depth of the beam and column as 95% of their actual depths to allow for the presence of plastic strain in the flanges, due to concurrent bending. Applying this reduction to both the depth of the beam (d_b) and the column (d_c), and also expressing the applied plastic moment (M_p) in ft-lbs rather than in.-lbs, this formula becomes:

$$\boxed{w_r = \frac{23{,}000\ M_p}{d_b\ d_c\ \sigma_y}} \qquad \text{(11)}$$

Here M_p = plastic moment, *ft.-lbs*

For most wide flange (WF) sections, the web thickness (w) will be less than the required value (w_r) above, and some form of stiffening will be required.

Web Doubler Plate

A web doubler plate, or a pair, may be used to bring the total web thickness up to the minimum (w_r) obtained above.

Welds should be arranged at the edges of doubler plates so as to transfer the shear forces directly to the boundary stiffeners and flanges.

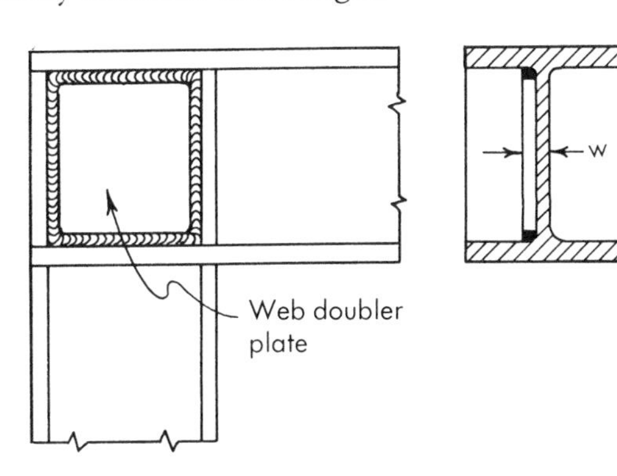

FIGURE 17

Diagonal Stiffeners

A symmetrical pair of diagonal stiffeners may be added to this connection to prevent the web from buckling. These stiffeners resist enough of the flange force (F) that the resulting shear (V) applied to this web is reduced sufficiently to prevent buckling.

Stiffeners having a thickness equal to that of the rolled section flange of the beam or column normally will be adequate, although this thickness will be greater than required. The minimum thickness of this stiffener may be found from the following:

The horizontal flange force (F_b) of the beam is resisted by the combined effect of the web shear (V) and the horizontal component of the compressive force (P) in the stiffener.

$$F = V + P \cos\theta$$

where

$$V = w\ d_c\ \tau_y = w\ d_c \frac{\sigma_y}{\sqrt{3}}$$

and since

$$F = \frac{M_p}{d_b}$$

$$\therefore \frac{M_p}{d_b} = w\ d_c \frac{\sigma_y}{\sqrt{3}} + P\cos\theta \qquad \text{or}$$

$$P = \frac{1}{\cos\theta}\left[\frac{M_p}{d_b} = \frac{w\ d_c\ \sigma_y}{\sqrt{3}}\right]$$

$$\therefore \boxed{A_s = \frac{1}{\cos\theta}\left[\frac{M_p}{d_b\ \sigma_y} - \frac{w\ d_c}{\sqrt{3}}\right]} \qquad \text{(12)}$$

where

θ = angle of diagonal stiffener with horizon,

$$\theta = \tan^{-1}\left(\frac{d_b}{d_c}\right)$$

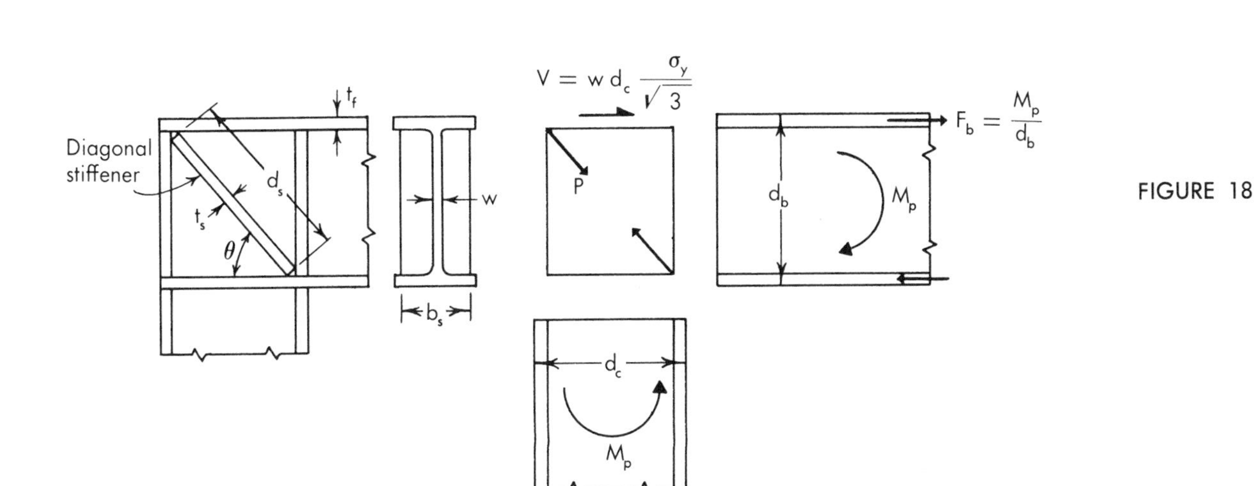

FIGURE 18

A_s = area of a pair of diagonal stiffeners,

$$A_s = b_s \, t_s$$

In the usual detailing of the connection, the required web thickness (w_r) is first found. The actual web thickness (w) of course is known, therefore it would be simpler to change this formula into the following so that the required area of the diagonal stiffener may be found from these two values (w_r) and (w):

From Formula 10,

$$w_r = \frac{\sqrt{3}\, M_p}{d_b \; d_c \; \sigma_y} \quad \text{or}$$

$$M_p = \frac{w_r \; d_b \; d_c \; \sigma_y}{\sqrt{3}}$$

and substituting this into Formula 12,

$$A_s = \frac{1}{\cos \theta} \left[\frac{M_p}{d_b \; \sigma_y} - \frac{w \; d_c}{\sqrt{3}} \right]$$

and since

$$\cos \theta = \frac{d_c}{d_s}$$

$$\therefore \boxed{A_s = \frac{d_c \; (w_r - w)}{\sqrt{3} \; \cos \theta}} \quad \ldots\ldots\ldots\ldots\ldots\ldots (13)$$

or

$$\boxed{A_s = \frac{d_s \; (w_r - w)}{\sqrt{3}}} \quad \ldots\ldots\ldots\ldots\ldots\ldots (14)$$

or could use

$$t_s = t_f$$

also in all cases

$$\boxed{\frac{b_s}{t_s} \leqq 17} \quad \ldots\ldots\ldots\ldots\ldots\ldots\ldots\ldots\ldots (15)$$

For full strength, stiffeners should be welded across their ends with either fillet welds or groove welds, and to the connection web with continuous fillet welds.

Problem 1

To design a 90° connection for a 21″ WF 62# roof girder to a 14″ WF 84# column. Use A36 steel and E70 welds. Load from girder: M_p ultimate plastic moment = 432 ft-kips.

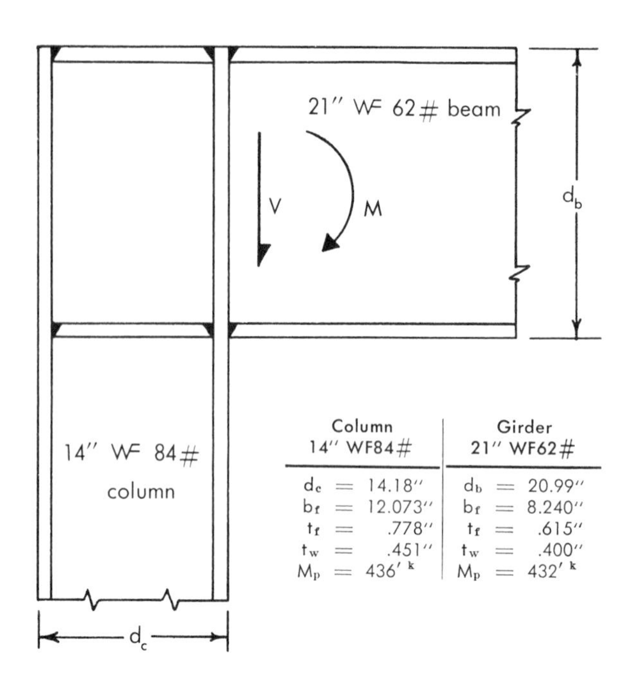

FIGURE 19

The required web reinforcement is determined as follows:

$$w_r \geqq \frac{\sqrt{3}\; M_p}{d_b \; d_c \; \sigma_y}$$

$$\geqq \frac{\sqrt{3}\;(432 \text{ ft-kips x } 12)}{(20.99'')(14.18'')(36 \text{ ksi})} \qquad \geqq 0.837''$$

web furnished by the 14″ WF 84# column = 0.451″

effective web to be furnished by stiffeners ≧ 0.386″

This reinforcement may be provided by one of two possible types of stiffeners as noted below.

(a) Web Doubler Plate

The additional web plate must be sufficient to develop the required web thickness. The welds should be arranged at the edges so as to transmit the shear forces directly to the boundary stiffeners and flanges. Plate must be .386″ thick, or use a 7/16″ thick plate.

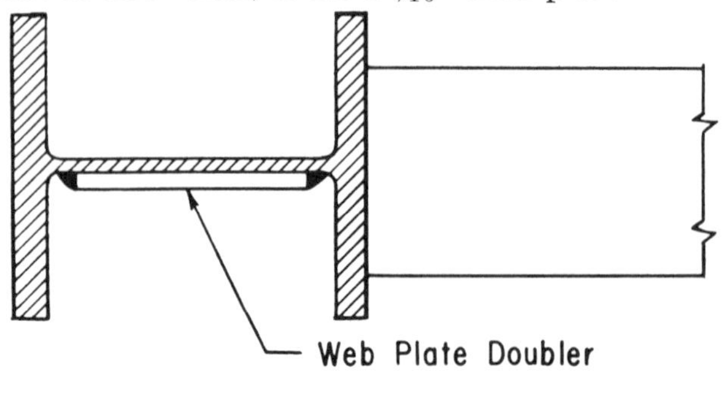

FIGURE 20

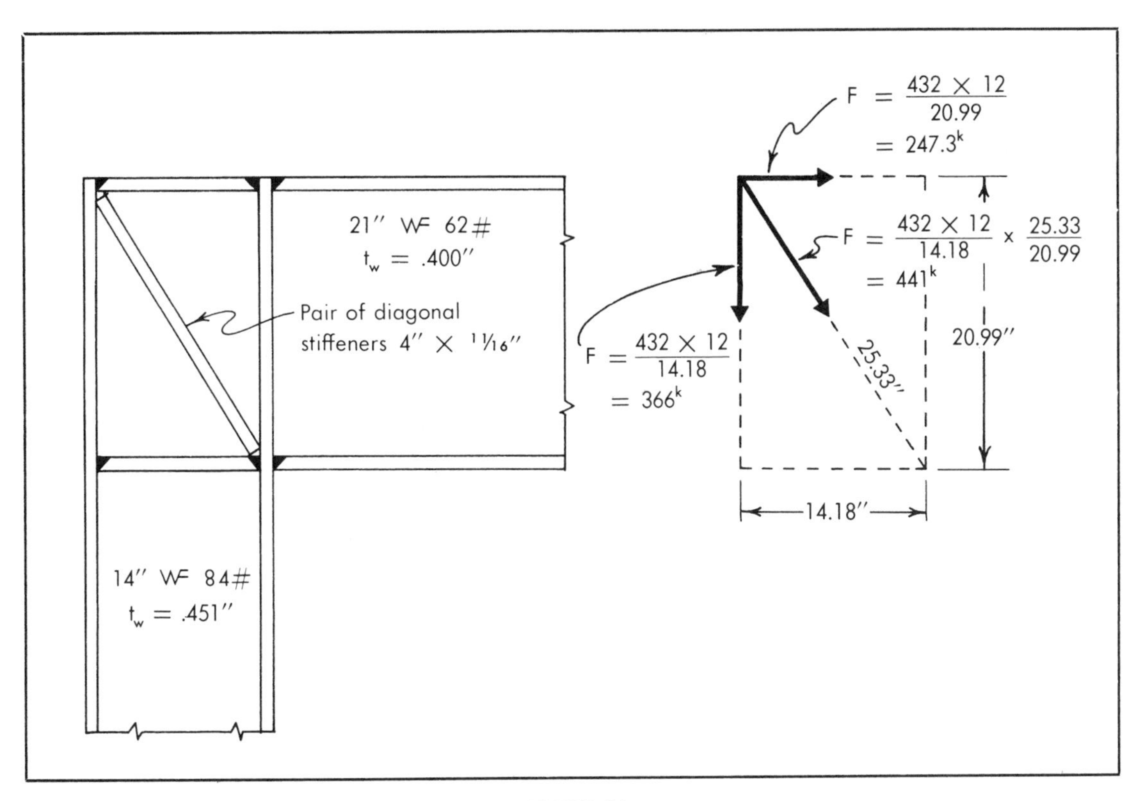

FIGURE 21

(b) Diagonal Stiffener

The diagonal stiffener will resist the diagonal component of the flange load as a compression strut. The flange force to be carried by the stiffener is the portion that exceeds the amount carried by the web. Assuming the bending moment to be carried entirely by the flanges, the compressive force in the diagonal stiffener is computed as in Figure 21.

Multiply this diagonal compressive force of 441 kips by the ratio of the additional thickness needed to that already in the web:

$$441\left(\frac{.386}{.837}\right) = 204 \text{ kips force on diagonal stiffener}$$

or

$$A_s = \frac{P}{\sigma_y}$$

$$= \frac{204 \text{ kips}}{36 \text{ ksi}}$$

$$= 5.65 \ in.^2 \text{ needed in the stiffener}$$

or use a pair of ¾″ x 4″ stiffeners, $A_s = 6.0 > 5.65$ OK

Now solve this portion of the problem by using Formula 3:

$$A_s = \frac{d_c}{\sqrt{3}\cos\theta}\ (w_r - w)$$

where:

$$\theta = \tan^{-1}\frac{d_b}{d_c}$$

$$= \tan^{-1}\frac{(20.99)}{(14.18)}$$

$$= \tan^{-1} 1.48 \qquad \text{or}$$

$$\theta = 55.93°$$

and

$$\cos 55.93° = .560$$

$$\therefore\ A_s = \frac{14.18}{\sqrt{3}\,(.560)}\ (.837 - .451)$$

$$= 5.65 \ in.^2 \text{ needed in the stiffener}$$

If $b_s = 8''$, then

$$t_s = \frac{A_s}{b_s}$$

$$= \frac{5.65}{8}$$

$$= .707'' \text{ or } use\ ¾''$$

Or use two plates, ¾″ x 4″, for the diagonal stiffeners. Check their width-to-thickness ratio:

$$\frac{b_s}{t_s} = \frac{8}{¾} = 10.7 < 17 \qquad \underline{\text{OK}}$$

Welds for Stiffener

Only nominal fillet welding is required between stiffener and connection web to resist buckling. These welds are used simply to hold the stiffeners in position. Welding at terminations of the stiffener should be sufficient to transfer forces.

To develop the full capacity of the stiffener, it may be butt welded to the corners, or full-strength fillet welds may be used.

The required leg size of fillet weld to match the ultimate capacity of the stiffener would be—

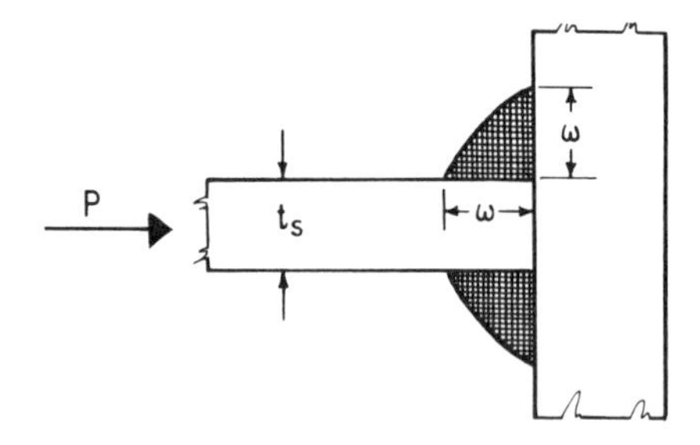

FIGURE 22

E60 Welds & A7, A373 Plate

$$2(9600\ \omega)1.67 = t_s\ 33{,}000$$

$$\omega = 1.03\ t_s$$

$$\boxed{\omega = t_s} \quad \text{..........................} \quad (16)$$

E70 Welds & A36 Plate

$$2(11{,}200\ \omega)1.67 = t_s\ 36{,}000$$

$$\omega = .96\ t_s$$

$$\boxed{\omega = t_s} \quad \text{..........................} \quad (16)$$

Hence, use ¾″ leg fillet welds across the ends of the stiffener.

It may be simpler to make the cross-sectional area of these diagonal stiffeners equal to that of the flange of the member whose web they reinforce.

5. HAUNCHED CONNECTIONS

Haunched connections, Figure 23, are sometimes used in order to more nearly match the moment requirements of a frame. This produces a deeepr section in the region of maximum moment, extending back until the moment is reduced to a value which the rolled section is capable of carrying. In this manner a smaller rolled section may be used for the remainder of the frame. This has been a rather standard practice in the conventional elastic rigid frame.

Haunched knees may exhibit poor rotational ability if the knee buckles laterally before the desired design conditions have been reached.

The haunch connection should be proportioned with sufficient strength and buckling resistance so that a plastic hinge may be formed at the end of the haunch where it joins the rolled member.

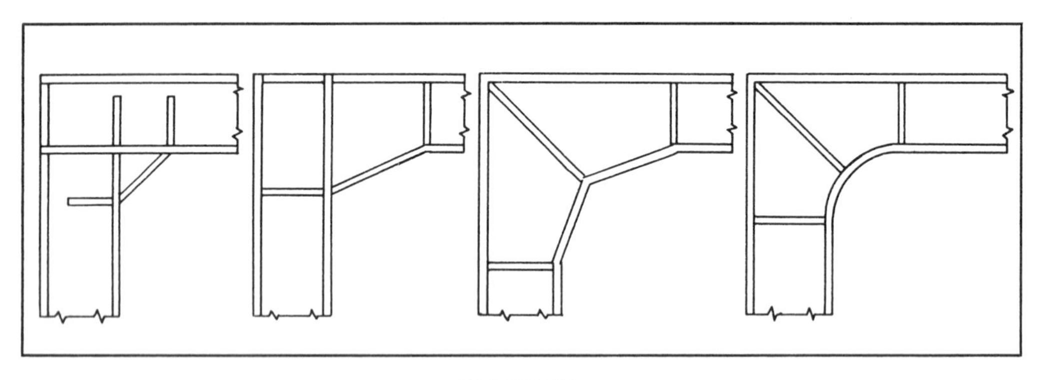

FIGURE 23

Lehigh University's extensive research in plastic design included the testing to destruction of full-scale structures such as this 40′ gabled frame.

Plastic design of this 8-acre rubber plant simplified mathematical analysis of the structure and moment distribution. Two results: a uniform factor of safety and a saving of 140 tons of structural steel.

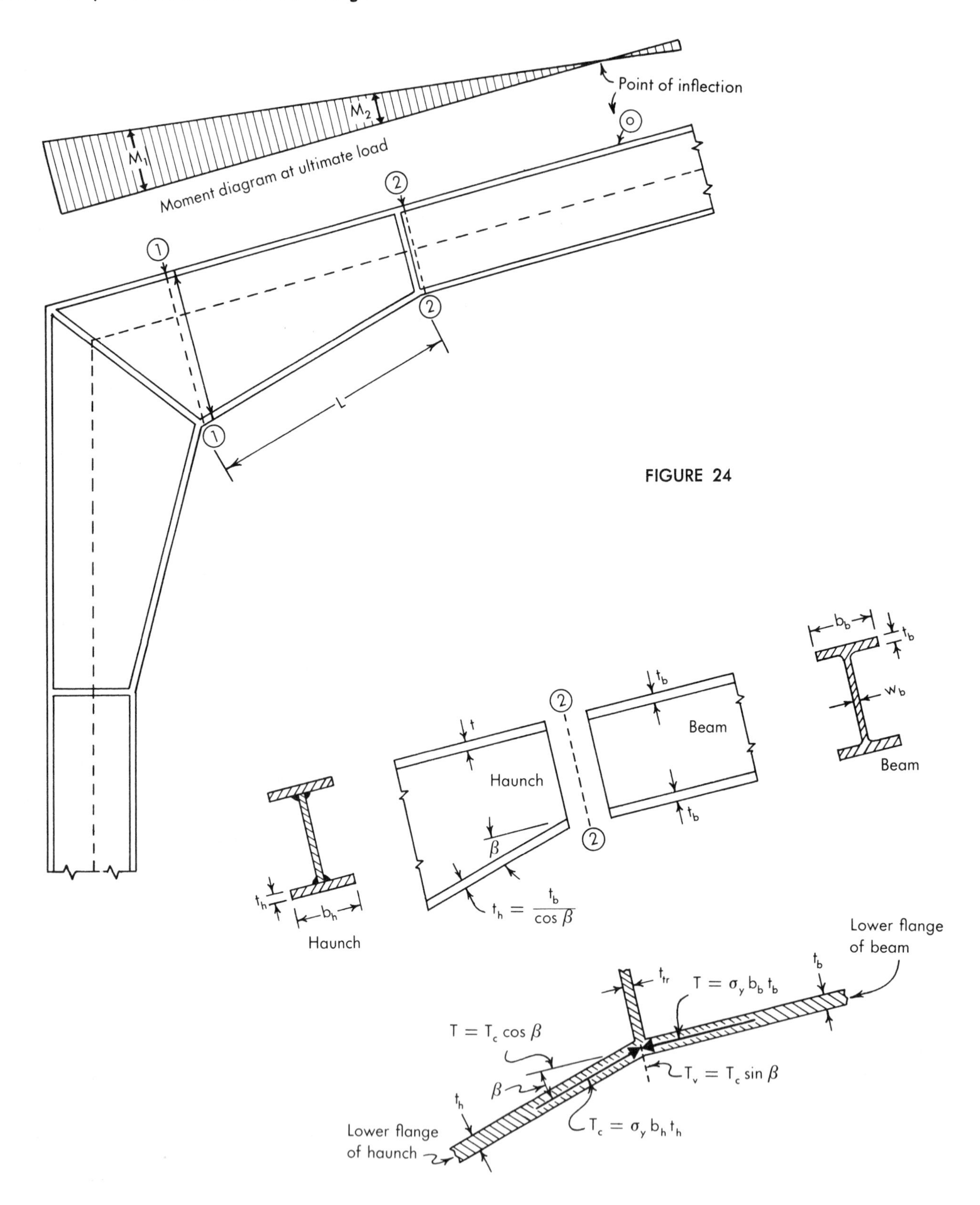

FIGURE 24

FIGURE 25

A. TAPERED HAUNCH CONNECTIONS

(See Figures 24 and 25, facing page)

Thickness of Top Flange and Web of Haunch

The thickness of the top flange and the web of the haunch should be at least equal to the thickness of the rolled beam to which it connects.

Thickness of Lower Flange of Haunch

The lower flange of the haunch must be increased in thickness so that when it is stressed to the yield point (σ_y), its horizontal component will be equal to the force in the lower beam flange stressed to yield.

The force in the sloping lower flange of the haunch at the plastic moment (M_p) is—

$$T_c = \sigma_y \, b_h \, t_h$$

The component of this force (T_c) in line with and against the force in the beam flange is—

$$T = T_c \cos \beta$$
$$= \sigma_y \, b_h \, t_h \cos \beta$$

and this must match the force (T) in the lower flange of the rolled beam, or:

$$T = \sigma_y \, b_h \, t_h \cos \beta \text{ must equal } T = \sigma_y \, b_b \, t_b$$

Assuming the same flange width for the haunch as the beam, i.e. $b_h = b_b$, gives—

$$\boxed{t_h = \frac{t_b}{\cos \beta}} \quad \ldots\ldots (17)$$

Transverse Stiffeners

$$T_v = T_c \sin \beta$$

or $\quad \sigma_y \, b_{tr} \, t_{tr} = \sigma_y \, b_h \, t_h \sin \beta$

Assuming the same flange width for the stiffener as the beam, i.e. $b_{tr} = b_b$, gives—

$$\boxed{t_{tr} = t_h \sin \beta} \quad \ldots\ldots (18)$$

AISC suggests making the total area of these stiffeners not less than ¾ of the haunch flange area (AISC Commentary p 37, item 4).

Required Haunch Section

Section (1-1), in the region of high moment, should be checked. The two flanges may vary in thickness, so for simplicity and a conservative value use the upper flange's thickness. Since this is the tension flange, it will be same or thinner than the lower (compression) flange. It can be shown that the plastic section modulus (Z) of an I section is:

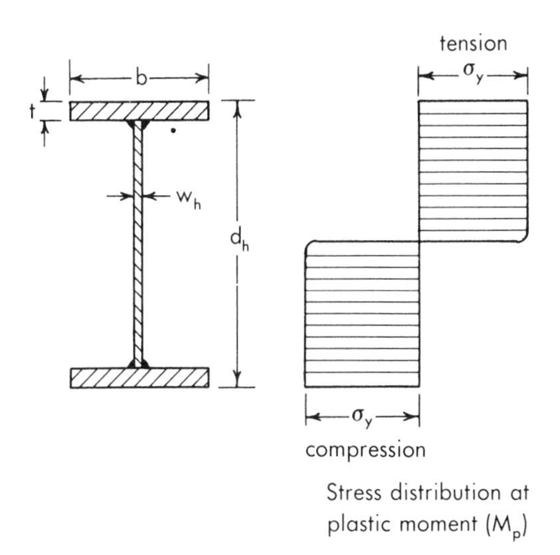

FIGURE 26

resisting plastic moment of section

$$M_p = 2 \, b \, t \, \sigma_y \left(\frac{d_h - t}{2}\right) + 2 \, w_h \left(\frac{d_h - 2t}{2}\right)\left(\frac{d_h - 2t}{4}\right)$$

since

$$\boxed{Z = \frac{M_p}{\sigma_y}} \quad \ldots\ldots (19)$$

$$\boxed{Z = b \, t \, (d_h - t) + \frac{w_h}{4} (d_h - 2t)^2} \quad .(20)$$

This increased plastic section modulus may be obtained by:

1. Increasing the depth (d_h) and holding the flange area constant, or

2. Increasing the flange thickness (t) and holding the depth (d_h) constant.

By assuming that ($d_h - t$) is equal to ($d_h - 2t$), and solving for the expression ($d_h - 2t$), it is found from the above formula that:

$$\boxed{d_h = 2\sqrt{\frac{b^2 t^2}{{w_h}^2} + \frac{Z}{w_h}} + 2t\left(1 - \frac{b}{w_h}\right)} \quad (21)$$

From this, the required depth (d_h) of the haunch may be found for any value of plastic section modulus (Z).

The haunch section must be able to develop the plastic moment at any point along its length:

$$\boxed{M_p = Z\,\sigma_y} \qquad (22)$$

or at any section (x-x)—

$$\boxed{\sigma_x = \frac{M_p}{Z} \leqq \sigma_y} \qquad (23)$$

Usually just the two ends of the haunch must be checked. This would be section (1-1) at the haunch point (H), and section (2-2) at the connection to the rolled beam. The latter finding will also dictate the required section modulus of the straight beam, since its highest moment will occur at section (2-2).

Beedle* points out that if the moment is assumed to increase linerally from the point of inflection (O) to the haunch point (H), and the distance (O-R) from the point of inflection to the end of the rolled beam is 3 d, then the critical section will always be along (2-2) if the angle β of the taper is greater than 12°; if this angle is less than 12°, then section (1-1) must *also* be checked.

Lateral Stability

Bracing should be placed at the extremities and the common intersecting points of the compression flange.

The commentary of the AISC specifications sets the following limits for lateral bracing.

The taper of the haunch may be such that the resulting bending stress at plastic loading, when computed by using the plastic modulus (Z), is approximately at yield (σ_y) at both ends ① & ②. If this is the case, then limit the unbraced length (L_h):

$$\boxed{L_h \leqq 6\, b_h} \qquad (24)$$

or as an alternate, increase the thickness of the haunch flanges by the factor:

$$\boxed{t = t_h \left[1 + 0.1 \left(\frac{L_h}{b_h} - 6 \right) \right]} \qquad (25)$$

If the bending stress at one end is approximately at yield (σ_y), using the plastic modulus (Z), and at the other end is less than yield ($\sigma_x < \sigma_y$) when using the secton modulus (S), limit the unbraced length (L_h):

$$\boxed{L_h \leqq (17.5 - 0.40\,\sigma_x)\, b_h} \qquad (26)$$

but

$$\boxed{L_h \geqq 6\, b_h}$$

If the bending stress computed on the basis of section modulus (S) is less than yield ($\sigma_x < \sigma_y$) at all transverse sections of the haunch from ① to ②, then check to see that greatest computed stress:

* "Plastic Design of Steel Frames" Lynn S. Beedle; John S. Wiley & Sons, publishers.

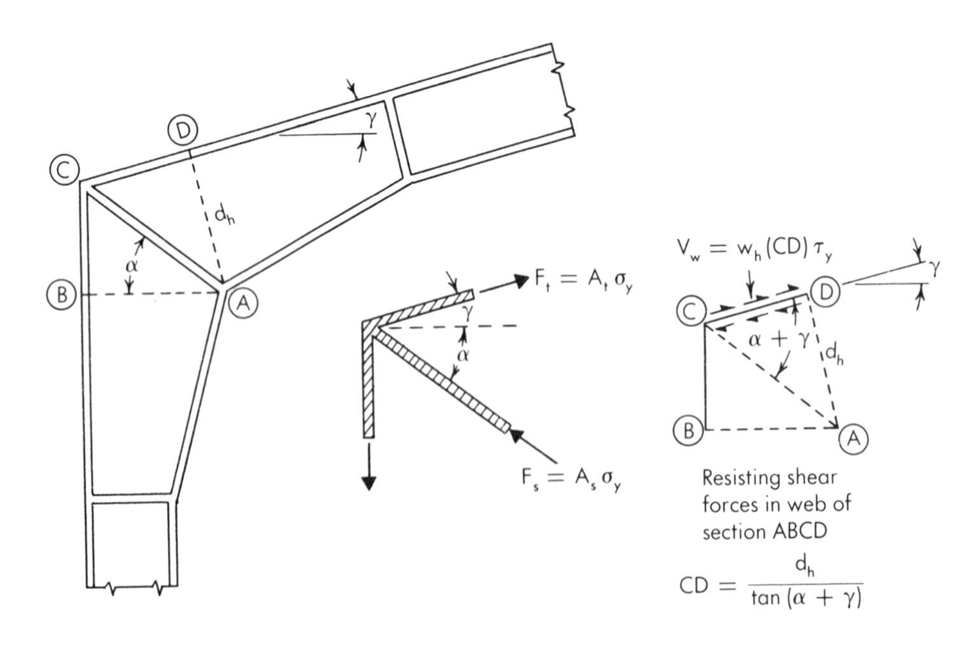

FIGURE 27

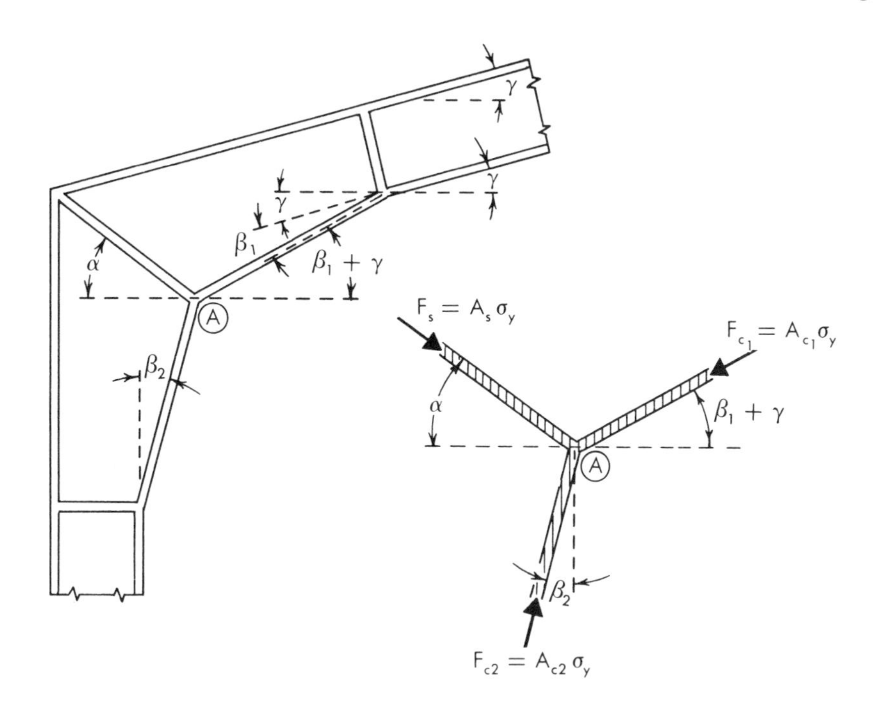

FIGURE 28

$$\sigma_x \leqq \frac{(12 \text{ x } 10^6)1.67}{\frac{L_h \, d_{max}}{A_c}} \quad \ldots\ldots\ldots\ldots\ldots\ldots\ldots (27)$$

Diagonal Stiffeners

The tapered haunch has an extra-large web area in the bend of the knee. This is subject to buckling, and should be strengthened by diagonal stiffeners. The required stiffener section area should be figured from the compressive force on the web diagonal resulting from the larger of two forces: (a) the tensile forces on the outer flange of the haunch at point (C), and (b) the compressive forces on the inner flange of the haunch at point (A)

(1) Based on tensile forces at (C)

The compressive force in the diagonal stiffener is found by taking the sum of the horizontal components of the forces in the outer flanges and setting them equal to zero. See Figure 27.

$$+ A_t \, \sigma_y \cos \gamma - \left(\frac{w_h \, d_h}{\tan(\alpha + \gamma)}\right)\left(\frac{\sigma_y}{\sqrt{3}}\right) \cos \gamma - A_s \, \sigma_y \cos \alpha = 0$$

or

$$A_s = A_t\left(\frac{\cos \gamma}{\cos \alpha}\right) - \left(\frac{w_h \, d_h \cos \gamma}{\sqrt{3} \tan(\alpha + \gamma) \cos \alpha}\right)$$

$$A_s = \frac{\cos \gamma}{\cos \alpha}\left[A_t - \frac{w_h \, d_h}{\sqrt{3} \tan(\alpha + \gamma)}\right] \quad .(28)$$

where:

A_t = area of top (tension) flange of haunch

A_s = total area of a pair of diagonal stiffeners

(2) Based on compressive forces at 

The compressive force in the diagonal stiffener is found in a similar manner as before; the horizontal components of the forces in the inner flanges are set in equilibrium. See Figure 28.

$$+ A_s \, \sigma_y \cos \alpha + A_{c2} \, \sigma_y \sin \beta_2 - A_{c1} \, \sigma_y \cos(\beta_1 + \gamma) = 0$$

or

$$A_s = \frac{A_{c1} \cos(\beta_1 + \gamma) - A_{c2} \sin \beta_2}{\cos \alpha} \quad \ldots .(29)$$

If $A_c = A_{c1} = A_{c2}$, this becomes—

$$A_s = \frac{A_c}{\cos \alpha}\left[\cos(\beta_1 + \gamma) - \sin \beta_2\right] \quad .(30)$$

(3) When outer (tensile) flanges form right angle

If the beam and column are at right angles to each other, $\gamma = 0$. See Figure 29.

and $\beta = \beta_1 = \beta_2$

$\alpha = 45°$

$A_c = A_{c1} = A_{c2}$

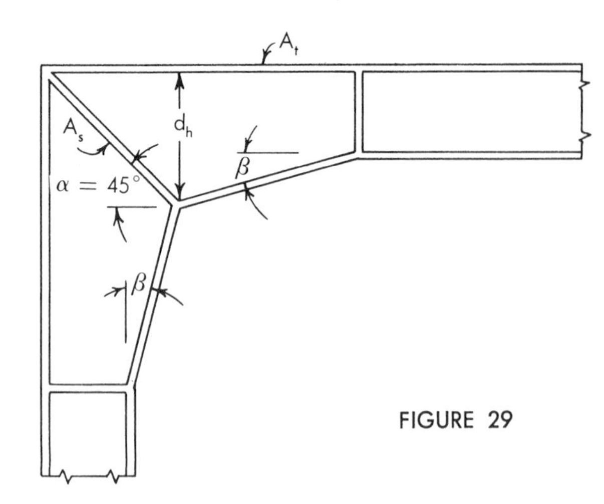

FIGURE 29

Then the preceding two formulas reduce to the following:

based on tensile forces in outer flanges and shear resistance of web

$$A_s \geqq \sqrt{2}\, A_t - 0.82\, w_h\, d_h \qquad (31)$$

based on compressive forces in inner flange

$$A_s \geqq \sqrt{2}\, A_c\, (\cos \beta - \sin \beta) \qquad (32)$$

also

$$\frac{b_s}{t_s} \leqq 17 \qquad (33)$$

The modified formulas above may also be used for convenience in finding the stiffener requirement of gable frames, but will provide a more conservative value.

Summary of Tapered Haunch Requirements

$$w_h \geqq w_{beam}$$

$$t_h \geqq \frac{t_b}{\cos \beta}$$

Based on load from tension flange—

$$A_s \geqq \sqrt{2}\, A_t - 0.82\, w_h d_h$$

Based on load from compression flange—

$$A_s \geqq \sqrt{2}\, A_c\, (\cos \beta - \sin \beta)$$

also $\dfrac{b_s}{t_s} \leqq 17$

$$t_{tr} \geqq t_h \sin \beta = \frac{b_h}{17}$$

$$t_{tr}\, b_{tr} \geqq \tfrac{3}{4}\, t_b b_b$$

$$Z_h = b\, t\, (d_h - t) + \frac{w_h}{4}\, (d_h - 2\, t)^2 \geqq \frac{M_p}{\sigma_y}$$

Check lateral stability of compression flange

(a) if both ends of haunch ① or ② are stressed to yield (σ_y) using Z

$$L_h \leqq 6\, b_h$$

or increase $t = t_h \left[1 + 0.1 \left(\dfrac{L_h}{b_h} - 6 \right) \right]$

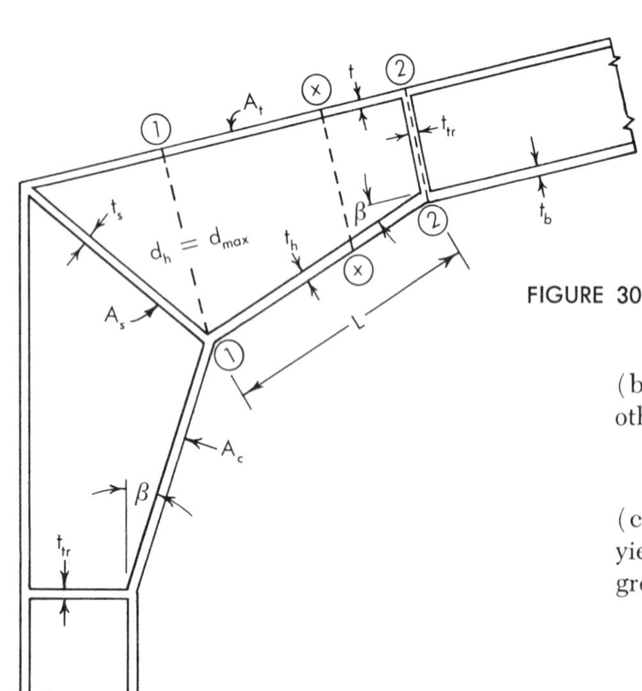

FIGURE 30

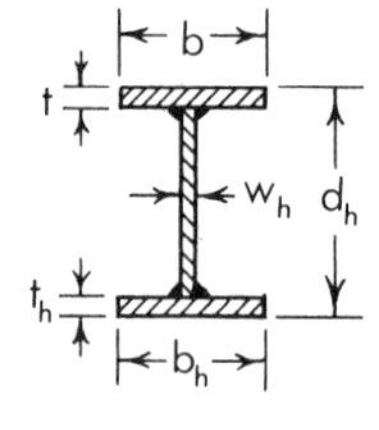

Section 1-1

(b) if one end is stressed to yield (σ_y) using Z, and other end is stressed below yield ($\sigma_x < \sigma_y$) using S

$$L_h \leqq (17.5 - 0.40\, \sigma_x)\, b_h \geqq 6\, b_h$$

(c) if entire haunch from ① to ② is stressed below yield ($\sigma_x < \sigma_y$) using S. Here, check to see that greatest commuted stress:

$$\sigma_x \leqq \frac{(12 \times 10^6)1.67}{\dfrac{L_h\, d_{max}}{A_c}}$$

B. CURVED HAUNCH CONNECTIONS

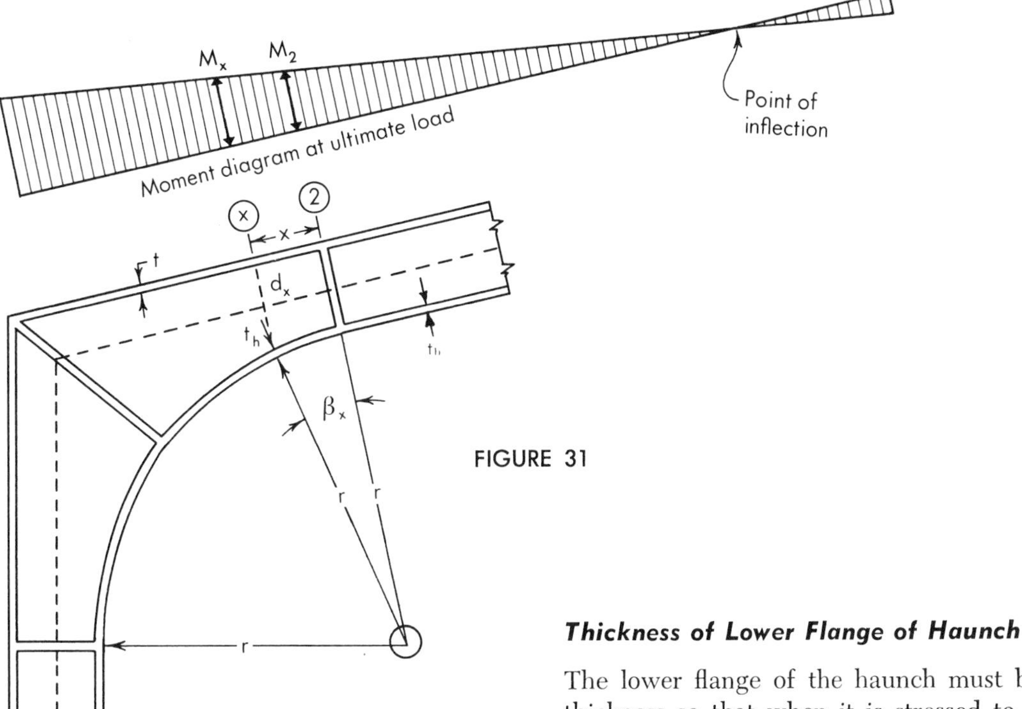

FIGURE 31

Here:

β = angle between tangents of given section and beam flange

r = radius of curvature of inner flange

d_x = depth of curved haunch at any section (x-x)

$= d_2 + r(1 - \cos \beta_x)$

$x = r \sin \beta_x$

It is seen in Figure 31 that the moment resulting from ultimate loading gradually increases out to the corner of the haunch. However, the depth of the haunch and therefore its bending stress also increases toward the corner, so that the critical section (x-x) within the haunch will occur at some distance (x) or some angle (β_x) from section 2-2. For most curved haunches, this angle (β_x) will be about 12°.

Thickness of Top Flange and Web of Haunch

The thickness of the top flange and of the web of the haunch should be at least equal to these features of the rolled beam to which it connects. If bending stress at ②, $\sigma_2 = \dfrac{M_2}{S} < \sigma_y$, then the outer flange thickness of the haunch (t) does not have to exceed the beam flange thickness (t_b) (AISC Commentary).

Thickness of Lower Flange of Haunch

The lower flange of the haunch must be increased in thickness so that when it is stressed to yield (σ_y), its component along the beam axis is equal to the force in the lower beam flange when stressed to yield.

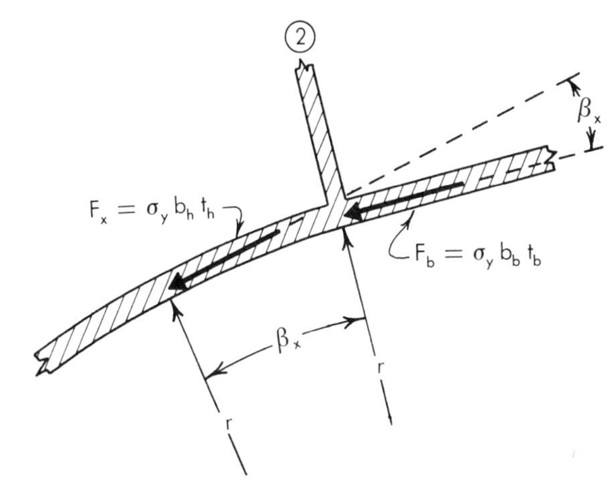

FIGURE 32

$$F_x = \frac{F_b}{\cos \beta_x}$$

$$\sigma_y \, b_h \, t_h = \frac{\sigma_y \, b_b \, t_b}{\cos \beta_x}$$

or

$$\boxed{t_h \geq \frac{t_b}{\cos \beta_x}} \qquad (34)$$

As in the tapered haunch, the plastic section modulus (Z) at any given point (X) is:

$$Z_x = b_h\, t_h\, (d_x - t_h) + \frac{w_h}{4}(d_x - 2\, t_h)^2 \quad \cdots (35)$$

For any given depth (d_x), the plastic section modulus (Z_x) may be increased by increasing the flange thickness (t_h).

Assuming the web thickness and flange width of the curved haunch is at least equal to that of the beam, the required thickness of the lower flange would be:

$$Z_x = b_h\, t_h\, (d_x - t_h) + \frac{w_h}{4}(d_x - 2\, t_h)^2$$

$$Z_x = b_h d_x t_h - b_h t_h^2 + \frac{w_h d_x^2}{4} - w_h d_x t_h + w_h t_h^2$$

$$t_h^2\,(b_h - w_h) - t_h\, d_x\,(b_h - w_h) - \frac{w_h\, d_x^2}{d} + Z_x = 0$$

$$t_h = \frac{d_x}{2} - \sqrt{\frac{\dfrac{d_x^2\, b_h}{4} - Z_x}{b_h - w_h}} \quad \cdots\cdots\cdots\cdots (36)$$

The AISC Commentary (Sec. 2.7) recommends that the thickness of this inner flange of the curved haunch should be—

$$t_h \geqq (1 + m)\, t \quad \cdots\cdots\cdots\cdots (37)$$

where values for (m) come from the graph, Figure 33.

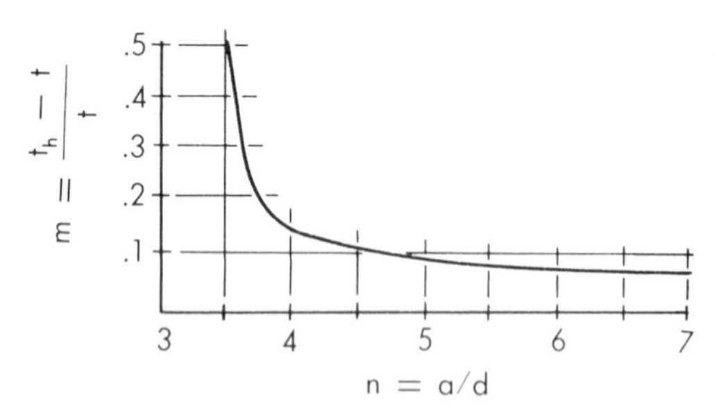

FIGURE 33

Here:

a = distance from point of inflection (M = 0) of the column to the point of plastic moment (M_p) in the haunch

d = depth of column section

In order to prevent local buckling of the curved inner flange, limit the radius of curvature to—

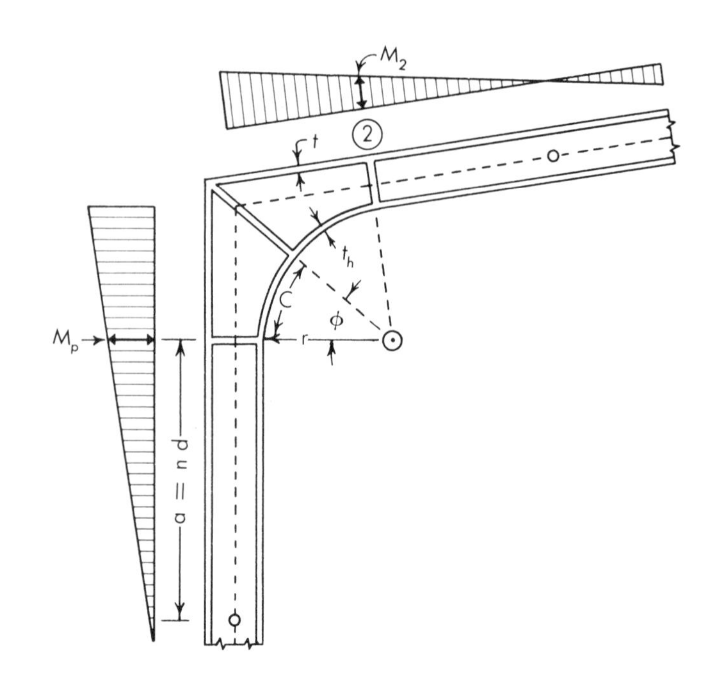

FIGURE 34

$$r \leqq 6\, b_h \quad ^{*} \cdots\cdots\cdots\cdots (38)$$

This is based on a 90° knee (outer flanges form a right angle), which is the most conservative.

The radius of curvature may be increased above this limit if additional points of support are added to decrease the critical arc length (C).

The unbraced length between points of lateral support must be held to—

$$C \leqq 6\, b_h \quad \cdots\cdots\cdots\cdots (39)$$

where

$C = r\, \phi$

ϕ = radian measure

If the unbraced length (C) exceeds this limit, the thickness of the curved inner flange must be increased by—

$$0.1\left(\frac{C}{b_h} - 6\right) t_h$$

or the final thickness will be—

$$t_h\left[1 + 0.1\left(\frac{C}{b_h} - 6\right)\right] \quad \cdots\cdots\cdots\cdots (40)$$

An alternate method would be to increase the width of the inner flange (b_h) to a minimum of C/6

* ASCE Commentary on Plastic Design in Steel, p. 116.

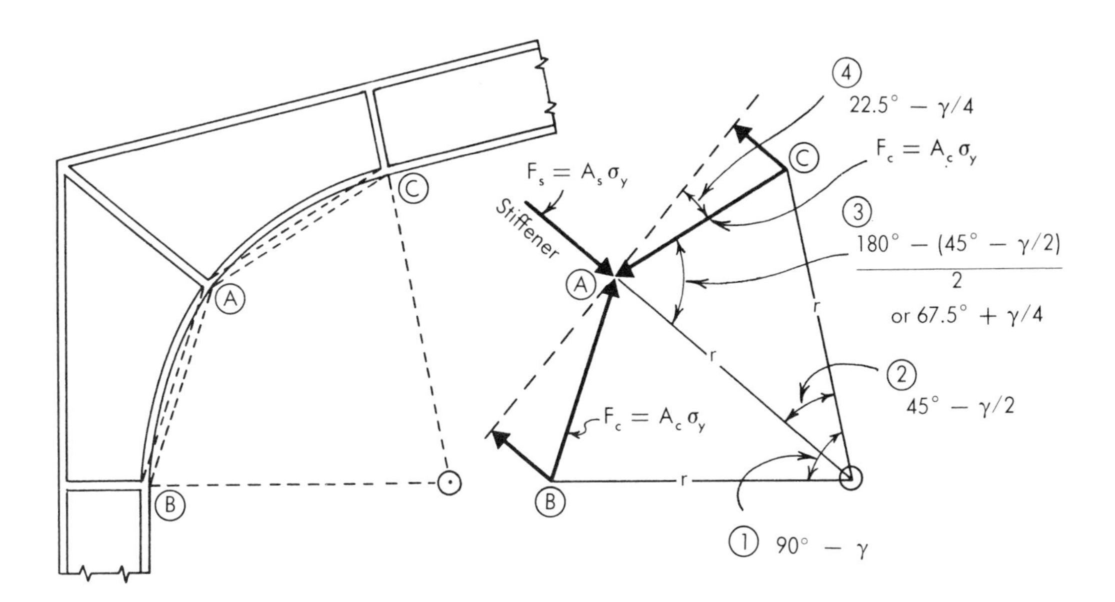

FIGURE 35

without decreasing the original flange thickness (t_h):

$$\boxed{b_h \geqq \frac{C}{6}} \quad \ldots\ldots\ldots\ldots\ldots\ldots\ldots\ldots (41)$$

Diagonal Stiffeners

(1) Based on compressive forces at (A)

An approximate value of the compressive force applied to the diagonal stiffener as a result of the compressive forces in the curved inner flange may be made by treating the curved haunch as a tapered haunch. See Figure 35.

$$A_s \sigma_y = 2\ A_c\ \sigma_y \sin\ (22.5° - \gamma/4)$$

or

$$\boxed{A_s \geqq 2\ A_c \sin\left(\frac{90° - \gamma}{4}\right)} \quad \ldots\ldots\ldots\ldots (42)$$

(2) Based on tensile forces at (C)

The compressive force in the diagonal stiffener is found by taking the horizontal components of these tensile flange forces, and setting them equal to zero. See Figure 36.

$$A_t\ \sigma_y \cos\gamma - \frac{w_h\ d_h}{\tan(\alpha + \gamma)}\ \frac{\sigma_y}{\sqrt{3}} \cos\gamma - A_s\ \sigma_y \cos\alpha = 0$$

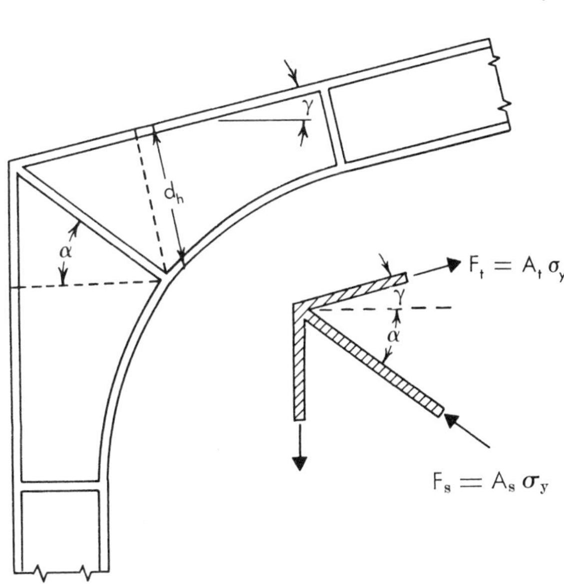

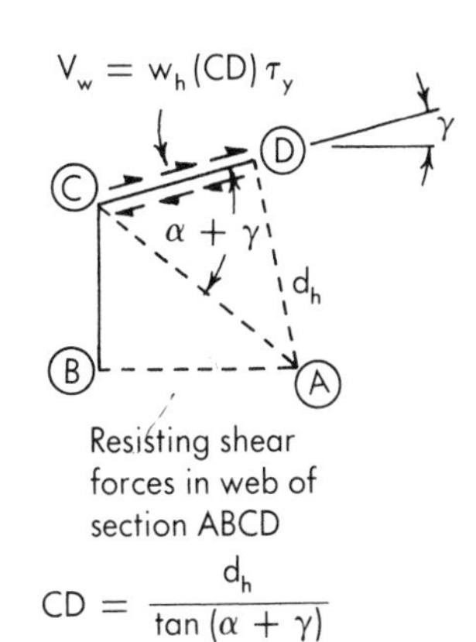

FIGURE 36

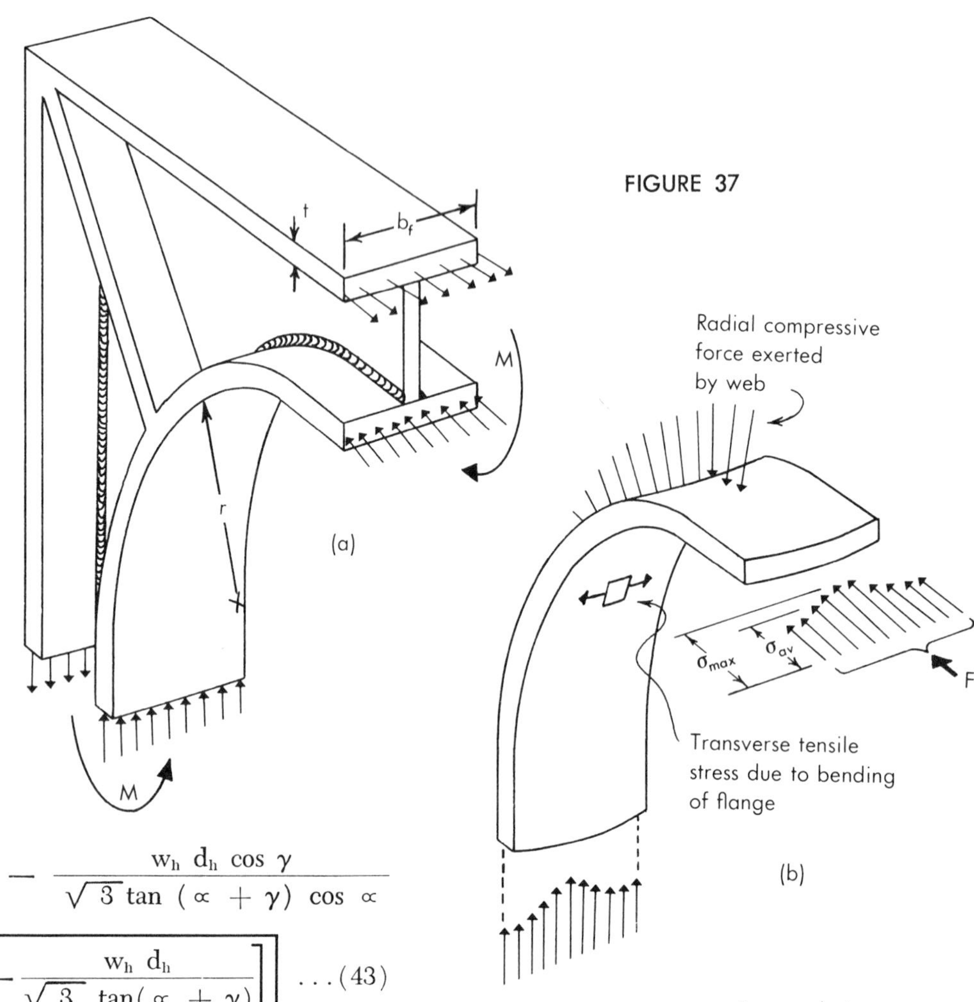

FIGURE 37

or

$$A_s = A_t \frac{\cos \gamma}{\cos \alpha} - \frac{w_h\, d_h \cos \gamma}{\sqrt{3} \tan(\alpha + \gamma) \cos \alpha}$$

$$\boxed{A_s \geq \frac{\cos \gamma}{\cos \alpha}\left[A_t - \frac{w_h\, d_h}{\sqrt{3}\ \tan(\alpha + \gamma)}\right]} \qquad \ldots (43)$$

where:

A_t = area of top (tension) flange of haunch

A_s = total area of a pair of diagonal stiffeners

Radial Support of Lower Flange

The radial components of force in the curved inner flange tend to push the flange in toward the web, and to bend the flange as shown in Figure 37(b). Because of the slight yielding of the outer edge of the flange, there is a non-uniform distribution of the flange stress (σ), Figure 37(a). This stress is maximum in line with the web. There is also a transverse tensile stress across the outer face of this flange, Figure 37(b).

The unit radial force (f_r) acting on the curved inner flange from the axial compressive force (F_c) within the flange, Figure 38, is—

$$f_r = \frac{F_c}{r} \quad \text{(lbs/cir inch)}$$

Treating a 1″ slice of this flange supported by the web of the haunch as a cantilever beam and uniformly loaded with this unit radial force (f_r), Figure 39:

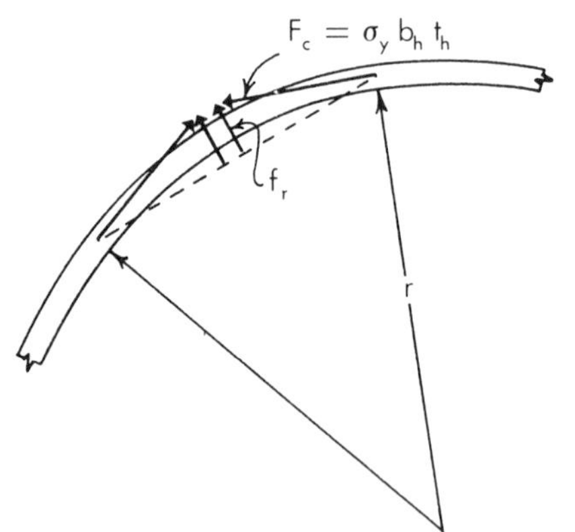

FIGURE 38

$$Z = \frac{t_h^2}{4}$$

$$f_r = \frac{F_c}{r} = \frac{\sigma_y\, b_h\, t_h}{r}$$

or unit load (p) on section:

$$p = \frac{\sigma_y\, t_h}{r}$$

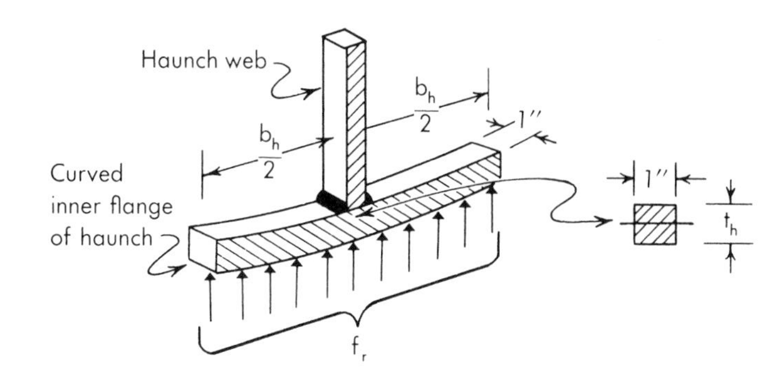

FIGURE 39

$$M = \frac{p}{2}\left(\frac{b}{2}\right)^2$$

$$M = \frac{\sigma_y\ t_h}{2\ r}\left(\frac{b_h}{2}\right)^2 = \frac{\sigma_y\ t_h\ b_h^2}{8\ r}$$

also

$$M \leqq \sigma_y\ Z \leqq \frac{\sigma_y\ t_h^2}{4}$$

$$\frac{b_h^2}{8\ r} \leqq \frac{t_h}{4}$$

or

$$\boxed{\frac{b_h^2}{r\ t_h} \leqq 2} \qquad (44)$$

Therefore limit the ratio of flange width to thickness (b_f/t_x) of the curved inner flange to the following, whichever is the smaller:

$$\boxed{\frac{b_h}{t_h} \leqq \frac{2\ r}{b_h} \leqq 17} \qquad (45)$$

Provide stiffeners at and midway between the two points of tangency. Make the total cross-sectional area of the pair of diagonal stiffeners at their midpoint not less than ¾ of the inner curved flange area.

Summary of Curved Haunch Requirements

thickness of outer flange $(t) \geqq t_b$

web of haunch $(w_h) \geqq w_b$

thickness of curved inner flange $(t_h) \geqq \dfrac{t_b}{\cos\beta}$

$$= (1 + m)\ t$$

(based on tensile flange)

$$A_s \geqq \frac{\cos\gamma}{\cos\alpha}\left[A_t - \frac{w_h\ d_h}{\sqrt{3}\tan(\alpha + \gamma)}\right]$$

(based on compressive flange)

$$A_s \geqq 2A_c \sin\left(\frac{90 - \gamma}{4}\right) \quad \text{and}$$

$$A_s \geqq \tfrac{3}{4}\ A_c$$

If bending stress at ② $\sigma_2 = \dfrac{M_2}{S} < \sigma_y$, then

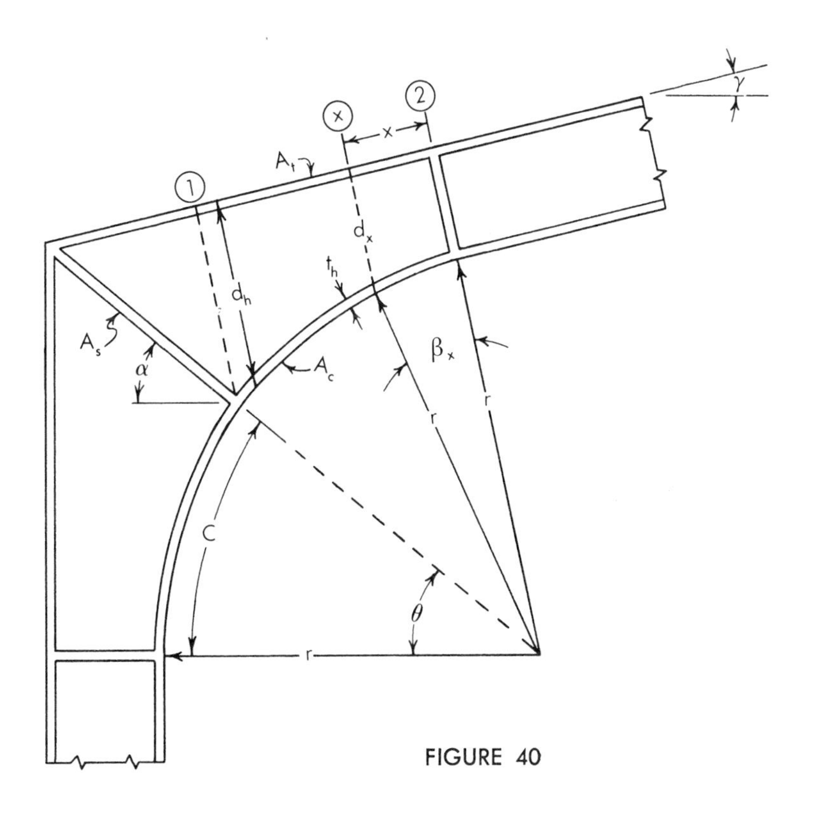

FIGURE 40

outer flange thickness (t) does not have to exceed beam flange (t_b).

$$r \leqq 6\ b_h$$

Otherwise, use additional lateral support to decrease arc length (C).

Assume critical section (x-x) at—

$$\beta_x = 12°$$

then

$$Z_x = b_h\ t_h\ (d_x - t_h) + \frac{w_h}{4}\ (d_x - 2\ t_h)^2$$

and

$$Z_x \geqq \frac{M_x}{x}$$

$$C \leqq 6\ b_h$$

where:

$C = r\ \phi$

ϕ = radian measure

Otherwise, increase the thickness of the curved flange to—

$$t_h \left[1 + 0.1 \left(\frac{C}{b} - 6 \right) \right]$$

or increase the width of the curved inner flange to—

$$b_h \geqq \frac{C}{6}$$

without decreasing the flange thickness.

$$\frac{b_h}{t_x} \leqq \frac{2\ r}{b_h} \leqq 17$$

6. BEAM-TO-COLUMN CONNECTIONS (Multiple Span)

Web Resisting Shear

When the moments in two beams framing into an interior column differ by a larger amount, this difference in moment will cause large shear forces to act on the connection web. The web must be checked to see if it has sufficient thickness; if not, it must be reinforced with either a web doubler plate or diagonal stiffeners. (See Figure 41.)

horizontal shear applied on connection web

along top portion

$$= F_2 - F_1 - V_4$$

$$= \frac{M_2}{d_2} - \frac{M_1}{d_1} - V_4$$

shear resisted by connection web

along top portion

$$= w\ d_c\ \tau_y$$

$$= w\ d_c\ \frac{\sigma_y}{\sqrt{3}} \qquad \text{or}$$

$$w\ d_c\ \frac{\sigma_y}{\sqrt{3}} = \frac{M_2}{d_2} - \frac{M_1}{d_1} - V_4$$

or

$$\boxed{w_r = \frac{\sqrt{3}}{d_c\ \sigma} \left[\frac{M_2}{d_2} - \frac{M_1}{d_1} - V_4 \right]} \qquad \text{.........(46)}$$

where:

V_4 = horizontal shear force in the column above the connection, lbs

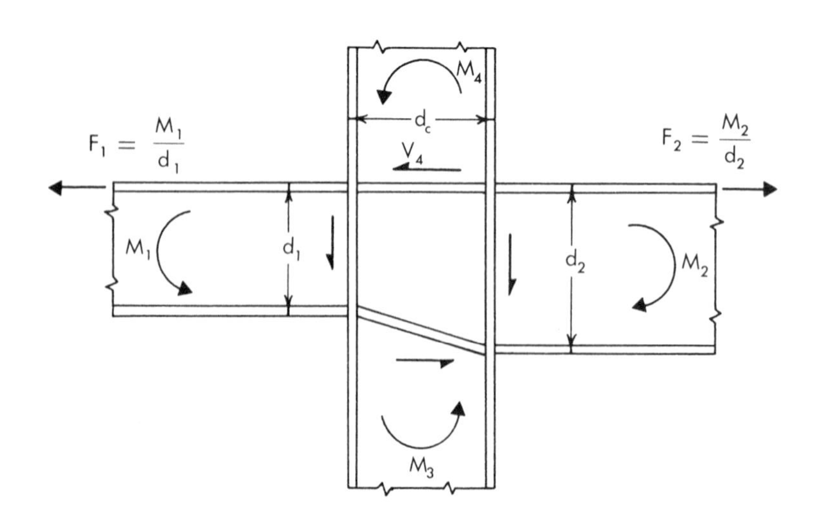

FIGURE 41

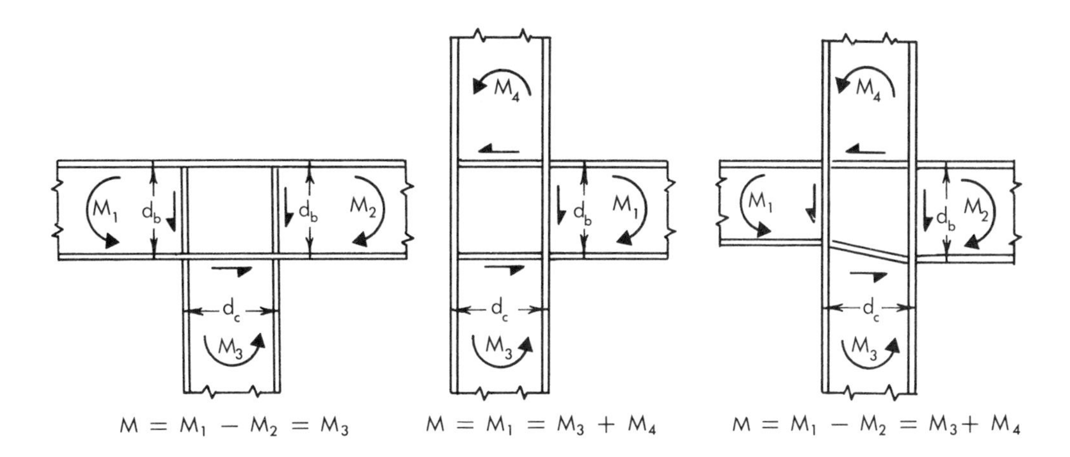

FIGURE 42

M_1 and M_2 = moments in beams (1) and (2), in.-lbs.

d_c = depth of column, in.

d_1 and d_2 = depth of beams (1) and (2)

w = thickness of connection web, in.

If it is assumed that:

1. the column height (h) has a point of inflection at mid-height,

2. the depth of the larger beam (d_2) is $\frac{1}{15}$ of the column height (h), or less,

3. the yield strength of the steel is σ_y = 33,000 psi, and

4. the unbalanced moment (M) is expressed in foot-kips,

this formula will reduce to the following:

$$w_r = \frac{19{,}400\ M}{d_b\ d_c\ \sigma_y} \qquad (47)$$

The method of determining the value of M is illustrated in Figure 42.

Web Resisting Thrust

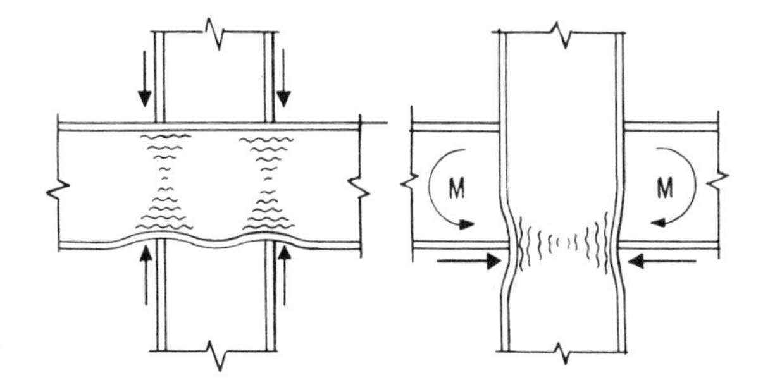

FIGURE 43

Stiffeners are quite often required on members in line with the compression flanges which act against them, to prevent crippling of the web where the concentrated compressive force is applied.

Where a beam supports a column, or a column supports a beam, on just one flange, the stiffeners on its web need only extend just beyond its neutral axis.

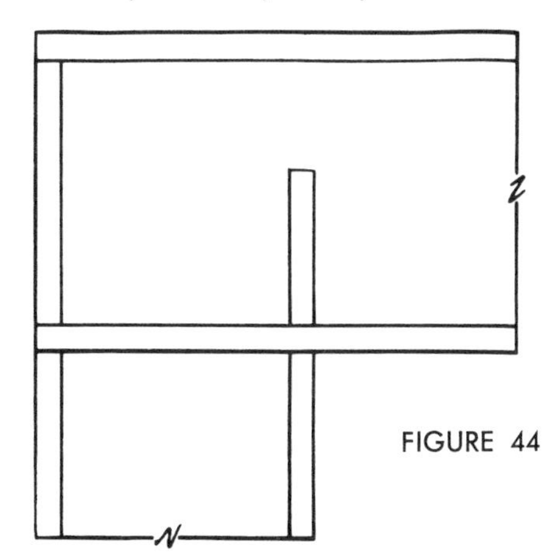

FIGURE 44

The following formulas will indicate when stiffeners are required, and also the necessary size of these stiffeners:

1. Web stiffeners are required adjacent to the beam tension flange if—

$$t_c < 0.4\ \sqrt{A_f} \qquad (48)$$

2. Web stiffeners are required adjacent to the beam compression flange if—

$$w_c \geqq w_r \qquad (49)$$

where:

$$w_r = \frac{A_f}{t_b + 5\ K_c}$$

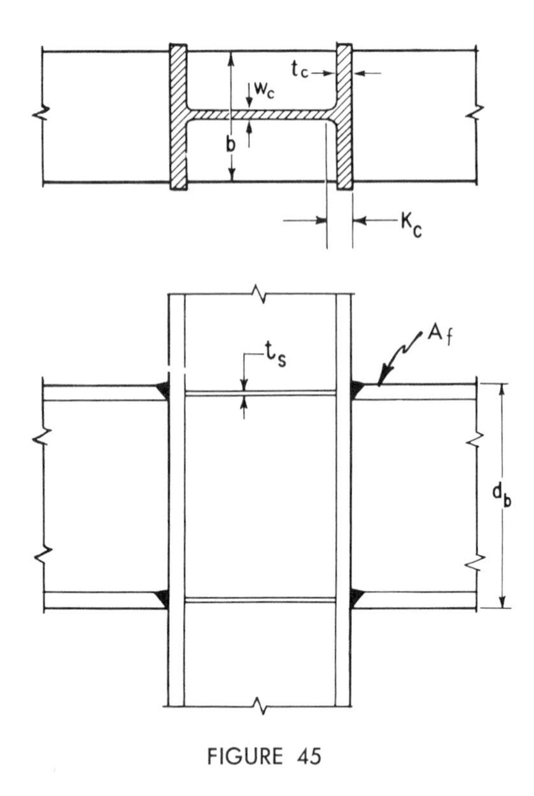

FIGURE 45

If horizontal flange plate stiffeners are used, Figure 45, their dimensions are found from the following:

$$t_s \geqq \frac{A_f - w_c\,(t_b + 5\,K_c)}{b_s} \qquad \text{.............} (50)$$

or

$$t_s \geqq \frac{A_f}{b_s}\left[1 - \frac{w_c}{w_r}\right] \qquad \text{.............} (51)$$

also

$$t_s \geqq \frac{b_s}{17} \qquad \text{.............} (52)$$

where:

$A_f = b_b \times t_b$

w_r = required thickness of connection web

w_c = actual thickness of column web; here actual thickness of connection web

(See Section 5.7 on Continuous Connections for further explanation.)

If vertical plate stiffeners are used, Figure 46, they should be proportioned to carry the excess of beam flange force over that which the column web is able to carry. It is assumed the beam flange extends almost the full width of the column flanges, and that the stiffeners are only half as effective, since they lie at the outer edge of the flange.

$$t_s \geqq \frac{A_f}{t_b + 5\,K_c} - w_c \qquad \text{.............} (53)$$

or

$$t_s \geqq w_r - w_c \qquad \text{.............} (54)$$

also

$$t_s \geqq \frac{d_c}{30} \qquad \text{.............} (55)$$

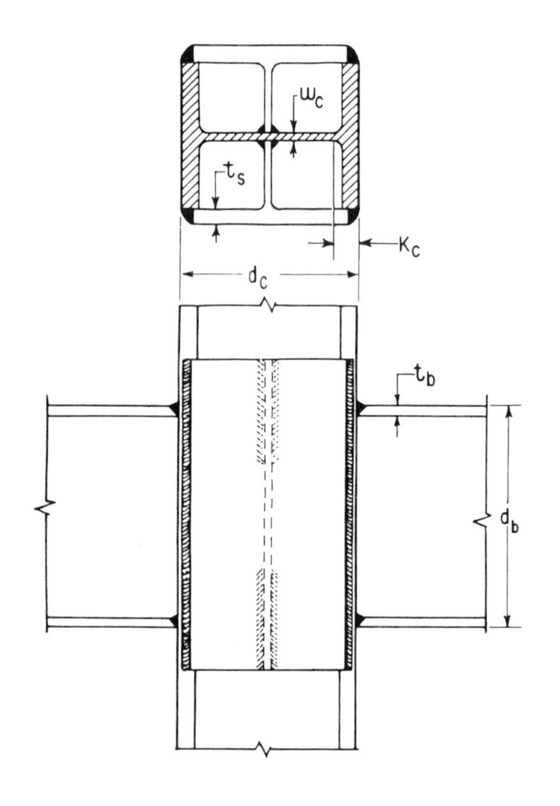

FIGURE 46

(See Section 5.7 on Continuous Connections for further explanation.)

The nomograph, Figure 47, may be used to find the distance $(t_b + 5\,K_c)$ over which the concentrated force from the beam flange spreads out into the column web. In the case of a built-up column, use the flange thickness (t_c) and find the distance $(t_b + 5\,t_c)$ from the nomograph.

This value of $(t_b + 5\,K_c)$ or $(t_b + 5\,t_c)$ can then be used in finding the required web thickness (w_r) from the nomograph, Figure 48.

FIGURE 47—Spread of Flange Thrust Into Column Web.

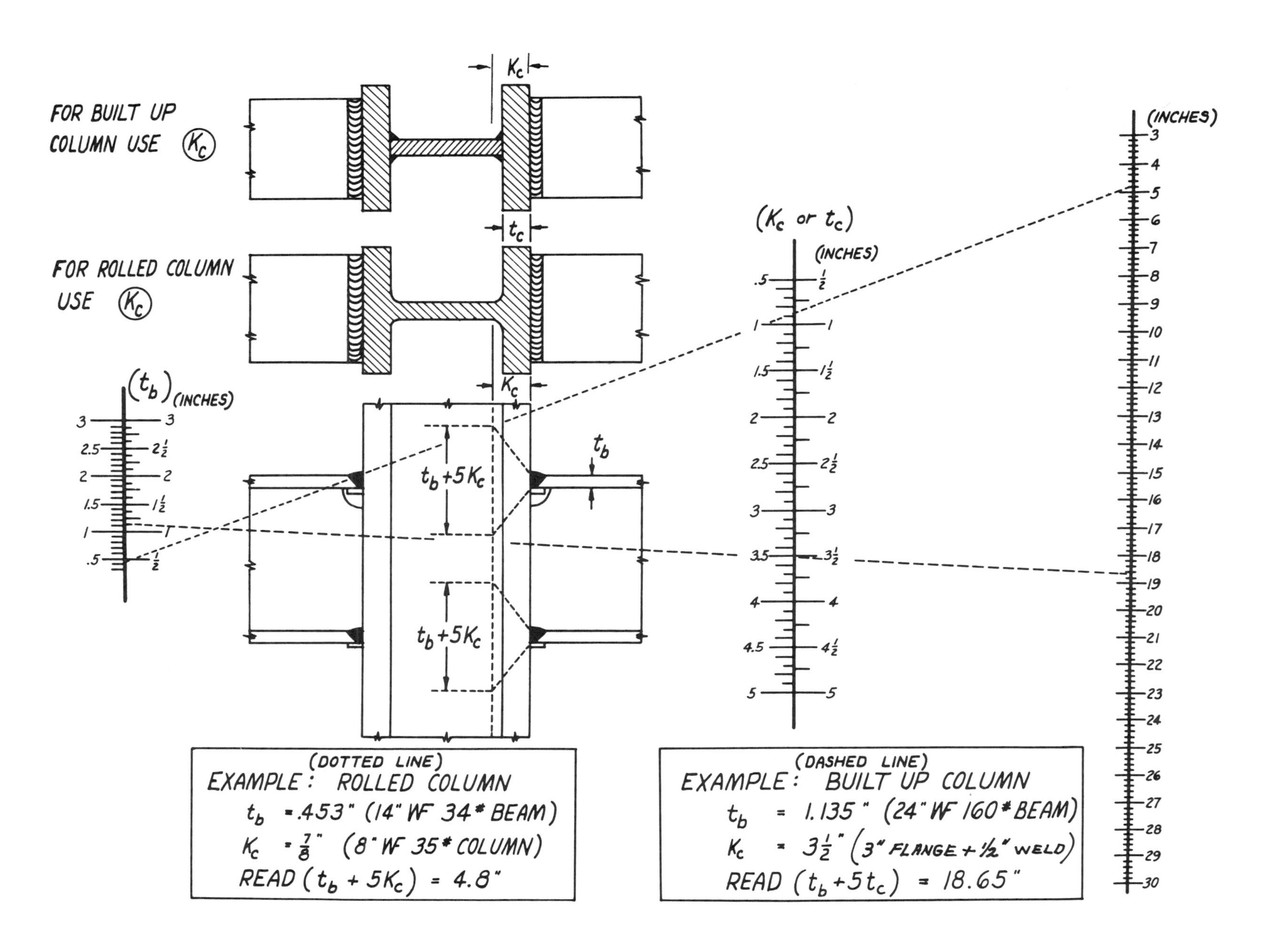

FIGURE 48—Thickness of Connection Web To Resist Thrust of Compression Flange.

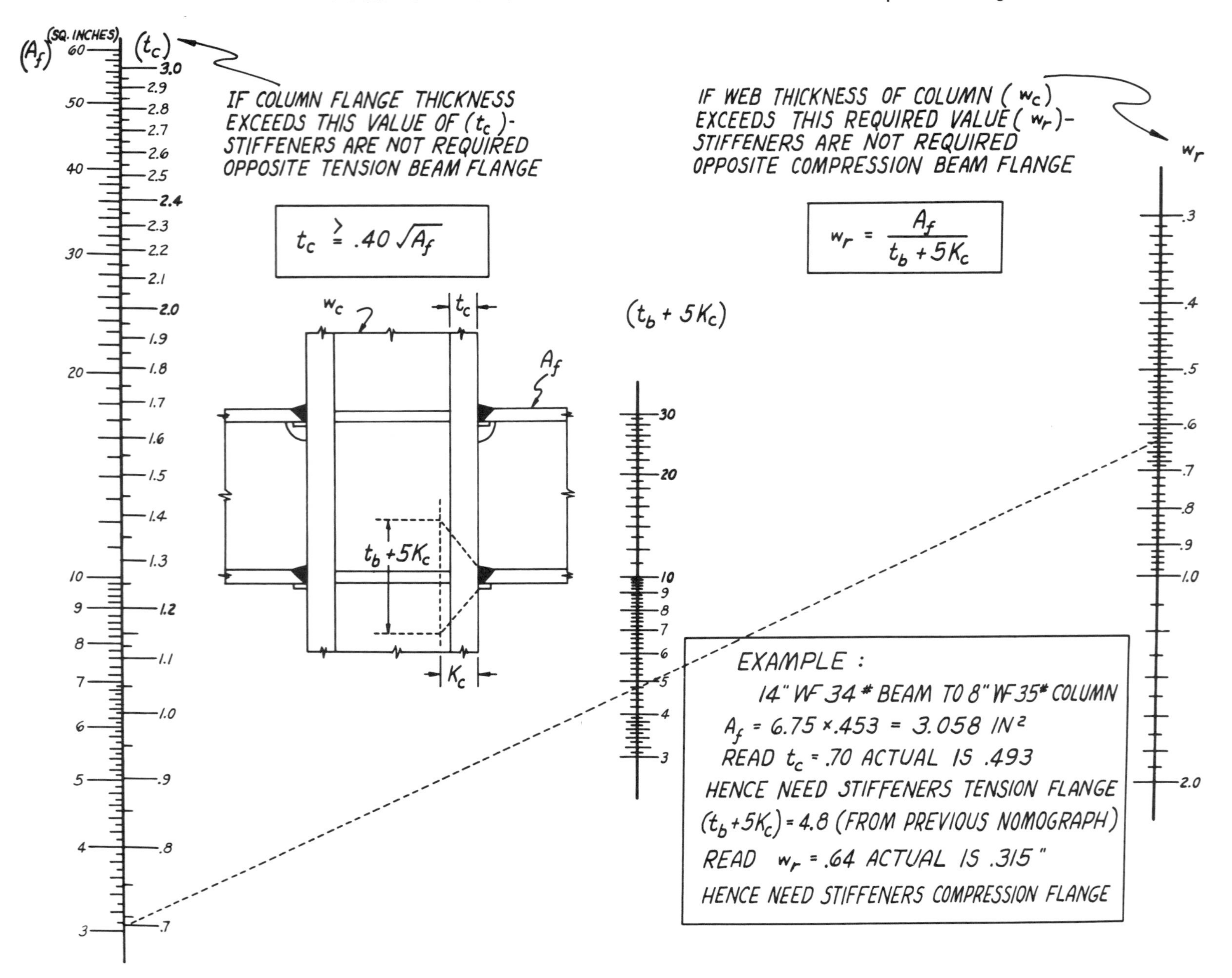
(A_f) (SQ. INCHES)
(t_c)
IF COLUMN FLANGE THICKNESS EXCEEDS THIS VALUE OF (t_c)- STIFFENERS ARE NOT REQUIRED OPPOSITE TENSION BEAM FLANGE
$t_c \geq .40\sqrt{A_f}$
IF WEB THICKNESS OF COLUMN (w_c) EXCEEDS THIS REQUIRED VALUE (w_r)- STIFFENERS ARE NOT REQUIRED OPPOSITE COMPRESSION BEAM FLANGE
$w_r = \frac{A_f}{t_b + 5K_c}$
w_r
($t_b + 5K_c$)
w_c
t_c
A_f
$t_b + 5K_c$
K_c
EXAMPLE :
14" WF 34# BEAM TO 8" WF 35# COLUMN
A_f = 6.75 × .453 = 3.058 IN²
READ t_c = .70 ACTUAL IS .493
HENCE NEED STIFFENERS TENSION FLANGE
(t_b+5K_c) = 4.8 (FROM PREVIOUS NOMOGRAPH)
READ w_r = .64 ACTUAL IS .315"
HENCE NEED STIFFENERS COMPRESSION FLANGE

Problem 2

Is reinforcement necessary at this interior connection? Moments at ultimate load are shown below. A36 steel and E70 welds.

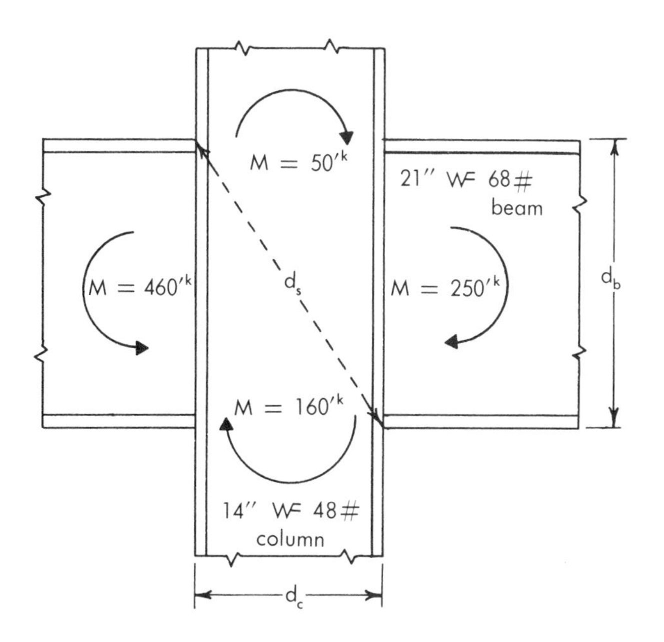

FIGURE 49

beam dimensions

$$d_b = 21.13''$$

$$b_b = 8.27''$$

$$w_b = .430''$$

$$t_b = .685''$$

column dimensions

$$d_b = 13.81''$$

$$w_c = .339''$$

$$b_c = 8.031''$$

$$K_c = 1\tfrac{3}{16}''$$

diagonal of connection web

$$d_s = \sqrt{d_b^2 + d_c^2}$$

$$= \sqrt{21.13^2 + 13.81^2}$$

$$= 23.18''$$

Web Resisting Shear

The necessary web thickness will be determined by the AISC requirements for webs in the connection region. The algebraic sums of the clockwise and counter-clockwise moments on opposite sides of the connection are:

$$M = 460 \text{ ft-kips} - 250 \text{ ft-kips}$$

$$= 210 \text{ ft-kips}$$

and

$$M = 160 \text{ ft-kips} + 50 \text{ ft-kips}$$

$$= 210 \text{ ft-kips}$$

required thickness of connection web

$$w_r = \frac{\sqrt{3}\, M}{d_b\, d_c\, \sigma_y}$$

$$= \frac{\sqrt{3}\,(210 \text{ ft-kips x } 12)}{(21.13)(13.81)(36 \text{ ksi})}$$

$$= .416''$$

Conclusions (Fig. 50)

(a) This required web thickness would be satisfied if the beam were allowed to run through the column. This would give a web thickness of .430". OK

(b) If the column were to run continuous through the beam, as illustrated above, then a ¼" doubler plate would be required in this connection area to make up the difference in thickness.

(c) Another choice would be to use a pair of diagonal stiffeners having the following cross-sectional area:

$$A_s = \frac{d_s\,(w_r - w_c)}{\sqrt{3}}$$

$$= \frac{(23.18)(.416 - .339)}{\sqrt{3}}$$

$$= 1.03 \text{ in.}^2$$

Or use a pair of 3" by ⅜" stiffeners, the area of which checks out as—

$$A_s = \tfrac{3}{8}''\ (2 \text{ x } 3'' + .339'')$$

$$= 2.38 \text{ in.}^2 > 1.03 \text{ in.}^2 \qquad \underline{\text{OK}}$$

Also, the required thickness is—

$$t_s \geq \frac{b_s}{17}$$

$$= \frac{2 \text{ x } 3''}{17}$$

$$= .35'' < \tfrac{3}{8}'' \qquad \underline{\text{OK}}$$

Web Resisting Thrust

In addition to this, the web of the column must be checked against buckling from the concentrated compressive forces applied by the beam flanges.

If the web thickness exceeds the following value, stiffeners are not needed opposite beam compression flange:

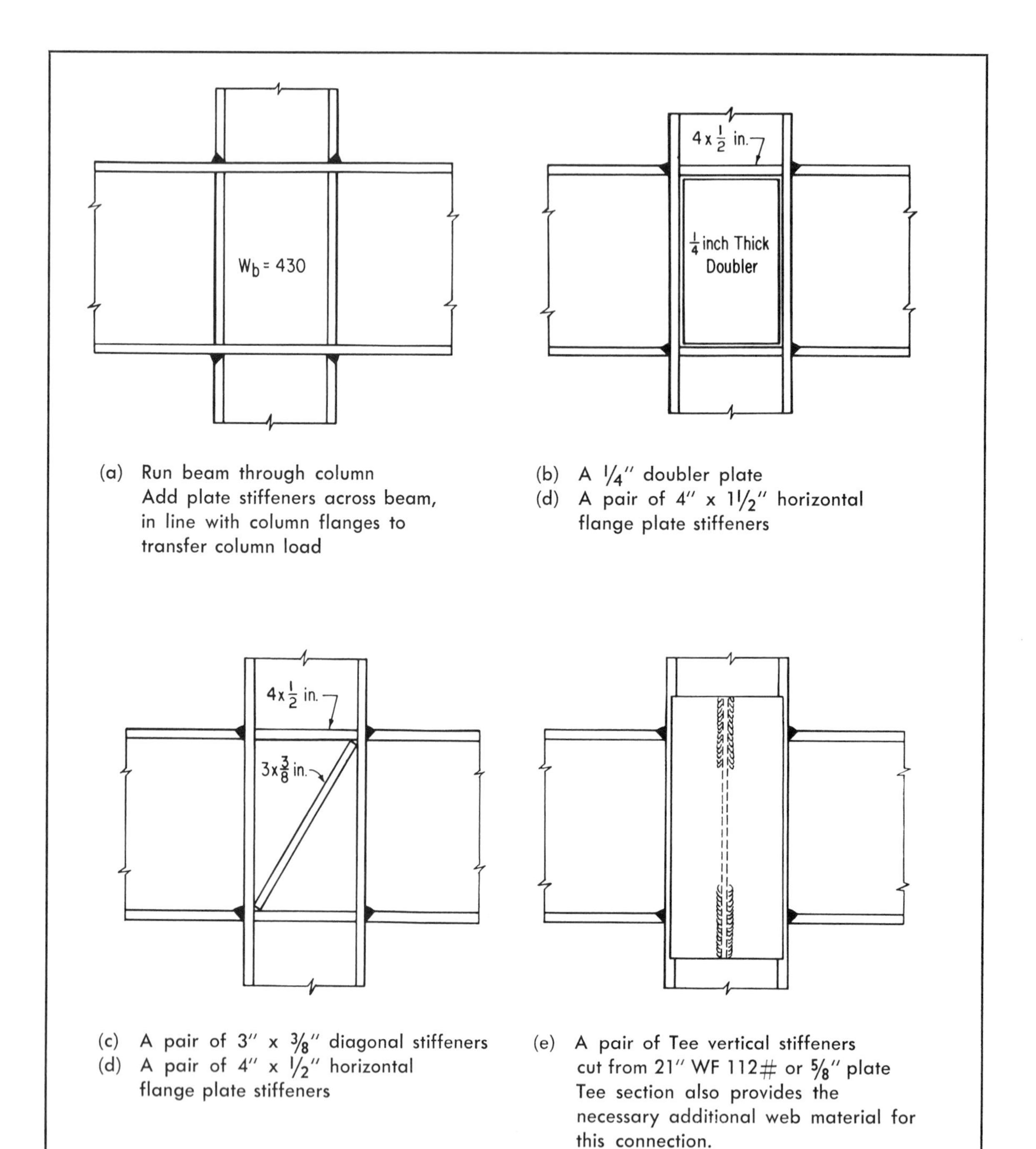

(a) Run beam through column
Add plate stiffeners across beam, in line with column flanges to transfer column load

(b) A 1/4″ doubler plate
(d) A pair of 4″ x 1½″ horizontal flange plate stiffeners

(c) A pair of 3″ x 3/8″ diagonal stiffeners
(d) A pair of 4″ x 1/2″ horizontal flange plate stiffeners

(e) A pair of Tee vertical stiffeners cut from 21″ WF 112# or 5/8″ plate
Tee section also provides the necessary additional web material for this connection.

FIGURE 50

$$w_r = \frac{A_f}{t_b + 5\ K_c}$$

$$= \frac{(8.27'' \times .687'')}{(.685'') + 5(1\tfrac{3}{16}'')}$$

$$= .856''$$

Since $w_c = .339''$, some additional stiffening is required. There are two solutions.

(d) *Horizontal flange plate stiffeners,* the required thickness of which is found from the following formula:

$$t_s \geqq \frac{A_f}{b_s}\left[1 - \frac{W_c}{w_r}\right]$$

$$\geqq \frac{(8.27'' \times .685'')}{(8'')}\left[1 - \frac{(.339'')}{(.856'')}\right]$$

$$\geqq .428''$$

but the following is called for—

$$t_s \geqq \frac{b_s}{17}$$

$$\geqq \frac{(2 \times 4'')}{16}$$

$$\geqq .47''$$

Hence, use a pair of 4″ x ½″ horizontal plate stiffeners.

(e) *Vertical stiffeners,* the required thickness of which is found from the following formula:

$$t_s \geqq w_r - w_c$$

$$\geqq .856'' - .339''$$

$$\geqq .517''$$

and this checks against the following requirement—

$$t_s \geqq \frac{d_s}{30}$$

$$\geqq \frac{(13.81'')}{30}$$

$$\geqq .46'' < .517''$$

This T section could be flame cut from a 12″ WF 112# section, which has a flange thickness of .865″ (we need .517″) and a flange width of 13.00″ (we need at least 12.625″). Otherwise, it could be fabricated from ⅝″ thick plate welded together.

Summary

There are four possible methods of making this connection, Figure 50. Each uses a combination of the preceding solutions to stiffen the connection web so it may safely transmit the shear forces resulting from the unbalanced moment as well as to prevent buckling from the concentrated compressive forces applied by the beam.

Shop-fabricated Vierendeel trusses lowered steel requirements and reduced time for erection of Hamburgers clothing store in Baltimore. Here a weldor is connecting a corner bracket between web member and bottom chord of the truss, using low-hydrogen electrode for root passes.

Welded Connections for Vierendeel Trusses

1. ADVANTAGES OF VIERENDEEL TRUSSES

A Vierendeel truss is in effect a rigid frame. It differs from the simple truss (Sect. 5.9), but it also differs in some respects from the usual rigid frame (Sect. 5.11).

Although the Vierendeel truss has been used widely in European bridge design, the relatively high cost of riveted construction precluded its early popularity in this country. Modern welding processes have changed the economics and several structures using the welded Vierendeel truss have been built here in recent years.

Currently the major field for welded Vierendeel trusses is in building design; Figure 1. For example, they have been used as roof supports to carry the extra load of a superstructure, as exterior floor-high members for rigid support of heavy masonry walls, and in exterior wall grid systems for aesthetic value as well as construction advantages.

In exterior use, the large panel areas provide adequate window area to be filled in by glass or translucent materials; chord and web members are sometimes faced with masonry. When used as interior members, the web openings permit savings in space since piping, conduits, and ducts may be fed through them.

Some Vierendeel trusses are fabricated from wide-flange beams, as shown at the top in Figure 2. Here the top and bottom chord members, as well as the verticals, are standard rolled beams. Additional plates are used to join these members.

At the center in Figure 2, the vertical rolled sections are extended all the way to the top and bottom members. A triangular gusset section or bracket is insected on each side of the connection. These gussets are flame cut from standard rolled sections, usually having the same flange width as the other members. This is a simpler method and therefore is widely used. However, it does not result in as smooth stress distribution at points of high bending moment as does a design with curved corners.

Another method of achieving these curved corners is illustrated at the bottom in Figure 2. Here the truss is flame cut from flat plate with flanges welded to it around the web openings and across top and bottom edges. Also see Open-Web Expanded Beams, Section 4.7.

FIGURE 1

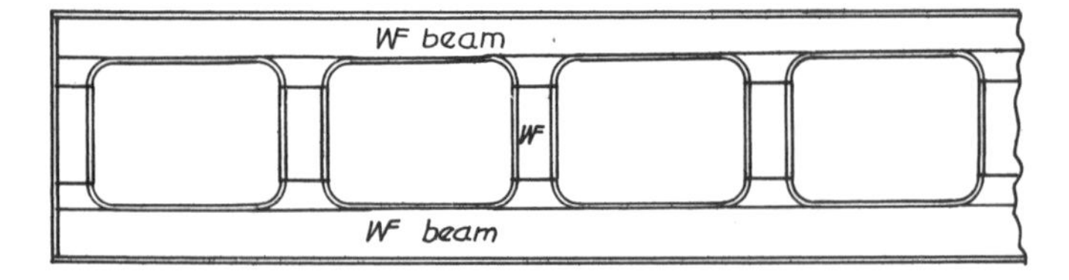

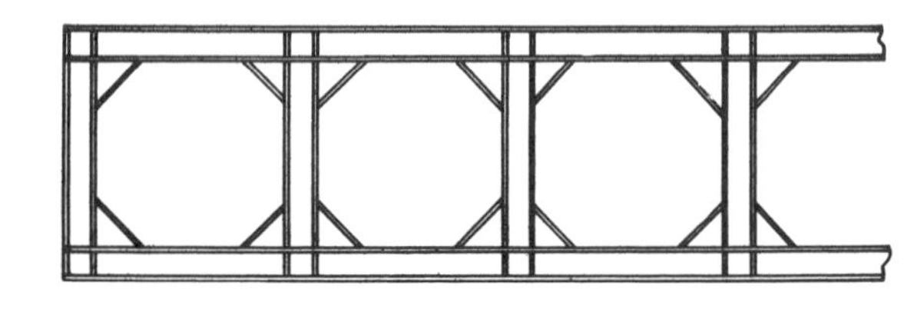

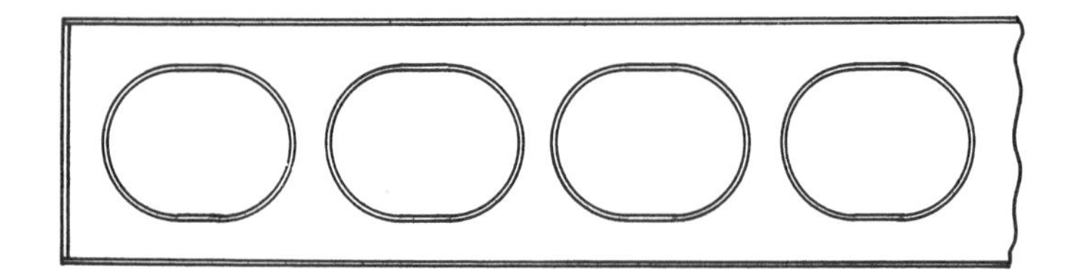

FIGURE 2

2. BASIC CONNECTION REQUIREMENTS

In the usual rigid-frame design certain assumptions are made: the beams and columns deflect, and the connections rotate; but within the connection itself, there is no appreciable movement. Of course the connection does undergo some movement (not to be confused with rotation). However, the distances over which this movement takes place are small compared with the lengths of the beams and columns. Consequently the movement within the joint has little effect on the final moment distribution in the frame.

The Vierendeel truss on the other hand is more compact; for example, the lengths of the vertical members often are relatively shorter. See Figure 3. The more massive connections thus occupy a larger portion of this frame than most others. Any angular movement of vertical members due to yielding within the connection itself will greatly increase the moments in horizontal members. There is no method of computing or predicting how much the connection will yield; therefore, every effort must be made to provide a connection at least as rigid as the adjoining members.

It might be thought that the simple square type of connection would naturally be as rigid as the members, since it is a continuation of the same section. In many cases this is true. However, it might be well to remember that stress causes strain, and the accumulation of strain over a distance results in appreciable movement of some kind: deflection, angular movement, etc. The sharp corner of this connection increases the stress in this area by several times. This stress concentration results in a higher strain and therefore greater movement in this small area. Since only flange stiffeners are added to this square-cornered connection, it is difficult to exceed the stiffness of the member. In most cases, it will just equal the member, and in some cases it will be less.

3. PLASTIC DATA HAS APPLICATION

There is little test data on the connections used in the Vierendeel truss. However, data available on the plastic design of corner connections or knees will be helpful.

FIG. 3—In this building addition, use of Vierendeel trusses will provide a column-free area of about 30′ x 60′ for large trucks and trailers to load and unload communications equipment.

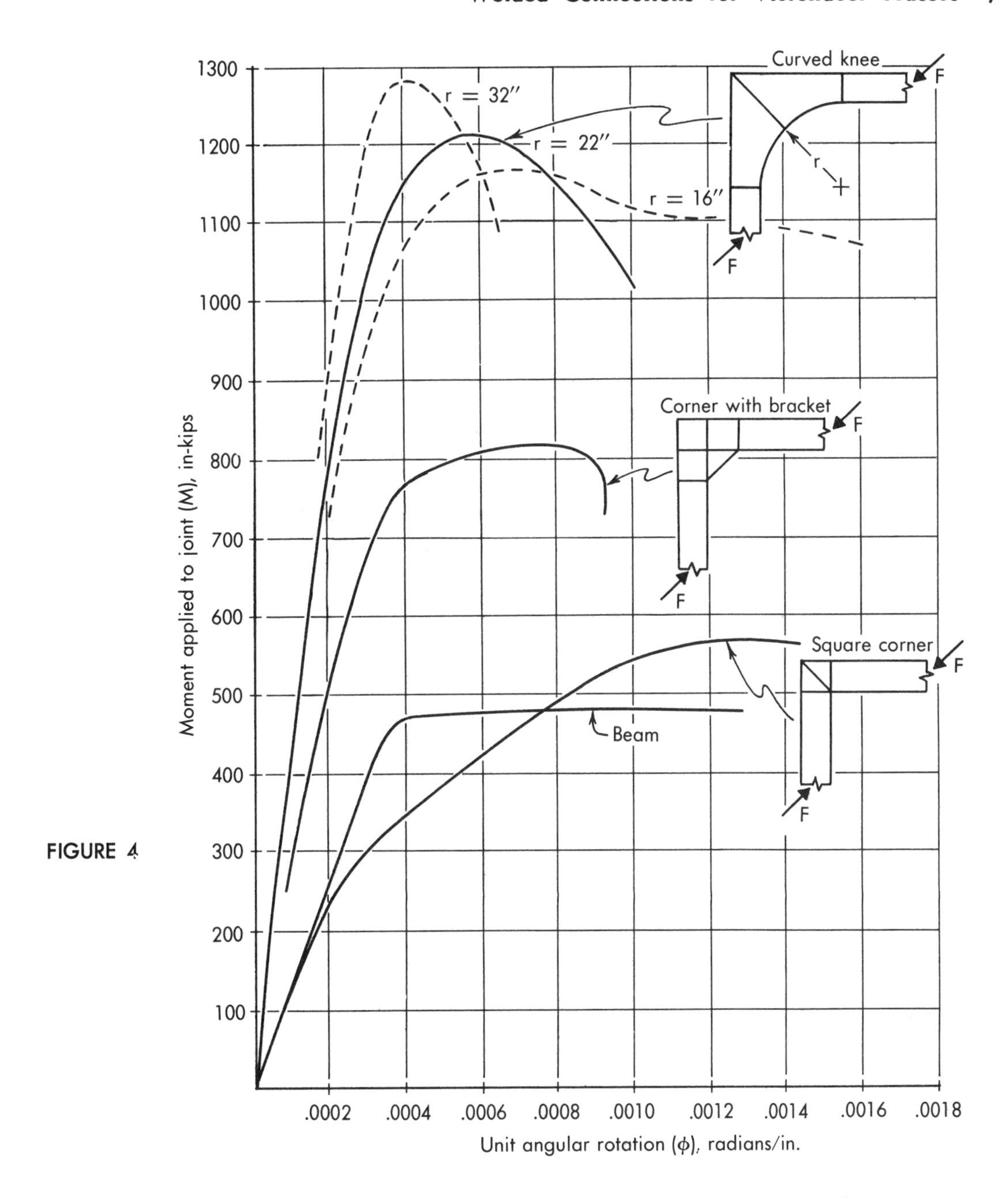

FIGURE 4

Figure 4 shows moment-rotation curves of various corner connections.* The vertical axis is the applied moment; the horizontal axis is the resulting rotation of the connection. The vertical height of the curve represents the maximum or ultimate strength moment of the connection. The slope of the straight portion of the curve represents the stiffness of the connection, with the more nearly vertical curves representing the stiffer connections. The right-hand extremity of the curve represents the rotational capacity of the connection.

In plastic design, it is necessary that the connection have high rotational capacity in addition to exceeding the moment capacity of the member. In Vierendeel trusses, it is more important that the connection have a stiffness equal to or exceeding that of the member, and a high moment capacity in order to safely carry accidental overloads. Here the extra rotational capacity would not be as important because it is an elastic design rather than a plastic design.

In Figure 4 notice that the square-corner connection is the most flexible. It falls slightly short of the beam itself, but does have the greatest rotational capacity. The corner with the bracket has greater stiffness and higher moment capacity, but less rotational capacity. Tapered haunch knees, not shown here, were found

* Figure 1 adapted from "Connections for Welded Continuous Portal Frames", Beedle, Topractsoglou and Johnston; AWS Journal; Part I July 1951, Part II August 1951, and Part III November 1952.

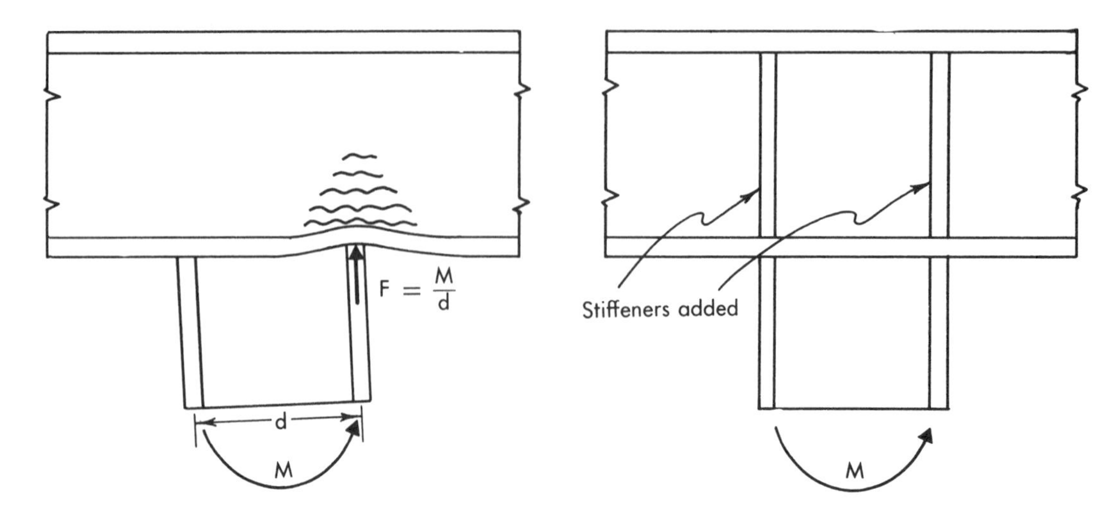

FIGURE 4

to behave similarly. The curved knees are the most rigid, have the highest moment capacity, and have a rotational capacity somewhere in between the simple square corner and the haunched knee. As the radius of curvature of this inner flange is increased, the stiffness and moment capacity increase slightly, with slightly lower rotational capacity.

4. SQUARE CONNECTIONS

When the flanges of one member intersect the flange of another, stiffeners should be added in line with the intersecting flanges. The stiffeners transfer the forces of the flange back into the web of the other member. See Figure 5. These flange forces are distributed as shear into the web along the full web depth. This will prevent the web from buckling due to the concentrated flange forces.

The unbalanced moment about a connection will cause shear forces around the periphery of the connection web, Figure 6. The vertical shear force and the horizontal shear force will result in a diagonal compressive force applied to the connection web. Unless the web has sufficient thickness or is reinforced, it may buckle. According to plastic design (and this may be used in elastic design), the required thickness of the joint web must be—

$$\tau \; t_w = f_v = \frac{F_h}{d_v} = \frac{M}{d_h \; d_v}$$

and:

$$\boxed{t_w = \frac{M}{d_h \; d_v \; \tau}} \qquad \cdots\cdots (1)$$

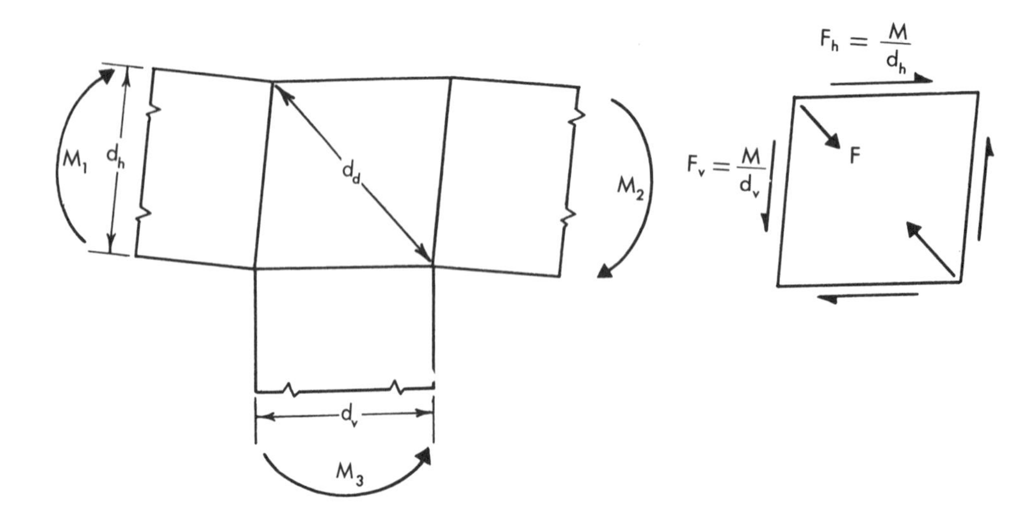

FIGURE 6

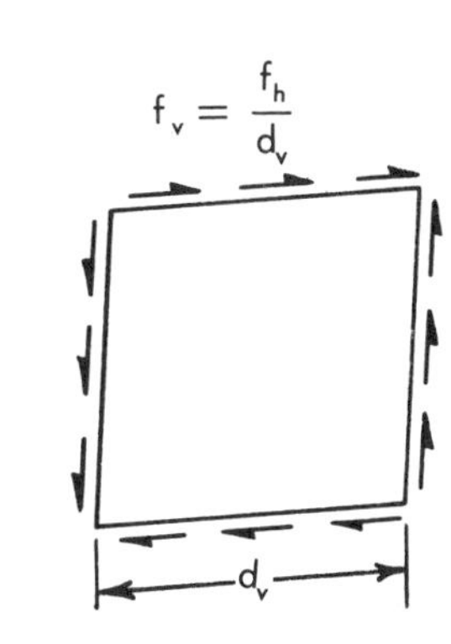

FIGURE 7

where:

t_w = thickness of connection web, inches

f_v = unit shear force, lbs/linear inch = $\tau\ t_w$

d_h = depth of horizontal member, inches

d_v = depth of vertical member, inches

M = algebraic sum of clockwise and counterclockwise moments applied by members framing to opposite sides of the joint web boundary at ultimate load, inch-pounds

For a panel subjected to shear forces and having a ratio of width to thickness up to about 70 (the connection webs will almost always be within this value), the critical shear stress (τ_{cr}) equals the yield shear stress (τ_y), or—

$$\tau_{cr} = \tau_y \qquad \text{and}$$

$$\tau_y = \frac{\sigma_y}{\sqrt{3}} \qquad \text{or:}$$

$$\boxed{t_w \geqq \frac{\sqrt{3}\ M}{d_h\ d_v\ \sigma_y}} \qquad (2)$$

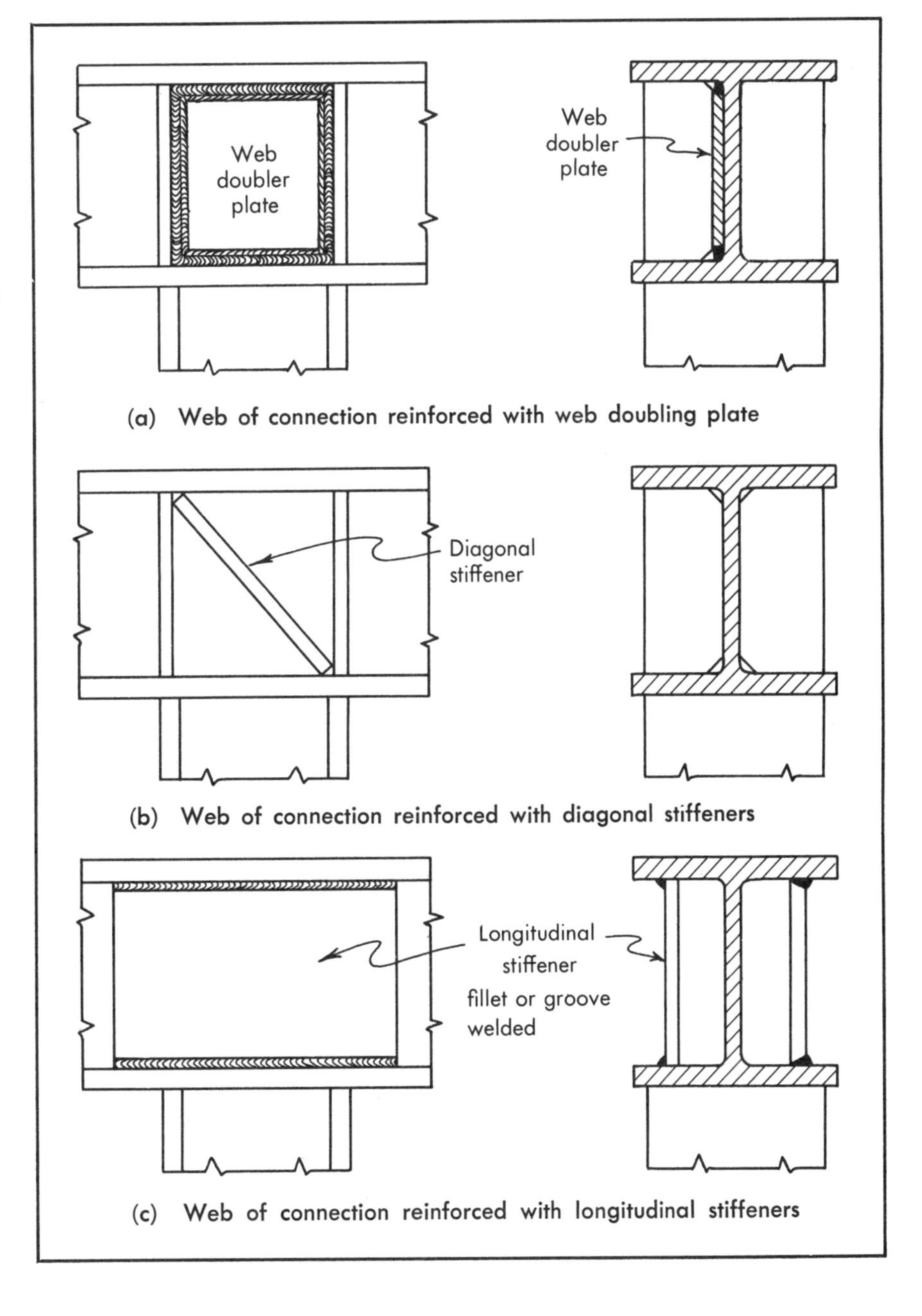

FIG. 8 Methods of obtaining web thickness to meet requirement of Formula #2.

If the thickness of the connection web should be less than this required value, AISC in their work on Plastic Design (which may also be used in Elastic Design) recommends adding either (a) a doubler plate to the web to get this required thickness, see Figure 8, or (b) a pair of diagonal stiffeners to carry this diagonal compression, the area of these stiffeners to be sufficient for just the additional requirements.

It seems reasonable that (c) a pair of longitudinal stiffeners extending through the connection area would be sufficient to resist this web shear. These stiffeners would be flat plates standing vertically between flanges of the chord member and welded to the flanges near their outer edges.

5. CURVED-KNEE CONNECTIONS

Tensile stress (σ_{mean}) in the inner flange of a curved knee tends to pull the flange away from the web, and to bend the curved flange as shown at the lower right of Figure 9. Because of the slight yielding of the flange's outer edge, there is a non-uniform distribution of flange stress (σ). This stress is maximum in line with the web.

In addition there is a transverse tensile bending stress (σ_t) in the curved flange. If this value is too high, stiffeners should be welded between this flange and the web. These keep the flange from bending and pulling away from the web. These stiffeners usually need not extend all the way between flanges, but may be a series of short triangular plates connecting with the curved flange.

In the following formulas, the values of factors $\propto$ and β come from the graph, Figure 10.*

longitudinal tensile stress in flange

$$\sigma_{max} = \frac{\sigma_{mean}}{\propto} \quad * \qquad (3)$$

transverse tensile bending stress in flange

$$\sigma_t = \beta \, \sigma_{max} \quad * \qquad (4)$$

radial force

$$f_r = \frac{F}{r} \qquad (5)$$

The radial force (f_r) acts transverse to the fillet welds connecting the flange and the web.

* From "Design of Rigid Frame Knees", by F. Bleich, AISC.

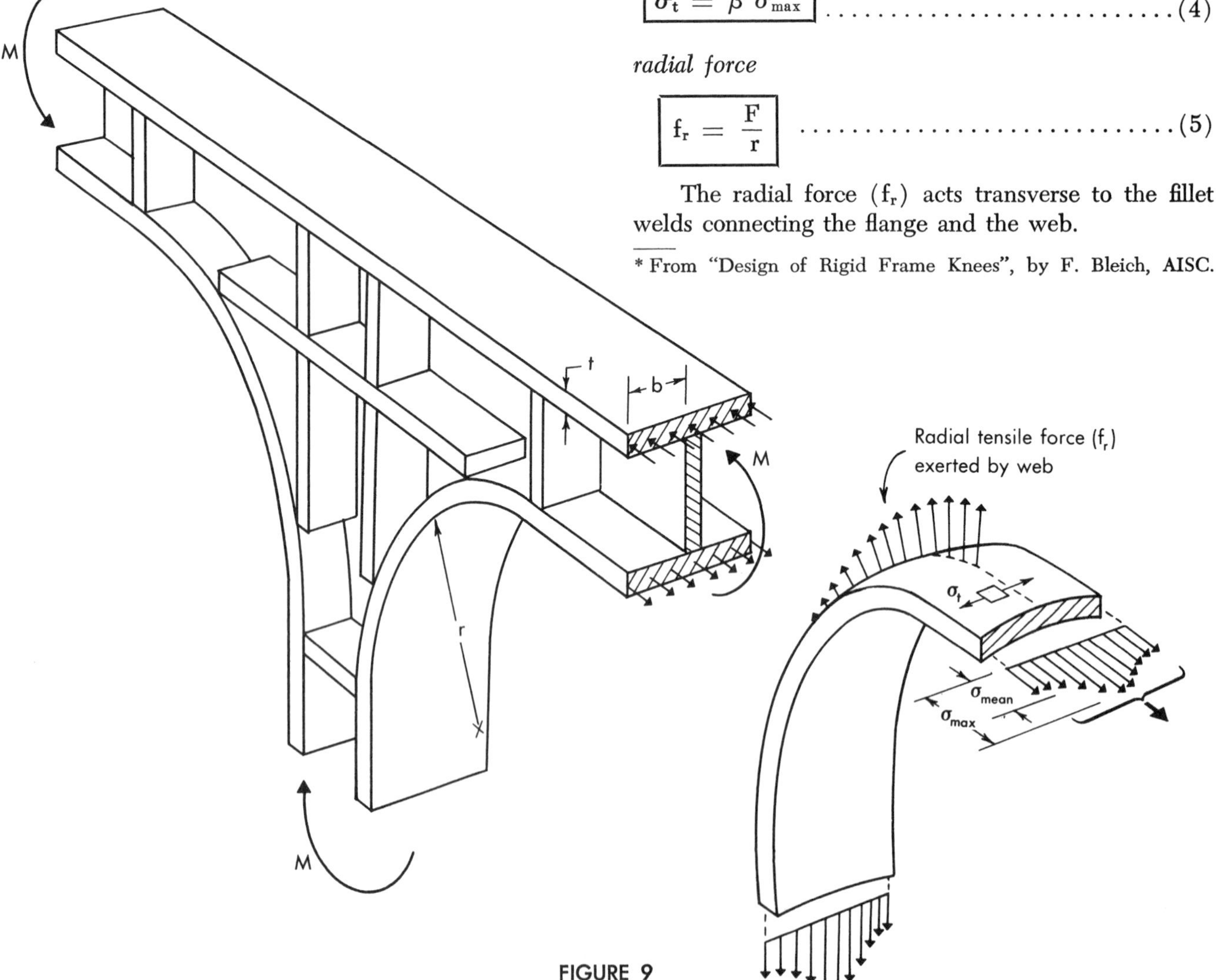

FIGURE 9

FIGURE 10

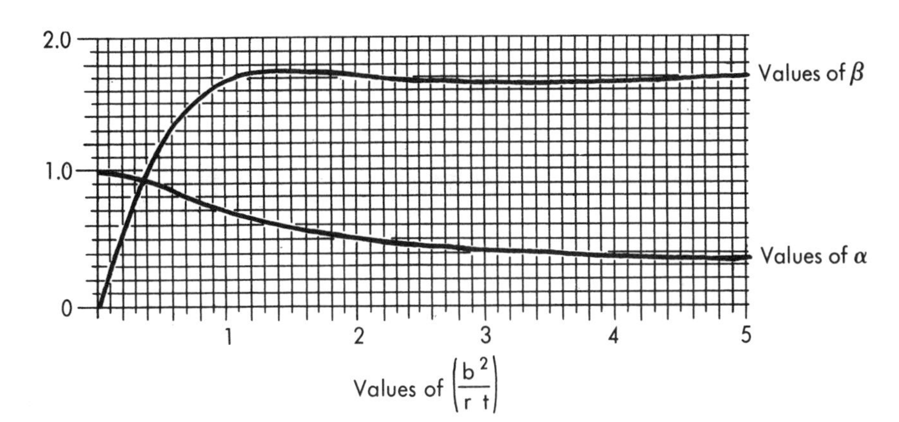

6. SUMMARY OF REQUIREMENTS

Here is a summary of the general requirements for these Vierendeel truss connections:

1. The bottom chord is in tension and the connections here must provide continuity of the member for this tensile force; the top chord is in compression and the connections here must provide continuity of the member for this compressive force. For these reasons, the inside flanges of the horizontal chords should be made continuous throughout the connection.

2. There may be some axial tension or compression in the vertical member, but this is usually of a smaller magnitude.

3. Large moments are applied by the horizontal and vertical legs to each connection.

4. A pair of connections, one above the other, tend to be restrained from rotation by the vertical member which connects them. The rotation of these connections due to deflection of horizontal and vertical members is taken into consideration when the truss is designed. However, yielding within the connection itself is not considered in the design and this could alter the moment distribution of the truss, therefore it is important that the connection have equal or greater stiffness than the members connecting to it.

5. The web of the connection must be stiffened against buckling due to the high shear stress resulting from the unbalanced moment of the two horizontal members connecting at the joint. This difference in moment is equal to the moment applied by the vertical member also connected there. This web must either have sufficient thickness or be reinforced with a doubler plate or some type of stiffeners.

6. Flange stiffeners should be used whenever there is an abrupt change in direction or curvature of the flange.

Vierendeel trusses in this addition to the New England Life Insurance Co. home office building permitted architect to match window openings in original buildings, yet accomplish significant savings in steel and in floor space. Design also provided stiffer construction, reducing danger of cracked masonry.

Use of Vierendeel trusses here provided a column-free area of about 30′ x 60′ for large trucks and trailers to load and unload communications equipment.

Design of Rigid Frames (Elastic Design)

1. METHODS OF ANALYSIS

There is no single best method to analyze statically indeterminate structures. There are many methods, and many combinations and adaptations of these methods. One method may be simple and quick, but can only be used to a limited extent. Another method may have wide application, but be so laborious that it is not used much.

Most texts on statically indeterminate structures start out with the various methods of determining deflections of the structure. They then consider the analysis of these structures. The methods of finding deflections are simple tools which may be used in the analysis of the structure.

There are actually about five basic, well used methods for the analysis of statically indeterminate structures encountered in rigid frame designing:

1. Least Work Method
2. General Method
3. Slope Deflection Method
4. Moment and Shear Distribution Method
5. Column Analogy Method

All of these methods, when applied to continuous beams and frames, give the resulting bending moments at various points along the structure. In order to proceed this far to get the resulting moments on the structure, it is first necessary to assume the moments of inertia of the members. This is usually a good guess or approximation. Then, from these resulting bending moments, the member is built up. If the final required moment of inertia is more than that which was started with, the work must be repeated, or adjusted, using this newer value. In some methods only the ratios of the various moments of inertia need be used.

Method of Least Work

The method of least work depends on the following. It is considered that a structure will deform under the application of a load, in such a manner that the internal work of deformation will be held to a minimum. This method may be outlined as follows:

1. Cut the structure so that it becomes statically determinate.
2. The unknown moments or forces become the redundants or unknown quantities.
3. Set up an equation for the internal work of the structure in terms of these redundants.
4. A derivative of this is then set equal to zero, and this will give the minimum value of this redundant force.

General Method

The general method consists of the following:

1. Cut the structure at the redundant or unknown force.
2. Determine the opening of this gap caused by the given load (while cut). Several methods may be used to find this deflection.
3. Apply a redundant force to close this gap.
4. From the given loads and this redundant force, make up a moment diagram and design the structure from this.

For more than one redundant force, cut all members at these redundant forces and close the gaps simultaneously.

To use the general method, the designer must be able to find deflections in Step 2. Some of the methods for finding deflections are as follows:

(a) Real Work
(b) Castigliano's Theorem
(c) Virtual Work
(d) Area Moment
(e) Conjugate Beam
(f) Angle Weights
(g) Willot-Mohr Diagram

Several of these methods are described in Section 2.5 on Deflection by Bending and will not be discussed here.

Slope Deflection Method

In the general method just outlined, the redundant or unknown forces and moments are found. In a similar manner, it is possible to solve for the unknown joint rotations and deflections. As soon as these are found, the end moments may be determined and these combined with the original moments from the applied load.

Moment and Shear Distribution Method

The moment distribution or Hardy Cross method consists of holding the joints in a frame fixed so that they cannot rotate. The end moments of each loaded member are found from standard beam diagrams in handbooks. Then, one at a time, a joint is released, allowed

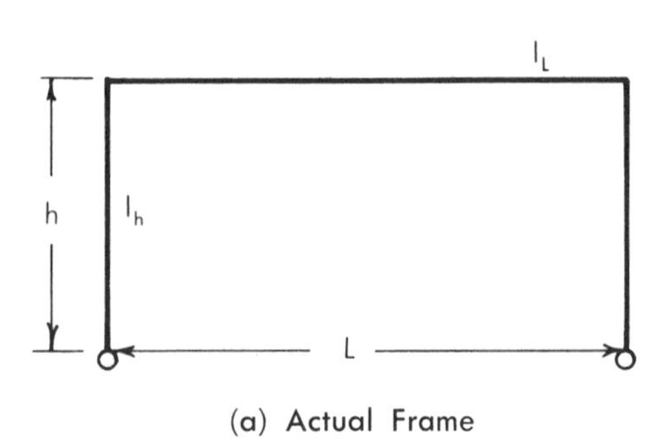

(a) Actual Frame

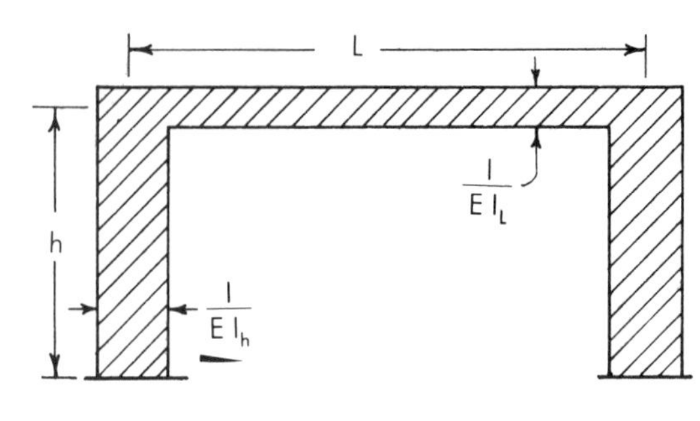

(b) Elastic area of analogous column

FIGURE 1

to rotate, and then fixed again. This release causes a new distribution of the moment about this point, and some of this change is carried over into the next joint. This procedure is followed for each joint in the entire frame, and then the whole process is repeated over all the joints as often as required until these corrections become very small.

This method is outlined as follows:

1. Fix the joints from rotation and find the moments, treating the member as a simple structure.
2. Remove the joint restraints one at a time, and balance moments about the joint. This unbalanced moment is then distributed about the joint.
3. Some of this distributed moment is then carried over into the other end of the member.
4. This is repeated until the unbalanced moments become very small. The final moments are then used to design the structure.

Column Analogy Method

The outline or over-all shape of the given frame is considered as a column cross-section, called an elastic area. The length of each portion of this elastic area is equal to the actual length of the corresponding member of the frame. The width of each portion of this elastic area is equal to the 1/EI of the corresponding member of the frame.

The properties of this elastic area are determined: area, center of gravity or elastic center, and moments of inertia about the two axes (x-x and y-y).

The statically indeterminate frame must be cut, usually at one of the supports, so that it becomes statically determinate. Under this condition, the moment diagram caused by the applied loads is constructed and then treated as a load (M/EI) applied to the elastic area of the analogous column.

Just as an eccentrically loaded column has an axial compressive stress and bending stresses about the two axes (x-x and y-y), so the analogous column has "stresses" at any point equal to the axial compressive "stress" and the two bending "stresses". These resulting "stresses" of the analogous column are the corrective moments which must be added to the statically determinate moments of the "cut" frame in order to bring the frame back to its original shape and condition before it was "cut".

This is outlined as follows:

1. Determine properties of the elastic area: area, center of gravity or elastic center, and moments of inertia about the two axes (x-x and y-y).
2. Cut the frame to make it statically determinate. Use moment diagram from applied loads as a load (M/EI) on the elastic area of the analogous column.
3. Determine axial "stress" and the two bending "stresses" of the analogous column. These become corrective moments which must be added to the statically determinate moment of Step 2 to give the final moments of the statically indeterminate frame.
4. From these moments, find the redundant forces at the cut portion of the frame.

2. COLUMN ANALOGY METHOD

The outline of the given frame is considered to be a column cross-section, called an elastic area; Figure 1.

The length of each member in the elastic area is considered equal to the actual length of the corresponding member of the actual frame.

The width of each member in the elastic area is equal to 1/EI of the corresponding member of the frame.

It is seen by Figure 1 that for a pinned-end frame the moment of inertia of the flexible pin is zero. Hence the width of the elastic area at this point is

$$\frac{1}{E\ I} = \frac{1}{0} = \infty$$

and the elastic area at this pinned end would equal ∞.

For a fixed end, the moment of inertia at this rigid support is assumed to be ∞. The resulting width of the elastic area at this point is—

$$\frac{1}{E\ I} = \frac{1}{\infty} = 0$$

and the elastic area at this fixed end would be zero.

The elastic area, with its dimensions now known

Length = L

Height = h

$$\text{Width} = \frac{1}{E\ I}$$

is now treated like any other cross-section, and its properties determined.

In this example of pinned ends:

Area

$$A = 2\left(\frac{1}{E\ I_h}\right) h + \left(\frac{1}{E\ I_L}\right) L + 2\left(\frac{1}{0}\right) = \infty$$

(2 columns) (beam) (pinned ends)

Elastic Center

The elastic center is found as though it were the center of gravity of the elastic area.

axis x-x

Taking moments about the base line, it is seen that the elastic axis x-x of the elastic area must pass through the frame base since, in the analogous column, the pinned ends have infinite (∞) area.

This may be proved by mathematically determining the elastic center of gravity:

$$C.G. = \frac{\Sigma\ M}{\Sigma\ A}$$

$$= \frac{2\left(\frac{1}{E\ I_h}\right) h\left(\frac{h}{2}\right) + \left(\frac{1}{E\ I_L}\right) L\ (h) + 2\ (\infty)\ (0)}{\infty}$$

$$= 0$$

axis y-y

By observation, it is seen that the y-y axis would pass through the center of this elastic area because of section symmetry.

Moment of Inertia

$$I_{x\text{-}x} = 2\left(\frac{1}{E\ I_h}\right)\frac{h^3}{3} + \left(\frac{1}{E\ I_L}\right) L\ h^2 + 2\left(\frac{1}{0}\right) 0$$

(2 columns) (beams) (pinned ends)

$$= \frac{h^2}{3\ E}\left(\frac{2\ h}{I_h} + \frac{3\ L}{I_L}\right)$$

Since the infinite elastic area at the pin lies along the elastic axis x-x, it will have no effect upon $I_{x\text{-}x}$.

$I_{y\text{-}y} = \infty$, since there is an infinite elastic area at the two pinned ends and these lie at the extreme ends of the section about axis x-x.

Apply Load to Elastic Area

The statically indeterminate frame, Figure 2(a), must have some portion cut, usually at one of the supports, so that it becomes statically determinate, Figure 2(b). Under this condition, the bending moment diagram caused by the applied loads is constructed, Figure 2(c). This is then treated as a load (M_s/EI) applied to the elastic area of the analogous column, Figure 3(a).

Just as an eccentrically loaded column has an axial load and tilting moments ($M_x = P\ y$, and $M_y = P\ x$),

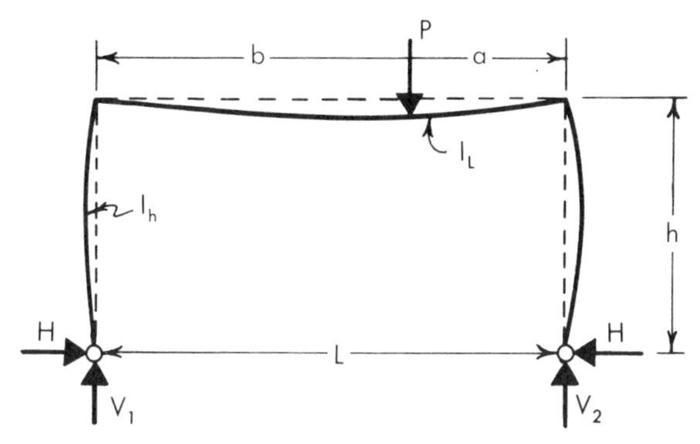

(a) Statically indeterminate frame

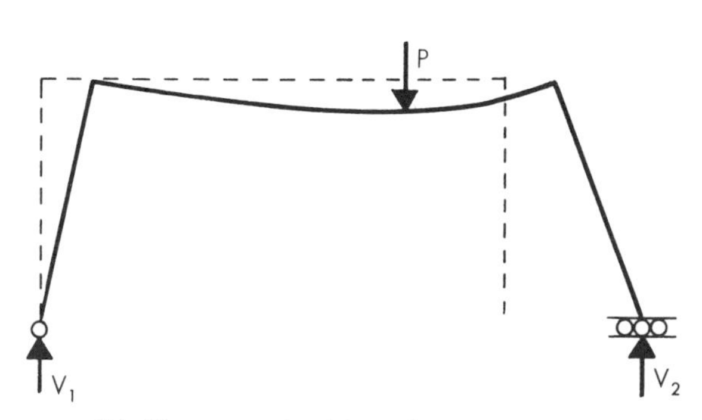

(b) One support cut to make frame statically determinate

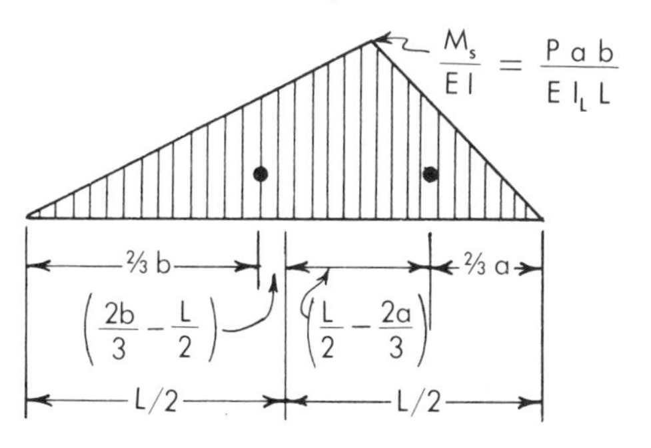

(c) Moment diagram for the statically determinate frame

FIGURE 2

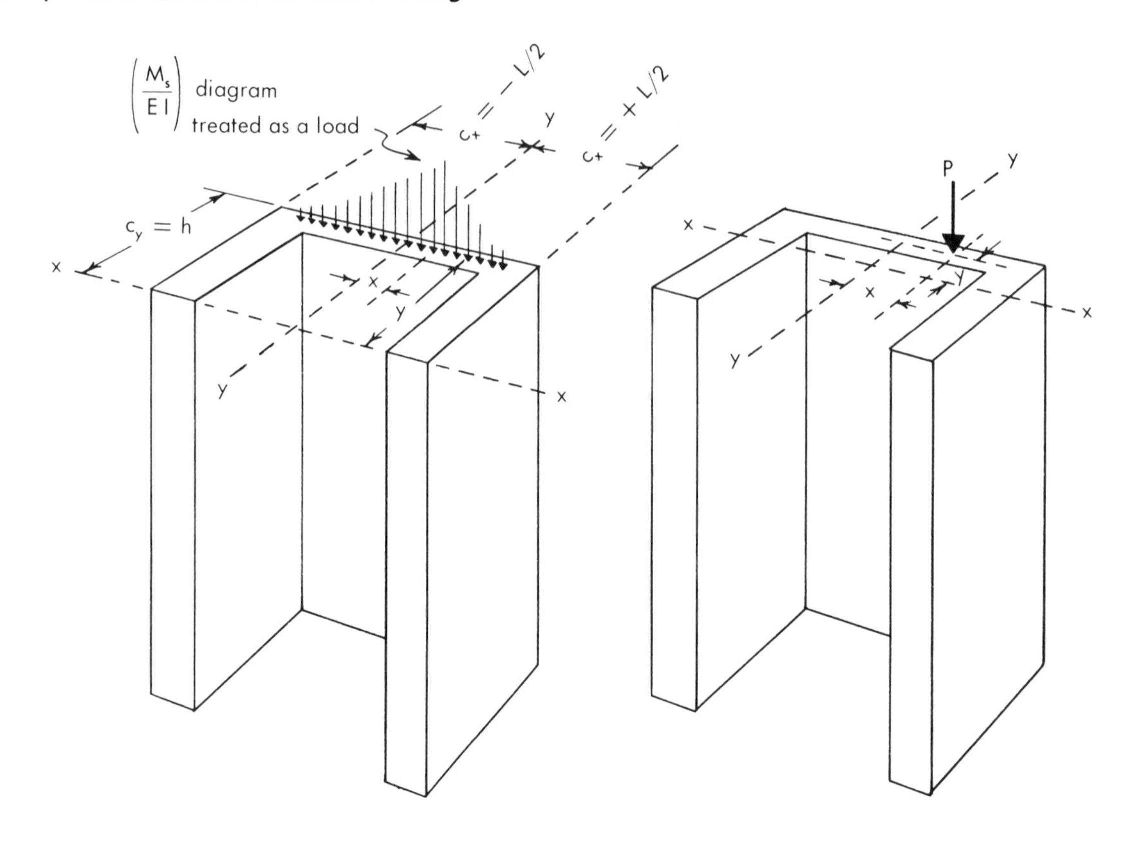

(a) Analogous column loaded with $\frac{M_s}{EI}$ (b) Actual column with eccentric load (P)

FIGURE 3

so the analogous column has an axial load and tilting moments. Consider the moment diagram divided by EI as the load about the two axes (x-x and y-y) through the elastic center:

axial load on analogous column

$$P = \frac{1}{2}\left(\frac{P\ a\ b}{E\ I_L\ L}\right) L$$

$$= \frac{P\ a\ b}{2\ E\ I_L}$$

moment about axis x-x on analogous column

$$M_{x\text{-}x} = \frac{1}{2}\left(\frac{P\ a\ b}{E\ I_L\ L}\right) L\ h$$

$$= \frac{P\ a\ b\ h}{2\ E\ I_L}$$

moment about axis y-y on analogous column

$$M_{y\text{-}y} = \frac{1}{2}\left(\frac{P\ a\ b}{E\ I_L\ L}\right) b \left(\frac{2b}{3} - \frac{L}{2}\right) + \frac{1}{2}\left(\frac{P\ a\ b}{E\ I_L\ L}\right) a \left(\frac{L}{2} - \frac{2a}{3}\right)$$

$$= \frac{P\ a\ b}{12\ E\ I_L\ L}\ (b - a)\ (4b + 4a - 3L)$$

Just as the eccentrically loaded column has stresses at any point equal to the axial compressive stress plus the two bending stresses—

$$\sigma = \sigma_a\ (\text{axial}) \pm \sigma_x\ (\text{bending}_{x\text{-}x}) \pm \sigma_y\ (\text{bending}_{y\text{-}y})$$

$$\text{or } \sigma = \frac{P}{A} \pm \frac{M_{x\text{-}x}\ c_y}{I_{x\text{-}x}} \pm \frac{M_{y\text{-}y}\ c_x}{I_{y\text{-}y}}$$

so the analogous column has "stresses" at any point equal to the axial "stress" (σ_a) plus the two bending "stresses" (σ_y & σ_x). These are the corresponding corrective moments (M_a, M_x, & M_y) which must be applied to the statically determinate moments of the "cut" frame in Figure 2(b) to bring the frame back to its original shape and condition, Figure 2(a).

$$\boxed{\sigma_a = -\ M_a = -\ \frac{P}{a}} \quad \cdots\cdots (1)$$

$$M_a = -\ \frac{\frac{P\ a\ b}{2\ E\ I_L}}{\infty}$$

$$= 0 \qquad \text{(See Figure 4.)}$$

$$\boxed{\sigma_x = -\ M_x = -\ \frac{M_{x\text{-}x}\ c_y}{I_{x\text{-}x}}} \quad \cdots\cdots (2)$$

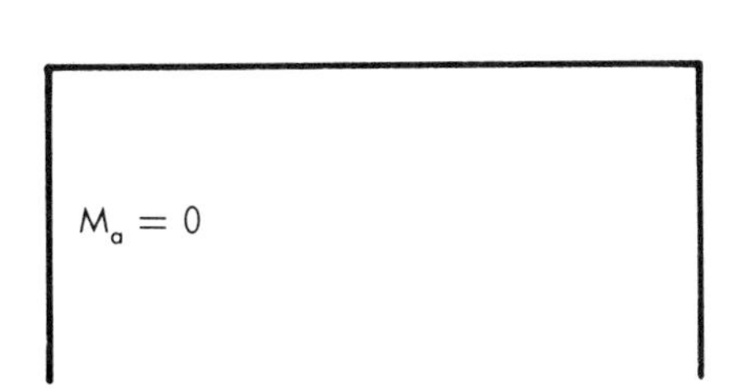

FIG. 4 No corrective moment to be added here.

when $c_y = +h$

$$M_x = -\frac{\left(\frac{P\,a\,b\,h}{2\,E\,I_L}\right) h}{\frac{h^2}{3\,E}\left(\frac{2\,h}{I_h} + \frac{3\,L}{I_L}\right)}$$

$$= -\frac{3\,P\,a\,b}{\frac{4\,h\,I_L}{I_h} + 6\,L}$$

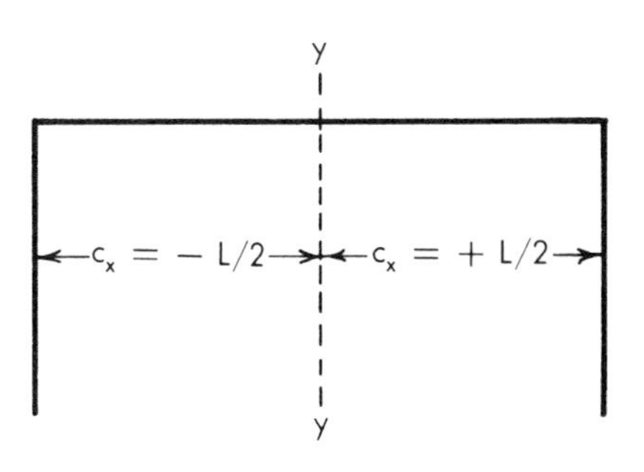

FIG. 6 No corrective moment to be added here.

when $c_y = 0$

$M_x = 0$ (See Figure 5.)

$$\sigma_y = -M_y = -\frac{M_{y\text{-}y}\,c_x}{I_{y\text{-}y}} \qquad \text{.............(3)}$$

Since $I_{y\text{-}y} = \infty$

$M_y = 0$ (See Figure 6.)

The final moment on the frame will be as given in Figure 7.

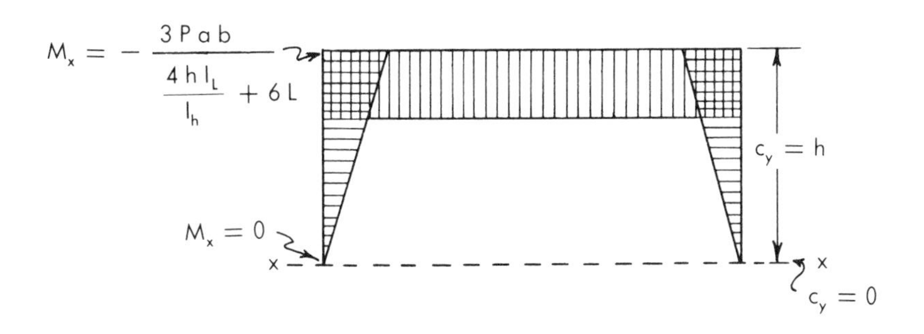

FIG. 5 Corrective moment to be added here.

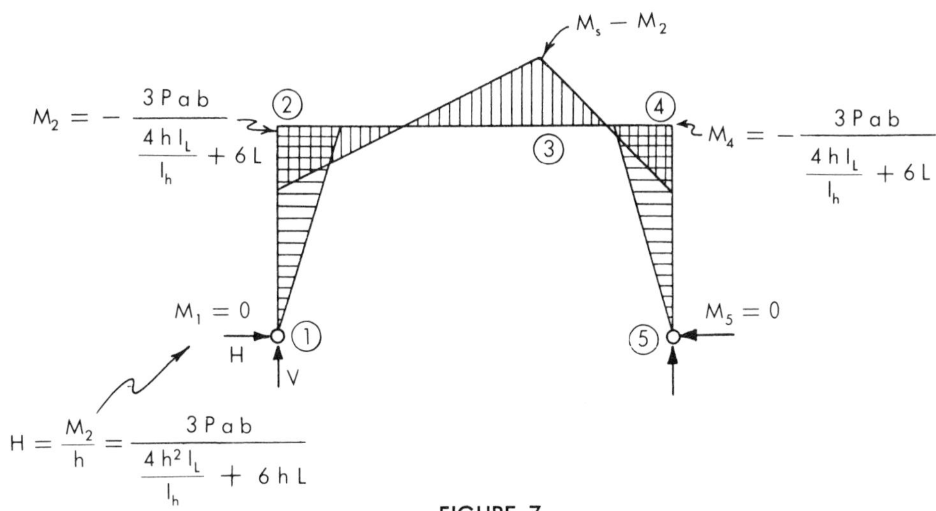

FIGURE 7

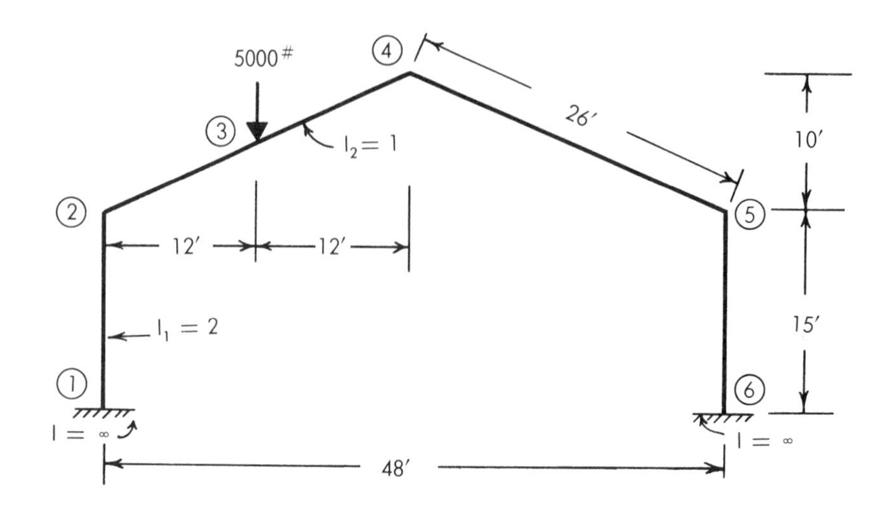

FIGURE 8

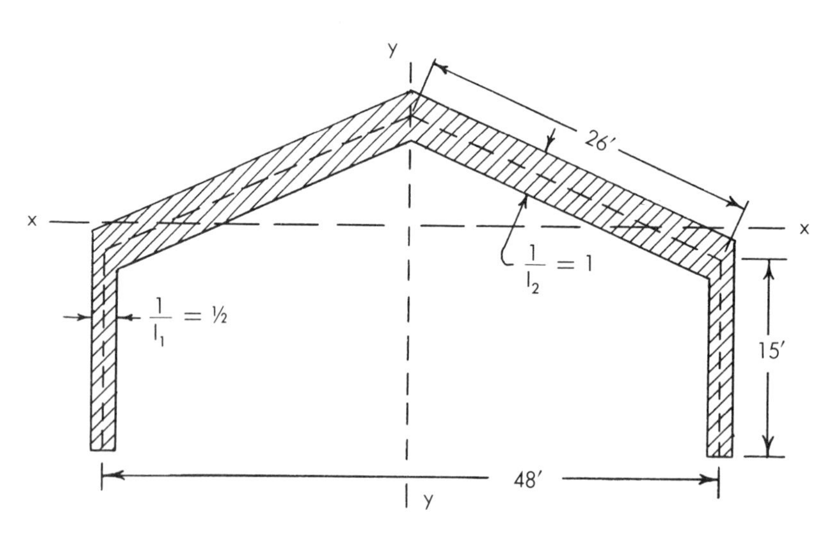

FIGURE 9

Problem 1

Find the moments (M) and the other redundant forces (H and V) of the following frame, having fixed ends, by means of the Column Analogy Method; Figure 8.

This frame must be transformed into the analogous column, and the properties of this equivalent elastic area determined; Figure 9.

Here:

$$A = 2\,\frac{15'}{I_1 = 2} + 2\,\frac{26''}{I_2 = 1} = 67$$

axis x-x of elastic center (See Figure 10.)

Use a reference axis (x′-x′) through the top of the column.

Member	A	y′	M = Ay′	$I_x' = M \cdot y'$	I_g
Columns	15	−7.5	−112.5	+ 843.75	281
Rafters	52	+5.0	+260	+1300	433
Total	67		+147.5	2856	

$$\text{elastic center} = \frac{M}{A} = \frac{+147.5}{67}$$

$= +\ 2.2'$ measured from reference axis (x′-x′)

$$\therefore I_{x\text{-}x} = I_x' + I_g - \frac{M^2}{A}$$

$$= 2856 - \frac{+147.5^2}{67}$$

$$= 2856 - 325$$

$$= 2531 \text{ in.}^4$$

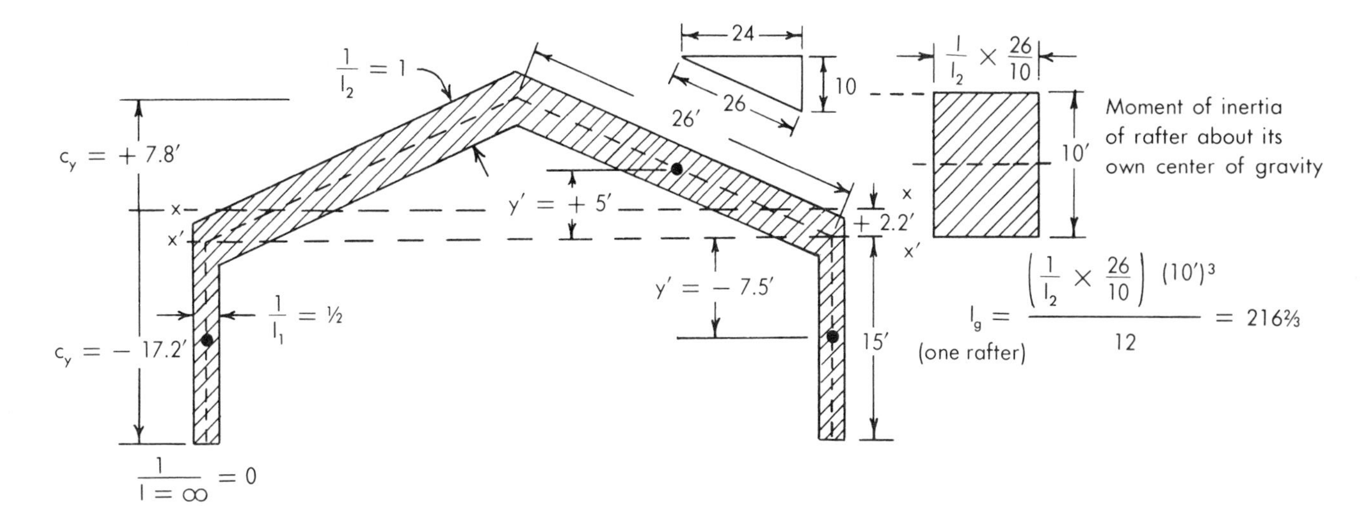

FIGURE 10

distance from elastic center (x-x) to outer fiber

(bottom) $c_y = -15 - 2.2 = -17.2'$

(top) $c_y = +10 - 2.2 = +7.8'$

axis y-y of elastic center (See Figure 11.)

By observation it is seen that this passes through the centerline of the frame:

$$I_{y\text{-}y} = 2(7.5)(24)^2 + 2(26)(12^2) + 2(1248)$$

(2 columns) (2 rafters)

$$= 18{,}624 \text{ in.}^4$$

distance from elastic center (y-y) to outer fiber

(right side) $c_x = +24$

(left side) $c_x = -24$

Cutting Frame So It Becomes Statically Determinate

The frame is now cut so that it becomes statically determinate. The resulting moment diagram, divided by the real moment of inertia (I), is treated as a load upon the analogous column or elastic area. (We don't divide by E here because E is constant; for steel, E = 30 x 10^6.) This may be done in several ways, principally:

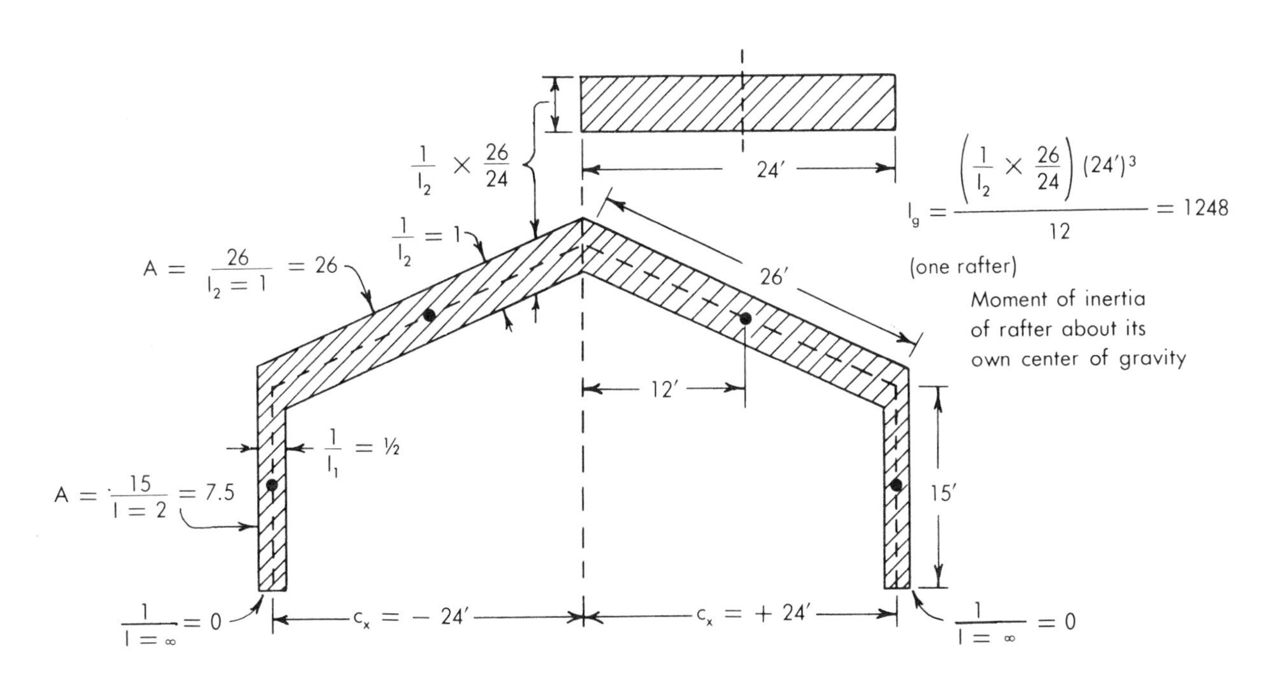

FIGURE 11

A. Cut the right fixed end support at ⑥. The portion of the rafter to the left of the applied load becomes a statically determinate cantilever beam.

B. Release the ends of the rafters at ② and ⑤. This becomes a statically determinate simply supported haunched beam.

Method A: Cut the frame at ⑥. With the load applied at ③, the rafter cantilevers out from ②. The end moment at ②, M = —60,000 ft-lbs, is also applied to the left column ①—②. (See Figure 15.)

the three loads on elastic area

$$P = \frac{-60{,}000 \times 15'}{I_1 = 2} + \frac{\tfrac{1}{2}(-60{,}000 \times 13')}{I_2 = 1}$$

$$= -450{,}000 - 390{,}000$$

$$= -840{,}000$$

$$M_{x\text{-}x} = (-450{,}000)(-9.7) + (-390{,}000)(-.53)$$

$$= +\ 4{,}571{,}700$$

$$M_{y\text{-}y} = (-450{,}000)(-24) + (-390{,}000)(-20)$$

$$= +\ 18{,}600{,}000$$

correction moment at ①

$c_y = -17.2'$

$c_x = -24'$

$$= \frac{P}{A} + \frac{M_{x\text{-}x}\, c_y}{I_{x\text{-}x}} + \frac{M_{y\text{-}y}\, c_x}{I_{y\text{-}y}}$$

$$= \frac{(-840{,}000)}{67} + \frac{(+4{,}571{,}700)(-17.2)}{2531} + \frac{(+18{,}600{,}000)(-24)}{18{,}624}$$

$$= -\ 67{,}570 \text{ ft-lbs}$$

HOW TO DETERMINE CORRECTIVE MOMENTS
(Diagrams Apply to Option *A*)

The moment diagram divided by the moment of inertia of the statically determinant frame is considered to be the load on the elastic area of the analogous column. (E is constant.)

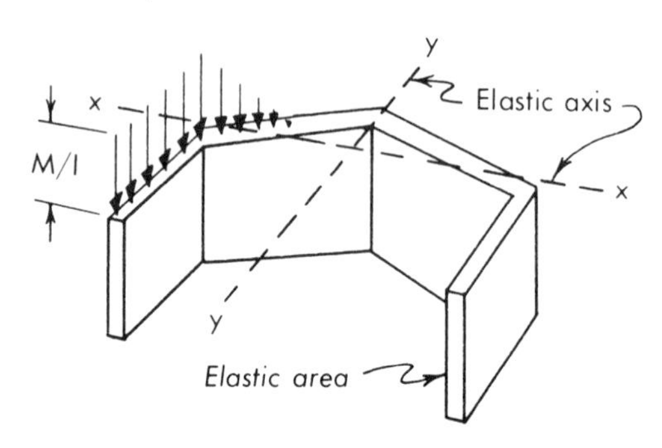

FIGURE 12

This total load on the elastic area may be broken down into 3 loads:

a. Axial load, P

b. Moment, $M_{x\text{-}x}$, about axis x-x

c. Moment, $M_{y\text{-}y}$, about axis y-y

These loads, in turn, result in 3 types of resisting "stresses":

$$\sigma_a = \frac{P}{a} \qquad \sigma_x = \frac{M_{x\text{-}x}\, c_y}{I_{x\text{-}x}} \qquad \sigma_y = \frac{M_{y\text{-}y}\, c_x}{I_{y\text{-}y}}$$

The resultant "stress" at any point of the elastic area may be found from the conventional stress in an eccentrically-loaded column:

$$\sigma = \frac{P}{a} + \frac{M_{y\text{-}y}\, c_y}{I_{y\text{-}y}} + \frac{M_{x\text{-}x}\, c_x}{I_{x\text{-}x}}$$

These "stresses" are the correcting moments, which must be applied to the original moments of the statically determinate frame to produce the final moments of the statically indeterminate frame.

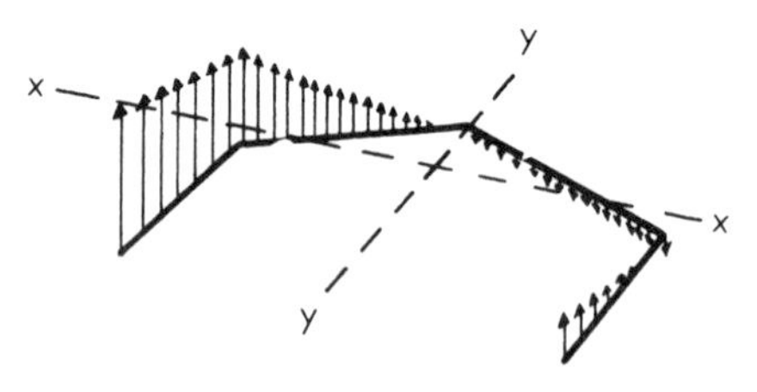

FIG. 14 Correcting moments

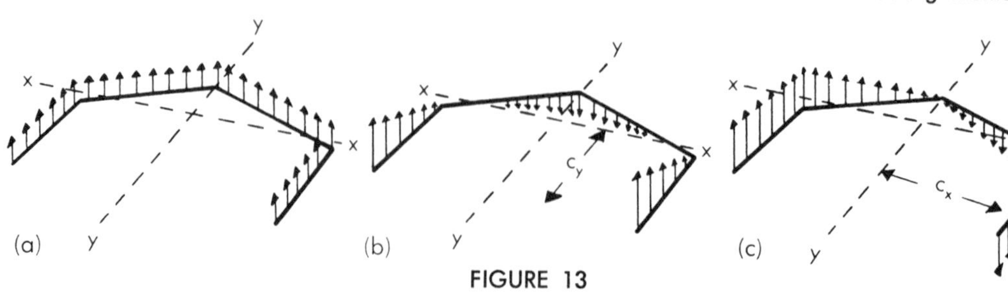

FIGURE 13

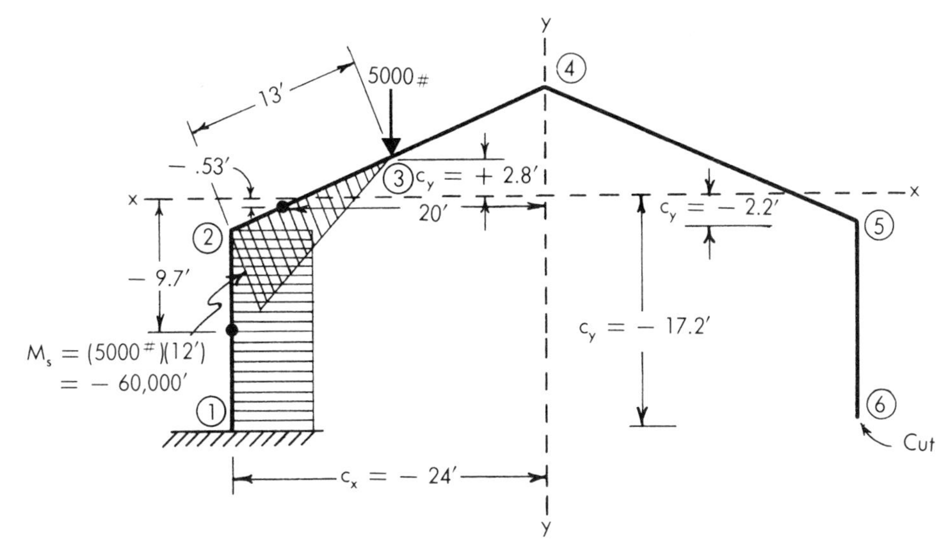

FIGURE 15

final moment = original moment − correction moment

$$M_1 = -60{,}000 + 67{,}620$$
$$= +7570 \text{ ft-lbs}$$

correction moment at ②

$$= \frac{P}{A} + \frac{M_{x\text{-}x}\, c_y}{I_{x\text{-}x}} + \frac{M_{y\text{-}y}\, c_x}{I_{y\text{-}y}} \qquad \begin{array}{|l} c_y = -2.2' \\ c_x = -24' \end{array}$$

$$= \frac{-840{,}000}{67} + \frac{(+4{,}571{,}700)(-2.2)}{2531} + \frac{(+18{,}600{,}000)(-24)}{18{,}624}$$

$$= -40{,}480 \text{ ft-lbs}$$

final moment = original moment − correction moment

$$M_2 = -60{,}000 + 40{,}480$$
$$= -19{,}520 \text{ ft-lbs}$$

correction moment at ③

$$= \frac{P}{A} + \frac{M_{x\text{-}x}\, c_y}{I_{x\text{-}x}} + \frac{M_{y\text{-}y}\, c_x}{I_{y\text{-}y}} \qquad \begin{array}{|l} c_y = +2.8' \\ c_x = -12' \end{array}$$

$$= \frac{-840{,}000}{67} + \frac{(+4{,}571{,}700)(+2.8)}{2531} + \frac{(+18{,}600{,}000)(-12)}{18{,}624}$$

$$= -19{,}460 \text{ ft-lbs}$$

final moment = original moment − correction moment

$$M_3 = 0 + 19{,}460$$
$$= +19{,}460 \text{ ft-lbs}$$

correction moment at ④

$$= \frac{P}{A} + \frac{M_{x\text{-}x}\, c_y}{I_{x\text{-}x}} + \frac{M_{y\text{-}y}\, c_x}{I_{y\text{-}y}} \qquad \begin{array}{|l} c_y = +7.8' \\ c_x = 0 \end{array}$$

$$= \frac{-840{,}000}{67} + \frac{(+4{,}571{,}700)(+7.8)}{2531} + \frac{(+18{,}600{,}000)(0)}{18{,}624}$$

$$= +1550 \text{ ft-lbs}$$

final moment

$$M_4 = -1550 \text{ ft-lbs}$$

correction moment at ⑤

$$= \frac{P}{A} + \frac{M_{x\text{-}x}\, c_y}{I_{x\text{-}x}} + \frac{M_{y\text{-}y}\, c_x}{I_{y\text{-}y}} \qquad \begin{array}{|l} c_y = -2.2' \\ c_x = +24' \end{array}$$

$$= \frac{-840{,}000}{67} + \frac{(+4{,}571{,}700)(-2.2)}{2531} + \frac{(+18{,}600{,}000)(+24)}{18{,}624}$$

$$= +7460 \text{ ft-lbs}$$

final moment

$$M_5 = -7460 \text{ ft-lbs}$$

correction moment at ⑥

$$= \frac{P}{A} + \frac{M_{x\text{-}x}\, c_y}{I_{x\text{-}x}} + \frac{M_{y\text{-}y}\, c_x}{I_{y\text{-}y}} \qquad \begin{array}{|l} c_y = -17.2' \\ c_x = +24' \end{array}$$

$$= \frac{-840{,}000}{67} + \frac{(+4{,}571{,}700)(-17.2)}{2531} + \frac{(+18{,}600{,}000)(+24)}{18{,}624}$$

$$= -19{,}640 \text{ ft-lbs}$$

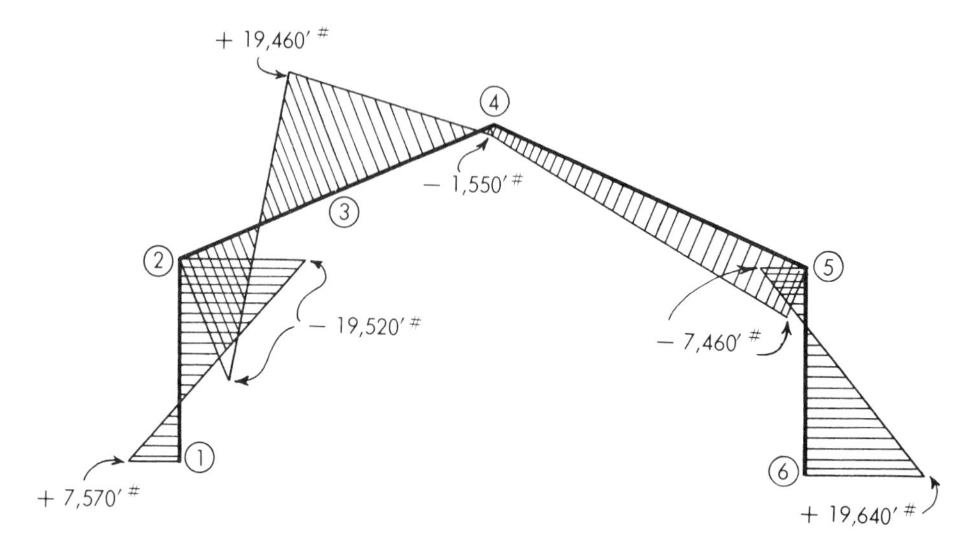

FIGURE 16

final moment

$$M_6 = + 19{,}640 \text{ ft-lbs}$$

The final moments of the statically indeterminate frame are diagrammed in Figure 16.

Horizontal Redundant Force

To find the horizontal redundant force (H) at the base of the column, first find the point of inflection (zero moment) in the column. Then find the horizontal force required at this point to equal the end moment at the base of the column.

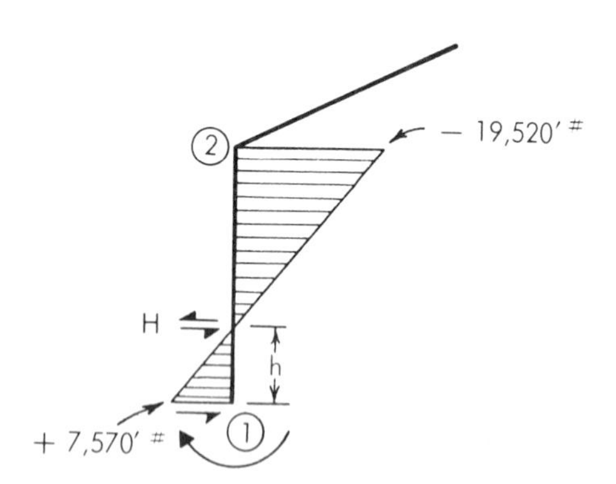

FIGURE 17

$$\frac{h}{15} = \frac{7570}{7570 + 19{,}520}$$

$$= .2794$$

$$\therefore h = 4.191'$$

$$H\,h = M_1$$

$$H = \frac{M_1}{h}$$

$$= \frac{7570 \text{ ft-lbs}}{4{,}191}$$

$$= 1806 \text{ lbs}$$

Vertical Reaction

To find the vertical reaction (V) at the base of the column, take the moments about the base of the opposite column and set them equal to zero. (See Figure 18.)

$$\Sigma M_6 = 0 \text{ or}$$

$$+ M_1 + V_1\,(48) - 5000(36) - M_6 = 0$$

$$V_1(48) = M_6 - M_1 + 5000(36)$$

$$= 19{,}640 - 7570 + 180{,}000$$

$$= 192{,}070$$

$$V_1 = \frac{192{,}070}{48}$$

$$= 4000 \text{ lbs}$$

Method B: Release ends of the rafters at ② and ⑤, so that the rafter becomes simply supported and statically indeterminate. (See Figure 19.)

the three loads on elastic area

$$P = \frac{\frac{1}{2}\,(+45{,}000)(13)}{I_2 = 1} + \frac{\frac{1}{2}\,(+15{,}000)(13)}{I_2 = 1} + \frac{(+30{,}000)(13)}{I_2 = 1} + \frac{\frac{1}{2}\,(+30{,}000)(26)}{I_2 = 1}$$

$$= + 292{,}500 + 97{,}500 + 390{,}000 + 390{,}000$$

$$= + 1{,}170{,}000$$

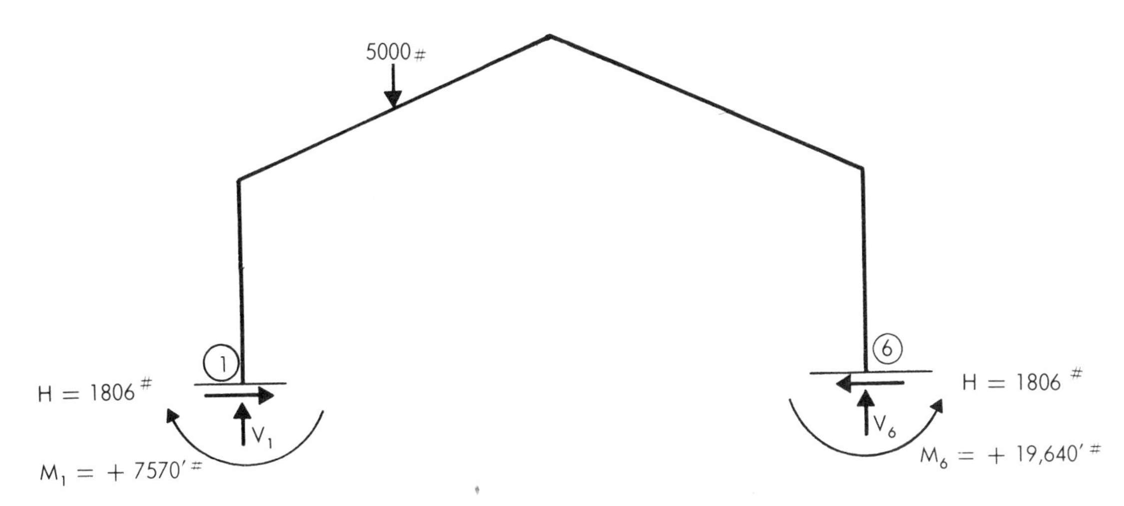

FIGURE 18

$$M_{x\text{-}x} = (+292{,}500)(+1.13) + (97{,}500)(+4.47) + (390{,}000)(+5.3) + (390{,}000)(+4.47)$$
$$= +\ 4{,}576{,}650$$

$$M_{y\text{-}y} = (+292{,}500)(-16) + (97{,}500)(-8) + (390{,}000)(-6) + (390{,}000)(+8)$$
$$= -\ 4{,}680{,}000$$

correction moment at ①

$$= \frac{P}{A} + \frac{M_{x\text{-}x}\ c_y}{I_{x\text{-}x}} + \frac{M_{y\text{-}y}\ c_x}{I_{y\text{-}y}} \qquad \begin{array}{|l} c_y = -\ 17.2' \\ c_x = -\ 24' \end{array}$$

$$= \frac{+1{,}170{,}000}{67} + \frac{(+4{,}576{,}650)(-17.2)}{2531} + \frac{(-4{,}680{,}000)(-24)}{18{,}624}$$

$$= -\ 7600 \text{ ft-lbs}$$

final moment = original moment — correction moment

$$M_1 = 0 + 7600$$
$$= +\ 7600 \text{ ft-lbs}$$

correction moment at ②

$$= \frac{P}{A} + \frac{M_{x\text{-}x}\ c_y}{I_{x\text{-}x}} + \frac{M_{y\text{-}y}\ c_x}{I_{y\text{-}y}} \qquad \begin{array}{|l} c_y = -\ 2.2' \\ c_x = -\ 24' \end{array}$$

$$= \frac{+1{,}170{,}000}{67} + \frac{(+4{,}576{,}650)(-2.2)}{2531} + \frac{(-4{,}680{,}000)(-24)}{18{,}624}$$

$$= +\ 19{,}520 \text{ ft-lbs}$$

final moment

$$M_2 = -\ 19{,}520 \text{ ft-lbs}$$

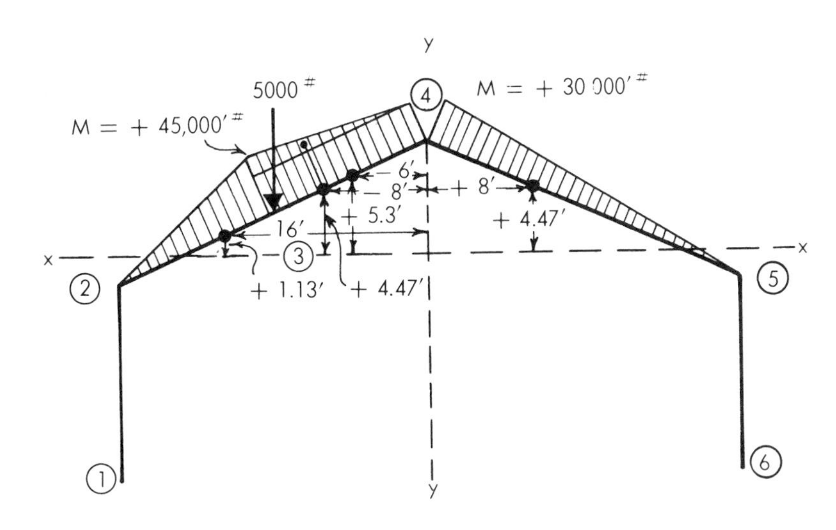

FIGURE 19

correction moment at ③

$$= \frac{P}{A} + \frac{M_{x\text{-}x}\ c_y}{I_{x\text{-}x}} + \frac{M_{y\text{-}y}\ c_x}{I_{y\text{-}y}} \qquad \begin{array}{|l} c_y = +\ 2.8' \\ c_x = -\ 12' \end{array}$$

$$= \frac{+1{,}170{,}000}{67} + \frac{(+4{,}576{,}650)(+2.8)}{2531} + \frac{(-4{,}680{,}000)(-12)}{18{,}624}$$

$$= +\ 25{,}540 \text{ ft-lbs}$$

final moment

$$M_3 = +\ 45{,}000 - 25{,}540$$
$$= +\ 19{,}460 \text{ ft-lbs}$$

correction moment at ④

$$= \frac{P}{A} + \frac{M_{x\text{-}x}\ c_y}{I_{x\text{-}x}} + \frac{M_{y\text{-}y}\ c_x}{I_{y\text{-}y}} \qquad \begin{array}{|l} c_y = +\ 7.8' \\ c_x = 0 \end{array}$$

$$= \frac{+1{,}170{,}000}{67} + \frac{(+4{,}576{,}650)(+7.8)}{2531} + \frac{(-4{,}680{,}000)(0)}{18{,}624}$$

$$= +\ 31{,}560 \text{ ft-lbs}$$

final moment

$$M_4 = +\ 30{,}000 - 31{,}560$$
$$= -\ 1560 \text{ ft-lbs}$$

correction moment at ⑤

$$= \frac{P}{A} + \frac{M_{x\text{-}x}\ c_y}{I_{x\text{-}x}} + \frac{M_{y\text{-}y}\ c_x}{I_{y\text{-}y}} \qquad \begin{array}{|l} c_y = -\ 2.2' \\ c_x = \quad 24' \end{array}$$

$$= \frac{+1{,}170{,}000}{67} + \frac{(+4{,}576{,}650)(-2.2)}{2531} + \frac{(-4{,}680{,}000)(+24)}{18{,}624}$$

$$= +\ 7450 \text{ ft-lbs}$$

final moment

$$M_5 = -\ 7450 \text{ ft-lbs}$$

correction moment at ⑥

$$= \frac{P}{A} + \frac{M_{x\text{-}x}\ c_y}{I_{x\text{-}x}} + \frac{M_{y\text{-}y}\ c_x}{I_{y\text{-}y}} \qquad \begin{array}{|l} c_y = -\ 17.2' \\ c_x = +\ 24' \end{array}$$

$$= \frac{+1{,}170{,}000}{67} + \frac{(+4{,}576{,}650)(-17.2)}{2531} + \frac{(-4{,}680{,}000)(+24)}{18{,}624}$$

$$= -\ 19{,}670 \text{ ft-lbs}$$

final moment

$$M_6 = 0 + 19{,}670$$
$$= +\ 19{,}670 \text{ ft-lbs}$$

Alternate Method

It is possible to work this problem in a slightly different manner. As before—

1. Determine the properties of the elastic area.
2. Cut the frame to make it statically determinate, as before.
3. Dividing the moment diagram of this cut frame by the moment of inertia of the corresponding members of the frame, treat it as the load on the elastic area. (E is constant.)
4. Find the resulting three parts of this load on the elastic area; that is,
   a. Load, P
   b. Moment, $M_{x\text{-}x}$
   c. Moment, $M_{y\text{-}y}$

Then find the three corrective actions—fixed end moment (M_{fe}), horizontal force (H), and vertical force (V)—which must be applied at the base of the frame to bring it back to the original shape and condition of the statically indeterminate frame. Find these from the following formulas:

$$M_{fe} = -\ \frac{P}{A}$$

$$H = -\ \frac{M_{x\text{-}x}}{I_{x\text{-}x}}$$

$$V = -\ \frac{M_{y\text{-}y}}{I_{y\text{-}y}}$$

Figure 20 shows their application to solution of the immediate problems.

The resulting moments about the frame for each of these corrective actions are determined and placed for convenience in table form. This facilitates totaling them to produce the final moments at any point of the statically indeterminate frame. See Figure 21.

3. FIXED END MOMENTS, STIFFNESS FACTORS, AND CARRY-OVER FACTORS

When some type of moment distribution is used for the analysis of continuous frames, it is necessary to know the following:

1. Fixed end moments (M_{fe}) of the beam.
2. Stiffness factor (K) for each end of the beam so the distribution factors may be determined.
3. Carry-over factor (C) of a moment from one end of the beam to the other end.

These items may be found from already-developed charts, or by use of the column analogy method which

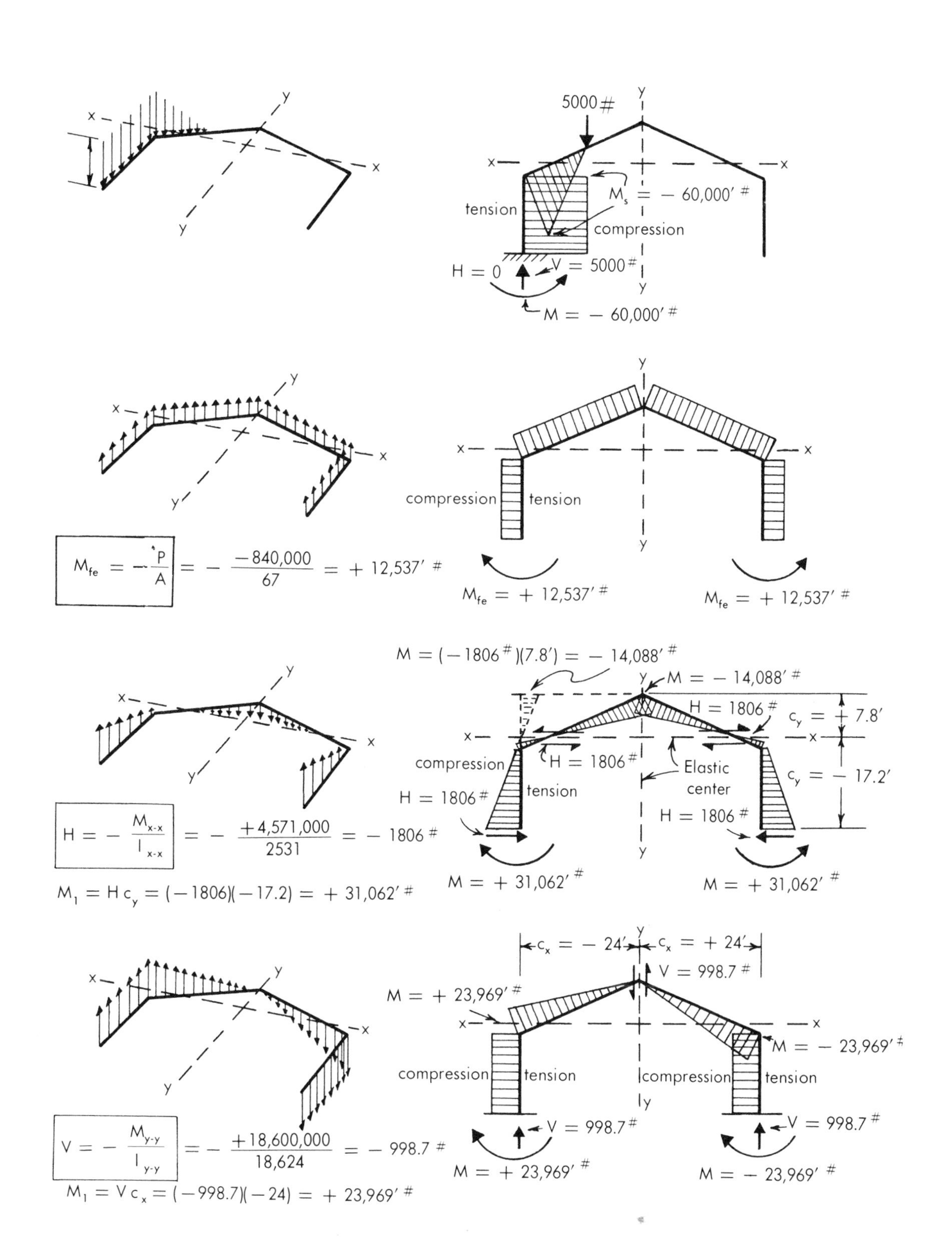
5000#
tension
M_s = − 60,000′ #
compression
H = 0
V = 5000 #
M = − 60,000′ #
compression
tension
$M_{fe} = -\frac{P}{A} = -\frac{-840,000}{67} = +12,537'$ #
M_{fe} = + 12,537′ #
M_{fe} = + 12,537′ #
M = (− 1806 #)(7.8′) = − 14,088′ #
M = − 14,088′ #
H = 1806 #
c_y = + 7.8′
compression
H = 1806 #
Elastic center
c_y = − 17.2′
H = 1806 #
tension
H = 1806 #
$H = -\frac{M_{x\text{-}x}}{I_{x\text{-}x}} = -\frac{+4,571,000}{2531} = -1806$ #
$M_1 = H c_y = (-1806)(-17.2) = +31,062'$ #
M = + 31,062′ #
M = + 31,062′ #
c_x = − 24′
c_x = + 24′
V = 998.7 #
M = + 23,969′ #
M = − 23,969′ #
compression
tension
compression
tension
$V = -\frac{M_{y\text{-}y}}{I_{y\text{-}y}} = -\frac{+18,600,000}{18,624} = -998.7$ #
$M_1 = V c_x = (-998.7)(-24) = +23,969'$ #
V = 998.7 #
V = 998.7 #
M = + 23,969′ #
M = − 23,969′ #

FIGURE 20

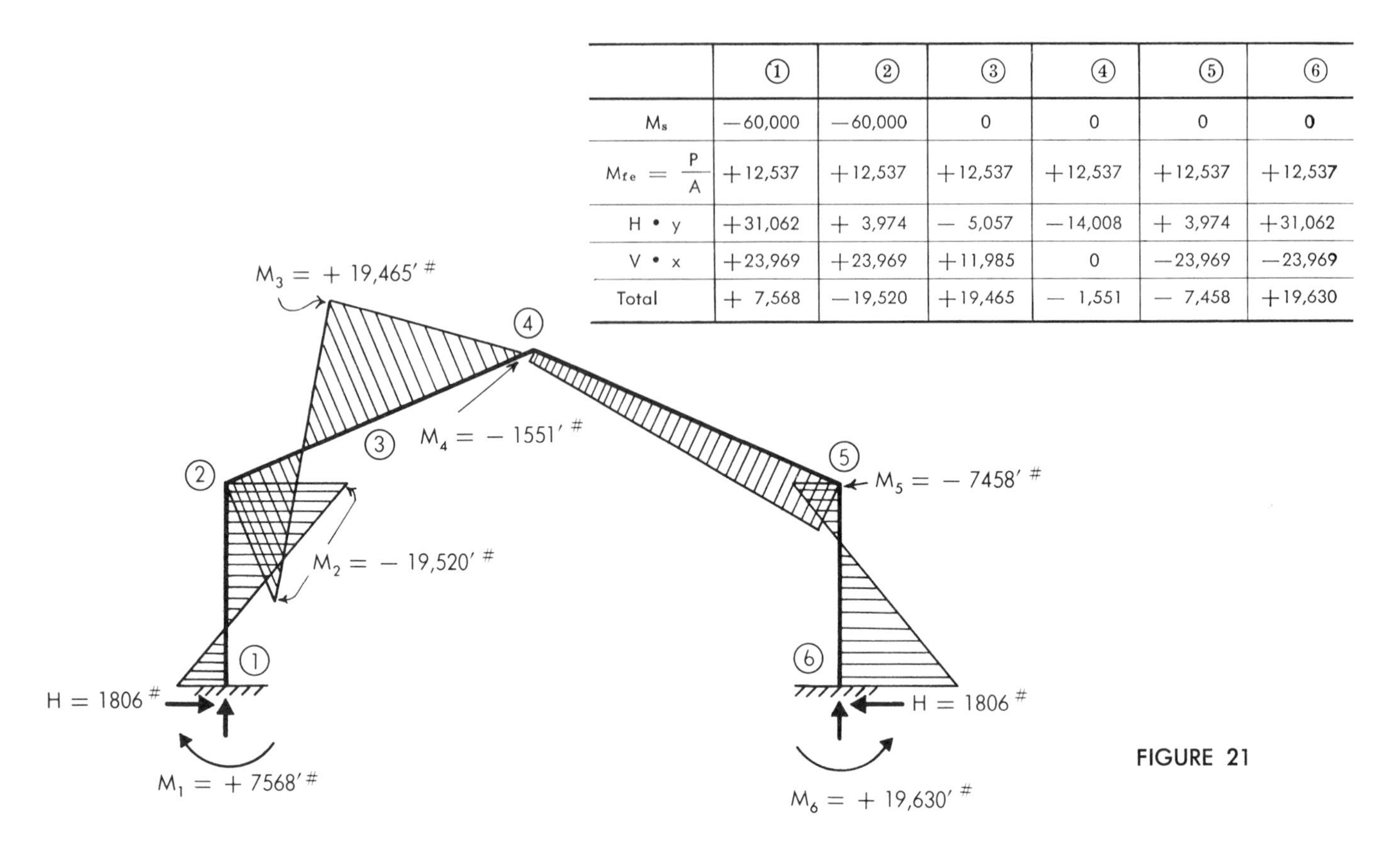

	①	②	③	④	⑤	⑥
M_s	−60,000	−60,000	0	0	0	0
$M_{fe} = \frac{P}{A}$	+12,537	+12,537	+12,537	+12,537	+12,537	+12,537
H • y	+31,062	+ 3,974	− 5,057	−14,008	+ 3,974	+31,062
V • x	+23,969	+23,969	+11,985	0	−23,969	−23,969
Total	+ 7,568	−19,520	+19,465	− 1,551	− 7,458	+19,630

FIGURE 21

is applicable to any type of beam, Figure 22.

The cover-plated beam is representative of any beam in which there is an abrupt change of section . . . and of moment of inertia. The other two common conditions in which there is an abrupt change of section are 1) where plate of heavier thickness is used for the flanges for a short distance at the ends of the beam, and 2) where short lengths of smaller beams are used below the regular beams to reinforce them at and near the points of support.

Constants to Help Calculate Final Moments

Charts have been developed by which the designer can readily find constants to use in determining stiffness factors, carry-over factors, and fixed-end moments for beams.

Sources include:

1. Bull. 176, R. A. Caughy and R. S. Cebula; Iowa Engineering Experiment Station, Iowa State College, Ames, Iowa. 36 charts for beams with cover plates at ends.

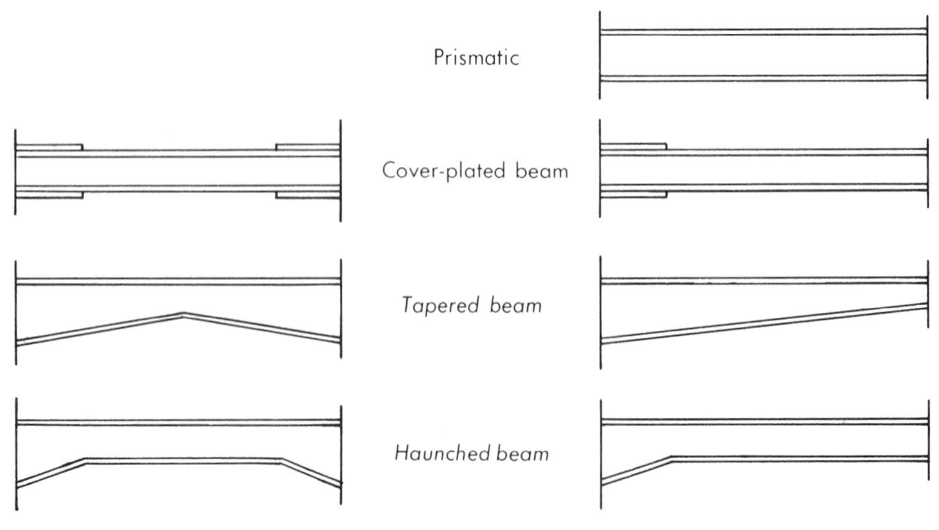

FIGURE 22

2. "Moment Distribution," J. M. Gere, 1963; D. Van Nostrand Co., 378 pages; 29 charts for beams with cover plates at ends; 42 charts for tapered beams.

4. FINDING FIXED END MOMENTS BY COLUMN ANALOGY

Referring back to Topic 2, The Column Analogy Method, the outline of the beam is considered to be the cross-section of a column (or elastic area). See Figure 23.

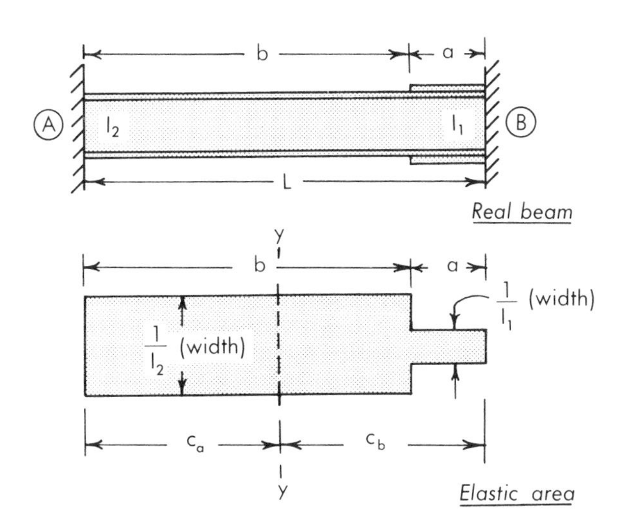

FIGURE 23

The length of the elastic area is equal to the length of the real beam, and the width at any point of the elastic area is equal to the 1/EI of the real beam at the corresponding point. Since we are dealing with steel, the modulus of elasticity (E) is constant and will drop out of the calculations. As the depth and moment of inertia of the real beam increases, the elastic area decreases.

The following design procedure may then be followed.

1. Determine the properties of the elastic area:
   a. Area of the elastic area (A).
   b. Location of axis y-y through the elastic center of the elastic area.
   c. Distance from the elastic center (y-y) to the outer fibers of the elastic area (c_A) and (c_B).
   d. Moment of inertia of the elastic area ($I_{y\text{-}y}$).

2. Release both ends Ⓐ and Ⓑ of the fixed-end beam and draw the moment diagram of this "simply-supported" beam. Use this moment diagram, divided by EI, as the load upon the elastic area (analogous column).

3. The resulting "stresses" at the ends Ⓐ and Ⓑ

$$\sigma = -\frac{P}{A} \pm \frac{M_{y\text{-}y}\ c}{I_{y\text{-}y}}$$

become the correction moments which must be added to the moment of the "simply-supported" beam to transform it back to the original fixed-end, statically indeterminate beam. Since in this case we started out with zero end moments for the "simply-supported" beam, these correction moments then become the fixed end moments of the final rigid beam:

M_{fe} at end Ⓐ

M_{fe} at end Ⓑ

Stiffness Factor by Column Analogy

The stiffness factor (K) is a measure of the resistance of the member against end rotation. It may be defined as the moment necessary to produce a unit end rotation at the same end, while the opposite end is held fixed:

$$K_A = M_A$$

Carry-Over Factor by Column Analogy

For any applied moment (M_A) at Ⓐ, the resulting moment (M_{AB}) at the other end Ⓑ is determined. The carry-over factor is the ratio of these two moments:

$$C_A = -\frac{M_{AB}}{M_A}$$

In both of these two cases, Stiffness Factor and Carry-Over Factor, the fixed-end beam is released at one end Ⓐ and rotated through a unit angle change (ϕ). The resulting end moments (M_A) at Ⓐ and (M_{AB}) at Ⓑ are found.

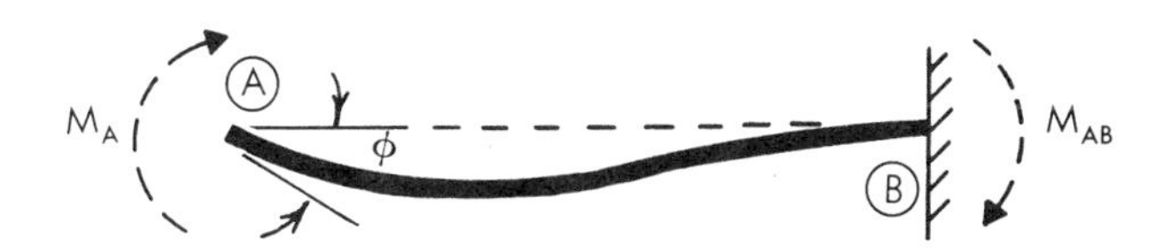

FIGURE 24

This unit angle rotation is applied as a single load at the outer edge of the elastic area (analogous column), just as an eccentric load might be applied to a real column. See Table 1.

For a uniformly loaded, simply supported beam, the bending moment has the shape of a parabola. It will be helpful to know the loads (P) and distances (e) at the center of gravity of these areas. See Table 2.

5. COLUMN ANALOGY METHOD APPLIED TO BEAMS HAVING ABRUPT CHANGE OF SECTION

The Column Analogy Method will now be used to find the fixed end moments, stiffness factor, and the carry-over factors for a fixed-end beam with cover plates at one end, supporting a uniform load (w). The technique would be applied similarly to any beam having abrupt change of section.

Figure 25 diagrams the real loaded beam, at top, and the elastic area of an analogous column, below. On this elastic area,

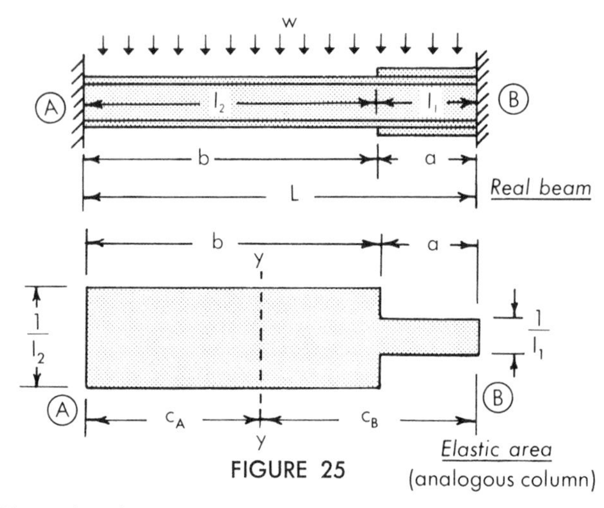

FIGURE 25

TABLE 1—Column Analogy: Unit Angle Rotation

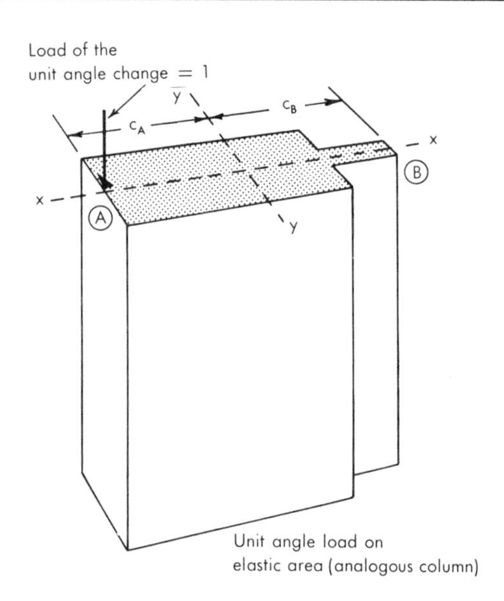

Unit angle change (load) placed at (A)

$$M_{y\text{-}y} = 1\ c_A$$

at (A)

$$M_A = \text{“}\sigma_A\text{”} = \frac{1}{A} + \frac{M_{y\text{-}y}\ c_A}{I_{y\text{-}y}} = \boxed{\frac{1}{A} + \frac{1\ c_A^2}{I_{y\text{-}y}}}$$

at (B)

$$M_{AB} = \text{“}\sigma_B\text{”} = \frac{1}{A} - \frac{M_{y\text{-}y}\ c_B}{I_{y\text{-}y}} = \boxed{\frac{1}{A} - \frac{1\ c_A c_B}{I_{y\text{-}y}}}$$

In same manner—
Unit angle change (load) placed at (B)

$$M_{y\text{-}y} = 1\ c_B$$

at (B)

$$M_B = \text{“}\sigma_B\text{”} = \boxed{\frac{1}{A} + \frac{1\ c_B^2}{I_{y\text{-}y}}}$$

at (A)

$$M_{BA} = \text{“}\sigma_A\text{”} = \boxed{\frac{1}{A} - \frac{1\ c_A c_B}{I_{y\text{-}y}}}$$

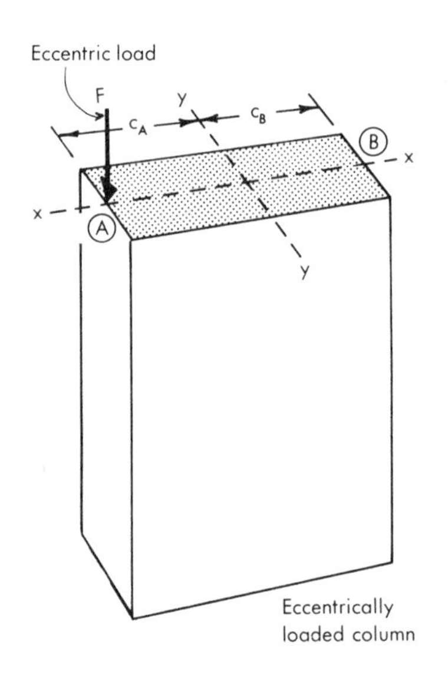

Load F placed at (A)

$$M_{y\text{-}y} = F\ c_A$$

at (A)

$$\sigma_A = \frac{F}{A} + \frac{M_{y\text{-}y}\ c_A}{I_{y\text{-}y}} = \frac{F}{A} + \frac{F\ c_A^2}{I_{y\text{-}y}}$$

at (B)

$$\sigma_B = \frac{F}{A} - \frac{M_{y\text{-}y}\ c_B}{I_{y\text{-}y}} = \frac{F}{A} - \frac{F\ c_A c_B}{I_{y\text{-}y}}$$

Load F placed at (B)

$$M_{y\text{-}y} = F\ c_B$$

at (B)

$$\sigma_B = \frac{F}{A} + \frac{F\ c_B^2}{I_{y\text{-}y}}$$

at (A)

$$\sigma_A = \frac{F}{A} - \frac{F\ c_A c_B}{I_{y\text{-}y}}$$

length = actual length of beam

$$\text{width} = \frac{1}{I_{beam}}$$

STEP 1: Determine Properties of this Elastic Area

area

$$A = \frac{a}{I_1} + \frac{b}{I_2}$$

elastic center (y-y)

Take moments about Ⓐ.

$$c_A = \frac{\Sigma\ M}{\Sigma\ A}$$

$$= \frac{\frac{a}{I_1}\left(b + \frac{a}{2}\right) + \frac{b}{I_2}\left(\frac{b}{2}\right)}{A}$$

$$c_A = \frac{\frac{a}{I_1}\left(a + 2\ b\right) + \frac{b^2}{I^2}}{2\ A}$$

$$c_B = L - c_A$$

moment of inertia ($I_{y\text{-}y}$)

$$I_{y\text{-}y} = \frac{1}{12}\left(\frac{1}{I_2}\right)b^3 + \frac{1}{12}\left(\frac{1}{I_1}\right)a^3 + \frac{b}{I_2}\left(c_A - \frac{b}{2}\right)^2 + \frac{a}{I_1}\left(c_B - \frac{a}{2}\right)^2$$

STEP 2: Determine the Fixed End Moments

Both ends Ⓐ and Ⓑ of the beam are released so that it now becomes simply supported. This moment diagram now becomes the load on the elastic area, Figure 26.

TABLE 2—Loads and Their Eccentricity

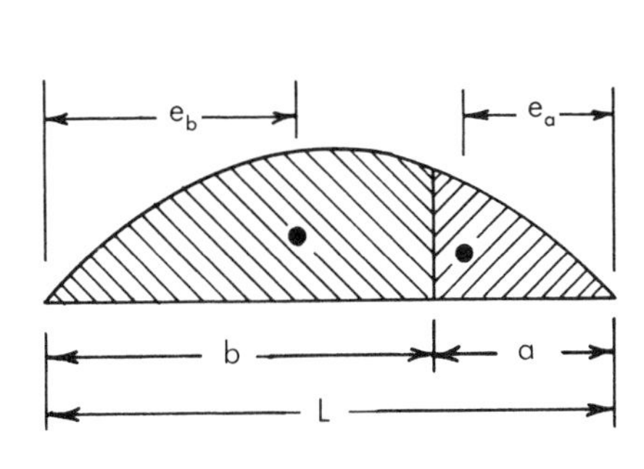

L = a + b

Load (P_a) or (P_b) of portion of moment diagram

$$P_b = \frac{w\ b^2}{12\ I_2}(3\ a + \ b)$$

$$P_a = \frac{w\ a^2}{12\ I_1}(a + 3\ b)$$

Distance to cg of this load

$$e_a = \frac{a}{2}\left(\frac{a + 4\ b}{a + 3\ b}\right)$$

$$e_b = \frac{b}{2}\left(\frac{4\ a + b}{3\ a \ + b}\right)$$

w = unit uniform load (lbs/in.)

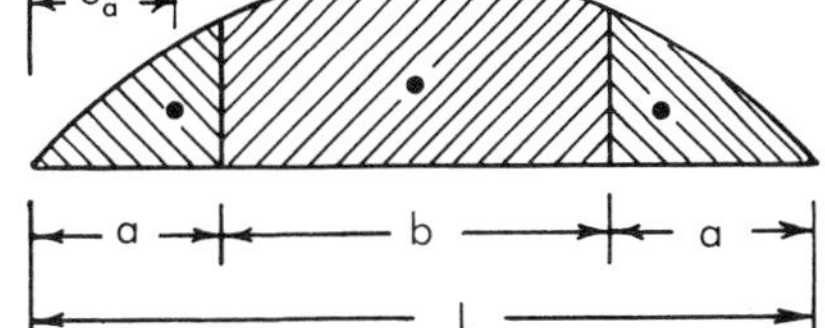

L = 2a + b

Load (P_a) or (P_b) of portion of moment diagram

$$P_b = \frac{w\ b}{12\ I_2}(6\ a^2 + 6\ a\ b + b^2)$$

$$P_a = \frac{w\ a^2}{12\ I_1}(4\ a + 3\ b)$$

Distance to CG of this load

$$e_a = \frac{a}{2}\left(\frac{5\ a + 4\ b}{4\ a + 3\ b}\right)$$

w = unit uniform load (lbs/in.)

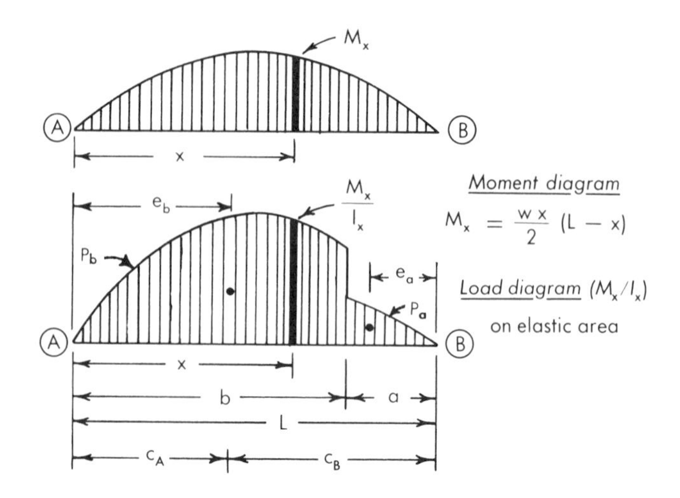

FIGURE 26

"axial" load (P)

$$P_a = \frac{w\ a^2}{12\ I_1}\ (a + 3\ b)$$

$$P_b = \frac{w\ b^2}{12\ I_2}\ (3a + b)$$

$$P = P_a + P_b$$

moment about elastic axis

$$M_{y\text{-}y} = P_a(c_B - e_a) + P_b(e_b - c_A)$$

fixed end moments

This load (P) and ($M_{y\text{-}y}$) on the elastic area causes "stresses" similar to those on an eccentrically loaded column. These "stresses" become the correction moments, or in this case the end moments of the fixed-end beam.

$$\sigma = \frac{P}{A} \pm \frac{M\ c}{I}$$

at A

$$M_{fe} = \frac{P_a + P_b}{A} - \frac{M_{y\text{-}y}\ c_A}{I_{y\text{-}y}}$$

at B

$$M_{fe} = \frac{P_a + P_b}{A} + \frac{M_{y\text{-}y}\ c_B}{I_{y\text{-}y}}$$

STEP 3: Determine Stiffness and Carry-Over Factors

A load of a unit angle change (ϕ) is applied to the elastic area at the outer edge Ⓐ, and the resulting end moments (M_A) at Ⓐ and (M_{AB}) at Ⓑ are found.

$$M_{y\text{-}y} = 1\ c_A$$

at Ⓐ

$$M_A = \frac{1}{A} + \frac{1\ c_A^2}{I_{y\text{-}y}}$$

at Ⓑ

$$M_{AB} = \frac{1}{A} - \frac{1\ c_A\ c_B}{I_{y\text{-}y}}$$

Now the load of a unit angle change (ϕ) is applied to the elastic area at the other outer edge Ⓑ, and the resulting end moment (M_B) at Ⓑ is found. Notice that the end moment (M_{BA}) at Ⓐ is equal to (M_{AB}) at Ⓑ which is already found.

$$M_{y\text{-}y} = 1\ c_B$$

at Ⓑ

$$M_B = \frac{1}{A} + \frac{1\ c_B^2}{I_{y\text{-}y}}$$

From these three values (M_A), (M_{AB}) and (M_B), the following may be found:

stiffness factor at Ⓐ

$$K_A = M_A$$

stiffness factor at Ⓑ

$$K_B = M_B$$

carry-over factor, Ⓐ to Ⓑ

$$C_{AB} = -\frac{M_{AB}}{M_A}$$

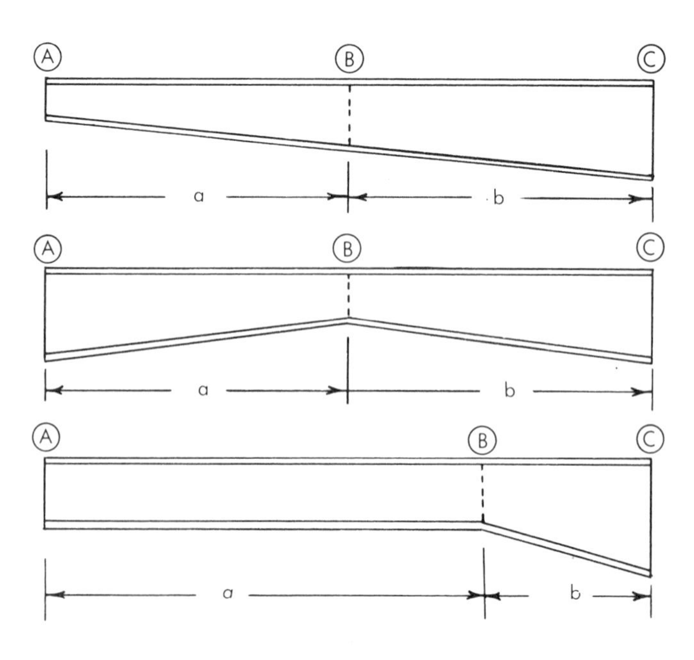

FIGURE 27

TABLE 3—Design Summary: Beam Cover Plated At One End

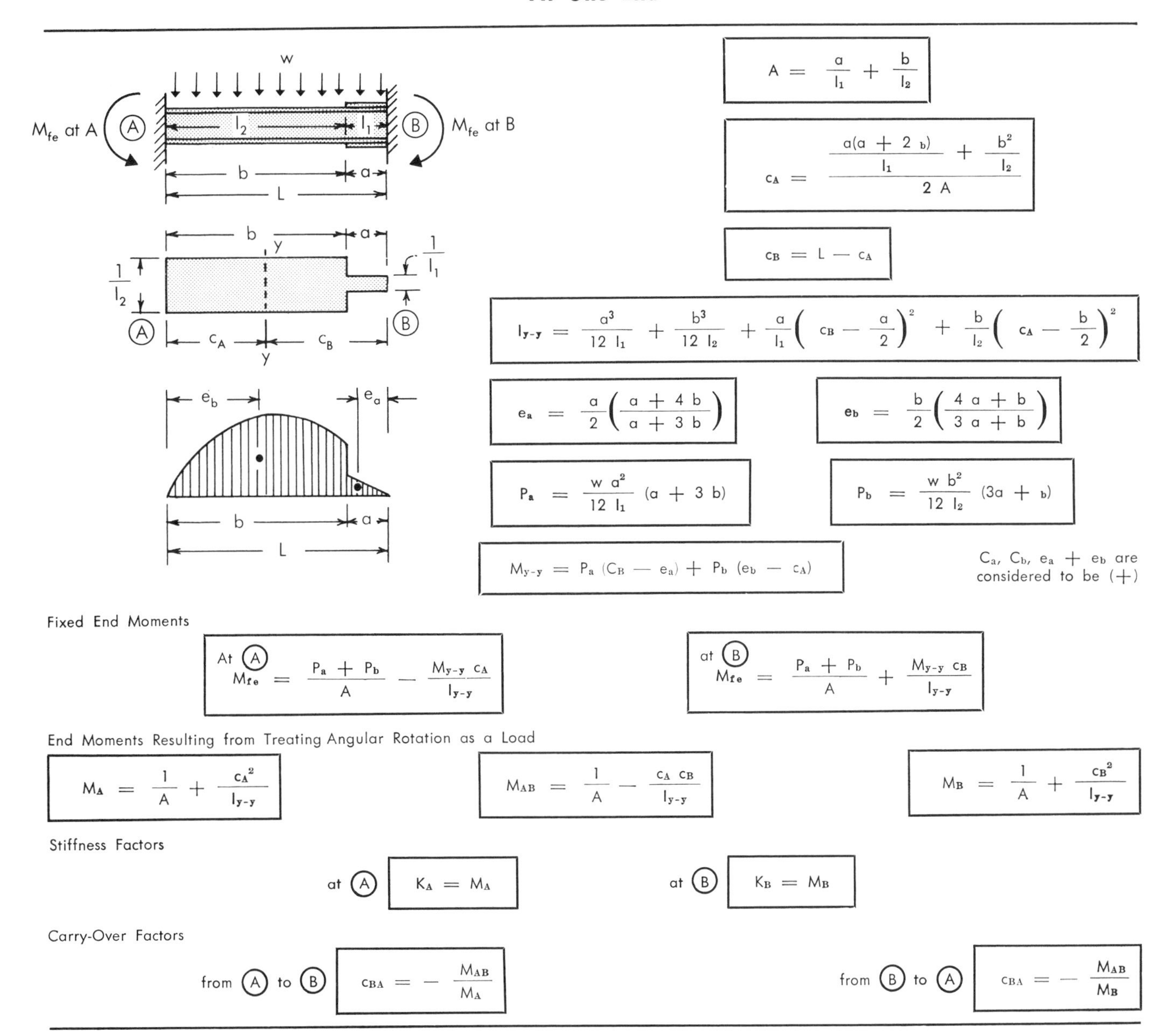

$$A = \frac{a}{I_1} + \frac{b}{I_2}$$

$$c_A = \frac{\frac{a(a + 2b)}{I_1} + \frac{b^2}{I_2}}{2A}$$

$$c_B = L - c_A$$

$$I_{y-y} = \frac{a^3}{12 I_1} + \frac{b^3}{12 I_2} + \frac{a}{I_1}\left(c_B - \frac{a}{2}\right)^2 + \frac{b}{I_2}\left(c_A - \frac{b}{2}\right)^2$$

$$e_a = \frac{a}{2}\left(\frac{a + 4b}{a + 3b}\right) \qquad e_b = \frac{b}{2}\left(\frac{4a + b}{3a + b}\right)$$

$$P_a = \frac{w\,a^2}{12 I_1}(a + 3b) \qquad P_b = \frac{w\,b^2}{12 I_2}(3a + b)$$

$$M_{y-y} = P_a(C_B - e_a) + P_b(e_b - c_A)$$

C_a, C_b, e_a + e_b are considered to be (+)

Fixed End Moments

At (A) $$M_{fe} = \frac{P_a + P_b}{A} - \frac{M_{y-y}\,c_A}{I_{y-y}}$$

at (B) $$M_{fe} = \frac{P_a + P_b}{A} + \frac{M_{y-y}\,c_B}{I_{y-y}}$$

End Moments Resulting from Treating Angular Rotation as a Load

$$M_A = \frac{1}{A} + \frac{c_A^2}{I_{y-y}} \qquad M_{AB} = \frac{1}{A} - \frac{c_A c_B}{I_{y-y}} \qquad M_B = \frac{1}{A} + \frac{c_B^2}{I_{y-y}}$$

Stiffness Factors

at (A) $K_A = M_A$ at (B) $K_B = M_B$

Carry-Over Factors

from (A) to (B) $$c_{BA} = -\frac{M_{AB}}{M_A}$$

from (B) to (A) $$c_{BA} = -\frac{M_{AB}}{M_B}$$

carry-over factor, (B) *to* (A)

$$C_{BA} = -\frac{M_{AB}}{M_B}$$

Summary

This example of the uniformly-loaded, fixed-end beam with cover plates at *one* end may be summarized as in Table 3.

Modified Example

Although the work is not shown, the same fixed-end beam with cover plates at *both* ends, uniformly loaded, may be summarized as in Table 4. (See next page)

6. COLUMN ANALOGY METHOD APPLIED TO BEAMS HAVING GRADUALLY VARYING SECTION

The following method may be used to find the fixed end moments, stiffness factors, and carry-over factors of beams which have constantly varying moments of inertia, such as haunched and tapered beams, Figure 27.

A beam which tapers along a straight line (in other words, its depth increases linearly along the length of the beam, see Fig. 28, top) will have a moment of inertia (I) which does not increase linearly

TABLE 4—Design Summary: Beam Cover Plated At Both Ends

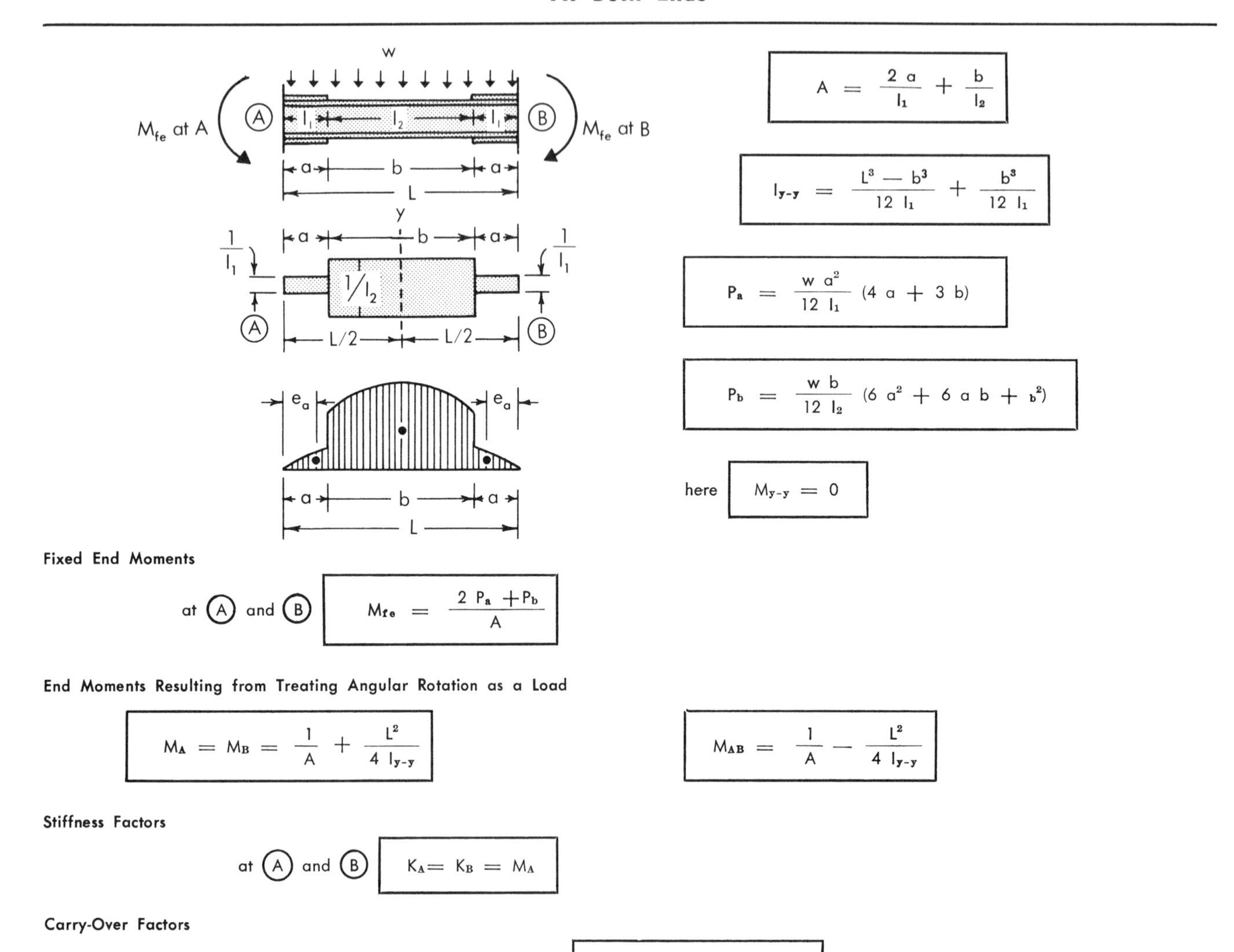

$$A = \frac{2\,a}{I_1} + \frac{b}{I_2}$$

$$I_{y\text{-}y} = \frac{L^3 - b^3}{12\,I_1} + \frac{b^3}{12\,I_1}$$

$$P_a = \frac{w\,a^2}{12\,I_1}(4\,a + 3\,b)$$

$$P_b = \frac{w\,b}{12\,I_2}(6\,a^2 + 6\,a\,b + b^2)$$

here $M_{y\text{-}y} = 0$

Fixed End Moments

at (A) and (B) $$M_{fe} = \frac{2\,P_a + P_b}{A}$$

End Moments Resulting from Treating Angular Rotation as a Load

$$M_A = M_B = \frac{1}{A} + \frac{L^2}{4\,I_{y\text{-}y}}$$

$$M_{AB} = \frac{1}{A} - \frac{L^2}{4\,I_{y\text{-}y}}$$

Stiffness Factors

at (A) and (B) $K_A = K_B = M_A$

Carry-Over Factors

from (A) to (B) or from (B) to (A) $$C_{AB} = C_{BA} = -\frac{M_{AB}}{M_A}$$

but will have a slight curve (see Fig. 28, center, solid line). This curve approaches a straight line as the beam becomes less tapered.

Although a slight error will be introduced, it will greatly simplify the analysis if we assume this moment of inertia distribution to be a straight (dotted) line. However, this slight error may be reduced by breaking the beam into two parts (see Fig. 28, bottom) and assuming a straight line variation of the moment of inertia between the three points (A), (B), and (C). This is represented by the dashed line in Figure 28, center.

STEP 1: Determine Properties of the Elastic Area

area of elastic area

$$A_x = \frac{a}{I_B - I_A} \log_e \frac{I_B}{I_A}$$

$$A_z = \frac{b}{I_C - I_B} \log_e \frac{I_C}{I_B}$$

moment of elastic area A_x about axis A-A

$$M_{Ax}/_{A\text{-}A} = \left(\frac{a}{I_B - I_A}\right)^2 \left(I_B - I_A - I_A \log_e \frac{I_B}{I_A}\right)$$

moment of elastic area A_z about axis B-B

$$M_{Az}/_{B\text{-}B} = \left(\frac{b}{I_C - I_B}\right)^2 \left(I_C - I_B - I_B \log_e \frac{I_C}{I_B}\right)$$

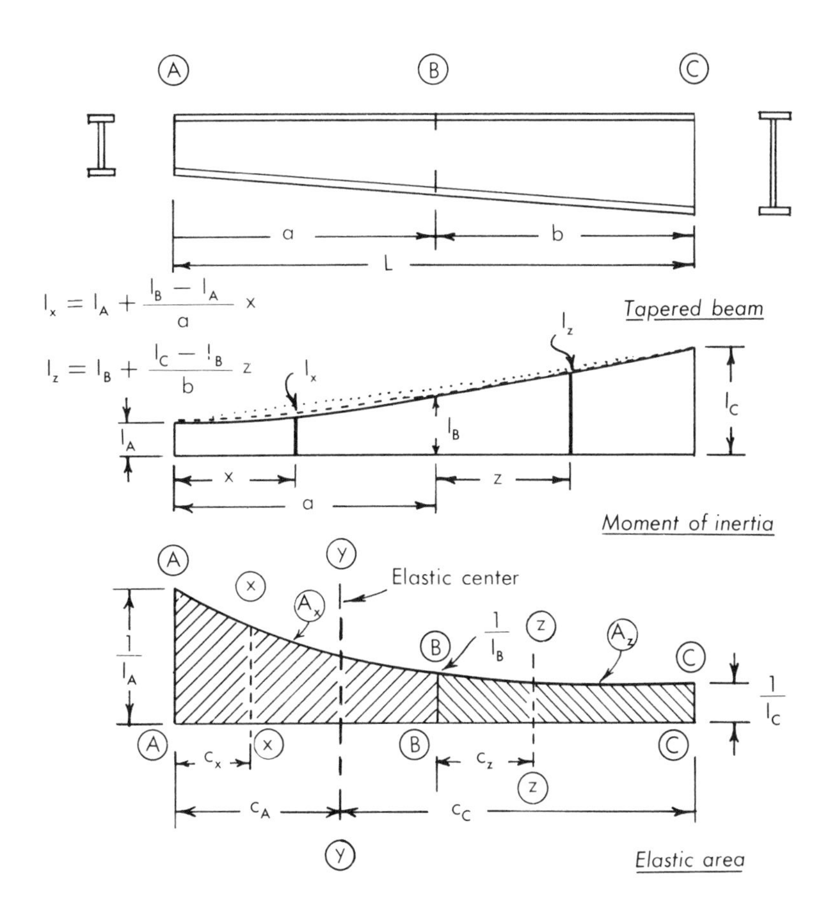

FIGURE 28

distance from C.G. of elastic area A_x to axis A-A

$$c_x = \frac{M_{Ax/A\text{-}A}}{A_x}$$

distance from C.G. of elastic area A_z to axis B-B

$$c_z = \frac{M_{Az/B\text{-}B}}{A_z}$$

moment of elastic area A_z about axis A-A

$$M_{Az/A\text{-}A} = a\ A_z + M_{Az/B\text{-}B}$$

total moment of elastic area about axis A-A

$$M_{A\text{-}A} = M_{Ax/A\text{-}A} + M_{Az/A\text{-}A}$$

elastic center (y-y)

$$c_A = \frac{M_{A\text{-}A}}{A}$$

$$c_C = L - c_A$$

moment of inertia of elastic area A_x about axis A-A

$$I_{Ax/A\text{-}A} = \left(\frac{a}{I_B - I_A}\right)^3 \left[\frac{(I_B - I_A)(I_B - 3\ I_A)}{2} + I_A^2 \log_e \frac{I_B}{I_A}\right]$$

moment of inertia of elastic area A_z about axis B-B

$$I_{Az/B\text{-}B} = \left(\frac{b}{I_C - I_B}\right)^3 \left[\frac{(I_C - I_B)(I_C - 3\ I_B)}{2} + I_B^2 \log_e \frac{I_C}{I_B}\right]$$

Since these moments of inertia can't be added, not being taken about the same axis, it will be necessary to shift axis B-B and axis A-A to the elastic center y-y. If axis A-A is always taken at the shallow end of the tapered beam, negative signs will be avoided in the calculations.

moment of inertia of elastic area A_x about axis y-y

Using the parallel axis theorem:

$$I_{Ax}/_{A\text{-}A} = I_{Ax}/_{x\text{-}x} + A_x\, c_x^2$$

$$\therefore \quad I_{Ax}/_{x\text{-}x} = I_{Ax}/_{A\text{-}A} - A_x\, c_x^2$$

Now we wish moments of inertia of A_x about the elastic axis y-y, and again using parallel axis theorem—

$$I_{Ax}/_{y\text{-}y} = I_{Ax}/_{x\text{-}x} + A_x(c_A - c_x)^2$$

$$\text{or } I_{Ax}/_{y\text{-}y} = I_{Ax}/_{A\text{-}A} - A_x\, c_x^2 + A_x(c_A - c_x)^2$$

$$\text{and } I_{Ax}/_{y\text{-}y} = I_{Ax}/_{A\text{-}A} + A_x\, c_A(c_A - 2\, c_x)$$

moment of inertia of elastic area A_z about axis y-y

in same manner—

$$I_{Az}/_{y\text{-}y} = I_{Az}/_{B\text{-}B} + A_z\,[(c_z + b - c_A)^2 - c_z^2]$$

total moment of inertia of elastic area

$$I_{y\text{-}y} = I_{Ax}/_{y\text{-}y} + I_{Az}/_{y\text{-}y}$$

STEP 2: Determine the Fixed End Moments

The moment diagram from the applied load on the real beam is divided by the moment of inertia (I) of the real beam, and becomes the load (M/I) on the elastic area which is treated as a column.

The axial load (P) applied to the elastic area is equal to the total M/I. This axial load applied at some distance from the elastic center of the elastic area causes a moment (M) on the elastic area.

Both of these loads cause "stresses" on the elastic area.

The following applies if the designer can assume a uniform load (w):

axial load (P) applied to elastic area

$$P_x = \frac{w}{2}\left(L\, M_{Ax}/_{A\text{-}A} - I_{Ax}/_{A\text{-}A} \right)$$

$$P_z = \frac{w}{2}\Big[- I_{Az}/_{B\text{-}B} + (L - 2\,a)\, M_{Az}/_{B\text{-}B} + a\,(L - a)\, A_y\Big]$$

and,

$$P = P_x + P_z$$

momen (M) applied to elastic area about its elastic center

$$M_x/_{y\text{-}y} = \frac{w}{2}\Big[- Q_x + (L + c_A)\, I_{Ax}/_{A\text{-}A} - c_A\, L\, M_{Ax}/_{A\text{-}A}\Big]$$

where:

$$Q_x = \left(\frac{a}{I_B - I_A}\right)^4 \left[\left(\frac{I_B - I_A}{6}\right)(2\, I_B^2 - 7\, I_B\, I_A + 11\, I_A^2) - I_A^3 \log_e \frac{I_B}{I_A}\right]$$

$$M_z/_{y\text{-}y} = \frac{w}{2}\Big[- Q_z + (L - 3\,a + c_A)\, I_{Az}/_{B\text{-}B} + [a(2\,L - 3a) - c_A(L - 2a)]\; M_{Az}/_{B\text{-}B} + a\,(L - a)(a - c_A)\, A_y\Big]$$

where:

$$Q_z = \left(\frac{b}{I_C - I_B}\right)^4 \left[\left(\frac{I_C - I_B}{6}\right)(2\, I_C^2 - 7\, I_C\, I_B + 11\, I_B^2) - I_B^3 \log_e \frac{I_C}{I_B}\right]$$

and the total moment—

$$M_{y\text{-}y} = M_x/_{y\text{-}y} + M_z/_{y\text{-}y}$$

fixed end moments

at Ⓐ

$$M_{fe} = \frac{P}{A} - \frac{M_{y\text{-}y}\, c_A}{I_{y\text{-}y}}$$

at Ⓒ

$$M_{fe} = \frac{P}{A} + \frac{M_{y\text{-}y}\, c_C}{I_{y\text{-}y}}$$

STEP 3: Determine Stiffness and Carry-Over Factors

$$M_A = \frac{1}{A} + \frac{c_A^2}{I_{y\text{-}y}}$$

$$M_{AC} = \frac{1}{A} - \frac{c_A\, c_C}{I_{y\text{-}y}}$$

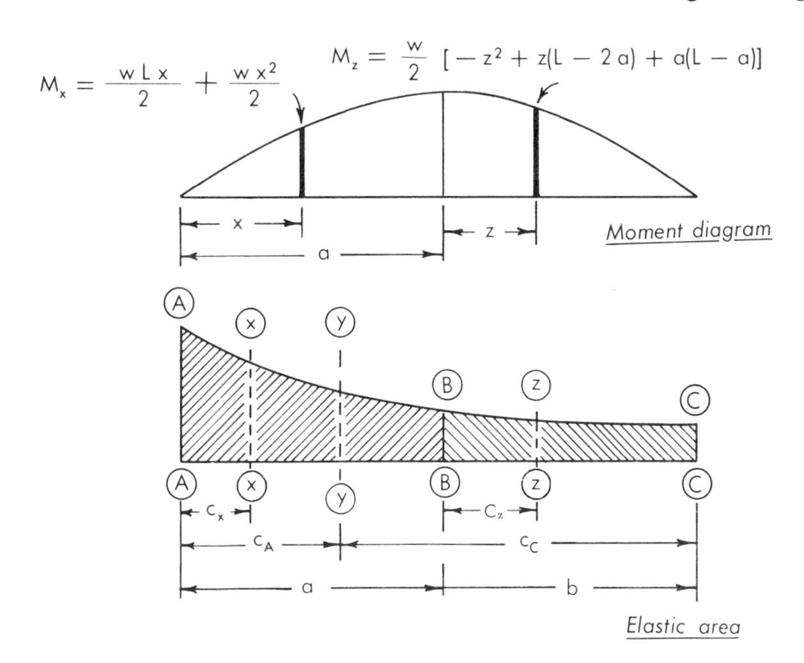

FIGURE 29

$$M_C = \frac{1}{A} + \frac{c_C^2}{I_{y\text{-}y}}$$

stiffness factor at Ⓐ

$$K_A = M_A$$

stiffness factor at Ⓒ

$$K_C = M_C$$

carry-over factor, Ⓐ *to* Ⓒ

$$C_{AC} = -\frac{M_{AC}}{M_A}$$

carry-over factor, Ⓒ *to* Ⓐ

$$C_{CA} = -\frac{M_{AC}}{M_C}$$

Problem 2

For the uniformly-loaded beam shown at top in Figure 30, having fixed ends, find the fixed end moments, stiffness factor, and carry-over factors.

At center in Figure 30, the solid curve is the actual moment of inertia (I) as it varies along the length of the beam. The dashed line is the assumed straight-line variation in moment of inertia along the two halves of the tapered beam.

The following properties are established:

$a = 100''$ $\qquad I_B{}^2 = 6.4516 \times 10^6$

$I_A = 646.7$ $\qquad I_B{}^3 = 1.6386 \times 10^{10}$

$I_A{}^2 = 4.1822 \times 10^5$ $\qquad L = 100''$

$I_A{}^3 = 3.678 \times 10^8$ $\qquad I_C = 5930$

$b = 100''$ $\qquad I_C{}^2 = 3.5163 \times 10^7$

$I_B = 2540$

Then proceed first to find formula elements made up of these properties:

$$\log_e n = 2.3026 \quad \log_{10} n$$

$$\log_e \frac{I_B}{I_A} = \log_e \frac{(2540)}{(6467)} = \log_e 3.9276$$

$$= 1.3680$$

$$\log_e \frac{I_C}{I_B} = \log_e \frac{(5930)}{(2540)} = \log_e 2.3346$$

$$= .84780$$

$$I_B - I_A = (2540) - (646.7)$$

$$= 1893.3$$

$$I_C - I_B = (5930) - (2540)$$

$$= 3390$$

$$\frac{a}{(I_B - I_A)} = \frac{(100)}{(1893.3)}$$

$$= .052813$$

$$\left(\frac{a}{(I_B - I_A)}\right)^2 = 2.7892 \times 10^{-3}$$

$$\left(\frac{a}{(I_B - I_A)}\right)^3 = 1.4731 \times 10^{-4}$$

$$\left(\frac{a}{(I_B - I_A}\right)^4 = .77800 \times 10^{-5}$$

$$\frac{b}{(I_C - I_B)} = \frac{(100)}{(3390)}$$
$$= .029499$$

$$\left(\frac{b}{(I_C - I_B)}\right)^2 = .8722 \times 10^{-3}$$

$$\left(\frac{b}{(I_C - I_B)}\right)^3 = 2.5728 \times 10^{-5}$$

$$\left(\frac{b}{(I_C - I_B)}\right)^4 = .75895 \times 10^{-6}$$

STEP 1: Determine Properties of the Elastic Area

area of elastic area

$$A_x = \frac{a}{(I_B - I_A)} \log_e \frac{I_B}{I_A}$$
$$= (.052813)(1.3680)$$
$$= .072252$$

$$A_z = \frac{b}{(I_C - I_B)} \log_e \frac{I_C}{I_B}$$
$$= (.029499)(.84780)$$
$$= .025008$$

$$A = A_x + A_z$$
$$= (.072252) + (.025008)$$
$$= .097260$$

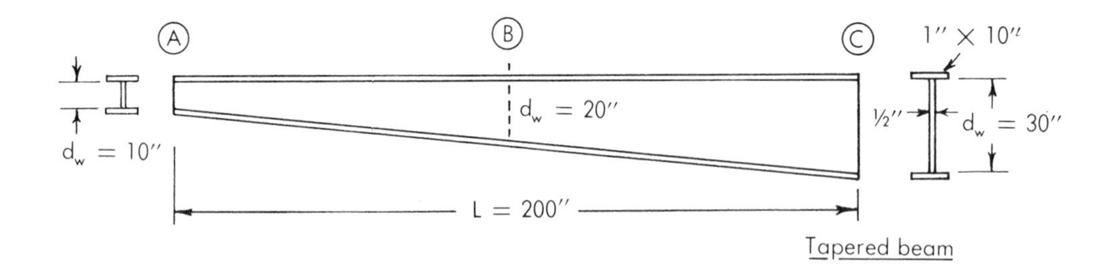

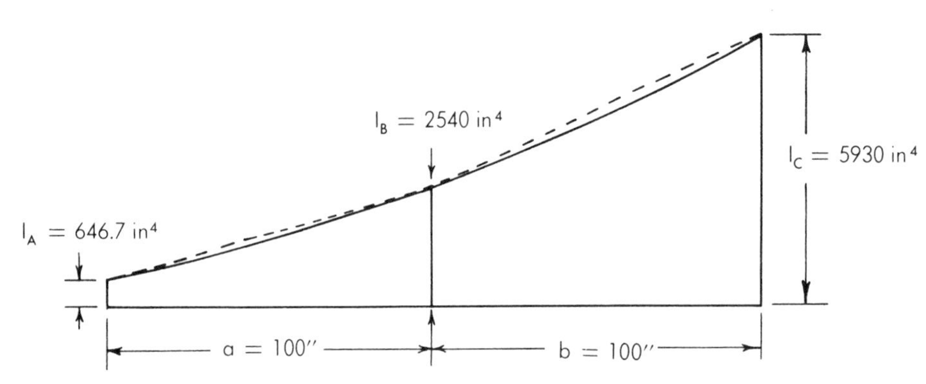

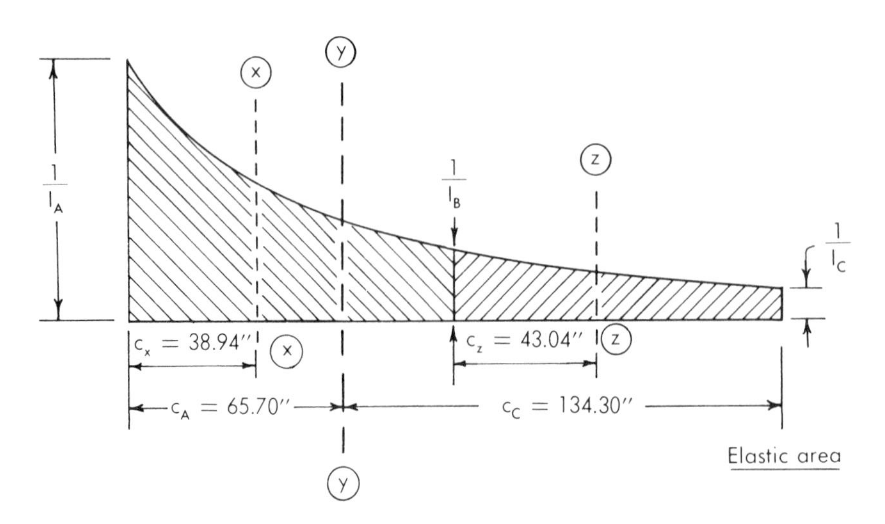

FIGURE 30

moments of elastic area

$$M_{Ax}/_{A\text{-}A} = \left(\frac{a}{(I_B - I_A)}\right)^2 \left(I_B - I_A - I_A \log_e \frac{I_B}{I_A}\right)$$

$$= (2.7892 \times 10^{-3})(1893.3 - 646.7 \times 1.3680)$$

$$= 2.8132$$

$$M_{Az}/_{B\text{-}B} = \left(\frac{b}{(I_C - I_B)}\right)^2 \left(I_C - I_B - I_B \log_e \frac{I_C}{I_B}\right)$$

$$= (.8722 \times 10^{-3})(3390 - 2540 \times .84780)$$

$$= 1.0762$$

$$c_x = \frac{M_{Ax}/_{A\text{-}A}}{A_x}$$

$$= \frac{(2.8132)}{(.072252)}$$

$$= 38.937''$$

$$c_z = \frac{M_{Az}/_{B\text{-}B}}{A_z}$$

$$= \frac{(1.0762)}{(.025008)}$$

$$= 43.038''$$

$$M_{Az}/_{A\text{-}A} = A_z a + M_{Az}/_{B\text{-}B}$$

$$= (.025008)(100) + (1.0762)$$

$$= 3.5570$$

$$M_{A\text{-}A} = M_{Ax}/_{A\text{-}A} + M_{Az}/_{A\text{-}A}$$

$$= (2.8132) + (3.5570)$$

$$= 6.3902$$

$$c_A = \frac{M_{A\text{-}A}}{A}$$

$$= \frac{(6.3903)}{(.097260)}$$

$$= 65.70''$$

$$c_C = L - c_A$$

$$= (200) - (65.70)$$

$$= 134.30''$$

$$I_{Ax}/_{A\text{-}A} = \left(\frac{a}{(I_B - I_A)}\right)^3 \left(\frac{(I_B - I_A)(I_B - 3\ I_A)}{2} + I_A^2 \log_e \frac{I_B}{I_A}\right)$$

$$= \left(1.4731 \times 10^{-4}\right)\left(\frac{1893.3 \times 599.9}{2} + 4.1822 \times 10^5 \times 1.3680\right)$$

$$= 167.93$$

$$I_{Az}/_{B\text{-}B} = \left(\frac{b}{(I_C - I_B)}\right)^3 \left(\frac{(I_C - I_B)(I_C - 3\ I_B)}{2} + I_B^2 \log_e \frac{I_C}{I_B}\right)$$

$$= \left(2.5728 \times 10^{-5}\right)\left(\frac{(3390)(-1690)}{2} + 6.4516 \times 10^6 \times .84790\right)$$

$$= 67.02$$

$$I_{Ax}/_{y\text{-}y} = I_{Ax}/_{A\text{-}A} + A_x\ c_A\ (c_A - 2\ c_x)$$

$$= (167.93) + (.072252)(65.70)(65.70 - 2 \times 38.937)$$

$$= 110.16$$

$$I_{Az}/_{y\text{-}y} = I_{Az}/_{B\text{-}B} + A_z \left[(c_z + b - c_A)^2 - c_z^2\right]$$

$$= (67.02 + .025008)\left[(43.04 + \frac{200}{2} - 65.70)^2 - 43.04^2\right]$$

$$= 170.28$$

$$I_{y\text{-}y} = I_{Ax}/_{y\text{-}y} + I_{Az}/_{y\text{-}y}$$

$$= (110.16) + (170.28)$$

$$= 280.44$$

$$P_x = \frac{w}{2}\left(L\ M_{Ax}/_{A\text{-}A} - I_{Ax}/_{A\text{-}A}\right)$$

$$= \frac{w}{2}\ (200 \times 2.8132 - 167.93)$$

$$= 197.36\ w$$

$$P_z = \frac{w}{2}\left(\frac{L^2}{4}\ A_z - I_{Az}/_{B\text{-}B}\right)$$

$$= \frac{w}{2}\left(\frac{200^2}{4}\ .025008 - 67.02\right)$$

$$= 91.53\ w$$

$$P = P_x + P_z$$

$$= (197.36\ w) + (91.53\ w)$$

$$= 288.89\ w$$

$$Q_x = \left(\frac{a}{(I_B - I_A)}\right)^4 \left[\left(\frac{(I_B - I_A)}{6}\right)(2\ I_B^2 - 7\ I_B\ I_A + 11\ I_A^2) - I_A^3 \log_e \frac{I_B}{I_A}\right]$$

$$= (.7780 \times 10^{-5}) \left[\frac{1893.3}{6}[2 \times 6.4516 \times 10^6 - 7(2450)(646.7) + 11(4.1822 \times 10^5] - 3.678 \times 10^8(1.3680)\right]$$

$$= 11{,}878$$

$$Q_z = \left(\frac{b}{(I_C - I_B)}\right)^4 \left[\left(\frac{(I_C - I_B)}{6}\right)(2\ I_C^2 - 7\ I_C\ I_B + 11\ I_B^2) - I_B^3 \log_e \frac{I_C}{I_B}\right]$$

$$= (.75895 \times 10^{-6}) \left[\left(\frac{3390}{6}\right)[2 \times 3.5163 \times 10^7 - 7(5930)(2540) - 11(6.4516 \times 10^6)] - 1.6386 \times 10^{10}(.84780)\right]$$

$$= 4827$$

$$M_{x/y\text{-}y} = \frac{w}{2}\left[- Q_x + (L + c_A)\ I_{Ax/A\text{-}A} - c_A\ L\ M_{AX/A\text{-}A}\right]$$

$$= \frac{w}{2}\left[- 11{,}878 + (265.70)167.93 - 65.70(200)(2.8132)\right]$$

$$= - 2113\ w$$

$$M_{z/y\text{-}y} = \frac{w}{2}\left[- Q_z + (L - 3\ a + c_A)\ I_{Az/B\text{-}B} + [a(2\ L - 3\ a) - c_A(L - 2\ a)]\ M_{Az/B\text{-}B} + a\ (L - a)(a - c_A)\ A_z\right]$$

$$= \frac{w}{2}\left[- 4827 + (-34.30)67.02 + 10{,}000(1.0762) + 343{,}000(0.25008)\right]$$

$$= 6107\ w$$

$$M_{y\text{-}y} = M_{x/y\text{-}y} + M_{z/y\text{-}y}$$

$$= (- 2113\ w) + (6107\ w)$$

$$= + 3994\ w$$

STEP 2: Determine the Fixed End Moments

at Ⓐ

$$M_{fe} = \frac{P}{A} - \frac{M_{y\text{-}y}\ c_A}{I_{y\text{-}y}}$$

$$= \frac{(288.89\ w)}{(.09726)} - \frac{(3994\ w)(65.70)}{(280.44)}$$

$$= \underline{2034.5\ w}$$

at Ⓒ

$$M_{fe} = \frac{P}{A} + \frac{M_{y\text{-}y}\ c_C}{I_{y\text{-}y}}$$

$$= \frac{(288.89\ w)}{(.09726)} + \frac{(3994\ w)(134.30)}{(280.44)}$$

$$= \underline{4882.8\ w}$$

STEP 3: Determine Stiffness and Carry-Over Factors

$$M_A = \frac{1}{A} + \frac{c_A^2}{I_{y\text{-}y}}$$

$$= \frac{1}{(.09726)} + \frac{(65.70^2)}{(280.44)}$$

$$= 25.67$$

$$M_{AC} = \frac{1}{A} - \frac{c_A\ c_C}{I_{y\text{-}y}}$$

$$= \frac{1}{(.09726)} - \frac{(65.70)(134.30)}{(280.44)}$$

$$= - 21.18$$

$$M_C = \frac{1}{A} + \frac{c_C^2}{I_{y\text{-}y}}$$

$$= \frac{1}{(.09726)} + \frac{(134.30^2)}{(280.44)}$$

$$= 74.59$$

stiffness factor at Ⓐ

$$K_A = M_A = \underline{25.67}$$

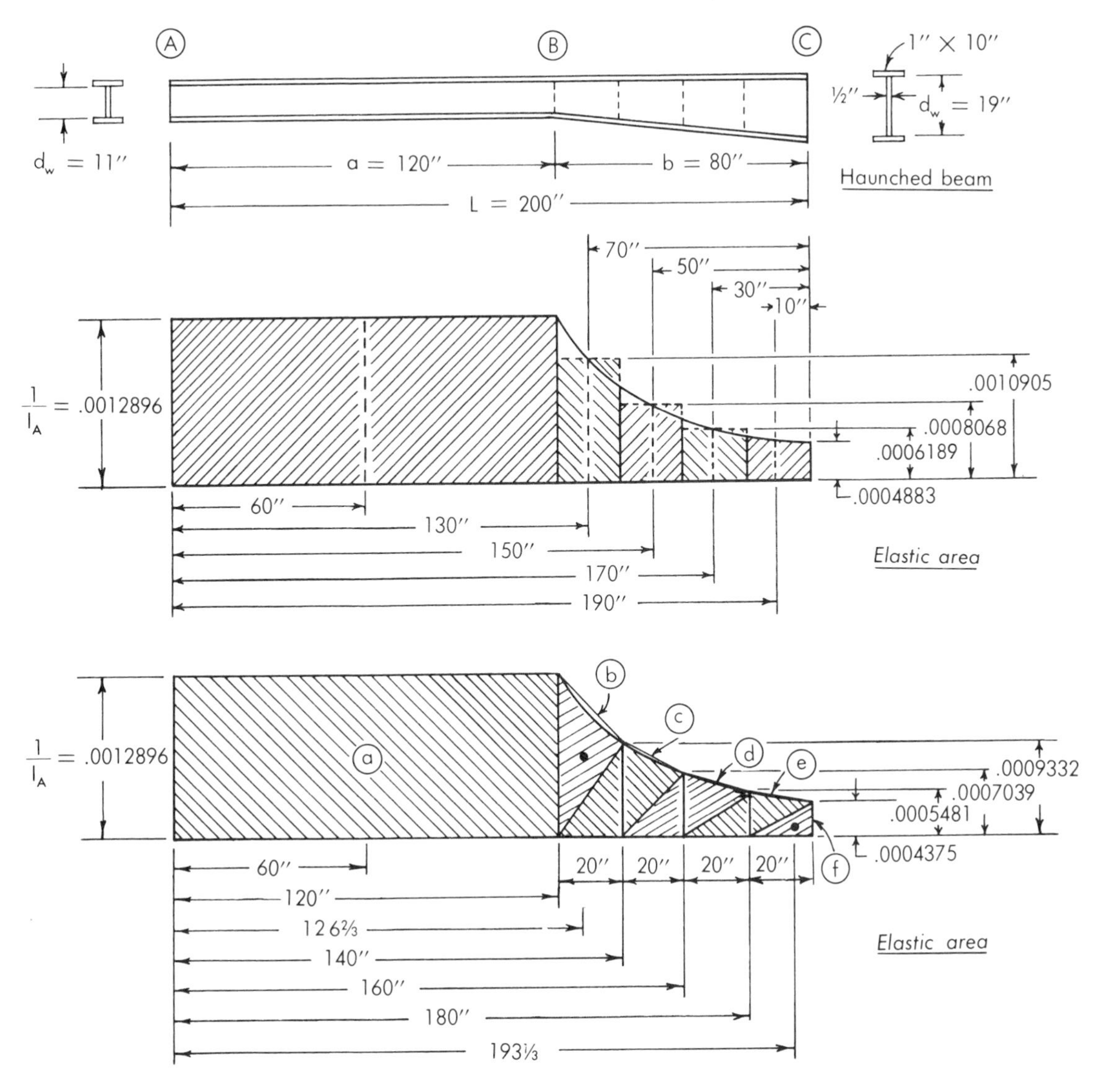

FIGURE 31

stiffness factor at Ⓒ

$$K_C = M_C = \underline{74.59}$$

carry-over factor, Ⓐ *to* Ⓒ

$$C_{AC} = -\frac{M_{AC}}{M_A}$$

$$= -\frac{(-21.18)}{(25.67)}$$

$$= \underline{.825}$$

carry-over factor, Ⓒ *to* Ⓐ

$$C_{CA} = -\frac{M_{AC}}{M_C}$$

$$= -\frac{(-21.18)}{(74.59)}$$

$$= \underline{.284}$$

Problem 3

For the haunched beam at top in Figure 31, having fixed ends, find the fixed end moments (uniformly loaded), stiffness factors, and carry-over factors. Break beam into sections and use numerical integration.

The elastic area could be divided into rectangular areas, as at center in Figure 31, and the resulting properties of the elastic area found in this manner. Of course some error will be introduced because these rectangular areas do not quite equal the actual curve of the elastic area. However, as the number of divisions is increased, this error will decrease.

Without any additional work, the following method will more nearly fit the outline of the elastic area and will result in less error. See lower diagram, Figure 31. The curved portion within the elastic area is divided into triangular areas. It is noticed that a pair of tri-

Section	A (area)		y'	M(moments)	$I_y' = M \cdot y'$	I_g
(a)	(.0012896) 120 =	.154752	60	9.2851	557.11	185.70
(b)	½(.0012896) 20 =	.012896	126⅔	1.6335	206.91	.29
(c)	½(.0009332) 40 =	.018664	140	2.6130	368.38	1.24
(d)	½(.0007039) 40 =	.014078	160	2.2525	360.40	.94
(e)	½(.0005481) 40 =	.010962	180	1.9732	355.17	.73
(f)	½(.0004375) 20 =	.004375	193⅓	.8458	163.52	.09
	Total →	.21573		18.6036	2199.69	

angular areas share the same altitude and since the division in length (s) is the same, they will have the same area. Therefore, the center of gravity of the two triangles lies along their common altitude. (This graphical method is applicable to any beam with a non-uniform change in moment of inertia along its length).

STEP 1: Determine the Properties of the Elastic Area

elastic center

$$c_A = \frac{M}{A}$$

$$= \frac{(18.6036)}{(.21573)}$$

$$= 86.23''$$

$$c_C = L - c_A$$

$$= (200) - (86.23)$$

$$= 113.77''$$

moment of inertia

$$I_{y\text{-}y} = I_y + I_g - \frac{M^2}{A}$$

$$= (2199.7) - \frac{(18.6036)^2}{(.21573)}$$

$$= 2199.7 - 1604.2 = 595.5$$

$$= 595.5$$

area (A) of section (a) of M_x/I_x diagram

$$A = \frac{w\ a^2}{12}\ (a + 3\ b)$$

$$= \frac{w(120)^2}{12}\ (120 + 3 \times 80)$$

$$= 557.10\ w$$

center of gravity of section (a)

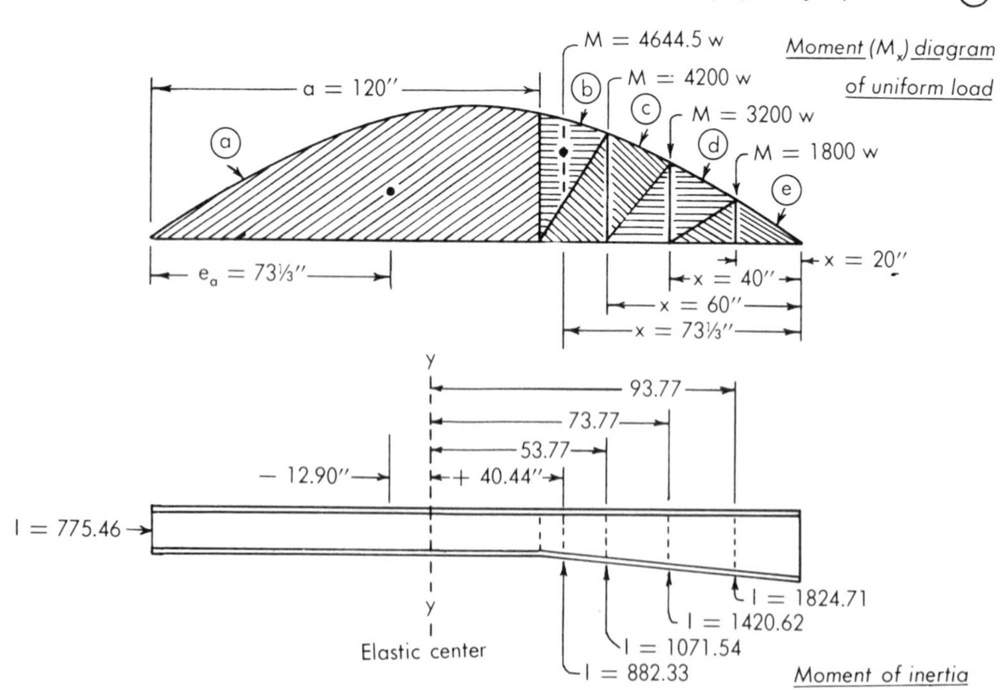

FIGURE 32

Section	C.G.	M_x	I_x	P (area of $\frac{M_x}{I_x}$ diagram)	y	$M_{y\text{-}y}$
a	$e_a = 73\frac{1}{3}$			see above 557.10 ω	−12.90	−7,186.5 w
b	$x = 73\frac{1}{3}$	4644.5 w	882.33	$\frac{1}{2}\left(\frac{4644.5\ w}{882.33}\right) 20 = 52.628\ \omega$	+40.44	+2,128.7 w
c	$x = 60$	4200.0 w	1071.54	$\frac{1}{2}\left(\frac{4200.0\ w}{1071.54}\right) 40 = 78.392\ \omega$	+53.77	+4,215.2 w
d	$x = 40$	3200.0 w	1420.62	$\frac{1}{2}\left(\frac{3200.0\ w}{1420.62}\right) 40 = 45.052\ \omega$	+73.77	+3,323.4 w
e	$x = 20$	1800.0 w	1824.71	$\frac{1}{2}\left(\frac{1800.0\ w}{1824.71}\right) 40 = 19.728\ \omega$	+93.77	+1,849.9 w
				Total → +752.91 ω		+4,321.7 w

$$e_a = \frac{a}{2}\left(\frac{a + 4\ b}{a + 3\ b}\right)$$

$$= \frac{(120)}{2}\left(\frac{120 + 4 \times 80}{120 + 3 \times 80}\right)$$

$$= 73\tfrac{1}{3}''$$

other properties of M_x/I_x diagram

These are shown in the table above.

STEP 2: Determine the Fixed End Moments

at (A)

$$M_{fe} = \frac{P}{A} - \frac{M_{y\text{-}y}\ c_A}{I_{y\text{-}y}}$$

$$= \frac{(+752.91\ w)}{(.21573)} - \frac{(+4321.7\ w)(86.23)}{(595.5)}$$

$$= +\ 2863.0\ w$$

at (C)

$$M_{fe} = \frac{P}{A} + \frac{M_{y\text{-}y}\ c_C}{I_{y\text{-}y}}$$

$$= \frac{(+752.91\ w)}{(.21573)} + \frac{(+4321.7\ w)(113.72)}{(595.5)}$$

$$= +4{,}3141.1\ w$$

STEP 3: Determine Stiffness and Carry-Over Factors

$$M_A = \frac{1}{A} + \frac{c_A^2}{I_{y\text{-}y}}$$

$$= \frac{1}{(.21573)} + \frac{(86.23)^2}{(595.5)}$$

$$= +\ 17.12$$

$$M_{AC} = \frac{1}{A} - \frac{c_A\ c_C}{I_{y\text{-}y}}$$

$$= \frac{1}{(.21573)} + \frac{(86.23)(113.72)}{(595.5)}$$

$$= -\ 12.10$$

$$M_C = \frac{1}{A} + \frac{c_C^2}{I_{y\text{-}y}}$$

$$= \frac{1}{(.21573)} + \frac{(113.72)^2}{(595.5)}$$

$$= +\ 26.35$$

stiffness factor at (A)

$$K_A = M_A = 17.12$$

stiffness factor at (C)

$$K_C = M_C = 26.35$$

carry-over factor, (A) *to* (C)

$$C_{AC} = -\frac{M_{AC}}{M_A}$$

$$= -\frac{(-12.10)}{(17.12)}$$

$$= .706$$

carry-over factor, (C) *to* (A)

$$C_{CA} = -\frac{M_{AC}}{M_C}$$

$$= -\frac{(-12.10)}{(26.35)}$$

$$= .460$$

7. READY-TO-USE DESIGN CONSTANTS

The following 36 charts—appearing on the following pages—give the fixed end moments, stiffness factors, and carry-over factors for beams with abrupt changes in moment of inertia and may be used for beams with cover plates. They were developed by R. A. Caughy, Professor of Civil Engineering, Iowa State College, and Richard S. Cebula, Head, Engineering Department, St. Martin's College. These charts appeared in Bull. 176 of the Iowa Engineering Experiment Station.

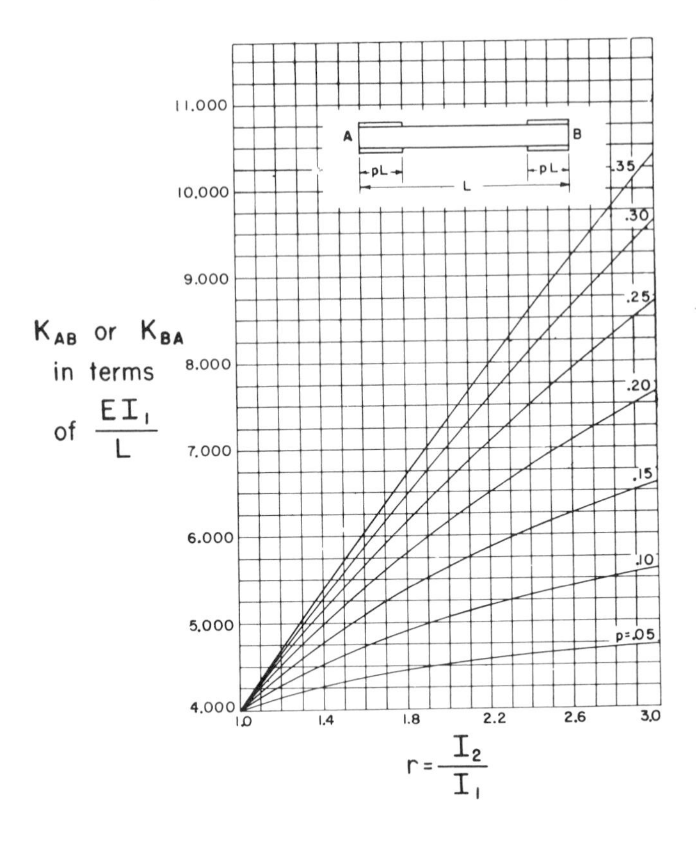

Chart 1. Stiffness factors at either end of symmetrical beam.

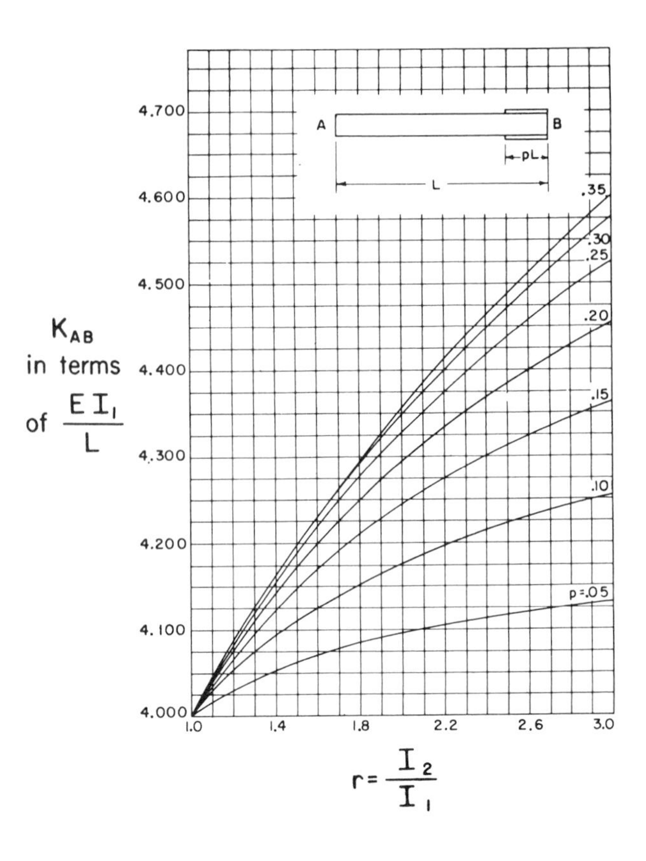

Chart 2. Stiffness factors at small end of unsymmetrical beam.

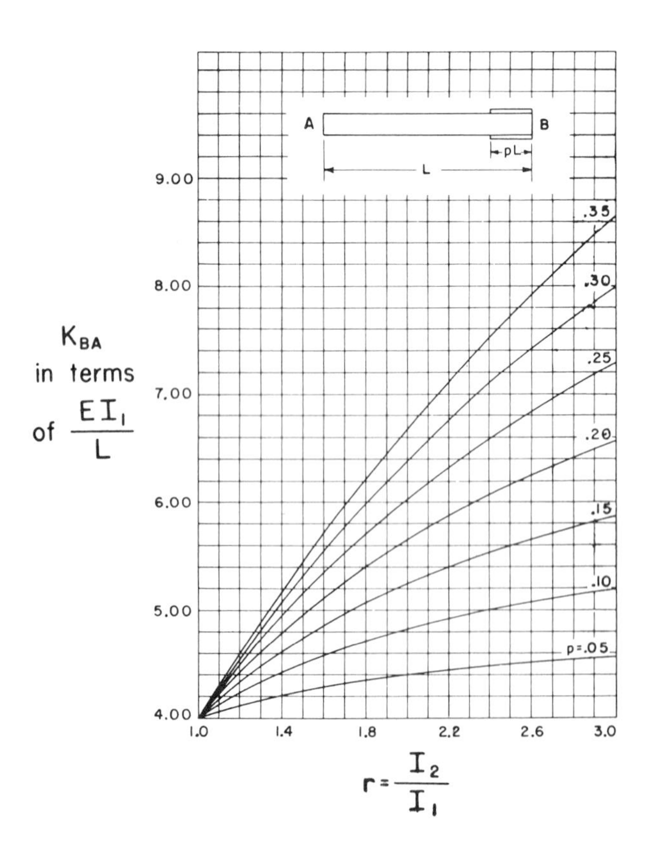

Chart 3. Stiffness factors at large end of unsymmetrical beam.

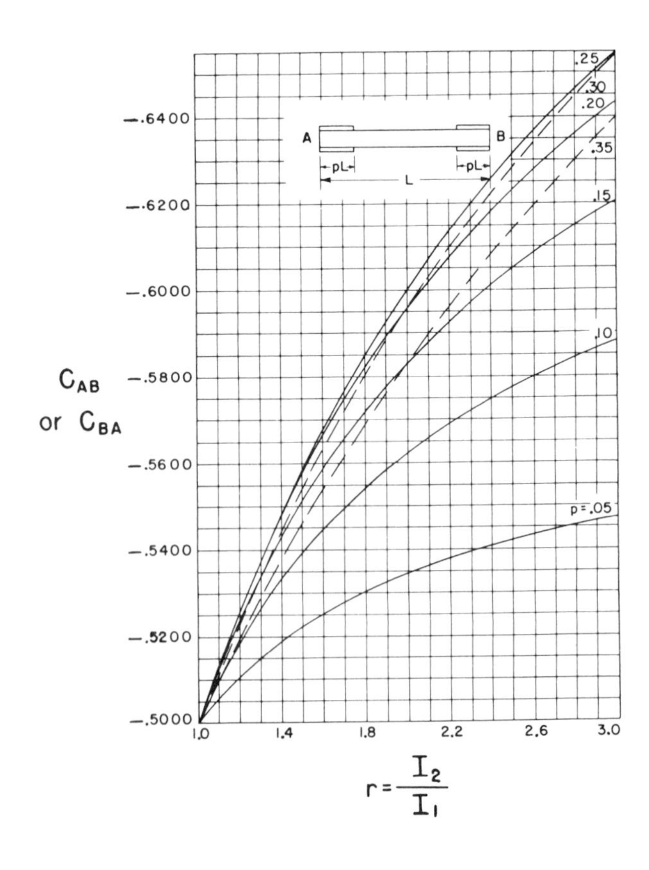

Chart 4. Carry-over factors for symmetrical beam from either end to the other.

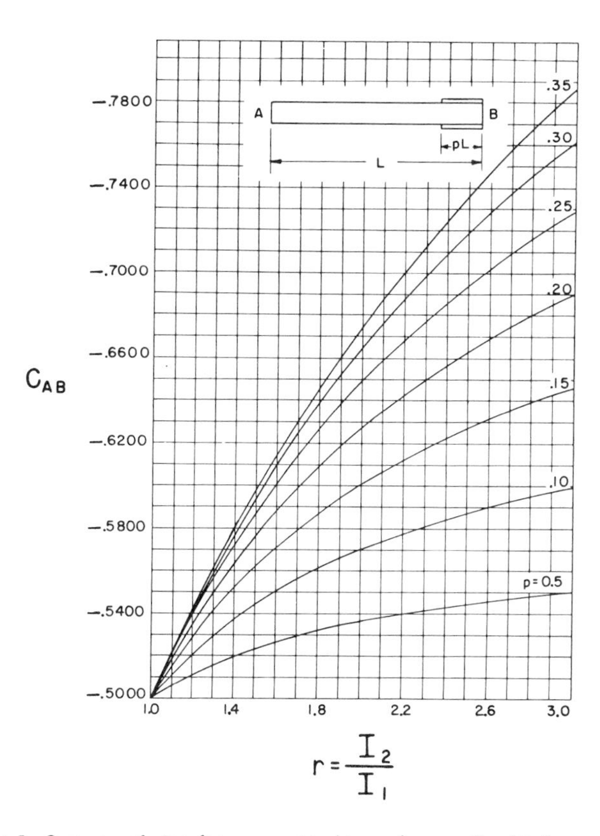

Chart 5. Carry-over factors for unsymmetrical beam from small end to large end.

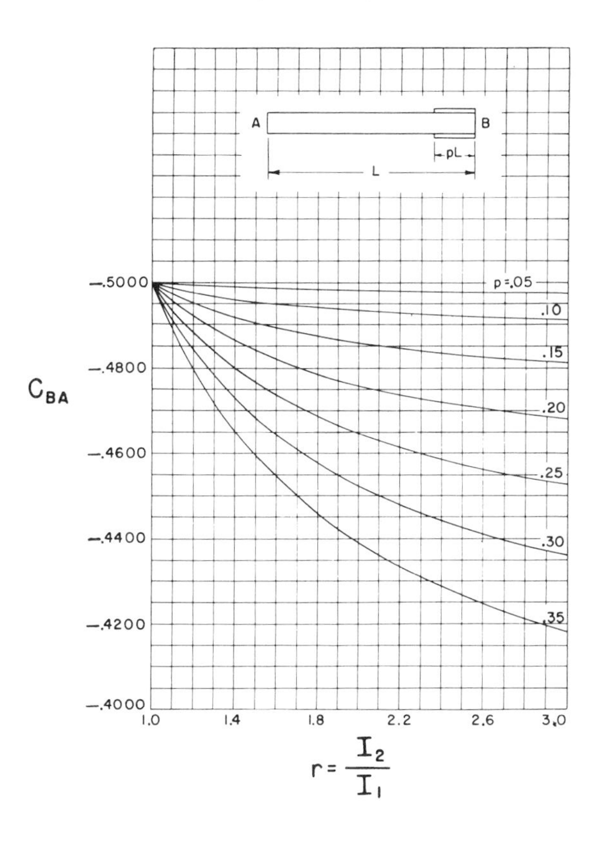

Chart 6. Carry-over factors for unsymmetrical beam from large end to small end.

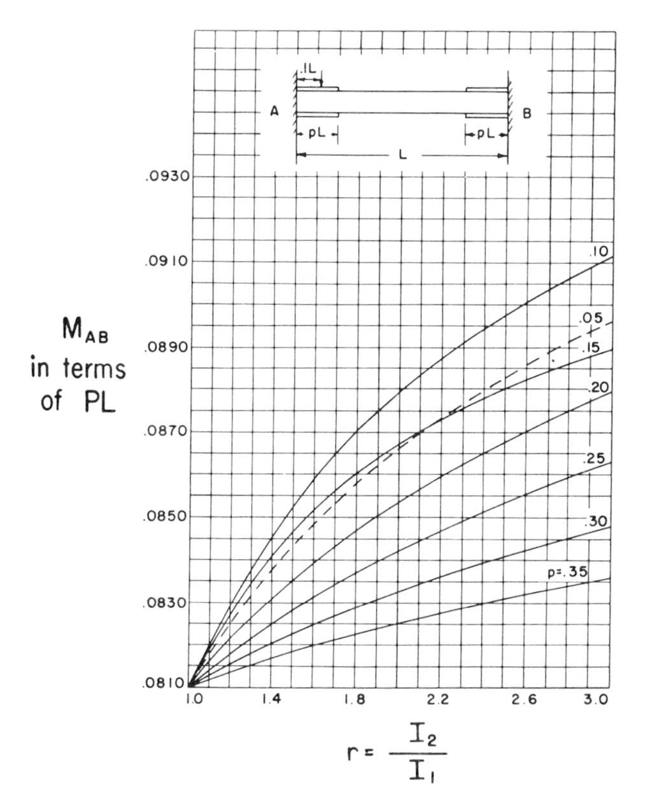

Chart 7. Fixed-end moments at left end of symmetrical beam for concentrated load at .1 point.

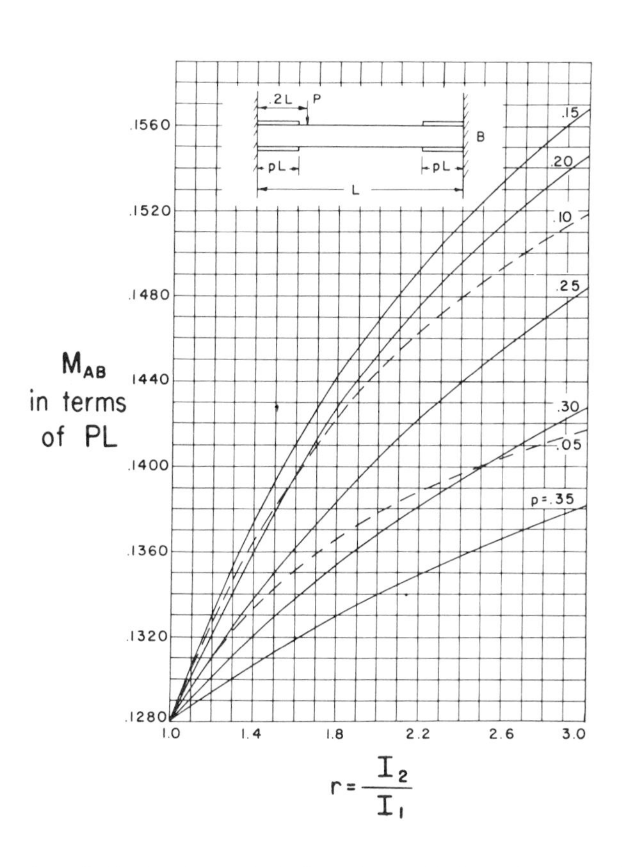

Chart 8. Fixed-end moments at left end of symmetrical beam for concentrated load at .2 point.

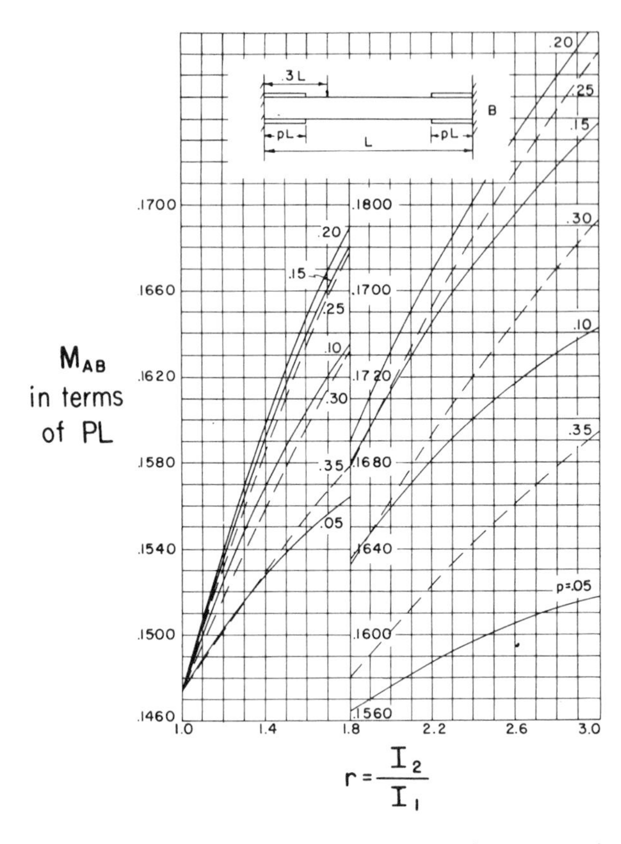

Chart 9. Fixed-end moments at left end of symmetrical beam for concentrated load at .3 point.

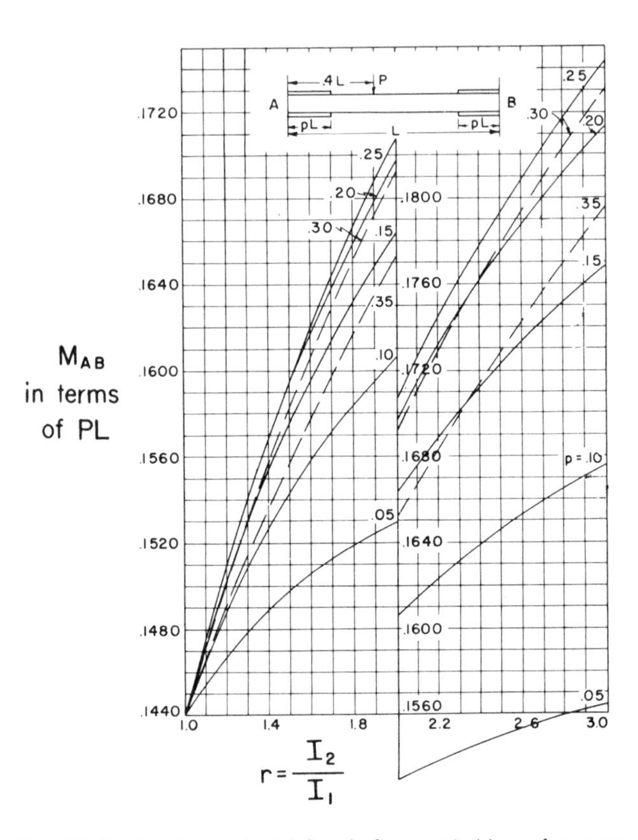

Chart 10. Fixed-end moments at left end of symmetrical beam for concentrated load at .4 point.

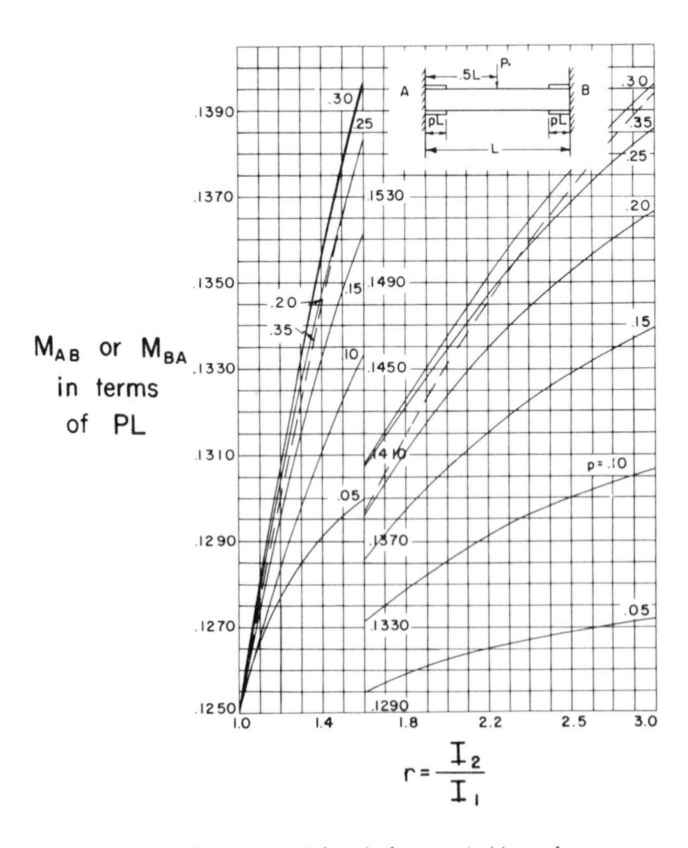

Chart 11. Fixed-end moments at left end of symmetrical beam for concentrated load at .5 point.

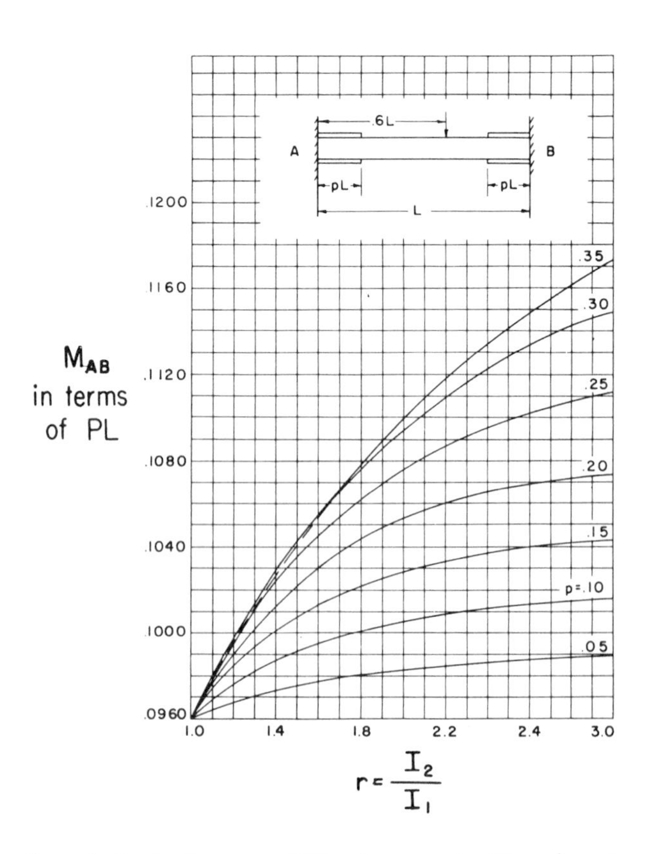

Chart 12. Fixed end moments at left end of symmetrical beam for concentrated load at .6 point.

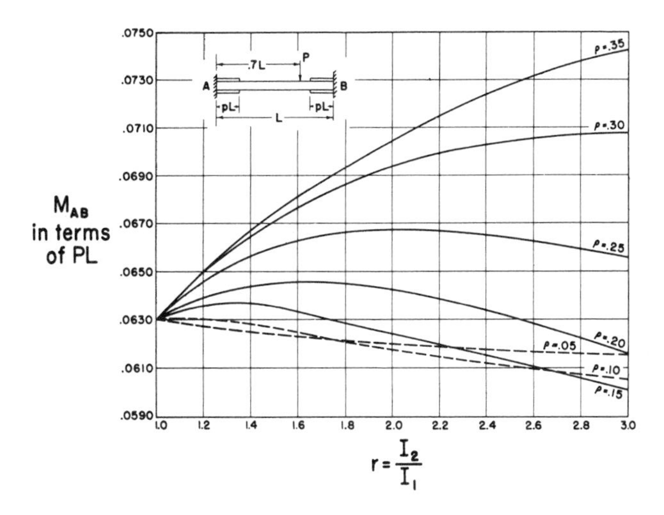

Chart 13. Fixed-end moments at left end of symmetrical beam for concentrated load at .7 point.

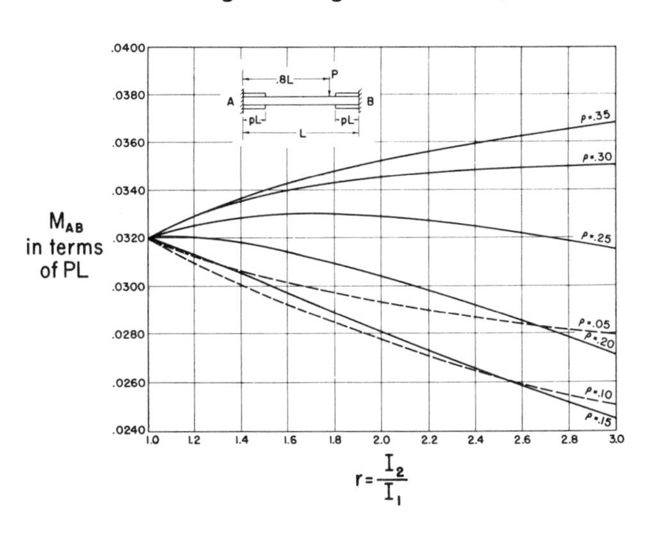

Chart 14. Fixed-end moments at left end of symmetrical beam for concentrated load at .8 point.

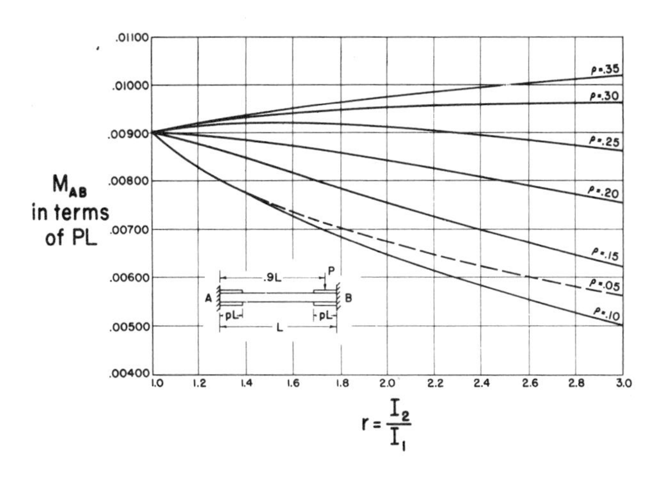

Chart 15. Fixed-end moments at left end of symmetrical beam for concentrated load at .9 point.

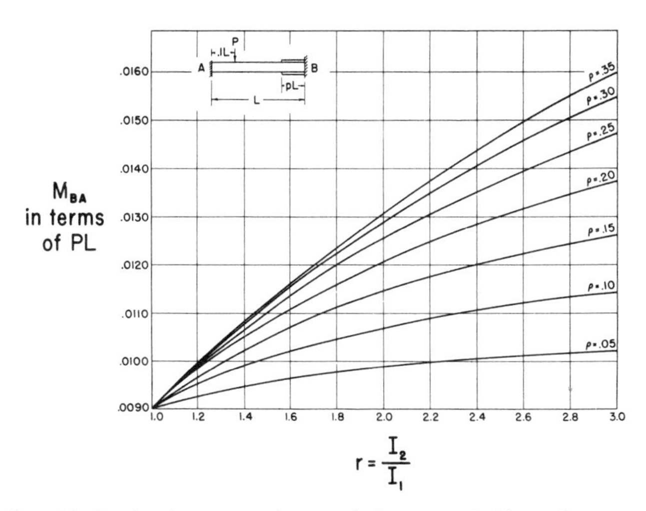

Chart 16. Fixed-end moments at large end of unsymmetrical beam for concentrated load at .1 point.

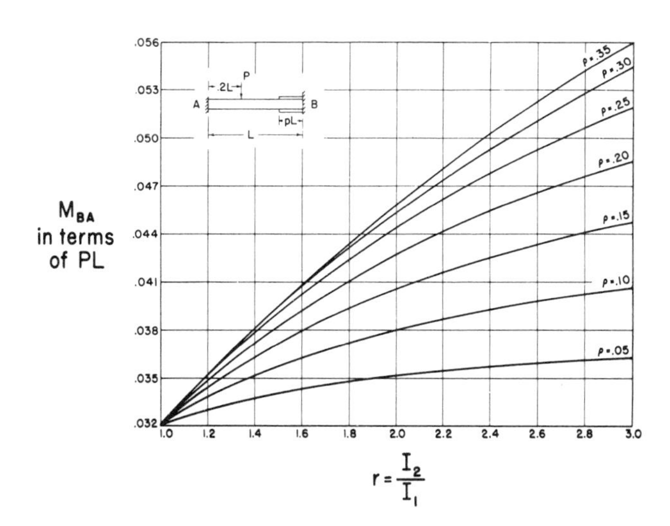

Chart 17. Fixed-end moments at large end of unsymmetrical beam for concentrated load at .2 point.

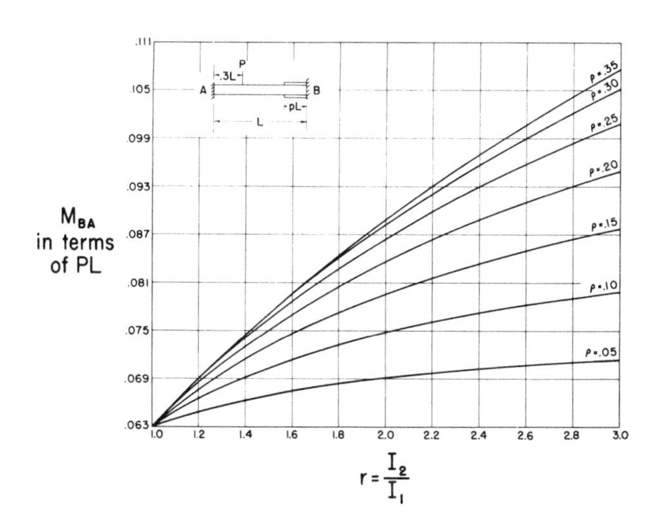

Chart 18. Fixed-end moments at large end of unsymmetrical beam for concentrated load at .3 point.

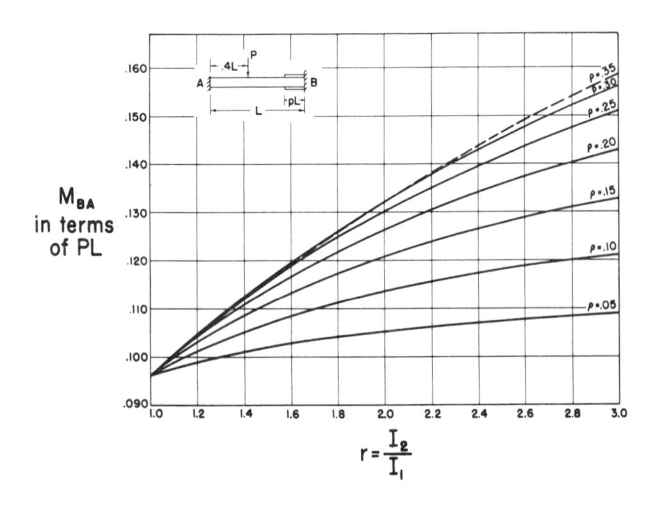

Chart 19. Fixed-end moments at large end of unsymmetrical beam for concentrated load at .4 point.

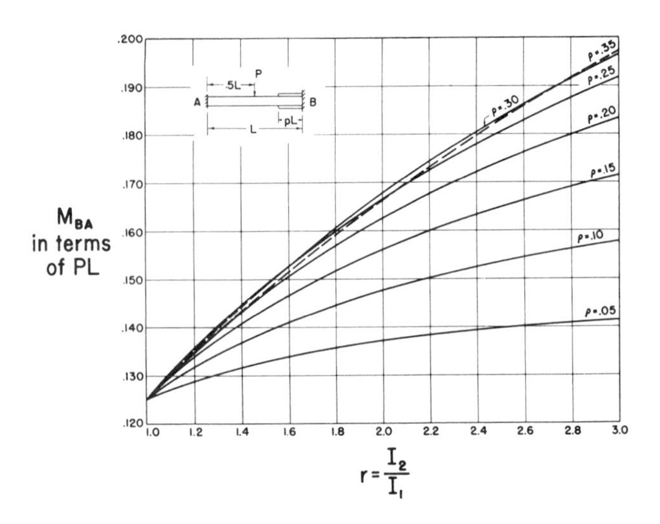

Chart 20. Fixed-end moments at large end of unsymmetrical beam for concentrated load at .5 point.

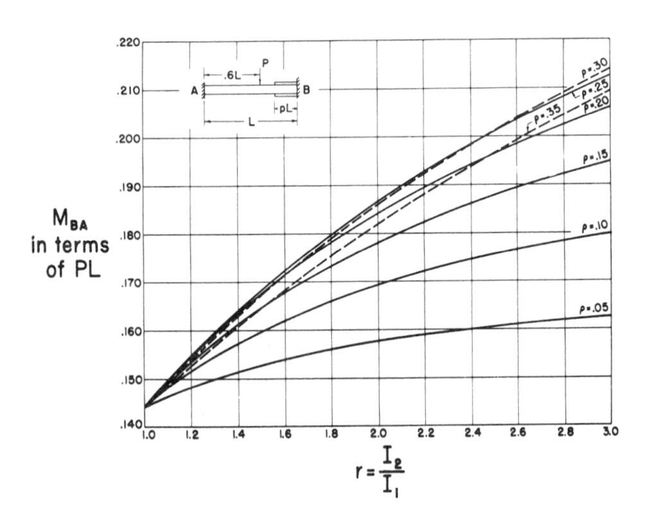

Chart 21. Fixed-end moments at large end of unsymmetrical beam for concentrated load at .6 point.

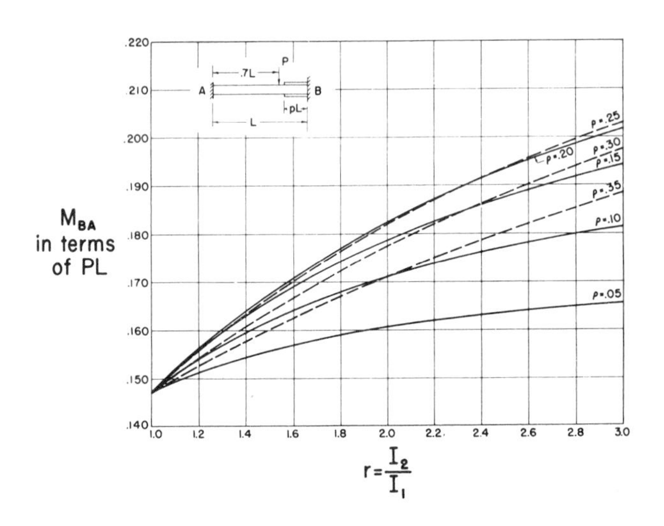

Chart 22. Fixed-end moments at large end of unsymmetrical beam for concentrated load at .7 point.

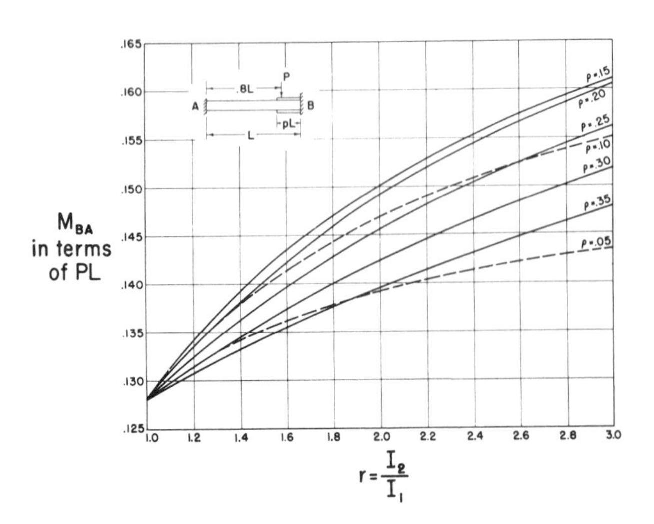

Chart 23. Fixed-end moments at large end of unsymmetrical beam for concentrated load at .8 point.

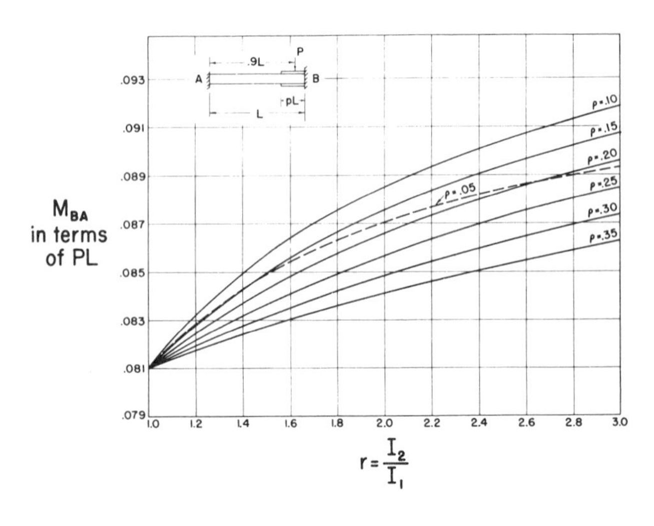

Chart 24. Fixed-end moments at large end of unsymmetrical beam for concentrated load at .9 point.

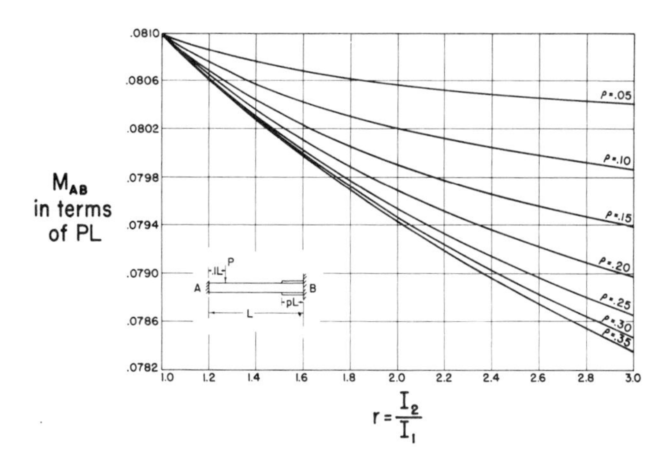

Chart 25. Fixed-end moments at small end of unsymmetrical beam for concentrated load at .1 point.

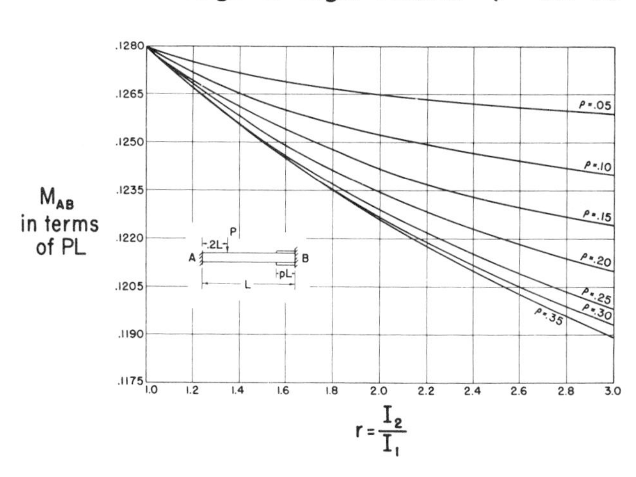

Chart 26. Fixed-end moments at small end of unsymmetrical beam for concentrated load at .2 point.

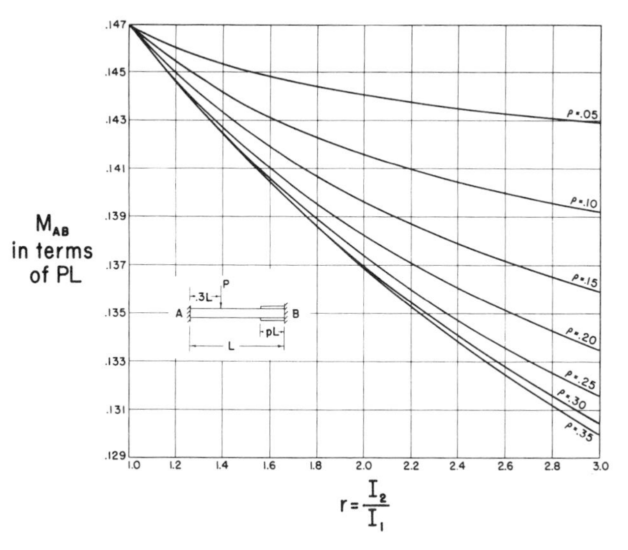

Chart 27. Fixed-end moments at small end of unsymmetrical beam for concentrated load at .3 point.

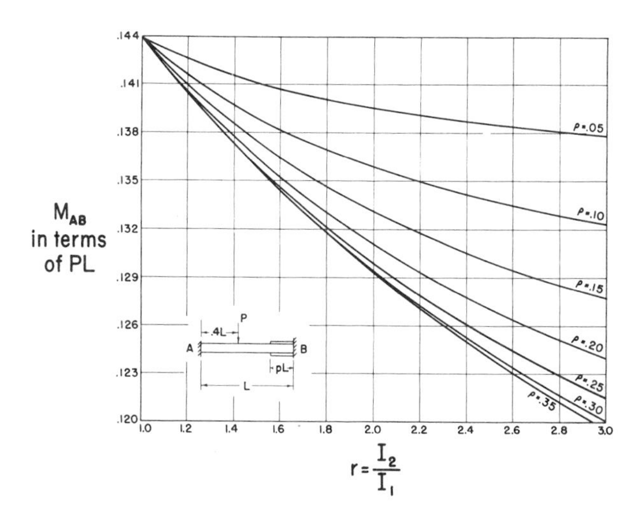

Chart 28. Fixed-end moments at small end of unsymmetrical beam for concentrated load at .4 point.

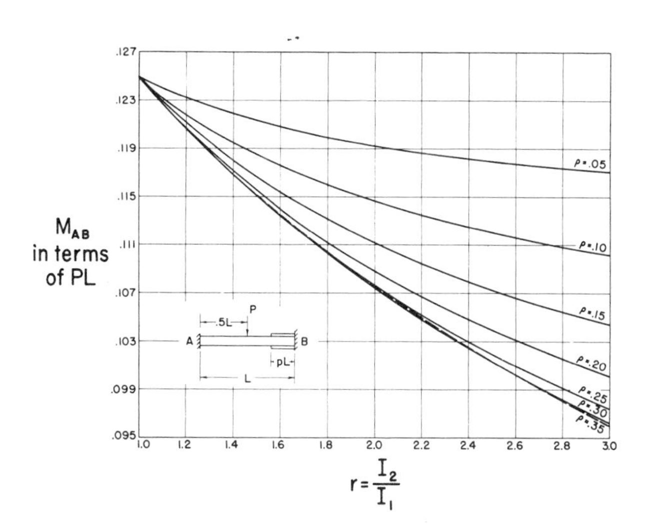

Chart 29. Fixed-end moments at small end of unsymmetrical beam for concentrated load at .5 point.

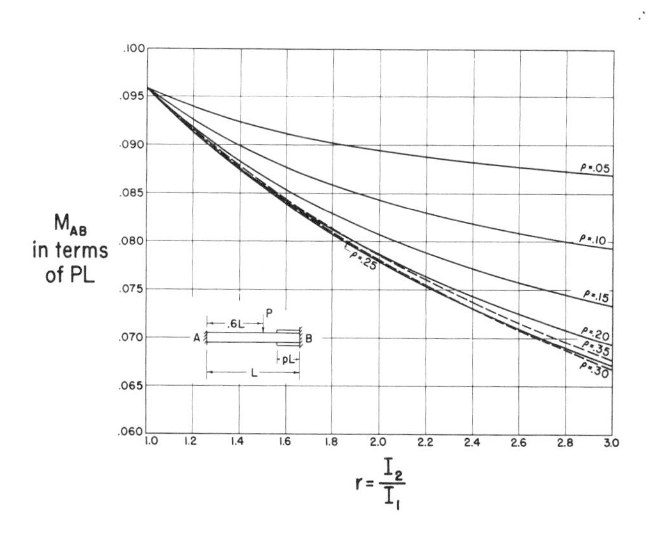

Chart 30. Fixed-end moments at small end of unsymmetrical beam for concentrated load at .6 point.

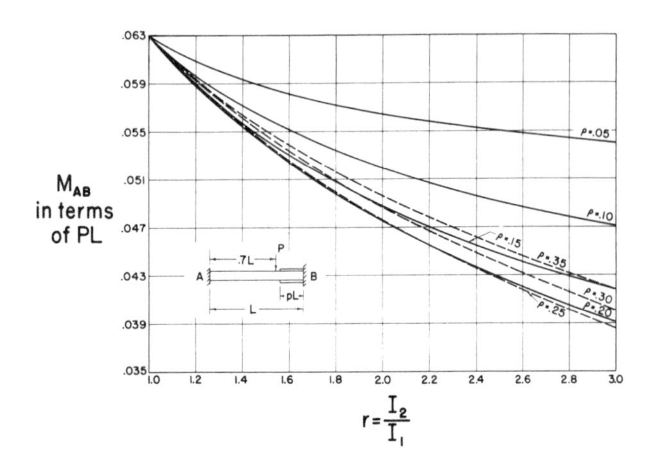

Chart 31. Fixed-end moments at small end of unsymmetrical beam for concentrated load at .7 point.

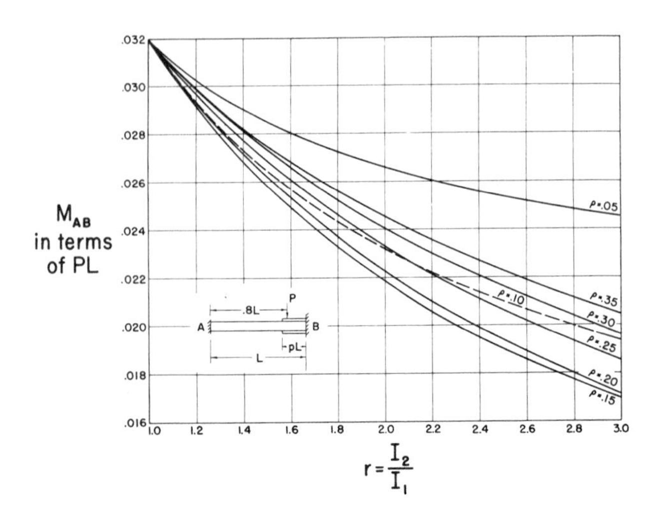

Chart 32. Fixed-end moments at small end of unsymmetrical beam for concentrated load at .8 point.

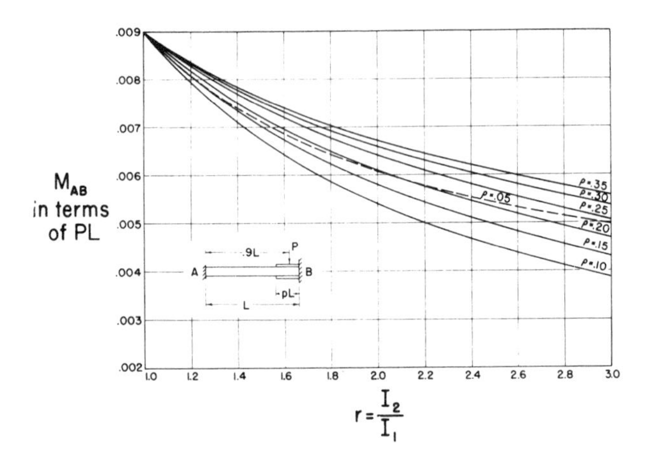

Chart 33. Fixed-end moments at small end of unsymmetrical beam for concentrated load at .9 point.

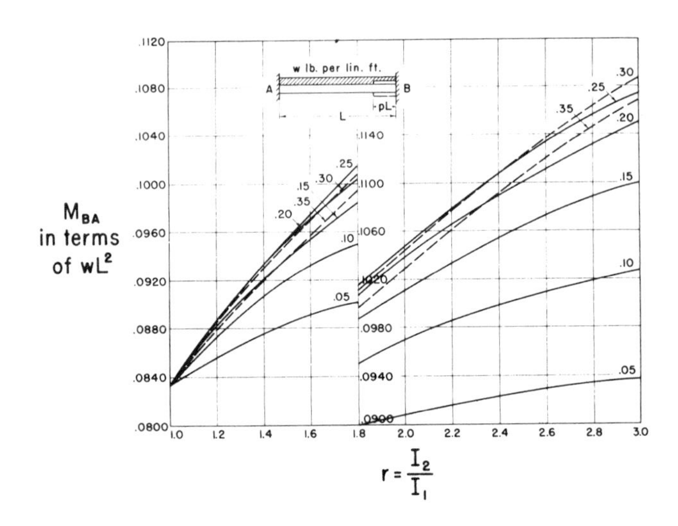

Chart 34. Fixed-end moments at large end of unsymmetrical beam for uniform load.

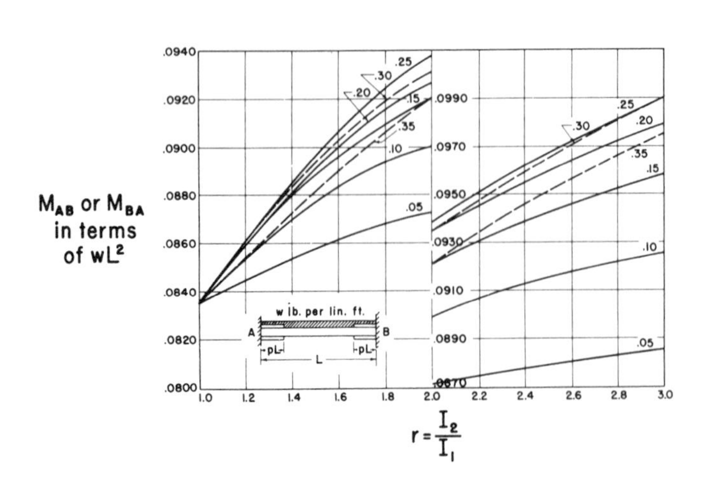

Chart 35. Fixed-end moments at either end of symmetrical beam for uniform load.

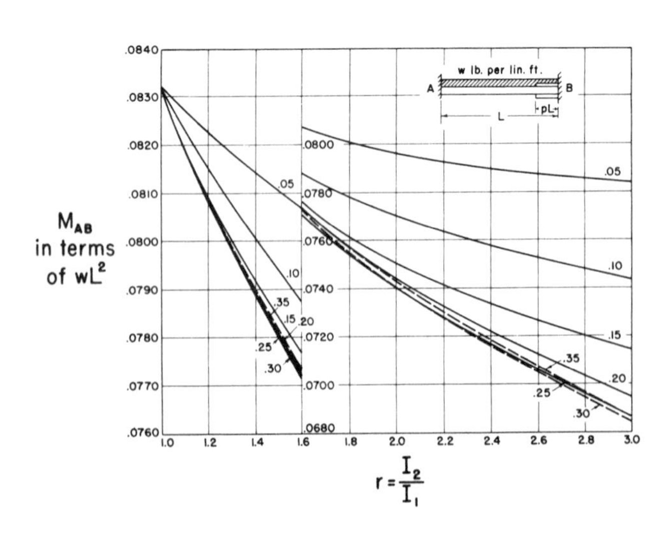

Chart 36. Fixed-end moments at small end of unsymmetrical beam for uniform load.

Open-Web Bar Joists

1. BAR JOISTS

Several available types of bar joists of patented design are fabricated by welding. Where design permits, it is usually more economical to use these standard bar joists than to fabricate special joists. However, to meet special design requirements bar joists can be quickly and easily fabricated. In some cases, this may be done on the construction site.

Figure 1 shows the framework of a factory building. Joists are spaced between beams and support the metal roof deck. The deck is plug welded to the joists by welding at intervals through the 20-ga metal.

Arc welding also provides an efficient means for securing bar joists to their supporting members. A short tack weld on each side of the bearing plate at the ends of the bar joist permanently joins the joist to the framework. Figure 2 shows bar joists arc welded in place. Thus, use of arc welding stiffens the entire structure by actually tying in the framework.

FIG. 2 Open-web bar joists are welded to beams and girders which support them. This stiffens the entire structure.

2. STANDARD SPECIFICATIONS

The Steel Joist Institute, and the American Institute of Steel Construction have set up standard specifications for the design of Open Web Steel Joists (High Strength Longspan or LH-Series). The following requirements are adapted from these (1962) specifications:

Allowable Stresses for Welds

E70XX manual electrodes or equivalent weld metal shall be used; E60XX electrodes or equivalent weld metal may be used on steels having a specified yield point of 36,000 psi.

fillet welds

	Shear at Throat of Weld Metal	Unit Force
E60XX	$\tau = 13,600$ psi	$f = 9,600\ \omega$
E70XX	$\tau = 15,800$ psi	$f = 11,200\ \omega$

groove welds

Tension or compression, same as connecting material.

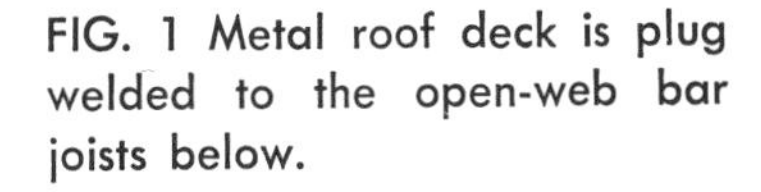

FIG. 1 Metal roof deck is plug welded to the open-web bar joists below.

Allowable Stresses for Members

The allowable stresses shall be based on yield strengths from 36,000 to 50,000 psi.

tension

$$= 0.60\ \sigma_y$$

compression

If $L/r \leqq C_c$

$$= \frac{\left[1 - \frac{1}{2}\left(\frac{(L/r)}{C_c}\right)^2\right]\sigma_y}{\frac{5}{3} + \frac{3}{8}\frac{L/r}{C_c} - \frac{1}{8}\left(\frac{(L/r)}{C_c}\right)^3}$$

If $L/r \geqq C_c$

$$= \frac{149{,}000{,}000}{(L/r)^2}$$

where:

$$C_c = \frac{23{,}900}{\sqrt{\sigma_y}}$$

L = length of member or component, center to center of panel point

r = least radius of gyration of member or component

L/r of web members may be taken as ¾ (L/r_x) or L/r_y, whichever is larger; r_x is in the plane of the joist, and r_y is normal to it.

bending

for chords and web members $= 0.60\ \sigma_y$
for bearing plates $= 0.75\ \sigma_y$

Maximum Slenderness (L/r) Ratios

Top chord interior panels	90
Top chord end panels	120
Other compression members	200
Tension members	240

Other Requirements for Members

The bottom chord is designed for tension.

The top chord is designed as a continuous member subject to axial compression stresses (σ_a) and bending stresses (σ_b). The sum of the two $(\sigma_a + \sigma_b) \leqq 0.60\ \sigma_y$ at the panel point.

The quality

$$\frac{\sigma_a}{\underline{\sigma_a}} + \frac{C_m\ \sigma_b}{\left(1 - \frac{\sigma_a}{\sigma'_e}\right)\underline{\sigma_b}} \leqq 1.0 \text{ at mid-panel}$$

where:

$C_m = 1 - 0.3\ \sigma_a/\sigma'_e$ for end panels
$C_m = 1 - 0.4\ \sigma_a/\sigma'_e$ for interior panels
σ_a = calculated axial unit compressive stress
σ_b = calculated bending unit compressive stress at joint under consideration

FIG. 3 In the fabrication of these bar joists, semi-automatic welding with self-shielding cored electrode substantially increased the arc speed over previous practice.

FIG. 4 Bar joist studs are quickly welded in place by means of efficient portable stud welders. The studs shown are used to anchor crossbracing rods running from top chord of one joint to bottom chord of another, to increase torsional resistance and prevent buckling.

σ_a = allowable axial unit compressive stress based upon (L/r) for the panel length, center to center of panel points

σ_b = allowable bending unit stress, 0.60 σ_y

$\sigma'_e = \frac{149,000}{(L/r_x)^2}$ where (L) is the full panel length, center to center of panel points

r_x = radius of gyration about the axis of bending

The radius of gyration of the top chord about its vertical axis $\leq$ L/170, where L is the spacing in inches between lines of bridging.

Chord Size	Minimum Spacing of Lines of Bridging
No. 02 to No. 08 incl.	11′
No. 09 to No. 14 incl.	16′
No. 15 to No. 19 incl.	21′

The top chord shall be considered to have lateral support if it is properly attached to the floor or roof deck at distances not to exceed 36″.

The vertical shear values to be used in the design of web members shall be determined from full uniform loading, but shall not be less than 25% of the rated end reaction.

Chord and web members in compression, composed of two components separated one from another, shall have fillers spaced so that the L/r ratio for each component shall not exceed the L/r ratio of the whole member; if in tension, the L/r ratio of each component shall not exceed 240. Fillers may be omitted in chords having interior panel lengths not over 24″ and in webs of joists not over 28″ in depth. In all of these cases, the least radius of gyration (r) is used.

Connection Requirements

Connections shall be designed to carry the design load, but not less than half of the allowable strength of the member. Butt welded joints shall be designed to carry the full allowable strength of the member.

Members connecting into a joint shall have their centers of gravity meet at a point, otherwise the bending stresses due to eccentricity shall be taken into account. Eccentricity on either side of the neutral axis of the chord members may be neglected if it does not exceed the distance between the neutral axis and back of the chord. When a single angle compression member is attached to the outside of the stem of a Tee or double angle chord, the eccentricity shall be taken into account.

High-strength steel reinforcing bars for concrete column verticals in the Washington National Insurance Bldg., Evanston, Ill., permitted reduction of column size and savings in floor space.

Reinforcing bars in concrete columns are field spliced. Simple positioning jig maintains proper alignment during welding. These large size AISI 4140 alloy steel bars were welded with low-hydrogen electrodes.

Reinforcing Bars

1. WELDING OF REINFORCING BARS

The American Welding Society has issued Bulletin D 12.1-61 giving the Recommended Practices for the Welding of Reinforcing Steel, and these should be followed. Table 1 of allowable stresses is adapted from the AWS bulletin.

Reinforcing steel may be spliced by butt welding two ends directly together, using either a single Vee or double Vee groove joint with an included groove angle of 45° to 60°, or a single bevel or double bevel groove joint with an included groove angle of 45°. These joints should have a root opening of ⅛″ and a root face or land of ⅛″.

This butt welded joint may be made with the aid of an additional splice member, for example a plate or angle connected with longitudinal flare-bevel welds, see Figure 1, or a sleeve connected by transverse fillet welds around the sleeve and bar, see Figure 2. The splice member should have a cross-sectional area equal to the strength of the connected bar.

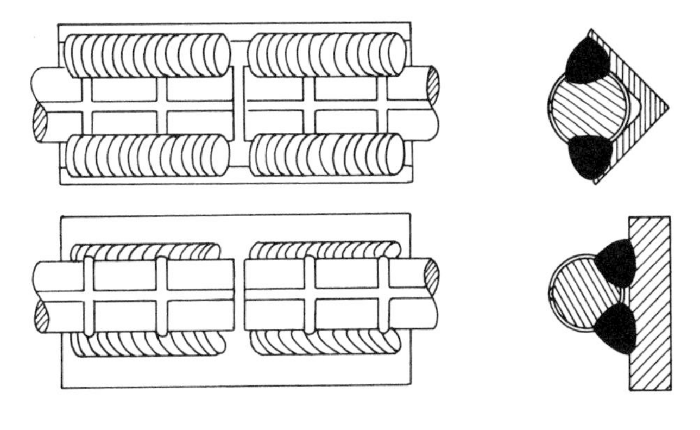

FIGURE 1

Reinforcing steel may also be spliced by a lap joint, either lapped directly together or with an insert plate between the two bars. When the two bars have

TABLE 1—Allowable Stresses for Joints in Reinforcing Rods

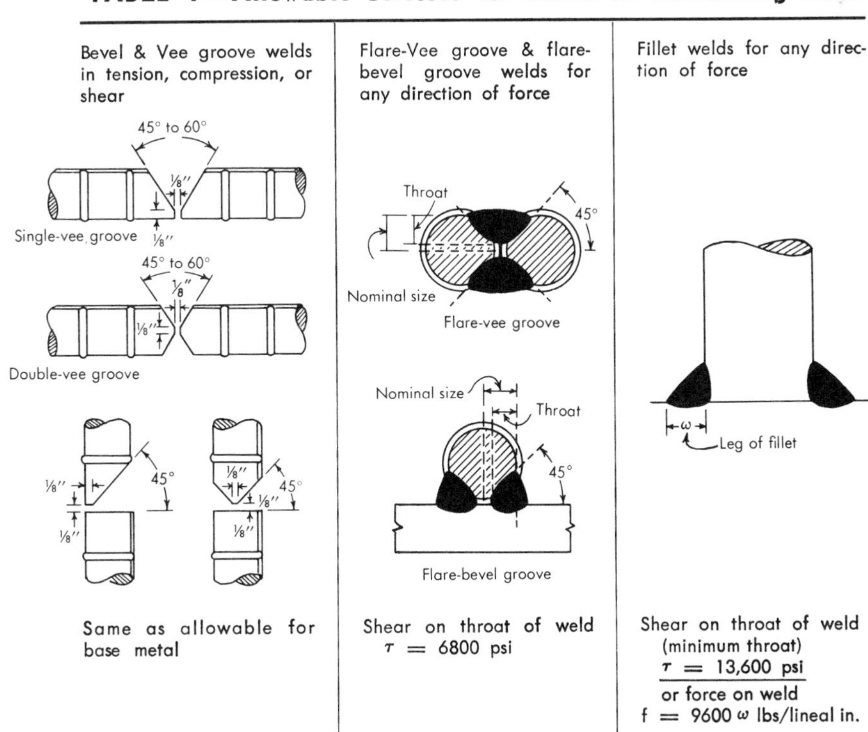

Bevel & Vee groove welds in tension, compression, or shear	Flare-Vee groove & flare-bevel groove welds for any direction of force	Fillet welds for any direction of force
Same as allowable for base metal	Shear on throat of weld $\tau = 6800$ psi	Shear on throat of weld (minimum throat) $\tau = 13{,}600$ psi or force on weld $f = 9600\,\omega$ lbs/lineal in.

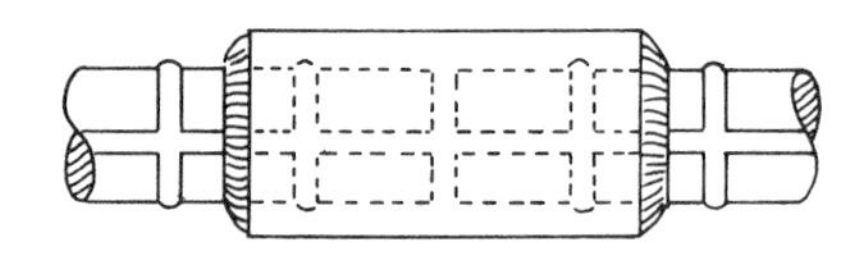
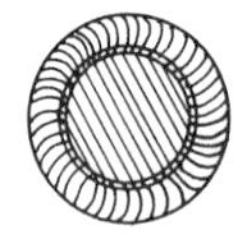

FIGURE 2

the same diameter, the nominal size of a flare-Vee groove weld is the radius of the bar. When the bars are of unequal diameter, the nominal size of the weld is the radius of the smaller bar. The nominal size of the flare-bevel groove weld is the radius of the bar.

In all of these cases, the nominal size is the throat on which the allowable shear stress of 6800 psi is applied. The actual required throat of the finished weld in a flare-Vee groove and flare-bevel groove weld should be at least ¾ the nominal size of the weld, which is the radius of the bar. The maximum gap between the bar and the splice plate should not exceed ¼ the diameter of the bar nor $\frac{3}{16}$″.

In general, it is easier to butt weld larger reinforcing bars together than to use a splice joint with longitudinal connecting welds. On smaller bars, it might be easier to use the longitudinally welded lap joint, although the doubling up of the bars within the connection region might take too much of the cross-section of the concrete member.

Figure 3 illustrates a good method to butt weld a reinforcing bar lying in the horizontal position. A thin backing strap, about ⅛″ thick, is tack welded to the bottom of the joint as shown in (a). After a portion of the groove weld is made, this backing strap is red hot and can easily be wrapped partially around the bar with the weldor's slag hammer as welding progresses, see (b) and (c). This provides just enough dam action to support the weld and yet does not interfere with the welding. Finally, the ends of this strap are tapped tight against the bar and the weld is completed, see (d).

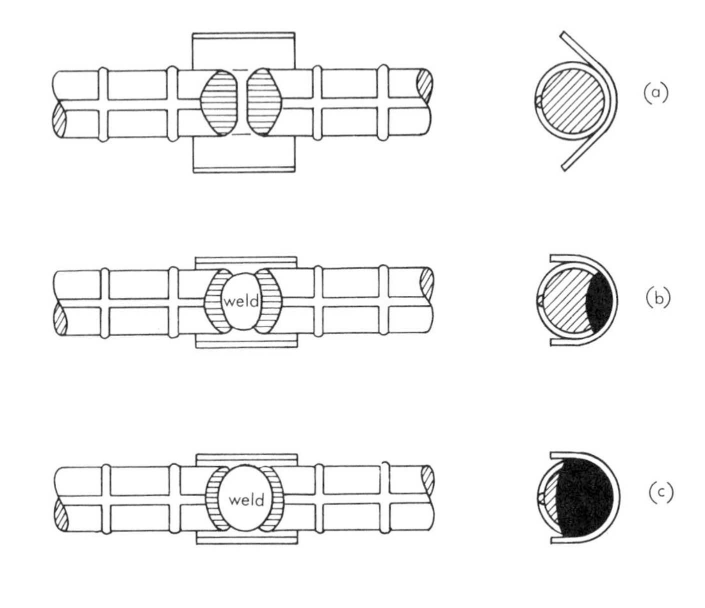

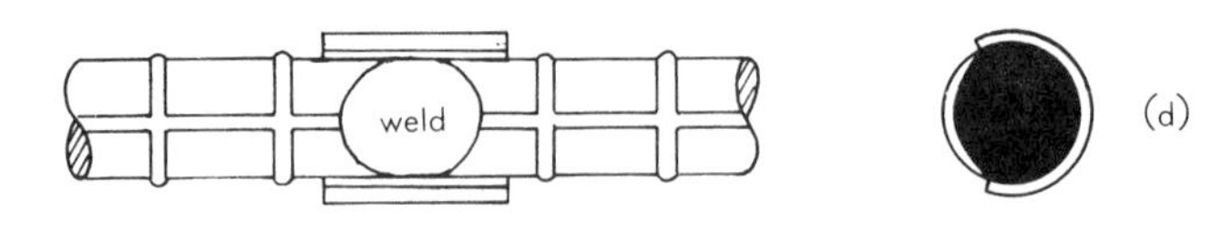

FIGURE 3

2. ROD MATERIAL AND WELDING PROCEDURE

Reinforcing bars are rolled from new steel produced in the open-hearth furnace, acid bessemer converter, electric furnace, or the basic oxygen process; or, they are re-rolled from discarded railroad rails or car axles.

It is necessary to obtain a Mill Report on the reinforcing bars to be welded; otherwise, they must be analyzed before setting up the welding procedure. See Table 2.

For manual welding, E60XX and E70XX electrodes should be used, and preferably be of the low-hydrogen type. Coverings of the low-hydrogen electrodes must be thoroughly dry when used.

TABLE 2—Recommended Welding Procedures for Reinforcing Rods of Various Analyses

C to .30 Mn to .60	C .31 to .35 Mn to .90	C .36 to .40 Mn to 1.30	C .41 to .50 Mn to 1.30	C .51 to .80 Mn to 1.30
Any E60xx or E70xx electrodes	Non low-hydrogen E60 or E70xx electrodes—	Low hydrogen E60xx to E70xx electrodes—	Low-hydrogen E60xx or E70xx electrodes—	Thermit or pressure gas welding
Preheat not required. If below 10°F, preheat to 100°F	Preheat to 100°F	Preheat to 200°F	Preheat to 400°F	Other procedures subject to procedure qualification or approval of the Engineer
	Low-hydrogen E60xx or E70xx electrodes Preheat not required. If below 10°F, preheat to 100°F		Could also use submerged-arc, thermit, or pressure gas welding	

How to Stiffen a Panel

1. INCREASING PANEL RIGIDITY

The efficient use of materials is the first essential to lower cost designs. One way to achieve such efficiency is to use lighter-gage plate that is easily fabricated and to add stiffeners as necessary for the required rigidity.

Regardless of how flexible or rigid the stiffeners are, they will increase the stiffness of the whole panel by increasing the moment of inertia (I) of the member panel sections.

The usual method is to consider a section of the panel having a width equal to the distance between centers of the stiffeners.* In this manner, just one stiffener will be included in the panel section. The resulting moment of inertia (I) of the stiffener and the section of the panel may be found from the following formula:

$$I = I_s + \frac{A_p\, t^2}{12} + \frac{A_s\, A_p\, d^2}{A_s + A_p} \qquad \text{..........(1)}$$

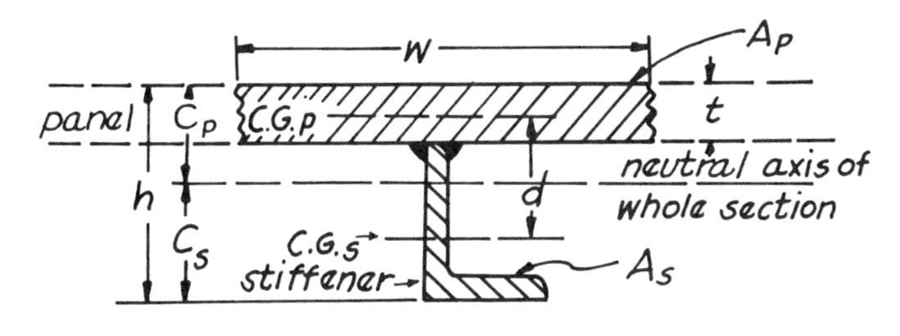

FIGURE 2

where:

* W = distance between stiffeners, in.

d = distance between center of gravity of panel and that of stiffener, in.

A_p = cross-sectional area of plate within distance b, in.[2]

** A_s = cross-sectional area of stiffener, in.[2]

t = thickness of panel, in.

** I_s = moment of inertia of stiffener, in.[4]

*If there is any question about the distance between stiffeners becoming too great, Section 2.12 will provide some guidance.
**Data obtained from any steel handbook

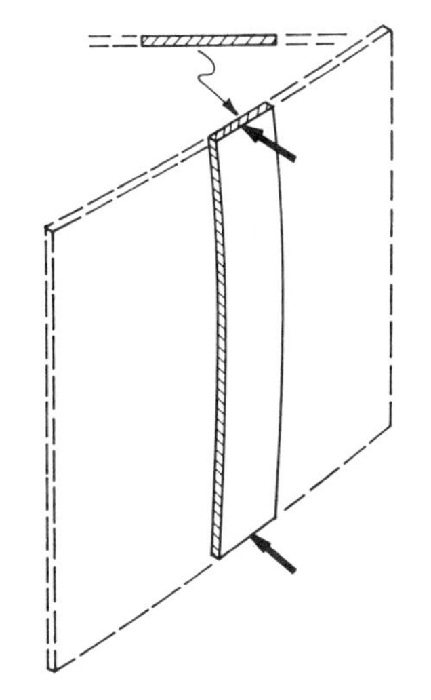

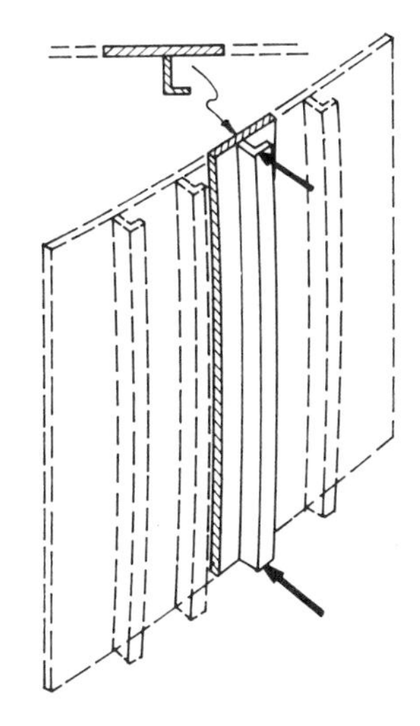

FIGURE 1

In figuring the maximum bending stress in this built-up section, the following distances to the outer fibers must be known.

$$c_p = \frac{A_s\, d}{A_s + A_p} + \frac{t}{2} \qquad \text{..................(2)}$$

$$c_s = h - c_p = h - \frac{t}{2} - \frac{A_s\, d}{A_s + A_p} \qquad \text{......(3)}$$

where:

c_p = distance from neutral axis of whole section to outer fiber of plate, in.

c_s = distance from neutral axis of whole section to outer fiber of stiffener, in.

The panel section may then be treated as a simply supported beam and designed with sufficient moment of inertia (I) to withstand whatever load is applied. Use a 1″ wide strip of this panel, and use uniform load of (w) lbs per linear inch; if entire width of panel (b), use uniform pressure of (p) psi.

Figure 3 illustrates the technique of treating a panel section as a beam under three different conditions. Formulas for finding maximum deflection, bending moment, and vertical shear are given, with p being the pressure in psi against the panel.

FIGURE 3—Properties of Panel Section Treated as a Beam

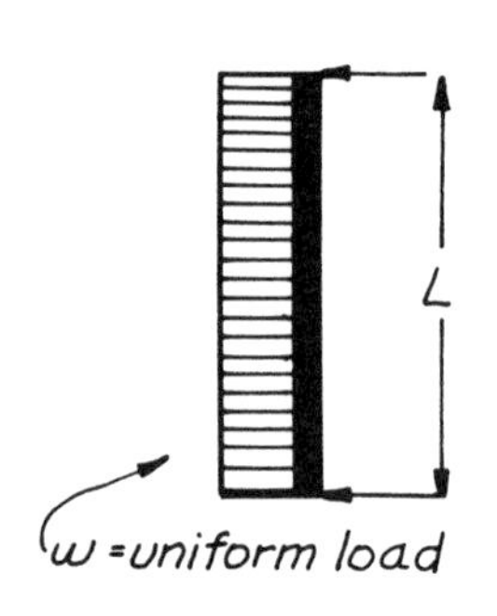

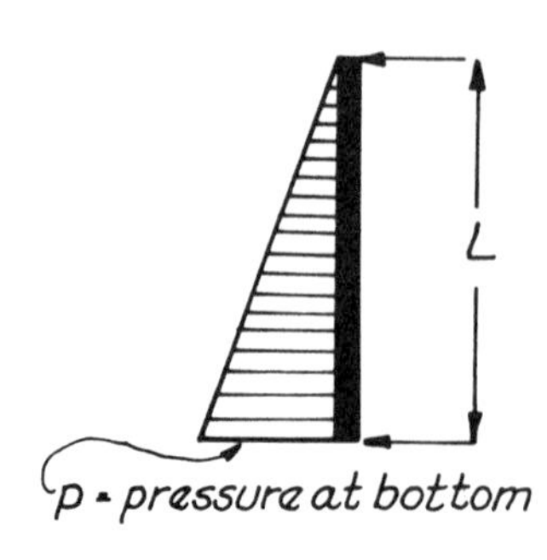

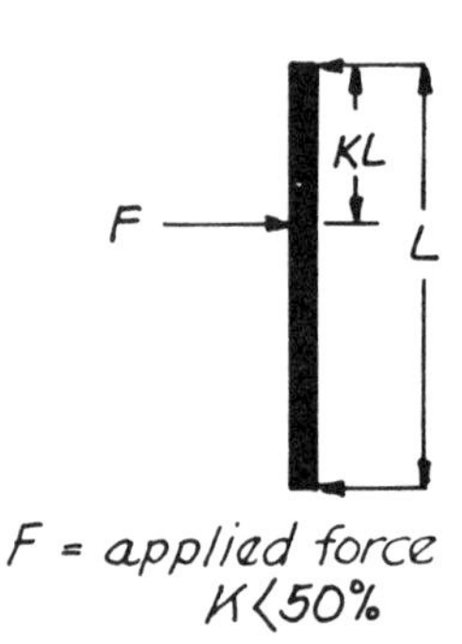

Condition A

$$\Delta_{max} = \frac{5\ p\ b\ L^4}{384\ E\ I} \quad ..(4)$$

$$M_{max} = \frac{p\ b\ L^2}{8} \quad ...(5)$$

$$V_{max} = \frac{p\ b\ L}{2} \quad ....(6)$$

Condition B

$$\Delta_{max} = 0.00652 \frac{p\ b\ L^4}{E\ I} \quad (7)$$

$$M_{max} = 0.0642\ p\ b\ L^2 \quad ...(8)$$

$$V_{max} = \frac{p\ b\ L}{3} \quad ....(9)$$

Condition C

$$\Delta_{max} = \frac{F\ L^3\ K}{27\ E\ I} \sqrt{3\ (1 - K^2)^3} \quad (10)$$

$$M_{max} = F\ L\ K\ (1 - K) \quad ....(11)$$

$$V_{max} = F\ (1 - K) \quad ....(12)$$

(With reference to Figure 3)
If due to weight of liquid or granular material:

$$p = h\ d = .006944\ H\ D$$
$$p = .0361\ h\ s = .4335\ H\ s$$

where:

h = height of liquid or material, in.

H = height of liquid or material, ft

s = specific gravity of liquid or material, lbs/cu in.

d = density of liquid or material, lbs/cu. in.

D = density of liquid or material, lbs/cu ft.

The maximum stress in the outer fibers of either the panel or the stiffener may be found by using the corresponding value of c and the maximum moment (M_{max}) in the following formulas:

for the panel

$$\sigma_p = \frac{M_{max}\ c_p}{I} \quad ....(13)$$

for the stiffener

$$\sigma_p = \frac{M_{max}\ c_s}{I} \quad ....(14)$$

2. RESISTING TORSION

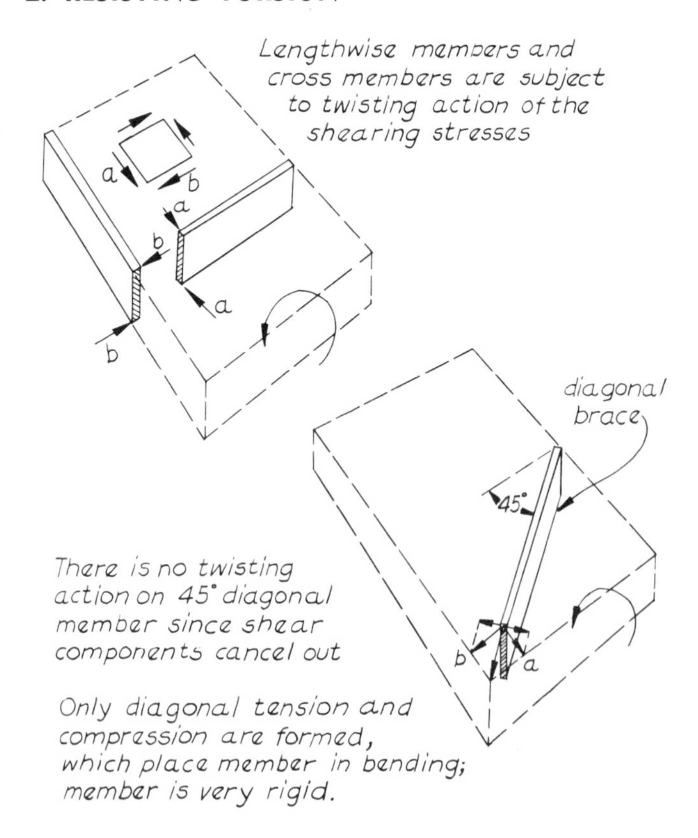

Lengthwise members and cross members are subject to twisting action of the shearing stresses
a
b
diagonal brace
45°
There is no twisting action on 45° diagonal member since shear components cancel out
Only diagonal tension and compression are formed, which place member in bending; member is very rigid.

FIGURE 4

Conventional cross stiffeners on a panel do not offer any resistance to twisting. However, if these stiffeners are placed at 45°, they will greatly increase the torsional resistance of a panel. There is no twisting action on the 45° stiffeners because the two components from the longitudinal and transverse shear stresses are equal and opposite and, therefore, cancel out.

3. WELD SIZE

The leg size of the continuous fillet weld required to join a stiffener to the panel may be found from the following formula:

$$\omega = \frac{V\ a\ y}{11{,}200\ I\ n} \quad \text{(E70 welds)}$$

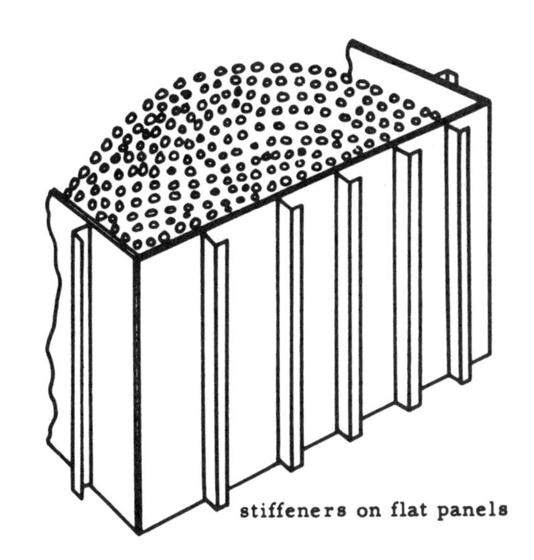

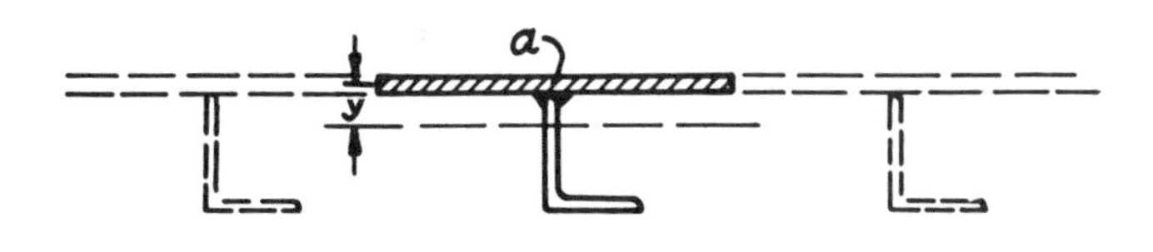

FIGURE 5

where:

ω = leg size of continuous fillet weld, in.

V = total shear on section at a given position along the beam, lbs

a = area held by weld, in.^{2}

y = distance between center of gravity of the area and neutral axis of whole section, in. $= c_p - \frac{1}{2}\, t$

I = moment of inertia of whole section, in.^{4}

n = number of continuous welds joining the stiffener to the panel

If intermittent fillet welds are to be used, calculate the continuous fillet weld leg size expressed as a decimal, and divide this by the actual leg size of intermittent fillet weld used. When expressed as a percentage this will give the amount of intermittent weld to be used per unit length. For convenience, Table 1 has various intermittent weld lengths and distance between centers for a given percentage of continuous weld.

TABLE 1—Intermittent Welds

Percent of Continuous Weld	Length of Intermittent Welds and Distance Between Centers		
75%		3 - 4	
66			4 - 6
60		3 - 5	
57			4 - 7
50	2 - 4	3 - 6	4 - 8
44			4 - 9
43		3 - 7	
40	2 - 5		4 - 10
37		3 - 8	
33	2 - 6	3 - 9	4 - 12
30		3 - 10	
25	2 - 8	3 - 12	
20	2 - 10		
16	2 - 12		

Weld fabrication of large panels, using proper stiffeners, provides required strength and rigidity, while keeping weight to a minimum.

Tanks, Bins and Hoppers

1. SCOPE

This is a broad classification, covering many types of containers. However, principles and formulas relating to their design are best discussed as a single group. Some of these containers have flat surfaces; some have curved surfaces; some have both. Some carry steam, gasses, or pressurized fluids that exert uniform pressure in all directions; others carry bulk materials such as grain, the weight of which exerts a varying horizontal pressure against the side walls.

The first requisite of a container is that it be tight. It must have sufficient strength to withstand the internal pressure to which it is subjected. In arc-welded construction, the joints are made as tight and strong as the plates joined. In large tanks built up from a number of plates or sheets, butt welds are customarily specified.

Many containers must be designed and fabricated according to the minimum requirements of certain codes, for example ASME. Most containers have thin shells in comparison to their diameters and come under the classification of thin-wall shells.

Types of Containers
Flat and/or Curved Surfaces

tanks	drums	chutes
vats	bins	stacks
hoppers	silos	pipe and piping systems and many others

2. ELEMENTS OF THE CONTAINER

The surfaces of any container must withstand pressure of some type, so it would be well to consider the strength and stiffness of various shapes and forms of plates under uniform pressure.

In analysis of a given container, the designer explodes it into its various elements and applies the corresponding formulas.

Flat Surfaces of Containers

3. GENERAL

Some containers are of box construction, made up entirely of flat surfaces. Other containers, many tanks for example, consist of a cylinder closed at each end by a flat plate.

Table 1 presents design formulas applicable to various flat plates subjected to internal pressure.

Problem 1

Determine the required plate thickness of the following tank to hold water, Figure 1.

Since the varying pressure against side walls is due to the weight of a liquid:

$$p = .4336\ H\ s$$
$$= .4336(6)(1)$$
$$= 2.6 \text{ psi}$$

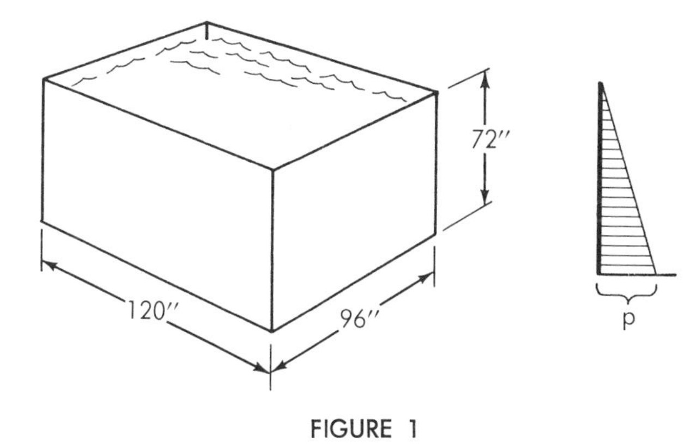

FIGURE 1

where:

H = the maximum height of the liquid, in feet

s = the specific gravity of the liquid

It is necessary to consider only the longest side plate, having the greatest span between supports:

120″. The top edge is free, the other three are supported. This is recognized as condition 4D in Table 1.

Since the ratio of plate height to width is—

$$\frac{a}{b} = \frac{72}{120} = .6$$

values are estimated from Table 1 to be—

$$\beta = .14 \qquad \text{and } \gamma = .030$$

Then the required plate thickness is derived from the maximum stress formula:

$$\sigma_{max} = \frac{\beta\, p\, b^2}{t^2}$$

or, assuming an allowable stress of 20,000 psi—

$$t^2 = \frac{\beta\, p\, b^2}{\sigma}$$

$$= \frac{(.14)(2.6)(120)^2}{20{,}000}$$

$$= .262$$

$$\therefore\ t = \sqrt{.262}$$

$$= .512'', \text{ or use } ½''\ ⅊$$

Checking the deflection of this plate—

$$\Delta_{max} = \frac{\gamma\, p\, b^4}{E\, t^3}$$

$$= \frac{(.030)(2.6)(120)^4}{(30 \times 10^6)(.5)^3}$$

$$= 4.3''$$

Since this deflection would be excessive, a stiffening bar must be added along the top edge of the tank to form a rectangular frame, Figure 2.

Tank with Top Edge Stiffener

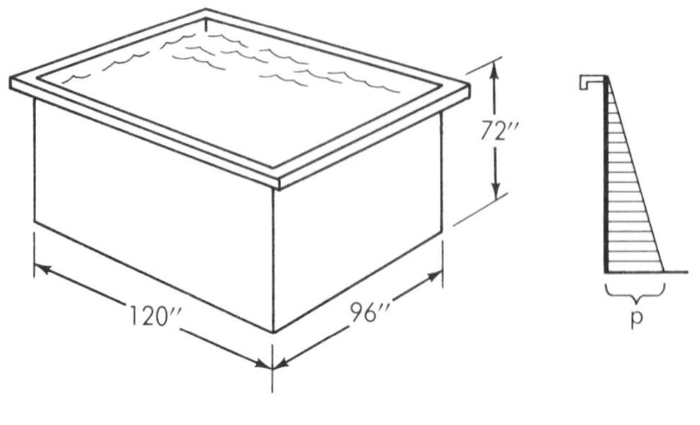

FIGURE 2

The modified tank now satisfies the condition 5A on Table 1, because the critical plate is supported on all four edges.

The ratio of plate height to width still being .6, values are estimated from Table 1 to be—

$$\beta = .102 \qquad \text{and } \gamma = .0064$$

Since the same maximum stress formula applies—

$$t^2 = \frac{\beta\, p\, b^2}{\sigma}$$

$$= \frac{(.102)(2.6)(120)^2}{20{,}000}$$

$$= .191$$

$$\therefore\ t = \sqrt{.191}$$

$$= .437'', \text{ or use } 7/16''\ ⅊$$

Checking the deflection of this plate—

$$\Delta_{max} = \frac{\gamma\, p\, b^4}{E\, t^3}$$

$$= \frac{(.0064)(2.6)(120)^4}{(30 \times 10^6)(.4375)^3}$$

$$= 1.37''$$

It might be advisable to go back to the ½″ plate thickness, still using the top edge stiffener, in which case the bending stress and deflection would be reduced to—

$$\sigma_{max} = 15{,}300 \text{ psi} \qquad \text{and } \Delta_{max} = .92''$$

There is another method of determining the bending stress and deflection. A description of this follows immediately.

Considering Plate Section as a Beam

A narrow section of the tank's side panel (width m = 1″) can be considered as a beam, Figure 3, using formulas taken from Reference Section 8.1 on Beam Diagrams.

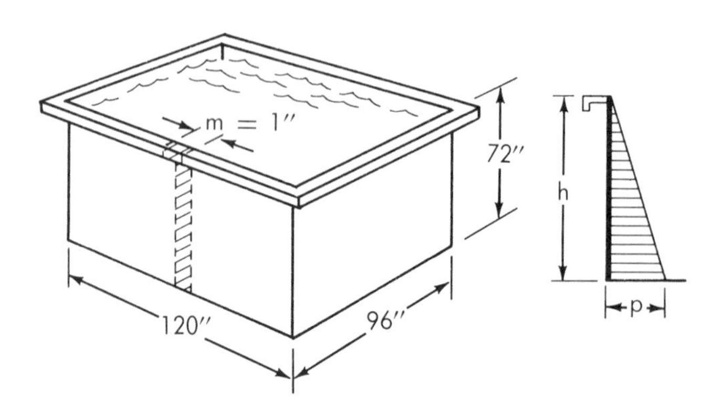

FIGURE 3

TABLE 1—Stress and Deflection, Flat Plates*
Subjected to Internal Pressure (p), psi

CIRCULAR PLATE

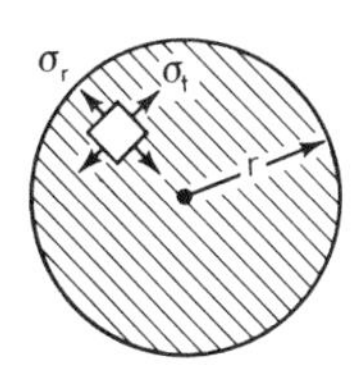

(1A) Edges supported; uniform load

At center:

$$(max)\ \sigma_r = \sigma_t = -\frac{1.24\ p\ r^2}{t^2}$$

$$\Delta_{max} = -\frac{.695\ p\ r^4}{E\ t^3}$$

(1B) Edges fixed; uniform load

At center:

$$\sigma_r = \sigma_t = -\frac{.488\ p\ r^2}{t^2}$$

$$\Delta_{max} = -\frac{.1705\ p\ r^4}{E\ t^3}$$

At edge:

$$(max)\ \sigma_r = \frac{3\ p\ r^2}{4\ t^2}$$

$$\sigma_t = \frac{.225\ p\ r^2}{t^2}$$

ELLIPTICAL PLATE

$$\alpha = \frac{b}{a}$$

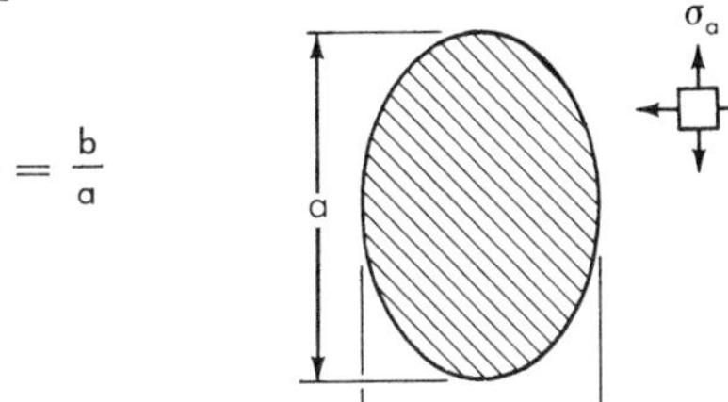

(2A) Edges supported; uniform load

At center:

$$(max)\ \sigma_b = -\frac{.3125\ (2 - \alpha)\ p\ b^2}{t^2}$$

$$(approx)\ \Delta_{max} = \frac{(.146 - .1\ \alpha)\ p\ b^4}{E\ t^3}$$

(2B) Edges fixed; uniform load

At center:

$$\sigma_a = -\frac{.075\ p\ b^2\ (10\ \alpha^2 + 3)}{t^2\ (3 + 2\ \alpha^2 + 3\ \alpha^4)}$$

$$\sigma_b = -\frac{.075\ p\ b^2\ (3\ \alpha^2 + 10)}{t^2\ (3 + 2\ \alpha^2 + 3\ \alpha^4)}$$

$$\Delta_{max} = -\frac{.1705\ p\ b^4}{E\ t^3\ (6 + 4\ \alpha^2 + 6\ \alpha^4)}$$

At edge:

$$(Span\ a)\ \sigma_a = \frac{1.5\ p\ b^2\ \alpha^2}{t^2\ (3 + 2\ \alpha^2 + 3\ \alpha^4)}$$

$$(max)\ (Span\ b)\ \sigma_b = \frac{1.5\ p\ b^2}{t^2\ (3 + 2\ \alpha^2 + 3\ \alpha^4)}$$

SQUARE PLATE

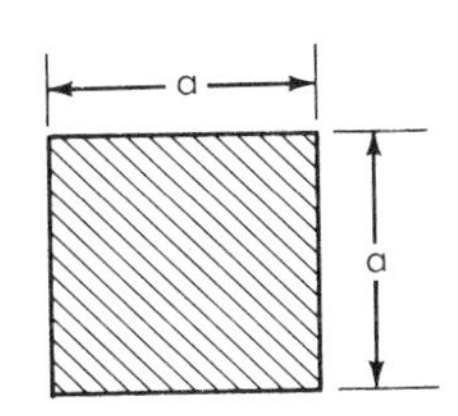

(3A) Edges supported (and held down); uniform load

At center:

$$(max)\ \sigma_a = -\frac{.2870\ p\ a^2}{t^2}$$

$$\Delta_{max} = \frac{.0443\ p\ a^4}{E\ t^3}$$

(3B) Edges fixed; uniform load

At center:

$$\sigma_a = -\frac{.166\ p\ a^2}{t^2}$$

$$\Delta_{max} = -\frac{.0138\ p\ a^4}{E\ t^3}$$

At midpoint of each edge:

$$(max)\ \sigma_a = +\frac{.308\ p\ a^2}{t^2}$$

*After Roark, "Formulas for Stress and Strain".

Table 1 continued on following page

Table 1 continued

RECTANGULAR PLATES

$$\alpha = \frac{b}{a}$$

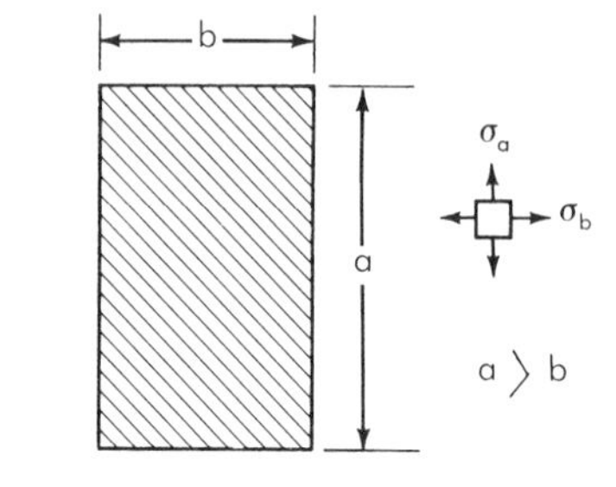

(4A) Edges supported; uniform load

At center:

$$\sigma_a = -\frac{p\,b^2\,(.225 + .382\,\alpha^2 - .320\,\alpha^3)}{t^2}$$

$$(\max)\ \sigma_b = -\frac{.75\,p\,b^2}{t^2\,(1 + 1.61\,\alpha^3)} \quad \text{or} = \frac{\beta\,p\,b^2}{t^2}$$

$$\Delta_{max} = -\frac{.1422\,p\,b^4}{E\,t^3\,(1 + 2.21\,\alpha^3)} \quad \text{or} = -\frac{\gamma\,p\,b^4}{E\,t^3}$$

(4B) Edges fixed; uniform load

At center:

$$\sigma_a = -\frac{.054\,p\,b^2\,(1 + 2\alpha^2 - \alpha^4)}{t^2}$$

$$\sigma_b = -\frac{.75\,p\,b^2}{t^2\,(3 + 4\,\alpha^4)}$$

$$\Delta_{max} = -\frac{.0284\,p\,b^4}{E\,t^3\,(1 + 1.056\,\alpha^5)} \quad \text{or} = -\frac{\gamma\,p\,b^4}{E\,t^3}$$

At midpoint of long edges:

$$(\max)\ \sigma_b = \frac{.5\,p\,b^2}{t^2\,(1 + .623\,\alpha^6)} \quad \text{or} = \frac{\beta\,p\,b^2}{t^2}$$

At midpoint of short edges:

$$\sigma_a = \frac{.25\,p\,b^2}{t^2}$$

See the following sub-tables for values of β and γ:

$\frac{a}{b}$	1.0	1.1	1.2	1.3	1.4	1.5	1.6	1.7	1.8	1.9	2.0	∞
FOR EDGES SUPPORTED												
β	.2874	.3318	.3756	.4158	.4518	.4542	.5172	.5448	.5688	.5910	.6102	.7500
γ	.0443	.0530	.0616	.0697	.0770	.0843	.0906	.0964	.1017	.1064	.1106	.1422
FOR EDGES FIXED												
β	.3078	.3486	.3834	.4122	.4356	.4252	.4680	.4794	.4872	.4932	.4974	
γ	.0138	.0164	.0188	.0209	.0226	.0240	.0251	.0260	.0267	.0272	.0277	

(4C) All edges supported; varying load

Load increasing uniformly from zero at one edge to a maximum of (p) psi at opposite edge (triangular load)

$$\sigma_{max} = \frac{\beta\,p\,b^2}{t^2}$$

$$\Delta_{max} = \frac{\gamma\,p\,b^4}{E\,t^3}$$

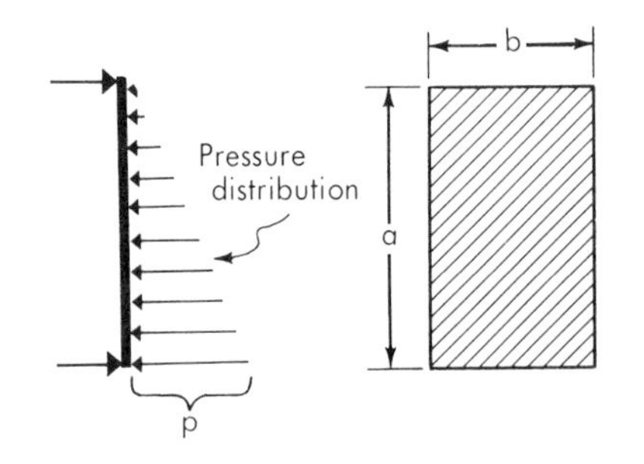

or

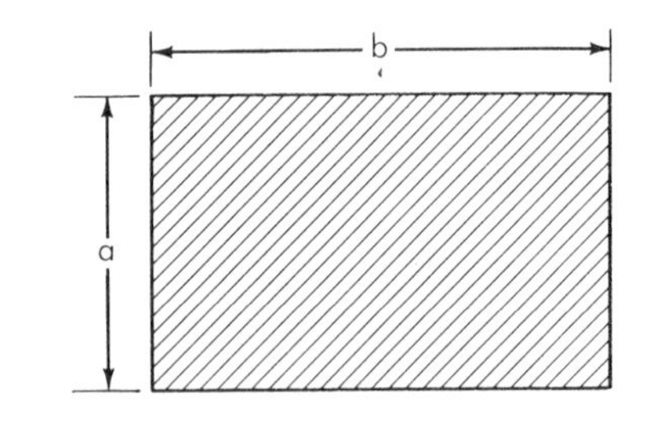

The following values apply to Condition 4C;

$\frac{a}{b}$	.25	.286	.333	.4	.5	.667	1.0	1.5	2.0	2.5	3.0	3.5	4.0
β	.024	.031	.041	.056	.080	.116	.16	.26	.32	.35	.37	.38	.38
γ	.00027	.00046	.00083	.0016	.0035	.0083	.022	.042	.056	.063	.067	.069	.070

Table 1 continued on facing page

Table 1 continued

(4D) Top edge free, other three edges supported; varying load

Load increasing uniformly from zero at top edge to a maximum of (p) psi at bottom edge (triangular load)

$$\sigma_{max} = \frac{\beta \; p \; b^2}{t^2}$$

$$\Delta_{max} = \frac{\gamma \; p \; b^4}{E \; t^3}$$

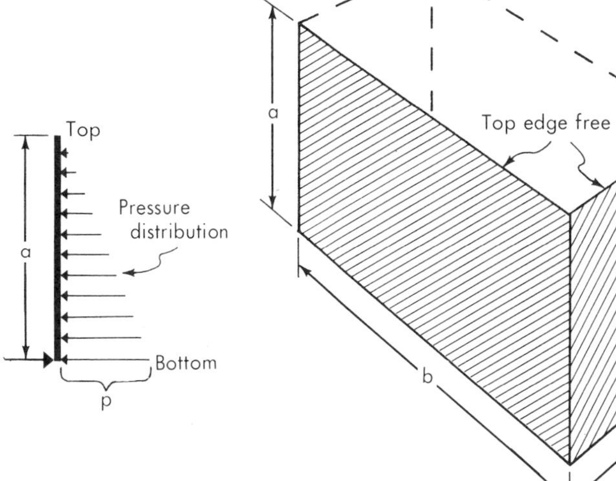

The following values apply to Condition 4D;

$\frac{a}{b}$	.5	.667	1.0	1.5	2.0	2.5	3.0	3.5	4.0
β	.11	.16	.20	.28	.32	.35	.36	.37	.37
β	.026	.033	.040	.050	.058	.064	.067	.069	.070

Since the maximum bending moment here is—

$$M_{max} = .0642 \; p \; h^2 \; m \text{ (with h expressed in inches)}$$

$$= .0642 \; (2.6)(72)^2(1)$$

$$= 865 \text{ in.-lbs}$$

$$\sigma_{max} = \frac{M}{S} = \frac{M \; 6}{t^2}$$

$$= 20{,}800 \text{ psi}$$

instead of the 15,300 psi obtained by considering the entire plate width; and—

$$\Delta_{max} = \frac{.0625 \; p \; h^4 \; m}{E \; I}$$

$$= \frac{.0625(2.6)(72)^4(1)(12)}{(30 \times 10^6)(.5)^3}$$

$$= 1.39''$$

instead of the .92″ obtained by considering the entire plate width.

This method of isolating a 1″ strip of the panel and considering it as a beam will indicate greater bending stress and deflection than actually exists. The reason is that the stiffening effect of the surrounding panel has been neglected for simplicity.

The previous method of considering the entire panel is recommended for its accuracy and for a more efficient design wherever it can be applied.

Adding Another Stiffener

When a panel is divided into two parts by a large stiffener, it becomes a continuous panel, triangularly loaded with a rather high negative moment at the stiffener which acts as a support. There is no simple formula for this; therefore the method of considering a 1″ strip will be used, and of course will result in a slightly greater stress value than actually exists.

The plate thickness in the tank being considered can probably be reduced by adding such a stiffener around the middle of the tank, Figure 4.

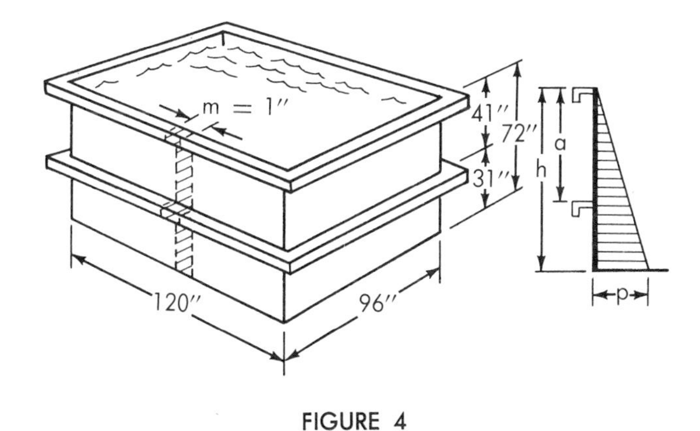

FIGURE 4

The first step is to locate the stiffener at the height which will produce the minimum bending moment in the panel, both above and below the stiffener.

(Again use formulas from Reference Section 8.1 on Beam Diagrams.) This dimension (a), the distance between the two stiffeners, is—

$$a = .57\ h = .57(72) = 41''$$

Then, at the middle stiffener—

$$M_{max} = .0147\ p\ h^2\ m$$
$$= .0147\ (2.6)(72)^2(1)$$
$$= 198\ \text{in.-lbs}$$

Trying 5/16″ ℄

$$\sigma_{max} = \frac{M}{S} = \frac{M\ 6}{t^2}$$
$$= \frac{(198)6}{(5/16)^2}$$
$$= \underline{12{,}200\ \text{psi}} \qquad \text{OK}$$

Container Surfaces Formed By A Figure of Revolution

4. STRESSES IN SHELL

The various container shapes illustrated in Table 2 are formed by a figure of revolution.

In any of these containers, the internal pressure (p) along with the weight of the gas, liquid or other media within the container produces three types of tensile stresses in the container's shell. These are:

1. σ_{mp} = tensile stress in the direction of a meridian. (A meridian is the curve formed by the intersection of the shell and a plane through the longitudinal axis of the container.) This stress is referred to as longitudinal stress.

2. σ_{cp} = tensile stress in the direction of a tangent to a circumference. (A circumference is the curve formed by the intersection of the shell and a plane perpendicular to the longitudinal axis of the container.) This stress is referred to as tangential or circumferential stress but is commonly called the hoop stress.

3. σ_{rp} = tensile stress in the radial direction.

For containers having relatively thin shells (generally considered as less than 10% of the mean radius) and no abrupt change in thickness or curvature, the radial tensile stress (σ_{rp}) and any bending stress may be neglected.

TABLE 2—Container Surfaces Formed By A Figure of Revolution

THIN WALL CONTAINERS		
CONTAINER SHAPE	UNIT WALL SEGMENT	TENSILE STRESS FORMULAE
CYLINDER (t_s, p, r_c)	(σ_{mp}, σ_{cp})	$\sigma_{mp} = \frac{p\,r_c}{2\,t_s}$ $\sigma_{cp} = \frac{p\,r_c}{t_s}$
SPHERE (t_s, p, r_c)	(σ_{mp}, σ_{cp})	$\sigma_{mp} = \sigma_{cp} = \frac{p\,r_c}{2\,t_s}$
ANY FIGURE OF REVOLUTION (t_s, p, r_m, r_c)	(σ_{mp}, σ_{cp})	$\frac{\sigma_{cp}}{r_{cp}} + \frac{\sigma_m}{r_m} = \frac{p}{t_s}$ $\sigma_{mp} = \frac{p\,r_c}{2t_s}$ $\sigma_{cp} = \frac{p\,r_c}{t_s}\left(1 - \frac{r_c}{2\,r_m}\right)$
CONE (α, t_s, p, r_c)	(σ_{mp}, σ_{cp})	$\sigma_{mp} = \frac{p\,r_c}{2t_s \cos\alpha}$ $\sigma_{cp} = \frac{p\,r_c}{t_s \cos\alpha}$

TABLE 3—Stresses in Thick-Wall Cylinders

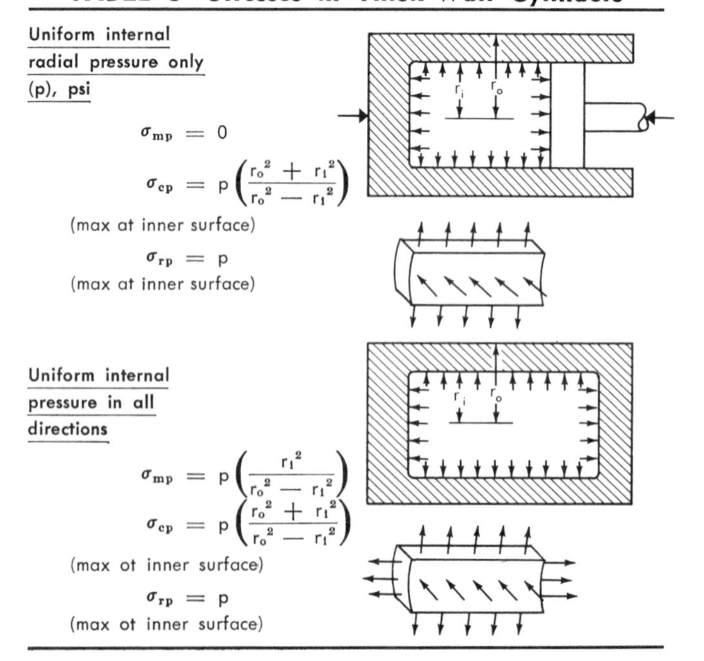

Uniform internal radial pressure only (p), psi

$$\sigma_{mp} = 0$$
$$\sigma_{cp} = p\left(\frac{r_o^2 + r_i^2}{r_o^2 - r_i^2}\right)$$
(max at inner surface)
$$\sigma_{rp} = p$$
(max at inner surface)

Uniform internal pressure in all directions

$$\sigma_{mp} = p\left(\frac{r_i^2}{r_o^2 - r_i^2}\right)$$
$$\sigma_{cp} = p\left(\frac{r_o^2 + r_i^2}{r_o^2 - r_i^2}\right)$$
(max at inner surface)
$$\sigma_{rp} = p$$
(max at inner surface)

The biaxial tensile stresses (σ_{mp}) and (σ_{cp}) in thin-wall containers can be calculated with the basic formulas shown in Table 2, where:

t_s = thickness of shell, in.

r_c = mean radius of a circumference of the shell, in.

r_m = mean radius of the meridian of the shell, in.

p = internal pressure, psi

5. THICK-WALLED CONTAINERS

In thin-walled containers, the hoop stress is assumed to be uniformly distributed across the shell thickness without serious error occurring in stress calculations. However, in a thick-walled container generated by a figure of revolution the decreasing variance of hoop stress from the inner surface to the outer surface of the shell wall must be considered.

Table 3 presents formulas for calculating the stresses in two common thick-walled cylinders. In the first condition, the internal pressure parallel to the structural (longitudinal) axis is balanced by the external force against the moving piston and by the resistance of the cylinder's support, and the resultant longitudinal stress (σ_{mp}) is zero. In the second condition, there is a longitudinal stress (σ_{mp}).

Unfired Pressure Vessels

6. ASME CODE—SECTION 8

Any pressure container of any importance undoubtedly must conform to the minimum requirements of the ASME, so it would be well to use ASME Section 8 "Unfired Pressure Vessels" as a guide. In general this covers containers for pressures exceeding 15 psi up to a maximum of 3,000 psi, and having a diameter exceeding 6″.

Table 4 presents the formulas for calculating the minimum required wall thickness of cylindrical shells and spherical shells, where:

p = internal pressure, psi

σ_a = allowable stress (See ASME Sec. 8, par USC-23)

E = joint efficiency (See ASME Sec. 8, par UW-12)

Table 5 presents the formulas for calculating the minimum required thickness of various types of heads. Turn to next page for Table 5.

TABLE 4—Wall Thickness of Shells
Subjected to Internal Pressure (p), psi
(ASME-8: Unfired Pressure Vessels)

CYLINDRICAL SHELLS (UG-27c and UA-1)	SPHERICAL SHELLS (UG-27d and UA-3)
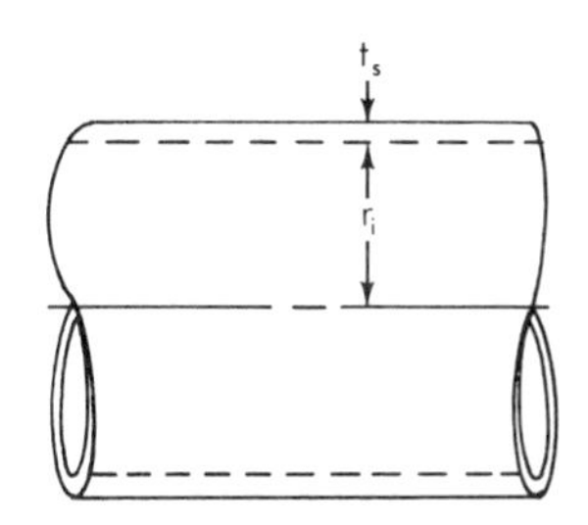	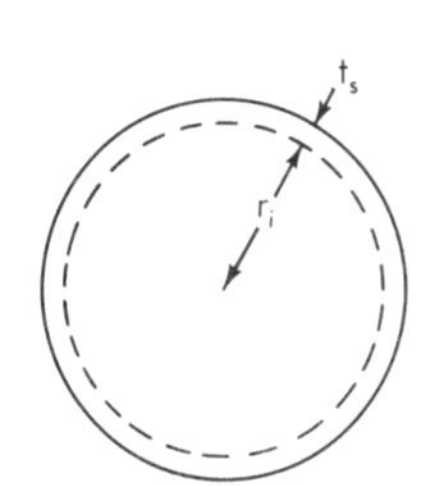
Thin shell — when $t_s < \frac{1}{2} r_i$ and $p < .385\ \sigma_a E$	Thin shell — when $t_s < .356\ r_i$ and $p < .665\ \sigma_a E$
$t_s = \dfrac{p\ r_i}{\sigma_a E - .6\ p}$	$t_s = \dfrac{p\ r_i}{2(\sigma_a E - .1\ p)}$
Thick shell — when $t_s > \frac{1}{2} r_i$ and $p > .385\ \sigma_a E$	Thick shell — when $t_s > .356\ r_i$ and $p > .665\ \sigma_a E$
$= r_i(\sqrt{Z} - 1)$	$t_s = r_i(\sqrt[3]{Y} - 1)$
where $Z = \dfrac{\sigma_a E + p}{\sigma_a Z - p}$	where $Y = \dfrac{2(\sigma_a E + p)}{2\ \sigma_a E - p}$

TABLE 5—Thickness of Formed Heads
Subjected to Internal Pressure (p) on Concave Side
(ASME-8: Unfired Pressure Vessels)

ELLIPSOIDAL HEAD
(UG-32d and UA-4c)

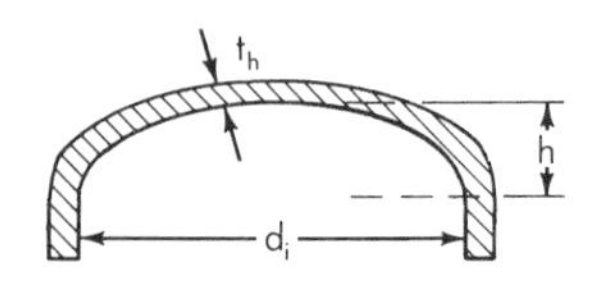

Standard head — where $h = d_i/4$

(h = minor axis: inside depth of head minus skirt)

$$t_h = \frac{p\ d_i}{2(\sigma_a\ E - .1\ p}$$

Head of other proportions

$$t_h = \frac{p\ d_i\ K}{2(\sigma_a\ E - .1\ p)}$$

where:

$$K = \frac{1}{6}\left[2 + \left(\frac{d_i}{2h}\right)^2\right]$$

TORISPHERICAL HEAD
(UG-32e and UA-4d)

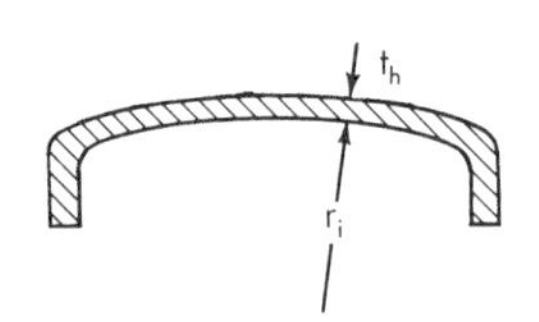

Standard head — where $r_k = .06\ r_i$

(r_k = knuckle radius)

$$t_h = \frac{.885\ p\ r_i}{\sigma_a\ E - .1\ p}$$

Head of other proportions

$$t_h = \frac{p\ r_i\ M}{2(\sigma_a\ E - .1\ p)}$$

where:

$$M = \frac{1}{4}\left[3 + \sqrt{\frac{r_i}{r_k}}\right]$$

HEMISPHERICAL HEAD
(UG-32f and UA-3)

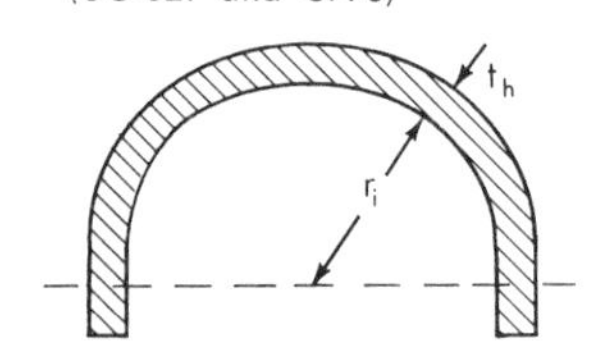

Thin head — when $t_h < .356\ r_i$ and $p < .665\ \sigma_a\ E$

$$t_h = \frac{p\ r_i}{2(\sigma_a\ E - .1\ p)}$$

Thick head — when $t_h > .356\ r_i$ and $p > .665\ \sigma_a\ E$

$$t_h = r_i\ (\sqrt[3]{Y} - 1)$$

where:

$$Y = \frac{2(\sigma_a\ E + p)}{2\ \sigma_a\ E - p}$$

FLAT HEAD (UG-34)

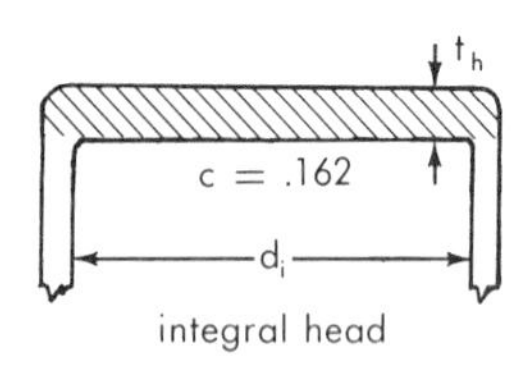

integral head

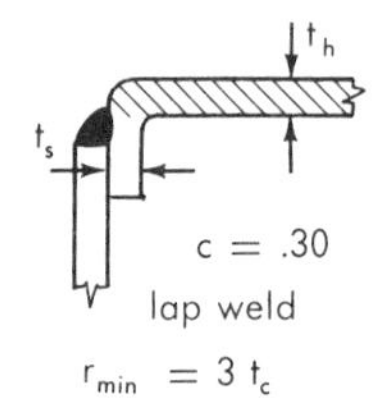

lap weld

$r_{min} = 3\ t_c$

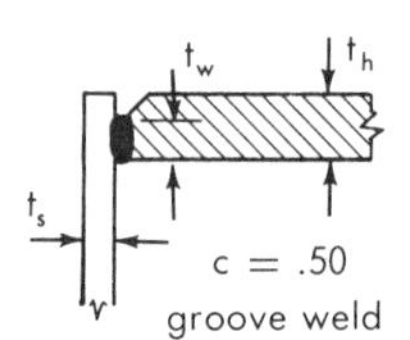

groove weld

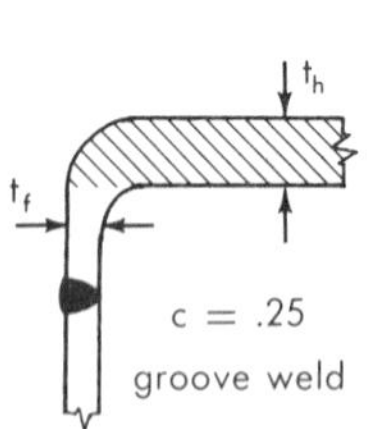

groove weld

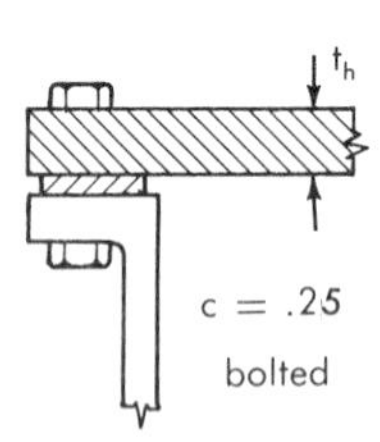

bolted

t_w = twice required thickness of spherical shell or 1.25 t_s and not greater than t_h

$$t_h = d_i\ \sqrt{\frac{c\ p}{\sigma_a}}$$

The Design of Hangers and Supports

1. BASIC FORCES AND STRESSES

Designing hangers or brackets for supporting a shell such as a pipe, tank or pressure vessel requires consideration of two important factors:

1. The additional stress of the support forces when combined with the working stress of the shell must not increase the stress in the shell above the allowable limit.

2. The support should not restrain the stressed shell so it becomes too rigid to flex under normal changes in working pressures or loads.

Many types of stresses are involved in any supporting structure. The more common types are the following:

1. The internal pressure of the gas or liquid in the shell, along with its weight, cause tangential (σ_{cp}) and longitudinal (σ_{mp}) tensile stresses in the shell.

2. Any radial force (F_1) acting on a section of the shell causes bending stresses in the ring of the shell (from the bending moment M_r) as well as axial tensile stresses (from the tensile force T), both of which act tangentially to the circumference of the shell.

3. The radial force (F_1) causes radial shear stresses in the shell, and the longitudinal force (F_2) causes longitudinal shear stresses, both adjacent to the hanger. These stresses usually will be low.

After proper analysis of the forces involved, the various stresses must be combined to determine the maximum normal stress (σ_{max}—tensile or compressive) and maximum shear stress (τ_{max}). If the resulting stresses are excessive, a simple study of the individual stresses will indicate what portion of the hanger is under-designed and should be strengthened.

For example, the bending stresses may be excessive, indicating that some type of stiffener ring should be attached to the shell between supports to substantially increase the moment of inertia of the shell section thereby decreasing the bending stress.

The following discussions identify and analyze the effect of various basic stresses and relate them to material thickness and curvature.

2. STRESSES IN SHELL FROM INTERNAL PRESSURE

As explained more fully in Section 6.5, internal pressure in a shell produces two tensile stresses of importance.

1. σ_{mp} = tensile stress in the direction of the meridian. This is called the longitudinal stress.

2. σ_{cp} = tensile stress in the direction of the tangent to the circumference. This stress is commonly called the hoop stress, but is also referred to as the tangential or circumferential stress.

The tensile stresses σ_{mp} and σ_{cp} can be calculated with the formulas presented in Table 2 of the preceding Section 6.5 and repeated here.

THIN WALL CONTAINERS

CONTAINER SHAPE	UNIT WALL SEGMENT	TENSILE STRESS FORMULAE
CYLINDER (t_s, p, r_c)	σ_{mp}, σ_{cp}	$\sigma_{mp} = \frac{p r_c}{2 t_s}$; $\sigma_{cp} = \frac{p r_c}{t_s}$
SPHERE (t_s, p, r_c)	σ_{mp}, σ_{cp}	$\sigma_{mp} = \sigma_{cp} = \frac{p r_c}{2 t_s}$
ANY FIGURE OF REVOLUTION (t_s, p, r_m, r_c)	σ_{mp}, σ_{cp}	$\frac{\sigma_{cp}}{r_{cp}} + \frac{\sigma_m}{r_m} = \frac{p}{t_s}$; $\sigma_{mp} = \frac{p r_c}{2 t_s}$; $\sigma_{cp} = \frac{p r_c}{t_s}\left(1 - \frac{r_c}{2 r_m}\right)$
CONE (α, t_s, p, r_c)	σ_{mp}, σ_{cp}	$\sigma_{mp} = \frac{p r_c}{2 t_s \cos \alpha}$; $\sigma_{cp} = \frac{p r_c}{t_s \cos \alpha}$

3. EFFECT OF HANGER OR SUPPORT WELDED TO SHELL

The force (P) applied to the hanger (see Figure 1) may be resolved into a radial component (F_1) and a longitudinal component (F_2) having the following values:

$$F_1 = P \cos \theta$$

$$F_2 = P \sin \theta$$

where θ is the angle between guy cable or support attached to the shell and the horizontal.

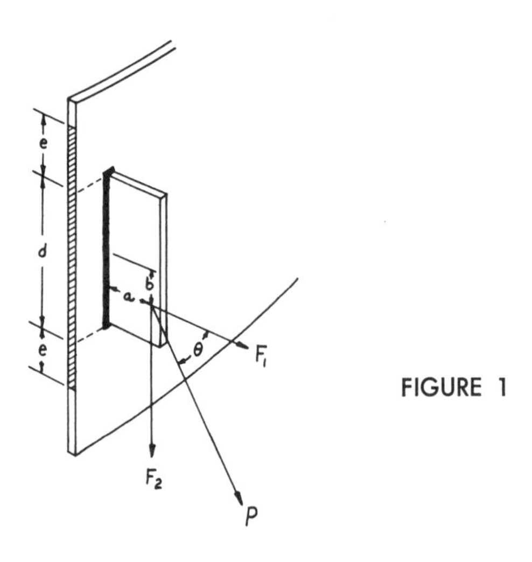

FIGURE 1

If these components are applied at some eccentricity (a and b), they will produce moments applied to the shell section by the hanger and having values:

$$M_1 = b\ F_1$$

$$M_2 = a\ F_2$$

Combining these values, observing proper signs, will give the total moment acting on the shell from the hanger:

$$M_h = M_1 + M_2$$

A study of stress distribution in the shell can be resolved into separate analyses of the radial and moment force distributions. Before analyzing these forces, however, the engineer should determine how much shell beyond the hanger is effective in resisting these forces.

The shell with stiffeners can be compared to a curved beam with an extremely wide flange, Figure 1. Von Karman* suggests that an effective width (e) of the flange on each side of the stiffening web is approximately—

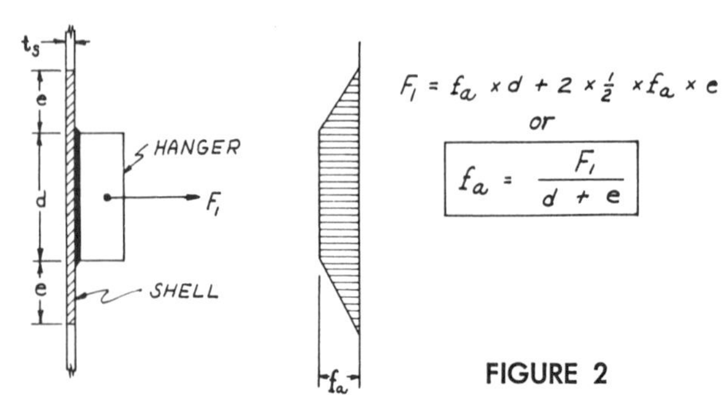

FIGURE 2

$$e = \frac{\sqrt{t_s\ r_c}}{2}$$

where:

r_c = radius of shell curvature, inches

t_s = thickness of shell, inches

The value of "e" should be limited to a maximum of $12t_s$.

The radial component (F_1) of the force (P) is applied directly to the shell. It is reasonable to assume that the radial forces applied to the additional shell width (e) would decrease linearly to almost zero at its outer limits. This assumed distribution of radial forces (f_a) due to the radial component (F_1) is sketched in Figure 2.

The value of f_a is equivalent to the force (lbs) on a 1″ wide ring of the shell.

The longitudinal component (F_2) of the force (P) because of its eccentricity (a), and the radial component (F_1) because of its eccentricity (b), combine into moment M_h and apply radial forces to the shell having a distribution similar to that of bending forces, i.e. maximum at the outer fibers and zero along the neutral axis. The assumed distribution of the radial forces (f_b) due to the action of the applied moment is indicated in Figure 3.

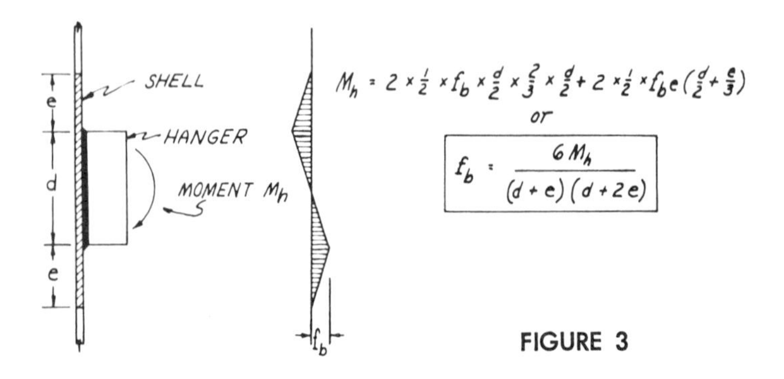

FIGURE 3

* "Analysis of Some Thin-Walled Structures", Von Karman, ASME paper AER-55-19C, Aer Eng, Vol. 5, No. 4, 1933.

The value of f_b is equivalent to the force (lbs) on a 1″ wide ring of the shell.

The resulting radial forces applied on the shell must be added, being careful to watch the signs:

$$f_1 = f_a + f_b$$

4. EFFECT OF ADDING STIFFENING RING

For additional stiffening of the shell at the support, rings may be welded to the shell. As before, the additional width of the shell on each side of the ring assumed to be effective in resisting these forces is—

$$e = \frac{\sqrt{t_s\, r_c}}{2}$$

with e not to exceed 12 t_s on each side of the ring.

The total radial force (F) applied to this built-up section is the radial force resulting from the longitudinal force (F_2), plus any radial force (F_1) applied at this point of support:

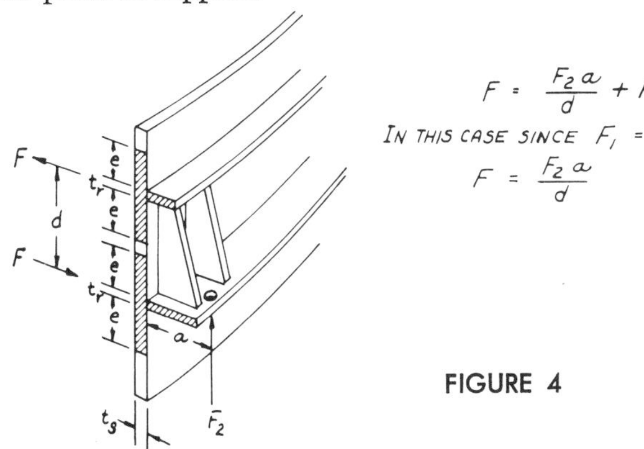

FIGURE 4

After determining the bending moment in this built-up ring resulting from the radial forces at the point of support, the moment of inertia (I) of the section is calculated. The bending stresses are then found and later combined with any other stresses.

5. EFFECT OF THESE FORCES UPON A SECTIONAL RING OF THE SHELL

Forces (f_1) normal to the shell set up tangential tensile forces (T) and bending moments (M_r) in the ring of the shell, Figure 5.

Stresses σ_{ct} and σ_{cb} are added to σ_{cp} to give σ_c = total tangential (or circumferential) stress in a section of the critical shell ring.

The maximum shear stress is equal to ½ the difference of the two principal stresses (σ) having the greatest algebraic difference. See Section 2.11, Topic 2.

The following are typical examples that demonstrate the use of these formulas for calculating the stresses in a shell.

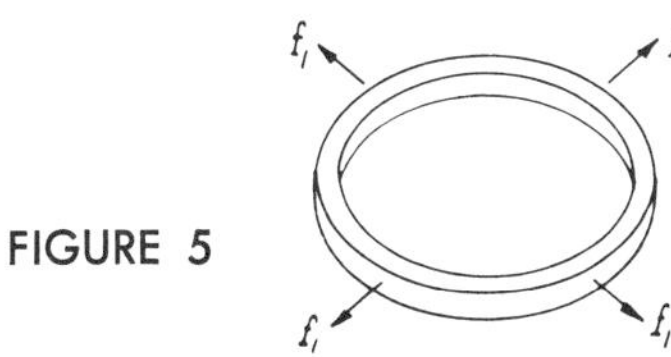

FIGURE 5

NOTE: FOR 1 INCH WIDE RING RADIAL FORCES ARE f_1; WHEN SECTION IS BUILT UP AS ILLUSTRATED IN PREVIOUS SKETCH, RADIAL FORCES ARE F.

THESE FORCES AND MOMENTS CAN BE TABULATED FOR VARIOUS SUPPORT CONFIGURATIONS:

TABLE I

	FORMULA FOR TANGENTIAL TENSILE FORCE $T = K_1 f_1$		FORMULA FOR BENDING MOMENT M_r in ring $M_r = K_2 f_1 r_c$	
	VALUES FOR K_1		VALUES FOR K_2	
NUMBER OF HANGERS	AT HANGERS	HALFWAY BETWEEN HANGERS	AT HANGERS	HALFWAY BETWEEN HANGERS
2	0	0.500	+ 0.318	− 0.182
3	0.289	0.577	+ 0.188	− 0.100
4	0.500	0.707	+ 0.136	− 0.071
6	0.866	1.000	+ 0.089	− 0.045
8	1.207	1.306	+ 0.065	− 0.033
	RESULTING TENSILE STRESS $\sigma_{c_t} = \frac{T}{A}$		RESULTING BENDING STRESS $\sigma_{c_b} = \frac{M_r}{S}$	

where:

A = area of shell ring cross-section or built-up section

S = section modulus of the same section.

Problem 1

Part A: Four hangers are used for guying a smoke stack with its axis in the vertical position, Figure 6.

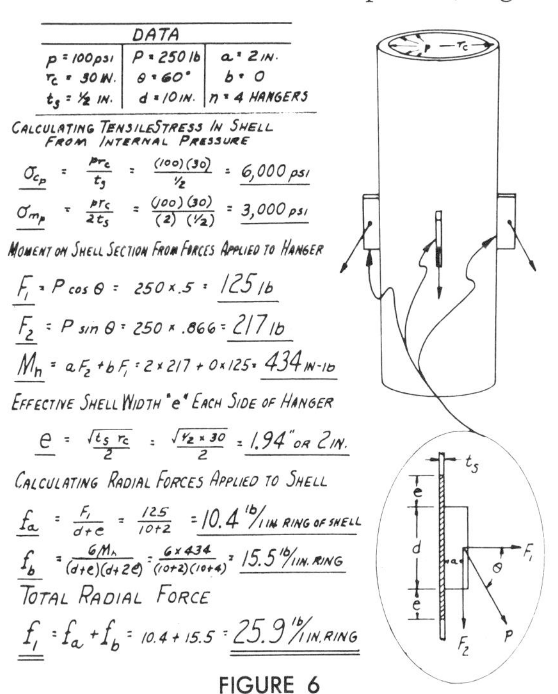

FIGURE 6

Determine the total radial force acting on the shell as a result of the force (P) applied to the hangers.

Part B: With tangential tensile force (T) and bending moment (M_r) per 1" wide ring of this shell resulting from radial forces (f_1) applied to the four hangers, calculate the tensile (σ_{ct}) and bending (σ_{cb}) stresses at the hangers.

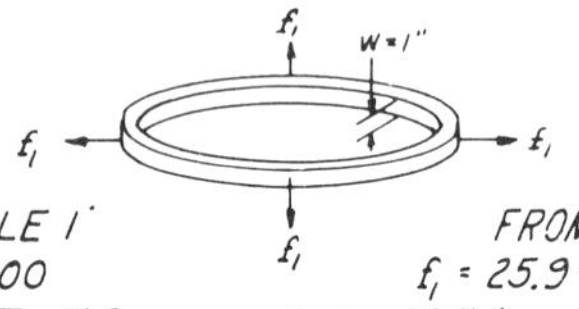

FIGURE 7

FROM TABLE I: $K_1 = 0.500$ FROM PART A: $f_1 = 25.9$ lb/in. ring

$T = K_1 f_1 = .500 \times 25.9 = 13$ lb/in. ring

A (area of 1" ring) $= w t_s = 1 \times 1/2 = \frac{1}{2}$ sq.in.

$\sigma_{cT} = \frac{T}{A} = \frac{13}{1/2} = 26$ psi (small can be neglected)

From Table I we know $M_r = K_2 f_1 r_c = .136 \times 26 \times 30 = 106$ in.-lb.

Section modulus $S = \frac{(1'')(1/2'')^2}{6} = \frac{1}{24}$ in^3

Then $\sigma_{cb} = \frac{M_r}{S} = \frac{106}{1/24} = 2,544$ psi

Conclusion: Combining these stresses in the outer fiber of the shell adjacent to the hanger shows our analysis of the shear stress (τ_{max}) to be—

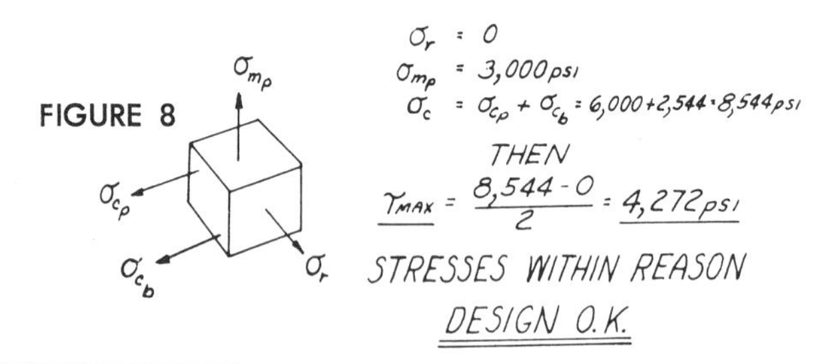
FIGURE 8

$\sigma_r = 0$

$\sigma_{mp} = 3,000$ psi

$\sigma_c = \sigma_{cp} + \sigma_{cb} = 6,000 + 2,544 = 8,544$ psi

THEN

$\tau_{max} = \frac{8,544 - 0}{2} = 4,272$ psi

STRESSES WITHIN REASON

DESIGN O.K.

Problem 2

DATA		
p = 100 psi	P = 600 lb.	a = 5 in.
r_c = 6.21 in.	θ = 90°	b = 0
t_s = .33 in.	d = 3 in.	n = 4 HANGERS

CALCULATING TENSILE STRESS IN SHELL FROM INTERNAL PRESSURE

$\sigma_{cp} = \frac{p r_c}{t_s} = \frac{100 \times 6.21}{.33} = 1,888$ psi

$\sigma_{mp} = \frac{p r_c}{2 t_s} = \frac{100 \times 6.21}{2 \times .33} = 9.42$ psi

MOMENT ON SHELL SECTION FROM FORCES APPLIED TO HANGER

$F_1 = P \cos\theta = 600 \times 0 = 0$ lb.

$F_2 = P \sin\theta = 600 \times 1 = 600$ lb.

$M_h = aF_2 + bF_1 = 5 \times 600 + 0 \times 0 = 3,000$ lb.

EFFECTIVE SHELL WIDTH "e" EACH SIDE OF HANGER

$e = \frac{\sqrt{t_s r_c}}{2} = \frac{\sqrt{.33 \times 6.21}}{2} = .72$ in.

CALCULATING RADIAL FORCES APPLIED TO SHELL

$f_a = \frac{F_1}{d+e} = \frac{0}{3+.72} = 0$ lb/in. ring of shell

$f_b = \frac{6M}{(d+e)(d+2e)} = \frac{6 \times 3000}{(3+.72)(3+1.44)} = 1,090$ lb/in. ring

TOTAL RADIAL FORCE

$f_1 = f_a + f_b = 0 + 1,090 = 1,090$ lb/in. ring of shell

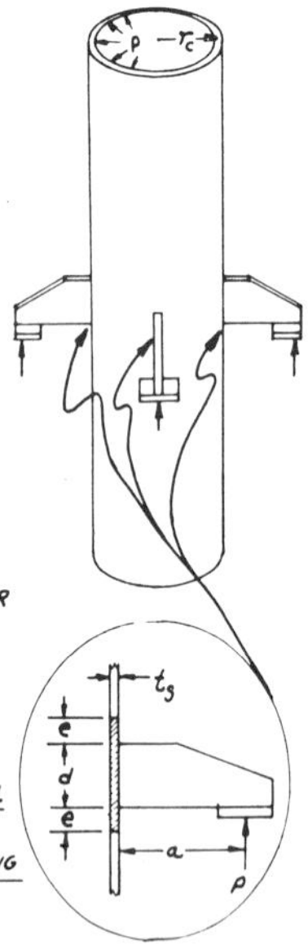

FIGURE 9

Part A: Four hangers are used to support a vertical 12" stand pipe, Figure 9. Determine the total radial force acting on the shell as a result of the force (P) applied to the hangers.

Part B: With tensile force (T) and bending moment (M_r) per 1" wide ring of this shell resulting from radial forces (f_1) applied at the four hangers, calculate the tensile (σ_{ct}) and bending (σ_{cb}) stresses at the hangers.

FROM TABLE I: $K_1 = 0.500$ FROM PART A: $f_1 = 1,090$ lb/in. ring

$T = K_1 f_1 = 0.500 \times 1,090 = 545$ lb/in. ring

A (area of 1" ring) $= W t_s = 1 \times .33 = .33$ sq. in

$\sigma_{cT} = \frac{T}{A} = \frac{545}{.33} = 1650$ psi

From Table I we know $M_r = K_2 f_1 r_c = .136 \times 1.090 \times 6.21 = 920$ in-lb

Section modulus $S = \frac{(1'')(.33)^2}{6} = .0181$ in^3

Then $\sigma_{cb} = \frac{M_r}{S} = \frac{920}{.0181} = 50,800$ psi (EXCESSIVE)

Since this bending stress in the ring of the shell is excessive, it is necessary to stiffen the shell in this region. To accomplish this, two ¼" × 2" ring stiffeners are added as illustrated, Figure 10.

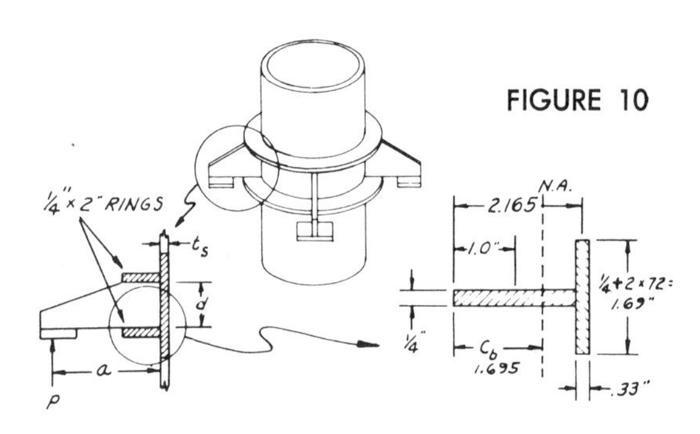

FIGURE 10

The effect of the bottom ring will be considered since it will apply radial tensile forces to the built-up ring and shell section. Using the method of finding moment of inertia by adding areas (Sect. 2.2), the properties of this section are as follows:

TABLE II

RING SECTION	A	d	M = Ad	$I_x = Md$	I_g
1.69 × .33	.557	+2.165	1.205	2.61	.005
¼ × 2.0	.500	+1.0	.500	.50	.167
TOTAL	1.057		1.705	3.282	

THEN MOMENT OF INERTIA ABOUT NEUTRAL AXIS WILL BE

$I_{NA} = I_x - \frac{M^2}{A} = 3.282 - \frac{1.705^2}{1.057} = 0.532$ in.^{4}

AND NEUTRAL AXIS WILL BE

$NA = C_b = \frac{M}{A} = \frac{1.705}{1.057} = +1.613$ in.

The radial force (F) acting on the ring section and resulting from the vertical force (P) is—

$$\underline{F} = \frac{F_2 a}{d} = \frac{600 \times 5}{3} = \underline{1000\ lb}$$

FIGURE 11

Part C: Recalculation of the tensile (σ_{ct}) and bending (σ_{cb}) stresses at the hangers yields the following results:

FROM TABLE I $K_1 = 0.500$ THE NEW F $F = 1{,}000$

$$\underline{T} = K_1 F = 0.500 \times 1{,}000 = \underline{500\ lb.}$$

$$\underline{A}\ (\text{TOTAL FROM TABLE 2}) = \underline{1.057\ sq. in.}$$

$$\underline{\sigma_{c_T}} = \frac{T}{A} = \frac{500}{1.057} = \underline{473\ psi}$$

FROM TABLE I WE KNOW $M_r = K_2 F r_c = .136 \times 1{,}000 \times 6.21 = \underline{845\ in.\text{-}lb.}$

$$\text{THEN } \underline{\sigma_{c_b}} = \frac{M_r c}{I} = \frac{845 \times 1.695}{.532} \quad \underline{2{,}690\ psi}$$

The hoop stress of $\sigma_{cp} = 1{,}888$ psi in the shell will be assumed to be reduced when considered to be acting over the entire cross-section of the built-up ring section:

$$\sigma_{c_p} = 1{,}888 \times \frac{\text{AREA SHELL IN RING SECTION}}{\text{AREA OF RING SECTION}}$$

$$\sigma_{c_p} = 1{,}888 \times \frac{1.69 \times .33}{1.057}$$

$$\underline{\sigma_{c_p}} = \underline{990\ psi}$$

Combining these stresses in the outer fiber of the lower ring, adjacent to the hanger, we find the maximum shear stress (τ_{max}) to be—

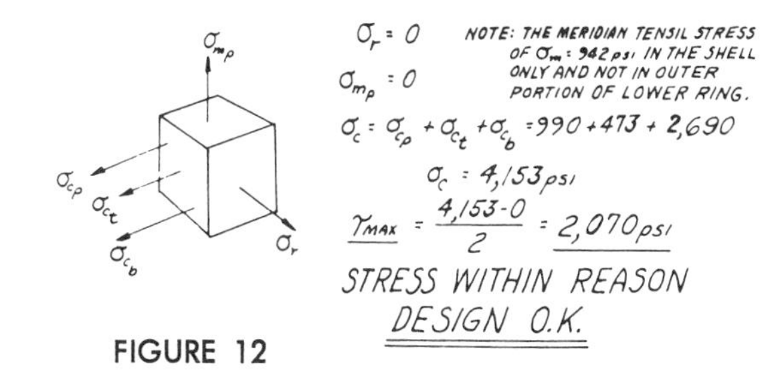
σmp
σcp
σct
σcb
σr
σr = 0
σmp = 0
NOTE: THE MERIDIAN TENSIL STRESS OF σm = 942 psi IN THE SHELL ONLY AND NOT IN OUTER PORTION OF LOWER RING.
σc = σcp + σct + σcb = 990 + 473 + 2,690
σc = 4,153 psi
τMAX = (4,153 - 0)/2 = 2,070 psi
STRESS WITHIN REASON
DESIGN O.K.

FIGURE 12

FIG. 13—Typical Hangers and Supports

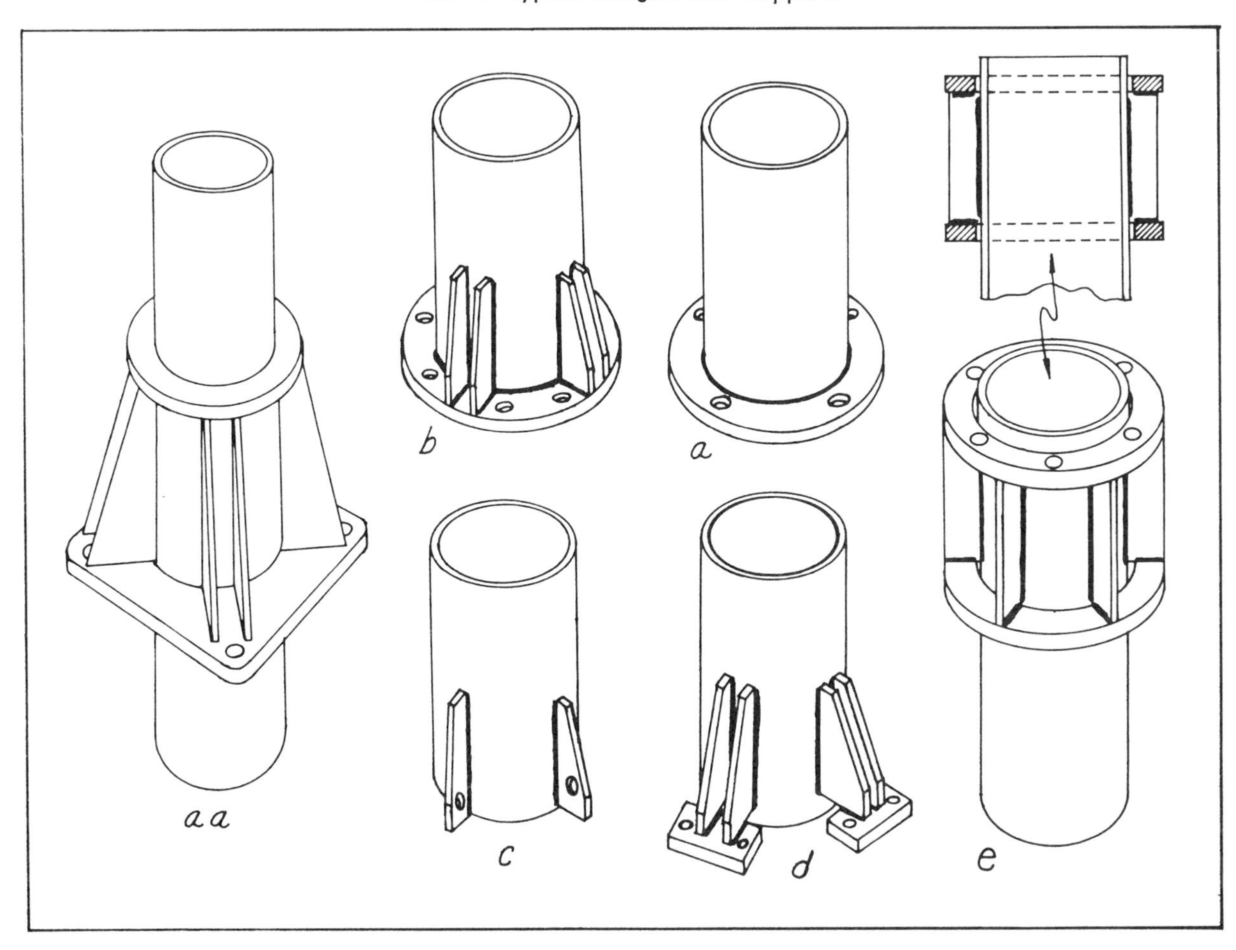
aa
b
a
c
d
e

Problem 3

Part A: What transverse or radial force (F_1) can be applied to the web of this I section through the gusset plate shown? See Figure 14. The resulting bending stresses are to be kept down to a reasonable value, such as $\sigma = 15{,}000$ psi, since the I section is already under applied load. The gusset plate intersects the web of the I section along a predetermined distance of d = 10″.

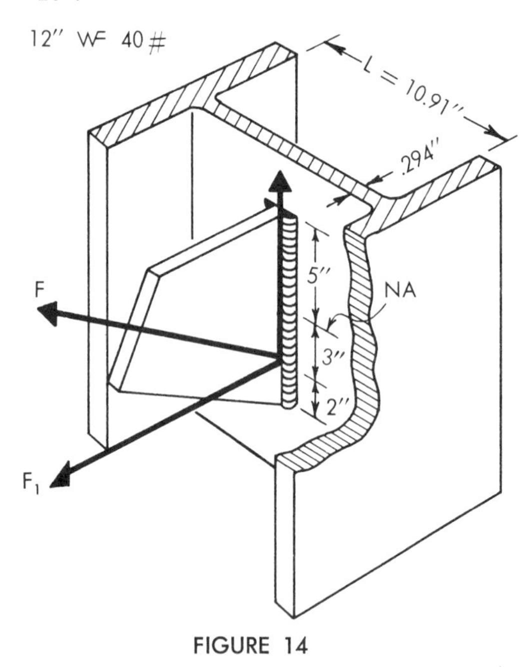

FIGURE 14

The analysis of this problem again stems from Figures 1, 2 and 3 and related text. Here, the gusset plate acts as a hanger.

Considering the web of the I section as a panel, the section flanges act as stiffeners and give the entire section a high moment of inertia about its x-x axis. However, to be conservative assume the width of web beyond the gusset that is effective in resisting the bending moment on the web to have a maximum value of 12 times the web thickness.

effective width of web

$$e = 12\ t_w$$
$$= 12\ (.294'')$$
$$= 3.53''$$

moment on web due to force on gusset

$$M = F_1 \times 3''$$

tangential forces applied to web (see Fig. 2)

$$f_a = \frac{F_1}{d + e}$$
$$= \frac{F_1}{(10) + (3.53)}$$
$$= .074\ F_1 \quad \text{lbs/in.}$$

$$f_b = \frac{6\ M}{(d + e)(d + 2e)}$$
$$= \frac{6\ (F_1 \times 3'')}{(10 + 3.53)(10 + 7.06)}$$
$$= .078\ F_1 \quad \text{lbs/in.}$$

total tangential forces applied to web

$$f = f_a + f_b$$
$$= .074\ F_1 + .078\ F_1$$
$$= .152\ F_1 \quad \text{lbs/in.}$$

Consider a 1″-wide strip of the web:

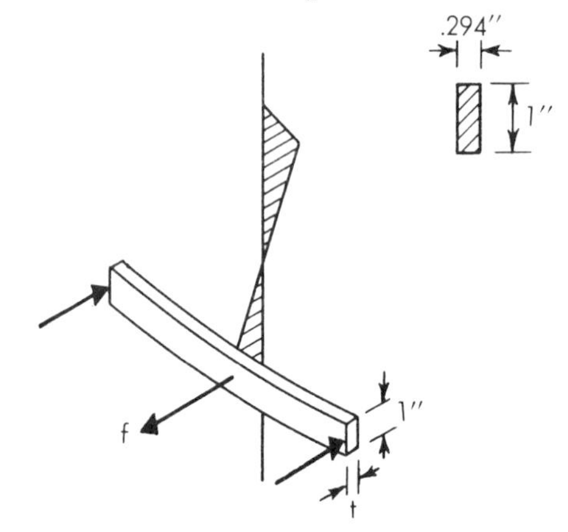

section modulus of strip

$$S = \frac{1''(.204)^2}{6}$$
$$= .0144\ \text{in.}^3$$

tangential force on strip

Since: $M_{℄} = \dfrac{f\ L}{4}$

$$f = \frac{4\ M_{℄}}{L} = \frac{4\ \sigma\ S}{L}$$
$$= \frac{4(15{,}000)(.0144)}{(10.91)}$$
$$= 79.2\ \text{lbs/1''-wide strip}$$

But:

$$f = .152\ F_1$$

$\therefore$ *allowable tangential force on web*

$$F_1 = \frac{79.2}{.152}$$
$$= 521\ \text{lbs}$$

Part B: What transverse force (F_1) can be applied if it is concentric with the center of gravity of the connection? See Figure 15. There would be no moment (M).

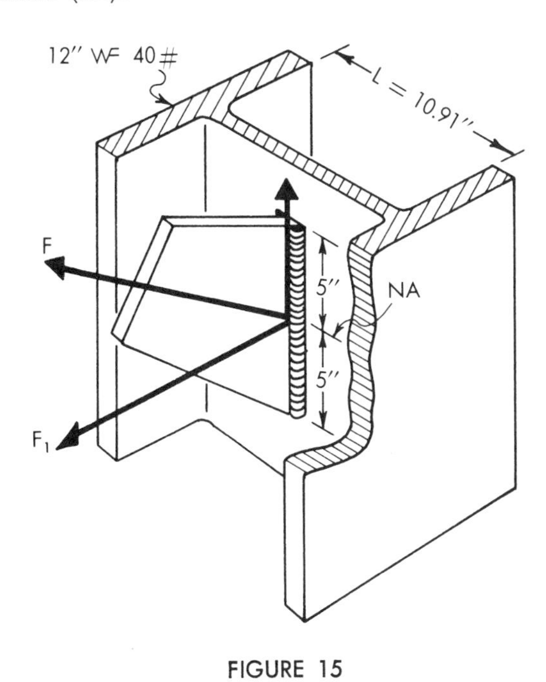

FIGURE 15

Here:

$$M = 0$$

hence:

$$f_b = 0$$

$$f_a = \frac{F_1}{d + e}$$

$$= \frac{F_1}{(10) + (3.53)}$$

$$= .074\ F_1$$

Consider a 1″-wide strip of the web. As before:

$$S = .0144 \text{ in.}^3$$

$$M_{\text{℄}} = \frac{f\ L}{4}$$

$$f = 79.2 \text{ lbs/1″-wide strip}$$

But:

$$f = .074\ F_1$$

$$\therefore\ F_1 = \frac{79.2}{.074}$$

$$= 1070 \text{ lbs}$$

General Formula

A general formula, if the transverse force (F_1) is concentric with the center of gravity of the connection, is—

$$\boxed{F_1 = \frac{4\ \sigma\ t_w^2\ (d + e)}{6\ L}}$$

Assume:
$e = 12\ t_w$

Part C: What transverse force (F_1) can be applied if a stiffener is added to the web section to increase its bending strength? See Figure 16.

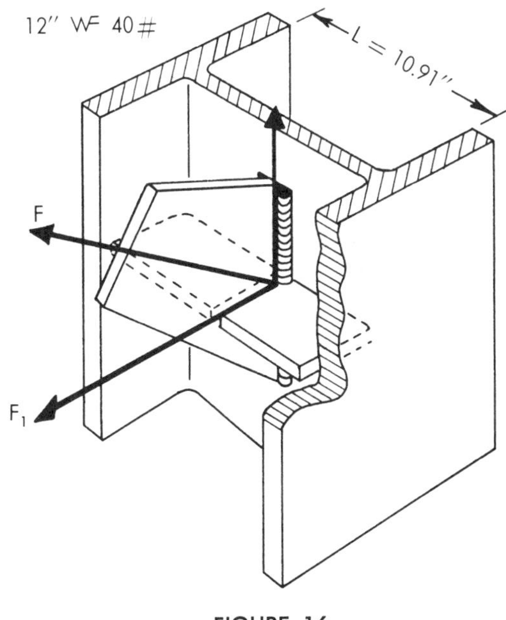

FIGURE 16

The stiffened web will now have a much greater moment of inertia in the direction of tangential force. Although the gusset plate intersects the web of the I for a distance of 10″, to be conservative only a portion of this ($b \leqq t_s + 2_e$) can be considered as resisting the moment on the web.

Following the analysis of a stiffened plate as given in Section 6.6:

Here:

$e = 3.53″$

$A_p = 2.2216 \text{ in.}^2$ (area of effective stiffened portion of web)

$I_p = .01601 \text{ in.}^4$

$A_s = 1.5 \text{ in.}^2$ (area of stiffener section)

$I_s = 1.125 \text{ in.}^4$

$d = 1.647″$ (distance, C.G. of stiffener to C.G. of web)

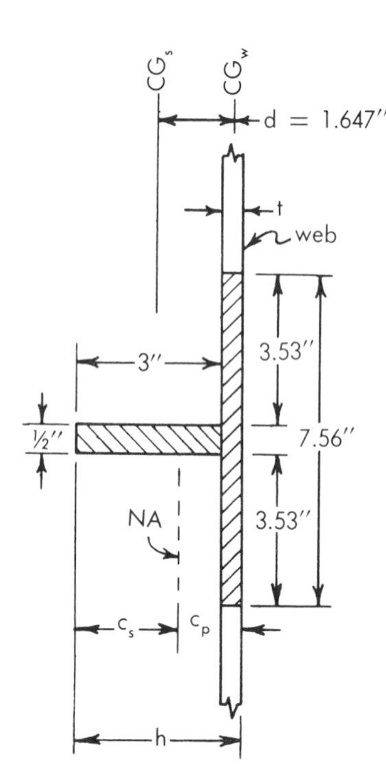

FIGURE 17

moment of inertia of entire section

$$I = I_s + I_p + \frac{A_s\ A_p\ d^2}{A_s + A_p}$$

$$= (1.25) + (.01601) + \frac{(1.5)(2.216)(1.647)^2}{(1.5) + (2.216)}$$

$$= 3.570 \text{ in.}^4$$

distance of N.A. to outer fiber

$$c_s = h - c_p$$

and since

$$c_p = \frac{A_s\ d}{A_s + A_p} + \frac{t}{2}$$

$$\therefore\ c_s = h - \frac{t}{2} - \frac{A_s\ d}{A_s + A_p}$$

$$= (3.294) - (.147) - \frac{(1.5)(1.647)}{(1.5) + (2.216)}$$

$$= 2.483''$$

section modulus of entire section resistant to force (F_1) which is maximum at extreme fiber

$$S = \frac{I}{c_s}$$

$$= \frac{(3.570)}{(2.483)}$$

$$= 1.438 \text{ in.}^3$$

and since

$$M = \frac{F_1\ L}{4}$$

$$\text{or } F_1 = \frac{4\ M}{L} = \frac{4\ \sigma\ S}{L}$$

$$= \frac{4\ (15{,}000)(1.438)}{(10.91)}$$

$$= 7920 \text{ lbs allowable tangential force on web}$$

Alternate Location of Stiffener

The web stiffener could be placed on the back side of the web (Fig. 18). However, additional brackets might have to be used to safely transfer the transverse force (F_1) back into the stiffener. Otherwise, both the gusset plate and the stiffener might be overstressed in a localized area where the two intersect (Fig. 19).

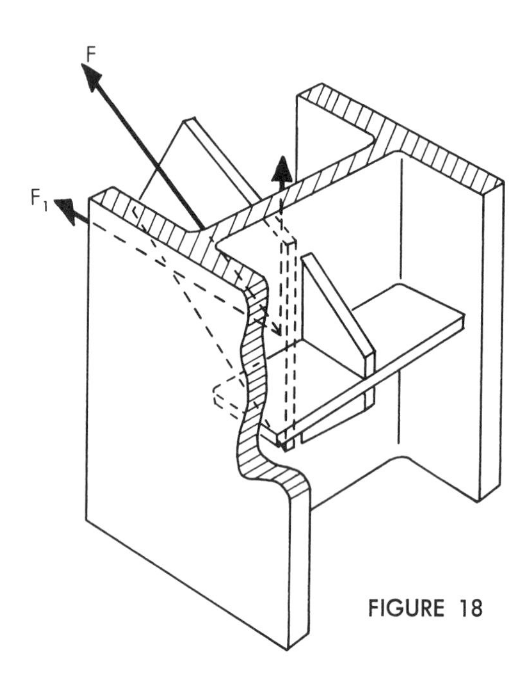

FIGURE 18

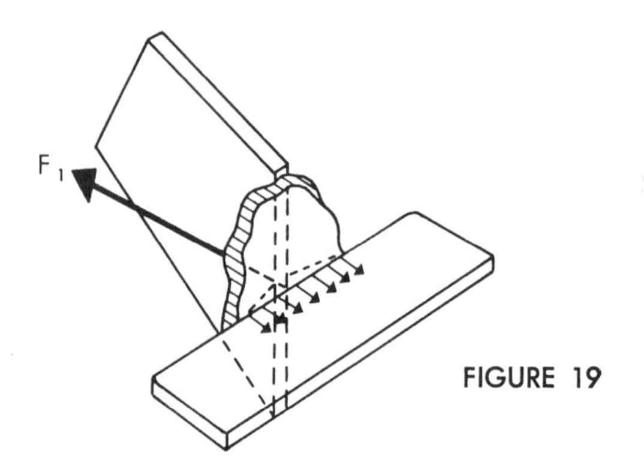

FIGURE 19

Selection of Structural Steel For Welded Construction

1. INTRODUCTION

With today's continuing progress in welding technology and the rapid expansion of welded construction, along with the development of new and better steels, the engineer or architect has a multiplicity of choices for a given project. The following information is designed to aid him in selecting the proper structural steel for his needs. . . on the basis of strength and cost.

In November of 1961, the American Institute of Steel Construction adopted a new "Specification for the Design, Fabrication and Erection of Structural Steel for Buildings". This Specification, which was revised in April 1963, includes design specifications for six American Society for Testing Materials grades of steel with specified minimum yield points ranging from 32,000 to 50,000 psi.

In addition to the steels specifically included in the AISC Specification, a number of proprietary structural steels are now being offered by various steel producers. These steels have specified minimum yield points ranging from 45,000 to 100,000 psi.

As a result, the engineer or architect today is faced with a problem he rarely encountered 10 years before: the selection of the proper structural steel that is best suited to his needs. Furthermore, since welded construction is increasingly being used for all types of structures, the designer must be assured that the welding of these steels is performed in a manner which will provide sound welds economically.

A. KNOWING THE STRUCTURAL STEELS

2. STEEL CLASSIFICATIONS

In the design of buildings, bridges, and similar structures, the engineer or architect is concerned primarily with three groups of structural steels:

A. Carbon Steels
B. High-Strength Low Allow Steels
C. Heat-Treated Constructional Alloy Steels

The first two of these categories include the six basic ASTM grades of structural steel included in the AISC Specification. The mechanical properties and chemistry limitations for these six ASTM grades are shown in Tables 1A and 1B.

3. CARBON STEELS
ASTM Grades A7, A373, and A36

The carbon steels for the structural field include ASTM Grades A7, A373, and A36. The principal strengthening agents in these steels are carbon and manganese. Specified minimum yield points range from 32,000 psi for A373 to 36,000 for A36.

ASTM A7

The first ASTM specification for steel used in building construction was proposed in 1900, and was adopted one year later as the "Standard Specification for Steel

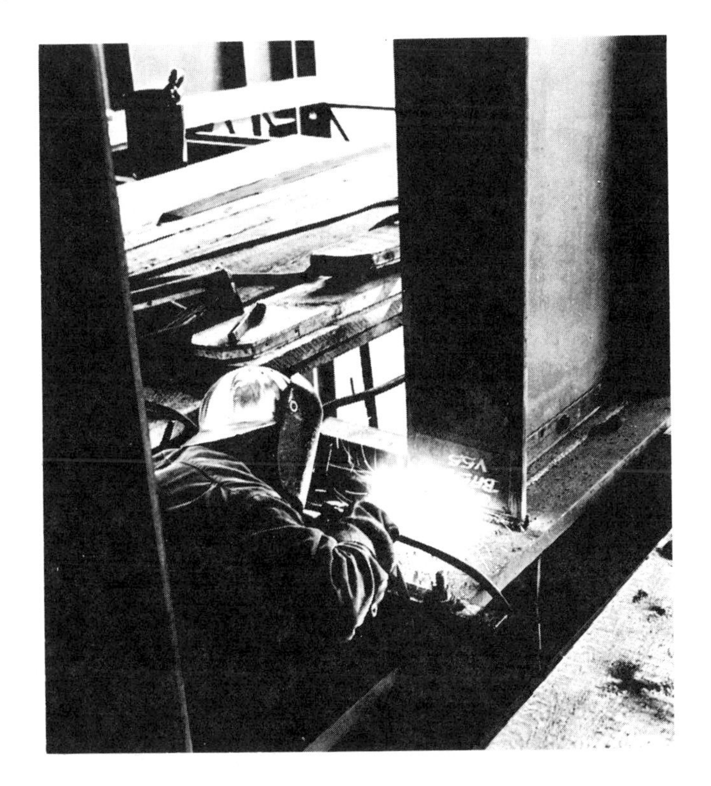

Field welding of vertical member to bottom chord of Vierendeel truss for 17-story Foundation House in Toronto, Canada. Truss is built of high-strength, low-alloy steel with 55,000 psi minimum yield strength.

for Buildings." When the ASTM adopted a numbering system for its specification in 1914, "Standard Specifications for Steel for Buildings" was designated as ASTM A9. The designation "ASTM A7" was given to "Standard Specifications for Steel for Bridges." In 1936 the ASTM combined A7 and A9 into one specification, ASTM A7, "Standard Specifications for Steel for Bridges and Buildings."

This specification was written to provide an economical as-rolled steel which would assure specific minimum strength requirements. The current version requires minimum tensile strength of 60,000 psi and minimum yield point of 33,000 psi. There are no limitations on chemistry except the sulphur and phosphorus maxima. The specification also includes a maximum tensile strength and minimum elongation requirements.

The most economical way to produce a steel of this nature is through the use of carbon and manganese in varying amounts. Carbon may be found in these steels in percentages ranging from a low of approximately 0.10 per cent to a maximum of 0.33 per cent or in some cases, even higher. Manganese is generally added to provide increased strength with less carbon to avoid the hardenability effect of high carbon in the steel. The manganese also improves hot rolling characteristics of the steel during production.

ASTM A373

With the increased use of welding after World War II, it became necessary to limit the carbon and manganese in A7 steel to screen out "high side" heats that sometimes presented welding problems.

In 1954, ASTM A373, "Structural Steel for Welding" was written. This specification limits the carbon and manganese, in addition to the maxima for phosphorus and sulphur, to insure good welds using stand-

TABLE 1A—A Comparison of Steels for Construction
ASTM Carbon Steels

ASTM Grade	Thickness		Min. Yield Point psi	Tensile Strength psi	Chemical Requirements (Ladle) Per Cent							
					C Max.	Mn	P Max.	S Max.	Si Max.	Cu Min.	V Min.	Other
A7	Shapes		33,000	60,000 to 75,000			0.04(1)	0.05		(2)		
	Plates & Bars	To 1½" incl.		60,000 to 72,000								
		Over 1½"		60,000 to 75,000								
A373	Shapes	Other than Group A(3)	32,000	58,000 to 75,000	0.28		0.04	0.05		(2)		
		Group A (3)				0.50/0.90						
	Plates	To ½" incl.			0.26							
		Over ½" to 1" incl.			0.25							
		Over 1" to 2" incl.			0.26	0.50/0.90			0.15/0.30			
		Over 2" to 4" incl.			0.27							
	Bars	To 1" incl.										
		Over 1"			0.28	0.50/0.90						
A36	Shapes		36,000	58,000 to 80,000	0.26		0.04	0.05	0.15/0.30	(2)		
	Plates	To ¾"			0.25							
		Over ¾" to 1½" incl.				0.80/1.20						
		Over 1½" to 2½" incl.			0.26							
		Over 2½" to 4" incl.			0.27	0.85/1.20						
		Over 4" to 8" incl.			0.29							
	Bars	To ¾" incl.			0.26							
		Over ¾" to 1½" incl.			0.27	0.60/0.90						
		Over 1½" to 4" incl.			0.28							

(1) Based upon basic steelmaking process.

(2) When copper steel is specified, the min. copper is 0.20%.

(3) Group A comprises the following wide flange beams (nominal sizes):
36 x 16½, 36 x 12, 36 x 15¾, 33 x 11½, 30 x 15, 30 x 10½, 27 x 14, 24 x 14, 21 x 13, 14 x 16, 14 x 14½, 12 x 12, 10 x 10

ard high speed welding procedures. However, the limits on carbon and manganese at that time necessitated a slight reduction in the strength of the steel, and the minimum yield point was placed at 32,000 psi. The specification further requires that plates over one inch thick be produced fully killed to insure a homogeneous steel in these heavier thicknesses.

With the establishment of A373 by the ASTM as a steel for welded construction, the Bureau of Public Roads designated this grade to be used for welded bridges.

ASTM A36

By 1960 the mapor producers of A7 steel had begun to realize the fruits of the modernization and expansion of their facilities after the war. Through improvements in quality control and through better heating and rolling techniques, they could produce an A7 type steel to a higher strength level while maintaining carbon and manganese within the limitations desirable for economical welding.

As a result of these improvements, ASTM A36 "Structural Steel" was proposed, and was adopted in 1960. This specification imposed controls on carbon and manganese to insure economical welding and specified a minimum yield point of 36,000 psi, a 10 per cent increase over A7. In 1962, A36 was revised to place further limitations on carbon and manganese and was subsequently accepted by the Bureau of Public Roads for welded bridges.

In essence, the new A36 specification combines all of the advantages of A373 in a steel which has a higher minimum yield point than A7, yet costs no more than A7 in shapes and costs only slightly more than A7 in plates.

4. HIGH-STRENGTH LOW ALLOY STEELS ASTM Grades A242, A440, and A441

The high-strength grades of steel, ASTM A242, A440, and A441, have minimum specified yield points varying from 42,000 psi to 50,000 psi depending on the thickness of the material.

ASTM A242

During the 1930's, a number of steel producers began offering proprietary grades of high-strength low alloy steels containing, in addition to carbon and manganese, such elements as vanadium, chromium, copper, silicon, and nickel. These steels were offered with specified minimum yield points from 42,000 psi to 50,000 psi. In addition, many of these steels provided greatly improved corrosion resistance over ASTM A7.

By 1941 it became apparent that a specification was desirable for these steels, and in that year the American Society for Testing Materials wrote A242, "High-Strength Low Alloy Structural Steel", ASTM A242 is primarily a strength specification with specified minimum yield points of:

50,000 psi for material up to and including ¾ inch thick

46,000 psi for material over ¾ inch thick to 1½ inches thick, inclusive

42,000 psi for material over 1½ inches thick to 4 inches thick, inclusive.

The chemical requirements are quite liberal. An attempt is made to insure economical welding of these steels by limiting carbon and manganese content. However, the presence of other elements such as silicon, copper, chromium, phosphorus, and nickel, which are often added to provide improved strength and corrosion resistance, may require a special welding procedure for some of these steels.

In addition, the specification requires that "these steels have enhanced corrosion resistance equal to or greater than carbon steels with copper." Carbon steels with copper—or "copper bearing" steels, as they are frequently called—have twice the atmospheric corrosion resistance of A7 steel. There are, however, certain proprietary grades of A242 having over four times the atmospheric corrosion resistance of A7 steel.

Consequently, in ordering A242 steel, the producer must be consulted to insure that the steel can be economically welded and has improved corrosion resistance if these properties are desired.

ASTM A440

In 1959 ASTM wrote Specification A440, "High-Strength Structural Steel", to provide a more economical high strength steel than A242 for structures to be riveted or bolted.

The same strength requirements are specified as for A242. The chemical requirements allow higher carbon and manganese contents than A242, so that the required strength can be reached without the addition of more expensive alloying elements. The specification limits the sulphur and phosphorus, and requires that the steel be "copper bearing" to improve its corrosion resistance over that of A7.

Because of the increased carbon and manganese contents, A440 requires special welding precautions. It is not recommended for economical welded construction.

ASTM A441

In 1960 ASTM A441, "High-Strength Low Alloy Structural Manganese Vanadium Steel", was written to provide an economically weldable high strength steel.

A441 specifies the same strength requirements as A242. The chemical requirements limit carbon and manganese to the same levels as A242, but add 0.02 per cent minimum vanadium to obtain the desired strength levels without the need for more expensive alloy additions. As in the case of A440, the Specification limits the sulphur and phosphorus, and requires that the steel be "copper bearing" to improve its corrosion resistance over that of A7.

5. HIGH-STRENGTH LOW ALLOY STEELS

Proprietary Grades

Proprietary grades of high-strength low alloy steels are available which are similar to the ASTM high-strength grades but differ in certain respects. These steels have specified minimum yield points ranging from 45,000 psi to 65,000 psi. Although these steels are widely used in manufacturing, they have only recently begun

TABLE 1B—A Comparison of Steels for Construction
ASTM High-Strength Steels

ASTM Grade	Thickness		Min. Yield Point psi	Tensile Strength psi	Chemical Requirements (Ladle) Per Cent							
					C Max.	Mn	P Max.	S Max.	Si Max.	Cu Min.	V Min.	Other
A440	Shapes	Group I (1)	50,000	70,000 min.	.28	1.10/1.60	.04(2)	.05	.30	.20		
		Group II (1)	46,000	67,000 min.								
		Group III (1)	42,000	63,000 min.								
	Plates & Bars	To 3/4" incl.	50,000	70,000 min.								
		Over 3/4" to 1 1/2" incl.	46,000	67,000 min.								
		Over 1 1/2" to 4" incl.	42,000	63,000 min.								
A441	Shapes	Group I (1)	50,000	70,000 min.	.22	1.25 max.	.04	.05	.30	.20	.02	
		Group II (1)	46,000	67,000 min.								
		Group III (1)	42,000	63,000 min.								
	Plates & Bars	To 3/4" incl.	50,000	70,000 min.								
		Over 3/4" to 1 1/2" incl.	46,000	67,000 min.								
		Over 1 1/2" to 4" incl.	42,000	63,000 min.								
		Over 4" to 8" incl.	40,000	60,000 min.								
A242	Shapes	Group I (1)	50,000	70,000 min.	.22	1.25 max.		.05				(3)
		Group II (1)	46,000	67,000 min.								
		Group III (1)	42,000	63,000 min.								
	Plates & Bars	To 3/4" incl.	50,000	70,000 min.								
		Over 3/4" to 1 1/2" incl.	46,000	67,000 min.								
		Over 1 1/2" to 4" incl.	42,000	63,000 min.								

(1) Groups I, II, III are defined as follows:

Group I	Group II		Group III	
	Wide Flange Shapes		Wide Flange Shapes	
	Nominal Size*, in.	Wt. per ft., lb.	Nominal Size*, in.	Wt. per ft., lb.
All shapes except those listed in Groups II & III	36 x 16 1/2	All weights	14 x 16	210 to 426 incl.
	33 x 15 3/4	All weights		
	14 x 16	142 to 211 incl.		
	12 x 12	120 to 190 incl.		
	Angles over 3/4" thick			

*Nominal depth and nominal width of flange

(2) Based on basic steelmaking process.

(3) The choice and use of alloying elements to produce the required strength or to improve corrosion resistance, or both, will vary with the manufacturer.

to be used in the design of buildings and bridges.

The first of this group of high-strength steels was commercially produced in 1958. At that time it was found that minor additions of columbium to plain carbon steel produced as-rolled yield points up to 60,000 psi in the thinner gauges in a weldable grade of steel. These "columbium steels", as they were called, were produced to specified minimum yield points of 45,000 psi, 50,000 psi, 55,000 psi, and 60,000 psi in limited thicknesses.

In 1962 another group of high-strength low alloy steels was introduced commercially which extended these high strengths to a broad range of thicknesses in plates and shapes. These steels resulted from the discovery that the addition of small amounts of nitrogen combined with vanadium in a carbon-manganese steel produced an increase in strength much greater than would be expected from the effects of these two elements individually, while eliminating the deleterious effects of adding nitrogen alone.

Similar high-strength steels are now available from several producers, in a wide range of shapes and plates with specified minimum yield points of 45,000, 50,000, 55,000, 60,000 and 65,000 psi. (See Table 1C). And the Bureau of Public Roads, in cooperation with the steel producers concerned, is currently (January, 1966) preparing a specification for these steels to allow their use in welded highway bridges.

The proprietary grades of high-strength steels are presently (January 1966) limited in their use in building and bridge construction because of code and specification requirements. These steels do not as yet have an ASTM designation. However, these steels offer the advantage of providing high strength at economical prices in a variety of yield points and they enable designers to obtain the strength they need without the necessity of paying for considerably more strength than required. Furthermore, the chemistry of these steels is controlled for economical welding. Consequently, engineers are taking advantage of the economies to be gained in the use of these steels and have used them on a great variety of structures including many buildings and several bridges.

6. HEAT-TREATED CONSTRUCTIONAL ALLOY STEELS

Proprietary Grades

In 1953, the first of the high-strength, heat treated, constructional alloy steels was marketed. These are low-carbon, quenched and tempered alloy steels with specified minimum yields points ranging from 90,000

TABLE 1C—A Comparison of Steels for Construction

Proprietary High-Strength Low Alloy Steels (1)

Mfr's Grade Classi-fication	Thickness		Min. Yield Point psi	Tensile Strength psi	Chemical Requirements (Ladle) Per Cent						
					N Max.	C Max.	Mn Max.	P Max.	S Max.	V Min.	Cu Min.
45	Shapes		45,000	65,000 min.		.22	1.25	.04	.05	.02	(2)
	Plates	To $1\frac{1}{2}''$ incl.									
50	Shapes	To $\frac{3}{4}''$ incl. (3)	50,000	70,000 min.		.22	1.25	.04	.05	.02	(2)
		Over $\frac{3}{4}''$ (3)			.015						
	Plates	To $\frac{3}{4}''$ incl.									
		Over $\frac{3}{4}''$ to $1\frac{1}{2}''$ incl.			.015						
55	Shapes	To $\frac{3}{8}''$ incl. (3)	55,000	70,000 min.		.22	1.25	.04	.05	.02	(2)
		Over $\frac{3}{8}''$ (3)			.015						
	Plates	To $\frac{3}{8}''$ incl.									
		Over $\frac{3}{8}''$ to $\frac{3}{4}''$ incl.			.015						
60	Shapes	To $\frac{3}{4}''$ incl. (3)	60,000	75,000 min.	.015	.22	1.25	.04	.05	.02	(2)
	Plates	To $\frac{3}{8}''$ incl.									
65	Shapes	To $\frac{3}{8}''$ incl. (3)	65,000	80,000 min.	.015	.22	1.25	.04	.05	.02	(2)
	Plates	To $\frac{3}{8}''$ incl.									

(1) Chemistry of high-strength low alloy steels varies with producers. This Table is based on Bethlehem V Steels as of January, 1964.

(2) When copper steel is specified, the minimum copper is 0.20%.

(3) For shapes, the thickness shown indicates web thickness.

to 100,000 psi, and ultimate strengths ranging from 105,000 to 135,000 psi, depending upon thickness. Originally these steels were available only in plates because of difficulties encountered during heat treating in maintaining the straightness of shapes. By 1961 many of these difficulties had been overcome, and these steels are now offered in certain structural shapes.

Because of the higher price of these steels, their use in building construction has so far been rather limited. However, they have been used to considerable advantage in several large bridges built in recent years, and in other types of structures. The major applications of these steels in construction occur when unusually high loads are encountered, particularly in tension members.

Heat-treated constructional alloy steels have the ASTM designation of A514-64. Where local codes permit the use of these steels and when loads are of sufficient magnitude, and tension loads are encountered or lateral buckling is restrained, economies can be gained through the use of the heat-treated constructional alloy steels.

B. SELECTING THE RIGHT STRUCTURAL STEEL

7. BASIS FOR SELECTION

With the adoption by the AISC of design specifications covering the use of six ASTM steels (A7, A373, A36, A440, A441, and A242), designers are now able to choose the particular steel which is best suited to the job at hand. However, before designers can take advantage of these steels, some insight must be acquired as to where each can be used to the greatest advantage.

To aid the designer in this selection, we shall compare the five ASTM steels recommended for welded construction on the basis of price, and also on what we call "yield strength per dollar".

We shall also present guides to aid in recognizing those situations wherein the use of high-strength steels has proven to be advantageous.

8. COMPARISON BASED ON PRICE

Price is, of course, a factor in the selection of a steel. Table 2A (for shapes) and Table 2B (for plates) show the comparative prices of the five ASTM structural steels and proprietary high strength, low alloy steels.

Carbon Steels

In carbon steel shapes, A36 steel is the same price as A7, has a 10 per cent higher specified minimum yield point, and can be welded with high speed, low cost procedures. The maximum carbon content is only 0.26 per cent. A373 has a higher maximum carbon content (0.28 per cent), a higher price, and a lower yield strength than A36. In shapes, therefore, A36 is by far the best bargain of the carbon steels.

In plates, the advantage of A36 is not quite as pronounced as in shapes. However, because of its higher specified minimum yield point, relative ease of welding, and the requirement that the steel be produced fully killed in thicknesses over 1½ inches thick, A36 is the best buy for construction purposes.

High-Strength Steels

In the high strength steels, for material thicknesses up to ⅜″ inclusive, A441 is the same price as A440. For thickness over ⅜″ to ¾″ inclusive, A441 is only slightly more expensive than A440. Since A440 steel is not generally recommended for economical welding, A441 is a more versatile and useful steel for construction purposes.

The A242 grades are substantially higher in cost than A441. Consequently, it would be uneconomical to use A242 unless improved corrosion resistance is desired. If this property is desired, it should be so specified; mere reference to the A242 specification does not assure improved corrosion resistance.

9. COMPARISON BASED ON YIELD STRENGTH PER DOLLAR

Price alone does not always give an accurate picture of the possible cost advantage of one steel over another, particularly where a difference in yield point is involved. Table 3A (for shapes) and Table 3B (for plates) compare the five ASTM structural steels on the basis of comparative yield point per dollar of cost, with A36 steel used as the basis for comparison.

Although such a comparison gives a more accurate picture than a comparison of price alone, a comparison of steels on the basis of the strength-to-price ratio must be made with the following qualifications:

a. Strength-price values are based on minimum yield point. Where factors other than yield point (such as limitations due to deflection, buckling or lateral stability) determine the allowable stress, strength-price values based on minimum yield point are not a valid comparison.

TABLE 2A—A Comparison of Prices of Steels for Construction
Base Price Plus Grade Extra Only, October, 1963 (1)
Structural Shapes

	Grade	Group and Thickness (2)		Min. Yield Point psi	$ Per Ton	Differential Over A36	Comparative Price (3)	Comparative Yield Strength per Dollar (4)
ASTM Carbon Steels	A36			36,000	114	0	1.00	1.00
	A7			33,000	114	0	1.00	0.92
	A373	Other Than Group A (5)		32,000	117	+3	1.03	0.86
		Group A (5)			121	+7	1.06	0.84
ASTM High-Strength Steels	A441	Group I (6)	To 3/8″ incl.	50,000	133	+19	1.17	1.19
			Over 3/8″ to 3/4″ incl.		139	+25	1.22	1.14
			Over 3/4″		147	+33	1.29	1.08
		Group II (6)	To 3/4″ incl.	46,000	139	+25	1.22	1.05
			Over 3/4″		147	+33	1.29	0.99
		Group III (6)	To 3/4″ incl.	42,000	139	+25	1.22	0.96
			Over 3/4″		147	+33	1.29	0.90
	A242 (7)	Group I (6)		50,000	164	+50	1.44	0.96
		Group II (6)		46,000				0.89
		Group III (6)		42,000				0.81
Proprietary High-Strength Low Alloy Steels (8)	45	To 3/8″ incl.		45,000	125	+11	1.10	1.14
		Over 3/8″ to 3/4″ incl.			130	+16	1.14	1.10
		Over 3/4″			137	+23	1.20	1.04
	50	To 3/8″ incl.		50,000	128	+14	1.12	1.24
		Over 3/8″ to 3/4″ incl.			134	+20	1.18	1.18
		Over 3/4″			142	+28	1.25	1.11
	55	To 3/8″ incl.		55,000	135	+21	1.18	1.29
		Over 3/8″ to 3/4″ incl.			141	+27	1.24	1.23
		Over 3/4″			151	+37	1.32	1.16
	60	To 3/8″ incl.		60,000	142	+28	1.25	1.33
		Over 3/8″ to 3/4″ incl.			150	+36	1.32	1.26
	65	To 3/8″ incl.		65,000	152	+38	1.33	1.36

(1) These figures are for comparative purposes only, and are not to be used for pricing purposes. Figures are based on Bethlehem Steel Company prices, October, 1963.

(2) Indicates web thickness.

(3) The ratio of the price of the steel to the price of A36.

(4) The yield strength of the steel per unit price of the steel (dollars per ton) compared to the yield strength per unit price for A36.

(5) See Table 1A, Note 3, for definition of Group A.

(6) See Table 1B, Note 1, for definition of Groups I, II, and III.

(7) Based upon Bethlehem's Mayari R A242 steel, **which has an atmospheric corrosion resistance of at least 4 to 6 times that of plain carbon steel.**

(8) Based on Bethlehem V Steels.

TABLE 2B—A Comparison of Prices of Steels for Construction
Base Price Plus Grade Extra Only, October, 1963 (1)
Structural Plates

Grade		Thickness	Min. Yield Point psi	$ Per Ton	Differential Over A36	Comparative Price (2)	Comparative Yield Strength Per Dollar (3)
ASTM Carbon Steels	A36	To ¾″ incl.	36,000	114	0	1.00	1.00
		Over ¾″ to 1½″ incl.		120			
		Over 1½″ to 8″ incl.		135			
	A7	To ¾″ incl.	33,000	113	−1	0.99	0.93
		Over ¾″ to 1½″ incl.			−7	0.94	0.98
		Over 1½″ to 4″ incl.		128		0.95	0.96
	A373	To ½″ incl.	32,000	114	0	1.00	0.89
		Over ½″ to ¾″ incl.		118	+4	1.04	0.85
		Over ¾″ to 1″ incl.			−2	0.98	0.91
		Over 1″ to 1½″ incl.		131	+11	1.09	0.82
		Over 1½″ to 4″ incl.		133	−2	0.99	0.90
ASTM High-Strength Steels	A441	To ⅜″ incl.	50,000	130	+16	1.14	1.22
		Over ⅜″ to ¾″ incl.		136	+22	1.19	1.17
		Over ¾″ to 1½″ incl.	46,000	144	+24	1.20	1.06
		Over 1½″ to 4″ incl.	42,000	151	+16	1.12	1.04
		Over 4″ to 8″ incl.	40,000	164	+29	1.21	0.91
	A242 (4)	To ¾″ incl.	50,000	161	+47	1.41	0.99
		Over ¾″ to 1½″ incl.	46,000		+41	1.34	0.95
		Over 1½″ to 4″ incl.	42,000	163	+28	1.21	0.96
Proprietary High-Strength Low Alloy Steels (5)	45	To ⅜″ incl.	45,000	122	+8	1.07	1.17
		Over ⅜″ to ¾″ incl.		127	+13	1.12	1.12
		Over ¾″ to 1½″ incl.		134	+14	1.12	1.12
	50	To ⅜″ incl.	50,000	125	+11	1.10	1.26
		Over ⅜″ to ¾″ incl.		131	+17	1.16	1.20
		Over ¾″ to 1½″ incl.		139	+19	1.16	1.20
	55	To ⅜″ incl.	55,000	132	+18	1.16	1.32
		Over ⅜″ to ¾″ incl.		138	+24	1.21	1.26
	60	To ⅜″ incl.	60,000	139	+25	1.22	1.37
	65	To ⅜″ incl.	65,000	149	+35	1.31	1.38

(1) These figures are for comparative purposes only, and are not to be used for pricing purposes. Figures are based on Bethlehem Steel Company prices, October, 1963.
(2) The ratio of the price of the steel to the price of A36.
(3) The yield strength of the steel per unit price of the steel (dollars per ton) compared to the yield strength per unit price for A36 steel in the same thickness.
(4) Based upon Bethlehem's Mayari R A242 steel, which has an atmospheric corrosion resistance of at least 4 to 6 times that of plain carbon steel.
(5) Based on Bethlehem V Steels.

b. Strength-price values are based on equivalent thicknesses of material. Use of a high-strength steel will usually result in a thinner section than that required with A36. Since the thinner material may be sold at a lower unit price, actual savings may therefore be greater than indicated by comparative strength-price ratios. It is also true that using higher strength, thinner sections will permit a reduction in weld size which offsets increased cost of preheat or other special welding procedures.

c. Strength-price values are based on material costs and do not include freight, fabrication, or erection.

Carbon Steels

Based on price alone, A36 was found to be the best buy in shapes and a good buy in plates. If we make our comparison on the basis of strength-to-price ratio, as in Table 3, A36 is found to be a better value than either A7 or A373 in both shapes and plates.

High-Strength Steels

Where full advantage can be taken of higher yield point levels, A441 is a better buy than A36, except for Group II* shapes over ¾ inch thick (web thickness) and for Group III* shapes.

The A242 steels are not recommended for economical design unless high corrosion resistance is a major requirement.

* Refer to note 1 on Table 1B.

TABLE 3A—Comparative Strength-to-Price Ratios
Comparative Yield Strength Per Dollar*
Structural Shapes

Grade		Group and Thickness (1)		.80 .90 1.00 1.10 1.20 1.30
ASTM Carbon Steels	A36			
	A7			
	A373	Other than Group A (2)		
		Group A (2)		
ASTM High-Strength Steels	A441	Group I (3)	To 3/8″ incl.	
			Over 3/8″ to 3/4″ incl.	
			Over 3/4″	
		Group II (3)	To 3/4″ incl.	
			Over 3/4″	
		Group III (3)	To 3/4″ incl.	
			Over 3/4″	
	A242	Group I (3)		
		Group II (3)		
		Group III (3)		
Proprietary High-Strength Low Alloy Steels (4)	V45	To 3/8″ incl.		
		Over 3/8″ to 3/4″ incl.		
		Over 3/4″		
	V50	To 3/8″ incl.		
		Over 3/8″ to 3/4″ incl.		
		Over 3/4″		
	V55	To 3/8″ incl.		
		Over 3/8″ to 3/4″ incl.		
		Over 3/4″		
	V60	To 3/8″ incl.		
		Over 3/8″ to 3/4″ incl.		
	V65	To 3/8″ incl.		

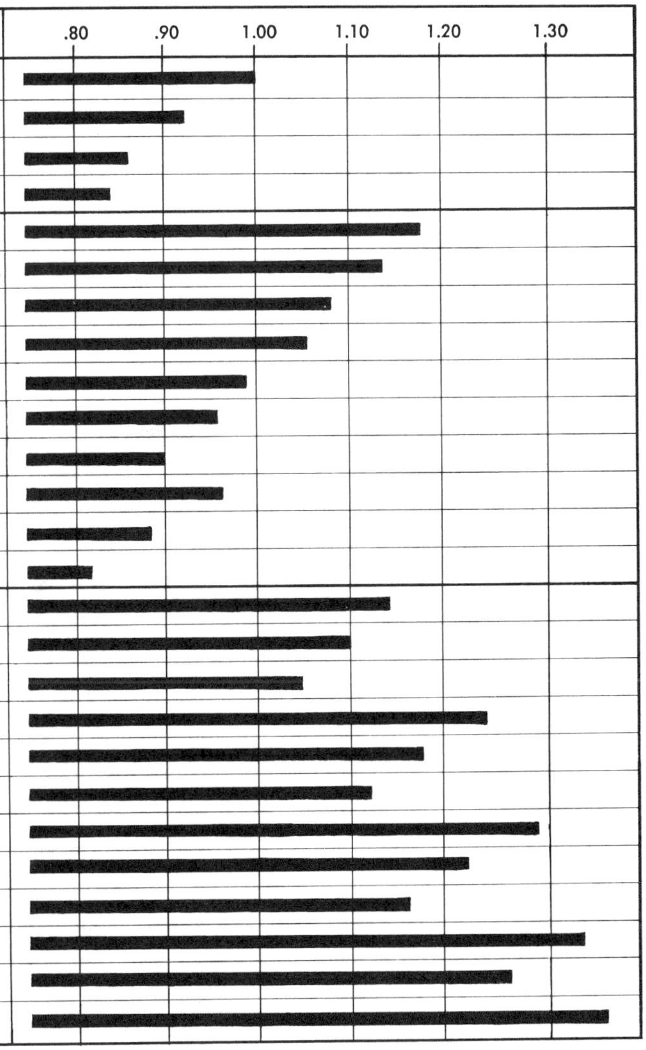

*The yield strength of the steel per unit price of the steel (dollars per ton) compared to the yield strength per unit price for A36.

(1) Indicates web thickness.

(2) See Table 1A, Note 3, for definition of Group A.

(3) See Table 1B, Note 1, for definition of Groups I, II, and III.

(4) Based on Bethlehem V Steels.

10. WHEN TO CONSIDER THE HIGH-STRENGTH STEELS

A36 is recommended as the most economical of the carbon steels. When advantage can be taken of the higher yield point levels of A441, the use of this steel rather than A36 can result in savings.

Tension Members

High-strength steels can usually be used to advantage in tension members, where a significant increase in design stress can result from increased yield strength. However, where connections are made with bolts or rivets rather than by welding, some advantage of the high-strength steels is lost because of the reduced net area at the holes.

Beams

The use of high-strength steels in beam design is usually limited to applications where deflections are either unimportant or can be minimized by special design procedures. The modulus of elasticity is the same for all these steels. Consequently, if we compare two beams of the same section and length, one an A36 beam loaded to a design stress of 24,000 psi and one an A441 beam loaded to a design stress of 33,000 psi, the A441 beam will deflect 38 per cent more than the A36 beam.

Columns and Compression Members

In columns and compression members, the slenderness ratio (L/r) will usually limit the allowable design

TABLE 3B—Comparative Strength-to-Price Ratios
Comparative Yield Strength Per Dollar (1)
Structural Plates

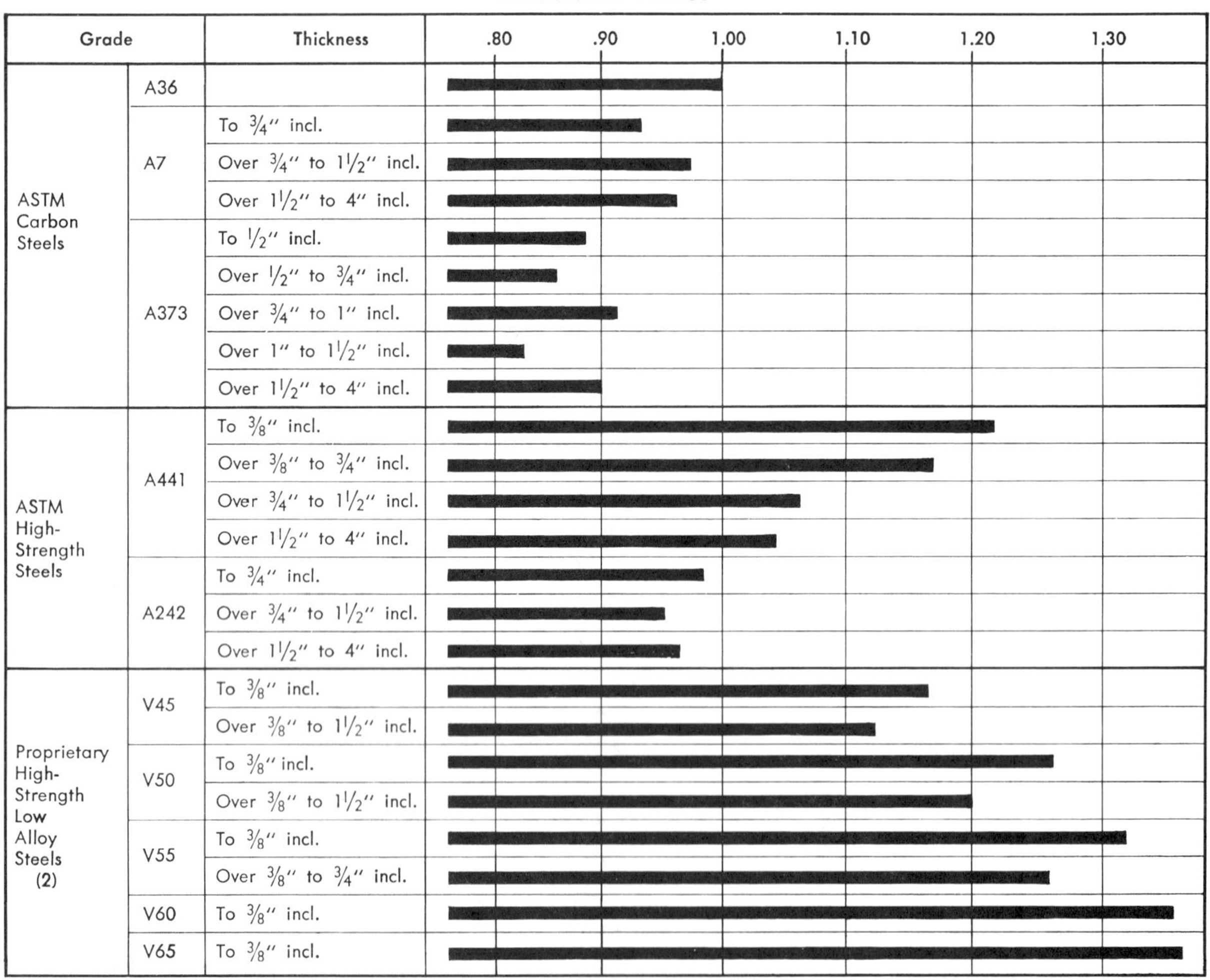

(1) The yield strength of the steel per unit price of the steel (dollars per ton) compared to the yield strength per unit price for A36 steel in the same thickness.

(2) Based on Bethlehem V Steels.

stress and often preclude advantageous use of high-strength steels.

For instance, if we consider an unbraced column length of 11 feet and compare the required column size of A36 and A441 for loads of 100^k, 400^k, and 1600^k we find savings as given in Table A.

TABLE A

Load (Kips)	Comparative Factors	ASTM	
		A36	A441
100^k	Size	8WF24	8WF24
	wt. Savings/ft.		0
	Cost Savings/ft. *		—$.22
400^k	Size	12WF79	12WF58
	wt. Savings/ft.		21
	Cost Savings/ft. *		+$.74
1600^k	Size	14WF287	12WF246
	wt. Savings/ft.		41
	Cost Savings/ft. *		—$1.25

* Saving of A441 over A36; (+) indicates a saving (based on prices in effect Oct., 1963). These values include base price and grade extra (shown in Table 2B) plus section and length extras.

Although there is a saving in weight using A441, the cost saving is variable and often nil. Because of the heavy section required for the 1600^k load, A441 has a minimum specified yield point of only 42,000 psi.

Weight Savings

The judicious use of high-strength steels will almost always result in an overall reduction in weight of the structure. Whenever this weight reduction can be translated into savings in the cost of foundations, supporting structures, or in handling, transportation, or erection costs, then the high-strength steels can and should be used to advantage.

Savings In Fabrication Costs

Whenever the need for built-up sections can be avoided through the use of high-strength steels, savings in fabricating costs can be realized. A common example is in the lower tier columns of multi-story buildings.

Proprietary Grades

Whenever high-strength steels can be used advantageously, serious consideration should be given to one or more of the proprietary steels, if these steels are acceptable under the local codes. Proprietary steels often provide increased economies over A441. For instance, if we compare the same column loads and column length (11 feet) as in Table A, we find savings for proprietary steels as given in Table B.

TABLE B

Load (Kips)	Comparative Factors	ASTM A36	Proprietary Steels* Guaranteed Min. Y.P.Ksi	
			50	55
100^k	Size	8WF24	8WF24	8WF24
	wt. Savings/ft.		0	0
	Cost Savings/ft.**		—$.16	—$.25
400^k	Size	12WF79	12WF58	12WF53
	wt. Savings/ft.		21	26
	Cost Savings/ft.**		+$.88	+$1.04
1600^k	Size	14WF287	14WF211	14WF193
	wt. Savings/ft.		86	94
	Cost Savings/ft.**		+$1.80	+$2.31

* Based on Bethlehem Steel Company's V50 and V55 Steels

**Saving of grade 50 or 55 over A36; (+) indicates a saving (based on prices in effect Oct., 1963. These values include base price and grade extra (shown in Table 2B) plus section and length extras.

Although the minimum specified yield point of A441 decreases as thickness increases, yield points for the above proprietary steels are 50,000 and 55,000 psi respectively for all available thicknesses. As can be seen in Tables A and B, the effect on cost of maintaining yield point throughout a broad range of thicknesses is quite evident.

C. THE MILL TEST REPORT: A GUIDE TO WELDABILITY

11. SPECIFICATION VS ACTUAL CHEMISTRY

The preceding material on the development of the construction steels and the specifications and merits of these steels should be helpful to the engineer or architect who is searching for the most economical design.

However, to the fabricator, who must determine the procedure to use for forming, burning or welding the steel, the paramount question is: "What is the chemical composition and what are the mechanical properties of the steel that I must work with?"

Many fabricators and engineers tend to rely on the specification of the steel for the answer to this question. But such practice has in many cases led to a welding procedure based on the worst combination of chemistry (as far as welding is concerned) that the specification will allow. This practice can result in a more costly welding operation than is necessary.

A more realistic answer to the establishment of welding procedure lies in the steel's "pedigree"—the mill test report. The mill test report is a certification of the chemical composition and physical properties of the steel in a specific shipment.

To cite an example, an investigation of the mill test reports from a certain mill disclosed that the steel supplied by that mill had a carbon and manganese content considerably less than the maximum allowed under the specification. In addition, 85 per cent of the steel purchased from this mill was less than ¾ inch thick. The average chemistry for plates up to ¾ inch thick rolled on this mill compares with the allowable specification chemistry as follows:

Grade		Carbon	Manganese
A36	Specification Mill Average	0.25% max .20	— .50%
A441	Specification Mill Average	.22% max. .18	1.25% 1.10

Although the above average figures are for a particular mill, they indicate that the carbon and manganese content is usually considerably less than the maximum of the specification and will be in a range that will permit significant variations in welding procedures.

12. MILL PROCEDURE

When a mill receives an order for a particular grade of steel, production of that item is scheduled to be rolled from a heat of steel meeting the chemical requirements of the grade ordered and which it is expected will provide the mechanical properties required in the finished product.

Each ingot poured from any heat of steel is identified with the heat number, and this identity is maintained throughout all subsequent rolling mill operations.

The rolling of steel has a definite effect on the mechanical properties of the finished product. Confirming mechanical tests (tensile strength, yield point, and per cent elongation) are, therefore, made after the steel has been rolled to final section and cooled.

The mechanical properties of the section and the chemical composition of the heat are recorded on the mill test report.

The mill test report is filed by the mill for its own record and certified copies are forwarded to the customer, when requested, for his use. The report's disclosure of the particular mill order's chemistry is a valuable guide to development of the most economical and satisfactory welding procedure.

The chemistry of the steel in a structural steel fabricator's shop can thus be readily determined from the mill test report. Furthermore, where necessary the chemistry of the steel can be anticipated to a reasonable degree far in advance of shipment by referring to previous mill test reports on similar products from the same mill.

For greater economy of welding, the structural steel fabricator or erector can and should base his welding procedure on the actual chemistry of the steel he is welding, rather than upon the worst possible combination of chemistry allowed under the specification.

CHECKLIST FOR USE OF HIGH-STRENGTH STEEL

In structural steel design, A36 is generally the most versatile and economical of the construction steels. However, there are occasions where the judicious use of high-strength steels can result in overall cost and weight savings, such as:

Tension Members

The high-strength steels can usually be used to advantage in tension members except when the members are relatively small in section or when holes (i.e. for bolts or rivets) substantially reduce the net section of the member.

Beams

a. When steel dead load is a major portion of design load.

b. When deflection limitations are not a major factor in determining section.

c. When deflections can be reduced through design features such as continuity or composite design.

d. When weight is important.

e. When fabricating costs can be reduced.

f. When architectural considerations limit the beam dimensions.

Columns And Compression Members

a. When steel dead load is a major portion of design load.

b. When the slenderness ratio (L/r) of the member is small.

c. When weight is important.

d. When fabricating costs can be reduced.

e. When architectural considerations limit the column dimensions.

Weldability and Welding Procedure

1. INTRODUCTION

Ordinarily, a correctly designed joint and properly made weld do not require special procedures to prevent cracks during welding or in service. The need for special procedures increases, however, with heavy plate structural members and is growing with the expanding use of steels having greater amounts of alloying elements in their chemistry.

This section first provides some insight into the factors that promote weld cracking and makes suggestions for welding procedures to correct or prevent a cracking problem. This section then will present a comprehensive discussion of when to use preheating to eliminate or prevent cracking. It will also present a new approach to establishing the preheat and interpass temperature, based on the heat input of the welding procedure, the critical cooling rate (determined by the chemistry of the steel), and the joint geometry, particularly the plate thickness.

2. WELDABILITY

Most steels can be commercially arc welded, with good results—sound, strong welded joints. The "weldability" of a metal refers to the relative ease of producing a satisfactory, crack-free, sound joint. A steel is said to be ideally weldable if the required weld joint can be made without difficulty or excessive cost.

Some steels are more suited to high-speed welding than others. Analysis of the electrode core wire is accurately controlled to produce good welds, but since the plate metal becomes part of the weld, control of the plate analysis is also important. When higher currents are used to get higher welding speeds, more of the plate metal mixes with the weld. If possible, select an easily welded steel that doesn't require expensive electrodes or complicated welding procedures. Table 1 gives a range of carbon steel analyses for maximum welding speed.

The commonly used mild steels fall within the

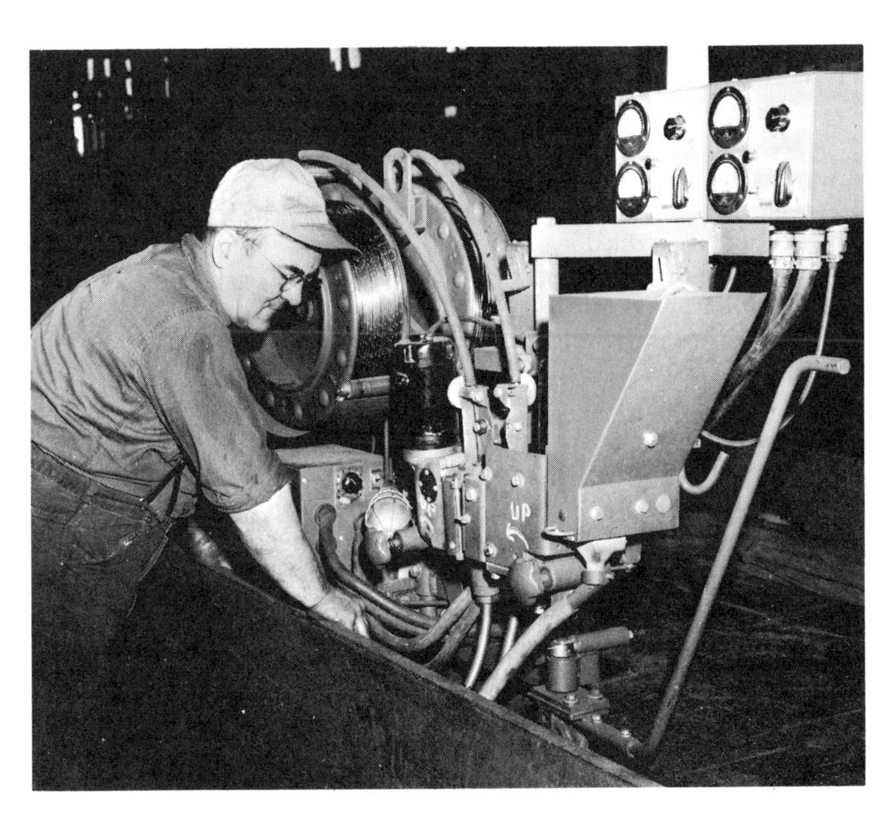

Tandem-arc and other modern automatic welding equipment have revolutionized the shop fabrication of large bridge girders, built-up columns, and other special structural members. The welding of thick plates, or of higher-strength alloys, may require preheating or other measures not needed with the more common mild steels.

The Shielded Arc Welding Process

In order to evaluate the weldability of steels, a limited knowledge of the basic arc welding process is advisable.

Welding consists of joining two pieces of metal by establishing a metallurgical bond between them. Many different welding processes may be used to produce bonding through the application of pressure and/or through fusion. Arc welding is a fusion process. The bond between the metals is produced by reducing to a molten state the surfaces to be joined and then allowing the metal to solidify. When the molten metal solidifies, union is completed.

In the arc welding process, the intense heat required to reduce the metal to a liquid state is produced by an electric arc. The arc is formed between the work to be welded and a metal wire or rod called the electrode. The arc, which produces a

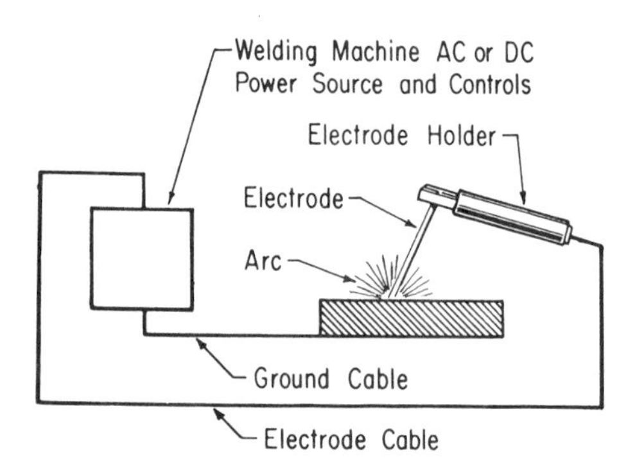

temperature of about 6500°F at the tip of the electrode, is formed by bringing the electrode close to the metal to be joined. The tremendous heat at the tip of the electrode melts filler metal and base metal, thus liquifying them in a common pool called a crater.* As the areas solidify, the metals are joined into one solid homogeneous piece. By moving the electrode along the seam or joint to be welded, the surfaces to be joined are welded together along their entire length.

The electric arc is the most widely used source of energy for the intense heat required for fusion welding. The arc is an electrical discharge or spark sustained in a gap in the electrical circuit. The resistance of the air or gas in the gap to the passage of the current, transforms the electrical energy into heat at extremely high temperatures. Electrical power consists of amperes and voltage. The amount of energy available is the product of the amperes and the voltage flowing through the circuit and is measured in watts and kilowatts. The energy used is affected by such variables as the constituents in electrode coatings, the type of current (AC or DC), the direction of current flow, and many others.

In all modern arc welding processes, the arc is shielded to control the complex arc phenomenon and to improve the physical properties of the weld deposit. This shielding is accomplished through various techniques: a chemical coating on the electrode wire, inert gases, granular flux compounds, and metallic salts placed in the core of the electrode. Arc shielding varies with the type of arc welding process used. In all cases, however, the shielding is intended: 1) to protect the molten metal from the air, either with gas, vapor or slag; 2) to add alloying and fluxing ingredients; and 3) to control the melting of the rod for more effective use of the arc energy.

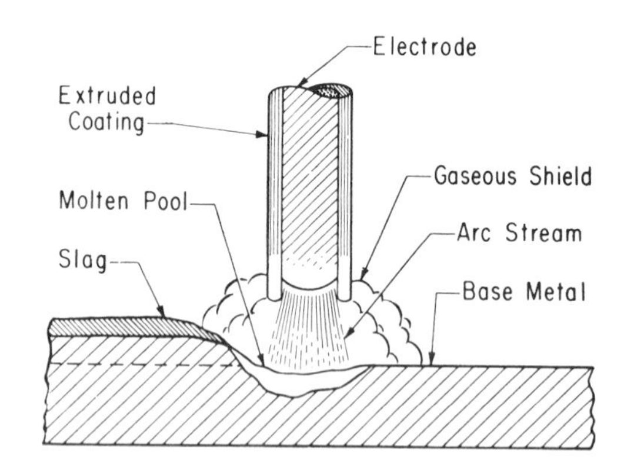

The arc welding process requires a continuous supply of electric current sufficient in amperage and voltage to maintain an arc. This current may be either alternating (AC) or direct (DC), but it must be provided through a source which can be controlled to satisfy the variables of the welding process: amperage and voltage.

* For some applications, filler metal is deposited by a consumable welding electrode; for others, a "nonconsumable" electrode supplies the heat and a separate welding rod the filler metal.

preferred analysis listed. Sulphur content of these steels is usually below 0.035%, although the specification limits permit as much as 0.050%.

Continued progress is being made in metallurgical control of steel, as well as in the development of welding processes, electrodes and fluxes. This tends to broaden the range of "weldability" with respect to steel analysis.

The six basic ASTM-specification construction steels usually do not require special precautions or special procedures.

However, when welding the thicker plates in even these steels the increased rigidity and restraint and the drastic quench effect makes the use of the proper procedure vitally important. In addition, thick plates usually have higher carbon content.

We also have an increase in the use of higher strength low alloy steels and the heat treated very high yield strength steels. These steels have some elements in their chemistry that exceed the ideal analysis, Table 1, for high speed welding.

Frequently pre-planned and proven welding procedures are required to assure the production of crack-free welds when joining thicker plates or the alloy steels. These procedures usually call for one or all of the following:

1. Proper bead shape and joint configuration.
2. Minimized penetration to prevent dilution of the weld metal with the alloy elements in the plate.
3. Preheating, controlled interpass temperature and sometimes even controlled heat input from the welding procedure to retard the cooling rate and reduce shrinkage stresses.

3. BASE PROCEDURE ON ACTUAL ANALYSIS

Published standard production welding procedures generally apply to normal welding conditions and the more common, "preferred analysis" mild steels.

When a steel's specification analysis falls outside the preferred analysis, the user often adopts a special welding procedure based on the *extremes* of the material's chemical content "allowed" by the steel's specification. However, since the chemistry of a specific heat of steel may run far below the top limit of the "allowables", a special procedure may not be required, or may require only a slight change from standard procedures and thereby minimize any increase in welding cost.

TABLE 1—Preferred Analysis Of Carbon Steel for Good Weldability

Element		Normal Range, %	Steel Exceeding Any One of the Following Percentages Will Probably Require Extra Care
Carbon	C	.06 - .25	.35
Manganese	Mn	.35 - .80	1.40
Silicon	Si	.10 max	.30
Sulphur	S	.035 max	.050
Phosphorus	P	.030 max	.040

For optimum economy and quality, under either favorable or adverse conditions, the welding procedure for joining any type of steel should be based on the steel's *actual* chemistry rather than the *maximum* alloy content allowed by the specification. This is because a mill's average production normally runs considerably under the maximum limits set by the specification.

Usually a Mill Test Report is available which gives the *specific* analysis of any given heat of steel. Once this information is obtained, a welding procedure can be set that will assure the production of crack-free welds at the lowest possible cost.

4. WELD QUALITY

The main objective of any welding procedure is to join the pieces as required with the most efficient weld possible and at the least possible cost. "As required" means the weld's size and quality must be consistent with the service requirements. Excessive precautions to obtain unnecessary quality, beyond that needed to meet service requirements, serve no practical purpose and can be expensive.

Because it greatly increases cost without any benefit, inspection should not request the correction of slight undercut or minor radiographic defects such as limited scattered porosity and slag inclusions, unless thorough study shows such defects cannot be tolerated because of specific service requirements.

Why Welds Crack and How to Prevent It

5. WELD CRACKS

A crack in a weld, however, is never minor and cannot be condoned. Good design and proper welding procedure will prevent these cracking problems:

1. weld cracks occurring during welding,
2. cracking in the heat affected zone of the base metal,
3. welded joints failing in service.

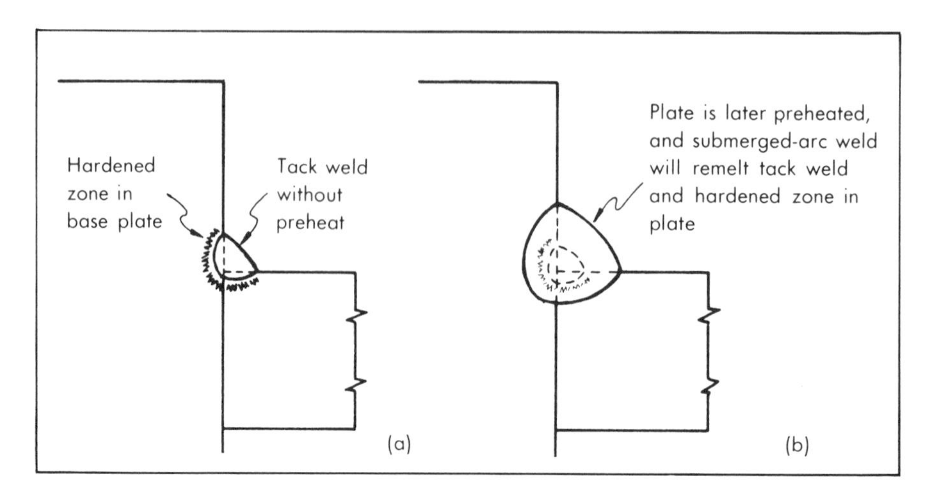

FIGURE 1

Factors that Affect Weld Cracking During Welding

1. *Joint Restraint* that causes high stresses in the weld.

2. *Bead Shape* of the deposited weld. As the hot weld cools, it tends to shrink. A convex bead has sufficient material in the throat to satisfy the demands of the biaxial pull. However, a concave bead may result in high tensile stresses across the weld surface from toe to toe. These stresses frequently are high enough to rupture the surface of the weld causing a longitudinal crack.

An excessively penetrated weld with its depth greater than its width under conditions of high restraint may cause internal cracks.

Both of these types of cracking are greatly aggravated by high sulphur or phosphorus content in the base plate.

3. *Carbon and Alloy Content* of the base metal. The higher the carbon and alloy content of the base metal, the greater the possible reduction in ductility of the weld metal through admixture. This contributes appreciably to weld cracking.

4. *Hydrogen Pickup* in the weld deposit from the electrode coating, moisture in the joint, and contaminants on the surface of the base metal.

5. *Rapid Cooling Rate* which increases the effect of items 3 and 4.

Factors that Affect Cracking in the Heat-Affected Zone

1. *High carbon or alloy content* which increases hardenability and loss of ductility in the heat-affected zone. (Underbead cracking does not occur in non-hardenable steel.)

2. *Hydrogen embrittlement* of the fusion zone through migration of hydrogen liberated from the weld metal.

3. *Rate of cooling* which controls items 1 and 2.

Factors that Affect Welded Joints Failing in Service

Welds do not usually "crack" in service but may "break" because the weld was of insufficient size to fulfill service requirements. Two other factors would be:

1. Notch toughness,* which would affect the breaking of welds or plate when subjected to high impact loading at extremely low temperatures.

2. Fatigue cracking* due to a notch effect from poor joint geometry. This occurs under service conditions of unusually severe stress reversals.

Items to Control

1. *Bead Shape.* Deposit beads having proper bead surface (i.e. slightly convex) and also having the proper width-to-depth ratio. This is most critical in the case of single pass welds or the root pass of a multiple pass weld.

2. *Joint Restraint.* Design weldments and structure to keep restraint problems to a minimum.

3. *Carbon and Alloy Content.* Select the correct grade and quality of steel for a given application, through familiarity with the mill analysis and the cost of welding. This will ensure balancing weld cost and steel price using that steel which will develop the lowest possible overall cost. Further, this approach will usually avoid use of inferior welding quality steels that have excessively high percentages of those elements that always adversely affect weld quality—sulphur and phosphorus.

Avoid excessive admixture. This can be accomplished through procedure changes which reduce penetration (different electrodes, lower currents, changing

---

* Neither notch toughness nor fatigue cracking are discussed here. See Section 2.1, "Properties of Materials," Section 2.8, "Designing for Impact Loads, and Section 2.9, "Designing for Fatigue Loads."

polarity, or improving joint design such as replacing a square edge butt weld with a bevel joint.)

4. *Hydrogen Pickup.* Select low-hydrogen welding materials.

5. *Heat Input.* Control total heat input. This may include preheat, welding heat, heating between weld passes to control interpass temperature and post heating to control cooling rate. Control of heat input lowers the shrinkage stresses and retards the cooling rate helping to prevent excessive hardening in the heat-affected zone, two primary causes of cracking.

6. TACK WELDS

The American Welding Society's Building Code and Bridge Specifications both require any tack welds that will be incorporated into the final joint, to be made under the same quality requirements, including preheat, as the final welds.

However, this does not recognize the deep penetration characteristics of some welding processes, for example, submerged-arc. If the initial tack welds are relatively small compared to the first submerged-arc weld pass, they will be entirely remelted along with the adjacent heat-affected area in the plate.

In this case, no preheat should be required for small single pass tack welds unless the plates are so thick and restrained that the tack welds are breaking. See Figure 1. If the tack welds are breaking, the corrective measures previously listed relating to bead shape and weld throat should be applied with preheating called for as a last resort. It is always a good idea to use low-hydrogen welding materials for tack welding plates over 1 in. thick.

7. THINNER PLATE

Welds that join thinner plates rarely show a tendency to crack. The heat input during welding and lack of mass of the thinner plate create a relatively slow cooling rate. This, plus the reduced internal stresses resulting from a good weld throat to plate thickness ratio and the fact that the thinner plate is less rigid and can flex as the weld cools and shrinks, controls the factors that induce cracking. Cracking is almost never a factor on thinner plate unless unusually high in carbon or alloy content.

8. THICK PLATES

In the steel mill, all steel plates and rolled sections undergo a rather slow rate of cooling after being rolled while red hot. The red hot thick sections, because of their greater mass, cool more slowly than thin sections. For a given carbon and alloy content, slower cooling from the critical temperature results in a slightly lower strength.

For the normal thicknesses, the mill has no difficulty in meeting the minimum yield strength required. However, in extremely thick mill sections, because of their slower cooling, the carbon or alloy content might have to be increased slightly in order to meet the required yield strength.

Since a weld cools faster on a thick plate than on

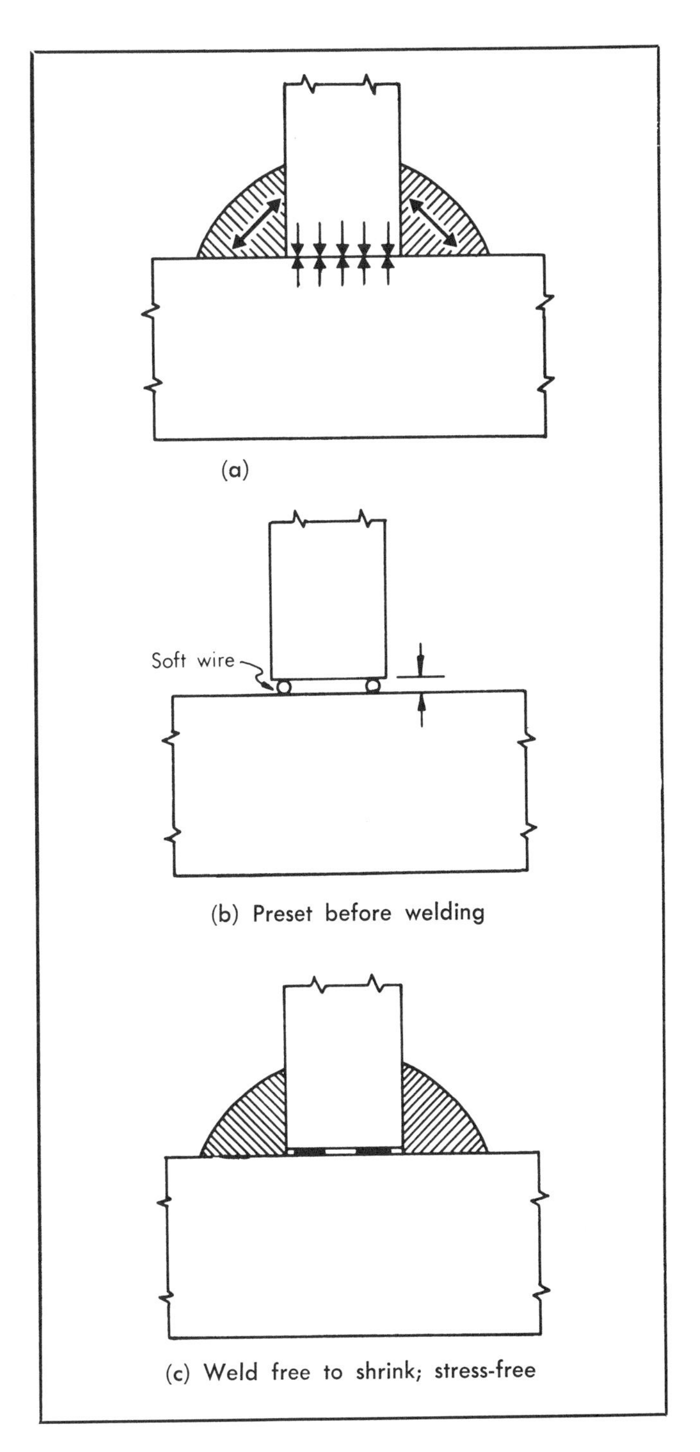

FIGURE 2

a thinner plate, and since the thicker plate will probably have a slightly higher carbon or alloy content, welds on thick plate (because of admixture and fast cooling) will have higher strengths but lower ductility than those made on thinner plate. Special welding procedures may be required for joining thick plate (especially for the first or root pass), and preheating may be necessary. The object is to decrease the weld's rate of cooling so as to increase its ductility.

In addition to improving ductility, preheating thick plates tends to lower the shrinkage stresses that develop because of excessive restraint.

Because of its expense, preheating should be selectively specified, however. For example, fillet welds joining a thin web to a thick flange plate may not require as much preheat as does a butt weld joining two highly restrained thick plates.

On thick plates with large welds, if there is metal-to-metal contact prior to welding, there is no possibility of plate movement. As the welds cool and contract, all the shrinkage stress must be taken up in the weld, Figure 2(a). In cases of severe restraint, this may cause the weld to crack, especially in the first pass on either side of the plate.

By allowing a small gap between the plates, the plates can "move in" slightly as the weld shrinks. This reduces the transverse stresses in the weld. See Figures 2(b) and 2(c). Heavy plates should always have a minimum of 1/32" gap between them, if possible 1/16".

This small gap can be obtained by means of:

1. Insertion of spacers, made of soft steel wire between the plates. The soft wire will flatten out as the weld shrinks. If copper wire is used, care should be taken that it does not mix with the weld metal.

2. A deliberately rough flame-cut edge. The small peaks of the cut edge keep the plates apart, yet can squash out as the weld shrinks.

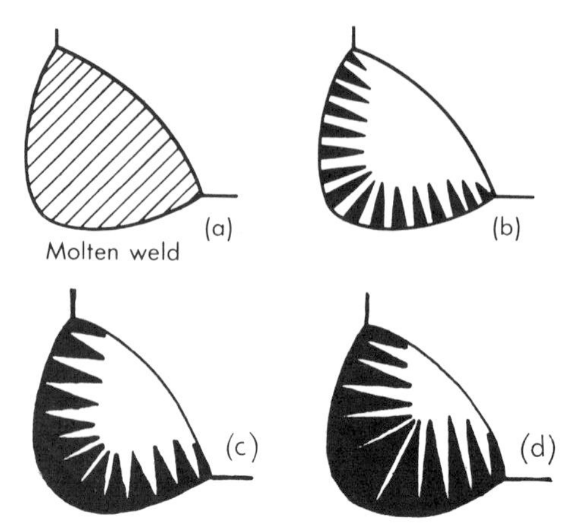

FIGURE 3

3. Upsetting the edge of the plate with a heavy center punch. This acts similar to the rough flame-cut edge.

The plates will usually be tight together after the weld has cooled.

Fillet Welds

The above discussion of metal-to-metal contact and shrinkage stresses especially applies to fillet welds. A slight gap between plates will help assure crack-free fillet welds.

Bead shape is another important factor that affects fillet weld cracking. Freezing of the molten weld, Figure 3(a), due to the quenching effect of the plates commences along the sides of the joint (b) where the cold mass of the heavy plate instantly draws the heat out of the molten weld metal and progresses uniformly inward (c) until the weld is completely solid (d). Notice that the last material to freeze lies in a plane along the centerline of the weld.

To all external appearances, the concave weld (a) in Figure 4 would seem to be larger than the convex weld (b). However, a check of the cross-

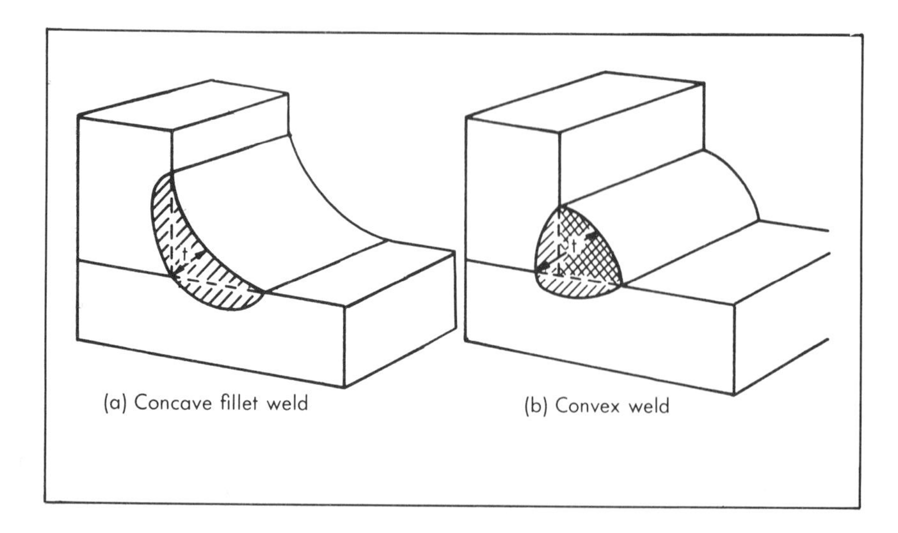

FIGURE 4

section may show the concave weld to have less penetration and a smaller throat (t) than first thought; therefore, the convex weld may actually be stronger even though it may have less deposited metal (darker cross-section).

Designers originally favored the concave fillet weld because it seemed to offer a smoother path for the flow of stress. However, experience has shown that single-pass fillet welds of this shape have a greater tendency to crack upon cooling, which unfortunately usually outweighs the effect of improved stress distribution. This is especially true with steels that require special welding procedures.

When a concave fillet weld cools and shrinks, its outer face is stressed in tension, Figure 5(a). If a surface shrinkage crack should occur, it can usually be avoided by changing to a convex fillet (b). Here the

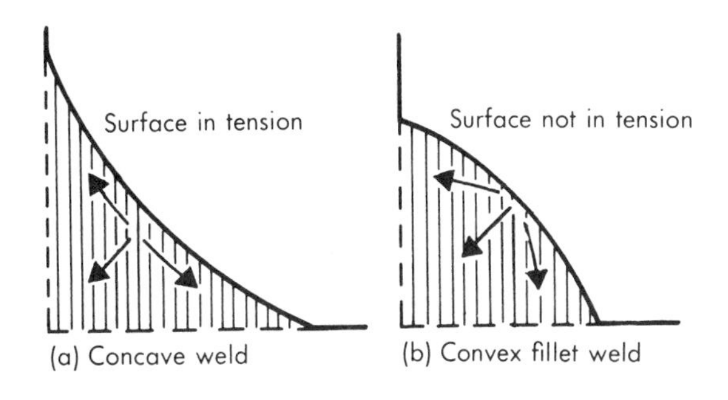

FIGURE 5

weld can shrink, while cooling, without stressing the outer face in tension and should not crack. For multiple-pass fillet welds, the convex bead shape usually applies only to the first pass.

For this reason, when concave welds are desired for special design considerations, such as stress flow, they should be made in two or more passes—the first slightly convex, and the other passes built up to form a concave fillet weld.

9. GROOVE WELDS

On heavy plate, it is usually the first (or root) pass of a groove weld that requires special precautions. This is especially true of the root weld on the back side of a double Vee joint because of the added restraint from the weld on the front side. The weld tends to shrink in all directions as it cools, but is restrained by the plate. Not only are tensile shrinkage stresses set up within the weld, but the weld frequently undergoes plastic yielding to accommodate this shrinkage.

Some idea of the possible locked-in stress and plastic flow of the weld may be seen in Figure 6. Imagine the plate to be cut near the joint, allowing the weld to freely shrink (dotted lines). Then pull the plates back to the original rigid position that they would normally be in during and after welding (solid lines). This necessitates a stretching of the weld.

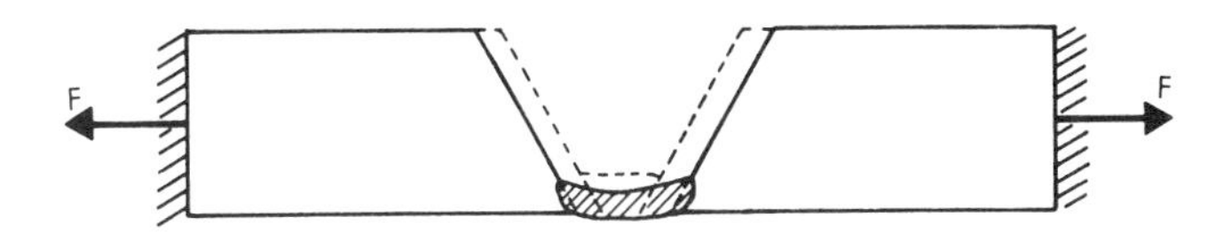

FIGURE 6

In actual practice all of this stretch or yielding can occur only in the weld, since the plate cannot move and the weld has the least thickness of the joint. Most of this yielding takes place while the weld is hot and has lower strength and ductility. If, at this time, the internal stress exceeds the physical properties of the weld, a crack occurs which is usually down the centerline of the weld.

The problem is enhanced by the fact that the first (or root) bead usually picks up additional carbon or alloy by admixture with the base metal. The root bead thus is less ductile than subsequent beads.

A concave bead surface in a groove weld creates the same tendency for surface cracking as described for fillet welds, Figure 7. This tendency is further increased with lower ductility.

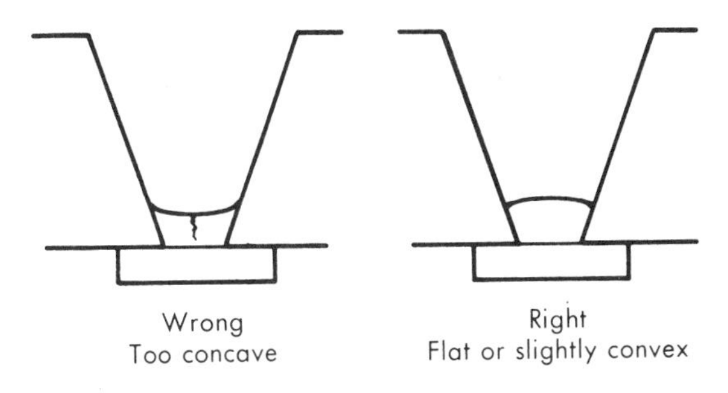

FIGURE 7

Increasing the throat dimension of the root pass will help to prevent cracking; use electrodes or procedures that develop a convex bead shape. Low hydrogen welding materials are sometimes useful and finally preheat can be specified. Obviously preheating should be adopted as a last resort since it will cause the greatest increase in weld cost.

The problem of centerline cracking can even occur in the succeeding passes of a multiple pass weld if the passes are excessively wide or concave. Corrective measures call for a procedure that specifies a narrower slightly convex bead shape, making the completed weld two or more beads wide, side by side, Figure 8.

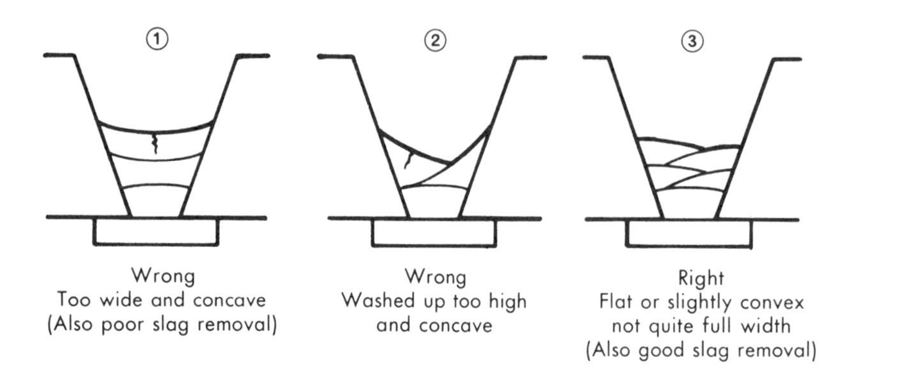

FIGURE 8

10. INTERNAL CRACKS AND WELD WIDTH TO DEPTH OF FUSION RATIO

Where a cracking problem exists due to joint restraint, material chemistry or both, the crack usually appears at the weld's face. In some situations, however, an internal crack can occur which won't reach the weld's face. This type of crack usually stems from the misuse of a welding process that can achieve deep penetration, or poor joint design.

The freezing action for butt and groove welds is the same as that illustrated for fillet welds. Freezing starts along the weld surface adjacent to the cold base metal, and finishes at the centerline of the weld. If, however, the weld depth of fusion is much greater than width of the face, the weld's surface may freeze in advance of its center. Now the shrinkage forces will act on the still hot center or core of the bead which could cause a centerline crack along its length without this crack extending to the weld's face, Figure 9(a).

Internal cracks can also result with improper joint design or preparation. Figure 9(b) illustrates the results of combining thick plate, a deep penetrating welding process, and a 45° included angle.

A small bevel on the second pass side of the double-V-groove weld, Figure 9(c), and arc gouging a groove too deep for its width, led to the internal crack illustrated.

Internal cracks can also occur on fillet welds if the depth of fusion is sufficiently greater than the face width of the bead, Figure 9(d).

Although internal cracks are most serious since they cannot be detected with visual inspection methods, a few preventive measures can assure their elimination. Limiting the penetration and the volume of weld metal deposited per pass through speed and amperage control and using a joint design which sets reasonable depth of fusion requirements are both steps in the right direction.

In all cases, however, the critical factor that helps control internal cracks is the ratio of weld width to depth. Experience shows that the weld width to depth of fusion ratio can range from a minimum of 1 to 1 to a maximum of 1.4 to 1.

$$\frac{\text{Width of Weld}}{\text{Depth of Fusion}} = 1 \text{ to } 1.4$$

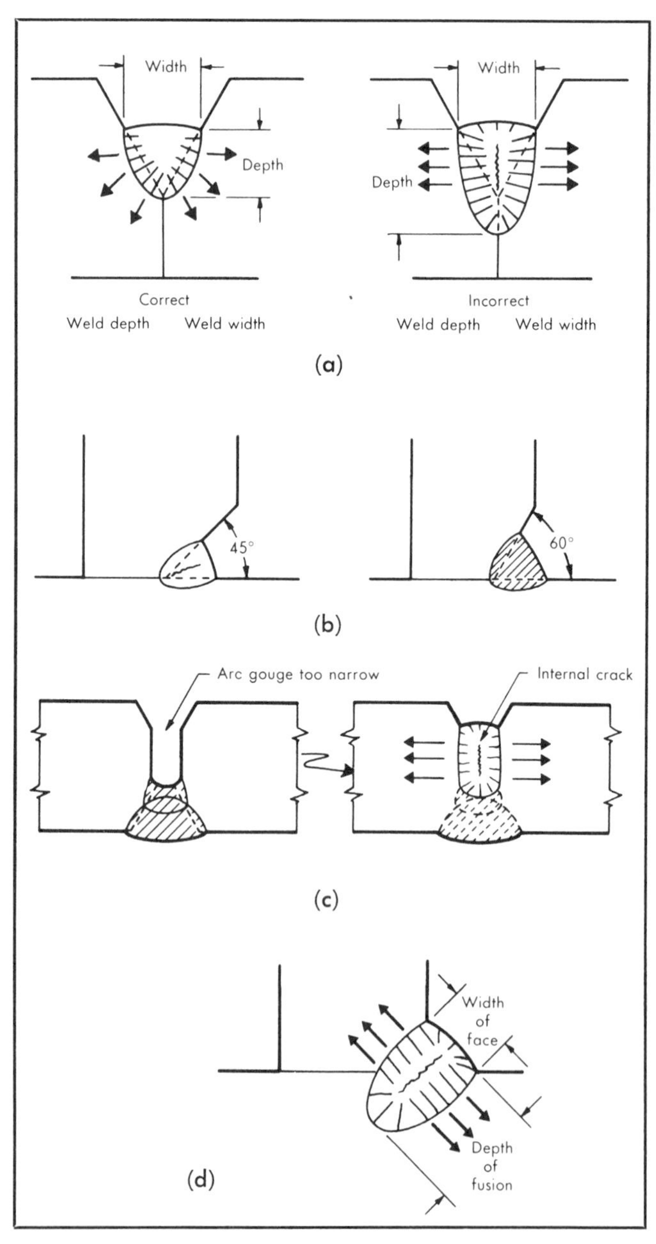

FIGURE 9

11. UNDERBEAD CRACKING

Underbead cracking is not a problem with the controlled analysis low carbon steels. This problem if it occurs is in the heat-affected zone of the base metal. It can become a factor with thick plate as the carbon or alloy content of the steel increases. As an example, this can occur with the heat treatable very high strength, high carbon low alloy steels like 4140 or 6150. The construction alloy steels which have over 100,000 psi tensile strength and are heat treated before welding, also can experience underbead cracking in thick plates. When armour plate was used, underbead cracking (toe cracks) was a problem. The point is that the problem is only important on hardenable steels.

Low-hydrogen processes should be used to join these materials since one cause of underbead cracking is hydrogen embrittlement in the heat-affected zone. Hydrogen in the welding arc, either from the electrode coating or from wet or dirty plate surfaces, will tend to be partially absorbed into the droplets of weld metal being deposited and absorbed into the molten metal beneath the arc.

As the welding arc progresses along the plate, the deposited hot weld metal (which has now solidified) and the adjacent base metal heated by the weld above the transformation temperature are both austenitic at this elevated temperature, and have a high solubility for hydrogen. Fortunately, a considerable amount of hydrogen escapes through the weld's surface into the air; however, a small amount may diffuse back through the weld into the adjacent base metal. (The rate of diffusion decreases with decreasing temperature.)

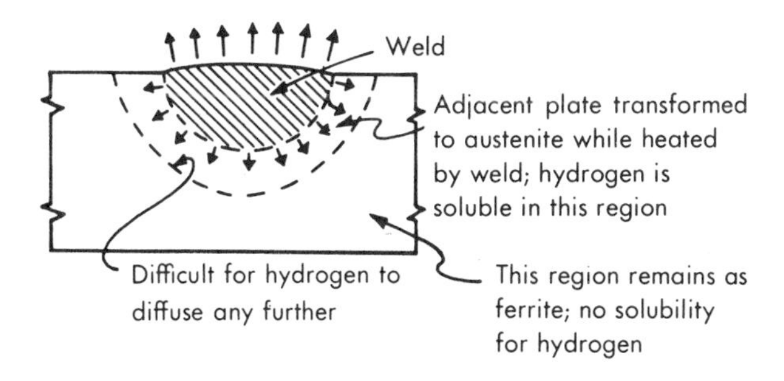

FIGURE 10

Beyond the boundary of the heat-affected zone, the base metal is in the form of ferrite, which has practically no solubility for hydrogen. This ferrite boundary becomes an imaginary fence, and the hydrogen tends to pile up here, going no farther. See Figure 10.

Upon further cooling, the heat-affected area transforms back to ferrite with almost no solubility for hydrogen. Any hydrogen present tends to separate out between the crystal lattice and builds up pressure. This pressure, when combined with shrinkage stresses and any hardening effect of the steel's chemistry, may cause tiny cracks. Since weld metal is usually of a lower carbon than the base plate, this trouble occurs mainly just beyond the weld along the austenite-ferrite boundary and is called "underbead cracking" See Figure 11. If some of these cracks appear on the

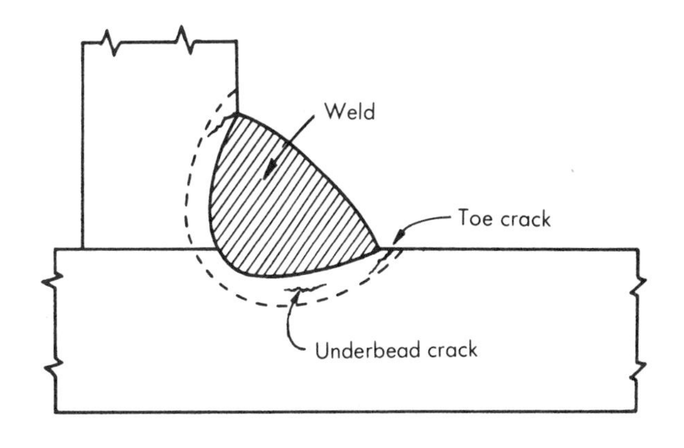

FIGURE 11

plate surface adjacent to the weld, they are called "toe cracks". Slower cooling by welding slower and preheating allows hydrogen to escape and helps control this problem.

The use of low-hydrogen welding materials eliminates the major source of hydrogen and usually eliminates underbead cracking.

12. SUMMARY ON CRACKING

The first requirement of any welded joint is to be crack-free. Cracking may occur in either the weld metal or the heat-affected zone of the base plates.

Most steels can be welded in the average plate thickness without worrying about weld cracking.

As plate thickness increases, and as the carbon and alloying content increase, weld cracks and underbead cracks may become problems and require special precautions for their control.

This necessitates in order of importance: a) good welding procedure, especially in respect to bead shape, control of admixture, b) reducing rigidity by intentional spacing of plates, c) use of low-hydrogen welding materials, and d) controlled cooling rate, including welding current and travel speed, and if needed control of preheat and interpass temperature.

Why Preheat and How to Determine Correct Preheat Temperature

13. WHEN AND WHY TO PREHEAT

Preheating, while not always necessary, is used for one of the following reasons:

1. To reduce shrinkage stresses in the weld and adjacent base metal; especially important in highly restrained joints.
2. To provide a slower rate of cooling through the critical temperature range (about 1800° F to 1330° F) preventing excessive hardening and lowered ductility in both weld and heat-affected area of the base plate.
3. To provide a slower rate of cooling through the 400°F range, allowing more time for any hydrogen that is present to diffuse away from the weld and adjacent plate to avoid underbead cracking.
4. To increase the allowable critical rate of cooling below which there will be no underbead cracking. Thus, with the welding procedure held constant, a higher initial plate temperature increases the maximum safe rate of cooling while slowing down the actual rate of cooling. This tends to make the heat input from the welding process less critical.

Cottrell and Bradstreet* show the following critical cooling rates (R_{cr}) for a given steel at 572°F (300°C) using low-hydrogen electrode in order to prevent underbead cracking for various preheats to be:

T_o (°F)	R_{cr} (°F/sec)
—58	6.8 — 9.9
68	8.6 — 11.7
212	21.6 — 37.8

5. To increase the notch toughness in the weld zone.
6. To lower the transition temperature of the weld and adjacent base metal.

Normally, not much preheat is required to prevent underbead cracking. This is held to a minimum when low-hydrogen welding materials are used. Higher preheat temperature might be required for some other reason, e.g. a highly restrained joint between very thick plates, or a high alloy content.

Preheating makes other factors less critical, but since it invariably increases the cost of welding, it cannot be indulged in unnecessarily.

* Cottrell and Bradstreet, "Effect of Preheat on Weldability", BRITISH WELDING JOURNAL, July 1955, p. 309.

14. AWS MINIMUM REQUIREMENTS

The AWS has set up minimum preheat and interpass requirements given in Table 2.

These minimum preheat requirements may need to be adjusted, according to welding heat input, specific steel chemistry, the joint geometry, and other factors.

TABLE 1—AWS Minimum Initial and Interpass Temperatures[1,2] (1966)

Thickness of Thickest Part at Point of Welding (inches)	Welding Process	
	Shielded Metal-Arc Welding with Other than Low-Hydrogen Electrodes A36[3], A7[3], A373[3]	Shielded Metal-Arc Welding with Low-Hydrogen Electrodes and Submerged Arc Welding A36[4], A7[4], A373[4], A441[5] A242[5] Weldable Grade
To 3/4, Incl.	none[6]	none[6]
Over 3/4 to 1 1/2, Incl.	150°F	70°F
Over 1 1/2 to 2 1/2, Incl.	225°F	150°F
Over 2 1/2	300°F	225°F

[1] Welding shall not be done when the ambient temperature is lower than 0°F.
[2] When the base metal is below the temperature listed for the welding process being used and the thickness of material being welded, it shall be preheated for both tack welding and welding in such manner that the surfaces of the parts on which weld metal is being deposited are at or above the specified minimum temperature for a distance equal to the thickness of the part being welded, but not less than 3 inches, both laterally and in advance of the welding. Preheat temperature shall not exceed 400°F. (Interpass temperature is not subject to a maximum limit.)
[3] Using E60XX or E70XX electrodes other than the low-hydrogen types.
[4] Using E60XX or E70XX low-hydrogen electrodes (EXX15, -16, -18, -28) or Grade SAW-1 or SAW-2.
[5] Using only E70XX low-hydrogen electrodes (E7015, E7016, E7018, E7028) or Grade SAW-2.
[6] When the base metal temperature is below 32°F , preheat the base metal to at least 72°F.

15. HEAT INPUT DURING WELDING

One factor that would reduce preheat requirements is the use of greater welding heat input; for example, the welding heat input for vertical welding with weave passes at an arc speed of 3 in./min. is greater than that of horizontal welding with stringer beads at 6 in./min. The heat input (J) for a specific welding procedure can be determined using the formula:

$$J = \frac{E\ I\ 60}{V} \qquad (1)$$

where:

J = Heat input in Joules/in. or watt-sec/in.
E = Arc voltage in volts
I = Welding current in amps
V = Arc speed in in./min

Since all of the welding heat input at the arc does not enter the plate, the following heat efficiencies are suggested for use with this formula and subsequent formulas, charts or nomographs:

75-80% manual welding

90-100% submerged arc welding

Most preheat and interpass temperature recommendations are set up for manual welding where there is a relatively low heat input. For example, a current of 200 amps and a speed of 6 in./min. would produce a welding heat input of about 48,000 joules/in. or watt-sec./in., assuming an efficiency of 80 percent. Yet, it might be necessary to weld a 12-gauge sheet to this plate in the vertical down position with 180 amps and a speed of 22 in./min. This would reduce the welding heat input to 9800 joules/in. If this were a thick plate, it would indicate the need, with this second procedure, for more preheat, although existing preheat tables do not recognize the effect of different welding heat inputs.

On the other hand, some downward adjustment in preheat from the value listed in the preheat tables should be made for standard welding procedures which provide a much greater welding heat input. We are considering here a stable heat-flow condition after some welding has progressed.

This does not consider the more severe cooling conditions at the moment welding commences. Undoubtedly, some initial heat could be supplied to a localized area at the start of the weld on thick plate. The question now becomes how much, if any, preheat is needed for the remaining length of joint.

For example, it is standard practice today to use submerged-arc automatic welding to build up columns and girders from heavy plate. One method of fabrication uses a single-arc, submerged-arc automatic weld at 850 amps and a speed of 20 in./min. (for a ⅜" fillet weld), with the girder positioned for flat welding. This would provide a heat input of 86,000 joules/in. An alternate method positions the girder with its web vertical so that both welds are made simultaneously in the horizontal position, and uses two sets of tandem arcs (each set with two welding heads); the heat input from each arc would be 73,600 joules/in.—a total of 147,000 joules/in. of weld for each fillet. Because of the resulting lower cooling rate, less preheat should be required once the weld has been started. This may be a considerable advantage for the comfort of welding operators, especially when welding inside large box girders.

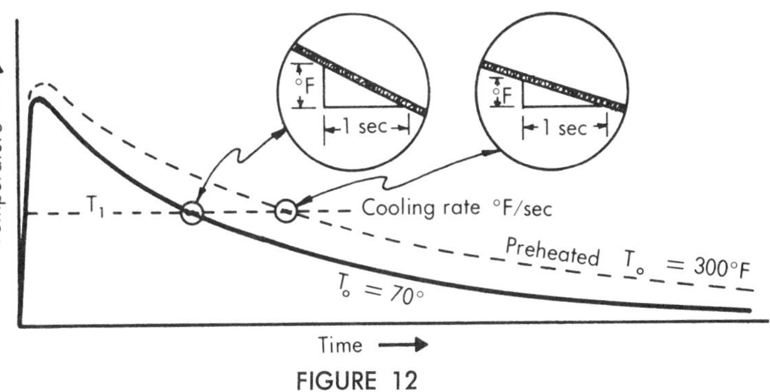

FIGURE 12

16. COOLING RATE

When a weld is made, the weld and adjacent plate cool very rapidly. The rate of cooling depends *first* on the combination of initial plate temperature (T_o) (including effects of preheat or interpass temperature) and the welding heat input (J), and *secondly*, on the plate's capacity to absorb this heat in terms of plate thickness and joint geometry.

Figure 12 illustrates the temperatures in the heat-affected zone of the plate as the welding arc passes by. Under a given set of conditions, the cooling rate will vary as represented by the changing slopes of both curves.

For a particular chemistry, at a given temperature level (T_1) there is a critical cooling rate (R_{cr}) which should not be exceeded in order to avoid underbead cracking. This temperature level is in the range of 400°F to 750°F. American investigators tend to use a higher value such as 750°, while English and Canadian investigators favor a lower value such as 300°C, or 572°F. In this discussion, we have placed this temperature level (T_1) at 572°F.

The investigation of cooling rates has been based largely on two extreme conditions, which have been developed mathematically.* These are:

1. The *thin plate,* in which the combination of

heat input and plate size permit assuming the temperature to be uniform throughout the thickness at any point; in other words, heat flows transversely in only two axes. See Figure 13.

FIGURE 13

thin plate

$$R = K_1 \left(\frac{t}{J}\right)^2 (T_1 - T_o)^3 \quad \ldots\ldots\ldots\ldots (2)$$

2. The *thick plate,* in which the combination of heat input and plate size permit assuming the bottom surface of the plate does not increase in temperature; in other words, heat flows transversely in three axes. See Figure 14.

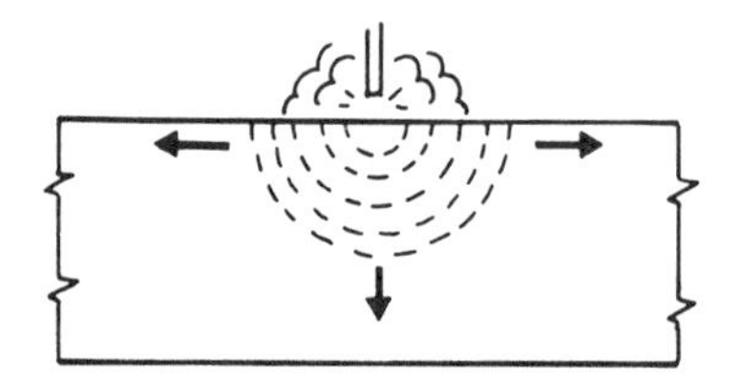

FIGURE 14

thick plate

$$R = \frac{K_2}{J}(T_1 - T_o)^2 \quad \ldots\ldots\ldots\ldots\ldots\ldots (3)$$

where:

R = cooling rate at temperature (T_1), °F/sec

T_1 = temperature at which cooling rate is considered, 572°F

T_o = initial plate temperature or preheat temperature when preheating is used, °F

K = thermal conductivity (the BTU loss per hour per square foot of surface divided by the temperature gradient of °F per foot of thickness.)

(K = 25.9 for mild steel at 572°F)

K_1 = constant, representing K, ρ, C at T_1

(K_1 = 161.48 for mild steel at 572°F)

K_2 = constant, representing K at T_1

(K_2 = 5.961 for mild steel at 572°F)

ρ = density, lbs/ft^3

(ρ = 489.6 lbs/ft^3 for mild steel)

C = specific heat, BTU/lb/°F

(C = .136 BTU/lb/°F for mild steel)

t = actual plate thickness, in.

J = welding heat input (formula 1)

Unfortunately, there is no clear definition of what is a "thin plate" and what is a "thick plate" relative to cooling rate. The actual condition often lies somewhere between these two extremes, and for this reason a certain amount of judgment is needed. For example, welding on a 1" plate with submerged arc at a current of 1000 amps and a speed of 10 in./min. would approach a "thin plate" condition; yet manual welding vertically down on a ¾" plate at a current of 120 amps and a speed of 12 in./min. would approach a "thick plate" condition.

In Figure 15, these two basic formulas are plotted for a given set of conditions: heat input (J), and preheat and interpass temperature (T_o).

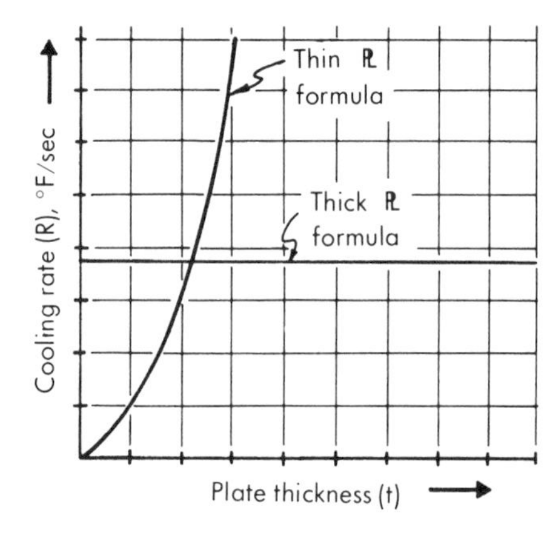

FIGURE 15

The formula for a "thin plate" recognizes the effect of plate thickness (t); and the resulting cooling rate (R) increases rapidly as the square of the plate thickness. When the cooling rate characteristics of a thick plate are studied, however, it soon becomes apparent that for a given welding procedure and an initial temperature, increasing the plate thickness beyond a certain dimension will not cause further change in the rate of cooling. For this reason, the formula for "thick plate"—Formula No. 3—does not include actual plate thickness (t) and the value of (R) does not vary with thickness but remains constant for a given

* D. Rosenthal, "Mathematical Theory of Heat Distribution During Cutting and Welding", WELDING JOURNAL, May 1941, p. 220-s.

heat input, preheat and interpass temperature. For a given heat input, the cooling rate indicated by the "thick plate" formula is the maximum (R_m) that can occur regardless of the plate thickness.

At any given plate thickness the lower cooling rate value is the more nearly correct. Using the two curves of Figure 15 as a limit and a guide, a new curve (solid line) has been drawn in Figure 16.

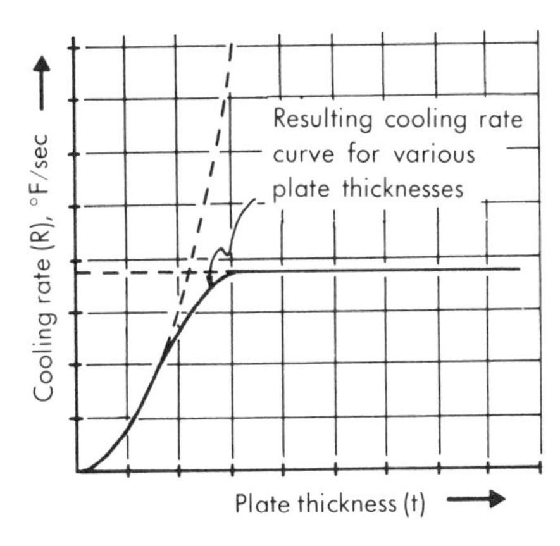

FIGURE 16

Notice, Figure 16, that the upper half of the variable part of this curve is almost a perfect reversal of the lower half, and the lower half belongs to the curve for the "thin plate". Therefore, the curved portions will be expressed mathematically as—

lower portion

$$R = 161.48 \left(\frac{t}{J}\right)^2 (572 - T_o)^3 \qquad (4)$$

upper portion

$$R = 5.961 \frac{(572 - T_o)^2}{J} \left(- 27.09\, t^2 \frac{(572 - T_o)}{J} + 14.72\, t \sqrt{\frac{572 - T_o}{J}} - 1 \right) \qquad (5)$$

If a welding procedure for a given plate thickness lies in the lower portion of the curve, it is easy to solve directly for the required preheat (T_o) using formula (4); however, this would be very difficult for the upper portion using formula (5).

The chart is further limited in use since it only covers a single value of preheat and heat input. Therefore, to expand the application of this approach, we will put both formulas (4) and (5) into more usable non-dimension formulas (6) and (7). This calls for inclusion of the maximum effective plate thickness (t_{me}), and the corresponding maximum effective preheat ($T_o/_{me}$) for this thickness.

lower portion

$$\frac{t}{t_{me}} = \sqrt{\frac{1}{2}\left(\frac{T_1 - T_o/_{me}}{T_1 - T_o}\right)^3} \qquad (6)$$

upper portion

$$\frac{t}{t_{me}} = \sqrt{\frac{T_1 - T_o/_{me}}{T_1 - T_o}} \left(1 - \frac{1}{\sqrt{2}} \sqrt{1 - \left(\frac{T_1 - T_o/_{me}}{T_1 - T_o}\right)^2} \right) \qquad (7)$$

where:

t = actual thickness of the plate, in.

t_{me} = maximum effective plate for given values of (J) and (R)

$$t_{me} = .4246 \sqrt[4]{\frac{J}{R}} \qquad (8)$$

T_1 = elevated temperature at which cooling rate is considered (572°F)

T_o = preheat temperature for given values of (J), (R), and (t), °F

$T_o/_{me}$ = maximum effective preheat temperature for a given value of (J) and (R), °F

$$T_1 - T_o/_{me} = \sqrt{\frac{R\,J}{5.961}} \qquad (9)$$

Formulas (6) and (7) produced the curve shown in Figure 17. This can be used to determine T_o the required preheat temperature.

17. BI-THERMAL VS. TRI-THERMAL HEAT FLOW

This work is based upon bi-thermal heat flow where the heat has two avenues for escape; for example, a conventional butt joint consisting of two plates, Figure 18(a).

Tri-thermal heat flow has three avenues for escape, an example is a tee joint made of three plates, Figure 18(b).

Where tri-thermal heat flow condition exists, the above work should be modified either by:

1. Using ⅔ of the actual heat input (J), or
2. Adjusting the plate thickness (t) to allow for the extra plate by using ½ of the sum of three thicknesses.

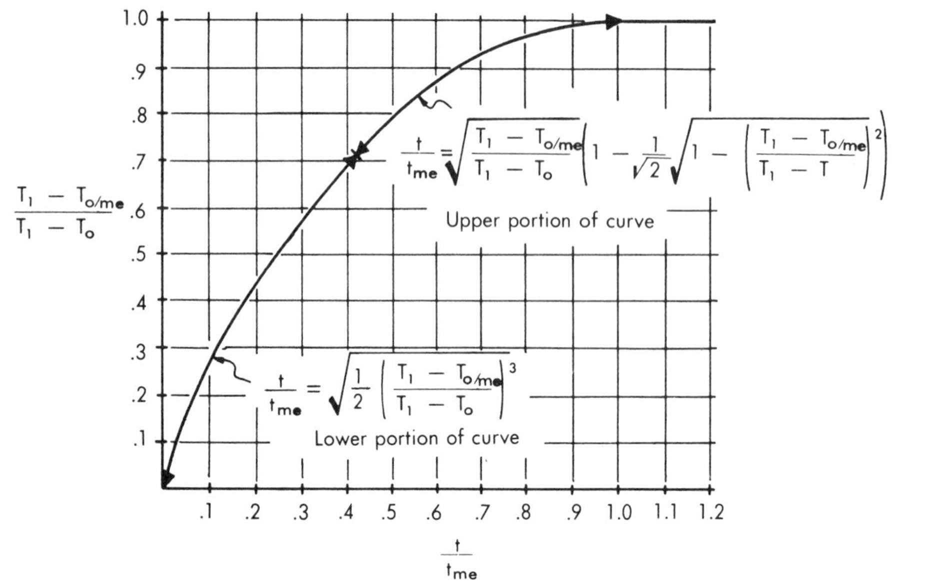

FIGURE 17

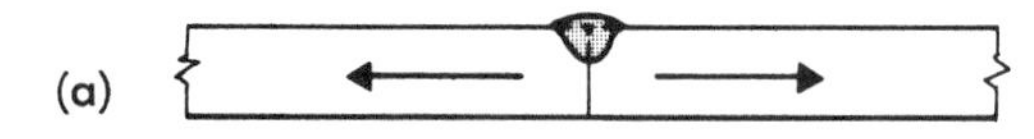

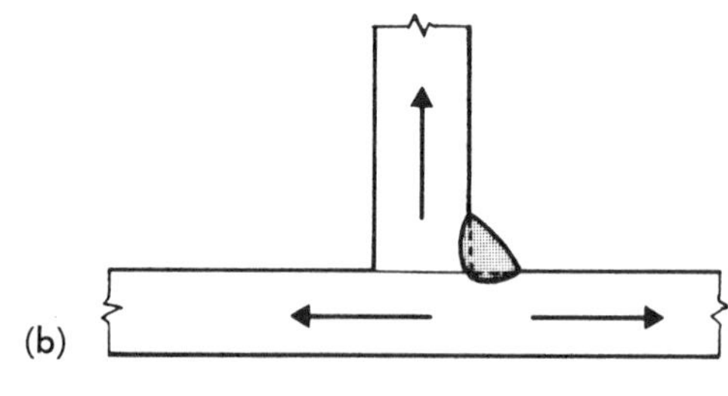

FIGURE 18

18. CARBON EQUIVALENT

As a result of recent experiments and studies, it is possible to simplify the relationship of all chemical elements in a steel to the occurrence of underbead cracking. The simplification is expressed in a single formula known as the carbon equivalent. This formula expresses the influence of each element relative to that of carbon.

Investigators* have shown a definite relationship in the percent of underbead cracking to the carbon equivalent. Figure 19 shows a 1″ thick test plate on which a single bead was deposited using ⅛″ E6010 electrode at 100 amps, 25 v, reversed polarity, at 10 in./min. The chart, Figure 20, shows the percentage of underbead cracking for different carbon equivalents that occurred with this test. A deposit made with low-hydrogen E6015 electrodes on a specimen of this thickness did not have underbead cracks. The AWS E6015 electrode is comparable to today's E7018. The results were plotted, Figure 20, to give curves for three different preheat temperatures (T_o).

K. Winterton* has listed 14 different carbon equivalent formulas and recommended the following:

$$C_{eq} = C\% + \frac{Mn\%}{6} + \frac{Ni\%}{20} + \frac{Cr\%}{10} - \frac{Mo\%}{50} - \frac{V\%}{10} + \frac{Cu\%}{40} \quad (10)$$

This formula is applicable to the low-carbon low-alloy steels for construction and machinery manufacturing.

19. COOLING RATE AND CARBON EQUIVALENT

Although not too well defined, for a given analysis of steel there is a maximum rate at which the weld and adjacent plate may be cooled without underbead cracking occurring.

* Stout and Doty, "Weldability of Steels", Welding Research Council, 1953, p. 150; Williams, Roach, Martin and Voldrich, "Weldability of Carbon-Manganese Steels", WELDING JOURNAL, July 1949, p. 311-s.

* K. Winterton, "Weldability Prediction from Steel Composition to Avoid Heat-Affected Zone Cracking", WELDING JOURNAL, June 1961, p. 253-s.

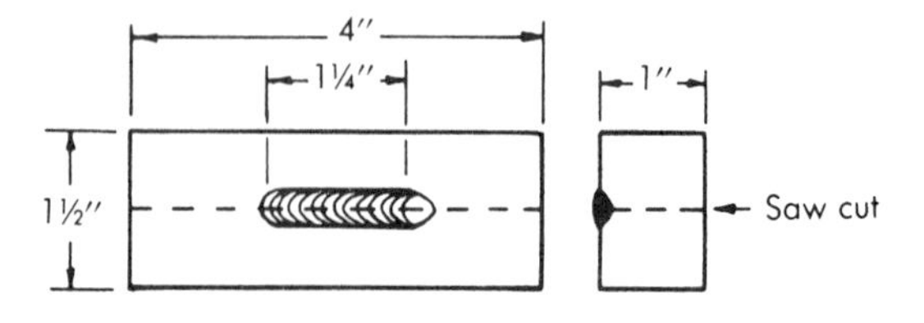

FIGURE 19

The higher the carbon equivalent, the lower will be this critical (allowable) cooling rate. Thus, the higher the steel's carbon equivalent, the more important becomes the use of low-hydrogen welding and preheating.

Cottrell and Bradstreet* have used a type of Reeve Restraint test, called the CTS (Controlled Thermal Severity) test. For any given steel, three thicknesses are tested — ¼, ½, and 1". Each test requires

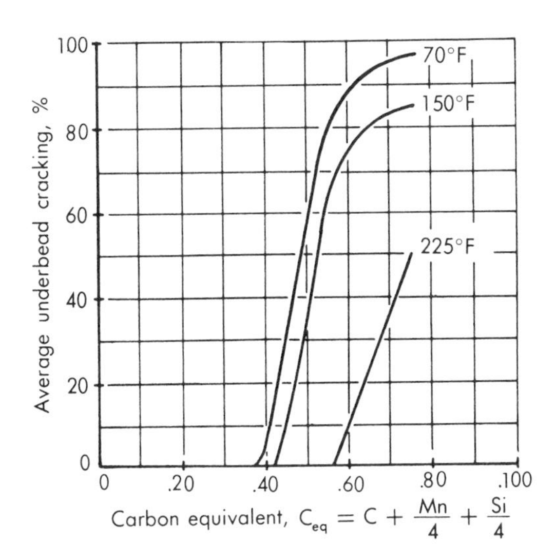

FIGURE 20

two fillet welds—one a bi-thermal weld (two avenues for heat to escape), the other a tri-thermal weld (three avenues for heat to escape). This gives a total of 6 different values for TSN (Thermal Severity Number), and for the given welding heat input (about 32,000 joules/in.) produces 6 different cooling rates. It is then observed at what cooling rate cracking does or does not occur, and the subsequent welding procedure is adjusted so this critical cooling rate will not be exceeded.

Both of these men have produced tables in which relative weldability has been expressed along with the critical cooling rate. More recently, Bradstreet** has tied in this relative weldability with carbon equivalent. By working back through this information, the carbon equivalent—critical cooling rate curve shown in Figure 21 has been produced to use as a guide in case the CTS test on the particular steel is not made. This curve may be expressed by the following formula:

$$R_{cr} = \frac{6.598}{C_{eq} - .3074} - 16.26 \quad \text{............(11)}$$

This is the critical cooling rate at T_1 — 572°F.

The critical cooling rate (R_{cr}) can be determined by a) actual test of the particular steel to see what cooling rate will not cause cracking, or b) using formula (11) based upon Canadian investigations.

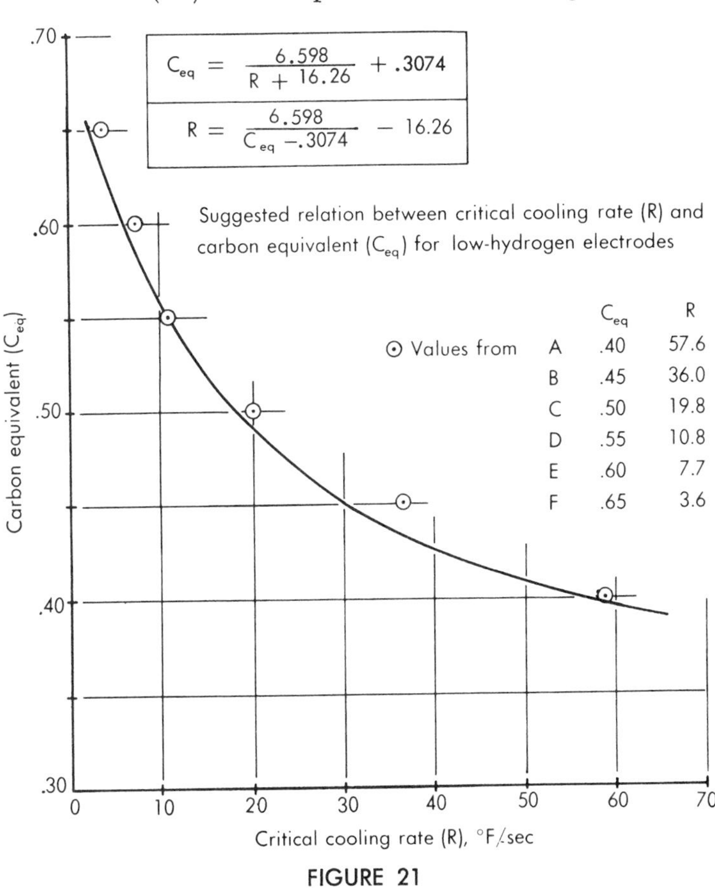

FIGURE 21

20. FINDING REQUIRED PREHEAT TEMPERATURE

To calculate the required preheat temperature (T_o) that will produce the required cooling rate (R) for a given heat input (J) and plate thickness (t), the following mathematical computations must be made:

a) Determine from formula (9) the value of $(T_1 - T_o/_{me})$.

b) Determine from formula (8) the value of (t_{me}).

c) From this (b) determine (t/t_{me}).

d) From the chart, Figure 17, using (c) read the value for

---

* C. L. M. Cottrell, "Controlled Thermal Severity Cracking Test Simulates Practical Welded Joints", WELDING JOURNAL, June 1953, p. 257-s; Cottrell and Bradstreet, "A Method for Calculating the Effect of Preheat on Weldability", BRITISH WELDING JOURNAL, July 1955, p. 305; Cottrell and Bradstreet, "Calculating Preheat Temperatures to Prevent Hard Zone Cracking in Low Alloy Steels", BRITISH WELDING JOURNAL, July 1955, p. 310.

** B. J. Bradstreet, "Methods to Establish Procedures for Welding Low Alloy Steels", ENGINEERING JOURNAL (Engineering Institute of Canada), November 1963.

$$\left(\frac{T_1 - T_{o/me}}{T_1 - T_o}\right)$$

e) Knowing this value (d) and the value of $(T_1 - T_{o/me})$ from item (a), determine the required preheat temeprature (T_o).

An easier and faster method for determining the required preheat uses the nomograph, Figure 22. This nomograph is actually two nomographs superimposed upon each other. The first nomograph (subscript a) will provide a value for $\left(\frac{T_1 - T_{o/me}}{T_1 - T_o}\right)$.
The second nomograph (subscript b) will provide the required preheat and interpass temperature (T_o).

A set of eight graphs, Figure 23, will also provide this same information.

Example Using Chart (Fig. 17)

Given:

$$J = 20{,}000 \ \frac{\text{watt-sec}}{\text{inch}}$$

$$R = 25 \ °F/sec$$

$$t = 1.0''$$

find required preheat temperature (T_o):

a) Determine $T_1 - T_{o/me} = \sqrt{\frac{R\,J}{5.961}}$

$$= \sqrt{\frac{(25)\ (20{,}000)}{5.961}}$$

$$= 289.6°F$$

b) Determine $t_{me} = .42457 \sqrt[4]{\frac{J}{R}}$

$$= .42457 \sqrt[4]{\frac{20{,}000}{25}}$$

$$= 2.26''$$

c) Determine relative thickness: $\frac{t}{t_{me}} = \frac{1''}{2.26''}$

$$= .4429$$

d) From chart, Figure 17, read relative preheat temperature: $\frac{T_1 - T_{o/me}}{T_1 - T_o} = .73$

e) Therefore: $T_1 - T_o = \frac{T_1 - T_{o/me}}{.73} = \frac{289.6}{.73}$

$$= 396.7$$

$$572 - T_o = 396.7$$

$$\text{or } T_o = \underline{175.3} \ °F$$

Example Using Nomograph (Fig. 22)

Given: $J = 20{,}000 \ \frac{\text{watt-sec}}{\text{inch}}$

$$R = 25 \ °F/sec$$

$$t = 1.0''$$

find preheat temperature (T_o):

1st nomograph

(1) $R = 25 \ °F/sec$

(2a) $J = 20{,}000 \ \frac{\text{watt-sec}}{\text{inch}}$

(3a) Read $t_{me} = 2.26''$

Use this number as a pivot point

(4a) $t = 1.0''$

(5a) Read $\% \ \frac{T_1 - T_{o/me}}{T_1 - T_o} = 73\%$

2nd nomograph

(1) $R = 25 \ °F/sec$

(2b) $J = 20{,}000 \ \frac{\text{watt-sec}}{\text{inch}}$

(3b) Read $T_{o/me} = 282 \ °F$

Use this number as a pivot point

(4b) $\% \ \frac{T_1 - T_{o/me}}{T_1 - T_o} = 73\%$ (from 1st nomograph)

(5b) Read $T_o = 175 \ °F$

21. OTHER POINTS OF CONSIDERATION

Test data has indicated that thin plates result in slightly higher cooling rates than calculated. It is believed this is because thin plates have a relatively greater surface area for heat loss per volume than thick plates.

Normally, in the investigation of a groove weld, the pass completing the joint is considered rather than the root pass. This is because the face pass usually has a slightly higher cooling rate due to the larger cross-section of the joint (assuming the same interpass temperature).

There is some indication that fillet welds have slightly higher cooling rates than the bead-on-plate welds used in the investigative work. This is because the 90° intersection of the two plates presents a larger area of contact with the weld, therefore absorbing heat at a slightly greater rate. A groove weld similarly would offer a larger area of plate contact with the weld than a bead-on-plate weld.

FIGURE 22—Estimated Preheat for Given Heat Input, Cooling Rate and Plate Thickness

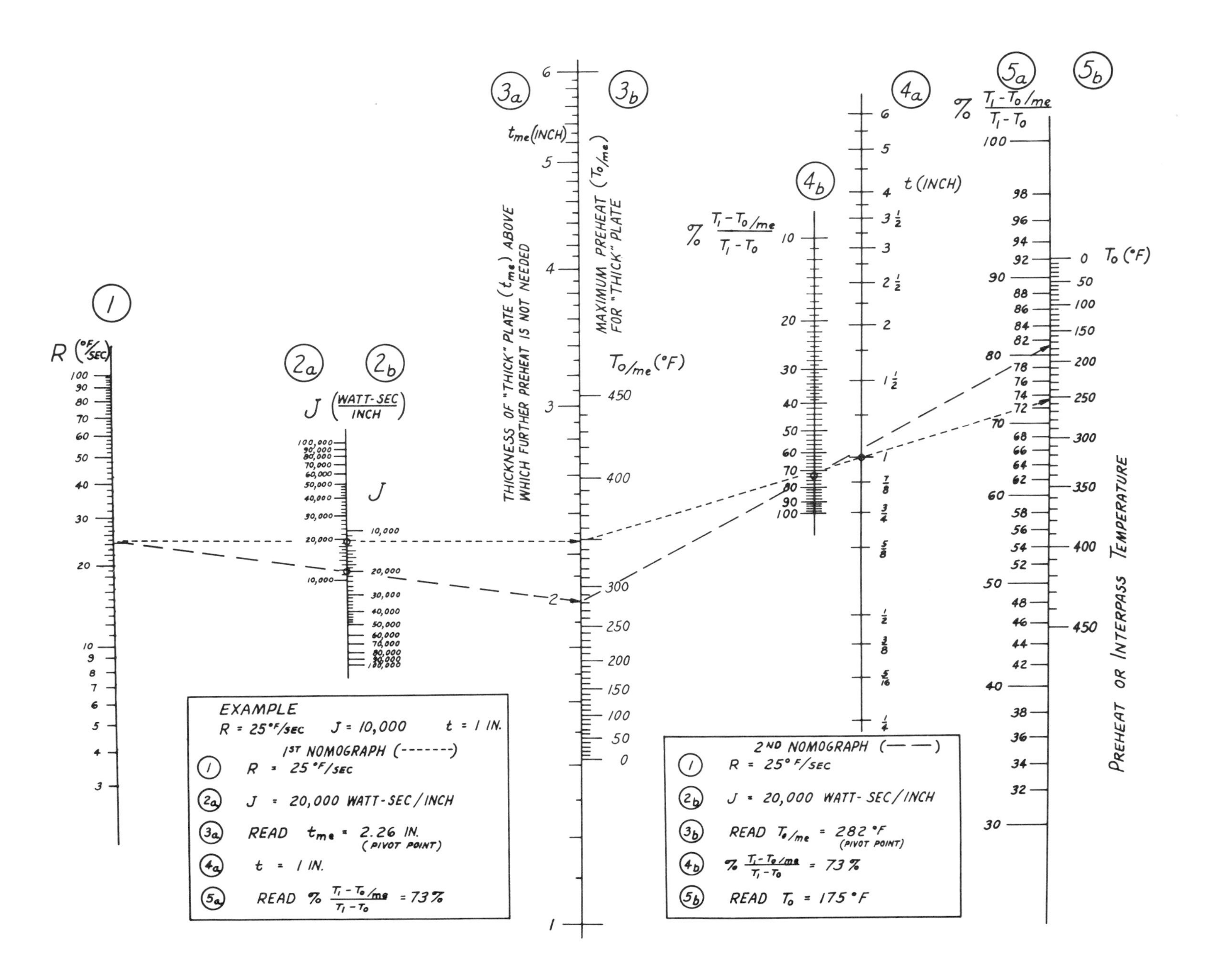

FIGURE 23—Estimated Preheat for Given Cooling Rate, Heat Input & Plate Thickness

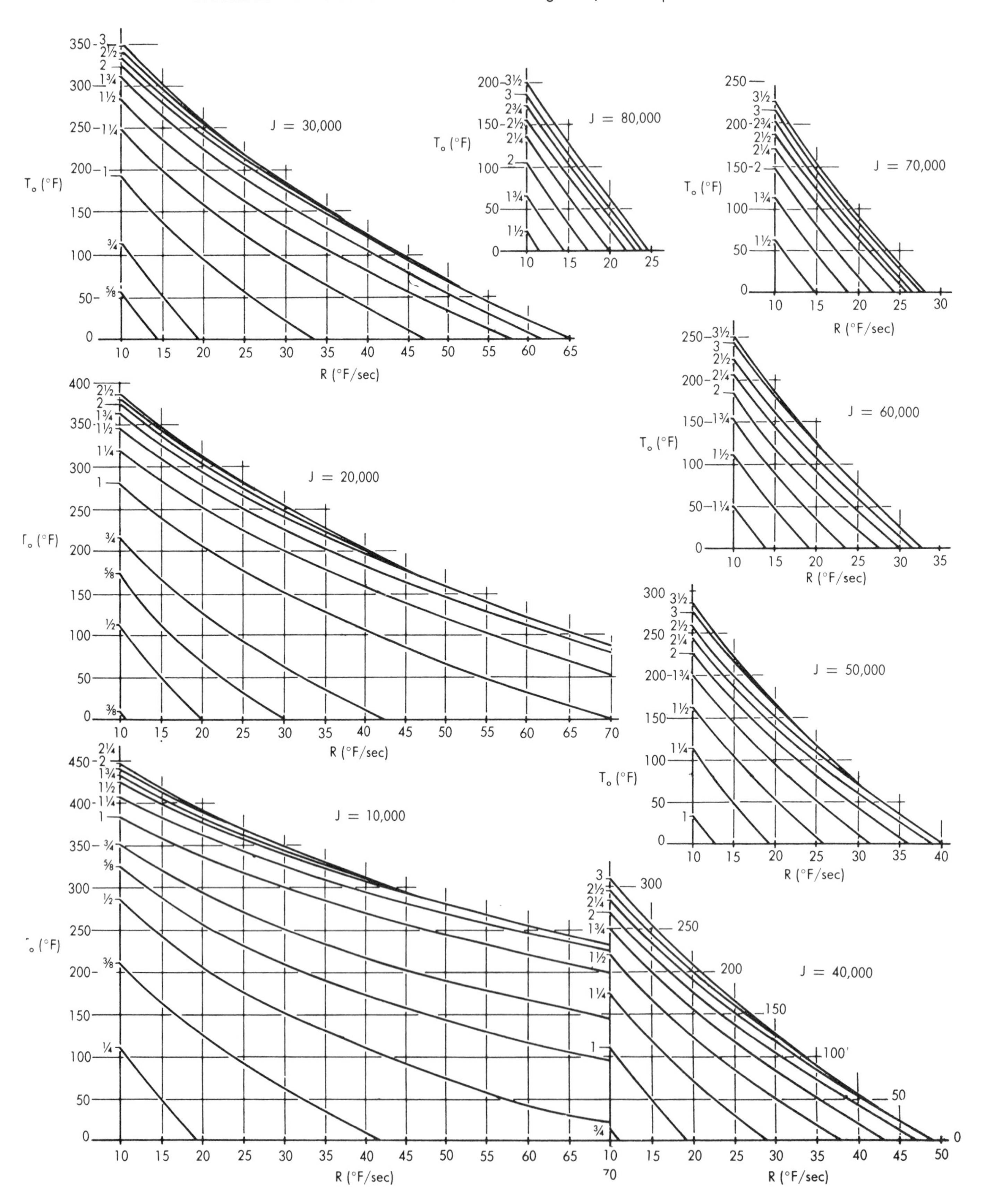

Joint Design

1. FACTORS AFFECTING PROCEDURES

For every welding job there is one procedure which will complete the joint at the lowest possible cost. The accomplishment of this task requires a knowledge of the factors affecting the type of weld to be performed.

The main factors to be considered are:

1. Type of joint to be made, included angle, root opening, and land (root face).
2. Type and size of electrode.
3. Type of current, polarity and amount (amperes).
4. Arc length (arc voltage).
5. Arc speed.
6. Position of welds (flat, horizontal, vertical, and overhead).

A large number of the above-mentioned factors can be determined by actually welding a sample joint. Such items as the type and size of electrode, polarity, current, arc characteristics, and shop techniques are best determined by the fabricator. The engineer must realize that these problems are present and should include them in his consideration of the joint designs.

Figure 1 indicates that the root opening (R) is the separation between the members to be joined.

A root opening is used for electrode accessibility to the base or root of the joint. The smaller the angle of the bevel, the larger the root opening must be to get good fusion at the root.

If the root opening is too small, root fusion is more difficult to obtain and smaller electrodes must be used, thus slowing down the welding process.

If the root opening is too large, weld quality does not suffer but more weld metal is required; this increases weld cost and will tend to increase distortion.

Figure 2 indicates how the root opening must be increased as the bevel's included angle is decreased. Backup strips are used on larger root openings. All three preparations are acceptable; all are conducive to good welding procedure and good weld quality. Selection, therefore, is usually based on cost.

Root opening and joint preparation will directly affect weld cost (pounds of metal required), and choice should be made with this in mind. Joint preparation includes the work required on plate edges prior to welding and includes beveling, providing a land, etc.

In Figure 3a if bevel and/or gap is too small, the weld will bridge the gap leaving slag at the root. Excessive back gouging is then required.

Figure 3b shows how proper joint preparation and

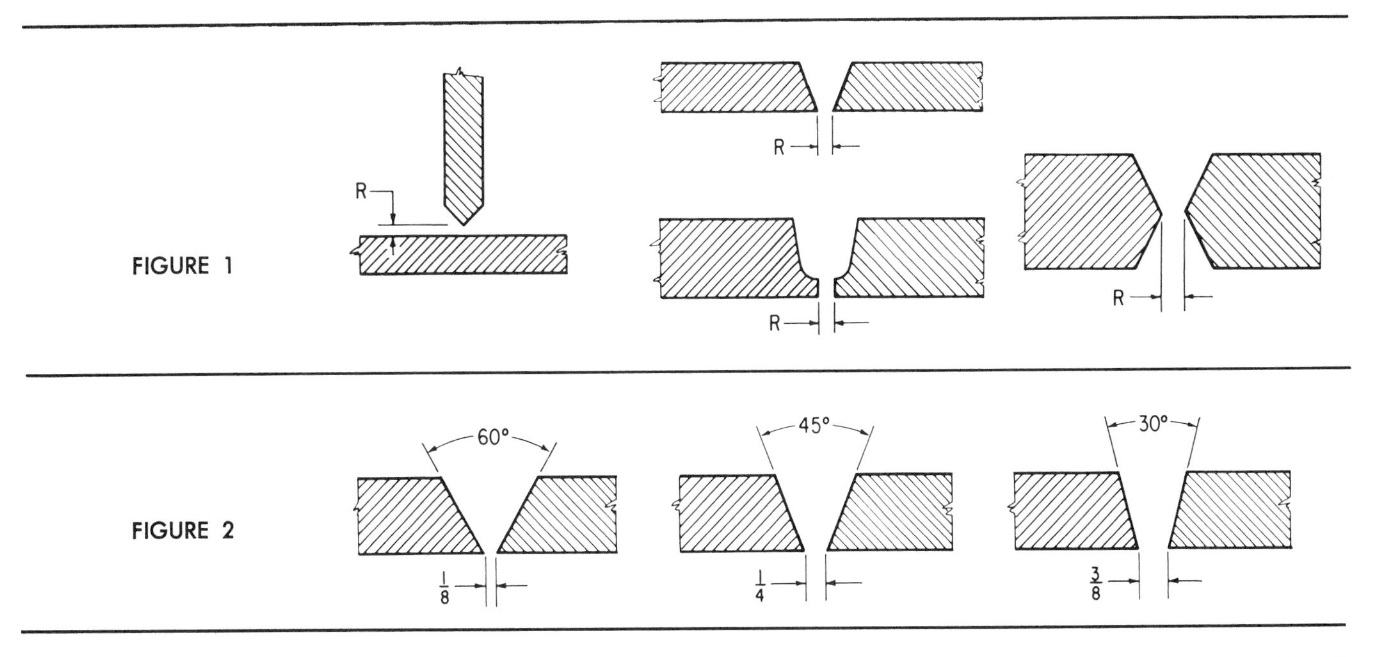

FIGURE 1

FIGURE 2

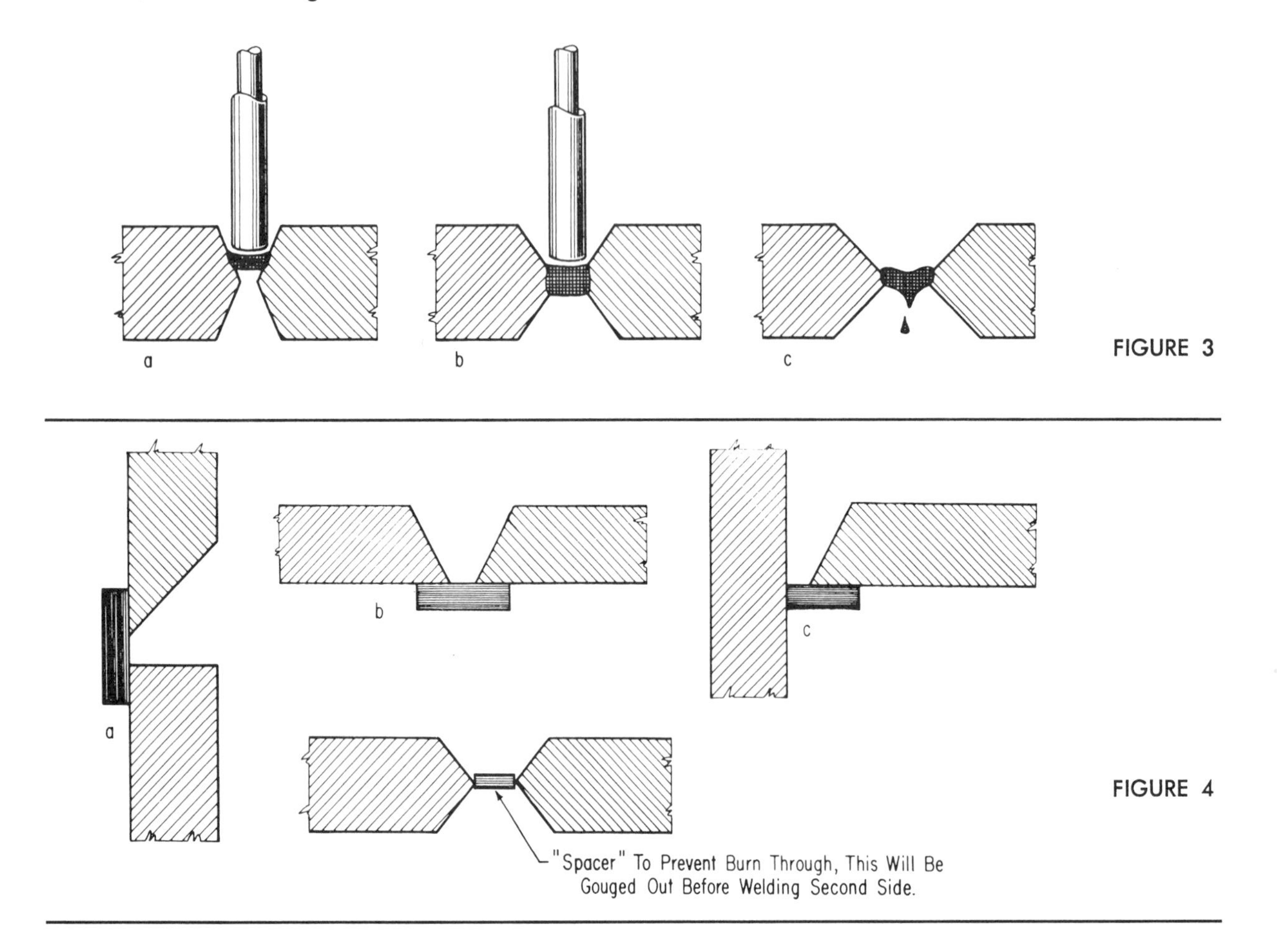
a
b
c
a
b
c
"Spacer" To Prevent Burn Through, This Will Be Gouged Out Before Welding Second Side.

FIGURE 3

FIGURE 4

procedure will produce good root fusion and will minimize back gouging.

In Figure 3c a large root opening will result in burn-through. Spacer strip may be used, in which case the joint must be back gouged.

Backup strips are commonly used when all welding must be done from one side, or when the root opening is excessive. Backup strips, shown in Figure 4a, b and c, are generally left in place and become an integral part of the joint.

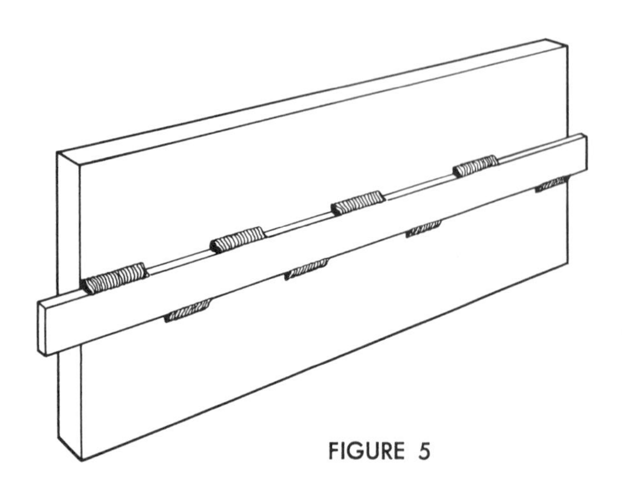

FIGURE 5

Spacer strips may be used especially in the case of double-vee joints to prevent burn-through. The spacer, Figure 4d, to prevent burn-through, will be gouged out before welding the second side.

Backup Strips

Backup strip material should conform to the base metal. Feather edges of the plate are recommended when using a backup strip.

Short intermittent tack welds should be used to hold the backup strip in place, and these should preferably be staggered to reduce any initial restraint of the joint. They should not be directly opposite one another, Figure 5.

The backup strip should be in intimate contact with both plate edges to avoid trapped slag at the root, Figure 6.

Weld Reinforcement

On a butt joint, a nominal weld reinforcement (approximately $1/16''$ above flush) is all that is necessary, Figure 7, left. Additional buildup, Figure 7, right, serves no useful purpose, and will increase the weld cost.

Care should be taken to keep both the width and the height of the reinforcement to a minimum.

2. EDGE PREPARATION

The main purpose of a land, Figure 8, is to provide an additional thickness of metal, as opposed to a feather edge, in order to minimize any burn-through tendency. A feather edge preparation is more prone to burn-through than a joint with a land, especially if the gap gets a little too large, Figure 9.

A land is not as easily obtained as a feather edge. A feather edge is generally a matter of one cut with a torch, while a land will usually require two cuts or possibly a torch cut plus machining.

A land usually requires back gouging if a 100% weld is required. A land is not recommended when welding into a backup strip, Figure 10, since a gas pocket would be formed.

Plate edges are beveled to permit accessibility to all parts of the joint and insure good fusion throughout the entire weld cross-section. Accessibility can be gained by compromising between maximum bevel and minimum root opening, Figure 11.

Degree of bevel may be dictated by the importance of maintaining proper electrode angle in confined quarters, Figure 12. For the joint illustrated, the minimum recommended bevel is 45°.

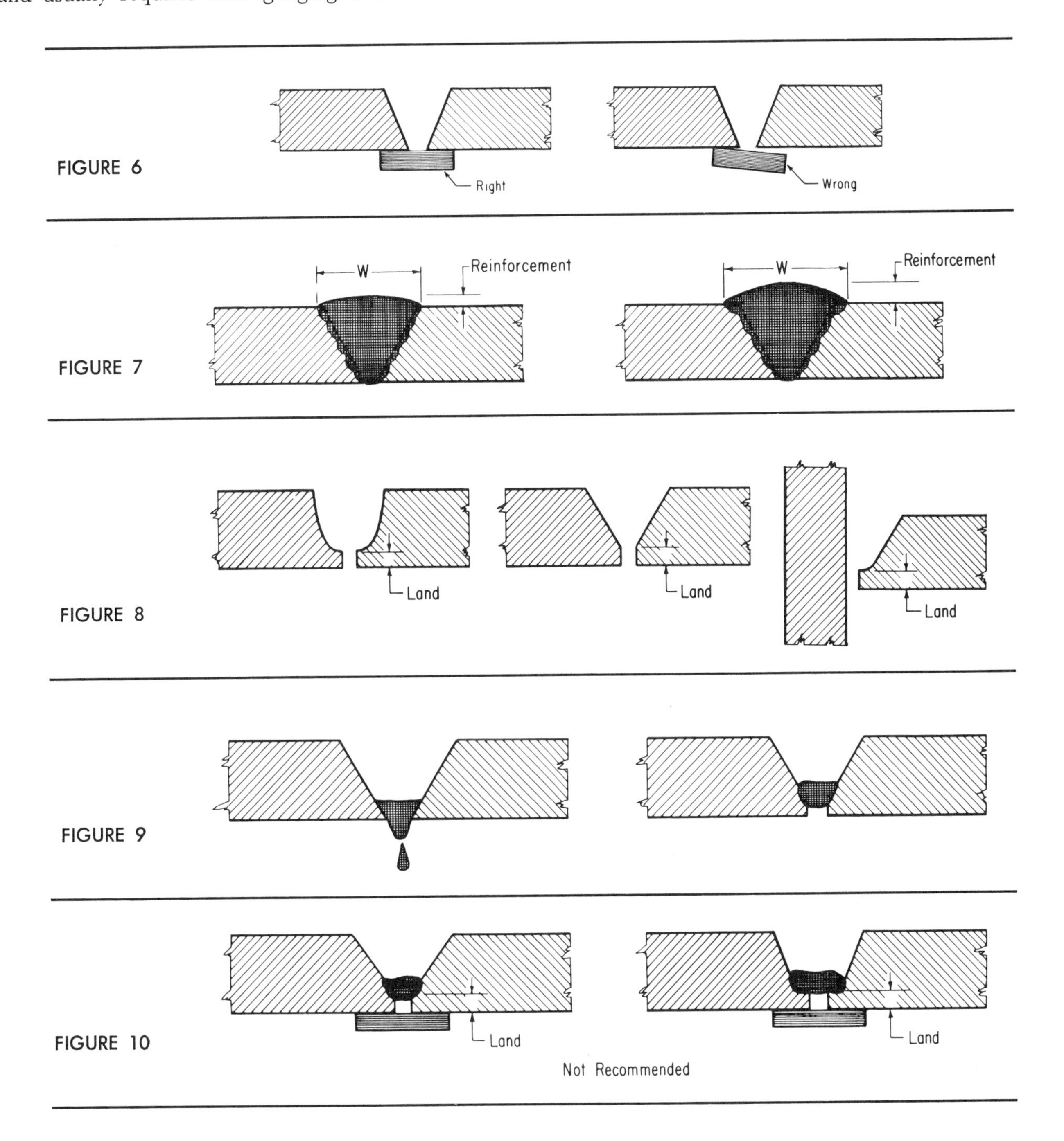

FIGURE 6

FIGURE 7

FIGURE 8

FIGURE 9

FIGURE 10

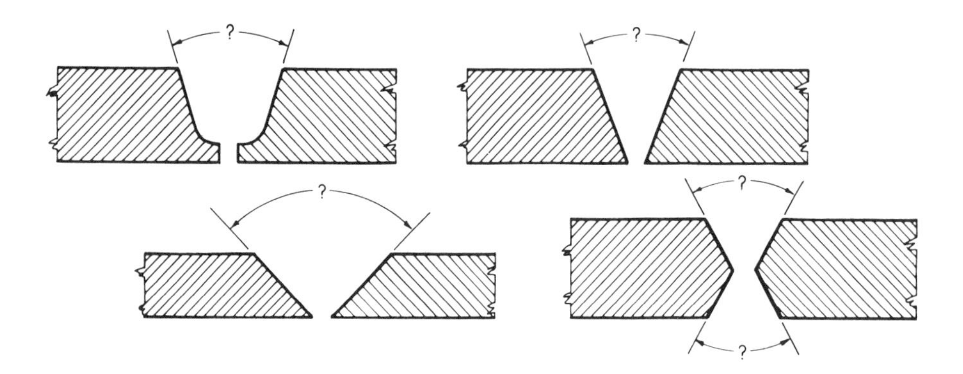

FIGURE 11

U and J versus Vee Preparations

J and U preparations are excellent to work with but economically they have little to offer because preparation requires machining as opposed to simple torch cutting. Also a J or U groove requires a land, Figure 13, and thus back gouging.

Back Gouging

To consistently obtain complete fusion when welding a plate, back gouging is required on virtually all joints except "vees" with feather edge. This may be done by any convenient means: grinding, chipping, or arc-air gouging. The latter method is generally the most economical and leaves an ideal contour for subsequent beads.

Without back gouging, penetration is incomplete, Figure 14. Proper back chipping should be deep enough to expose sound weld metal, and the contour should permit the electrode complete accessibility, Figure 15.

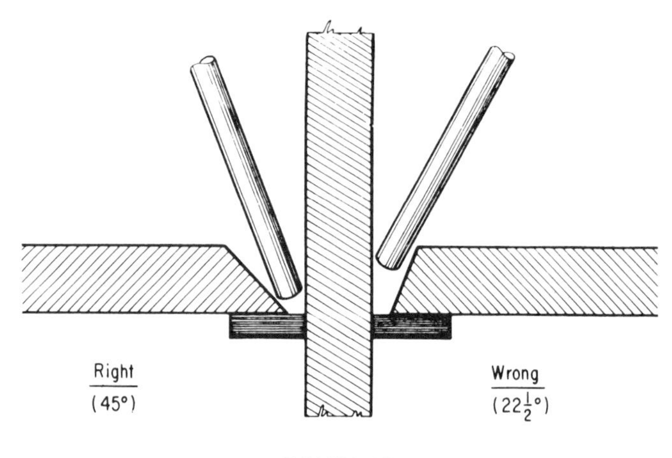

FIGURE 12

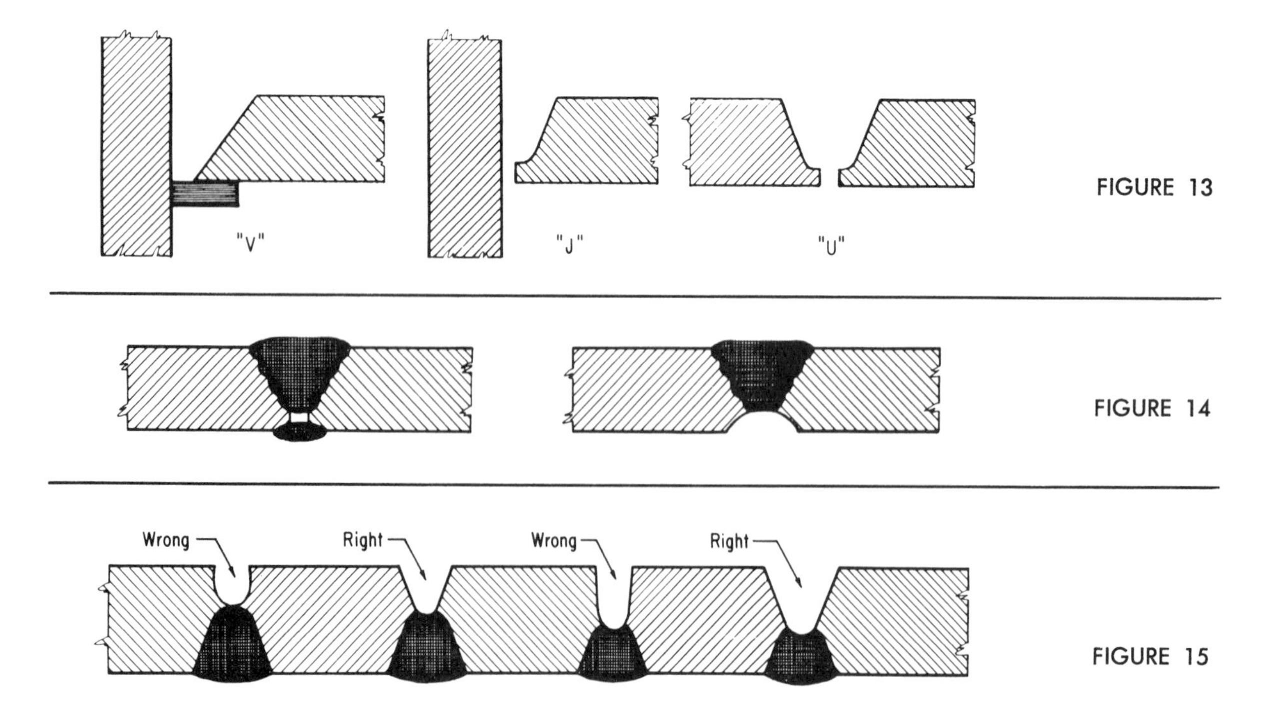

FIGURE 13

FIGURE 14

FIGURE 15

FIGURE 16A—Prequalified AWS Building Joints (Manual Welding)
Complete Penetration Groove Welds—Par. 209

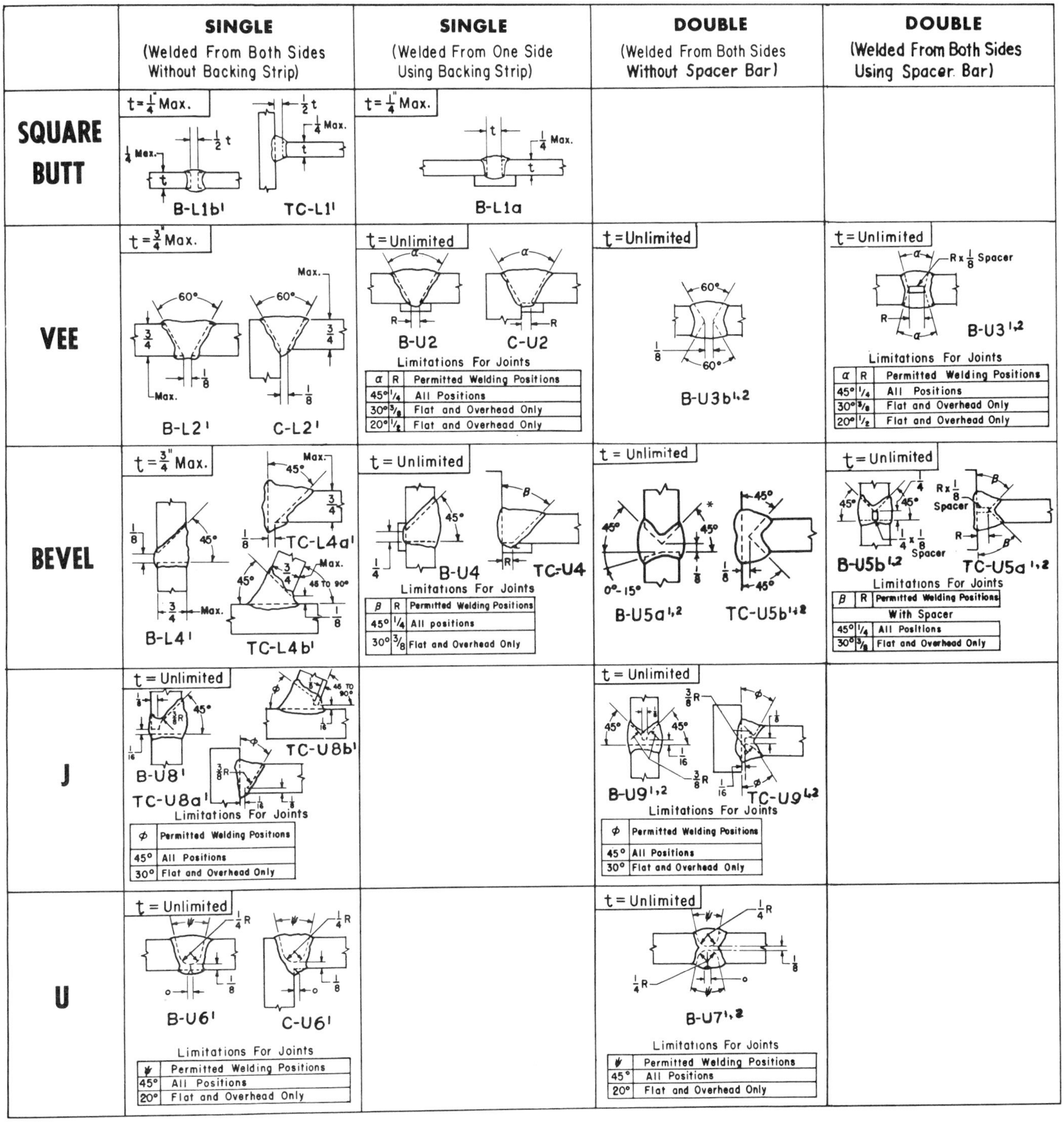

	SINGLE (Welded From Both Sides Without Backing Strip)	SINGLE (Welded From One Side Using Backing Strip)	DOUBLE (Welded From Both Sides Without Spacer Bar)	DOUBLE (Welded From Both Sides Using Spacer Bar)
SQUARE BUTT	t = 1/4" Max.; B-L1b[1]; TC-L1[1]	t = 1/4" Max.; B-L1a		
VEE	t = 3/4" Max.; 60°; B-L2[1]; C-L2[1]	t = Unlimited; B-U2; C-U2	t = Unlimited; 60°; B-U3b[1,2]	t = Unlimited; R x 1/8 Spacer; B-U3[1,2]
BEVEL	t = 3/4" Max.; 45°; B-L4[1]; TC-L4a[1]; TC-L4b[1]	t = Unlimited; 45°; B-U4; TC-U4	t = Unlimited; 45°; 0°–15°; B-U5a[1,2]; TC-U5b[1,2]	t = Unlimited; R x 1/8 Spacer; 1/4 x 1/8 Spacer; B-U5b[1,2]; TC-U5a[1,2]
J	t = Unlimited; 45°; 3/8 R; B-U8[1]; TC-U8a[1]; TC-U8b[1]		t = Unlimited; 45°; 3/8 R; B-U9[1,2]; TC-U9[1,2]	
U	t = Unlimited; 1/4 R; B-U6[1]; C-U6[1]		t = Unlimited; 1/4 R; B-U7[1,2]	

Limitations For Joints (B-U2, C-U2)

α	R	Permitted Welding Positions
45°	1/4	All Positions
30°	3/8	Flat and Overhead Only
20°	1/2	Flat and Overhead Only

Limitations For Joints (B-U3)

α	R	Permitted Welding Positions
45°	1/4	All Positions
30°	3/8	Flat and Overhead Only
20°	1/2	Flat and Overhead Only

Limitations For Joints (B-U4, TC-U4)

β	R	Permitted Welding Positions
45°	1/4	All positions
30°	3/8	Flat and Overhead Only

Limitations For Joints (B-U5b, TC-U5a)

β	R	Permitted Welding Positions With Spacer
45°	1/4	All Positions
30°	3/8	Flat and Overhead Only

Limitations For Joints (B-U8, TC-U8a, TC-U8b)

φ	Permitted Welding Positions
45°	All Positions
30°	Flat and Overhead Only

Limitations For Joints (B-U9, TC-U9)

φ	Permitted Welding Positions
45°	All Positions
30°	Flat and Overhead Only

Limitations For Joints (B-U6, C-U6)

ψ	Permitted Welding Positions
45°	All Positions
20°	Flat and Overhead Only

Limitations For Joints (B-U7)

ψ	Permitted Welding Positions
45°	All Positions
20°	Flat and Overhead Only

NOTE: The size of the fillet weld reinforcing groove welds in Tee and corner joints shall equal t/4 but shall be 3/8" max.

1. Gouge root before welding second side (Par 505i)
2. Use of this weld preferably limited to base metal thickness of 5/8" or larger.

* When lower plate is bevelled, first weld root pass this side.

FIGURE 16B—Prequalified AWS Building Joints (Manual Welding)
Partial Penetration Groove Welds—Par. 210 $t_e \geq \sqrt{\frac{t}{6}}$

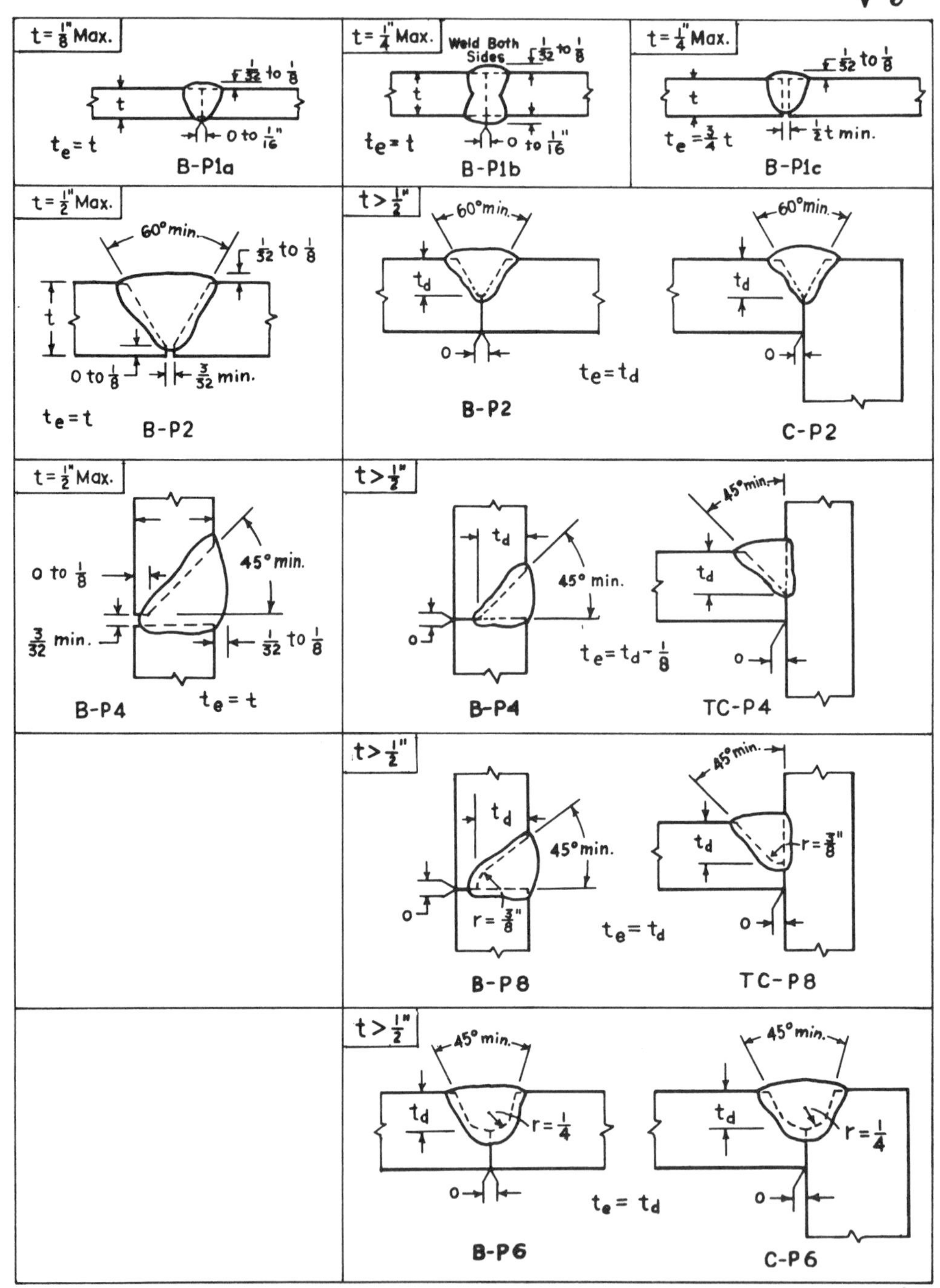

NOTE: 1. Gouge root before welding second side (Par 505i)
2. Use of this weld preferably limited to base metal thickness of 5/8" or larger.
* When lower plate is bevelled, first weld root pass this side.

3. TYPES OF JOINTS

The type of joint to be made depends on the design condition and may be one of the following: groove, fillet, plug or T joint. These joints may be made using various edge preparations, such as: square butt, Vee, bevel, J, or U. Certain of these joints have been prequalified by the American Welding Society (AWS) and are illustrated in two charts, Figure 16 for manual welding and in Figure 17 for submerged-arc automatic welding.

The choice between two or more types of joint

FIGURE 17A—Prequalified AWS Building Joints (Submerged-Arc Automatic Welding)

Complete Penetration Groove Welds—Par. 211

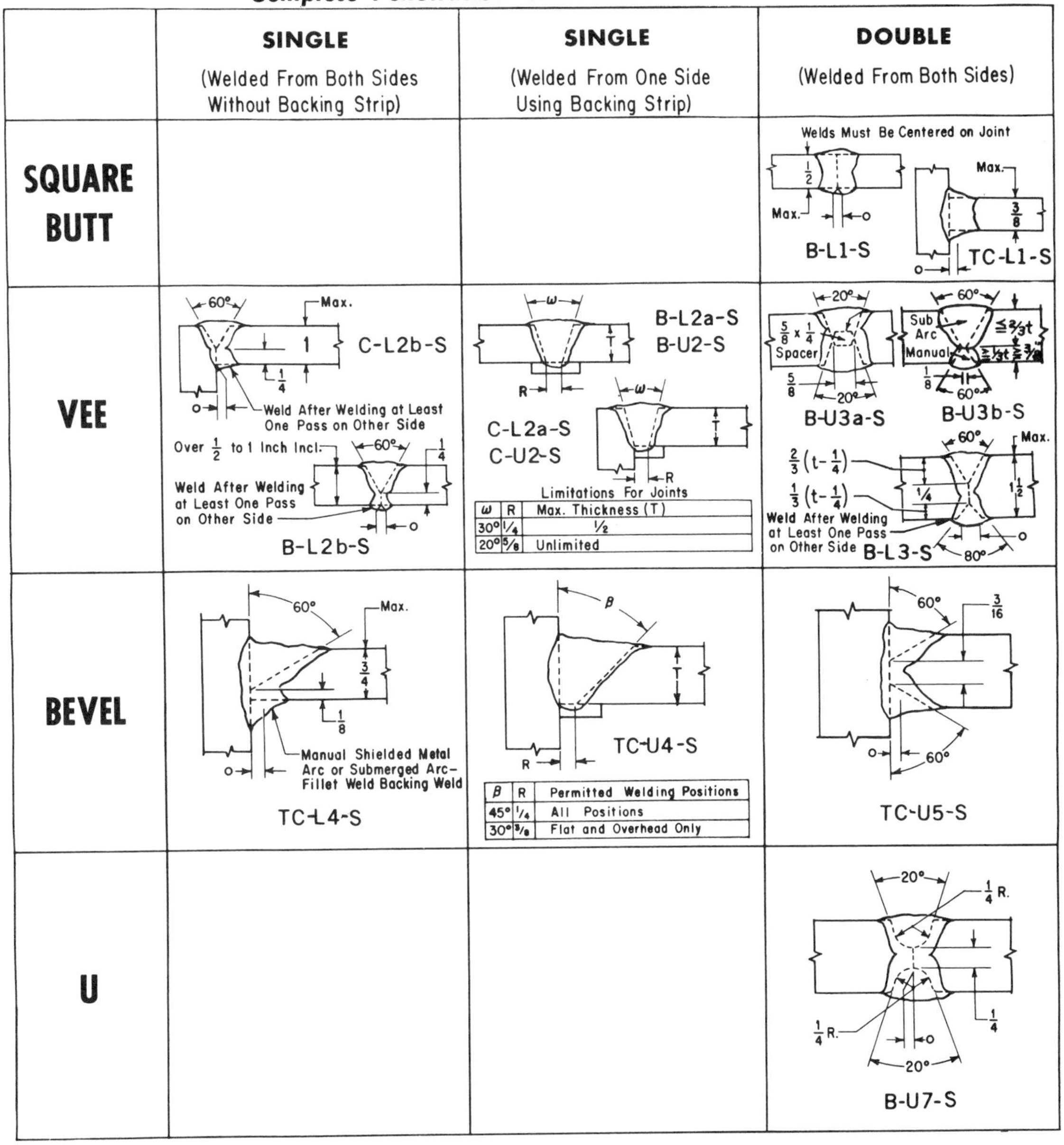

	SINGLE (Welded From Both Sides Without Backing Strip)	SINGLE (Welded From One Side Using Backing Strip)	DOUBLE (Welded From Both Sides)
SQUARE BUTT			Welds Must Be Centered on Joint; B-L1-S; TC-L1-S
VEE	C-L2b-S; B-L2b-S; Weld After Welding at Least One Pass on Other Side; Over ½ to 1 Inch Incl.	B-L2a-S; B-U2-S; C-L2a-S; C-U2-S	B-U3a-S; B-U3b-S; B-L3-S; Weld After Welding at Least One Pass on Other Side
BEVEL	TC-L4-S; Manual Shielded Metal Arc or Submerged Arc–Fillet Weld Backing Weld	TC-U4-S	TC-U5-S
U			B-U7-S

Limitations For Joints

ω	R	Max. Thickness (T)
30°	¼	½
20°	⅝	Unlimited

β	R	Permitted Welding Positions
45°	¼	All Positions
30°	⅜	Flat and Overhead Only

NOTE: The size of the fillet weld reinforcing groove welds in Tee and corner joints shall equal t/4 but shall be ⅜″ max.

1. Gouge root before welding second side (Par 505i)
2. Use of this weld preferably limited to base metal thickness of ⅝″ or larger.

* When lower plate is bevelled, first weld root pass this side.

is not always dictated solely by the design function. The choice often directly affects the cost of welding. For example, Figure 18 illustrates this influence. The choice is to be made between 45° fillet welds or some type of T groove joints.

(a) For full-strength welds, the leg of the fillet weld must be about 75% of the plate thickness.

(b) Full strength may also be obtained by double beveling the edge of the plate 45° and spacing the plate so the root opening is ⅛″ to allow for complete penetration. The amount of weld metal compared to the conventional fillet weld varies from 75% for a 1″ plate to 56% for a 4″ plate. For plates up to about 1½″ thickness, the extra cost of beveling the plate and the probable need to use lower welding current in the 45° groove tend to offset the lower cost of weld metal for this type of joint. But for heavier plate the reduction in weld metal is great enough to overcome any extra preparation cost.

(c) Full strength may also be obtained by bevel-

FIGURE 17B—Prequalified AWS Building Joints (Submerged-Arc Automatic Welding)

Partial Penetration Groove Welds—Par. 212

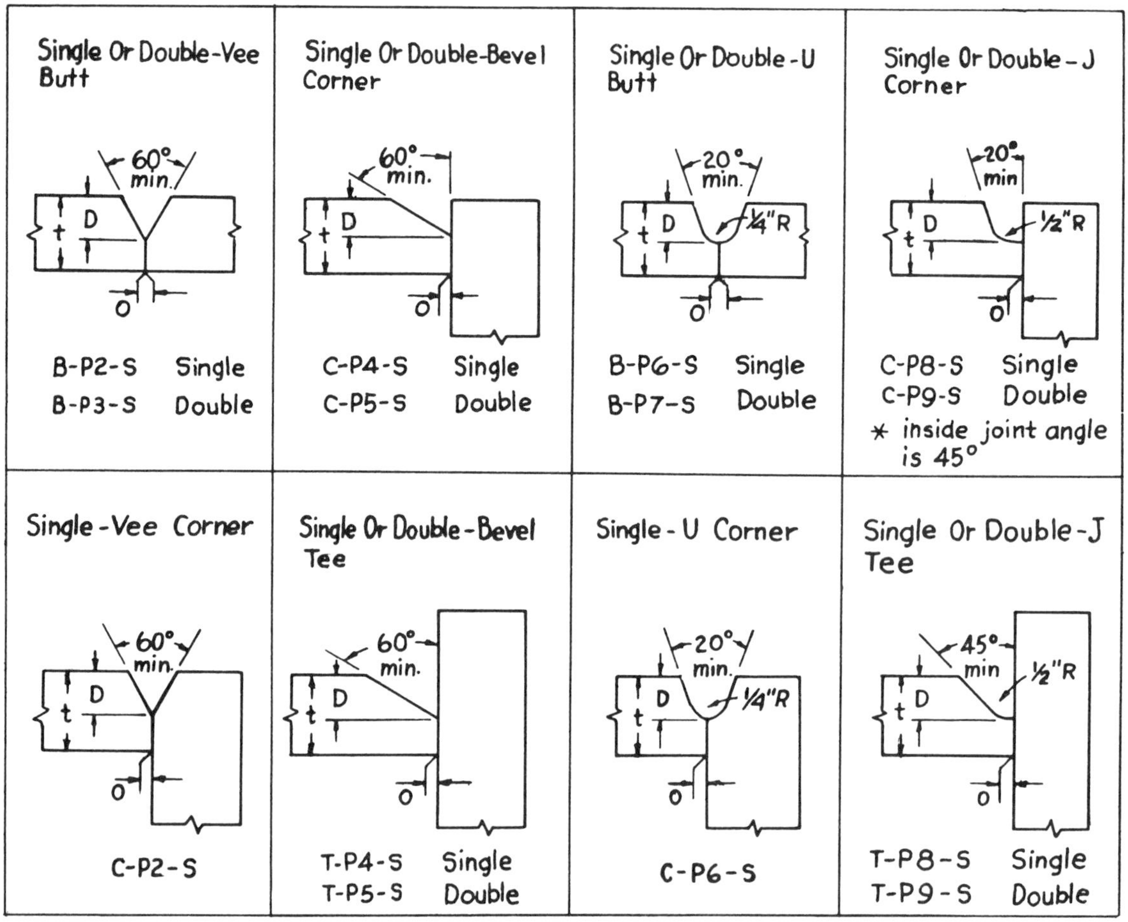

Single Or Double-Vee Butt	Single Or Double-Bevel Corner	Single Or Double-U Butt	Single Or Double-J Corner
60° min.; D; t; O	60° min.; D; t; O	20° min.; D; t; 1/4"R; O	20° min; D; t; 1/2"R; O
B-P2-S Single B-P3-S Double	C-P4-S Single C-P5-S Double	B-P6-S Single B-P7-S Double	C-P8-S Single C-P9-S Double * inside joint angle is 45°
Single-Vee Corner	**Single Or Double-Bevel Tee**	**Single-U Corner**	**Single Or Double-J Tee**
60° min.; D; t; O	60° min.; D; t; O	20° min.; D; t; 1/4"R; O	45° min; D; t; 1/2"R; O
C-P2-S	T-P4-S Single T-P5-S Double	C-P6-S	T-P8-S Single T-P9-S Double

NOTES:

- Welded in the flat position.
- If root face is less than 1/4", there should be at least one manual bead to prevent burnthrough.
- Minimum effective throat $= \sqrt{t/6}$, where t is thickness of thinner part.
- Plate thickness: single groove joint $t \geqq 3/4''$; double groove joint $t \geqq 1\frac{1}{4}''$.
- Effective throat $= t_d$.

ing the edge of the plate 60° so as to place some of the weld within the plate; a 60° fillet is then placed on the outside. The minimum depth of bevel and the additional leg of fillet are both equal to 29% of the plate thickness. For all plate thicknesses, the amount of weld metal is approximately half that of the conventional fillet. This joint has the additional advantage that almost high welding current may be used as in the making of the fillet weld.

All of this is shown in the graph, Figure 18. The cross-over point in this chart between the conventional fillet welds and the 45° full penetrated T groove joint is about 1½" plate. The 60° bevel, partly penetrated joint, with 60° fillets appears to be the lowest in cost above 1" in thicknesses. The relative position of these curves will vary according to the welding and cutting costs used.

It would be a good idea for each company to make a similar cost study of the welding in their shop for guidance of their engineers in quickly selecting the most economical weld. Naturally the various costs (labor, welding, cutting, handling, assembly, etc.) will vary with each company.

4. WELDING SYMBOLS

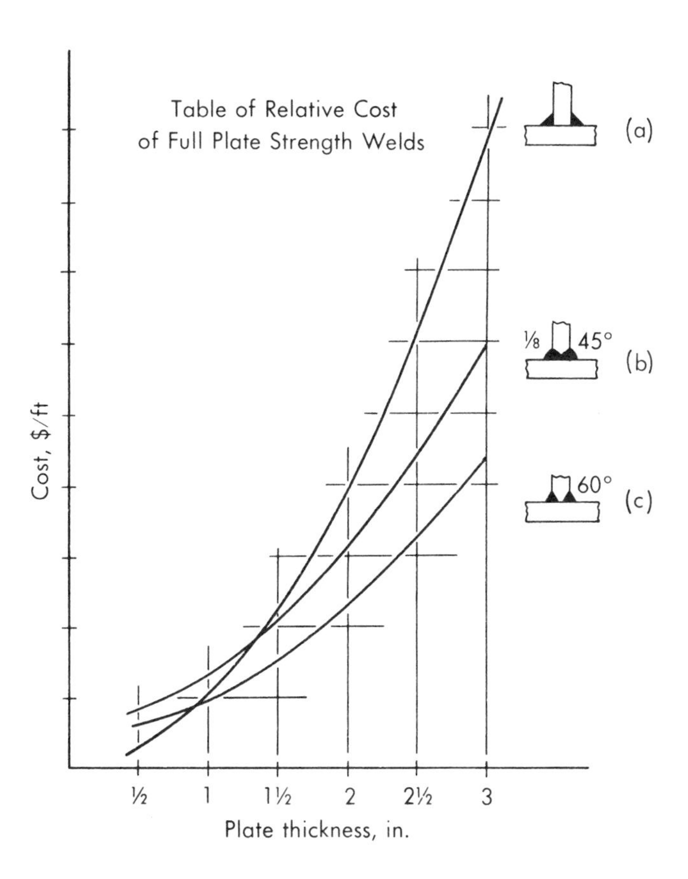

FIGURE 18

The symbols in the chart, Figure 19, denoting the type of weld to be applied to a particular weldment have been standardized and adopted by the American Welding Society. Like any systematic plan of symbols, these welding notations quickly indicate to the designer, draftsman, production supervisor, and weldor alike, the exact welding details established for each joint or connection to satisfy all conditions of material strength and service required. Adapting this system of symbols to your engineering department will assure that the correct welding instructions are transmitted to all concerned and prevent misinterpretation of instructions, and resulting production cost increases.

Although at first it may appear that many different symbols are involved, the system of symbols is broken down into basic elements or fundamentals. Any combination of these elements can then be built up to conform to any set of conditions governing a welded joint.

Therefore, it is wise in the initial stages to limit the use of symbols to just fillet welds and simple groove welds and to detail any special welds on the drawings. After the shop and draftsmen get used to these simple symbols, then they can branch into the ones that are more rarely used. Figure 20 shows the practical application of these symbols to various typical joints.

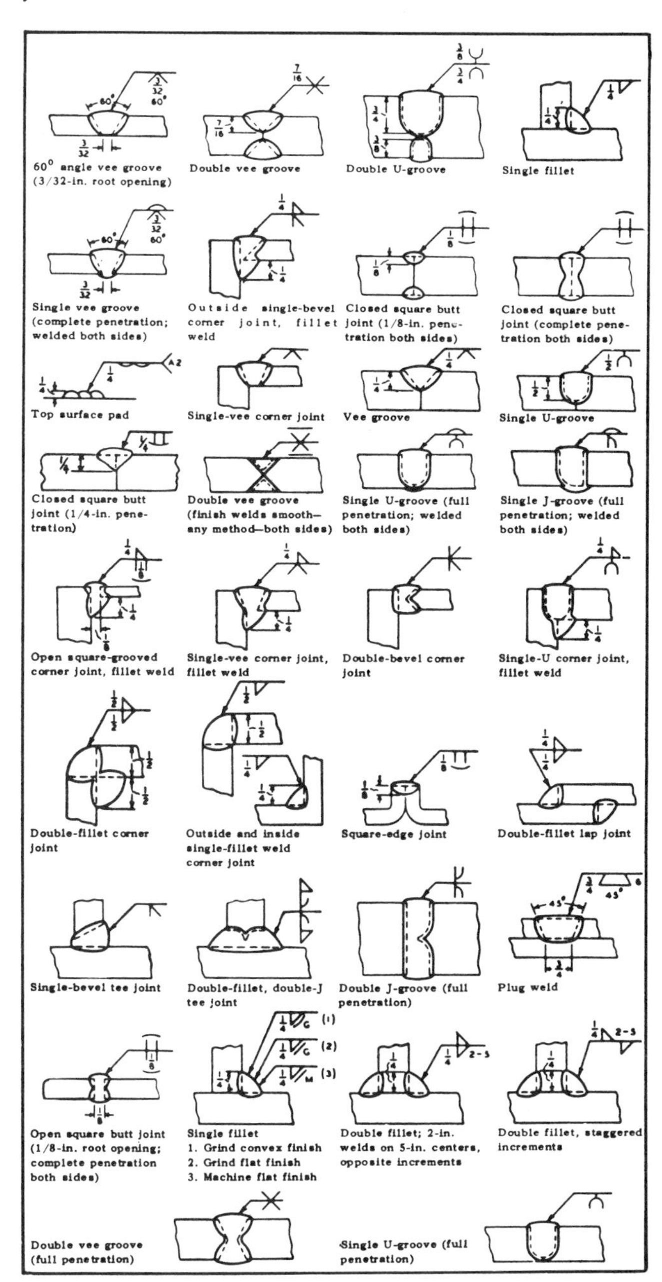

FIG. 20—Typical Applications of AWS Drafting Symbols for Welds.

FIGURE 19

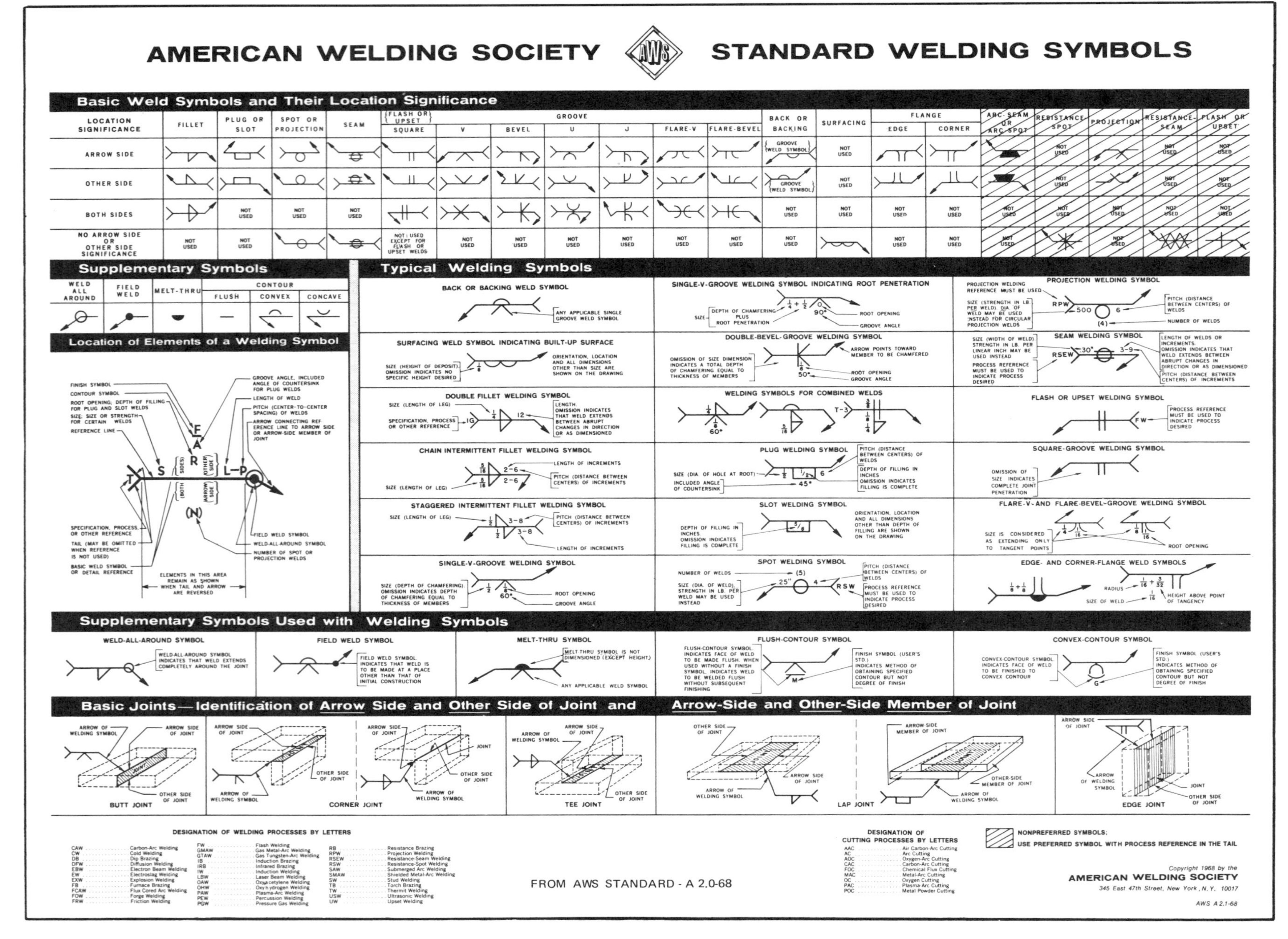
AMERICAN WELDING SOCIETY
STANDARD WELDING SYMBOLS
Basic Weld Symbols and Their Location Significance
LOCATION SIGNIFICANCE
FILLET
PLUG OR SLOT
SPOT OR PROJECTION
SEAM
GROOVE
BACK OR BACKING
SURFACING
FLANGE
ARROW SIDE
OTHER SIDE
BOTH SIDES
NO ARROW SIDE OR OTHER SIDE SIGNIFICANCE
Supplementary Symbols
Location of Elements of a Welding Symbol
Typical Welding Symbols
BACK OR BACKING WELD SYMBOL
SINGLE-V-GROOVE WELDING SYMBOL INDICATING ROOT PENETRATION
PROJECTION WELDING SYMBOL
SURFACING WELD SYMBOL INDICATING BUILT-UP SURFACE
DOUBLE-BEVEL-GROOVE WELDING SYMBOL
SEAM WELDING SYMBOL
DOUBLE FILLET WELDING SYMBOL
WELDING SYMBOLS FOR COMBINED WELDS
FLASH OR UPSET WELDING SYMBOL
CHAIN INTERMITTENT FILLET WELDING SYMBOL
PLUG WELDING SYMBOL
SQUARE-GROOVE WELDING SYMBOL
STAGGERED INTERMITTENT FILLET WELDING SYMBOL
SLOT WELDING SYMBOL
FLARE-V- AND FLARE-BEVEL-GROOVE WELDING SYMBOL
SINGLE-V-GROOVE WELDING SYMBOL
SPOT WELDING SYMBOL
EDGE- AND CORNER-FLANGE WELD SYMBOLS
Supplementary Symbols Used with Welding Symbols
WELD-ALL-AROUND SYMBOL
FIELD WELD SYMBOL
MELT-THRU SYMBOL
FLUSH-CONTOUR SYMBOL
CONVEX-CONTOUR SYMBOL
Basic Joints—Identification of Arrow Side and Other Side of Joint and Arrow-Side and Other-Side Member of Joint
BUTT JOINT
CORNER JOINT
TEE JOINT
LAP JOINT
EDGE JOINT
DESIGNATION OF WELDING PROCESSES BY LETTERS
FROM AWS STANDARD - A 2.0-68
DESIGNATION OF CUTTING PROCESSES BY LETTERS
NONPREFERRED SYMBOLS;
USE PREFERRED SYMBOL WITH PROCESS REFERENCE IN THE TAIL
Copyright 1968 by the
AMERICAN WELDING SOCIETY
345 East 47th Street, New York, N.Y. 10017
AWS A2.1-68

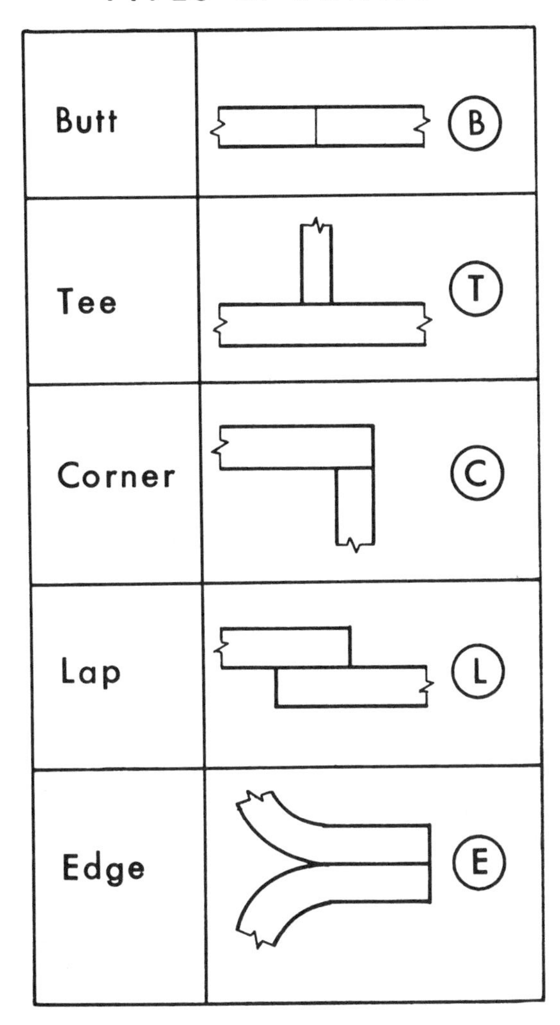

TYPES of WELDS

	Single	Double
Fillet		
Square	* 1	* 1
Bevel Groove	* 4	* 5
Vee Groove	* 2	* 3
J Groove	* 8	* 9
U Groove	* 6	* 7

*Same Number Used on AWS Prequalified Joints, See Figures 16A & B, 17A & B.

FIGURE 21

5. TERMINOLOGY

People who specify or are otherwise associated with welding often use the terms "joint" and "weld" rather loosely. For clarity in communication of instructions, it is desirable to keep in mind the basic difference in meaning between these two terms. This is illustrated by Figure 21.

The left-hand chart shows the five basic types of joints: butt, tee, corner, lap, and edge. Each is defined in a way that is descriptive of the relationship the plates being joined have to each other. Neither the geometry of the weld itself nor the method of edge preparation has any influence on the basic definition of the joint. For instance, the tee joint could be either fillet welded or groove welded.

The right-hand chart shows the basic types of welds: fillet, square, bevel-groove, V-groove, J-groove, and U-groove. The type of joint does not affect what we call the weld. Although the single bevel-groove weld is illustrated as a butt joint, it may be used in a butt, tee or corner joint.

The complete definition of a welded joint must include description of both the joint and the weld.

Efficient fabrication of large curved roof girders for the University of Vermont gymnasium was assured by submerged-arc welding, using semi-automatic guns mounted on self-propelled trackless tractors.

Here production of large box-section bridge girders is speeded by submerged-arc welding and self-propelled trackless trolley which follows the joint with minimum guidance.

Determining Weld Size

1. WHEN TO CALCULATE WELD SIZE

Overwelding is one of the major factors of welding cost. Specifying the correct size of weld is the first step in obtaining low-cost welding. This demands a simple method to figure the proper amount of weld to provide adequate strength for all types of connections.

In strength connections, complete-penetration groove welds must be made all the way through the plate. Since a groove weld, properly made, has equal or better strength than the plate, there is no need for calculating the stress in the weld or attempting to determine its size. However, the size of a partial-penetration groove weld may sometimes be needed. When welding alloy steels, it is necessary to match the weld-metal strength to plate strength. This is primarily a matter of proper electrode selection and of welding procedures.

With fillet welds, it is possible to have too small a weld or too large a weld; therefore, it is necessary to determine the proper weld size.

Strength of Welds

Many engineers are not aware of the great reserve strength that welds have. Table 1 shows the recognized strength of various weld metals (by electrode designation) and of various structural steels.

Notice that the minimum yield strengths of the ordinary E60XX electrodes are over 50% higher than the corresponding minimum yield strengths of the A7, A373 and A36 structural steels for which they should be used.

Since many E60XX electrodes meet the specifications for E70XX classification, they have about 75% higher yield strength than the steel.

Submerged-Arc Welds

AWS and AISC require that the bare electrode and flux combination used for submerged-arc welding shall be selected to produce weld metal having the tensile properties listed in Table 2, when deposited in a multiple-pass weld.

2. FILLET WELD SIZE

The AWS has defined the effective throat area of a fillet weld to be equal to the effective length of the weld times the effective throat. The effective throat is defined as the shortest distance from the root of the diagrammatic weld to the face.

According to AWS the leg size of a fillet weld is measured by the largest right triangle which can be inscribed within the weld, Figure 1.

This definition would allow unequal-legged fillet welds, Figure 1(a). Another AWS definition stipulates the largest isosceles inscribed right triangle and would limit this to an equal-legged fillet weld, Figure 1(b).

Unequal-legged fillet welds are sometimes used to get additional throat area, hence strength, when the

TABLE 1—Minimum Strengths Required of Weld Metals and Structural Steels *(AWS A5.1 & ASTM A233)* *(as-welded condition)*

	Material	Min. Yield Strength psi	Min. Tensile Strength psi
Weld Metals	E6010	50,000 psi	62,000 psi
	E6012	55,000	67,000
	E6024	58,000	62,000
	E6027	50,000	62,000
	E70XX	60,000	72,000
Steels	A7	33,000	60,000
	A373	32,000	58,000
	A36	36,000	58,000
	A441	42,000 46,000 50,000	63,000 67,000 70,000

TABLE 2—Minimum Properties Required of Automatic Submerged-Arc Welds *(AWS & AISC) (as-welded; multiple-pass)*

Grade SAW—1	
tensile strength	62,000 to 80,000 psi
yield point, min.	45,000 psi
elongation in 2 inches, min.	25%
reduction in area, min.	40%

Grade SAW—2	
tensile strength	70,000 to 90,000 psi
yield point, min.	50,000 psi
elongation in 2 inches, min.	22%
reduction in area, min.	40%

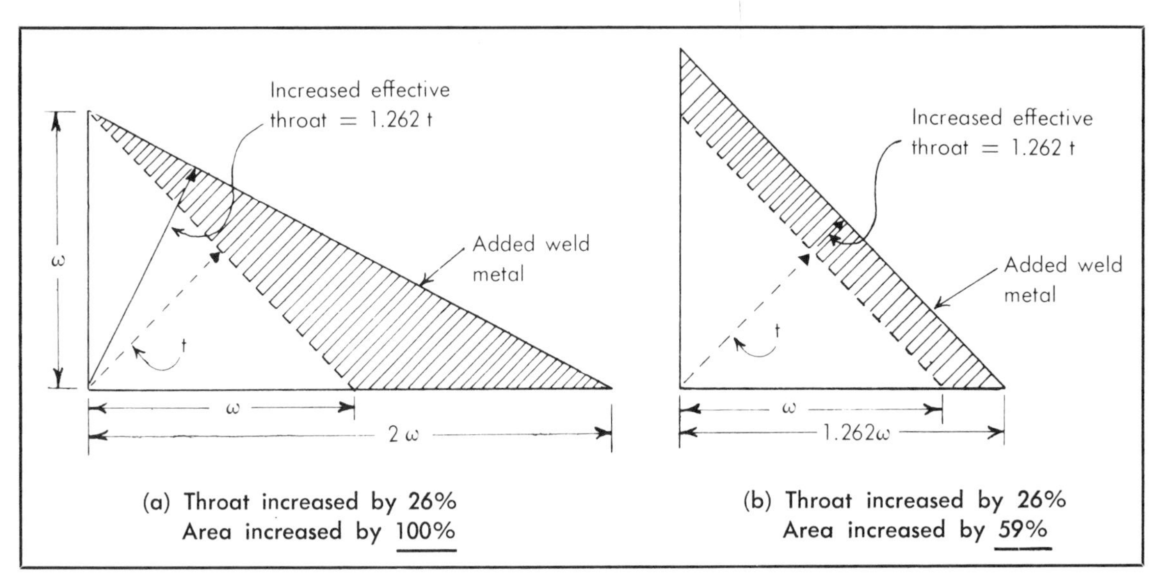

FIGURE 1

vertical leg of the weld cannot be increased. See Figure 2(a).

Where space permits, a more efficient means of obtaining the same increase in throat area or strength is to increase both legs to maintain an equal-legged fillet weld with a smaller increase in weld metal. See Figure 2(b).

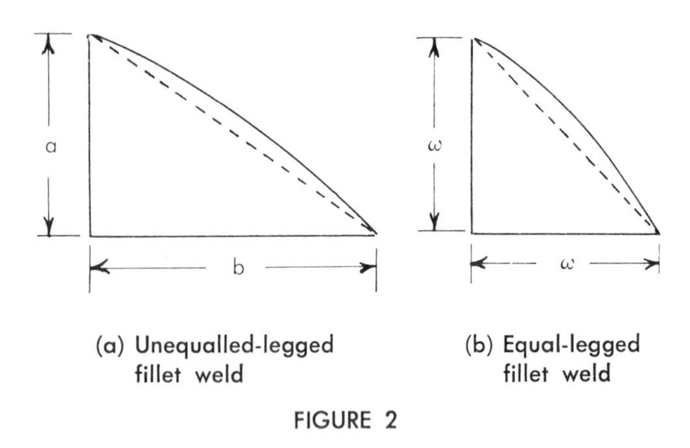

FIGURE 2

One example of this would be the welding of channel shear attachments to beam flanges, Figure 3. Here the vertical leg of the fillet weld must be held to the thickness at the outer edge of the channel flange. Additional strength must be obtained by increasing the horizontal leg of the fillet.

The effective length of the weld is defined as the length of the weld having full throat. Further, the AWS requires that all craters shall be filled to the full cross-section of the weld.

In continuous fillet welds, this is no problem because the weldor will strike an arc for the next electrode on the forward edge of the crater of the previous weld, then swing back into the crater to fill it, and then proceed forward for the remainder of the weld. In this manner no crater will be left unfilled.

In practically all cases of intermittent fillet welds, the required length of the weld is marked out on the plate and the weldor starts welding at one mark and continues to weld until the rim of the weld crater passes the other mark. In other words, the crater is beyond the required length of the intermittent fillet weld and is not counted.

There may be some cases where the crater is filled and included in the weld length. This may be accomplished by filling the crater, or by using a method of welding part way in from one end, breaking the arc and welding in from the other end, and then overlapping in the central portion, thus eliminating any crater.

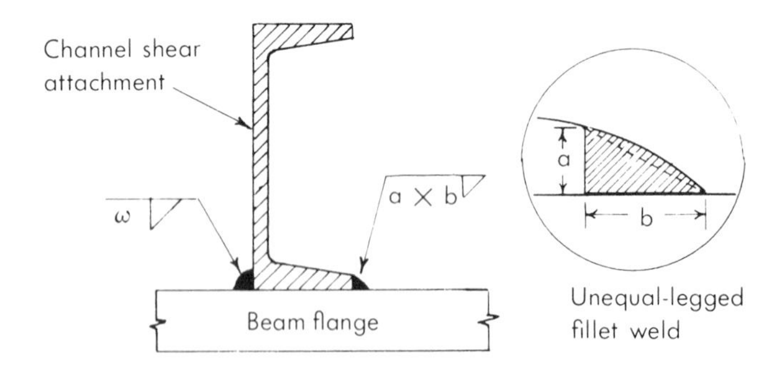

FIGURE 3

The effective throat is defined as the shortest distance between the root of the joint and the face of the diagrammatical weld. This would be a line from the root of the joint and normal to the flat face, Figure 4.

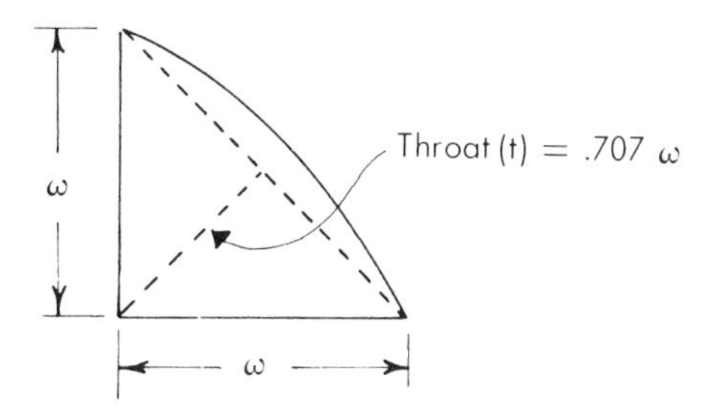

FIGURE 4

For an equal-legged fillet weld, the throat is equal to .707 times the leg size (ω):

$$t = .707\ \omega$$

The allowable force on the fillet weld, 1″ long is—

$$\boxed{f = .707\ \omega\ \tau} \qquad \ldots\ldots\ldots\ldots\ldots\ldots\ldots\ldots (1)$$

where:

f = allowable force on fillet weld, lbs per linear inch

ω = leg size of fillet weld, inches

τ = allowable shear stress on throat of weld, psi

The AWS has set up several shear stress allowables for the throat of the fillet weld. These are shown in Tables 6 and 7 for the Building and Bridge fields.

Minimum Weld Size

(AWS Bldg Art 212(a)1, AWS Bridge Par 217(b), AISC 1.17.4)

In joints connected only by fillet welds, the minimum leg size shall correspond to Table 3. This is determined by the thickness of the thicker part joined, but does not have to exceed the thickness of the thinner part joined.

The American Welding Society recognizes that thick plates offer greater restraint, and produce a faster cooling rate for the welds.

Table 3 is predicated on the theory that the required minimum weld size will provide sufficient welding heat input into the plate to give the desired slow rate of cooling.

This is not a complete answer to this problem; for example, a plate thicker than 6″ would require a minimum weld size of 5/8″, yet in actual practice this would be made in several passes. Each pass would be equivalent to about a 5/16″ fillet, and have the heat input of approximately a 5/16″ weld which may not be sufficient unless the plates are preheated.

A partial solution to this problem would be the following: Since the first pass of the joint is the most critical, it should be made with low-hydrogen electrodes and a rather slow travel speed. Resulting superior weld physicals, weld contour, and maximum heat input provide a good strong root bead.

TABLE 3—Minimum Weld Sizes for Thick Plates (AWS)

THICKNESS OF THICKER PLATE JOINED t	MINIMUM LEG SIZE OF FILLET WELD ω
to 1/2″ incl.	3/16″
over 1/2″ thru 3/4″	1/4″
over 3/4″ thru 1 1/2″	5/16″
over 1 1/2″ thru 2 1/4″	3/8″
over 2 1/4″ thru 6″	1/2″
over 6″	5/8″

Minimum leg size need not exceed thickness of the thinner plate.

Maximum Effective Weld Size

(AWS Bldg Art 212(a)2, AWS Bridge Par 217(c), AISC 1.17.5)

Along the edge of material less than 1/4″ thick, the maximum effective leg size of fillet weld shall be equal to the plate thickness (t):

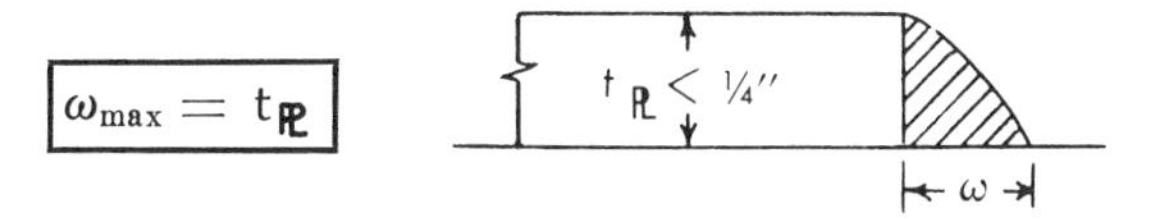

FIGURE 5

Along the edges of material 1/4″ or more in thickness, the maximum effective leg size of fillet weld shall be equal to the plate thickness (t) less 1/16″, unless noted on the drawing that the weld is to be built out to full throat:

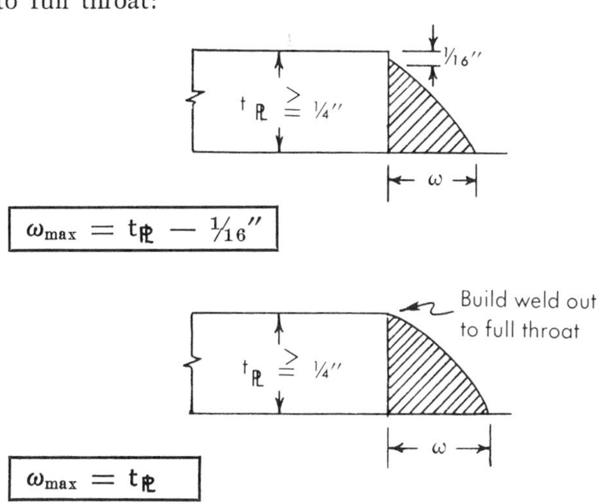

FIGURE 6

Minimum Effective Length

(AWS Bldg Art 212(a)4, AWS Bridge Par 217(d), AISC 1.17.6)

The minimum effective length (L_e) of a fillet weld designed to transfer a force shall be not less than 4 times its leg size or 1½″. Otherwise, the effective leg size (ω_e) of the fillet weld shall be considered not to exceed ¼ of the actual length (short of the crater unless filled).

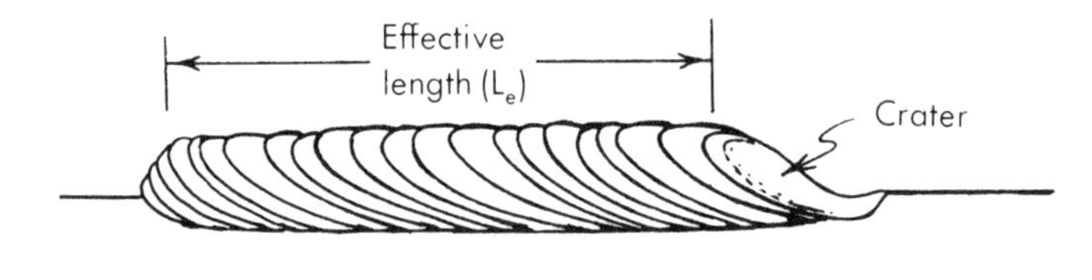

FIGURE 7

$$L_e \geqq 4\ \omega \geqq 1\tfrac{1}{2}''^*$$

Otherwise,

$$\omega_e \leqq \tfrac{1}{4}\ L$$

If longitudinal fillet welds are used alone in end connections of flat bar tension members:

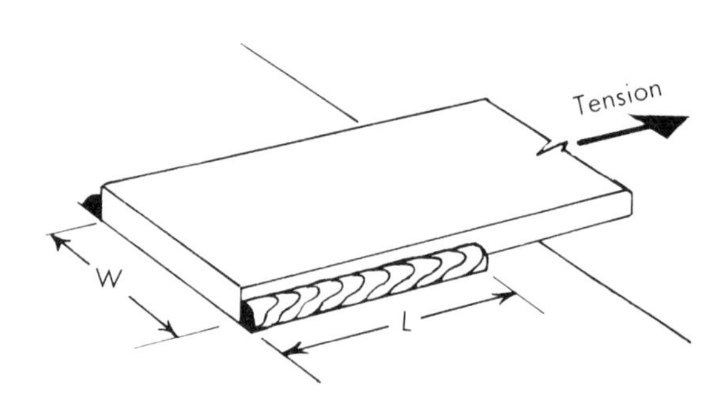

FIGURE 8

(AWS Bldg Art 212(a)3, AISC 1.17.6)

$$L_e \geqq W$$
$$W \leqq 8''$$

unless additional welding prevents transverse bending within the connection.

*In addition, the effective length (L_e) of an intermittent fillet weld shall not be less than 1½″ (AISC 1.17.7).

3. OTHER WELD REQUIREMENTS

Minimum Overlap of Lap Joints

(AWS Bldg Art 212(b)1, AISC 1.17.8)

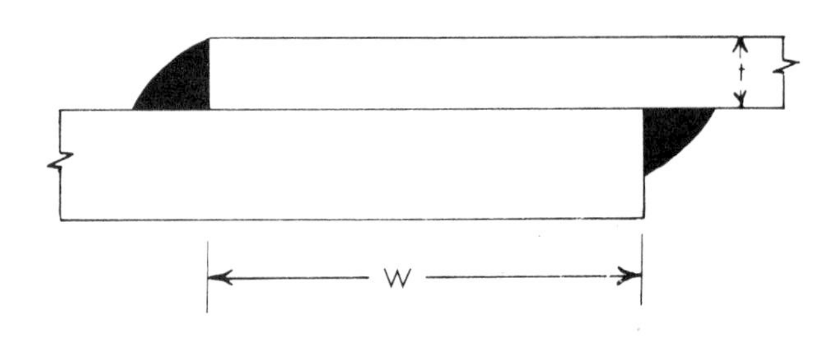

FIGURE 9

$$W \geqq 5\ t \geqq 1''$$

where t = thickness of thinner plate

Thickness of Plug or Slot Welds

(AWS Bldg Art 213, AWS Bridge Par 218, AISC 1.17.11)

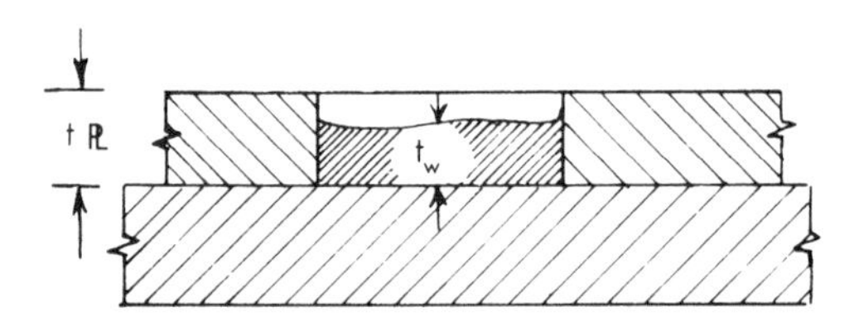

FIGURE 10

1. If $t_{℞} \leqq ⅝''$
   then $t_w = t_{℞}$
2. If $t_{℞} > ⅝''$
   then $t_w \geqq \tfrac{1}{2}\ t_{℞} \geqq ⅝''$

Spacing and Size of Plug Welds

(AWS Bldg Art 213, AWS Bridge Par 218, AISC 1.17.11)

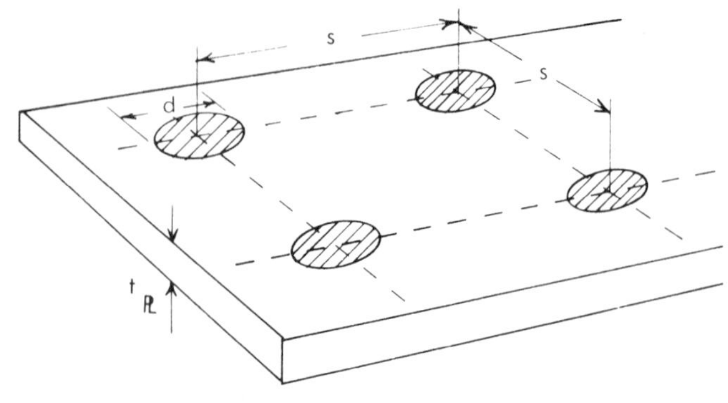

FIGURE 11

$s \geqq 4\ d$

$d \geqq t_{PL} + 5/16'' < 2\frac{1}{4}\ t_w$

Spacing and Size of Slot Welds

$L \leqq 10\ t_w$

$W \geqq t_{PL} + 5/16'' \leqq 2\frac{1}{4}\ t_w$

$s_T \geqq 4\ W$

$s_L \geqq 2\ L$

$r \geqq t_{PL}$

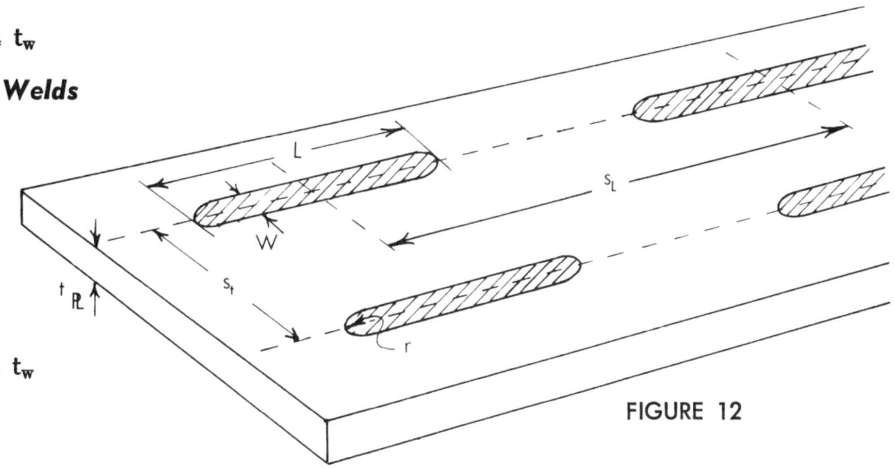

FIGURE 12

4. PARTIAL-PENETRATION GROOVE WELDS

Partial-penetration groove welds are allowed in the building field. They have many applications; for example, field splices of columns, built-up box sections for truss chords, etc.

For the V, J or U grooves made by manual welding, and all joints made by submerged-arc welding, it is assumed the bottom of the joint can be reached easily. So, the effective throat of the weld (t_e) is equal to the actual throat of the prepared groove (t). See Figure 13.

If a bevel groove is welded manually, it is assumed that the weldor may not quite reach the bottom of the groove. Therefore, AWS and AISC deduct ⅛″ from the prepared groove. Here the effective throat (t_e) will equal the throat of the groove (t) minus ⅛″. See Figure 13(a).

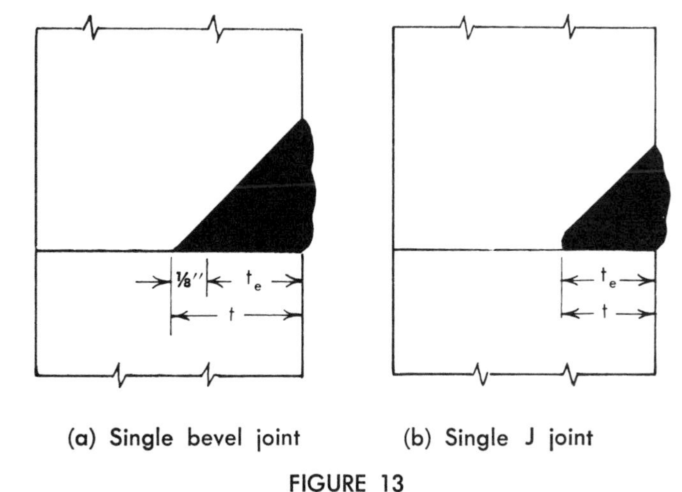

(a) Single bevel joint (b) Single J joint

FIGURE 13

Tension applied parallel to the weld's axis, or compression in any direction, has the same allowable stress as the plate.

Tension applied transverse to the weld's axis, or shear in any direction, has a reduced allowable stress, equal to that for the throat of a corresponding fillet weld.

Just as fillet welds have a minimum size for thick plates because of fast cooling and greater restraint, so partial-penetration groove welds have a minimum effective throat (t_e) which should be used —

$$t_e \geqq \sqrt{\frac{t_p}{6}}$$

where:

t_p = thickness of thinner plate

5. TYPES OF WELDS

a. Primary welds transmit the entire load at the particular point where they are located. If the weld fails, the member fails. The weld must have the same property as the member at this point. In brief, the weld becomes the member at this point.

b. Secondary welds simply hold the parts together, thus forming the member. In most cases, the forces on these welds are low.

c. Parallel welds have forces applied parallel to their axis. In the case of fillet welds, the throat is stressed only in shear. For an equal-legged fillet, the maximum shear stress occurs on the 45° throat.

d. Transverse welds have forces applied transversely or at right angles to their axis. In the case of fillet welds, the throat is stressed both in shear and in tension or compression. For an equal-legged fillet weld, the maximum shear stress occurs on the 67½° throat, and the maximum normal stress occurs on the 22½° throat.

TABLE 4—Determining Force on Weld

	Type of Loading	standard design formula stress lbs/in^2	treating the weld as a line force lbs/in
	PRIMARY WELDS transmit entire load at this point		
	tension or compression	$\sigma = \frac{P}{A}$	$f = \frac{P}{A_w}$
	vertical shear	$\sigma = \frac{V}{A}$	$f = \frac{V}{A_w}$
	bending	$\sigma = \frac{M}{S}$	$f = \frac{M}{S_w}$
	twisting	$\sigma = \frac{T\,C}{J}$	$f = \frac{T\,C}{J_w}$
	SECONDARY WELDS hold section together - low stress		
	horizontal shear	$\tau = \frac{V\,A\,y}{I\,t}$	$f = \frac{V\,A\,y}{I\,n}$
	torsional horizontal shear*	$\tau = \frac{T}{2\,At}$	$f = \frac{T}{2\,A}$

A = area contained within median line.
(*) applies to closed tubular section only.

6. SIMPLE TENSILE, COMPRESSIVE OR SHEAR LOADS ON WELDS

For a simple tensile, compressive or shear load, the given load is divided by the length of the weld to arrive at the applied unit force, lbs per linear inch of weld. From this force, the proper leg size of fillet weld or throat of groove weld may be found.

7. BENDING OR TWISTING LOADS ON WELDS

The problem here is to determine the properties of the welded connection in order to check the stress in the weld without first knowing its leg size. Some design texts suggest assuming a certain weld-leg size and then calculating the stress in the weld to see if it is overstressed or understressed. If the result is too far off, then the weld-leg size is readjusted.

This has the following disadvantages:

1. Some decision must be made as to what throat section is going to be used to determine the property of the weld. Usually some objection can be raised to any throat section chosen.

2. The resulting stresses must be combined and, for several types of loading, this can be rather complicated.

In contrast, the following is a simple method to determine the correct amount of welding required for adequate strength. This is a method in which the weld is treated as a line, having no area, but a definite length and outline. This method has the following advantages:

1. It is not necessary to consider throat areas because only a line is considered.

2. Properties of the welded connection are easily found from a table without knowing weld-leg size.

3. Forces are considered on a unit length of weld instead of stresses, thus eliminating the knotty problem of combining stresses.

4. It is true that the stress distribution within a fillet weld is complex, due to eccentricity of the applied force, shape of the fillet, notch effect of the root, etc.; however, these same conditions exist in the actual fillet welds tested and have been recorded as a unit force per unit length of weld.

8. DETERMINING FORCE ON WELD

Visualize the welded connection as a single line, having the same outline as the connection, but no cross-sectional area. Notice, Figure 14, that the area (A_w) of the welded connection now becomes just the length of the weld.

Instead of trying to determine the stress on the weld (this cannot be done unless the weld size is known), the problem becomes a much simpler one of determining the force on the weld.

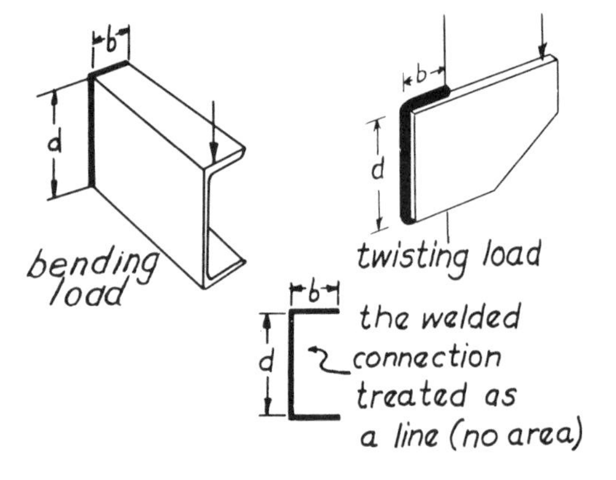

FIG. 14 Treating weld as a line.

By inserting the property of the welded connection treated as a line into the standard design formula used for that particular type of load (see Table 4), the force on the weld may be found in terms of lbs per linear inch of weld.

Example: Bending

Standard design formula (bending stress)	Same formula used for weld (treating weld as a line)
$\sigma = \frac{M}{S} = \frac{lbs}{in.^2}$ stress	$f = \frac{M}{S_w} = \frac{lbs}{in.}$ force

Normally the use of these standard design formulas results in a unit stress, psi; however, when the weld is treated as a line, these formulas result in a force on the weld, lbs per linear inch.

For secondary welds, the weld is not treated as a line, but standard design formulas are used to find the force on the weld, lbs per linear inch.

In problems involving bending or twisting loads Table 5 is used to determine properties of the weld treated as a line. It contains the section modulus (S_w), for bending, and polar moment of inertia (J_w), for twisting, of some 13 typical welded connections with the weld treated as a line.

For any given connection, two dimensions are needed, width (b) and depth (d).

Section modulus (S_w) is used for welds subject to bending loads, and polar moment of inertia (J_w) for twisting loads.

Section moduli (S_w) from these formulas are for maximum force at the top as well as the bottom portions of the welded connections. For the unsymmetrical connections shown in this table, maximum bending force is at the bottom.

If there is more than one force applied to the weld, these are found and combined. All forces which are combined (vectorially added) must occur at the same position in the welded joint.

Determining Weld Size by Using Allowables

Weld size is obtained by dividing the resulting force on the weld found above, by the allowable strength of the particular type of weld used (fillet or groove), obtained from Tables 6 and 7 (steady loads) or Tables 8 and 9 (fatigue loads).

If there are two forces at right angles to each other, the resultant is equal to the square root of the sum of the squares of these two forces.

$$f_r = \sqrt{f_1^2 + f_2^2} \quad \text{..................(3)}$$

If there are three forces, each at right angles to each other, the resultant is equal to the square root of the sum of the squares of the three forces.

$$f_r = \sqrt{f_1^2 + f_2^2 + f_3^2} \quad \text{..................(4)}$$

One important advantage to this method, in addition to its simplicity, is that no new formulas must be used, nothing new must be learned. Assume an engineer has just designed a beam. For strength he has used the standard formula $\sigma = M/S$. Substituting the load on the beam (M) and the property of the beam (S) into this formula, he has found the bending stress (σ). Now, he substitutes the property of the weld, treating it as a line (S_w), obtained from Table 5, into the same formula. Using the same load (M), $f = M/S_w$, he thus finds the force on the weld (f) per linear inch. The weld size is then found by dividing the force on the weld by the allowable force.

TABLE 5—Properties of Weld Treated as Line

Outline of Welded Joint b = width d = depth	Bending (about horizontal axis x-x)	Twisting
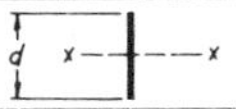	$S_w = \frac{d^2}{6}$ in.^{2}	$J_w = \frac{d^3}{12}$ in.^{3}
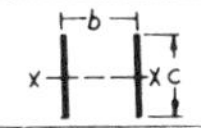	$S_w = \frac{d^2}{3}$	$J_w = \frac{d(3b^2 + d^2)}{6}$
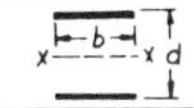	$S_w = bd$	$J_w = \frac{b^3 + 3bd^2}{6}$
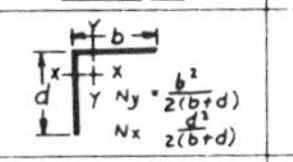 $N_y = \frac{b^2}{2(b+d)}$ $N_x = \frac{d^2}{2(b+d)}$	$S_w = \frac{4bd+d^2}{6}$ (top) $= \frac{d^2(4b+d)}{6(2b+d)}$ (bottom)	$J_w = \frac{(b+d)^4 - 6b^2d^2}{12(b+d)}$
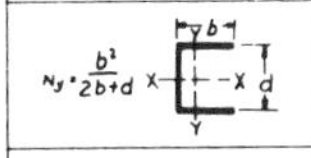 $N_y = \frac{b^2}{2b+d}$	$S_w = bd + \frac{d^2}{6}$	$J_w = \frac{(2b+d)^3}{12} - \frac{b^2(b+d)^2}{(2b+d)}$
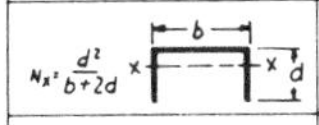 $N_x = \frac{d^2}{b+2d}$	$S_w = \frac{2bd+d^2}{3}$ (top) $= \frac{d^2(2b+d)}{3(b+d)}$ (bottom)	$J_w = \frac{(b+2d)^3}{12} - \frac{d^2(b+d)^2}{(b+2d)}$
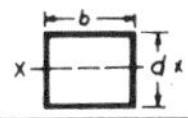	$S_w = bd + \frac{d^2}{3}$	$J_w = \frac{(b+d)^3}{6}$
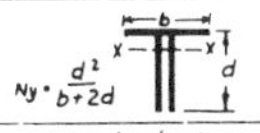 $N_y = \frac{d^2}{b+2d}$	$S_w = \frac{2bd+d^2}{3}$ (top) $= \frac{d^2(2b+d)}{3(b+d)}$ (bottom)	$J_w = \frac{(b+2d)^3}{12} - \frac{d^2(b+d)^2}{(b+2d)}$
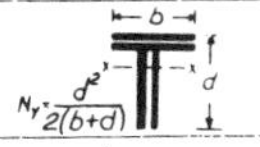 $N_y = \frac{d^2}{2(b+d)}$	$S_w = \frac{4bd+d^2}{3}$ (top) $= \frac{4bd^2+d^3}{6b+3d}$ (bottom)	$J_w = \frac{d^3(4b+d)}{6(b+d)} + \frac{b^3}{6}$
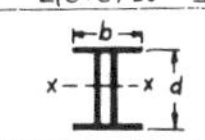	$S_w = bd + \frac{d^2}{3}$	$J_w = \frac{b^3 + 3bd^2 + d^3}{6}$
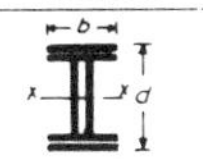	$S_w = 2bd + \frac{d^2}{3}$	$J_w = \frac{2b^3 + 6bd^2 + d^3}{6}$
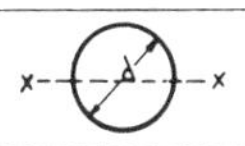	$S_w = \frac{\pi d^2}{4}$	$J_w = \frac{\pi d^3}{4}$
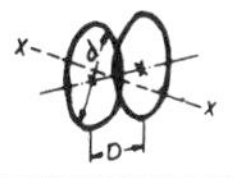	$I_w = \frac{\pi d}{2}\left(D^2 + \frac{d^2}{2}\right)$ $S_w = \frac{I_w}{c}$ where $c = \frac{\sqrt{D^2+d^2}}{2}$	

Applying System to Any Welded Connection

1. Find the position on the welded connection where the combination of forces will be maximum. There may be more than one which should be considered.

2. Find the value of each of the forces on the welded connection at this point. (a) Use Table 4 for the standard design formula to find the force on the weld. (b) Use Table 5 to find the property of the weld treated as a line.

3. Combine (vectorially) all of the forces on the weld at this point.

4. Determine the required weld size by dividing this resultant value by the allowable force in Tables 6, 7, 8, or 9.

TABLE 6—Allowables for Welds—Buildings (AWS Bldg & AISC)

Type of Weld	Stress	Steel	Electrode	Allowable
Complete-Penetration Groove Welds	tension compression shear	A7, A36, A373	‡E60 or SAW-1	same as PL
		A441, A242*	E70 or SAW-2	
Partial-Penetration Groove Welds	tension transverse to axis of weld or shear on effective throat	A7, A36, A373	E60 or SAW-1	σ or τ = 13,600 psi
		A441, A242*	E60 low-hydrogen or SAW-1	
		A7, A373	E70 or SAW-2	
		A36	E70 or SAW-2	σ or τ = 15,800 psi
		A441, A242*	E70 low-hydrogen or SAW-2	
	tension parallel to axis of weld or compression on effective throat	A7, A36, A373	‡E60 or SAW-1	same as PL
		A441 or A242*	E70 or SAW-1	
Fillet Weld	shear on effective throat	A7, A36, A373	E60 or SAW-1	τ = 13,600 psi or f = 9600 ω lb/in
		A441, A242*	E60 low-hydrogen or SAW-2	
		A7, A373	E70 or SAW-2	
		A36	E70 or SAW-2	τ = 15,800 psi or f = 11,200 ω lb/in
		A441, A242*	E70 low-hydrogen or SAW-2	
Plug and Slot	shear on effective area	Same as for fillet weld		

* weldable A242
‡ E70 or SAW-2 could be used, but would not increase allowable

TABLE 7—Allowables for Welds—Bridges (AWS Bridge)

Type of Weld	Stress	Steel	Electrode	Allowable
Complete-Penetration Groove Welds	tension compression shear	A7, A373	‡E60 or SAW-1	Same as PL
		A36 ≦ 1″ thick		
		A36 > 1″ thick	‡E60 low-hydrogen or SAW-1	
		A441, A242*	E70 low-hydrogen or SAW-2	
Fillet Welds	shear on effective throat	A7, A373	‡E60 or SAW-1	τ = 12,400 psi or f = 8800 ω lb/in
		A36 ≦ 1″ thick		
		A36 > 1″ thick	‡E60 low-hydrogen or SAW-1	
		A441, A242*	E70 low-hydrogen or SAW-2	τ = 14,700 psi or f = 10,400 ω lb/in
Plug and Slot	shear on effective area	A7, A373, A36 ≦ 1″ thick	‡E60 or SAW-1	12,400 psi
		A36 > 1″ thick A441, A242*	‡E60 low-hydrogen or SAW-1	

* weldable A242
‡ E70 or SAW-2 could be used, but would not increase allowable

Problem 1

Determine the size of required fillet weld for the bracket shown in Figure 15, to carry a load of 18,000 lbs.

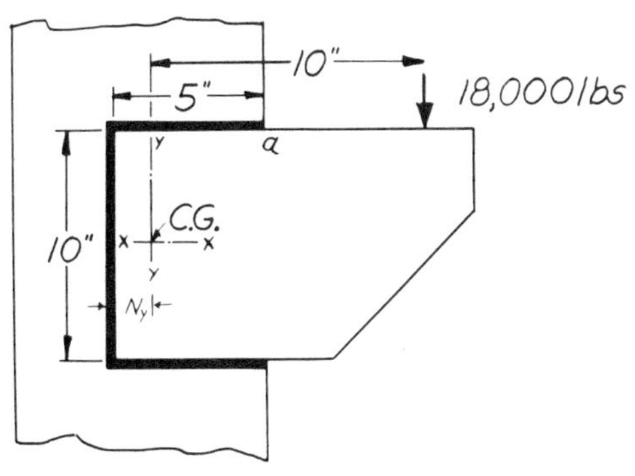

FIGURE 15

Step 1: FIND PROPERTIES OF WELD, TREATING IT AS A LINE (use Table 5).

$$N_y = \frac{b^2}{2\,b + d}$$

$$= \frac{(5)^2}{2\,(5 + 10)}$$

$$= 1.25''$$

$$J_w = \frac{(2\,b + d)^3}{12} - \frac{b^2\,(b + d)^2}{(2\,b + d)}$$

$$= \frac{(2 \times 5 + 10)^3}{12} - \frac{(5)^2\,(5 + 10)^2}{(2 \times 5 + 10)}$$

$$= 385.9 \text{ in.}^3$$

$$A_w = 20''$$

(Continued on page 10)

TABLE 8—Allowable Fatigue Stress for A7, A373 and A36 Steels and Their Welds

	2,000,000 cycles	600,000 cycles	100,000 cycles	But Not to Exceed
Base Metal In Tension Connected By Fillet Welds	(1) $\sigma = \frac{7500}{1 - 2/3\,K}$ psi	(3) $\sigma = \frac{10,500}{1 - 2/3\,K}$ psi	(5) $\sigma = \frac{15,000}{1 - 2/3\,K}$ psi	$\frac{2\,P_c}{3\,K}$ psi
But not to exceed	P_t	P_t	P_t	
Base Metal Compression Connected By Fillet Welds	(2) $\sigma = \frac{7500}{1 - 2/3\,K}$ psi	(4) $\sigma = \frac{10,500}{1 - 2/3\,K}$ psi	(6) $\sigma = \frac{15,000}{1 - 2/3\,K}$ psi	P_c psi $\frac{P_c}{1 - \frac{K}{2}}$ psi
Butt Weld In Tension	(7) $\sigma = \frac{16,000}{1 - \frac{8}{10}K}$ psi	(11) $\sigma = \frac{17,000}{1 - \frac{7}{10}K}$ psi	(15) $\sigma = \frac{18,000}{1 - \frac{K}{2}}$ psi	P_t psi
Butt Weld Compression	(8) $\sigma = \frac{18,000}{1 - K}$ psi	(12) $\sigma = \frac{18,000}{1 - .8K}$ psi	(16) $\sigma = \frac{18,000}{1 - \frac{K}{2}}$ psi	P_c psi
Butt Weld In Shear	(9) $\tau = \frac{9,000}{1 - \frac{K}{2}}$ psi	(13) $\tau = \frac{10,000}{1 - \frac{K}{2}}$ psi	(17) $\tau = \frac{13,000}{1 - \frac{K}{2}}$ psi	13,000 psi
Fillet Welds ω = Leg Size	(10) $f = \frac{5100\,\omega}{1 - \frac{K}{2}}$ lb/in.	(14) $f = \frac{7100\,\omega}{1 - \frac{K}{2}}$ lb/in.	(18) $f = \frac{8800\,\omega}{1 - \frac{K}{2}}$ lb/in.	8800 ω lb/in.

Adapted from AWS Bridge Specifications. K = min/max
P_c = Allowable unit compressive stress for member.
P_t = Allowable unit tensile stress for member.

Step 2: FIND THE VARIOUS FORCES ON WELD, INSERTING PROPERTIES OF WELD FOUND ABOVE (see Table 4).

Point a is where combined forces are maximum. Twisting force is broken into horizontal and vertical components by proper value of c (see sketch).

twisting (horizontal component)

$$f_{t_h} = \frac{T\ c_h}{J_w}$$

$$= \frac{(180{,}000)(5)}{(385.9)}$$

$$= 2340 \text{ lbs/in.}$$

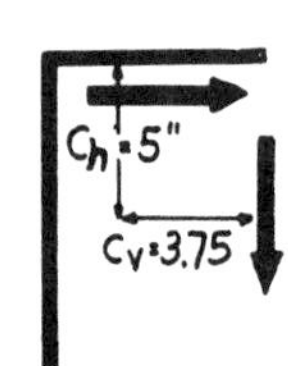

twisting (vertical component)

$$f_{t_v} = \frac{T\ c_v}{J_w}$$

$$= \frac{(180{,}000)(3.75)}{(385.9)}$$

$$= 1750 \text{ lbs/in.}$$

vertical shear

$$f_{s_v} = \frac{P}{A_w}$$

$$= \frac{(18{,}000)}{(20)}$$

$$= 900 \text{ lbs/in.}$$

(Continued on page 11)

TABLE 9—Allowable Fatigue Stress for A441 Steel and Its Welds

	2,000,000 cycles	600,000 cycles	100,000 cycles	But Not to Exceed
Base Metal In Tension Connected By Fillet Welds	(1) $\sigma = \frac{7500}{1 - 2/3\ R}$ psi	(3) $\sigma = \frac{10{,}500}{1 - 2/3\ R}$ psi	(5) $\sigma = \frac{15{,}000}{1 - 2/3\ R}$ psi	$\frac{2\ P_c}{3\ R}$ psi P_t psi
Base Metal Compression Connected By Fillet Welds	(2) $\sigma = \frac{7500}{1 - 2/3\ R}$ psi	(4) $\sigma = \frac{10{,}500}{1 - 2/3\ R}$ psi	(6) $\sigma = \frac{15{,}000}{1 - 2/3\ R}$ psi	$\frac{P_c}{1 - \frac{1}{2} R}$ psi P_c psi
Butt Weld In Tension	(7) $\sigma = \frac{16{,}000}{1 - .8\ R}$ psi	(11) $\sigma = \frac{19{,}000}{1 - .7\ R}$ psi	(15) $\sigma = \frac{24{,}000}{1 - \frac{1}{2} R}$ psi	P_t psi
Butt Weld Compression	(8) $\sigma = \frac{24{,}000}{1 - 1.7\ R}$ psi	(12) $\sigma = \frac{24{,}000}{1 - R}$ psi	(16) $\sigma = \frac{24{,}000}{1 - \frac{1}{2} R}$ psi	P_c psi
Butt Weld In Shear	(9) $\sigma = \frac{9000}{1 - \frac{1}{2} R}$ psi	(13) $\sigma = \frac{10{,}000}{1 - \frac{1}{2} R}$ psi	(17) $\sigma = \frac{13{,}000}{1 - \frac{1}{2} R}$ psi	13,000 psi
Fillet Welds ω = leg size	(10) $f = \frac{5100\ \omega}{1 - \frac{1}{2} R}$ lb/in.	(14) $f = \frac{7100\ \omega}{1 - \frac{1}{2} R}$ lb/in.	(18) $f = \frac{8800\ \omega}{1 - \frac{1}{2} R}$ lb/in.	* $f = 10{,}400\ \omega$ lb/in.

Adapted from AWS Bridge Specifications.
* if SAW-1, use 8800
R = min/max load
P_t = Allowable unit compressive stress for member.
P_c = Allowable unit tensile stress for member.

Step 3: DETERMINE ACTUAL RESULTANT FORCE ON WELD.

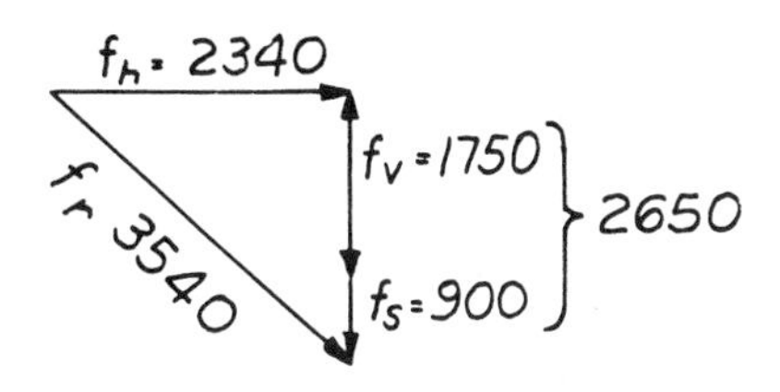

$$f_r = \sqrt{f_{t_h}{}^2 + (f_{t_v} + f_{s_v})^2}$$
$$= \sqrt{(2340)^2 + (2650)^2}$$
$$= 3540 \text{ lbs/in.}$$

Step 4: NOW FIND REQUIRED LEG SIZE OF FILLET WELD CONNECTING THE BRACKET.

$$\omega = \frac{\text{actual force}}{\text{allowable force}}$$
$$= \frac{3540}{11{,}200}$$
$$= .316 \text{ or use } 5/16'' \triangle$$

9. HORIZONTAL SHEAR FORCES

Any weld joining the flange of a beam to its web is stressed in horizontal shear (Fig. 16). Normally a designer is accustomed to specifying a certain size fillet weld for a given plate thickness (leg size about ¾ of the plate thickness) in order for the weld to have full plate strength. However, this particular joint between the flange and web is one exception to this rule. In order to prevent web buckling, a lower allowable shear stress is usually used; this results in a thicker web. The welds are in an area next to the flange where there is no buckling problem and, therefore, no reduction in allowable load is used. From a design standpoint, these welds may be very small, their actual size sometimes determined by the minimum allowed because of the thickness of the flange plate, in order to assure the proper slow cooling rate of the weld on the heavier plate.

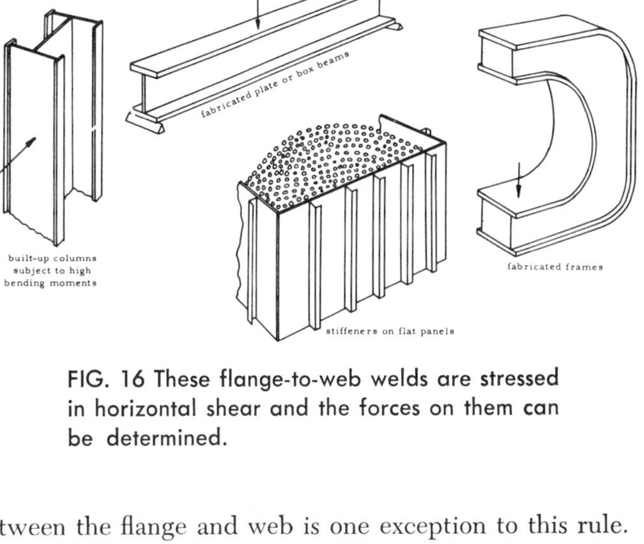

FIG. 16 These flange-to-web welds are stressed in horizontal shear and the forces on them can be determined.

General Rules

Outside of simply holding the flanges and web of a beam together, or to transmit any unusually high force between the flange and web at right angles to the member (for example, bearing supports, lifting

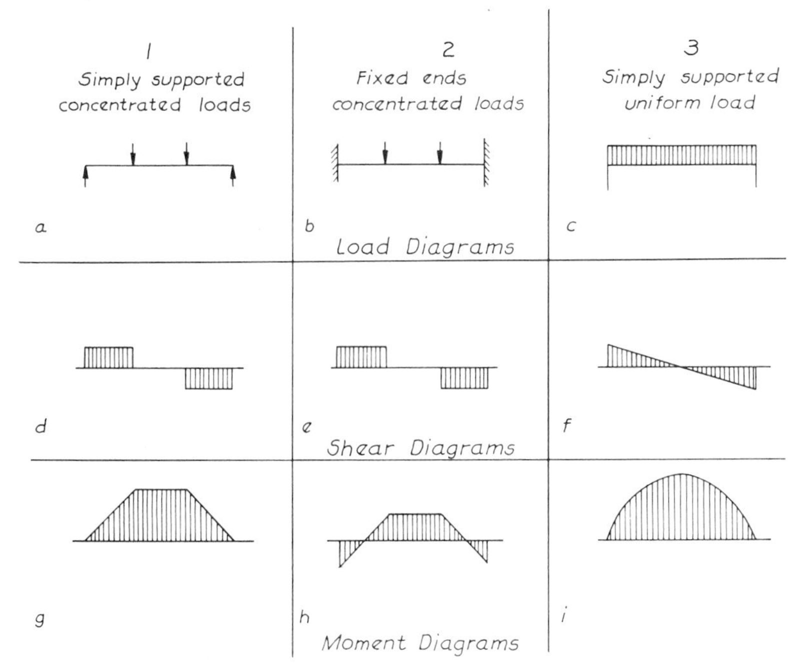

FIG. 17 Shear diagram pictures the amount and location of welding required to transmit horizontal shear forces between flange and web.

lugs, etc.), the real purpose of the weld between the flange and web is to transmit the horizontal shear forces, and the size of the weld is determined by the value of these shear forces.

It will help in the analysis of a beam if it is recognized that the shear diagram is also a picture of the amount and location of the welding required between the flange and web.

A study of Figure 17 will show that 1) loads applied transversely to members cause bending moments; 2) bending moments varying along the length of the beam cause horizontal shear forces; and 3) horizontal shear forces require welds to transmit these forces between the flange and web of the beam.

Notice: 1) Shear forces occur only when the bending moment varies along the length. 2) It is quite possible for portions of a beam to have little or no shear—notice the middle portions of beams 1 and 2—this is because the bending moment is constant within this area. 3) If there should be a difference in shear along the length of the beam, the shear forces are usually greatest at the ends of the beam (see beam 3). This is why stiffeners are sometimes welded continuously at their ends for a distance even though they are welded intermittently the rest of their length. 4) Fixed ends will shift the moment diagram so that the maximum moment is less. What is taken off at the middle of the beam is added to the ends. Even though this does happen, the shear diagram remains unchanged, so that the amount of welding between flange and web will be the same regardless of end conditions of the beam.

To apply these rules, consider the welded frame in Figure 18. The moment diagram for this loaded frame is shown on the left-hand side. The bending moment is gradually changing throughout the vertical portion of the frame. The shear diagram shows that this results in a small amount of shear in the frame. Using the horizontal shear formula ($f = Vay/In$), this would require a small amount of welding between the flange and web. Intermittent welding would probably be sufficient. However, at the point where the crane bending moment is applied, the moment diagram shows a very fast rate of change. Since the shear value is equal to the rate of change in the bending moment, it is very high and more welding is required at this region.

Use continuous welding where loads or moments are applied to a member, even though intermittent welding may be used throughout the rest of the fabricated frame.

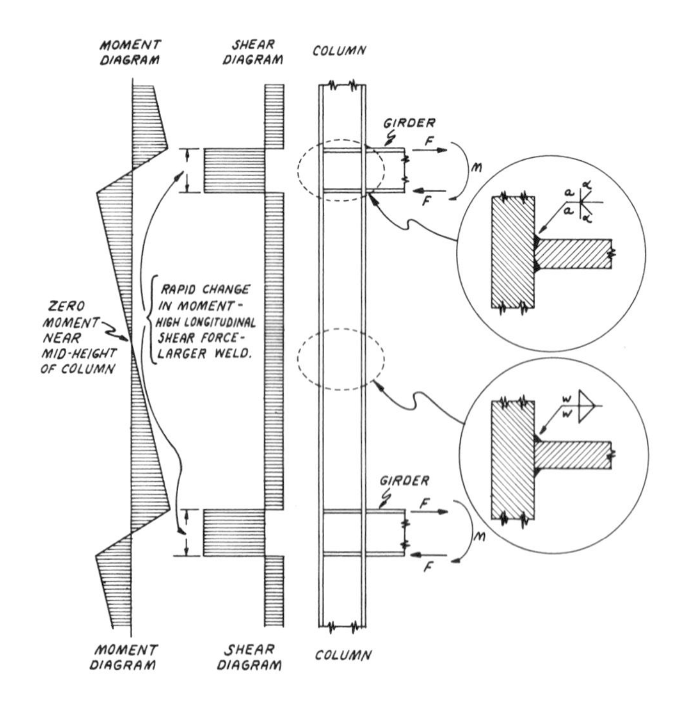

FIG. 18 Shear diagram of frame indicates where the amount of welding is critical.

Finding Weld Size

The horizontal shear forces acting on the weld joining a flange to web, Figures 19 and 20, may be found from the following formula:

$$f = \frac{V\,a\,y}{I\,n} \qquad (5)$$

where:

f = force on weld, lbs/lin in.

V = total shear on section at a given position along beam, lbs

a = area of flange held by weld, sq in.

y = distance between the center of gravity of flange area and the neutral axis of whole section, in.

I = moment of inertia of whole section, $in.^4$

n = number of welds joining flange to web

FIG. 19 Locate weld at point of minimum stress. Horizontal shear force is maximum along neutral axis. Welds in top example must carry maximum shear force; there is no shear on welds in bottom example.

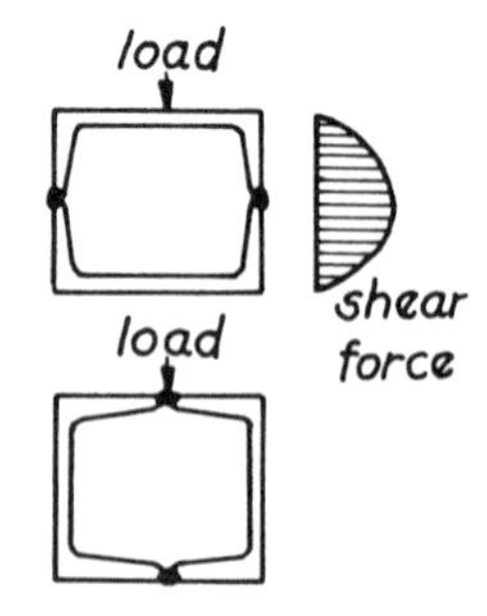

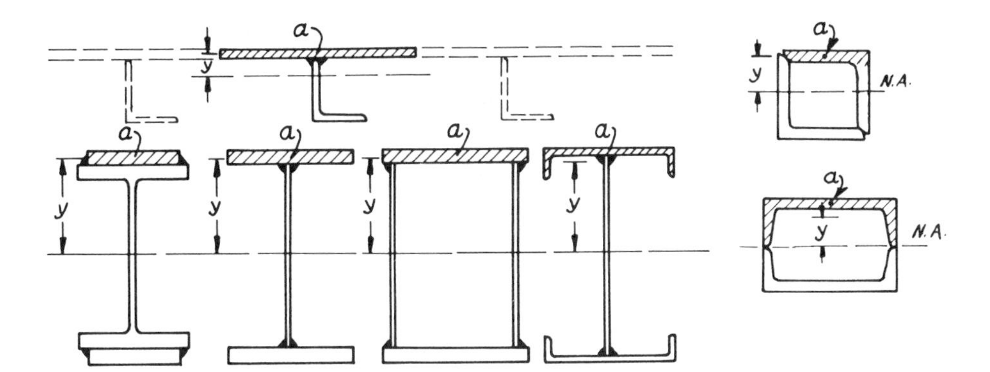

FIG. 20 Examples of welds in horizontal shear.

The leg size of the required fillet weld (continuous) is found by dividing this actual unit force (f) by the allowable for the type of weld metal used.

If intermittent fillet welds are to be used divide this weld size (continuous) by the actual size used (intermittent). When expressed as a percentage, this will give the length of weld to be used per unit length. For convenience, Table 10 has various intermittent weld lengths and distances between centers for given percentages of continuous welds.

$$\% = \frac{\text{calculated leg size (continuous)}}{\text{actual leg size used (intermittent)}}$$

Problem 2

For the fabricated plate girder in Figure 21, determine the proper amount of fillet welds to join flanges to the web. Use E70 welds.

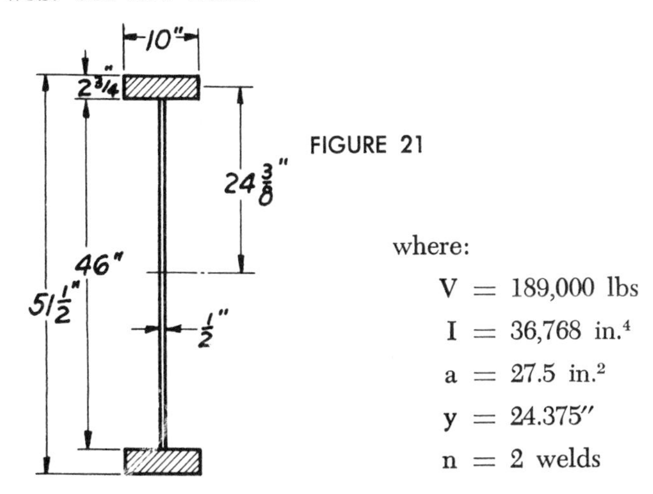

FIGURE 21

where:

$$V = 189{,}000 \text{ lbs}$$
$$I = 36{,}768 \text{ in.}^4$$
$$a = 27.5 \text{ in.}^2$$
$$y = 24.375''$$
$$n = 2 \text{ welds}$$

horizontal shear force on weld

$$f_h = \frac{V\ a\ y}{I\ n}$$

$$= \frac{(189{,}000)(27.5)(24.375)}{(36{,}768)(2)}$$

$$= 1720 \text{ lbs/in.}$$

required leg size of weld

$$\omega = \frac{\text{actual force}}{\text{allowable force}}$$

$$= \frac{1720}{11{,}200}$$

$$= .153''$$

This would be the minimum leg size of a *continuous* fillet weld; however, ½" fillet welds are recommended because of the thick 2¾" flange plate (see table). In this particular case, the leg size of the fillet weld need not exceed the web thickness (thinner plate). Because of the greater strength of the ½" fillet, intermittent welds may be used but must not stress the web above 14,500 psi. Therefore, the length of weld must be increased to spread the load over a greater length of web.

Weld vs Plate

$$2\ (11{,}200\ \omega)\ L \leqq 14{,}500 \text{ psi } t \times L$$

$$\omega \leqq \frac{14{,}500 \text{ psi } t}{2(11{,}200)} \leqq .643\ t$$

$$\text{or} \quad \boxed{\omega \leqq \tfrac{2}{3}\ t}$$

TABLE 10—Intermittent Welds
Length and Spacing

Continuous weld, %	Length of intermittent welds and distance between centers, in.		
75	. .	3-4	. .
66	. .	. .	4-6
60	. .	3-5	. .
57	. .	. .	4-7
50	2-4	3-6	4-8
44	. .	. .	4-9
43	. .	3-7	. .
40	2-5	. .	4-10
37	. .	3-8	. .
33	2-6	3-9	4-12
30	. .	3-10	. .
25	2-8	3-12	. .
20	2-10	. .	. .
16	2-12	. .	. .

For this reason the size of intermittent fillet weld *used in design calculations or for determination of length* must not exceed ⅔ of the web thickness, or here:

$$\tfrac{2}{3} \text{ of } \tfrac{1}{2}'' \text{ (web)} = .333''$$

The percentage of continuous weld length needed for this intermittent weld will be—

$$\% = \frac{\text{continuous leg size}}{\text{intermittent leg size}}$$

$$= \frac{(.153'')}{(.333'')}$$

$$= 46\%$$

Hence, use—

½″ ◺ 4″ — 8″ (see Table 10)

Problem 3

A fillet weld is required, using

⅜″ ◺ 4″ — 12″

that is, intermittent welds having leg size of ⅜″ and length of 4″, set on 12″ centers. A ⅜″ fillet weld usually requires 2 passes, unless the work is positioned. A 2-pass weld requires more inspection to maintain size and weld quality. The shop would like to change this to a 5⁄16″ weld. This single-pass weld is easier to make and there is little chance of it being undersize.

This change could be made as follows:

The present ⅜″ ◺ is welded in lengths of 4″ on 12″ centers, or 33% of the length of the joint, reducing the leg size down to 5⁄16″ ◺ or ⅚ of the previous weld. This would require the percentage of length of joint to be increased by the ratio 6 / 5 or 33% (6⁄5) = 40%.

Hence, use—

5⁄16″ ◺ 4″ — 10″

In other words, ⅜″ intermittent fillet welds, 4″ long on 12″ centers, may be replaced with 5⁄16″ welds, 4″ long on 10″ centers, providing same strength. This change would permit welding in one pass instead of two passes, with a saving of approx. 16⅔% in welding time and cost.

Problem 4

Determine the leg size of fillet weld for the base of a signal tower, Figure 22, assuming wind pressure of 30 lbs/sq ft or pressure of p = .208 psi. Use A36 Steel & E70 welds.

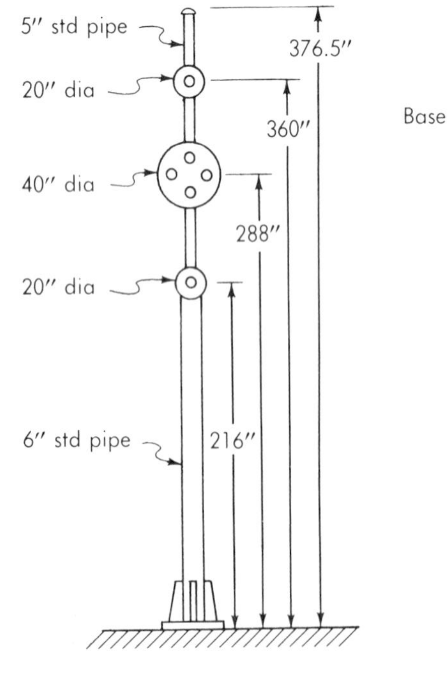

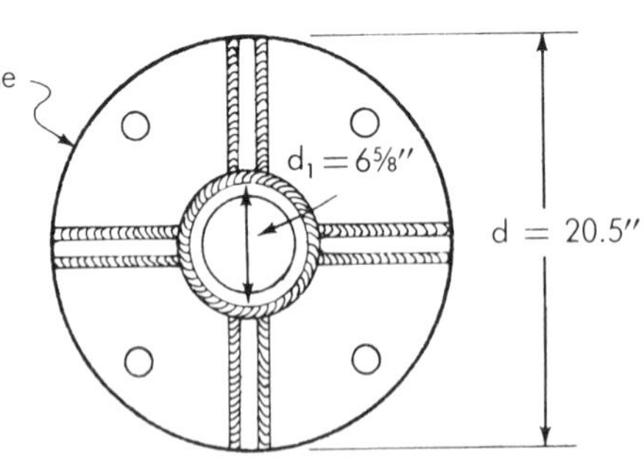

FIGURE 22

Step 1: FIND PROPERTIES OF WELD, TREATING IT AS A LINE.

$$I_w = \frac{d^3 - d_1^3}{6}$$

$$= \frac{(20.5)^3 - (6\tfrac{5}{8})^3}{6} \qquad = 1386 \text{ in.}^3$$

$$I_w = \frac{\pi\ d_1^3}{8}$$

$$= \frac{\pi\ (6\tfrac{5}{8})^3}{8} = \qquad 114 \text{ in.}^3$$

$$\text{Total } I_w = 1500 \text{ in.}^3$$

$$S_w = \frac{I_w}{d/2}$$

$$= \frac{1500}{10.25}$$

$$= 146 \text{ in.}^2$$

Step 2: FIND THE FORCE INVOLVED.

Moment acting on tower due to wind pressure:

$$M = (.208)\left(\frac{\pi\ 20^2}{4}\right)(360)$$

$$+ (.208)\left(\frac{\pi\ 40^2}{4}\right)(288)$$

$$+ (.208)\left(\frac{\pi\ 20^2}{4}\right)(216)$$

$$+ (.208)(556)(160.5)(296.3)$$

$$+ (.208)(6\tfrac{5}{8})(216)(108)$$

$$= 200{,}000 \text{ in.-lbs}$$

bending stress in pipe (column)

$$\sigma = \frac{M\ c}{I}$$

$$= \frac{(200{,}000)(3.3125'')}{(28.14 \text{ in.}^4)}$$

$$= \underline{23{,}600 \text{ psi}}$$

Step 3: FIND FORCE ON FILLET WELD AT COLUMN BASE.

$$f = \frac{M}{S_w}$$

$$= \frac{(200{,}000 \text{ in.-lbs})}{(146 \text{ in.}^2)}$$

$$= 1370 \text{ lbs/linear in.}$$

Step 4: NOW FIND REQUIRED LEG SIZE OF FILLET WELD AT BASE.

$$\omega = \frac{\text{actual force}}{\text{allowable force}}$$

$$= \frac{1370}{11{,}200}$$

= .123″ but <u>use 5/16″ ◺ all around,</u> the minimum fillet weld size for 1″ base plate

Problem 5

To determine amount of fillet weld to attach masonry plate to beam, using E70 welds. The following conditions exist:

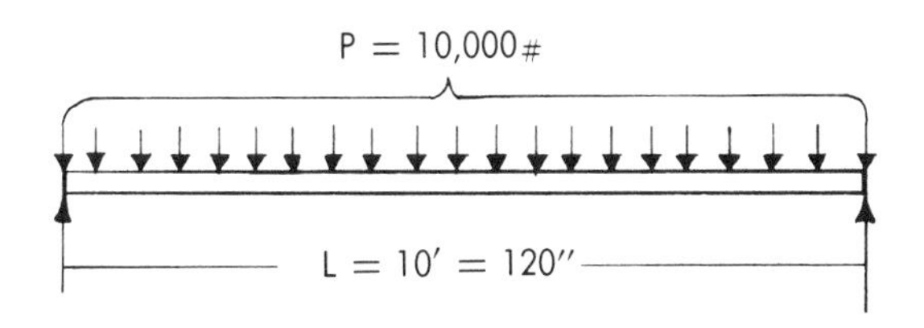

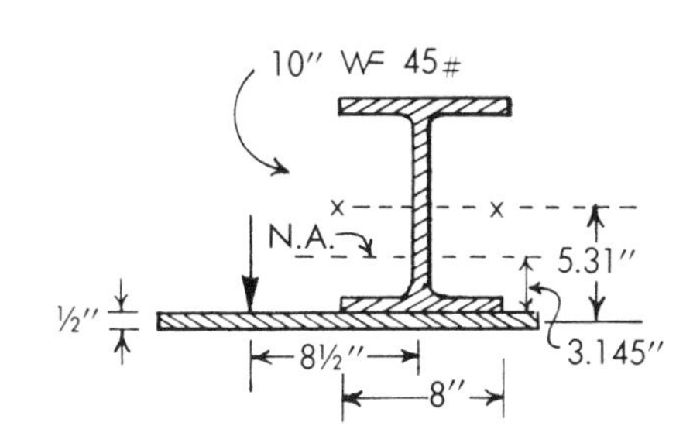

FIGURE 23

Built-up member	A	d	M	I_x	I_g
10″ WF 45#	13.24	0	0	0	248.6
18″ x ½″	9.00	— 5.31	—47.79	+253.8	—
Total ➻	22.24		—47.79	502.4	

properties of section

$$NA = \frac{M}{A} = \frac{(-47.79)}{(22.24)}$$

$$= -2.145'' \text{ below axis x-x}$$

$$\therefore \frac{M_2}{A} = (-2.145)(-47.79)$$

$$= +\ 102.7$$

$$I_{NA} = I_x - \frac{M^2}{A}$$

$$= (502.4) - (102.7)$$

$$= 399.7 \text{ in.}^4$$

horizontal shear force on weld

$$f_h = \frac{V\ a\ y}{I\ n}$$

$$= \frac{(5000)(9.0)(3.415)}{(399.7)(2 \text{ welds})}$$

$$= 192.0 \text{ lbs/in., max. at ends}$$

properties of weld, treating it as a line

$$S_w = b\ d$$

$$= (120)(8)$$

$$= 960 \text{ in.}^2$$

d = 8″

b = 120″

$$A_w = 2\ b$$

$$= 2(120)$$

$$= 240''$$

bending force on weld

$$f_b = \frac{M}{S_w}$$

$$= \frac{(10{,}000)(8.5)}{(960)}$$

$$= 88.5 \text{ lbs/in.}$$

vertical shear force on weld

$$f_v = \frac{V}{A_w}$$

$$= \frac{(5000)}{(120)}$$

$$= 41.7 \text{ lbs/in.}$$

resultant force on weld

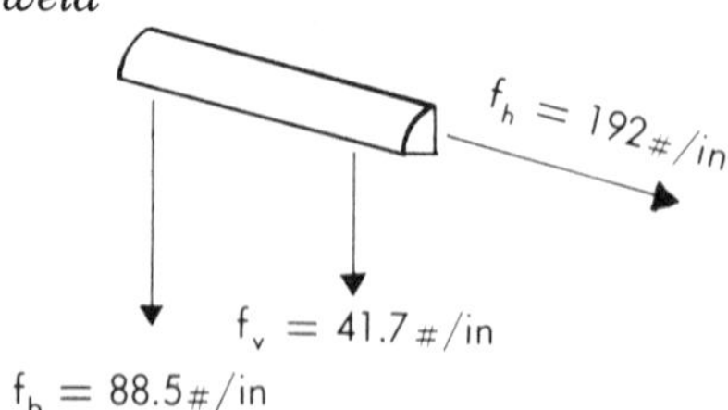

$$f_r = \sqrt{(f_b + f_v)^2 + f_h^2}$$

$$= \sqrt{(88.5 + 41.7)^2 + (192)^2}$$

$$= 232 \text{ lbs/in.}$$

leg size of weld

$$\omega = \frac{232}{11{,}200}$$

$$= .0207'' \text{ if continuous}$$

If using 3/16″ intermittent weld, then

$$\% = \frac{\text{calculated continuous leg size}}{\text{actual intermittent leg size used}}$$

$$= \frac{.0207''}{3/16''}$$

$$= 11\%$$

Hence, use

3/16″ ⊿ 2 — 8 on each side (25%)

Problem 6

DRIVE ROLL FOR CONVEYOR BELT

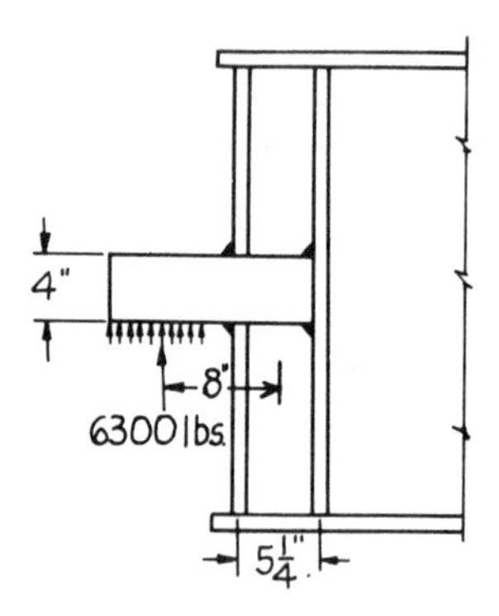

FIGURE 24

Determine size of required fillet weld for hub shown in Figure 24. The bearing load is 6300 lbs. Torque transmitted is 150 HP at 100 RPM, or:

$$T = \frac{63{,}030 \times HP}{RPM}$$

$$= \frac{63{,}030 \times (150)}{(100)}$$

$$= 94{,}500 \text{ in.-lbs.}$$

Step 1: FIND PROPERTIES OF WELD, TREATING IT AS A LINE (use Table 5).

$$J_w = 2\ \frac{\pi\ d^3}{4}$$

$$= 2\ \frac{\pi\ (4)^3}{4}$$

$$= 100.5 \text{ in.}^3$$

D

d

$$I_w = \frac{\pi\, d}{2}\left(D^2 + \frac{d^2}{2}\right) = \frac{\pi\, 4}{2}\left[(5\tfrac{1}{4})^2 + \frac{(4)^2}{2}\right]$$

$$= 223.3 \text{ in.}^3$$

$$c = \tfrac{1}{2}\sqrt{D^2 + d^2} = \tfrac{1}{2}\sqrt{(5\tfrac{1}{4})^2 + (4)^2}$$

$$= 3.3''$$

$$S_w = \frac{I_w}{c} = \frac{(223.3)}{(3.3)}$$

$$= 67.6 \text{ in.}^2$$

$$A_w = 2\,\pi\,d$$

$$= 2\,\pi\,(4)$$

$$= 25.2''$$

Step 2: FIND THE VARIOUS FORCES ON WELD, INSERTING PROPERTIES OF WELD FOUND ABOVE (use Table 4).

bending

$$f_b = \frac{M}{S_w} = \frac{(6300)(8)}{(67.6)} = 746 \text{ lbs/in.}$$

twisting

$$f_t = \frac{T\,c}{J_w}$$

$$= \frac{(94{,}500)(2)}{(100.5)}$$

$$= 1880 \text{ lbs/in.}$$

vertical shear

$$f_v = \frac{V}{A_w}$$

$$= \frac{(6300)}{(25.2)}$$

$$= 250 \text{ lbs/in.}$$

Step 3: DETERMINE ACTUAL RESULTANT FORCE AND ALLOWABLE FORCE ON THE WELD.

$f_b = 451$ — 1 inch of fillet weld at hub — $f_v = 250$ — $f_t = 1880$

$$f_r = \sqrt{f_b^2 + f_t^2 + f_v^2}$$

$$= \sqrt{(746)^2 + (1880)^2 + (250)^2}$$

$$= 2040 \text{ lbs/in.} \quad \text{(actual resultant force)}$$

Since this is fatigue loading, assume service life of N = 2,000,000 cycles and use Table 8 formula. In this case, assume a complete reversal of load; hence K = min/max = −1 and:

$$f = \frac{5100}{1 - \frac{K}{2}}$$

$$= \frac{5100}{1 + \tfrac{1}{2}}$$

$$= 3400 \text{ lbs/in.} \quad \text{(allowable force)}$$

Step 4: NOW REQUIRED LEG SIZE OF FILLET WELD AROUND HUB CAN BE FOUND.

$$\omega = \frac{\text{actual force}}{\text{allowable force}}$$

$$= \frac{(2040)}{(3400)}$$

$$= .600'' \text{ or use } \tfrac{5}{8}''$$

Problem 7

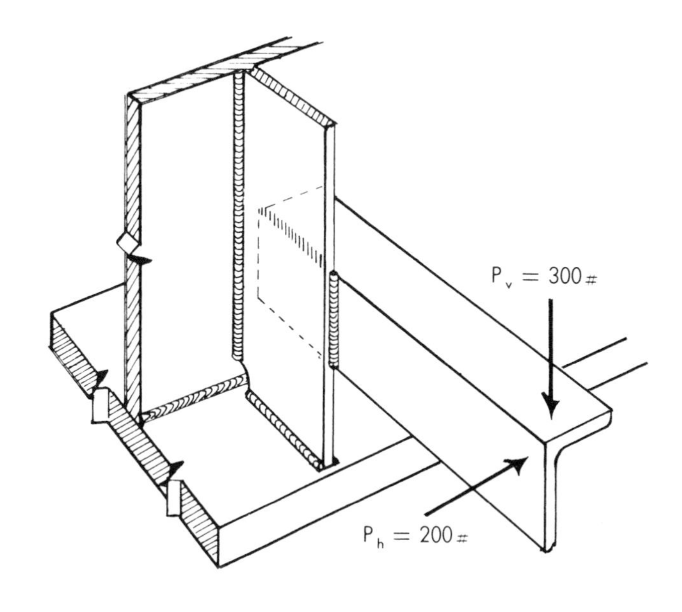

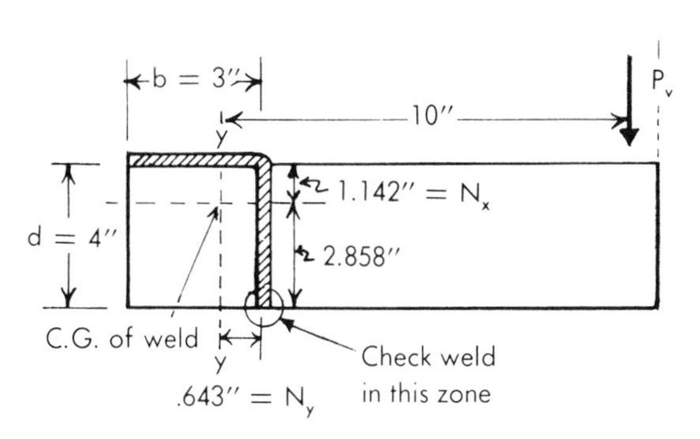

FIGURE 25

A 3″ × 4″ angle for support of a pipe extends out from the transverse intermediate stiffeners on a plate girder, Figure 25. This must be field welded. It will be difficult to weld in the overhead position along the bottom edge of the angle as well as to make the vertical weld along the end of the angle next to the girder web because of poor accessibility. Check whether just two fillet welds would be sufficient, assuming the pipe's weight on the hanger is 300 lbs and a possible horizontal force of approximately 200 lbs is applied to the hanger during erection of the pipe.

$$N_y = \frac{b^2}{2(b + d)} = \frac{(3)^2}{2(3 + 4)} = .643''$$

$$N_x = \frac{d^2}{2(b + d)} = \frac{(4)^2}{2(3 + 4)} = 1.142''$$

properties of weld treated as a line

1. For twist about connection's center of gravity, due to P_v

$$J_w = \frac{(b + d)^4 - 6\, b^2\, d^2}{12\,(b + d)} = \frac{(3 + 4)^4 - 6(3)^2(4)^2}{12\,(3 + 4)} = 18.3 \text{ in.}^3$$

2. For bending about (y-y) axis, due to P_h

$$S_w = \frac{4\,bd + b^2}{6} = \frac{4(3)(4) + 3^2}{6} = 9.5 \text{ in.}^2$$

twisting force on weld

1. Horizontal

$$f_{h_1} = \frac{T\, c_h}{J_w} = \frac{(300 \times 10)(2.858)}{(18.3)} = 470 \text{ lbs/in.}$$

2. Vertical

$$f_{v_1} = \frac{T\, c_v}{J_w} = \frac{(300 \times 10)(.643)}{(18.3)} = 105 \text{ lbs/in.}$$

vertical shear

$$f_{v_2} = \frac{P}{L} = \frac{(300)}{(3 + 4)} = 43 \text{ lbs/in.}$$

bending force on weld (about y-y), due to P_h

$$f_{h_2} = \frac{M}{S_w} = \frac{(200 \times 10)}{(9.5)} = 211 \text{ lbs/in.}$$

resultant force on weld at bottom of connection

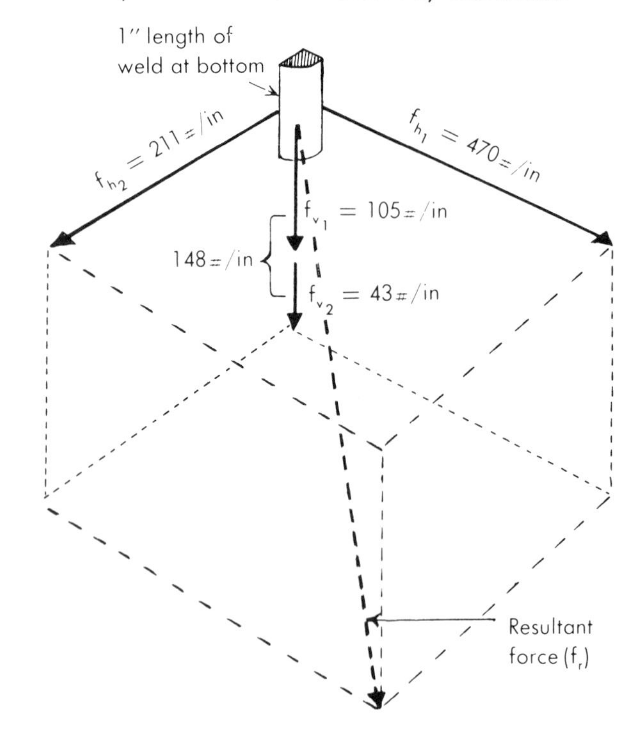

FIGURE 26

$$f_r = \sqrt{f_{h_1}{}^2 + f_{h_2}{}^2 + f_v{}^2} = \sqrt{(470)^2 + (211)^2 + (148)^2} = 536 \text{ lbs/in.}$$

leg size of fillet weld

$$\omega = \frac{536}{11{,}200}$$

$$= .048'' \text{ or } \tfrac{3}{16}'' \text{ would be sufficient}$$

10. HOW TO MEASURE SIZE OF FILLET WELDS

The size of a fillet weld is difficult to measure without proper gages. Fillet shapes are concave, convex, or flat. They may have equal or unequal legs. However, the true fillet size is measured by finding the leg-length of the largest isosceles right triangle (a triangle with a 90° corner and legs of equal length) which can be inscribed within the weld cross-section, with the legs in line with the original surface of the metal.

The gages shown in Figure 27 give quick, easy measurement of fillet size. Two gage types are available: one for a convex fillet, another for a concave fillet. See Section 7.10 for series of illustrations which dramatically show how poor gaging can seriously offset the accuracy of engineered welds.

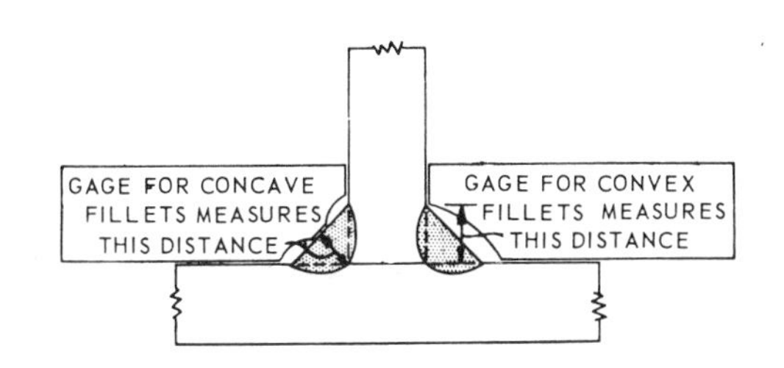

FIG. 27 Convex fillets may be measured with gage of type shown on right; in this case it measures the leg size. Concave fillets are measured with gage like the one on left; in this case it measures the weld throat.

TABLE 11—Maximum Allowable Shear Stress and Shear Force For Given Applied Normal Stress on Fillet Weld or Partial-Penetration Groove Weld

Applied normal stress (σ) parallel to weld (psi)	Max. allowable shear stress (τ) which may be applied to throat of fillet weld or partial penetration groove weld (psi)		Max. allowable shear force (f) which may be applied to fillet weld (lbs/lineal inch)	
	E60 welds	E70 welds	E60 welds	E70 welds
zero	13,600	15,800	9,600	11,170
1,000	13,590	15,790	9,600	11,160
2,000	13,560	15,770	9,590	11,150
3,000	13,520	15,720	9,560	11,110
4,000	13,450	15,660	9,510	11,070
5,000	13,380	15,600	9,460	11,030
6,000	13,270	15,510	9,380	10,970
7,000	13,130	15,410	9,280	10,890
8,000	13,000	15,290	9,190	10,810
9,000	12,840	15,140	9,080	10,710
10,000	12,650	14,990	8,940	10,600
11,000	12,430	14,810	8,790	10,470
12,000	12,200	14,610	8,630	10,330
13,000	11,940	14,400	8,440	10,180
14,000	11,660	14,160	8,240	10,010
15,000	11,340	13,910	8,020	9,840
16,000	11,000	13,620	7,780	9,630
17,000	10,620	13,320	7,510	9,420
18,000	10,200	12,980	7,210	9,180
19,000	9,730	12,630	6,880	8,930
20,000	9,220	12,230	6,520	8,650
21,000	8,640	11,810	6,110	8,350
22,000	8,000	11,340	5,660	8,020
23,000	7,260	10,840	5,130	7,660
24,000	6,400	10,280	4,530	7,270

11. WELDS SUBJECT TO COMBINED STRESS

Although the (1963) AISC Specifications are silent concerning combined stresses on welds, the previous specifications (Sec 12 b) required that welds subject to shearing and externally applied tensile or compressive forces shall be so proportioned that the combined unit stress shall not exceed the unit stress allowed for shear.

Very rarely does this have to be checked into. For simply supported girders, the maximum shear occurs near the ends and in a region of relatively low bending stress. For built-up tension or compression members, the axial tensile or compressive stresses may be relatively high, but theoretically there is no shear to be transferred.

In the case of continuous girders, it might be well to check into the effect of combined stress on the connecting welds in the region of negative moment, because this region of high shear transfer also has high bending stresses.

Even in this case, there is some question as to how much a superimposed axial stress actually reduces the shear-carrying capacity of the weld. Unfortunately there has been no testing of this. In general, it is felt that the use of the following combined stress analysis is conservative and any reduction in the shear-carrying capacity of the weld would not be as great as would be indicated by the following formulas. See Figure 28.

In Figure 28:

τ = shear stress to be transferred along throat of weld, psi

σ = normal stress applied parallel to axis of weld, psi

From the Mohr's circle of stress in Figure 28:

$$\sigma_{max} = \frac{\sigma_1}{2} + \sqrt{\left(\frac{\sigma_1}{2}\right)^2 + \tau_3^2} \quad \ldots\ldots\ldots\ldots (6)$$

$$\tau_{max} = \sqrt{\left(\frac{\sigma_1}{2}\right)^2 + \tau_3^2} \quad \ldots\ldots\ldots\ldots (7)$$

From these formulas for the resulting maximum shear stress and maximum normal stress, the following is true:

For a given applied normal stress (σ), the greatest applied shear stress on the throat of a partial-penetration groove weld or fillet weld (and holding the maximum shear stress resulting from these combined stresses within the allowable of τ = 13,600 psi for E60 welds, or τ = 15,800 psi for E70 welds) is—

for E60 welds or SAW-1

$$\tau \leqq \sqrt{13{,}600^2 - \frac{\sigma^2}{4}} \quad \ldots\ldots\ldots\ldots (7a)$$

for E70 welds or SAW-2

$$\tau \leqq \sqrt{15{,}800^2 - \frac{\sigma^2}{4}} \quad \ldots\ldots\ldots\ldots (7b)$$

This same formula may be expressed in terms of allowable unit force (lbs/linear inch) for a fillet weld:

for E60 welds or SAW-1

$$f \leqq \omega \sqrt{9600^2 - \frac{\sigma^2}{8}} \quad \ldots\ldots\ldots\ldots (8a)$$

for E70 welds or SAW-2

$$f \leqq \omega \sqrt{11{,}200^2 - \frac{\sigma^2}{8}} \quad \ldots\ldots\ldots\ldots (8b)$$

For the same given applied normal stress (σ), the greatest applied shear stress (τ) on the throat of a groove weld or fillet weld (and holding the maximum normal stress resulting from these combined stresses within the allowable of σ = .60 σ_y) is—

$$\tau \leqq \sqrt{(.60\ \sigma_y)^2 - (.60\ \sigma_y)\ \sigma} \quad \ldots\ldots\ldots (9)$$

Formulas #7 and #8 are expressed in table form, as in Table 11. The general relationship of these formulas is illustrated by the graph, Figure 29.

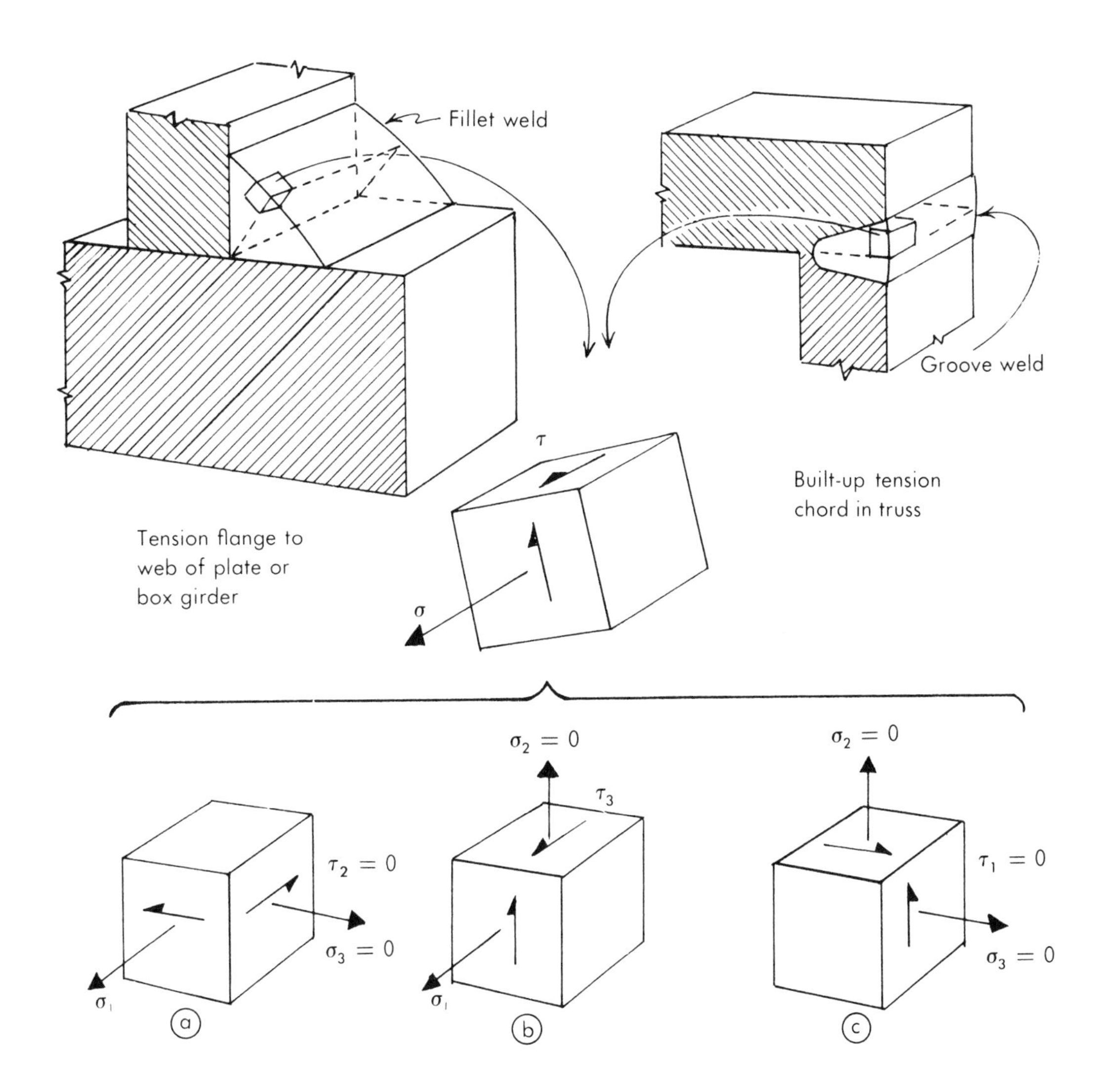

FIG. 28 Analysis of weld, using Mohr's Circle of Stress.

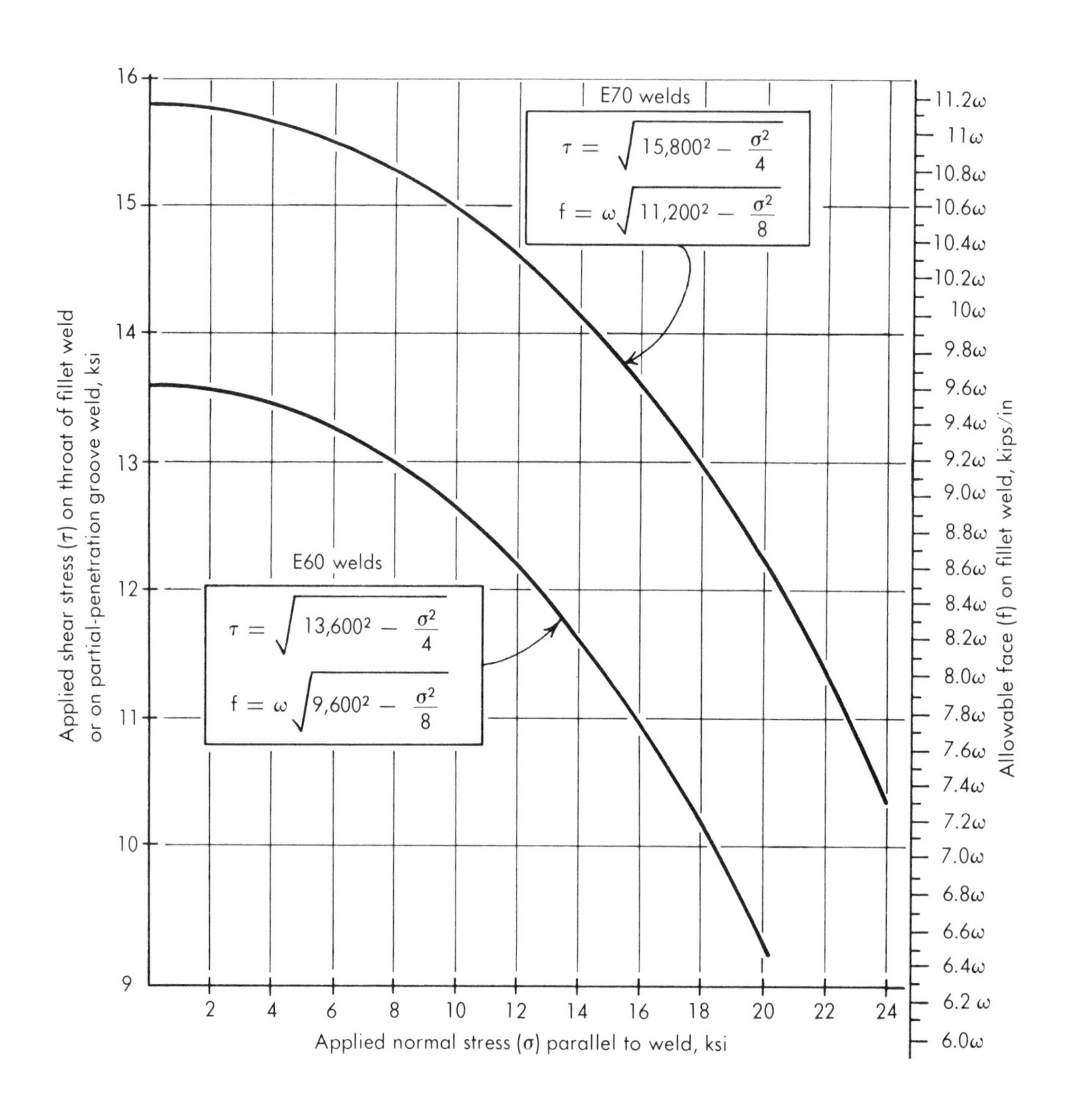

FIG. 29 Relationship of Formulas #8 and #9; see Table 11, page 19.

Estimating Welding Cost

1. COST FACTORS

There are several methods which may be used to study welding cost, and these depend on the need for such a study. For example, is it needed to estimate a new job for bidding? Or, it is needed to compare one procedure against another? Or, is the chief need one of determining the amount of electrode to order?

A good method of cost estimating should give the final cost quickly; yet indicate what portion of the operation is more expensive, i.e. where the welding dollar is really being spent.

The final cost includes at least these items: a) labor and overhead for plate preparation, assembling, welding, cleaning, and sometimes stress-relieving; b) electrode, flux, and gas; and c) electric power.

Table 1 includes a number of useful formulas for determining various cost components.

Unfortunately there is no one all-inclusive formula by which all types of welding jobs may be studied. The simplest type of cost estimation is a job that requires a long, single-pass fillet or groove weld. Next comes the long, multi-pass weld, where a different procedure may be used for each pass. In both examples, it is sufficient to assume a reasonable operating factor due to the downtime between electrodes consumed and to apply this to the actual arc time. This downtime is affected by the weldor, as well as the job. A more complicated weld may require a handling time factor. This handling time is affected more by the job, than by the welding.

Three items which are difficult to tie down, yet greatly affect the cost of a weld, are these:

1. The amount of filler weld metal required; this varies with size of weld, size of root opening or fit up, amount of reinforcement, included angle of groove, etc.
2. The operating factor used, i.e. the ratio of actual arc time to the over-all welding time.
3. The amount of handling and cleaning time.

This section includes various tables and nomographs which are helpful in making true cost estimates. No estimating system, however, is satisfactory without the estimator applying his good judgment and perception.

2. COST OF WELD METAL

The cost of welding is directly affected by the amount of weld metal required. Very few people realize the great increase in weld metal and cost that results from a slight increase in weld size.

The cross-sectional area of a weld generally varies as the square of the weld size. For example, making a 5⁄16" leg size fillet weld when a ¼" weld is desired, increases the leg by 25% but the area is increased by 56%. The amount of reinforcement is difficult to specify and control; yet the range of its variance can substantially affect the amount of weld metal required. A slight increase in root opening increases the amount of weld metal for the entire thickness and length of the weld. The resulting percentage increase in weld metal is usually surprising.

Computing Weld Weight

Designers or associated personnel frequently have to compute the weight of weld metal required on a particular job, as a matter of either cost estimating or determining the amount of material to be ordered for a particular job. Sometimes these computations must be based on the size and configuration of the joint. The normal procedure to follow in such a case is to compute the cross-sectional area of the joint in square inches and then convert this into pounds per linear foot by multiplying by the factor 3.4. To simplify these computations, Table 2 (weight in lbs/linear ft) has been developed; its use is illustrated in Problem 1.

Tables 3, 4, and 5 provide precalculated weights for specific joints and read directly in lbs per foot of joint. Table 6 is a similar table for AWS prequalified joints. Tables for the direct reading of weld metal for partial-penetration groove or fillet welds are included in Section 3.6, "Fabrication of Built-Up Columns."

For estimating the weight of manual electrode required, roughly add another 50% to this amount of weld metal.

In order to arrive at the labor cost per foot of joint, it is necessary to know the speed at which the joint can be welded. This may be found in prepared data on standard welding procedures, both for manual welding as well as the submerged-arc process. For special joints for which no information is available, the deposition rate (lbs/hr) may be determined from tables and charts for given welding currents. The joint speed is then found by dividing this deposition rate by the amount of weld metal required (lbs/linear ft.).

TABLE 1—Useful Welding Cost Formulas

SPEED	TIME	JOINT SPEED
$\frac{ft}{hr} = 5\ \frac{in}{min}$	$\frac{min}{ft} = \frac{60}{ft/hr} = \frac{12}{in/min}$	$S = \frac{1}{\frac{1}{S_1} + \frac{1}{S_2} + \frac{1}{S_3}}$

JOINT SPEED	ROD MELTED PER FOOT	ROD MELTED PER HOUR
$\frac{ft}{hr} = \frac{60\ D}{J}$	$\frac{\text{lb rod melted}}{\text{ft weld}} = \frac{1200\ M}{N\ L_m\ S}$	$\frac{\text{lb rod melted}}{\text{hr}} = \frac{6000\ M\ (OF)}{N\ L_m}$

ROD MILEAGE	ROD CONSUMED PER FOOT	ROD CONSUMED PER HOUR
$\frac{\text{in of weld}}{\text{one rod}} = L_w = \frac{L_m\ S}{M}$	$\frac{\text{lb rod consumed}}{\text{ft weld}} = \frac{1200\ M}{N\ L_m\ S}$	$\frac{\text{lb rod consumed}}{\text{hr}} = \frac{6000\ M\ (OF)}{N\ L_m}$

APPROXIMATE MELT OFF RATE

$$= \frac{E(\text{arc volts})\ I(\text{welding current})}{1000} = \frac{\text{lb rod melted}}{\text{hr}}$$

APPROXIMATE COST OF SUBMERGED ARC AUTOMATIC WELD

$$= \frac{¢}{ft} = \frac{.0065\ I\ (F+W) + 20\ L}{S}$$

WELD COST

	per foot of each pass	per lb of deposit
LABOR OVERHEAD	$\frac{¢}{ft} = \frac{20\ L}{S\ (OF)}$	$\frac{¢}{lb} = \frac{5\ L}{3\ D\ (OF)}$
MANUAL ELECTRODE	$\frac{¢}{ft} = \frac{1200\ M\ W}{N\ L_m\ S}$	$\frac{¢}{lb} = \frac{W}{E_2}$
AUTOMATIC WIRE & FLUX	$\frac{¢}{ft} = \frac{12\ m\ (W+RF)}{S} = \frac{J\ (W+RF)}{E_2}$	$\frac{¢}{lb} = \frac{W+RF}{E_2}$
GAS	$\frac{¢}{ft} = \frac{20\ G}{S}$	$\frac{¢}{lb} = \frac{5\ G}{3\ D}$

L = labor + overhead ($/hr)
W = wire or rod cost (¢lb)
F = flux cost (¢/lb)
G = gas cost ($/hr)
R = ratio of flux to wire
D = (lb weld deposited/min)
M = (in rod melted/min) = L_m/T
C = (lb rod consumed/min) with stub
m = (lb rod melted/min) no stub

W_r = weight one rod with stub (lbs) = 100/N
W_s = weight of one stub (lbs)
E_1 = deposition efficiency $\frac{\text{lb weld deposited}}{\text{lb rod melted}} = \frac{D}{m}$
E_2 = overall deposition efficiency $\frac{\text{lb weld deposited}}{\text{lb rod consumed}} = \frac{D}{C} = E_1\ E_3$
E_3 = melting efficiency $\frac{\text{lb rod melted}}{\text{lb rod consumed}} = \frac{m}{C} = \frac{W_r - W_s}{W_r}$

N = number rods/100 lbs
I = welding current (amperes)
S = (in weld/min) = L_w/T
T = time to melt one rod (min)
L_m = (in rod melted/rod)
L_w = (in weld/rod)
J = (lb weld/ft of joint)
OF = operating factor

TABLE 2—Weight of Weld Metal (Pounds Per Foot of Joint) *Based on Joint Design*

"d" or "r"	BUTT WELDS																FILLET WELDS		
Dimension	"t" Dimension						"t" Dimension				Segment of Weld Bead	Included Angle					Values below are for leg size 10% oversize, consistent with normal shop practices. (leg size increased 10%)		
	1/16"	1/8"	3/16"	1/4"	3/8"	1/2"	1/16"	1/8"	3/16"	1/4"		14°	20°	60°	45° (1/2 of 90°)	70°	flat	convex	concave
1/16"											.021								
1/8"	.027	.053	.080	.106	.159	.212					.083	.0065	.0094	.031	.027	.037	.032	.039	.037
3/16"	.040	.080	.119	.159	.239	.318	.027				.188	.0147	.021	.069	.060	.084	.072	.087	.083
1/4"	.053	.106	.159	.212	.318	.425	.035				.334	.026	.037	.123	.106	.149	.129	.155	.147
5/16"	.066	.133	.199	.265	.390	.531	.044				.531	.041	.059	.192	.166	.232	.201	.242	.230
3/8"	.080	.159	.239	.318	.478	.637	.053	.106			.750	.059	.084	.276	.239	.334	.289	.349	.331
7/16"	.091	.186	.279	.371	.557	.743	.062	.124	.186		1.02	.080	.115	.376	.326	.456	.394	.475	.451
1/2"	.106	.212	.318	.425	.637	.849	.071	.142	.212		1.33	.104	.150	.491	.425	.595	.514	.620	.589
9/16"	.119	.239	.358	.478	.716	.955	.080	.159	.239			.132	.190	.621	.538	.753	.651	.785	.745
5/8"	.133	.265	.398	.531	.796	1.06	.089	.177	.266			.163	.234	.766	.664	.930	.804	.970	.920
11/16"	.146	.292	.438	.584	.876	1.17	.097	.195	.292	.389		.197	.283	.927	.804	1.13			
3/4"	.159	.318	.478	.637	.955	1.27	.111	.212	.318	.424		.234	.337	1.11	.956	1.34	1.16	1.40	1.32
13/16"	.172	.345	.517	.690	1.04	1.38	.114	.230	.345	.460		.275	.396	1.30	1.12	1.57			
7/8"	.186	.371	.557	.743	1.11	1.49	.124	.248	.372	.490		.319	.459	1.50	1.30	1.82	1.58	1.90	1.80
15/16"	.199	.398	.597	.796	1.19	1.59	.133	.266	.398	.530		.367	.527	1.73	1.50	2.07			
1"	.212	.425	.627	.849	1.25	1.70	.142	.282	.418	.566		.417	.599	1.96	1.70	2.38	2.06	2.48	2.36
1-1/16"	.226	.451	.677	.902	1.35	1.80	.150	.301	.451	.602		.471	.676	2.22	1.92	2.68			
1-1/8"	.239	.478	.716	.955	1.43	1.91	.159	.318	.477	.637		.528	.758	2.48	2.15	3.02	2.60	3.14	2.98
1-3/16"	.252	.504	.756	1.01	1.51	2.02	.168	.336	.505	.672		.588	.845	2.77	2.40	3.36			
1-1/4"	.265	.531	.796	1.06	1.59	2.12	.177	.354	.531	.706		.651	.936	3.07	2.66	3.72	3.21	3.88	3.68
1-5/16"	.279	.557	.836	1.11	1.67	2.23	.186	.372	.557	.743		.718	1.03	3.38	2.93	4.10			
1-3/8"	.292	.584	.876	1.17	1.75	2.34	.195	.389	.584	.777		.789	1.13	3.71	3.21	4.50	3.89	4.69	4.45
1-7/16"	.305	.610	.915	1.22	1.83	2.44	.203	.407	.610	.814		.836	1.24	4.05	3.51	4.91			
1-1/2"	.318	.637	.955	1.27	1.91	2.55	.212	.425	.636	.849		.938	1.35	4.42	3.82	5.36	4.62	5.58	5.30
1-9/16"	.332	.664	.995	1.33	1.99	2.65	.221	.442	.664	.884		1.02	1.46	4.79	4.15	5.81			
1-5/8"	.345	.690	1.04	1.38	2.07	2.76	.230	.460	.690	.920		1.10	1.58	5.18	4.49	6.29	5.43	6.55	6.22
1-11/16"	.358	.716	1.07	1.43	2.15	2.87	.239	.477	.716	.956		1.19	1.71	5.59	4.84	6.80			
1-3/4"	.371	.743	1.11	1.49	2.23	2.97	.249	.495	.743	.990		1.28	1.84	6.01	5.20	7.29	6.29	7.59	7.21
1-13/16"	.385	.769	1.15	1.54	2.31	3.08	.257	.513	.770	1.03		1.37	1.97	6.45	5.58	7.81			
1-7/8"	.390	.796	1.19	1.59	2.39	3.18	.266	.531	.796	1.06		1.47	2.10	6.90	5.97	8.36	7.23	8.72	8.28
1-15/16"	.411	.822	1.23	1.65	2.47	3.29	.274	.549	.823	1.10		1.56	2.25	7.36	6.38	8.94			
2"	.425	.849	1.27	1.70	2.55	3.40	.283	.566	.849	1.13		1.67	2.40	7.85	6.80	9.52	8.23	9.93	9.43

TABLE 3—Weight of Weld Metal (lbs/ft of Joint)

↓ Plate thickness	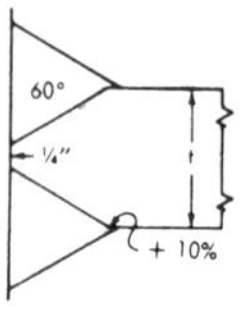 60°, 1/4", + 10%		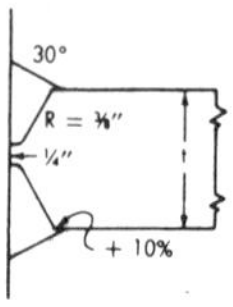 30°, R = 3/8", 1/4", + 10%		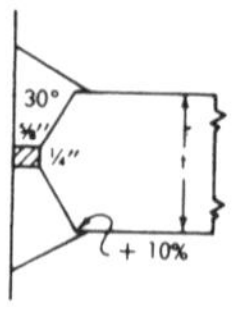 30°, 3/8", 1/4", + 10%		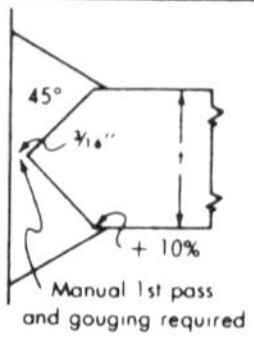 45°, 3/16", + 10%, Manual 1st pass and gouging required		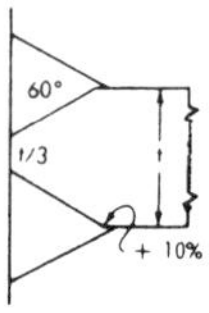 60°, 1/3, + 10%
	30° reinforcement	20° reinforcement	30° reinforcement	20° reinforcement	30° reinforcement	20° reinforcement	30° reinforcement	20° reinforcement	30° reinforcement
5/8	.456	.364	.544	.452	2.53	1.96	1.33	1.11	.427
3/4	.811	.649	.735	.626	3.02	2.40	1.71	1.43	.616
7/8	1.26	1.01	1.01	.830	3.54	2.86	2.14	1.79	.901
1	1.82	1.46	1.33	1.06	4.07	3.34	2.61	2.19	1.09
1 1/8	2.48	1.99	1.62	1.30	4.63	3.84	3.13	2.64	1.39
1 1/4	3.24	2.60	1.93	1.56	5.19	4.35	3.70	3.12	1.71
1 3/8	4.11	3.28	2.26	1.83	5.80	4.89	4.30	3.63	2.07
1 1/2	5.07	4.06	2.62	2.13	6.41	5.45	4.96	4.19	2.46
1 5/8	6.14	4.91	3.01	2.45	7.06	6.02	5.66	4.78	2.89
1 3/4	7.30	5.84	3.41	2.79	7.72	6.62	6.40	5.41	3.35
2	9.94	7.94	4.29	3.52	9.11	7.85	8.03	6.79	4.38
2 1/8	11.4	9.12	4.75	3.91	9.85	8.51	8.91	7.54	4.94
2 1/4	13.0	10.4	5.25	4.32	10.6	9.18	9.83	8.32	5.54
2 3/8	14.7	11.7	5.77	4.75	11.4	9.87	10.8	9.14	6.18
2 1/2	16.4	13.1	6.31	5.20	12.2	10.6	11.8	10.0	6.85
2 5/8	18.3	14.7	6.88	5.67	13.0	11.4	12.9	10.9	7.55
2 3/4	20.3	16.2	7.46	6.16	13.8	12.1	14.0	11.8	8.28
3	24.6	19.6	8.71	7.20	15.5	13.6	16.3	13.8	9.85

TABLE 4—Weight of Weld Metal (lbs/ft of Joint)

↓ Plate thickness	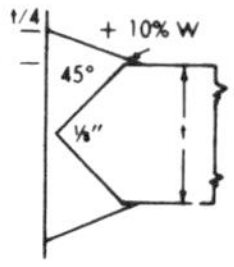 1/4, + 10% W, 45°, 1/8"	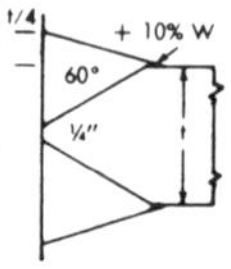 1/4, + 10% W, 60°, 1/4"	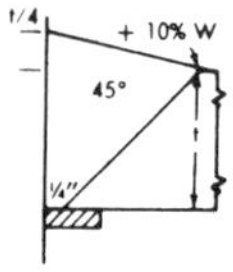 1/4, + 10% W, 45°, 1/4"	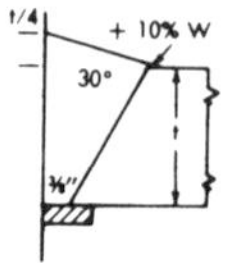 1/4, + 10% W, 30°, 3/8"	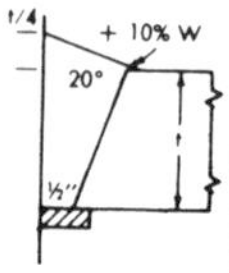 1/4, + 10% W, 20°, 1/2"	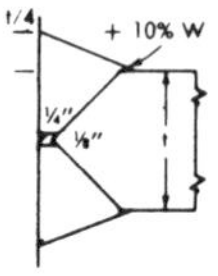 1/4, + 10% W, 1/4", 1/8"	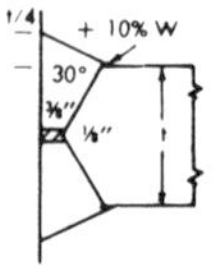 1/4, + 10% W, 30°, 3/8", 1/8"
5/8	.854	.501	1.45	1.39	1.52	1.09	1.15
3/4	1.15	.805	1.95	1.79	1.89	1.45	1.49
7/8	1.48	1.18	2.50	2.22	2.29	1.99	1.85
1	1.86	1.63	3.13	2.70	2.72	2.30	2.23
1 1/8	2.28	2.14	3.83	3.22	3.17	2.79	2.63
1 1/4	2.74	2.73	4.59	3.76	3.55	3.31	3.06
1 3/8	3.24	3.39	5.42	4.26	4.15	3.88	3.52
1 1/2	3.78	4.12	6.31	4.99	4.67	4.49	3.99
1 5/8	4.36	4.92	7.28	5.56	5.22	5.14	4.49
1 3/4	4.99	5.80	8.32	6.36	5.80	5.83	5.02
2	6.35	7.76	10.6	7.90	7.02	7.33	6.14
2 1/8	7.10	8.85	11.8	8.73	7.67	8.05	6.74
2 1/4	7.88	9.99	12.1	9.58	8.33	9.00	7.35
2 3/8	8.73	11.3	14.5	10.5	9.04	9.91	8.00
2 1/2	9.60	12.5	15.9	11.4	9.66	10.9	8.66
2 5/8	10.5	13.9	17.5	12.4	10.5	11.8	9.35
2 3/4	11.5	15.3	19.0	13.4	11.3	12.8	10.1
3	13.5	18.4	22.4	15.6	12.9	15.0	11.6

TABLE 5—Weight of Weld Metal
(lbs/ft of Joint)
Reinforcement: 10% W, Width of Joint

Plate thickness ↓	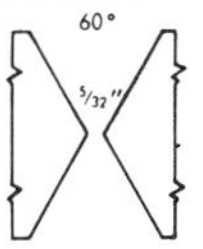 60°, 5/32"	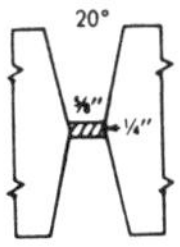 20°, 3/8", 1/4"	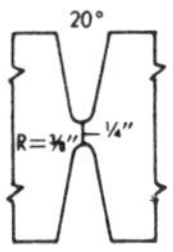 20°, R=3/8", 1/4"	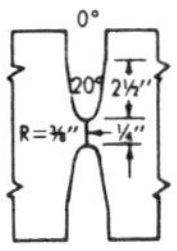 0°, 20°, 2 1/2", R=3/8", 1/4"	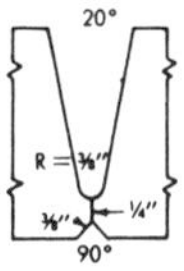 20°, R=3/8", 3/8", 1/4", 90°	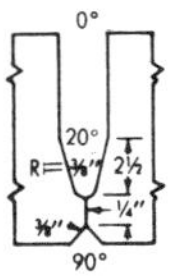 0°, 20°, R=3/8", 2 1/2, 1/4", 3/8", 90°
1	1.81	2.24	1.82		1.54	
1 1/8	2.17	2.61	2.17		1.89	
1 1/4	2.61	2.99	2.52		2.27	
1 3/8	3.09	3.37	2.88		2.65	
1 1/2	3.57	3.76	3.27		3.07	
1 5/8	4.12	4.18	3.65		3.50	
1 3/4	4.67	4.59	4.05		3.94	
2	5.93	5.44	4.87		4.91	
2 1/8	6.58	5.88	5.28		5.40	
2 1/4	7.32	6.34	5.72		5.94	
2 3/8	8.05	6.80	6.16		6.50	
2 1/2	8.87	7.28	6.63		7.06	
2 5/8	9.67	7.76	7.10		7.65	
2 3/4	10.5	8.26	7.57		8.25	
3	12.4	9.27	8.55		9.54	
3 1/8	13.3	9.80	8.90		10.2	10.2
3 1/4	14.5	10.3	9.40		10.8	10.8
3 1/2	16.5	11.2	10.6		12.3	12.1
3 3/4	18.8	12.5	11.6		13.8	13.3
4	21.2	13.7	12.9		15.4	14.7
4 1/2	26.4	16.2	15.2		18.9	17.2
5	32.3	18.8	17.8		22.6	19.8
5 1/2	38.7	21.6	20.5	20.4	26.7	22.3
6	45.7	24.6	23.4	23.0	31.0	25.0
6 1/2	53.3	27.8	26.4	25.4	35.6	27.0
7	61.4	30.4	29.6	28.1	40.5	30.1
7 1/2	70.0	34.3	32.9	30.6	46.0	32.8
8	79.5	37.9	36.4	33.3	51.7	35.3
9	99.9	45.5	43.9	38.4	63.9	40.4
10	122.6	53.8	52.0	43.5	77.4	45.6

FIG. 1—Weight of Weld Metal
(lbs/ft of Joint)
Based on Procedures, Using Submerged-Arc Process

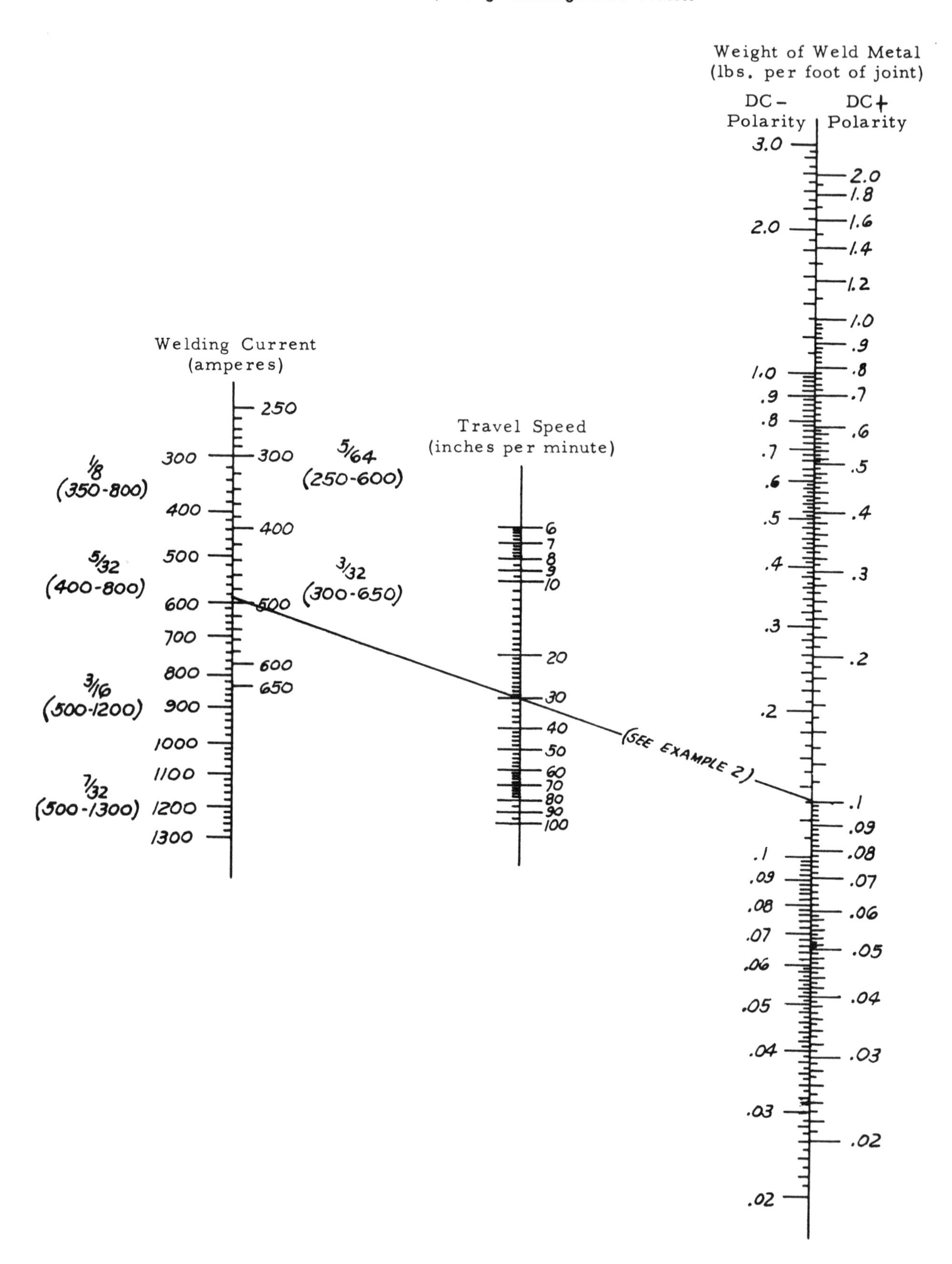

Problem 1

Computing the Weight of Weld Metal Based on Joint Design

With Table 2, computations based on joint design are easy. Essentially, it is a matter of dividing the cross-section of the area to be filled with weld metal, into standard geometric areas. The contributions of the individual areas can be found in the chart. Totaling these, gives the pounds of weld metal per foot required by the joint. For example, consider the following joint design (Fig. 2):

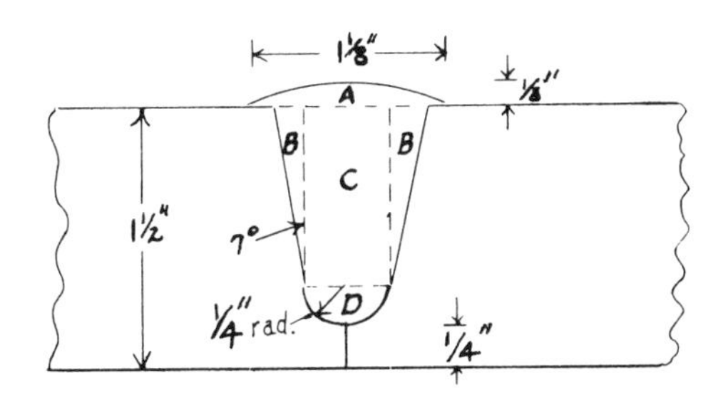

FIGURE 2

This joint can be broken into component areas A, B, C and D. Referring to Table 2, the contribution of each of these component areas to the total weight of weld metal required by the joint is simply picked off the chart as follows (Fig. 3):

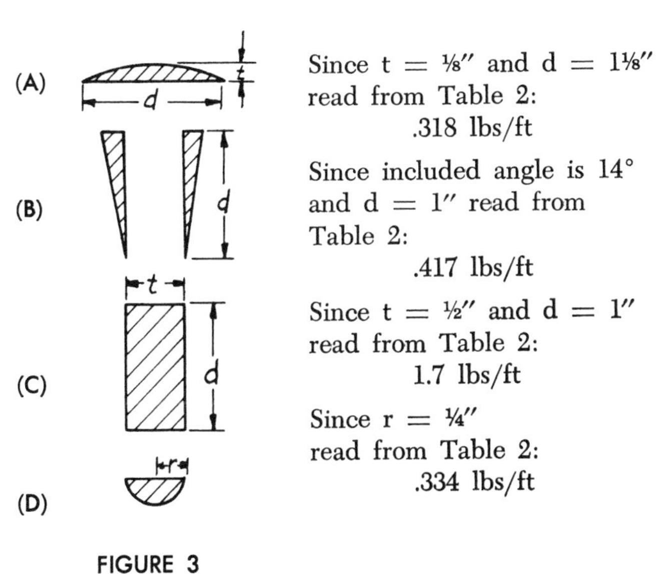

Since t = ⅛" and d = 1⅛" read from Table 2:
.318 lbs/ft

Since included angle is 14° and d = 1" read from Table 2:
.417 lbs/ft

Since t = ½" and d = 1" read from Table 2:
1.7 lbs/ft

Since r = ¼" read from Table 2:
.334 lbs/ft

FIGURE 3

Adding these, the total weight becomes 2.77 lbs of weld metal per foot of joint.

Problem 2

Computing the Weight of Weld Metal Based on Welding Procedures

When the welding procedures for a particular job are known, it is a simple matter to determine the weight of weld metal that will be deposited per foot of joint through the use of the nomograph for submerged arc welding Figure 1. Simply line up a straight-edge through the point on the left scale that represents the welding current being used and the point on the middle scale that represents the travel speed being used. Where the straight-edge intersects the right scale, read the amount of weld metal per foot of joint.

There is one note of caution. Be sure to use the proper side of the *Welding Current* scale, depending on the size of electrode used, and the correct side of the *Weight of Weld Metal* scale, depending on the polarity used.

As an example, the line drawn on the nomograph represents the procedure which uses 590 amps on ⅛" electrode at a travel speed of 30 in./min. The resultant weight of weld metal is .10 lbs per foot of joint if DC positive polarity is used, or .13 lbs if DC negative polarity is used.

Problem 3

Adjusting Procedures to Provide the Required Amount of Weld Metal

For some types of joints, there are no established welding procedures. When such is the case, the normal method is to find an established procedure for a similar joint and alter it slightly to accommodate the desired joint. The nomograph for submerged-arc welding, Figure 1, can eliminate a lot of hit-and-miss approaches to the selection of the proper procedure.

For example, consider the following submerged-arc automatic joint (Fig. 4):

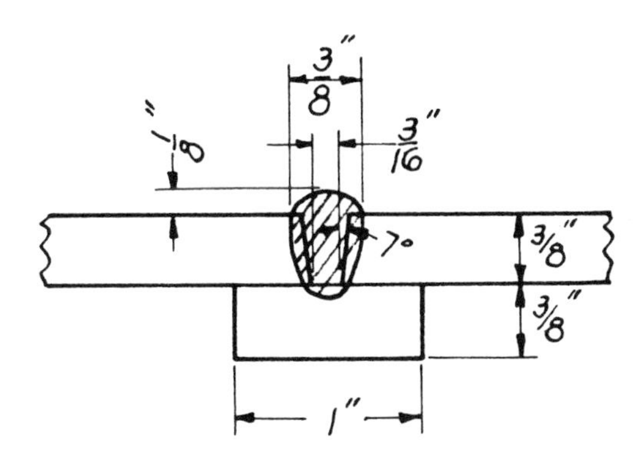

FIGURE 4

There are no established procedures for this joint. Probably the closest is that for the following joint (Fig. 5):

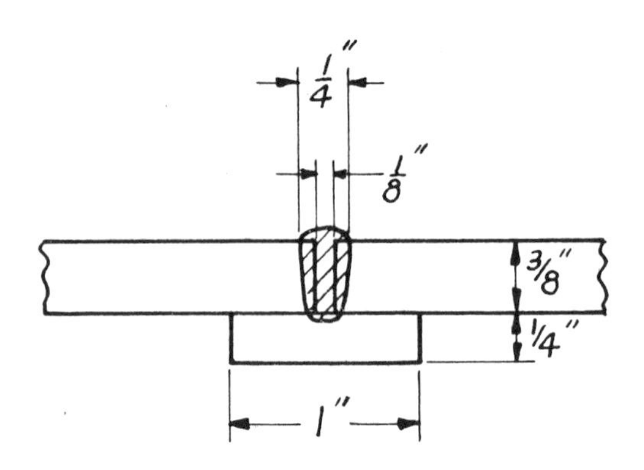

FIGURE 5

Power:	DC+
Amperes:	670
Volts:	29
Electrode Size:	5/32"
Travel Speed:	16"/min.

In adjusting this procedure to the new joint, it is reasonable to assume that the 670 amps would be about right and, therefore, the simplest thing to do would be to slow down the welding speed enough to provide the amount of fill required. To do this, first determine the amount of weld metal required to fill the new joint in the manner outlined in Problem 1. In this case, it is determined to be .404 lbs/ft of joint.

Then, use the nomograph to determine the proper speed setting as follows.

Locate 670 amps on the left-hand side of the welding scale (for 5/32" electrode) and .404 lbs/ft on the DC+ polarity side of the weld metal scale. Draw a straight line between them. This intersects the travel speed line at 9"/min, which is an estimate of the speed which should be used to provide adequate fill in the joint. With this much of the procedure fixed, it is a simple matter to adjust the voltage to provide the desired bead shape.

* * * *

3. OPERATING FACTOR

The selection of a proper operating factor (OF) is difficult, and yet affects the final cost more than any other single item. Even though some difficulty is encountered in obtaining this value, it is necessary to establish an approximately true value rather than to simply ignore it or assume it to be 100%. Consider the following:

METHOD A	METHOD B
1/4" electrode A @ 20¢/lb	1/4" electrode B @ 14¢/lb
uses 1/4 # rod/ft of weld	uses 1/4 # rod/ft of weld
speed is 18 in./min	speed is 16 in./min
labor & overhead, $6.00/hr	labor & overhead, $6.00/hr
Total cost of welding using 100% operating factor: 11.7 ¢/ft	Total cost of welding using 100% operating factor: 10.9 ¢/ft
This indicates that, with 100% operating factor, electrode B would have the least cost, and would save 6.6%.	
Total cost of welding using 30% operating factor 27.2 ¢/ft	Total cost of welding using 30% operating factor 28.4 ¢/ft
This indicates that, with 30% operating factor, electrode A would have the least cost and would save 4.1%.	

In other words, the operating factor does affect the welding cost sufficiently to be considered.

Since one might question the practice of assuming the same operating factor for various electrodes and procedures, consider the following example.

A welding engineer is interested in replacing his present E-6012 electrode on a certain job with the iron powder E-6024 electrode. The following is his cost study:

E-6012 ELECTRODE	E-6024 ELECTRODE
5/16" leg fillet .30# rod/ft	5/16" leg fillet .30# rod/ft
5/16" E-6012 rod @ 375 amps AC	5/16" E-6024 rod @ 375 amps AC
melt-off rate M = 7¾ in./min	melt-off rate M = 10.2 in./min
speed S = 9 in./min	speed S = 13 in./min
length rod melted L_m = 16"	length rod melted L_m = 16"
time T = 2.06 min/rod	time T = 1.57 min/rod

Assume a 50% operating factor (OF)
and $6.00/hr labor and overhead (L)

labor cost	labor cost
$\frac{20L}{S\ (OF)} = \frac{(20)(6)}{(9)(50\%)} = 26.7$ ¢/ft	$\frac{20\ L}{S\ (OF)} = \frac{(20)(6)}{(13)(50\%)} = 18.5$ ¢/ft

or a saving in labor of 30.7% by using the iron powder electrode E-6024.

But this analysis reveals the following: The arc time for the E-6012 electrode per rod is 2.06 minutes; using a 50% operating factor, this represents a downtime of 2.06 minutes per rod. This downtime between electrodes includes time to lift up the helmet, clean the slag off the weld, insert a new electrode into the holder, etc. On the same basis the arc time for the E-6024 electrode would be 1.57 minutes per rod; and using the same operating factor of 50%, this means a downtime of only 1.57 minutes per rod.

It might appear at first that simply substituting the E-6024 electrode into the holder would decrease the downtime; i.e. the operator can lift up his helmet faster, knock off the slag faster, pick up and insert the next electrode faster, etc. Of course this is not true.

A more accurate method would be to use a fixed downtime, adjusting the operating factor accordingly. Re-examine this cost study, using an average downtime between electrodes of 2.06 minutes:

E-6012 ELECTRODE	E-6024 ELECTRODE
operating factor = 50%	operating factor $= \frac{1.57}{(1.57) + (2.06)} = 43.5\%$
labor cost	labor cost
$\frac{20\ L}{S\ (OF)} = \frac{(20)(6)}{(9)(50\%)} = 26.7$ ¢/ft	$\frac{20\ L}{S\ (OF)} = \frac{(20)(6)}{(13)(43.5\%)} = 21.2$ ¢/ft

or a saving in labor cost of 21% by using the E-6024 electrode.

$$\text{Assume } E = \frac{\text{lbs rod melted}}{\text{lbs rod consumed}} = 90\%$$

rod cost	rod cost
$\frac{1200\ M\ W}{N\ L_m\ S\ E_3} = \frac{(1200)(7\ 3/4)(14.9)}{(219)(16)(9)(90\%)} = 4.9$ ¢/ft	$\frac{1200\ M\ W}{N\ L_m\ S\ E_3} = \frac{(1200)(10.2)(16.9)}{(218)(16)(13)(90\%)} = 5.1$ ¢/ft
Total 26.7 + 4.9 = 31.6 ¢/ft	Total 21.2 + 5.1 = 26.3 ¢/ft

or a total saving in labor and rod cost of 16.8% by using the E-6024 electrode.

Notice that the decreased arc time with the E-6024 results in a slightly lower operating factor, 43.5% instead of 50%, although the joint does cost less.

One might further suggest using a downtime per electrode and a handling time per foot of weld. These figures, if available, would give a more true picture of the welding cost, but it would mean making a time study of the job, which we are trying to avoid.

The nomograph, Figure 6, may be used to quickly read the labor and overhead cost per foot of weld.

4. COST PER HOUR

As a matter of interest, consider the cost per hour for these two procedures:

E-6012 ELECTRODE	E-6024 ELECTRODE
rod consumed per hr	rod consumed per hr
$\frac{6000\,M\,(OF)}{N\,L_m\,E_3} = \frac{(6000)(7\ 3/4)(50\%)}{(219)(16)(90\%)}$	$\frac{6000\,M\,(OF)}{N\,L_m\,E_3} = \frac{(6000)(10.2)(43.5\%)}{(218(16)(90\%)}$
= 7.37 lbs/hr	= 8.49 lbs/hr
rod cost	rod cost
7.37 x 14.9 ¢/lb = $1.10/hr	8.49 x 16.9 ¢/lb = $1.44/hr
labor cost = 6.00	labor cost = 6.00
Total = $7.10/hr	Total = $7.44/hr

It can be expected then that the cost per hour for making the same size weld will increase slightly with faster procedures. Obviously the increase equals the difference in cost of electrode consumed. Of course the number of units turned out per hour is greater, so the unit cost is less.

5. ESTIMATING ACTUAL WELDING TIME

After the length and size of the various welds have been determined, there are three ways to estimate the actual welding time:

1. Convert these values into weight of weld metal per linear foot, and total for the entire job. Determine the deposition rate from the given welding current, and from this find the arc time. This method is especially useful when there is no standard welding data for the particular joint.
2. If standard welding data is available in tables, giving the arc travel speeds for various types and sizes of welds, in terms of inches per minute, apply this to the total lengths of each type and size of weld on the job.
3. Time the actual weld or job.

Most welding procedures are based on good welding conditions. These assume a weldable steel, clean smooth edge preparation, proper fit-up, proper position of plates for welding, sufficient accessibility so the welding operator can easily observe the weld and place the electrode in the proper position, and welds sufficiently long so the length of crater is not a factor in determining weld strength. Under these standard conditions, the weld should have acceptable appearance. Failure to provide these conditions requires a substantial reduction in welding current and immediately increases cost.

It is impossible to put a qualitative value on these factors, therefore the designer or engineer must learn to anticipate such problems and, by observation or consulting with shop personnel or other engineers who have actual welding experience, modify his estimate accordingly.

FIG. 6—Welding Cost Estimator
(Does Not Include Cost of Filler Metal)

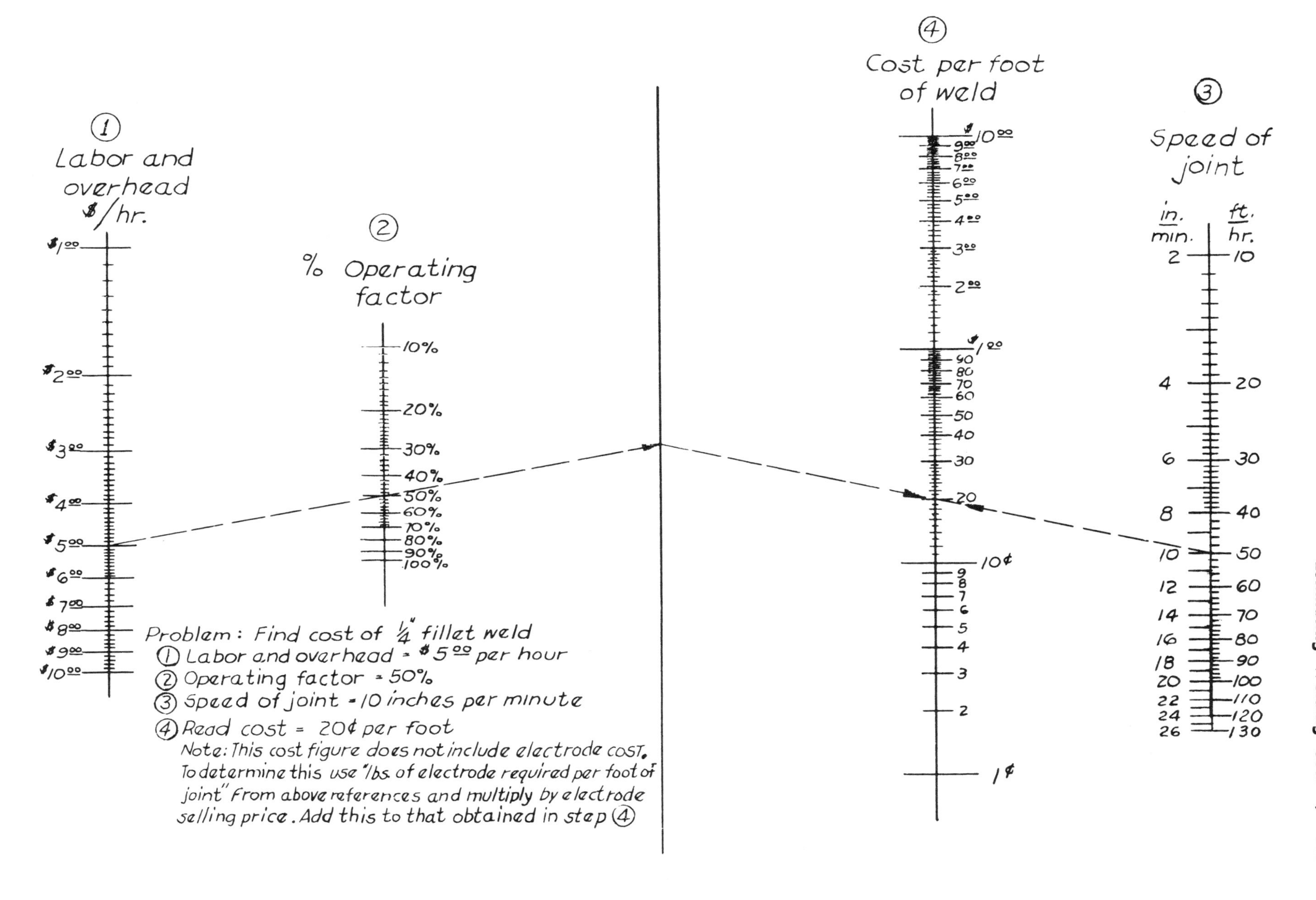

TABLE 6—Weight of Weld Metal
(lbs/ft of Joint)

Plate Thickness	Unlimited † Flat and Overhead 30° 1/16"	Unlimited † All Positions 45° 1/16"	Unlimited † Flat and Overhead 20° 1/8"	Unlimited † All Positions 45° 1/8"	Unlimited † Double V* / Max. 3/4" † Single V* 60° 1/8"	Unlimited † All Positions 45° 1/4"	Unlimited † Flat and Overhead 30° 3/8"	Unlimited † Flat and Overhead 20° 1/2"	Unlimited † Double Bevel* / Max. 3/4" † Single Bevel* 45° 1/8"	Unlimited † All Positions 45° 1/4"	Unlimited † Flat and Overhead 30° 3/8"
1/2"	.58	.65	.68	.67	.84	.89	.98	1.12	.74	1.00	1.01
3/4"	.90	1.40	1.27	1.35	1.70	1.60	1.60	1.80	1.52	1.87	1.65
1"	1.78	2.32	1.96	2.23	2.83	2.57	2.41	2.50	2.47	2.97	2.51
1 1/4"	2.40	3.65	2.60	3.32	4.27	3.67	3.35	3.30	3.70	4.35	3.45
1 1/2"	3.54	4.99	3.37	4.60	5.98	5.03	4.35	4.18	5.17	5.93	4.55
1 3/4"	4.65	6.70	4.20	6.06	7.93	6.55	5.55	5.17	6.87	7.80	5.80
2"	5.87	8.64	5.20	7.76	10.32	8.31	6.75	6.20	8.85	9.87	7.12
2 1/4"	7.20	10.80	6.23	9.35	12.90	10.23	8.15	7.32	11.10	12.20	8.60
2 1/2"	8.74	13.27	7.34	11.71	15.81	12.37	9.67	8.50	13.57	14.79	10.22
2 3/4"	10.40	15.90	8.60	14.00	19.00	14.70	11.37	9.85	16.30	17.75	12.00
3"	12.20	18.93	9.87	16.50	22.48	17.20	13.08	11.15	19.17	20.69	13.87

* All Positions
A.W.S. Highway and R.R. Bridge 1956—Prequalified Joints 9-5-57

Welding on Existing Structures

1. LOAD CARRYING CAPACITY OF CONNECTION

In the modification or repair of buildings, it may be necessary to weld to the existing steel framework.

When welding and riveting are combined on the same strength joint, the riveted portion of the joint may slip or yield slightly, thus throwing the entire load eventually on the weld. Normally, on new construction where welding and riveting are combined, the joint would be figured on the basis of the weld taking the entire load. Since 1930, most of the old riveted railroad trestles have been reinforced by welding because of the newer and heavier locomotives.

Riveted connections can be reinforced with plates, with holes to fit over the rivets. The plate is welded to the existing connection with fillet welds all around its edge, and is plug welded to the plate at each rivet hole. This technique, however, requires a considerable amount of out-of-position welding with small electrodes.

2. EFFECT OF WELDING HEAT ON MEMBER'S STRENGTH

Frequently, a question arises as to the effect of welding on the strength of an existing structure already under a stress. Actually the strength of steel does not drop off upon heating, until a temperature of about 650°F is reached. This is brought out in the table of allowable strengths of materials in the ASME Unfired Pressure Vessels, Section 8. Here the same allowable is used from minus 20°F all the way up to 650°F. The ASME code body recognizes the fact that the strength of steel rises slightly upon heating and does not start to drop off until a temperature of 600°F or 700°F is reached.

In welding to an existing structure, the amount of material actually heated momentarily above 700° would be a very small spot right at the welding arc. Figure 1 shows the temperature rise in a plate while making a 5⁄16″ fillet weld in the vertical-up position. This indicates that in using a 3⁄16″ E6010 electrode, the temperature on the back side of the ¾″ thick plate opposite the weld was held below 600°F. Figure 2 shows the same weld using a 5⁄32″ E6010 electrode. Here the temperature on the back side of the ½″ thick plate was held below 650°F. Also see Figure 3.

The very tiny area of the member heated above this temperature does not represent a sizable percentage of the entire cross-section of the stress carrying member. This has been the opinion of many fabricators and erectors who have been welding on existing structures for several years.

All welds will, however, shrink. This creates a shrinkage force which, if welds are not placed symmetrically about the member, will result in some distortion of that member. This could occur in welding to an existing member if most of the welding is done on one side. For example, if all of the welding is done on the bottom flange of a beam, the unsymmetrical welding will tend to distort the beam upward in the

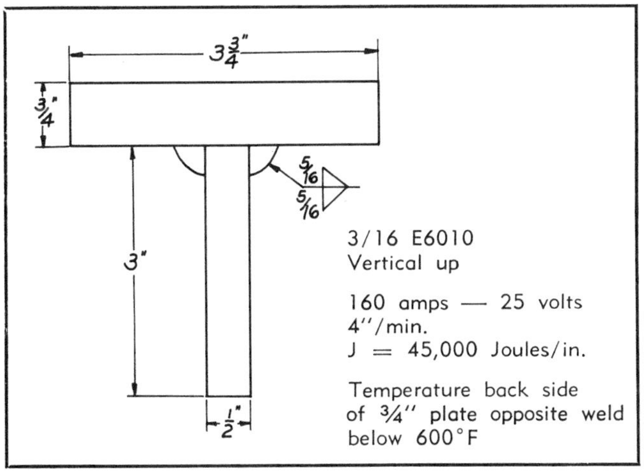

3¾″
¾″
3″
½″
5⁄16
5⁄16
3/16 E6010
Vertical up
160 amps — 25 volts
4″/min.
J = 45,000 Joules/in.
Temperature back side of ¾″ plate opposite weld below 600°F

FIGURE 1

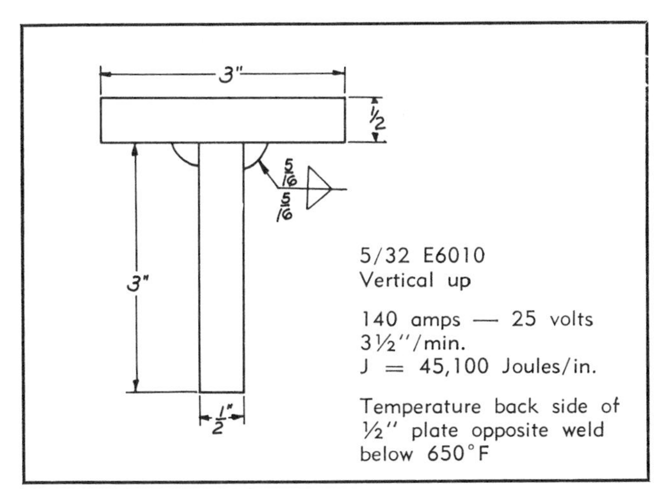

FIGURE 2

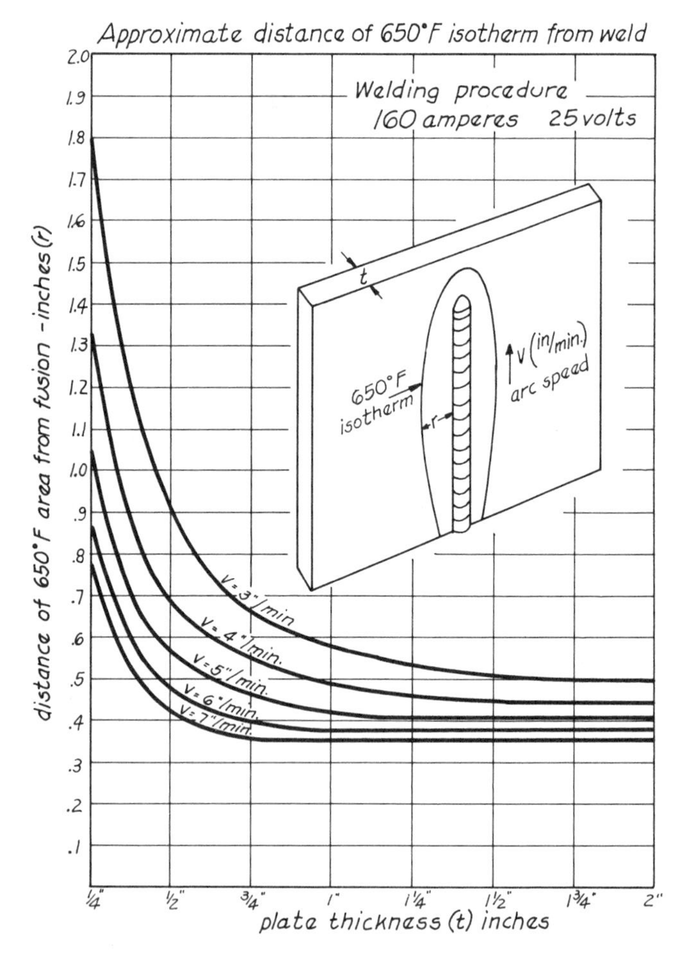

FIG. 3 A guide to establishing proper welding procedures for minimum heat input.

opposite direction as the applied load to the beam. If the welding were done along the top flange only, this would tend to distort the beam downward in the same direction as the applied load. Therefore, it might be well, in some cases, to temporarily shore up a beam in order to reduce some or all of the beam load while welding.

3. AWS, AISC AND AASHO SPECIFICATIONS

Section 7 of the present AWS Code for Welding in Building Construction, and the Specifications for Welded Highway and Railway Bridges, cover the strengthening and repairing of existing structures.

The engineer shall determine whether or not a member is permitted to carry live load stresses while welding or oxygen-cutting is being performed on it, taking into consideration the extent to which the member's cross-section is heated as a result of the operation being performed.

If material is added to a member carrying a dead load stress of 3000 psi, either for repairing corroded parts or for strengthening, it is desirable to relieve the member of dead load stresses, or to pre-stress the material to be added. If neither is practical, the new material to be added shall be proportioned for a unit stress equal to the allowable unit stress in the original member minus the dead load unit stress in the original member.

Problem 1

To reinforce an existing member to withstand an additional live load of 20,000 lbs. The existing section has a cross-sectional area of 10.0 in.², with an allowable working stress of $\sigma = 18{,}000$ psi. The original design loads—dead (DL), live (LL), and impact (I)—gave the following:

DL force	100,000 lbs ÷ 10.0 in.² =	10,000 psi
LL + I force	80,000 lbs ÷ 10.0 in.² =	8,000 psi
DL + LL + I force	180,000 lbs	18,000 psi
	and 18,000 psi ≦	18,000 psi OK

The member must now be increased in section for an additional 20,000 lbs of live load (LL):

Allowable stress in original member =	18,000 psi
Dead load stress in original member =	10,000 psi
To be used in new steel to be added =	8,000 psi

$$\frac{20{,}000 \text{ lbs}}{8{,}000 \text{ lbs}} = 2.5 \text{ in.}^2 = \text{area of new steel to be added}$$

Check this as follows:

DL force	100,000 lbs ÷ 10.0 in.² =	10,000 psi
LL + I force	100,000 lbs ÷ 12.5 in.² =	8,000 psi
DL + LL + I	200,000 lbs	18,000 psi
	and 18,000 psi ≦	18,000 psi OK

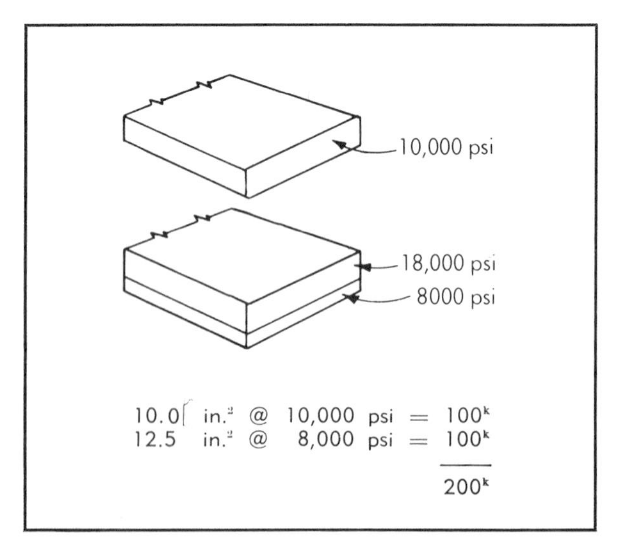

FIGURE 4

In making alterations to structures, existing rivets may be utilized for carrying stresses resulting from dead loads and welding shall be provided to carry all additional stress. However, if the framing is shored during repairs and the member to be reinforced is thus relieved of stress, the welding shall carry the entire stress.

AISC Requirements

AISC Sec 1.15.10: Rivets and Bolts in Combination with Welds. In new work, rivets, bolts or high strength bolts used in bearing type connections shall not be considered as sharing the stress in combination with welds. Welds, if used, shall be provided to carry the entire stress in the connection. High strength bolts installed in accordance with the provisions of Sec 1.16.1 as friction-type connections prior to welding may be considered as sharing the stress with the welds. In making welded alterations to structures, existing rivets and properly tightened high strength bolts may be utilized for carrying stresses resulting from existing dead loads, and the welding need be adequate only to carry all additional stress.

AASHO Requirements

AASHO 1.12.7: The unit working stresses used in determining the load-carrying capacity of each member of a structure shall take into account the type of material from which the member is made. The unit working stress assumed for the inventory rating shall not exceed 0.545% of the yield point and for the operating rating shall not exceed 0.82 of the yield point.

Where information concerning the specification under which the metal was supplied is not available, it will be assumed that the yield point does not exceed 30,000 psi for all bridges built after 1905.

Bridges built previous to 1905 shall be checked to see that the material is not of a fibrous nature. If it is fibrous or of doubtful character, the yield point will be assumed to be equal to that of wrought iron which shall be taken as 26,000 psi.

In the absence of definite information, it shall be assumed that the yield point of wrought iron is 26,000 psi, and the unit working stress shall be taken as 14,000 psi.

4. GENERAL

Proposed repairs and methods should be considered and approved by a qualified engineer. Welding on a job of this type should be of the best quality and adequately inspected. An E6010 type of electrode would normally be recommended for this welding, if it involves vertical and overhead positions or painted or dirty material. Material should be cleaned as thoroughly as possible before welding. If the material is unusually thick, a low-hydrogen electrode should be used, and it would be well to check for any preheat which might be recommended. See the following topic, Temperature for Welding.

When making a repair on a structure it is necessary to know the type of steel it is made of. It may be possible to get a mill report from the steel mill which furnished the steel. Sometimes on very old structures this information cannot be obtained. If this is an important structure, it would be a good idea to get test drillings and have them analyzed.

An experienced weldor will sometimes weld a small piece of mild steel to the structure and then knock it off with a hammer. If the weld cracks out of the base metal, taking some of it with the weld, this indicates that the steel is hardenable and the heat-affected zone adjacent to the weld has been hardened. If the weld itself cracks, this indicates higher carbon or alloy in the steel which has been picked up in the molten weld and become hard during cooling. In both cases, preheating and low hydrogen electrodes should be used. If the mild steel bar bends down without the weld breaking, this indicates good weldable ductile steel.

All structural work for a major addition to the Jordan-Marsh Department Store in Boston was completed without interruption of business. The concrete wall was penetrated and new steel welded successfully to vintage steel under load —without removal of the load.

There is little chance that the structure to be repaired is made of wrought iron, which was used in structures prior to 1900. Wrought iron contains slag rolled into it as tiny slag inclusions or laminations, and is low in carbon. The slag pockets might bother the welding operator a little, but this should be no real problem. Some engineers recommend that extra effort be made to fuse or penetrate well into the wrought iron surface, especially if the attached member is going to pull at right angles to the wrought iron member; otherwise, they reason, the surface might pull out because of the laminations directly below the surface.

It is also possible for the sulphur content of wrought iron to be excessive, and it should be checked. Keep in mind that any chemical analysis for sulphur represents the average value in the drillings of steel taken for analysis. It is possible in wrought iron to have the sulphur segregated into small areas of high concentrations. The low-hydrogen electrodes (EXX15, EXX16 and EXX18) should be used where sulphur might be a problem.

The AISC published in 1953 a complete listing of steel and wrought iron beams and columns that were rolled between 1873 and 1952 in the United States.

5. TEMPERATURE FOR WELDING

The AWS Building and Bridge codes require that welding shall not be done when the ambient temperature is lower than 0°F. When the base metal temperature is below 32°F, preheat the base metal to at least 70°F, and maintain this temperature during welding.

Under both codes, no welding is to be done on metal which is wet, exposed to ice, snow, or rain, nor when the weldors are exposed to inclement conditions, including high wind, unless the work and the weldors are properly protected.

In general, the AISC and AWS specifications on minimum temperature for welding are a good guide to follow. See Table 1. The following thoughts might supplement them in producing better welds at these cold temperatures.

Welding on plates at cold temperatures results in a very fast rate of cooling for the weld metal and adjacent base metals. With thicker sections of mild steel, A7, A373, and A36, this exceptionally fast rate of cooling traps hydrogen in the weld metal. This reduces ductility and impact strength of the weld and may cause cracking, especially of the root bead or first pass. This type of weld cracking has been shown to occur almost entirely in the temperature range below 400°F.

With a preheat or interpass temperature of 200°F, this cracking does not occur, even with the organic type of mild steel electrodes. This is because the higher temperature results in a slower cooling rate, and more time for this entrapped hydrogen to escape.

Low-hydrogen electrodes greatly reduce the source of hydrogen and, therefore, the cracking problem. This weld metal has greater impact strength and a lower transition temperature. In general, the use of low-hydrogen electrodes will lower any preheat requirement by approximately 300°F.

The fastest cooling rate occurs with so-called "arc strikes", when at the start of a weld the electrode is scratched along the surface of the plate without any metal being deposited. This can be damaging and

TABLE 1—Minimum Preheat and Interpass Temperatures [1, 2]

Thickness of Thickest Part at Point of Welding, in inches	Welding Process	
	Shielded Metal-Arc Welding with Other than Low-Hydrogen Electrodes	Shielded Metal-Arc Welding with Low-Hydrogen Electrodes or Submerged Arc Welding
	ASTM A36[3], A7[3, 4], A373[3]	ASTM A36[5], A7[4, 5], A373[5], A441[6]
To 3/4, incl.	None[7]	None[7]
Over 3/4 to 1 1/2, incl.	150°F	70°F
Over 1 1/2 to 2 1/2, incl.	225°F	150°F
Over 2 1/2	300°F	225°F

[1] Welding shall not be done when the ambient temperature is lower than 0°F.
[2] When the base metal is below the temperature listed for the welding process being used and the thickness of material being welded, it shall be preheated for all welding (including tack welding) in such manner that the surfaces of the parts on which weld metal is being deposited are at or above the specified minimum temperature for a distance equal to the thickness of the part being welded, but not less than 3 in., both laterally and in advance of the welding.
Preheat temperature shall not exceed 400°F. (Interpass temperature is not subject to a maximum limit.)
[3] Using E60XX or E70XX electrodes other than the low-hydrogen types.
[4] See limitations on use of ASTM A7 steel in Par. 105(b).
[5] Using low-hydrogen electrodes (E7015, E7016, E7018, E7028) or Grade SAW-1 or SAW-2.
[6] Using only low-hydrogen electrodes (E7015, E7016, E7018, E7028) or Grade SAW-2.
[7] When the base metal temperature is below 32°F, preheat the base metal to at least 70°F.

should be avoided. Next to this in seriousness are very short tack welds.

The following will illustrate the effect which weld length has on cooling rate. The length of time to cool from 1600°F to 200°F when a single weld is placed on a ¾″ plate is:

Length of Weld	2½″	4″	9″
Time (Seconds)	90.	300.	2000.

A weld 9″ long made at a temperature of 70°F has about the same cooling rate as the same weld 3″ long at a preheat of 300°F. Welds of larger cross-section have greater heat input per inch of weld. High welding current and slow travel speeds slow down the rate of cooling and decrease the cracking problem.

Perhaps the greatest difficulty in cold temperature welding is the discomfort of the welding operator. It becomes more awkward to move around the weld because of the extra clothing required. The welding lens continually becomes frosted or fogged from the breath of the operator. The helmet must be removed and the lens wiped.

6. WELDING OF INSERT PLATES

For thick plates, a double V or U joint would reduce the amount of weld metal and therefore transverse shrinkage. The balanced weld would preclude any angular distortion.

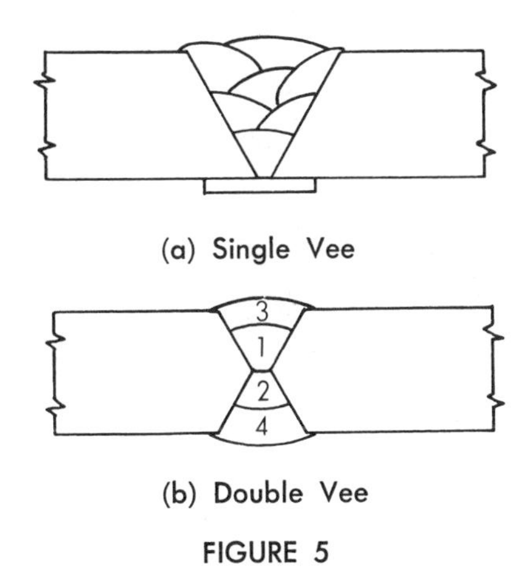

(a) Single Vee

(b) Double Vee

FIGURE 5

The use of round corners will tend to reduce any notch effect at the corners of the welded insert.

Sometimes the plate to be inserted is pre-dished, providing a little excess material in the plate to offset the transverse shrinkage. However, longitudinal shrinkage stresses will build up around the periphery of the plate, because the edge welded lies in a flat plane and therefore is more restrained.

The following sequence is usually used:

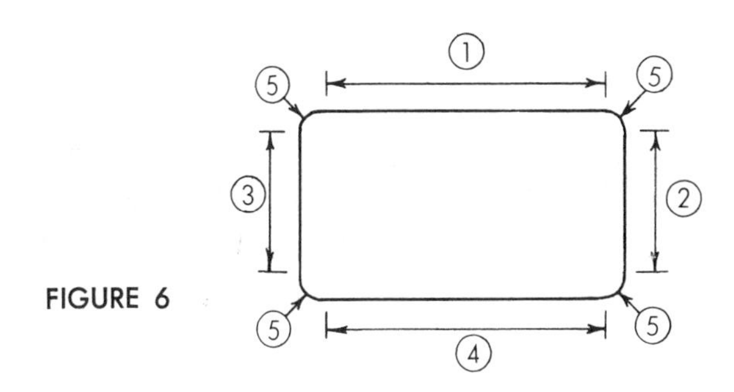

FIGURE 6

Weld side (1) complete. So far this should be rather unrestrained. A few tack welds on the opposite side might crack; if so, they should be realigned and rewelded. Weld side (2) complete. It might be argued that this is free to shrink because the opposite side (3) is unwelded. However there is some restraint offered by the weld along side (1). Now side (3) directly opposite side (2) is welded; this will start to lock-up now. Then weld side (4) opposite side (1). If either weld (3) or (4) should crack, it should be gouged out to sound metal and rewelded. Finally, the four corners (5) are completed.

Another suggestion is to estimated the amount of transverse shrinkage and to open up the joint initially by this amount, by driving in several hardened steel drift pins. The joint is then welded, full throat, up to these pins. The pins are then removed, and the joint completed.

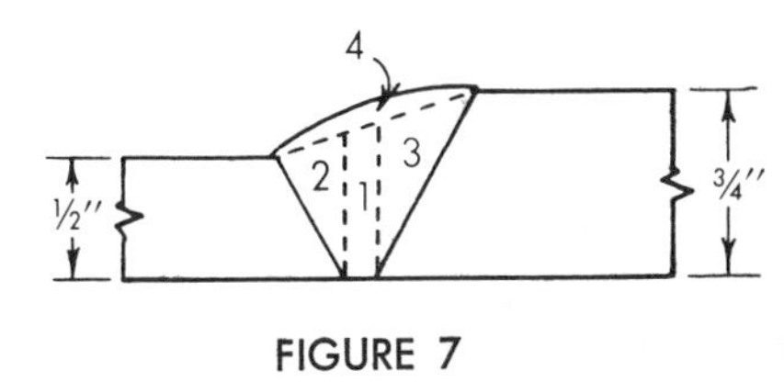

FIGURE 7

Figure 7 illustrates the geometrical method of obtaining the weld area. This value is needed to determine transverse shrinkage:

$$\text{transverse shrinkage } (\Delta) = 10\% \, \frac{\text{weld area}}{\text{thickness}}$$
$$= 10\% \text{ average width of weld}$$

area of weld

$$\begin{aligned}
(\tfrac{3}{16}'')(.62'') &= .1162 \\
\tfrac{1}{2}\,(.62'')(.30'') &= .0930 \\
\tfrac{1}{2}\,(.90'')(.30'') &= .1350 \\
\tfrac{2}{3}\,(1.0'')(.10'') &= .0667 \\
\hline
&\ .4109 \text{ in.}^2
\end{aligned}$$

$$\therefore \Delta = .10 \, \frac{(.411)}{\left(\dfrac{\tfrac{1}{2}'' \times \tfrac{3}{4}''}{2}\right)}$$

$$= \underline{.07''}$$

In production of large plate girders, flange is commonly tack welded to the web. Then, with the girder web held at a 45° angle, the web-to-flange weld can be efficiently made using a self-propelled submerged-arc welding unit. This 1/2" fillet is here being made in two passes. Flange is 4" thick, web 3/4". Improvements in equipment and technique are currently permitting many 1/2" fillets to be made in a single pass.

Control of Shrinkage and Distortion

1. WELDING FACTORS THAT CAUSE MOVEMENT

In making a weld, the heating and cooling cycle always causes shrinkage in both base metal and weld metal, and shrinkage forces tend to cause a degree of distortion. Designers and engineers must anticipate and provide control of this shrinkage to achieve the full economies of arc-welded steel construction. Suggested solutions for correction or elimination are based on both theoretical analysis and the practical experience of fabricating shops.

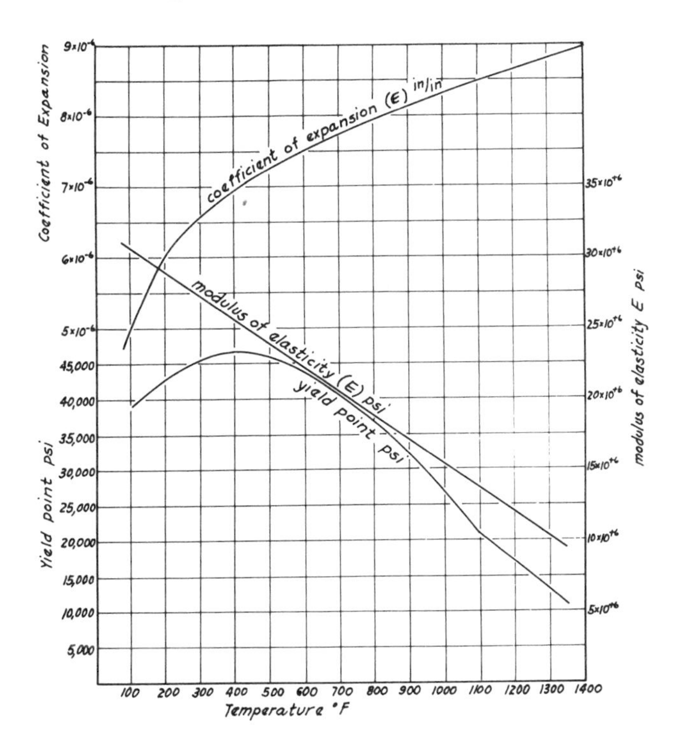

FIG. 1 Properties of a metal change at elevated temperatures, complicating the analysis of weld shrinkage. Graph is for mild steel.

The enormous temperature differential in the arc area, creates a non-uniform distribution of heat in the part. As the temperature increases, such properties as yield strength decrease, the modulus of elasticity decreases, the coefficient of thermal expansion increases, the thermal conductivity decreases, and the specific heat increases. See Figure 1. To anticipate the movement of material from a straightforward analysis of heat is difficult.

Restraint from external clamping, internal restraint due to mass, and the stiffness of the steel plate itself also must be considered. All these factors have a definite influence on the degree of movement.

Finally it is necessary to consider the factor of time as it affects the rapidly changing conditions. The period of time during which a specific condition is in effect controls the importance of that condition.

These variable conditions are further influenced by the welding process itself. Different welding procedures, type and size of electrode, welding current, speed of travel, joint design, preheating and cooling rates—all these bear significantly on the problem.

It is obvious that distortion cannot be analyzed

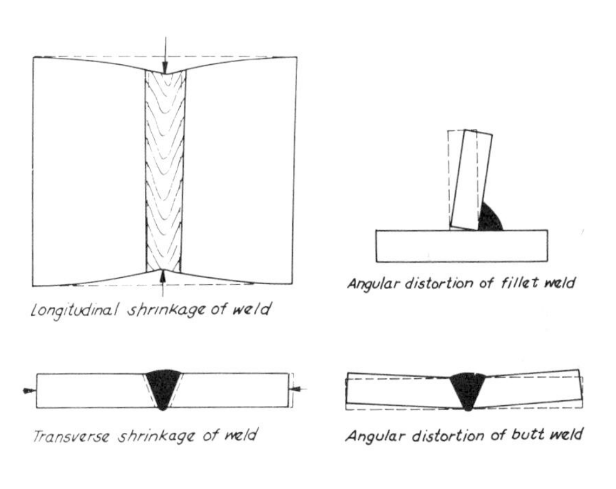

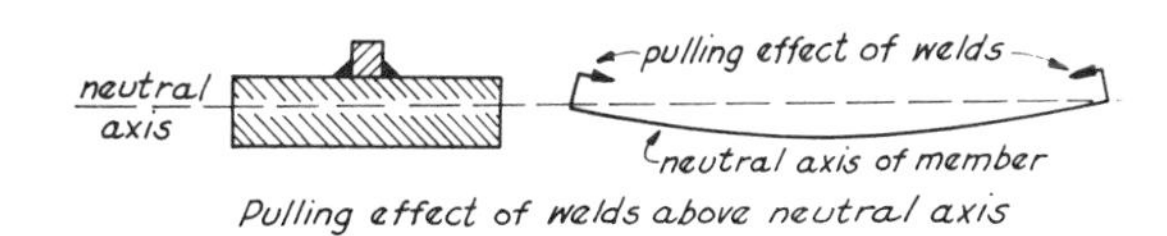

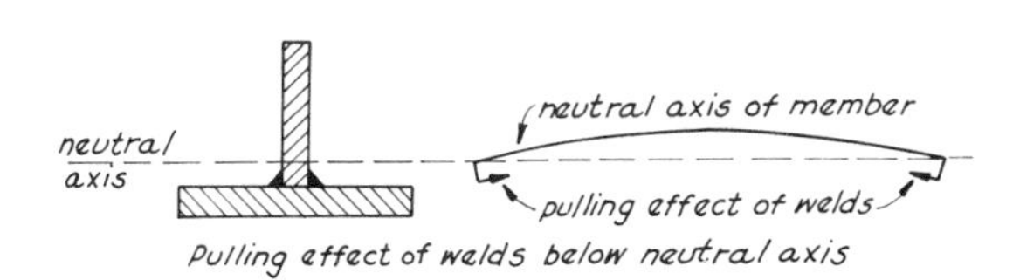

FIG. 2 An unbalance of forces resulting from shrinkage of weld deposit tends to cause angular distortion or bowing.

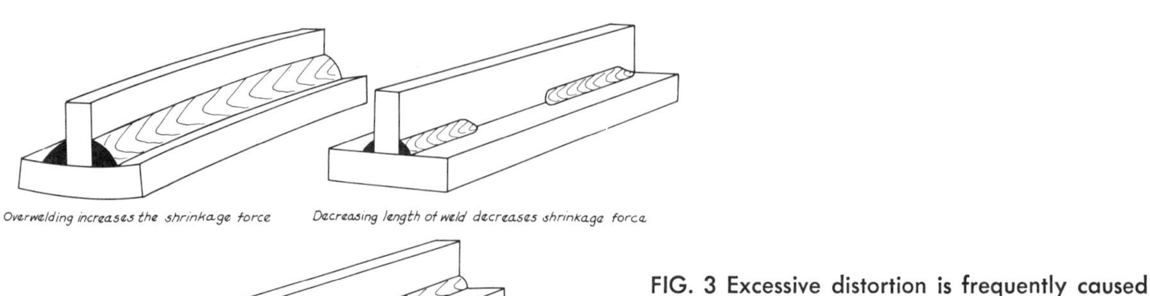
Overwelding increases the shrinkage force
Decreasing length of weld decreases shrinkage force
Decreasing leg size of weld decreases shrinkage force

FIG. 3 Excessive distortion is frequently caused by overwelding.

by viewing each one of these factors separately. A solution based on correcting the combined effect is the only practicable approach.

2. EVIDENCES AND CAUSE OF DISTORTION

When distortion occurs, it appears as a shortening of the weld area. This generally can be cataloged as longitudinal shrinkage and transverse shrinkage, Figure 2. Further, if transverse shrinkage is not uniform throughout the thickness of the weld, angular distortion will result. When longitudinal shrinkage acts in a direction that is not along the neutral axis of the member, the result is bowing or cambering (also shown in Fig. 2).

Distortion results when a condition of non-uniform expansion and contraction is created. Distortion can be anticipated by evaluating the following factors:

1. The weld along with some adjacent metal contracts on cooling, producing a shrinkage force, F.

2. The shrinkage force acts about the neutral axis of a member. The distance between the center of gravity of the weld area and this neutral axis represents the moment arm, d.

3. The moment of inertia of the section, I, resists this contraction. The I of a section also resists straightening, should it be necessary.

3. THE INFLUENCE OF OVERWELDING

Overwelding increases the shrinkage force, F, and the tendency to distort. Anything that reduces the amount of welding such as decreasing the leg size, reducing the weld length, or using intermittent welding techniques, will minimize this condition. See Figure 3.

Overwelding can be caused inadvertently by a chain of events. The designer may specify the next larger weld size because of a lack of confidence in welding. When the part reaches the shop floor, the shop foreman, wishing to play it safe, marks the piece up for the next weld size. The weldor, having just been criticized for making undersize welds, makes real sure that these welds are still larger. The result—a ¼″ fillet has become a ½″ weld. These men usually do not realize that weld metal increases as the square of the leg size. The apparently harmless ¼″ increase in the leg size has increased the amount of weld metal deposited, the weld shrinkage and the weld cost by 4 times.

4. CONTROL OF WELD SHRINKAGE

One technique used to control weld shrinkage involves prebending the member or presetting the joint before welding. In this way the net effect of weld shrinkage pulls the member or connection back into proper alignment (Fig. 4).

Whenever possible, welding should be balanced around the neutral axis of the member. This makes the moment arm, d, equal to zero. Even though a shrinkage force, F, does exist, the shrinkage moment ($d \times F$) becomes zero (Fig. 5).

Frequently the neutral axis of the member is below

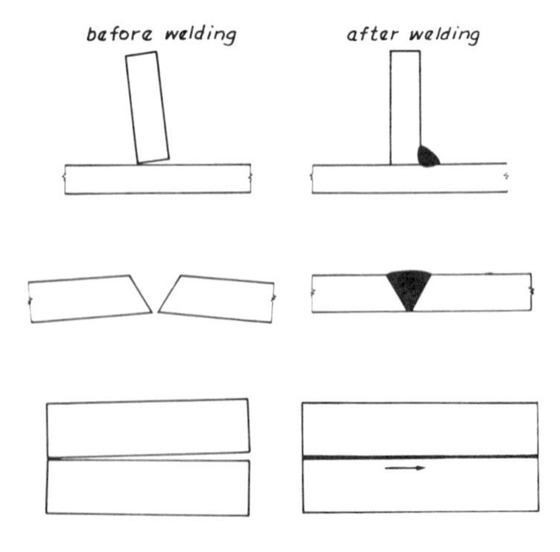
before welding
after welding

FIG. 4 Parts are often present so that weld shrinkage will pull them back into correct alignment.

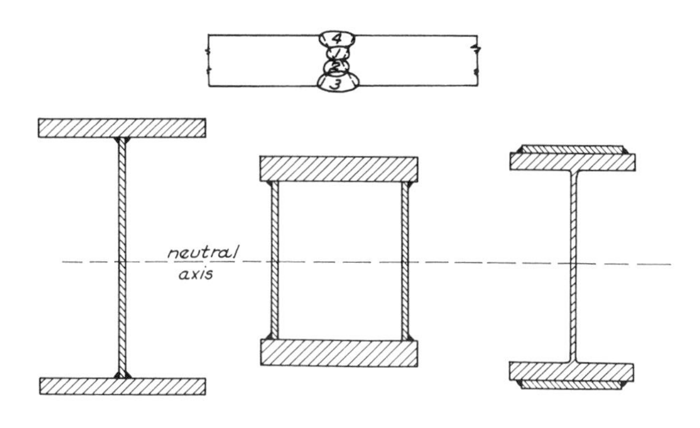

FIG. 5 Balancing welds or weld beads about the neutral axis of the member, reduces angular distortion to zero.

the center of gravity of the welds as shown in Figure 6. By making the welds with the submerged-arc automatic welding process, the deep penetration characteristic of this process further lowers the center of gravity of the weld deposit and reduces the moment arm, thereby reducing the shrinkage moment.

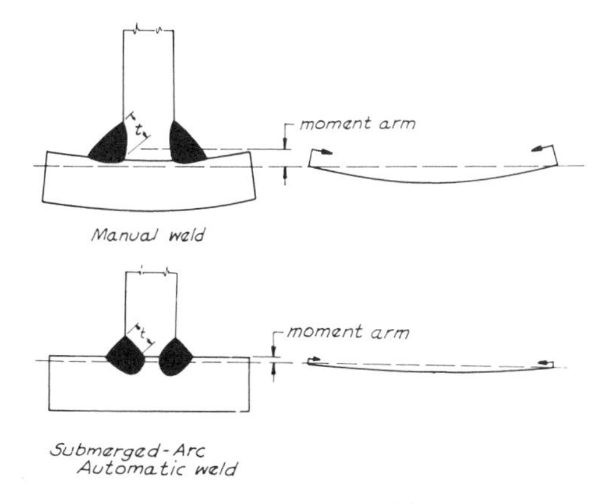

FIG. 6 Deep-penetration welding processes and procedures places the weld closer to the neutral axis, reducing moment arm and net effect of shrinkage forces.

Adjacent Base Metal

Shrinkage of weld metal alone is not sufficient to account for the amount of shrinkage sometimes actually encountered. The heat of welding causes the metal just adjacent to the weld deposit to expand. However, this metal is restrained by the relatively cooler sections of the remainder of the plate. Almost all the volume expansion must take place in thickness. On cooling, this heated section undergoes volume contraction, building up shrinkage stresses in the longitudinal and transverse direction, and this adjacent base metal tends to shrink along with the weld metal.

Effect of High Welding Speeds

The volume of this adjacent base metal which contributes to the distortion can be controlled by welding procedures. Higher welding speeds through the use of powdered-iron-type manual electrodes, semi-automatic and fully automatic submerged-arc welding equipment, or vapor-shielded automatic welding equipment reduces the amount of adjacent material affected by the heat of the arc and progressively decreases distortion.

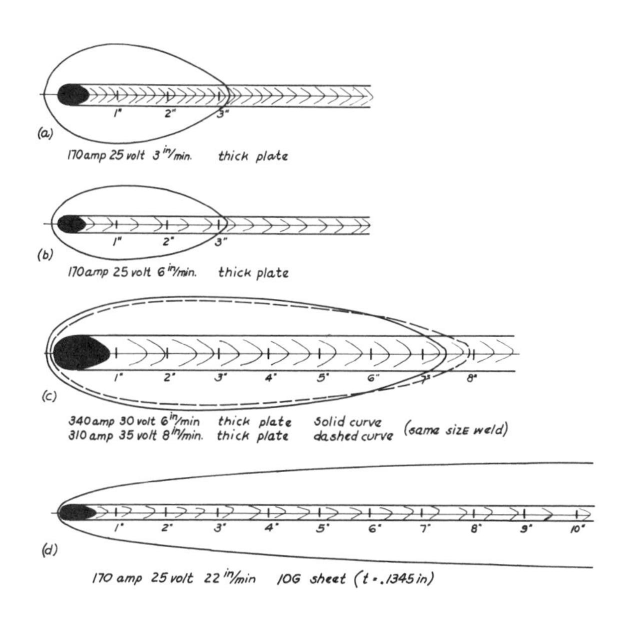

FIG. 7 Variance of welding technique. In each case, surface isotherm of 300°F is shown surrounding welding source.

The effect of welding current and arc speed on adjacent base metal is illustrated in Figure 7. Approximately the same weld size was produced with procedures (a) and (c). The important difference lies in the fact that the higher-speed welding technique produced a slightly narrower isotherm, measuring outward from the edge of the molten pool. The width of this isotherm of 300°F can be used to indicate the amount of adjacent metal shrinkage along with the weld, and therefore distortion; this helps to explain why in general faster welding speeds result in less distortion. This slight difference is also evident in a comparison of the quantity of welding heat applied to the plate.

For (a),

$$\frac{E\,I\,60}{V} = \frac{(25\text{ v})(170\text{ amp})(60)}{3''/\text{min}}$$

$$= 85{,}000 \text{ Joules/linear in. of weld}$$

For (c),

$$\frac{E\,I\,60}{V} = \frac{(35\ v)(310\ amp)(60)}{8''/min}$$

$$= 81{,}000\ \text{Joules/linear in. of weld}$$

Another condition can be observed by using conditions (a) and (b) of Figure 7. Two butt joints were made, one in the vertical position and the other in the horizontal position, using a multiple-pass groove weld. The same welding current (170 amps) was used in both joints. The vertical joint used a vertical-up weaving procedure, 3 passes at a speed of 3″/min., procedure (a). The horizontal joint used a series of 6 stringer passes at a speed of 6″/min., procedure (b). The faster welding of (b), 6″/min., produces a narrower isotherm. However, it required 6 passes rather than 3 of procedure (a), and the net result is an over-all cumulative shrinkage effect greater than that for (a).

This helps to explain why a given weld made with more passes will have slightly greater transverse shrinkage than one made with fewer passes. The transverse shrinkage can be reduced by using fewer passes. A further reduction can also be achieved by using larger electrodes.

In the weld on sheet metal, Figure 7 (d), it is noticed that a greater portion of the adjacent base metal is affected as compared to the weld itself. This, combined with the fact that the thin sheet metal is less rigid than the thick plate (its rigidity varies as its thickness cubed), helps to explain why sheet metal always presents more of a distortion problem.

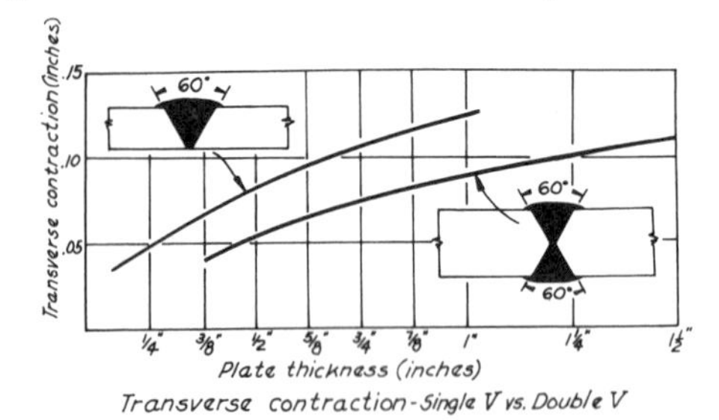

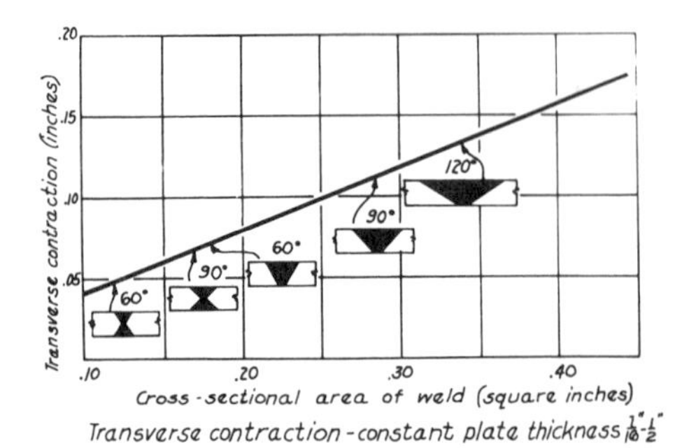

FIG. 8 Transverse shrinkage varies directly with amount of weld deposit.

5. TRANSVERSE SHRINKAGE

Transverse shrinkage becomes an important factor where the net effect of individual weld shrinkage can be cumulative.

The charts in Figure 8 throw some light on transverse shrinkage. In the lower chart transverse shrinkage, for a given plate thickness, is seen to vary directly with the cross-sectional area of the weld. The large included angles only help to illustrate this relationship and do not represent common practice. The relative effects of single and double V-joints are seen in the upper chart. Both charts assume no unusual restraint of the plates against transverse movement. Calculations show that transverse shrinkage is about 10% of the average width of the cross-section of the weld area.

$$\Delta_{trans} = .10\ \frac{A_{weld}}{t}$$

$$= .10 \times \text{aver. width of weld}$$

Where the submerged-arc process is involved, the cross-section of the fused part of the joint is considered rather than simply the area of the weld metal deposited.

Problem 1

Estimate the transverse shrinkage to be expected after welding two 1″ plates together if plates are free to pull in. Use a double-V groove weld, Figure 9.

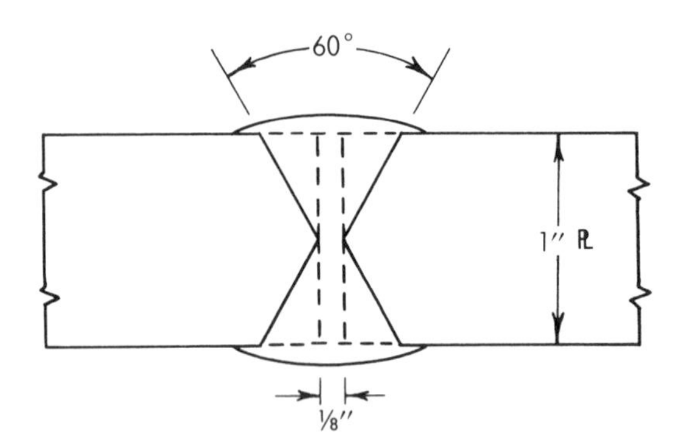

FIG. 9 Transverse shrinkage of this weld can be closely estimated from computed cross-sectional area of the weld.

area of weld

$$(1/8'')(1'') = .125$$
$$2(1/2)(1/2'')(.58'') = .29$$
$$2(2/3)(1'')(1/16'') = .083$$
$$A_w = .498\ \text{in.}^2$$

shrinkage

$$\Delta_{trans} = .10 \frac{A_w}{t}$$

$$= .10 \frac{(.498)}{(1'')}$$

$$= \underline{.05''}$$

Iron powder electrodes should reduce this shrinkage, and submerged-arc automatic welding should further reduce it. Also, a procedure resulting in fewer passes should reduce the shrinkage.

Notice that Figure 8 would indicate a transverse shrinkage of about .08″. However, in the above work, if the root opening were increased to ¼″ rather than the ⅛″ shown here and if the reinforcement were increased accordingly, the weld area would be increased to .75 in.². Thus the indicated shrinkage would increase to .075″. This shows good correspondence between Figure 8 and the above method of estimating shrinkage.

Use of Tables 6 and 7 in Section 7.5 (for weight of weld metal for various joints) makes it unnecessary to compute the cross-sectional area of the weld. Simply divide the weight of the weld (lbs/ft) by 3.4 to obtain the weld area in square inches.

For example, this 1″ double-V joint is equal to two ½″ single-V joints. From Table 6 (Sect. 7.5),

$$W_t = 2\ (.84\ \text{lbs/ft})$$

$$= 1.68\ \text{lbs/ft}$$

area of weld

$$A_w = \frac{(1.68)}{3.4}$$

$= .494$ in.², and from this

transverse shrinkage

$$\Delta_{trans} = .10 \frac{(.494)}{(1.0)}$$

$= \underline{.05''}$ the same as before

Problem 2

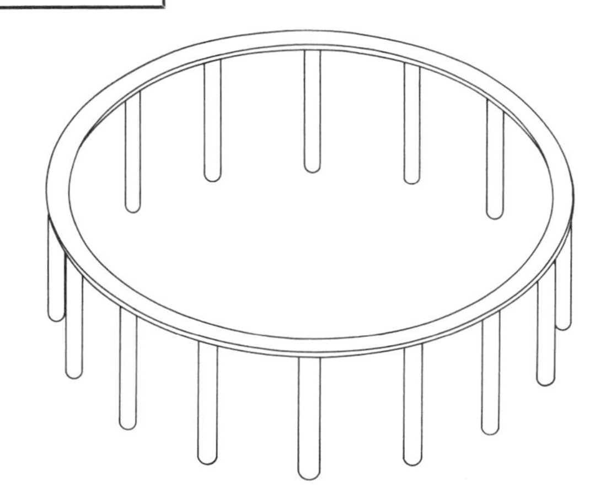

FIG. 10 Radial movement can be expected after welding large multi-segment ring as the cumulative effect of transverse shrinkage of each weld.

A steel tension ring, ½″ × 10″, is to support a dome of 136′ diameter. Each segment of this ring is to be groove welded to a steel insert plate directly over each of the 24 columns. See Figure 10. When fabricated, no allowance was made for the transverse shrinkage of these field welds. It was later found that the circumference of this ring had shrunk, causing each column to pull inward about ½″.

How should this have been estimated in order to open up the joints by this amount before welding?

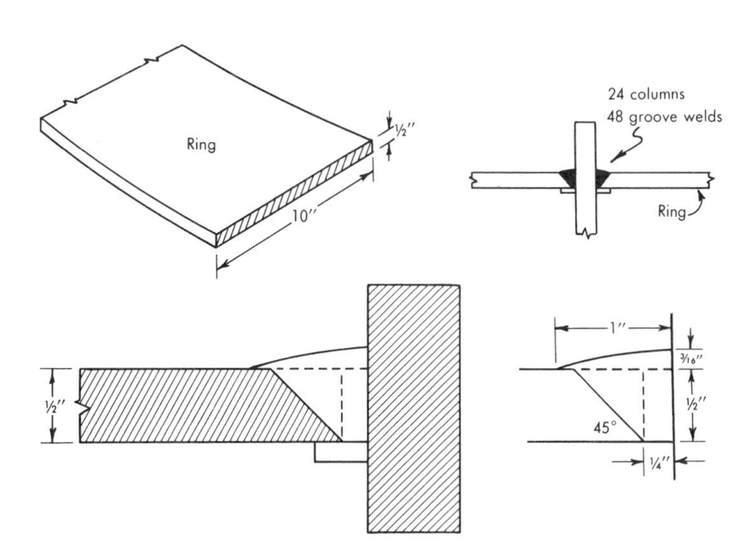

FIG. 11 Pull-in can be estimated readily.

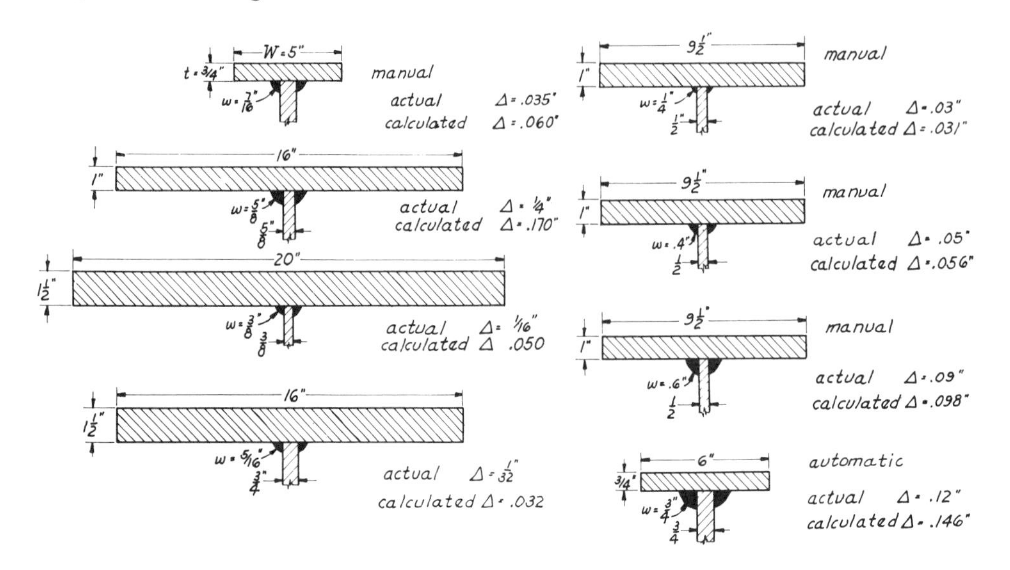

FIG. 12 Warpage varies directly with flange width and weld size, and inversely with plate thickness.

area of weld

$$\tfrac{2}{3}(1'')(\tfrac{3}{16}'') = .125$$
$$(\tfrac{1}{4}'')(\tfrac{1}{2}'') = .125$$
$$\tfrac{1}{2}(\tfrac{1}{2}'')(\tfrac{1}{2}'') = .125$$
$$A_w = .375'' \text{ in.}^2$$

average width of weld

$$\frac{.375 \text{ in.}^2}{{}^{11}\!/_{16}''} = .545''$$

transverse shrinkage

$$\Delta_{trans} = .10\ (.545'')$$
$$= .055'' \text{ estimated}$$

Since there are 24 columns or 48 groove welds,

overall shrinkage in circumference

$$\Delta_{circ} = 48\ (.055'')$$
$$= 2.64'' \text{ or a}$$

radial pull-in of columns

$$\Delta_{rad} = \frac{(2.64'')}{2\ \pi}$$
$$= .42''$$

Of course any poor fitup (increasing the root opening) or excessive weld reinforcement will greatly increase this transverse shrinkage.

6. ANGULAR DISTORTION

The formula for calculating warpage is—

$$\Delta = \frac{0.02\ W\ \omega^{1.3}}{t^2}$$

Figure 12 gives both the actual and calculated warpage for each of eight different flanges, fillet welded as indicated. The close agreement between the two values verifies the formula used. Only three exceed the American Welding Society allowable (½% of the width of the flange). It should be noted that these were overwelded.

7. BENDING OF LONGITUDINAL MEMBERS

Distortion or bending of longitudinal members results from development of a shrinkage force applied at some distance from the neutral axis of the member. The amount of distortion is directly controlled by the magnitude of the shrinkage moment and the member's resistance to bending as indicated by its moment of inertia.

Assuming no unusual initial stresses, the following formula indicates the amount of distortion or bending that will result from any longitudinal welding on a given member:

$$\Delta = 0.005\ \frac{A_w\ d\ L^2}{I}$$

where:

A_w = total cross-sectional area within the fusion line, of all welds, in.^{2}

d = distance between the center of gravity of the weld group and the neutral axis of the member, in.

L = length of the member, assuming welding the full length, in.

I = moment of inertia of the member, in.^{4}

Δ = resulting vertical movement, in.

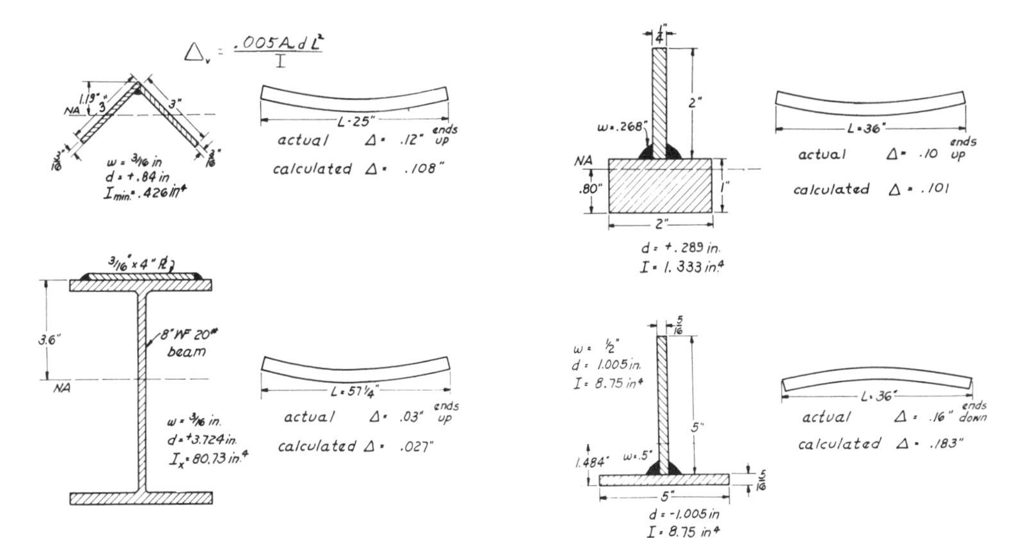

FIG. 13 Actual measured distortion corresponds well with calculated distortion, using the formula given.

Measurement of actual distortion verifies the formula for theoretical calculation of distortion, Figure 10.

In some instances when equal welds are positioned symmetrically around neutral axis of a member, a certain amount of distortion still occurs even though the magnitudes of the shrinkage moments are equal and opposite. It is believed some plastic flow or upset occurs in the compressive area next to the weld area after the first weld is made. Because of this upset, the initial distortion, from the first weld, is not quite offset by the second weld on the opposite side. Where multiple-pass welding is involved, this condition can be corrected, as illustrated in the groove-weld sequence, Figure 5. Here Pass 1 is on the top side. Pass 2, deposited on the opposite side, does not quite pull the plates back into flat alignment; therefore Pass 3 is added to the same side. The net result will usually pull the plate slightly beyond the flat position and Pass 4, on the top side, should bring this plate back into flat alignment. Frequently this problem is of no major importance since the sections to be welded are large enough in respect to the size of the weld to prevent the occurrence of this upsetting. As a result, on large sections the second weld on the opposite side is just as effective as the first weld.

In cases where the welds are not symmetrically balanced about the neutral axis of the section, advantage may be taken of this difference in distortion by first completing the joint nearest the neutral axis (it has the shorter moment arm) and then welding the joint on the side farthest from the neutral axis (taking advantage of its greater moment arm). See Figure 14, which illustrates a masonry plate welded to the bottom flange of a rolled beam. On the left, the welds are not symmetrical, so weld (a) was made first. Weld (b) follows since it has a greater moment arm. On the right, the wider masonry plate extends slightly on the left, and allows both welds to be made at the same time (since they are both in the flat position). The equal moment arms in this situation should result in no sweep of the beam. In both cases the welds will produce some camber but this is usually desirable.

Many long slender members are made by welding together two light-gage formed sections. Waiting until the first weld has cooled before making the second

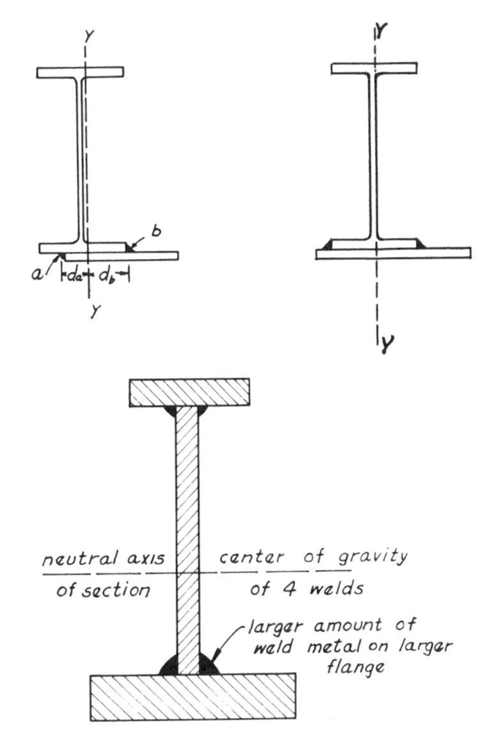

FIG. 14 Where welds are not balanced about the neutral axis of the section, distortion can be minimized by welding first the joint nearest the neutral axis and then the joint farthest from the neutral axis. Similarly, weld sizes may be varied to help balance forces.

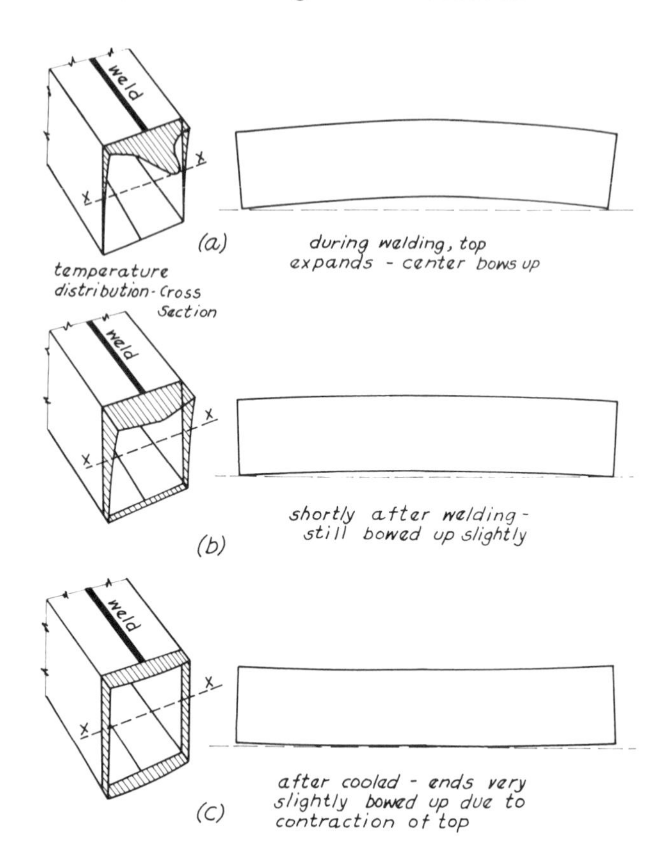

FIG. 15 To avoid bowing of long, thin box sections welded up from two channels, the first weld is protected against cooling until the second weld is completed. The two welds are then allowed to cool simultaneously.

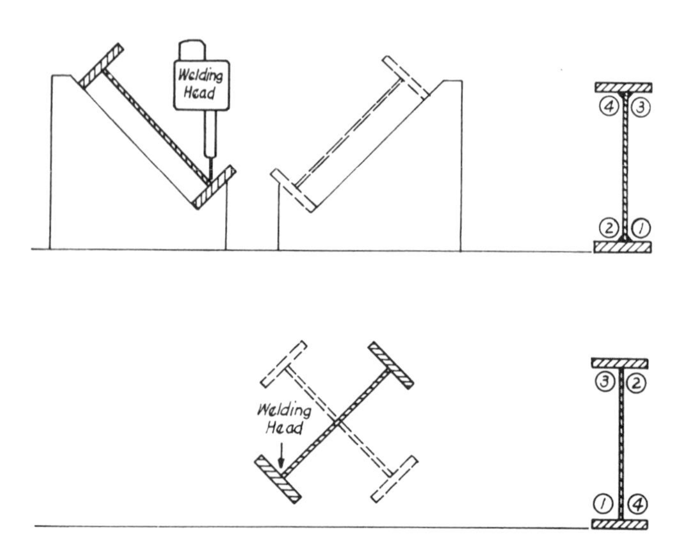

FIG. 16 Proper welding position and sequence for fabrication when girder is supported by inclined fixture (top) or trunnion-type fixture (bottom).

weld on the opposite side, usually results in some final bowing since the second weld may not quite pull the member back, Figure 15. Notice (a) the heating of the top side of the member by the first weld initially causes some expansion and bowing upward. Turning the member over quickly while it is still in this shape and depositing the second weld, increases the shrinking effect of the second weld deposit and the member is usually straight after cooling to room temperature.

The sequence for automatic welding to produce the four fillets on a fabricated plate girder can be varied without major effect on distrotion. In most cases this sequence is based on the type of fixture used and the method of moving the girder from one welding position to another (Fig. 16). When a single automatic welder is used, the girder is usually positioned at an angle between 30° and 45°, permitting the welds to be deposited in the flat position. This position is desirable since it makes welding easier and slightly faster. It also permits better control of bead shape and the production of larger welds when necessary.

Permissible AWS tolerances for most welded

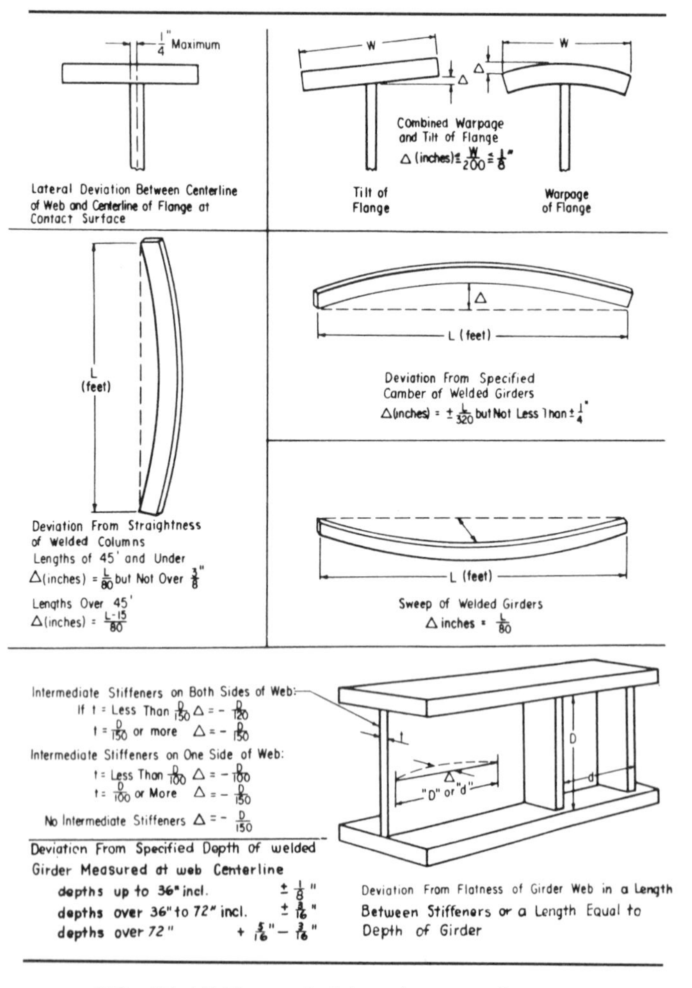

FIG. 17 AWS permissible tolerances for common welded members.

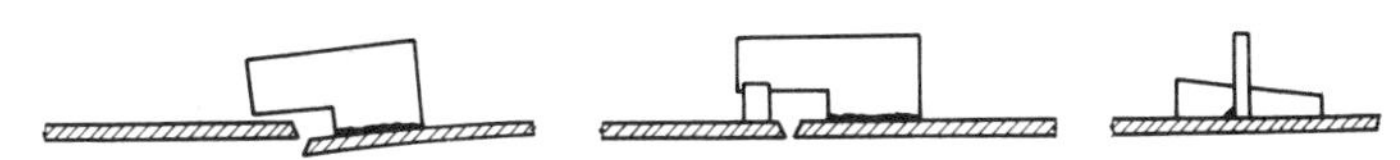

Weld clip along one edge only so it may be removed easily with a hammer. Drive a steel wedge below clip until edges of plate are in alignment.

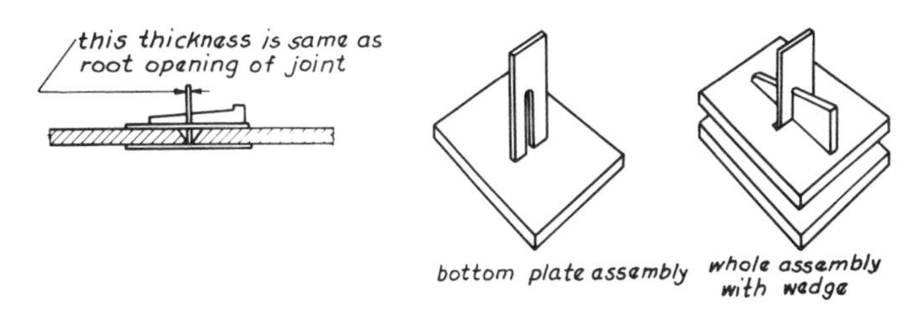

FIG. 18 Small clip angles and wedges can be used to economically maintain alignment of plates during welding. If clips are welded on one side only, they can later be knocked off with a hammer.

members are illustrated in Figure 17: (a) deviation between centerline of web and centerline of flange; (b) camber or sweep of columns; (c) at left, tilt of flange, and at right, warpage of flange; (d) deviation of camber of girders; (e) sweep of girders; (f) deviation from flatness of girder web.

8. PROPER ALIGNMENT OF PLATES

Various methods have been used for pulling plate edges into alignment and maintaining this alignment during welding. The most widely used technique (Fig. 18) calls for welding small clips to the edge of one plate. Driving a steel wedge between each clip and the second plate brings both edges into alignment. Welding the clips on one side only, simplifies removal.

In the top part of Figure 19, pressure is applied by steel wedges whereas, in the bottom part of this figure, pressure is applied by tightening the strongbacks with bolts previously welded to the plate.

9. PEENING AND FLAME SHRINKING

Peening is used occasionally to control distortion. Since the weld area contracts, peening, if properly applied, tends to expand it. However, this expansion occurs only near the surface.

Upsetting or expansion of the weld metal by peening is most effective at higher temperatures where the yield strength of the metal is rather low. Unfortunately, most of the distortion occurs later at the lower temperatures after the yield strength has been restored to its higher value. For this reason, peening does not accomplish the desired results. An additional disadvantage of peening is that it work-hardens the surface of the metal and uses up some of the available ductility.

Flame shrinking or flame straightening is another method of correcting distortion, through localized heating with a torch. The heat causes the metal in this area to expand, and this expansion is restrained in all directions by the surrounding cooler metal. As a result, this

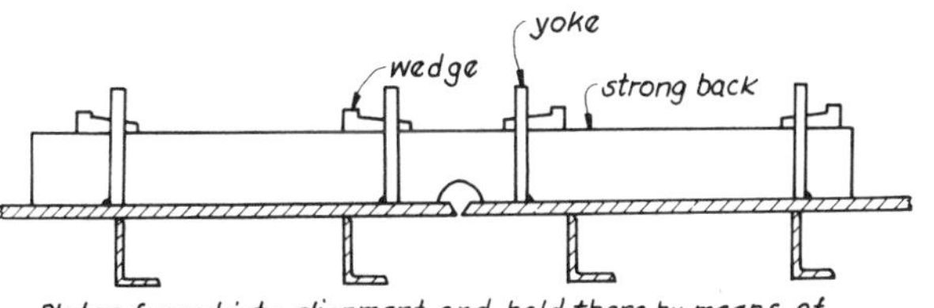

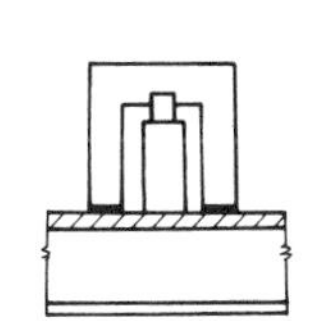

FIG. 19 Large plates can be aligned against strongbacks, the plates being pulled up by means of yoke and wedge combination; or, bolts are welded to the plates and run through the strongbacks to facilitate alignment.

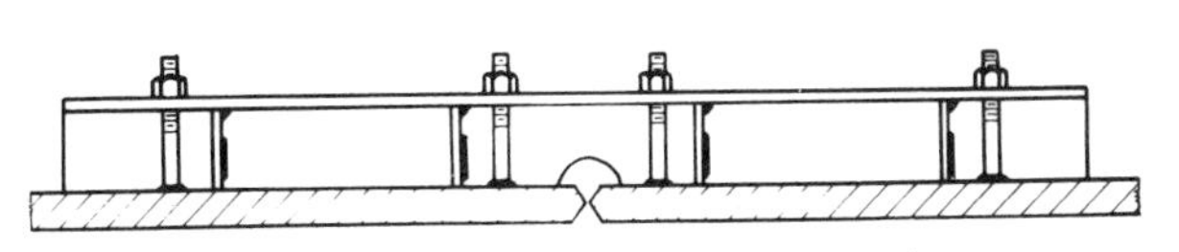

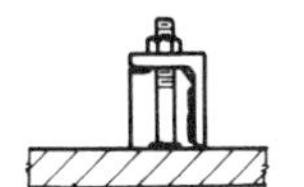

area of the metal expands abnormally through its thickness and upon cooling tends to become shorter in all directions. The section so treated will become shorter and stressed in tension with each successive application of heat.

The bending of a member by welding and its straightening by flame shrinking is analogous to the case of a stool which will tilt to one side when the legs on one side are shortened but will again become erect when the opposite legs are also shortened the same amount.

10. SUMMARY AND CHECK LIST

Transverse distortion

1. Depends on restraint.

2. Is equal to about 10% of the average width of the weld area.

3. Increases with the weld area for the same plate thickness.

4. Increases with the root opening and the included angle.

5. Is directly proportional to the welding heat input per inch, that is, Joules per inch.

Angular distortion can be reduced by:

1. Use of a double bevel, V, J, or U for butt joints.

2. Alternating welds from side to side.

3. Beveling the web of a T-joint; this will reduce the moment arm of the weld and reduce the angular movement.

4. Use of the smallest leg size for fillet welds, since the distortion varies approximately with the 1.3 power of the leg size of such a weld.

5. Use of thicker flanges; distortion varies approximately inversely with the square of the flange thickness.

Bending of long members by longitudinal welds can be partially controlled by:

1. Balancing welds about the neutral axis of the member.

a. Making welds of the same size at the same distance on the opposite side of the neutral axis of the member.

b. For welds of different sizes—if at different distances from the neutral axis of the member—making the welds that are farther away smaller.

2. If the welding is not symmetrical, this result is achieved by:

a. Prebending the member.

b. Supporting the member in the middle and letting the ends sag, and for the opposite effect, by supporting the member at the ends and letting the middle sag.

c. Breaking the member into sub-assemblies so that each part is welded about its own neutral axis.

Deflection is directly proportional to the shrinkage moment of the welds (weld area times its distance from the neutral axis of the member) and inversely proportional to the moment of inertia of the member. Although a high moment of inertia for the member is desired to resist bending, it also makes the member more difficult to straighten, once it has become distorted. Flame shrinking may be applied to the longer side if welding has bent the member.

Assembly procedures that help control distortion:

1. Clamp the member in position and hold during welding.

2. Preset the joint to offset expected contraction.

3. Prebend the member to offset expected distortion.

4. Before welding, clamp two similar members back to back with some prebending.

5. If stress-relieving is required, weld two similar members back to back and keep fastened until after stress relief.

6. Use strong-backs.

7. Use jigs and fixtures to maintain proper fit-up and alignment during welding.

8. Make allowances for contraction when a joint is assembled.

9. Arrange the erection, fitting, and welding sequence so that parts will have freedom to move in one or more directions as long as possible.

10. Use subassemblies and complete the welding in each before final assembly and welding together.

11. If possible break the member into proper sections, so that the welding of each section is balanced about its own neutral axis.

12. Weld the more flexible sections together first, so that they can be easily straightened before final assembly.

Painting & Corrosion of Welded Structures

1. THE NATURE OF RUSTING

Any steel surface* will gradually and progressively rust if left unprotected. For this reason it is important to keep most steel structures painted.

Most of us are so familiar with the rusting of steel that we fail to recognize several important facts about this:

$$\underset{(steel)}{4\ Fe} + \underset{(air)}{3\ O_2} \xrightarrow[(moisture)]{} \underset{(rust)}{2\ Fe_2O_3}$$

1. Most chemical reactions will come to a stop if just one of the required elements or compounds is not supplied, or if one of the products is not removed from the reaction.

2. A moist condition (water) is required for steel to rust in the presence of air (oxygen). Steel will not rust in dry air.

3. Under ordinary conditions, there is a continuous supply of air (oxygen) and moisture, so this reaction never comes to equilibrium. The result is a continuous rusting action, unless prevented by some protective coating.

2. PROTECTION OF TUBULAR AND OTHER CLOSED SECTIONS

It is believed the inside of closed-in hollow box structural sections can be left unpainted. This is because any slight oxidation of the steel would soon come to equilibrium, since there is no continual supply of air and moisture.

The question is whether box sections must be made airtight, merely protected from rain, or left completely open. If airtight, should any precaution be taken to dry the air before sealing, and should any unusual test methods be taken to insure complete tightness?

To shed more light on these questions, comments were solicited from several leading authorities in the structural field in the United States, Canada, and Europe. Foreign reaction is particularly significant since the adoption of welded box-section structurals has progressed further there than in this country, notably in German bridges built in the past 15 years. What follows is a symposium of their replies.

* The rusting of certain proprietary steels produces a thin protective oxide layer that inhibits further corrosion. Such steels (for example, A242) are often used unpainted.

• From an article, "Corrosion Prevention Inside Closed Hollow Bodies, by Seils and Kranitzky, in DER STAHLBAU (Germany), February, 1959, pp 46-53. (Translated in abstract form.):

Investigations on behalf of the German railroads are reported on six groups of welded structures: Four railroad bridges; three highway bridges; hollow supports on a Munich railroad station; a locomotive turntable; traveling platform on a rail car; and one experimental weldment.

These welded steel towers carry two 30″ pipelines ½ mile across the river. The 273′ towers are hermetically-sealed box-section members internally reinforced to keep skin from buckling. They will stand for many years without concern for internal corrosion.

Detailed inspection substantiated the present assumption that condensation in hollow steel sections is very slight. Inaccessible or difficult-to-reach sections should always be welded airtight. Any manholes should be closed with rubber gaskets. With these precautions, corrosion protection of inner parts becomes unnecessary.

Wherever possible, large, accessible hollow weldments should be made as airtight as is practical. Closure does not lead to any observable tendency for water condensation and resulting corrosion. If sections are to be ventilated, adequate numbers of openings should be provided on the front and side walls to allow for some circulation of air. Openings in the floor are not very suitable for ventilation, particularly when sidewalls have no openings. Under this condition humidity could be higher.

If water pipes have to pass through hollow sections, there should be an opening in the hollow member to allow water to escape in case the pipe should later develop a leak. This opening, however, can be provided with a type of relief or check valve which will automatically open when required and later reseal. Areas in the vicinity of any of these openings should be particularly well protected. The pipe system itself should be insulated to avoid possible condensation.

Experience has shown that if any condensation does occur in the interior of sealed sections, the upper cover plate is the most vulnerable area.

In contrast to the outside coatings, a simpler corrosion protection can be applied to the inside surfaces. Areas subject to frequent use, such as manhole openings or in some cases the bottom side of a cover plate, should be given additional protective coating.

A recent type of corrosion protection for the interior of hollow sections is zinc powder paints. They have two important properties: First, they are largely unaffected by the welding heat; and, secondly, they do not influence the quality of the weld metal.

• Several of the new multi-span German bridges across the Rhine make use of welded orthotropic (orthagonal anisotropic) plate decks, with savings in dead weight of steel as high as 50% over conventional bridges. In this section, floor beams and longitudinal ribs are shop welded to the top deck plate, the latter thus serving as a common top flange.

Many times torsionally rigid ribs are used, either U-shaped or trapezoidal, forming a closed box section with the top deck plate. Thickness seldom exceeds 5⁄16″, and occasionally is as little as 3⁄16″. The box-shaped ribs are either butt welded to the webs of the floor beams at each intersection, or pass through them and are attached with fillet welds.

Orthotropic plate decks naturally have many sealed sections. They are not given any special corrosion protection inside. It is felt that after the initial minor corrosion resulting from entrapped moist air, little further advance will be experienced, and even under the most adverse conditions could not detract from the strength of the section.

• From a structural engineer at Eindhoven, Netherlands, representing an American international construction company:

"All modern fabricators make completely closed sections. There are a few which have taken some precautions for corrosion protection, probably at the insistence of the customer. One has used a normal type of manhole in large girders, for inspection purposes. The girders were not painted on the inside.

"Another company is using this construction in columns. Near the bottom of the column is a hole about ¾″ diameter, drilled and then closed with a plug. The hole is used in two ways. First, before the column is shipped, pressure is applied to the inside to determine whether welds are airtight. If they are, the plug is replaced, the column erected and then inspected after a few years by removing the plug, to see if any water has collected. Until now, there has never been any water found inside the columns.

"E.D.F. in France has in use a large number of long welded steel columns closed at both ends, with no access holes.

"It is bad practice to completely close columns filled with concrete. Holes should be punched or drilled to avoid the possibility of explosion in case of fire. Water in the concrete may vaporize under heat, causing tremendous pressure on the inside if no escape hole is present."

• From a London structural engineering director, active with one of the largest companies in the field there:

"This 'bogey' of internal corrosion in hollow sections is constantly cropping up. . . In general, in order to be absolutely certain of the absence of internal corrosion, it is always preferable to insure that the structure is sealed completely."

• The paper, L'ENERGIA ELETTRICA (Italy), July, 1953, discusses the mechanics by which water can enter an imperfectly sealed structure—condensation, breathing resulting from heating and cooling, capillary infiltration, etc.

A passage from this research study is worth quoting for its basic information.

"To produce internal corrosion, one essential condition must be fulfilled, i.e., an aperture of appreciable size in order that water and oxygen can be present in sufficient quantity and a lack of either will delay corrosion. In the case of a closed tube, chemical equilibrium between water, oxygen and rust is reached as soon as a practically imperceptible layer of oxide has been formed.

"Tests we have made indicated that corrosion was unlikely to occur through holes having direct access to the atmosphere, provided they were shielded from actual films of water. The test, of course, refers to structures under ordinary atmospheric conditions where no artificial agency was tending to draw air into the structure.

"We would prefer that a hollow welded section be airtight, and if this is done there is no need to dry the air before sealing unless, of course, a slight initial corrosion must be avoided."

• From the chief structural engineer of an eastern structural fabricator and erector:

"On light structures such as schools, we have observed many designs which use tubular sections. Some are filled with concrete and many are not. Some require sealing and others do not. Apparently no concern is shown in regard to the rusting of the unsealed sections.

"If tubular sections are used and moisture is apt to accumulate, provision should be made to drain them. To seal fully tubular sections does not appear a feasible proposition."

• A consulting engineer in Phoenix, Ariz., now active on highway work in Alaska has this to say:

"There has always been a question in my mind as to the feasibility of closing the box sections so as not to permit the circulation of air through the member. I believe that if air is allowed to circulate, rusting will take place, but any good paint should take care of that and will last considerably longer if not exposed directly to the air and light.

"Some of the states have used a galvanized pipe or square section for a (bridge) railing member; however, galvanizing would be impracticable for a large bridge member. I have placed some hopes on the new epoxy resin which apparently has characteristics making it an almost permanent protection coat."

• From the assistant chief engineer of a major steel producing company:

"Our own corrosion experts have assured me that if the box member is completely sealed, any moisture or other corrosion causing substance will soon react and become neutralized, so that after a very slight amount of corrosion there will be no further action. However, if there is any opening to permit any air circulation, there will be new un-neutralized moisture from condensation, etc., and corrosion will be continued.

"If, however, sealed members are used, then some provision should be made for frequent checking of the seal by testing the tightness of the box under air pressure."

• From the general secretary of the American Welding Society:

"For many years elevated storage tanks in this country have been supported by towers consisting of closed tubular members. Companies in the structural field have had extensive experience in the use of such closed sections in which normally the internal surface receives no special treatment. Some of these have been sealed sections and some not sealed. Service generally has been entirely satisfactory in both cases. Where the section has been sealed, no effort has been made to dry the contained air before sealing."

Tower masts, roof girders and haunched frames for the Tulsa (Oklahoma) Exposition Center are box sections, entirely weld fabricated. Members such as these are capped to prevent entry of water; otherwise receive no special protection against internal corrosion.

• From a partner in a New York city consulting engineering firm:

"Closed box sections should be sealed, but if possible should be covered with a protective interior paint beforehand. The use of higher alloy steels, such as weldable A242, adds a measure of protection at low additional cost, and the added strength may offset the extra cost.

"I have seen no general applications in this country. However, some of the older bridges using the old Phoenix shapes (arc form with ends bent up at right angles) have been sealed and have stood up well.

"The subject of interior corrosion is very important, not only for columns but also for large closed box girders which at some future time may become popular in this country."

• From the manager of technical research for a Canadian bridge company:

"One of our erection engineers who has worked on bridge erection in England, India and other countries states that bridge box chords, either welded or riveted, are often sealed to avoid air movements. This sealing is accomplished by gasketing the manway openings into the chords. When this is done, painting on the inside can be a single coat or can be eliminated entirely. Sealing of box sections to avoid rusting on the inside is increasing in popularity.

"It is presumed that where welding is continuous to seal any box section completely, rusting will be inconsequential, being limited by the amount of air present when sealed."

• The chief engineer of the same company's Vancouver, B.C., plant adds:

"The practice of hermetically sealing structural members to avoid inside painting and corrosion originated in Europe when closed welded sections were introduced. No type of closure short of hermetic sealing is dependable. In such structures, no manholes were provided and no paint was applied on the inside."

"Completely logical" is how this engineer describes the practice of hermetically sealing closed welded members.

• The Port Mann arch bridge in British Columbia uses an orthotropic deck. The longitudinal stiffeners are U-shaped and when continuously welded to the deck, form a closed tubular section. The ends of the stiffeners have openings for field bolting. At a distance of 15″ from each end of each stiffener, diaphragms are continuously welded inside to seal off the remaining length from the outside. This sealed portion of the stiffener was not painted on the inside.

3. PAINTING OVER WELDS

There may be an occasional problem with paint discoloring, flaking, or blistering over welds or in an immediate adjacent area. There are several possible reasons for this. Dust, smoke film, iron-oxide film, grease and similar materials on the surface of the weld and immediate adjacent area prevent the paint from coming in contact with the surface of the steel and properly bonding to it. These materials form a barrier between the paint and the steel surface. A surface that has been burnished very smooth with a power wire brush might also prevent proper bonding.

Elements in the fumes of welding, when deposited in the slag as a film on the steel surface, may combine with moisture in the air to produce an alkaline solution that reacts with paint. This may cause discoloring and blistering. This problem increases with increasing humidity.

Submerged-arc welds are relatively free of paint problems because the slag is nearly always removed and the process leaves no film of smoke or iron oxide on the adjacent plate.

Cleaning is the obvious first step. Removing slag, spatter, smoke film, iron-oxide film, and other similar materials, helps eliminate both causes of problems. First, it provides a clean surface to which the paint can bond. Secondly, it removes from weld deposits most of the chemicals that might react with a paint. In most cases, cleaning will eliminate paint problems, but don't burnish the surface with a power brush.

If discoloration or blistering prevails after normal cleaning, two additional steps will help. First, a wash in a mild acid solution, such as boric acid, followed by a good rinse with clear water will neutralize the alkaline solution so that it won't affect the paint. Secondly, a more alkaline-resistant paint may be substituted. Paints with a vinyl, epoxy or chlorinated rubber base are the best.

Just wiping the surface with a shop rag will remove much of the film and improve paint bonding. Painting with a brush instead of a sprayer helps the paint get under the film and make a better bond to the surface. Painting the affected area as quickly as possible after welding will prevent the chemicals in the deposited film from picking up much moisture. Therefore less alkaline solution will be formed to attack the paint. Two coats, including an alkaline-resistant primer put on as soon as practical, is usually better than a single coat.

Weld Quality and Inspection

1. REJECTION VS. PREVENTION

The structural welding of buildings and bridges enjoys a good reputation in the sense that weld failures of a catastrophic nature have not occurred. But, it is not uncommon to find welds which have failed in the sense that they did not meet final inspection requirements.

There are many reasons why welds may be rejected at final inspection. Before repairing the weld, however, several very appropriate questions should be resolved. For example, it is always good policy to review the inspection methods; to look for and insist upon some reliable correlation between the reasons for rejection and the service conditions. When such correlation does exist, prompt action should be taken to correct the rejected welds and to prevent their recurrence. If, on the other hand, the inspection methods are unrealistic or inappropriate, they should be replaced.

When weld rejection is justified, a person can be certain that somebody either did not know what his job was, or just did not do it properly. There is a logical explanation for any serious weld defect, and there is an equally logical remedy and correction. Many weld defects are related to procedures and can be visually detected as the job progresses.

Early detection of weld defects permits economical correction. If left for final inspection after the job is complete, a major loss of time and money usually results. Performance standards on the production floor and the erection site are needed to assure the quality of the weld being produced.

2. WHAT IS A GOOD WELD?

To a great many people, the answer to "What is a good weld?" would be, "Any weld that passes final inspection." We can hardly blame production-minded people for going along with this answer. But is this a good answer when you realize that frequently there is little or no connection between the defects found during inspection and the performance of the weld in service? (See Section 1.1, an Introduction to Welded Design.)

An improved definition would be, "A good weld is any weld which will continue indefinitely to do the job for which it was intended." The problem with this definition is that we do not have any thoroughly satisfactory nondestructive testing device that can provide a "yes" or "no" answer. Instead, we look for, and hope not to find, weld defects. If they are found, the weld is judged "good" or "bad" as we think the defects may or may not influence its performance in service.

3. WHAT IS THE SOLUTION?

First, find out what these defects are and what causes them. Second, set up welding procedures that will eliminate them. This is not as difficult as it might appear. It does, however, mean that a great many small, but important, details must be spelled out and accounted for.

It is encouraging to note that good qualified weldors and welding machine operators understand the importance of these small details. They are also generally capable of predicting exactly what final inspection will reveal. A conscientious weldor or welding operator can provide full-time visual inspection. Since he sees every bead, he is better informed than any inspector who only sees a finished weld or some small portion of the weld as it is being made.

4. WHEN DOES INSPECTION START?

The decision to inspect only after welding is completed is extremely dangerous and not the best way to assure product quality. This puts the inspector in the position of a combination physician-coroner with the dubious distinction of being the one to declare the weld dead or alive, and if dead, to decide "the cause of death."

A better approach to quality control allows inspection to provide constant checkups as welding progresses—preventive inspection. This promotes early detection of symptoms and correction of procedures as well as minor flaws, both of which might otherwise lead to serious defects. When this approach is followed, final inspection becomes a routine function to confirm the fact that good welding procedures have been employed and that objectionable defects have not been permitted to occur.

Inspection should start before the first arc is struck and should not be the sole responsibility of an inspector *per se*. Everyone involved in the preparation and production of a welded connection or joint should at least visually inspect his own work to make sure that

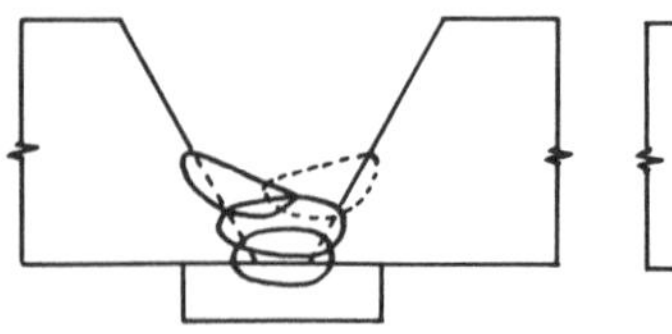

(a) No problem for next pass to fuse properly into side of joint and weld

(b) Not enough room left between side of joint and last pass; will not fuse properly; may trap slag

FIG. 1 The conscientious weldor visually inspects each bead as it is made. He knows that bad bead contour, poor wash-in at the edges or uneven edges are symptoms of trouble and takes steps to correct them before they produce weld rejects.

it has been done properly and in a manner consistent with the established standards of quality. This goes for people who prepare plate edges, assembly men, weld tackers, welding operators, weldors' helpers, and everyone whose efforts can in any way affect the quality of the welds.

5. RECOGNIZE SMALL DEFECTS AND CORRECT THEM

Perhaps the most common weld rejections occur as a result of radiographic inspection. This method has the ability to expose lack of fusion and/or slag inclusions that would not be apparent to visual final inspection techniques.

With very few exceptions, a good, conscientious weldor can tell by visual inspection whether or not he is getting good fusion, Figure 1. This includes what he sees as he makes the bead as well as what he sees when the bead is concluded. Bad bead contour, poor wash-in at the edges or uneven edges are all indications of poor fusion at the moment, or that it will occur on subsequent beads.

There are many symptoms of trouble which the weldor can spot. This is the time to correct the condition either by gouging out the questionable portion and/or changing the procedure. The wrong attitude at a time like this is to assume, as some weldors are inclined to, that "the defect can be 'burned out' on the next pass." This is a game of Russian Roulette that invariably pays off only in weld rejects.

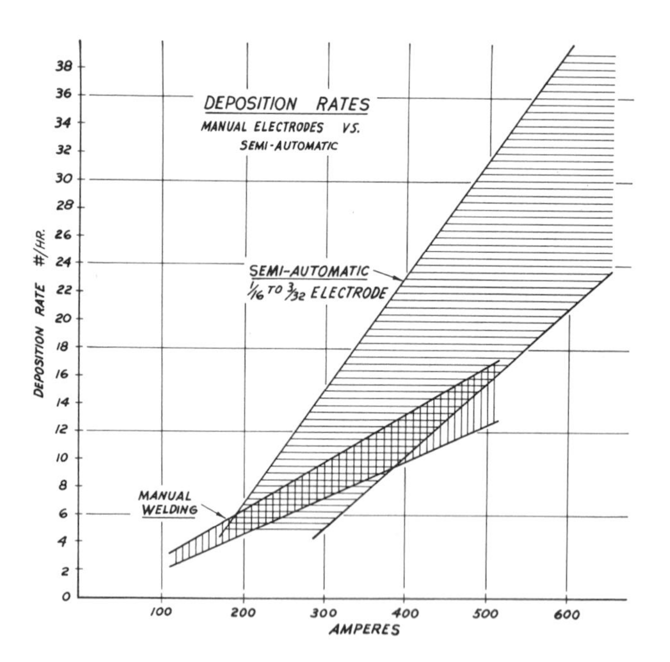

FIG. 2 Correct application of the various semi-automatic welding processes can tremendously increase deposition rate and lower costs.

6. "PREQUALIFIED JOINTS"

The term "prequalified joints" has led to some misunderstanding and, in a sense, it is a misnomer. It is certainly a mistake to think that just because prequalified joints have been used the final results will be completely satisfactory.

The AWS Code for Welding in Building Construction (AWS D1.0-66) and AWS Specifications for Welded Highway and Railway Bridges (AWS D2.0-66) do not suggest that it is that simple. They say that these joints are to be "welded in accordance with Sections 3 and 4," and then they may be considered "prequalified." A careful study of Sections 3 and 4 reveals 12 pages of good sound advice, recommendations, restrictions, etc., all aimed in the direction of producing good welds.

If joints are prepared as "prequalified joints" and all of the requirements of Sections 3 and 4 have been met, it would appear to be nearly impossible to produce welds which would not pass final inspection. Also, it should be understood that prequalified joints have been put in the code and are recommended only because past experience has demonstrated that these joints are capable of producing good weld quality *when they are used together with good welding procedures.*

The establishment of prequalified joints, however, does not preclude the fact that other joint designs can lead to equally satisfactory results. The progressive-minded fabricator or constructor who wishes to use other joint preparations and has valid reasons should be encouraged to do so.

The code allows adoption of alternate joint designs. It also logically requires special tests be performed to prove the acceptability of welds made with the alternate design. In most cases, these special tests, although admittedly time consuming, are worth completing to permit the application of a progressive procedure that leads to improved performance or cost reduction.

7. GOOD COMMUNICATIONS ARE NEEDED

With the broad latitude that welding offers to the designer, it is only natural that bridges and buildings take on a "one of a kind" nature. These connection variations present a challenge which welding is quite capable of meeting. But not without good communications between all interested parties.

Communicating is most important early in the game, especially while welding procedures are being worked out. This is the time for design vs. production discussions to bring up and solve questionable issues before they become points of major disagreement.

8. FIVE P'S OF GOOD STRUCTURAL WELDING

There are five areas which require close attention to assure good weld quality:

1. Process selection (welding process must be right for the job).
2. Preparation (joint preparation must be compatible with the process being used).
3. Procedures (detailed procedures are essential to assure uniform results).
4. Personnel (qualified personnel should be assigned to the job).
5. Prove it (pretest procedures and preparations to prove needed weld quality will result with their use).

Process Selection

The first and most important step is selecting the best welding process for the job. This is a very challenging decision to make, especially if the job is suited to semi-automatic welding where there are so many different choices. And yet, in this area lies the greatest opportunity for improvement, Figure 2. Since manual welding is inherently slow and expensive and subject to the human element, it is becoming a matter of economic survival to convert whenever possible to a semi-automatic process, Figure 3.

The entire industry is involved in this transition, but the progress is relatively slow. This is due in part to the natural reluctance to accept new methods. It is also true that each of the newer processes has its own peculiarities, advantages and limitations, and all introduce some problems affecting weldor training, joint preparation and welding procedures.

The semi-automatic processes (exclusive of submerged-arc) do not enjoy the "prequalified" status of manual and submerged-arc welding. This should not, however, prevent their use, since the AWS Code and Specifications state, "other welding processes and procedures may be used, provided the contractor qualifies them in accordance with the requirements of Article 502."

Selection of a semi-automatic process may also require joint qualification since appropriate joint prepa-

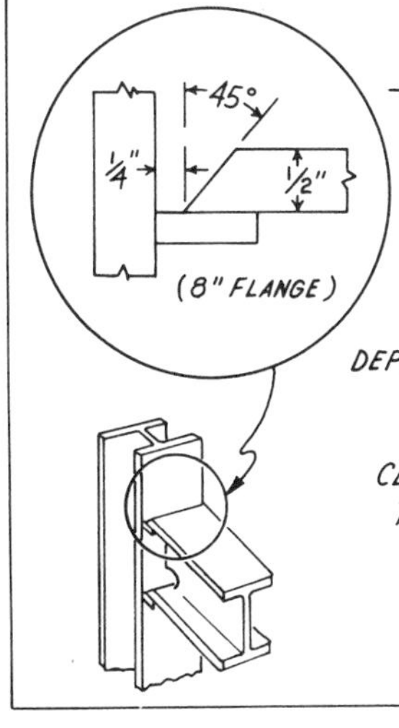

45°
1/4"
1/2"
(8" FLANGE)

PROCESS	CORED WIRE	SUB-ARC	MANUAL	MANUAL
WIRE / FLUX	3/32" NS-3M	5/64" L-60 780 FLUX	3/16" & 7/32" E6027	3/16" E6018
CURRENT	325-350	350-375	300 - 350	200 -225
VOLTAGE	30-31	30-31		
POLARITY	DC+	DC+	AC	DC+
DEPOSITION RATE #/HR. (100% O.F.)	12-13	10.5-11.0	9.5-10.5	5-6
ARC TIME (MIN.)	3.2	3.8	3.9	8.3
CLEANING TIME (MIN.)	1.0	.7	1.0	2.3
TOTAL TIME (MIN.)	4.2	4.5	4.9	10.6
TIME FACTOR	1.0	1.1	1.2	2.5

FIG. 3 This cost comparison of manual and semi-automatic welding methods demonstrates the important role process selection plays in the control of weld costs.

ration may not be the same as "prequalified manual" or "prequalified submerged-arc joints."

Where conditions permit, the use of full-automatic welding provides even greater economy and control of weld quality.

Preparation

Acceptable butt joint preparations are nothing more than a compromise between the included angle of bevel and the root spacing dimension. A large included angle will permit a smaller root spacing; conversely, a small included angle requires a larger root spacing. The type of joint, the welding position, and the process being used will all influence the bevel and root spacing. All of these factors have been taken into consideration in the prequalified joints.

The joints detailed in the appendix of the code book indicate a nominal dimension for bevel and root spacing. Since the joint design (bevel angle root spacing) must provide access of the arc to the base of the joint, it is important to understand that the dimensions of the root opening and groove angle of the joints are minimum values. (All of this and more is covered in the fine print of the specification.) Also see Section 7.3 on Joint Design.

Not only must the root spacing and bevel be

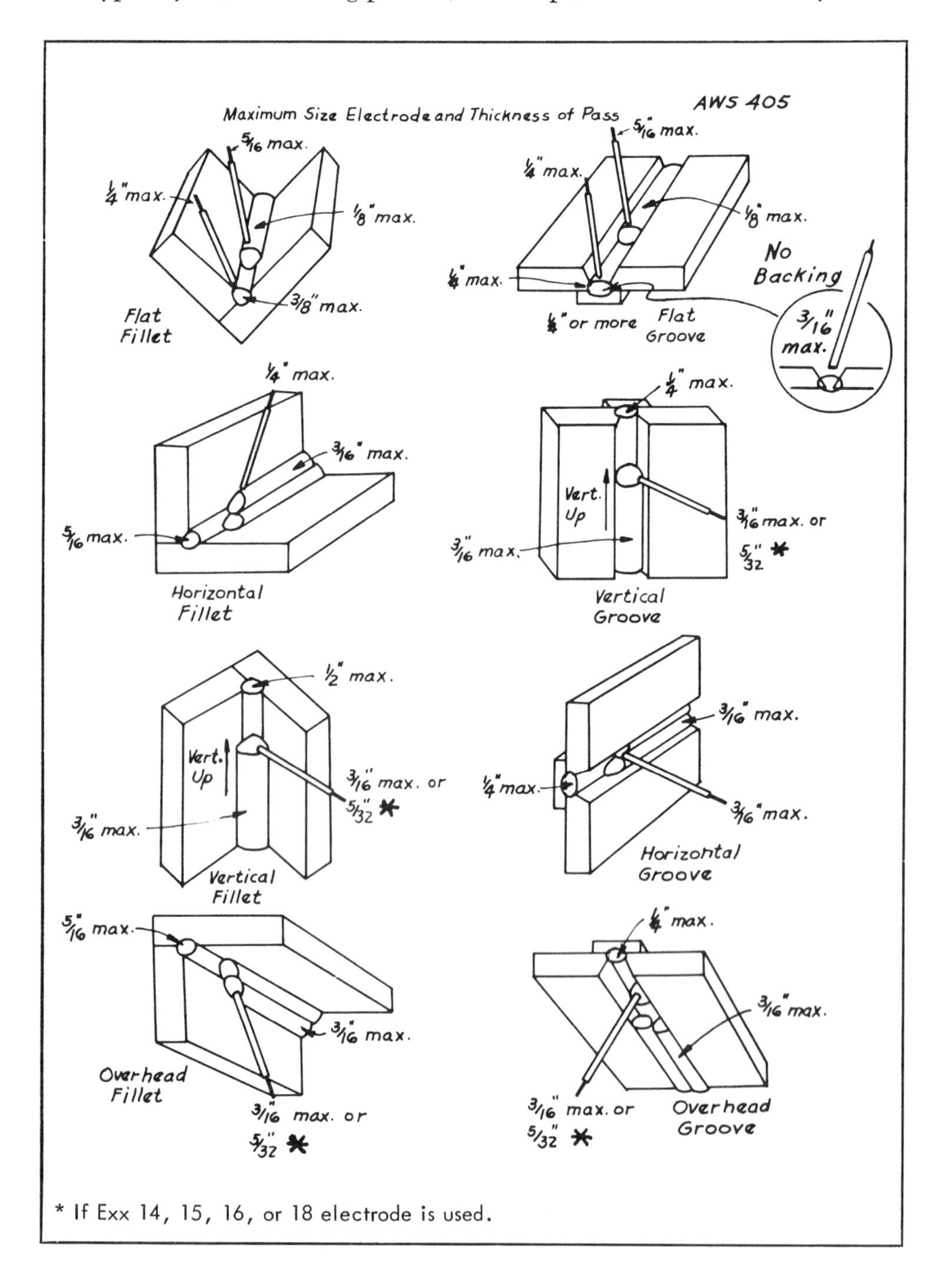

FIG. 4 The code book places specific limits on electrode size for specific joint designs and weld positions.

FIG. 5 Mock-up welds, such as shown here, provide a first-hand check of welding procedures before they reach the production floor. They can later be used as workmanship samples.

treated as minimum dimensions, but the electrode size must be compatible with the combination being used. Here again, the AWS Code and AWS Specification specifies maximum permissible electrode sizes which may be used under certain conditions Figure 4.

The first inspection action considered vitally important is to check the joint preperation before welding. Make sure that the joint preparation corresponds to the joint details as specified on the procedure. Be sure that the joint has been properly assembled and correct fit-up and root spacing obtained.

Procedures

The important welded connections of any structure deserve a well planned, thoroughly investigated and completely detailed welding procedure.

Reliable welding procedures are best obtained through first-hand experience. In the structural field, it is often helpful to produce a full scale mock-up of the actual joint prior to its release to the production floor. If possible, use the identical steel, same type, chemistry, sizes and shapes that will be used on the job. Figure 5 contains examples of "mock-up" welds.

A procedure properly developed under these conditions would include:

1. Identification of the joint.
2. Joint dimension details and tolerances.
3. Identification of the welding process.
4. Type and size of electrode.

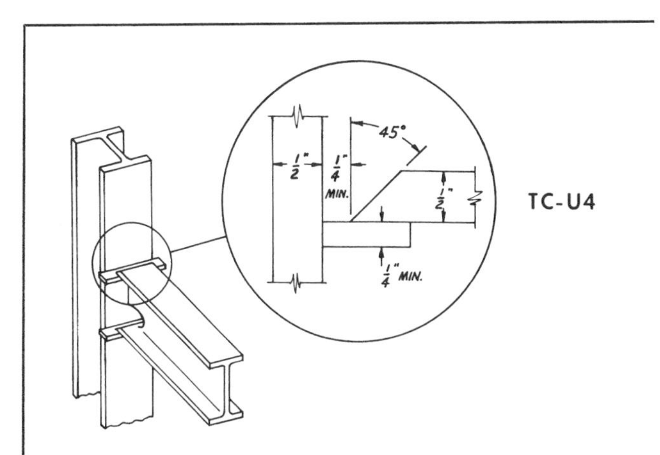

WELDING PROCEDURE:

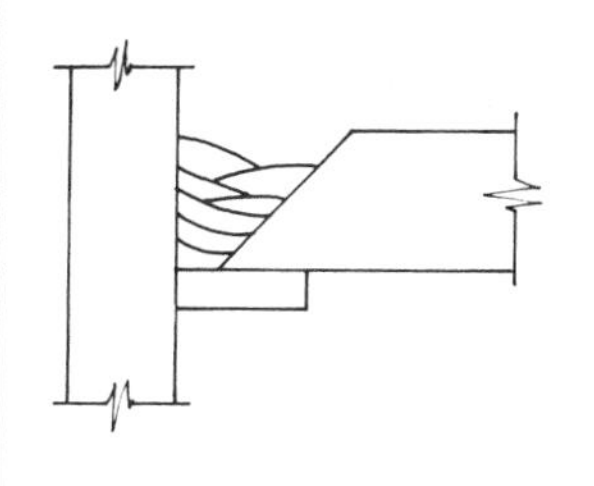

Electrode:

Current:

Pass Sequence:

Technique:

Preheat:

Inspection Req'd.:

FIG. 6 A completely detailed welding procedure helps guarantee uniform weld quality. It provides a road map for the weldor and a check list with which inspection can check weldor performance. In some cases more details will be required than are shown in this example.

5. Type of flux, gas, etc. (as required).

6. Current and voltage (with changes as required for different passes).

7. Preheat and interpass temperature.

8. Pass sequence (show sketch if necessary).

9. Type of inspection required.

10. Any comments or information that will help the weldor, such as special techniques, electrode angles, weld bead placement, etc., Figure 6.

This method of establishing the welding procedure takes time. It, nevertheless, is an almost foolproof approach to guaranteeing weld quality since it provides firsthand experience, workmanship samples, samples for destructive testing and positive evidence that the adopted procedure can produce the required results. And perhaps most important of all, it gives all weldors one "proved procedure" so that the job is no longer subject to the multiple choice of several weldors.

Personnel

In the case of manual welding, it is true that the weld quality cannot be any better than the skill of the weldor. This skill should be evaluated before the man is permitted to do any actual welding.

The simple and relatively inexpensive device for doing this is the AWS weldor qualification test, Figure

Summary of AWS Weldor Qualification Test Requirements

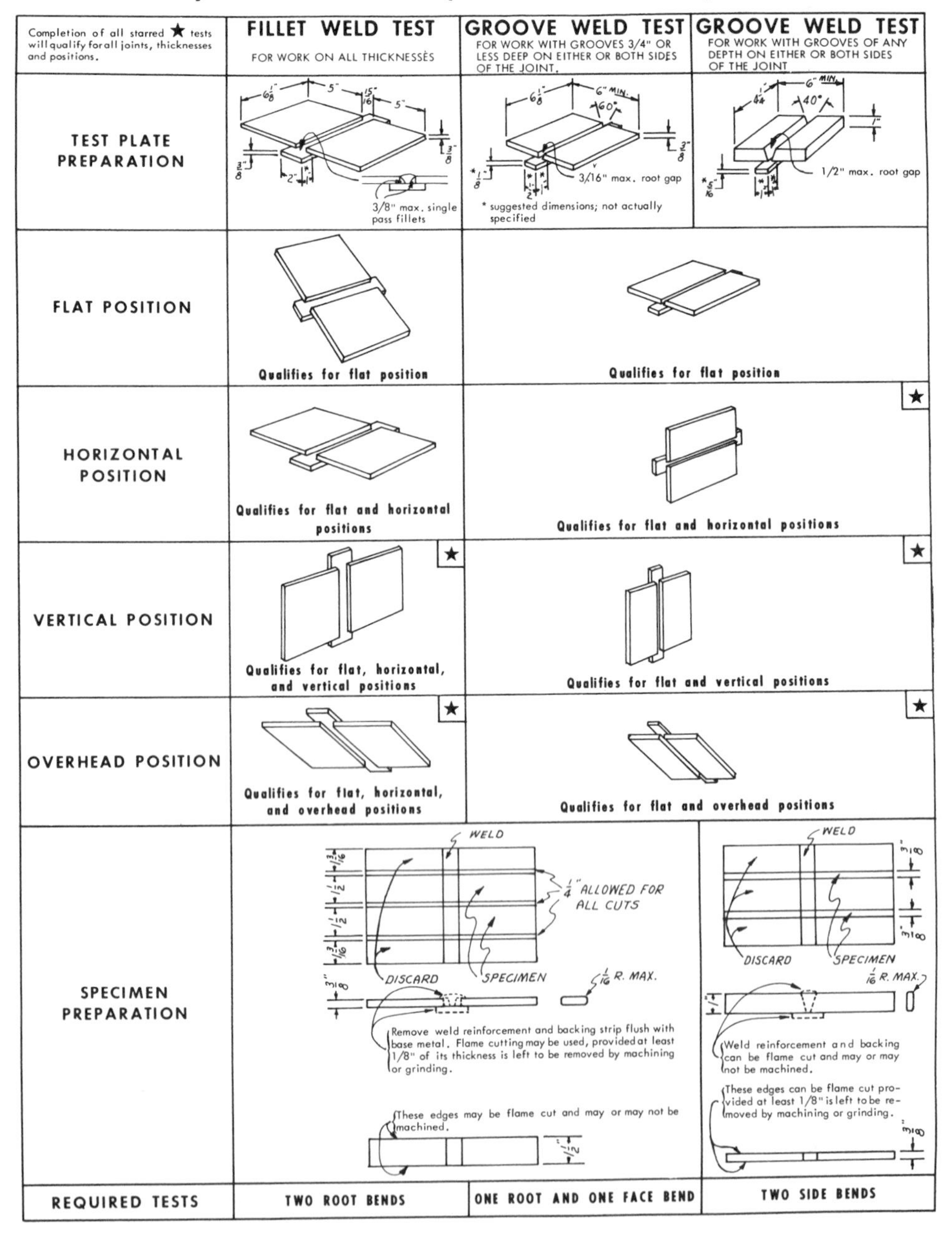

FIG. 7 AWS Weldor Qualification Test requirements are completely detailed in the code books.

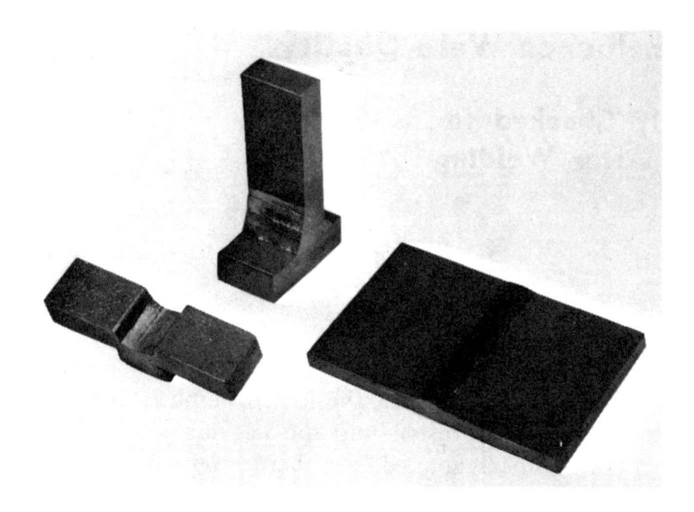

FIG. 8 Sample welds, such as those shown, made under typical conditions should be made and subjected to the various types of destructive and nondestructive tests needed to establish the degree of quality required for the job. With this approach, many tests can be applied that might be impractical or impossible to use during final inspection.

7. This test is usually adequate. But in a great many instances, it is questionable whether this simple test establishes the ability of the weldor to do the actual job and proves that he can make the welds on the job that will satisfy final inspection requirements.

For example, if the weldor will be required to make vertical butt welds on ¾″ thick plate and final inspection calls for radiographic inspection (Section 409 of the Bridge Specifications), will the AWS weldor qualification test prove the weldor can produce these welds in a satisfactory manner? Obviously, it will not because radiographic inspection is not normally called for in the AWS weldor qualification test. The test becomes more meaningful if radiographic inspection is added to the normal testing requirements.

The contractor is in the best position to evaluate the actual skill required for the job as opposed to the skill required to pass an AWS weldor qualification test. When the actual job demands more of the man than he would otherwise be able to demonstrate on a standard weldor qualification test, the contractor for his own protection is justified in requiring more realistic tests.

Most semi-automatic processes present some problems relative to weldor training. If, however, the process has been properly selected for the job and correct welding procedures have been worked out, weldor training should not pose a difficult problem. With competent instruction, this can be handled as a joint weldor-training, weldor-qualification program.

The question of properly qualified personnel also involves people other than weldors, and attention should be given to their training also.

Pretest It

Once a welding procedure has been established, nobody should be more eager to prove it than the contractor, and nobody is in a better position to do so. Mock-up sample welds made under typical conditions can be subjected to all kinds of destructive and nondestructive tests, Figure 8. Many of these tests would be completely impractical or even impossible as a final inspection requirement. Testing at this stage is relatively inexpensive, and the latitude is much broader than would be permitted or desired as final inspection. Maximum testing at this time gives assurance that final inspection can be held to a minimum.

9. PREVENTIVE INSPECTION

In summary, it should be universally recognized that inspection after welding, while often essential, is somewhat too late. Any excessive weld cracks, undercuts, undersize welds, poor fusion or other defects detected that late will be expensive to correct. All parties concerned should insist on good welding, supervision, conscientious qualified weldors, and a thorough system of preventive inspection.

Preventive inspection, in which everyone concerned should share responsibility, involves a systematic observation of welding practices and adherence to specifications before, during, and after welding in order to visually detect and stop any occurrences that may result in substandard welds. The check list that follows will aid in developing this pattern of operation.

FIG. 9 This "mock-up" beam-to-column connection was made with scrap ends, prepared and assembled to specifications then welded to work out procedure details.

Check List of Items That Influence Weld Quality

Points to be Visually Checked for Before, During and After Welding

● ○ ○ Check Before Welding
○ ● ○ Check During Welding
○ ○ ● Check After Welding

(1) Proper Included Angle

● ○ ○

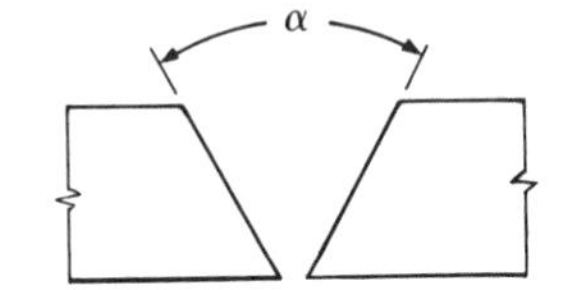

The included angle must be sufficient to allow electrode to reach root of joint, and to ensure fusion to side walls on multiple passes. In general, the greater this angle the more weld metal will be required.

(2) Proper Root Opening (Fit-Up)

● ○ ○

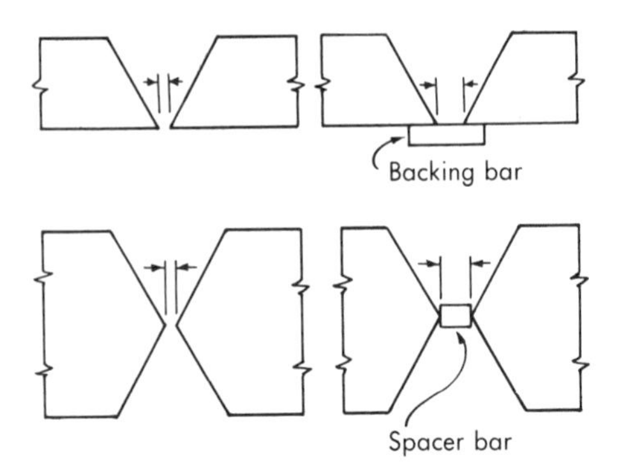

Without a backing bar, there is a possibility of burning through on the first pass; so, the root opening is reduced slightly. Lack of fusion of the root pass to the very bottom of the joint is no real problem because the joint must be back gouged before the pass may be made on the back side.

With a backing bar, the root opening is increased to allow proper fusion into the backing bar, since it will not be back gouged; also there is no burn-through.

With a spacer bar, it serves as a backing bar but must be back gouged before welding on the back side to ensure sound fusion.

(3) Proper Root Face

● ○ ○

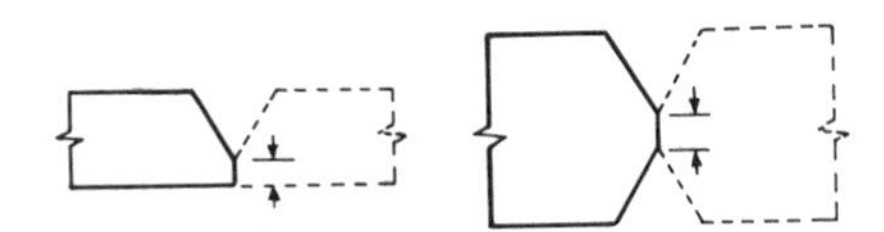

A root face is usually specified in joints welded by the submerged-arc process to prevent burn-through on the first or root pass; therefore, there is a minimum limit to this dimension. There is also a maximum limit so that the back pass, when made, will fuse with the first root pass to provide a sound joint. This fusion of root and back passes can be checked after welding, if the joint runs out to an exposed edge of the plate and onto run-off bars.

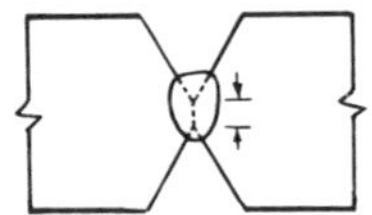

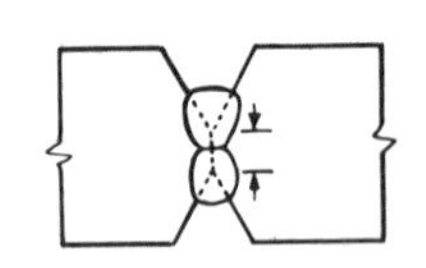

(a) Too small root face; burn-through (b) Too large root face; lack of penetration (c) Proper root face; proper penetration

The above items, included angle (1) and root opening (2), go hand in hand to ensure clearance for the electrode to enter the joint sufficiently for proper fusion at the root, and yet not require excessive weld metal.

In general, as the included angle is decreased to reduce the amount of weld metal, the root must be opened up to maintain proper fusion of weld metal at the joint root. For any given thickness of plate, there is a range in the combination of included angle and root opening that will result in a minimum amount of weld metal consistent with the required weld quality.

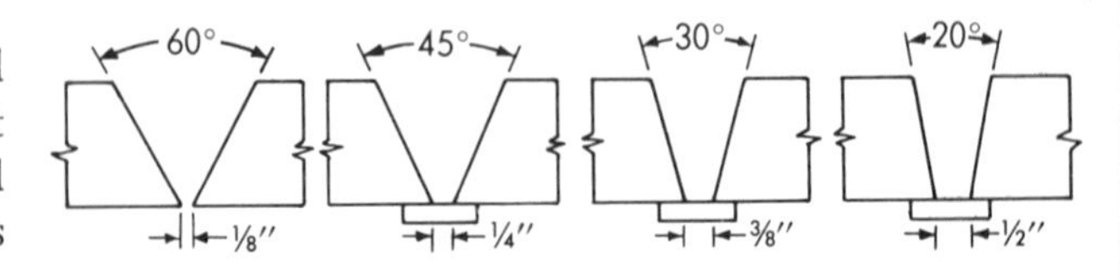

(4) Proper Alignment

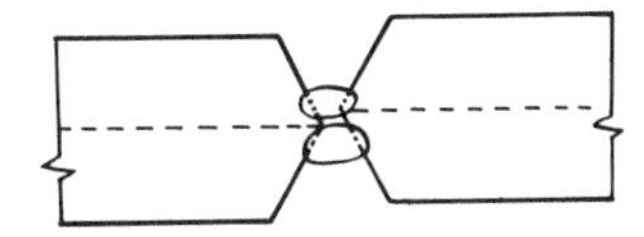

Misalignment of plates being joined may result in an unpenetrated portion between root and back passes. This would require more back gouging.

(5) Cleanliness of Joint

● ● ●

Joint and plate surface must be clean of dirt, rust, and moisture. This is especially important on those surfaces to be fused with the deposited weld metal.

(6) Proper Type and Size of Electrode

○ ● ○

Electrodes must suit the metal being joined, the welding position, the function of the weld, the plate thickness, the size of the joint, etc. Where standard procedures specify the electrodes, periodic checks should be made to ensure their use.

(7) Proper Welding Current and Polarity

○ ● ○

Welding current and polarity must suit the type electrode used and the joint to be made.

(8) Proper Tack Welds

○ ● ○

These should be small and long, if posible, so they won't interfere with subsequent submerged-arc welds. On heavy plates, low-hydrogen electrodes should be used.

(9) Good Fusion

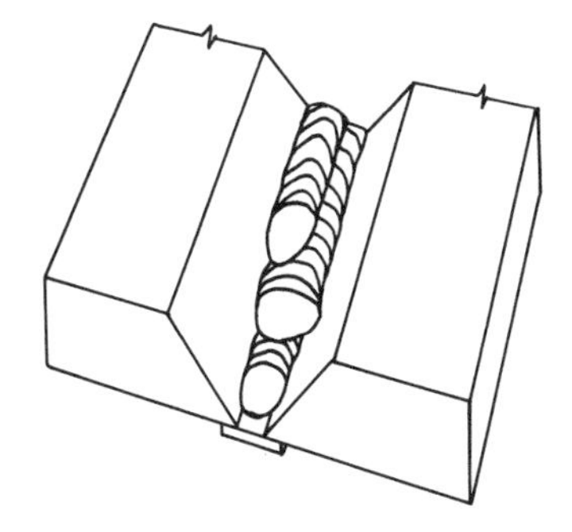

Each pass should fuse properly into any backing plate, preceding pass, or adjacent plate metal. No unfilled or unfused pockets should be left between weld beads.

(10) Proper Preheat and Interpass Temperature

○ ● ○

The need for preheat and required temperature level depends on the plate thickness, the grade of steel, the welding process, and ambient temperatures. Where these conditions dictate the need, periodical checks should be made to ensure adherence to requirements.

(11) Proper Sequencing of Passes

○ ● ○

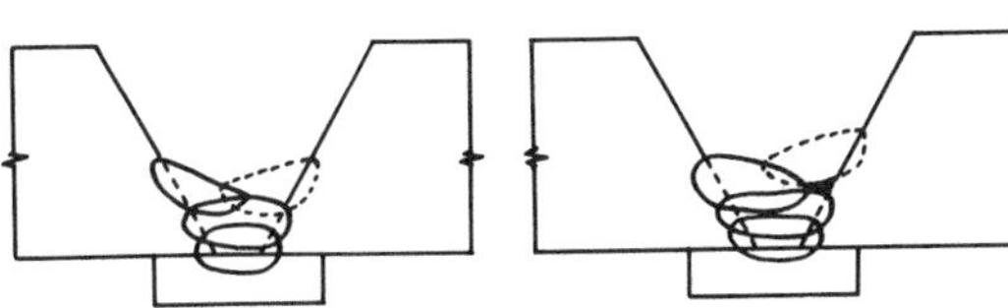

(a) No problem for next pass to fuse properly into side of joint and weld

(b) Not enough room left between side of joint and last pass; will not fuse properly; may trap slag

The sequencing of passes should be such that no unfused portion results, nor distortion.

(12) Proper Travel Speed

○ ● ○

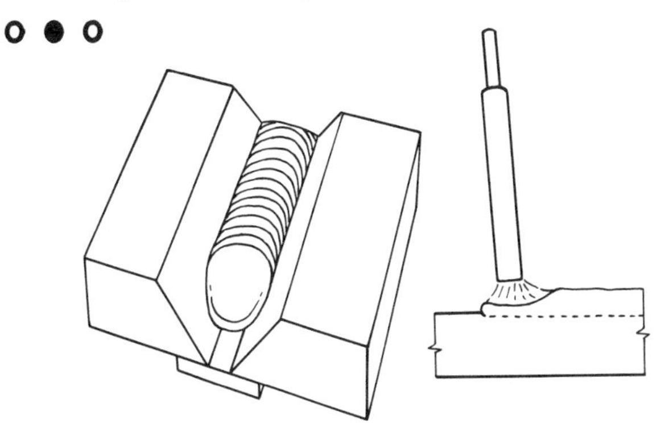

If travel speed is too slow, molten weld metal and slag will tend to run ahead and start to cool; the main body of weld metal will run over this without the arc penetrating far enough, and the trapped slag will reduce fusion.

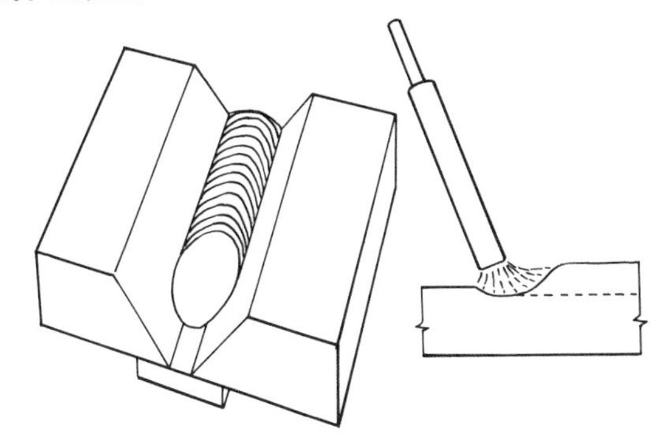

If travel speed is increased, good fusion will result because the molten weld metal and slag will be forced backward, with the arc digging into the plate.

(13) Absence of Overlap

○ ● ●

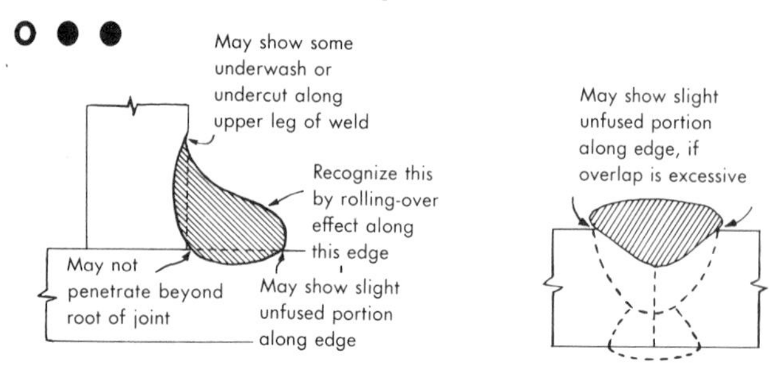
May show some underwash or undercut along upper leg of weld
Recognize this by rolling-over effect along this edge
May not penetrate beyond root of joint
May show slight unfused portion along edge
May show slight unfused portion along edge, if overlap is excessive

if speed of travel is too slow, the excessive amount of weld metal being deposited will tend to roll over along the edges, preventing proper fusion. This roll-over action is easily noticed during welding. The correction is very simple; increasing the travel speed will achieve the desired effect (below).

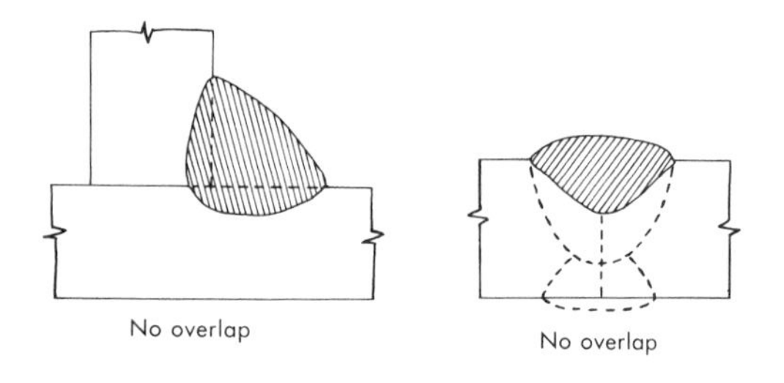
No overlap
No overlap

(14) In Vertical Welding, Tilt of Crater

○ ● ○

The crater position should be kept tilted slightly so slag will run out toward the front of weld and will not interfere. This will help ensure good fusion.

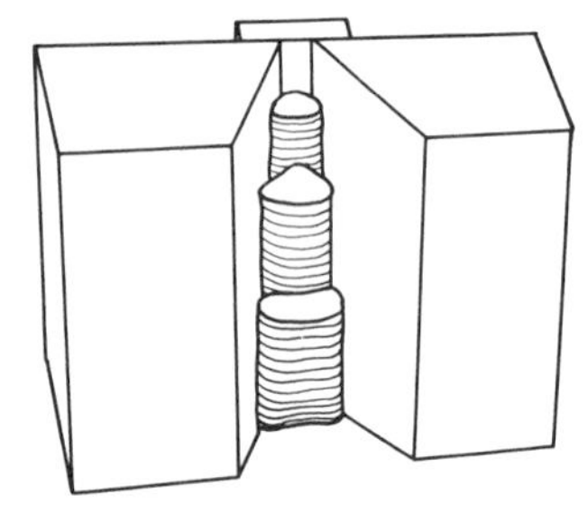

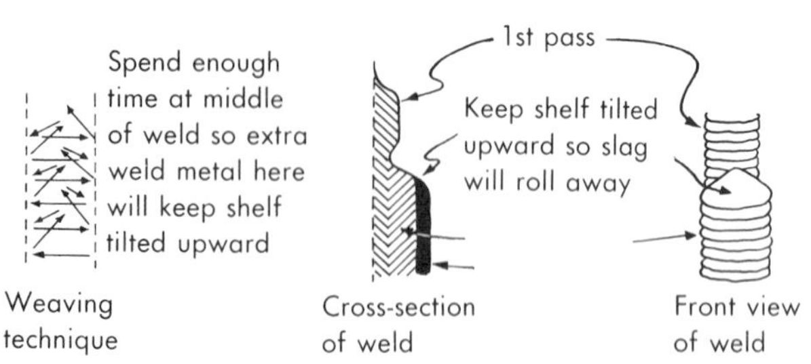
Spend enough time at middle of weld so extra weld metal here will keep shelf tilted upward
1st pass
Keep shelf tilted upward so slag will roll away
Weaving technique
Cross-section of weld
Front view of weld

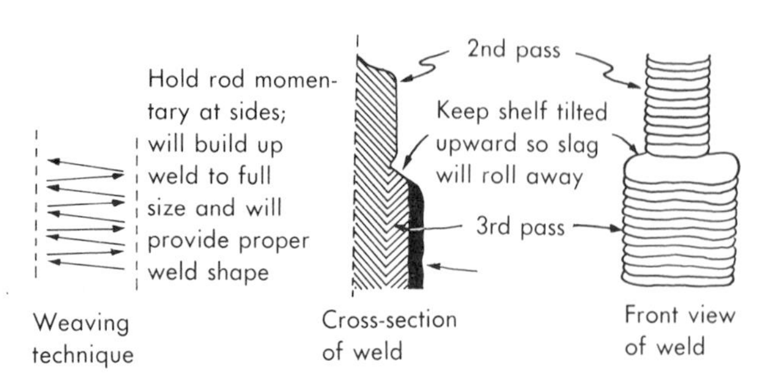
Hold rod momentary at sides; will build up weld to full size and will provide proper weld shape
2nd pass
Keep shelf tilted upward so slag will roll away
3rd pass
Weaving technique
Cross-section of weld
Front view of weld

(15) Filled Craters

○ ● ●

It might be argued that craters are a problem if—

1) they are undersize, i.e. not full throat, and/or

2) they are concave, since they might crack upon cooling; of course, once they cool down to room temperature, this would no longer be a problem.

Normally, on continuous fillet welds, there is no crater problem because each crater is filled by the next weld. The weldor starts his arc at the outer end of the last crater and momentarily swings back into the crater to fill it before going ahead for the next weld.

For a single connection, it is important at the end of the weld not to leave the crater in a highly stressed area. If necessary to do so, extra care should be taken to carefully fill the crater to full throat.

• Example: On a beam-to-column connection using a top connecting plate, the crater of the fillet weld joining the plate to the beam flange should be made full throat.

• Example: In shop welding a flexible seat angle to the supporting column flange, the welding sequence should permit the weld to start at the top portion of the seat angle, and carry down along the edge, with the crater at the bottom; as shown.

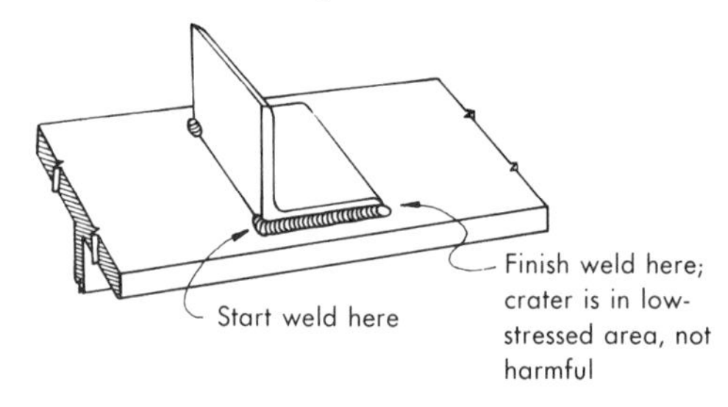
Start weld here
Finish weld here; crater is in low-stressed area, not harmful

On intermittent fillet welds, unfilled craters should normally be no problem because:

1. The additional strength obtained by filling the crater would not be needed in this low-stressed joint, for which intermittent fillet welds are sufficient.

2. Any notch effect of an unfilled crater should be no worse than the notch presented by the start end of the fillet weld; shown below. No matter what is done to the crater, it will still represent the termination of the weld, in other words an unwelded portion meeting a welded portion.

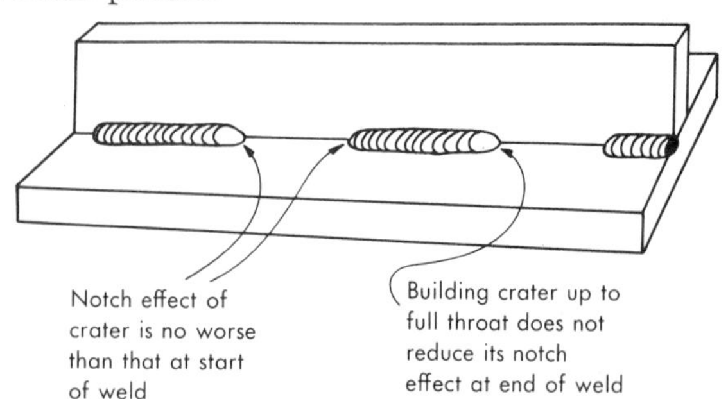
Notch effect of crater is no worse than that at start of weld
Building crater up to full throat does not reduce its notch effect at end of weld

(16) Absence of Excessive Undercut

○ ● ●

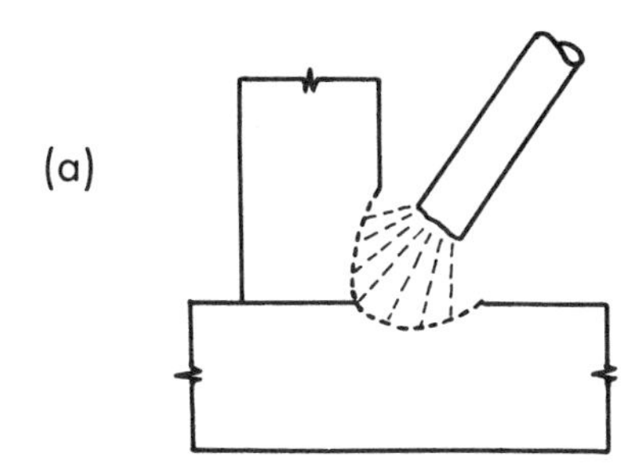
(a)

(a) The digging effect of the arc melts a portion of the base plate.

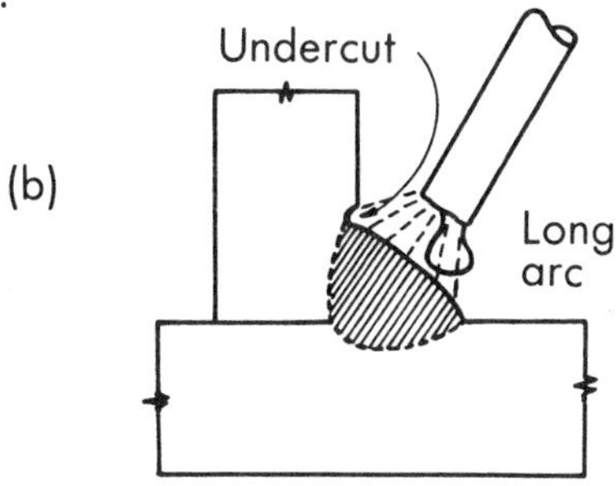
Undercut
(b)
Long
arc

(b) If the arc is too long, the molten weld metal from the end of the electrode may fall short and not completely fill this melted zone, thus leaving an undercut along the upper leg of the weld.

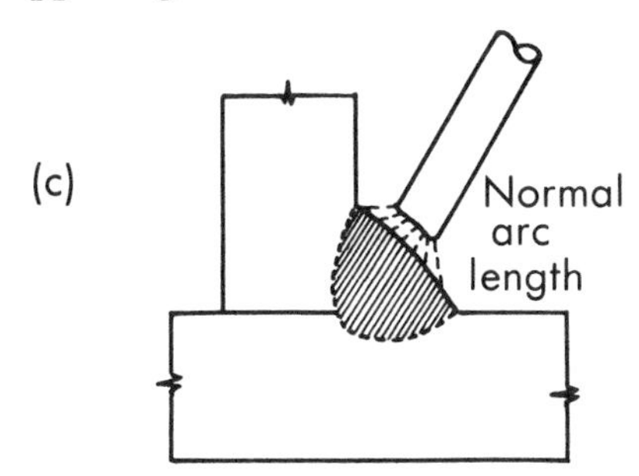
(c)
Normal
arc
length

(c) If the arc is shortened to the proper arc length, the molten weld metal from the end of the electrode will completely fill this melted zone and will leave no undercut.

Undercut should not be accepted on a recurring basis since it can be eliminated with proper welding procedure. If, however, undercut does occur, the question to be answered at this point is whether it is harmful and needs repair.

(1st) If the undercut results in a sizeable loss of net section that cannot be allowed.

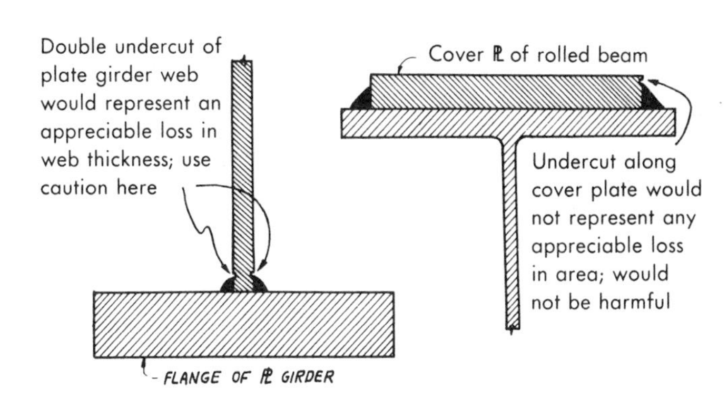
Double undercut of
plate girder web
would represent an
appreciable loss in
web thickness; use
caution here
Cover ℄ of rolled beam
Undercut along
cover plate would
not represent any
appreciable loss
in area; would
not be harmful
FLANGE OF ℄ GIRDER

(2nd) If a force must be transferred transverse to the axis of the undercut, which may then act as a notch or stress riser.

(a) Here the tensile force is applied transverse to the undercut and presents a stress riser. This *would be* harmful.

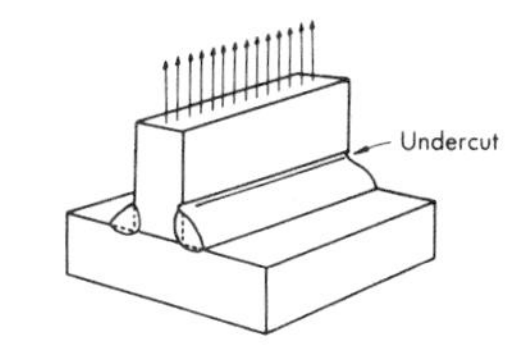
Undercut

(b) Here the axial tensile stresses are applied parallel to the undercut and would not present a stress riser. This should *not* be harmful.

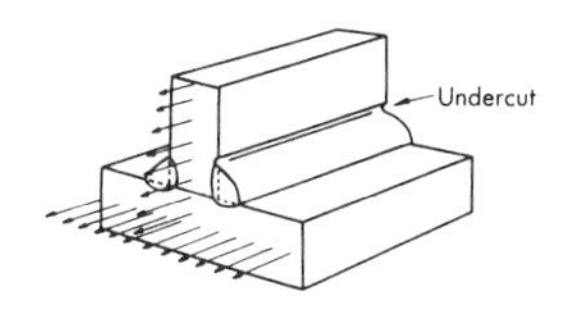
Undercut

(c) Here the shear force is applied parallel to the undercut and would not present a stress riser. This should *not* be harmful.

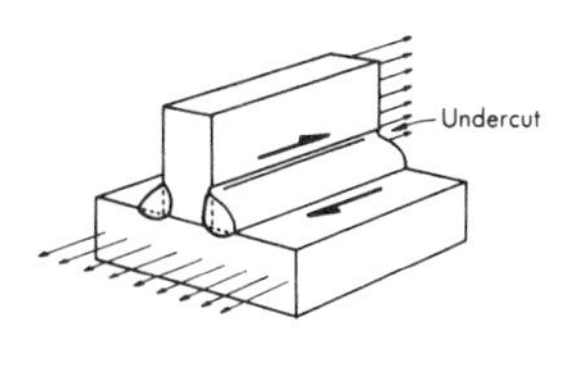
Undercut

The AWS allows undercut up to 0.01″ in depth if it lies transverse to the applied force, and 1/32″ if it lies parallel to the force.

• Although both undercuts in this tensile joint are transverse to the notch, the upper undercut undoubtedly has less effect upon producing a stress raiser because the stress flows smoothly below the surface of the root of the notch. On the other hand, the lower undercut does represent a stress raiser because the flow of stress is greatly disturbed as it is forced to pass sharply around the root of the notch.

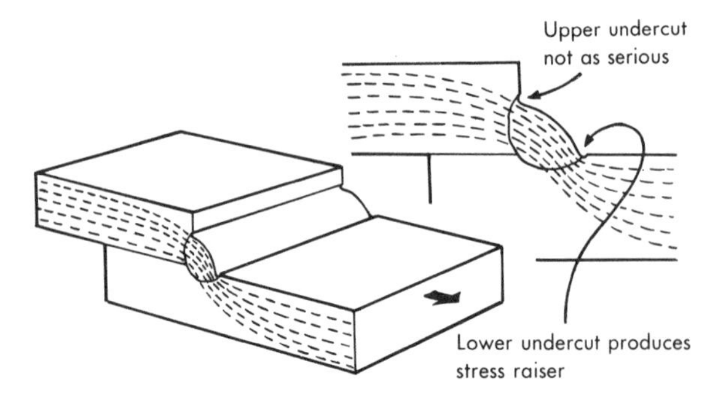

• In addition, any eccentricity would produce bending stresses in the region of the lower undercut.

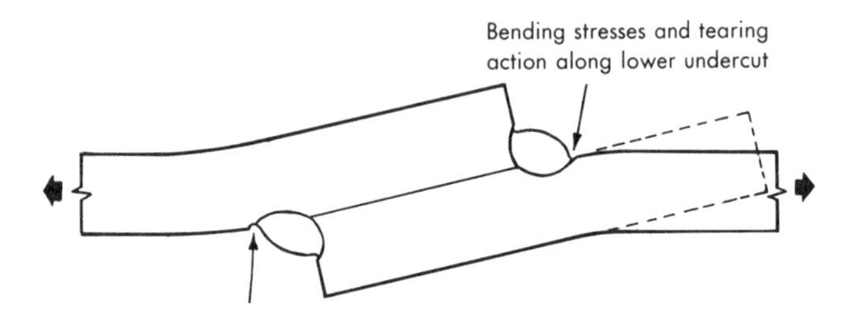

(17) Slight Reinforcement on Groove Welds

O ● ●

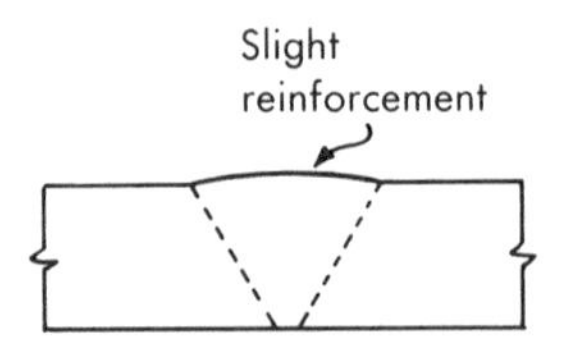

A nominal weld reinforcement (about $\frac{1}{16}''$ above flush) is required. Any more than this is unnecessary and increases the weld cost.

(18) Full Size on Fillet Welds

O O ●

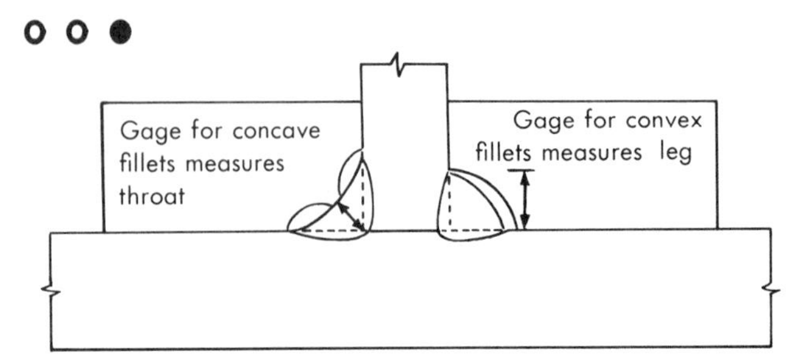

Proper gaging of fillet welds is important to ensure adequate size.

(19) Absence of Cracks

O ● ●

There should be no cracks of any kind, either in the weld or in the heat-affected zone of the welded plate.

Beam Diagrams and Formulas

The following beam diagrams and formulas have been found useful in the design of welded steel structures.

Proper signs, positive (+) and negative (—), are not necessarily indicated in the formulas. The following are suggested:

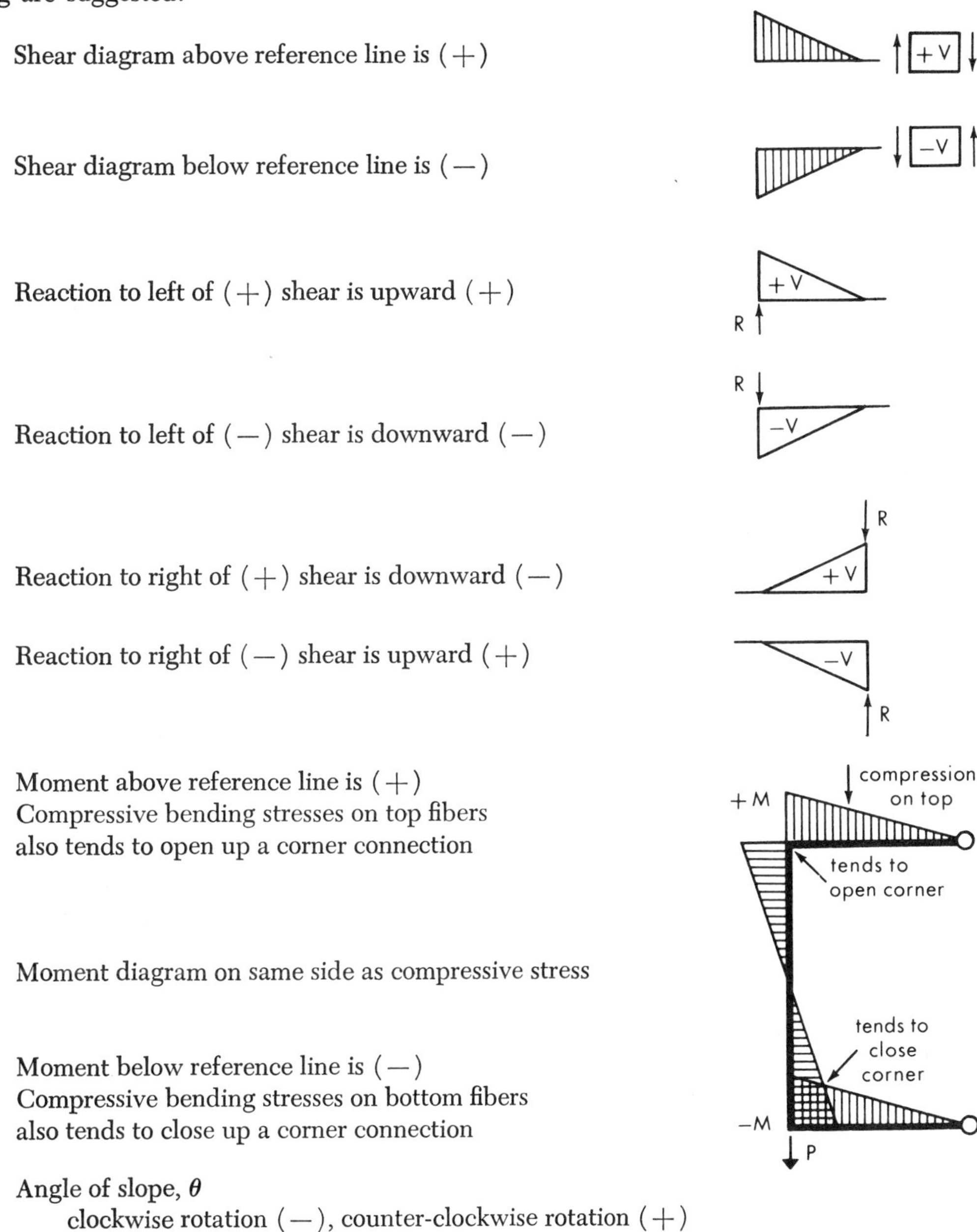

Shear diagram above reference line is (+)

Shear diagram below reference line is (—)

Reaction to left of (+) shear is upward (+)

Reaction to left of (—) shear is downward (—)

Reaction to right of (+) shear is downward (—)

Reaction to right of (—) shear is upward (+)

Moment above reference line is (+)
Compressive bending stresses on top fibers
also tends to open up a corner connection

Moment diagram on same side as compressive stress

Moment below reference line is (—)
Compressive bending stresses on bottom fibers
also tends to close up a corner connection

Angle of slope, θ
clockwise rotation (—), counter-clockwise rotation (+)

On the next page is a visual index to the various beam diagrams and formulas. As indicated, these are keyed by number to the type of beam and by capital letter to the type of load.

For some conditions, influence curves are included to illustrate the effect of an important variable. These are keyed to the basic beam diagram and are positioned as close as practical to the diagram.

VISUAL INDEX TO FORMULAS ON FOLLOWING PAGES FOR VARIOUS BEAM-LOAD CONDITIONS

Type of LOAD / Type of BEAM	(A) Concentrated force (P)	(B) Uniform load entire span (w)	(C) Uniform load partial span (w)	(D) Varying load (W)	(E) Couple (M_o)
(1) Cantilever (free, fixed)	1Aa 1Ab	1B	1C	1Da 1Db	1E
(2) guided, fixed	2A	2B			
(3) Simply supported (supported)	3Aa 3Ab 3Ac 3Ad	3B	3C	3Da 3Db 3Dc	3Ea 3Eb 3Ec
(4) fixed	4Aa 4Ab 4Ac	4Ba 4Bb	4C	4D	4E
(5) supported, fixed	5Aa 5Ab	5B	5C	5Da 5Db	5E
(6) Single span with overhang	6Aa 6Ab	6Ba 6Bb	6Ca 6Cb		
(7) Continuous two span	7Aa 7Ab	7B		7D See adjacent to (3D)	For other multi-span load conditions, see discussion under (7)

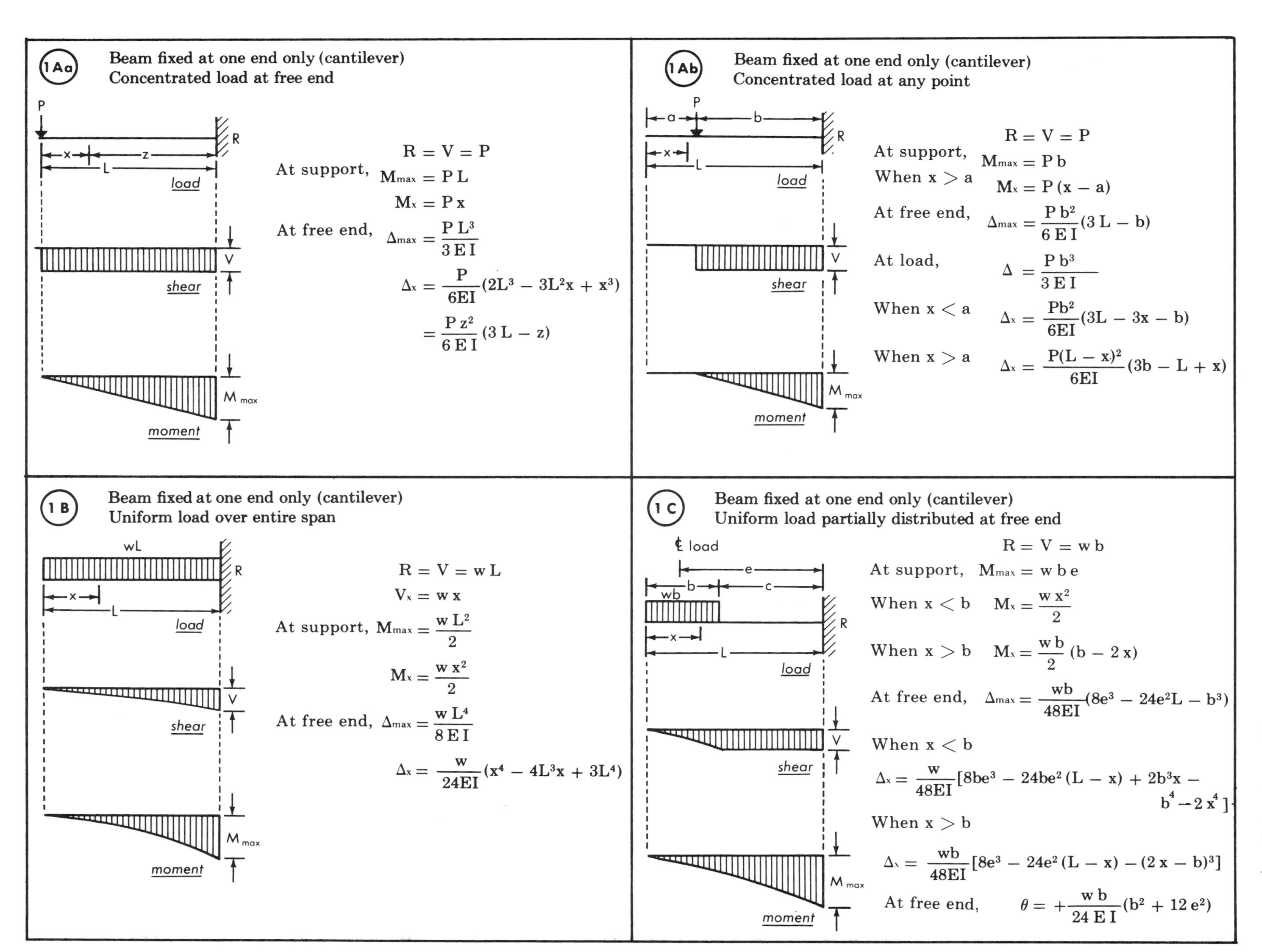
1Aa
Beam fixed at one end only (cantilever)
Concentrated load at free end
P
x
z
L
R
load
shear
V
moment
M max
At support,
$R = V = P$
$M_{max} = P L$
$M_x = P x$
At free end,
$\Delta_{max} = \frac{P L^3}{3 E I}$
$\Delta_x = \frac{P}{6EI}(2L^3 - 3L^2x + x^3)$
$= \frac{P z^2}{6 E I}(3 L - z)$
1Ab
Beam fixed at one end only (cantilever)
Concentrated load at any point
P
a
b
x
L
R
load
shear
V
moment
M max
At support,
$R = V = P$
$M_{max} = P b$
When $x > a$
$M_x = P (x - a)$
At free end,
$\Delta_{max} = \frac{P b^2}{6 E I}(3 L - b)$
At load,
$\Delta = \frac{P b^3}{3 E I}$
When $x < a$
$\Delta_x = \frac{Pb^2}{6EI}(3L - 3x - b)$
When $x > a$
$\Delta_x = \frac{P(L - x)^2}{6EI}(3b - L + x)$
1 B
Beam fixed at one end only (cantilever)
Uniform load over entire span
wL
x
L
R
load
shear
V
moment
M max
$R = V = w L$
$V_x = w x$
At support,
$M_{max} = \frac{w L^2}{2}$
$M_x = \frac{w x^2}{2}$
At free end,
$\Delta_{max} = \frac{w L^4}{8 E I}$
$\Delta_x = \frac{w}{24EI}(x^4 - 4L^3x + 3L^4)$
1 C
Beam fixed at one end only (cantilever)
Uniform load partially distributed at free end
℄ load
e
b
c
wb
x
L
R
load
shear
V
moment
M max
$R = V = w b$
At support,
$M_{max} = w b e$
When $x < b$
$M_x = \frac{w x^2}{2}$
When $x > b$
$M_x = \frac{w b}{2}(b - 2 x)$
At free end,
$\Delta_{max} = \frac{wb}{48EI}(8e^3 - 24e^2L - b^3)$
When $x < b$
$\Delta_x = \frac{w}{48EI}[8be^3 - 24be^2 (L - x) + 2b^3x - b^4 - 2 x^4]$
When $x > b$
$\Delta_x = \frac{wb}{48EI}[8e^3 - 24e^2 (L - x) - (2 x - b)^3]$
At free end,
$\theta = +\frac{w b}{24 E I}(b^2 + 12 e^2)$

(1Da) Beam fixed at one end only (cantilever)
Varying load increasing uniformly from free end to support

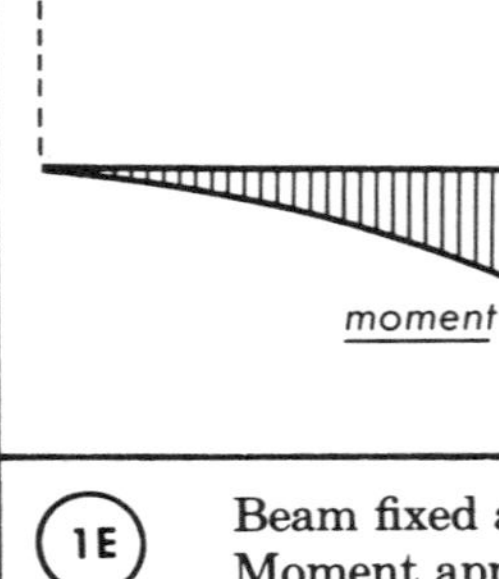

$$W = \frac{p\,L}{2}$$

$$R = V = W$$

$$V_x = W\frac{x^2}{L^2}$$

At support, $$M_{max} = \frac{W\,L}{3}$$

$$M_x = \frac{W\,x^3}{3\,L^2}$$

At free end, $$\Delta_{max} = \frac{W\,L^3}{15\,E\,I}$$

$$\Delta_x = \frac{W}{60EIL^2}(x^5 - 5L^4x + 4L^5)$$

At free end, $$\theta = +\frac{W\,L^2}{12\,E\,I}$$

(1Db) Beam fixed at one end only (cantilever)
Varying load increasing uniformly from support to free end

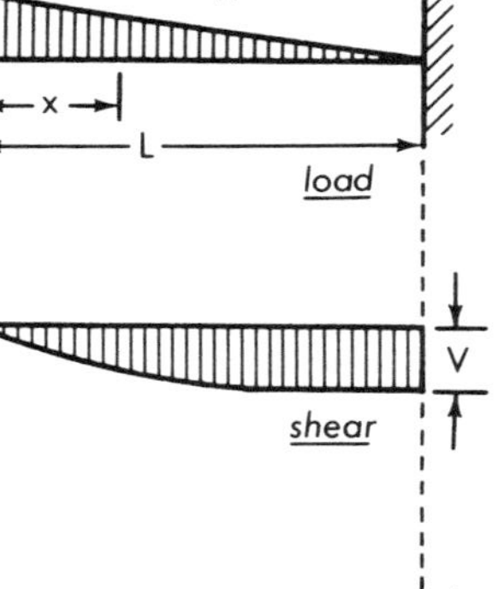
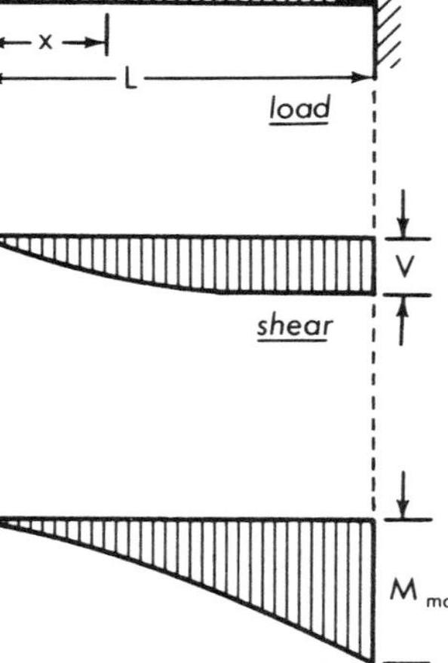
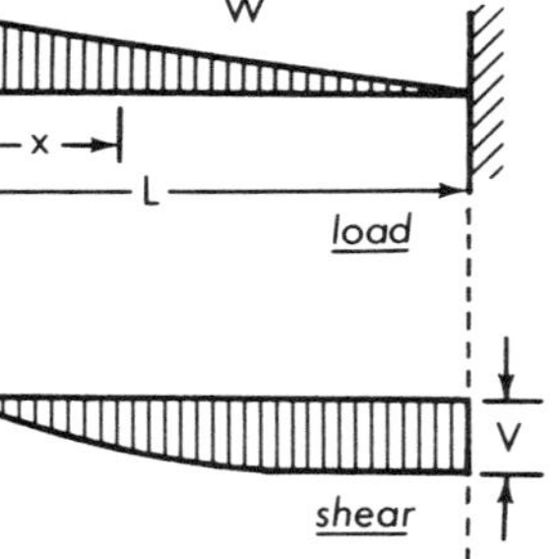
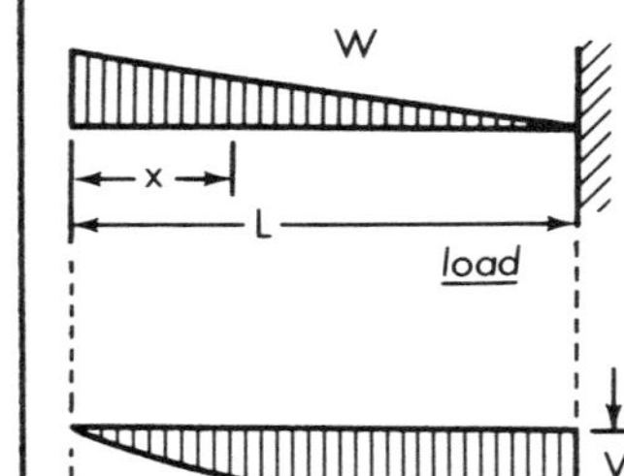
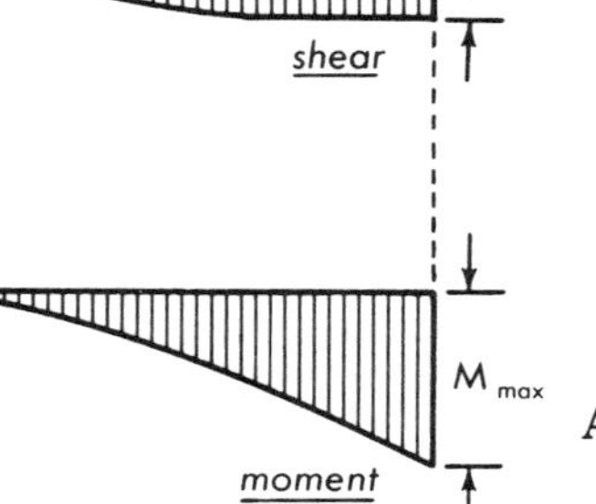
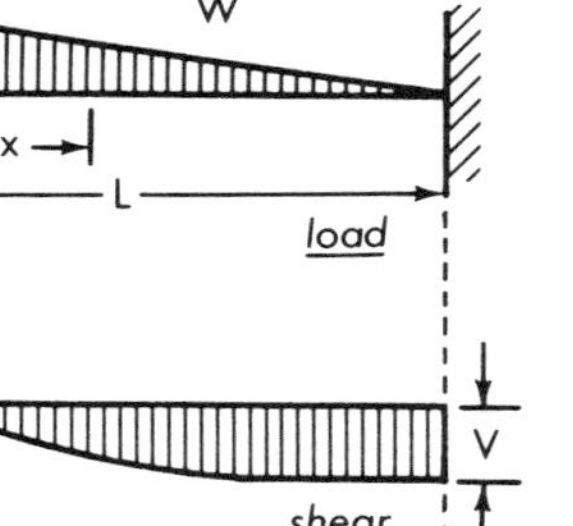

$$R = V = W$$

$$V_x = \frac{2\,W\,x}{L^2}\left(L - \frac{x}{2}\right)$$

At support, $$M_{max} = \frac{2\,W\,L}{3}$$

$$M_x = \frac{W\,x^2}{3\,L^2}(x - 3\,L)$$

At free end, $$\Delta_{max} = \frac{11\,W\,L^3}{60\,E\,I}$$

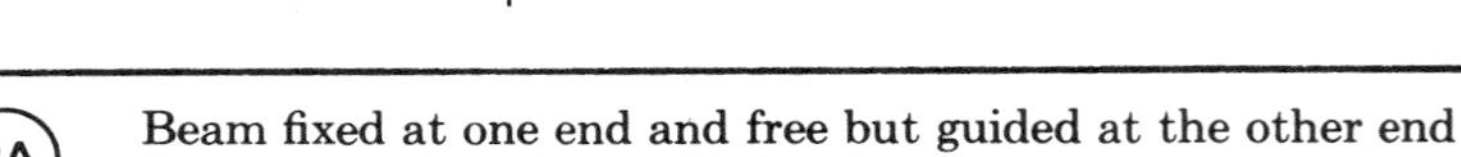

$$\Delta_x = \frac{W}{60EIL^2}[L^4(15x - 11L) - x^4(5L - x)]$$

At free end, $$\theta = +\frac{W\,L^2}{4\,E\,I}$$

(1E) Beam fixed at one end only (cantilever)
Moment applied at free end

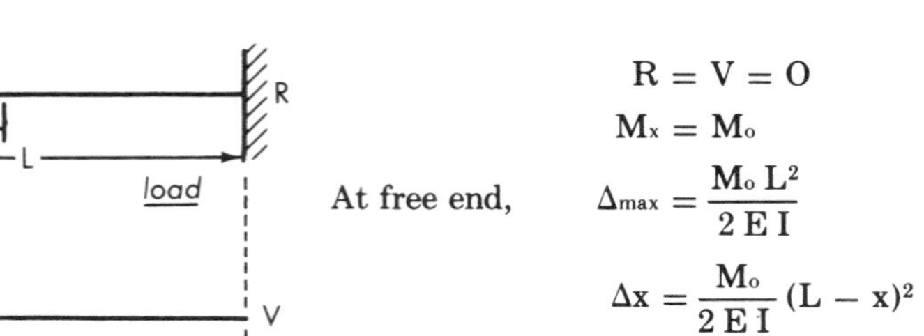
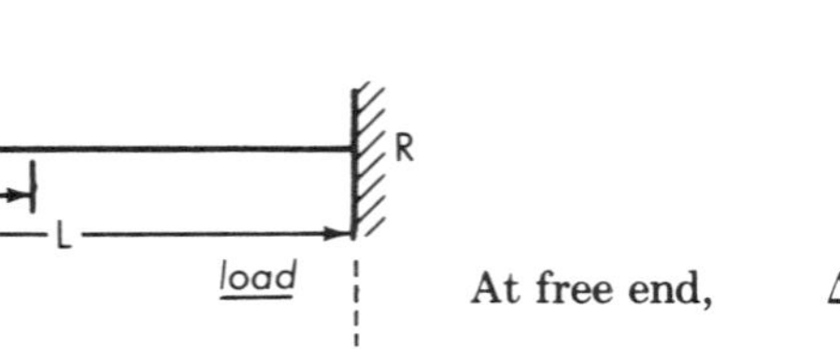
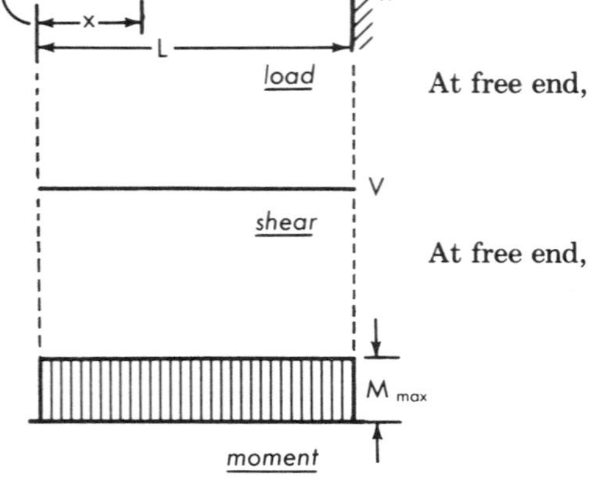

$$R = V = O$$

$$M_x = M_o$$

At free end, $$\Delta_{max} = \frac{M_o\,L^2}{2\,E\,I}$$

$$\Delta x = \frac{M_o}{2\,E\,I}(L - x)^2$$

At free end, $$\theta = -\frac{M_o\,L}{E\,I}$$

(2A) Beam fixed at one end and free but guided at the other end
Concentrated load at guided end

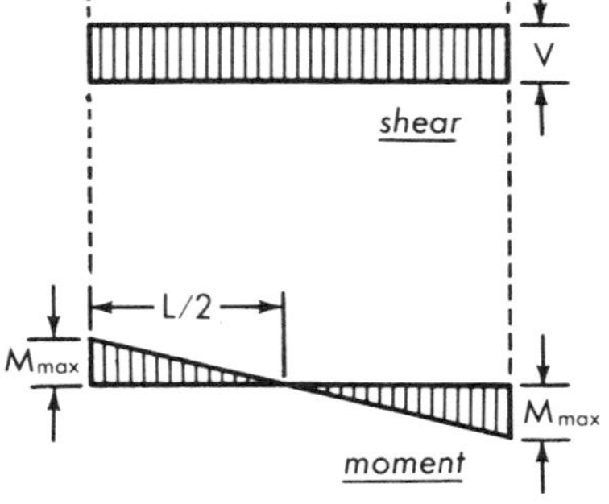
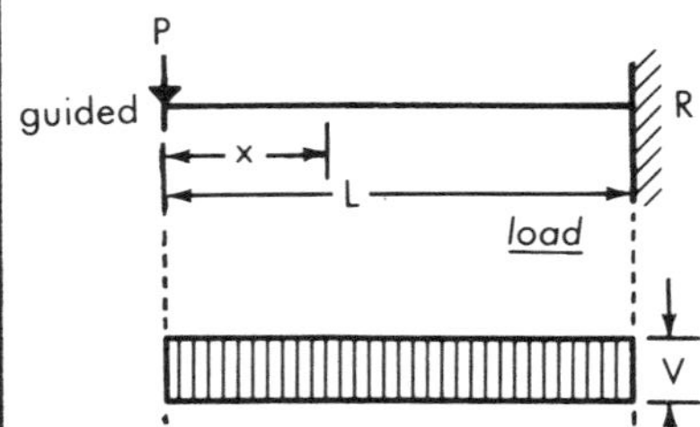

$$R = V = P$$

At both ends, $$M_{max} = \frac{P\,L}{2}$$

$$M_x = P\left(\frac{L}{2} - x\right)$$

At guided end, $$\Delta_{max} = \frac{P\,L^3}{12\,E\,I}$$

$$\Delta_x = \frac{P\,(L - x)^2}{12\,E\,I}(L + 2x)$$

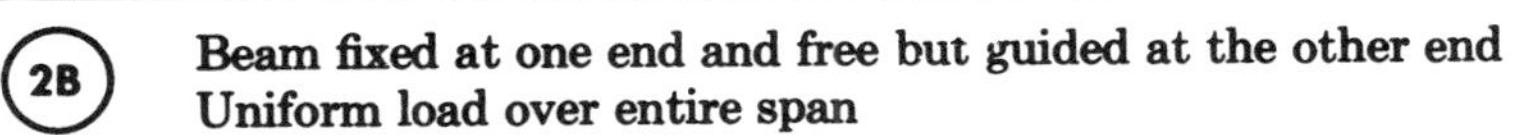

(2B) Beam fixed at one end and free but guided at the other end
Uniform load over entire span

$$R = V = w\,L$$

$$V_x = w\,x$$

At support, $M_{max} = \dfrac{w\,L^2}{3}$

At guided end, $M_1 = \dfrac{w\,L^2}{6}$

$$M_x = \frac{w}{6}(L^2 - 3\,x^2)$$

At guided end, $\Delta_{max} = \dfrac{w\,L^4}{24\,E\,I}$

$$\Delta_x = \frac{w\,(L^2 - x^2)^2}{24\,E\,I}$$

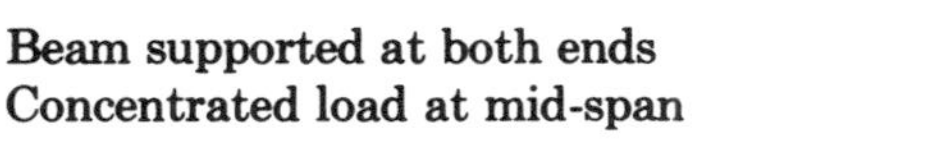

(3Aa) Beam supported at both ends
Concentrated load at mid-span

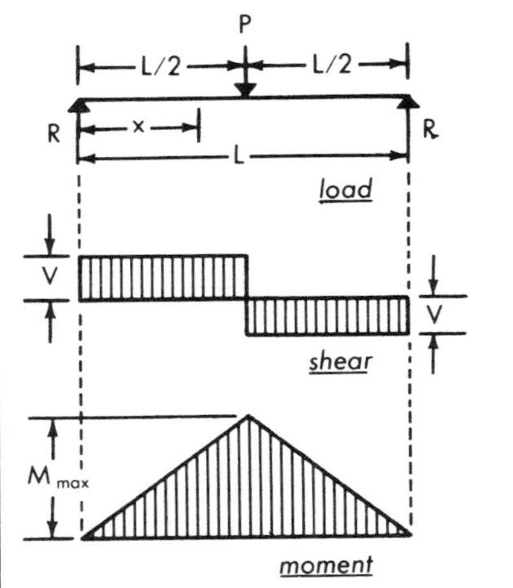

$$R_1 = R_2 = V = P/2$$

At load, $M_{max} = \dfrac{P\,L}{4}$

When $x < L/2$ $\quad M_x = \dfrac{P\,x}{2}$

At load, $\Delta_{max} = \dfrac{P\,L^3}{48\,E\,I}$

When $x < L/2$ $\quad \Delta_x = \dfrac{P\,x}{48\,E\,I}(3\,L^2 - 4\,x^2)$

At end, $\theta_1 = -\dfrac{P\,L^2}{16\,E\,I} = -\theta_2$

(3Ab) Beam supported at both ends
Concentrated load at any point

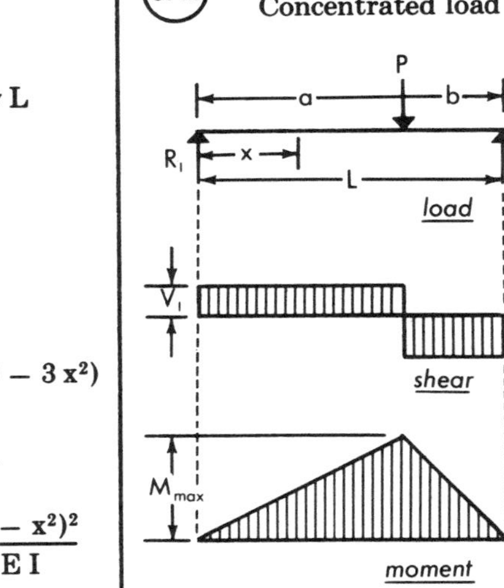

Max when $a < b$ $\quad R_1 = V_1 = \dfrac{P\,b}{L}$

Max when $a > b$ $\quad R_2 = V_2 = \dfrac{P\,a}{L}$

At load, $M_{max} = \dfrac{P\,a\,b}{L}$

When $x < a$ $\quad M_x = \dfrac{P\,b\,x}{L}$

At $x = \sqrt{\dfrac{L^2 - b^2}{3}}$

when $a > b$ $\quad \Delta_{max} = \dfrac{Pb}{3EIL}\sqrt{\left(\dfrac{L^2 - b^2}{3}\right)^3}$

At load, $\Delta = \dfrac{P\,a^2\,b^2}{3\,E\,I\,L}$

When $x < a$ $\quad \Delta_x = \dfrac{Pbx}{6EIL}(L^2 - b^2 - x^2)$

When $a < b$ $\quad \Delta_{\mathcal{L}} = \dfrac{Pa}{48EI}(3L^2 - 4a^2)$

At ends,

$$\theta_1 = -\frac{P}{6EI}\left(2aL + \frac{a^3}{L} - 3a^2\right)$$

$$\theta_2 = +\frac{P}{6EI}\left(aL - \frac{a^3}{L}\right)$$

3Ac

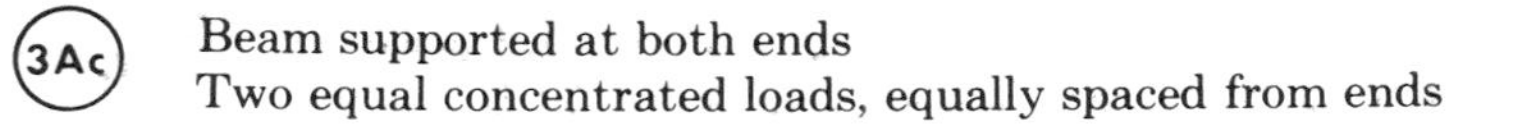

Beam supported at both ends
Two equal concentrated loads, equally spaced from ends

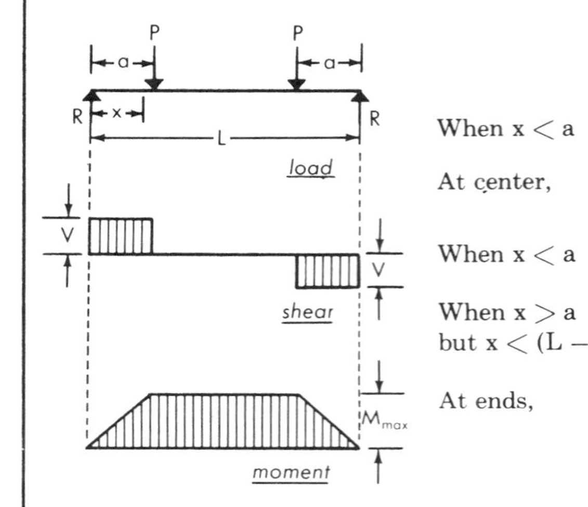

$R = V = P$

$M_{max} = P\,a$

When $x < a$ $\quad M_x = P\,x$

At center, $\quad \Delta_{max} = \dfrac{P\,a}{24\,E\,I}(3\,L^2 - 4\,a^2)$

When $x < a$ $\quad \Delta_x = \dfrac{Px}{6EI}(3La - 3a^2 - x^2)$

When $x > a$ but $x < (L - a)$ $\quad \Delta_x = \dfrac{Pa}{6EI}(3Lx - 3x^2 - a^2)$

At ends, $\quad \theta = \dfrac{P\,a}{2\,E\,I}(L - a)$

3Ad

Beam supported at both ends
Two unequal concentrated loads, unequally spaced from ends

$R_1 = V_1 = \dfrac{P_1(L - a) + P_2 b}{L}$

$R_2 = V_2 = \dfrac{P_1 a + P_2(L - b)}{L}$

When $x > a$ but $x < (L - b)$ $\quad V_x = R_1 - P_1$

Max when $R_1 < P_1$ $\quad M_1 = R_1\,a$

Max when $R_2 < P_2$ $\quad M_2 = R_2\,b$

When $x < a$ $\quad M_x = R_1\,x$

When $x > a$ but $x < (L - b)$ $\quad M_x = R_1\,x - P_1\,(x - a)$

3C

Beam supported at both ends
Uniform load partially distributed over span

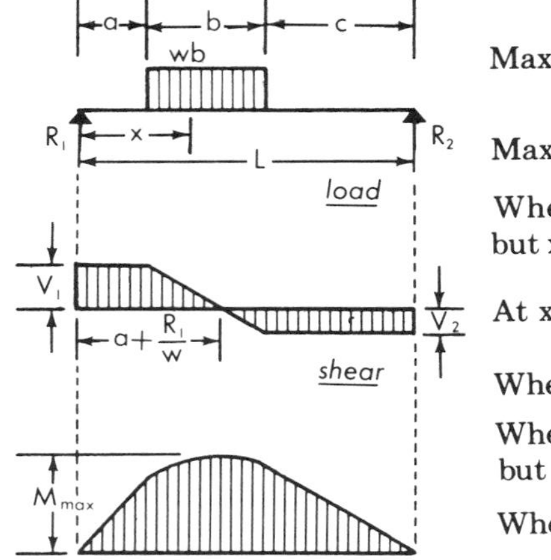

Max when $a < c$ $\quad R_1 = V_1 = \dfrac{wb}{2L}(2c + b)$

Max when $a > c$ $\quad R_2 = V_2 = \dfrac{wb}{2L}(2a + b)$

When $x > a$ but $x < (a + b)$ $\quad V_x = R_1 - w\,(x - a)$

At $x = a + \dfrac{R_1}{w}$ $\quad M_{max} = R_1\left(a + \dfrac{R_1}{2\,w}\right)$

When $x < a$ $\quad M_x = R_1\,x$

When $x > a$ but $x < (a + b)$ $\quad M_x = R_1 x - \dfrac{w}{2}(x - a)^2$

When $x > (a+b)$ $\quad M_x = R_2\,(L - x)$

When $a = c$

$R = V = \dfrac{w\,b}{2}$

$V_x = w\left(a + \dfrac{b}{2} - x\right)$

At center, $\quad M_{max} = \dfrac{w\,b}{2}\left(a + \dfrac{b}{4}\right)$

When $x < a$ $\quad M_x = \dfrac{w\,b\,x}{2}$

When $x > a$ but $x < (a + b)$ $\quad M_x = \dfrac{wbx}{2} - \dfrac{w}{2}(x - a)^2$

At center, $\quad \Delta_{\mathfrak{c}} = \dfrac{wb}{384EI}(+8L^3 - 4b^2L + b^3)$

(3B) Beam supported at both ends
Uniform load over entire span

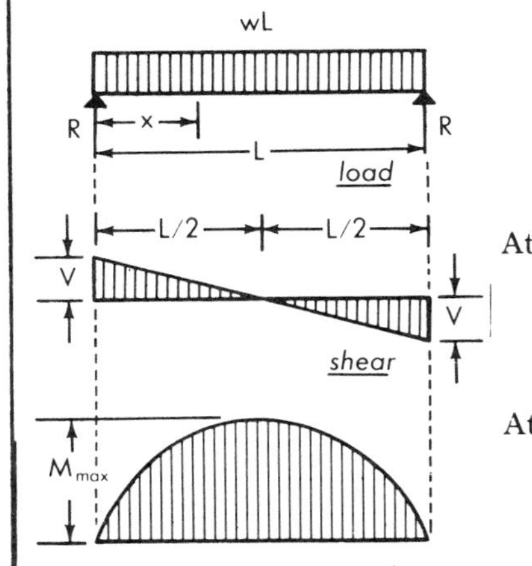

$$R = V = \frac{w\,L}{2}$$

$$V_x = w\left(\frac{L}{2} - x\right)$$

At center, $$M_{max} = \frac{w\,L^2}{8}$$

$$M_x = \frac{w\,x}{2}(L - x)$$

At center, $$\Delta_{max} = \frac{5\,w\,L^4}{384\,E\,I}$$

$$\Delta_x = \frac{wx}{24EI}(L^3 - 2Lx^2 + x^3)$$

At ends, $$\theta = \frac{w\,L^3}{24\,E\,I}$$

(3Db) Beam supported at both ends
Varying load, increasing uniformly to center

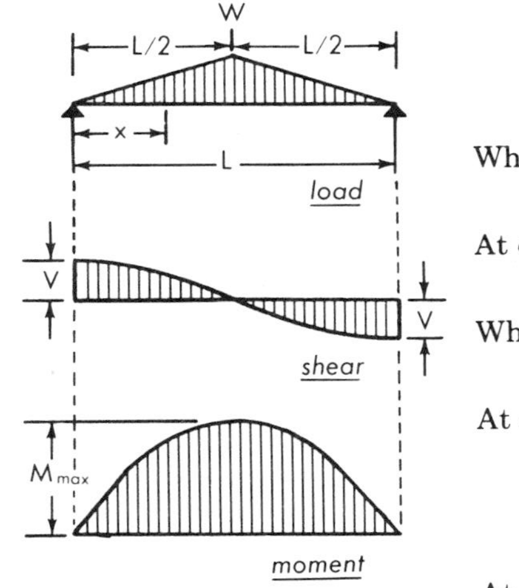
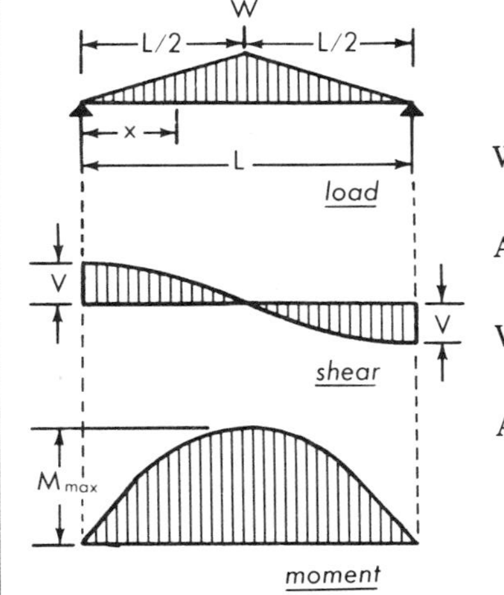
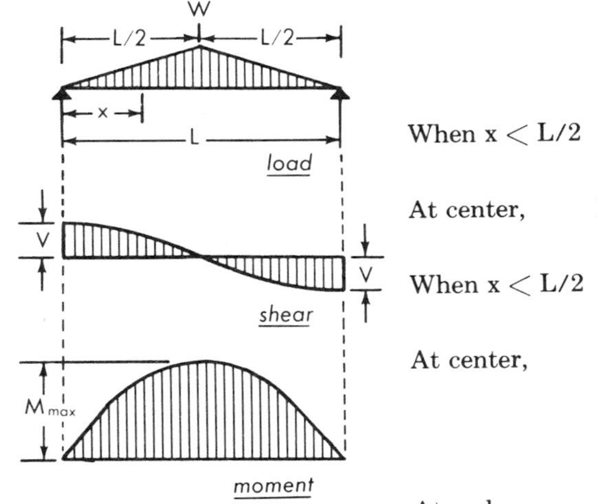

$$R_1 = R_2 = V = \frac{W}{2}$$

When $x < L/2$ $$V_x = \frac{W}{2\,L^2}(L^2 - 4\,x^2)$$

At center, $$M_{max} = \frac{W\,L}{6}$$

When $x < L/2$ $$M_x = W\,x\left(\frac{1}{2} - \frac{2\,x^2}{3\,L^2}\right)$$

At center, $$\Delta_{max} = \frac{W\,L^3}{60\,E\,I}$$

$$\Delta_x = \frac{Wx}{480EIL^2}(5L^2 - 4x^2)^2$$

At ends, $$\theta = \frac{5\,W\,L^2}{96\,E\,I}$$

(3Da) Beam supported at both ends
Varying load, increasing uniformly to one end

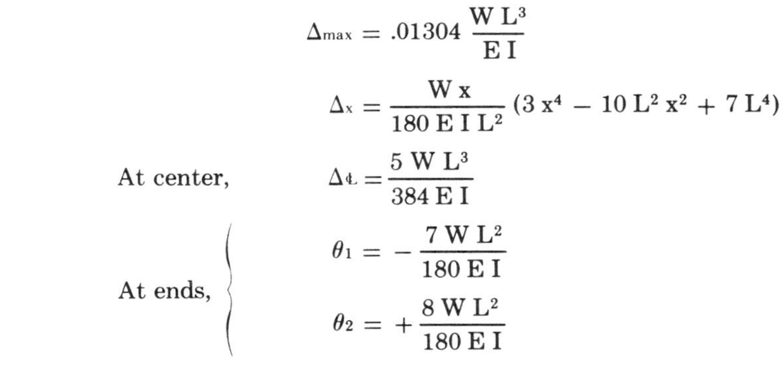

$$W = \frac{P\,L}{2}$$

$$R_1 = V_1 = \frac{W}{3}$$

$$R_2 = V_{2\,(max)} = \tfrac{2}{3}\,W$$

$$V_x = \frac{W}{3} - \frac{W\,x^2}{L^2}$$

At $x = L/\sqrt{3} = .5744\,L$

$$M_{max} = \frac{2\,W\,L}{9\sqrt{3}} = .1283\,W\,L$$

$$M_x = \frac{W\,x}{3\,L^2}(L^2 - x^2)$$

At $x = L\sqrt{1 - \sqrt{8/15}} = .5193\,L$

$$\Delta_{max} = .01304\,\frac{W\,L^3}{E\,I}$$

$$\Delta_x = \frac{W\,x}{180\,E\,I\,L^2}(3\,x^4 - 10\,L^2\,x^2 + 7\,L^4)$$

At center, $$\Delta_{c\!\!\!L} = \frac{5\,W\,L^3}{384\,E\,I}$$

At ends,
$$\theta_1 = -\frac{7\,W\,L^2}{180\,E\,I}$$
$$\theta_2 = +\frac{8\,W\,L^2}{180\,E\,I}$$

Also see formulas on page 8

BEAM FORMULAS APPLIED TO SIDE OF TANK, BIN OR HOPPER

(p = pressure, psi; m = width of panel considered)

3Da

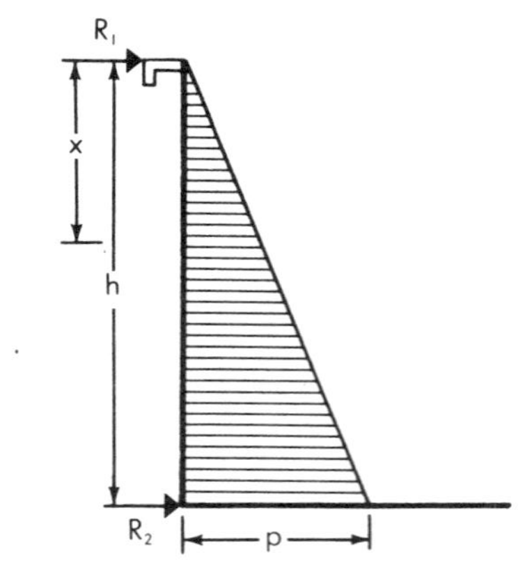

$R_1 = \frac{p\,h\,m}{6} \qquad R_2 = \frac{p\,h\,m}{3} = V_{max}$

$M_{max} = \frac{p\,h^2\,m}{9\sqrt{3}} = .0642\,p\,h^2\,m$

$M_x = \frac{p\,x\,m}{6\,h}(h^2 - x^2)$

$\Delta_{℄} = \frac{5\,p\,h^4\,m}{768\,E\,I}$

$\Delta x = \frac{p\,x\,m}{360\,E\,I\,h}(3\,x^4 - 10\,h^2\,x^2 + 7\,h^4)$

$\Delta_{max} = .00652\,\frac{p\,h^4\,m}{E\,I}$

(at x = .5193 h)

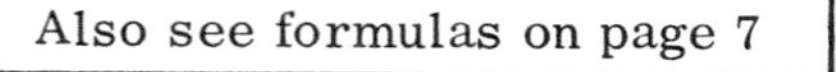

Also see formulas on page 7

3Dc

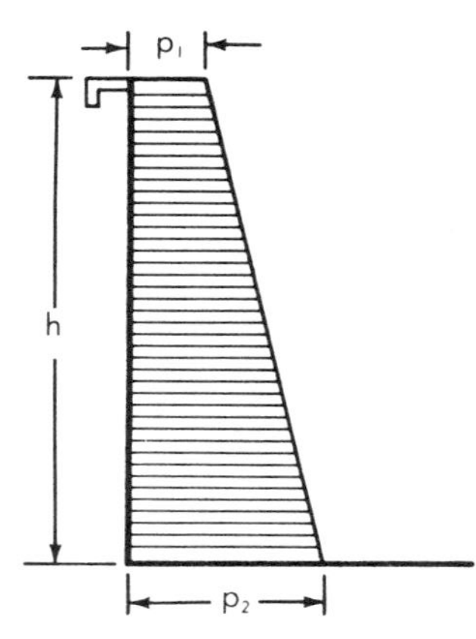

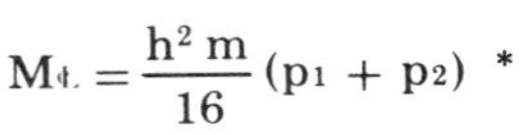

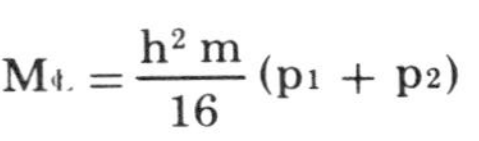

$M_{℄} = \frac{h^2\,m}{16}(p_1 + p_2)$ *

$\Delta_{℄} = \frac{5\,h^4\,m}{768\,E\,I}(p_1 + p_2)$ *

$V_{max} = \frac{m\,h}{6}(p_1 + 2\,p_2)$

(* These values are within 98% of maximum.)

7D

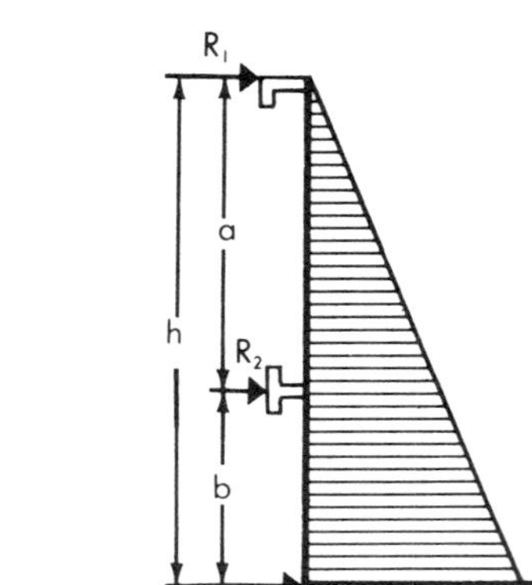

Maximum bending moment is least when

a = .57 h

b = .43 h

$M_{max} = .0147\,p\,h^2\,m$

(negative moment at middle support, 2)

$R_1 = +\,.030\,p\,h\,m$

$R_2 = +\,.320\,p\,h\,m$

$R_3 = +\,.150\,p\,h\,m$

$V_{max} = +\,.188\,p\,h\,m$

(at middle support, 2)

7D

Influence Lines

Effect of location of middle support (2) upon reactions (R) and moments (M)

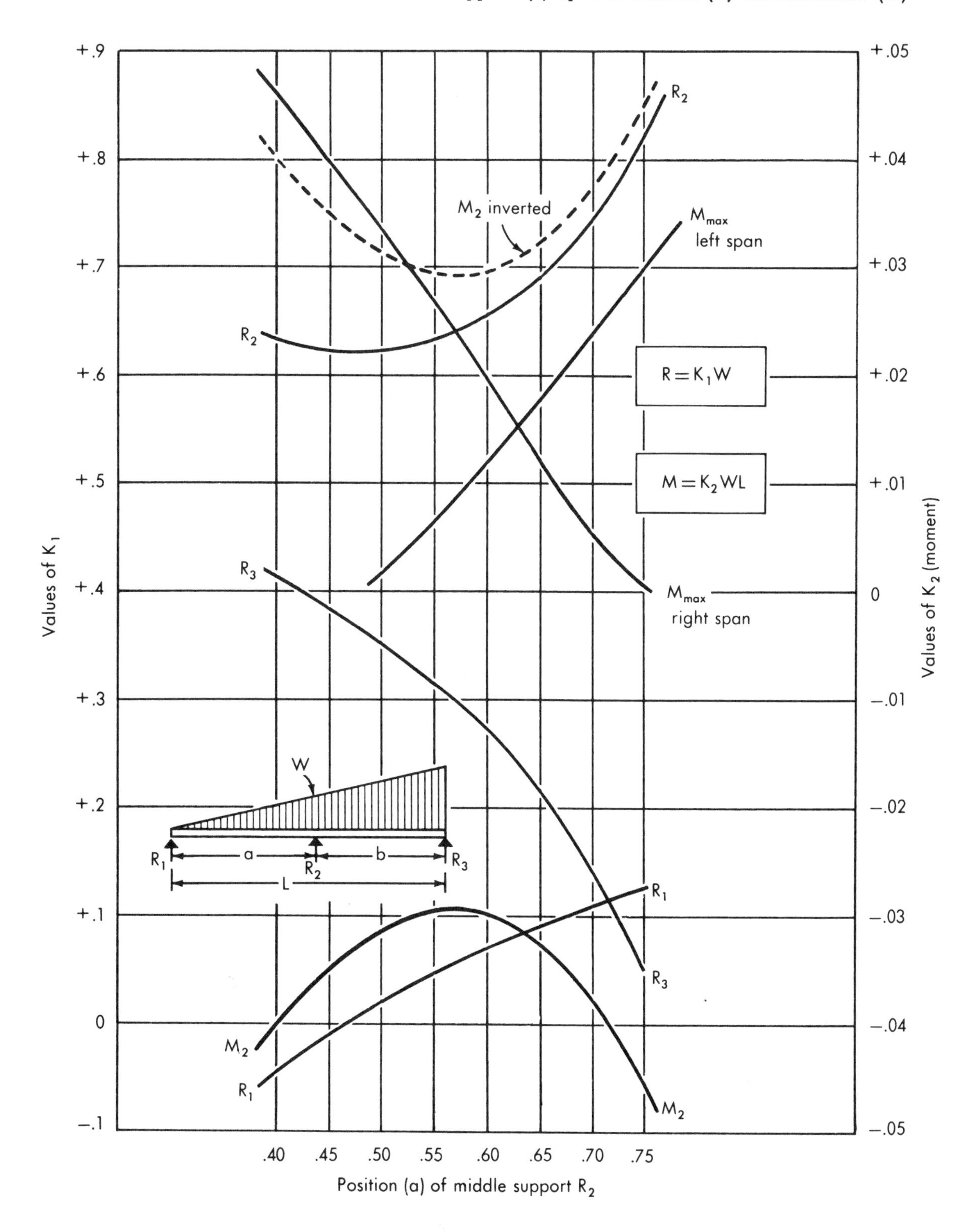

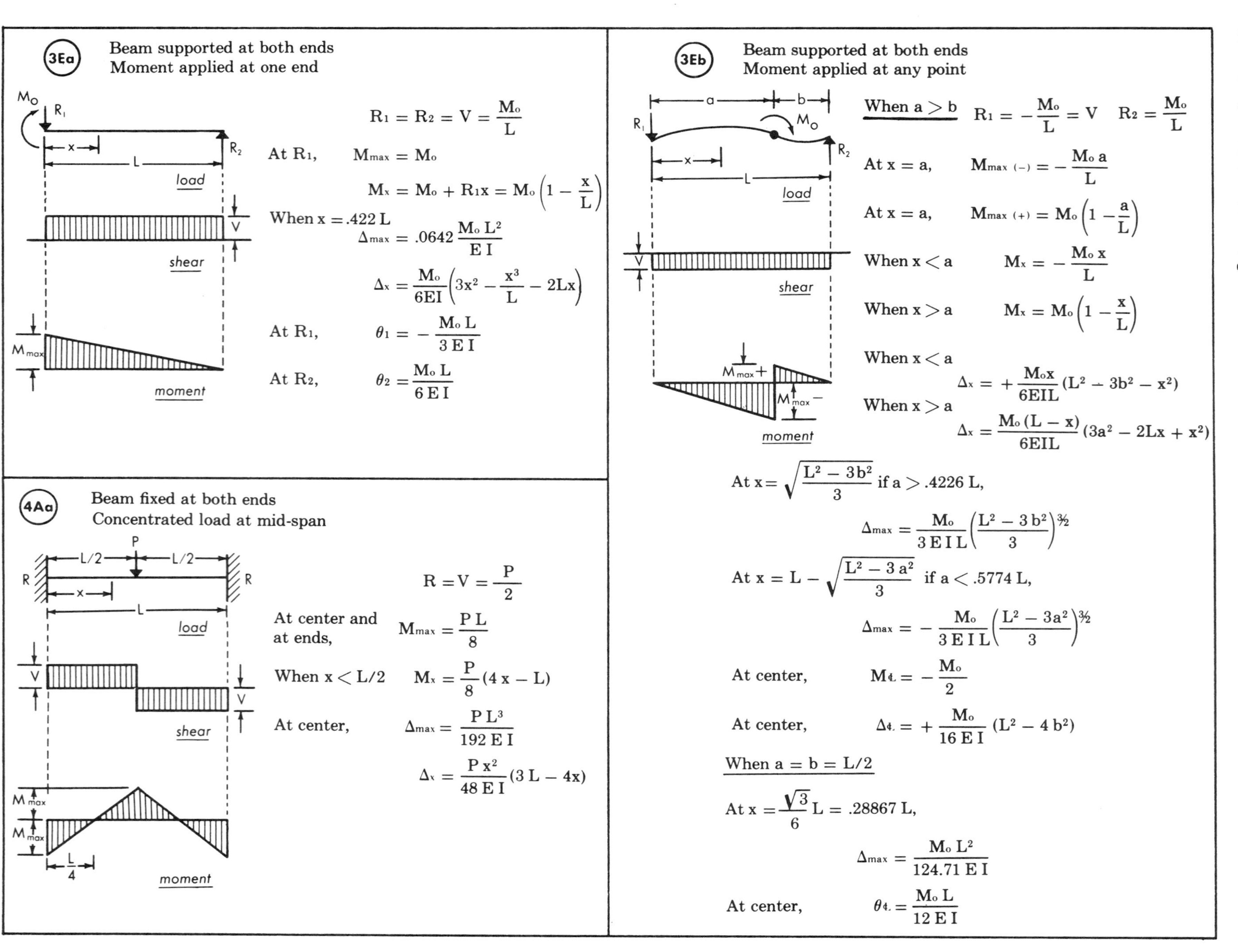

3Ea Beam supported at both ends
Moment applied at one end

$$R_1 = R_2 = V = \frac{M_o}{L}$$

At R_1, $M_{max} = M_o$

$$M_x = M_o + R_1 x = M_o\left(1 - \frac{x}{L}\right)$$

When $x = .422\,L$ $\quad \Delta_{max} = .0642\,\frac{M_o L^2}{E\,I}$

$$\Delta_x = \frac{M_o}{6EI}\left(3x^2 - \frac{x^3}{L} - 2Lx\right)$$

At R_1, $\theta_1 = -\frac{M_o L}{3\,E\,I}$

At R_2, $\theta_2 = \frac{M_o L}{6\,E\,I}$

3Eb Beam supported at both ends
Moment applied at any point

When $a > b$ $\quad R_1 = -\frac{M_o}{L} = V \quad R_2 = \frac{M_o}{L}$

At $x = a$, $\quad M_{max\,(-)} = -\frac{M_o\,a}{L}$

At $x = a$, $\quad M_{max\,(+)} = M_o\left(1 - \frac{a}{L}\right)$

When $x < a$ $\quad M_x = -\frac{M_o\,x}{L}$

When $x > a$ $\quad M_x = M_o\left(1 - \frac{x}{L}\right)$

When $x < a$

$$\Delta_x = +\frac{M_o x}{6EIL}(L^2 - 3b^2 - x^2)$$

When $x > a$

$$\Delta_x = \frac{M_o(L - x)}{6EIL}(3a^2 - 2Lx + x^2)$$

At $x = \sqrt{\frac{L^2 - 3b^2}{3}}$ if $a > .4226\,L$,

$$\Delta_{max} = \frac{M_o}{3\,E\,I\,L}\left(\frac{L^2 - 3\,b^2}{3}\right)^{3/2}$$

At $x = L - \sqrt{\frac{L^2 - 3\,a^2}{3}}$ if $a < .5774\,L$,

$$\Delta_{max} = -\frac{M_o}{3\,E\,I\,L}\left(\frac{L^2 - 3a^2}{3}\right)^{3/2}$$

At center, $\quad M_{℄} = -\frac{M_o}{2}$

At center, $\quad \Delta_{℄} = +\frac{M_o}{16\,E\,I}(L^2 - 4\,b^2)$

When $a = b = L/2$

At $x = \frac{\sqrt{3}}{6}L = .28867\,L$,

$$\Delta_{max} = \frac{M_o L^2}{124.71\,E\,I}$$

At center, $\quad \theta_{℄} = \frac{M_o L}{12\,E\,I}$

4Aa Beam fixed at both ends
Concentrated load at mid-span

$$R = V = \frac{P}{2}$$

At center and at ends, $\quad M_{max} = \frac{P\,L}{8}$

When $x < L/2$ $\quad M_x = \frac{P}{8}(4\,x - L)$

At center, $\quad \Delta_{max} = \frac{P\,L^3}{192\,E\,I}$

$$\Delta_x = \frac{P\,x^2}{48\,E\,I}(3\,L - 4x)$$

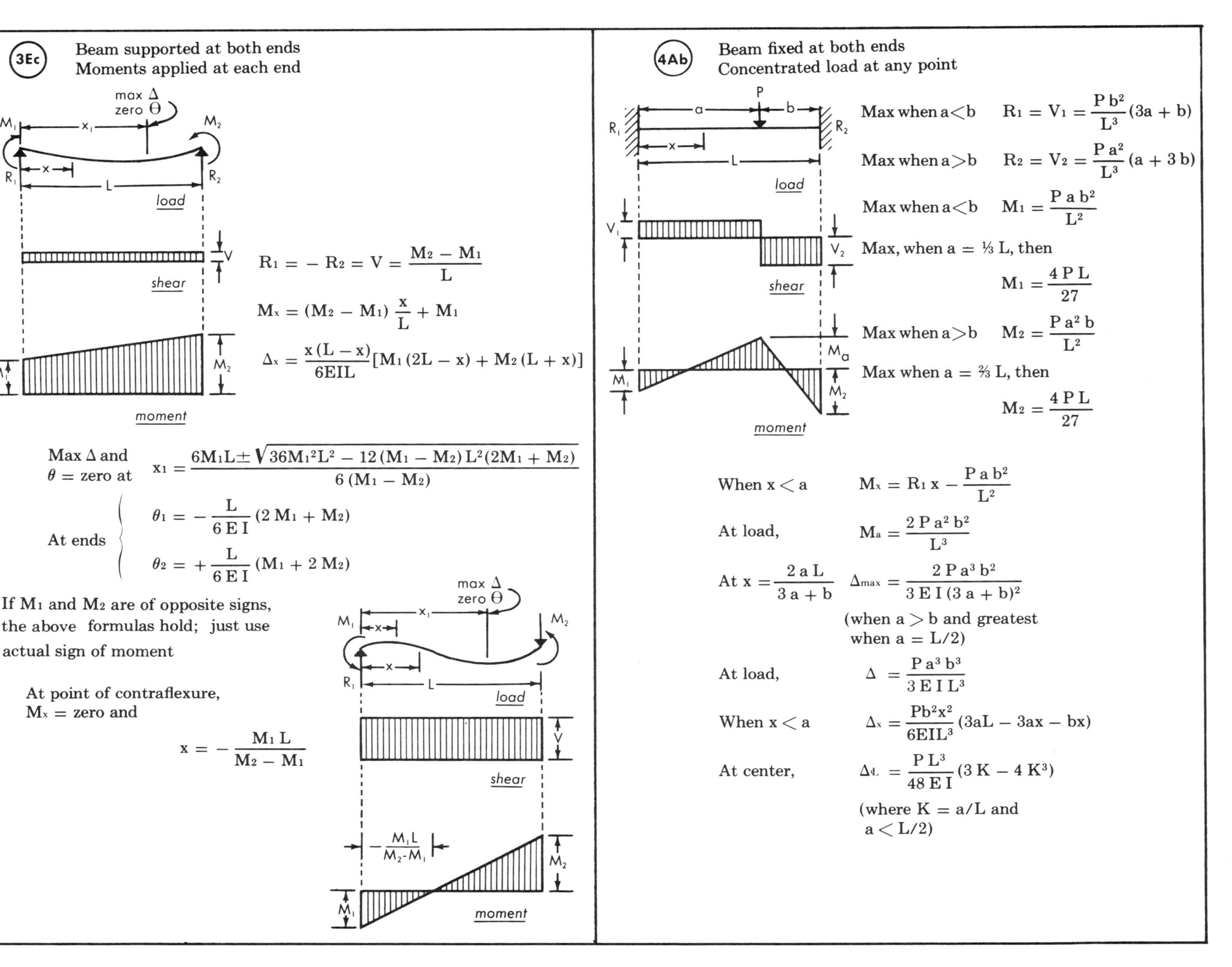

(3Ec) Beam supported at both ends. Moments applied at each end

$$R_1 = -R_2 = V = \frac{M_2 - M_1}{L}$$

$$M_x = (M_2 - M_1)\frac{x}{L} + M_1$$

$$\Delta_x = \frac{x(L-x)}{6EIL}[M_1(2L-x) + M_2(L+x)]$$

Max Δ and θ = zero at

$$x_1 = \frac{6M_1L \pm \sqrt{36M_1^2L^2 - 12(M_1 - M_2)L^2(2M_1 + M_2)}}{6(M_1 - M_2)}$$

At ends

$$\theta_1 = -\frac{L}{6EI}(2M_1 + M_2)$$

$$\theta_2 = +\frac{L}{6EI}(M_1 + 2M_2)$$

If M_1 and M_2 are of opposite signs, the above formulas hold; just use actual sign of moment

At point of contraflexure, M_x = zero and

$$x = -\frac{M_1 L}{M_2 - M_1}$$

(4Ab) Beam fixed at both ends. Concentrated load at any point

Max when a<b $\quad R_1 = V_1 = \frac{Pb^2}{L^3}(3a + b)$

Max when a>b $\quad R_2 = V_2 = \frac{Pa^2}{L^3}(a + 3b)$

Max when a<b $\quad M_1 = \frac{Pab^2}{L^2}$

Max, when a = ⅓ L, then $\quad M_1 = \frac{4PL}{27}$

Max when a>b $\quad M_2 = \frac{Pa^2b}{L^2}$

Max when a = ⅔ L, then $\quad M_2 = \frac{4PL}{27}$

When $x < a$ $\quad M_x = R_1 x - \frac{Pab^2}{L^2}$

At load, $\quad M_a = \frac{2Pa^2b^2}{L^3}$

At $x = \frac{2aL}{3a+b}$ $\quad \Delta_{max} = \frac{2Pa^3b^2}{3EI(3a+b)^2}$

(when a > b and greatest when a = L/2)

At load, $\quad \Delta = \frac{Pa^3b^3}{3EIL^3}$

When $x < a$ $\quad \Delta_x = \frac{Pb^2x^2}{6EIL^3}(3aL - 3ax - bx)$

At center, $\quad \Delta_{℄} = \frac{PL^3}{48EI}(3K - 4K^3)$

(where K = a/L and a < L/2)

(4Ab) Influence Lines

Effect of position of force (F) upon moments M_a, M_1, M_2 and upon Δ_{max}

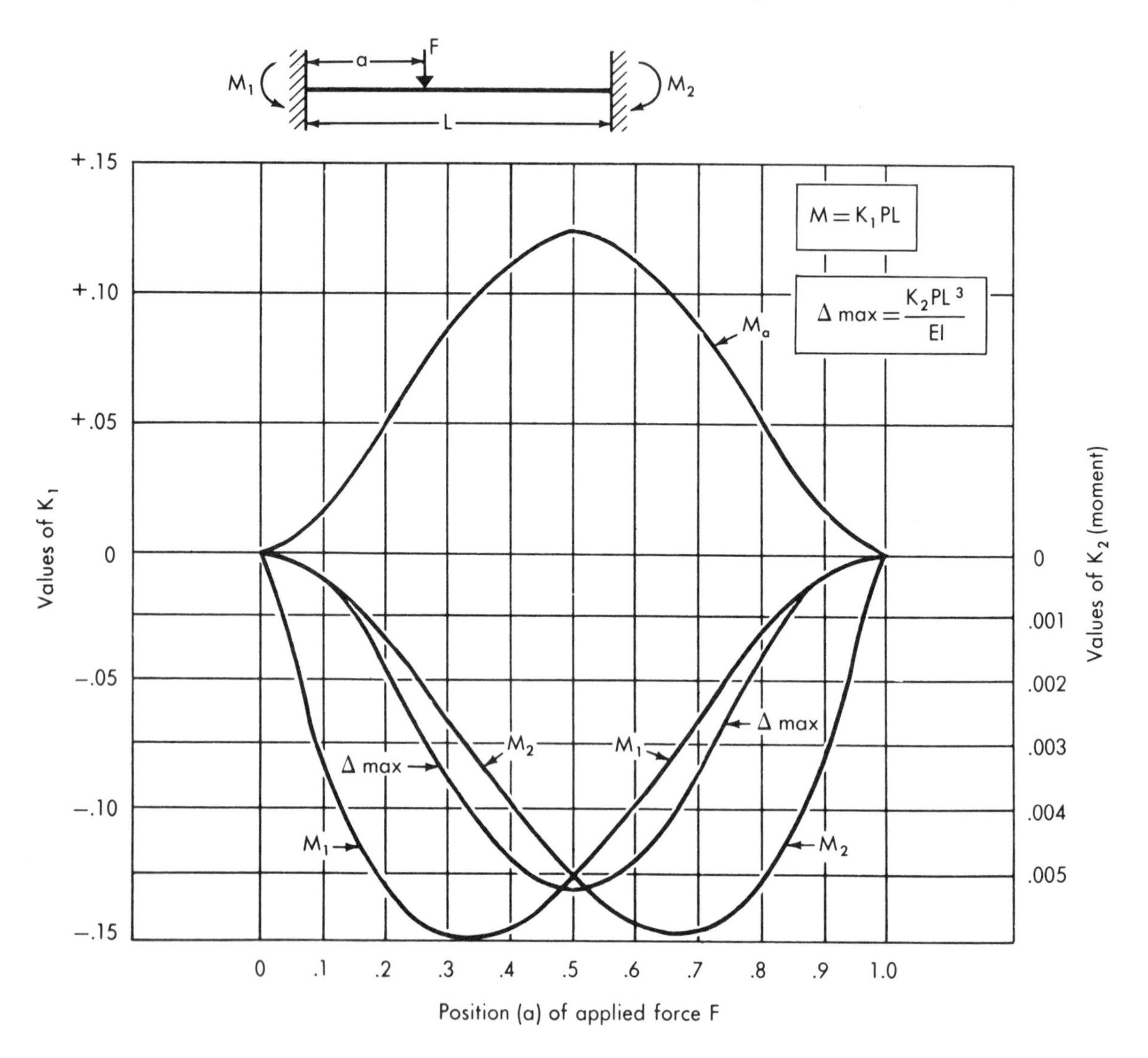

4Ac

Beam supported and partially restrained at both ends
Concentrated load at any point

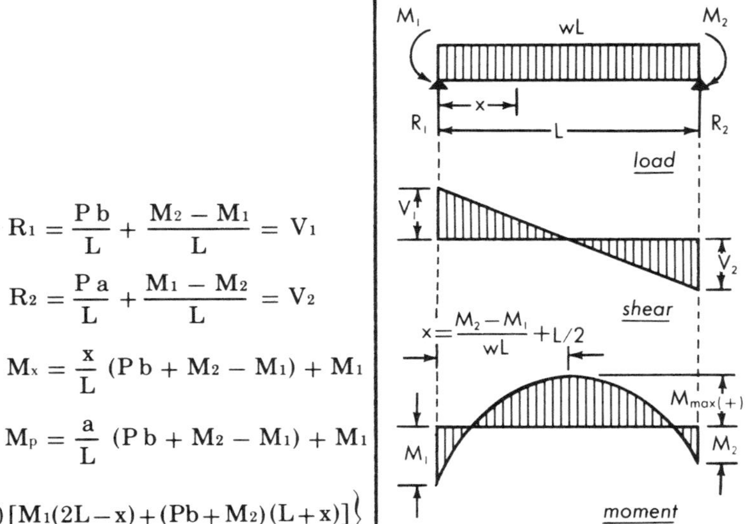

Here $a > b$

$$R_1 = \frac{P\,b}{L} + \frac{M_2 - M_1}{L} = V_1$$

$$R_2 = \frac{P\,a}{L} + \frac{M_1 - M_2}{L} = V_2$$

When $x < a$ $\quad M_x = \frac{x}{L}\,(P\,b + M_2 - M_1) + M_1$

At load, $\quad M_P = \frac{a}{L}\,(P\,b + M_2 - M_1) + M_1$

When $x < a$ $\quad \Delta_x = \frac{-x}{6EIL}\left\{Pb^3 - (L-x)\,[M_1(2L-x) + (Pb+M_2)(L+x)]\right\}$

4Ba

Beam fixed at both ends
Uniform load over entire span

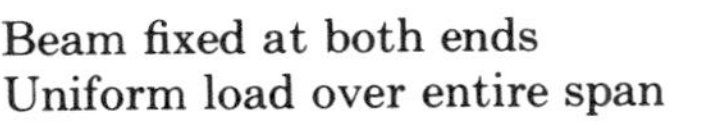

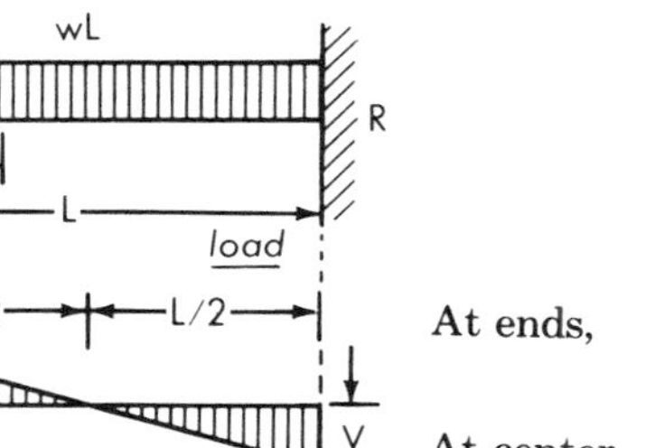

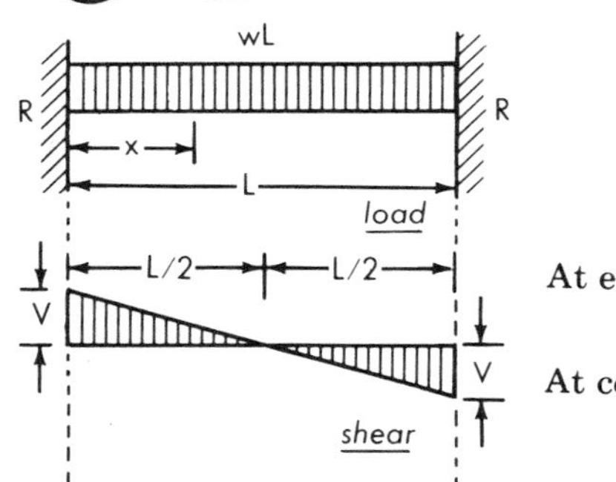

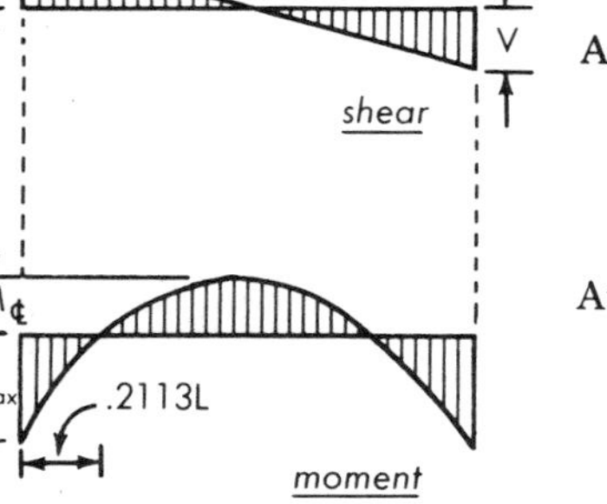

$$R = V = \frac{w\,L}{2}$$

$$V_x = w\left(\frac{L}{2} - x\right)$$

At ends, $\quad M_{max} = \frac{w\,L^2}{12}$

At center, $\quad M_{℄} = \frac{w\,L^2}{24}$

$$M_x = \frac{w}{12}\,(6Lx - L^2 - 6x^2)$$

At center, $\quad \Delta_{max} = \frac{w\,L^4}{384\,E\,I}$

$$\Delta_x = \frac{w\,x^2}{24\,E\,I}\,(L - x)^2$$

4Bb

Beam supported and partially restrained at both ends
A portion of a continuous beam
Uniform load over entire span

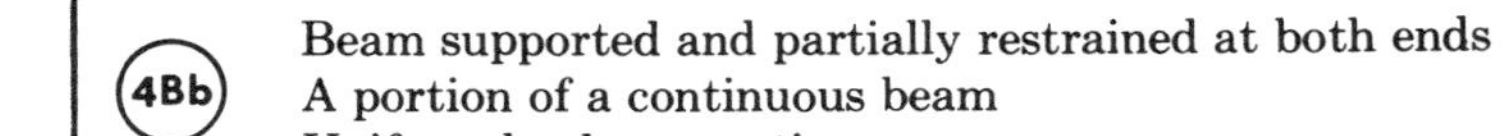

(Use actual signs of moments)

$$V_1 = \frac{M_2 - M_1}{L} + \frac{w\,L}{2}$$

$$V_2 = \frac{M_1 - M_2}{L} + \frac{w\,L}{2}$$

$$M_x = \frac{wx}{2}\,(L - x) + M_1\left(\frac{L - x}{L}\right) + M_2\frac{x}{L}$$

When $x = \frac{M_2 - M_1}{w\,L} + \frac{L}{2}$

$$M_{max\,(+)} = \frac{wL^2}{8} + \frac{M_1 + M_2}{2} + \frac{(M_2 - M_1)^2}{2wL^2}$$

To find value of x for a given value of M_x:

$$\underbrace{x^2}_{a} - x\underbrace{\left[\frac{2\,(M_2 - M_1)}{wL} + L\right]}_{b} + \underbrace{\frac{2}{w}\,(M_x - M_1)}_{c} = 0$$

and $x = \frac{-b \pm \sqrt{b^2 - 4ac}}{2a}$

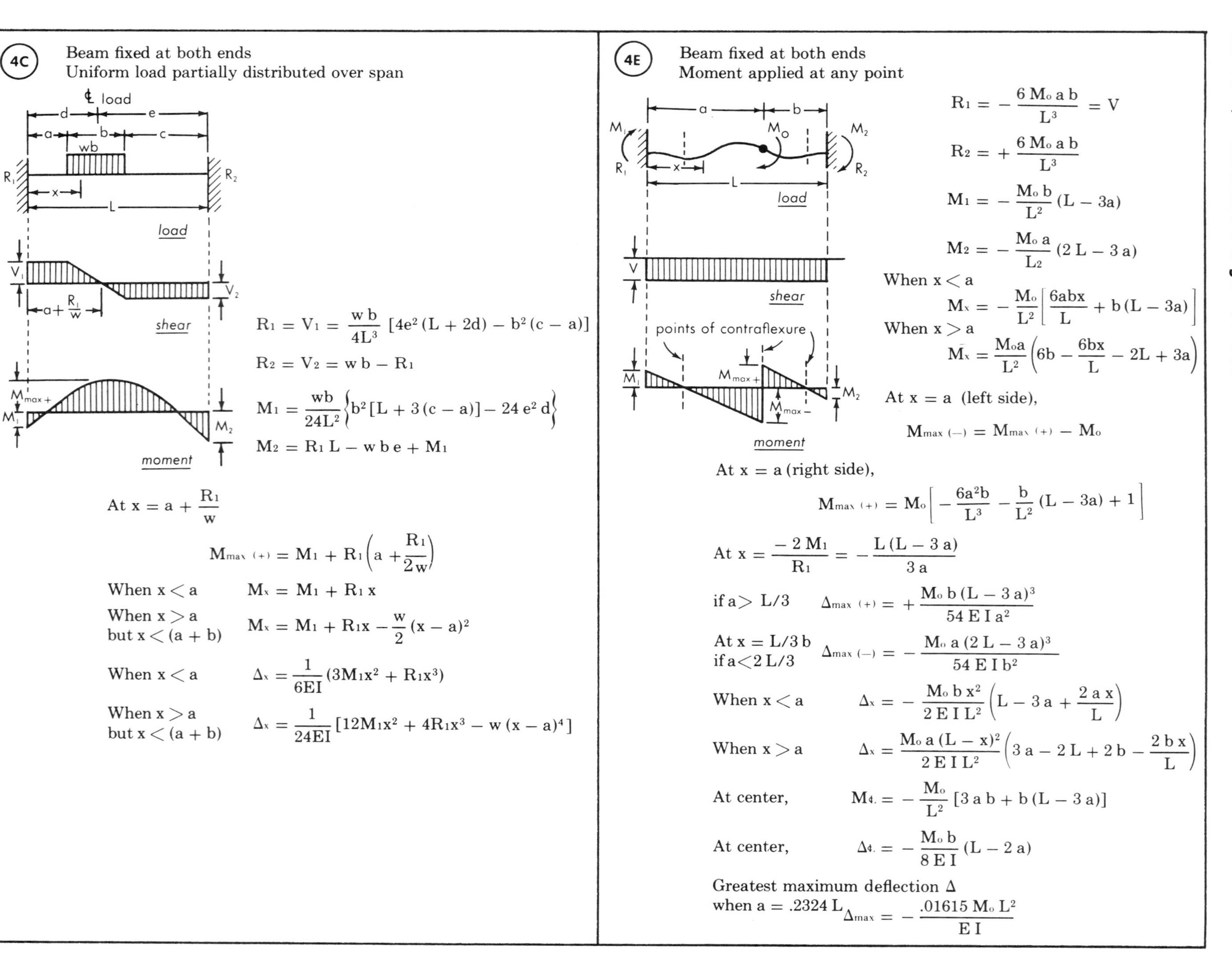

4C Beam fixed at both ends
Uniform load partially distributed over span

$$R_1 = V_1 = \frac{w\,b}{4L^3}\,[4e^2(L + 2d) - b^2(c - a)]$$

$$R_2 = V_2 = w\,b - R_1$$

$$M_1 = \frac{wb}{24L^2}\left\{b^2[L + 3(c - a)] - 24\,e^2\,d\right\}$$

$$M_2 = R_1 L - w\,b\,e + M_1$$

At $x = a + \frac{R_1}{w}$

$$M_{max\,(+)} = M_1 + R_1\left(a + \frac{R_1}{2w}\right)$$

When $x < a$ $\qquad M_x = M_1 + R_1 x$

When $x > a$ but $x < (a + b)$ $\qquad M_x = M_1 + R_1 x - \frac{w}{2}(x - a)^2$

When $x < a$ $\qquad \Delta_x = \frac{1}{6EI}(3M_1x^2 + R_1x^3)$

When $x > a$ but $x < (a + b)$ $\qquad \Delta_x = \frac{1}{24EI}[12M_1x^2 + 4R_1x^3 - w(x - a)^4]$

4E Beam fixed at both ends
Moment applied at any point

$$R_1 = -\frac{6\,M_o\,a\,b}{L^3} = V$$

$$R_2 = +\frac{6\,M_o\,a\,b}{L^3}$$

$$M_1 = -\frac{M_o\,b}{L^2}(L - 3a)$$

$$M_2 = -\frac{M_o\,a}{L_2}(2L - 3a)$$

When $x < a$

$$M_x = -\frac{M_o}{L^2}\left[\frac{6abx}{L} + b(L - 3a)\right]$$

When $x > a$

$$M_x = \frac{M_o a}{L^2}\left(6b - \frac{6bx}{L} - 2L + 3a\right)$$

At $x = a$ (left side),

$$M_{max\,(-)} = M_{max\,(+)} - M_o$$

At $x = a$ (right side),

$$M_{max\,(+)} = M_o\left[-\frac{6a^2b}{L^3} - \frac{b}{L^2}(L - 3a) + 1\right]$$

At $x = \frac{-2M_1}{R_1} = -\frac{L(L - 3a)}{3a}$

if $a > L/3$ $\qquad \Delta_{max\,(+)} = +\frac{M_o\,b\,(L - 3a)^3}{54\,E\,I\,a^2}$

At $x = L/3b$ if $a < 2L/3$ $\qquad \Delta_{max\,(-)} = -\frac{M_o\,a\,(2L - 3a)^3}{54\,E\,I\,b^2}$

When $x < a$ $\qquad \Delta_x = -\frac{M_o\,b\,x^2}{2\,E\,I\,L^2}\left(L - 3a + \frac{2ax}{L}\right)$

When $x > a$ $\qquad \Delta_x = \frac{M_o\,a\,(L - x)^2}{2\,E\,I\,L^2}\left(3a - 2L + 2b - \frac{2bx}{L}\right)$

At center, $\qquad M_{℄} = -\frac{M_o}{L^2}[3ab + b(L - 3a)]$

At center, $\qquad \Delta_{℄} = -\frac{M_o\,b}{8\,E\,I}(L - 2a)$

Greatest maximum deflection Δ when $a = .2324\,L$ $\qquad \Delta_{max} = -\frac{.01615\,M_o\,L^2}{E\,I}$

(4E) Influence Lines

Effect of position of moment (M_o) upon M_1, M_2, M+ and M−

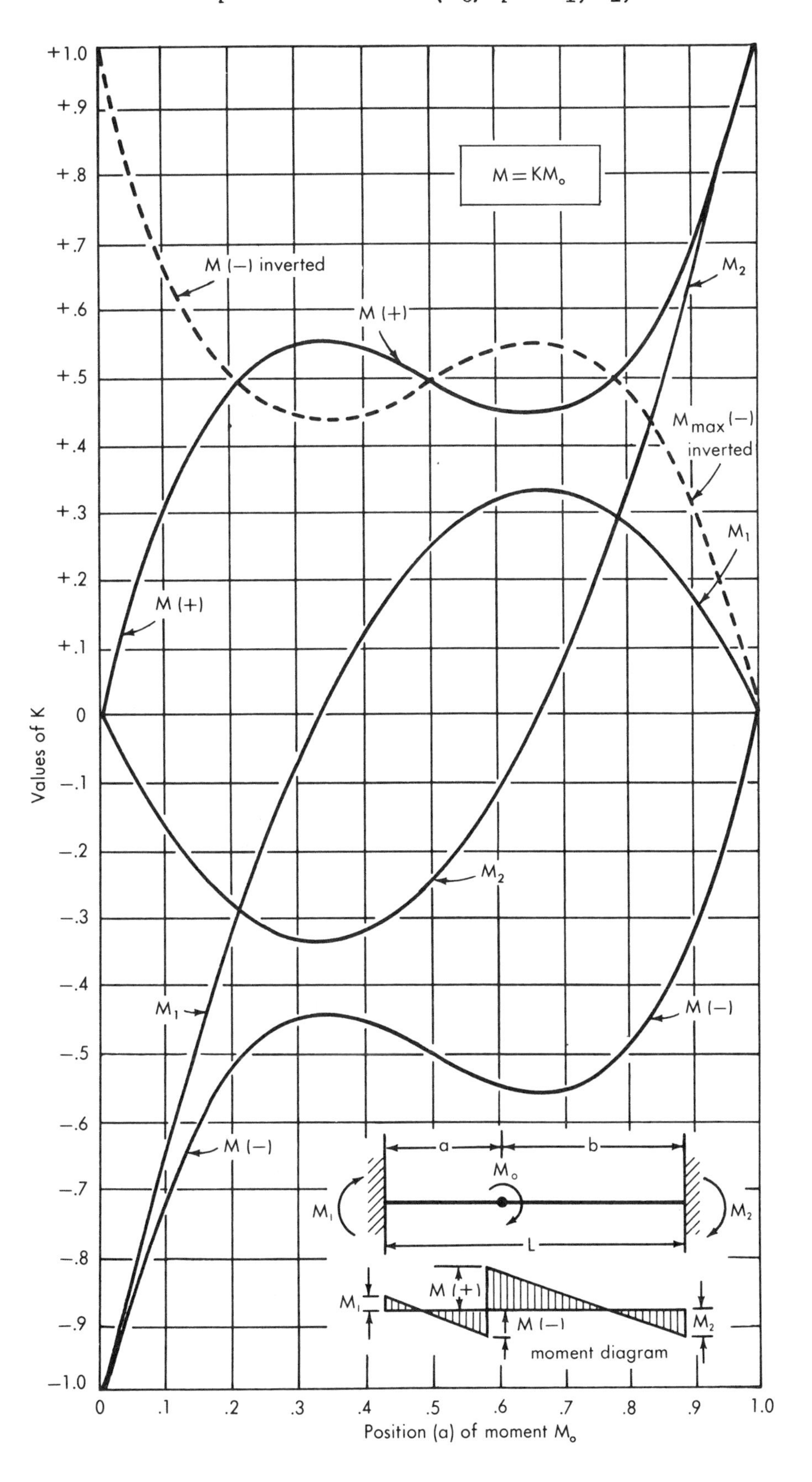

(4E) Influence Line for Maximum Deflection

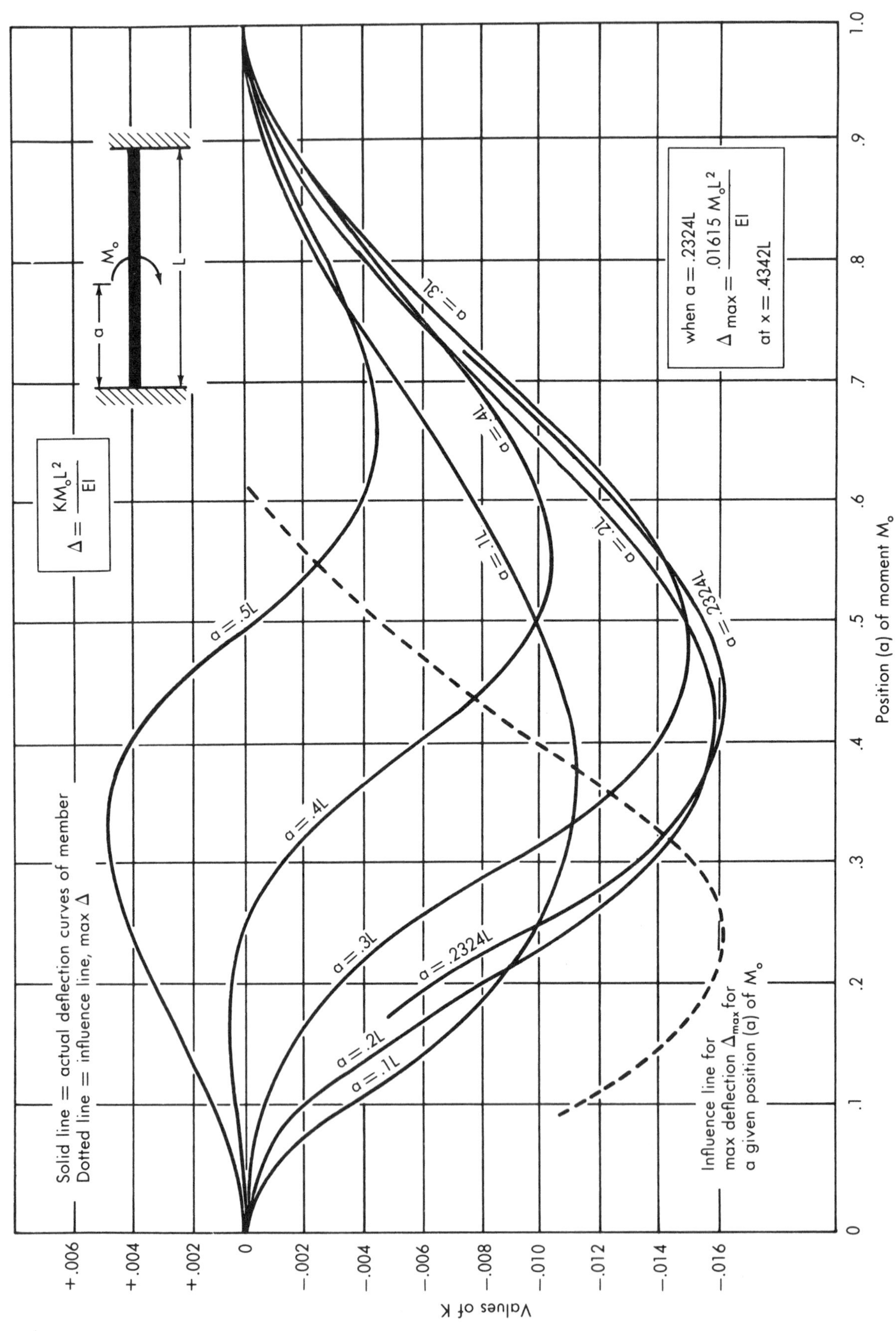

5Aa Beam fixed at one end and supported at the other end
Concentrated load at mid-span

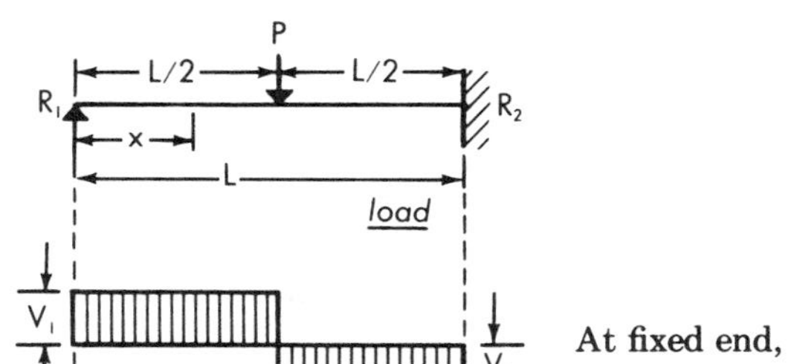

$$R_1 = V_1 = \frac{5P}{16}$$

$$R_2 = V_{2\,max} = \frac{11P}{16}$$

At fixed end, $M_{max} = \frac{3PL}{16}$

At load, $M_1 = \frac{5PL}{32}$

When $x < L/2$ $\quad M_x = \frac{5Px}{16}$

When $x > L/2$ $\quad M_x = P\left(\frac{L}{2} - \frac{11x}{16}\right)$

At $x = L\sqrt{.2} = .4472\,L$,

$$\Delta_{max} = \frac{PL^3}{48EI\sqrt{5}} = .009317\frac{PL^3}{EI}$$

At load, $\Delta = \frac{7PL^3}{768EI}$

When $x < L/2$ $\quad \Delta_x = \frac{Px}{96EI}(3L^2 - 5x^2)$

When $x > L/2$ $\quad \Delta_x = \frac{P}{96EI}(x - L)^2(11x - 2L)$

5Ab Beam fixed at one end and supported at the other end
Concentrated load at any point

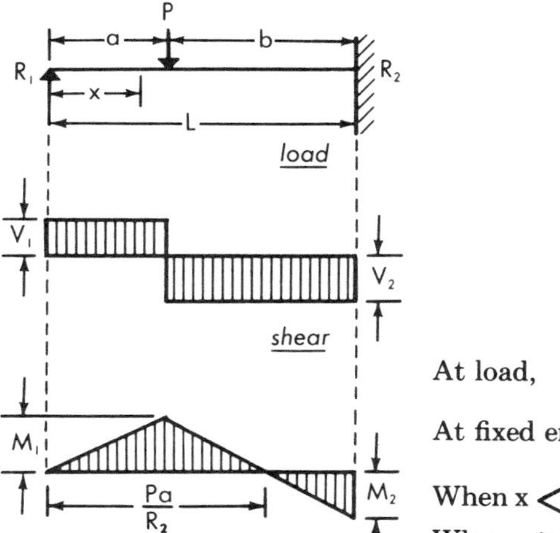

$$R_1 = V_1 = \frac{Pb^2}{2L^3}(a + 2L)$$

$$R_2 = V_2 = \frac{Pa}{2L^3}(3L^2 - a^2)$$

At load, $M_1 = R_1 a$

At fixed end, $M_2 = \frac{Pab}{2L^2}(a + L)$

When $x < a$ $\quad M_x = R_1 x$

When $x > a$ $\quad M_x = R_1 x - P(x - a)$

At $x = L\frac{L^2 + a^2}{3L^2 - a^2}$

$$\Delta_{max} = \frac{Pa}{3EI}\frac{(L^2 - a^2)^3}{(3L^2 - a^2)^2} \quad \text{when } a < .414\,L$$

At $x = L\sqrt{\frac{a}{2L + a}}$

$$\Delta_{max} = \frac{Pab^2}{6EI}\sqrt{\frac{a}{2L + a}} \quad \text{when } a > .414\,L$$

At load, $\Delta = \frac{Pa^2b^3}{12EIL^3}(3L + a)$

When $x < a$ $\quad \Delta_x = \frac{Pb^2x}{12EIL^3}(3aL^2 - 2Lx^2 - ax^2)$

When $x > a$ $\quad \Delta_x = \frac{Pa}{12EIL^3}(L - x)^2(3L^2x - a^2x - 2a^2L)$

5B

Beam fixed at one end and supported at the other end
Uniform load over entire span

$$R_1 = V_1 = \frac{3\,w\,L}{8}$$

$$R_2 = V_2 = \frac{5\,w\,L}{8}$$

$$V_x = R_1 - w\,x$$

$$M_{max} = \frac{w\,L^2}{8}$$

At $x = 3/8\ L$, $M_1 = \frac{9}{128}\,w\,L^2$

$$M_x = R_1\,x - \frac{w\,x^2}{2}$$

At $x = \frac{L}{16}(1 + \sqrt{33}) = .4215\ L$, $\Delta_{max} = \frac{w\,L^4}{185\,E\,I}$

$$\Delta_x = \frac{wx}{48EI}(L^3 - 3Lx^2 + 2x^2)$$

$$\theta_1 = \frac{w\,L^3}{48\,E\,I}$$

5C

Beam fixed at one end and supported at the other end
Uniform load partially distributed over span

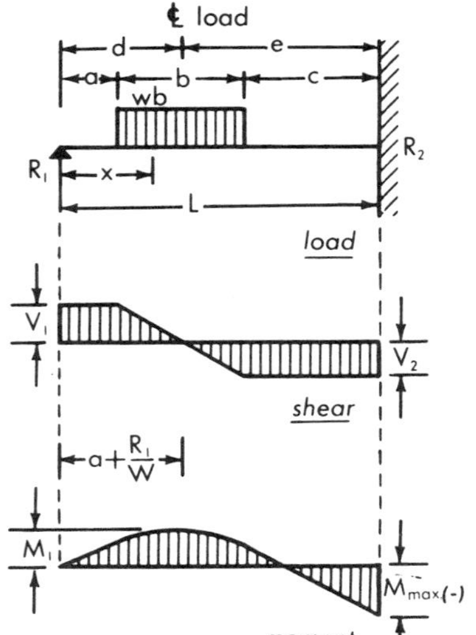

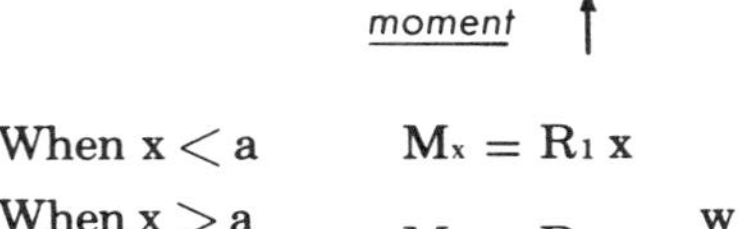

$$R_1 = V_1 = \frac{wb}{8L^3}(12e^2L - 4e^3 + b^2d)$$

$$R_2 = V_2 = w\,b - R_1$$

$$M_{max\,(-)} = \frac{wb}{8L^2}(12e^2L - 4e^3 + b^2d - 8eL^2)$$

$$M_1 = R_1\left(a + \frac{R_1}{2\,w}\right)$$

When $x < a$: $M_x = R_1\,x$

When $x > a$ but $x < (a+b)$: $M_x = R_1\,x - \frac{w}{2}(x - a)^2$

When $x > (a + b)$ but $x < L$: $M_x = R_1\,x - w\,b\,(x - d)$

When $x < a$: $\Delta_x = \frac{x}{24EI}[4R_1(x^2 - 3L^2) + wb(b^2 + 12e^2)]$

When $x > a$ but $x < (a + b)$: $\Delta_x = \frac{1}{24EI}[4R_1x(x^2 - 3L^2) + wbx(b^2 + 12e^2) - w(x - a)^4]$

When $x > (a + b)$ but $x < L$: $\Delta_x = \frac{1}{6EI}[3M_{max}(L - x)^2 + R_2(L - x)^3]$

5E

Beam fixed at one end and supported at the other end
Moment applied at the flexible end

$$R_1 = R_2 = V = \frac{3\,M_o}{2\,L}$$

$$M_1 = M_o$$

$$M_2 = 1/2\,M_o$$

$$M_x = \frac{M_o}{2\,L}(2\,L - 3x)$$

At $x = L/3$, $\Delta_{max} = \frac{M_o\,L^2}{27\,E\,I}$

$$\Delta_x = \frac{M_o\,x}{4\,E\,I\,L}(L - x)^2$$

At supported end, $\theta = -\frac{M_o\,L}{4\,E\,I}$

6Aa Single span, simply supported beam, with overhang — Concentrated load at any point between supports

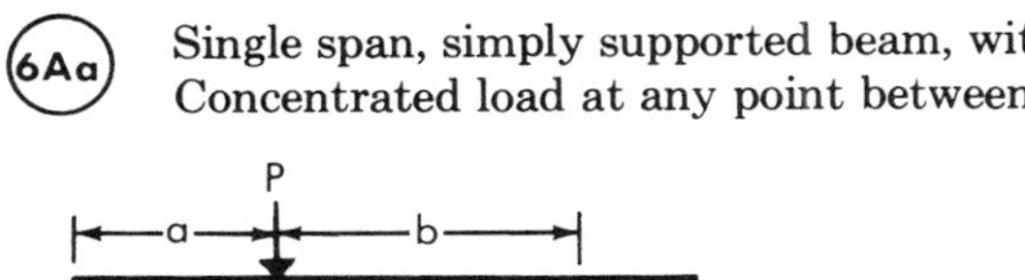
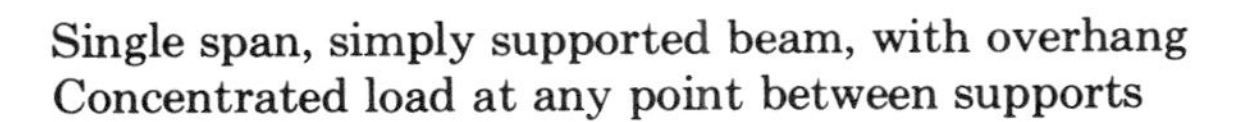

$$R_1 = V_1 \begin{pmatrix} \text{max} \\ \text{when} \\ a < b \end{pmatrix} = \frac{P\,b}{L}$$

$$R_2 = V_2 \begin{pmatrix} \text{max} \\ \text{when} \\ a > b \end{pmatrix} = \frac{P\,a}{L}$$

At load, $M_{max} = \dfrac{P\,a\,b}{L}$

When $x < a$ $\quad M_x = \dfrac{P\,b\,x}{L}$

At $x = \sqrt{\dfrac{a\,(a + 2\,b)}{3}}$

$$\Delta_{max} = \frac{Pab\,(a+2b)\sqrt{3a\,(a+2b)}}{27EIL} \quad \text{when } a > b$$

At load, $\quad \Delta = \dfrac{P\,a^2\,b^2}{3\,E\,I\,L}$

When $x < a$ $\quad \Delta_x = \dfrac{P\,b\,x}{6\,E\,I\,L}\,(L^2 - b^2 - x^2)$

When $x > a$ $\quad \Delta_x = \dfrac{Pa\,(L-x)}{6EIL}\,(2Lx - x^2 - a^2)$

For overhang, $\quad \Delta_{x1} = -\dfrac{P\,a\,b\,x_1}{6\,E\,I\,L}\,(L + a)$

6Ab Single span, simply supported beam, with overhang — Concentrated load at outer end

$$R_1 = V_1 = \frac{P\,a}{L}$$

$$R_2 = V_1 + V_2 = \frac{P}{L}\,(L + a)$$

$$V_2 = P$$

At R_2, $\quad M_{max} = P\,a$

Between supports, $M_x = \dfrac{P\,a\,x}{L}$

For overhang, $\quad M_{x1} = P\,(a - x_1)$

Between supports at $x = L/\sqrt{3}$,

$$\Delta_{max} = -\frac{P\,a\,L^2}{9\sqrt{3}\,E\,I}$$

For overhang $x_1 = a$,

$$\Delta_{max} = \frac{P\,a^2}{3\,E\,I}\,(L + a)$$

Between supports, $\quad \Delta_x = -\dfrac{P\,a\,x}{6\,E\,I\,L}\,(L^2 - x^2)$

For overhang, $\quad \Delta_{x1} = \dfrac{Px_1}{6EI}\,(2aL + 3ax_1 - x_1^2)$

(6Ba) Single span, simply supported beam, with overhang
Uniform load over entire beam

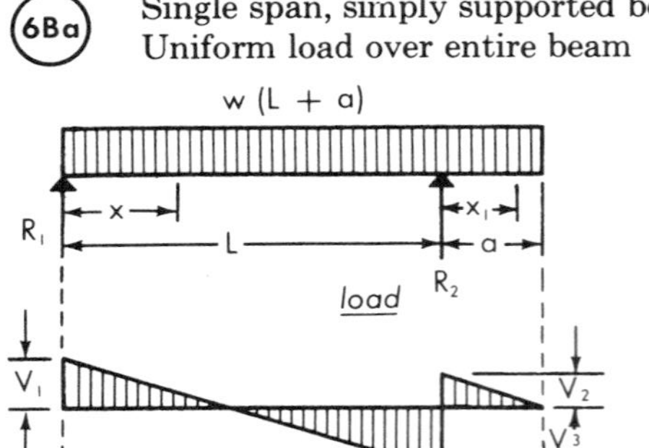

$$R_1 = V_1 = \frac{w}{2L}(L^2 - a^2)$$

$$R_2 = V_2 + V_3 = \frac{w}{2L}(L + a)^2$$

$$V_2 = w\,a$$

$$V_3 = \frac{w}{2L}(L^2 + a^2)$$

Between supports, $V_x = R_1 - w\,x$

For overhang, $V_{x1} = w(a - x_1)$

At $x = \frac{1}{2}\left(L - \frac{a^2}{L}\right)$

$$M_1 = \frac{w}{8L^2}(L^2 - a^2)^2$$

At R_2, $M_2 = \frac{w\,a^2}{2}$

Between supports, $M_x = \frac{w\,x}{2L}(L^2 - a^2 - x\,L)$

For overhang, $M_{x1} = \frac{w}{2}(a - x_1)^2$

Between supports, $\Delta_x = \frac{w\,x}{24\,EIL}(L^4 - 2L^2x^2 + L\,x^3 - 2a^2L^2 + 2a^2x^2)$

For overhang, $\Delta_{x1} = \frac{w\,x_1}{24\,E\,I}(4a^2L - L^3 + 6a^2x_1 - 4\,a\,x_1^2 + x_1^3)$

At free end, $\Delta = \frac{w\,a}{24\,E\,I}(3a^3 + 4a^2L - L^3)$

When $a = .414\,L$, $M_1 = M_2 = .08579\,w\,L^2$

(6Bb) Single span beam, overhanging at both ends
Uniform load over entire beam

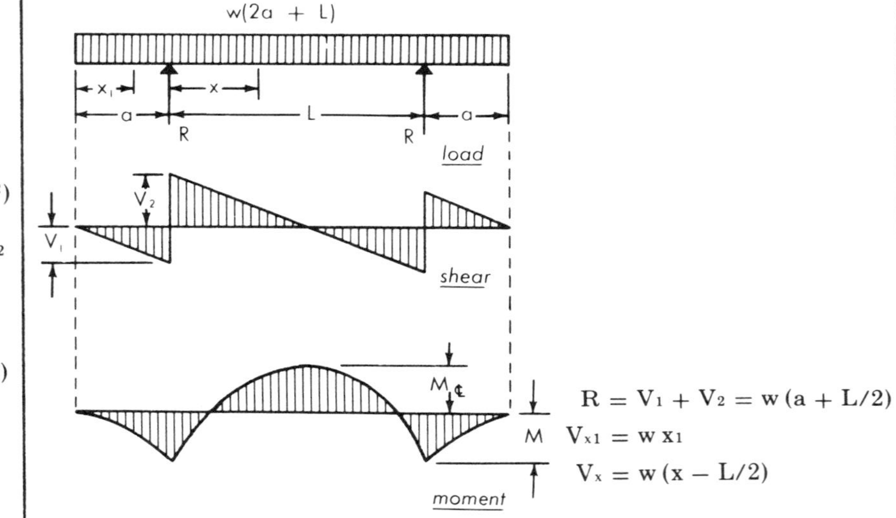

$$R = V_1 + V_2 = w(a + L/2)$$

$$V_{x1} = w\,x_1$$

$$V_x = w(x - L/2)$$

For overhang, $M_{x1} = \frac{w\,x_1^2}{2}$

At support, $M = \frac{w\,a^2}{2}$

Between supports, $M_x = \frac{w}{2}(L\,x - x^2 - a^2)$

At center, $M_{℄} = \frac{w}{8}(L^2 - 4a^2)$

At ends, $\Delta = \frac{wa}{24EI}(L^3 - 6a^2L - 3a^3)$

At center, $\Delta_{℄} = \frac{wL^2}{384EI}(5L^2 - 24a^2)$

When $a = .207 \times$ total length
or $a = .354\,L$

$$M = M_{℄} = \frac{w\,L^2}{16}$$

6Ca Single span, simple supported beam, with overhang
Uniform load over entire span

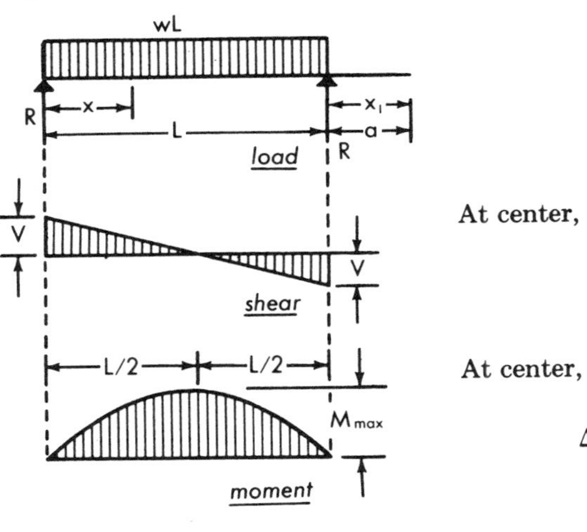

$$R = V = \frac{w\,L}{2}$$

$$V_x = w\left(\frac{L}{2} - x\right)$$

At center, $$M_{max} = \frac{w\,L^2}{8}$$

$$M_x = \frac{w\,x}{2}(L - x)$$

At center, $$\Delta_{max} = \frac{5\,w\,L^4}{384\,E\,I}$$

$$\Delta_x = \frac{wx}{24EI}(L^3 - 2Lx^2 + x^3)$$

$$\Delta_{x1} = \frac{w\,L^3\,x_1}{24\,E\,I}$$

6Cb Single span, simply supported beam, with overhang
Uniform load on overhang

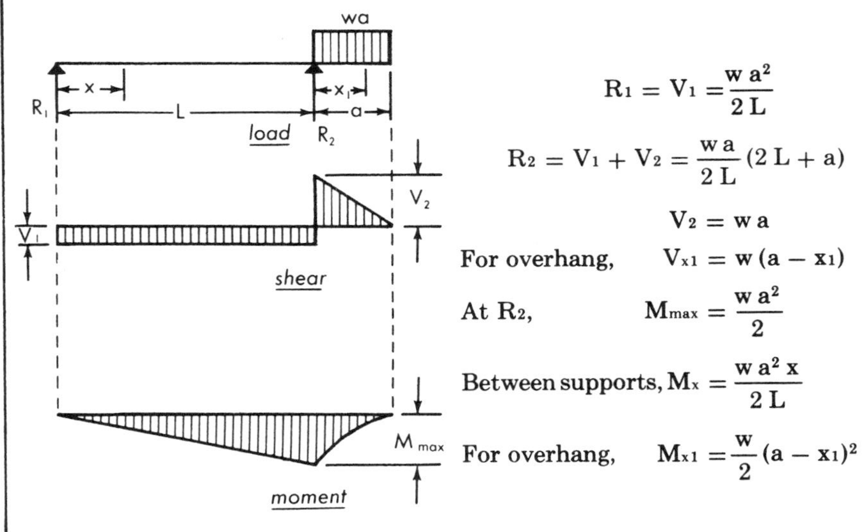

$$R_1 = V_1 = \frac{w\,a^2}{2\,L}$$

$$R_2 = V_1 + V_2 = \frac{w\,a}{2\,L}(2\,L + a)$$

$$V_2 = w\,a$$

For overhang, $$V_{x1} = w\,(a - x_1)$$

At R_2, $$M_{max} = \frac{w\,a^2}{2}$$

Between supports, $$M_x = \frac{w\,a^2\,x}{2\,L}$$

For overhang, $$M_{x1} = \frac{w}{2}(a - x_1)^2$$

At $x = L/\sqrt{3}$, $$\Delta_{max} = -\frac{w\,a^2\,L^2}{18\sqrt{3}\,E\,I}$$

At free end, $$\Delta_{max} = \frac{w\,a^3}{24\,E\,I}(4\,L + 3\,a)$$

Between supports, $$\Delta_x = -\frac{w\,a^2\,x}{12\,E\,I\,L}(L^2 - x^2)$$

For overhang, $$\Delta_{x1} = \frac{wx_1}{24EI}(4a^2L + 6a^2x_1 - 4ax_1^2 + x_1^3)$$

(7) THEORY OF THREE MOMENTS

Consider the following continuous beam:

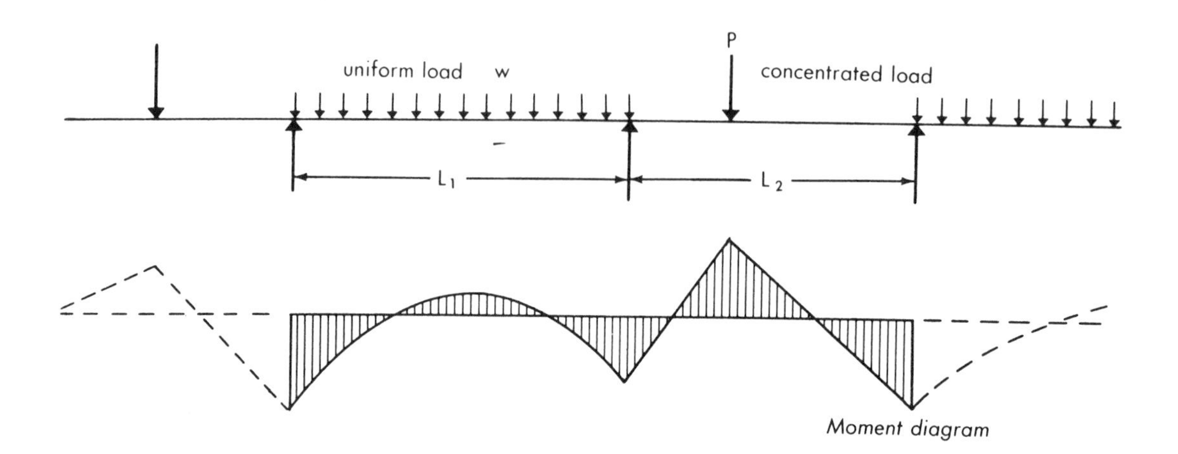

The above moment diagram may be considered as made up of two parts: the positive moment due to the applied loads, and the negative moment due to the restraining end moments over the supports.

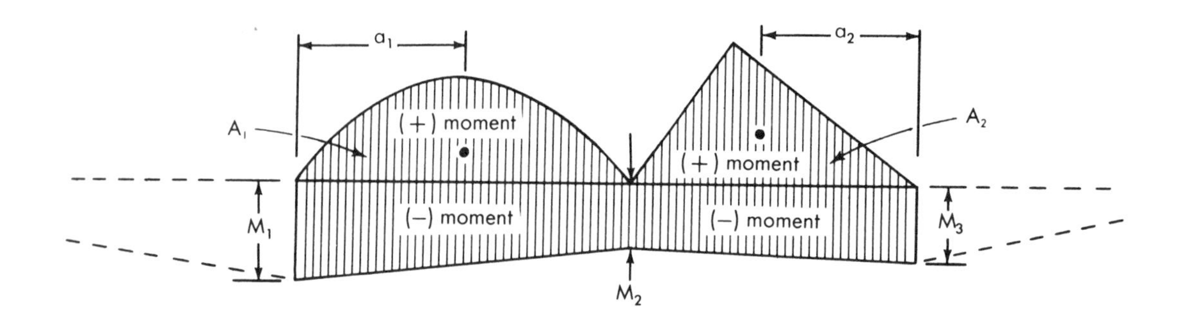

For any two adjacent spans, the following relationship is true:

$$+\frac{M_1 L_1}{6 E I_1} + \frac{M_2}{3E}\left(\frac{L_1}{I_1} + \frac{L_2}{I_2}\right) + \frac{M_3 L_2}{6 E I_2} + \frac{A_1 a_1}{E I_1 L_1} + \frac{A_2 a_2}{E I_2 L_2} = 0$$

where:

M_1, M_2, and M_3 are the end moments at the 1st, 2nd, and 3rd supports.

L_1 and L_2 are the lengths of the 1st and 2nd span.

I_1 and I_2 are the moments of inertia of the 1st and 2nd span.

A_1 and A_2 are the areas under the positive moment diagrams of the 1st and 2nd span.

a_1 and a_2 are the distance of the centroids of the areas of the positive moment diagrams to the 1st and 3rd outer supports.

By writing this equation for each successive pair of spans, all of the moments may be found.

The moment diagram for a simply supported, uniformly loaded beam is a parabola; and a concentrated load produces a triangular moment diagram. The following shows the area and distance to the centroid of these areas.

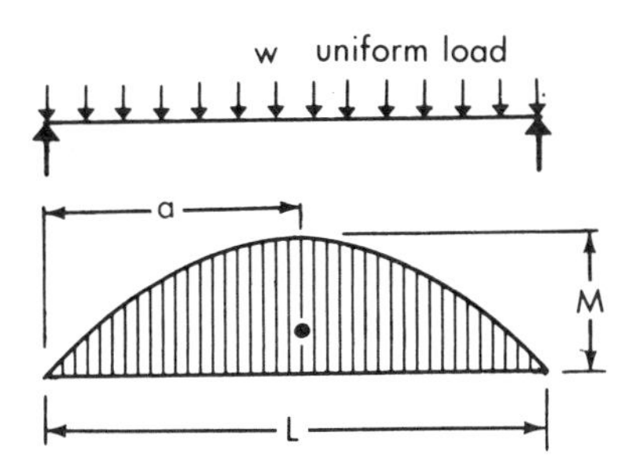

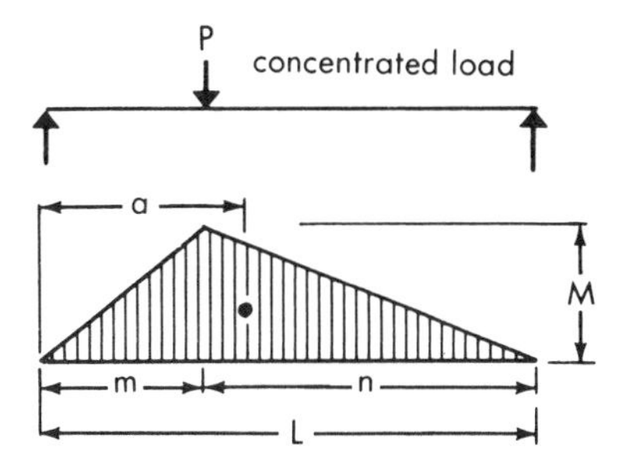

Area

$A = 2/3\,M\,L$

Distance to centroid

$a = L/2$

Area

$A = 1/2\,M\,L$

Distance to centroid

$$a = \frac{m + L}{3}$$

7Aa Two span, continuous beam — Concentrated load at center of one span only

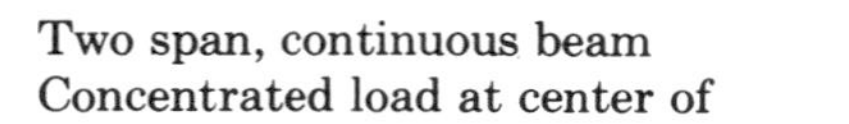

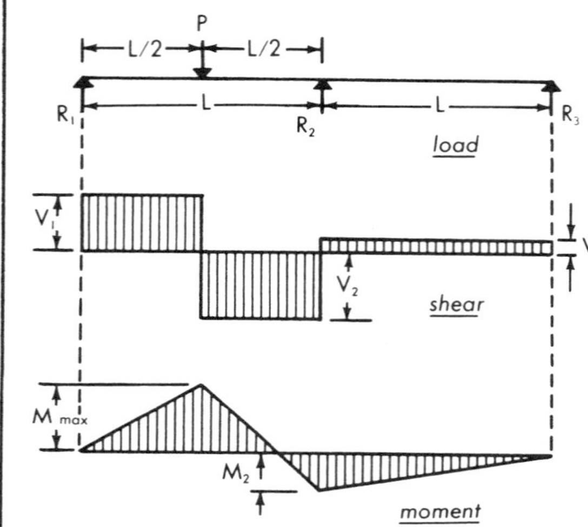

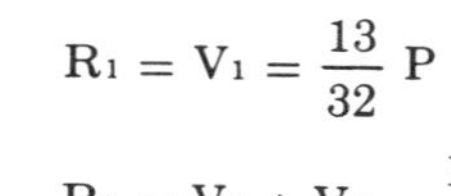

$$R_1 = V_1 = \frac{13}{32} P$$

$$R_2 = V_2 + V_3 = \frac{11}{16} P$$

$$R_3 = V_3 = \frac{3}{32} P$$

$$V_2 = \frac{19}{32} P$$

At load, $M_{max} = \frac{13}{64} P L$

At R_2, $M_2 = \frac{3}{32} P L$

7Ab Two span, continuous beam — Concentrated load at any point of one span only

$$R_1 = V_1 = \frac{Pb}{4L^3}\left[4L^2 - a(L+a)\right]$$

$$R_2 = V_2 + V_3 = \frac{Pa}{2L^3}\left[2L^2 + b(L+a)\right]$$

$$R_3 = V_3 = \frac{P a b}{4 L^3}(L + a)$$

$$V_2 = \frac{P a}{4 L^3}\left[4 L^2 - b(L + a)\right]$$

At load, $M_{max} = \frac{P a b}{4 L^3}\left[4 L^2 - a(L + a)\right]$

At R_2, $M_2 = \frac{P a b}{4 L^2}(L + a)$

7B Two span, continuous beam — Uniform load over one span only

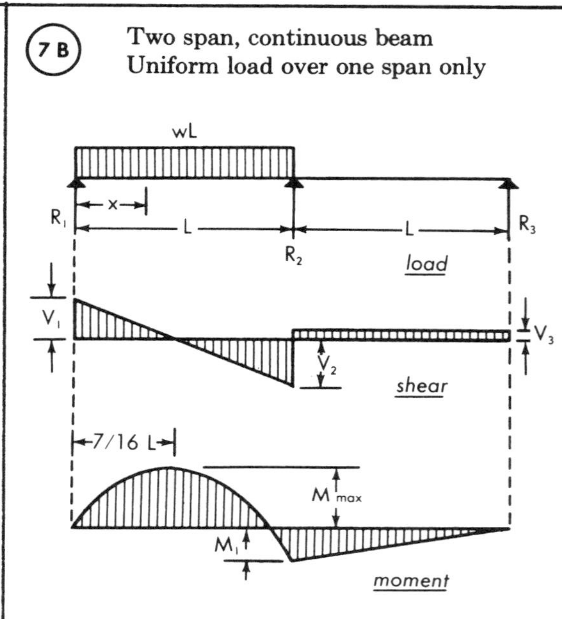

$$R_1 = V_1 = \frac{7}{16} w L$$

$$R_2 = V_2 + V_3 = \frac{5}{8} w L$$

$$R_3 = V_3 = \frac{1}{16} w L$$

$$V_2 = \frac{9}{16} w L$$

At $x = 7/16\,L$, $M_{max} = \frac{49}{512} w L^2$

At R_2, $M_1 = \frac{w L^2}{16}$

When $x < L$, $M_x = \frac{w x}{16}(7 L - 8 x)$

See pages 8 and 9 for beam-load condition 7D

Torsion Diagrams and Formulas

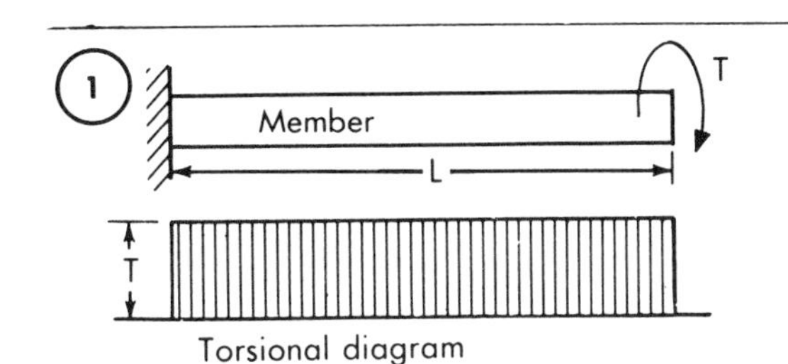

$$T = T$$

At support, $\theta = \dfrac{T\,L}{E_s\,R}$

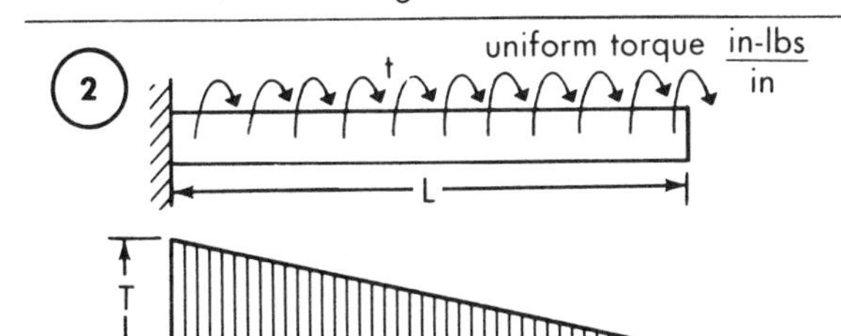

At support, $T = t\,L$

$$\theta = \frac{t\,L^2}{2\,E_s\,R}$$

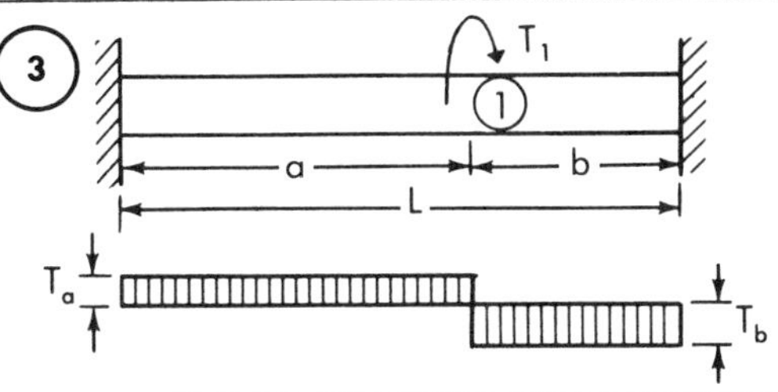

Section a: $T_a = \dfrac{T_1\,b}{L}$

Section b: $T_b = \dfrac{T_1\,a}{L}$ $\qquad \theta_1 = \dfrac{T_1\,a\,b}{L\,E_s\,R}$

When $a = b = L/2$ $\qquad \theta_{\mathcal{L}} = \dfrac{T\,L}{4\,E_s\,R}$

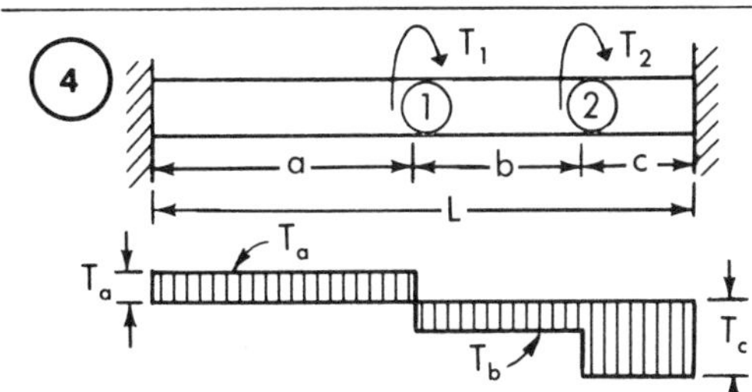

Section a: $T_a = \dfrac{T_1\,(b + c) + T_2\,c}{L}$ $\qquad \theta_1 = \dfrac{T_a\,a}{E_s\,R}$

Section b: $T_b = \dfrac{T_2\,c - T_1\,a}{L}$ $\qquad \theta_2 = \dfrac{T_c\,c}{E_s\,R}$

Section c: $T_c = -\dfrac{T_1\,a + T_2\,(a + b)}{L}$

When $a = b = c = L/3$

$T_1 = T_2 = T/2$

and $\theta_1 = \theta_2 = \dfrac{T\,L}{6\,E_s\,R}$

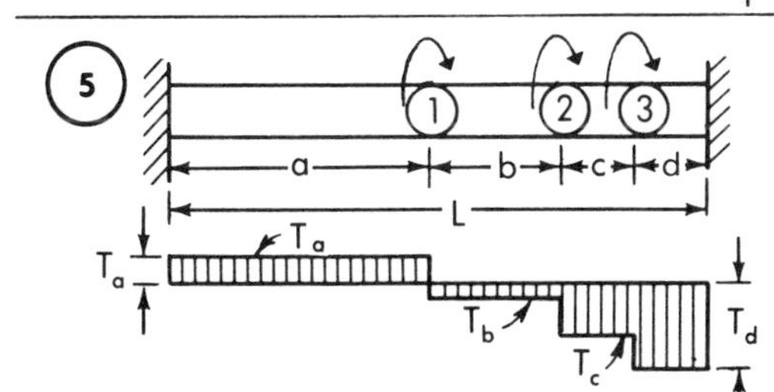

$$T_a = \frac{T_1\,(b + c + d) + T_2\,(c + d) + T_3\,d}{L}$$

$$T_b = \frac{-\,T_1\,a + T_2\,(c + d) + T_3\,d}{L}$$

$$T_c = \frac{-\,T_1\,a - T_2\,(a + b) + T_3\,d}{L}$$

$$T_d = \frac{-\,T_1\,a - T_2\,(a + b) - T_3\,(a + b + c)}{L}$$

$$\theta_1 = \frac{T_a\,a}{E_s\,R}$$

$$\theta_2 = \frac{T_b\,b + T_a\,a}{E_s\,R}$$

$$\theta_3 = \frac{T_d\,d}{E_s\,R}$$

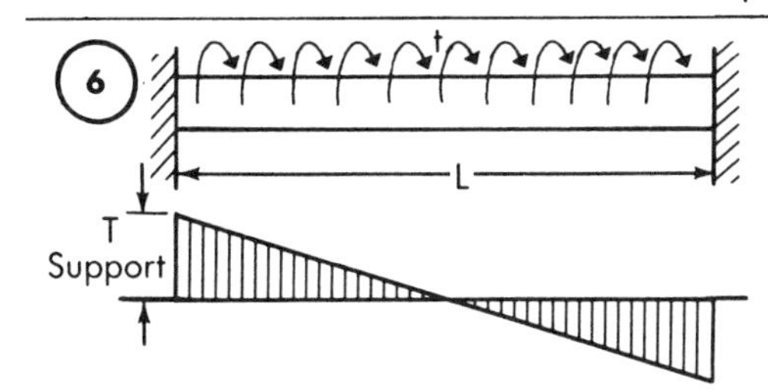

$$T_{support} = \frac{t\,L}{2}$$

$$\theta_{\mathcal{L}} = \frac{t\,L^2}{8\,E_s\,R}$$

FIGURE 1 - BEAMS ON A HORIZONTAL CURVE, UNDER UNIFORM LOAD (w)

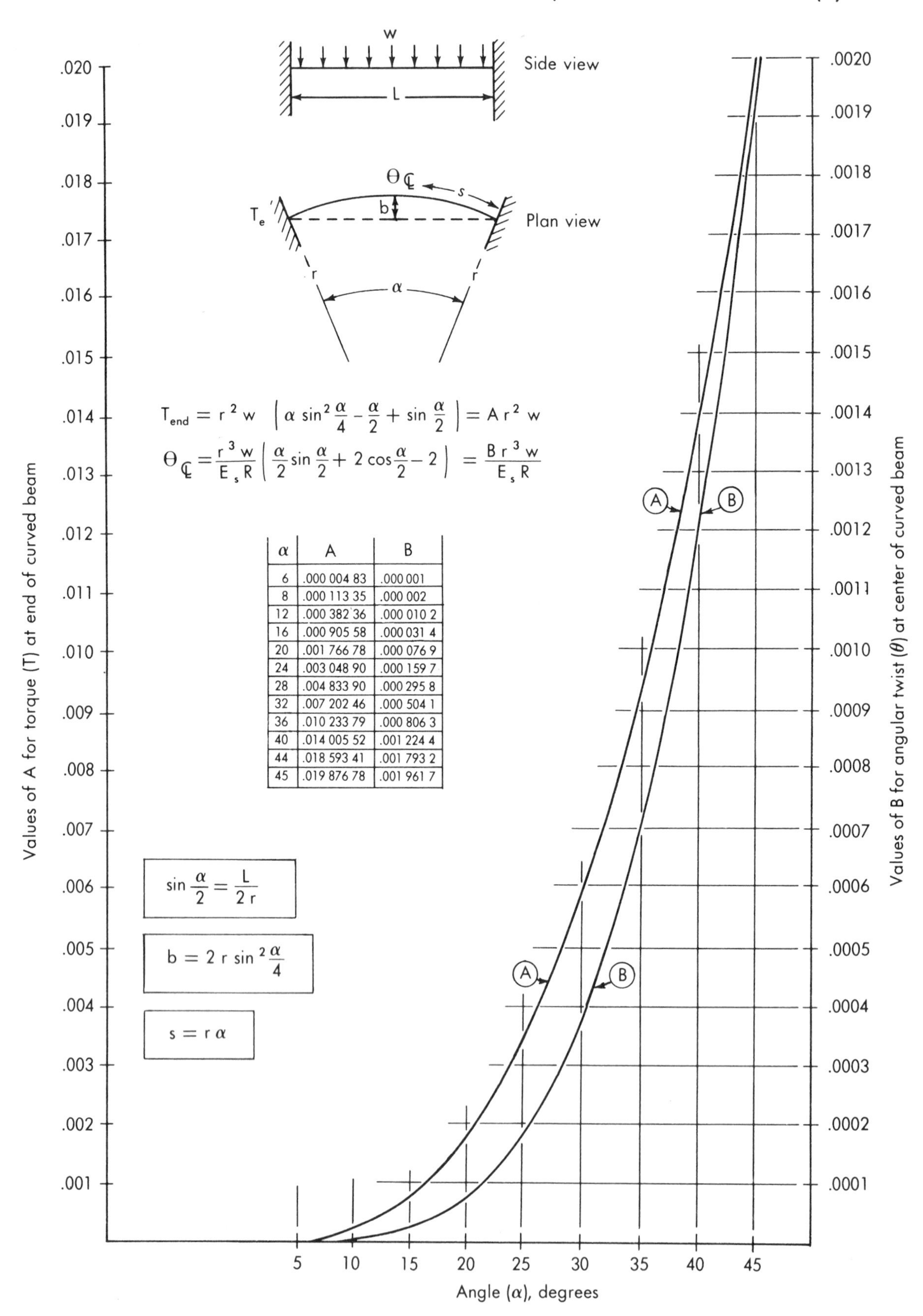

α	A	B
6	.000 004 83	.000 001
8	.000 113 35	.000 002
12	.000 382 36	.000 010 2
16	.000 905 58	.000 031 4
20	.001 766 78	.000 076 9
24	.003 048 90	.000 159 7
28	.004 833 90	.000 295 8
32	.007 202 46	.000 504 1
36	.010 233 79	.000 806 3
40	.014 005 52	.001 224 4
44	.018 593 41	.001 793 2
45	.019 876 78	.001 961 7